AMERICAN
ART DIRECTORY

AMERICAN ART DIRECTORY

1978

Edited by JAQUES CATTELL PRESS

R. R. BOWKER COMPANY
New York & London

705
Am35am

Published by R. R. Bowker Co.
1180 Avenue of the Americas, New York, NY 10036

Copyright © 1978 by Xerox Corporation

All rights reserved. Reproduction of this book, in whole or in part,
without written permission of the publisher is prohibited.
International Standard Book Number: 0-8352-1037-5
International Standard Serial Number: 0065-6968
Library of Congress Catalog Card Number: 99-1016
Printed and bound in the United States of America

All precautions have been made to avoid errors. However, the publishers
do not assume and hereby disclaim any liability to any party for any loss
or damage caused by errors or omissions in the *American Art Directory*,
whether such errors or omissions result from negligence, accident or
any cause.

Contents

Advisory Committee

Paul B Arnold, President
National Association of Schools of Art
c/o Department of Art
Oberlin College, Oberlin, Ohio 44074

Mario Cooper, President
American Watercolor Society
1083 Fifth Avenue
New York, New York 10028

Mark Freeman, President
National Society of Painters
   in Casein & Acrylic
307 East 37th Street
New York, New York 10016

Kenneth S Friedman, Director
Institute for Advanced Studies
   in Contemporary Art
6361 Elmhurst Drive
San Diego, California 92120

Bill Gallo, President
National Cartoonists Society
9 Ebony Court
Brooklyn, New York 11229

Judith Hoffberg, Editor
Umbrella
PO Box 3692
Glendale, California 91201

Konrad Kuchel, Coordinator of Loans
The American Federation of Arts
41 East 65th Street
New York, New York 10021

John J Mahlmann, Executive Director
National Art Education Association
1916 Association Drive
Reston, Virginia 22091

Laurence McGilvery
Rare Art Book Dealer
PO Box 852
La Jolla, California 92037

Margaret Mills, Executive Director
American Academy & Institute of
   Arts & Letters
633 West 155th Street
New York, New York 10032

Paul C Mills, Secretary
Association of Art Museum Directors
c/o Santa Barbara Museum of Art
1130 State Street
Santa Barbara, California 93101

Claire Stein, Executive Director
National Sculpture Society
777 Third Avenue
New York, New York 10017

Preface

The 47th edition of the *American Art Directory* contains data for more than 4467 art museums, art libraries, art associations, and art schools and studios, including universities and colleges with art departments and museums, in the United States, Canada and abroad. Also listed are museums of a general nature with collections relevant to art as indicated by their listing. 2300 museums in the United States, 223 in Canada, and 393 abroad; 1404 art schools in the United States, 44 in Canada and 103 abroad.

The arrangement continues to be geographical; however, the style has changed. Beginning with this edition, all departments at one institution have been grouped in a single entry. In addition, there are sections listing state arts councils, directors and supervisors of art education in the school systems of the United States, art magazines, newspapers carrying art notes and their critics, scholarships and fellowships, open exhibitions, and traveling exhibitions with booking agencies. An added feature is a section listing corporations having art collections for public viewing.

This is the first edition published without the sponsorship of The American Federation of Arts. In its stead, the editors have assembled an advisory committee whose responsibilities will include critiquing this edition of both the *American Art Directory* and its companion volume, *Who's Who in American Art,* to provide nominations of qualified artists or organizations not already listed, as well as suggestions for improvement of format and data. In addition, the editors will look to the advisory committee for advice when settling interpretation and criteria problems during compilation of future editions. We are very pleased to have this cooperation and support from these distinguished members of the art community.

All material submitted was carefully edited to established format and proofread. While all precautions have been taken to avoid errors, the publishers do not assume and hereby disclaim any liability to any party for any loss or damage caused by errors or omissions, whether such errors or omissions result from negligence, accident or any other cause. In any event, the sole responsibility of the publishers will be the entry of corrected data in a succeeding edition.

Comments and reviews are invited and should be addressed to The Editors, *American Art Directory,* P.O. Box 25001, Tempe, Arizona 85282.

Ann Gammons, *Sponsoring Editor*
Anne Rhodes, *Managing Editor*
Steve Nichols, *General Manager*
JAQUES CATTELL PRESS

July 1978

ART ORGANIZATIONS

ARRANGEMENT AND ABBREVIATONS
KEY TO ART ORGANIZATIONS

ARRANGEMENT OF DATA

Name of institution and address, zip code; telephone number where possible.

Name of director (Dir), curator (Cur) and other key personnel.

Hours open; date established (Estab) and purpose; description of gallery; annual average attendance; membership.

Income including how financed; purchases.

Collections.

Exhibitions.

Publications.

Activities including classes for adults or children; dramatic programs; docent training; lectures and number of lecturers per year; concerts; gallery talks; tours; competitions and awards; scholarships and fellowships; artmobile; lending program and material available; sales or museum shop.

Library showing librarian, volumes, periodical subscriptions, audio-visual and other holdings; Special Subjects; Special Collections.

ABBREVIATIONS AND SYMBOLS

Admin — Administration, Administrative
Adminr — Administrator
Admis — Admission
Adv — Advisory
AM — Morning
Ann — Annual
Approx — Approximate, Approximately
Asn — Association
Assoc — Associate
Asst — Assistant
Av — Audio-Visual
Bldg — Building
c — circa
Chap — Chapter
Chmn — Chairman
Circ — Circulation
Cl — Closed
Coll — Collection
Comt — Committee
Coordr — Coordinator
Corresp — Corresponding
Cur — Curator
Dept — Department
Dir — Director
Dist — District
Div — Division

Ed — Editor
Educ — Education
Enrl — Enrollment
Ent — Entrance
Estab — Established
Exec — Executive
Exhib — Exhibition
Exten — Extension
Fel(s) — Fellowship(s)
Fri — Friday
Ft — Feet
Gen — General
Hon — Honorary
Hr — Hour
Inc — Incorporated
Incl — Including
Jr — Junior
Lect — Lecture(s)
Lectr — Lecturer(s)
Librn — Librarian
Mem — Membership
Mgr — Manager
Mon — Monday
Mss — Manuscripts
Nat — National
PM — Afternoon

Pres — President
Prin — Principal
Prog — Program
Pub — Public
Publ — Publication, Publish
Res — Residence, Resident
Sat — Saturday
Schol — Scholarship
Secy — Secretary
Soc — Society
Sq — Square
Sr — Senior
Sun — Sunday
Supt — Superintendent
Supv — Supervisor
Thurs — Thursday
Treas — Treasurer
Tues — Tuesday
Tui — Tuition
TV — Television
Univ — University
Vol — Volunteer
VPres — Vice President
Wk — Week
Wed — Wednesday
Yr — Year(s)

*No response to questionnaire
†Used in text to denote collections currently being enlarged.

National and Regional Organizations In The United States

ALLIED ARTISTS OF AMERICA, INC, 1083 Fifth Ave, New York, NY 10028. *Pres* Dale Meyers; *VPres* William Gorman; *Treas* Moses Worthman; *Corresponding Secy* Diana Kan.
Estab 1914, inc 1922, as a self-supporting exhibition cooperative, with juries elected each year by the membership, to promote work by American artists. Mem: Active 350, assoc 225; dues $15 and $12 respectively.
Exhibitions: Annual exhibition in the fall at National Academy of Design; numerous awards, medals; prizes total approx $4500 each year.
Activities: Conducts demonstrations during the period of Annual Exhibition. Awards scholarship through the National Academy of Design.

AMERICAN ABSTRACT ARTISTS, 218 W 20th St, New York, NY 10011. *Pres* Leo Rabkin; *Secy* Ruth Eckstein; *Treas* Esphyr Slobodkina; *Exhib Chmn* Nick Kazak.
Estab 1936, active 1937, to further cause; develop and educate through exhibitions and publications. Mem: 60; meeting held quarterly.
Income: Financed by membership.
Exhibitions: Held at Betty Parsons Gallery.
Publications: Books and catalogs.
Activities: Traveling exhibitions organized and circulated.

AMERICAN ACADEMY AND INSTITUTE OF ARTS AND LETTERS, 633 W 155th St, New York, NY 10032. Tel: 212-368-5900. *Pres* Jacques Barzun; *VPres Art* John Heliker; *Treas* William Schuman; *Secy Academy* John Cheever; *Secy Institute* Ralph Ellison; *Exec Dir* Margaret M Mills.
Open Tues - Sun 1 - 4 PM during exhibitions, by appointment other times. Estab 1898 as an honorary society of artists, writers and composers whose function it is to foster, assist and sustain an interest in literature, music and the fine arts. Formed by 1976 merger of the American Academy of Arts and Letters and the National Institute of Arts and Letters. Maintains two galleries separated by a terrace. Average Annual Attendance: 6000. Mem: 250; membership is by election; no dues; annual meeting May.
Income: $750,000 (financed by endowment). Purchases: $50,000.
Collections: Works by members.
Exhibitions: Memorial Exhibitions for Deceased Artist Members; Exhibition of Candidates for Art Awards; Exhibition of Paintings Eligible for Hassam Fund Purchase; Newly Elected Members Exhibitions; Recipients of Honors and Awards.
Publications: Proceedings; exhibition catalogs.
Activities: Awards given, Gold Medal, Richard and Hings Rosenthal Foundation award, Marjorie Peabody Waite Award, Arnold W Brunner Memorial Prize in Architecture; Award of Merit of the Academy.
Library. Librn Hortense Zera. Open to scholars by appointment for reference. Special Subjects: Books and photography of work by members; books about members; exhibition catalogs. Special Collections: Paintings and drawings by Childe Hassam and Eugene Speicher; photography by Van Vechten.

AMERICAN ANTIQUARIAN SOCIETY,* 185 Salisbury St, Worcester, MA 01609. Tel: 617-755-5221. *Dir & Librn* Marcus A McCorison; *Cur Graphic Arts* Georgia B Bumgardner.
Open 9 AM - 5 PM; cl Sat, Sun & holidays. No admis. Inc 1812 to collect, preserve and encourage serious study of the materials of American history and life through 1876. Mem: hon 320; meetings semi-annual third Wed Apr & Oct.
Collections: Early American portraits; Staffordshire pottery, †bookplates; †prints; †lithographs; †cartoons; †engraving; colonial furniture.
Income: $200,000. Purchases $50,000.
Publications: Proceedings, semi-annually; monographs.

Activities: Guided tours; temporary exhibitions; lectures; sponsors fellowships.
Library: Holdings—Titles 750,000 dating before 1877. Special Subjects: Early American books on art; 20th century books and periodicals relating to the history and culture of the United States before 1877.

AMERICAN ARTISTS PROFESSIONAL LEAGUE, INC,* 215 Park Ave S, New York, NY 10003. Tel: 212-475-6650. *Pres* Frank C Wright; *Secy* Mary Keim Tietze.
Estab 1928 to advance the cause of fine arts in America, through the promotion of high standards of beauty, integrity and craftsmanship in painting, sculpture and the graphic arts; to emphasize the importance of order and coherent communication as prime requisites of works of art through exhibitions and publications; Average Annual Attendance: 20,000 - 30,000. Mem: 1000; monthly meetings Oct - May.
Income: $800 - $10,000 (financed by membership).
Exhibitions: Annually.
Publications: AAPL News Bulletin, irregularly.
Activities: Classes for adults and children; lect open to the public; demonstrations, exhibitions, paintings, sculpture, graphics available to members and state chapters on consignment; broadcasts, telecasts.

AMERICAN ASSOCIATION OF MUSEUMS, 1055 Thomas Jefferson St NW, Washington, DC 20007. Tel: 202-338-5300. *Pres* Kenneth Starr; *Dir* Lawrence L Reger; *Asst Dir* Michael Warner; *Editor* Ellen C Hicks.
Open Mon - Fri 9 AM - 5 PM. No admis. Estab 1906, to promote the welfare and advancement of museums as educational institutions, as agencies of scientific and academic research and as cultural centers of the community, to encourage interest and inquiries in the field of museology; to increase and diffuse knowledge of all matters relating to museums. Mem: 6000.
Publications: Museum News, six times year; Aviso, monthly; Official Museum Directory, biennially; reprints and books.
Library: Open to public for reference only. Special Subjects: Museum information.

AMERICAN ASSOCIATION OF UNIVERSITY WOMEN,* 2401 Virginia Ave NW, Washington, DC 20037. Tel: 202-785-7700. *Gen Dir* Helen B Wolfe.
Estab 1882 to unite alumnae of different institutions for the purpose of continuing their intellectual growth, furthering the advancement of women and providing enlightened leadership. Mem: 193,000 at biennial conventions.
Publications: The Journal (magazine), semi-annually; Journal (newspaper), five times a year; occasionally feature arts in education.
Activities: Association's Educational Center has available guidance in a wide range of the arts, including studio painting, writing, music structure, acting, dance, development of environmental awareness and action. Awards for women in the creative arts are made annually to enable practicing artists to advance their careers in printmaking, photography, painting, sculpture and film-making.

AMERICAN CERAMIC SOCIETY, 65 Ceramic Dr, Columbus OH 43214. Tel: 614-268-8645. *Pres* Lyle A Holmes; *VPres* John B Wachtman, Jr; *Exec Dir* Frank P Reid.
Open Mon - Fri 8:30 AM - 5 PM. No admis. Estab 1899 to promote the arts, science and technology of ceramics. Mem: 8000; dues $30; annual meeting May.
Income: 1,000,000 (financed by membership).
Publications: American Ceramic Society Bulletin, monthly; Journal and Abstracts, bimonthly.

AMERICAN COUNCIL FOR THE ARTS (formerly Associated Councils of the Arts), 570 Seventh Ave, New York, NY 10018. Tel: 212-354-6655. *Pres* Michael Newton; *VPres* Nancy Bush; *Secy* Anne Bartley; *Conf Dir & Publns Dir* Raymond Baron.
Estab 1960 as a national organization to provide services—management training, advocacy, news and publications—which address needs that cut across art forms. Mem: 3500; dues student $20, individual $30, library $35, universities and art organizations $100, business $200, councils $60-$500 depending on size of budget.
Publications: ACA Reports, 8 times a yr; Word from Washington, 10 times a yr.
Activities: Sponsors competitions.

AMERICAN COUNCIL FOR THE ARTS IN EDUCATION, 115 E 92nd St, New York, NY 10028. Tel: 212-831-8110. *Pres* Eldon Winkler; *VPres* Robert Glidden; *Secy-Treas* Gerry J Martin.
Estab 1957, a federation of national organizations concerned with furthering the cause of all the arts in American education. Mem: 25; meetings winter Jan or Feb, summer June or July.
Income: Financed by membership, Foundation grants, federal grants and contract research.

AMERICAN CRAFTS COUNCIL, 44 W 53rd St, New York, NY 10019. Tel: 212-977-8989. *Pres* Samuel Scherr; *VPres* Laurence Maloy; *Secy* Nicholas Angell; *Dir Mus Contemporary Crafts* Paul Smith; *Editor-in-Chief Crafts Horizons* Rose Slivka; *Dir Nat Programs* Lois Moran.
Estab 1943 as a national organization to develop appreciation for the work of contemporary American craftsmen; maintains museum (see entry under New York City). Mem: 34,000; dues $18 and higher; National conference every 3-4 years.
Income: $1,500,000 (financed by endowment, membership and donations).
Publications: Craft Horizons, bimonthly; Exhibition catalogs.
Activities: Regional workshops and conferences; sponsors Young Americans, a crafts competion for persons 18-30 years old, approx every 6 years; travel stipend; over 100 slide kits—a national audio-visual service called Your Portable Museum—for rent; traveling exhibitions organized and circulated.
Resource Center: Librn Joanne Polster. Open to the public for reference.
Holdings: Vols 2300; Other—Data on craft courses, organizations, supplies, shops, films, vertical files on craft subjects. Special Subjects: American crafts, principally 20th century. Special Collections: Portfolio files on practicing American craftsmen; 1000 exhibition catalogs; bound sets of craft periodicals; photographic archives of Museum of Contemporary Crafts.

THE AMERICAN FEDERATION OF ARTS, 41 E 65th St, New York, NY 10021. *Pres Bd of Trustees* Bayard Ewing; *VPres* Arthur D Emil; *Secy* Francis E Brennan; *Dir* Wiler Green; *Asst Dir & Dir Exhib* Jane S Tai; *Coordr Loans* Konrad G Kuchel; *Exhib Coordr* Susanna D'Alton; *Registrar* Melissa Meigham; *Dir Film Prog* Steven Aronson; *Dir Membership* Margot Linton; *Graphic Designer* Michael Shroyer; *Coordr Museum Publications Distribution Serv* Alice S Zimet; *Controller* Stanley W Berger.
Estab 1909, nonprofit educational institution, which organizes circulating art exhibitions and file programs for museums, art centers, universities, colleges, schools and libraries. Mem: 2000; dues individual $25 - $100, institutions $75 and up.
Income: Financed by endowment and membership.
Exhibitions: American Folk Painting; Tsutsumu; The Art of the Japanese Package; Alberto Giacometti; Sculptor and Draftsman; The Dyer's Art; Ikat; Batik; Plangi; The Art of Tibet; Survival: Life and Art of the Alaskan Eskimo; Art from Zaire; Photography in China, 1850-1920; From Type to Landscape, Designs, Projects and Proposals by Herbet Bayer, 1923-1973; A History of the American Avant-Garde Cinema; Murals without Walls; 200 Years of American Architectural Drawing; Masters of the Camera; Stieglitz, Steichen and Their Successors; Court House; A Photographic Document; Room for Wonder; Indian Paintings of the British Period; Young Americans; Fiber/Wood/Plastic/Leather; Five Centuries of Tapestry; Prints From the Guggenheim Collection.
Publications: Exhibition catalogs; Catalog of Museum Catalogs.
Activities: Traveling exhibitions organized and circulated.

AMERICAN INSTITUTE OF ARCHITECTS, 1735 New York Ave NW, Washington, DC 20006. Tel: 202-785-7300. *Pres* Elmer E Botsai; *VPres* Ehrman B Mitchell, Jr; *Secy* Robert M Lawrence; *Exec VPres* David Olan Meeker, Jr.
Open Mon - Fri 8:30 AM - 5 PM. No admis. Estab 1857 to organize and unite the architects of the United States and to promote the esthetic, scientific and practical efficiency of the profession. The Octagon, town house for Colonel John Tayloe, built in 1800 and designed by architect William Thornton serves as a gallery owned and operated by the American Institute of Architects Foundation.
Income: Financed by Membership.
Collections: The Octagon has collection of period paintings and furniture.
Exhibitions: Maine Forms of American Architecture; The Tall Grass Prairie; Selections from the AIA Architectural Archives; Dolley and the Great Little Madison; special Christmas exhibition.
Publications: AIA Journal, monthly; AIA Memo, (newsletter), biweekly.
Activities: Continuing education prog; awards given, Gold Medal, Kemper Award, Architectural Firm Award, R S Reynolds Memorial Award; Reynolds Aluminum Prize Citation of Honor.
—Library. *Librn* Susan Holton.
Open to the public, lending provided for members.
Holdings: Vols 20,000; Per subs 150.
Special Subjects: Architecture; architectural history.

AMERICAN INSTITUTE OF GRAPHIC ARTS, 1059 Third Ave, New York, NY 10021. Tel: 212-752-0813. *Pres* Richard Danne; *Exec Dir* Caroline Hightower.
Open Mon - Fri 9:30 AM - 5 PM. No admis. Estab 1914 as a national non-profit educational organization devoted to raising standards in all branches of the graphic arts; maintains gallery. Mem: 1700; dues nonresident $40, resident $75, corporation $300 - $1500, professional $100, student $20.
Income: Financed by membership.
Exhibitions: (1976-78) Show and Inside Show; Packaging Show and Illustration Show; Communication Graphics Show; Book Show; Federal Design Response Show.
Publications: AIGA catalogs.
Activities: Clinics on aspects of book production and seminars on design and production problems; plant tours; awards AIGA Medal for distinguised contributions to the graphic arts; traveling exhibitions organized and circulated.

AMERICAN INTERNATIONAL SCULPTORS SYMPOSIUMS, INC, 799 Greenwich St, New York, NY 10014. Tel: 212-242-3374. *Pres & Exec Dir* Verna Gillis; *VPres* Bradford Graves; *Secy* Benay Rubenstein.
Estab 1971 to promote art in public places.
Income: $45,000 (financed by state appropriation and NEA-corporate support).
Publications: Poem cards.
Activities: Lectr, 10 vis lectr per yr; Poetry in Public Places, placement of poem cards in buses throughout New York state; competitions; awards; traveling exhibitions organized and circulated; sales shop selling slides and poem cards.

AMERICAN NUMISMATIC ASSOCIATION, 818 N Cascade, Colorado Spring, CO 80909. Tel: 303-473-9142. *Pres* Col Grover C Criswell; *Exec VPres* Edward C Rochette; *Asst to Exec VPres & Acting Mus Cur* Kenneth L. Hallenbeck; *Asst to Exec VPres* Ruthann Brettell.
Open Mon - Fri 10 AM - 5 PM. No admis. Estab 1891 as an international organization to promote numismatics as a means of recording history; maintains a museum and library; seven galleries display numismatic material from paper money through coins and art medals. Average Annual Attendance: 3000. Mem: 34,000; to qualify for membership, a person must be at least eleven years of age and interested in coin collecting; dues $12 plus one-time initiation fee of $5; annual meeting second or third week of August.
Income: $500,000 - $1,000,000 (financed by endowment, donations and miscellaneous sources).
Collections: Robert T Herdegen Memorial Collection of coins of the world; Norman H Liebman Collection of Abraham Lincoln on paper money; several other collections from donations by members.
Exhibitions: Three galleries open to the public during the year with permanent exhibits—Colonial Gallery exhibiting coins of the American Colonial period; Americana Galleries exhibiting United States coins, 1792 to date; and the Gallery of Modern Medallic Art exhibiting contemporary medals.
Publications: The Numismatist, monthly.
Activities: Classes for adults and children; annual seminar on campus of Colorado College, Colorado Springs; lect open to the public, 6 vis lectrs per yr; tours; sponsors National Coin Week third week in April when members throughout the United States promote their avocations through exhibits in local areas; awards given; scholarships; sales shop selling books, magazines, slides, medals and souvenir jewelry.
Library: Librn Mrs Genie Karlson. Open to the public for reference; members may borrow contents. Holdings: Vols 11,000; AV—motion pictures; slide presentations 40; audiovisual library available to member clubs for borrowing.

AMERICAN NUMISMATIC SOCIETY, Broadway at 155th St, New York, NY 10032. Tel: 212-234-3130. *Pres* Harry W Bass, Jr; *VPres* Harry W Fowler; *Dir & Secy* Leslie A Elam; *Chief Cur* Margaret Thompson.

Open Tues - Sat 9 AM - 4:30 PM; Sun 1 - 4 PM; cl Mon. No admis. Estab 1858 as an international organization for the advancement of numismatic knowledge; maintains museum and library; two exhibition halls, one devoted to medals and decorations, the other to Money in Early America. Average Annual Attendance: 15,000. Mem: 1842 members interested in numismatics; dues assoc $15; annual meeting second Sat in January.
Income: Financed by endowment.
Collections: Universal numismatics.
Publications: Numismatic Literature, semiannually; MuseumNotes, annually.
Activities: Lect open to the public, 2 vis lectrs per yr; scholarships.
Library. Librn Francis D Campbell, Jr. Open to the public. Holdings: Vols 50,000; per sub 300; Other—Manuscripts, auction catalogs, slides.

AMERICAN RED CROSS, 17th & D Sts NW, Washington, DC 20006. Tel: 202-737-8300. *Pres* George M Elsey; *Senior VPres* Frederic S Laise; *Counselor & Secy* John L Currin.
Open Mon - Fri 8:30 AM - 4:45 PM. No admis. Estab 1881 to improve the quality of human life and enhance individual self-reliance and concern for others. Mem: 33,065,741; dues $1.
Income: Financed by membership.
Collections: Oil and poster paintings.
Activities: Occasionally sponsors art competitions by youth. International-intercultural Art Exchange Program is designed to foster human understanding through the arts by providing children and youth opportunities to share art education and social service experiences with young people in the United States and in countries served by other Red Cross societies.

AMERICAN SOCIETY OF CONTEMPORARY ARTISTS,* c/o Rose Hart Betensky, Pres, 66 Hayloft Place, Roslyn Heights, NY 11577. Estab 1917. Mem: 110 elected of basis of high level of professional distinction; annual meeting Apr.
Exhibitions and demonstrations of graphic technique, watercolor, oil and sculpture, gives citations to individuals dedicated to arts.

AMERICAN SOCIETY FOR AESTHETICS, c/o James R Johnson, Secy-Treas, School of Fine Arts, University of Connecticut, Storrs, CT 06268. Tel: 203-485-3016. *Pres* Jerome Stolnitz, Lehman College, Bronx, NY 10468; *Journal Editor* John J Fisher, Temple University, Philadelphia, PA 19122.
Estab 1942 for the advancement of philosophical and scientific study of the arts and related fields. Mem: Open to qualified persons in the fields of Society interest; annual meeting; regional meetings.
Publications: Journal of Aesthetics and Art Criticism, quarterly.

AMERICAN SOCIETY OF BOOKPLATE COLLECTORS AND DESIGNERS, 1206 N Stoneman Ave, 15, Alhambra, CA 91801. Tel: 213-283-1936. *Dir & Editor* Audrey Spencer Arellanes.
Estab 1922 as an international organization to foster an interest in the art of the bookplate through the publication of a Yearbook, and to encourage friendship and a greater knowledge of bookplates among members by an exchange membership list. Mem: 200 who are interested in bookplates as either a collector or artist, or just an interest in bookplates and graphic arts; dues $25 which includes quarterly newsletter and Yerbook.
Income: Financed by membership.
Publications: Bookplates in the News, quarterly newsletter; Yearbook, annually.
Activities: Contributes bookplates to the Prints and Photographs Division of the Library of Congress and furnishes them with copies of Newsletter and Yearbook; lectures given upon request; traveling exhibitions organized and circulated.

AMERICAN SOCIETY OF INTERIOR DESIGNERS, 730 Fifth Ave, New York, NY 10019. Tel: 212-586-7111. *Pres* Irving D Schwartz; *VPres* Rita St Clair; *Secy* Bruce Stodola; *Exec Dir* John J Mead; *Dir Mem & Chapter Services* Ed Gips; *Dir Educ* Russell Radley.
Estab 1975 as a national organization to advance standards of interior design, to uphold in practice a code of ethics and professional practices of mutual benefit in professional, public and trade relations, and to promote educational programs to improve the art of interior design. Mem: 15,000; members are selected according to their education and professional experience in the field; dues professional $175; annual meeting July 22 - 25, 1978, August 3 - 6, 1979.
Income: Financed by membership.
Publications: ASID Report, monthly; Student Career Guide; research papers.
Activities: Carried on through National committees; local activities conducted through 44 chapters. Annual competition for designers of fabrics, furniture, floor coverings, wall coverings and lighting produced and offered for sale during the year; annual scholarship design competitions for students in schools and colleges in the United States and Canada offering courses in interior design; cash prize awards and honorable mentions;

Educational Foundation finances educational research and awards special grants.
Library: Interior design books and publications.

AMERICAN WATERCOLOR SOCIETY, 1083 Fifth Ave, New York, NY 10028. Tel: 212-876-6622. *Pres* Mario Cooper; *VPres* Samuel Leitman; *Second VPres* William Strosahl; *Secy* Maxwell Desser; *Treas* Elsie Ject-Key; *Recording Secy* Mina Kocherthaler.
Open during exhibitions 1 - 5 PM. No admis. Estab 1866 as a National organization to foster the advancement of the art of watercolor painting and to further the interests of painters in watercolor throughout the United States; rests the National Academy Galleries for three weeks each year for annual exhibition. Annual Average Attendance: 1200. Mem: Approx 550; to qualify for membership, an artist must exhibit in three annuals within past ten years, then submit application to membership chairman; dues $15; annual meeting in April.
Income: Financed by membership.
Publications: AWS Newsletter, semiannually.
Activities: Demonstrations during annual exhibitions; awards given at annual exhibitions (approx $13,000 in 1978); traveling exhibitions organized and circulated.

ARCHAEOLOGICAL INSTITUTE OF AMERICA, 260 W Broadway, New York, NY 10013. Tel: 212-925-7333. *Pres* Robert H Dyson, Jr; *VPres* Claireve Grandjouan; *Gen Secy* Elizabeth A Whitehead; *Acting Managing Dir* R John Carpenter; *Exec Assts* Carol Smallman and James G Hamilton, Jr.
Estab 1879 as an international organization concerned with two major areas of responsibility—facilitating archaeological research and disseminating the results to the public. Mem: 7445 consisting of professionals and laypersons interested in archaeology; dues $25; annual meeting Dec. 27 - 30.
Income: Financed by endowment and membership.
Publications: Archaeology Magazine, bimonthly; American Journal of Archaeology, quarterly.
Activities: Lect open to the public, 270 vis lectr per year; annual award given for distinguished archaeological achievement; one or more fellowships awarded for an academic year.

ART DEALERS ASSOCIATION OF AMERICA, INC, 575 Madison Ave, New York, NY 10022. Tel: 212-644-7150. *Pres* Leo Castelli; *VPres* Norman Hirschl & William Acquavella; *Secy* Gilbert S Edelson; *Admin VPres & Counsel* Ralph F Colin.
Estab 1962 as a national organization to improve the stature and status of the art dealing profession. Mem: 104; membership by invitation, must have been in business for five years; dues $250.
Income: Financed by membership.
Publications: Handbook of Members.
Activities: Gives Adam Award for excellence in art history.

ART DIRECTORS CLUB, INC, 488 Madison Ave, New York, NY 10022. Tel: 212-838-8140. *Pres* David Davidian; *VPres* William Taubin; *Secy* Robert Reed; *Exec Dir* Diane Herzman.
Estab 1920 as an international organization to protect, promote and elevate the standards of practice of the profession of art directing; owns gallery. Mem: 620; criteria for membership—qualified art director, at least 21 years of age, of good character and at lest two years of practical experience in creating and directing in the visual communication or graphic arts industry; dues regular $150, nonresident $75, junior $25.
Income: Financed by membership.
Exhibitions: Bimonthly shows conceived to provide a showcase for works and ideas not readily viewed otherwise. They cover new art, design, lettering and graphics by illustrators, alumni art directors, ad agencies and individuals; annual exhibition of advertising and editorial art and design, presenting the best work in art directing in all media for the preceding year.
Publications: The Art Directors Annual, annually; Newsletter, bimonthly.
Activities: Portfolio Review Programs, Adoption Program, Seminars; lect open to the public; gallery talks; annual exhibition with Gold & Silver Medals, Gold, Silver and Distinctive Merit Certificates; scholarships; traveling exhibitions organized and circulated.
Library: Open to the public for reference. Holdings: Vols 56.

ARTISTS EQUITY ASSOCIATION, INC, 3726 Albemarle St NW, Washington, DC 20016. Tel: 202-244-0209. *Pres* Gilda Ellis; *Secy* Michael C Gast; *Exec Dir* Gail Rasmussen; 5 Regional VPres.
Estab 1947 as a national non-profit, aesthetically non-partisan organization working for social, economic and legislative change for all artists. Mem: 3000 who have given evidence of professional status; dues $20 and $30; annual meeting in June.
Income: $37,000 (financed by membership and grants).
Publications: AEA News, quarterly; Legislative Update, bimonthly; seven Action Kits available.

Activities: Lect open to the public at annual meeting only; chapters occasionally organize and circulate traveling exhibitions.

ARTISTS GUILD INC OF NEW YORK, 25 West 36th St, New York, NY 10018. Tel: 212-239-1348. *Chmn* John Josephs; *Pres* Dean Powell; *Secy* Joan De Katch; *Treas* Thomas Connolly.
Estab 1920 as a national organization to help establish better business relations between the buyers and sellers of art; Charter member of Joint Ethics Committee formed in 1945. Artist of the Year Award given yearly since 1960. Mem: 200 - 300; membership open to professional commercial and fine artists, salaried or free-lance; dues active $25, assoc $15, nonres $15 student $15.
Income: Financed by membership.

ASSOCIATION OF AMERICAN EDITORIAL CARTOONISTS, 475 School St SW, Washington, DC 20024. *Pres* Tom Curtis of Milwaukee Sentinel; *VPres* Jeff McNalley of Richmond Times-Dispatch; *Secy* Jim Lange, Oklahoma City Oklahoman.
Estab 1957 by John Stampone of the Army Times, Washington, DC, as an international organization of professional editorial cartoonists for newspapers and newspaper syndicates. Mem: 225; to qualify for membership an editorial cartoonists must produce at least one editorial cartoon per week for publication; dues $25; annual meeting.
Income: Financed by membership.
Exhibitions: University of Southern Mississippi Touring Exhibition of Association's editorial cartoons.
Publications: AAEC News Magazine.

ASSOCIATION OF ART MUSEUM DIRECTORS,* PO Box 620, Lenox Hill Station, New York, NY 10021. Tel: 212-249-5236. *Exec Secy* Millicent Hall Gaudieri.
Estab 1916; meets twice a year for discussion of the work of art museum executives. Mem: 118.
Publications: Conference Proceedings; Professional Practices in Art Museums.

ASSOCIATION OF COLLEGIATE SCHOOLS OF ARCHITECTURE, 1735 New York Ave NW, Washington, DC 20006. Tel: 202-785-2324. *Pres* D Nuzum; *VPres* B Turner; *Secy* B Honikman; *Exec Dir* R Schluntz; *Admin Asst* I Deshler; *Journal Exec Editor* D Clarke.
Open daily 9 AM - 5 PM. No admis. Estab 1912 as an international organization furthering the advancement of architectural education. Mem: 3400 faculty members; membership open to schools (and their faculty) that offer professional degrees in architecture; school dues $650-$900; annual meeting in April.
Income: $200,000 (financed by endowment, membership and state appropriation).
Publications: ACSA News, 6 times per yr; Journal of Architectural Education, quarterly.
Activities: Educ Dept; sponsors competitions occasionally; gives awards; sales shop selling books and magazines.

ASSOCIATION OF JUNIOR LEAGUES, INC, 825 Third Ave, New York, NY 10022. Tel: 212-355-4380. *Pres* Alice Weber; *VPres* Margaret Graham; *Exec Dir* Dean Londa.
Estab 1921 by the 30 Leagues then in existence to unite the member Leagues and to promote their individual purposes by offering them leadership and assistance. The purpose of each Junior League is to promote voluntarism, to develop the potential of its members for voluntary participation in community affairs and to demonstrate the effectiveness of trained volunteers. Mem: 235 Junior Leagues with approx 122,000 members; annual conference.
Publications: AJL Review, 4 times per yr.
Activities: The Junior Leagues are responsible for initiating the arts council movement and subsequently have been involved in the establishment of approximately 40 arts councils. They have acted as catalysts in starting a number of arts, history and science centers and arts festivals. They established the first museum docent programs in North America using volunteers. They are involved in historic preservation. A recent thrust is programs relating to building the arts into general education. Administrative, volunteer and financial resources are invested by Leagues in these programs.

ASSOCIATION OF MEDICAL ILLUSTRATORS, 6650 Northwest Hwy, Suite 112, Chicago, IL 60631. Tel: 312-763-7350. *Pres* Gottfried Goldenberg; *VPres* Martin Finch; *Corresp Secy* Phyllis Wood; *Assoc Dir* Larry Offriecht; *Chmn Public Relations* William Winn.
Open daily 8:30 AM - 5 PM. No admis. Estab 1945 as an international organization to encourage the advancement of medical illustration and allied fields of visual education; to promote understanding and cooperation with the medical and related professions. Mem: 540—active 284, assoc 92, honorary 5, sustaining 4, emeritus 38, student 104 overseas 6, associate overseas 7; dues active $75, assoc $60, overseas and assoc overseas $25, sustaining $200; annual meeting in October.

Income: Financed by membership.
Exhibitions: Members' work is exhibited at annual meeting.
Publications: Newsletter, 6 times per yr; Medical Illustration, brochure; Journal of Biocommunications, 3 times per yr.
Activities: Individual members throughout the world give lectures on the profession; awards given for artistic achievements submitted to salon each year; student scholarships to members of AMI accredited schools only; traveling exhibitions organized and circulated; a traveling art salon (20-30 pieces 11 x 14 in) will be available for loan by Sept. 1, 1978, from the central office; matted prints of illustrations.

AUDUBON ARTISTS, INC, 1083 Fifth Ave, New York, NY 10028. Tel: 212-369-4880. *Pres* Mark Freeman, 307 E 37th St, New York, NY 10016; *VPres* Howard Mandel; *Secy* Mervin Honig.
Open during annual exhibition. Admis 50¢. Estab 1944 as a national organization for the presentation of annual exhibitions in all media—oil, acrylics, watercolors, graphics, sculpture, open to nonmembers. Gallery not maintained; exhibitions held at the National Academy of Design. Average Annual Attendance: 1000-1500 during three weeks of exhibition. Mem: 400; membership by invitation; dues $20; annual meeting in April.
Income: Approx $15,000 (financed by membership and exhibition admission).
Publications: Illustrated catalog, each January.
Activities: Annual exhibition lasting three weeks; demonstrations in all media; medals and cash prizes.

COLLEGE ART ASSOCIATION OF AMERICA, 16 E 52nd St, New York, NY 10022. Tel: 212-755-3532. *Pres* Marilyn Stokstad; *VPres* Joshua C Taylor; *Secy* Lucy Freeman Sandler; *Exec Secy* Rose R Weil.
Estab 1912 as a national organization to further scholarship and excellence in the teaching and practice of art and art history. Average Annual Attendance: 3500-6000 at annual meeting. Mem: 9200; open to all individuals and institutions interested in the purposes of the Association; dues individual $30-$40 (scaled to salary), student $17.50, institution $50, life $1000; annual meeting end of Jan or beginning of Feb.
Income: Financed by membership.
Publications: The Art Bulletin, quarterly; Art Journal, quarterly; CA Newsletter, 4-5 times per yr.
Awards: Distinguished Teaching of Art History Award; Distinguished Teaching of Art Award; Charles Rufus Morey Book Award; Frank Jewett Mather Award for Distinction in Art and Architectural Criticism; Arthur Kingsley Porter Prize for best article by younger scholar in The Art Bulletin.

COUNCIL OF AMERICAN ARTIST SOCIETIES,* 215 Park Ave S, New York, NY 10003. Tel: 212-475-6650. *Pres* Frank C Wright; *First VPres* Donald DeLue; *VPres, Treas & Gen Counsel* John S Dole; *Recording Secy* Florence Whitehill. Estab 1962, a national, tax-free, nonprofit incorporated educational council to educate, motivate and protect art and artists; to further traditional art at the highest esthetic level; policies and management controlled by artists. Mem: 100 societies; no dues; annual meeting in May.
Income: Financed by endowment.
Publications: Annual Report; monographs.
Activities: Presents awards to art organizations; awards and citations for excellence in art; medals and awards; circulates exhibitions; provides some scholarships.

FEDERATION OF MODERN PAINTERS AND SCULPTORS, 340 W 72nd St, New York, NY 10023. Tel: 212-362-4608. *Pres* Ahmet Gursoy; *VPres* Theo Hios, Barbara Krashes & Louise Nevelson; *Secy* Elisabeth Model.
Estab 1940 as a national organization to proote the cultural interests of free progressive artists working in the United States. Mem: 69; selected by membership comt; dues $10; meeting every two months.
Income: Financed by membership and New York State Council on the Arts.
Exhibitions: 35th Annual Exhibition traveling in New York State.
Activities: Lect open to the public, 1 - 2 vis lectrs per yr; traveling exhibitions organized and circulated.

GENERAL FEDERATION OF WOMEN'S CLUBS,* 1734 N St NW, Washington, DC 20036. Tel: 202-347-3168. *Exec Secy* Mrs W Ed Hamilton.
Estab 1890 as an international organization with members in 36 countries to unite the women's clubs and like organizations throughout the world for the purpose of mutual benefit, and for the promotion of their common interest in educational, industrial, philanthropic, literary, artistic and scientific culture as interpreted and implemented by established policy. Mem: 700,000 in 14,000 clubs in the United States; annual meeting in June, 1978 in Phoenix, AZ, 1979 in New Orleans, LA and 1980 in St Louis, MO.

Income: Many activities financed through the Pennies for Art Fund, estab 1930, to which each member is asked to donate just pennies. Proceeds are used within the state where collected.
Publications: General Federation Clubwoman News, 9 times per yr.
Activities: State Federation and local clubs provide art scholarships; sponsor state and local contests for high school seniors; art classes; present works of American artists as awards to schools or clubs for outstanding services to art or to hospitals and public buildings; conduct state art surveys; exhibit the work of state and local artists; observe American Art Week.

GENERAL SERVICES ADMINISTRATION,* Public Buildings Service Fine Arts Program, 18th & F Sts NW, Washington, DC 20405. Tel: 202-963-5131. *Dir Fine Arts Program* Donald W Thalacker.
The Fine Arts Program office directs the work of artists commissioned to design and execute sculpture, murals, tapestries and other art work incorporated as part of the design of new Federal Buildings, except Post Offices and Veterans Administration buildings. The scope of work is determined by the size and character of the building with allowances up to .5% of the estimated construction cost.
Artists are commissioned by direct selection by agency upon recommendation by a panel of distinguished art professionals appointed by the National Endowment for the Arts and the architect for the building.
Estimated annual budget: $1,000,000.

GUILD OF BOOK WORKERS, 1059 Third Ave, New York, NY 10021. Tel: 212-752-0813. *Pres* Mary C Schlosser; *VPres* Jeanne F Lewisohn; *Secy* Grady E Jensen.
Estab 1906 as a national organization to establish and maintain a feeling of kinship and mutual interest among workers in the several hand book crafts. Mem: 300; membership open to all interested parties; dues national $36, New York City area $60; annual meeting May or June.
Income: Financed by membership.
Exhibitions: Held every two or three years; hand bookbinding; calligraphy; decorated papers.
Publications: Newsletter, quarterly; Guild of Book Workers Journal, 3 times per yr; Membership List, annually; Supply List, biennially; Opportunities for Study in Hand Bookbinding and Calligraphy, directory, published 1977.
Activities: 2 - 4 lectures annually, some open to the public and some for members only.
Library, c/o Boston Athenaeum, 10½ Beacon St, Boston, MA 02108. *Librn* Stanley E Cushing. Open to Guild members for lending and reference; by appointment to others. Holdings: Vols 500; books related to the hand book crafts.

INDUSTRIAL DESIGNERS SOCIETY OF AMERICA, 1750 Old Meadow Rd, McLean, VA 22101. Tel: 703-893-5575. *Pres* Richard Hollerith; *VPres* Robert Smith; *Secy* Allace H Appel; *Exec Dir* Brian J Wynne; *Mem Secy* Celia Shifflett.
Open daily 8 AM - 5 PM. No admis. Estab and inc 1965 as a non-profit national organization representing the profession of industrial design. Mem: 1200, dues full, assoc, affiliate, sustaining and student from $25 to $125; annual meeting Sept 26 - Oct 1, 1978.
Publications: IDSA Newsletter, monthly; Membership Directory; other surveys and studies.
Activities: IDSA Student Chapters; IDSA Student Merit Awards; lectures and competitions.

INTERMUSEUM CONSERVATION ASSOCIATION, Allen Art Bldg, Oberlin, OH 44074. Tel: 216-775-7331. *Pres* Bret Waller; *VPres* Budd Bishop; *Secy-Treas & Dir* Marigene H Butler; *Admin Asst-Art Historian* Ricardo Barreto; *Chief Conservator* Philip Vance; *Painting Conservators* Leni Potoff, Carol Mancusi-Ungaro, Mervin Richard; *Paper Conservator* vacant; *Secy-Acct* Ruth E Spitler.
Not open to public. Estab 1952 as a non-profit conservation laboratory to aid in the maintenance of the collections of its member museums. Mem: 17, must be a non-profit cultural institution.

INTERNATIONAL COUNCIL OF MUSEUMS COMMITTEE OF THE AMERICAN ASSOCIATION OF MUSEUMS, 1055 Thomas Jefferson St NW, Washington, DC 20007. Tel: 212-338-5300. *Prog Coordr* Maria Papageorge.
Open 9 AM - 5 PM. No admis. Estab 1973; The AAM represents international museum interests within the United States through the AAM/ICOM office which disseminates information on international conferences, publications, travel and study grants, museum jobs, training programs and museum collections. The AAM/ICOM office also maintains an international network of museum professionals' visits to United States museums. Mem: 900; members must be museum professionals or institutions holding membership in the American Association of Museums.
Income: Financed by membership.

Publications: AAM/ICOM Newsletter, quarterly; ICOM News, quarterly.
Activities: Specialty committees; serves as liaison for the organization and circulation of traveling exhibitions.

INTERNATIONAL FOUNDATION FOR ART RESEARCH, INC, 24 E 81st St, New York, NY 10028. Tel: 212-879-1780. *Pres* Edwin L Weisl, Jr; *Exec Dir* Elizabeth B Burns; *Dir Art Theft Archive* Bonnie Burnham.
Open Mon - Fri 9 AM - 5 PM. No admis. Estab 1968 to provide a framework for impartial consideration by experts on questions concerning attribution and authentication of major works of art; expanded in 1945 to include an Art Theft Archive for the collection and cataloging of information on art theft.
Income: Financed by donations.
Publications: Brochure; Bulletin; report on the problem of art theft.
Activities: The Foundation examines art objects submitted by private owners and public institutions in order to resolve questions of authenticity and proper attribution. The Foundation accepts paintings, sculpture, prints and pottery for study. It's examinations consist of a laboratory examination, including all relevant physical tests, and a stylistic examination by leading experts in the field. A written report of the experts' conclusions is issued to the owner in the name of the Foundation. Fees vary according to costs of examination. Under the Foundation's Museum Program, these services are offered to small museums to aid in the resolution of questions dealing with the proper attribution of works of art in their collections. Funds are available to museums for the service through the aid of NEA and NYSCA.
The *Art Theft Archive* is a research program of the Foundation, funded by a special grant. The Archive collects and catalogs records of art thefts, and provides information on stolen objects to individuals, institutions, government agencies and other organizations involved in the fine arts, in order to prevent the circulation of stolen works and aid in their recovery. The Archive contains reports from a wide range of domestic and international sources. A comprehensive report on the problem of art theft is also available, including museum and dealer surveys, international statistics, and an evaluation of the legal context of this problem.

INTER-SOCIETY COLOR COUNCIL, c/o Dr Fred W Billmeyer, Jr, *Secy*, Rensselaer Polytechnic Institute, Troy, NY 12181. Tel: 518-270-6458. *Pres* Franc Grom; *VPres* William D Schaeffer; *Treas* S Leonard Davidson.
Estab 1931 as a national organization to stimulate and coordinate the study of color in science, art and industry. Mem: 850; members must show an interest in color and in the aims and purposes of the Council; dues $15; annual meeting usually in Apr.
Income: $10,000 (financed by membership.).
Publications: Inter-Society Color Council Newsletter, bimonthly.
Activities: Lectures open to the public; also at meetings; gives Macbeth Award and Godlove Award.

KAPPA PI INTERNATIONAL HONORARY ART FRATERNITY, PO Box 7843, Midfield, Birmingham, AL 35228. Tel: 205-428-4540. *Pres* Miss Garnet R Leader; *VPres* Dr Ralph M Hudson; *Secy* Elmer J Porter; *Treas* Mrs Myrtle Kerr; *Editor* Arthur Kennon.
Estab 1911 as an international honorary art fraternity for men and women in colleges, universities and art schools.
Income: Financed by membership.
Publications: Bulletin, annually in the fall; Sketch Book, annual magazine in the spring.
Activities: Sponsors competitions in photography; annual scholarships available to active members.
Chapter Roll
Alpha—University of Kentucky, Lexington, KY 40506
Theta—Birmingham Southern College, Birmingham, AL 35204
Iota—Iowa Wesleyan College, Mount Pleasant, IA 52641
Kappa—Lindenwood College, St Charles, MO 63301
Lambda—Oklahoma City University, Oklahoma City, OK 73106
Mu—Western New Mexico University, Silver City, NM 88061
Nu—Fort Hays State College, Hays, KS 67601
Xi—University of Montevallo, Montevallo, AL 35115
Omicron—Western Montana College, Dillon, MT 69725
Pi—University of Georgia, Athens, GA 30602
Rho—Mississippi University for Women, Columbus, MS 39701
Sigma—Huntingdon College, Montgomery, AL 36106
Phi—Central State University, Edmond, OK 73034
Chi—Eastern Illinois University, Charleston, IL 61920
Psi—Southern Illinois University, Carbondale, IL 62901
Omega—Indiana State University, Terre Haute, IN 47809
Alpha Alpha—Samford University, Birmingham, AL 35209
Alpha Beta—Central Washington State College, Ellensburg, WA 98926
Alpha Delta—University of Arkansas, Fayetteville, AR 72701
Alpha Epsilon—Mary Hardin-Baylor College, Belton, TX 76513
Alpha Eta—Florida Southern College, Lakeland, FL 33802

Alpha Theta—Winthrop College, Rock Hill, SC 29733
Alpha Iota—DePauw University, Greencastle, IN 46135
Alpha Kappa—Baylor University, Waco, TX 76703
Alpha Lambda—Sam Houston State University, Huntsville, TX 77340
Alpha Mu—University of Minnesota, Duluth, MN 55812
Alpha Xi—Kansas Wesleyan Univresity, Salina, KS 67401
Alpha Omicron—Georgetown College, Georgetown, KY 40324
Alpha Pi—Southwest Texas State University, San Marcos, TX 78666
Alpha Rho—Brenau College, Gainesville, GA 30501
Alpha Sigma—Our Lady of the Lake University, San Antonio, TX 78207
Alpha Tau—John B Stetson University, DeLand, FL 32720
Alpha Upsilon—Winona State University, Winona, MN 55987
Alpha Chi—Black Hills State College, Spearfish, SD 57783
Alpha Psi—University of South Carolina, Columbia, SC 29208
Alpha Omega—Wicheta State University, Wichita, KS 67208
Alpha Alpha Alpha—Oregon College of Education, Monmouth, OR 97361
Alpha Alpha Beta—Oklahoma Baptist University, Shawnee, OK 74801
Alpha Alpha Delta—Western State College, Gunnison, CO 81230
Alpha Alpha Epsilon—Southwestern College, Winfield, KS 67156
Alpha Alpha Zeta—Carthage College, Kenosha, WI 53140
Alpha Alpha Eta—University of Southern California, Los Angeles, CA 90007
Alpha Alpha Theta—University of Tampa, Tampa, FL 33606
Alpha Alpha Iota—University of Miami, Coral Gables, FL 33124
Alpha Alpha Kappa—Arkansas State University, Jonesboro, AR 72467
Alpha Alpha Lambda—Southwestern Oklahoma State University, Weatherford, OK 73096
Alpha Alpha Mu—Eastern Washington State College, Cheney, WA 99004
Alpha Alpha Nu—University of Texas at El Paso, El Paso, TX 79968
Alpha Alpha Xi—Phillips University, Enid, OK 73701
Alpha Alpha Omicron—Eastern New Mexico University, Portales, NM 88130
Alpha Alpha Pi—Oregon State University, Corvallis, OR 97331
Alpha Alpha Rho—University of Southern Mississippi, Hattiesburg, MS 39401
Alpha Alpha Sigma—New Mexico Highlands University, Las Vegas, NM 87701
Alpha Alpha Tau—West Liberty State College, West Liberty, WV 26074
Alpha Alpha Upsilon—St Cloud State University, St Cloud, MN 56301
Alpha Alpha Phi—University of North Carolina, Chapel Hill, NC 27514
Alpha Alpha Chi—Murray State University, Murray, KY 42071
Alpha Alpha Psi—Eastern Kentucky University, Richmond, KY 40475
Beta Alpha—Baker University, Baldwin City, KS 66006
Beta Beta—Kearney State College, Kearney, NE 68847
Beta Gamma—Southeast Missouri State University, Cape Girardeau, MO 63701
Beta Delta—University of Alabama, University, AL 35486
Beta Epsilon—North Texas State University, Denton, TX 76203
Beta Zeta—Heidelberg College, Tiffin, OH 44883
Beta Theta—Wayne State College, Wayne, NE 68787
Beta Iota—Stephen F Austin State University, Nacogdoches, TX 75961
Beta Kappa—Queen's College of the City University of New York, Flushing, NY 11367
Beta Lambda—Hofstra University, Hempstead, NY 11550
Beta Mu—Frostburg State College, Frostburg, MD 21532
Beta Nu—Hunter College of the City University of New York, New York, NY 10021
Beta Xi—University of Evansville, Evansville, IN 47702
Beta Omicron—Lewis and Clark College, Portland, OR 97219
Beta Pi—West Texas State University, Canyon, TX 79016
Beta Rho—University of Northern Iowa, Cedar Falls, IA 50613
Beta Sigma—Drew University, Madison, NJ 07940
Beta Tau—Lamar University, Beaumont, TX 77710
Beta Upsilon—Harris Teachers College, St Louis, MO 63103
Beta Phi—Texas Wesleyan College, Fort Worth, TX 76105
Beta Chi—Hardin-Simmons University, Abilene, TX 79601
Beta Psi—Concord College, Athens, WV 24712
Beta Omega—Seattle Pacific College, Seattle, WA 98119
Gamma Alpha—Northwest Missouri State University, Maryville, MO 64468
Gamma Beta—Fairmont State College, Fairmont, WV 26554
Gamma Gamma—Union College, Barbourville, KY 40906
Gamma Delta—University of Wisconsin-Eau Claire, Eau Clair, WI 54701
Gamma Epsilon—University of Houston, Houston, TX 77004
Gamma Zeta—Hastings College, Hastings, NE 68901
Gamma Eta—Chadron State College, Chadron, NE 69337
Gamma Theta—Montclaire State College, Upper Montclair, NJ 07043
Gamma Iota—Eastern Oregon College, LaGrande, OR 97850
Gamma Kappa—Madison College, Harrisonburg, VA 22801

Gamma Lambda—Abilene Christian University, Abilene, TX 79601
Gamma Mu—Northwestern State University, Natchitoches, LA 71457
Gamma Nu—University of Southwestern Louisiana, Lafayette, LA 70504
Gamma Xi—Louisiana College, Pineville, LA 71360
Gamma Omicron—Centenary College of Louisiana, Shreveport, LA 71104
Gamma Pi—Western Kentucky University, Bowling Green, KY 42101
Gamma Rho—Northwestern Oklahoma State University, Alva, OK 73717
Gamma Sigma—Adelphi University, Garden City, NY 11530
Gamma Tau—California State University at Los Angeles, Los Angeles, CA 90032
Gamma Upsilon—University of Alaska, Fairbanks, AK 99506
Gamma Phi—National Photographic, Box 7843, Midfield, Birmingham, AL 35228
Gamma Chi—Alaska Methodist University, Anchorage, AK 99504
Gamma Psi—San Diego State University, San Diego, CA 92812
Gamma Omega—West Virginia Wesleyan College, Buckhannon, WV 26201
Delta Alpha—Northeast Louisiana University, Monroe, LA 71201
Delta Beta—Mississippi College, Clinton, MS 39058
Delta Gamma—Mankato State University, Mankato, MN 56001
Delta Delta—Western Illinois University, Macomb, IL 61455
Delta Epsilon—University of Bridgeport, Bridgeport, CT 06602
Delta Zeta—State University of New York College at New Paltz, New Paltz, NY 12561
Delta Eta—Northern Montana College, Havre, MT 59501
Delta Iota—Morehead State University, Morehead, KY 40351
Delta Kappa—University of the Phillippines, Quezon City, Philippines
Delta Lambda—Delta State University, Cleveland, MS 38732
Delta Mu—University of North Alabama, Florence, AL 35630
Delta Nu—Belhaven College, Jackson, MS 39202
Delta Xi—Arkansas Tech University, Russellville, AR 72801
Delta Omicron—Long Island University CW Post Center, Greenvale, NY 11548
Delta Pi—University of North Carolina at Asheville, Asheville, NC 28801
Delta Rho—Ottawa University, Ottawa, KS 66067
Delta Sigma—Keuka College, Keuka Park, NY 14478
Delta Tau—Alabama State University, Montgomery, AL 36101
Delta Upsilon—Troy State University, Troy, AL 36081
Delta Phi—College of Mount Saint Vincent, Riverdale, NY 10471
Delta Chi—California State University, Fullerton, CA 92634
Dlta Psi—Waynesburg College, Waynesburg, PA 15370
Delta Omega—Louisiana Tech University, Rushton, LA 71270
Epsilon Alpha—Baldwin-Wallace College, Berea, OH 44012
Epsilon Gamma—Middle Tennessee State University, Murfreesboro, TN 37130
Epsilon Delta—Minot State College, Minot, ND 58701
Epsilon Zeta—Dickinson State College, Dickinson, ND 58601
Epsilon Eta—University of Central Arkansas, Conway, AR 72032
Epsilon Theta—McMurray College, Abilene TX 79605
Epsilon Kappa—Montreat-Anderson College, Montreat, NC 28757
Epsilon Lambda—University of Wyoming, Laramie, WY 82071
Epsilon Mu—Boise State University, Boise, ID 83725
Epsilon Xi—John F Kennedy College, Wahoo, NE 68066
Epsilon Omicron—Herbert H Lehman College of the City University of New York, Bronx, NY 10468
Epsilon Pi—Carson Newman College, Jefferson City, TN 37760
Epsilon Rho—Friends University, Wichita, KS 67213
Epsilon Sigma—Ohio Northern University, Ada, OH 45810
Epsilon Tau—University of Alabama in Huntsville, Huntsville, AL 35807
Epsilon Upsilon—Saint Mary's College, Saint Mary's City, MD 20686
Epsilon Phi—Mississippi State University, Mississippi State, MS 39762
Epsilon Chi—Bethany College, Bethany, WV 26032
Epsilon Omega—Instituto Allende, San Miguel de Allende GTO, Mexico

MID-AMERICA COLLEGE ART ASSOCIATION,* c/o G Alden Smith, Pres, Art Dept, Wayne State University, Detroit, MI 48202. Tel: 313-577-2424.
Estab 1938 to promote better teaching of art and art history in colleges and universities. Average Annual Attendance: 700. Mem: 200 college and university art departments in 24 states and 4 Canadian provinces; annual meeting and elections in October.

MIDWEST ART HISTORY SOCIETY. Dept of Art History, Northwestern University, Evanston, IL 60201. Tel: 312-492-3741. *Pres* James D Breckenridge; *VPres & Secy* Edward J Olszewski.
Estab 1973 to further art history in the Midwest as a discipline and a profession. Average Annual Attendance: 150 at meetings. Mem: 410;

membership is open to institutions, students and academic and museum art historians in the Midwest; dues institution $5, professional $2; annual meeting March 29th-31st.
Income: $900 (financed by membership).
Publications: Midwest Art History Society Newsletter, October.
Activities: Lectures provided.

NATIONAL ARCHITECTURAL ACCREDITING BOARD, INC, 1735 New York Ave NW, Washington, DC 20006. Tel: 202-833-1180. *Exec Dir* Dr Hugo G Blasdel.
Estab 1940 to produce and maintain a current list of accredited programs in architecture in the United States and its jurisdictions, with the general objective that a well-integrated program of architectural education be developed which will be national in scope.
Publications: List of Accredited Programs in Architecture, annually; Criteria and Procedures, pamphlet.

NATIONAL ART EDUCATION ASSOCIATION, 1916 Association Dr, Reston, VA 22091. Tel: 703-860-8000. *Exec Dir* John J Mahlmann; *Pres* Dr Elliot W Eisner, Dept Art, Stanford University, Stanford, CA 94305; *Pres-Elect* Dr Kent Anderson, Milwaukee Public Schools, PO Drawer 10K, Milwaukee, WI 53201.
Estab 1947 throught the affiliation of four regional groups—Eastern, Western, Pacific and Southeastern Arts Associations—the NAEA is a national organization devoted to the advancement of the professional interests and competence of teachers of art at all educational levels. Mem: Approx 10,000 art teachers, administrators, supervisors and students; fee active $35, institutional comprehensive $100; National Conference held in Apr—1977 in Philadelphia, PA, 1978 in Houston, TX, 1979 in San Francisco, CA, 1980 in Atlanta, GA.
Income: Programs financed through membership, sales of publications, and occasional grants for specific purposes.
Publications: Journal of Art Education, 8 issues per year; Studies in Art Education, 3 times per year; Art Teacher, 3 times per year; special publications.
Activities: Promotes the study of the problems of teaching art; encourages research and experimentation; facilitates the professional and personal cooperation of its members; holds public discussions and programs; publishes desirable articles, reports, and surveys; integrates efforts of others with similar purposes.

NATIONAL ASSOCIATION OF SCHOOLS OF ART, 11250 Roger Bacon Dr, 5, Reston, VA 22090. Tel: 703-437-0700. *Pres* Paul B Arnold, *Chmn Dept Art,* Oberlin College, Oberlin, OH 44074; *Exec Secy* Samuel Hope.
Formerly the National Conference of Schools of Design, holding its first conference in 1944. Changed name 1948, at which time its Constitution and By-Laws were adopted. Changed its name again in 1960 from National Association of Schools of Design to National Association of Schools of Art.
NASA is the national accrediting agency for higher educational institutions in the visual arts and is so recognized by the US Office of Education and the Council on Postsecondary Accreditation.
The organization is established to develop a closer relationship among schools and departments of art for the purpose of examining and improving their educational practice and professional standards in design and art.
Membership is open to schools and departments of art established for the purpose of educating designers and artists in the visual arts, and giving evidence of permanence and stability; possessing an approved organization, administration, faculty and facilities; and maintaining standards agreed upon by the Association.

NATIONAL ASSOCIATION OF WOMEN ARTISTS, INC, 41 Union Square, New York, NY 10003. Tel: 212-675-1616. *Pres* Elizabeth Horman.
Estab 1889 as a national organization to provide opportunities for women artists (members) to exhibit and sell their work. Mem: 650; mem work is juried prior to selection; dues $25; annual meetings Nov & May.
Income: Financed by membership.
Exhibitions: Annual members' exhibition in spring with awards; annual traveling exhibitions of oils, watercolors and graphics; annual New York City shows of oils, watercolors, graphics and sculpture.
Publications: Annual Exhibition Catalog.
Activities: Lect open to the public, 1 vis lect per yr; awards given during annual exhibition; traveling exhibitions organized and circulated.

NATIONAL CARTOONISTS SOCIETY,* 9 Ebony Court, Brooklyn, NY 11229. Tel: 212-743-6510. *Pres* Bill Gallo; *Secy* Bill Kresse; *Scribe* Marge Duffy Devine.
Estab March 1946 to advance the ideals and standards of the profession of cartooning; to assist needy, or incapacitated cartoonists; to stimulate interest in the art of cartooning by cooperating with established schools; to encourage talented students; to assist governmental and charitable institutes. Mem: 480; annual Reuben Awards Dinner in April.
Collections: National Cartoonists Society Collection; Milt Gross Collection.
Publications: Newsletter, monthly; The Cartoonist, annually; roster.
Activities: Educ Dept to supply material and information to students; traveling exhibitions organized and circulated; original cartoons lent to schools, libraries, galleries; tape recordings; individual cartoonists to lecture, chalktalks can be arranged; occasional cartoon auctions; proceeds from traveling exhibitions and auctions support Milt Gross Fund assisting needy cartoonists, widows and children; gives Reuben Award to Outstanding Cartoonist of the Year; Silver Plaque Awards to best cartoonists in individual categories of cartooning—advertising, animation, comic books, editorial, gags, humor strips, sports, story strips, syndicated panels.
Library: Tape recordings by famous cartoonists on the subject of cartooning and the profession.

NATIONAL COUNCIL FOR ARTS AND EDUCATION, 743 Fifth Ave, New York, NY 10022. Tel: 212-759-5800. *Chairperson* Henry Fonda: *Exec Dir* Frances Richard.
Open 9:30 AM - 5:30 PM. No admis. Estab June 1976 as a national organization to support innovative funding proposals to insure financial stability for arts, education and cultural institutions in the United States.
Income: Financed by state appropriation and private contributions.
Publications: NCAE News, quarterly.
Activities: Docent training; NCAE Information, Inc (educational arm) educates and informs the public of the reality and nature of fiscal stress in all arts and humanities related endeavors.

NATIONAL COUNCIL OF ARCHITECTURAL REGISTRATION BOARDS,* 1735 New York Ave NW, Suite 700, Washington, DC 20006. Tel: 202-659-3996. *Exec Dir* Hayden P Mims.
Estab 1920 as a clearinghouse for architects registering from state to state. All now have laws regulating the practice of architecture. Mem: 55 officials of state architectural registration boards of the United States, Puerto Rico, Canal Zone, Virgin Islands and Guam; annual meeting June, 1978 in Los Angeles, CA.
Publications: Newsletter, quarterly; Annual Report; Architectural Registration Handbook, annually.

NATIONAL ENDOWMENT FOR THE ARTS, 2401 E St NW, Washington, DC 20506. Tel: 202-634-6369. *Chmn* Livingston L Biddle, Jr.
Open 9 AM - 5:30 PM. No admis. Estab 1965 as a national organization to make the arts available to more people across the country, to strengthen cultural institutions so they can better serve the people, and to advance cultural legacy.
Income: $114,600,000 appropriation for fiscal year 1978 for programming Federal funds that are given through grants to individuals and nonprofit organizations. Grants to organizations must be matched at least dollar for dollar by private, state, or local funds.
Publications: Guide to Programs (summary of grant programs available), annually; Annual Report; Cultural Post, bimonthly.
Library: *Librn* Chris Morrison. Open to Arts Endowment employees and scholars in arts fields for lending and reference. Holdings: Vols 2000; Per subs 220. Special Subjects: Arts, Arts Administration, Cultural Policy.

NATIONAL INSTITUTE FOR ARCHITECTURAL EDUCATION,* 139 E 52nd St, New York, NY 10022. Tel: 212-759-9154. *Chmn Bd Trustees* Hugh N Romney; *VChmn* Byron Bell; *Secy* Herman C Litwack; *Treas* Sidney L Katz; *Dir Educ* Howard H Juster; *Exec Secy* Lilian Marus.
Open Mon - Fri 9 AM - 5 PM. Inc 1894 as Society of Beaux-Arts Architects, which was dissolved Dec 1941; Beaux-Arts Institute of Design estab 1916, name changed 1956 to above. Mem: Approx 250; dues $20; annual meeting first week in Dec.
Exhibitions: Prize-winning drawings of competitions held during year.
Publications: Yearbook, annually in October.
Activities: Trustee for the Lloyd Warren Fellowship (Paris Prize in Architecture) for study and travel abroad; Hirons Alumni Scholarship to winner not enrolled in school; William Van Alen Architect Memorial Award (international competition) annual scholarship for further study or research project of some architectural nature; and other trust funds for prize awards for study and travel abroad and educational activities in the United States.

NATIONAL SCULPTURE SOCIETY, 777 Third Ave, New York, NY 10017. Tel: 212-838-5218. *Pres* Charles Parks; *VPres* John Terken; *Secy* Marilyn Newmark; *Exec Dir* Claire A Stein.
Open Mon - Fri 9 AM - 5 PM. No admis. Estab 1893 as a national organization to spread the knowledge of good sculpture. Average Annual Attendance: 4000 at annual exhibition. Mem: 350; work juried for sculp-

tor membership; vote of Bd of Directors for allied professional and patron membership; dues $10-$50 depending on class; annual meeting second Tues in Jan.
Income: Approx $80,000, not counting magazine income; (financed by endowment, membership, state appropriation and donations).
Exhibitions: Annual juried exhibition open to all United States residents; 1976, 1977 and 1978 annual exhibitions were held at the Equitable Gallery.
Publications: National Sculpture Review, quarterly; Exhibition Catalog, annually; Membership Book.
Activities: Educ Comt chooses recipients for NSS scholarships; lect open to the public, 5 vis lectr per yr; gallery talks and tours with annual exhibition; youth awards annually; exhibition prizes in the past provided consultation for large annual competitions; i.e, reverses of the dollar, half-dollar and quarter in 1976 for the US Mint, Libby Dam sculpture for US Army Corps of Engineers; scholarships offered to accredited art schools; exhibitions organized for other institutions.
Library: Open to the public for reference; a few volumes and periodicals, and photographic and original archival materials. Special Subjects: American sculpture; marketing; law; biography; history.

NATIONAL SOCIETY OF MURAL PAINTERS, INC,* 41 E 65th St, New York, NY 10021. Tel: 212-988-7700. *Secy* Lloyd L Goff.
Estab and inc 1895 to encourage and advance the standards of mural painting in America; to formulate a code for decorative competitions and by-laws to regulate professional practice. Mem: 200; dues $15, non-res $10.
Publications: Annual Bulletin of photographs of contemporary work of members; biographies and articles pertinent to the mural painting profession.
Activities: Exhibitions held in collaboration with allied professions; Ernest Piexotto Prize awarded to young artists for work in relation to architecture.

NATIONAL SOCIETY OF PAINTERS IN CASEIN AND ACRYLIC, INC, 1083 Fifth Ave, New York, NY 10028. Tel: 212-686-2659. *Pres* Mark Freeman, 307 E 37th St, New York, NY 10016; *VPres* Mina Kocherthaler & Walter Scott; *Secy* Lily Shuff, 155 W 68th St, New York, NY 10023.
Open in December during annual exhibition. Admis 50¢. Estab 1952 as a national organization for a showcase for artists in casein and acrylic; galleries rented from National Academy of Design. Average Annual Attendance: 600-1000 during exhibition. Mem: 120; membership by invitation; work must pass three juries; dues $15; annual meeting Apr.
Income: $3000 (financed by membership).
Publications: Annual catalog for the exhibition.
Activities: Demonstrations; medals and $2500 in prizes given at annual exhibition; traveling exhibitions organized and circulated.

PRINT COUNCIL OF AMERICA,* National Gallery of Art, Constitution Ave at Sixth St NW, Washington, DC 20565. Tel: 202-737-4215. *Pres* Andrew Robison; *Treas* Grace M Mayer.
Estab 1956, a nonprofit organization fostering the study and appreciation of fine prints, new and old; issues occasional publications on old and modern prints. Mem: 100 museum and university professionals and private individuals interested in prints; annual meeting April or May.

PROFESSIONAL ARTISTS GUILD, 69 Shelter Lane (Mailing Add: PO Box 11, Roslyn Heights, NY 11577. Tel: 516-621-4792. *Pres* Anne Orling; *VPres* Rhoda Sherbell; *Secy* Lucille Orzack; *Treas* Sunya Levy.
Estab 1963 as an international non-profit organization that has been serving the artist, the public and educational institutions through exhibitions, lectures, public meetings and demonstrations of the various art media. Mem: 90; membership is juried and must have had shows in a professional gallery or museum or educational institution. Dues $20; meeting first Mon every month except summer.
Income: $2500 (financed by membership and sales).
Exhibitions: Royal Academy, Stockholm, Sweden; Lincoln Center, New York City; C W Post College Art Center, Greenvale, NY; Union Carbide Building Gallery, New York City; Adelphi University, Garden City, NY.
Publications: Newsletter, monthly except during summer.
Activities: Lect open to the public, 10-12 vis lectrs per yr; individual paintings lent to public institutions; traveling exhibitions organized and circulated.

SALMAGUNDI CLUB,* 47 Fifth Ave, New York, NY 10003. Tel: 212-255-7740. *Chmn of Bd* Martin Hannon; *Corresp Secy* Ruth R Reininghaus. Gallery open during exhibitions 1 - 6 PM. No admis. Estab 1871, inc. 1880; building purchases 1917; clubhouse with living quarters for men, restaurant, gallery and library. Mem 600; dues junior $120; res artist $212, res layman $288; nonres artist $162, nonres layman $174; scholarship graduated to scale.
Exhibitions: Seven per year by artist members with cash awards.

Publications: Centennial Roster published in 1972; Salmagundi Membership Roster, biennially; Salmagundian, monthly except for summer.
Activities: Acts as organizing and screening agency between the US Navy and all qualified American artists; under its Naval Art Cooperation and Liaison (NACAL) Committee, artists are chosen and sent on short painting trips around the world to interpret the daily life and traditions of the US Navy. Lectures; art classes; awards, scholarships and prizes; buys paintings to present to museums.
Library: Over 6000 volumes with notable collection of art reference.

SOCIETY OF AMERICAN GRAPHIC ARTISTS, 1083 Fifth Ave, New York, NY 10028. Tel: 212-289-1507. *Pres* Stanley Kaplan; *VPres* Robert Conover; *VPres* Jan Gelb; *Treas* Helen Gerardia; *Corresp Secy* Bernice B Hunter; *Recording Secy* Christine Engler.
Estab 1915 as a society of printmakers; sponsors competitive and members exhibits with awards, traveling exhibits; presentation prints for associate members. Mem: Over 200 voted in by merit; dues $10; annual meeting May.
Income: Financed by membership and associate memberships.
Exhibitions: Semiannual Open Competition National Print Exhibition; Semiannual Closed Members Exhibit; National Traveling Exhibitions every two years.
Publications: Exhibition Catalog, annual; Presentation Prints for Associate Membership.
Activities: Lect open to public, 1 vis lectr per yr; competitions, cash and purchase awards; original objects of art lent; lending collection contains original prints; traveling exhibitions organized and circulated.

SOCIETY OF ANIMAL ARTISTS, INC, 151 Carroll St, City Island, Bronx, NY 10464. Tel: 212-885-2181. *Pres* Paul Branson; *VPres* Albert Gilbert; *Secy* Patricia Allen Bott; *Treas* Beverly Bender; *Mem Jury* Douglas Allen, William F Bartlett, Louis DeDonato, Richard Ellis, Donald Miller and Douglas MacClintock.
Open during exhibitions. No admis. Estab 1960 to make the people of the United States and Canada more aware of the artists who explore the beauty and habits of animals, and by so doing help ecology and the environment. Mem: 150; artists must pass jury of admissions to become a member; dues $25; meetings twice a year, or more often if needed.
Income: Financed by membership.
Exhibitions: Grand Central Art Galleries (1976 & 1977); Sportsmans Edge, New York City and Owens Gallery, Oklahoma City (1978).
Publications: Newsletter, every other month, sometimes more often.
Activities: Lectures for members only, 3 visit lectr per yr; gallery talks; slide lectures of trips with animal art by members; advisory board for those who want to study animal art and wildlife; paintings and individual objects of art lent to members, wildlife organizations, Audubon, World Wildlife Special Exhibitions; catalogs, slides, prints, color and framed reproductions, sculpture, photographs and slides all in lending collection; organize and circulate traveling exhibitions; prints, reproductions and original art sold at gallery shows.

SOCIETY OF ARCHITECTURAL HISTORIANS, 1700 Walnut St, Room 716, Philadelphia, PA 19103. Tel: 215-735-0224, 735-0246. *Pres* Adolf K Placzek; *First VPres* David Gebhard; *Second VPres* Damie Stillman; *Secy* David T Van Zanten; *Exec Secy* Rosann S Berry.
Open daily 8:30 AM - 4:30 PM. No admis. Estab to provide an international forum for those interested in architecture and its related arts, to encourage scholarly research in the field and to promote the preservation of significant architectural monuments throughout the world. Mem: 4500 who show an interest in architecture, past, present and future; dues $25; annual meeting April—Savannah, GA, April 4-8, 1979 and Madison, WI, April 23-27, 1980.
Income: Financed by membership.
Publications: Journal, quarterly; Newsletter, bimonthly.
Activities: Sponsors competitions; Alice Davis Hitchcock Book Award and Founders' Award given annually; scholarships given to student members for graduate work in architecture and architectural history; sales shop selling architectural guides and booklets and also back issues of the Journal.

SOCIETY OF ILLUSTRATORS, 128 E 63rd St, New York NY 10021. Tel: 212-838-2560. *Pres* Charles McVicker; *Exec Dir* Arpi Ermoyan.
Open Mon - Fri 10 AM - 5 PM. No admis. Estab 1901 as a national organization of professional illustrators and art directors; gallery has group, theme, one-man and juried shows, approx every three weeks. Mem: 730; monthly meeting.
Publications: Illustrators Annual.
Activities: Lectures open to public; holds annual national exhibition of best illustrations of the year; awards scholarships.

SOCIETY OF MEDALISTS,* c/o Donald A Schwartz, Treas, Old Ridgebury Rd, Danbury CT 06810. Tel: 203-792-3000. *Pres* Donald A Eifert; *Art Advisory Bd* Elvira Clain-Stefanelli, Frank Eliscu, Christopher Parks, Eric Sloane and Albert Wein.
Estab 1930 by the late art patron, George DuPont Pratt, to stimulate interest in medallic sculpture. The Society of Medalists has granted two commissions annually since 1930 to American sculptors to execute bas-relief medallic sculpture. The finished high-relief fine art medals struck by the Society are then distributed to dues paying members of the nonprofit organization. Free illustrated brochures, membership information and artists' submission inquiries will be accommodated by writing to the above address. Mem: 1200.
Publications: News Bulletin, yearly.
Activities: Medals are exhibited annually at the American Numismatic Association Convention. Complete collections of Society medals are on permanent exhibition at the World Heritage Museum, University of Illinois, 484 Lincoln Hall, Urbana, IL 61801 and R W Norton Gallery, 4747 Creswell Ave, Shreveport, LA 71106.

SOCIETY OF NORTH AMERICAN ARTISTS, INC, PO Box 37072, Millard Station, Omaha, NE 68137. Tel: 402-895-4252. *Pres* Eugene H Grimm; *VPres* Gloria D Grimm; *Secy* Michele K Berry.
Open Mon - Fri 9 AM - 4 PM. Estab October 1970 as an international organization, founded to provide all artists a simplified, expedient and low cost method to register their original work in a permanent public record for the immediate and long range future. Mem: 450; a minimum of three registrations required, original work only.
Publications: Fine Art Registry, distributed annually to members and selected public libraries.

SOUTHEASTERN COLLEGE ART CONFERENCE, Box 1022, Chapel Hill, NC 27514. Tel: 919-933-6981. *Pres* Virginia Rembert, University of Arkansas at Little Rock, AR 72204; *VPres* Martha B Caldwell, James Madison University, Harrisonburg, VA 22801; *Secy* Anne W Thomas, University of North Carolina at Chapel Hill, NC 27514; *Staff Asst* Marion Kay Smith.
Estab as a regional organization to promote art at higher education level. Mem: 300; members must be interested in purpose of organization and have paid entrance dues; dues student $5, regular $10, institutional $25; annual meeting in fall.
Publications: Annual Review.

SOUTHERN ASSOCIATION OF SCULPTORS, INC, c/o Jeffrey Bayer, University of Alabama, Huntsville, AL 35805. Tel: 205-985-6492.
Estab 1965, inc 1967, to promote the exchange of ideas and information among its members, assist institutions, museums and the public in developing an understanding of sculpture through exhibitions, demonstrations and publications. Mem: 210, participating mem restricted to Ala, Ark, DC, Fla, Ga, Ky, La, Md, Miss, NC, SC, Tenn, Va, WVa; assoc mem open to any US sculptor; annual meeting fall.
Exhibitions: Annual juried sculpture exhibition is national open exhibits; area invitations exhibitions.
Publications: Southern Association of Sculptors, quarterly; Job Information Center Bulletin, 9 times per year; periodic technical publications; Illustrated Sculptors Directory, every 2 years.
Activities: traveling exhibitions organized and circulated.
Library: AV—Slides 500 for loan.

STAINED GLASS ASSOCIATION OF AMERICA, c/o Naomi Mundy, Exec Secy, 1125 Wilmington Ave, Saint Louis, MO 63111. Tel: 314-353-5128. *Pres* Patrick J White, 3110 Glenn Pl NW, Canton, OH 44708; *VPres* H W Cummings, The Windsor Mill, North Adams, MA 01247; *Secy* Kenneth Urschel, 701 Elmhurst Ave, Valparaiso, IN 46383.

Estab 1903 as an international organization to promote the development and advancement of the stained glass craft. Mem: 500; there are four categories of membership—active member, active artist member, craft supplier member, and associate member; various criteria apply to each membership; dues vary for members with size of studio; associate members $30; semi-annual meetings, Jan and June.
Publications: Stained Glass, quarterly magazine.
Activities: Educ Dept with two and three week courses and an apprenticeship program; competitions sponsored for apprentices only, every two years with cash prizes given.

UNITED STATES COMMITTEE OF THE INTERNATIONAL ASSOCIATION OF ART, INC, c/o Dorothy Paris, VPres, 33 W 67th St, New York, NY 10023. Tel: 212-787-7063.
Estab 1952, inc March 1955 to promote greater appreciation of contemporary fine arts, regardless of genre, to uphold the status of the artists and to defend their rights, primarily on the national level, then on the international level, evaluating by comparison and appraisal; also to stimulate international cultural relations and exchanges of art and artists free of any aesthetic or other bias. Mem: 12 national art organizations of painters, sculptors and graphic arts in the United States; triennial congress—West Germany, 1979.
Publications: Information, three times per year.

VISUAL ARTISTS AND GALLERIES ASSOCIATION, INC, One World Trade Center, Suite 1535, 10048. Tel: 212-466-1390. *Exec Dir* Dorothy M Weber; *Artist Trustees* Will Barnet; Ernst Beadle; Romare Bearden; Robert Motherwell; James Rosenquist; Estate of Ben Shahn; *Gallery Trustees* Leo Castelli; Sylvan Cole; Lawrence A Fleishman; Meredith Long; Alex Rosenberg.
Open daily 9 AM - 5 PM. Estab 1976 as a nonprofit venture to help artists control and police the reproduction of their works for anything, from textile designs to photographs in text books; to act as a clearinghouse for licensing reproduction rights and set up a directory of artists and other owners of reproduction rights for international use. Mem: American 300, European 4000; all artists eligible for membership; dues $10.
Income: Financed by membership.

WESTERN ASSOCIATION OF ART MUSEUMS, PO Box 9989, Mills College, Oakland, CA 94613. Tel: 415-568-2773. *Pres* Henry T Hopkins; *VPres* Terry Melton; *Secy* Lewis Story; *Exec Dir* Lynn Jorgenson; *Prog Dir* Linda E Evans; *Exhib Adminr* Gil Dobbs.
Open Mon - Fri 9 AM - 5 PM. No admis. Estab as an international nonprofit membership organization which circulates traveling exhibitions, offers fine art insurance, and organizes educational seminars for museum professionals. Mem: Over 500; members selected by accreditation and approval of membership committee; dues active $150; annual meeting October.
Income: Over $250,000.
Publications: Exhibition Catalogs; educational publications printed in conjunction with seminars.
Activities: Seminars for museum professionals; lectures; Ilo Liston Publication Award competition is sponsored annually to award graphic design excellence in museum publications including posters, books, catalogs, annual reports, and others; scholarships and fellowships offered; member and non-member institutions may rent exhibitions organized for circulation.

ALABAMA

BIRMINGHAM

ALABAMA MUSEUM OF PHOTOGRAPHY, 4322 Glenwood Ave, 35222. Tel: 205-595-6980. *Pres & Dir* Ed Willis Barnett; *VPres* James S Larkin.
Open by appointment and invitation. No admis. Estab 1974 to promote photography as a fine art; to procure outstanding photographs from over the world and mount exhibitions in America; to maintain a laboratory for experimentation. Collections are housed in a residence, on display for students and small groups.
Income: Financed by donations, grants from National endowment for the Arts, and Alabama State Council.
Collections: Man Ray (rayographs, portraits, scenes); Samuel Chamberlain (30 photographs used to illustrate his books); Ed Willis Barnett (many photographs, color and black and white); collection of Fincken, Gore, Underwood, Widder, Fischer, and others.
Activities: Traveling exhibitions organized and circulated.

BIRMINGHAM MUSEUM OF ART, 2000 Eighth Ave N, 35203. Tel: 205-254-2565. *Dir* John David Farmer; *Cur* Edward F Weeks; *Asst Cur Decorative Arts* Gail C Andrews; *Registrar* Patricia Johnston.
Open Mon - Wed & Fri - Sat 10 AM - 5 PM; Thur 10 AM - 9 PM; Sun 2 - 6 PM. No admis. Estab 1951 as a general art museum with collections from earliest manifestation of man's creativity to contemporary work. Its goal is to illustrate the highest level of man's artistic work in an art historical context. The 24 galleries are climate controlled; lighting system is modern and controlled to latest safety standards. Average Annual Attendance: 100,000. Mem: 1000; dues $5 - $100.
Income: $600,000 (financed by membership, city appropriation and annual donations). Purchases: $80,000.
Collections: Ancient art; Revies Collection of Palestinian art; American Indian art; †Pre-Columbian; †old master painting and sculpture; †art of the American West; †contemporary American art; †Asian art; †Beeson Collection of Wedgwood; Frances Oliver Collection; of porcelain †American and English silver; †prints and drawings; Lamprecht Collection of 19th century German cast iron.
Exhibitions: Esmark Currier and Ives Collection; Folk Art from the Rockefeller Collection; Birmingham Collections; American Art before 1918; Five American Artists of Greek Ancestry; The Tiepolos: Painters to Princes and Prelates, Rubens and Humanism.
Publications: Calendar, monthly; bulletin, quarterly.
Activities: Classes for adults and chidren; docent training; lect open to the public, 12 - 15 vis lectr per yr; concerts; gallery talks; tours. Competitions; artmobile; individual paintings lent to city offices; traveling exhibitions organized and circulated; museum shop selling reproductions, prints and gifts.
Library: Open to the public by request. Holdings: Vols 5000.

BIRMINGHAM PUBLIC LIBRARY,* 2020 Seventh Ave, N, 35203, Tel: 205-254-2551. *Dir* George R Stewart.
Open Mon - Fri 9 AM - 9 PM; Sat 9 AM - 6 PM; Sun 3 - 6 PM. Estab 1909; gallery opened 1927; Art Department opened 1946.
Holdings: Vols 16,000; Per subs 1420; Other—Pictures, mounted and unmounted 40,000.
Special Collections: Small permanent collection of prints, paintings and Mexican pottery.

KAPPA PI INTERNATIONAL HONORARY ART FRATERNITY, PO Box 7843, Midfield, 35228. Tel: 205-428-4540. *Pres* Miss Garnet R

Leader; *VPres* Dr Ralph M Hudson; *Secy* Elmer J Porter; *Treas* Mrs Myrtle Kerr; *Editor* Arthur Kennon.
For further information see National and Regional Organizations.

FAIRHOPE

PERCY H WHITING ART CENTER,* 401 Oak St, 36532. Tel: 205-928-2228. *Pres* Mrs CD Harrell, Jr.
Open Mon - Sat 10 AM - Noon, 2 - 5 PM; cl New Year's, Thanksgiving, Christmas. No admis. Estab 1952. Mem: Dues single $5, sustaining $10, life $500.
Collections: Small collection of paintings.
Activities: Art classes for adults and children; demonstrations; gallery talks; films; temporary exhibitions.

HUNTSVILLE

HUNTSVILLE ART LEAGUE AND MUSEUM ASSOCIATION, INC, 206 B Bob Wallace, 35801. Tel: 205-534-2511. *Pres* Shirley Feaux; *VPres* Mary Gamble McGaha; *Secy* Robin Estell; *Treas* Chuck Long; *Gallery Exhibits Chmn* Louise Hope and Ophelia Ealy; *Educational Chmn* Louise Smith and Gail Hansen.
Open Mon - Fri 10 AM - 2 PM. Estab 1957, the League is a nonprofit organization dedicated to promoting and stimulating the appreciation of the visual arts. Average Annual Attendance: 10,000. Mem: 600; dues student $5, adults $10, and higher for additional members of family; annual meeting August.
Exhibitions: Annual Clothesline Shows at the Heart of Huntsville Mall and downtown around the Square in the spring; continuous exhibitions throughout Huntsville.
Publications: Monthly newsletter on activities plus exhibition opportunities in the Southeast.
Activities: Classes for adults and children; film series; competitions.

HUNTSVILLE MUSEUM OF ART, 700 Monroe St SW, 35801. Tel: 205-534-4566. *Chmn Bd* Joyce Griffin; *VChmn Bd* L Tennent Lee, III; *Secy Bd* Ruth Linde; *Treas Bd* William B Thomas; *Dir* Thomas A Bowles, III; *Bus Officer* Nancy W Holliman; *Cur* Carolyn Wood; *Admin Asst* Beverly Humphrey.
Open Tues - Sat 10 AM - 5 PM; Sun 1 - 5 PM; Thurs Eve 7 - 9 PM; cl Mon and month of August. No admis, small donation requested for special exhibitions. Estab 1970 to provide for the exhibition, particularly to students of the public schools and in general to the population of the City, of statuary and all forms of the graphic and decorative arts and other fine arts; to encourage by appropriate means the cultivation of artistic talents and recognition of artistic achievements. Gallery is located in the Von Braun Civic Center; 16,000 sq ft of atmospherically-controlled exhibition galleries, carpentry shop, art storage area and vault. Average Annual Attendance: 40,000. Mem: 1500; dues vol/students $5, individual $10, Family $15, contributing $25, sustaining $50, patron $100; annual meeting last Mon in November.
Income: $330,700 (financed by membership, city appropriation, grants and support groups). Purchases: $348,000.
Collections: †Contemporary American Graphics portion of Comprehensive Graphics Collection; collection of Japanese and Chinese objects including porcelain, jade, bronze and ivory carvings.
Exhibitions: Paintings of Maurice Groser; Royal Copenhagen Porcelain; City of Huntsville Bicentennial Exhibition; Images for Eternity: 3000 years of Egyptian Art; Al Beyer, one-man show; Contemporary Courtroom Art; Jewels of Peter Carl Faberge and Other Master Jewelers;

Watercolors of John Marin; Contemporary Enamelists; New Orleans: The City that Care Forgot; Old Master and Contemporary Printmakers; Ballet Theatre Design; California Bay Area Art; Art of China and Japan; Alice in Wonderland by Nall; Works of Hans Grohs; Historical Porcelain Figures by Martha Darwin Thompson; Art of the Space Era; Models of Leonard da Vince Drawings; Russian Space Art.
Publications: Museum Newsletter, quarterly.
Activities: Docent training; lect open to public, 9 vis lect per yr; concerts; gallery talks; tours. exten dept for art enrichment lectures presented by volunteers in fifth and sixth grades in city and county schools; individual paintings lent to other museums; traveling exhibitions organized and circulated; sales shop selling books, original art, reproductions, prints, slides, jewelry, stationery and seasonal items.
Library: *Vol* Sophye Lowe Young. Open to public upon individual request. Holdings: Vols 800; Per subs 12; Other—Cassettes 20; Sales catalogs 87; Exhibition catalogs 400, Unbound per 700.

MOBILE

ART PATRONS LEAGUE OF MOBILE, Box 8055, 36608. Tel: 205-344-2148. *Pres* Mrs Joe Gunter Jr; *VPres* Mrs Medford Roe; *Secy* Mrs Claude Warren III.
Estab 1964 to promote the education and appreciation of the visual and graphic arts in the Mobile area. Mem: 425; dues active $12, assoc $20.
Income: $50,000 (financed by membership). Purchases: $28,000.
Activities: Classes for adults and children; workshops; lect open to public, 3 vis lectr per yr; gallery talks; tours; sales shop selling original art, prints, and reproductions.

FINE ARTS MUSEUM OF THE SOUTH, Langan Park. (Mailing Add: PO Box 8404, 36608). Tel: 205-342-4642. *Chmn Bd* Kenneth M Hannon; *Dir* Mary O'Neill Victor; *Asst Dir* Harold M Wittmann; *Secy* Kathryn W Lewis.
Open Tues - Sat 10 AM - 5 PM; Sun Noon - 5 PM; cl Mon. Estab 1964 to foster the appreciation of art and provide art education programs for the community. Average Annual Attendance: 100,000. Mem: 1800; dues associate $250, patron $100, supporting $50, family $25, individual $15.
Income: Financed by membership and city appropriation.
Collections: 19th & 20th century American and European paintings, sculpture, prints, and decorative arts; Wellington Collection of wood engravings; †American crafts; Oriental art; African art.
Exhibitions: Visions of Courtly India; Presidential China; Lion Rugs from Fars; Locks from Iran; American Folk Art; Pennsylvania Quilts; Forms in Metal; Jewish Art: A Continuing Heritage; Cleveland Woodward: Painter by God's Good Light.
Publications: Calendar, quarterly.
Activities: Classes for adults and children; docent training; lect open to public; competitions; Junior Discovery Museum opening in Fall 1978.
Library: *Dir* Mary O'Neill; *Librn* Debra Bryant. For reference only. Holdings: I Vols 850; AV—Slides 2000; Other—Clipping files, exhibitions catalogs, framed reproductions, pamphlets, photographs, reproductions.

MOBILE ART ASSOCIATION, INC,* c/o Vasco Geer Jr, *Pres,* 39 Alverson Rd, 36608. Tel: 205-344-7073. *Secy* Mrs George Ide; *Treas* Louis S Conover.
Estab 1943 to promote and support a cultural program among artists, sculptors, and craftsmen in the field of fine arts. Mem: 436; annual meeting May.
Income: Financed by membership.
Collections: Annual fall juried show collection.
Exhibitions: Fall juried show; Dauphin Island Show; Old Mobile Show; Spring non-juried show.
Publications: Mobile Art Association, Inc. Yearbook.
Activities: Classes for adults and children; competitions; co-sponsor of Mobile Museum of the South at Mobile.

MUSEUM OF THE CITY OF MOBILE, Reference Library, 355 Government St, 36609. Tel: 205-438-7569. *Museum Dir* Caldwell Delaney; *Registrar* Roy U Tallon.
Open Tues - Sat 10 AM - 5 PM; cl Mon. Estab 1954 as a reference library for scholars doing research on local history; gallery not maintained.
Income: $1500 (financed by city appropriation).
Holdings: AV—Slides; Other—Clipping files, manuscripts, original art works, original documents, photographs, prints.
Special Collections: Armistead Collection of glass negatives of subjects related to Mobile area; Fenollosa Collection of Chinese and Japanese art.

UNIVERSITY OF SOUTH ALABAMA, Ethnic American Slide Library, College of Arts & Sciences, University Blvd, 36688. Tel: 205-460-6337. *Head* James E Kennedy.

Open Daily 8 AM - 5 PM. Estab for the acquisition of slides of works produced by Afro-American, Mexican American and native American artists and the distribution of duplicate slides of these works to educational institutions and individuals engaged in research.
Holdings: Other—Slides.
Special Collections: 19th and 20th century ethnic American art works in drawing, painting, printmaking, photography, ceramics and sculpture.
Publications: Slide Catalog.

MONTEVALLO

UNIVERSITY OF MONTEVALLO, The Gallery, 35115. Tel: 205-665-2521, exten 224. *Art Dept Chmn* Dr Frank McCoy; *Dir of Gallery* Ted Metz.
Open Mon - Fri 9 AM - 5 PM; No admis. Estab Sept 1977 to supply students and public with high quality contemporary art; also special exhibitions; gallery 27 x 54 ft, track lighting, floors and walls carpeted; no windows. Average Annual Attendance: 1500 - 2000.
Income: $2000 - $2500. (financed by state appropriation and regular department budget).
Publications: High quality posters and catalogs.
Activities: Management classes; lect open to the public, 6 vis lectr per year; gallery talks; traveling exhibitions organized and circulated.

MONTGOMERY

ALABAMA STATE DEPARTMENT OF ARCHIVES AND HISTORY, 624 Washington Ave, 36130. Tel: 205-832-6510. *Dir* Milo B Howard Jr.
Open Mon - Fri 8 AM - 5 PM; Sat, Sun & holidays 8 AM - 11:30 AM & 12:30 - 5 PM; Open to research Mon - Fri 8 AM - 4:30 PM. No admis. Estab 1901 to preserve the history of Alabama through artifacts and archives; art gallery maintained.
Income: Financed by state appropriation.
Collections: All collections are permanent; portraits of prominent Alabamians; paintings depicting Alabama life; engraving and etchings of Alabama scenes; military artifacts; Indian artifacts; historical collections concerning history of the Unived States. Also fine arts, as porcelain; china; silver; portraits; William Rufus King Room; French Room.
Publications: Alabama Historical Quarterly; Alabama Official and Statistical Register, quadrennial.

MONTGOMERY MUSEUM OF FINE ARTS, 440 S McDonough St, 36104. Tel: 205-834-3490. *Dir* Henry Flood Robert, Jr; *Asst Dir* Theodore W James; *Cur* Diane J Gingold; *Cur Educ* Thomas A Rhodes; *Registrar* Barbara J Redjinski; *Pres Asn* Mrs Frederick W Wilkerson; *First VPres* J L Sabel; *Second VPres* Mrs. Robert Arrington; *Secy* Mrs. W Kendrick Upchurch, Jr; *Treas,* Mrs Jack P Evans; *Past Pres* Mrs Robert S. Weil.
Open Tues - Sat 10 AM - 5 PM; Thurs 10 AM - 10 PM; Sun 1 - 6 PM; cl Mon. No admis. Estab 1930 to generally promote the cultural artistic and higher educational life of the city of Montgomery by all methods that may be properly pursued by a museum or art gallery. The gallery occupies the upper floor of a two-story museum/library structure built by the city in the late 1950s. Five galleries provide the necessary space for displaying the permanent collection and circulating shows; 180 seat auditorium. Average Annual Attendance: 70,000. Mem: 1400; dues regular $10 - $30, associate $50 - $150, leadership $250 - $5000; annual meeting Oct.
Income: $425,000 (financed by membership, city and county appropriations and grants). Purchases: $15,200.
Collections: †Paintings by American artists from early 19th century through the present; master prints of the 15th and 19th centuries; †contemporary graphics and other works on paper by artists living in the South; decorative arts.
Exhibitions: The Five Sense Store and Space Place; The Work of Charles White: An American Experience; Afro-American Art from Alabama Collections; Christmas Trees Around the World; The George Verdak Collection: Eras of the Dance; Permanent Collections Survey; Drawings by Ronald Milhoan; Montgomery Art Guild 16th Annual Exhibition; Antique Silver; In-Museum Studio; Throne of the Third Heaven of the Nations Millenium General Assembly; 18th Dixie Annual; Anne Goldthwaite, 1869-1944; Life in Colonial America; 10th Annual South Central Alabama High School Art Exhibition; Lila J Wells: Paintings; A Phillip Coley: Paintings; The Arthur M Sackler Collection: Piranesi, Drawings and Etchings at the Avery Architecture Library, Columbia University, New York; Shakespeare Portfolio from the Folger Shakespeare Library, Washington, DC; American Quilts; Montgomery Photographers: James Russell Baxley, Jr, Robert M Guy, Reginald Jenkins, Jr, Mike Mayo, Philip Scarsbrook and Lewis Ware; Paper Negatives: Photographs by Hampton Link; Tiffany Favrile Glass; Folk Art and Crafts: The Deep South; Master Prints from the 15th through 18th Centuries; Barbara Gallagher: Paintings.

Publications: Calendar of Events, quarterly; Annual Report; exhbitions catalogs for selected shows.
Activities: Classes for children; docent training; films; lect open to the public, 4 - 8 vis lectr per yr; concerts; gallery talks; tours; competitions; individual paintings and original objects of art lent to museums and art galleries, lending collection of cassettes, film strips, 275 original prints, 450 paintings, 1300 slides; traveling exhibitions organized and circulated; museum shop selling books, original art, reproductions, prints, crafts, stationery and jewelry.
Library: For reference. Holdings: Vols 400; Per subs 22.
—**Alabama Art League,*** 440 S McDonough St, 36104. Tel: 205-263-2519. *Pres* Philip Coley; *Secy* Janice Ross.
Estab 1929 to build a museum in the capital city of Montgomery and help the artists of Alabama in every way possible. Mem: 300; annual meeting first Sat in Nov.
Income: Financed by endowment, membership, city and state appropriation.
Exhibitions: Exhibitions by members at Montgomery Museum of Fine Arts; Birmingham Museum of Art; Mobile Art Gallery; George Washington Carver Museum; Tuskegee Institute; Goodwater Public Library; Convention hall; Gadsden; The Governor's Mansion and WSFA-TV, Montgomery.
Publications: Alabama Art League Quarterly (newsletter).
Activities: Lect open to the public, 1 vis lectr per yr; competitions; schol; lending collection consisting of all media.

OPELIKA

LEWIS COOPER JUNIOR MEMORIAL LIBRARY AND ARTS CENTER, 200 S Sixth St, 36801. (Mailing Add: PO Box 125, 36801). Tel: 205-749-1426. *Dir* Mrs Sammie D Meadows; *Librn* Roberta Greene.
Open Mon - Thurs 9 AM - 7:30 PM; Fri 9 AM - 5 PM; Sat 9 AM - Noon. Estab 1941 to provide free library service to all residents of the community, district or region without discrimination. Under the direction of the Opelika Arts Association. Circ: 60,000.
Income: Approx $60,000 (financed by city appropriation). Purchases: $8000.
Holdings: Vols 25,000; Per subs 45; AV—Cassettes, phonorecords; Other—Clipping files, framed reproductions.

SELMA

STURDIVANT HALL, 713 Mabry St (Mailing Add: PO Box 1205, 36701). Tel: 205-872-5626. *Pres* J Mel Gilmer; *Cur* Mrs Jefferson Ratcliffe.
Open Tues - Sat 9 AM - 4 PM; Sun 2 - 4 PM. Admis adult $2; student $1. Estab 1957 as a museum with emphasis on the historical South. Period furniture of the 1850's in a magnificent architectural edifice built 1852-53. Average Annual Attendance: 10,000. Mem: 480; dues $10 - $1000; annual meeting April.
Income: Financed by membership, city and state appropriations.
Collections: †Period furniture; objects of art; textiles.
Publications: Brochure.
Activities: Lect open to public; tours.

TALLADEGA

TALLADEGA COLLEGE, Savery Art Gallery, 627 W Battle St, 35160. Tel: 205-362-4961. *Dir* Edward Jennings.
Open 9 AM - 5 PM. No admis. Estab to exhibit student art work, faculty art work and traveling exhibitions; gallery is 25 x 35 ft, has adjustable lights; located in Library Bldg. basement. Average Annual Attendance: 1500.
Income: Financed by college funds.
Collections: Gallery maintains a collection, but no additional artwork has been added in some time.
Exhibitions: Photo Exhibit; Student Exhibit; Art Instructor Exhibit; Arts Festival Exhibit.
Activities: Lects open to the public, 12 vis lectr per yr; concerts; gallery talks; individual paintings lent to faculty, students and administration personnel; lending collection contains prints of paintings; museum shop and sales shop.

THEODORE

BELLINGRATH GARDENS AND HOME, Rt 1 (Mailing Add: Box 60, 36582). Tel: 205-973-2217. *General Mgr* John M Brown.
Open daily 7 AM to dusk. Admis Gardens $3; Home $3.75 additional. Estab 1932 to perpetuate and educate appreciation of nature, and display man-made objets d'art; the gallery houses the world's largest public display of Boehm porcelain, and the Bellingrath Home contains priceless antiques. Average Annual Attendance: 250,000.
Income: Financed by Foundation.

Collections: Boehm Porcelain; Antiques from Europe and America.
Publications: Brochures, available on request; Hardbound book, available.
Activities: Classes for children; tours; lending collection contains kodachromes, motion pictures, slides; sales shop selling books, magazines, reproductions, prints, slides.

TUSCALOOSA

ARTS AND HUMANITIES COUNCIL OF TUSCALOOSA COUNTY, INC, Box 1117, 35401. Tel: 205-553-3671. *Pres* Mrs J D Leapard; *Exec Dir* Tom Boozer.
Open Weekdays 8 AM - 5 PM. No admis. Estab June 26, 1970 for the development, promotion and coordination of educational, cultural and artistic activities of the city and county of Tuscaloosa. Mem: 410 individual, 30 organization; dues individual, $5, organization; $25, annual meeting in June, meetings quarterly.
Income: Financed by endowment, membership, city and state appropriation.
Publications: Lively Arts Calendar, quarterly.
Activities: Dramatic programs; concerts; competitions.

TUSCUMBIA

TENNESSEE VALLEY ART CENTER, 511 N Water St (Mailing Add: PO Box 474, 35674). Tel: 205-383-0533. *Pres* Mary B Brown; *First VPres* Nelle Bigbee; *Second VPres* Edward B Johnson; *Treas* Louise Mays; *Chmn of Bd* Katherine M Owen; *Coordinator* Ina Guise; *CETA Dir in Training* Julie Beckman.
Open Tues - Sun 1 - 5 PM; Cl last week of each month. No admin to members; adults 50 cents, children 25 cents. Chartered 1963; building completed 1973; to create a higher level of culture in the arts in this metro area and to bring together all persons interested in the arts with planned programs, classes, workshops and special events; the gallery is 60 x 40 ft buff brick with three arches and two columns; main Big Gallery has track lights, the small gallery has well-lighted work room that sometime serves as offices; an upstairs area is used for working or storage; gallery was designed for additional expansion; it is located one block from the birthplace of Helen Keller on the Commons in Tuscumbia. Average Annual Attendance: No figures available. Mem: 300; dues $3 & $5; annual meetings third Mon in Mar.
Income: $12,000 (financed by membership and state appropriation).
Collections: Very small with only donated artwork and things.
Exhibitions: (1976-77) Exhibition South 77; Children Art; Annual Juried Photography Show; Annual Outdoor Art Show.
Publications: Monthly newsletter and calendar of events. Calendar of Local Scenes.
Activities: Classes for adults and children; dramatic programs; special workshops; lectr open to the public, 5 vis lectr per yr; concerts; gallery talks; tours; competitions; exten dept serving senior citizens; sponsor rotating art exhibits by member artists in public and private buildings; traveling exhibitions organized and circulated; sales shop selling original art; prints and small crafts and sculptures.
Library: Reference material from library of Sheldon Chaney noted author on drama, music architecture and art donated; currently uncataloged.

TUSKEGEE

TUSKEGEE INSTITUTE,* George Washington Carver Museum, 36088. Tel: 205-727-8479. *Dir & Cur* Elaine F Thomas; *Art Gallery Dir* Stefania Jarkowski.
Open Mon - Sat 10 AM - 4 PM; Sun 1 - 4 PM. No admis. Estab 1938 to house Dr Carver's extensive collections of native plants, minerals, birds, his products from the peanut, sweet potato, and clay. Average Annual Attendance: Approximately 13,000.
Income: Financed by the college.
Collections: Gallery maintains a permanent collection of traditional and contemporary paintings and sculpture; achievements of Dr George Washington Carver in science and art; African art; historical dioramas; artifacts of Tuskegee Institute.
Exhibitions: Dr Carver's permanent exhibit of vegetables he started in 1904; traveling and monthly exhibitions.
Publications: Museum brochures; art gallery exhibition catalogs; historical dioramas.
Activities: Classes for adults and children; dramatic programs; material available to museums and educational institutions; lect open to the public, 5 vis lectr per yr; concerts; gallery talks; tours; competitions; exten department serving the entire United States; individual paintings and

original objects of art lent; lending collection contains paintings, original art works, photographs, traveling exhibitions organized and circulated; book shop.

UNIVERSITY

UNIVERSITY OF ALABAMA ART GALLERY, Garland Hall, (Mailing Add: Box F, 35486). Tel: 205-348-5967. *Dir* Angelo Granata. Open Mon - Sat 8 AM - 5 PM; Sun 2 - 5 PM. No admis. Estab 1946.
Collections: Small collection of paintings, prints, photography, drawings, sculpture and ceramics, primarily modern.
Exhibitions: Approximately 15 exhibitions per year.

ALASKA

ANCHORAGE

ALASKA ARTISTS GUILD, PO Box 1888, 99501. *Pres* Ric Swenson; *VPres* Dieter Doppelfield and Susan LaGrand-Fisher; *Secy* Pat Fridley; *Funding* Marie Shaunnessy; *Newsletter Editors* Caryl Strom and An-Morgan-Curry; *Publicity* Linda Brady.
Estab 1972 to provide an association for the educational interaction of qualified artists and to provide an education focus for the visual arts in the community. Mem: 87; qualification for membership requires talent and training and/or experience in the visual arts; dues $15; meetings second Tues each month.
Income: $1500 (financed by membership).
Exhibitions: Alaska Festival of Mus Art Exhibit.
Publications: Alaska Artists Guild Newsletter, monthly except July and August.
Activities: Lectr open to the public, 3 - 4 vis lectr per yr; gallery talks; competitions Betty Park Memorial painting award given; schol; individual paintings and original objects of art lent to colleges and school by members.

ANCHORAGE HISTORICAL AND FINE ARTS MUSEUM, 121 W Seventh Ave, 99501. Tel: 907-264-4326. *Dir* R L Shalkop; *Cur of Educ* Patricia Wolf: *Cur of Exhibits* Juan Alvarez; *Cur of Coll* Walter Van-Horn.
Open Sept - May, Tues - Sat 9 AM - 5 PM; Sun 1 - 5 PM. June - Aug, Mon, Wed, Fri & Sat 9 AM - 5 PM; Tues & Thurs 9 AM - 9 PM; Sun 1 - 5 PM. No admis. Estab 1968 to collect and display Alaskan art and artifacts of all periods; to present changing exhibitions of the art of the world. Average Annual Attendance: 107,000 (1977). Mem: 900; dues $5 up; annual meeting Oct.
Income: $667,000 (financed by city appropriation). Purchases: $150,000.
Collections: †Alaskan Eskimo and Indian; †Alaskan history; †Alaskan art; American art; Primitive art (nonAmerican).
Exhibitions: (1976-78) The Athapaskans; North to the Pole; Early Missions in Alaska; Eustace Ziegler Retrospective; All Alaska Exhibition; Alaska Festival of Native Arts; Earth, Fire and Fibre Show.
Publications: Newsletter, monthly.
Activities: Classes for children; dramatic programs; lect open to the public, 10 vis lectr per yr; concerts; tours; competitions; individual paintings lent to municipal offices; lending collection contains original art works 150; traveling exhibitions organized and circulated; museum shop selling books, magazines, original art, prints, slides and Alaskan Native art.
—**Archives.** Tel. 907-264-4326. *Museum Archivist* M Diane Brenner.
Open Tues - Fri 9 AM - 5 PM. Estab 1968 to maintain archives of Alaska materials, chiefly the Cook Inlet area.
Income: Financed by city appropriation. Purchases: $3000.
Holdings: Vols 2000; Per subs 28; AV—Audio tapes, cassettes; motion pictures, phonorecords, slides; Other—Clipping files, exhibition catalogs, memorabilia, original documents, pamphlets, photographs 5000.
Special Subjects: Alaska Native peoples, Alaska history and culture, American art, and Museum techniques.
Special Collections: Mostly photograph collections as the Hinchey-Alagco Photograph Collection of approximately 4000 pictures of the Waldex/Copper River area.
Publications: Museum newsletter, monthly; occasional papers and exhibition catalogs.

FAIRBANKS

ALASKA ASSOCIATION FOR THE ARTS,* PO Box 2786, 99707. Tel: 907-456-6485. *Pres* Donna Matschke; *First VPres* Walter Ensign; *Second VPres* Carol Thomson; *Secy* Mary K Barsdale; *Treas* Molly Heath; *Historian* Mildred Wenger; *Exec Dir* Irene Carr-Bayless.
Open office Mon - Fri 9 AM - 5 PM; gallery Mon - Fri 10 AM - 5 PM; Sat, Sun & holidays 2 - 4 PM. Estab Nov 1965 to expand the opportunities for citizens to enjoy and participate in cultural programs; to assist and promote the programs of existing art organizations and to encourage formation of new ones in community; to encourage educational programs

designed to strengthen and improve the arts; to facilitate touring of professional performers and exhibits; to act as coordinator between local arts groups and the national and state council on the arts; management of Civic Center Building at Alaskaland. Average Annual Attendance: 8000 - 10,000. Mem: 93, comprised of individuals, businesses and art groups; annual meeting in April.
Income: $24,000 (financed by city and state appropriation, and national grant).
Publications: Cultural Calendar, bi-monthly, Sept - May.
Activities: Dramatic programs; art exhibits and auctions; art balls; film programs for adults and children; demonstrations and workshops; educational TV programs; Artist-in-the Schools and Artist-in-Residence programs; sponsorship; provide administrative service on grants for other art organizations.

UNIVERSITY OF ALASKA

—**Museum,** 99701. Tel: 907-479-7505. *Dir* L J Rowinski; *Cur* D Larsen; *Coordr Exhib & Educational Programs* T Dickey.
Open Summer 9 AM - 5 PM; Winter 1 - 5 PM. No admis. Estab 1929 to collect, preserve and interpret the natural and cultural history of Alaska; gallery contains 6000 sq ft of exhibition space. Average Annual Attendance: 78,000.
Income: Financed by state appropriation.
Activities: Educ dept; lect, 1 - 2 vis lectr per yr; school tours; traveling exhibitions organized and circulated; museum shop selling pamphlets.
—**Elmer E Rasmuson Library,** 99701. Tel: 907-479-7224. *Dir* H Theodore Ryberg; *Head Catalog Dept* Sharon West; *Head Reader Services* David A Hales; *Head Archives* Paul McCarthy; *Head Acquisitions Dept* William Smith; *Head Media Services* Edmund Cridge.
Open Mon - Thurs 7:30 AM - 10 PM; Fri 7:30 AM - 6 PM; Sat 1 - 6 PM; Sun 1 - 8 PM; when school not in session 8 AM - 5 PM. Estab 1922 to support research and curriculum of the university. Circ: 57,000.
Income: Financed by state appropriation.
Holdings: Vols 500,000; Per subs 2500; AV—Audio tapes, cassettes, film strips, microfiche, microfilm, motion pictures, phonorecords, slides, video tapes; Other—Original documents; photographs.
Special Collections: 70,000 print reference photograph collection on Alaska and the Polar Regions; paintings by Alaskan artists—C Rusty Heurlin and Claire Fejes; lithographs of Fred Machetanz; photographs of early Alaskan bush pilots are displayed in the library.

HAINES

SHELDON MUSEUM AND CULTURAL CENTER, Box 236, 99827. Tel: 907-766-2128. *Dir Sheldon Museum* Elisabeth S Hakkinen; *Pres Chilkat Valley Historical Society* Karl Ward; *VPres* Carl Heinmiller; *Secy* Jean Smith; *Treas* Retha Young.
Open daily 2 - 4 PM. Admis adults 50¢, children 25¢. Estab 1925, under operation of Chilkat Valley Historical Society since 1975, for the purpose of collecting, displaying and explaining local and Alaskan history, artifacts and mementoes; the gallery is presently located in a warehouse but new building will be available later. Average Annual Attendance: 1500. Mem: 74; dues $5; annual meeting 2nd Thurs Jan.
Income: Financed by membership and other sources.
Collections: Indian artifacts, basically Tlingit.
Publications: Historical column in newspaper, weekly.
Activities: Lect open to the public; sales shop selling books; Children's Corner.
Library. Dir Elisabeth S Hakkinen. Open to the public for reference only. Holdings: Vols 200.

JUNEAU

ALASKA STATE MUSEUM, Whittier St, (Mailing Add: Pouch FM, 99811). *Dir* Richard Engen; *Chief Cur* Alan Munro, *Dep Chief Cur* Dan Monroe, *Cur Collections* Bette Hulbert; *Cur Temporary Exhib* Kesler Woodward; *Cur Exhib* Ed Way; *Cur Educ* Martha Stevens; *Conservator* May Pat Wyatt.
Open Weekdays 9 AM - 5 PM; weekends 1 - 5 PM; summer weekdays 9 AM - 9 PM. No admis. Estab 1900 to collect, preserve, exhibit and interpret objects of special significance or value in order to promote public appreciation of Alaska's cultural heritage, history, art and natural environment. Gallery occupies two floors; first floor houses permanent and temporary exhibits on 1400 sq ft with 14 ft ceiling; second floor houses permanent exhibits. Average Annual Attendance: 75,000 with more than 100,000 including outreach programs.
Income: Financed by state appropriation and grants. Purchases: $50,000.
Collections: †Alaskan ethnographic material including Eskimo, Aleut, Athabaskan, Tlingit, Haida and Tsimshian artifacts; †historical and contemporary Alaskan art; †Gold Rush and early Alaskan industrial-historical material.

Exhibitions: (1976-78) Alaska Positive; monthly one-person or group shows by Alaskan and non-Alaskan artists/craftsman; Works from the Canadian Art Bank.
Publications: Museum Alaska, monthly.
Activities: Educ dept; docent training; circulate learning kits to Alaska public schools; concerts; gallery talks; tours; competitions; exten dept; individual paintings and original objects of art lent to other museums, libraries, historical societies; lending collection contains original prints, photographs, 8 traveling exhibits of photographs, prints, etc.
Library: Cur of Educ Martha Stevens. Open to staff, others on request. Holdings: Vols 1500 Per subs 25.

NOME

NOME ARTS COUNCIL, Box 233, 99762. *Pres* John J Shaffer; *VPres* Delores Orman; *Secy* Barbara Shaffer.
Estab to assist local museum in gathering American Native (Eskimo) and historic artifacts and artwork.
Income: Financed by membership, state appropriation and national funds.

NOME MUSEUM,* Front St, 99762. Tel: 907-443-2440. *Chief Cur & Librn* Dave Wellman.
Open Mon - Sat Noon - 8 PM; cl Sun & legal holidays. No admis. Estab 1964.
Income: Financed by city appropriation.
Collections: Historical material covering Nome's Gold Rush; Eskimo artifacts; archaeology; nature art; contemporary art; paintings.
Exhibitions: Permanent exhibitions from the collection; temporary exhibitions.
Library: Open to the public. Holdings: 4000 vols.

SITKA

SHELDON JACKSON COLLEGE, Sheldon Jackson Museum, Lincoln St (Mailing Add: PO Box 479, 99835). Tel: 907-747-5228. *Dir/Cur* Peter L Corey; *Museum Aide* Elizabeth F Goodwin.
Open Oct - April Tues - Fri & Sun 1 - 4 PM; May - Sept Mon - Sun 8 AM - 5 PM. Admis $1 for over 18. Estab 1888, the first museum in Alaska, for the purpose of collecting and preserving the cultural remains of the Alaskan natives in the form of artifacts; museum occupies one room with permanent displays concerned with Tlingit, Haida, Aleut, Athabascan and Eskimo culture. Average Annual Attendance: 35,000.
Income: $30,000 (financed by admission fee, sales, donation and college support). Purchases: $500.
Collections: Ethnographic material from Tlingit, Haida, Aleut, Athabascan, Eskimo, and some Russian.
Publications: Brochures: catalogs of Ethnological Collections.
Activities: Lect open to the public, 1-2 vis lectr per yr; gallery talks; tours; traveling exhibitions organized and circulated; museum shop selling books, magazines, original art, prints, slides.

SOUTHEAST ALASKA REGIONAL ARTS COUNCIL, INC,* PO Box 678, 99835. Tel: 907-747-8581. *Exec Dir* Jan Craddick; *Secy & Coordinator* Elinora Brandner; *Pres* Linda Larsen; *VPres* Twyla Coughlin; *Secy* Judy Auger; *Treas* Corrinne Kenway.
Open 9 - 4:30 PM. Estab in 1973 as a coordinating agency for arts organization and community arts councils in Southeast Alaska. Mem: arts councils from 13 communities, serves additional communities in Southeast; annual meeting first weekend in Oct.
Income: Financed by membership, local school districts and municipalities, local contributions, and grants from the Alaska State Council on the Arts, National Endowment for the Arts, American Revolution Bicentennial Commission. Purchases: $200,000.
Publications: Who Has An Idea (book of stories, articles and poems by children).
Activities: Classes; workshops, two-week camp for junior and senior high school students offering enrichment programs in dance, drama, music and visual arts; seven-community theater design project; concert tours.

ARIZONA

DOUGLAS

DOUGLAS ART ASSOCIATION, Little Gallery, 11th St at Pan American Ave (Mailing Add: PO Box 256, 85607). Tel: 602-364-2633. *Pres* Bee Jay Zans; *First VPres* Hope Ramos; *Second VPres* Gayle Bell; *Secy* Dorothy Fernandez.
Open Daily 1:30 - 4 PM; cl Mon. No admis. Estab 1960 as a non-profit tax exempt organization dedicated to promoting the visual arts and general cultural awareness in the Douglas, Arizona and Agua Prieta, Sonora

area; the Little Gallery is operated in a city-owned bldg with city cooperation. Average Annual Attendance: 2000. Mem: 100; dues $7.50 and $10.
Income: Financed by membership and fund raising events.
Collections: †Two Flags Festival International Collections for the cities of Douglas and Agua Prieta, Mexico.
Exhibitions: Monthly exhibitions by local and regional arts and craftsmen; Annual Two Flags Festival Exhibit; Outdoor Show.
Publications: Monthly newsletter.
Activities: Classes for adults and children; workshops in painting and various art activities; lect open to the public; gallery talks; competitions with cash awards; school; sales shop selling books and donated items.

DRAGOON

AMERIND FOUNDATION, INC, Triangle T Road (Mailing Add: PO Box 248, 85609). Tel: 602-586-3003. *Dir* Dr Charles C Di Peso.
Open Mon - Fri 8 AM - Noon & 1 - 5 PM. No admis. Estab 1937 for archaeological research primarily on Southwest, and maintaining a museum and art gallery. Average Annual Attendance: 6000.
Income: Financed by private foundation.
Collections: American Indian Art and other American art.
Publications: Amerind Publications, Nos 1-9.
Activities: Museum shop.
—Amerind Research Library.
Open to scholars by appointment.
Holdings: Vols 16,000; Per subs 350.
Special Subjects: Archaeological and ethnological materials.

FLAGSTAFF

MUSEUM OF NORTHERN ARIZONA, Route 4, Box 720, 86001. Tel: 602-774-5211. *Dir* Dr Hermann K Bleibtreu; *Pres Bd Trustees* Dr Edward B Danson; *Cur Anthropology* Dr Alexander J Lindsay.
Open Mon - Sat 9 AM - 5 PM; Sun 1:30 - 5 PM. No admis. Estab 1928 to maintain a museum where the story of the geological history and prehistory of northern Arizona can be told and where archaelogical and ethnological treasures of northern Arizona can be preserved. . .to protect our historic and prehistoric sites, works of art, scenic places and wildlife from needless destruction; to provide facilities for research and to offer opportunities for aesthetic enjoyment. Average Annual Attendance: 100,000. Mem: 1000; dues $25 - $100.
Income: $2,500,000 (financed by endowment, membership and earned income).
Collections: (art) Ethnographic collection; Archaeological collection; Art collection.
Exhibitions: Sacred Paths: Aspects of the native American and Hispanic religious experience in the Southwest; Philip Hyde Photographic Show; Hopi Show; Navajo Show; Art Institute Show; Flagstaff Handweavers Guild; Northern Arizona Art Invitational.
Publications: Museum Notes, bimonthly; Plateau, quarterly.
Activities: Classes for adults and children; docent training; expeditions; lect open to public, 25 vis lectr per yr; tours; competitions; exten dept serving the Southwestern states; individual paintings and original objects of art lent to various institutions; lending collection contains nature artifacts; original art works; original prints; paintings; photographs; sculpture; traveling exhibitions organized and circulated; museum shop selling books, magazines, and original art.
—Harold S Colton Memorial Library. Tel: 602-774-5211, exten 56.
Open Mon - Fri 9 AM - 5 PM. Estab 1928. It is a repository of material relating to the Colorado Plateau. Its primary function is to serve the needs of the Museum's research staff, although visiting scholars are welcome. Circ: Limited to Museum Staff (4000).
Income: Financed by endowment.
Holdings: Vols 18,000; Per subs 400; Other—Clipping files, manuscripts, photographs.
Special Collections: Navajo sandpainting reproductions.

NORTHERN ARIZONA UNIVERSITY ART GALLERY, Creative Arts Building, Room 231.(Mailing Add: NAU Art Gallery, Box 6021, 86011). Tel: 602-523-3471. *Dir Art Gallery* Joel S Eide; *Dean College Creative Arts* Charles H Aurand.
Open Mon - Fri 8 AM - 5 PM; Tues 6:30 - 8:30 PM; Sun 3 - 5 PM; cl Sat. No admis. Estab 1968 for the continuing education and service to the students and the Flagstaff community in all aspects of fine arts.
Collections: Master prints of the 20th century and American painting of the Southwest.
Activities: Concerts; gallery talks; competitions; annual toy show.

JEROME

VERDE VALLEY ART ASSOCIATION, INC, Main St, (Mailing Add: PO Box 985, 86331). Tel: 602-634-5466. *Pres* Susan Dowling; *VPres* Diane Koble; *Secy* Neil Heinrich; *Dir* Hank Chaikin.
Open daily 10 AM - 5 PM; cl Christmas. Admis by donation.
Estab 1977 to promote and further the arts in Northern Arizona, particularly the Verde Valley, in all its forms—visual arts, performing arts and educational programs; 1000 sq ft gallery with changing monthly exhibitions. Average Annual Attendance: 30,000. Mem: 115; dues variable; annual meeting third Tues in June.
Income: $4000 (financed by membership and CETA funding).
Collections: Small 8-piece permanent collection of original works and prints.
Exhibitions: (1977-78) Third Annual Jerome Theme Show; John Waddell; Artist Hopid; John Salter; Ray Fink; Joseph Coco; Four Prescott Artists; Dr Harry Wood; Children's Art Invitational; Yavapai College Verde Campus Student Art Exhibit.
Publications: Verde Artist Bulletin, monthly.
Activities: Lect open to public, 4 vis lectr per yr; concerts; gallery talks; competitions, prizes, purchase awards and gift certificates.
Library: Open to the public. Holdings: Vols 72; Per subs 6.

PATAGONIA

STRADLING MUSEUM OF THE HORSE, INC,* Box 413, 85624. Tel: 602-394-2264. *Dir & Cur* Anne C Stradling; *Deputy Dir* Floyd M Stradling; *Asst Dir* Beulah Brearton.
Open daily & holidays 9 AM - 6 PM; cl Thanksgiving & Xmas. Admis adults 50¢, no admis children & special groups. Estab 1960.
Collections: Saddles, blankets, reins and other horse trappings collected from all over the world; American Indian artifacts; painting; sculpture.
Activities: Guided tours. Sales shop selling saddlery, Indian rugs, art, china and jewelry.
Library: Open to the public. Holdings: 800 vols. Special Subjects: Indian history; horses; art history.

PHOENIX

ARIZONA ARTIST GUILD, 8912 N Fourth St, 85020. Tel: 602-944-9713. *Pres* Mary Arendt; *First VPres Mem* Shirley Murray; *Second VPres Shows* Bobie Moore; *Recording Secy* Sidney Moxham; *Treas* LaVona Campbell; *Corresp Secy* Charlee Wallace.
No admis. Estab 1928 to foster guild spirit, to assist in raising standards of art in the community, and to assume civic responsibility in matters relating to art. Average Annual Attendance: 300. Mem: 210; dues $15; meetings 3rd Mon each month.
Income: Financed by endowment and membership.
Exhibitions: Fall for members only; Dimensions, open to whole state; Horizons, each spring, members only.
Publications: AAG News, monthly.
Activities: Classes for adults; lect sometimes open to the public, usually for members only, 12 or more vis lectrs per yr; gallery talks; competitions, with four $50 awards each show; schol.
Library: Open to members only for reference.

ARIZONA WATERCOLOR ASSOCIATION, 8122 N Eighth Ave, 85021. *Pres* Clarence Shanks; *First VPres* Jacqueline Shultz; *Second VPres* Ann Mary Seyfert; *Third VPres* Mickey Daniels; *Recording Secy* Harriet Mularz; *Corresponding Secy* Anne M Balentine; *Treas* Jewel Bales; *Dir* Val Muggeridge, Lily Ham, Marge Young and Adrian Hansen.
Estab 1960 to further activity and interest in the watercolor medium, promote growth of individuals and group and maintain high quality of professional exhibits. Mem: 100; qualifications for membership jurying of paintings by membership committee; dues $12; annual meetings vary.
Publications: AWA Newsletter, every 2 months.
Activities: Lectr; competitions; traveling exhibitions organized and circulated.

HEARD MUSEUM, 22 E Monte Vista Rd, 85004. Tel: 602-252-8848. *Dir* Patrick T Houlihan; *Cur Anthropology* H Thomas Cain; *Cur Coll* Jon T Erickson; *Cur Exhib* Patrick Neary; *Cur Educ* Camille Tumolo; *Cur Anthropology* Erin Younger; *Cur Harvey Coll* Cynthia Davies.
Open Mon - Sat 10 AM - 5 PM; Sun 1 - 5 PM. Admis adult $1.00, children 50¢. Estab 1929 to collect and exhibit anthropology and art; collections built around works of Indians of the Americas; primitive arts from the cultures of Africa, Asia and Oceania; archaeology; ethnology; paintings and sculpture; Fred Harvey Fine Arts Collection. Average Annual Attendance: 250,000.
Income: $400,000 (financed by endowment, membership).
Collections: American Indian; African; Oceania; Fred Harvey Fine Arts Collection.

Publications: African Art; The CG Wallace Collection of American Indian Art; Dancing Kachinas; Fred Harvey Fine Arts Collection; Heard Museum Book; Indian Art of the Americas; Kachinas, the Goldwater Collection at the Heard Museum; Kachinas, a Hopi Artist's Documentary; Navajo Textiles from the Read Mullan Collection.
Activities: Docent training; lect open to public, 15 vis lectr per yr; lect at schools; original objects of art lent to accredited museums; lending collection contains framed reproductions, original prints, paintings 600, photographs 200, sculpture and slides 600; traveling exhibitions organized and circulated; museum shop selling books, original art, reproductions, prints, and slides.
—Library. Tel: 602-252-8848. *Librn* Carol Ruppe.
Open Mon - Fri 10 AM - 5 PM. Estab 1929 as a research library for the museum staff and members. Circ: Loan privileges in house and interlibrary loan only.
Income: $8000 (financed by membership and museum budget).
Holdings: Vols 8000; Per subs & series 69; AV—Microfiche, phonorecords; Other—Exhibitions catalogs, pamphlets.
Special Subjects: Anthropology, American Indian, primitive art.

PHOENIX ART MUSEUM, 1625 N Central Ave, 85004. Tel: 602-257-1222. *Pres* Mary Dell Pritzlaff; *Secy* EV O'Malley Jr; *VPres* Donald Kauffman & Don B Tostenrud; *Treas* Robert Applewhite; *Dir* Ronald D Hickman; *Asst Dir* Robert H Frankel.
Open Tues - Sat 10 AM - 5 PM; Wed 10 AM - 9 PM; Sun 1 - 5 PM; cl Mon. No admis. Estab 1925; museum constructed 1959. Average Annual Attendance: 180,000. Mem: 4300; dues $15 and up; annual meeting April.
Income: $507,000.
Collections: Medieval; Renaissance; Baroque; 19th century; contemporary paintings, sculptures and graphics; Oriental arts collection; Mexican art and Western art; Thorne Miniature rooms.
Exhibitions: Changing exhibitions in all areas of art including photography and graphics.
Publications: Calendar, monthly; annual report; exhibition catalogs; catalog of permanent collection.
Activities: Classes for adults; lect open to public; concerts; movie series; docent training; museum shop; Junior Museum.
—Reference Library. *Librn* Shirley H Russell.
Open Tues - Thurs 10 AM - 5 PM. Estab 1959 to serve reserence reference needs of the museum staff, docents, membership and students for reference only.
Income: Financed by endowment and membership. Purchases: $3500.
Holdings: Vols 4000; Per subs 35. Other—Clipping files, exhibitions catalogs, pamphlets, reproductions Arizona artist index, auction catalogs, museum archives.
Special Subjects: Painting, sculpture.
Special Collections: Rembrandt etching catalogs; Ambrose Lansing Egyptian Collection.
Exhibitions: (1976) Rare Book Bindings; (1977) Titlepiece and Frontispage; one museum exhibition per year.

SCOTTSDALE

COSANTI FOUNDATION, 6433 Doubletree Rd, 85253. Tel: 602-948-6145. *Pres* Paolo Soleri; *VPres & Secy* Corolyn Soleri. Open Mon - Sun 9 AM - 5 PM. Admis $1 per person. Estab 1956 as a non-profit, educational organization by Paolo Soleri pursuing the research and development of an alternative urban environment; gallery, The North Studio, has on display original sketches, sculptures and graphics by Paolo Soleri. Average Annual Attendance: 40,000.
Income: Financed by state appropriation and sales of art objects.
Collections: Permanent Collection of architectural designs, drawings by Paolo Soleri.
Exhibitions: Permanent exhibit in North Studio; Toward Arcology-Works in Progress, traveled to 35 colleges and universities; 2 Suns Arcology-The City Energized by the Sun, sponsored by Xerox Corp, traveled to three East Coast Museums.
Publications: Publications available at any time.
Activities: Classes for adults; docent training; Arcosanti Workshop Program, experiential construction workshops; lect open to the public; gallery talks; tours; schol; traveling exhibits organized and circulated; sales shop selling books, original art, prints, reproductions, slides.

SCOTTSDALE ARTISTS' LEAGUE, PO Box 1071, 85252. Tel: 602-996-1994. *Pres* Doreen Kennedy.
Estab 1961 to encourage the practice of art and to support and encourage the study and application of art as an avocation, to promote ethical principals and practice, to advance the interest and appreciation of art in all its forms and to increase the usefulness of art to the public at large; maintains Upstairs Gallery in Camelview Plaza Mall and gallery in Scottsdale Hospital. Mem: 553; dues individual $10, family $15; monthly meetings first Tues.

Exhibitions: Yearly juried exhibition for members only; yearly juries exhibition for Air Arizona artists (open show).
Activities: Lecturers and demo demonstrations for members only.
Publications: Art Beat, monthly.

TEMPE

ARIZONA STATE UNIVERSITY
—**University Art Collections,** Mathews Center, 85281. Tel: 602-965-2874. *Dir* Rudy H Turk; *Registrar* Mary Jane Williams.
Open Mon - Fri 8 AM - 5 PM; Sun 1 - 5 PM. No admis. Estab 1950 to provide esthetic and educational service for student and the citizens of the state; three permanent exhibition galleries featuring American, European and Latin American art; two changing galleries and two changing area; 48 shows annually. Average Annual Attendance: 40,000.
Income: $100,000 (financed by city and state appropriations, donations and earnings). Purchases: Varies, approx $25,000.
Collections: †American painting and sculpture (1700 to the present); †print collection (1500 to the present); †American crafts especially ceramics; †Latin American art.
Exhibitions: Crime by Cuevas; The Flute and the Brush; Indian Miniatures; First Annual Arizona Print Competition: works by David Sklar; Indians Forever by Fritz Scholder; Mexican Folk Retrospect; Tramp Art; Antique Coverlets and Chests.
Activities: Educ dept; dramatic programs; docent training; special events; lectr open to the public, 12 vis lectr per yr; gallery talks; tours; competitions; individual paintings and original objects of art lent to campus offices; traveling exhibitions organized and circulated; museum shop selling books, original art, slides and crafts.
Library: Registrar Mary Jane Williams. Open to public for reference. Holdings: Per subs 13; increasing holdings in catalogs, invitations, posters and brochures.
—**Memorial Union Gallery,** 85281. Tel: 602-965-6649. *Dir/Adv* Mark Miller.
Open Mon - Fri 9 AM - 5 PM. Estab to exhibit work that has strong individual qualities from the United States also some Arizona work that has not been shown on campus. The gallery is contained in two rooms with 1400 sq ft space, fireplace, one wall is glass, 20 ft ceiling, 26 4 x 8 partitions, track lighting, one entrance and exit, located in area with maximum traffic. Average Annual Attendance: 30,000.
Income: $400 (financed by city appropriation). Purchases: $2000.
Collections: Painting and print primarily Mahaffey, Schoulder, Altman and Gorman.
Exhibitions: New Southwest Landscapes; Jim Waid; The Shamen and the Goddess an Environment; Edith Weff; Dan O'Dowdy; Barbara MacCallum; Linda S Munswiler; Dina Yellen; Susan Weil; Beth Ames Swartz; Adrianne Wartzel; Marcia Wallace.
Activities: Educ dept; internships; lectr open to the public, 4 vis lectr per yr; gallery talks; competitions; traveling exhibitions organized and circulated.
—**Howe Architecture Library,** College of Architecture, Planning and Design Sciences, 85281. Tel: 602-965-6400. *Head Dept* Stan Jones; *Librn Asst* Betty Dong; *Architecture Specialist* Jane Henning.
Open Mon - Thurs 8 AM - 10 PM; Fri 8 AM - 5 PM; Sat Noon - 5 PM; Sun 5 - 10 PM. Estab 1959 to serve the architecture college and the university community with reference and research material in the subject of architecture. Circ: 13,500.
Income: Financed by state appropriation.
Holdings: Vols 15,000; Per subs 180; AV—Audio tapes, cassettes, microfilm, motion pictures, video tapes; Other—Manuscripts, memorabilia, original art works, original documents, pamphlets, photographs, prints.
Special Collections: Paola Soleri Archive; Frank Lloyd Wright rare material.
Publications: New Books List, semi-annual; Guide to the Library, Annual; Information Brochure, Annual.

TUBAC

TUBAC CENTER OF THE ARTS,* Santa Cruz Valley Art Association, Box 1314, 84540. *Pres* Richard Wormser.
Open Tues - Sat 1 - 5 PM; Sun & holidays 1 - 5 PM; cl Mon. No admis. Estab 1971.
Collections: Works by former and present Tubac artists.
Activities: Docent training; lectures; guided tours; films; arts festivals. Sales Shop.

TUCSON

CENTER FOR CREATIVE PHOTOGRAPHY, University of Arizona, 843 E University, 85710. Tel: 602-884-4636. *Dir* James Enyeart; *Cur & Libr Photography Archive* Terence R Pitts.

Open Mon - Fri 9 AM - 6 PM; Thur 9 AM - 9 PM. Estab 1975 to house and organize the archives of numerous major photographers and to act as a research center in 20th century photography; gallery exhibitions changing approximately every 6 weeks. Average Annual Attendance: 15,000.
Income: Financed by city appropriation, grants and donations.
Collections: Archives of Ansel Adams, Wynn Bullock, Harry Callahan, Aaron Siskind, Paul Strand, Frederick Sommer and W Eugene Smith.
Publications: Center for Creative Photography, approx 5 times per yr.
Activities: Lect open to public, 12 - 15 vis lectr per yr; gallery talks; tours; original objects of art lent to qualified institutions; lending collection 5000 photographs; traveling exhibitions organized and circulated.
Library: Librn Terrence R Pitts. Open to public for lending and reference. Holdings: Vols 3000; Pers subs 30. Special Collections: Limited edition books; hand-made books; books illustrated with original photographs.

TUCSON MUSEUM OF ART, 235 W Alameda, 85701. Tel: 602-624-2333. *Dir* Paul M Piazza; *Asst Dir* Gerrit C Cone; *Cur Educ* David L Jones; *Cur Historic Sites* Bettina Lyons; *Asst Cur Educ* Libby Stiff; *Registrar* Rene Verdugo; *Museum Educ Coordr* Toby Falk; *Public Relations & Media Coordr* Adina Wingate; *Admin Asst* Toby Engler; *Membership* Margorie Sherrill.
Open Tues - Sat 10 AM - 5 PM; Sun 1 - 5 PM. No admis. Estab 1924 to operate a nonprofit civic art gallery to promote art education, to hold art exhibitions and to further art appreciation for the public. Upper gallery—changing exhibitions; sales gallery—contemporary crafts by Arizona artists; lower galleries—permanent collection. Average Annual Attendance: 60,000. Mem: 2275; dues league $6, student $10, individual $20, family $25, donor $50, sponsor $100, patron $250, benefactor $500, Angel $1000 or more; annual meeting in May.
Income: $410,000 (financed by endowment, membership, city and state appropriations; and contributions). Purchases $5000.
Collections: †Pre-Columbian; †Spanish Colonial/Mexican; †19th and 20th century Oriental; †European painting and sculpture; †art of the Americas.
Exhibitions: Robert Motherwell, selected print 1961-1974; Tucson Heritage Photo Exhibition; Arizona's Outlook 76 & 78; Tucson Collects; The Great War and the Great American Quilt; Craft Encore; Imagenes Hispanoamericanas; Watercolor Southwest, II; Arizona Crafts 77; Ancient Roots/New Visions; Selections from the Permanent Collections; Current Directions; Twelve from the Soviet Underground; Silver Works from Rio de la Plata; The Dyer's Art; Photographs by Peter MacGill; History of Navajo Weaving; Czechoslovakian Graphics; Tucson Collects: The Year of the Snake; The Year of the Horse.
Publications: Calendar, monthly; exhibition catalogs; Arizona Artist Newsletter, six times a yr.
Activities: Classes for adults and children; docent training; lect open to the public, 20 vis lectr per yr; concerts; gallery talks; tours; competitions; exten dept serving Tucson school districts; individual paintings lent and original objects of art lent to art rental gallery for public use; lending collection contains, original prints, paintings and photographs; traveling exhibitions organized and circulated; museum shop selling magazines, original art with emphasis on crafts.
—**Library.** *Librn* Dorcas Worsley.
Open to the public for reference lending to members only.
Holdings: Vols 4500; Per subs 12; AV—Slides 16,000; Other—Vertical files on Arizona Artists; pamphlet material on all artists; archives; back files of periodicals.
Special Subjects: Pre-Columbian Art; African art; Oceanic art, Southwestern art; contemporary art.

UNIVERSITY OF ARIZONA, Museum of Art, Olive & Speedway Sts, 85721. Tel: 602-884-2173. *Acting Dir* Kathryn C Jessup.
Open Mon - Sat 9 AM - 5 PM; Sun 12 Noon - 5 PM. Estab 1955 to share the treasures of three remarkable permanent collection, the C Leonard Pfeiffer Collection, Samuel H Kress Collection and the Edward J Gallagher, Jr Collection with the Tucson community, visitors and the university students; also one of the most important functions is to reach out to the public school districts around Tucson through the education department. Special exhibitions are maintained on the first floor of the museum; the three permanent collections are housed on the second floor. Average Annual Attendance: 80,000.
Income: Financed by state appropriation.
Collections: C Leonard Pfeiffer Collection of American artists of the 30s, 40s and 50s; Samuel H Kress Collection of 26 Renaissance works and 26 paintings of the 15th century Spanish Retablo by Fernando Gallego; Edward J Gallagher Collection of over a hundred paintings of national and international artists.
Exhibitions: (1976) Masters of Fine Art Exhibit; Photography of Jerry Uelsman; Graphic Art of Francisco Goya; First Flowers of Our Wilderness (early American paintings, lithographs and samplers); (1977-78) German Graphics; Ad Reinhart Prints; National Copper, Brass and

Bronze Competition; Arcology, Paolo Soleri; Waid-Miller-Rod Exhibit; Vault Show I (from the permanent collection in the vault); Oriental Prints (from the collection of Mr and Mrs Murphey).
Publications: Fully illustrated catalogs on all special exhibitions.
Activities: Educ dept; docent training; tours of museum and out reach tours to public schools; lectr; gallery talks; tours; artmobile; individual paintings and original objects of art lent; lending collection contains original art works, original prints, paintings, photographs and sculpture; traveling exhibitions organized and circulated; sales shop selling books, reproductions and poster reproductions.
Library: Fine Arts Library. *Librn* Barbara Kittle. Open to staff only for reference. Holdings: Vols: 500; Per subs 16; Other—Slide library collection of permanent collection.

WICKENBURG

DESERT CABALLEROS WESTERN MUSEUM, 20 N Frontier St (Mailing Add: Box 1446, 85358). *Pres* Roy Coxwell; *Exec VPres and Cur* Harry T Needham; *Asst Cur* Ann ImOberstag; *Chmn of the Bd* H K MacLennan; *Treas* H D Murphy.
Open Tues - Sat 10 AM - 4 PM; Sun 1 - 4 PM, cl Mon. Admis by donation. Est (reopened) in 1975 to show the development of Wickenburg from prehistoric to present day; the museum houses western art gallery, mineral room, Indian room, period rooms, and gold mining equipment. Average Annual Attendance: 16,000. Mem: 200; dues vary; annual meeting 2nd Mon April.
Income: $25,000 - $35,000 (financed by membership).
Collections: (Art) Indian artifacts, western art, and a special display of western bronzes of George Phippen.
Activities: Museum shop selling books, prints.
Library. Open to members for reference only. Holdings: Vols 200; Per subs 6.

WINDOW ROCK

NAVAJO TRIBAL MUSEUM, Highway 264 (Mailing Add: Box 308, 86515). Tel: 602-871-6457. *Acting Dir* Russell P Hartman.
Open daily 8 AM - 5 PM; cl major holidays. No admis. Estab 1961 to preserve and display items related to the history and culture of Navajo Indians and of natural history of Navajoland; exhibit space is divided into two rooms and covers approximately 2500 sq ft. Average Annual Attendance: 50,000.
Income: Financed by state appropriation and tribal budget. Purchases: Approx $2500.
Collections: Works in all media by well-known Southwest Indian artists, with emphasis on Navajo artists.
Exhibitions: (1977) Exhibition of paintings by Theresa Potter depicting deAnza Expedition in 1776. (1978) Selection of R C Gorman prints sponsored by Arizona Commission for the Arts and Humanities.
Activities: Individual paintings and original objects of art lent to other museums; lending collection contains original art works.
Navajo Nation Library. *Librn* Richard Heiser. Open to the public for reference only. Holdings: Vol 3000.

YUMA

YUMA ART CENTER, 281 Gila St, (Mailing Add: PO Box 1471, 85364). Tel: 602-782-9261. *Dir* Laurel Meinig; *Admin Asst,* Susan Kalicki; *Supt & Preparator* Roberto Espinoza; *Prog Coordr* Corinne Christian.
Open Tues - Sun 10 AM - 5 PM. No admis. Estab 1962 to foster the arts in the Yuma area and to provide a showing space for contemporary Arizona artists; gallery is housed in restored Southern Pacific Railway depot built in 1926. Average Annual Attendance: 12,000. Mem: 500; dues $5 - $1000.
Income: $100,000 (financed by endowment, membership and city appropriation). Purchases: $3000.
Collections: Contemporary Arizona.
Exhibitions: 10th, 11th & 12th; Southwestern Invitational; The Railroad: Focus on the Southwest; Rookwood Pottery.
Publications: Bimonthly membership bulletin.
Activities: Educ dept; classes for children; dramatic programs; docent training; lect open to public, 10 - 12 vis lectr per yr; concerts; gallery talks; tours; individual painting and original objects of art lent to members and businesses; traveling exhibitions organized and circulated; museum shop selling original art, reproductions and prints.

ARKANSAS

CLARKSVILLE

COLLEGE OF THE OZARKS ART DEPARTMENT LIBRARY,* 610 Johnson St, 72830. *Head, Art Dept* Lyle Ward; *Librn* Jan Cole.
No admis. Estab 1834 as a four-year liberal arts college.
Income: $1000 (financed by endowment). Purchases: $100 - $200.
Holdings: Vols 73,000.
Special Collections: Original print collection; graduate students' painting collection.
Activities: Lect open to the public, 9 vis lectr per yr; dramatic programs; Elementary and Secondary Education programs meeting for state certification requirements; schol; individual paintings lent to schools; lending collection contains color reproductions 100, 16mm films.

CROSSETT

CROSSETT ART LEAGUE,* 125 Main, 71635. Tel: 501-364-3606. *Pres* Sunny Fisher; *Secy* Olivia Bingham.
Estab to promote and encourage art skills and art appreciation. Mem: 41; dues $5.
Income: Financed by membership and federal matching funds.
Exhibitions: Held at El Dorado Art Center, Arkansas. Junior League Arts and Crafts Fair and Ashley County Fair.
Publications: Monthly newsletter.
Activities: Classes for adults and children; sponsor trips to cultural centers for sixth graders.

EL DORADO

SOUTH ARKANSAS ART LEAGUE,* 110 E Fifth St, 71730. Tel: 501-862-5474. *Pres* Carl W Egerer, *Secy* Ann S Plair.
Open 9 AM - 5 PM. No admis. Estab 1955 for the promotion, enrichment and improvement of the visual arts by means of exhibits, lectures and instruction, and through scholarships to be offered whenever possible; gallery maintained. Mem: 170; dues $5; annual meeting fourth Tues in May.
Income: Financed by membership, and city and state appropriation.
Collections: All paintings and collections are under jurisdiction of South Arkansas Arts Center.
Exhibitions: Various art shows in this and surrounding states; gallery shows ten guest artists annually; two months dedicated to local artists; works by local artists handing in corridor year-round.
Publications: Artifacts, quarterly.
Activities: Classes for adults and children; lect open to the public; gallery talks; competitions; schol.
Library. Holdings—Vols 135.

SOUTH ARKANSAS ARTS CENTER,* 110 E Fifth St, 71730. Tel: 501-862-5474. *Pres* Jerome Orr, *Secy* Maurice Mims.
Open Mon - Fri 10 AM - 5 PM; Sat, Sun & holidays 2 - 5 PM. No admis. Estab 1964 to furnish arts to the South Arkansas Area; two art galleries.
Income: Financed by endowments and contributions.
Publications: Artifacts, quarterly.
Activities: Classes for adults and children; dramatic programs; ballet company; lect open to the public; concerts; competitions; schol.

EUREKA SPRINGS

EUREKA SPRINGS GUILD OF ARTISTS AND CRAFTS PEOPLE, PO Box 182, 72632. *Chairperson* Hank Kaminsky; *Vice Chairperson* Henry Menke; *Secy* Lee Ericson; *Treas* Bernice Pereboom.
Estab 1976 to encourage quality art work and to provide various art oriented services. Mem: Approx 60; dues $20 - $32; monthly meetings.
Income: Approx $6000 (financed by membership).
Exhibitions: (1978) Spring Art Fair.
Publications: Gentians from the Mountain, a directory of members.
Activities: Educ dept; films, workshops; lect open to public, 2 - 3 vis lectrs per yr; gallery talks; competitions; lending collections contains books 200; traveling exhibitions organized and circulated.
Library: Holdings: Vols approx 300; Per subs 10 - 12; Other—Files of fair and exhibitions.

FAYETTEVILLE

UNIVERSITY OF ARKANSAS
—Fine Arts Center Gallery, Garland St, 7 2701. Tel: 501-575-3706. *Gallery Coord* Martha Sutherland.

Open August to May weekdays 9 AM - 5 PM. No admis. Estab 1950 as a teaching gallery in fields of painting, drawing, sculpture, and architecture, both inreach and outreach programs; one gallery with moveable display panels covers 80 x 80 ft.
Income: Financed by state appropriation.
Collections: Permanent Collection of †paintings, prints, sculpture and photographs.
Exhibitions: Sixteen exhibitions per year, of which eight are in-house, art department related; one regional exhibit; one public school exhibit; one architecture exhibit; traveling shows.
Activities: Classes for adults; lect open to the public, 4 - 6 vis lectr per yr; concerts, gallery talks; competitions with purchase award; exten dept.
—**Fine Arts Library** (Mailing Add: FA-103, 72701). Tel: 501-575-4708. *Librn* Eloise E McDonald.
Open Mon - Thurs 8 AM - 10 PM; Fri 8 AM - 5 PM; Sat 9 AM - 1 PM; Sun 2 -10 PM. Estab 1951 to provide support materials for undergraduate curriculum in art, music, and architecture, for graduate curriculum in music and art, for faculty members with adequate research material. Circ: approx 31,000.
Income; $13,000 - $16,000. Purchases: $10,000 - $15,000.
Holdings: Vols 28,400; Per subs 155 reference: Other—Clipping files, exhibition catalogs.
Publications: Occasional bibliographies.
Activities: Tours.

FORT SMITH

FORT SMITH ART CENTER,* 423 N Sixth St, 72901. Tel: 501-782-6371. *Dir* Polly Crews; *Pres* Marcia Edwards.
Open daily 10 AM - 4 PM; Sun 2 - 4 PM; cl Mon, New Year's, July 4, Labor Day, Thanksgiving and Christmas. No admis. Estab 1957 to provide art museum, art association and art education. Mem: 292, dues $15. Average Annual Attendance: 5000.
Income: $25,000 financed by endowment.
Collections: †American painting, graphic, drawings.
Publications: Bulletin, monthly.
Activities: Classes for adults; films; lect open to the public, competitions; traveling exhibitions organized and circulated; sales gallery.
Library maintained.

HELENA

PHILLIPS COUNTY MUSEUM, 623 Pecan St, 72342. Tel: 501-338-3537. *Pres* Mrs Floyd E Curtis.
Open Mon - Sat 9 AM - 5 PM; cl national holidays. Estab 1929 as an educational and cultural museum; to impart an appreciation of local history and to display objects of art from all over the world. Average Annual Attendance: 5000. Mem: 250; dues $2; annual meeting May.
Income: Financed by endowment, membership and city appropriation.
Collections: (Art) China; glassware; paintings.

HOT SPRINGS

SOUTHERN ARTISTS ASSOCIATION, Fine Arts Center, 815 Whittington Ave, 71901. Tel: 501-623-0836. *Pres* Margaret Pedersen; *VPres* Bruce Richards; *Secy* Theresa Kosics, *Staff Secy* Lucille Chick; *Gallery Dir* Violet Richard.
Open Wed - Sat 10 AM - 4 PM; Sun 1:30 - 5 PM; cl Mon & Tues. No admis. Estab 1951 to provide the community with a yearly calendar of art exhibitions, to provide gallery space for members, to provide educational program in art for the community and serve as a statewide art association. Mem: 137; dues $15; meetings monthly.
Income: Financed by membership, city appropriation and commission from sales of artwork.
Exhibitions: (1978) Annual Arts Festival; Semiannual Outdoor Exhibitions; one-man shows, traveling exhibitions from many sources.
Activities: Classes for adults and children; art films; workshop; lect open to the public, 3 - 4 vis lectr per yr; gallery talks; competitions with prizes, awards and honorable mentions given.

LITTLE ROCK

ARKANSAS ARTS CENTER, MacArthur Park, (Mailing Add: PO Box 2137, 72203. Tel: 501-372-4000. *Exec Dir* Townsend D Wolfe, III; *Asst to the Dir* Leon Kaplan; *Dir State Services* June Freeman; *Neighborhood Arts Coordr* Brenda Reese; *Museum Registrar* Margaret Wickard; *Dir Educ* Rebecca Rogers Witsell.
Open Mon - Sat 8 AM - 5 PM; Sun & holidays Noon - 5 PM. No admis to galleries; admission charged for theatre activities. Estab 1960 to further the development, the understanding and the appreciation of the visual and performing arts; five galleries four used for circulating exhibitions on for art educational gallery for young people. Average Annual

Attendance: 509,000 include state services program. Mem: 3324; dues from student $5 to sustaining $1000; annual meeting of board of trustees July 1.
Income: FInanced by endowment, membership, city and state appropriation and earned income.
Collections: Paintings, prints and drawings prior to the 20th century; †prints; †drawings; decorative arts.
Exhibitions: (1977-78) The American Westward Movement; Toys Designed by Artists; Painting: Materials and Techniques; Photographic Imagemaking; Portraits; Wil Winslow Homer's Work in Black & White; Selections for the Permanent Collection; Robert Motherwell Exhibition; Thomas Hart Benton's Illustrations from Mark Twain; The Work of Charles White: An American Experience; Drawings USA/75; Line of Vision—Latin American Drawings: American Drawings 1976; Contemporary Egyptian Tapestries; Bolivian Handicraft Exhibit: 20th Annual Delta Art Exhibition; Serge Lifar Collection of Ballet Set and Costume Designs; Collector's Show; Edvard Munch: The Major Graphics; Stitchery 77: Mid-Southern Watercolorists Exhibition; Antwerp Drawings and Prints from the 16th and 17th Centuries; Artists' Stamps and Stamp Images; Young Arkansas Artists; 11th Annual Prints, Drawings and Crafts Exhibition; Treasures by Peter Carl Faberge.
Publications: Members Bulletin, monthly; Annual Catalog; Annual Report.
Activities: Classes for adults and children; dramatic programs; docent training; lect open to the public, 6 - 10 vis lectr per yr; concerts; gallery talks; tours; competitions: exten dept serving the state of Arkansas; artmobile; individual paintings and original objects of art lent to schools, civic groups and churches; lending collection contains, motion pictures, original prints, paintings; phonorecords 4300, slides 16,000; traveling exhibitions organized and circulated; museum shop selling books, slides, gifts, jewelery and crafts; junior museum.
—**Elizabeth Prewitt Taylor Memorial Library.** *Librn & Vol Activities* Evelyn McCoy.
Open to Center members, class participants, educators and public for reference only.
Holdings: Vols 6000; Per subs 125; AV—Films, phonorecords, slides.
Special Subjects: Fine Arts and drama.
Special Collections: John Reid Collection of early American Jazz including books, catalogs, recordings and memorabilia; George Fisher Political cartoons.

ARKANSAS HISTORY COMMISSION,* Old State House (West Wing), 300 W Markham St, 72201. Tel: 501-371-2141. *Dir* Dr John L Ferguson.
Open Mon - Fri 8 AM - 4:30 PM. No admis. Museum includes gallery of †paintings of noted Arkansans.
Collections: Harry B Solmson Collection of Confederate and Southern State Currency; A Howard Stebbins Collection of Arkansas Obsolete Currency.
Library: †Rare Arkansiana.

ARKANSAS TERRITORIAL RESTORATION,* Territorial Square, 72201. Tel: 501: 501-374-5544. *Dir* William B Worthen Jr.
Open daily 9 AM - 5 PM; Sun 1 - 5 PM; cl New Year's, Easter, Thanksgiving, Christmas Eve, & Christmas. Admis to museum houses adults $1, children (6 and under) 25¢, senior citizens (65 and over) 25¢; admis free to reception center. Restoration completed 1941; owned by the State, operated by the Arkansas Territorial Restoration Commission; a group of 13 buildings dating from 1820s-1840s. Average Annual Attendance: 70,000.
Collections: †Furnishings of the period; †porcelain hands; †watercolors; prints dating from the early 19th Century, including early copies and one original Audubon bird print of Arkansas birds.
Activities: Reception center with space for history and pre-tour lectures; slide shows; lending collection contains photographs and art of historical and regional interest; lending box program; traveling and temporary exhibitions of objects.
Library: Volumes on art, furniture, garden and history.

MID-SOUTHERN WATERCOLORISTS, 6632 Waverly Place, 72207. Tel: 501-666-8431. *Pres* James W Wood; *VPres* Peggy Johnston; *Secy* Drenda Alstadt. Estab June 26, 1970 to elevate the stature of watercolor and educate the public to the significance of watercolor as an important creative permanent painting medium; gallery not maintained. Mem: 216; Qualif for mem: approval of membership; dues $15.
Income: Financed by membership.
Publications: Newsletter, monthly.
Activities: Competitions; schol; traveling exhibitions organized and circulated.

PINE BLUFF

SOUTHEAST ARKANSAS ARTS AND SCIENCE CENTER,* Civic Center, 71601. Tel: 501-536-3375. *Dir* Philip A Klopfenstein; *Dir Theatre* Brad Ford; *Cur of Educ* James Loney; *Chmn of the Board* changes yearly.
Open Mon - Sat 10 AM - 5 PM; cl Sun and holidays. No admis. Opened in 1968 in Civic Center Complex; governing authority, city of Pine Bluff. Average Annual Attendance: 55,000. Mem: 750; dues family $15.
Income: Budget $150,000.
Collections: Contemporary art assembled by gifts and purchases; prints of American college professors.
Activities: Art gallery exhibitions; annual art festival; annual statewide competition; docent tours, theatre workshops, theatre productions, concert series, music concerts; art sales gallery; regional advisory activities for cultural programs in 11 counties; film series for adults and children; original art print sales, publications.

SPRINGDALE

COUNCIL OF OZARK ARTISTS AND CRAFTSMEN, INC,* Arts Center of the Ozarks, Arts Bldg, 216 W Grove Ave (Mailing Add: PO Box 725, 72764). Tel: 501-751-5441. *Pres* Mrs Fred McCuistion; *Dir Arts Center* Geneva Powers; *VPres Arts Div & Exhibit Chmn* Mrs Nick S Matthews; *Workshop Chmn* Mrs Luther S Cammack; *Special Exhibit Chmn* Rolf W Brandt.
Open Mon - Fri 1 - 5 PM. No admis. Estab 1948, merged with the Springdale Arts Center, to become Arts Center of the Ozarks, 1973, to preserve the traditional handcrafts, to promote all qualified contemporary arts and crafts, to help find markets for artists and craftsmen. Mem: 70; annual meeting third Mon in Aug.
Income: Financed by membership, and city and state appropriations.
Exhibitions: Springdale Invitational Arts and Crafts Fair (annually in June); Prairie Grove Clothesline Fair (annually on Labor Day weekend).
Publications: Arts Center Events, monthly; bimonthly newsletter.
Activities: Instruction in the arts, music, dance and drama, run concurrently with other activities; evening classes in painting; schedules workshops in handcrafts.

STATE UNIVERSITY

ARKANSAS STATE UNIVERSITY ART GALLERY, JONESBORO, Caraway Rd, Jonesboro (Mailing Add: Box 846, 72467). Tel: 501-972-3050. *Dir* Evan Lindquist; *Chmn Dept Art* Karl Richards; *Chmn Exhib* Donn Hedman.
Open weekdays 8 AM - 4 PM. No admis. Established 1967 for education objectives; recognition of contemporary artists and encouragement to students. Located in the Fine Art Center, the well-lighted gallery measures 45 x 45 ft plus corridor display areas. Average Annual Attendance: 10,500.
Income: $3000 (financed by city appropriation).
Collections: Historical and contemporary prints; contemporary paintings; some contemporary sculpture.
Exhibitions: Jim Eisentrager; Virginia Myers; Ray George; Duane Crigger-Jerry Hatch-John Walker; Jane Asbury; Rimas Visgerda-Herb Schumacher-Chas Counts-Erik Gronborg-Dick Luster.
Publications: Exhibition catalogs.
Activities: Lectr open to the public, 4 - 6 vis lectr per yr; gallery talks; competitions; traveling exhibitions organized and circulated.

STUTTGART

GRAND PRAIRIE ART COUNCIL, INC, PO Box 65, 72160. Tel: 501-673-8443. *Pres* Mrs E A McCracken; *Secy* Mrs Robert L Fischer.
Estab 1956, inc. 1964, to encourage cultural development in the Grand Prairie area; to sponsor the Grand Prairie Festival of Arts held annually in September at Stuttgart; and to work toward the establishment of an arts center for junior and senior citizens. Average Annual Attendance: Approx 9000 at Grand Prairie Festival of Arts. Mem: 15, representing 6 civic organizations; annual meeting Jan for election of officers.
Income: $3000 - $4000 (financed by contributions).
Collections: Very small permanent collection started by donations.
Publications: Festival invitations in July, programs in Sept.
Activities: Schools divisions in festival.

CALIFORNIA

ALHAMBRA

AMERICAN SOCIETY OF BOOKPLATE COLLECTORS AND DESIGNERS, 1206 N Stoneman Ave, 15, 91801. Tel: 213-283-1936. *Dir & Editor* Audrey Spencer Arellanes. For further information see National and Regional Organizations.

BAKERSFIELD

KERN COUNTY MUSEUM,* 3801 Chester Ave, 93301. Tel: 805-861-2132. *Dir* Richard C Bailey; *Secy* Patti Binns.
Open Mon - Fri 8 AM - 5 PM; Sat & Sun Noon - 7 PM; cl New Years, Thanksgiving & Christmas. Admis to Pioneer Village adults 50¢, adult groups 35¢, juniors 35¢, children 25¢. Estab 1945. Average Annual Attendance: 150,000.
Collections: California primitive paintings; Pioneer Village covering 12 acres.
Publications: Guide to the Museum.
Activities: Prepares data for circulation and program tours and visits by school and civic groups.
Library: Open for reference only. Holdings: Vols 1700; Other—Photograph collection of 500 prints.

BERKELEY

BERKELEY ART CENTER,* 1275 Walnut St, 94709. Tel: 415-849-4120. *Dir* Carl Worth; *Exhib Specialist* Richard Sargent.
Open Tues - Sun 11 AM - 5 PM; cl. Mon & National holidays. No admis. Estab 1967.
Income: Financed by city appropriation.
Collections: Paintings, sculpture, and environments.
Exhibitions: Loan exhibitions and shows by Bay Area artists.
Activities: Dramatic programs; films; gallery talks; concerts; arts festivals.

BERKELEY PUBLIC LIBRARY, Art and Music Section, 2090 Kittredge St, 94704. Tel: 415-664-6787 & 644-6785. *Head Art & Music Section* vacant.
Open Mon - Thur 9 AM - 9 PM; Fri - Sat 9 AM - 6 PM; Sun 1 - 5 PM. Estab 1960 for general circulation and reference for the residents of Berkeley and its affiliate library, Oakland Public Library System; Circ: 221,271.
Income: $28,126.
Holdings: Vols 18,419; Per subs 103; AV—Cassettes 381; records 8000; slides 11,158; miniature scores 377; framed prints 385; Other—Framed reproductions.

JUDAH L MAGNES MEMORIAL MUSEUM, Western Jewish History Center, 2911 Russell St, 94705. Tel: 415-849-2710. *Dir* Seymour Fromer; *Cur* Ruth Eis; *Registrar* Ted A Greenberg.
Open Sun - Fri 10 AM - 4 PM; cl Jewish and legal holidays. No admis. Estab 1962 to preserve, collect and exhibit Jewish artifacts and art from around the world; the museum also does research in the establishment of the Jewish community in the Western part of the US from 1849 to the present; the first floor has changing exhibition space and painting gallery, and the second floor contains the permanent exhibition area. Average Annual Attendance: 5100.
Income: Financed by membership and donations.
Collections: †Hannukah lamps; †textiles; †prints and graphics; †spice boxes; Synagogue art and objects, †manuscripts and rare books.
Exhibitions: Ketubah; Woodcuts by Stavroulakis; Ben Kutcher Retrospective; Transparencies and Reflections: Sculptures by Jacques Schnier; Collectors Choice: Baila Feldman (paintings); Mission to Israel: Paintings by Henrietta Berk; Brochard; Woodcuts by Jacob Pins; Contemporary Ketubot by David Moss and Sculpture by Elbert Weinberg; Garvey: We Are the Wall Itself; Creative Frontier; Ruth Eis; Orloff; Lee Waisler; Richard Kamler; Laura Ziegler; Podwal; Wolpert.
Publications: Pamphlets, exhibition catalogs, and bibliographies.
Activities: Classes for adults, lect open to the public; gallery talks; tours; individual paintings and original objects of art lent to museums, synagogues, exhibition halls and Jewish organizations; traveling exhibitions organized and circulated; museum shop selling books, magazines, original art, reproductions, prints and original jewelry, note cards, posters, postcards.
—**Morris Goldstein Library.** Tel: 415-849-2710. *Librn* James Weinberger.
Open Mon & Wed 1 - 4 PM; Sun 10 AM - 4 PM. Estab 1966 as a center for the study and preservation of Judaica.
Income: $1900 (financed by membership).
Holdings: Vols 10,000 for reference; Per subs 15 for reference; AV—Film strips, motion pictures, slides; Other—Clipping files, exhibition catalogs, manuscripts, memorabilia, original documents, pamphlets, reproductions.
Special Subjects: Judaica; Hebraica; rare book and mss; Jewish art and music; music of the Yiddish theater; Soviet Jewry; religious thought; ethics; philosophy; mysticism; history; literature in English, Hebrew, Yiddish and Ladino.

Special Collections: 16th to 19th Century rare printed editions, books and mss; Ukrainian pogroms (Belkin docs); Karaite community (Egypt); Passover Haggadahs (Zismor); Holocaust material (Institute for Righteous Acts); community collections from Cochin, India, Egypt, Morocco and Czechoslovakia.

UNIVERSITY OF CALIFORNIA, BERKELEY

—**University Art Museum,** 2626 Bancroft Way, 94720. Tel: 415-642-1207. *Dir* James Elliott; *Asst Dir* for Admin Ronald Egherman; *Chief Cur* David Ross; *Cur of Coll* Mark Rosenthal; *Registrar* Gretchen Glicksman; *Cur of Film* Tom Luddy.
Open Wed - Sun 11 AM - 5 PM. No admis. Estab 1965; new museum bldg opened in 1970, and was designed by Mario Ciampi, Richard Jorasch, and Ronald E Wagner of San Francisco; there are eleven exhibition galleries, a sculpture garden and 200-seat theater. Average Annual Attendance: 350,000. Mem: 1300; dues vary.
Income: $1,300,000 operating budget 1977-78 (financed by university funds, and income programs).
Collections: 20th century European and American painting and sculpture; Hans Hofmann's gift of 45 of his paintings is housed in the Hans Hofmann Gallery; a small group of pre-20th century paintings and sculpture; a small group of Chinese and Japanese paintings.
Exhibitions: The Museum offers over 20 exhibitions annually. Small exhibitions are originated for study purposes. Several galleries display works from the permanent collection.
Publications: Art Museum Council publishes a newsletter, bimonthly; handbills and brochures with most exhibitions.
Activities: Lectures open to the public, 5-10 vis lectr per yr; gallery talks; slide lectures; traveling exhibitions organized and circulated; museum shop selling books, magazines, crafts, posters, jewelry, art materials.
Library. The University Library at Berkeley and its various departmental branches house the largest collection of art books on the West Coast. The Museum maintains a collection of exhibition catalogs and related materials for reference use, as well as videotapes and over 3000 film prints in the Pacific Film Archive. The Pacific Film Archive offers over 800 public film programs annually, as well as film programs for classes and research screenings.
—**R H Lowie Museum of Anthropology,*** 103 Kroeber Hall, 94720. Tel: 415-642-3681. *Dir* William Bascom; *Asst Dir* Frank A Norick; *Sr Cur Anthropologist* Dave D Herod.
Open Mon - Fri 10 AM - 4 PM, Sat & Sun Noon - 4 PM; cl major national holidays. Admis adults 25¢, children 10¢. Estab 1901 as a research museum for the training and educating of undergraduate and graduate students; a resource for scholarly research; and to collect preserve, educate and conduct research. Average Annual Attendance: 65,000.
Income: Over $250,000 (financed by city and state appropriations).
Collections: Approx 3.5 million objects of anthropological interest, both archeological and ethnological. Ethnological collections from Africa, Oceania, North America (Plains, Arctic and Sub-Arctic); archaeological collections from Egypt, Peru, California, and Africa.
Exhibitions: (Anthropology) Traditions in Transition; Games of Skill, Chance and Strategy; Indians of Panama; Artisans of India; Ishi, The Last Survivor of a California Indian Tribe; Sons of Vishvakarma—Artisans of India.
Publications: Annual Report; Exhibition Guides.
Activities: Classes for adults; lect open to public; gallery talks; tours; book shop.
Library: Open for reference and research. Holdings: Vols 2000; Other—Photographs; prints 20,000.
—**Pacific Film Archive,** 2625 Durant Ave, 94720. Tel: 415-642-1412. *Cur Film* Tony Luddy; *Film Consultant* Linda Artel; *Technical Dir* Daniel Tanner; *Librn* Linda Provinzano; *Asst Programmer* Edith Kramer.
Open Mon - Fri 8 AM - Noon & 1 - 5 PM. Estab 1971, the Archive is a cinematheque showing a constantly changing repertory of films; a research screening facility; a media information service and an archive for the storage and preservation of films.
Income: Financed by endowment, membership and student fees.
Holdings: Vols 500; Per subs 30; AV—Cassettes, motion pictures; Other—Clipping files; stills and posters.
Special Collection: Japanese film collection; experimental and animated films; Soviet silents.
Publications: Monthly calendar.
Activities: Dramatic programs; special daytime screenings of films; lectures 50 - 75 vis filmmakers per yr.

BEVERLY HILLS

BEVERLY HILLS PUBLIC LIBRARY, Fine Arts Library, 444 N Rexford Dr, 90210. Tel: 213-550-4720. *Fine Art Librn* Nicholas Cellini; *AV Librn* Kandy Brown.
Open Mon - Thurs 10 AM - 9 PM; Fri & Sat 10 AM - 6 PM. Estab 1973 to make art materials available to the general public; the library concentrates on 19th and 20th century art.

Income: Financed by city appropriation and Friends of Library.
Holdings: Vols 20,000; Per subs 200; AV—Cassettes, kodachromes, microfiche, microfilm, motion pictures, phonorecords, slides; Other—Clipping files, exhibition catalogs, pamphlets, photographs, prints.
Special Subjects: Art; Music; Dance; Costume; Architecture; Minor Arts; Film.
Special Collections: Will Rogers Collection; Dorathi Bock Pierre Dance Collection.
Exhibitions: (1977) Contemporary African Makonde Sculpture Exhibition.
Activities: Lect open to the public, 3 vis lectr per yr; gallery talks; tours.

FOWLER MUSEUM,* 9215 Wilshire Blvd, 90210. Tel: 213-278-8010. Tel: 213-278-8010. *Cur* Basil W R Jenkins.
Open Mon - Sat 1 - 5 PM; cl Sun & holidays. No admis. Estab 1953.
Collections: Russian art; Oriental art; antique European and American paperweights; drinking cups; 15th - 19th century English, early American and Continental silver; European & Asiatic decorative arts.
Activities: Lectures; guided tours.

CARMEL

CARMEL MISSION BASILICA,* 3080 Rio Rd, 93921. Tel: 408-624-9848. *Mgr* Katie Ambrosio; *Cur* Sir Harry Downie.
Open Mon - Sat 9:30 AM - 5 PM; Sun 10:30 AM - 5 PM; cl Thanksgiving & Xmas, Donations welcome. Estab 1770.
Collections: Indian artifacts; sculpture; textiles.
Activities: Sales shop selling religious articles, souvenir books and postcards.
Library: Books published between 1615 - 1833 available for research by appointment.

FRIENDS OF PHOTOGRAPHY, Ninth and San Carlos (Mailing Add: PO Box 239, 93921). Tel: 408-624-6330. *Pres* Ansel Adams; *VPres* Peter C Bunnell; *Secy* Ralph Tutzker; *Exec Dir* James Alinder; *Exec Asst* David Featherstone.
Open Tues - Sun 1 - 5 PM. No admis. Estab 1967 to serve the field of serious art photography through exhibitions, workshops, publications, and critical inquiry. Maintains an art gallery with continuous exhibitions. Average Annual Attendance: 7000. Mem: 1800; dues $18; annual meeting Feb.
Income: $173,000 (financed by endowment, membership, city and state appropriations, federal grants, and patrons).
Exhibitions: Eikoh Hosoe; Ken Graves; Paul Caponigro; Abigail Heyman; Barbara Crane; Eva Rubenstein; Brett Weston; Classics of Documentary Photography; Emerging Los Angeles Photographers; New Portfolios; Norman Locks; Lou Stoumen; Bernard Freemesser; Harold Jones; Arthur Tress; Jerome Liebling; Vilem Kriz; Bruguiere; Photography as Artifice.
Publications: Journal of the Friends, quarterly; Newsletter, monthly.
Activities: Classes for adults; workshops; lect open to the public; competitions, with cash awards; sales shop selling books and photographs.

CATHEDRAL CITY

MUSEUM OF ANTIQUITIES AND ART, Hotel Arner, Glenn Grove & Plumley Place, 92234. *Founder & Cur* Samuel DeWalt Arner.
Open (Nov 15 - May 1) 3 - 5 PM & 7 - 9 PM. Estab 1960 for educational purposes. Permanent gallery of Western historical figures, mostly oil portraits by Arner over 50 year period.
Income: Financed by founder, Samuel DeWalt Arner.
Collections: Pre-Columbian artifacts; artifacts from Isreal, Turkey, Lebanon, Egypt, Italy, India, Japan, and China; ancient coins; ancient arms; fossils; gemstones; mineral specimens; portraits by Arner.
Activities: Lect to visitors and large groups from schools and colleges.
Library: Holdings—Vols 3000-4000, for reference on archaeology.

CHERRY VALLEY

RIVERSIDE COUNTY ART AND CULTURAL CENTER, Edward-Dean Museum of Decorative Arts, 9401 Oak Glen Rd, 92223. Tel: 714-845-2526. *Dir* Mary Jo O'Neill.
Open Tues - Sat 10 AM - 5 PM; Sun 1 - 5 PM. No admis. Built in 1957, and given to the County of Riverside in 1964, and is is a division of the Parks Dept. The South Wing of the gallery displays antiques and decorative arts as permanent collections; the North Wing has monthly exhibits by contemporary artists. Average Annual Attendance: 55,000. Mem: 250; dues $10 min; monthly meetings.
Income: Financed by county funding.
Collections: Antiques; decorative arts; David Roberts (original watercolors); Boulle cabinet; Meisen; Wedgwood; Sevres; Lowestoft; Capo di Monte; Chinese export wares, and other fine porcelains.

Exhibitions: (1978) Robert H Meltzer (watercolors); Evelyn Gathings Butler (oils); Museum Board Annual Special Exhibit featuring Jane Maleung (traditional Chinese watercolor and oil); AWS National Invitational Watercolors; Gloria White (mixed media); AWS Traveling Exhibit; San Ildefonso Pueblo Pottery by Maria Martinez and family; Mas Konatsu (acrylics); Betty Davenport Ford (sculpture); Annual Friends Special Exhibit.
Publications: Friends of the Museum Bulletin, quarterly.
Activities: Docent training; lect for members only; individual paintings and original objects of art lent; traveling exhibitions organized and circulated; sales shop selling books, original art, prints, slides and crafts.
Library. Open to the public for reference only. Holdings: Vols 1200; Per subs 10. Special Subjects: Decorative arts, paintings, porcelains, furnitures, crystals. Special Collections: David Roberts (original lithograph set of Holy Land.)

CHICO

CALIFORNIA STATE UNIVERSITY, CHICO, Art Gallery, Normal and Salem Sts, 95929. Tel: 916-895-5331 or 895-5218. *Chmn* Richard Hornaday; *Secy* Janet Karolyi.
Open daily 8 AM - 10 PM. No admis. Estab to afford broad cultural influences to the massive North California region. Average Annual Attendance: 15,000.
Income: Financed by state appropriations.
Collections: The Behrick Oriental Ceramics Collection.
Exhibitions: Jan Wagstaff; The Los Angeles Fine Arts Squad; Art, Theory and Criticism; Roland Reiss; Perceptual Truths and Created Fakes; Jim Gale: Monster Environments; Sculpture by Val Zarins; Student Exhibits.
Activities: Classes for adults and children; lect open to public; competitions with awards; scholarships; exten dept serving the region.
Library: Learning Activities Resource Center. *Dir* P Busch. Open to students and the public.

CHULA VISTA

SOUTHWESTERN COMMUNITY COLLEGE ART GALLERY,* 900 Otay Lakes Rd, 92010. Tel: 714-420-1080, exten 283. *Dir* Geraldine Turley.
Open Mon - Fri 10 AM - 2 PM; Mon - Thurs 6 - 9 PM; No admis. Estab 1961 to show contemporary artists' work who are of merit to the community and the school, as a service and an educational service. Gallery is approx 3000 sq ft. Average Annual Attendance: 10,000.
Income: Financed by city and state appropriations.
Collections: Permanent collection of mostly contemporary work.
Publications: Show announcements, every 3 weeks.
Activities: Classes for adults; lect open to public, 3 vis lectr per yr; gallery talks; competitions; individual paintings and original objects of art lent; lending collection contains color reproductions, photographs, and original art works; junior museum.

CLAREMONT

GALLERIES OF THE CLAREMONT COLLEGES, Montgomery Art Gallery—Pomona College, Lang Art Gallery—Scripps College, 91711. Tel: 714-621-8000, exten 2241. *Dir* David W Steadman; *Asst Dir* David S Rubin; *Registrar* Kay Koeninger; *Galleries Mgr.* Doug Humble; *Galleries Coordr* Charmaine Soldat.
Open Daily 1 - 5 PM; Wed 7 - 9 PM; cl national and school holidays. No admis. Estab 1974 to present balanced exhibitions useful not only to students of art history and studio arts but also to the general public; Montgomery Art Gallery—Pomona College contains one large and two smaller galleries with two exhibitions corridors. The Lang Art Gallery—Scripps College contains one large and three smaller galleries one of which can be closed off from the rest of the building. Average Annual Attendance: 15,000.
Income: $80,000 (financed by endowment). Purchases: Varies.
Collections: American painting; Samuel H Kress Collection of Renaissance paintings; Old Master and contemporary graphics; photographs; Oriental art; African Art.
Exhibitions: (1977-78) Works on Paper 1900-1960 from Southern California Collection; American Art from Permanent Collections; Paper Art; The Wonderful World of Dr Seuss; The Art of J M Whistler; Color Consciousness; 34th Ceramics Annual; Photographs of Wright Morris; Pomona and Scripps Colleges Student Exhibitions; Pomona and Scripps Colleges Seniors Exhibitions.
Publications: Art Publications List, annual.

Activities: Educ dept; docent training; lectr open to the public 7 - 10 vis lectr per yr; gallery talks; tours; competitions; individual paintings and original objects of art lent; lending collection contains original art works, original prints, paintings and photographs; traveling exhibitions organized and circulated; sales shop selling books, posters and cards.

CYPRESS

CYPRESS COLLEGE FINE ARTS GALLERY,* 9200 Valley View St, 90630.
Open Mon - Fri 11 AM - 3 PM; Tues & Thurs 7 - 9 PM during exhibitions. No admis. Estab 1969 to bring visually enriching experiences to the school and community.
Income: Financed by school budget.
Collections: Student works; purchase awards.
Exhibitions: Faculty Art Shows; Architectural Crafts Invitational; Annual Juried Student Show; Community College Ceramics; Annual High School Invitational; Craft Design Invitational; Aridian Techniques and Design; plus many others.

DAVIS

UNIVERSITY OF CALIFORNIA, DAVIS
—**The Gallery,** Fourth Floor, Memorial Union, 95616. Tel: 916-752-2885. *Asst Dir* Christi Olson.
Open Mon - Fri 8 AM - 5 PM; Tues 8 AM - 7 PM. No admis. Estab 1965 to provide facility for students, faculty and townspeople to enjoy Northern California talent and other events while on campus; gallery consists of North Gallery and South Gallery (hallway gallery); two separate shows; North Gallery is one large room.
Publications: Monthly calendar.
Activities: Classes for adults; lect open to public, 5 vis lectr per yr; concerts; film competitions.
—**Richard L Nelson Gallery,** Dept of Art, 95616. Tel: 916-752-0105. *Cur* L Price Amerson, Jr.
Open Mon - Fri Noon - 5 PM. No admis. Estab 1976 to provide exhibitions of contemporary art as well as historical importance as a service to the teaching program of the department of art and other departments, the university and the public; contains main gallery and small gallery. Average Annual Attendance: 5000.
Income: Financed by university appropriation.
Collections: Opeated in connection with the Department of Art's permanent collection.
Exhibitions: (1977-78) The Nagel Collection of South and East Asian Ceramics and Sculpture; A Survey of Relief Printmaking; A Survey of Intaglio Printmaking; A Survey of Planographic and Stencil Printmaking; MFA Retrospective I: 1970-1976; MA/MFA: 24 Artists Then and Now; History of Photography I: Invention to World War I; History of Photography II: World War I Through the Present; Fred Martin: New Paintings; Kaplan and Rukhin: Works by Two Contemporary Soviet Jewish Artists; Recent Work by First Year MFA Students; A Mona Lisa Scrapbook; Garner Tullis: Sculptured Print; John Spence Weir: Recent Photographs; 1977 MFA Exhibitions: Linda Horning, Mary Gould, Kevin Kearney and Paula Nees; Joan Brown: Drawings-Ashland Printmakers: Five Years Later; London: From the Great Fire to the Great War; Satire and Caricature of British Prints from Hogarth through Rowlandson; Poetry: The Resurrection of the Body. An Exhibit of Paintings and Works on Paper by Jarrold Hines; Barbara Kasten: Non-Camera Blueprints; Ceramics: Ann Adair and Richard Shaw; The Photographer as a Collector; Jack Welpott: Recent Photographs; Guzel Amalrik and Henry Elinson: Paintings and Drawings by Two Russian Emigre Artists; Artists Working in Wood; Darrell Forney: Large Letter Postcard Paintings, 1968-1978.
Publications: Exhibition catalogs occasionally.
Activities: Lect open to the public, 3 - 5 vis lectr per yr.
—**Art Dept Library,** 95616. *Librn* Barbara Hoermann.
Open to students and faculty.
Holdings: Vols 2500; Per subs 34; AV—Microfiche: mounted reproductions 26,500.
Special Collections: Decimal index of the art of the low countries.

DOMINGUEZ HILLS

ART GALLERY OF CALIFORNIA STATE COLLEGE, DOMINGUEZ HILLS,* 1000 E Victoria, 90747. Tel: 213-515-3372.
Open Mon - Fri Noon - 2 PM. Estab 1973 to exhibit faculty, student, and outside art.
Income: Financed by state appropriations.

DOWNEY

DOWNEY MUSEUM OF ART, 10419 S Rives Ave, 90241. Tel: 213-861-0419. *Dir* Ronald E Steen.

Open Wed - Sun 1 - 5 PM. No admis. Estab 1957 as an aesthetic and educational facility and located in Furman Park, it is the only municipal art museum with a permanent collection in Southeast Los Angeles which includes in its area 27 neighboring communities of such significant ethnic range, and a total population close to one million; the facility has four gallery areas plus classroom space; Gallery I covers 15 x 39 ft, Gallery II covers approx 12 x 12 x 24 ft, Gallery III covers 15 x 20 ft, and Gallery IV covers 23 x 39 ft. The Museum is continuing a program for new artists which was originally funded by Los Angeles County but is now paid for by museum operating funds. Average Annual Attendance: 7500. Mem: 110; dues $15; annual meeting April.
Income: $20,000 (financed by membership, and city appropriation).
Collections: Many pieces produced by Southern California artists over the past 20 years—Billy Al Bengston, Corita Kent, Don Emery, Sabato Fiorello, Luckman Glascow, Stephen Longstreet, Anna Mahler, Shirley Pettibone, Betye Saar.
Exhibitions: Twelve to fourteen shows a year featuring painting, sculpture, crafts, prints and other visual forms. Recent shows included Beyond the Garden Wall (relationships of women and children in art); Los Angeles Printmaking Society National Exhibition; Festival of Holiday Trees (involving area schools and businesses); Hollywood: the Matrix (Hollywood film costumes); monthly Round Robin Art Competition; and co-sponsors a carnival and art fair in association with the Downey Training Center for the Retarded and the Department of Parks and Recreation. (1976) A Treasury of Historical Prints (Recollections of Times Past, Part I, II, III); A Retrospective of Donna Norine Schuster: 1883-1953; Time Remembered: Antique Clocks. (1978) Southern California Industrial Ceramics, Part I: 1912-1942 by Ernest Batchelder, Part II: 1927-1942 by Southern California Pottery.
Activities: Classes for children; lect open to the public, 4 vis lectr per yr; gallery talks; tours; traveling exhibitions organized and circulated; museum shop selling reproductions, prints.

EL CAJON

GROSSMONT COMMUNITY COLLEGE GALLERY, 8800 Grossmont College Drive, 92020. *Dir* Gene Kennedy.
Open Mon - Fri 10 AM - 4 PM & 6 - 9 PM. No admis. Estab 1970 as a co-curricular institution which cooperates with and supports the Art Dept of Grossmont College and which provides a major cultural resource for the general public in the eastern part of the greater San Diego area. Two galleries, one 30 x 40 ft, the other 30 x 20 ft. Average Annual Attendance: 20,000.
Income: Financed through College.
Collections: Prints; photographs; clay objects; large Tom Holland painting.
Exhibitions: Patti Warashina; Erik Gronborg; Garry Winogrand; Victor Lance Henderson; Henry Wessel Jr; William Wareham; Jaye Lawrence; James Edwards; Jean St Pierre; Sam Wilson; Jud Yalkut; Los Angeles Printmakers; Kathe Kollwitz: The Weavers' Revolt; Viewpoint: Ceramics; Carol Shaw-Sutton.
Publications: Catalogs, 5 - 6 per yr.
Activities: Lect open to public, 6 vis lectr per yr; concerts; original objects of art lent to institutions; lending collection contains photographs; traveling exhibitions organized and circulated.

EUREKA

HUMBOLDT ARTS COUNCIL,* PO Box 221, 95501. *Pres* Ardene Janssen; *Secy* Kathleen Timm.
Estab 1966 to encourage, promote and correlate all forms of activity in the arts and to make such activity a vital influence in the life of the community. Mem: 250. Annual meeting Oct.
Income: $10,000 (financed by membership).
Collections: Art Bank, consisting of the yearly award winner from the juried Redwood Art Association Spring Show; other purchases and donated works of art.
Activities: Concerts; competitions; scholarships; traveling exhibitions organized and circulated; individual paintings and original objects of art lent; photograph collection.

FRESNO

FRESNO ARTS CENTER, 3033 E Yale, 93703. *Exec Dir* R Andrew Maass; *Asst to Dir* Dorys L Beck.
Open Mon - Sun 10 AM - 4:30 PM; Wed 7 - 9:30 PM. No admis. Estab 1960 as a visual arts gallery to provide Fresno and its environs with a community oriented visual arts center. The Center exhibits works of internationally known artists, and arranges shows of local artists. Three galleries plus entry for exhibits. Average Annual Attendance: 60,000. Mem: 1200; dues $25; annual meeting March.
Income: $150,000 (financed by membership, city and state appropriations, and fund-raising efforts). Purchases: $2250.

Collections: Works of prominent Central valley artists; Oriental art; Mexican folk art and Mexican graphic arts.
Exhibitions: Masterworks of Modern Sculpture; California Contemporary Stained Glass; BJ McCoon; Varaz Samuelian; Alex Katz; 200 Years of American Painting; Ruth Azawa.
Activities: Classes for adults and children; docent training; lect open to public, 12 vis lectr per yr; gallery talks; individual paintings and original objects of art lent to city and county offices and other institutions; lending collection contains framed reproductions, original art works, original prints, and slides; traveling exhibitions organized and circulated; museum shop selling books, original art, reproductions, prints, cards, and local craft.

FULLERTON

CALIFORNIA STATE UNIVERSITY, FULLERTON, ART GALLERY, 800 N State College Blvd, 92634. Tel: 714-870-3262. *Gallery Dir* Dextra Frankel; *Tech Asst* Steve Stark; *Secretarial Asst* Barbara McAlpine.
Open during exhibits, Mon - Fri 1 - 4 PM; Sun Noon - 4 PM. No admis. Estab 1963 to bring to the campus carefully developed art exhibits that instruct, inspire, and challenge the student to the visual arts, to present to the student body, faculty and community exhibits of national interest; acting as an educational tool, creating interaction between various departmental disciplines, and promotion of public relations between campus and community. Four to five exhibits are presented each year with organizational activity stemming from a class, Display and Exhibition Design. The students have the opportunity to work in an actual gallery environment rather than one which is only theoretical—designing, constructing and installing. Average Annual Attendance: 5000 - 7000.
Income: Financed by state appropriation, grants and donations.
Collections: The Art Department as a whole, not the Gallery, is the holder of the permanent collection.
Exhibitions: (1976-78) Jewelers, USA; California White Paper Painters; Jud Fine—Confessions and Related Work 1970-1976; Shaw/Blackburn/Costanzo/Ekks/Roloff; Sam Richardson "Coordinate Line/Motion Broken By Boulder"; John Okulick; Overglaze Imagery: Cone 019-016; Faculty Collects; Gallery as Studio: Lithography & Society; Art Student Art.
Publications: Exhibition catalogs.
Activities: Educ dept; college course; lect open to public, 4-6 vis lectrs per yr; traveling exhibitions organized and circulated.
Library: *Librn* Ernest Toy, Jr. Open to students for reference only. Holdings: Catalogs of exhibitions.

MUCKENTHALER CULTURAL CENTER, 1201 W Malvern, 92633. Tel: 714-879-6860. *Dir Civic Arts* Donald E Knaub; *Prog Coordr* Martha L Bartholomew; *Gallery Dir* Ronald Salgado; *Exec Secy* Norman Bricker.
Open Tues - Sun Noon - 5 PM. No admis. Estab 1966 for the promotion and development of a public cultural center for the preservation, display and edification in the arts for the purpose of encouraging aesthetic appreciation and creative expression particularly in the field of fine arts; gallery contains 2500 sq ft; three galleries, the larger also used for the performing arts. Average Annual Attendance: 60,000. Mem: 450; dues $10 and up; annual meeting June.
Income: $116,000 (financed by endowment, membership and city appropriation).
Exhibitions: (1977-78) Four from Gallery Four (watercolor); Specific Observations, Sights Unseen (photography); Native American Woman's Poems: An Exhibition of Navajo Blankets and Pomo Baskets, Jim Nash (furniture); 19th Century Posters; Holiday Faire.
Publications: Catalogues in conjunction with exhibitions.
Activities: Classes for adults and children; lect open to public, 40 vis lectr per yr; concerts; gallery talks; tours; competitions; individual paintings lent; traveling exhibitions organized and circulated; sales shop selling books, magazines and original art.

GARDEN GROVE

MILLS HOUSE ART GALLERY,* 12732 Main St, 92640. Tel: 714-638-6707. *Pres Mills House Volunteers* Rachel Casey; *Secy Mills House Volunteers* Barbara Burby; *Dir* Richard Conrad; *Cultural Arts Coordr* Sondra Evans.
Open Thurs - Mon Noon - 4 PM; cl Tues & Wed. No admis. Estab 1964 to promote the visual arts in the city of Garden Grove, serving student, local and regional artists. Average Annual Attendance: 6000. Mem: 50.
Income: Financed by city appropriation.
Activities: Lect open to public; gallery talks; tours.

ORANGE COUNTY PUBLIC LIBRARY, Garden Grove Regional Branch, 11200 Stanford Ave, 92640. Tel: 714-530-0711. *County Librn* Harry M Rowe Jr; *Dir Public Services* (vacant); *Dir Special Services* Nadine Leffler; *Regional Librn* Irmgard Bassen; *Regional Librn* Ann

Ague; *Regional Branch Librn* Katherine Spencer; *Dir Reference Center* Carin Tong; *Special Projects & AV Librn* Richard Dimmitt.
Open Mon - Thurs 10 AM - 9 PM; Fri - Sun 1 - 5 PM. Estab 1921 for public library services. Circ. 300,117.
Income: Financed by county appropriations.
Holdings: Vols 87,500; Per subs 1050, AV—Cassettes, motion pictures 740, phonorecords; Other—Framed reproductions, pamphlets, color reproductions 400, graphics 14.
Activities: Lect open to the public; tours.

GILROY

GAVILAN COLLEGE ART GALLERY, 5055 Santa Therese Blvd, 95020. Tel: 408-847-1400. *Gallery Adviser & Humanities Div Dir* Kent Child; *Community Services Dir* Ken Cooper.
Open Mon - Fri 8 AM - 9:30 PM. No admis. Estab 1967 to serve as a focal point in art exhibitions for community college district, and as a teaching resource for the art department. Gallery is in large lobby of college library with 25 ft ceiling, redwood panelled walls, and carpeted floor.
Income: Financed through college.
Collections: Approx 25 paintings purchased as award-purchase prizes in college art competitions.
Exhibitions: Changing monthly exhibits of student, local artist, and traveling shows.
Activities: Lending collection contains books, cassettes, color reproductions, film strips, Kodachromes, paintings; sculpture.

GLEN ELLEN

JACK LONDON STATE HISTORIC PARK, London Ranch Rd (Mailing Add: PO Box 358, 95441). Tel: 707-938-5216.
Open daily 10 AM - 5 PM; cl Thanksgiving, Christmas, New Year's Day. Admis adults 50¢. Estab 1959 for the interpretation of the life of Jack London; the fieldstone home was constructed in 1919 by London's widow; the collection is housed on two floors in the House of Happy Walls, and is operated by Calif. Dept. of Parks & Recreation. Average Annual Attendance: 125,000.
Income: Financed by state appropriation.
Collections: (Art) Artifacts from South Sea Islands; original illustrations.
Activities: Museum shop selling books.

GLENDALE

BRAND LIBRARY AND ART CENTER,* 1601 W Mountain St, 91201. Tel: 213-956-2051. *Librn* Jane Hagan; *Asst Librn* Marilyn Costamagna; *Exhib Coordr* Burdette Peterson.
Open Tues & Thurs Noon - 9 PM; Wed, Fri & Sat Noon - 6 PM; Sun 1 - 5 PM; cl Mon. No admis. Estab 1956 as art and music departments of the Glendale Public Library. A large and a small gallery with a contemporary art program and crafts. Average Annual Attendance: 72,000. Dues: $15 - $500.
Income: Financed by city and state appropriations.
Holdings: Vols 28,000; AV—Cassettes 300, records 18,000; Other—Color slides 4000.
Special Collections: Works on history, theory, criticism and techniques, specialized encyclopedias, dictionaries, indexes and other guides to art and music literature; piano rolls; 78-rpm records, Dieterle picture collection, early photography journals.
Activities: Lect open to the public; tours; concerts; competitions; lending collection contains color reproductions 2286, Kodachromes 4000.

FOREST LAWN MUSEUM,* 1712 Glendale Ave, 91209. Tel: 213-254-3131. *Dir* Frederick Llewellyn; *Mgr* Jane E Llewellyn.
Open daily 10 AM - 6 PM. No admis. Estab 1951 as a community museum offering education and culture through association with the architecture and the art of world masters. There are four galleries in the museum and several smaller galleries in buildings throughout the four parks. Average Annual Attendance: 200,000.
Collections: American Western bronzes; reproductions of Michelangelo's greatest sculptures; ancient Biblical and historical coins; stained glass window of the Last Supper; Crucifixion Painting by Paderewski (195 x 45 ft); The Resurrection Painting by Robert Clark; reproductions and originals of famous sculptures, paintings, and documents.
Activities: Lending collection contains reproductions of the crown jewels of England; documents for the Smithsonian Institution Bicentennial Collection; scholarships; memento shop selling books and art works.
Library: For use of employees. Holdings: Vols 3000.

IRVINE

UNIVERSITY OF CALIFORNIA, IRVINE ART GALLERY,* 92717. *Dir* Melinda Wortz; *Admin Asst* Linda Rosengarten.

Open Oct - June, Tues - Sat Noon - 5 PM. No admis. Estab 1965 to house changing exhibitions devoted to contemporary art.
Income: Financed by city and state appropriations, and by interested private collectors.
Publications: Exhibition catalogs.
Activities: Monthly lect on each exhibit.

KENTFIELD

COLLEGE OF MARIN ART GALLERY, 94904. *Art Gallery Dir* Ann L Jack.
Open Mon - Fri 8 AM - 10 PM; Open also during all performances for Drama, Music and Concert/Lecture series. No admis. Estab 1970 for the purpose of education in the college district and community; gallery is housed in the entrance to Fine Arts Complex, measures 3600 sq ft of unlimited hanging space; has portable hanging units and locked cases. Average Annual Attendance: 100 - 300 daily.
Income: Financed by state appropriation and community taxes. Purchases: $300.
Collections: Art Student Work; miscellaneous collection.
Exhibitions: Eight yearly; Faculty and Art Student; Fine Arts and Decorative Arts.
Publications: Catalogs, 1 - 2 per year.
Activities: Docent training; Gallery Design/Management; gallery talks; tours.

LA JOLLA

LA JOLLA MUSEUM OF CONTEMPORARY ART, 700 Prospect St, 92037. Tel: 714-454-9719. *Pres Bd of Trustees* Mrs Lynn G Fayman; *Dir* Sebastian Adler; *Financial Coordr* Ratchel Lingren; *Admin Asst to Dir* Ulla Burg; *Sr Cur* Richard Armstrong; *Cur* Christopher Knight.
Open Tues - Fri 10 AM - 5 PM; Sat & Sun 12:30 - 5 PM; Wed eve 7 - 10 PM; cl Mon, New Years, Thanksgiving & Christmas. No admis, suggested contribution adults $1, children 50¢. Founded 1941 for exhibition and understanding of the visual arts. Nonprofit organization, tax exemp. 500-seat auditorium, classrooms, exhibition space; six-acre sculpture garden under development. Average Annual Attendance: 100,000. Mem: 1300; dues $15 - $1000; annual meeting Oct.
Income: $400,000 (financed by endowment, membership and Combined Arts and Education Council of San Diego County).
Collections: Substantial representtion from all major painting and sculptural styles since 1930.
Exhibitions: Angel of Mercy, Eleanor Antin; The Modern Chair: Its Origins and Evolution; Richard Anuszkiewicz Retrospective; A View of California Architecture 1965-75; Four Californians: Krebs, Spence, Therrien, Georgesco; Rope Drawings by Patrick Ireland.
Publications: Newsletter, monthly; exhibition catalogs.
Activities: Classes for children; dramatic programs; lect open to public; individual paintings lent; traveling exhibitions organized and circulated; museum shop; films; gallery talks; tours; schol; docent program; intermuseum loans.
—**Helen Palmer Geisel Library.** Tel: 714-454-9717. *Librn* Gail Richardson.
Open Tues - Fri 10 AM - 5 PM; Sat & Sun 12:30 - 5 PM; Wed 7 - 10 PM. Estab 1941 for reference use by staff, docents, others by appointment.
Income: Financed by membership, gifts and grants.
Holdings: Vols revision and inventory in process; Per subs 30; AV—Slides; Other—Exhibition catalogs, pamphlets, vertical file: artist information.
Special Subjects: Contemporary art, international in scope.
Exhibitions: (1976) The Substance of Light: Charles Ross; New Industrial Parks Near Irvine, California; Sculpture by Dennis O'Leary; Naives and Visionaries; North, East, West, South and Middle; Christo's Running Fence; by Richard Artschwager, Chuck Close, Joe Zucker; Work by Bernard Venet; (1977) Who is Dr Seuss?; 48 Rugged Wheels in 7 Ways - Marc van der Marck; Stories and Posters by Christian Boltanski; Improbable Furniture; View of California Architecture 1960-1976; (1978) Recent Acquisitions; Probing the Earth: Contemporary Land Projects; Selections from the Permanent Collection; Herbert Rockere: Recent Work; Paintings by Manny Farber.

LIBRARY ASSOCIATION OF LA JOLLA, Athenaeum Music and Arts Library, 1008 Wall St, 92037. Tel: 714-454-5872. *Adminr* Lynn Neumann.
Open Tues - Sat 10 AM - 5:30 PM. Estab 1899 for the use of the people in the community, endeavoring to provide material not otherwise available. Circ. 15,000. No established gallery.
Income: $27,622 (financed by endowment and membership). Purchases: $5181.
Holdings: Vols 4200; Per subs 42. AV—Cassettes, records; Other—Clipping files, memorabilia, pamphlets.

Special Collections: Bach Werke, 47 vols.
Exhibitions: Monthly one-man shows.
Activities: Lect open to public, 10 vis lectr per yr; concerts; library tours.

UNIVERSITY OF CALIFORNIA, SAN DIEGO
—Mandeville Art Gallery, B-027, 92093. Tel: 714-452-2860. *Dir* Gerry McAllister.
Open Sun - Fri 12 - 5 PM; Wed 7 - 10 PM. No admis. Estab 1967 to provide changing exhibitions of interest to the visual arts majors, university personnel and the community at large including an emphasis on contemporary art; located on west end of Mandeville Center, flexible open space approx 40 x 70 ft. Average Annual Attendance: 12,000.
Income: Financed by state appropriations and student registration fees.
Collections: Small Impressionist Collection owned by UC Foundation, presently on loan to San Diego Fine Arts Gallery, Balboa Park.
Exhibitions: Three Performers (Hershman, Laub, Goodell); Faculty Exhibitions; Alexis Smith's Star Material; Illusins in the Gallery (Bill Lundberg and Alan Turner): King Ubu; Mary Beth Edelson Exhibition and Performance; The Artist's Book; Wendy Clarke Interactive Video Exhibition; Arbus/Avedon Photographic Exhibition; Paul Conrad's Political Cartoons; Tom Wudl's Paintings; Frid Kahlo Painting Retrospective.
Publications: Exhibition announcements.
Activities: Approx. 10 vis lectr sponsored by Dept of Visual Arts.
Library: Gallery contains current periodical library.
—Central University Library. Tel: 714-452-3336. *Art Librn* Donald McKie.
Open Mon - Fri 8 AM - 10 PM; Sat 8 AM - 5 PM; Sun 2 - 10 PM. Estab 1960 as a general university library.
Income: Financed by state appropriation. Purchases: $40,000.
Holdings: Vols 25,000; Per subs 160. AV—Slides.
Special Subjects: Architecture; Renaissance Art; 19th - 20th century art.

LAGUNA BEACH

LAGUNA BEACH MUSEUM OF ART, Pacific Coast Highway at Cliff Dr, 92651. Tel: 714-494-6531. *Dir* Tom K Enman; *Secy* Mary Jacob.
Open six days a week 11:30 AM - 4:30 PM. No admis. Estab 1918 as an art association; two large galleries, two small galleries, museum store and offices. Average Annual Attendance: 37,000. Mem: 1050; dues $21; annual meeting Sept.
Income: 74,000 (financed by endowment and membership).
Collections: Emphasis on early 20th century California painting.
Exhibitions: Conrad Buff (1898-1975) Retrospective; All California Photography Show; Illusionistic Realism (contemporary ceramics); William Wendt (1865-1946) Retrospective; Roger Kunts (1926-1975) Retrospective; Japanese Prints—Edo Period—from Norton Simon Museum.
Activities: Classes for adults and children; docent training; lect open to public; museum shop selling books, magazines, original art, reproductions, and prints.

LONG BEACH

CALIFORNIA STATE UNIVERSITY, LONG BEACH
—The Art Galleries, 1250 Bellflower Blvd, 90840. Tel: 213-498-5761. *Dir* Constance W Glenn; *Asst Dir* Jane K Bledsoe.
Open Mon - Fri Noon - 4 PM; Sun 1 - 4 PM. No admis. Estab 1949 to be an academic and community visual arts resource. Three galleries situated adjacent to the fine arts patio. Average Annual Attendance: 30,000.
Income: Financed by city appropriation.
Collections: Collection of the 1965 Sculpture Symposium; prints; drawings; photographs.
Exhibitions: Roy Lichtenstein: Ceramic Sculpture; George Segal: Pastels 1957-1965; Lucas Samaras: Photo-Transformations; The Photographs as Artifice; The Black Dolphin Press; Egypt in Los Angeles; MC=E^2: Merce Cunningham; Anna A Hills: California Impressionist.
Publications: Exhibition catalogs, 5-6 per year.
Activities: Docent training; scheduled tours; lect, 10 vis lectr per yr; traveling exhibitions organized and circulated.
—Library. Tel: 213-498-4047. *Dir* Peter Spyers-Duran; *Assoc Dir* Lloyd A Kramer; *Fine Arts Librn* Henry J DuBois.
Open Mon - Thurs 7:30 AM - Midnight; Fri 7:30 AM - 5 PM; Sat 9 AM - 5 PM; Sun 1 - 10 PM. Estab 1949 to support and augment the curriculum offered by the University's Art Department and to provide enrichment and recreational materials for all the campus community.
Income: Financed by city appropriation. Purchases: $18,500.
Holdings: Vols, Per subs & Serials 27,000; AV—Audio tapes, cassettes, film strips, microfiche, phonorecords, slides and video tapes; Other—Clipping files; pamphlets, and reproductions.

LONG BEACH MUSEUM OF ART, 2300 E Ocean Blvd, 90803. Tel: 213-439-2119. *Dir* Russell J Moore; *Cur* Nancy Drew; *Mgr Publications* Barbara Hendrick.
Open Wed - Sun Noon - 5 PM; cl New Year's, Thanksgiving and Christmas. No admis. Opened in 1951 as a Municipal Art Center under the city library department; in 1957 the Long Beach City Council changed the center to the Long Beach Museum of Art, a department of municipal government. Average Annual Attendance: Approx 60,000.
Collections: †Paintings, †sculpture, †prints, †drawings, crafts and photography; 850 items with emphasis on West Coast and California contemporary; small collection of African artifacts; sculpture garden.
Exhibitions: Continuous exhibition of permanent collection; Arts of Southern California Exhibition (one every three years), a traveling exhibition of contemporary art, invitational and organized by the museum under a grant from Los Angeles County; one-man and group exhibitions in diversified media; extensive video division.
Publications: Quarterly bulletin, catalogs, announcements.
Activities: Classes for adults and children; receptions; art festivals; lect series; gallery talks; tours; films and chamber music concerts; art rental and sales service; sales shop selling books, magazines, original folk art, ceramics and jewelry.
Library: Open for staff reference with restricted lending of books, publications and slides. Holdings: Vols 1500.

LONG BEACH PUBLIC LIBRARY, 101 Pacific Ave, 90802. Tel: 213-437-2949. *Dir Library Services* Frances Henselman; *Assoc Dir Library Services Long Beach Museum of Art* Russell Moore.
Open Mon - Thurs 10 AM - 9 PM; Fri & Sat 10 AM - 5:30 PM; Sun 1:30 - 5 PM. Estab 1897. Maintains gallery at Long Beach Museum of Art.
Holdings: Vols 706,763; AV—Audio tapes, cassettes, microfiche, microfilm, motion pictures, phonorecords, video tapes; Other—Clipping files, exhibition catalogs, framed reproductions, memorabilia, original art works, pamphlets, photographs, prints, reproductions, sculpture.
Activities: Exhibitions organized and circulated.

LOS ANGELES

ADVOCATES FOR THE ARTS, University of California, Los Angeles, School of Law, 405 N Hilgard Ave, 90024. Tel: 213-825-3309. *Dir* Monroe E Price; *Coordr* Audrey Greenberg; over 60 vol lawyers.
Founded 1974 to provide free legal assistance to visual and performing artists, and art organizations who otherwise would be unable to afford counsel. Besides providing legal support to art groups and individuals, the program seeks to encourage research and understanding of arts-related issues by University of California, Los Angeles students.
Activities: Research in arts-related topics and historic preservation, copyright, contracts, and libel; legal seminars; research into funding sources for community art; voluntary legal services and assistance to community groups fostering public arts.

AMERICAN ART SOCIETY, 810 S Lucerne Blvd, 90005. Tel: 213-935-9728. *Dir* Harry Muir Kurtzworth; *Art Research Dir* Nicholas B Barton; *Psychology Research Dir* E Franck Lee; *Educ Dir* Payne Thebaut.
Estab 1935, as a nonprofit educational institution, to help art museums achieve facilities enabling the public to appreciate art and the written word, to understand and use positive emotions for the betterment of all with the help of the Lucideum, the Compass of Human Destiny and the experiences of the Constructive Process.

ARCO CENTER FOR VISUAL ART, 505 S Flower St, 90071. Tel: 213-488-0038. *Gallery Asst* Deborah Perrin.
Estab 1976; the Atlantic Richfield Company is the corporate sponsor of the center, which is a not-for-profit gallery for changing exhibitions. The gallery has two show spaces—the larger is used for painting, sculpture and installations; the smaller for photography and drawing. Shows are changed every six weeks, with a staggered opening schedule so that there is something new every three weeks. Average Annual Attendance: Approx 75,000.
Exhibitions: Contemporary California artists; Jim Turrell (installation); David Gilhooly (ceramics); Herbert Bayer (photographic works).
Publications: Brochures; catalog.

CALIFORNIA MUSEUM OF SCIENCE AND INDUSTRY,* 700 State Dr, Exposition Park, 90037. Tel: 213-749-0101. *Museum Dir* William J McCann; *Asst Dir* Henry D Sturr; *Dir Exhib* Norman C Bilderback.
Open daily 10 AM - 5 PM. Dynamically tells the story of science, industry and commerce to the public by tempting each visitor to take part in a sensory learning experience and education adventure. The museum has 9

halls housing 20 permanent exhibits and more than 60 temporary exhibits among which are Sister Cities Youth Art Exhib and Sister Cities in Focus that appear throughout the year.
Income: Financed by state appropriation and California Museum Foundation.
Permanent Exhibitions: (Art) Hall of Fame Exhibit.
Temporary Exhibitions: (Art) Annual Union Artist Exhibit (paintings and sculpture by all unions in AFL-CIO); annual showcase of the best in student design from jewelry to furniture to wallpaper; Key Art Awards (annual showing of posters, logos, word-styles promoting movies or TV shows); National Hobby Show; Of Medicine and Art (sculpture, paintings and medical memorabilia).
Publications: Notices of temporary exhibits, maps, pamphlets.
Activities: Formal science-art education programs for school groups and the public; competitions, scholarships; auditorium seating 500.

CALIFORNIA STATE UNIVERSITY, LOS ANGELES, Fine Arts Gallery, 5151 State University Dr, 90032. Tel: 213-224-3521. *Dir* Daniel Douke; *Asst to Dir* James Halverson; *Gallery Asst* Glenn Hing.
Open Mon - Thurs Noon - 5 PM; Sun 1 - 5 PM. No admis. Estab 1954 as a forum for advanced works of art and their makers; so that education through exposure to works of art can take place. Gallery has 1400 sq ft, clean white walls, 11 ft high ceilings with an entry and catalog desk. Average Annual Attendance: 30,000.
Income: Financed by endowment, and state appropriation.
Publications: Exhibition catalogs, 3 per year.
Activities: Educ Dept; lect open to public, 10 - 20 per yr; gallery talks; exten dept.

CITY OF LOS ANGELES, Municipal Arts Dept, Room 1500, City Hall, 90012. Tel: 213-485-2433. *Gen Mgr* Kenneth Ross; *Asst Gen Mgr* Rodney L Punt; *Dir, Municipal Art Gallery* Josine Ianco-Starrels; *Dir, Junior Arts Center* Claire Isaacs; *Dir, Bureau of Music* George Milan; *Dir, Cultural Heritage* Ileana Welch; *Dir, Gallery Theater* Larry Scott Lane; *Dir, Watts Towers Arts Center* John Outerbridge; *Architect* Forrest Scott, AIA; *Pres, Municipal Arts Commission* Susan Hines; *Pres, Cultural Heritage Board* Carl Dentzel.
Estab 1925 to bring to the community the cultural and aesthetic aspects of Los Angeles; to encourage citizen appreciation and participation in cultural activities and developing art skills; the art areas are the Municipal Arts Dept, the Junior Arts Center Gallery, and the Watts Towers Art Center Gallery. Average Annual Attendance: 250,000.
Income: $1,125,000 (financed by city appropriation).
Collections: Portraits of Mayors of Los Angeles; works by local area artists; gifts to the city from other countries.
Exhibitions: (1976-78) All City Outdoor Arts Festival; Artists Investigate the Environment; Charles White; An American Experience; A Tribute to Martin Luther King; Joyce Treiman Retrospective; Greene & Greene; Another Magical Mystery Tour; Newcomers; Still and Not So Still Lives; Fabric of a Nation.
Activities: Classes for adults and children; dramatic programs; docent training; lect open to the public; concerts; gallery talks; tours; competitions; sales shop selling books, original art, reproductions, prints; Junior Arts Center Gallery at Barnsdall Park.

CRAFT AND FOLK ART MUSEUM,* 5814 Wilshire Blvd, 90036. Tel: 213-937-5544. *Dir* Edith R Wyle; *Admin Dir* Patrick H Ela; *Preparator* Roman Janczak. Open Sat - Wed 11 AM - 5 PM; Thurs & Fri 11 AM - 8 PM. No admis. Estab 1976 as The Egg and The Eye.
Collections: Folk paintings; Japanese folk art; East Indian quilts.
Publications: Newsletter, quarterly; exhibition catalogs.
Activities: Educational programs; workshops; films; lectures; exhibitions; community outreach programs.
Library: Holdings—300 vols.

HARBOR COLLEGE ART GALLERY, 1111 Figueroa Pl, 90744. Tel: 213-518-1000 exten 474. *Dir Art Gallery* Judith Lea Kunda.
Open Mon, Wed & Thurs Noon - 4 PM; Tues & Fri 10 AM - 2 PM; Wed Eve 7 - 9 PM. No admis. Estab 1960 to educate and elevate mind and spirit; gallery is approximately 28 ft square. Average Annual Attendance: 1500.
Income: Financed by community services.
Publications: Catalogs occasionally.
Activities: lect open to the public, 4 vis lectr per yr; gallery talks; museum and sales shop.

HEBREW UNION COLLEGE, Skirball Museum, 32nd and Hoover Sts, (Mailing Add: 3077 University Mall, 90007). Tel: 213-749-3424. *Dir* Nancy Berman; *Cur* Alice Greenwald; *Educ Cur* Ester Duenyas; *Cataloger* Leslie Blacksberg; *Admin Secy* Carole Kirschner; *Slide Librn* Gloria Blumenthal.
Open Tues - Fri 11 AM - 4 PM; Sun 10 AM - 5 PM. No admis. Estab 1913 as part of the library of Hebrew Union College in Cincinnati, Ohio, and moved in 1972 to the California branch of the College, and renamed the Skirball Museum; to collect and display artifacts of Jewish culture;

5575 sq ft in gallery, divided into four rooms—main or permanent installation, mini-exhibit room (changing gallery), large changing exhibits gallery (north gallery), and ceremonial art gallery (northeast gallery); plus lobby/gift shop area. Average Annual Attendance: 18,500. Mem: 876; dues varied, contributions.
Income: Financed by city appropriation and federal funds.
Collections: Archaeological objects 2000 from the Near East, primarily Palestinian; prints and drawings 4000 from Western Europe, spanning four to five centuries; textiles 2000 from Germany, France, Italy, Near East, America, also spanning four centuries; ceremonial objects; primarily Western European, but some exotic, Oriental pieces as well—Chinese Torah case.
Exhibitions: A Centennial Sampler—One Hundred Years of Collecting at Hebrew Union College; Jerusalem-City of Mankind (photographic exhibit) by Ludwig Yehuda Wolpert; Jews of Yemen, a Retrospective; textiles and ceremonial art; And There was Light, Studies by Abraham Rattner for the Stained Glass Windows of the Chicago Loop Synagogue; Selections from the Louis and Jennie Rattner Allen Collection; For Meyer Schapiro: #48; Twelve from the Soviet Underground; Maranova: A Modern Graphic Interpretation of Kafka's The Trial; permanent installation: A Walk through the Past.
Publications: Calendar of Events.
Activities: Docent training; lect open to the public; competitions; lending collections contain slides 7000; museum shop selling books, reproductions, prints and slides.
—**Frances Henry Library.** 213-749-3424. *Librn* Harvey Horowitz.
Open to the public.
Holdings: Vols 60,000; Per subs 250.

JUNIOR ARTS CENTER,* 4814 Hollywood Blvd, 90027. Tel: 213-666-1093. *Chmn Bd Trustees* Mrs Gavin Miller; *Dir* Claire Isaacs Deussen; *Admin Asst* Thomas Mathews; *Art Cur* Ron Layborteaux; *Educ Coordr* Richard Ellis.
Open Mon - Sat 9 AM - 5 PM. No admis. Estab 1967 to stimulate and assist in the development of art skills and creativity. A Division of Municipal Arts Dept, City of Los Angeles. The gallery offers exhibitions of interest to children and young people and those who work with the young. Average Annual Attendance: 50,000. Mem: 350; dues $5 - $1000; annual meeting of Friends of the Junior Arts Center May.
Income: Financed by city appropriation, and Friends of the Junior Arts Center.
Collections: Two-dimensional works on paper; 8mm film by former students.
Publications: Schedule of art classes, quarterly; exhibition notices.
Activities: Art classes for young people in painting, drawing, etching, general printmaking, photography, filmmaking, photo silkscreen, three-dimensional photography, ceramics, film animation; workshops for teachers; concerts; lect; films; improvisational groups for students and the public.
Library: Open for reference. Holdings: Vols 700; Other—slides 15,000.

LOS ANGELES ART ASSOCIATION AND GALLERIES, 825 N LaCienega Blvd, 90069. Tel: 213-652-8272. *Pres* Stephen Longstreet; *Chmn* Lorser Feitelson; *Dir* Helen Wurdemann, *VPres* Shirley Burden; *Treas* Oscar Grossman.
Open Tues - Fri Noon - 5 PM; Sat Noon - 4 PM; Sun 2 - 4 PM; cl Mon. Estab 1925 to discover and present young professional artists, and to exhibit the work of established California artists. Regional contemporary gallery shows established artists. North and South galleries and little gallery for works not part of shows. Average Annual Attendance: 25,000. Mem: 600; dues $30; annual meeting April.
Income: Financed by membership.
Exhibitions: (1978) Abstract Water Color Exhibition; monthly exhibitions.
Publications: Announcements of exhibitions; pamphlets; folders.

LOS ANGELES COUNTY MUSEUM OF ART, 5905 Wilshire Blvd, 90036. Tel: 213-937-4250. *Chmn* Franklin D Murphy; *Pres* Richard E Sherwood; *VPres* Anna Bing Arnold; *VPres* Charles E Ducommun; *VPres* Mrs F Daniel Frost; *Treas* Dr Charles Z Wilson Jr; *Secy* Mrs Norman F Sprague, Jr; *Dir* Kenneth Donahue; *Deputy Dir Fine Arts* Rexford Stead; *Deputy Dir Admin* Morton Golden; *Cur of Exhib and Publ* Jeanne D'Andrea; *Sr Cur of Prints and Drawings* Ebria Feinblatt; *Cur of European Sculpture* Peter Fusco; *Cur of Decorative Arts* William E Jones; *Sr of Far Eastern Art* George Kuwayama; *Sr Cur of Indian and Islamic Art* Pratapaditya Pal; *Cur of American Art* Michael Quick; *Sr Cur of Modern Art* Maurice Tuchman; *Registrar* Patricia Nauert; *Dir of Public Information* Philippa Calnan; *Coord of Educ Services* Rex Moser; *Dir of Film Programs* Ronald Haver.
Open Tues - Fri 10 AM - 5 PM; Sat & Sun 10 AM - 6 PM; cl Mon, Thanksgiving and Christmas. No admis to permanent collection; adults $1, students and senior citizens 50¢ for special exhibitions. Estab 1910 as Division of History, Science and Art; estab separately in 1961, for the purpose of acquiring, researching, publishing, exhibiting and providing for the educational use of works of art from all parts of the world in all

media, dating from prehistoric times to the present; complex of three buildings and Sculpture Garden. Average Annual Attendance: 1,500,000. Mem: 60,000; dues $20 - $1000.

Income: Approx $5,500,000 (financed by endowment, membership, and county appropriation). Purchases: $2,000,000.

Collections: †American Art; †decorative arts; †Far Eastern art; †Ancient art, †Indian and Islamic art; †modern art; †prints and drawings; †European painting and sculpture; †textiles and costumes, †contemporary art.

Exhibitions: (1976) Master Paintings from the Hermitage; Nepal: Where the Gods are Young; Old Master Drawings from American Collections; Folk Sculpture USA; Leonardo Da Vinci Anatomical Drawings from the Queen's Collection at Windsor Castle; Two Centuries of Black American Art; (1977) The World of Franklin and Jefferson; Women Artists: 1550 - 1950; The Gilbert Collections: Monumental Silver and the Art of Mosaics; Richard Diebenkorn: Paintings and Drawings, 1943-1976; (1978) The Sensuous Immortals: Sculptures from the Pan-Asian Collection; Treasures of Tutankhamun; Treasures of Mexico; Venetian Paintings: Giovanni Bellini to Early El Greco.

Publications: Members' Calendar, monthly; Bulletin, annually; Biennial Report; exhibition catalogs, 3 - 4 yearly; special installation brochures, 12 - 18 yearly.

Activities: Classes for adults and children; dramatic programs; docent training; films; workshops; lect open to the public, 30 vis lectr per yr; concerts; gallery talks; tours; competitions with awards; individual paintings and original objects of art lent to other AAM-accredited museums for special exhibitions; lending collection contains original art works, original prints, paintings and slides 88,000; traveling exhibitions organized and circulated; museum shop selling books, magazines, reproductions, prints, slides, gifts, posters, postcards and antiquities.

—**Art Research Library.** Tel: 213-937-4250. *Librn* Eleanor C Hartman.
Open to museum members, staff, volunteers and scholars for reference only.

Holdings: Vols 53,000; Per subs 256; AV—Microfiche, microfilm; Other—Clipping files, vertical files of one-man show announcements 22, catalogs, auction catalogs.

LOS ANGELES INSTITUTE OF CONTEMPORARY ART, 2020 S Robertson Blvd, 90034. Tel: 213-559-5033. *Dir* Bob Smith; *Gallery Coordr* Lorig Injejikian; *Dir Develop* Tobi Smith; *Printer* Terrel Anderson; *Audience Develop Specialist* Irene Borger; *Admin Asst for CETA Programs* Sherry Brody; *Asst Gallery Preparator* James Evans; *Film & Video Coordr* Morgan Fisher; *Special Projects Coordr* Bridget Reak-Johnson; *Information Specialist* Susan Rosenfeld; *Gallery Preparator* David Sabol; *Asst Gallery Coordr* Judith Vogt.
Open Tues - Sat Noon - 6 PM. No admis. Estab 1974 to be a major resource for exhibition of contemporary art; the gallery maintains 4500 sq ft of exhibition space to be used for static and temporal work; film and video facilities. Average Annual Attendance: 50,000. Mem: 1500; dues artist/student $15, active $25, contributing $50, sponsor $100, patron/corporate $500.

Income: $105,000 (financed by membership, city appropriation and state appropriation, NEA and CETA).

Exhibitions: Joan Snyder; Fred Eversley; Exposing: Photographic Definitions; Michael Asher; David Askerold and Richard Long; Unstretched Surfaces; Architectural Views; Physical Fact, Psychic Effect; Women's Video: Public Domain/Private Shadows; Artworks/Bookworks; Pat Hogan; The Museum of Drawers; plus others.

Publications: LAICA Journal, quarterly; LAICA Newsletter, monthly.

Activities: Lect open to the public; concerts; gallery talks; artists performances; sales shop selling books, magazines, artists books and art periodicals.

—**Art Information Center.** *Information Specialist* Susan Rosenfeld.
Open to everyone for reference.

Special Subjects: Art catalogs, periodicals on contemporary art, painting, sculpture, installation, performance, photography and video.

Special Collections: Documentation of 34 arts groups covered by CETA title VI grants.

—**Artists Registry.**

Special Collections: Slides and biographical data of over 1500 Southern California artists.

LOS ANGELES PUBLIC LIBRARY, 630 W Fifth St, 90071. Tel: 213-626-7461. *Art & Music Librn* Katherine Grant.
Open Mon - Thurs 10 AM - 9 PM; Fri & Sat 10 AM - 5:30 PM; cl Sun & holidays. No admis. Estab 1872.

Income: Financed by municipality.

Holdings: (Art & Music Dept) Vols 156,000; Other—Music scores, recreation materials, prints including original etchings 670, woodcuts, lithographs and drawings.

Special Collections: Twin Prints 54; Japanese prints including a complete set of Hiroshige's Tokaido Series.

LOS ANGELES TRADE-TECHNICAL COLLEGE LIBRARY, 400 W Washington Blvd, 90015. Tel: 213-746-0800 exten 217. *Coordinator of Learning Resources* Harold Eckes.
Open 7 AM - 8:30 PM. Estab 1920 for academic/vocational/trade/technical education; mini-gallery located in new Learning Resources Center. Circ: 21,500.

Income: $500,000 (budget), (financed by district tax base). Purchases: $125,000.

Holdings: Vols 90,000; Per subs 700; AV—Audio tapes, cassettes, film strips, kodachromes, microfiche, microfilm, motion pictures, phonorecords, reels, slides, video tapes; Other—Memorabilia, pamphlets, photographs, prints.

Special Subjects: Art; Art History; Apparel Arts; Art Trades; Photography; Graphic Arts; Illustrations.

Special Collections: Vocational/Trade/Technology Education; Career Information.

Publications: LATTC Learning Resources Center Newsletter.

Activities: Classes for adults; competitions; schol.

LOYOLA MARYMOUNT UNIVERSITY, Malone Art Gallery, Loyola Blvd at W 80th, 90045. Tel: 213-642-2880. *Dir* Ellen Ekedal.
Open Mon - Fri 11 AM - 4 PM; Sun 1 - 4 PM. No admis. Estab 1971 to hold exhibitions. Gallery is 20 x 60 ft with 15 ft ceilings, track lighting and carpeted floors. Average Annual Attendance: 10,000.

Income: $10,000 (financed by university).

Exhibitions: (1977-78) Six Printmakers; Four Sculptors; Shades of Grey—A Drawing Survey; Faculty Exhibitions; Contemporary Themes, Traditional Means; Student Exhibition.

Publications: Catalogs.

Activities: Lect open to the public, 2 vis lectr per yr; concerts; gallery talks; traveling exhibitions organized and circulated.

MOUNT ST MARY'S COLLEGE ART GALLERY, * Art Dept, 12001 Chalon Rd, 90049. Tel: 213-272-8791. *Gallery Dir* Jim Murray.
Open Wed - Sun 1 - 4 PM. No admis. Estab to present works of art of various disciplines for the enrichment of students and community.

Income: Financed by College.

Collections: Collection of and by Jose Drudis-Blada.

Publications: Exhibitions catalogs, 2 - 3 per yr.

Activities: Lect open to public, 2 - 3 vis lectr per yr; scholarships.

NATIONAL WATERCOLOR SOCIETY, * c/o Ruth Rossman, 401 Cascada Way, 90049. *Pres* Ruth Rossman; *First VPres* Morten E Solberg; *Treas* Frank Nestler; *Recording Secy* Sylvai Gavurin; *Corresp Secy* Ruth Erich.
Estab 1921 to sponsor art exhibits for the cultural and educational benefit of the public. Mem: 400; dues $20 (must be juried into membership); annual meeting Jan.

Collections: Purchase award-winning paintings from 1954 to present.

Exhibitions: All-membership show; annual exhibition.

Activities: Docent training; slide/cassette program of members' works; traveling exhibitions organized and circulated; competitions with cash awards.

NATURAL HISTORY MUSEUM OF LOS ANGELES COUNTY, 900 Exposition Blvd, 90007. Tel: 213-746-0410, exten 316. *Dir* Giles W Meas; *Asst Dir* Leon Arnold; *Asst Dir* Gurdon Wood; *Pres Board Governors* Ed Harrison; *Chief Exhib* Robert Wade.
Open daily 10 AM - 5 PM. No admis. Estab 1913 to collect, hold and research collection in life science, earth science and history and to exhibit these collections for public education. Average Annual Attendance: 1,500,000. Mem: 11,000; dues $15 - $100.

Income: Financed by county appropriation.

Collections: (Art) Pre-Columbian artifacts.

Exhibitions: (Art) Art from Zaire; American Indian Images of Edward S Curtis.

Publications: Science Bulletin; Contributions in Science; Terra Quarterly Magazine; Terra Monthly Calendar.

Activities: Classes for adults and children; docent training; school tours; film program; saturday workshops; concerts; galley talks; tours; museum shop selling books, original art, reproductions, prints, slides.

Library: *Librn* Katharine Donohue. Open to staff and to the public by appointment for reference only. Holdings: Vols 30,000.

OCCIDENTAL COLLEGE, Thorne Hall, 1600 Campus Rd, 90041. Tel: 213-259-2737. *Dir* Constance M Perkins.
Open Mon - Fri 9 AM - 3 PM. No admis. Estab 1938 to support the academic program of the College and the community; gallery is located in the foyer of the auditorium. Average Annual Attendance: 19,500.

Income: $2600.

Activities: Lect open to public; gallery talks.

OTIS ART INSTITUTE GALLERY, 2410 Wilshire Blvd, 90057. Tel: 213-387-5288. *Gallery Dir* Hal Glicksman; *Asst Cur* Helen Lewis; *Chairperson of the Otis Art Gallery Committee Otis Art Assoc* Carolyn Vena.

Open Tues - Sat 10:30 AM - 5 PM; Sun 1 - 5 PM. No admis. Estab 1954 as a forum for contemporary art; gallery is flawless white drywall, two rooms each measuring 35 x 40 ft, with 16 ft ceilings. Average Annual Attendance: 20,000. Mem: 670; dues $25 and up, meeting May & Dec.

Income: Financed by endowment, membership.

Collections: No permanent collection except Otis Graduate Collection.

Exhibitions: (1976-78) Richard Tuttle; New Topographics; The Great American Quilts; Parasol Press; Five Contemporary Artists; Alice Aycock & Jane Reynolds; Dan Flavin; Carl Andre; Corporate Art Collections; Animated Films of John & Faith Hubley; Hap Tivey & John Knight; On Kawara; Drawing Towards a More Modern Architecture; Sam Francis; Peasant Paintings from Huhsien County; Peoples Republic of China.

Publications: Dan Graham-For Publication; Dan Favin; Carl Andre; On Kawara, 2 a year; posters.

Activities: Classes for adults; lect open to the public and/or members, 2-3 vis lectr per yr, gallery talks; individual paintings and original objects of art lent to County Agencies to hang in offices; museum shop selling books, magazines, posters, postcards.

Library: Librn Joan Hugo. 627 S Carondelet St. Open to faculty/students. Holdings: Vols 24,000; Per subs 310.

RUSKIN ART CLUB,* 800 S Plymouth Blvd, 90005. Tel: 213-937-9641.

Estab 1888, inc 1905. Owns club building. Mem: 60; dues $20; annual meeting Apr. First two public art exhibitions in Los Angeles held by Ruskin Art Club were in 1890 and 1891.

Activities: Weekly art study program.

SOUTHWEST MUSEUM, 234 Museum Dr (Mailing Add: PO Box 42128, Highland Park Station, 90042). Tel: 213-221-2163.

Open daily 1 - 4:45 PM, cl Mon and certain holidays. No admis. Estab 1907 to maintain a free public museum of history, science and art, as manifested in the native cultures of America and especially of the Southwest; owns museum building, also Casa de Adobe, replica of Spanish-California ranch house. Mem dues student $10, others $15 up.

Income: Financed by membership and other funds.

Collections: An extensive collection of Aboriginal American Art of Pre-Columbian and Post-Columbian periods; Caballeria collection of oil paintings from California missions; paintings of Western scenes and Indian subjects; collections of native American arts, crafts, textiles, ceramics and lithic arts.

—**Braun Research Library.**

Holdings: Vols 160,000 (archaeological, ethnological and anthropological).

UNIVERSITY OF CALIFORNIA, LOS ANGELES

—**Grunwald Center for the Graphic Arts,** 405 Hilgard Ave, 90024. Tel: 213-825-3783. *Dir & Cur* Dr E Maurice Bloch; *Asst to Cur* Michael W Schantz.

Open Mon - Fri 9 AM - Noon & 1 - 5 PM. No admis. Estab 1956 as a research and study center for the graphic arts.

Collections: Prints and drawings, 15th century to the present; German Expressionism; French Impressionism; Japanese woodblock; Tamarind Lithography Workshop impressions (complete); Ornament; Renoir; Picasso; Matisse and Rouault.

Activities: Original objects of art lent; lending collection contains original prints 25,000.

—**Museum of Cultural History,** 55A Haines Hall, 405 Hilgard Ave, 90024. Tel: 213-825-4361. *Dir* Dr Christopher B Donnan; *Asst Dir* George R Ellis; *Admin Asst* Beverly Jo Haughey; *Registrar* Nancy L Ellis; *Museum Asst* Anne Bomeisler; *Publ Dir* Raul A Lopez; *Cur New World Coll* Raul A Lopez; *Cur Textiles & Folk Art* Patricia B Altman; *Cur Africa, Oceania & Indonesia* George R Ellis.

Not open to the public. Scholars or students with special interests may make arrangements to view collections with appropriate curator. Estab 1963 to collect, preserve, and make available for research and exhibition objects and artifacts from cultures considered to be outside the Western tradition. The Museum does not have its own gallery; the Frederick S Wight Art Gallery (part of UCLA's Art Dept) is used for annual major exhibition. In 1978, a small exhibition gallery will be opened on the premises; it will be utilized for exhibitions and for seminars and teaching purposes as well.

Income: Financed by endowment, state appropriation, and private donations.

Collections: Approx 120,000 objects primarily from non-Western cultures—Africa, Asia, the Americas, Oceania, the Near East, and parts of Europe. Archeological as well as ethnographic collections.

Exhibitions: Asian Puppets: Wall of the World; Reflections: Images of Los Angeles; The Arts of Ghana; The Loom, the Needle, and the Dye Pot: Selected Textiles from the Museum of Cultural History; Moche Art of Peru: Pre-Columbian Symbolic Communication.

Publications: Exhibition catalogs; monographs; occasional papers.

Activities: Educ dept; lect to school children; filmstrip series on non-Western art; lect open to public, 1-3 vis lectr per yr; competitions; traveling exhibitions organized and circulated; museum shop selling books, original art, reproductions, prints, slides.

Library: Open for reference to UCLA students, and the public. Holdings: Vols 5000; Per subs 30. Special Subjects: Art, anthropology, and archaeology of non-Western cultures.

—**Frederick S Wight Art Galleries.*** Tel: 213-825-1461. *Acting Dir* Jack Carter; *Admin Asst* Marian Eber.

Open Tues - Fri 11 AM - 5 PM; Sat & Sun 1 - 5 PM; cl Mon and during Aug. No admis. Estab 1952. The Galleries serve both the University and the general public; the program is integrated with the curricula of the Art Department. Average Annual Attendance: 175,000.

Collections: Franklin D Murphy Sculpture Garden; 54 sculptures from the 19th-20th centuries including Arp, Calder, Lachaise, Lipchitz, Moore, Noguchi, Rodin and Smith; the Willitts J Hole Collection of approx 50 paintings of the Italian, Spanish, Dutch, Flemish and English schools, from the 15th - 19th century; 20th century painting, sculpture and photographic collections.

Exhibitions: twelve exhibitions annually, painting and sculpture, prints and drawings, architecture and design; operates in close conjunction with the Museum of Cultural History, and the Grunwald Center for the Graphic Arts. One of the exhibitions is regularly sponsored by the UCLA Art Council, the supporting organization of the Galleries.

—**Student Union Art Gallery,*** 5151 State University Dr, 90039. Tel: 213-224-2189. *Arts & Crafts Coordr* Frank Brown.

Open Mon - Thurs 11 AM - 7 PM; Fri 11 AM - 1 PM. No admis. Estab 1975 as a fine arts gallery.

Income: Financed by city and state appropriations.

Exhibitions: Works by established professional artists as well as work by students and faculty.

Publications: Catalogs; artists books, 4 - 5 per year.

Activities: Classes for adults and children; dramatic programs; lect open to public, 20 vis lectr per yr; concerts; individual paintings and original objects of art lent; traveling exhibitions organized and circulated; book shop.

—**Art Library.*** An integral part of the University Library.

Holdings: Vols 45,000; Other—Slide Library 158,000.

Special Collections: A copy of Princeton's Index of Christian Art.

—**Elmer Belt Library of Vinciana.** Tel: 213-825-3817. *Art Librn* Joyce Ludmer; *Belt Library Asst* Victoria Erpelding.

Open Mon - Fri 9 AM - 5 PM. Estab 1961. It is a special collection of rare books, incunabula, and related materials in Renaissance studies, with a focus on Leonardo da Vinci, his manuscripts, his milieu, his art, and thought. Non-circulating.

Income: Financed by state appropriation.

Holdings: Vols 15,000; Other—Clipping files, exhibition catalogs, framed reproductions, manuscripts, original art works, original documents, pamphlets, photographs, and reproductions.

Special Subjects: Leonardo da Vinci.

—**Architecture and Urban Planning Library,** 1302 Architecture Bldg, 90024. Tel: 213-825-2747. *Head Librn* Jon S Greene.

Open Winter Mon - Thur 8 AM - 10 PM; Fri 8 AM - 5 PM; Sat 9 AM - 5 PM; Sun 1 - 5 PM; Summer and intersessions Mon - Fri 8 AM - 5 PM; cl Sat, Sun & Evenings. Estab 1969 to provide the basic materials for the study of architecture and urban planning at the professional graduate level. Circ: 21,000.

Income: Financed by endowment and state appropriation. Purchases: $15,000.

Holdings: Vols 9000; Per subs 225; AV—Cassettes, microfilm.

UNIVERSITY OF SOUTHERN CALIFORNIA

—**University Galleries,** 823 Exposition Blvd, 90007. Tel: 213-741-2799 and 213-741-7624. *Dir* Donald Brewer; *Cur* Doris Kent.

Open Mon - Fri Noon - 5 PM; cl Sat & Sun except for special exhibitions. No admis. Estab 1939 as an educational department of the university; the Fisher Gallery consists of three rooms, two for changing exhibitions, the third for permanent collection display; the Lindhurst Gallery displays student work. Average Annual Attendance: 18,000. Dues $100; meeting second Tuesday monthly.

Income: Financed by endowment.

Collections: The Galleries house the permanent collections of paintings of 17th century Dutch, Flemish and Italian, 18th century British, 19th century French and American landscape and portraiture schools.

Exhibitions: Wayne Thiebaud.

Publications: In conjunction with exhibitions, the galleries publish an average of three catalogs annually.

Activities: Lect open to the public; films; gallery talks.

—**Architecture and Fine Arts Library,** Watt Hall, University Park, 90007. Tel: 213-741-2798. *Librn* Alson Clark; *Slide Curator* Justine Clancy; *Library Asst* Helen Robischon.

Open Mon - Thurs 8:30 AM - 10 PM; Fri 8:30 AM - 5 PM; Sat 10 AM - 5 PM; Sun 1 - 8 PM. Estab 1925 to provide undergraduate and graduate level students and the teaching and research faculty materials in the areas of architecture and fine arts needed to achieve their objectives; branch library in the central library system is supported by the University. Circ 65,000.

Income: Financed by University funds. Purchases $35,000.

Holdings: Vols 35,000; Per subs 200 for reference; AV for reference—Microfilm 200, slides 105,000; Other—Exhibition catalogs, pamphlets, photographs, architectural drawings 1000.

Activities: Tours.

MALIBU

J PAUL GETTY MUSEUM, 17985 Pacific Coast Highway, 90265. Tel: 213-459-2306. *Dir* Stephen Garrett; *Cur of Paintings* Burton Fredericksen; *Cur of Antiquities* Dr Jiri Frel; *Cur of Decorative Arts* Gillian Wilson.

Open Tues - Sat (summer Mon - Fri) 10 AM - 5 PM. No admis. Estab 1953 to display art objects for public viewing and to promote scholarly research in the fields represented; the museum building is a recreation of an ancient Roman villa, and consists of 38 galleries. Average Annual Attendance: 300,000.

Income: Financed by endowment.

Collections: †Greek and Roman antiquities; †Western European paintings; †French decorative arts.

Publications: Calendar, quarterly; Museum Journal.

Activities: Docent training; slide show for children; classroom materials; lect open to the public, 10 - 12 vis lectr per yr; concerts; original objects of art lent occasionally to other museums for special exhibitions; museum shop selling books, reproductions, slides, museum publications.

—**Research Library.** *Head Librn* vacant; *Assoc Librn* Bethany Mendenhall.

Open Tues - Fri 10 AM - 5 PM. Noncirculating library.

Holdings: Vols 30,000; AV—Microfiche; microfilm; Other—Clipping files, exhibitions catalogs, sales catalogs.

Special Subjects: Greek and Roman art; European painting; French decorative art.

—**Photo Archives.** Tel: 312-459-2306. *Personnel* Laurie Fusco; Yole Lehmann; Stephen Bailey; Constantina Oldknow.

Open Tues - Fri 10 AM - 5 PM; summers hours Mon - Fri 10 AM - 5 PM by appointment. Estab 1972 to provide scholars with a research facility of photographs of works of art in international collections. Non circulating.

Income: Financed by endowment.

Holdings: Other—Photographs 34,000 cataloged, 20,000 uncataloged.

Special Subjects: Ancient art (Greek, Etruscan and Roman); Western European painting (from the 14th - 19th centuries); Western European decorative arts particularly French 18th century.

Special Collections: Decimal Index of the art of low countries; Courtauld Institute of Photo Survey of private collections; Bartsch series of early prints; paintings and decorative arts from major auction houses; the William Suhr restoration photos of paintings.

MENDOCINO

MENDOCINO ART CENTER GALLERY, 45200 Little Lake St (Mailing Add: Box 36, 95460). Tel: 707-937-5818. *Exec Dir* Robert N Avery, Jr; *Pres Bd Trustees* Elaine C Lackey; *Gallery Mgr* Marjorie LeRay.

Open Mon - Fri 10 AM - 4 PM; Sat - Sun 10 AM - 5 PM. No admis. Estab 1959 as a rental/sales gallery for exhibition and sales of member work; also to sponsor traveling and museum exhibits oriented to education in the arts; two major gallery rooms, approx 1500 sq ft; one free-to-the-artist gallery room 500 sq ft; one gallery room available for rental for one-man shows. Average Annual Attendance: 10,000. Mem: 900; dues $10; annual meeting Oct.

Income: $50,000-60,000 galleries only (financed by membership and commissions).

Collections: Paintings, sculpture and graphics which have been donated to the Center.

Exhibitions: (1976-78) One person shows—Anthony Senna, Judith Greenleaf, N'ima Leveton, Conrad Smeeth, William DeLappa, Michael Levin and Stephen Gillette; Mushrooms for Color (traveling museum exhibit); annual open juried competition (painting/drawing 1977).

Publications: Arts & Entertainment, monthly.

Activities: Classes for adults and children; dramatic programs; textile apprenticeship; lectr open to public, 4 - 10 vis lectr per yr; concerts; gallery talks; tours; competitions with cash awards; individual painting and original objects of art lent to businesses and public places by application or to individuals on rental; lending collection contains 300 Kodachromes, motion pictures, original art works, original prints; paintings, photographs, sculpture, and 300 slides; sales shop selling books, original art, reproductions and crafts.

Library: *Librn* Beth Deaward. Open to members and public for reference. Holdings: Vols 1200; Per subs 5; Other—Collection of theatrical plays; specialized architectural materials.

MISSION HILLS

SAN FERNANDO VALLEY HISTORICAL SOCIETY,* 10940 Sepulveda Blvd, 91340. Tel: 213-365-7810. *Pres* Elva Meline.

Open Sat - Sun 1 - 4 PM; weekdays by appointment; cl holidays. No admis. Estab 1943. The Society acquired an 1834 adobe where they house their collection. Mem: Dues active, sustaining and organization $10, Life $100.

Income: Financed by city appropriation and by membership.

Collections: Historical material; Indian artifacts; paintings; costumes; decorative arts; manuscripts.

Activities: Lectures; films; permanent and temporary exhibitions; guided tours.

Library: Open to the public for research on the premises. Holdings: 2400 vols.

MONTEREY

CASA AMESTI,* 516 Polk Street, 93940. Tel: 408-372-8173.

Open Sat & Sun 2 - 4 PM. Admis 50¢, free to National Trust members. Bequeathed to the National Trust in 1953 by Mrs. Frances Adler Elkins. It is an 1833 adobe structure reflecting phases of the history and culture of the part of California owned by Mexico, after the period of Spanish missions and before development of American influences from the Eastern seaboard. It is a prototype of what is now known as Monterey style architecture. The Italian-style gardens within the high adobe walls were designed by Mrs. Elkins, an interior designer, and her brother, Chicago architect David Adler. the furnishings, largely European, collected by Mrs. Elkins are displayed in a typical 1930's interior. The property is a National Trust historic house. The Old Capital Club, a private organization, leases, occupies and maintains the property for social and educational purposes.

Activities: Volunteers from the Monterey History and Art Assoc provide interpretive services for visitors on weekends.

MONTEREY HISTORY AND ART ASSOCIATION,* 412 Pacific St (Mailing Add; P.O. Box 805, 93940). Tel: 408-372-2311. *Pres* Raymond M Smith.

Casa Serrano open Sat - Sun 1 - 4 PM; cl holidays. No admis. Estab 1931; the association owns the 1845 Serrano Adobe, the 1845 Fremont House, the 1865 Francis Doud House, the 1876 St James Chapel Library and the Allen Knight Maritime Museum. They commemorate the historic landing at Monterey by Commodore John Drake Sloat in 1846. Mem: Dues junior $1, single $10, couple $20, life $250.

Collections: Paintings, costumes and manuscripts.

Publications: Noticias del Puerto de Monterey; quarterly bulletin.

Activities: Permanent and temporary exhibitions; guided tours.

Library: Open to the public. Holdings: 500 vols.

—**Allen Knight Maritime Museum,*** 550 Calle Principal (Mailing Add: P.O. Box 805, 93940). Tel: 408-372-2608. *Dir* R Admr Earl E Stone, USN (Ret).

Open summer Tues - Fri 10 AM - Noon & 1 - 4 PM; Sat - Sun 2 - 4 PM; Sept 1 - June 15 afternoons only; cl Mon & National holidays. No admis. Estab 1971. Mem: Dues junior $1, single $10, couple $15, sustaining single $20, sustaining couple $30, life $250.

Collections: Marine artifacts, ship models, paintings, photographs.

Activities: Permanent and temporary exhibitions; lectures; guided tours.

Library: *Librn* Prof G R Giet. Open for research on the premises. Holdings: 200-300 vols and manuscripts.

Publications: Brochure of museum with map.

MONTEREY PENINSULA MUSEUM OF ART, 559 Pacific St, 93940. Tel: 408-372-5477. *Pres* Mrs George Dietterle; *VPres* Maj Gen Lee Cagwin (Ret), Harold Hallett and Elizabeth Sherman; *Recording Secy* William F Stone, Jr; *Corresp Secy* Mrs Roger Bailey; *Treas* Roland Tavernetti; *Dir* June Elder Braucht; *Museum on Wheels Coordinator* Ilene Tuttle; *Museum on Wheels Dir* Kay Cline.

Open Tues - Fri 10 AM - 4 PM; Sat & Sun 1 - 4 PM; cl Mon and holidays. No admis. Estab 1959 to perpetuate knowledge of an interest in the arts; to encourage a spirit of fellowship among artists and to bring together the artist and the community at large. It recognizes the need for the collection, preservation and exhibition or art works, especially the best of those done in the area; the main gallery 30 x 60 ft houses monthly temporary exhibitions; Leonard Heller Memorial Gallery, revolving permanent collection; Armin Hansen Gallery, William Ritschel Memorial Gallery, Folk Art Gallery for collection of international folk arts and hallways which are used to show permanent collection. Average Annual Attendance: 26,000. Mem; 1760; dues individual $10; annual meeting Jan.

Income: $85,000 (financed by endowment, membership and fund-raising functions).

Collections: †Regional art, past and present; international folk art, photography, graphics; Armin Hansen Collection; William Ritschel Collection.

Exhibitions: (1976) Lithography by Garo Antreasian; Intaglios by Haku Maki; Woodblocks by Fumiaki Fuhito; Paintings by Frank Ewing, Jr and Abel Warshawsky; Group Photography Show; Jewelry by Stephen Bondi and Marguerite Stuade; Monterey County Art-1976; Survey of the Architecture of Monterey County; Paintings by Henry Wo Yue Kee (Chinese paintings); Jewelry by Douglas Steakley; Bicentennial Exhibition: A Look at 200 Years on the Monterey Peninsula; Alan Parker Retrospective Exhibition; Haitian Primitive Paintings; Four Watercolorists; Two Mexicos. Steve Crouch and Jim Hill (photography); Winners of Monterey County Art 1976; The California Craftsman; Harriet Zeitlin's Bicentennial Graphics; Photography Invitational; Graphics by George Young; (1977) Ecuadorian Artifacts (William Cameron Collection); Drawings and Watercolors by Roger Bailey; Paintings by Paul Mays, Cornelia Wattley, Merilyn Brown, Howard Smith, Stone and DeGuire; Photographys by Pamela Harris; Monterey County Art 1977; The Many World of Chesley Bonestell; Architectural Awards of Monterey County (photographic); Gloria Brown-paintings and Barbara Spring-Sculpture; Santa Cruz Graphics Workshop; Watercolors by Ron Lee; Egyptian Folk Tapestries; Diana Cheng's Serigraphs; Drawings by Henry Elinson; Monterey Peninsula Collectors; Sculpture by Philip Augerson and David McFadden; Graphics on Handmade Paper by Claudia Bibber; Photography Invitational; Primitive Paintings by Marguerite Pendergast; (1978) Paintings and Drawings by Christine Fry-Loftis and Stephen Lang; Photography by Betty Peckinpah; Watercolors by Richard Bennett; Drawings by Michael and Melinda Wright; Watercolors of Organic Forms by Anita Tortorici.

Publications: Courier, monthly; Yesterday's Artists on the Monterey Peninsula, book; exhibition catalogs.

Activities: Classes for adults and children; docent training; Museum on Wheels teaches craft classes in schools; lectr open to the public, 4 vis lectr per yr; concerts; gallery talks; tours; competitions; exten dept serving three rural county areas; museum shop selling books, reproductions, prints and museum replicas and folk art objects.

Library: Librn Ethel Solliday. Open to the public for reference when supervised or by appointment. Holdings: Vols 1300; Per subs 3 Other—Catalogs.

MONTEREY PUBLIC LIBRARY, 625 Pacific St, 93940. Tel: 408-372-7391. *City Libr* Dorothy Steven.
Open Mon - Fri 9 AM - 9 PM; Sat 9 AM - 6 PM; Sun 1 - 5 PM. Estab 1849 as a library for the city of Monterey. Circ: 300,000.

Income: Financed by membership and city appropriation.

Holdings: Vols 114,000; Per subs 200; AV—Cassettes, microfilm, motion pictures, phonorecords, slides; Other—Clipping files, framed reproductions, manuscripts, original art works, pamphlets, photographs, reproductions.

Special Subjects: Local history.

Special Collections: Volumes on Raiquel, Adler, Elkins collection on architecture and interior design, especially 17th - 19th Century English, Italian and French.

SAN CARLOS CATHEDRAL, * 550 Church St, 93940. Tel: 408-373-2628. *Rector* Msgr Brendan McGuinness.
Open daily 8 AM - 6 PM. No admis. Built in 1970, now a branch of the Monterey Diocese. The art museum is housed in the 1794 Royal Presidio Chapel.

Collections: Spanish religious paintings and sculpture of the 18th and 19th century.

Activities: Guided tours.

NATIONAL CITY

MUSEUM OF AMERICAN TREASURES, 1315 E Fourth St, 92050. Tel: 714-GR7-7489. *Owner and Founder* Hans K Lindemann.
Open Sat 10 AM - dusk and by special arrangements for groups. Estab 1954 as the Museum of Glass of suncolored glass later other acquisitions in the arts were made.

Collections: Imarivase from Japan; world's largest desert glass collection, some 10,000 items; 82 ft elephants tusk carving; bronze Buddha; marble statue; clock called the Goddess of Fortune with coins from various countries; commemorative medals, plates and ashtrays; artillery shells hammered into vases and ashtrays; door knockers in likeness of lions, ea-

gles, Egyptians and Abraham Lincoln; documents signed by several presidents; campaign buttons from presidential candidates, including Ulysses S Grant; handblown glass replica of the royal barge of the King of Siam; world's largest ivory carved chess set; world's largest bust of Princess Piccarda of the Medici family; woodcarvings; old books dating back as far as 1508.

NEWHALL

WILLIAM S HART MUSEUM, 24151 N Newhall Ave, 91321. Tel: 805-259-0855. *Regional Park Supt* Curt Ferguson; *Grounds Maintenance Supv* Mike Dortch; *Head Tour Guide* Kathy Siegwart.
Open Tues - Sun 10 AM - 5 PM. No admis. Estab 1958 to maintain the park and museum as center for leisure enjoyment to the opulation of Southern California. The retirement home of William S Hart is full of Western art. Average Annual Attendance: 120,000.

Income: Financed by county appropriation.

Collections: Western art; Charles M Russell (bronzes, oils, watercolors, grisalle, pen & ink); Remington; Christadoro; Joe de Yong; James M Flagg; Schrezvogel; Robert L Lamdin.

Activities: Classes for children.

NEWPORT BEACH

NEWPORT HARBOR ART MUSEUM, 850 San Clemente Dr, 92660. Tel: 714-759-1122. *Pres* Leon Lyon; *Secy* Mrs Richard S Jonas; *Treas* Charles Hester; *Dir* Thomas H Garver; *Cur Exhib & Coll* Betty Turnbull; *Cur Educ* Phyllis Lutjeans; *Registrar/Editor* Sue Henger; *Adminr* Jean Smock.
Open Tues - Sun 11 AM - 4 PM; Fri 6 - 9 PM. Admis by contribution. Estab 1962 as a museum of the Art of our Time serving Orange County and Southern California. The building completed in 1977 contains three galleries of various sizes—1200, 1600 and 500 sq ft, plus lobby exhibition and sculpture garden. Average Annual Attendance: 70,000. Mem: 2000; dues $7.50, $15, $18, $20, $50, $100, $250 and $1000.

Income: $550,000 (financed by endowment and membership). Purchases $50,000.

Collections: A small collection of contemporary American art—paintings by Josef Albers, Robert Irwin, Gene Davis, Kenzo Okada and Julian Stanczakand and California artists—Richard Diebenkorn, Masami Teraoka, John Altoon, Jean St Pierre and George Herms; works by Ron Davis, Billy Al Bengston, Joan Brown, Nathan Oliveira, John Okulick, Bruce Richards and Ed Ruscha.

Exhibitions: (1976-1978) The Flute and the Brush: Indian Paintings from the Collection of William Theo Brown and Paul Wonner; The Last Time I Saw Ferus: Paintings and Sculpture by Artists of the Ferus Gallery in Los Angeles (1957-1966); Three Directions: Drawing by Channa Horwitz, Agnes Denes, Joyce Cutler Shaw; David Park (paintings); The Figure More or Less: Sculpture Survey; William Baziotes (retrospective paintings and watercolor drawings).

Publications: Bimonthly Calendar.

Activities: Classes for adults and children; dramatic programs; docent training; in-training session for teachers; lectr open to the public and occasionally for members only, 15 vis lectr per yr; concerts; gallery talks; tours; individual paintings and original objects of art lent to qualified art museums; lending collection contains original prints, paintings and sculpture; traveling exhibitions organized and circulated; museum shop selling books, magazines, original art.

Library: Librn Ruth Roe. Open for reference by appointment. Holdings Vols 1000; Per subs 6; Other—Exhibition and sales catalogs. Special Subjects: Contemporary art.

NORTHRIDGE

CALIFORNIA STATE UNIVERSITY, NORTHRIDGE, Fine Arts Gallery, 18111 Nordhoff St, 91330. Tel; 213-885-2192. *Dir* Jean-Luc Bordeaux; *Asst Dir* Louise Lewis; *Installations Dir* Phil Morrison; *Gallery Asst* Steve Peters.
Open Tues - Fri 10 AM - 4 PM; Sun 1 - 4 PM. No admis. Estab 1971 to serve the needs of the four art departments and to provide a source of cultural enrichment for the community at large; exhibitions in main gallery have average duration of four weeks. Gallery II for weekly MA candidate solo exhibitions. Average Annual Attendance: 35,000. Mem: Arts Council for CSUN 300; dues $25; annual meeting June.

Income: $10,000 (financed by city and state appropriation).

Exhibitions: Art of the Upper and Lower Niger; A Collection without Walls: Studies in Connoisseurship; Fundamental Aspects of Modernism; Recent Abstract Painting from New York; Harry Callahan.

Publications: Catalogs of exhibitions, with introduction average 2 per yr.

Activities: Docent training; gallery talks; tours; competitions; traveling exhibitions organized and circulated; sales shop selling books, magazines, reproductions and slides.

OAKLAND

CALIFORNIA COLLEGE OF ARTS & CRAFTS, Meyer Library, Broadway & College Aves, 94618. Tel: 415-653-8118. *Head Librn* Robert L Harper; *Asst Librn* Fraiser McConnell.
Open Mon - Thur 8 AM - 7 PM; Fri 8 AM - 5 PM. Estab 1907 to support the studio and academic requirement for BFA and MFA.
Income: $76,676 (financed by tuition). Purchases, $18,970.
Holdings: Vols 27,500; Per subs 232. AV—Microfilm, records. Other—Clipping files, exhibition catalogs, original art works, photographs, prints and reproductions.
Special Collections: Jo Sinel Collection of his pioneering work in industrial design.
Exhibitions: Library mounts small shows on free-standing panels.

JUNIOR CENTER OF ART AND SCIENCE, 3612 Webster St, 94609. Tel: 415-655-3226. *Dir* Jane McCaffery.
Open Tues - Fri 10 AM - 5 PM; Sat 10 AM - Noon. Estab 1949 as a non-profit organization existing for the benefit of children of the community. Sponsored by the Art League of the East Bay and East Bay Children's Theatre. Mem: Dues family $15, contributing $25, sustaining $50, sponsor $100, business $25-$550.
Income: Financed by membership, donations, memorial gifts and raising.
Activities: Classes for children; exhibitions; music and movies.

MILLS COLLEGE, Art Gallery, Seminary and MacArthur Blvd (Mailing Add: PO Box 9973, 94613). Tel: 415-632-2700 exten 310. *Acting Dir* Paul Tomidy; *Asst to the Dir* Gail Cates.
Open Wed - Sun Noon - 4 PM. No admis. Estab 1925 to show contemporary painting, sculpture and ceramics and exhibitions from permanent collection and loan collections; Gallery is Spanish-type architecture and has 120 ft main exhibition space, with skylight full length of gallery. Average Annual Attendance: Approx 7000.
Income: Financed by college funds. Purchases: $1500.
Collections: †Regional collection of California paintings, drawings and prints; †extensive collection of European and American prints and drawings; Guatemalan textiles; photographs and slides.
Exhibitions: (1976-77) Selected major exhibitions; Ralph DuCasse; Thirty Year Retrospective; Ansel Adams & Roi Patridge exhibition.
Activities: Lect open to the public, 3 vis lectr per yr; gallery talks.

OAKLAND MUSEUM,* Art Department, 1000 Oak St, 94607. Tel: 415-273-3005. *Museum Dir* John E Peetz; *Cur Art* George W Newbert; *Deputy Cur Art* Harvey L Jones; *Sr Cur Prints & Photographs* Therese Heyman; *Assoc Cur* Hazel Bray, Terry St John; *Registrar* Barbara Savinar.
Open Tues - Thurs & Sat 10 AM - 5 PM; Fri 10 AM - 10 PM; Sun 10 AM - 6 PM; cl Mon, New Year's, Thanksgiving, and Christmas. Admis 25¢ to each gallery plus additional for most exhibits in the Great Hall; School children, children under 13, and museum members free. The New Oakland Museum is comprised of three departments, Natural Sciences (formerly the Snow Museum of Natural History, founded 1922), History (formerly the Oakland Public Museum, founded 1910), and the Art Department (formerly the Oakland Art Museum, founded 1916). Internationally recognized as a brilliant contribution to urban museum design, The Oakland Museum occupies a four-square-block, three-studded site on the south shore of Lake Merritt. Designed by Kevin Roche, John Dinkeloo and Assoc, the Museum is a three-tiered complex of exhibition galleries, with surrounding gardens, pools, courts and lawns, constructed so that the roof of each level becomes a garden and a terrace for the one above. The Art Department has a large hall with 20 small exhibition bays for the permanent collection and a gallery for one-person or group shows as well as the Oakes Art Observatory and Gallery.
Collections: Paintings, sculpture, prints, illustrations, photographs, and craftwork created either by California artists or artists dealing with California subjects, in a range that includes sketches and paintings by early artist-explorers, Gold Rush genre pictures, massive Victorian landscapes, examples of the California Decorative Style, Impressionist, Post-Impressionist, Abstract Expressionist, and other contemporary works.
Exhibitions: Study collections, a multimedia presentation in the Oakes Art Observatory and Gallery; photography and print collections; a wide variety of temporary monthly exhibitions.
—The Oakland Museum Association. A separately incorporated auxiliary for all three departments with over 5000 members. From its membership, the OMA provides assistance and support for museum educational and cultural programs, through its Women's Board, Docent Council, and its Art, History, and Natural Sciences Guilds, which coordinate volunteer activities in the museum's three Departments.

OAKLAND PUBLIC LIBRARY, Fine Arts Section, Room 218, Main Library, 125 14th St, 94612. Tel: 415-273-3176. *Dir Library Services* Lelia White; *Sr Librn in Charge* Richard Colvig.
Open Mon 12:30 - 9 PM; Tues, Wed & Thurs 9 AM - 9 PM; Fri & Sat 9 AM - 5:30 PM; cl Sun & holidays. Cooperation with the Oakland Museum and local groups.
Purchases: Approx $24,000.
Holdings: Circulating and reference books on architecture, costumes, dance, fine and applied arts, music, theatre and sports, AV—Musical scores, choral music, records and tape cassettes are available, as well as 16mm film; Other—For circulation and reference, a picture collection estab 1910, contains clipped and mounted pictures 300,000, posters and stereographs; framed and unframed reproductions 100 of famous paintings.
Special Collections: Biographical file of California artists; original prints, museum catalogs.

WESTERN ASSOCIATION OF ART MUSEUMS, PO Box 9989, Mills College, 94613. Tel: 415-568-2773. *Pres* Harry T Hopkins; *VPres* Terry Melton; *Secy* Lewis Story; *Exec Dir* Lynn Jorgenson; *Prog Dir* Linda E Evans; *Exhib Adminr* Gil Dobbs.
For further information see National and Regional Organizations.

OJAI

OJAI VALLEY ART CENTER, 113 S Montgomery, 93023. Tel: 805-646-0117, *Pres* Lee Horovitz; *VPres* Bob Rowlson; *Secy* Joyce Chell; *Treas* Louise Low; *Dir* Rick Hallmark.
Open Mon - Sat 9 AM 5 PM. No admis. Estab 1939 and dedicated to the advancement and development of the arts; gallery is 40 x 50 ft, high ceilings, large hanging area. Average Annual Attendance: 52,000 - 60,000. Mem: 300; dues adult $10; family $25; annual meeting first Mon Jan.
Income: $50,000 (financed by membership, class and special event fees).
Exhibitions: Twelve monthly exhibitions.
Publications: Newsletter, monthly.
Activities: Classes for adults and children: dramatic programs; workshops; dance classes; craft fair; competitions.

ONTARIO

ONTARIO CITY LIBRARY, 215 East C St, 91764. Tel: 714-984-2758. *Library Dir* James Housel; *Prin Librn* Barbara Flynn; *Sr Librn Adult Services* Kay Pearlman; *Sr Librn Children's Services* Julie Robinson.
Open Mon - Thurs 9:30 AM - 9 PM; Fri & Sat 9:30 AM - 5 PM; Sun 1 - 5 PM. Circ: 500,000. Maintains an art gallery to display local artists' works.
Holdings: Vols 180,000; Per subs 640; AV—Cassettes, film strips, microfiche, microfilm, motion pictures, phonorecords, slides, video tapes, multimedia kits; Other-Clipping files, exhibition catalogs, framed reproductions, memorabilia, original art works, original documents, pamphlets, photographs, prints.
Special Subjects: Music, art.
Special Collections: Depository for United States and California documents; local history.
Exhibitions: Monthly art exhibits, occasional sculpture exhibits.
Activities: Lect open to public; gallery talks; tours.

PACIFIC GROVE

PACIFIC GROVE ART CENTER, 568 Lighthouse Ave (Mailing Add: Drawer 700, 93950). Tel: 408-375-2208. *Pres* Craig Comstock, PhD; *Secy* Martha Larson: *Dir* Aloha Pettit Schaefer.
Open Tues - Sat 1 - 5 PM; cl Sun, Mon and holidays. No admis. Estab 1968 to promote the arts and encourage the artists of the Monterey Peninsula; galleries are available to organizations to exhibit their work; Main Gallery used for exhibiting the works of individuals, organizations, or community oriented shows, while Photo Gallery is used primarily for photography. Mem: 200; dues single $6, family $10, business/club $25.
Income: Financed by membership, rental or donations.
Publications: Newscalendar, monthly.
Activities: Museum shop selling original art.
Library: Open to members for reference only.

PALM SPRINGS

PALM SPRINGS DESERT MUSEUM,* 101 Museum Dr (Mailing Add: PO Box 2288, 92262). Tel: 714-325-7186. *Pres* Walter Annenberg; *Secy* Dr Roy F Hudson; *Exec Dir* Frederick W Sleight.
Open Sept - May, Tues - Sat 10 AM - 5 PM; Sun 2 - 5 PM; cl Mon. Admis general public $1; members, teachers, students and children free; Tues free. Estab and inc 1938. Mem: 1700; dues $15 - $5000; annual meeting Mar.

Collections: Modern American painting, prints and sculpture, specializing in California artists; interpretation of natural sciences of the desert; Southwestern Indian crafts.
Exhibitions: Approx 30 per year.
Publications: Calendar of Events, monthly; special exhibition catalogs; Parade, seasonal newsletter.
Activities: Classes for adults and children; docent training; Living Desert Reserve; lect; films; gallery talks; tours; concerts.
Library: Open for reference. Holdings: Vol 2500; Other—Photographs 2500.

PALO ALTO

PALO ALTO CULTURAL CENTER, 1313 Newell Rd, 94303. Tel: 415-329-2543. *Dir* Candace Carpenter; *Office Mgr* Beverly Michaud; *Vol Coordinator* Beth Fair; *Workshop Supv* Gary Clarien; *Coordinating Cur* Linda Langston.
Open Tues - Sat 10 AM - 5 PM; Tues - Thurs Eve 7 - 10 PM; Sun 1 - 5 PM; cl Mon. No admis. Estab 1971 to serve and inform the entire community in the area of visual arts and their purpose; one main gallery, one small gallery and a lobby are all used for exhibits.
Income: Financed by city appropriation.
Publications: Exhibition announcement, 4 - 8 weeks.
Activities: Classes for adults and children; dramatic programs; docent training; receptions; lect open to the public; concerts; gallery talks; tours; competitions; sales shop selling books, original art, prints, postcards and stationery.

PALO ALTO JUNIOR MUSEUM AND ZOO,* 1451 Middlefield Road, 94301. Tel: 415-329-2111. *Supv* Mearl Carson; *Instructor Arts & Crafts* Gale Bruce.
Open Tues - Sat 10 AM - 5 PM; Sun 1 - 4 PM; cl Mondays and holidays. No admis. Estab 1932, completely renovated in 1969. Average Annual Attendance: 100,000.
Income: $60,000 (financed by city appropriation).
Collections: Art and artifacts.
Publications: Notes, monthly; Prehistoric Palo Alto (brochure).
Activities: Classes; guided tours; sciencemobile; exten dept.
Library: Books and magazines on arts, crafts, natural science, ethnology—1000 items.

PASADENA

PACIFICULTURE-ASIA MUSEUM, 46 N Los Robles Ave, 91101. Tel: 213-449-2742. *Dir* David Kamansky.
Open Wed - Sun Noon - 5 PM; Estab 1943 to promote understanding of the cultures of the Pacific and Far East through exhibitions, lectures, dance, music and concerts. Through these activities, the museum helps to increase mutual respect and appreciation of both the diversities and similarities of Eastern and Western cultures. The buildings was designed by Marston, Van Pelt and Maybury architects for Grace Nicholson. The building is listed in the National Register of Historic Places as the Grace Nicholson Building. Mem: Dues individual $15, family $20, sustaining $50, patron $100, sponsor $250, donor $500, benefactor $1000.
Collections: Oriental objects of art.
Exhibitions: Japanese Screen Painting; Chinese Painting—The Last 100 Years; The Rug as an Art Form; Arts of China, I, I, III; Contemporary Painting of India; Calligraphy—Its Influence on the Arts of East and West; Women Painters East-West; Korean Folk Painting; Han and T'ang Murals.
Activities: Classes for adults; docent training; lectures; sales shop selling Asian art books.

PASADENA CITY COLLEGE ART GALLERY, 1570 E Colorado Blvd, 91106. Tel: 213-578-7238. *Gallery Dir* John H Jacobs.
Open Mon - Thurs 11 AM - 4 PM; Eve Mon, Tues, & Wed 7 - 9 PM. No admis. Estab to show work that relates to class given at Pasadena City College; gallery is housed in separate building 1000 sq ft. Average Annual Attendance: 20,000.
Income: $2800 (financed by school budget).
Exhibitions: Painting; sculpture; clothing design; Faculty Show; advertising design, Student Show.
Publications: Mailers for each show.

PASADENA PUBLIC LIBRARY,* 285 E Walnut St, 91101. Tel: 213-577-4049. *Library Dir* Robert Conover; *Head, Fine Arts Div* Josephine Pletscher.
Open Mon - Thurs 9 AM - 9 PM; Fri & Sat 9 AM - 6 PM; cl Sun. No admis. Art Department estab 1927.
Income: $24,000 (financed by endowments and gifts, for materials only).

Holdings: Vols 21,022; Per subs 133; Other—Records 12,796, clipped and mounted pictures 130,335; 16mm sound films 219; pamphlet file; scrapbooks on local architecture, artists and musicians.

NORTON SIMON MUSEUM, Colorado and Orange Grove Blvds, 91105. Tel: 213-449-6840. *Pres* Alvin E Toffel; *Dir* Norton Simon; *Cur* Sara Campbell; *Research Cur* David Steadman & Selma Holo.
Open Thurs - Sun Noon - 6 PM. Admis adults $1.50, students and sr citizens 50¢, members free. Estab 1924. It brings to the Western part of the United States one of the worlds great collections of paintings, tapestries, prints and sculptures for the cultural benefit of the community at large. It is oriented toward the serious and meticulous presentation of masterpiece art. Dues: $25 - $1,000.
Income: Financed by endowment, membership, and city appropriation.
Collections: Art spanning 14 centuries: including paintings, sculptures, tapestries and graphics from the early Renaissance through the 20th century; Indian and Southeast Asian sculpture; paintings, etchings and lithographs by Picasso; Goya graphics; masterpieces by Rubens, Tiepolo, Matisse, Rembrandt, Van Gogh, Cezanne, Degas, Monet, Raphael, Zurbaran, Henry Moore, Rodin and others; Blue Four Galka Scheyer Collection of German Expressionism; Photography of Weston, Cunningham and others.
Exhibitions: Picasso; Southeast Asian and Indian Sculpture; Goya Prints; Degas bronze sculptures; Claude Lorrain drawings; etchings of Rembrandt.
Publications: Catalogs of exhibitions.
Activities: Private guided tours; museum shop selling books, original art, reproductions, prints, slides and postcards.
—*Library.* *Librn* Amy Navratil.
Open to staff for reference; to scholars by appointment.
Holdings: Vols 5000; Per subs 34; Other—Knoedler library on microfiche - auction and exhibition catalogues dating from the 18th century to 1970.
Special Collections: Archival material and books relating to the Blue Four.

PLEASANT HILL

DIABLO VALLEY COLLEGE MUSEUM, 321 Golf Club Rd, 94523. Tel: 415-685-1230. *Cur* Erda Labuhn.
Open Mon - Fri 8:30 AM - 4:30 PM except Thurs; Sat 11:30 AM - 4:30 PM. No admis. Estab 1959 as a community service to the public, and to schools, and as a resource for the college; gallery measures 85 x 60 ft. Average Annual Attendance: 11,621.
Income: Financed by county taxes. Purchases: $2000 - $4000.
Exhibitions: (1976-77) Creative Growth; Estebaney Sculpture; Fantasy and Science Fiction Art; Sculpture by Rosa; Christmas Cards, Christmas Cards; The Images of Mainland China.
Activities: Classes for children; docent training; individual paintings lent to college students, faculty and staff; lending collection contains nature artifacts 202, original prints 120l; paintings, sculpture.
Library: For reference only; Holdings: Vols 150; Per subs 8.

RANCHO PALOS VERDES

PALOS VERDES ART CENTER, 5504 W Crestridge Rd, 90274. Tel: 213-541-2479. *Exec Dir* Susan Heinz; *Secy* Carol Ritscher; *Exhibit Coordr* Pam Merrill.
Open Mon - Fri 9 AM - 4 PM; Sat 11 AM - 2 PM; Sun 1 - 4 PM. No admis. Estab 1974 to provide a multifaceted program of classes, exhibits and lectures in the visual arts; rental/sales gallery; changing exhibits gallery. Mem: 1775; dues $15 - $100.
Income: Financed by membership.
Collections: Small purchase prize collection.
Publications: Chronicle, bimonthly.
Activities: Classes for children; docent training; lect open to public; gallery talks.

RED BLUFF

KELLY-GRIGGS HOUSE MUSEUM,* 311 Washington St (Mailing Add: 1248 Jefferson St, 96080). Tel: 916-527-1129. *Pres* Fred B Godbolt.
Open Thurs - Sun 2 - 5 PM; cl holidays. Donations welcome. Estab 1965, a history museum in a home built in 1880. Mem: Dues student $1, assoc $10, sustaining $50, charter $100 plus $10 annually, memoriam $100, life $200, patron $500, benefactor $1000.
Collections: Pendleton Art Collection spanning over a century of art; Indian artifacts; antique furniture; Victorian costumes.
Activities: Permanent and temporary exhibitions; guided tours.
Publications: Brochure; annual letter.

REDDING

REDDING MUSEUM AND ART CENTER, 1911 Rio Dr (Mailing Add: PO Box 427, 96001). Tel: 916-243-4994. *Pres* Noreen Braithwaite; *VPres* Judge Richard B Eaton; *Secy* Betty Carrick; *Treas* Cindy Howland; *Dir* Carolyn Bond; *Arts Cur* John Harper.
Open Summer Tues - Sat 10 AM - 5 PM; Winter Tues - Fri Noon - 5 PM; Sat & Sun 10 AM - 5 PM; cl Mon. Estab 1963 to encourage the understanding of, and appreciation for, man's accomplishments throughout history and pre-history; two galleries present changing monthly contemporary art exhibits. Average Annual Attendance: 25,000. Mem: 500; dues $10 - $100; annual meeting second Wed June.
Income: Financed by membership, city appropriation.
Collections: Central American Pre-Columbian pottery; Native American baskets; local Shasta County historical artifacts and documents.
Exhibitions: (1976-78) Pencil Works of David Hoppe; Oils by Paul A Feldhaus; Collected Works of Dottie Godden; Juried Art Show Winners; Art Faire; WAAM Bag Show; Christmas Arts and Crafts show; E M Escher Prints; Bob Nugent (handmade paper); Clayton Bailey (ceramics); Gary Jensen (landscape paintings); Berton J Oldham (paintings); Patrick Pry (photography); Susan Conaway (graphite and water color); Sacramento Weaver's Guild; Nancy Lawton (drawings); Richard Wilson (paintings); Cairulea—Eleanor Rappe and Eleanore Bender; Horace Washington (ceramics); Kenji Nanao (lithographer).
Publications: The Covered Wagon, published by Shasta Historical society, an affiliated organization.
Activities: Classes for adults and children; docent training; lect open to the public; gallery talks; competitions; museum shop selling books, magazines, reproductions, prints and crafts; Junior Museum, Shasta Natural Science Museum.
Museum Research Library. Open by appointment for reference only.
Special Collections: Photographs of Shasta County.

REDLANDS

LINCOLN MEMORIAL SHRINE,* Eureka & Vine (Mailing Add: P.O. Box 751, 92373). Tel: 714-793-6622. *Cur* Larry E Burgess.
Open Tues - Sat 1 - 5 PM; other hours by appointment; cl Sun, Mon & holidays. No admis. Estab 1932, operated as a section of the Smiley Public Library.
Collections: Manuscripts and documents of Lincoln and the Civil War period; sculptures, paintings, murals.
Activities: Docent program; temporary art exhibitions; lectures; guided tours.
Holdings: 4500 vols of rare and new books for use on the premises.

REDLANDS ART ASSOCIATION,* 12 E Vine St, 92373.
Open daily 10 AM - 2 PM; cl Sun. No admis. Estab 1964 to promote interest in the visual arts,to provide a gallery for artists. Mem: 265.
Exhibitions: Lyon Gallery exhibitions at least 6 times a year; many media juried shows.
Publications: Bulletin, monthly.
Activities: Classes for children through teens; lect open to public, 4 vis lectr per yr; tours; competitions; scholarships.

UNIVERSITY OF REDLANDS,* Peppers Art Center, 1200 W Colton Ave, 92373. Tel: 714-793-2121. *Chmn Art Dept* John P Brownfield.
Open Tues - Fri 1 - 5 PM; Sat & Sun 2 - 5 PM; cl Mon. No admis. Estab 1909.
Income: Financed by endowment.
Collections: Ethnic Art; graphics; a few famous artists.
Exhibitions: Various kinds during fall, winter, spring.
Activities: Art classes; individual paintings and original objects of art lent to schools.
Library: Holdings—Books and slides.

RICHMOND

RICHMOND ART CENTER, Civic Center, 25th and Barrett Ave, 49804. Tel: 415-234-2397 exten 370. *Dir* Ernie Kim; *Cur* James Soult; *Supervising Art Instructor* A Martin Cooke.
Open Mon - Fri 10 AM - 5:30 PM; Thurs eve 4:30 - 9:30 PM; Sun noon - 4:30 PM; cl Sat and holidays. No admis. Estab preliminary steps 1936-44; formed in 1944 to establish community center for Arts; to afford to the community an opportunity to experience and to improve knowledge and skill in the arts and crafts at the most comprehensive and highest level possible; a large gallery, small gallery and entrance corridor total 4757 sq ft, and a rental gallery covers 1628 ft; an outdoor sculpture court totals 8840 sq ft. Average Annual Attendance: 7000. Mem: 1300; dues $10 up; annual meeting fourth Wed May.
Income: $175,000 (financed by membership, city and state appropriations, and Art Center Asn).
Collections: †Primarily contemporary art and crafts of Bay area.

Exhibitions: (1976-77) Ten changing exhibitions including annual juried designer-craftsman show; annual Public Secondary School Show; two-week annual Spring Rental Gallery Show; seven changing exhibitions in balanced varied media.
Publications: Show announcements for exhibitions; newsletter, bi-monthly; catalog for designer-craftsman show.
Activities: Classes for adults and children; docent training; lect open to the public, 6 vis lectr per yr; gallery talks; exten dept serving community; individual paintings and original objects of art lent to offices, businesses, and homes; museum shop selling crafts, some prints, vignette paintings, cards.
Library: Class Supv A Martin Cooke. Open to Art Center members. Holdings: Books on paintings, crafts, and some slides. Special Collections: Contemporary Bay area Fine Arts and Crafts.

RIVERSIDE

RIVERSIDE ART CENTER AND MUSEUM,* 3425 Seventh, 92501. Tel: 714-684-7111. *Pres* Mary Jane Spiel; *VPres* Ruth Place; *Dir* Alan T Garrett; *Exec Secy* Daniel H Smith; *Educ Coordr* Virginia Massingale.
Open Tues - Sat 10 AM - 5 PM; Sun 1 - 5 PM; cl Mon, August and holidays. No admis. Estab 1931 to enlighten and refine the thinking of interested people through the visual arts and crafts. Exhibition gallery and sales and rental gallery maintained. Mem: 1000; dues student and sr citizen $1.50, general $20, family $30, supporting $40, patron $75 and up; annual meeting Apr.
Income: Financed by membership.
Collections: 50 pieces dating from late 1800's to present of a mixture of media.
Exhibitions: Annual Members Show; Annual Purchase Prize Competition: Annual High School Press Enterprise Show.
Publications: Artifacts, monthly (Sept-July).
Activities: Art classes, beginning to advanced studio instruction; art program presented in public school system; staffs and funds 50% of free art class for disadvantaged children; lect open to public, 6 vis lectr per yr; tours; competitions; scholarships.
Library: Holdings—Vols 400.

UNIVERSITY OF CALIFORNIA, RIVERSIDE, University Art Galleries and California Museum of Photography, 3401 Watkins Dr, 92521. Tel: 714-787-4636. *Dir Art Galleries* Kirk de Gooyer; *Admin Asst Art Galleries* Phyllis Gill; *Cur Slide Libr* Helene Kosher; *Asst Cur Slide Libr* Barbara Frank; *Dir Mus* Edward Beardsley; *Cur 20th-Century Art* Joe Deal; *Special Asst to the Dir* Kirk de Gooyer; *Art & Photography Librn* Lyndy K Zoeckler.
Open Mon - Fri 10 AM - 4 PM; Sun 1 - 5 PM. Gallery estab 1963, Museum 1972. The galleries present major temporary exhibitions; the museum program has both temporary exhibits and permanent installation; the Museum is also a major research center. The main gallery contains 1500 sq ft, Gallery B 250 sq ft and the Museum gallery 18,000 sq ft. Average Annual Attendance: Galleries 28,000, Museum 35,000.
Income: Financed by endowment and university funds.
Collections: Museum—†Bingham Collection of photographic apparatus approximately 5000 items; †19th and 20th century print collection; Keystone Mast Collection of stereoptics and sterographs, some 340,000 items; Raoul Collection of prints.
Exhibitions: Three Bay Area Artists—Bowers, Foster and Schutte.
Publications: Exhibition catalogs.
Activities: Classes for adults; lect open to the public, 6 vis lectr per yr; gallery talks; tours; competitions; original objects of art lent to museums and art center; lending collection contains color reproductions 17,000, photographs 341,450 and slides 65,000; traveling exhibitions organized and circulated.
Library: Open to staff and selected private researchers for reference only.

ROHNERT PARK

SONOMA STATE COLLEGE ART GALLERY, 1801 E Cotati Ave, 94928. Tel: 707-664-2054. *Acting Gallery Dir* Inez Storer; *Asst Dir* Joanna Kollen; *Dept Chmn* Susan Moulton.
Open Mon - Fri 10 Am - 4 PM. No admis. Estab 1978 to provide exhibitions of quality to the college and northern California community. Exhibitions of work by major artists and shows with historical and cultural implications which coordinate with traditional college courses. 2800 sq ft of exhibition space designed to house monumental sculpture and painting.
Income: Financed through College.
Collections: Garfield Collection of Oriental art.
Exhibitions: Major Artists from Northern California: Bill Allen, Fletcher Benton, Joan Brown, de Forest, Diebenkorn, Sam Francis, Cornelia Schulz, William Wiley, Peter Voulkos, Mark de Suvero, Bill Geis, Wally Hedrick, Ed Moses, Harold Paris, Sam Richardson.
Publications: Bulletins and announcements of exhibitions.

Activities: Classes for adults; lect open to public, 30 vis lectr per yr; gallery talks; tours; competitions; enten dept.

ROSS

MARIN ART & GARDEN SOCIETY, Marin Society of Artists, Inc, Sir Francis Drake Blvd (Mailing Add: PO Box 203, 94957). Tel: 415-454-9561. *Pres* Jane Santucci; *VPres* Margaret Atchley; *Secy* Helena Irons; *Office Mgr* Jo Smith.
Open daily 1 - 4 PM. No admis. Estab 1926 to foster cooperation among artists and to continually develop public interest in art; gallery is located in a garden setting; is approximately 3500 sq ft of well lighted exhibit space. Average Annual Attendance: 75,000. Mem: 600; Qualif for membership: Previous exhibition in a juried show, and must reside in Bay Area if active; dues $15; meeting May & Sept.
Income: Financed by membership, sale and rental of art.
Exhibitions: Ten exhibitions annually, some are open to non-member artists residing in San Francisco-Bay Area.
Activities: Lect open to the public, 2 - 3 vis lectr per yr; competitions with cash award of approximately $3000 annually; schol; sales shop selling original art, original prints, handcrafted jewelry, ceramics, and fiberworks.

SACRAMENTO

CALIFORNIA STATE FAIR & EXPOSITION ART SHOW,* 1600 Exposition Bldg, 95815. Tel: 916-641-2311. *Mgr* Thomas E Blair; *Secy* Audrey Corcoran; *Exhib Supv* Edward J Lynam.
Open Aug 21 - Sept 9, 10 AM - 10 PM. Estab 1854 to exhibit work of artists of the State of California. Average Annual Attendance: 450,000.
Income: $20,000.
Collections: Oils; watercolors; prints; ceramics and enameling; textiles; photographs; color slides.
Publications: Art catalog, annually; Premium Book.
Activities: Art in Action demonstrations; dramatic programs; individual paintings and original objects of art lent; traveling exhibitions organized and circulated.

CALIFORNIA STATE UNIVERSITY, SACRAMENTO, LIBRARY, Humanities Reference, Media Services Center, 2000 Jed Smith Drive, 95819. Tel: 916-454-6291. *Univ Librn* Gordon P Martin; *Assoc Humanities Reference Librn* Eugene N Salmon; *Sr Asst Humanities Reference Librn* Clifford P Wood; *Asst Humanities Reference Librn* Donna Ridley; *Slide Cur I* Della Schalansky.
Open Mon - Thurs 7:45 AM - 11 PM; Fri 7:45 AM - 5 PM; Sat 9 AM - 5 PM; Sun 1 - 9 PM (during Semester and Summer Sessions). Estab 1947. The art collection is developed to support the curriculum of the Art Department on campus and the Home Economics Department (design, architecture). Circ: 400,858. The Art Department maintains a gallery in the Art Building and a gallery in the University Union.
Income: Financed through the University.
Holdings: Vols 616,649; AV—Cassettes, film strips, microfiche, microfilm, slides, video tapes; Other—Clipping files; exhibition catalogs; original art works, pamphlets, reproductions.
Special Subjects: Book arts.
Publications: Series of bibliographies.

E B CROCKER ART GALLERY, 216 O St, 95814. Tel: 916-446-4677. *Dir* Richard Vincent West; *Chief Cur* Roger D Clisby; *Registrar* Joanna Ownby; *Mus Serv* Susan von Berckefeldt.
Open Wed - Sun 10 AM - 5 PM; Tues 2 - 10 PM; cl Mon. No admis. Estab 1873; municipal art museum since 1885; original gallery building designed by Seth Babson completed in 1873; R A Herold Wing opened in 1969; ARTSPACE (downtown gallery) opened in 1977. Average Annual Attendance: 100,000. Mem: 1700; annual meeting Mar 31.
Income $500,000 (financed by membership and city appropriation). Purchases $30,000 - $50,000 per annum.
Collections: †Old master drawings; †American painting of the 19th century with emphasis on California painting 1850-1900; †Contemporary California painting, sculpture and crafts; †European painting 1500-1900; †prints and photographs; Oriental art; European decorative arts, American decorative art and costumes 1850-1900.
Exhibitions: 18th Century Drawings from California Collections; Charles Christian Nahl: Artist of the Gold Rush; The Chicago Connection; California Crafts X; Crocker-Kingsley Annual (juried); The Santa Show; Munich and American Realism in the 19th Century.
Publications: Calendar, 10 times per annum; Report, biannually.
Activities: Classes for children; docent training; lect open to public; concerts; gallery talks; tours; annual juried competition; museum shop selling books, magazines, original art, reproductions and slides.

Library: *Librn* Ethel Fry. Open to staff, docents and others upon application. Holdings: Vols 1400; Per subs 24; Other—Sales catalogs; dissertations, microfiche and bulletins.

SAINT HELENA

SILVERADO MUSEUM, 1347 Railroad Ave (Mailing Add: PO Box 409, 94574). Tel: 707-963-3757. *Dir* Norman H Strouse; *Cur* Ellen Shaffer.
Open Tues - Sun Noon - 4 PM; cl Mon & holidays. No admis. Estab 1969 the museum is devoted to the life and works of Robert Louis Stevenson, who spent a brief but important time in the area; the object is to acquaint people with his life and works, and familiarize them with his stay; the museum has five wall cases and three large standing cases, as well as numerous bookcases. Average Annual Attendance: Approx 8700.
Income: Financed by the Vailima Foundation, set up by Mr and Mrs Norman H Strouse.
Collections: First editions, variant editions, fine press editions of Robert Louis Stevenson, letters, manuscripts, photographs, sculptures, paintings and memorabilia.
Exhibitions: A different exhibition devoted to some phase of Stevenson's work is mounted every two months.
Activities: Lect open to the public; gallery talks; sales shop selling books, postcards.
Library. Tel: 707-963-3757. For reference only. Holdings: Vols 2500.

SALINAS

HARTNELL COLLEGE GALLERY, 156 Homestead Ave, 93901. Tel: 408-758-8211 Ext 261 & 250. *Dir* Gary T Smith.
Open Mon - Thur 10 AM - 4 PM and 6 - 9 PM; Fri 10 AM - 4 PM. No admis. Estab 1959 to bring to students and the community the highest quality in contemporary and historical works of all media; main gallery 40 by 60 ft, brick floor; south gallery 15 by 30 ft, brick floor. Average Annual Attendance: 7500.
Collections: Approximately 45 works on paper from the San Francisco Bay Area WPA.
Exhibitions: Ralph Eugene Meatyard; Orange Crate Labels; Six Artists Six Concepts; Helen Escobedo; Faculty Show; Michael Arntz; Lee Wolcott; Retablos; Classical Narratives in Master Drawings; Selection; Historical and Contemporary Objects; Marion Post-Wolcott; Student Show, Children's Art.
Publications: Three small catalogs per year.
Activities: Classes for adults; dramatic programs; gallery management training; individual paintings lent to qualifying educational institutions; lending collection contains original art works; traveling exhibitions organized and circulated.

SAN BERNARDINO

CALIFORNIA STATE COLLEGE SAN BERNARDINO, College Art Galleries, 5500 State College Parkway, 92407. Tel: 714-887-7459. *Dir* Poppy Solomon; *Chmn Art Dept* Julius Kaplan.
Open Mon - Fri 9 AM - Noon, 1 - 3 PM; Sat 1 - 4 PM. No admis. Estab 1972 for the purpose of providing high quality exhibitions on varied subjects suitable for both campus and community; Gallery 2 opened in April 1978 as an exhibit area for senior shows and student work. Average Annual Attendance: 5500.
Income: Financed by membership, city and state appropriation.
Collections: Small collection of prints.
Exhibitions: (1976-78) Faculty Show: Joe Moran, Don Woodford, Leo Doyle, Poppy Soloman, Jan Mzronsky; L A Communications; Tradition and Continuity in the Art of Black Africa; Patterns, Structures and Grids: Richard Amen, Charles Arnold, Chris Burosu, Gloria Kisch, Frank Stella, Don Sorensen, Bob Walker, Greg Wolf, Tom Wudt; West Mexican Tomb Sculpture; Stamps/Art - Art/Stamps: Stamps and Paul Dillon, Ave Pildas, Stephanie Franklin, Margit Omar; Volcano - Don Woodford; Annual Juried Student Show.
Publications: Catalogs, infrequently; Personas de los Tumbas - West Mexican tomb sculpture.
Activities: Classes for adults; lect open to the public, 1 - 3 vis lectr per yr; gallery talks; competitions.

SAN BERNARDINO ART ASSOCIATION, INC, 1640 E Highland Ave (Mailing Add: PO Box 2272, 92406). *Pres,* Mrs G W Jacka; *VPres* Marie Hall; *Secy* Helen Kuhl; *Second VPres* Marion Stone; *Treas* Catherine Daschbach; *Corresp Secy* Ellen Karschnick; *Newsletter* Loretta Stirnaman.
Open to the public. No admis. Estab 1934 as a non-profit organization; maintains gallery. Mem: 140; dues $10; meets monthly.
Exhibitions: Inland Exhibit.
Publications: Newsletter.

Activities: Lect open tis lectr per yr; tours; competitions with awards; schol; sales shop selling original art.

SAN DIEGO

FINE ARTS GALLERY OF SAN DIEGO, Balboa Park (Mailing Add: PO Box 2107, 92112). Tel: 714-232-7931. *Dir* Henry G Gardiner; *Asst Dir* Steven L Brezzo; *Cur Paintings* Martin E Petersen; *Cur Exhib* Dennis Komac; *Bus Adminr* Ellen Harrison; *Mgr Book Store* Janet Spector; *Secy to Dir* Sandra Erb; *Cur Secy* Michaleen Sawka; *Activities Coordinator* Sharon Hemus; *Membership Secy* Sheila Hittle; *Mgr Art Sales & Rental* Denise Draper.
Open Tues - Sun 10 AM - 5 PM; cl Mon. No admis. Estab 1925. The gallery was built in 1926 by a generous patron in a Spanish Plateresque design; the West wing was added in 1966 the East wing in 1974. Average Annual Attendance: 370,000. Mem: 4648; dues student (undergraduate to age 21) $5, individual $15, family $20, sustaining $35, Friends of the Gallery $100, life $1500; annual meeting May.
Income: $750,000 (finance by endowment, membership, city and county appropriations). Purchases: $175,000.
Collections: Italian Renaissance and Baroque painting, Spanish Baroque, Flemish, Dutch and English schools; 19th and 20th century American and European sculpture and paintings; extensive print collection containing American, European and Oriental schools; Oriental arts—sculpture, paintings, ceramics and decorative arts; decorative arts—American furniture and glass, English and Georgian silver.
Exhibitions: (1978) Five Centuries of Tapestry; Zenga and Nanga: Paintings by Japanese Monks and Scholars; Studies in Connoisseurship; Giacomo Manzu; American Folk Painting.
Publications: Annual Report; catalogs of collections; exhibition catalogs; Membership Calendar, monthly.
Activities: Classes for adults and children; docent training; lectr open to the public; gallery talks; tours; competitions; original objects of art lent to city and county offices; traveling exhibitions organized and circulated; museum and sales shops selling books, original art, reproductions, prints, cards, jewelry and ceramics.
—**Art Reference Library.** Tel: 714-232-7931. *Librn* Nancy Andrews.
Open Tues - Sat 10 AM - 5 PM; Mon, Thanksgiving, Christmas and New Year's day. Estab 1925 for curatorial research; for reference and limited lending.
Holdings: Vols 12,000; Per subs: 35; AV—Audio tapes, slides 16,300; Other—Clipping files; exhibition catalogs, vertical files containing biographical material.
Special Subjects: Asian, Italian Renaissance, Spanish Baroque.
Special Collections: Bibliography of artists in exhibitions catalogs.

INSTITUTE FOR ADVANCED STUDIES IN CONTEMPORARY ART, 6361 Elmhurst Drive, 92120. Tel: 714-583-7935. *Exec Dir* Dr Kenneth S Friedman; *Research Dir* Dr Marilyn Ekdahl Ravicz.
Open by appointment only. Estab 1966 as a national research center to provide information and services on contemporary art to arts institutions, artists, publishers, scholars and research specialists in a wide variety of topics. Work is done on a project-oriented basis through the College of Fellows, many of whom also serve as arts professionals in a wide variety of institutions across the nation.
Income: Financed by gifts, grant funding, lecture and consulting fees for work by senior staff, and other means.
Collections: Contemporary art including works by Christo, Joseph Beuys, Dick Higgins, Arman, George Maciunas, Alison Knowles, Endre Tot, Don Boyd, Julius Schmit, Tommy Mew. The collections are housed primarily at The La Jolla Museum for Contemporary Art.
Activities: Educ prog available by arrangement; lecture; workshops; seminars; competitions, occasionally with awards.
Library: Open only to research scholars by appointment or to Institute staff. Vols 15,000. Special Subjects: Sociology of art, arts biographical studies, artists' books, European art information, concrete poetry, ephemeral media, aesthetic anthropology and fine arts administration.

MARITIME MUSEUM ASSOCIATION OF SAN DIEGO,* 1306 N Harbor Dr, 92101. Tel: 714-234-9153. *Pres & Exec Dir* Capt Carl G Bowman, USCG (Ret); *Fleet Capt* Capt Kenneth D Reynard.
Open daily 9 AM - 8 PM. Admis adults $2, families $5, service personnel $1.50, children under 12 50¢, in groups 25¢, discount to adult groups. Estab 1948, a maritime museum in a fleet of three ships—Star of India (1863), Berkeley (1898 steamer) and Medea (1904 steam yacht). Mem: Dues regular $12, supporting $25, development $50, life $250.
Collections: Maritime artifacts; antiques; maritime art.
Publications: Mains'l Haul, quarterly newsletter; Star of India, They Came by Sea.
Activities: Temporary and traveling exhibitions; lectures; guided tours; films. Sales shop selling maritime books, artifacts and souvenirs.
Holdings: Vols. 500. Other—Historical photograph collection.

SAN DIEGO PUBLIC LIBRARY, Art and Music Section, 820 E St, 92101. Tel: 714-236-5810. *Supv Librn* Barbara A Tuthill; *Sr Librn* Patricia K Katka; *Picture Specialist* Gale Griffin; *Librn* Evelyn Kooperman.
Open Mon - Thurs 10 AM - 9 PM; Fri - Sat 9:30 AM - 5:30 PM. Estab 1954 to provide information and reference services in the fine arts with expanding collection of books, both reference and circulating; Corridor Gallery monthly exhibits art work by local artists and art groups.
Income: Financed by city and state appropriation. Purchases: $40,450.
Holdings: Vols 69,000; AV—Cassettes, motion pictures, records 18,500; Other—Clipping files, exhibition catalogs, pamphlets, picture and postcards 460,000, sheet music, music scores.
Special Collections: Includes former libraries of William Templeton Johnson, architect, and Donal Hord, sculptor; emphasis is on Spanish, Mediterranean, Italian and French Renaissance architecture and Oriental art, sculpture and ceramics; books on the theatre including biographies of famous actors and actresses as well as histories of the American, London and European stages, gift of Elwyn B Gould, local theatre devotee.
Exhibitions: Clairemont Art Guild; San Diego Watercolor Society; Designers Workshop with one-man shows by local artists.
Activities: Lect open to public; concerts; opera previews.

SAN DIEGO STATE UNIVERSITY ART GALLERY, 5402 College Ave, 92182. *Chmn Dept Art* Dr Winifred H Higgins; *Dir* Moira Roth.
Open daily 9 AM - 4 PM. No admis. Estab to provide exhibitions of importance for the students, faculty, and public of the San Diego environment; for study and appreciation of art and enrichment of the university. Average Annual Attendance: 35,000.
Income: Financed by city and state appropriations.
Collections: Contemporary print collection; Oriental sculpture and prints; graduate student sculpture and painting; crafts collection.
Exhibitions: National Printmaking Annual; National Small Sculpture and Drawing; National Crafts Exhibition; Graduate & Undergraduate Students Exhibitions.
Activities: Lect open to the public; original objects of art lent to university only.

TIMKEN ART GALLERY, Balboa Park, 92101. Tel: 714-239-5548. *Chmn Bd* Walter Ames; *Pres Bd* A J Sutherland; *Exec VPres* Josiah L Neeper; *Exec Asst* Nancy A Petersen.
Open Tues - Sat 10 AM - 4:30 PM; Sun 1:30 - 4:30 PM; cl Mon. No admis. Estab to display and preserve Old Master's paintings; six galleries. Average Annual Attendance: 75,000.
Income: Financed by Endowment.
Collections: †Dutch/Flemish, †French, †Spanish, †Italian and †American paintings and Russian Icons. All paintings owned by Putnam Collection are on permanent display.
Publications: Pamphlets which are distributed free to visitors.
Activities: Docent training, tours.

UNIVERSITY OF SAN DIEGO,* Founders' Gallery, Alcala Park, 92110. Tel: 714-291-6480. *Dir* Therese T Whitcomb.
Open Mon - Fri 10 AM - 4 PM. Estab 1971 to enrich the goals of the art department and university by providing excellent in-house exhibitions of all eras, forms and media, and to share them with the community. Gallery is an architecturally outstanding facility with foyer, display area and patio, parking in central campus. Average Annual Attendance: 1500.
Collections: South Asian textiles and costumes of 19th & 20th centuries; Tibetan and Indian looms, Ghandi etc, spinning wheels; †19th & 20th century American folk sculpture; 17th, 18th & 19th century French tapestries and furniture.
Exhibitions: 7 shows each year.
Activities: Lect open to public; tours; competitions; scholarships; original objects of art lent; lantern slides 5000.

SAN FRANCISCO

ACADEMY OF THE MUSEUM OF CONCEPTUAL ART, 75 Third St, 94103. Tel: 415-495-3193. *Dir* Tom Marioni; *Preparator* Tony Labot; *Video Cur* Burt Arnowitz.
Open Wed PM or for events. Estab 1970 for actions and situational art, preservation of old site, and social activities for artists; gallery maintained and covers 10,000 sq ft, on two floors.
Income: Financed by endowment.
Holdings: AV reference—Audio tapes, cassettes, film strips, kodachromes, motion pictures, phonorecords, reels, slides, video tapes; Other reference—Exhibition catalogs, original art works, original documents, pamphlets, photographs, prints, sculpture.
Special Subjects: Cafe Society, every Wednesday, in Breen's Cafe, first floor of Museum.

Exhibitions: Vito Acconci; Robert Barry; Lowell Darling; Restoration of Back Wall; Bar Room Video; A Tight Thirteen Minutes.
Publications: Vision, annually.

ART COMMISSION—CITY AND COUNTY OF SAN FRANCIS-CO, 165 Grove St, 94102. Tel: 415-558-3465. *Pres Commission* Ray Taliaferro; *Asst Dir* Joan Ellison; *Dir Neighborhood Art Prog* Mark Denton; *Coordr Street Artist Prog* Howard Lazar; *Dir Cultural Affairs* Martin Snipper; *Visual Arts Dir* Elio Benvenuto; *Cur Capricorn Asunder Gallery* Ansel Wettersten.
Open daily 10 AM - 4:30 PM. No admis. Estab 1932; consists of 9 professional and 3 lay members appointed by the Mayor with advice of art societies, and 5 ex-officio members. Monthly meetings.
Passes on all buildings and works of art placed on property of City or County; supervises and controls all appropriations made by the Board of Supervisors of music and the advancement of art and music; may volunteer advice to private owners who submit plans for suggestions; maintains a Civic Chorale and Neighborhood Arts Program; administers ordinance providing 2% of cost of public construction for art; also, a municipal collection for art for embellishing public offices purchases for enlarging collection are made from the Annual Art Festival; maintains art gallery and presents various concerts; licenses street artists; responsible for cataloging and maintaining all public works of art.
Income: Purchases—over $5000 annually.

ASIA FOUNDATION GALLERY, The Asia Foundation, 550 Kearny St, Fifth Floor, 94108. (Mailing Add: PO Box 3223, 94119). Tel: 415-982-4640. *Pres* Dr Haydn Williams.
Open 9 AM - 5 PM. No admis. Estab 1954. The Foundation's gallery is made available to Asian artists to give them the opportunity to display their works. The gallery also is open to art collections of Asian-related works. Lobby area of Foundation headquarters and long hallway especially constructed to display works of art. Average Annual Attendance: 250. Quarterly meetings.
Exhibitions: Photographs of Asia; Chinese calligraphy and painting exhibits; collection of Jain Indian art; Indonesian batiks.
Publications: Rarities of the Asian Art Museum: The Avery Brundage Collection, program bulletin.

ASIAN ART MUSEUM,* Center of Asian Art & Culture, Golden Gate Park 94118. Tel: 415-558-2993. *Dir & Chief Cur* Rene-Yvon Lefebvre d'Argence; *Sr Cur* Clarence F Shangraw; *Cur Chinese Art* Sylvia Chen Shangraw; *Cur Indian Art* Terese Tse Bartholomew; *Cur Japanese Art* Yoshiko Kakudo; *Cur Educ* Diana Turner; *Pres* Mrs Philip McCoy; *Secy* Marjorie D Schwarz; *Exec Secy* Betty F Walters.
Open daily 10 AM - 5 PM. No admis. Estab 1958 for illustrated lectures on specialized subjects; for small study groups on specific aspects of Asian Art; for support of the research library in the center. Mem: 1065; dues active $15, student $5; annual meeting Apr or May.
Collections: Nearly 10,000 objects of Asian art, including the Avery Brundage Collection and the Roy C Leventritt Collection.
Publications: Society for Asian Art Newsletter, 3 per year; catalogs on museum collections and traveling shows.
Activities: lect open to public; gallery talks; classes for adults; tours; docent council; docent training; traveling exhibitions organized and circulated.
Library: Open for reference. Holdings: Vols 10,000.

CALIFORNIA HISTORICAL SOCIETY, 2090 Jackson St, 94109. Tel: 415-567-1848. *Pres* Mr North Baker; *Vpres* Robert Carpenter; *Dir* vacant; *Treas* George Hale; *Exec Asst* Pamela Seager; *Comptroller* Joan Kerr; *Cur Exhib & Coll* Catherine Hoover; *Dir Publ* Marilyn Ziebarth; *Prog* Renee Grignard Eaton; *Membership* Ingrid Ford.
Open Wed, Sat & Sun 1 - 5 PM. Admis nonmem $1.00, seniors and students 50¢. Estab 1871 to collect and disseminate information pertaining to the history of California and the West; changing exhibit gallery in headquarters building and in an adjunct regional office in San Marino; history center at 2300 Wilshire Blvd in Los Angeles. Average Annual Attendance: 15,000. Mem: 7500; dues $20 and up; annual meeting Mar.
Income: $550,000 (financed by endowment, membership and funding from private and public agencies).
Collections: Fine arts includes California lithography and other graphics, oils, watercolors, drawings, furniture and artifacts to 1915.
Exhibitions: A Photographic History of Golden Gate Park; The Image of America in Caricature and Cartoon (produced by the Amon Carter Museum); An Earlier Era; Selected Paintings from the California Historical Society Collection.
Publications: California History, quarterly; California Historical Courier (newspaper), five times per yr.
Activities: Classes for adults; docent training; programs, lectures, tours and films throughout the state; lect open to public; concerts; gallery talks; tours; awards given for participation in the field of California history; individual paintings and 3000 original objects of art lent; traveling exhibitions organized and circulated; sales shop selling CHS books only.

—Library, 2099 Pacific Ave, 94109. Tel: 415-567-1848. *Dir* Gary Kurutz; *Cur Photography* LaVerne Dicker; *Manuscripts* Karl Feichtneir; *Genealogy* Gerry Wright; *Kemble Collection* Bruce Johnson.
Open Wed - Sat 10 AM - 5 PM. Estab 1922 to collect books, manuscripts, photographs, ephemera, maps and posters pertaining to California history; for reference and research only.
Holdings: Vols 25,000; AV—Microfilm; Other—Clipping files, exhibition catalogs, manuscripts, memorabilia, original documents, pamphlets, photographs 200,000.
Special Collections: Kemble Collection of California printing and publishing; title insurance and trust photo collection; C Templeton Crocker Collection; Florence Keen Collection of California literature; early voyages of exploration; missions; Mexican War; Gold Rush; overland journeys; transcontinental railroad; Early California imprints country and municipal histories.

FINE ARTS MUSEUMS OF SAN FRANCISCO, M H de Young Memorial Museum, Golden Gate Park, 94118. Tel: 415-558-2887. California Palace of the Legion of Honor, Lincoln Park, 94121. Tel: 415-558-2881. *Pres* Walter S Newman; *Dir* Ian McKibbin White; *Dir Emeritus* Dr Thomas Carr Howe; *VDir Educ* Thomas K Seligman; *VDir Admin & Personnel* Steven E Dykes; *Exec Secy Board of Trustees* Delores Malone; *Development Officer* Katherine Livingston; *Cur in Charge Exhib* Susan Levitin; *Asst Cur in Charge Exhib* Susan Melim; *Cur in Charge Decorative Arts* Michael Conforti; *Cur in Charge Prints & Drawings* Robert F Johnson; *Cur Prints & Drawings Achenbach Foundation for Graphic Arts* Maxine Rooston; *Cur in Charge Art School* Ela Cameron; *Cur Painting* Thomas P Lee; *Asst to Dir* Bruce Merley; *Asst Dir Educ* Charles Mills; *Cur in Charge Department Textiles* Anna Bennet; *Librn & Cur Dept of Ancient Art* James Nelson; *Registrar* de Young Museum DeRenne Coerr; *Registrar* Legion of Honor Paula March; *Public Information Officer* Charles Long; *Conservator Paper* Robert Futernick; *Conservator Painting* Teri Oikawa-Picante, *Conservator Furniture* Gene Munsch.
Open Daily 10 AM - 5 PM. Admis adults 75¢, youth 25¢, senior citizens and children under 12 and members no admis; no admis first day of each month. The de Young Museum estab 1895, Legion of Honor estab 1924, merged 1972 as a department of the city and county of San Francisco. Average Annual Attendance: 1,000,000. Mem: 18,000; dues junior $7.50, senior $10, active $20, contributing $30, sustaining $50, supporting $100, donor $250, sponsor $500, guarantor $1000.
Income: $2,000,000 (financed by city appropriation).
Collections: *de Young Museum*—12th - 20th century European and American paintings, sculpture and decorative arts, including tapestries, silver, furniture, porcelain, glass and period rooms; arts of ancient Egypt, Greece and Rome; traditional arts of Africa, Oceania and the Americas. *Legion of Honor*—14th - 20th century French paintings, sculpture and decorative arts, including tapestries, furniture, porcelain, silver and period rooms; Rodin sculpture collection; Achenbach Foundation for Graphic Arts (Department of Prints and Drawings) hold approx 100,000 works from Europe, America and Asia, 15th century to the present.
Publications: Members' monthly calendar; exhibitions catalogs.
Activities: de Young Museum Art School; docent council for volunteer guided tours; lectures; films; concerts; Trip-Out Truck (community outreach); art book shops; cafe, temporary exhibitions.
—de Young Museum Library.
Holdings: Vols 20,000.
Special Collections: Archives of American Art West Coast Offices (branch of Smithsonian Institution) microfilm library located at the de Young Museum.

GALERIA DE LA RAZA,* 2851 24th St, 94110. Tel: 415-826-8009. *Co-Dir* Ralph Yanez; *Co-Dir* Ralph Maradiaga; *Cur & Researcher* Elisa Borrego; *Documentation of Exhib & Slides* Francisco Garcia.
Open Wed - Sun Noon - 5 PM. Estab 1969 as a community gallery and museum to exhibit works by Mexican-American and Latin-American artists, contemporary as well as cultural folk art. Average Annual Attendance: 35,000. Mem: 150; dues $12; monthly meetings.
Income: Financed by endowment.
Collections: Leopoldo Mendez prints from Mexico; Huichol yarn paintings from Peter Young Collection; folk art from Mexico; textiles from the Americas.
Exhibitions: Changing monthly exhibits, twelve per year.
Publications: Newsletter, monthly; Calendar, yearly; Children's Coloring Book; original screen prints editions of 100.
Activities: Classes for adults and children; lect open to public, 24 vis lectr per yr; gallery talks; tours; individual paintings and original objects of art lent; traveling exhibitions organized and circulated; art book store.

LA MAMELLE INC, 70 Twelfth St (Mailing Add: Box 3123 Rincon, 94119). Tel: 415-431-7524. *Pres* Carl E Loeffler.
Estab 1975 support network for contemporary art; gallery houses new, contemporary art.
Income: Financed by endowment, membership, and state appropriation.

Collections: Video art, artists books, marginal works.
Exhibitions: West Coast Conceptual Photographers; All Xerox; Photography and Language; Rubber Stamp Art; Recorded Works; Davi-Det-Hompson; Endre-Tot; Ecart; Women in the Printing Arts.
Publications: La Mamelle Magazine: Art Contemporary; quarterly.
Activities: Lect open to the public; concerts; gallery talks; original objects of art lent; lending collection contains video tapes; traveling exhibitions organized and circulated; sales shop selling books, magazines, original art.
—**Contemporary Art Archives.** Tel: 415-431-7524. For reference only.

LONE MOUNTAIN COLLEGE ART DEPARTMENT GALLERY,* 2800 Turk Blvd, 94118. Tel: 415-752-7000, exten 240 and 241. *Chmn* Robert Brawley; *Admin Asst* Patricia Shih.
Open Mon, Tues, Thurs, Fri & Sat Noon - 4 PM; cl Wed & Sun. Estab in 1930 as San Francisco College for Women, renamed in 1970. 25 x 45 ft gallery with 12 ft ceilings, track lighting and hardwood floor.
Exhibitions: Bay Area Artists Series (3 exhibitions); Young Artist Exhibition Series (5 exhibitions); Tibetan Art Exhib; Art of Retarded People; graduate, undergraduate and faculty exhibitions.
Publications: Gazette; bulletins.
Activities: Classes for adults; dramatic programs; concerts.
Library: Holdings—Vols 175,000.

JOSEPHINE D RANDALL JUNIOR MUSEUM,* 199 Museum Way, 94114. Tel: 415-863-1399. *Dir* Dr A Kirk Conragan; *Cur Arts & Crafts* Marie Anido.
Open Tues - Sat 10 AM - 5 PM; Sun 11 Am - 5 PM; cl Mon, New Year's and Christmas. No admis. Estab 1945 as part of the San francisco Recreation and Park Dept. Average Annual Attendance: 120,000.
Collections: Children's art; Indian artifacts.
Activities: Classes in ceramics; weaving, leaded glass, painting, art history, jewelry, and stitchery; tours; lect; films; individual paintings and original objects of art lent to other museums; traveling exhibitions organized and circulated.
Library: Open for reference. Holdings: Vols 8500; Other—Map files.

SAN FRANCISCO ART INSTITUTE,* 800 Chestnut St, 94133. Tel: 415-771-7020. *Dir* Philip Linhares; *Asst Dir* David Loveall.
Open Mon - Sat 10 AM - 4 PM. No admis. Estab 1871, inc 1889 to foster the appreciation and creation of the fine arts and maintain a school and museum for that purpose. Average Annual Attendance: 60,000. Mem: 1300; dues $15 - $100 and up; annual meeting June.
Collections: Emanual Walter Collection; San Francisco Art Institute Collection; Sloss Bequest.
Exhibitions: Emanuel Walter Gallery for exhibitions of contemporary art, open to the public, admission free; Atholl McBean Gallery for exhibitions of recent works by SFAI faculty on a two and three-man basis; Diego Rivera Gallery for exhibition of works by SFAI students; SFAI Photo Gallery for exhibitions of photographs by participating photographers invited by SFAI Photo Department.
Activities: Traveling exhibitions organized and circulated.
—**The Anne Bremer Memorial Library.** *Librn* Elisabeth Cunkle.
Holdings: Vols 21,000; Other—Slides 6500, reproductions 2000.

SAN FRANCISCO MARITIME MUSEUM ASSOCIATION,* Foot of Polk St, 94109. Tel: 415-673-0700. *Dir* Karl Kortum; *Asst Dir* David Nelson; *Cur* Harlan Soeten; *Photograph Archivist* Matilda Dring.
Open daily 10 AM - 5 PM. No admis. Estab 1951; museum was built in 1939, a terazzo and stainless steel structure with a nautical theme. Mem: Dues quarterdeck $10, contributing $25, sustaining $100, life $250.
Collections: 100,000 photographs and negatives of ships and other naval memorabilia; ship models; paintings; recordings; sailing ship and paddlewheeler.
Publications: Newsletter; booklets.
Library: *Librn* David Hull. Open to the public for research on premises. Holdings: 8000 vols.

SAN FRANCISCO MUSEUM OF MODERN ART, Van Ness at McAllister, 94102. Tel: 415-863-8800. *Dir* Henry T Hopkins; *Dep Dir* Michael McCone; *Chief Cur* Suzanne Foley; *Controller* S C St John.
Open Tues - Fri 10 AM - 10 PM; Sat - Sun 10 AM - 5 PM; cl Mon. No admis for permanent collection; $1.50 for temporary exhibitions. Estab 1935 to collect and exhibit art of the 20th century; Museum occupies two floors; four major galleries 35 by 180 ft; six corridor galleries; six smaller galleries. Average Annual Attendance: 300,000. Mem: 8000; dues $25.
Income: $1,200,000 (financed by endowment, membership, city appropriation, earnings and grants). Purchases: $60,000.
Collections: Clyfford Still; †California clay; †photography, †painting and †sculpture.
Exhibitions: Clyfford Still; Picasso/Braque/Leger; People's Murals; The Wild Beasts; Fauvism and its Affinities; Photographs by John Gutmann; Painting and Sculpture in California; The Modern Era: A View of California Architecture 1960-1976.

Publications: Calendar, monthly.
Activities: Classes for adults and children; docent training; lect open to public, 6 - 8 vis lectr per yr; concerts; gallery talks; tours; traveling exhibitions organized and circulated; museum shop selling books, magazines, reproductions and slides.
—**Louise Sloss Ackerman Fine Arts Library.** *Librn* Eugenie Candau.
Open to the public for reference.
Holdings: Vols: 6000; Per subs 100; Other—Exhibition catalogs 40,000; artists files; museum archives.
Special Subjects: Modern and contemporary art including photography and architecture.
Special Collections: Margery Mann Collection of books in the history of photography.

SAN FRANCISCO PUBLIC LIBRARY, Art & Music Department, Civic Center, 94102. Tel: 415-558-3687. *Librn in charge:* Mary Ashe.
Open Mon - Thurs 9 AM - 9 PM; Fri & Sat 9 AM - 6 PM. Estab 1878.
Income: Financed by city and state appropriations.
Holdings: AV—Phonorecords; Other—Framed reproductions, prints.

WINE MUSEUM OF SAN FRANCISCO, 633 Beach St, 94109. Tel: 415-673-6990. *Dir* Ernest G Mittelberger, *Hospitality Dir* Edwin Brown; *Art Consultant* Robert Emory Johnson; *Consulting Cur* Melinda Young Frye; *Asst to the Dir* Mary M Rodgers; *Preparator* Karl L Folsom.
Open Tues - Sat 11 AM - 5 PM; Sun Noon - 5 PM; cl Mon. No admis. Estab 1974 for the purpose of learning about the rituals and history of wine and its enjoyment, and as a demonstration of the quality and diversity of artistic expressions created by man as a record of his appreciation of wine from the earliest times to the present; one large room is divided into following sections: Grape, Vineyard and Harvest; Winemaking and the Vintner; Ancient Drinking Vessels; Wine in Mythology; In Celebration of Wine and Life; and a changing exhibition area. Average Annual Attendance: 100,000.
Income: Financed by private sponsor.
Collections: †Christian Brothers Collection of original graphics and decorative arts; Franz W Sichel Collection of glass drinking vessels spanning 2000 years.
Exhibitions: (1976) Thomas Jefferson and Wine in Early America. (1977) Bacchus Today - Fifty years of Wine Cartoons from the New Yorker. (1978 projection) The Wine Bottle through the Ages.
Publications: The Wine Museum of San Francisco, Brochure.
Activities: Docent training; lect open to the public, 5 vis lectr per yr; gallery talks; tours; individual prints and original objects of art lent to other museums who have proper security and insurance systems; traveling exhibitions organized and circulated; museum shop selling books, reproductions.
—**The Alfred Fromm Rare Wine Books Library.** Tel: 415-673-6990. *Librn* Mary M Rodgers.
Open to writers, researchers, scholars for reference only.
Holdings: Vols 1000.

SAN JOSE

ROSICRUCIAN EGYPTIAN MUSEUM AND ART GALLERY, Park and Naglee, 95191. Tel: 408-287-9171, exten 229. *Dir* Ralph M Lewis; *Cur* Curt Schild.
Open Tues - Fri 9 AM - 4:45 PM. No admis. Estab 1929, in present building 1967, to present to the public a collection of the works of the Ancient Egyptians, reflecting their lives and culture; A Gallery contains funereal works, Babylonian and Assyrian collection; B Gallery contains mummies, replica of tomb; C Gallery, Tel-El-Armana room, amulets, cosmetics, writing implements; D Gallery contains jewelry, pottery, model of King Zoser's tomb complex. Average Annual Attendance: 500,000.
Income: Financed by Rosicrucian Order
Collections: All parts of the museum are being added to over the years. French Room contains a collection of Louis 14 - Louis 16 furniture donated by the Vadenais family.
Exhibitions: Monthly exhibitions, majority are one-man shows.
Activities: Sales shop selling books, reproductions, prints, slides, jewelry, records and posters.

SAN JOSE MUSEUM OF ART, 110 S Market St, 95113. Tel: 408-294-2787. *Dir* Albert G Dixon Jr; *Cur* Elizabeth Gaidos; *Office Mgr* Judith Bolin; *Development Officer* Charlotte Wendel.
Open Tues - Sat 10 AM - 4:30 PM; Sun Noon - 4 PM. No admis. Estab 1968 to provide the citizens of San Jose and the South Bay region with a changing exhibition schedule featuring local, regional, national and international exhibitions; the museum is housed in an 1892 sandstone structure in the Romanesque style; it was a federal post office building in San Jose, and was renovated for museum use in 1975-76. Average Annual Attendance: 40,000. Mem dues: $8 - $1000; annual meeting June.
Income: Financed by membership, city appropriation.

Collections: Principally California contemporary paintings, sculptures, prints and drawings.
Exhibitions: Approximately 55 - 60 exhibitions per year.
Publications: Newsletter, monthly; exhibition catalogs.
Activities: Docent training; lect open to the public; concerts; traveling exhibitions organized and circulated; museum shop selling books, original art, reproductions.
Library: Tel: 408-294-2787. Open to the museum staff and volunteers for reference only. Holdings: Vols 200.

SAN JOSE STATE UNIVERSITY
—Art Gallery, Ninth and San Carlos, 95192. Tel: 408-277-2716. *Gallery Dir* Mark Glazebrook.
Open Mon - Fri 11 AM - 4 PM during term. No admis. Estab 1960 as part of the university Art Dept; gallery is 34 x 28 ft with 12 ft ceiling. Average Annual Attendance: 9000.
Income: Financed by city and state appropriations.
Collections: †Work by Faculty, students and ex-students; †Contemporary and historical graphics, including Klee, Chagall (neither collection normally on display but lent out individually).
Exhibitions: (1977-78) Fred Martin (visiting artist); Small is Beautiful (55 items borrowed from collections or Faculty); David Hockney (The Blue Guitar etchings); The Box Show; Punk Rock; Poland Now, Aspects of Culture; Pre-Columbian Ceramics of West Mexico; Three California Sculptors (David Boitini, Robert Graham, Geoff Sanders).
Publications: Exhibition catalogs.
Activities: Classes for adults; lect open to the public; individual paintings and original objects of art lent to university offices; lending collection contains original prints, paintings 200, sculpture; traveling exhibitions organized and circulated; catalogs sometimes sold.
—Union Gallery, S Ninth St, Student Union, 95192. Tel: 408-277-3221. *Dir & Cur* Stephen Moore; *Asst Dir* Dorothy Torres; *Registrar* Bonnie Cook; *Exhib Coordinator* Gratia Rankin.
Open Mon - Fri 10:30 AM - 4 PM; Wed & Thurs 6 - 8 PM. No admis. Estab 1968 to supplement the San Jose State University Students in the appreciation of the Arts. The Gallery consists of two main spaces: Main Gallery, with an additional entrance Gallery for smaller exhibitions. Average Annual Attendance: 30,000.
Income: Financed by state appropriation and through the University.
Collections: Paintings, graphics, and sculpture.
Exhibitions: The Printed Work; Juried Student Art Exhibition; Drawings; Bruce Fier: The Sound Frame; Convention: Art Publishers; Darryl Sapien; Configuration.
Publications: Exhibition catalogs.
Activities: Lect open to public, 9 vis lectr per yr; gallery talks; competitions; individual paintings and original objects of art lent to other galleries or museums; lending collection contains cassettes, original art works, original prints, paintings, phonorecords, photographs, sculpture, slides; traveling exhibitions organized and circulated; sales shop.

SAN MARCOS

PALOMAR COMMUNITY COLLEGE, Boehm Gallery, 1140 W Mission Road, 92069. *Gallery Dir* Russell W Baldwin; *Gallery Asst* Laurie A Brindle; *Gallery Secy* Dori Marzkiw.
Open Mon - Thurs 7:30 AM - 8:30 PM; Fri 7:30 AM - 4 PM; Sat 10 AM - 2 PM; cl Sun & Holidays. No admis. Estab 1964 to provide the community with fine art regardless of style, period and approach. The gallery is 35 x 35 ft, no windows, 18" brick exterior, 1 in plywood with ½ in drywall interior, acoustic ceiling, and asphalt tile floor. Average Annual Attendance: 50,000.
Income: $8000 (exhibition budget). Financed by city and state appropriataions.
Collections: †Contemporary art by nationally acclaimed artists.
Exhibitions: Faculty show; Harry Partch: Music Instruments; Invitational Crafts exhibit; James Collins: Romantic Conceptualization; Christine Oatman: Fantasy Landscapes; Wayne Theibaud: Recent Paintings and Drawings; William Wiley: Recent Sculpture and Drawings: Annual Student Art Show.
Activities: Lect open to public, 12 vis lectr per yr; competitions; individual paintings and original objects of art lent to reputable museums and galleries; lending collection contains original prints, paintings, and sculpture.
—Fine Arts Library. Tel: 714-744-1150, exten 277. *Reference Librn* Judy Jerstad Cater: *Library Technical Asst* Doris C Devel.
Open Mon - Thurs 7:30 AM - 8:40 PM, Fri 7:30 AM - 4 PM; Sat 10 AM - 2 PM. Estab 1967 to support the curriculum offered by the departments of Art and Music; to provide community access to crafts and fine arts materials. Circ: 16,000.
Holdings: Vols 11,000; Per subs 100; AV—Phonorecords, Other—clipping files, exhibition catalogs, pamphlets.
Special Collections: Sheet music from the 1890's-1950's.

SAN MARINO
HUNTINGTON LIBRARY, ART GALLERY AND BOTANICAL GARDENS, 1151 Oxford Road, 91108. Tel: 213-792-6141, exten 28. *Dir* James Thorpe; *Cur Art Coll* Robert R Wark.
Open Tues - Sun 1 - 4:30 PM; cl Mon, major holidays and Oct. No admis. Estab 1919 by the late Henry E Huntington as a free research library, art gallery, museum and botanical garden; exhibitions opened to the public in 1928 for educational and cultural purposes. Average Annual Attendance: 600,000. Mem: 2000 supporters of the institution who give $25 or more annually and are known as the Friends of the Huntington Library.
Income: Financed by endowment, state appropriation, and gifts.
Collections: British art of the 18th and early 19th centuries with a strong supporting collection of French furniture, decorative objects, and sculpture of the same periods.
Exhibitions: Rotating exhibitions from the permanent collection.
Publications: The Calendar, every other month.
Activities: Dramatic programs; lect open to public; gallery talks; tours; fellowships; sales shop selling books, prints, reproductions, slides, and postcards.
Library: Open to qualified scholars for reference. Special Subjects: British art of the 18th and early 19th centuries. Special Collections: British drawings and watercolors. Probably the largest collection of books, photographs and other materials for the study of British art that exists outside London.

SAN MATEO

COLLEGE OF SAN MATEO LIBRARY, 1700 W Hillsdale Blvd, 94402. Tel: 415-574-6100. *Head Librn* John B Dooley; *Librn* Gregg Atkins, Gladys Chaw, Colette Norman, and Barlow Weaver.
Open Mon - Fri 7:30 AM - 10 PM; Sun 1 - 5 PM; cl Sat. Estab 1922. Maintains an art galleryith monthly exhibits.
Income: Financed by state appropriation.
Holdings: Vols 110,000; Per subs 800; AV—Audio tapes, cassettes, film strips, kodachromes, lantern slides, microfiche, microfilm, motion pictures, phonorecords, reels, slides, video tapes; Other—Clipping files, framed reproductions, memorabilia, original documents, pamphlets, photographs, prints, reproductions.
Special Subjects: European and Oriental art; crafts.
Exhibitions: Young European artists: paintings and prints; student prints from Ljubljana, Yugoslavia; faculty art show: paintings, prints, and sculpture; Mexican folklore; mathematical forms: polyhedra models; community college student show: paintings, prints, and sculpture.

SAN MIGUEL

MISSION SAN MIGUEL, Mission St, 93451. Tel: 805-467-3256. Superior Rev Reginald McDonough; Pastor Rev Hilary Hobrecht.
Open daily 10 AM - 5 PM; cl New Year's, Easter, Thanksgiving, and Christmas. Admis by free will offering. Estab 1797 as The Old Mission church; the original is still the parish church and the entire Mission has been restored; throughout the Mission there are paintings dating back to the Mission days; the frescoes are the original, untouched or done over. Average Annual Attendance: 50,000.
Income: Financed by Franciscan Friars.
Activities: Concerts; museum and sales shops selling books, reproductions, prints, slides, and gifts.

SANTA ANA

BOWER'S MUSEUM,* 2002 N Main St, 92706. Tel: 714-834-4024. *Dir* Reilly P Rhodes; *Cur Art* Larry L Bruns; *Registrar* Margaret A Key; *Exhib Specialist* Paul Maull.
Open Tues - Sat 9 AM - 5 PM; Sun 1 - 5 PM; Wed & Thurs 7 - 10 PM; cl Mon. No admis. Estab 1934 to provide an active general museum for the community. The Charles W Bower Museum is housed in an authentic California mission-style home amid expansive fountain-studded grounds, originally devoted to the display of antique furniture, Indian relics and historical items of early California families. A new wing has been added with an exhibition program of contemporary art. Average Annual Attendance: 61,500. Mem: 400; dues from student $5 - life $1000.
Income: Financed by city appropriation supplemented by Foundation Board.
Collections: (Art) 19th century American textiles, decorative arts and patterned glass; 19th & 20th century American Indian baskets; 19th & early 20th century North and South American costumes; late 19th century Oriental costumes; early California history; Indian artifacts; Asian, African, contemporary American art; Pre-Columbian ceramics; some 16th & 17th century items on loan.

Exhibitions: Temporary exhibits program supplemented by permanent exhibits, one added each year by purchase; Contemporary Reflections; New Guinea Objects; Pre-Columbian Art of Mexico.
Publications: Museum calendar, onthly; exhibition catalogs; brochures.
Activities: Classes for adults and children; docent guild; lect open to public; films; gallery talks; tours; study clubs; individual paintings and original objects of art lent to other museums, and to the public; traveling exhibitions organized and circulated.
Library: Open for reference. Holdings: Vols 500; Other—Photographs and study files.

SANTA BARBARA

FAULKNER MEMORIAL ART WING, Santa Barbara Public Library, 40 E Anapamu St (Mailing Add: Box 1019, 93102). *Library Dir* Robert A Hart.
The Santa Barbara Public Library, in which the Faulkner Memorial Art Wing is housed, is operating in temporary quarters while the library building is being renovated. New facilities are expected to open during the summer of 1979.

SANTA BARBARA MUSEUM OF ART, 1130 State St, 93101. Tel: 805-963-4364. *Dir* Paul C Mills; *Asst Dir for Admin* Carl Vance; *Asst Dir for Activities* Shelley Ruston; *Cur of Coll* Katherine H Mead; *Registrar* Elaine Dietsch.
Open Tues - Sat 11 AM - 5 PM; Sun Noon - 5 PM cl Mon. No admis. Estab 1941 as an art museum. Average Annual Attendance: 200,000. Mem: 3000, dues $15 up; annual meeting January.
Income: $300,000 (financed by endowment, membership, city appropriation and sales).
Collections: American and European paintings, sculpture, drawings, prints; Oriental sculpture, paintings and ceramics; Greek and Roman Art; Henry Eichheim Collection of Oriental Musical Instruments; Alice F Schott Doll Collection.
Exhibitions: Changing exhibitions through the year.
Publications: Museum calendar and exhibition/collection catalogs, monthly.
Activities: Classes for adults and children; docent training; lect open to the public, 12 vis lectr per yr; concerts; gallery talks; tours; individual paintings and original objects of art lent to other museums and University galleries; traveling exhibitions organized and circulated; Junior Museum.
Library. *Librn* John Crozier. Open- to staff, scholars for reference only. Holdings: Vols 2000; Per subs 35; Other—Exhibit catalogs 13,000.

UNIVERSITY OF CALIFORNIA, SANTA BARBARA, Art Museum, 93106, Tel: 805-961-2951. *Dir* David Gebhard; *Cur* Phyllis Plous; *Designer of Exhib* Steven Slaney; *Designer of Exhib* Paul Prince; *Admin Asst/Registrar* Pamela Koe.
Open Tues - Sat 10 AM - 4 PM; Sun & holidays 1 - 5 PM. No admis. Estab 1961 and directed at both the needs of university students of art and the community, trying for a wide range of exhibitions both contemporary and historical; located on the UCSB campus and within the Museum complex, there are three galleries for changing exhibits, and three which exhibit part of the permanent collection. Average Annual Attendance: 30,000.
Financed by university funds.
Collections: Collection of architectural drawings by Southern California architects, including R M Schindler, Irving Gill, Kem Weber and George Washington Smith; Sedgwick Collection of 16th - 18th Century Italian, Flemish and Dutch artists; Morgenroth Collection of Renaissance medals; Ala Story Print Collection.
Exhibitions: Each exhibition year includes an annual undergraduate and graduate exhibition and exhibits by MFA candidates, all from the Art Department, UCSB. (1976-77) Approaches to Paintings: New York; Regional Styles of Drawing in Italy: 1600 - 1700; The Cult of Images: Baudelaire and the 19th Century Media Explosion. (1977-78) Contemporary Tableaux/Constructions; Contemporary Drawing/New York; Palladio; and Prelude to the Fifth Sun: Contemporary/ Traditional Chicano and Latino Art.
Publications: Exhibition catalogs, 3 - 6 per yr.
Activities: Lect upon request; lending collection contains original art works 3000, original prints 800, paintings 300, sculpture 40, architectural drawings 100,000; traveling exhibitions organized and circulated; sales shop selling exhibition catalogs.
—Arts Library. Tel: 805-961-2850. *Art Librn* William Treese; *Asst Art Librn* Susan Wyngaard.
Open Mon - Thurs 9 AM - 11 PM; Fri & Sat 9 AM - 6 PM; Sun 2 - 11 PM. Estab 1969 as the University Art Library to support academic programs.
Income: Financed by city appropriation.

Holdings: Vols 75,000; Per subs 350; AV reference—Cassettes, microfiche, microfilm, video tapes; Other—Exhibition catalogs, pamphlets, photographs, reproductions.
Special Subject: Research collection to support academic programs in Greek, Roman and Etruscan art; Medieval Art; Renaissance and Baroque Art; 18th, 19th and 20th Century Art; Oriental Art; primitive and exotic arts; and history of architecture.
Special Collections: Major collection of art exhibition catalogs, cataloged by computer-based program.
Publications: Catalogs of the Art Exhibition Catalogs of the Arts Library, University of California, Santa Barbara; Teaneck, NJ, Somerset House, 1978.
Activities: Tours.

SANTA CLARA

TRITON MUSEUM OF ART, 1505 Warburton Ave, 95050. Tel: 408-248-4585. *Acting Dir* Jo Farb Hernandez; *pres* Austen Warburton; *VPres* Hamp Gillespie; *Secy* Shirley Reich.
Open Tues - Fri Noon - 4 PM; Sat - Sun Noon - 5 PM. No admis. Estab 1956 to offer a rich and varied cultural experience to members of the community through the display of works of art by American artists, particularly Artists of California, and through related special events and programs; the museum consists of four buildings constructed in an architectural style that blends Oriental and Spanish elements; each pavilion is designed somewhat differently so as to lend variety to the gallery space. Average Annual Attendance: 5000 Mem: 350; dues $5 - $1000.
Income: $46,250 (financed by endowment, membership and city appropriation).
Collections: Oil paintings by Theodore Wores; American ceramics and glass collection, the heart of which is the Vivian Woodward Elmer Majolica Collection; American painting and sculpture.
Exhibitions: Charles Harmon; ADM Cooper; Fiber Coalition; Frank Van Sloan; Two Hundred Years of Santa Clara Valley Architecture; American Carousel Art; Santa Clara Valley Quilt Association; Maynard Dixon; International Children's Book Illustrations; New Testament Narratives in Master Drawings; Seat of American Invention: Chairs of the 19th Century; T Wores: Other Japanese Years.
Publications: Newsletter, bimonthly; occasional catalogs.
Activities: Classes for children; dramatic programs; docent training; lect open to public, 10 vis lectr per yr; concerts; gallery talks; tours; museum shop selling books, reproductions and postcards.
Library: *Librn* Jo Farb Hernandez. Open to members for reference. Holdings: Vols 150; Per subs 5.

UNIVERSITY OF SANTA CLARA, de Saisset Art Gallery & Museum, 95053. Tel: 408-984-4528. *Acad VPres* William Donnelly; *Dir* Lydia Modi Vitale; *Fiscal Consult* Marc Vitale; *Preparator* James Zingheim; *Secy* Cheryl Raasch.
Open Tues - Fri 10 AM - 5 PM; Sat - Sun 1 - 5 PM; cl Mon and all national holidays. No admis. Estab 1955 as a major cultural resource in Northern California; in recent years the art gallery and museum has dramatically broadened its cope, exhibiting some of the world's leading avant-garde artists while not losing sight of the traditional; the gallery has 20,000 sq ft of floor space in a concrete structure adjacent to the Mission Santa Clara on the University of Santa Clara campus, two stories of galleries with a balcony for small exhibitions, plus offices and a gallery shop as well as workrooms. Average Annual Attendance: 250,000. Dues $15 annual, $25 sustaining; $100 sponsor, $250 benefactor, $500 patron.
Income: $96,000 (financed by endowment, membership). Purchases: $2000.
Collections: Videotape repository; New Deal art repository; paintings; sculpture; graphics, china; silver; ivory; 17th and 18th century tapestries; antiques; D'Berger Collection of French furniture and ivories; African collection; Arnold Mountfort Collection; Kolb Collection of 17th and 18th century graphics.
Exhibitions: (1976-78) New Deal Art California; Westward Ho (Frederic Remington & Charles Russell); A Luta Kontinua (Beni Casselle); Mirror Horizon (Carleen Jiminez); Michael Koehne' Photography; A Survey of the Selected Works of James McManus; Sculpture and Drawings of Luis Jimenez; Photography of Judy Steiner; Paintings of Fratel Venzo; Italian Post-Impressionist and Works of Michael Cascella with Photography by Hella Hammid; The Flute and the Brush.
Publications: Quarterly calendar of events; exhibition catalogs.
Activities: Lect open to public, 15 vis lectr per yr; concerts; gallery talks; tours; individual paintings lent to on-campus personnel for offices on campus; traveling exhibitions organized and circulated; museum shop selling books, original art, prints, jewelry, antiques and artifacts.

Library: *Dir* Lydia Modi Vitale. Open by special request to the director. Holdings: Vols 500; Per subs 22. Special Collections: New Deal California; video tape collection; 250 vols of California mission period manuscripts and books.

SANTA CRUZ

SANTA CRUZ ART LEAGUE, INC, 526 Broadway, 95060. Tel: 408-426-5787. *Pres* Margaret Newsome; *VPres* Laurie Murphy, *Secy* Clem Schnabel; *Treas* Ione Riedel; *Cur* June Baker.
Open daily 1 - 5 PM. No admis. Estab 1919, Inc. 1949, to further interest in art; gallery displays paintings in representational art hung by members and changed monthly. Average Annual Attendance: 11,000. Mem: 225, qualifications for membership: Executive Board of Art League judge three original artworks; lay $7; Associate $10; Active $15; annual meeting second Wed in May, monthly meetings.
Income: Financed by donations.
Collections: Permanent display of wax figures of Last Supper from DaVinci painting.
Publications: Monthly bulletin.
Activities: Classes for adults; classes in painting, demonstration by professional artist at monthly meetings; 12 vis lectrs per yr; gallery talks; Schol.

SANTA CRUZ PUBLIC LIBRARY, Art, Music, Film Department, 224 Church St, 95060. Tel: 408-429-3530. *Dir* Charles K Atkins; *Art & Music Librn* Alma Westberg; *Librn* Joan Nordquist; *Asst* Anita Cowen.
Open Mon - Fri 9 AM - 9 PM; Sat 9 AM - 5 PM. Estab 1881 for the cultural enrichment and enjoyment of the citizens; gallery maintained in local and western art of variety of media. Circ: 11,000.
Income: $10,000 (financed by city and state appropriation). Purchases: $10,000.
Holdings: Vols 11,000; Per subs 48; AV—Audio tapes, cassettes, film strips, motion pictures, phonorecords, reels, slides; Other—Clipping files, framed reproductions, pamphlets, prints.
Special Subjects: Musical scores; opera libretti; older popular sheet music from 19th Century to 1960's.
Special Collections: Popular sheet music (non-current).
Exhibitions: (1976-78) Paintings and sculpture by local artists; Annual Handweavers Guild; Asian-American artists; local 19th Century lithographs; graphic arts; photography; Chicano arts; Art by exceptional children; University of California Santa Cruz Bachelor of Fine Arts Program; Contemporary Quilts; Symphony Poster contest; Bicentennial arts.
Activities: Classes for children; film programs; tours; exten dept serving Santa Cruz County.

SANTA MONICA

SANTA MONICA COLLEGE ART GALLERY, 1900 Pico Blvd, 90405. Tel: 213-450-5150, exten 340. *Dir* William M Hill; *Secy* Judy Booth.
Open Mon - Fri 10 AM - 3 PM; Thurs 7 - 9 PM; cl academic holidays. No admis. Estab 1973 to provide a study gallery for direct contact with contemporary and historic works of art. Average Annual Attendance: 25,000.
Income: Financed by membership, city and state appropriations. Purchases: $1000.
Collections: Southern California prints and drawings.
Exhibitions: Eight per year.
Activities: Lect open to public; gallery talks; tours; original objects of art lent.

SANTA MONICA HIGH SCHOOL, Roberts Art Gallery, 601 Pico Blvd, 90405. Tel: 213-395-3204, exten 246. *Dir* Eileen Sturgeon.
Open Mon - Fri 8:30 AM - 2:30 PM. No admis. Estab 1936, new space 1962. The gallery is a vital part of the school and brings to students exposure that would otherwise not be available. This is the only high school in the nation to have a professional art gallery. Exhibition area is 22 x 45 ft. Average Annual Attendance: Over 2500.
Collections: Large Federal Art Project collection; works by Stanton MacDonald Wright; Conrad Buff; Donal Hord, Boris Deutsch, Tyrus Wong, Rex Brandt and Herman Cherry.
Exhibitions: (1977-78) Schmidt and Schmidt (graphics); Wrought Iron (three artists); Mixed Media; Written by Hand; Art of the Great Depression; Fine Arts Festival.
Publications: Announcement of current exhibits.
Activities: Lect open to the public, 6 vis lectr per yr; gallery talks; competitions.

SANTA ROSA

SANTA ROSA JUNIOR COLLEGE ART GALLERY, 1501 Mendocino Ave, 95401. Tel: 707-527-4298. *Dir* John Watrous.

Open Tues - Fri 10 AM - 4 PM; Sun 1 - 4 PM. No admis. Estab 1973. Gallery is 40 x 42 ft, 12 ft walls, peaked roof with four skylights. Average Annual Attendance: 9000.
Publications: Annual report.
Activities: Lect open to public, 6 vis lectr per yr; concerts; gallery talks; traveling exhibitions organized and circulated.
Library: For reference. Holdings: Vols 100; Per subs 2.

SARATOGA

VILLA MONTALVO CENTER FOR THE ARTS, * 14800 Montalvo Rd (Mailing Add: PO Box 158, 95070). Tel: 408-867-3421. *Exec Dir* George Barati.
Open Tues - Sun 1 - 4 PM; cl Mon and holidays. Admis Tues - Fri free; Sat & Sun 25¢. Estab 1953; administered by Montalvo Association, Villa Montalvo is part of a cultural center for the development of art, literature, music and architecture by artists and promising students; facilities for artists in residence. The home of the late US Senator and Mayor of San Francisco, James Duval Phelan, was bequeathed as a Cultural Center, and is conducted as a non-profit enterprise by the Board of Trustees of the Montalvo Association. Average Annual Attendance: 50,000. Mem: 800; dues $15 and up; annual meeting Nov.
Collections: Paintings; sculpture; decorative arts; graphics; manuscripts.
Exhibitions: Monthly exhibitions of jewelry, ceramics, photography, paintings, drawings, crafts, graphic arts by California and other artists, and by students and faculty of Montalvo; traveling exhibitions.
Activities: Classes for adults and children; lect open to public; dramatic programs; films; gallery talks; concerts, traveling exhibitions organized and circulated.
Publications: James D Phelan (pamphlet); calendar monthly.

STANFORD

STANFORD UNIVERSITY, Museum of Art and T W Stanford Art Gallery, Museum Way & Lomita Dr, 94305. Tel: 415-497-4177. *Dir* Dr Lorenz Eitner; *Asst Dir* Dr Carol Osborne; *Cur of Prints & Drawings* Betsy G Fryberger; *Dir of Oriental Art* Dr Patrick Maveety; *Registrar* Voy Stone; *Cur of Photography* Anita V Mozley.
Open Tues - Fri 10 AM - 4:45 PM; Sat & Sun 1 - 4:45 PM. No admis. Estab 1891 as a teaching museum and laboratory for University's Department of Art. Average Annual Attendance: 85,000. Mem: 1440; dues $7.50 - $100; annual meeting May.
Income: Financed by endowment, membership, and university funds.
Collections: †Ancient art; †Oriental art: †Western art to the 20th Century; †20th Century art; †Contemporary art; †B G Cantor Gallery of Rodin sculpture; †American Indian art; Stanford Family Collection.
Exhibitions: (1976-78) Richard Diebenkorn, Monotypes; Imogen Cunningham, A Celebration; Keith Boyle (drawings); Piranesi; Portraits of Artists and Studios; Portraits; African Sculpture; Northern Renaissance Prints; Killing Likeness: Caricature & Satire; Japonisme; Camera Work: Journal of the Photo-Secession; recent acquisitions; Whistler: Themes and Variations; The Romantic Illustrated Book; Court Robes of Imperial China; two exhibitions every two months.
Publications: The Stanford Museum, biennially.
Activities: Docent training; lect open to the public, 15 vis lectr per yr; gallery talks; tours; exten dept serving the community; traveling exhibitions organized and circulated; museum shop selling books, reproductions, prints, cards.
—**Art Library of The Stanford University Libraries.** Tel: 415-497-4177. *Librn* Alex Ross. Open to the public for reference only.

STOCKTON

PIONEER MUSEUM AND HAGGIN GALLERIES, 1201 N Pershing Ave, 95203. Tel: 209-462-4116. *Pres* E Urban Ernst; *Secy* Constance Miller; *Treas* Dahl C Burnham; *Dir* Keith E Dennison; *Admin Asst* Setsuko Ryuto; *Cur of History* Raymond Hillman, *Registrar* Richard Casagrande.
Open Tues - Sun 1:30 - 5 PM. No admis. Estab 1928 to protect, preserve and interpret for present and future generations, historical and fine arts collections that pertain to the museum's disciplines; the gallery covers 34,000 sq ft of exhibit space housing art and history collections. Average Annual Attendance: Approx 50,000. Mem: 830; dues $15 up; annual meeting third Tues Jan.
Income: $175,000 (financed by endowment, membership, city and county appropriation).
Collections: 19th Century French, American and European paintings; graphics; and decorative arts. Extensive history collection contains items on Stockton, San Joaquin County and California history.
Publications: Museum Calendar, bimonthly.
Activities: Classes for children; docent training; lect open to the public, 4-5 vis lectr per yr; concerts; gallery talks; tours; competitions; individual paintings and original objects of art lent.

—**Petzinger Memorial Library.** Tel: 209-462-4116. *Librn* Richard Casagrande; *Dir* Keith E Dennison.
Open Tues - Sat by appointment only. Estab 1941 to supply material to those interested in the research of California and San Joaquin County history as well as the history of Stockton.
Income: $5400. Purchases: $700.
Holdings: Vols 7000; AV—Lantern slides, motion pictures, slides. Other—Clipping files, exhibition catalogs, manuscripts, memorabilia, original art works, original documents, pamphlets, photographs, prints, reproductions.
Special Collections: Roland Art collection.
Activities: Lectr open to the public, 3 vis lectr per yr; concerts; gallery talks.

UNIVERSITY OF THE PACIFIC, University Center Gallery, 3601 Pacific Ave, 95211. Tel: 209-946-2171. *Dir* Gary Kleemann.
Open 9 AM - 5 PM. No admis. Estab 1975 to expose the University community to various art forms.
Activities: Lect open to public, 2 vis lectrs per yr.

TORRANCE

EL CAMINO COLLEGE ART GALLERY, 16007 Crenshaw Blvd, 90506. *Dir* David Patterson; *Dean Fine Arts* Dr Lewis Hiigel; *Dean Community Services* Dr Robert Haag.
Open Mon - Fri 9 AM - 3 PM; Mon & Thurs 6 - 9 PM; Sun Noon - 4 PM. No admis. Estab 1970 to exhibit professional, historical and student art. Larger main gallery fifty feet square, smaller lounge gallery 18 x 22 ft.
Collections: Small print collection; small sculpture collection.
Publications: Exhibit catalogs.
Activities: Lect open to public; concerts; gallery talks, tours.

TURLOCK

CALIFORNIA STATE COLLEGE, STANISLAUS, 800 Monte Vista, 95380.
—**Art Gallery.** Tel: 209-633-2431. *Chmn of Art Dept* Winston McGee; *Dir of Gallery* Martin Camarata.
Open Mon - Fri 11 AM - 4 PM. No admis. Estab 1967 for the purpose of community and cultural instruction; gallery is small, covering 250 ft running. Average Annual Attendance: 10,000.
Income: $500 (financed by state appropriation). Puchases: $500.
Collections: Permanent collection of graphics and small contemporary works.
Exhibitions: (1977-78) Janssens; Gordon Cook; Walter Askin; CSCS Art Exhibition; CSCS Art Auction; Hank Baum Graphics; CSCS Art Faculty: Roten Gallery; David King Sculpture; High School Exhibition; Roland Peterson; CSCS Senior Show.
Publications: Exhibition catalogs.
Activities: Classes for adults; lect open to the public, 11 vis lectr per yr; concerts; gallery talks; tours; exten dept serving summer school; individual paintings and original objects of art lent to the campus community; lending collection contains film strips, 35mm lantern slides 15,000, motion pictures 20, original art works 25, original prints 40; traveling exhibitions organized and circulated.
—**Library.** Tel: 209-633-2232. *Librn Dir* R Dean Galloway; *Bibliographer* Bob Santos; *Head of Public Services & Asst Lib Dir* J Carlyle Parker; *Head of Technical Services* Peter C Mollema Jr.
Open Mon - Thurs 7:30 AM - 10 PM; Fri 7:30 AM - 5 PM; Sat 9 AM - 5 PM; Sun 1 - 9 PM. Estab 1957 to support curriculum of liberal arts, undergraduate and limited number of graduate programs. Circ 129,000.
Income: $5600 (financed by state appropriation). Purchases: $5600.
Holdings: Vols 7000; Per subs 77; AV—Cassettes, microfiche, microfilm, slides, video tapes; Other—Exhibition catalogs.
Special Subjects: Emphasis on 19th and 20th Century Art.

VALENCIA

CALIFORNIA INSTITUTE OF THE ARTS LIBRARY, 24700 McBean Parkway, 90038. Tel: 805-255-1050. *Dir* Elizabeth Armstrong; *Assoc Librn & Head, Technical Processes* James Elrod; *Cataloger* Joan Anderson; *Head Public Services* Frederick Gardner; *Film Librn* Margie Hanft; *Art & Slide Librn* Evelyn White.
Open Mon - Thurs 10 AM - Midnight; Fri 10 AM - 5 PM; Sun Noon - 9 PM; cl Sat. Estab 1961, first classes 1970, designed to be a community of practicing artists working in schools of art, design, film, music, theatre, and dance.
Income: Financed by endowment.
Holdings: Vols 85,311; Per subs 535; AV—Audio tapes, cassettes, microfiche, microfilm, motion pictures, phonorecords, slides, video tapes; Other—Exhibition catalogs.

Special Subjects: Art & design; dance; film & video; music; theatre; critical studies.
Exhibitions: Student work only, about 20 annually.
Publications: CalArts Admission Bulletin, yearly.

WALNUT

MOUNT SAN ANTONIO COLLEGE ART GALLERY, 1100 N Grand Ave, 91789. Tel: 714-598-2811, exten 207. *Dir* Michael Andrew Preble; *Secy to Dir* Myrtle Gebbie.
Open Mon - Thurs 11 AM - 3 PM; Tues & Wed 6:30 - 9 PM; Fri 11 AM - 1 PM. No admis. Estab c. 1950 as an art gallery for art and cultural exhibitions of interest and use by the college and resident communities; two galleries — East and West. Average Annual Attendance: 7000.
Income: Financed by city and district appropriations.
Collections: 30 works from past biennial exhibitions and donations; small collection of local artifacts and historical items.
Exhibitions: Ynez Johnston Retrospective; Michael Mollett Exhibition of Conceptual Art; Media—paper; Contemporary Designs—wood; Four Fantastic Imagists.
Publications: Occasional catalogs.
Activities: Educational emphasis upon college and resident communities; tours available.

WALNUT CREEK

WALNUT CREEK CIVIC ARTS GALLERY, 1641 Locust St, (Mailing Add: 1445 Civic Dr, 94596). *Dir Civic Arts* Gary F Schaub; *Exhib Specialist* Marvin Schneck; *Educ Specialist* Kathy Nelson.
Open Tues - Sat Noon - 5 PM; Fri - Sat 7:30 - 9:30 PM. No admis. Estab 1963 to offer varied and educational changing exhibitions to the community and surrounding area, guided by a professional staff following a course of pre-planned shows of the highest calibre of artistic intent and widespread public appeal; gallery contains 396 running ft, 2300 sq ft including mezzanine gallery. Average Annual Attendance: 24,000. Mem: 500; dues $10.
Purchases: $2000.
Collections: General city collection consisting of paintings, prints, photographs and crafts, enlarged periodically.
Exhibitions: (1976-78) Contemporary Japanese Prints, Dimondstein (sculpture) and St John (paintings); Touching All Things; Young Art; Three Views of Nature (DeVivieros, Hocking and Robb); West Coast Contemporary (photography); Solstice; Craft Competition; Puppet Show; Fine Arts Presses (printmaking); Edward Curtis and Joseph Sharpe; New Guinea Artifacts.
Publications: Three catalogs per yr; Artscene (newsletter).
Activities: Classes for adults and children; dramatic programs; docent training; lect open to public, 6 - 10 vis lectr per yr; concerts; gallery talks; tours; competitions; sales shop selling books, original art, slides and catalogs.
Library: Open to local schools, docents and civic arts members. Holdings in the process of being cataloged.

WHITTIER

RIO HONDO COLLEGE ART GALLERY, 3600 Workman Mill Road, 90608. Tel: 714-692-0921, exten 361. *Gallery Dir* Linda Ann Valeri; *Gallery Asst* Greg Allen.
Open Mon - Fri 11 AM - 4 PM & 6:30 - 9 PM. No admis. Estab 1967 to bring to the college students a wide variety of art experiences that will enhance and develop their sensitivity and appreciation of art. Small gallery about 1000 sq ft located within the art facility. Average Annual Attendance: 8000.
Income: Financed through college. Purchases: $1000.
Collections: Contemporary paintings and graphics by local artists (southern California area).
Exhibitions: Contemporary Applique; Recent works by Neda Al-Hilali; Contemporary Photography; Bill Lane (paintings); Group Show in Crafts; Childrens Art; American Indian Art.
Activities: Classes for adults; dramatic programs; lect open to public; artmobile.

YOSEMITE NATIONAL PARK

YOSEMITE MUSEUM COLLECTIONS, National Park Service, Box 577, 95389. Tel: 209-372-4461 exten 61. *Cur* Jack Gyer.
Open on prior request. No admis. Estab 1926 to interpret the natural sciences and human history of the Yosemite area. Mem: 1000 (Yosemite Natural History Asn members); dues $5 up.
Income: Financed by federal appropriation.

Collections: Photographic (with a special collection of early photographs of the area); Fine Arts; Indian Cultural artifacts; pioneer Caucasian artifacts.

Publications: Publication list available from Yosemite Natural History Association, Box 545, Yosemite National Park, CA 95389.

Activities: Lect open to the public; individual paintings and original objects of art lent on special exhibits only; lending collection contains original prints 20,000, photographs; sales shop selling books; junior museum.

Library. Librn Stephen Medley. For reference only. Holdings: Vols 7000.

COLORADO

BLACK HAWK

BLACKHAWK MOUNTAIN SCHOOL OF ART, The Gallery, 251 Main St, 80422. Tel: 303-582-5235. *Dir, Pres Bd Directors* Michael S Parfenoff; *VPres* Michael J Reardon.

Open 10 AM - 5 PM (June, July & Aug). No admis. Estab 1972 to exhibit works of art of students, faculty and friends of the School. The Gallery is part of the educational experience for the students. They organize exhibits, staff the gallery, and carry out all necessary functions of the gallery. 300 sq ft of exhibition space.

BOULDER

UNIVERSITY OF COLORADO, Fine Arts Building Gallery, Fine Arts Building, 80309. Tel: 303-402-6504. *Dir Exhib & Cur Permanent Coll* Jean-Edith V Weiffenbach.

Open Mon - Fri 8 AM - Noon & 1 - 5 PM. No admis. Estab 1939 to maintain and exhibit art collection. The gallery has 249 linear feet of wall space, and is 2133 sq ft.

Income: Financed through University.

Collections: †Prints, drawings, and watercolors of the 15th-20th centuries; †19th & 20th century paintings; †sculpture and ceramics of the 15th-20th centuries; †photographs, 20th century.

Exhibitions: Peter Plagens: Works on Paper; Portraits and Landscapes from the Permanent Collection; Two Photographers: Les Krims and Tod Papageorge (organized by Gary Metz); Late Renaissance Prints and Drawings; Billbored: American Billboards—A Slide Documentary; Judith Bernstein: Drawings 1966-1976; Acquisitions in Photography; Allusions: Gianakos, Schmidt, Strider; Sol Lewitt: Drawings, Structures and Prints; 18th Century Prints and Drawings; Xerox/Xerox/Xerox; Under Consciousness: Works by Rosemarie Castoro; Bruce Conner: Drawings and Lithographs; First Steps and Last Tangos (student exhibition); Vessel & Image: rehistoric Southwest Indian Pottery; Boulder Artists' Collaborative Exhibition; Daniel Buren: Impromptu—Two Complementary Works In Situ; Graduate Student Exhibition; Ann Leda Shapiro: Paintings; Late Renaissance Prints and Drawings.

Publications: Exhibition catalogs and brochures.

Activities: Lect open to public, 12 vis lectr per yr; individual paintings and original objects of art lent to museums; lending collection contains original art works, original prints, paintings, photographs, sculpture, original drawings; traveling collection organized and circulated.

—**Henderson Building Fine Arts Gallery,** * 80309. Tel: 303-402-6892.

Open Mon - Fri 8:30 AM - 5 PM; Sat 9 AM - 4 PM; Sun 10 AM - 4 PM. No admis. Gallery has 86 linear feet of wall space and an area of 987 sq ft.

Exhibitions: Continuous exhibitions of painting, graphic arts, photography, and sculpture from the Dept of Fine Arts Collection and from those of major museums and galleries throughout the country.

CENTRAL CITY

GILPIN COUNTY ARTS ASSOCIATION, Eureka St, 80427. Tel: 303-582-5952.

Pres Mrs John Rentz; *VPres* Randall Palser; *Secy* Mrs William McFarland and Mrs William Rossell; *Gallery Mgr* Richard Emmert.

Open daily 11 AM - 6 PM. No admis. Estab 1947 to offer a juried exhibition of Colorado artists; a gallery is maintained. Average Annual Attendance: 24,000. Mem: 300; dues $5 to $100; ann meeting third Sun in Aug.

Income: Financed by membership, sales and entry fee.

Publications: Catalog.

Activities: Funds given yearly for local elementary school art program; juried, competitions, with awards; sales shop selling original art.

COLORADO SPRINGS

AMERICAN NUMISMATIC ASSOCIATION, 818 N Cascade, 80909. Tel: 303-473-9142. *Pres* Col Grover C Criswell; *Exec VPres* Edward C Rochette; *Asst to Exec VPres & Acting Mus Cur* Kenneth L Hallenbeck; *Asst to Exec VPres* Ruthann Brettell.

For further information see National and Regional Organizations.

COLORADO SPRINGS FINE ARTS CENTER, 30 W Dale St, 80903. Tel: 303-634-5581. *Dir* Arne Hansen; *Adminr* G W Engle; *Cur Fine Arts Coll* William Henning; *Cur Taylor Mus* William Wroth; *Dir Mus Educ* Rod Rhodes; *Dir Performing Arts* Thomas Bourke; *Dir Bemis Art Sch for Children* Joyce Robinson; *Registrar* Kay Morris; *Dir Pub Information* Gwen Shuster-Haynes; *Dir Exhib & Physical Plant* Charles Guerin.

Open Tues & Thurs 10 AM - 9 PM; Wed, Fri & Sat 9 AM - 5 PM; Sun 1:30 - 5 PM. No admis. Estab 1936 as a forum, advocate and programmer of visual and performing arts activities for the community. Eleven galleries range in size from quite small to large. Average Annual Attendance: Over 220,000. Mem: Over 2000, dues $15 - $1000; annual meeting third Thurs in Feb.

Income: $750,000 (financed by endowment, membership, city and state appropriations, and revenue producing enterprises).

Collections: Southwestern Spanish Colonial and native American art; ethnographic collections; fine arts collections; American paintings, sculpture, graphics and drawings with emphasis upon art west of the Mississippi; 19th and 20th century art and survey collection of world art.

Exhibitions: (1976-77) American Painting: 1900-1932; Hispanic Crafts of the Southwest; Blumenschein: Retrospective; Between Traditions, Navajo Weaving Toward the End of the 19th Century; Christo's Valley Curtain; Chapel of Our Lady of Talpa; Great American Rodeo; Myth, Metaphor and Mimbreno Art, Parts I & II; Duane Hanson sculptures; Jose and J Rafael Aragon: 19th Century Santeros of New Mexico; Pikes Peak Regional Juried Exhibition.

Publications: Artsfocus, monthly bulletin; scholarly publications: Hispanic Crafts of the Southwest and Ernest L Blumenschein; annual report and various exhibition catalogs.

Activities: Classes for adults and children; dramatic programs; docent training; lect open to public, 12 vis lectr per yr; concerts; gallery talks; tours; competitions; individual paintings and original objects of art lent to AAM accredited museums and fine arts centers; lending collection contains 15,000 books; traveling exhibitions organized and circulated; sales shop selling books, magazines, original art, reproductions, prints, slides and imported and local gifts, including cards, objects of interest, hangings, and others.

—*Library.* Tel: 303-634-5581. *Librn* Roderick Dew; *Reference & Special Research Librn* Elsa Reich.

Open Tues - Sat 10 AM - 5 PM; Sun 1:30 - 5 PM; cl Mon. Estab 1936 as a fine arts reference library in support of the museum's collection and activities; open to public reference, but lending restricted to members of the center and local university students and faculty only.

Income: Financed by endowment, membership and state appropriation. Purchases: $4500 for books and periodicals.

Holdings: Vols 15,000; Per subs 100; Other—Clipping files, exhibition catalogs, memorabilia, pamphlets, prints and reproductions.

Special Subjects: Art and anthropology of the United States Southwest.

Special Collections: Taylor Museum Collection of books and periodicals on the art and anthropology of the United States Southwest.

Activities: Tours given as requested.

DENVER

COLORADO HISTORICAL SOCIETY, Colorado Heritage Center, 1300 Broadway, 80203. Tel: 303-839-2136. *Exec Dir* W E Marshall; *State Historic Preservation Officer* Arthur Townsend; *Cur Documentary Resources* Maxine Benson; *Asst to Dir* Walter R Borneman; *Cur Bldgs & Sites* Roger Doherty; *Cur Historic Preservation* James Hartman; *Cur Publications* Cathryne Johnson; *Cur Formal Education* Nancy Markham; *Cur Exhib* Loretta Slota Marshall; *Cur Material Culture* Joseph Morrow; *State Archaeologist* Bruce Rippeteau.

Open Mon - Fri 9 AM - 5 PM; Sat, Sun & holidays 10 AM - 5 PM; cl Christmas. No admis. Estab 1879 to collect, preserve, and interpret the history of Colorado. Main level exhibit space of 35,000 sq ft to be developed over the next 5-10 years; special exhibits gallery. Average Annual Attendance: 180,000. Mem: 3000; dues $10; annual meeting Dec.

Income: $1,600,000 (financed by endowment, membership, state and federal appropriations).

Collections: The Coloradoans: introduction to the peoples of Colorado.

Exhibitions: Colorado on Glass (photographs); From the Hands of the Ancient Ones (pre-historic Indian pottery).

Publications: Mountain Plain History Notes, monthly; The Colorado Magazine, quarterly.

Activities: Classes for children; docent training; lect open to public, 9 vis lectr per yr; exten dept serving the state; individual paintings and original objects of art lent to museums; traveling exhibitions organized and circulated; sales shop selling books, reproductions, slides.
—**Library,** Documentary Resources Department. Open to public for reference.
Holdings: Vols 40,000; Other—Newsfilm 12,000, microfilm 26,000, manuscripts 1,000,000, photographs 250,000, maps 2500, serials (bound volumes) 20,000, tape and phonograph recordings 600. Special Collections: William Henry Jackson glass plate negatives of views west of the Mississippi.

COLORADO WOMEN'S COLLEGE,* Lyle True Gallery, Montview at Quebec, 80220. Tel: 303-394-6012. *Dir* Maynard Whitney. Gallery maintained.
Income: Financed by endowment and student tuition.
Exhibitions: 3 - 5 exhibitions per year by nationally-known artists, plus faculty and student exhibitions.
Activities: Classes for adults; dramatic programs; lect open to the public; concerts, schol; field trips to regional and national museums and galleries; book shop.
Library maintained.

DENVER ART MUSEUM, 100 W 14th Ave Parkway, 80204. Tel: 303-575-2793. *Dir* Thomas N Maytham; *Assoc Dir* Lewis W Story; *Publ Relations Dir* Patricia D Stooker.
Open Tues - Sat 9 AM - 5 PM; Wed 6 - 9 PM; Sun 1- 5 PM; cl Mon. No admis. Estab 1893, new building opened 1971, to provide a number of permanent and rotating art collections for public viewing, as well as a variety of art education programs and services. The Museum is a seven-story building composed of two cubes, place like a square-cornered figure eight. The building contains 210,000 sq ft of space, 117,000 of which is exhibit space. Average Annual Attendance: 500,000. Mem: 10,000; dues individual $15, family $25; annual meeting April.
Income: Financed by membership, city and state appropriation, private funding.
Collections: Contemporary; Native American; Native Arts; American; New World; European; Oriental; costumes and textiles.
Exhibitions: Armand Hammer Collection; Kenneth Noland Retrospective; The Sensuous Immortals; Giacometti; Through Closed Doors (Western influence on Japanese Art); Noguchi Retrospective.
Publications: Calendar, monthly; catalogues for exhibitions.
Activities: Classes for adults and children; dramatic programs; docent training; lect open to public, 20 vis per yr; concerts; gallery talks; tours artmobile; individual paintings and original objects of art lent to museums; traveling exhibitions organized and circulated; museum shop selling books, reproductions, prints, slides, jewelry, and native American arts.

DENVER ARTISTS GUILD,* c/o Dorothy Trent, 355 Ingalls St, Lakewood, 80226. Tel: 303-237-7366. *Pres* Emily F Spillman; *Secy* Beulah Beardsley.
Estab 1928 to promote the highest professional standards in original works of art by artists in the community, and appreciation of the fine arts. Mem: 90; dues $10; annual meeting fourth Wed in April.
Activities: Classes; critiques; exhibitions; lectures.

DENVER PUBLIC LIBRARY, 1357 Broadway, 80203. Tel: 303-573-5152. *Librn* Henry G. Shearouse, Jr; *Head Arts & Recreation Dept* Georgiana Tiff.
Open Mon - Thurs 10 AM - 9 PM; Fri & Sat 10 AM - 5:30 PM. Estab 1889.
Holdings: Vols 65,391; AV—Audio tapes, cassettes, film strips, microfiche, microfilm, motion pictures, phonorecords, video tapes; Other—Clipping files; exhibition catalogs, framed reproductions, manuscripts, memorabilia, original art works, original documents, pamphlets 177,726, photographs 14,752, prints 1384, reproductions, sculpture, 16mm films 1060.
Activities: Frequent exhbitions from the book and picture collections; cooperates closely with the Denver Art Museum, schools, collegess and clubs throughout the region.

ROCKY MOUNTAIN SCHOOL OF ART, 1441 Ogden St, 80218. Tel: 303-832-1557. *Dir* Philip J Steele; *Asst Dir* Marc Conly; *Secy & Registrar* Karen Tussey.
Open Mon - Fri 8 AM - 4:30 PM. Vocational School in the Fine Arts.
Exhibitions: Annual art show; student work on display.
Publications: Spectrum, quarterly; catalogs, as needed.
Library: Librn Betty St John. Open to students. Holdings: Vols 500, Per subs 10.

WESTERN STATES ARTS FOUNDATION, 428 E Eleventh Ave, 80203. Tel: 303-832-7979. *Pres* Richard L Harcourt; *Dir of Programs* Frank Jacobson; *Dir of Research & Marketing* Richard Mason; *Dir of Visual Arts Services* Janice Steinhauser; *Fiscal/Operations Officer* Arlene Davis; *Publ Dir* Maripat Murphy.
Open daily 8 AM - 5:30 PM. No admis. Estab 1974 to increase the accessibility of quality arts through cost-effective, cooperative multi-state programs and services which expand and work in conjunction with state arts agency programs.
Income: Financed by NEA, private funds.
Exhibitions: (1977-78) Ten Artists Touring Exhibition. (1978-79) Contemporary Crafts Touring Exhibition.
Publications: Emphasis, newsletter, monthly; Annual program brochure.
Activities: Competitions with cash prizes; fels; traveling exhibitions organized.

GOLDEN

FOOTHILLS ART CENTER, INC, 809 15th St, 80401. Tel: 303-279-3922. *Exec Dir* Marian J. Metsopoulos.
Open Mon - Sat 9 AM - 4 PM; Sun 1 - 4 PM. No admis. Estab 1968 to provide a cultural center which embraces all the arts, to educate and stimulate the community in the appreciation and understanding of the arts, to provide equal opportunities for all people to participate in the further study and enjoyment of the arts, and to provide artists and artisans with the opportunity to present their work; housed in the former First Presbyterian Church of Golden, the oldest part was built in 1872, the manse (a part of the whole layout) was built in 1892; there are five galleries, offices, a kitchen and classrooms. Average Annual Attendance: 10,000. Mem: 800; dues $15; annual meeting Dec.
Income: $71,321 (financed by membership, city appropriation, donations, commissions, and rental of rooms).
Collections: About 6 paintings in permanent collection.
Exhibitions: Rocky Mountain National Watermedia Exhibition; North American Sculpture Exhibition in 1979; numerous open juried competitions; Threads Unlimited.
Publications: Foothills Flyer and poetry newsletter, monthly.
Activities: Classes for adults and children; lectr open to the public, 2 - 3 vis lectr per yr; concerts; gallery talks; tours; competitions; individual paintings and original objects of art lent to businesses.
—**Mary S Robinson Art Library.** *Vol* Jean Nelson.
Open to members only.
Holdings: Vols 2140; Per subs 3.

GRAND JUNCTION

WESTERN COLORADO CENTER FOR THE ARTS, INC, 1803 North Seventh, 81501. Tel: 303-243-7337. *Exec Dir* Vacant; *Exec Secy* Suzanne Willcoxon; *Pres of Board of Trustee* Charles L Greenslit.
Open Tues - Sat 10 AM - 5 PM; Sun 2 - 5 PM. No admis. Inc in 1953 to provide an appropriate setting to involve individuals in the appreciation of, and active participation in the arts; one large hexagonal gallery with small stage area; approx 2048 sq ft of floor space; approx 1000 sq ft of wall space. Average Annual Attendance: 6000 - 8000. Mem: 800; dues individual $7.50, family $15; annual meeting Feb.
Income: $38,000 (financed by endowment and membership).
Collections: Permanent collection of four Harold Bryant canvases from a private donor, plus a number of canvases from different artists, which were given to the center.
Exhibitions: Monthly exhibitions; several traveling exhibitions each year; 8-West; Objects.
Publications: Monthly newsletter for members.
Activities: Classes for adults and children; dramatic programs; lect open to the public; competitions; museum shop selling original art, reproductions, handcrafted jewelry and imports.
Library: Open to members and public for reference. Holdings: Vols 400; Per subs 4.

GREELEY

UNIVERSITY OF NORTHERN COLORADO,* John Mariana Art Gallery, Department of Fine Arts, 80639. Tel: 303-351-2143. *Dir* Fredric L Myers.
Open Mon - Fri 9 AM - 4 PM; Sun 1 - 4 PM. No admis. Estab Sept 1973 to bring in art exhibitions not usually seen in the area for benefit of the University and the surrounding community. Average Annual Attendance: 5000.
Income: Financed by endowment and city and state appropriation.
Publications: Schedule of exhibitions, quarterly.

GUNNISON

WESTERN STATE COLLEGE, Quigley Hall Art Gallery, 81230. *Dir* Harry Heil; *Dept Head* August J Grosland.
Open Mon - Fri 1 - 5 PM. No admis. Estab 1967 for the purpose of exhibiting student, staff and traveling art; approximately 300 running ft, fireproof brick walls, security lock-up iron grill gate. Average Annual Attendance: 6000.
Income: $500 (financed by state appropriation).
Collections: Original prints; original paintings.
Exhibitions: (1976-78) Various student and staff exhibitions; One-day exhibition and sale of Original Prints (Ferdinand-Roten Galleries); Original Drawings by Robert Hench; Various one-man shows and group shows from neighboring colleges and universities.
Activities: Competitions with purchase prizes; traveling exhibitions organized and circulated.

LA JUNTA

KOSHARE INDIAN MUSEUM, INC, 18th & Santa Fe, 81050. Tel: 303-384-4801. *Dir* J F Burshears.
Open summer 9 AM - 9 PM; winter 1 - 5 PM. No admis. Estab 1949 for the exhibition of Indian artifacts and paintings. Average Annual Attendance: 10,000.
Activities: Individual paintings and original objects of art lent; museum shop.
Library: Open to members only, for reference. Holdings: Vols 2000.

LEADVILLE

LAKE COUNTY CIVIC CENER ASSOCIATION, INC, Heritage Museum & Gallery, 100-102 W Ninth St (Mailing Add: PO Box 962; 80461). Tel: 303-486-1878. *Exec Dir* Georgina Brown; *Pres Bd of Dir* Neil Reynolds; *Treas Bd of Dir* Harold Neufeld; *Secy Bd of Dir* Shirley Campbell.
Open from Memorial Day through Labor Day, Mon - Sun 10 AM - 6 PM. Admis adult $1, children 12 - 18 years 50¢, under 12 free, family $2, members free. Estab 1972 to promote historical preservation/restoration in the Lake County area; to encourage study of the rich history of the area; to provide area for displays of art, both local and from outside the area; to provide educational assistance where possible, both to the public schools and to individuals interested; the Museum and Gallery owns no art works of its own, but displays a variety of art, on a changing basis. Average Annual Attendance: 11,000 - 12,500. Mem: 330; dues associate $10, patron $25, contributing $50, donor $100; annual meeting fourth Sunday in Feb.
Income: $7,000 - $8,000 (financed by membership and admissions fees). Purchases $500 - $1000.
Exhibitions: Changing display of various types of art: Paintings (watercolors and oils); photography; craft work. (1977) Currier & Ives display; and Colorado on Glass display.
Publications: The Talleyboard, newsletter, quarterly; Mountain Diggings, annual.
Activities: Lect open to the public; competitions; sales shop selling books, slides, papers, postcards, rock samples.
Library: Lake County Public Library, 1115 Harrison, 80461. *Librn* Roger McClurg. Open to the public for reference only. Holdings: Colorado Mountain History Collection; Others—Old Photographs.

LOVELAND

LOVELAND MUSEUM,* 503 Lincoln, 80537. Tel: 303-667-6070. *Cur & Dir* David S Brandon; *Asst Dir & Cur Educ* Kathryn Maddy; *Cur Coll* Helen Fellows.
Open Mon - Wed & Fri 9 AM - 4 PM; Thurs 9 AM - 8 PM; Sat 10 AM - 4 PM; Sun 1 - 4 PM; cl National holidays. No admis. Estab 1929. Art gallery in historic home.
Income: Financed by city appropriation.
Collections: Historical material; archaeology; art; period rooms; dioramas.
Activities: Outreach school programs; lectures; guided tours; loan program. Library of regional and state history available for inter-museum and inter-library loan.

PUEBLO

SANGRE DE CRISTO ARTS & CONFERENCE CENTER, 210 N Santa Fe, 81003. Tel: 303-543-0130. *Dir* Darrell A Bohlsen; *Development Mgr* Maggie Divelbiss; *Workshop & Exhibition Coordinator* Jane Brown, *Rentals Coordinator* Tom Segura; *Admin Asst* Priscilla Jimenez; *Admin Asst* Mary Eversole.

Open Mon - Sat 9 AM - 5 PM. No admis. Estab 1972 to promote the educational and cultural activities of all kinds related to the fine arts in southern Colorado and the management of conventions specifically those which may be concerned with and related to the fine arts; the Studio Gallery in one building has 12 running ft of wall space, 1000 sq ft of floor space and secured; the Conference Gallery located in another building covers 110 ft x 62 ft. Average Annual Attendance: 120,000. Mem: 450; dues $15 - $500; annual meeting third Wed Dec.
Income: $340,000 (financed by membership, city appropriation, and county appropriation).
Exhibitions: (1976) Robert Hench (drawings); Edward Sajbel (watercolors & collage); Artists of the Rockies Invitational; Channel 8 Auction; Community Women in Art; Colorado Intercollegiate Exhibitions; Colorado Art Ed Association Members Exhibitions; Weaver's Guild; Kites; Anita and Jan Fahs; Muriel Sibell Wolle Exhibition; Bruck Buck Exhibition; Pottery sale. (1977) Pueblo Weaver's Guild; Mola Exhibition; Women in Art; Pre-Columbian Exhibition; American Folk Art Exhibition; Charles Frizzel (paintings); Robert McPhee (photography); Own your Own Art Show; Pottery sale. (1978) Harmsen's Najavo Rug Exhibition; The Recent Paintings of Steven Seals; Ten Years of Contemporary Print Making (1967-1977); Invitational Stained Glass Exhibition; Channel 8 Auction; Colorado Artist Craftsmen Exhibition; Prismatic Reflections in Weaving; First National Spoon and Ash Tray Show; Fibers, Sculpture, and Painting (Lin Fife & Ron Snapp); Own your Own Art Show; Annual Invitational Pottery Sale.
Publications: Town & Center Mosaic, nine times a year.
Activities: Classes for adults and children; dramatic programs; docent training; workshops; lect open to the public, 3 vis lectr per yr; concerts; gallery talks; tours.

UNIVERSITY OF SOUTHERN COLORADO,* Creative and Performing Arts Center, Belmont Campus, 2200 Bonfort Ave, 81001. Tel: 303-549-2552. *Center Dir* Jim Duncan; *Art Dept Chmn* Ed Sajbel; *Gallery Dir* Robert Hench.
Open hours vary. Estab 1933 as an educational institution with gallery, music, dance and art center within the university.
Income: Financed by city and state appropriation.
Collections: Prints and drawings, mostly recent American; student and faculty work, 2 and 3 dimensional.
Publications: Creative Arts Quarterly for students and faculty, issued 3-4 times per year.
Activities: Classes for adults; dramatic programs; special educational department; lect open to the public; concerts; gallery talks; tours; competitions; individual paintings & original objects of art lent; traveling exhibitions organized and circulated; book shop.
Library maintained.

CONNECTICUT

BRIDGEPORT

BRIDGEPORT ART LEAGUE,* 528 Clinton Ave, 06605. Tel: 203-335-6250. *Pres* Mrs Alexander Mazur; *First VPres* Mrs Matthew Bobowick; *Art Chmn* Mrs Paul Lengyel.
Open 10:30 AM - 5 PM; cl Sun. No admis. Organized 1895, inc 1916. Average Annual Attendance: 200. Mem: 150, 85 patrons, 25 voting and honorary mem; annual meeting May.
Exhibitions: Special monthly shows by local artists; annual exhibition in April with jury and awards, open to non-members; Members Exhibition in May, of work completed in classes during the year.
Activities: Classes in arts and crafts; lect.
Library: Limited to reference works.

HOUSATONIC COMMUNITY COLLEGE, Housatonic Museum of Art, 510 Barnum Ave, 06608. Tel: 203-579-6400. *Dir* Burt Chernow; *Assoc Cur* David Kintzler, Michael Stein and Ronald Abbe.
Open Mon - Thurs 8 AM - 9 PM; Fri 8 AM - 5 PM. No admis. Estab 1968 for educational purposes; the collection is located on five floors throughout college facilities with changing exhibition galleries on the second and fourth floors. Average Annual Attendance: 8,000 - 12,000.
Income: Financed by state appropriation, from student goverment and other groups and by donations.
Collections: Extensive 19th and 20th century drawings, paintings and sculpture—Picasso, Matisse, Calder, Rivers, Lindner, Derain, Warhol, DeChirico, Marisol, Lichtenstein, Avery, Rauchenberg, Baskin, Wesselmann, Gottlieb, Miro, Chagall, Dubuffet, Cassat, Vasarely, Shahn, Daumier, Pavia and others. Extensive ethnographic collections including—Africa, South Seas and others; smaller holdings from various historical periods; Collections enlarged through grants.
Exhibitions: Monthly exhibitions.
Publications: Periodic catalogs for certain exhibitions, one or two per year.

Activities: Classes for adults; college art courses; lect open to public, 1 - 3 vis lectr per yr; concerts; gallery talks; tours; individual paintings and original objects of art lent to various institutions; lending collection contains paintings 1000; slides 20,000; traveling exhibitions organized and circulated.
Library: Librn Robert Martinson. College library with extensive art section. Open to students and community; Holdings: Vols 1000; Per subs; Other—Fiche.

MUSEUM OF ART, SCIENCE AND INDUSTRY, 4450 Park Ave, 06604. Tel: 203-372-3521. *Pres* Bradley Brewer; *Chief Educ* Raymond J Fennelly; *Cur Exhib* Herbert Davidson.
Open Tues - Sun 2 - 5 PM; cl Mon & holidays. Estab 1958 to provide exhibitions and educational programs in the arts and sciences for a regional audience. Average Annual Attendance 164,000. Mem: Dues $10 - $2500; annual meeting June.
Collections: Paintings; antique furniture; Indian Artifacts.
Exhibitions: Temporary and permanent exhibitions.
Activities: Classes for adults and children; lectures; gallery talks; tours.

DANBURY

DANBURY SCOTT-FANTON MUSEUM AND HISTORICAL SOCIETY, INC,* 43 Main St, 06810. Tel: 203-743-5200. *Pres* Robert J Sallick; *Dir* Dorothy T Schling.
Open Wed - Sun 2 - 5 PM; cl Mon, Tues & holidays. No admis. Estab June 24, 1921 as historic house. Merged with Museum and Arts Center by Legislative Act 1947. Operates the 1785 John and Mary Rider House as a museum of early Americana, and the 1790 Dodd Hat Shop with exhibits relating to hatting. Huntington Hall houses frequently changing exhibits. Ives Homestead, located at Rogers Park in Danbury is to be restored and opened to the public as a memorial to American composer, Charles Edward Ives. At present, there is a Charles Ives Parlor in the Rider House, recreating the period with Ives furnishings and memorabilia. Average Annual Attendance: 5000. Mem: 5000; dues students $2 up to life $1000; annual meeting in Nov.
Income: Financed by endowment and membership.
Publications: Newsletter, monthly; reprints.
Activities: Classes for adults and children; special exhibits; open house; lect; concerts.
Library: Historic material for reference only; photograph collection.

SOCIETY OF MEDALISTS,* c/o Donald A Schwartz, Treas, Old Ridgebury Rd, 06810. Tel: 203-792-3000. *Pres* Donald A Eifert; *Art Advisory Bd* Elvira Clain-Stefanelli, Frank Eliscu, Christopher Parks, Eric Sloane and Albert Wein.
For further information see National and Regional Organizations.

WOOSTER COMMUNITY ART CENTER, Ridgebury Rd, 06810. Tel: 203-743-6311. *Dir* Roger O Prince.
Open Mon - Fri 9 AM - 10 PM. Estab 1965 as a Community Art Center for exhibitions and art classes. Average Annual Attendance: 3000.
Exhibitions: Will Barnet; Ed Giobbi; B Roll; Robert Andrew Parker; Mike Nevelson; Fred Baur; George Chaplin; Bryan Kay; Sperry Andrews; Thomas Stearns; Nancy Tholen; Roger Prince; C Augusine; M Carstanjen; A Shundi; P Warfield; A Werner; L Archacki; R Hare and R Riche.
Activities: Classes for adults, high school and elementary students; 2-year Certificate Program for adults; Advance Placement.
Library: Maintains a small library with collection of slides 2200 and photographs 170.

ESSEX

ESSEX ART ASSOCIATION, INC., N Main St (Mailing Add: PO Box 193, 06426). Tel: 203-767-8996. *Pres* Florence Guerrant; *VPres* Suzanne Peckham; *Secy* Adele Clement; *Treas* E Gould Chalker; *Corresp Secy* Nancy Tighe; *Coordinator* Helen Miller.
Open daily 1 - 5 PM (June - Labor Day). Admis non-members 50¢; members free. Estab 1946 as a non-profit organization for the encouragement of the arts and to provide and maintain suitable headquarters for the showing of art. Maintains a small, well-equipped one-floor gallery. Average Annual Attendance: 2500. Mem: 360; dues artists $7.50, assoc $10; annual meeting Sept.
Income: $3000 (financed by membership).
Exhibitions: Three annual exhibits each year plus one or two special exhibits; usually one high school or grammar school exhibit.

FAIRFIELD

FAIRFIELD HISTORICAL SOCIETY, 636 Old Post Rd, 06430. Tel: 203-259-1598. *Pres* Edward E Harrison; *Cur* C Elizabeth Johnson.

Open Mon - Fri 9:30 AM - 4:30 PM. No admis. Estab 1902 to collect, preserve and interpret artifacts and information relating to the history of Fairfield. Average Annual Attendance: 3000. Mem: 750; dues $10 - $500; meeting varies.
Income: Approximately $50,000 (financed by endowment, membership, city and state appropriation).
Collections: (Art) Ceramics, paintings, furniture, textiles and costumes, photographs, prints, greeting cards, silver, jewelry.
Exhibitions: A Stitch in Time (textiles); three costume exhibits; Fairfield Landscape in Transition (photography); Jar Tar (maritime).
Publications: Newsletter, quarterly.
Activities: Classes for children; docent training; lect open to the public, 2 - 4 lectrs per yr; concerts; individual paintings and original objects of art lent to other institutions.
Library: Open to the public for reference only. Holdings: Vols 8000; Per subs 19; Other—Manuscripts, maps, diaries, documents, and photographs. Special Subjects: Genealogy.

FARMINGTON

FARMINGTON MUSEUM, Stanley-Whitman House, 37 High St, 06032. Tel: 203-677-9222. *Pres* Mrs A D Barney; *Cur* Mrs Mark Riemer.
Open April 1 - Nov 30 Wed - Sat 10 AM - Noon & 2 - 5 PM; Tues, Thurs & Fri 2 - 5 PM; Dec 1 - Mar 31 Fri 2 - 5 PM; Sat 10 AM - Noon & 2 - 5 PM; Sun all year 2 - 5 PM. Admis adults $1, children 50¢. Estab 1935 to preserve the 17th century house, furnished in the style of its period and used to display historical collections. The house and land on which it is located have been deeded in trust to the Farmington Village Green and Library Association, a specially chartered non-profit association. The Stanley-Whitman House was designated a registered National Historic Landmark in October, 1960. Annual meeting Sept.
Collections: Early American furniture; glass; china; silver; pewter; manuscripts; historical material.

HILL-STEAD MUSEUM, 671 Farmington Ave (Mailing Add; PO Box 353, 06032). Tel: 203-677-9064. *Pres* Mrs Erdman Harris; *VPres* George Heard Hamilton; *Secy-Treas* Marguerite Weaver; *Cur* Jarold D Talbot.
Open Wed, Thurs, Sat & Sun 2 - 5 PM; cl Thanksgiving & Christmas. Admis adults $1, children under 12 50¢. Estab 1946. The art collection is housed in turn-of-the-century house by Stanford White; contains original furnishings and collection of Alfred Atmore Pope. The museum is kept as if lived in by original owners; paintings were collected between 1880 and 1907. Average Annual Attendance; 10,000. Mem: 250; dues $5 - $300; meetings Nov and June.
Income: $95,000 (financed by endowment and admissions sales desk).
Collections: French impressionists—Degas, Monet, Manet, Cassatt, Whistler and Carriere; sculpture—Barye, Calder, Manship and others; prints—Whistler, Meryon, Durer, Piranesi, Haydon, Hiroshige, Hokusai and Utamara; Chinese porcelains; Oriental rugs; silver; 18th century French and English furniture; library contains Goya's Disasters of War, mezzotints by Joshua Reynolds, and an aquatint by Mary Cassatt.
Publications: Catalog of Hill-Stead Paintings, Hill-Stead Yesterdays; slide brochure.
Activities: Docent training; guided tours, groups by reservation; lect for members only; 3 vis lectr per yr; sales shop selling books, slides and postcards.
Library: Shown as part of museum, open to authorized scholars. Holdings: Vols 5000.

GREENWICH

ART BARN,* 143 Lower Cross Rd, 06830. Tel: 203-661-9048. *Pres* Blanche Hart; *Secy* Phoebe Biscow; *Exec Dir* Rebecca Bernstein; *Gallery Dir* Mildred Birnbaum; *Treas* David Jensen.
Open Mon - Fri 9:30 AM - 3 PM, also some weekends. No admis. Estab Mar 1962 to provide a stimulating atmosphere which encourages self-expression and growth without competitive pressures and by bringing sculptors, painters, printmakers and handcrafters from all parts of the country to exhibit at the Art Barn; gallery located in a converted dairy barn. Average Annual Attendance: 2500. Mem: 350; dues $15 - $25; annual meeting June.
Income: Financed by membership, from workshops, gallery and shop sales.
Exhibitions: Ten per year.
Activities: Classes for adults and children; workshops; demonstrations; schol.
Library: Holdings—Vols 500.

BRUCE MUSEUM,* Bruce Park, Steamboat Road, 06830. Tel: 203-869-0376. *Dir* Raymond M Owen Jr; *Cur of the Art Dept* Gordon Schmidt; *Secy and Asst to the Dir* Lee St German.

Open Mon - Fri 10 AM - 5 PM; Sun 2 - 5 PM; cl Sat. No admis. Estab 1908 by Robert M Bruce as a natural history, historical and art museum. Average Annual Attendance: 40,000.

Income: $115,000 supported by the Town of Greenwich, Connecticut.

Collections: 17th century Italian, 19th century European and 20th century American paintings; sculpture; Oriental porcelains; ivory; art objects; †53 Dioramas pertaining to natural history; history of the region and the American Indian.

Activities: Lect; films; special exhibitions; cooperates with schools; loan collections.

Library: Holdings—Vols 1000.

GREENWICH ART SOCIETY AND ART CENTER,* 449 Pemberwick Rd, 06830. Tel: 203-531-4010. *Publicity* Mrs John Dixon; *Treas* Mrs Walter I Bradbury; *Dir Art Center* Mrs George Huyer.

Estab 1912, a nonprofit organization to further art education and to awaken and stimulate broader interest in arts and crafts in the town of Greenwich; studio at Art Center is used for classes and meetings. Mem: 500; dues junior (18 and under) $3, student (19 - 24 years) $5, regular $15, family $20.

Income: (1975) $30,000 (financed by membership). Expenses: $29,100.

Exhibitions: Annual Sidewalk Show, open to all artists in area; Juried Annual Fall Show held at Greenwich Public Library Gallery; addition exhibitions at Historical Society, Bruce Museum, Garden Club and Union Trust Banks.

Publications: Bulletin of program for the year and class schedule.

Activities: Day and evening classes for adults, special classes for children; critiques and demonstrations; lect open to the public; individual paintings lent to schools, schol.

MUSEUM OF CARTOON ART,* 384 Field Point Rd, 06830. Tel: 203-661-4502. *Dir & Cur* Jack Tippit; *Asst Cur* Brian Walker.

Open Tues - Fri 10 AM - 4 PM; Sun 1 - 5 PM; cl Sat, Mon. Donations welcome.

Collections: Comics collection from 1896 to the present; early and contemporary original cartoon art; Walt Disney display showing the various steps used to produce animated cartoons; Cartoon Hall of Fame.

Publications: Inlings, quarterly; catalogs; brochures; Classic Comics Collection, 1640 to Present; Story of America in Cartoons.

Activities: Education program; lectures. Sales shop.

Library: Archives collection.

HARTFORD

CONNECTICUT HISTORICAL SOCIETY LIBRARY, 1 Elizabeth St, 06105. Tel: 203-236-5621. *Dir* Thompson R Harlow; *Cur* Philip H Dunbar; *Library Dir* Christopher P Bickford.

Open Mon - Fri 9:30 AM - 5:30 PM; cl Sun, holidays and Sat (June 1 - Sept 1). Estab 1825 to collect and preserve materials of Connecticut interest; to encourage an interest in Connecticut history. Maintains an art gallery. Exhibition space totals 6500 sq ft, two-thirds of it devoted to permanent exhibitions; one-third to changing exhibits.

Income: $250,000 (financed by endowment, and membership). Purchases: $50,000.

Holdings: Vols 70,000; Per subs 75; AV—Kodachromes and microfilm; Other—Clipping files, exhibition catalogs; manuscripts; original art works; original documents; pamphlets; photographs; prints; maps and posters.

Special Subjects: Local Connecticut history and genealogy; children's books; reference books on decorative arts of New England; Connecticut printing; maps; prints; broadsides, printed ephemera.

Exhibitions: Engravings by Amos Doolittle; Paintings by Charles Noel Flagg; Connecticut Pewter.

Publications: Connecticut Historical Society Bulletin, quarterly; Annual Report; Notes & News, five times a year.

Activities: Gallery talks; library tours; traveling exhibitions organized and circulated.

CONNECTICUT STATE LIBRARY, Museum of Connecticut History, 231 Capitol Ave, 06115. Tel: 203-566-3056. *Museum Dir* David O White.

Open Mon - Fri 9 AM - 5 PM; Sat 9 AM - 1 PM; cl holidays. Estab 1910 to collect, preserve and display artifacts and memorabilia reflecting the history and heritage of Connecticut; for reference only; Portraits of Connecticut's governors are on display in the museum's Memorial Hall; other paintings are displayed from time to time as part of special exhibits.

Holdings: Vols 500,000. AV—Cassettes, microfiche, microfilm, motion pictures and video tapes; Other—Clipping files, manuscripts, memorabilia, original art works, original documents, pamphlets, photographs and prints.

Special Subjects: Connecticut; firearms, numismatics.

Exhibitions: (1976-78) Connecticut and the American Revolution; P T Barnum; Photographic Essay of Eastern Connecticut; Sam Colt; The Man, the Gun, the Factory; World War I Posters.

Activities: Library tours; schol.

HARTFORD PUBLIC LIBRARY, 500 Main St, 06103. Tel: 203-525-9121 exten 32. *Dept Head* Vernon Martin.

Open hours vary. Estab 1774 as a free public library; a gallery is maintained on wall space and glass cases.

Income: Financed by endowment, membership, city appropriation.

Holdings: AV—Motion pictures, phonorecords; Other—Sculpture, pictures 300,000.

Exhibitions: Changing exhibit each month.

Activities: Dramatic programs; concerts.

STOWE-DAY FOUNDATION, 77 Forest St, 06105. Tel: 203-522-9258. *Pres* H Burton Powers; *VPres* Helen D Perkins & Mrs Ellsworth Grant; *Secy* Thomas L Archibald; *Dir* Joseph S Van Why; *Librn* Diana Royce; *Cur* Ellicel Schofield; *Nook Farm Visitors Center Adminr* Andrea Rudy.

Open daily June - Aug 10 AM - 4:30 PM; Sept - May, Tues - Sat 9:30 AM - 4 PM; Sun 1 - 4 PM. Estab 1941 to properly maintain, have open to the public and interpret the restored H B Stowe House; operate the Stowe-Day Library; oversee a publishing program to make available reprints of Mrs. Stowe's works and new books; to educate the public through workshops and lectures. Average Annual Attendance: 22,000. Mem: 170; dues single $10, couple $15, special $25; fall and spring meetings.

Income: $200,000 (financed by endowment). Purchases: $15,000 (library).

Collections: (Art) †Architecture of 19th century: books, plans & drawings, trade catalogs; †decorative arts, books, trade catalogs, study samples of wallpapers.

Exhibitions: Portraits of a 19th century family (Lyman Beecher & children) with illustrated book of five lectures; Nook Farm: Corner on the World; Victorian Christmas; George Keller, Architect; Trade cards and catalogs of the 19th century.

Publications: The American Woman's Home; Portraits of a 19th Century Family; Poganuc People; Eminent Victorian Americans; The Papers of Harriet Beecher Stowe; The Minister's Wooing; George Keller, Architect; H B Stowe & American Literature.

Activities: Classes for adults; teacher workshops, lect open to public, 1 - 2 vis lectr per yr; individual paintings and original objects of art lent to other institutions; sales shop selling books, prints, slides, reproductions of Victorian games, patterns for stencils, needlework.

—**The Stowe-Day Library.** *Pres* Joseph S Van Why; *Head Librn* Diana Royce; *Librn Photographs & Prints* Paige Savery; *Catalogue Librn* Marion Carmichael.

Open Mon - Fri 9 AM - 5 PM; cl national holidays. Estab 1965; concentrates on architecture, the decorative arts, history and literature of the United States of the 19th century with emphasis on residents of Hartford's 19th century neighborhood known as Nook Farm.

Income: Financed by endowment. Purchases: $5000.

Holdings: Vols 15,000; Per subs 6; 12; AV—Film strip, lantern slides, microfiche and microfilm, slides; Other—Clipping file, exhibition catalogs, manuscripts 100,000, memorabilia, original art works, original documents, pamphlets, photographs, prints, sculpture.

Special Subjects: Abolition movement; architecture; personal correspondence, diaries, of various members of the Beecher and Foote families and of John Calvin Day and Katharine S Day; the decorative arts (books, trade catalogues, sample studies of wallpaper); the woman suffrage movement; first editions and inscribed copies of the works of Harriet Beecher Stowe, Mark Twain, C D Warner, Isabella B Hooker, William Gillette.

TRINITY COLLEGE, Austin Arts Center, Summit St, 06106. Tel: 202-527-3151. *Chmn, Dept Fine Arts* Michael Mahoney; *Dir, Studio Arts Prog* George Chaplin; *Adminr & Technical Dir* John Woolley.

Open daily 1 - 5 PM (when college is in session). No admis. Estab 1957. A building housing the teaching and performing aspects of music, theater and studio arts at a liberal arts college. Widener Gallery—exhibition space mainly for student and faculty works, plus outside exhibitions.

Income: Financed by college appropriation.

Collections: Samuel H Kress Study Collection; Edwin M Blake Memorial and Archive; George F McMurray Loan Collection; College Collection.

Exhibitions: Antonio Frasconi; Richard Lytle; Lloyd Glasson; Richard Ziemann; Andrew Stasik; Carol Kreeger Davidson; Robert Cale; George Chaplin; Steve Wood.

Activities: Lect open to public, 6 vis lectr per yr; lending collection contains original art works 500, slides 85,000.

MARK TWAIN MEMORIAL,* 351 Farmington Ave, 06105. Tel: 203-247-0998. *Dir* Dexter B Peck; *Cur* Wilson H Faude.

Open June 1 - Aug 10 AM - 4:30 PM; Sept 1 - May Tues - Sat 9:30 AM - 4 PM; Sun 1 - 4 PM; cl Mon, Jan 1, Easter, Labor Day, Thanksgiving and Dec 25. Guided tours adults $1.50, children 16 and under 75¢, special group tour rates with advance arrangements. Estab 1929 to restore and maintain Mark Twain's Hartford home, to collect research materials needed for the project and to keep before the public the life and work of Mark Twain. Maintains Historic House Museum with period interiors, museum room of memorabilia. National Shrine status, US Dept of Interior. Occasional exhibitions. Average Annual Attendance: 70,000. Mem: Approximately 1000; dues $10 and higher; annual meeting May.
Collections: Mark Twain memorabilia, photographs, manuscripts; period and original furnishings; Tiffany Collection; Candace Wheeler Collection; Lockwood deForest Collection.
Activities: Group tours; Open House; Victorian Christmas; Frog Jump; Museum shop.
Library: Reference; photograph collection.
—Nook Farm Research Library.
Holdings: Vols 13,000; Other—Manuscripts 6500, pamphlets 4500, incorporating the Mark Twain Memorial Collection.

WADSWORTH ATHENEUM,* 600 Main St, 06103. Tel: 203-278-2670. *Dir* James Elliott, *Asst to the Dir* Lynn Traiger; *Chief Cur & Cur Painting & Sculpture* Peter O Marlow; *Educ Dir* Susan E Gans; *Pub Relations Dir* Jean C Burnett; *Cur Textiles & Costumes* J Herbert Callister; *Cur Dept Decorative Arts* Philip M Johnston; *Assoc Cur Paintings* Mark Rosenthal; *Conservator* Roland C Cunningham.
Open Tues - Sat 11 AM - 4 PM; Sun 1 - 5 PM; cl Mon, New Year's Day, July 4, Thanksgiving and Christmas. No admis. Estab 1842 by Daniel Wadsworth as Atheneum Gallery of Fine Arts; now occupies entire city block square on Main St, downtown Hartford. There are more than 60 galleries in 5 interconnected buildings, plus lecture room, classrooms, 299 seat theatre, Matrix Gallery of contemporary art and Lions Gallery of the Senses. Renovation and expansion of facilities includes James Lippincott Goodwin Building, along with sculpture court, restaurant, additional classrooms, offices and a lecture room. Average Annual Attendance: 250,000. Mem: 3200; dues $15 and higher; annual meeting March.
Income: Financed by private funds.
Collections: Arts of Europe, Asia, Africa and the Americas illustrated; J P Morgan Collection of antique bronzes, Italian Majolica, English and American silver and French and Meissen porcelain, the later among the finest in existence; Wallace Nutting Collection of furniture; †European and American painting from 1400 to the present, including fine examples of Baroque painting and arts of the Middle Ages and The Renaissance; European tapestries; sculpture; ceramics; glass; Pre-Columbian art; Lifar Collection of ballet designs; European and American prints and drawings; †American decorative arts; Continental decorative arts; Oriental art; †Modern art; American and European costumes.
Exhibitions: Varied major exhibitions of ancient-modern art.
Publications: Newsletter, monthly, to members.
Activities: Classes for adults and children, lectures and gallery talks by staff on art and related subjects (including docent talks and lectures); dance concerts; free Sunday concerts from Oct to June; gallery tours; outside lectures; 6 - 10 film series per year; Children's Holiday Festival; members' exhibition previews and various special events; Atheneum Shop selling books, reproductions, photographs, cards and gifts.
Library: Art reference. Holdings—Vols 15,000; AV—Slides 35,000; Other—Catalogs, pamphlets.

KENT

KENT ART ASSOCIATION, INC GALLERY, Box 202 Route 7, 06757. Tel: 203-927-4289. *Pres* Dorothy Stewart; *First VPres* Barbara Goodspeed; *Second VPres* George-Ann Gowan; *Recording Secy* Maggie Smith; *Corresp Secy* Frances Townley; *Treas* Jaune McGarvey.
Open during exhibitions only 2 - 5 PM.
Estab 1923; inc. 1935; annual meeting Oct. Average Annual Attendance: 2500. Mem: 375; dues assoc $5, sustaining $15, patron $25, life $100.
Exhibitions: Kent Art Association Exhibit; Spring Exhibition; Associated Members Show; Fall exhibition.
Activities: Maintains gallery for changing exhibitions; lect; demonstrations.

LITCHFIELD

LITCHFIELD HISTORICAL SOCIETY, On-the-Green (Mailing Add: PO Box 385, 06759). Tel: 203-567-5862. *Pres* John Mayher; *VPres* Whitney L Brooks; *Secy* Gordon Hamlin; *Dir* Lockett Ford Ballard, Jr.
Open Tues - Sat 11 AM - 5 PM; Apr 1 - Nov 30. No admis. Estab 1856, inc 1897 for the collection and utilization of local history collections; an art gallery is maintained containing American decorative arts from 1750-1970. Average Annual Attendance: 8,000-10,000. Mem: 500; dues stu-

dent (under 21) $2, senior citizen $4, individual $6, family $10, contributing $25, donor $50, benefactor $100. Annual meeting second Fri in Sept.
Income: $40,000 (financed by endowment and membership).
Collections: American and Connecticut decorative arts, pewter, costumes, textiles, paintings, silver, pottery, and graphics.
Exhibitions: (1976) Local History Exhibits; (1977) WWI French and American Posters; regional contemporary art; silver collection; early American domestic utensils; (1978) The 19th Century (paintings, graphics, miniatures, daguerreotypes and costumes).
Activities: Provides lect open to the public, 8 vis lectrs per yr.
—Ingraham Memorial Research Library. Tel 203-567-5862. *Librn* Mrs Hugh Todd.
Open Tues - Sat 9 AM - 5 PM. Estab 1856 as a center of local history and genealogy study; gallery contains changing exhibits of graphics collections 1700-1950.
Income: $10,000 (financed by endowment and membership).
Holdings: Vols 10,000; Per subs 35; AV—Kodachromes, slides; Other—Clipping files, exhibition catalogs, manuscripts, memorabilia, original art works, original documents, pamphlets, photographs, prints and sculpture.
Special Subjects: Litchfield, Connecticut history.
Special Collections: 40,000 manuscripts in local history.
Activities: Lect open to public, 6 vis lectr per yr.

MERIDEN

ARTS AND CRAFTS ASSOCIATION OF MERIDEN, INC, PO Box 348, 06450. Tel: 203-634-1381. *Pres* Dolores Bartlett; *VPres* Irma Morse; *Secy* Virginia Birch.
Open Daily including Sun 2 - 5 & 7 - 9 PM. No admis. Estab 1907 to encourage appreciation of the arts in the community. Mem: 300, qualifications for mem, payment of dues and acceptance of principles of organization. Dues $5 and up. Annual meeting May.
Income: Financed by membership, state appropriation and fund raising.
Collections: Permanent Museum Collection (110 pieces to date).
Exhibitions: (1978) 54th Annual Exhibition of paintings, crafts, sculpture, prints, drawings, and photography; Expo 78.
Activities: Classes for adults and children; dramatic programs; lect open to public, 9 vis lectr per yr; gallery talks; tours; competitions with awards; individual paintings and original objects of art lent to public; sales shop selling original art.
Library: Indiana Thomas Book Collection, Miller St. Holdings: Over 250 Vols; Per subs.

MIDDLETOWN

WESLEYAN UNIVERSITY,* Davison Art Center, 301 High St, 06457. Tel: 203-347-9411. *Cur* Dr Richard S Field.
Open Mon - Sat 10 AM - 4 PM; Sun & holidays 2 - 5 PM; cl weekends during summer. No admis. The majority of the collection has been presented to Wesleyan University by George W and Harriet B Davison, who began their donations in 1938 and continued to add to the collection until 1953 when George W Davison died. Since 1952 the collection, with its comprehensive and steadily growing reference library on the graphic arts, has been housed in the historic Alsop House (1838-1840), acquired by the University in 1949 and transformed into the Davison Art Center.
Collections: The print collection, comprising several thousand items, covers the entire field of print-making from the 15th century to the present day and contains many items of outstanding rarity and importance (Master E S, Nielli, Mantegna, Pollaiuolo, and others). The European Masters such as Dürer, Cranach, Rembrandt, Canaletto, Piranesi, Goya, Meryon and others are very well represented. The Millet Collection, one of the finest and most complete collections of this master, deserves special mention. A collection of about 600 Japanese prints supplements the collection of Western prints. Since 1955 acquisition funds have made it possible to build up the collection in the field of contemporary art and to complete many areas in the field of old masters. The collection now comprises about 14,000 items.
Exhibitions: Print exhibitions are frequently arranged in the gallery which was added to the Alsop House in 1952.
Friends of the Davison Art Center—Estab 1961, a membership group formed for the purpose of supporting and augmenting the activities of the Davison Art Center. Through its membership contributions the acquisition fund of the collection has increased.

MYSTIC

MYSTIC ART ASSOCIATION, INC, Water St (Mailing Add: PO Box 259, 06355). Tel: 203-536-7601. *Pres* David Suydam; *VPres* Lil Maxwell; *Secy* Beonne Boronda; *Treas* Horace Jones IV; *Financial Adv* John Lazerek; *Adv* Cheryl Barrett, Clara Balhatchet, Paul White and Nancy Klotz.

Open daily 11 AM - 5 PM. No admis. Estab 1920 to maintain an art museum to promote cultural education, local philanthropic and charitable interests. The association owns a colonial building on the bank of Mystic River with spacious grounds; there is one small gallery and one large gallery with L-shaped corridor for crafts. Average Annual Attendance: 2000 - 3000. Mem: 450, active mem must have high standards of proficiency and be elected by ⅔ vote; dues Associate $7 - $15; Active $10; meetings held in May and Sept.
Income: $10,000 - $15,000 (financed by membership).
Collection: Works donated by deceased members shown in Groton Savings Bank.
Exhibitions: First Scapes and Shapes (marine oriented); 21st Annual Regional Exhibition; members show; non-members invitational.
Activities: Occasional classes for children; lect open to public; 3 or 4 vis lectr per yr; concerts; gallery talks; competitions with cash awards; individual paintings lent.

MYSTIC SEAPORT, INC, Greenmanville Ave, 06355. Tel: 203-536-2631. *Chmn Bd Trustees* William C Ridgway; *Pres* Clifford D Mallory; *Dir* J Revell Carr; *Deputy Dir* Franklin Kneedler; *Development Dir* Michael Sturges; *Munson Institute Dir* Benjamin Labaree.
Open daily 9 AM - 5 PM (Apr-Nov); 9 AM - 4 PM (Dec-Mar). Admis adult $5; child (6-12 yrs) $2.50 (Apr-Nov); adult $4, child $2.25 (Dec-Mar). Estab 1929 to preserve America's maritime heritage. This is an outdoor museum of about forty buildings which include approx sixty exhibits. Three areas are for Formal Exhibits. Average Annual Attendance: 500,000. Mem: 15,868; dues individual $15, family $25; annual meeting Oct.
Income: Financed by endowment, membership, admissions.
Collections: Village Area—historic shops and homes in which craft demonstrations take place and appropriate artifacts are on view: shipcarver, smith, cooper, chandler, ropewalk, sailmaker's loft, weave shop; Shipyard—which also includes vessels, the wooden whaleship *Charles W Morgan*, squarerigger *Joseph Conrad*, fishing schooner *LA Donton*, operating passenger-carrying steamboat *Sabino*, about 200 traditional small craft, an operating shipyard facility where these ships and boats are regularly cared for. No traveling exhibitions, pieces brought out of reserve collections for exhibit periodically.
Publications: The Log, quarterly; The Windrose, eight times per year; also books.
Activities: Classes for adults and children; six-week university courses in American maritime history; lect open to public, 3 vis lectr per yr; tours; traveling exhibitions organized and circulated; museum shop selling books, magazines, crafts, reproductions, prints, slides; junior museum.
—G W Blunt White Library. *Librn* Gerald E Morris.
Open to members, serious researchers, and students.
Holdings: Vols 30,000; Per subs 300; Other—Manuscripts 250,000, ships plans 15,000; charts 5000.
Special Subjects: American Maritime History.
—Children's Museum, 06355. Tel: 203-536-2631. *Dir* J Revell Carr.
Open daily summer 9 AM - 5 PM; grounds close at 6 PM; winter 10 AM - 4 PM grounds close at 5 PM; cl Christmas & New Year's. Admis summer adults $5, children $2.50; winter adults $4.50, children $2.25; adult and children tickets good for two consecutive days admission to museum in winter, $6 and $2.75 respectfully during summer; group rates on request; Estab as a view into the life of children who went to sea in the late 19th century. A representation of a ship's cabin depicts the living quarters of a captain's family, complete with furnishings typical of a large sailing vessel. Yard with a boat and mast for climbing.
Exhibition: Children Who Went to Sea.

NEW BRITAIN

CENTRAL CONNECTICUT STATE COLLEGE MUSEUM, 1615 Stanley St, 06050. Tel: 203-287-7325. *Dir* Isabel S Fairchild.
Estab to collect, display and interpret works of art and ethnic materials related to their art education program.
Collections: With exception of pieces on loan, collection is currently in storage awaiting construction of a fine arts center for housing.

NEW BRITAIN MUSEUM OF AMERICAN ART, 56 Lexington St, 06052. Tel: 203-229-0257. *Dir* Charles B Ferguson; *Asst to Dir* Lois L Blomstrann.
Open Tues - Sun 1 - 5 PM. No admis. Estab 1903 to exhibit, collect and preserve American Art; 18 galleries. Average Annual Attendance: 20,000. Mem: 1000; dues $10.
Income: Financed by endowment.
Collections: Murals by Thomas Hart Benton; American Art from Colonial Period (1740) to contemporary—Copley, West, Bierstadt, Church, Homer, Eakins, Sargent, Whistler, Cassatt, Wyeth.
Publications: Newsletter, quarterly.

Activities: Docent training; lect open to public, 4 vis lectr per yr; gallery talks; tours; competitions; individual paintings and original objects of art lent to other museums and institutions; traveling exhibitions organized and circulated; museum shop selling books, reproductions, prints, slides and postcards.
Library: Maintains a small library.

NEW CANAAN

SILVERMINE GUILD SCHOOL OF THE ARTS, Silvermine Guild of Artists, 1037 Silvermine Rd, 06840. Tel: 203-866-0411 and 866-5617, Exten 18. *Pres Bd of Trustees* Spencer Stuart; *Gallery Dir* Mrs D Robinson; *School Dir* Robert Franco; *Publicity Dir* Marcia S Fox.
Open daily 12:30 - 5 PM; cl Mon. No admis. Estab 1922 as an independent art center for the exchange of ideas, to provide a place for member-artists to show and sell their work, and to offer the community a wide variety of artistic and cultural activities; four exhibition galleries and Farrell Gallery, containing over 1000 paintings and sculptures for purchase or loan with intent to purchase. Average Annual Attendance: 16,000. Mem: 800; dues from individual $25—Benefactor $1000 grants; monthly meetings.
Income: Financed by membership and city appropriation.
Collections: Permanent print collection containing purchase prizes from National Print Exhibition.
Exhibitions: Biennial National Print Exhibition; New England Exhibition of Painting and Sculpture.
Publications: Bimonthly newsletter for members.
Activities: Classes for children; lect not open to the public, 4 vis lectr per year; concerts; competitions; individual paintings and original objects of art lent to corporations, banks and department stores; museum shop selling original art and prints.
Library: *Librn* Mrs Bobbe Adams. Open to students and members. Holdings: Vols 5000.

NEW HAVEN

MUNSON GALLERY, 33 Whitney Ave, 06511. Tel: 203-865-2121. *Pres* Larom B Munson.
Open Tues - Fri 9:30 AM - 5:30 PM; Sat 9:30 AM - 5 PM. No admis. Estab 1860 to encourage interest in the arts by regular exhibitions of painting, sculpture, graphics, framing and restoration. Located in restored foundry building in New Haven Audubon Street Arts complex.
Exhibitions: Modern Tapestries; Joseph Albers; Cynthia Bloom; Mary Buckley; J B Thompson.

NEW HAVEN COLONY HISTORICAL SOCIETY,* 114 Whitney Ave, 06510. Tel: 203-562-4183. *Pres* Charles C Kingsley; *Secy* Reverdy Whitlock; *Dir* Joseph Johnson Smith; *Cur* Robert Egleston.
Open Tues - Fri 10 AM - 5 PM; Sat, Sun & major holidays 2 - 5 PM; cl Mon. No admis. Estab 1862 for the preservation, exhibition and research of local scholarly materials, memorabilia and arts. Average Annual Attendance: 15,000. Mem: 1000; dues students $7.50, others $15 - $50; annual meeting Nov.
Collections: †Connecticut pewter, †New Haven silver, local furniture, paintings, drawings and graphics, and items of local historic interest. Morris House (c 1685-1780).
Publications: Quarterly Journal; Newsletter.
Activities: Exhibitions, morning and evening lecture series, active school program; gift shop.
—Reference Library: Tel: 203-562-4183. *Librn & Mss Cur* Ottilia Koel; *Ref Librn* Lysbeth Andrews-Zike; *Archivist* Zofia Sywak.
Open Tues - Fri 10 AM - 5 PM. Estab 1862 to collect, preserve, make available, and publish historical and genealogical material relating to the early settlement and subsequent history of New Haven, its vicinity and incidentally other parts of the USA; The Society has three departments: museum, library/archives, educational, with the museum staff taking care of the gallery.
Income: Financed by endowment, membership, and grants.
Holdings: Vols 25,000; Per subs 55; AV—Lantern slides, microfiche, microfilm; Other—Clipping files, exhibition catalogs, manuscripts, memorabilia, original documents, pamphlets, photographs, prints, glass plate negatives 30,000.
Special Subjects: History; genealogy; decorative arts; early photography.
Special Collections: Noah Webster Collections; John W Barber Collection.
Publications: Journal, quarterly/irregular; News and Notes, monthly; also monographs and exhibition catalogs.
Activities: Tours; arrangement with local colleges for internship programs and work/study programs, have students from Southern Conn State College library school to do field work here for credit and give seminars for graduate students in library science.

NEW HAVEN FREE PUBLIC LIBRARY, 133 Elm St. 06510. Tel: 203-562-0151, exten 408. *Librn* Meredith Bloss; *Art Librn* Helen B Worobec.
Open Mon - Thurs 9 AM - 8 PM; Fri 9 AM - 6 PM; Sat 9 AM - 5 PM; cl Sun. No admis. Estab 1886, art dept 1921.
Special Subjects: Art, music, photography, architecture.
Special Collections: Art books, portfolios of plates, music books inluding both scores and music theory, phonograph records, and mounted pictures on a great variety of subjects, and 8mm films.
Exhibitions: Works of local artists are held throughout the year.
Activities: Circulates a collection of mounted and unmounted pictures; works with public schools.

NEW HAVEN PAINT & CLAY CLUB, INC,* The John Slade Ely House, 51 Trumbull St, 06510. Tel: 203-624-8055. *Pres* Jordan Abeshouse; *Secy* Shirley Price.
Open Tues - Fri 1 - 4 PM; Sat & Sun 2 - 5 PM; cl Mon. Estab 1900, inc 1928. Permanent collection is on display in the Upstairs Galleries of the John Slade Ely House at all times when the House is open. Mem: active 230, assoc & sustaining 60; qualif for mem: open to artists working in any media whose work has been accepted two times in the Annual juried show; dues active $10, assoc $5, sustaining $20, life $200 once; annual meeting May.
Income: In excess of $1000. Purchases: $1000.
Exhibitions: Annual exhibition in spring open to all artists, working in any medium; selection and award of prizes by jury. Purchase fund: work added to club's Permanent Collection. In the fall there is an exhibition for members only.

SOUTHERN CONNECTICUT STATE COLLEGE, The Art Gallery, 501 Crescent St (Mailing Add: PO Box 3144, 06515). Tel: 203-397-4262. *Dir* Olafs Zeidenbergs.
Estab April 1976 to build a collection of works of art to be used for educational purposes, gallery now in process of development. Mem: 250; dues $6 and up.
Income: $7500 (financed by membership, state appropriation, and fund raising).
Activities: Lect open to the public, 6 vis lectr per yr; gallery talks; tours; exten dept; individual paintings and original objects of art lent to administrative offices.

YALE UNIVERSITY
—Art Gallery, 1111 Chapel St (Mailing Add: Box 2006 Yale Station, 06520). Tel: 203-436-0574. *Dir* Alan Shestack; *Cur Prints, Drawings & Photographs* James D Burke; *Cur Oriental Art* Mary G Neill; *Registrar* Fernande Ross; *Cur Educ* Janet S Dickson; *Information & Membership* Caroline Rollins; *Superintendent* Robert Soule.
Open Tues - Sat 10 AM - 5 PM; Sun 2 - 5 PM; cl Mon. No admis. Estab 1832 to exhibit fine works of art from ancient times to the present day; organize special exhibitions and stimulate research; gallery is a 5-story building designed by Louis Kahn and completed in 1953; Average Annual Attendance: 150,000. Mem: 1500; dues $20 - $1000.
Income: Financed by endowment, membership, and annual fund-raising.
Collections: Stoddard Collection of Greek vases; Jarves Collection of Italian primitive painting; Trumbull history paintings and portraits; Garvan Collection of American furniture and silver; †European and American painting and sculpture; †20th century art.
Exhibitions: Traces of the Brush: Studies in Chinese Calligraphy; Towards Independence: American Art, 1750-1800; Greek Vases at Yale; Josef Albers (paintings); The Graphic Art of Federico Barocci.
Publications: The Yale University Art Gallery Bulletin, twice annually.
Activities: Classes for adults and children; guided tours weekly, Sunday lecture program, lunchtime Mini-lectures; lect open to the public, 10 vis lectr per yr; concerts; gallery talks; tours; individual paintings and original objects of art lent; traveling exhibitions organized and circulated; museum shop and sales shop selling books, magazines, reproductions, prints, jewelry, postcards.
—The Yale Center for British Art, 1080 Chapel St (Mailing Add: Box 2120 Yale Station, 06520). Tel: 203-432-4594. *Dir* Edmund P Pillsbury; *Cur Paintings* Malcolm Cormack; *Cur Prints & Drawings* Andrew Wilton; *Cur Rare Books* Joan Friedman; *Paper Conservator* Ursula Dreibholz; *Asst Cur Paintings* Susan Casteras; *Asst Cur Prints & Drawings* Patrick Noon.
Open Tues - Sat 10 AM - 5 PM; Sun 2 - 5 PM; cl Mon. No admis. Estab April 15, 1977 to foster a wider appreciation and knowledge of British art; to support advanced research by historians of British art; to encourage interdisciplinary use of the collections by social and cultural historians; to assist in the development of a special program of courses for Yale undergraduates in British Studies; principal resource in the collection of works of art and illustrated books which houses a nearly encyclopedic survey of the pictorial arts in Britain from the middle of the 16th century to the middle of the 19th century.
Income: Financed by private funding.
Collections: Paintings 1500, drawings 8000, prints 6000, sculptures.

Exhibitions: (1977-78) The Pursuit of Happiness—A View of Life in Georgian England; English Landscape, 1630-1850 (drawings, prints and books from the Paul Mellon Collection); Fifty Beautiful Drawings; Seascapes; The Cottage of Content, or Toys, Games and Amusements of Nineteenth Century England; Rowlandson Drawings from the Paul Mellon Collection; The Animal Kingdom: Wildlike in British Art; Travels with Pen, Pencil and Ink—Prints and Drawings by David Hockney; Color Printing in England: 1486-1870.
Publications: Books to coincide with major exhibitions.
Activities: Dramatic programs; films; lect open to the public; concerts; gallery talks; tours; museum shop selling books, prints, slides.
—Art Reference Library. Tel: 203-432-4594. *Librn* Anne-Marie Logan. Open to any interested person.
Holdings: Vols 20,000; Other—Photographs 90,000.

NEW LONDON

LYMAN ALLYN MUSEUM, 100 Mohegan Ave (entrance off Williams St), 06320. Tel: 203-443-2545. *Dir* Dr Edgar deN Mayhew; *Secy* Mrs Willard Shepard; *Cur* Mrs Arvin Karterud; *Educ Coordinator* Mrs James McGuire; *Conservator* David Kolch; *Docent* Mrs Edward Gipstein.
Open Tues - Sat 1 - 5 PM; Sun 2 - 5 PM; cl Mon. No admis. Estab 1932 for the education and enrichment of the community and other visitors. The current building consists of nine permanent galleries and four for changing exhibitions. Average Annual Attendance: 22,000. Mem: 750; dues from individual $10 to life $1000.
Income: $133,951 (financed by endowment, membership, and gifts). Purchases: $6000.
Collections: Paintings; sculpture; drawings; prints; decorative arts.
Exhibitions: Jan Werle One-man Show; Aaron Draper Shattuck Collection; Young Peoples Art Classes Show; New London Art Students Show; New London Bi-Centennial Exhibition; Photographs by Trager.
Publications: New London County Furniture from 1640-1840; New London Silver, a catalog; Handbook of the Museum's Outstanding Holdings.
Activities: Classes for adults and children; docent training; school tours and programs; lect for members; museum shop selling small antiques.
—Lyman Allyn Museum Library. *Librn* Marianne Dinsmore.
Estab 1926 to compliment the collections of Lyman Allyn Museum.
Holdings: Vols 7750; Other—Exhibition catalogs, framed reproductions, memorabilia, original art works, original documents, pamphlets, photographs, prints, reproductions and sculpture.
Special Subjects: Fine and applied arts.

NORWALK

LOCKWOOD-MATHEWS MANSION MUSEUM, 295 West Ave, 06850. Tel: 203-838-1434. *Pres* Mrs Andrew A Roóney; *Chmn* Mrs Moreau D Brown; *Dir* Mrs S B Hamilton Jr.
Open Mon - Thurs 9:30 AM - 2:30 PM; Sun 1 - 4 PM. Admis, suggested donation $1, students and sr citizens 50¢. Estab 1968 to completely restore this 19th century 50-room mansion as a historic house museum. Now a registered National Historic Landmark. Average Annual Attendance: 10,000. Mem: 500; annual meeting May.
Income: $29,000 (fiananced by membership, city and state appropriation, federal grant).
Publications: Newsletter, quarterly.
Activities: Docent training; lect open to public, 6 vis lectr per yr; gallery talks; tours; museum shop selling books, reproductions, prints, Victorian toys and games.

NORWICH

NORWICH FREE ACADEMY, Slater Memorial Museum & Converse Art Gallery, 108 Crescent St, 06360. Tel: 203-887-2505, exten 218. *Dir* Joseph P Gualtieri; *Museum Asst* Marie E Noyes; *Docent* Mary-Anne Stumpo; *Registrar* Judith Hamblen.
Open Sept - May Mon - Fri 9 AM - 4 PM; Sat & Sun 1 - 4 PM; June - Aug Tues - Sun 1 - 4 PM; cl holidays throughout the year. No admis. Estab 1888, the collection is housed in two buildings. Average Annual Attendance: 34,000. Mem: 400; dues single $5, family $8, associate $10; annual meeting usually April.
Income: Financed by endowment, student tuition paid by towns.
Collections: American art and furniture from the 17th - 20th century; American Indian artifacts; Vanderpoel Collection of Oriental art; African art, Egyptian art objects and textiles.
Exhibitions: Special exhibitions changed monthly.
Publications: Catalogs for special exhibitions.

Activities: Lect open to the public; competitions; individual paintings and original objects of art lent to museums, historical societies; shop selling postcards.

OLD LYME

LYME ART ASSOCIATION, INC, Lyme St (Mailing Add: PO Box 222, 06371). Tel: 203-434-7802. *Pres* E G Chandler; *VPres* Alex Poplaski; *Secy* Jessie Hull Mayer; *Treas* H Gil-Roberts; *Publ* E B Atwood; *Printing* Doris Jorgensen.
Open seasonally 10 AM - 5 PM. Admis 50¢. Estab 1901 to present fine arts in the traditional manner; maintains four large sky-lighted galleries. Mem: 30 qualifications for mem is invitational, following acceptance by ful mem jury; dues $25; annual meeting Sept.
Income: Financed by membership and associate members.
Exhibitions (1978): Three annual open exhibitions, five biweekly shows for members only.
Activities: Building houses the Lyme Academy of Fine Arts in downstairs teaching studios; open to the public; gallery talks.
Library: Open to members for reference.

LYME HISTORICAL SOCIETY, INC, Florence Griswold House, 96 Lyme St, 06371. Tel: 203-434-5542. *Pres* Daniel Woodhead Jr; *Dir* Jeffrey W Andersen.
Open (June - Aug) Tues - Sat 10 AM - 5 PM; Sun 1 - 5 PM; (Sept - May) Wed - Fri & Sat 1 - 5 PM. No admis. Estab 1953 for the purpose of collecting, preserving and exhibiting the history of Lyme and Old Lyme. Average Annual Attendance: 3000. Mem: 920; dues individual $10, family $20; annual meeting May.
Income: $50,000 (financed by endowment, membership and city appropriation). Purchases: 1500.
Collections: †Old Lyme Art Colony Paintings; Clara Champlain Griswold Toy Collection; †Decorative Arts and Furnishings; Local Historical Collections.
Exhibitions: The Ancient Town of Lyme; A Child's World; American Prints; Paintings by Gregory Smith; The Goodman Presentation Case; This Was Connecticut; Installation of the 1840 Bedroom.
Publications: The Lyme Ledger, quarterly.
Activities: Classes for adults and children; dramatic programs; docent training; field trips; lect open to public, 12 vis lectr per yr; tours; competitions; traveling exhibitions organized and circulated; museum shop selling books.
Library: Lyme Historical Society Archives. *Librn* Jeff Andersen. Open to the public for reference. Holdings: Vols 300; Other—Documents, diaries, letters, inventories, business records, town records pertaining to Lyme & Old Lyme. Special Subjects: History of Lyme

RIDGEFIELD

ALDRICH MUSEUM OF CONTEMPORARY ART, 258 Main St, 06877. *Pres* Robert Faesy; *Dirs* Carlus and Ruth Dyer; *Cur Educ & Pub Relations Coordinator* Jacqueline Moss; *Registrar* Louise Parrington.
Open Wed, Sat & Sun 1 - 5 PM, group visits by appointment. Admis adults $1, students, children and senior citizens 50¢. Estab 1964 for the presentation of contemporary painting and sculpture and allied arts; to stimulate public awareness of contemporary art through exhibitions and education programs; nine galleries on three floors of a totally renovated colonial building, provide well lit exhibition space. Average Annual Attendance: 8000. Mem: 300; dues from $25 - $1000.
Income: $130,000 (financed by membership, federal and state grants, corporate and private foundations).
Collections: Aldrich Collection; †museum collection of emerging Artists; †extended loan collection; print collection.
Exhibitions: (1975-78) Contemporary Reflections (ann); Fall Selections 1976; Selections 77; 16 Contemporary Polish Artists; Charles Shaw Perspective; 18 CAPS Photographers; (Fall 1977) Contemporary Collectors; Richard Lindner (lithographs); Jasper Johns (screenprints); Alexander Calder (woven mats).
Publications: Fully illustrated catalogs of two major exhibitions ann; members Newsletter, four times a yr.
Activities: Classes for adults; docent training; lect open to public, 20 vis lectr per yr; concerts; gallery talks; tours; individual paintings lent to museums, university galleries, and corporate patrons.

ROWAYTON

ROWAYTON ARTS CENTER, 145 Rowayton Ave, 06853. Tel: 203-866-2744.
Open daily 2 - 5 PM. No admis. Estab 1960, as a non-profit association, to promote arts in the area and to give members an opportunity to exhibit; Exhibition gallery downstairs; upstairs, studio room used for classes, slide shows, etc. Mem: 400; dues $20; annual meeting April.

Income: Financed by membership, state appropriation, fund raising events.
Exhibitions: Changed monthly and remain approximately three weeks and are varied.
Publications: Arts Center (newsletter), bi-monthly.
Activities: Classes for adults and children; workshops; individual paintings and original objects of art lent to local bank for monthly display.

STAMFORD

COUTURIER GALERIE, 1814 Newfield Ave, 06903. Tel: 203-322-2405. *Dir* Marion B Couturier; *Assoc Dir* Darrel J Couturier.
Open Mon, Thur, Fri & Sat 11 AM - 4 PM; cl Tues, Wed & Sun; open Eve & Sun by special appointment. No admis. Estab 1961 to promote and exhibit quality fine art by young artists from around the world with occasionally special exhibitions by well established artists. The gallery exhibits paintings, sculptures and original graphics; at Christmas original ceramics and handblown glass are featured.
Exhibitions: Two Painters and a Sculptor (Favus, Paskin, Bezalel); International Guest Exhibition of Paintings and Sculpture; Naive Painters and Canadian Indian Graphics; Sculpture by Francois and Bernard Baschet from France, (kinetic, musical); Christmas from Around the World and Pre-Columbian Art.
Activities: Classes for adults, some courses on art history; original objects of art lent; loan exhibitions arranged for schools, museums and occasionally fund raising projects; lending collection contains original art works and prints, paintings, sculpture and pre-Columbian art.

FERGUSON LIBRARY, 96 Broad St, 06901. Te: 203-325-4354. *Dir* Ernest A DiMattia, Jr; *Art & Music Librn* Phyllis Massar.
Open Mon - Fri 9 AM - 9 PM; Sat 9 AM - 5:30 PM. Estab 1880 as a public library dedicated to serving the information needs of the community.
Income: Financed by city appropriation. Purchases: Art and music books $10,000, records $7000, films $16,000.
Holdings: Vols 12,600; AV—Records, cassettes 7500, color slides 2000, films 800, picture file of circulating pictures 2700.
Special Collections: Comprehensive reference ollection of photography of Old Stamford.
Exhibitions: The Stamford Collection and outside sources.

STAMFORD MUSEUM AND NATURE CENTER, * High Ridge and Scofieldtown Rds, 06903. Tel: 203-322-1646. *Pres* R D Rich Jr; *Dir* Gerald E Rasmussen; *Asst Dir* James S Dunn.
Open Mon - Sat 9 AM - 5 PM; Sun & holidays 1 - 5PM; Nov - Mar, Mon 1 - 5 PM; cl Thanksgiving, Christmas, New Year's Day; parking fee. Estab 1936, Art Department 1955. Average Annual Attendance: 250,000. Mem: 4000; dues $10 and up; annual meeting June; art class enrl 1100.
Income: $360,000.
Collections: Painting, sculpture, American crafts, American Indian, sculpture garden.
Publications: Newsletter, monthly; pamphlets.
Activities: Classes in painting, drawing, sculpture, ceramics, modern dance; lectures to school groups; museum shop selling books, prints, crafts.

STONY CREEK

WILLOUGHBY WALLACE MEMORIAL LIBRARY, 146 Thimble Islands Rd, 06405. Tel: 203-488-8702. *Librn* Annelaine Lotreck.
Open Mon - Fri 2 - 5 PM and 7 - 9 PM; Sat 10 AM - 5 PM. Estab 1958 to collect, organize and make available print and nonprint resources; provide information, education and recreation for all members of the community. Circ: 25,000 annually. An art gallery is maintained.
Income: Financed by endowment, city and state appropriation.
Holdings: Vols 21,000; Per subs c 70; AV—Cassettes, phonorecords; Other—Framed reproductions.
Special Subjects: Sailing and art.
Exhibitions: Four group shows, plus rotating one-man shows of local artists are sponsored and organized by friends of the library throughout the year.
Activities: Concerts.

STORRS

AMERICAN SOCIETY FOR AESTHETICS, c/o James R Johnson, *Secy-Treas,* School of Fine Arts, University of Connecticut, 06268. Tel: 203-485-3016.
For further information see National and Regional Organizations.

UNIVERSITY OF CONNECTICUT
—**William Benton Museum of Art**, 06268. Tel: 203-486-4520 or 486-4521. *Dir* Paul F Rovetti; *Asst Dir* Stephanie Terenzio; *Cur* Thomas P Bruhm; *Registrar* George Mazeika.
Open during exhibitions Mon - Sat 10 AM - 4:30 PM; Sun 1 - 5 PM; cl summers. No admis. Estab 1966, a museum of art, operating as an autonomous department within the university; serving the student, faculty and general public; contributing to the field at large through research, exhibitions and publications and by maintaining a permanent collection of over 2,000 objects; the main gallery measures 36 x 116 ft with a balcony (with exhibit walls); running on three walls and two small pendant galleries 20 x 31 ft. Average Annual Attendance: 25,000. Mem: 1200; dues double $12.
Income: $9000 (financed by membership and state appropriation).
Collections: Principally paintings and graphics; Western European and American c 1600 to present; †American painting and graphics early 20th century; †German and French graphics late 19th and 20th century; †selected 17th and 18th century European paintings, sculpture and graphics.
Exhibitions: Edvard Munch, The Major Graphics; Watercolors of Reginard Marsh; Oscar Kokoschka, Literary & Graphic Works; Nicolas Vasilieff, A Retrospective.
Publications: Bulletin, annually, contains at least two works from the permanent collection.
Activities: Lectr open to the public, 4 - 5 vis lectr per yr; concerts; gallery talks; tours; individual paintings and original objects of art lent to accredited institutions for exhibition purposes; lending collection contains original prints, paintings and sculpture; traveling exhibitions organized and circulates; sales shop selling books, original art, reproductions, prints and museum related art objects and jewelry.
Library: Open to students and faculty for reference; library consists primarily of reference books directly related to the collections and catalogs exchanged with other museums and institutions throughout the US and Europe.
—**Jorgensen Gallery**, U-104, 06268. Tel: 203-486-4226. *Manager* Jorgensen Auditorium* Jack Cohan; *Assoc Manager* Edmund O Seagrave; *Coordr* Stephen E Gerling.
Open Mon - Fri 10 AM - 5 PM; Sat - Sun 1 - 5 PM. No admis. Estab 1967 to present works by leading contemporary artists of contemporary trends chiefly of American art. Serve the public as well as the university community. Gallery has large space 80 x 45 ft with 11 ft ceiling; six portable, self-lit room dividers; track type incandescent lighting; off-white tile floor; neutral colored burlap walls. Average Annual Attendance: 25,000.
Exhibitions: Philip Gravsman Sculpture; Frank Ballard Puppetry; Nathan Olivers Painting; Peter Mihon Prints; Clinton Hill Prints; Martha and Walter Erdebacher Painting and Sculpture; Push-Pin Studios; John Matt Sculpture; Richard Blake Sculpture; Richard Yorde Painting; Larry Miller Photography; John Pfahl Photography; Jan Groover Photography; Renda North Photography; Stephen Green Photography; Alfred Leslie Drawing; Jerry Pojo Theatre Design.
Publications: Season announcement; show announcements.
Activities: Dramatic programs; lect open to the public, 10 vis lectr per yr; concerts; gallery talks.

WALLINGFORD

WALLINGFORD ART LEAGUE, Box 163, 06492. *Pres* B Jeanne Kovacs; *VPres* Ray Lynn Farkas; *Secy* Carol Carr.
Estab 1945. Average Annual Attendance: approx 200. Mem: 62; dues $5; Meetings Oct - June, second Thurs each month.
Income: Approx $500 (financed by membership).
Activities: Classes for adults; lect open to public, 4 vis lectr per yr; schol.

WASHINGTON DEPOT

WASHINGTON ART ASSOCIATION, 06793. Tel: 203-868-2878. *Pres* Donald Harrison; *VPres* Mrs William Burnet; *VPres* Mrs Robert Middlebrook; *VPres* Mrs Robert Frost; *Secy* Mrs Harold Kihl; *Exec Secy* Mrs William Talbot.
Open Mon, Tues, Thur & Fri 2 - 5 PM; Wed 10 AM - Noon; Sat & Sun 2 - 5 PM. Estab 1952 to make available to all interested people a rich variety of art experiences through exhibitions, classes in arts and crafts; theatre, museum and concert trips, lectures and demonstrations and to offer exhibition opportunity to young and area artists; gallery is located in three rooms downstairs and one room upstairs for temporary exhibitions. Average Annual Attendance: 4000. Mem: 500; dues individual $8, family $12; annual meeting third week in Aug.
Income: $18,000 (financed by endowment, membership and fund-raising events).
Exhibitions: (1976) Turn of the Century; Members Show; Nancy LaSau (drawings); Kermit Adler; Jos Kleiner (painting); Morton Matthew (paper sculpture); Mark & Barbara (pottery); Art in Education; Allen Blagden (minerals); The Horses of Toal Mayon (Ben Gonzales, sculp-

ture); Roger Barnes (prints & sculpture); Bicentennial Invitational; Crafts Invitational; Bessie Landon; Lucie Spniyl; William Copley (paintings); Techaika (paintings); George Englert; Grace Anglada McCracken; Dobson (painting); Christmas Sale and Show; Ila Pal; (1977) Clapp/Schecter (painting & sculpture); Jean Dell (painting); Rimsky Memorial (painting); Members Show; Eight Plus One (drawing, painting & sculpture); George Knavs; Neufeld Family (painting, drawing, enamels, fabric collage); Open Photography; Peter Whitney (photography); Patricia Reynolds; Freida Mill; Seton Shanley; Ferdinand Roten Galleries Prints; Perlowsky (shaped canvases); Mineral Show (J Brunet); Arthur Getz (New Yorker covers & paintings); Crafts Show; Ann Chapman (paintings, abstract); Simeon Braguin (painting); Plus Hill Studio; Rhys Caparn; William Hoppin; Lois Dodd; Spaces Beyond (group show); Amy Besser (painting); Hatian Show; Students of Arthur Getz; Christmas Show; (1978) Helene Glass (Watercolors on Oriental paper); Winners: Photography Show (Reeves, Russell McGovern); Members Show; Eleanor Hubbard (paper sculpture); Lorraine Archacki (drawings & prints); Humor Show (cartoonists); Rosalind Schwarts-Berg; Charles Ferguson (acrylics); Anne Close (watercolors); Art in Bloom; Marion Humfeld (painting); Philip Grausman (sculpture); Handmade Paper Works (Kathryn Lipke); Mercedes Matter (drawings); Jane Morse (sculpture & drawings); Karen DiMeglio (paintings); M Lowell Peyton (watercolors); Craft Show; Wykeham Rise Alumni; Peter Poskas (painting); Georgia Middlebrook (drawing & painting); Mary Bonkemeyer (figure drawing); Christmas Show.
Publications: Events bulletin biannually.
Activities: Classes for adults and children; trips to major museum, theatre and Tanglewood concerts; lect open to the public, 2-3 vis lectr per yr; competitions.
Library: *Acting Librn* Mrs Theodore Fowler. Open to members and teachers for reference.

WATERBURY

MATTATUCK HISTORICAL SOCIETY, Mattatuck Museum, 119 W Main St, 06702. Tel: 203-754-5500. *Pres* Orton P Camp, Jr; *VPres* W Fielding Secor; *Secy* Mrs William W Brown; *Dir* Ann Smith; *Educ Dir* Dorothy Cantor; *Asst to Dir* Rosemarie A DiChiara.
Open Tues - Sat 12 - 5 PM; Sun 2 - 5 PM; cl Mon. No admis. Estab 1877 to collect and preserve the arts, history of the State of Connecticut, especially of Waterbury and adjacent towns; an art gallery is maintained. Average Annual Attendance: 25,000. Mem: 1000; dues from $10 - $500 per yr; annual meeting Nov.
Income: $65,000 (financed by endowment, membership and grants).
Collections: Connecticut Artists Collection; local history and industrial artifacts; decorative arts collection; period rooms.
Publications: Annual Report.
Activities: Classes for adults and children; lect open to public, 5 vis lectr per yr; gallery talks; tours; lending collection contains photographs and slides.

SILAS BRONSON LIBRARY,* 267 Grand St, 06702. Tel: 203-574-8221. *Dir* Stanford Warshasky; *Head Art Music & Theatre Dept* Patricia Veneziano.
Open Mon, Wed & Thurs 9 AM - 9 PM; Tues, Fri & Sat 9 AM - 5:30 PM. Estab 1869 to provide a free public library for the community; a spotlighted gallery wall is used for art exhibits, also a locked glass exhibition case.
Income: Financed by endowment and city appropriation.
Exhibitions: By local artists in various media.
Activities: Lect open to the public; concerts; individual paintings lent; lending collection contains film strips 16 in sets of 4, motion pictures 265, framed art prints 135, pictures 25,000.
Library: Holdings—Vols 160,761; Other—Pictures in children's department 25,000.

WEST HARTFORD

HARTFORD ART SCHOOL, Anne Bunce Cheney Library, Univ of Hartford, 200 Bloomfield Ave, 06117. Tel: 203-243-4397. *Art Librn* Jean J Miller; *Asst Art Librn* Laurie A Fox.
Open Mon - Thurs 8:30 AM - 10 PM; Fri 8:30 AM - 5 PM; Sat & Sun Noon - 5 PM. Estab 1964. Circ: 11,180.
Income: Financed through University Library.
Holdings: Vols 9,815; Per subs 83; Other—Exhibition catalogs, pamphlets and reproductions.

WILTON

CRAFT CENTER MUSEUM, 80 Danbury Rd, 06897. Tel: 203-762-8363. *Pres* Kenneth Lynch; *Secy* Otto Gust; *Dir* Carroll Cavanaugh & Harvey Muston; *Cur* Joseph Henry.

Open Mon - Fri 10 AM - 4 PM (Mar - Dec); cl Jan - Feb. No admis. Estab 1956 to exhibit and explain 17th - 19th century handwork, blacksmithing, casting, and woodwork; Maintains gallery for exhibitions. Mem: 12; annual meeting in Apr.

Collections: Armor; tools and finished products in areas of metal spinning; furnishing; copper; lead; wood; leather; lighting; brass casting; silversmithing.

Library: Holdings—Vols 3000; Other—Photographs.

DELAWARE

NEWARK

UNIVERSITY OF DELAWARE*
—**Student Center Art Gallery,** 19711. Tel: 302-738-2630. *Dir* Jack S Sturgell.

Open daily Noon - 5 PM; (shorter hours during vacations). Estab 1926 to enlarge the student's acquaintance with art in its various aspects. The public is also invited to all exhibitions. Average Annual Attendance: 10,000.

Exhibitions: Changed monthly; include traveling exhibitions from prominent museums and organizations as well as from the University collections: annual exhibition of University students' work; yearly juried show of regional artists.
—**University Art Collections,** 19711. Tel: Archivist's Office 302-738-2750; Art History Collection 302-738-2418. *Univ Archivist & Dir Permanent Art Coll* John M Clayton; *Coordr Cultural Prog* Patricia Kent; *Cur Slide & Photograph Library & Art History Teaching Coll* Charlotte Kelly.

Morris Library open daily 8:30 AM - 10 PM; Clayton Continuing Education Center open Mon - Fri 8:30 AM - 5 PM. No admis. Estab to consolidate the gifts of art to the University and to provide exhibitions of art objects from these collections to increase visual awareness on the campus. Several exhibition areas around campus Morris Library, Clayton Hall, Smith Hall mini-exhibition cases. Average Annual Attendance: 4000.

Income: Financed by state appropriation.

Collections: Permanent Collection of 500 art objects including painting, sculpture and prints; Art History Teaching Collection of 600 art objects including painting, sculpture (primarily American, African and pre-Columbian), and prints.

Publications: Bulletins.
—**Morris Library,** South College Ave, 19711. Tel: 302-738-2965. *Dir of Libraries* Dr John M Dawson; *Chief Reference Librn* Katharine M Wood; *Reference Librn (Art & Art History)* Susan A Davi.

Open Mon - Thurs 8 AM - 11:30 PM; Fri 8 AM - 10 PM; Sat 9 AM - 5 PM; Sun 1 - 11:30 PM (when in session). Estab 1834 as University Library.

Income: Financed through the University. Purchases: $56,000 for Art History only.

Holdings: (Art and Art History) Vols 30,000; Per subs 100; AV—Microfiche, microfilm, phonorecords; Other—Exhibition catalogs, pamphlets.

Special Subjects: American art, architecture & decorative arts, 19th & 20th century European art.

Special Collections: Material on Ornamental Horticulture; American Art & Architecture; early 20th century European art.

REHOBOTH BEACH

REHOBOTH ART LEAGUE, INC, Dodd's Lane, Henlopen Acres (Mailing Add: PO Box 84, 19971). Tel: 302-227-8408. *Pres* Lucile K Megee; *Exec VPres* Sandford B Leach; *Exec Secy* Ruth Chambers Stewart; *Asst Secy* Mary L Pearce.

Open May 1 - Sept 30 10 AM - 5 PM. No admis. Estab 1938 for art education; to nurture the creative arts in Rehoboth Beach community and Sussex County, Delaware, to hold art shows, musical concerts and lectures; two galleries display members' works and outstanding invited artists; one small sales gallery for members' works. Mem: 1050; dues $15 and up; ann meeting last Mon in Aug.

Income: Financed by membership, donation and fund raising sales of paintings.

Collections: Small permanent collection from gifts; enlargement is planned from purchase fund.

Exhibitions: Bicentennial Exhibition; annual exhibitions.

Publications: Brochure of yearly events; newsletters.

Activities: Classes for adults and children; lect open to public; concerts; competitions; schol; artmobile; sales shop selling original art and prints.

WILMINGTON

COUNCIL OF DELAWARE ARTISTS,* c/o Elinor H Gray, *Pres,* 803 W duPont Rd, Westover Hills, 19807. Tel: 302-654-0249. *VPres* Anne Genge; *Secy* Pauline McLean.

Estab 1955 to educate the membership and the public about significant aspects of the creative arts including discussions, lectures and exhibitions pertaining to the visual arts and to provide continuous exposure of members' work through exhibitions; to establish an atmosphere of fellowship and cooperation among professional artist members. Mem: 60; dues $10; annual meeting May.

Publications: Newsletter, as indicated.

Activities: Lect open to public, 9 vis lectr per yr; individual paintings lent to schools, public offices, retirement homes and banks; traveling exhibitions organized and circulated.

DELAWARE ART MUSEUM, 2301 Kentmere Parkway, 19806. Tel: 302-571-9590. *Dir* Charles L Wyrick, Jr; *Cur* Rowland Elzea; *Asst Cur & Cur John Sloan Archives* Elizabeth Hawkes; *Educ Dir* Marion F T Johnson; *Prog Asst* Stephen Bruni; *Downtown Gallery Mgr* Eric Robinson; *Public Relations Asst* Jean Allman Gilmore; *ArtReach Dir* Thomas L Sherman; *Registrar* Mary Holahan.

Open Mon - Sat 10 AM - 5 PM; Sun 1 - 5 PM. Admis Adults $1, students 50¢, persons under 12 and over 65 free. Incorporated 1912 as the Wilmington Society of Fine Arts; present building completed in 1935; is a privately funded, non-profit cultural and educational institution dedicated to the increase of knowledge and pleasure through the display and interpretation of works of art and through classes designed to encourage an understanding of and a participation in the fine arts; six galleries are used for exhibition; five usually hold permanent or semi-permanent exhibitions of works from the permanent collection; one is used for special exhibitions which change at approximately six week intervals. Exhibitions are also held in the library and the education wing. The Downtown Gallery located in the Bank of Delaware, 901 Market Street, serves businessmen and shoppers in the downtown area. Average Annual Attendance: 35,000. Mem: 2000; dues individual $15, family $25; annual meeting third Tues in Oct.

Income: $552,000 (financed by endowment, membership and grants).

Purchases: $6500.

Collections: Bancroft Collection of English Pre-Raphaelite paintings; †Copeland Collection of works by local artists; Phelps Collection of Andrew Wyeth works; †American paintings and sculpture, including many Howard Pyle works and complete etchings and lithographs of John Sloan.

Exhibitions: (1976) Thomas George An American Artist in China; Artists in the Schools; The Studio at Cogslea; The Delaware Art Museum Presents: Dan Teis; The Pre-Raphaelite Era: 1848-1914; (1976-77) Douglas Duer; American Paintings and Sculpture: A Bicentennial Selection; Photographs from Delaware Collections; 62nd Annual Delaware Exhibition; 1776-1876 in Delaware: A Century of Change; Delaware Architecture, 1776-1976; 20th Annual Contemporary Crafts Exhibition; Collector's Opportunity; The Poster Decade: American Posters of the 1890s; Metroscope Photographers; W H D Koerner; Rosamond Wolff Purcell; Symbolism of Light: The Photographs of Clarence H White; (1977-78) Kirk Sterling: Craftmanship in Silver; Charles Lee Reese, Print Collector; Stitchery 77; Russell Paterson; New Deal for Art; Accessible Arts; Flaking, Foxing, and Fine Works: A Conservation Exhibition; Photographs by Arnold Newman; Julio Da Cunha; 63rd Annual Delaware Exhibition; 21st Annual Contemporary Crafts Exhibition. France Views America; American Art Pottery; F O C Darley; Delaware Exhibition Prizewinners: Frederick Guthrie, Stephen Tanis, Donna Usher; Hayley Lever; Art Off the Picture Press; Bertha Corson Day; 64th Annual Delaware Exhibition; 22nd Annual Contemporary Crafts Exhibition; (1979) Edward Moran.

Publications: DAM Bulletin, monthly.

Activities: Classes for adults and children; docent training; workshops; lectr open to the public and occasionally to members only, 6 vis lectr per yr; concerts; gallery talks; tours; competitions; exten department serving schools and community groups offering two-week programs in visual education; traveling exhibitions organized and circulated; museum and sales shops selling books, original art, reproductions, prints, slides, jewelry, crafts, candles, note cards and paper.
—**Library.** *Librn* Phyllis J Nixon.

Open to students, scholars for reference only.

Holdings: Vols 20,000; Per subs 100; Other—Auction catalogs, clipping files, exhibition catalogs.

Special Subjects: Pre-Raphaelites; American art history; Howard Pyle and his pupils also illustration in general; John Sloan and the Eight.

Special Collections: Samuel and Mary R Bancroft Pre-Raphaelite Library; Howard Pyle Collection; John Sloan Memorial Library; N C W Wyeth Collection; Frank E Schoonover Collection; Gayle P Hoskins Collection.

HAGLEY MUSEUM, Eleutherian Mills-Hagley Foundation, Barley Mill Rd and Brandywine Creek (Mailing Add: PO Box 3630, Greenville, 19807). Tel: 302-658-2401, exten 257. *General Dir* Dr Walter J Heacock; *Museum Deputy Dir* Joseph P Monigle.

Open Tues - Sat 9:30 AM - 4:30 PM; Sun 1 - 5 PM. Admis adults $2.50, children under 14 with adults free, students $1, sr citizens $1.25. Estab 1952, museum first opened to public in 1957, to preserve and interpret the site of the original Du Pont black powder works and tell the story of the early history of industry on the Brandywine. The 1803 home of E I duPont, furnished to illustrate the lifestyle of five generations of duPonts, is open year round. Average Annual Attendance: 100,000. Mem: 400; dues single $15; family $25.

Income: Financed by endowment and grants.

Exhibitions: France Views America; changing exhibits.

Publications: Newsletter, three times a year; Annual Report; Guide Books.

Activities: Lect for members; focus tours; tours for students; traveling exhibitions organized and circulated; museum shop selling books, reproductions, prints, slides.

Library: Eleutherian Mills Historical Library. *Dir* Dr Richmond Williams. Open Mon - Fri to students, and to researchers by appointment. Holdings: Vols 120,000; Other—Manuscripts 10 million, photographs 246,000.

HISTORICAL SOCIETY OF DELAWARE,*
—**Museum, Old Town Hall,** 6th & Market Sts, 19801. Tel: 302-655-7161.
—**Read House, The Strand,** 19801. Tel: 302-322-8411. *Pres* Walter J Heacock; *Virst VPres* William Poole; *Exec Dir* Dale Fields; *Museum Cur* Roland H Woodward; *Managing Editor* George Gibson.
Museum open Tues - Fri Noon - 4 PM; Sat 10 AM - 4 PM. No admis. Read House open Wed - Sat 10 AM - 4 PM; Sun Noon - 4 PM. Admis adults $2, children 75c; cl holidays and month of Aug. Estab 1864 to record and preserve Delaware History. Average Annual Attendance: 15,000. Mem: 1200; dues $10 and up.

Income: $100,000.

Collections: †Delaware pictures; †silver; †furniture; manuscripts; costumes.

Activities: Educ prog; lect; tours; special prog arranged.
—**Library,** 505 Market St, 19801. Tel: 302-655-7161. *Dir of Libraries* Gladys M Coghlan.

Holdings: Vols 75,000.

Special Subjects: Delaware and American history.

WINTERTHUR

WINTERTHUR MUSEUM AND GARDENS, Rte 52, six miles northwest of Wilmington, 19735. Tel: 302-656-8591. *Pres* John A Herdeg; *Dir* James Morton Smith; *Deputy Dir Finance & Admin* Wesley A Adams; *Cur* Charles F Hummel; *Coordr of Research* John A H Sweeney; *Head of Educ Div* Scott T Swank; *Registrar* Nancy Goyne Evans; *Editor Publications Office* Ian M G Quimby; *Head of Public Relations* Catherine Wheeler; *Cur Corbit-Sharp and Wilson-Warner Houses* Horace L Hotchkiss Jr.

Main Museum tours by reservation only early June - mid April daily except Mon & major holidays; non-reserved tours Tues - Sat 10 AM - 4 PM; Sun Noon - 4 PM except major holidays. Admis $6 for each reserved tour ($3 for ages 12-16; under 12 not admitted to the Main Museum); non-reserved tour description and prices vary with season. Corporation estab in 1930; museum opened in 1951; 200 rooms and display areas featuring decorative arts made or used in America between 1640 and 1840; sixty acres of horticultural displays in the Gardens. Average Annual Attendance: 80,000. Mem: 2300; dues $25 - $35.

Income: Approximately $5,000,000 (financed by endowment, membership, grants for special projects).

Collections: Furniture; Pennsylvania German folk art; metals; glassware; ceramics; interior architecture; textiles; needlework; paintings; and prints.

Exhibitions: Loan exhibit of objects from collection—Beyond Necessity: Art in the Folk Tradition, Brandywine River Museum, Chadds Ford, PA.

Publications: Publications and articles by staff, including Winterthur Portfolio, annual, first issued in 1963; Annual Report, first issued in 1962.

Activities: Dramatic programs, docent training; Winterthur program in Early American Culture, a graduate program sponsored with the University of Delaware; lect open to the public and to members only; individual paintings and original objects of art lent to museums and historical societies; museum shop selling books, slides, gifts, postcards, plants.
—**Historic Odessa.** Corbit-Sharp House (1774), and Wilson-Warner House (1769).
Open to public Tues - Sat 10 AM - 5 PM, Sun 2 - 5 PM, cl National holidays.

Located 23 miles south of Wilmington, Odessa is a community of restored 18th and 19th century houses, including many fine examples of early Delaware Valley architecture.

Library: *Librn* Frank H Sommer III. Open to the public on a need-to-know basis for reference.

DISTRICT OF COLUMBIA

WASHINGTON

AMERICAN ASSOCIATION OF MUSEUMS, 1055 Thomas Jefferson St NW, Washington, DC 20007. Tel: 202-338-5300. *Pres* Kenneth Starr; *Dir* Lawrence L Reger; *Asst Dir* Michael Warner; *Editor* Ellen C Hicks.

For further information see National and Regional Organizations.

AMERICAN ASSOCIATION OF UNIVERSITY WOMEN,* 2401 Virginia Ave NW, Washington, DC 20037. Tel: 202-785-7700. *Gen Dir* Helen B Wolfe.

For further information see National and Regional Organizations.

AMERICAN INSTITUTE OF ARCHITECTS, 1735 New York Ave NW, Washington, DC 20006. Tel: 202-785-7300. *Pres* Elmer E Botsai; *VPres* Ehrman B Mitchell, Jr; *Secy* Robert M Lawrence; *Exec VPres* David Olan Meeker, Jr.

For further information see National and Regional Organizations.

AMERICAN INSTITUTE OF ARCHITECTS FOUNDATION, The Octagon, 1799 New York Ave NW, 20006. Tel: 202-638-3105. *Pres Found and Owner House* Jeanne F Butler; *Cur Octagon* Alison M MacTavish.

Open Tues - Fri 10 AM - 4 PM; Sat & Sun 1 - 4 PM. Admis by donation; groups over 10 charged $1 per person except student and senior citizens groups 50¢ per person. Opened as house museum in 1970; formerly a federal townhouse built by Col John Tayloe III to serve as White House during War of 1812, furnished with late 18th and early 19th century decorative arts; changing exhibition program in second floor galleries; 4 - 5 exhibitions yearly relating to architecture, history and decorative arts. Average Annual Attendance: 18,000.

Income: $85,000 (financed by state appropriation and the Institute).

Collections: Permanent collection of furniture, paintings, ceramics, kitchen utensils.

Exhibitions: Harold Sterner: A Retrospective; Armin Landeck: The Catalog Raisonne of his Prints; Travel Sketches of Louis I Kahn; Christmas at the Octagon.

Publications: Exhibition catalogs; The Octagon Being an Account of a Famous Washington Residence: Its Great Years, Decline and Restoration, book; Competition 1792/Designing a Nation's Capitol, book; William Thornton: A Renaissance Man in the Federal City, book; Selections from the AIA Architectural Archives, book; Dolley and the Great Little Madison, book.

Activities: Educ dept; dramatic programs, docent training; scheduled tours for docents; lectr for member only, 2 - 3 vis lectr per yr. sales shop selling, books, prints and slides.

Library: *Librn* Alison M MacTavish. Open to the public for reference; but primarily used by staff. Holdings: Vols 200; Per subs 10. Special Subjects: Decorative arts; architecture, history of the Octagon and the Tayloe family.

AMERICAN RED CROSS, 17th & D Sts NW, 20006. Tel: 202-737-8300. *Pres* George M Elsey; *Senior VPres* Frederic S Laise; *Counselor & Secy* John L Currin.

For further information see National and Regional Organizations.

AMERICAN UNIVERSITY, Watkins Art Gallery, Dept of Art, Massachusetts and Nebraska Ave NW, 20016. Tel: 202-686-2114. *Chmn* Ben L Summerford.

Open Mon - Fri 10 AM - Noon & 1 - 4 PM. No admis. Estab 1943 to exhibit art of interest to public and university art community; schedule includes occasional education or theme shows and student exhibits; one large room with moveable panels and one small exhibit room with attendant's desk. Average Annual Attendance: 2000 plus art students.

Collections: Watkins Collection of 19th and 20th century American and European paintings.

Exhibitions: (1976-77) Robert D'Arista Prints; Makonda Art; Luciano Penay Paintings; Jack Boul-Monoprints; Norvan Ives Collages and Prints; Marjorie Hirano and Michael Graham Drawings; Charles Cajori Drawings.

Activities: Educ dept; docent training; lectr open to the public, 3 - 5 vis lectr per yr; individual paintings and original objects of art lent to museums and university galleries; traveling exhibitions organized and circulated on occasion.

ANACOSTIA NEIGHBORHOOD MUSEUM, * 2405 Martin Luther King, Jr, Ave, SE, 20020. Tel: 202-381-5656. *Dir* John R Kinard; *Exhibits Mgr* Charles Mickens; *Supervisory Exhibits Specialist* James E Mayo.
Open Mon - Fri 10 Am - 6 PM; Sat, Sun & holidays 1 - 6 PM; cl Xmas. No admis. Estab 1967, a non-profit federally chartered corporation to record and research African, Black American and Anacostia history and urban problems.
Collections: (Art) Afro-American history; Afro-American and African art.
Publications: Educational booklets; exhibit programs; museum brochures.
Activities: Lectures; guided tours; gallery talks; arts festivals; formally organized programs for children and adults; traveling exhibitions. Sales shop.
Library: Open to the public for research on the premises. Holdings: 1000 vols.

ANDERSON HOUSE MUSEUM, * Society of the Cincinnati, 2118 Massachusetts Ave, NW 20008. Tel: 202-785-2040. *Dir* John D Kilbourne.
Open Tues - Sun 2 - 4 PM; special hours on request by groups for guided tours; cl Thanksgiving and Christmas. No admis. the Society of the Cincinnati was founded in May 1783; the museum was opened to the public in 1938. Anderson House Museum is a National museum for the custody and preservation of historical documents, relics and archives, especially those pertaining to the American Revolution. Because of its superb building (1905, Little and Browne, Boston architects), original furnishings and collections of Western and Oriental art, Anderson House Museum is also a Historic House Museum. Average Annual Attendance: 5600.
Collections: †Historical material; figurines of the French Regiments who fought at Yorktown, Va, 1781, and others; collection of paintings, 16th & 17th century Flemish tapestries, sculpture, period furniture; Oriental works of art, Japanese screens, bronzes, ceramics, jade.
Exhibitions: Rotating exhibitions; the permanent collection.
Publications: Annual Report of the director; The Society of the Cincinnati and its Museum; Oriental Art at Anderson House; A Few Questions and Answers regarding the Society of the Cincinnati.

ARCHIVES OF AMERICAN ART, Eighth & G Sts NW, (Administrative Headquarters Mailing Add: 41 E 65th St New York, NY 10021). Tel: 202-381-6174. *Chmn* Mrs Otto L Spaeth; *Pres* Dr I F Burton; *Secy* Mrs Dana M Raymond; *Dir* William E Wolfenden; *Archivist* Garnett McCoy; *Cur of Manuscripts* Arthur Breton.
Open 9 Am - 5 PM. Estab 1954 and joined the Smithsonian Institution in 1970. A national research institute whose purpose is to collect basic documentary source materials on American painters, sculptors, and craftsmen, as well as records of collectors, dealers, art historians, curators, museum, societies and institutions. Mem: 1600; dues $25 and up; Annual meeting first Tues in December.
Income: Financed by membership and federal funds.
Collections: Every known art auction catalog published in this country from 1785-1963; records and papers of the Macbeth Gallery containing 150,000 items dating from its opening in 1892 until its closing in 1954; the complete records of the Downtown Gallery 1926-1969; notebooks and sketchbooks kept by the contemporary sculptor David Smith; some seven million manuscripts and documents; 150,000 photographs; 2000 tapes interviews.
Publications: Archives of American Art Journal, quarterly.

ARTISTS EQUITY ASSOCIATION, INC, 3726 Albemarle St NW, 20016. Tel: 202-244-0209. *Pres* Gilda Ellis; *Secy* Michael C Gast; *Exec Dir* Gail Rasmussen; 5 Regional VPres.
For further information see National and Regional Organizations.

ARTS CLUB OF WASHINGTON, * James Monroe House, 2017 Eye St NW, 20006. Tel: 202-331-7282. *Pres* Dr Henry Lea Mason; *VPres* C Dudley Brown; *Treas* Albert L Yarashus; *Recording Secy* Mary Cates; *Corresp Secy* Jeanne Rose.
Open daily 11 AM - 5 PM; cl holidays. Founded 1916. The James Monroe House (1803-1805) was built by Timothy Caldwell of Philadelphia. It is registered with the National Register of Historic Places, the Historical Survey 1937 and 1968, and the National Trust for Historic Preservation. James Monroe, fifth President of the United States, resided in the house while he was Secretary of War and State. During the first six months of his Presidency (1817-1825) the house served as the Executive Mansion, since the White House had been burned in the War of 1812 and had not yet been restored. Mem: 250; annual meeting Apr.

Activities: Monthly lectures; periodic exhibitions; social and educational activities: scholarships; sketch group.

ASSOCIATION OF AMERICAN EDITORIAL CARTOONISTS, 475 School St SW, 20024. *Pres* Tom Curtis of Milwaukee Sentinel; *VPres* Jeff McNalley of Richmond Times-Dispatch; *Secy* Jim Lange, Oklahoma City Oklahoman.
For further information see National and Regional Organizations.

ASSOCIATION OF COLLEGIATE SCHOOLS OF ARCHITECTURE, 1735 New York Ave NW, 20006. Tel: 202-785-2324. *Pres* D Nuzum; *VPres* B Turner; *Secy* B Honikman; *Exec Dir* R Schluntz; *Admin Asst* I Deshler; *Journal Exec Editor* D Clark.
For further information see National and Regional Organizations.

B'NAI B'RITH EXHIBIT HALL, * 1640 Rhode Island Ave NW, 20036. Tel: 202-293-5284. *Cur & Dir* Anna R Cohn.
Open Sun - Fri 10 AM - 5 PM; cl Sat, national and Jewish holidays. No admis. Estab 1957 for exhibits of Jewish faith artists. Two gallery rooms.
Income: Financed by membership.
Collections: American Jewish history and art; Israeli art; Jewish ceremonial objects; archives of B'nai B'rith.
Exhibitions: Approx 9 one-person shows annually.
Publications: Brochures for art exhibits; historical pamphlets, occasionally; Lincoln and the Jews (portfolio); Ceremonies of Jews (portfolio).
Activities: Tours; collections of graphics lent to other institutions; traveling exhibitions organized and circulated; book shop.
Library: Holdings—Vols 8000; Other—Photographs, Manuscripts.

CATHOLIC UNIVERSITY OF AMERICA, Humanities Division - Mullen Library, Michigan Ave & Harewood Rd, NE, 20064. Tel: 202-635-5075. *Head, Humanities Div* B Gutekunst.
Open fall & spring terms Mon - Thurs 9 AM - 10 PM; Fri - Sat 9 AM - 5 PM; Sun 1 - 10 PM. Estab 1958 to offer academic resources and services that are integral to the work of the institution.
Holdings: Vols 6700; Other—Prints 200.

COMMISSION OF FINE ARTS, * 708 Jackson Place, NW, 20006. Tel: 202-343-5324. *Chmn* J Carter Brown; *Secy Admin Officer* Charles H Atherton.
Open daily 8 AM - 4:30 PM. Estab by Act of Congress in 1910 to advise the President, Members of Congress, and various governmental agencies on matters pertaining to the appearance of Washington, DC. The Comission of Fine Arts is composed of seven members, three architects, one landscape architect, one painter, one sculptor, and one layman, who are appointed by the President for four-year terms. Report issued periodically.
Plans for all new projects in the District of Columbia under the direction of the Federal and District of Columbia Governments which in any important way affect the appearance of the city, and all questions involving matters of art with which the Federal Government is concerned, must be submitted to the Commission for comment and advice before contracts are made. Also gives advice on suitability of designs of private buildings in certain parts of the city adjacent to the United States Capitol, the White House, the headquarters of the various departments and agencies of the District and Federal Governments, the Central Mall, Rock Creek Park, and Georgetown.

CORCORAN GALLERY OF ART, * 17th St & New York Ave NW, 20006. Tel: 202-638-3211. *Pres* David Lloyd Kreeger; *Dir* Roy Slade; *Chief Cur* Jane Livingston; *Cur Coll* Dorothy Phillips; *Registrar* Susan Grady.
Open Tues - Sun 11 AM - 5 PM; cl Mon, New Year's Day, Independence Day, Thanksgiving, and Christmas. No admis. Estab 1859, inc 1869, primarily for the encouragement of American art. Average Annual Attendance: 200,000. Mem: 3000; dues student & single $15, family $25, Friends of the Corcoran $100, sponsor $250, contributing $500 and up.
Collections: William Wilson Corcoran Collection consisting chiefly of †American paintings; James Parmelee Collection of American paintings and sculpture; Mary E Maxwell Collection of †American prints from the 18th century to the present; the American collections of †paintings, watercolors, drawings and sculpture from the 18th century through the 20th century is being constantly increased by purchases, gifts, and bequests; Edward C and Mary Walker Collection of 19th century paintings; bronzes by Antoine Louis Barye; the W A Clark Collection includes paintings and drawings by Dutch, Flemish, English and American artists; Gothic and Beauvais tapestries; an important triptych by Andrea di Vanni; an 18th century French salon; furniture, laces, rugs, mostly of the Herat style; majolica; Greek antiquities; a 13th century stained glass window; sculpture.
Exhibitions: One-person exhibitions of contemporary American artists; biennial exhibition of contemporary American painting; a program of exhibitions of Washington area artists, both one-person and group exhibits, and a program of historical exhibitions of American art.

Publications: Calendar of Events, monthly; exhibition catalogs; color reproductions; handbooks of the collections.
Activities: Children's programs; docent service; lect; concerts; gallery shop.
Library: Holdings—Vols 4500.

DAR MUSEUM (NATIONAL SOCIETY DAUGHTERS OF THE AMERICAN REVOLUTION), 1776 D St NW, 20006. Tel: 202-628-1776. *Cur* Jean Taylor Federico.
Open Mon - Fri 9 AM - 4 PM. No admis. Estab 1890 for collection and exhibition of decorative arts used in America from 1700-1840, for the study of objects, and preservation of Revolutionary artifacts (including uniforms and weapons), and documentation of American life; there are 29 period rooms which reflect the decorative arts of particular states, a museum which houses large collections grouped by ceramics, paintings, glass, and furniture. Average Annual Attendance: 12,000. Mem: 205,000; dues $15 - $17; ann meeting Apr.
Income: Under $100,000 (financed by membership). Purchases: Under $20,000.
Collections: †Ceramics, †prints, †paintings, †furniture.
Exhibitions: Special exhibitions arranged and changed periodically, usually every 2 - 3 months.
Activities: Classes for children; docent training; a suitcase, traveling museum to local schools, Touch Program; 3 - 4 vis lectr per yr; gallery talks; tours; exten dept serving third - sixth grades, schools in area; individual paintings and original objects of art lent to museums for special exhibitions; sales shop selling books, slides, stationery, dolls, and DAR souvenirs.
Library: Open to public by advance notice; for reference only. Holdings: Vols 1700; Per subs 4. Special Subjects: American decorative arts.

DECATUR HOUSE, 748 Jackson Pl, NW, 20006. Tel: 202-387-4062. *Adminr* Earl James; *Asst Adminr* Robert Mawson; *Admin Asst* Vicki Sopher.
Open Mon - Fri 10 AM - 2 PM; Sat & Sun Noon - 4 PM. Admis adults $1.50, students & sr citizens 50¢, Nat Trust Mem free. Estab 1958, bequeathed to National Trust for Historic Preservation by Mrs Truton Beale to foster appreciation and interest in the history and culture of the city of Washington, DC and in the benefits of historic preservation. Decatur House, a Federal period townhouse, was completed in 1819; designed by Benjamin Henry Latrobe. Average Annual Attendance: 15,000. Mem: National Trust members.
Income: Financed by endowment and membership.
Collections: Federal furniture and memorabilia representing the Decatur period; late 19th and 20th century furnishings (Victorian) representing the ninety years Beale lived in the house.
Activities: Lect open to public, 5 vis lectr per yr; gallery talks; individual paintings and original art objects lent to qualified non-profit corporations; sales shop selling books.

DEPARTMENT OF STATE, Diplomatic Reception Rooms, 2201 C St, NW, 20520. Tel: 202-632-0298. *Cur* Clement E Conger; *Cur Asst* Gail F Daly; *Clerk* Camille L Bradley; *Staff Asst* Patricia Heflin.
Open Mon - Fri, 3 public tours by reservation only. No admis. Estab 1961 (unofficially), 1971 (officially). The Diplomatic Reception Rooms were created in order to entertain foreign dignitaries. The decision to use museum quality 18th century American furniture came about in order to allow these foreign visitors to view furniture made by American craftsmen when this country existed as colonies of the British Empire. Nine separate rooms furnished with American 18th century furniture, 18th century American silver, 18th century Chinese porcelain made for the American trade and antique Persian rugs. Average Annual Attendance: 70,000.
Collections: 18th century American furniture, American silver and Chinese porcelain; antique Persian rugs.
Publications: Guidebook, 1975; Silver Supplement to the Guidebook, 1973.
Activities: Individual paintings and original objects of art lent to special national antique furniture and art gallery exhibitions.

FEDERAL DESIGN COUNCIL, PO Box 7537, 20044. *Pres* Robert Schulman; *VPres* Elaine Hamilton & Amy Millen; *Secy* Marian S Osher.
Organized in 1970 by a group of Federal art directors and design managers concerned with the design image of the Government. The Council has worked with the National Endowment for the Arts; with the Civil Service Commission; with the Government Printing Office and the General Services Administration. Qualif for Mem: Anyone concerned with the design image of the Government; dues $20; regular meetings held.
Income: Financed by membership.
Exhibitions: Federal Design Response exhibition.
Publications: Next Issue (newsletter), 4-6 issues.

Activities: Visual communications programs; lect open to members only, 5-8 vis lectr per yr; tours.

FOLGER SHAKESPEARE LIBRARY, 201 E Capitol St SE, 20003. Tel: 202-546-4800. *Dir* O B Hardison Jr; *Assoc Dir* Philip A Knachel; *Dir Research Activities* John F Andrews.
Open (Exhibition Gallery) Mon - Sat 10 AM - 4:30 PM; Sun from Apr 15 - Labor Day. Estab 1932 as an international center for the study of all aspects of the European Renaissance and civilization in the 16th & 17th centuries. Maintains an art gallery; permanent display of Shakesperean items and changing topical exhibits of books, manuscripts, paintings and sculpture; contemporary art exhibited in lower gallery.
Income: Financed by endowment.
Holdings: Vols 217,500; Per subs 180; AV—Audio tapes, film strips, microfilm, motion pictures, phonorecords and slides; Other—Exhibition catalogs, manuscripts, memorabilia, original art works, original documents, pamphlets, photographs, prints, reproductions and sculpture.
Special Subjects: History of English civilization in 16th & 17th centuries; history of Western civilization in 16th & 17th centuries; history of the theatre in England, especially 16th - 18th centuries; Renaissance drama and literature.
Special Collections: Shakespeare; playbills; promptbooks.
Exhibitions: Shakespeare in America; Medicine and Health in the Renaissance; Renaissance Art of War; Sir Thomas More, the Man and his Age.
Publications: Newsletter, five times a year; Shakespeare Quarterly.
Activities: Seminars for advanced graduate students; lect open to public; concerts; gallery talks; schol; traveling exhibitions organized and circulated.

FRANCISCAN MONASTERY,* Holy Land of America, 14th & Quincy St, NE, 20017. Tel: 202-526-6800. *Cur* Bro Joseph Pounds.
Open daily 8 AM - 5 PM; cl New Year's, Good Friday, Thanksgiving, Christmas. No admis. Estab 1898, affiliated with the Franciscan Custody of the Holy Land. The Monastery covers 44 acres with rose gardens, a reproduction of the Portiuncula Chapel, Assisi, and replicas of chapels and shrines of the Holy Land.
Collections: Frescos of early Christian art; pearl carvings; bronzes; antiquities; coins; ceramics; glassware; silver; gold; jewelry; pottery; icons and crusader artifacts.
Publications: The Crusader's Almanac, quarterly.
Activities: Guided tours; sales shop.

FREER GALLERY OF ART, Twelfth and Jefferson Dr, SW, 20560. Tel: 202-381-5344. *Dir* Thomas Lawton; *Head Conservator, Technical Laboratory* W T Chase; *Assoc Cur, Near Eastern Art* Dr. Esin Atil; *Assoc Cur, Chinese Art* Mrs. Hin-cheung Lovell.
Open daily 10 AM - 5:30 PM; cl Christmas. No admis. Estab 1906 under Smithsonian Institution to exhibit its outstanding masterpieces of American and Oriental art; to carry out research and publication in the history of civilizations represented by objects in the collections. Average Annual Attendance: 220,000.
Income: Financed by endowment and Federal appropriation.
Collections: †Art of the Near and Far East (paintings, sculpture, objects in stone, wood, jade, glass, porcelain, bronze, gold, silver, lacquer, metalwork); manuscripts (early Christian); Collection of works by James McNeill Whistler and some of his contemporaries.
Activities: Lect, 6 vis lectr per yr; tours; museum shop selling books, reproductions, slides, needlepoint, objects in the round, desk accessories and postcards.
—*Library.* *Librn* Priscilla P Smith.
Open to the public for reference.
Holdings: Vols 25,000; Per subs 100.
Special Subjects: Volumes relate to cultural and historical background of the collection.

GENERAL FEDERATION OF WOMEN'S CLUBS,* 1734 N St NW, 20036. Tel: 202-347-3168. *Exec Secy* Mrs W Ed Hamilton.
For further information see National and Regional Organizations.

GENERAL SERVICES ADMINISTRATION,* Public Buildings Service Fine Arts Program, 18th & F Sts NW, 20405. Tel: 202-963-5131. *Dir Fine Arts Program* Donald W Thalacker.
For further information see National and Regional Organizations.

GEORGE WASHINGTON UNIVERSITY,* Lower Lisner Auditorium, 20006. Tel: 202-676-7091—Dimock Gallery. *Cur* LeNore D Miller.
Open Mon - Fri 10 AM - 5 PM; cl Sat, Sun & National holidays; no admis. Estab 1964 to provide graduate and undergraduate programs in museum problems, research in art history and documentation of permanent collections.

Collections: Paintings; sculpture; graphic arts from the 18th, 19th and 20th centuries with special emphasis on American art; W. Lloyd Wright Collection of Washingtoniana; works pertaining to George Washington; US Grant Collection of photographs, historial material, prints; collection of prints by Joseph Pennell.
Exhibitions: Temporary exhibitions staged during academic year.
—Cloyd Heck Marvin Center Art Gallery.
Exhibitions: Monthly exhibitions of local, national and international artists.

GEORGETOWN UNIVERSITY ART AND HISTORY MUSEUM,* Box 1595, Hoya Station, 20007. Tel: 202-625-4085. *Cur* Clifford T Chieffo; *Assoc Cur* Patricia H Chieffo.
Open during University hours according to yearly schedule; cl holidays. No admis. University estab 1789; the museum is on the Georgetown University campus in Healy Hall (1879).
Collections: Paintings; sculpture; graphics; American portraits; religious art; works by Van Dyck and Gilbert Stuart; historical objects.
Publications: Collection catalog; exhibit catalogs.
Activities: Educational programs for undergraduate students; gallery talks; guided tours; arts festivals; temporary exhibitions.

HARVARD UNIVERSITY, Dumbarton Oaks Research Library and Collections,* 1703 32nd St, NW, 20007. Tel: 202-232-3101. *Dir* William R Tyler; *Dir Center for Byzantine Studies* William C Loerke; *Dir Center for Pre-Columbian Studies* Elizabeth P Benson; *Librn* Irene Vaslef.
Collections and Gardens open Tues - Sun 2 - 4:45 PM; cl Mon, holidays and July through Labor Day. Conveyed in 1940 to Harvard University by Mr and Mrs Robert Woods Bliss as a research center in the Byzantine and Mediaeval humanities and subsequently enlarged by them through gifts and bequests. Average Annual Attendance: 100,000.
Collections: †Byzantine devoted to Early Christian and Byzantine mosaics, textiles, bronzes, sculpture, ivories, metalwork, jewelry, glyptics, and other decorative arts of the period; †Pre-Columbian devoted to sculpture, textiles, pottery, gold ornaments, and other objects from Middle and South America, dating from 800 BC to the early 16th century; also a small group of European and American paintings, sculpture, and decorative arts.
Publications: Handbooks and catalogs of the Byzantine and Pre-Columbian collections.
Activities: Lect and conferences on Byzantine subjects, Pre-Columbian, and landscape architecture and gardening
—Library, Resources for Byzantine research.
Holdings: Vols 108.733.
Special Collection: Photographic copy of the Princeton Index of Christian Art; the Dumbarton Oaks Census of Early Christian and Byzantine Objects in American Collections; collection of over 50,000 photographs.
Pre-Columbian Library. Holdings: Vols 4400.
Garden Library. Holdings: Vols 2400 rare books; Other—Prints and drawings, other volumes 10,000.

HIRSHHORN MUSEUM AND SCULPTURE GARDEN, Eighth & Independence Aves, SW, 20560. Tel: 202-381-6512. *Dir* Abram Lerner; *Deputy Dir* Stephen Weil; *Adminr* Nancy Kirkpatrick; *Chief Cur* Charles Millard; *Cur* Cynthia McCabe & Inez Garson; *Chief, Educ Dept* Edward P Lawson; *Registrar* Douglas Robinson; *Chief Exhib* Joseph Shannon; *Chief Conservator* Laurence Hoffman.
Estab 1966 under the aegis of the Smithsonian Institution; building designed by Gordon Bunshaft of the architectural firm of Skidmore, Owings & Merrill. Opened in 1974.
Collections: Approx 6000 paintings and sculptures donated to the nation by Joseph H Hirshhorn, emphasizing the development of modern art from the latter half of the 19th century to the present; American art beginning with a strong group of Thomas Eakins' and going on to Sargent, Eastman Johnson, Chase, Hartley, Gorky, De Kooning, Rothko, Noland, Rivers and Frank Stella; European painting of the last 3 decades represented by Balthus, Bacon, Miro, Ernst, Agam and Vasarely; sculpture collection includes works by Daumier, Rodin, Degas, Brancusi, Giacometti, Arp, Moore, Manzu and David Smith, Caro and Nadelman.
Exhibitions: Permanent collection and special loan exhibitions.
Activities: Docent training; lect open to public; concerts; films; tours; lending program.
—Library. Tel: 202-381-6702. *Librn* Anna Brooke.
Estab 1974; for reference only.
Income: Financed by federal funds. Purchases: 6500.
Holdings: Vols 7000; Per subs 50; AV—Cassettes, microfiche, microfilm, slides; Other—Exhibition catalogs, memorabilia, auction catalogs.
Special Subjects: American painting 1850 to the present; International modern sculpture.
Special Collections: 5 Samuel Murray scrapbooks; Eakins memorabilia; Armory show memorabilia.

HOWARD UNIVERSITY GALLERY OF ART,* College of Fine Arts, Sixth & Fairmont Sts, NW 20001. Tel: 202-636-7047. *Dir* Dr Jeff R Donaldson; *Cur* Dr Albert J Carter.
Open Mon - Fri 9 AM - 4 PM; Sat Noon - 4 PM; cl Sun. No admis. Estab 1930 to stimulate the study and appreciation of the fine arts in the University and community. Three air-conditioned art galleries in Childers Hall—James V Herring Heritage Gallery, James A Porter Gallery, and the Student Gallery; also Gumbel Print Room. Average Annual Attendance: 24,000.
Collections: Kress Study Collection of Renaissance paintings and sculpture; Alain Locke Collection of African art; Irving R Gumbel Collection of prints; †Agnes Delano Collection of contemporary American watercolors and prints; †University collection of painting, sculpture and graphic arts by Afro-Americans.
Publications: Native American Arts (serial), exhibition catalogues, informational brochures; catalogue of the African and Afro-American collections.
Activities: Changing exhibitions monthly; bi-monthly gallery lectures and community programs.
—Art Seminar Library:
Holdings: Vols 2100; Other—Photographs 18,000, slides 12,000.

INDIAN ARTS AND CRAFTS BOARD, U.S. Department of the Interior, Room 4004, 20240. Tel: 202-343-2773. *Chmn* Lloyd New; *General Mgr* Robert G Hart; *Dir Museums, Exhib & Publications* Myles Libhart.
Open Mon - Fri 8 AM - 5 PM; cl Sat, Sun and Federal holidays. No admis. Estab 1935 to promote the development of contemporary native American arts and crafts in the United States. Under its Museum Program, the Board administers and operates three museums—Southern Plains Indian Museum, Anadarko, Oklahoma; Sioux Indian Museum, Rapid City, South Dakota and the Museum of the Plains Indian, Browning, Montana. Separate entries for each appears under their respective locations.
Publications: Source Directory of Contemporary Native American Arts and Crafts Business, biennial.

INTERNATIONAL COUNCIL OF MUSEUMS COMMITTEE OF THE AMERICAN ASSOCIATION OF MUSEUMS, 1055 Thomas Jefferson St NW, 20007. Tel: 212-338-5300. *Prog Coordr* Maria Papageorge.
For further information see National and Regional Organizations.

JOHN F KENNEDY CENTER FOR THE PERFORMING ARTS,* 20566. Tel: 202-872-0466. *Chmn of the Board of Trustees* Roger L Stevens.
The center opened in Sept 1971. Facilities include the 2200-seat Opera House, 2750-seat Concert Hall, 1130-seat Eisenhower Theater and 224-seat film theater operated by the American Film Institute.
Established in 1958 by Act of Congress as the National Cultural Center. A bureau of the Smithsonian Institution, but administered by a separate Board of Trustees; the Center is the sole official memorial in Washington to President Kennedy. Although the Center does not have an official collection, gifts in the form of art objects from foreign countries are on display throughout the Center.

LIBRARY OF CONGRESS, Prints and Photographs Division, First St Between E Capitol St & Independence Ave, 20540. Tel: Reference 202-426-6394; Offices 426-5836; Motion Pictures 426-5840. *Librn of Congress* Daniel J Boorstin; *Asst Chief, Prints & Photographs Division* Dale Haworth; *Head, Reference Section* Jerry L Kearns; *Acting Head, Motion Picture Section* Paul Spehr; *Collections Planner & Coordinator* Jerald Maddox.
Open Exhib Halls 8:30 AM - 9:30 PM; Sat & Sun 8:30 AM - 6 PM. Reading Room of the Division open Mon - Fri 8:30 - 5 PM; cl legal holidays. Estab 1897. For reference only.
Holdings: AV—Motion Pictures and reels 200,000; Other—Manuscripts, memorabilia, original art works, original document, photographs 8,000,000, prints & drawings 177,000, posters 70,000.
Collections: Original prints of all schools and periods, increased annually by the Gardiner Greene Hubbard and J & E R Pennell endowments.†Pennell Collection of Whistleriana; †early American lithographs; Japanese prints; †original drawings by American illustrators; †pictorial Archives of Early American Architecture including the Historic American Buildings Survey; Archive of Hispanic Culture; †Civil War drawings, prints, photographs and negatives; †outstanding among the collection of photographs and photographic negatives are the Farm Security Administration Collection, Red Cross Collection, Arnold Genthe, F B Johnston, Toni Frissell, Look Magazine. †The Motion Picture Section contains over 5000 motion pictures made between 1894 and 1912 and a large collection of German, Japanese, and Italian documentaries and feature films made prior to 1945.The bulk of the collection consists of selections among films registered for copyright since 1942. A cooperative acquisition and preser-

vation program between the Library and the American Film Institute attempts to collect American films printed on perishable nitrate stock and to preserve them through transfer on safer film.

Exhibitions: Biennial National Exhibition of Prints made within the preceding two years, of which a catalog is published and which is available on loan (the 25th exhibition held in 1977, in collaboration with National Collection of Fine Arts, Smithsonian; exhibitions from the collection are held at intervals.

Publications: Guide to the Special Collections of Prints and Photographs in the Library of Congress (1955-out of print); American Prints in the Library of Congress, published for Library of Congress by the Johns Hopkins Press, Baltimore (1970); Viewpoints (1975), for sale by Superintendent of Documents, US Govt Printing Office.

Activities: The division has an internship program for advanced undergraduate and graduates who wish to work with and study the collections of the division.

MINIATURE PAINTERS, SCULPTORS AND GRAVERS SOCIETY OF WASHINGTON, DC, 1711 Massachusetts Ave NW, 20036. *Pres* Edith Trifiletti; *VPres* Bonita Valien; *Secy* Mary Edmondson; *Treas* Eunice Haden; *Recorder* Elinor Cox.

Open daily, the hours vary. No admis. Estab 1931 to encourage and stimulate public interest in the arts in miniature, by exhibiting them in their values, apart from larger works. Mem: 65, artist must have exhibited with society for 3 years, been sponsored and voted on at annual meeting; ann meeting dates vary.

Exhibitions: Arts Club of Washington, DC (annual).

Activities: Competitions with Boardman Memorial, Founders, Jamieson, Muth, King, and Miniature Society of New Jersey Awards given.

MUSEUM OF AFRICAN ART, 316-332 A St NE, 20002. *Dir* Warren M Robbins; *Deputy Dir* Jean Salan; *Cur Coll* Lydia Puccineli; *Program Dir* Amina Dickinson; *Acad Coordr* Ed Lifschitz.

Open Mon - Fri 11 AM - 5 PM; Sat & Sun Noon - 5 PM. Admis voluntary. Estab 1963, open 1964 to reveal African art as one of the great cultural heritages of mankind; to help replace myth and misconception with valid scientific and historical information; to provide proper representation of African art in the spectrum of museums of Washington; 12 galleries display 500 objects of traditional African sculpture, plus a period-furnished memorial room to Frederick Douglass, 19th century abolitionist, orator, publisher, statesman in whose first Washington residence the Museum is located. Average Annual Attendance: 100,000. Mem: 1100; dues $10 - $5000.

Income: $750,000 (financed by membership foundations and national endowments).

Collections: African sculpture, textiles, crafts, musical instruments some 7000 items, 19th century Afro-American art; Eliot Elisofon Memorial Archives of 150,000 photos, slides and films.

Exhibitions: Traditional African Art; The Influence of African Sculpture on Modern Art; The African Photography of Eliot Elisofon; Permanent Outdoor color wall mural of the N'Debele villages of South Africa.

Publications: Two exhibitions catalogs per yr; Multimedia slide kit; pamphlets and booklets.

Activities: Classes for adults and children; docent training; tours in sign language; lect open to the public, 12 vis lectr per yr; concerts; gallery talks; tours; individual paintings and original objects of art lent to museums, universities, public officials and conferences; lending collection contains; motion pictures, paintings, photography, sculpture, slides and textiles; museum and sales shop selling books, magazines, original art, reproductions, prints, slides boutique African featuring quality crafts, jewelry, and other imports from Africa.

—Library. *Librn* Robert M Myers.

Open to student and scholars for reference by appointment.

Holdings: Vols 6000; Per subs 10; Other—Exhibition catalogs, maps.

Special Subjects: African Art and Culture; lesser emphasis Afro-American art and culture.

MUSEUM OF MODERN ART OF LATIN AMERICA, 201 18th St NW (Mailing Add: 17th and Constitution, NW, 20006). Tel: 202-331-1010. *Dir* José Gómez-Sicre; *Exhib Coordinator:* Jane Harmon de Ayoroa; *Public Relations Coordinator* Rafael Sardá.

Open Tues - Sat 10 AM - 5 PM. No admis. Estab 1976 to bring about an awareness and appreciation of contemporary Latin American art. Maintains an art gallery with the focus on contemporary Latin American art. Average Annual Attendance: 100,000.

Collections: Contemporary Latin American art.

Activities: Lect open to public, 4 vis lectr per yr; gallery talks; tours; individual paintings and original objects of art lent to museums; traveling exhibitions organized and circulated.

—Archive of Contemporary Latin American Art. Open to scholars and others involved in research.

Special Subjects: Contemporary Latin American Art.

MUSEUM OF THE UNITED STATES DEPARTMENT OF THE INTERIOR,* C St between 18th & 19th Sts NW, 20240. Tel: 202-343-5016. *Ex-officio* Secy of the Interior; *Exhib Specialist* Herbert Hallman.

Open Mon - Fri 8 AM - 4 PM. No admis. Estab 1938 to visualize and explain to the public through works of art and other media the history, aims, and activities of the Department. The Museum occupies 10 galleries in a wing on the first floor of the Interior Department Building. Average Annual Attendance: 100,000.

Collections: Oil paintings of early American explorers by William Henry Jackson; oil paintings of Western conservation scenes by Wilfrid Swancourt Bronson; Wildlife paintings by Walter Weber; Antarctic painting by Leland Curtis; miniature dioramas; sculpture groups; watercolor and black and white illustrations; Indian arts and crafts; Colburn Collection of Indian basketry; Gibson Collection of Indian materials. †General collection of Indian, Eskimo, and South Sea Islands and Virgin Islands arts and crafts, documents, maps, charts, etc.

Publications: Illustrated museum brochure.

NATIONAL AIR AND SPACE MUSEUM,* 7th & Independence Ave SW, 20560. Tel: 202-381-4156.

Open 10 AM - 9 PM during the summer; 10 AM - 5 PM during the winter; cl Christmas. No admis. Estab 1946 (art acquisitions are more recent) to memorialize the national development of aviation and space flight with about 5000 square feet of gallery devoted to the theme, Flight and the Arts.

Income: Financed through the Smithsonian Institution.

Exhibitions: Art exhibitions; Permanent, temporary and traveling exhibitions.

Activities: Special educational activities; guided tours; gallery talks; lect open to the public; Museum shop selling books.

Library: Holdings—Vols 12,000; Other—Manuscripts, extensive files of aerospace related photographs for reference.

NATIONAL ARCHITECTURAL ACCREDITING BOARD, INC, 1735 New York Ave NW, 20006. Tel: 202-833-1180. *Exec Dir* Dr Hugo G Blasdel.

For further information see National and Regional Organizations.

NATIONAL COLLECTION OF FINE ARTS,* Eighth & G Sts NW, 20560. Tel: 202-381-5180. *Dir* Joshua C Taylor; *Asst Dir* Hary Lowe; *Asst Dir for Admin* Harry Jordan; *Registrar* W Robert Johnston; *Cur 20th Century Painting & Sculpture* Walter Hopps; *Cur 18th & 19th Century Painting & Sculpture* William H Truettner; *Assoc Cur 18th & 19th Century Painting & Sculpture* Robin Bolton-Smith; *Cur Prints & Drawings* Janet A Fint; *Cur Educ* Peter Bermingham; *Research Cur* Lois M Fink; *Consultant 20th Century Painting & Sculpture* Adelyn D Breeskin; *Coordr Bicentennial Inventory of American Paintings* Abigail Booth; *Chief Office of Exhib & Design* David Keeler; *Chief Office of Exhib Abroad* Lois A Bingham; *Conservator* Thomas Carter; *Conservator* Stefano Scafetta; *Conservator* Katherine Eirk; *Editor Office of Publications* Carroll Clark; *Chief Office of Public Affairs* Margery Byres; *Photographer Office of Registrar* Michael Fischer.

Open Daily 10 AM - 5:30 PM; cl Christmas. Estab 1846 as part of the Smithsonian Institution and designated the National Gallery of Art in 1906. The title was changed to the National Collection of Fine Arts in 1937. The museum is now primarily concerned with the study and presentation of American art from its beginning to the present. The Explore Gallery on the first floor offers a stimulating range of exploratory experiences in art both for children and adults. An adjacent gallery, Discover, is devoted to challenging exhibitions of various kinds. Average Annual Attendance: 322,000.

Collections: The collection of paintings, sculpture, prints and drawings number over 17,000. It represents a wide range of American work, particularly late 19th and early 20th century. Major collections include those of Harriet Lane Johnston (1906), William T Evans (1907), John Gellatly (1929), and more recently the S C Johnson and Son Collection of paintings from the 1960s. There is a sizeable collection of portrait miniatures. All works not on display are available for examination by scholars.

Exhibitions: A representative selection of works from the collection are on permanent display in the galleries, providing a comprehensive view of the varied aspects of American art. Most temporary exhibitions, some twenty-five a year, are originated by the staff, many as part of the program to investigate less well-known aspects of American art. They include both studies of individual artists, such as W H Johnson, Ilya Bolotowsky and Lilly Martin Spencer, and thematic studies such as Art of the Pacific Northwest, Pennsylvania Academy Moderns, and the Academic Tradition in American Art. A small area is devoted to a representation of other than American works. Major exhibitions for 1976 included—1876: American Art of the Centennial; Behind the Scenes at NCFA; America as Art.

Publications: Major exhibitions are accompanied by authoritative publications; small exhibitions are accompanied by checklists.

Activities: The Department of Education carries on an active program with the schools and the general public, offering imaginative participatory tours for children, a Discover Graphics program which includes a print workshop and varied presentations of exhibitions, lectures, symposia and concerts. A research program in American art is maintained for visiting scholars and training is carried on through internship in general museum practice and conservation. The museum also circulates exhibitions abroad on a regular basis. The *Bicentennial Inventory of American Paintings Executed Before 1914* is compiling a computer list of largely uncatalogued works from throughout the country.
—**Library of the National Collection of Fine Arts and the National Portrait Gallery.** Tel: 202-381-5118, 381-5853. *Chief Librn* William B Walker; *Reference Librn* Katharine M Ratzenberger; *Cataloger* Charles H King, Jr.
Open Mon - Fri 10 AM - 5 PM. Estab 1964 to serve the reference and research needs of the staff and affiliated researchers of the National Collection of Fine Arts, the National Portrait Gallery, the Archives of American Art, and other Smithsonian bureaus. Open to graduate students and other qualified adult researchers. Circ: 7940.
Income: $160,000 (financed by federal appropriation). Purchases: $30,000.
Holdings: Vols 36,000; Serial subs 900; AV—Microfiche, microfilm; Other—Clipping files, exhibition catalogs, manuscripts, original documents, pamphlets, reproductions.
Special Subjects: American art especially painting, drawing, sculpture and graphic arts; contemporary art; American history and biography.
Special Collections: Ferdinand Perret Art Reference Library—collection of scrapbooks of clippings and pamphlets; special section on California art and artists consisting of approx 325 ring binders on art/artists of Southern California; vertical file of 300 file drawers of material on art and artists with increasing emphasis on American art/artists.
Activities: Library tours by appointment only.
—**Renwick Gallery,** 17th St & Pennsylvania Ave NW, 20560. Tel: 202-381-5811. *Dir* Lloyd E Herman.
Open Daily 10 AM - 5:30 PM; cl Christmas. Designed in 1859 by architect James Renwick, Jr, as the Corcoran Gallery of Art, the building was renamed for the architect in 1965 when it was transferred by the Federal government to the Smithsonian Institution for restoration. Restored to its French Second Empire elegance after 67 years as the United States Court of Claims, the building has two public rooms with period furnishing, the Grand Salon and the Octagon Room, as well as eight exhibition areas for American crafts and design exhibits.
Exhibitions: Since its opening the Renwick Gallery has presented 36 special exhibitions. During 1976 exhibitions included—Signs of Life: Symbols in the American City; Arne Jacobsen, Danish Architect and Designer; Man Made Mobile: The Western Saddle; Boxes and Bowls. Decorated Containers by 19th Century Haida, Tlingit, Bella Bella and Tsimshian Indian Artists; Paintings lent by The Corcoran Gallery of Art.
Publications: Major exhibitions are accompanied by publications, smaller exhibitions by checklists.
Activities: Docent training; film programs, lectr emphasizing the creative work of American designers and craftsmen as well as complementing the exhibitions from other countries; demonstrations; tours.

NATIONAL COUNCIL OF ARCHITECTURAL REGISTRATION BOARDS,* 1735 New York Ave NW, Suite 700, 20006. Tel: 202-659-3996. *Exec Dir* Hayden P Mims.
For further information see National and Regional Organizations.

NATIONAL ENDOWMENT FOR THE ARTS, 2401 E St NW, 20506. Tel: 202-634-6369. *Chmn* Livingston L Biddle, Jr.
For further information see National and Regional Organizations.

NATIONAL GALLERY OF ART,* Constitution Ave at Sixth St NW, 20565. Tel: 202-737-4215. Board of Trustees: *Chmn* The Chief Justice of the United States; The Secretary of State; The Secretary of the Treasury; The Secretary of the Smithsonian Institution; Paul Mellon, John Hay Whitney, Franklin D Murphy, Lessing J Rosenwald and Stoddard M Stevens. Officers and Staff *Pres* Paul Mellon; *VPres* John Hay Whitney; *Dir* J Carter Brown; *Consult Building Program* David W Scott; *Construction Manager* Robert C Engle; *Asst to Dir Music* Richard Bales; *Asst to Dir National Programs* W Howard Adams; *Asst to Dir Public Information* Katherine Warwick; *Asst to Dir Special Events* Robert L Pell; *Admin Asst* Elizabeth J Foy; *Secy & Gen Counsel* Robert Amory, Jr; *Gen Attorney* Mabel A Barry; *Asst Dir* Charles P Parkhurst; *Cur American Painting & Index of American Design* William P Campbell; *Cur Sculpture* C Douglas Lewis, Jr; *Research Cur* Konrad Oberhuber; *Chief Educ & Public Programs* Margaret I Bouton; *Cur Photographic Archives* Alessandro Contini-Bonacossi; *Editor* Theodore S Amussen; *Chief Exhibitions* Jack C Spinx; *Chief Conservator* Victor Covey; *Registrar* Peter Davidock; *Chief Photographic Laboratory* Henry B Beville; *Cur French Painting since 1700* David E Rust; *Cur Gaillard F Ravenel; Cur H Diane Russell; Treas* Lloyd D Haynes; *Adminr* Joseph E English; *Asst Adminr* George W Riggs; *Cur Northern European Painting to 1700* John Hand; *Cur Graphic Arts* Andrew Robinson, Jr; *Cur Later Italian*

Painting Sheldon Grossman; *Cur British Painting* Ross Watson; *Cur 20th Century Art* E A Carmean; *Cur Italian Renaissance Painting* David Brown; *Cur Early Italian Painting* Anna M Coris; *Cur Analytical Laboratory* Robert L Feller; *Cur Art Infomation* Elsie V H Ferber.
Open Mon - Fri 10 AM - 5 PM; Sun Noon - 9 PM; Apr 1 through Labor Day Mon - Fri 10 AM - 9 PM, Sun Noon - 9 PM; cl Christmas and New Year's Day. No admis. Estab 1937; gallery opened 1941. The original building was a gift from Andrew Mellon; the new East building opening June 1978 is gift of Paul Mellon and his late sister Ailsa Mellon Bruce. Designed by I M Pei in the shape of an isoceles triangle it will give new perspective to the traditional art gallery; the galleries in its towers are hexagonal in varying sizes; some 1500 sq ft in size; the temporary exhibition space the flexible space for temporary shows on the concourse level covers 18,000 sq ft. Average Annual Attendance: 2,000,000.
Income: Financed by private endowment and Federal appropriation.
Collections: Contains the Andrew W Mellon Collection of 126 paintings and 26 pieces of sculpture, which includes such masterpieces as Raphael's The Alba Madonna, the Niccolini-Cowper Madonna, and St George and the Dragon; van Eyck'a Annunciation; Botticelli's Adoration of the Magi; nine Rembrandts. Twenty-one of these paintings came from the Hermitage; Also in the original gift were the Vaughan Portraits of George Washington, by Gilbert Stuart, and the Washington Family, by Edward Savage. The National Gallery's Collection continues to be built by private donation, rather than through government funds, which serve solely to operate and maintain the Gallery, and other donations quickly followed Mr Mellon's. The Samuel H Kress Collection, given to the nation over a period of years, includes the great tondo to The Adoration of the Magi by Fra Angelico and Fra Filippo Lippi, the Laocoön by El Greco, and fine examples of by Giorgione, Titian, Grunewald, Durer, Memling, Bosch, Francois Clouet, Poussin, Watteau, Chardin, Boucher, Fragonard, David and Ingres. Also included were a number of masterpieces of Italian and French sculpture. The Widener Collection consists of fourteen Rembrandts, eight van Dycks, two Vermeers, major works of Italian, Spanish, English and French painting and Italian and French sculpture and decorative arts. The Chester Dale Collection included masterpieces by Manet, Cezanne, Renoir, Toulouse-Lautrec, Mont, Modigliani, Pissarro, Degas, van Gogh, Gauguin, Matisse, Picasso, Braque, and the American painter, George Bellows. Several major works of art by some of the most important artists of the last hundred years, such as Picasso, Cezanne, Gauguin and the American painter Walt Kuhn, were given to the Gallery in 1972 by the W Averell Harriman Foundation in memory of Marie N Harriman. Paintings to round out the collection have been bought with funds provided by the late Ailsa Mellon Bruce. Most important among them is the portrait of Ginevra de Benci, the only generally acknowledged painting by Leonardo da Vince outside Europe. Among other are Ruben's Daniel in the Lions' Denn, Claude Lorrain's Judgement of Paris, St George and the Dragon attributed to van der Weyden, and a number of American paintings, including Thomas Cole's second set of the Voyage of Life. Among recent acquisitions is Picasso's Femme Nue, key work of the artist's analytical cubist period. The National Gallery's rapidly expanding graphic arts holdings, in great part given by Lessing J Rosenwald, numbers about 30,000 items and dates from the 12th century to the present. Mr Rosenwald's gift, one of the world's great collections of prints and drawings, forms the nucleus of the Gallery's holdings in this field. The *Index of American Design* contains over 17,000 watercolor renderings and 22,000 photographs of American crafts and folk arts.
Exhibitions: Numerous exhibitions among them the first showing of the Treasures of Tutankhamen.
Publications: Calendar of Events, monthly.
Activities: Sunday lectures by distinguished guest speakers and members of the Gallery staff are given throughout the year. The A W Mellon Lectures in the Fine Arts are delivered as a series each spring by an outstanding scholar; Concerts are held in the East Garden Court each Sunday evening between September and June at 7 PM without charge. General tours and lectures are given in the Gallery by members of the Education department throughout the week. Special tours are arranged for groups. An electronic guide service on exhibits in 30 rooms broadcasts brief lectures. This service, called LecTour, as well as the Acoustiguide, which includes a Director's Tour and guides to special exhibitions, are available for a small rental fee. Films on art are presented on a varying schedule. Sends art loans, traveling exhibitions and multimedia programs to 4000 communities throughout the country.
—**Library.** Tel: 202-737-4215. *Chief Librn* J M Edelstein; *Reader Services Librn* Caroline H Backlund; *Cur Photographic Archives* Ruth Philbrick.
Open Tues - Fri 10 AM - 5 PM. Estab 1941 to support the National Gallery's curatorial, educational and research activities and serve as a research center for graduate students, visiting scholars and researchers in the visual arts. For Reference only.
Income: Financed by Federal appropriations and trust funds.
Holdings: Vols & Bound Per 65,000; Titles 524; AV—Microfiche; microfilm; Other—Clipping files, exhibition catalogs.
Special Subjects: Western European and American art.

Special Collections: Art exhibition, art sales and private art collection catalogs, artist monographs, Leonardo da Vinci.
Activities: Library tours on request.
—**Photography Archives.**
To open 1979.
Holdings: Photographs 800,000.
Special Subjects: Black/white photography on Western European art.

NATIONAL MUSEUM OF HISTORY AND TECHNOLOGY, Smithsonian Institution, Constitution Ave between 12th & 14th Sts NW, 20560. Tel: 202-628-4422. *Dir* Brook Hindle; *Deputy Dir* Silvio A Bedini; *Asst Dir for Admin* Robert G Tillotson; *Asst Dir for Exhibits* Benjamin W Lawless.
Open daily 10 AM - 5:30 PM; Apr 1 - Labor Day 10 AM - 9 PM; cl Christmas Day. No admis. Estab 1964. The Museum tells the story of American achievements from Colonial Times to the present, from man's basic needs of food, clothing and shelter, to the men and women who shaped our heritage and our progress in science and technology. Average Annual Attendance: 6 million.
Collections: (Art) Textiles, ceramics, glass, graphic arts and photography, numismatics, and archaeology.
Exhibitions: A Nation of Nations; We the People; Atom Smashers; and more.
Publications: Exhibition catalogs; Studies in History and Technology series.
Activities: Docent training; museum shop selling books, prints and slides.
Library: NMHT Branch of Smithsonian Institution Libraries. *Librn* Frank Pietropaoli. Open to staff and visiting scholars.

NATIONAL PORTRAIT GALLERY, F St at Eighth NW, 20560. Tel: 202-381-5380. *Dir* Marvin Sàdik; *Asst Dir* Douglas E Evelyn; *Cur* Robert G Stewart; *Historian* Marc Pachter; *Chief Exhib Design* Nello Marconi; *Cur Exhib* Beverly Coz; *Cur Education* Dennis O'Toole; *Cur Photographs* William F Stapp; *Cur Prints* Wendy C Wick; *Registrar* Suzanne Jenkins; *Keeper Catalog American Portraits* Mona Dearborn; *Catalog of American Portraits Survey Coordr* Richard K Doud; *Conservator* Felrath Hines; *Chief Public Information* Susanne Roschwalb.
Open daily 10 AM - 5:30 PM; cl Christmas. No admis. Estab 1962 as a museum of history and biography, told through portraiture and statuary depicting the men and women who have made significant contributions to the history, development and culture of the people of the United States; the Gallery is located in what was once the United States Patent Office Building, constructed between 1836 and 1867. The permanent collection of portraits of eminent Americans is located on the second floor. Sections of the first floor are devoted to major loan exhibitions, as well as photographs, prints and drawings from the permanent collection. Special rooms have been installed for a collection of 763 portrait engravings by C B J F de Saint-Memin and silhouettes by Auguste Edouart. The third floor, a two-story hall finished in a Victorian Renaissance style is also used occasionally for special exhibitions. Average Annual Attendance: 475,000.
Income: Approx $2,100,000 (financed by federal appropriation).
Collections: Collections constantly being enlarged include portraits of important Americans, preferably executed from life, in all traditional media; portraits of American Presidents from George Washington to Jimmy Carter:
Exhibitions: (1976 - 78) Abroad in America: Visitors to the New Nation, 1776 - 1914; Christian Gullager: Portrait Painter to Federal America; Wedgwood Portraits and the American Revolution; The President's Medal, 1789 - 1977; The Time of Our Lives; Facing the Light, Historic American Daguerreotype Portraits.
Publications: Large-scale monographs in connection with all major exhibitions, occasional teaching guides in booklet form for secondary school use, an illustrated checklist and studies independent of exhibitions on various aspects of the permanent collection, American portraiture and biography.
Activities: Classes for children; docent training; lect open to the public; gallery talks; tours; individual painting and original objects of art lent to other museums; lending collection contains motion pictures, original art works, slides; traveling exhibitions organized and circulated; museum shop selling books, magazines, reproductions, prints and slides.
Library: Shared with and maintained at the National Collection of Fine Arts.

NATIONAL TRUST FOR HISTORIC PRESERVATION, 740-748 Jackson Place NW, 20006. Tel: 202-638-6200. *Chmn Board Trustees* Carlisle H Humelstein; *Pres* James Biddle; *Exec VPres* Douglas P Wheeler; *Asst Exec VPres* Will Arey; *Dir Maritime Preservation* Harry C Allendorfer, Jr; *Comptroller & VPres for Finance* David A Dawson; *Acting VPres Historic Properties* Theodore A Sande; *VPres & Editor Preservation Press* Terry B Morton; *VPres Preservation Services* Russell V Keune; *VPres Public Affairs* Lyn Snoddon; *VPres for Real Estate and Legal Services* Joe E Moody; *Dir Division Properties Mgt* Charles Lyle;

AIA Historic Architect Nathaniel P Neblett; *Historic Landscape Architect* John Goodman; *Architectural Historian* Gale Alder; *Assoc Cur* Nancy Richards; *Registrar* Susan Leidy.
The National Trust for Historic Preservation is the only national, nonprofit, private organization chartered by Congress to encourage public participation in the preservation of sites, buildings and objects significant in American history and culture. Its services—counsel and education on preservation, and historic property interpretation and administration—are carried out at national and regional headquarters in consultation with advisors in each state and U.S. Territory. Mem dues adult $15.
Income: Financed by membership dues, contributions and matching grants from the U.S. Department of the Interior, National Park Service, under provision of the National Preservation Act of 1966.
Collections: Fine and decorative arts furnishing nine historic house museums—Chesterwood, Stockbridge, Mass; Cliveden, Philadelphia, Pa; Decatur House and Woodrow Wilson House, Washington, DC; Drayton Hall, Charleston, SC; Lyndhurst, Tarrytown, NY; Oatlands, Leesburg, Va; The Shadows-on-the-Teche, New Iberia, La; Woodlawn Plantation, Mt Vernon, Va. For additional information see separate listings.
Publications: Historic Preservation, quarterly; Preservation News, (newspaper) monthly.
Library: *Librn* Brigid Rapp. For reference only.

PHILLIPS COLLECTION, 1600-1612 21st St, NW, 20009. Tel: 202-387-2151. *Dir* Laughlin Phillips; *Cur* James McLaughlin; *Registrar & Archivist* John Gernand; *Dir Music* Charles Crowder; *Assoc Cur* Willem de Looper & Kevin Grogan; *Preparator* William Koberg; *Exec Asst* Louise Steffens; *Gift Shop Mgr* William Ryan.
Open Tues - Sat 10 AM - 5 PM; Sun 2 - 7 PM. No admis. Inc 1920 and opened to the public 1921 to show and interpret the best of contemporary painting in the context of outstanding works of the past; to underscore this intent through the presentation of concerts and lectures. Original building a residence designed by the firm of Hornblower & Marshall, built in 1897; additions constructed in 1907 and 1917; annex, designed by Frederick Weeks, constructed in 1959-60 and opened to the public late 1960. Average Annual Attendance: 85,000.
Income: $281,000 (financed by endowment, gifts and grants).
Collections: 19th and 20th century American and European painting with special emphasis on several artists whose work was acquired and assembled as a "unit," including Bonnard, Cezanne, Daumier, Braque, deStael, Marin, Dove and Rothko.
Exhibitions: Paintings by Eugene Rukhin; Abstract Paintings by Arthur G Dove; Recent Photographs by Glenn Rudolph; The Drawings of Morris Graves; Henry Moore: Prints since 1970; Paintings by The Group of Seven; Paintings by Horace Pippin; The Human Form: Sculpture, Prints and Drawings by Fritz Wotruba; Paintings by Sarah Baker; The Transforming Eye: Photographs by Clarence Jhn Laughlin; Alan Fenton: Watercolors and Drawings; Paintings by Stefan Hirsh; Color Monotypes by Matt Phillips; American Folk Painting: Selections from the Collections of Mr & Mrs William E Wiltshire, III; Tapestries by Annette Kaplan; Pottery by Vally Possony; Carol Summers: Woodcuts, 1951 - 1976; Peruvian Folk Art; Paintings by Philip C Curtis. Lect open to public, 3 vis lect per yr; group tours by appointment; concerts, films, museum shop selling books, reproductions, prints, slides and exhibit catalogs.
—**Library.** *Dir* Kevin Grogan; *Librn* Judith Richilieu.
Open to students, writers and museum professionals for reference.
Holdings: Vols 4000; Per subs 40.
Special Collections: The Phillips Collection itself, as well as the artists and periods represented in it.

PRINT COUNCIL OF AMERICA,* National Gallery of Art, Constitution Ave at Sixth St NW, 20565. Tel: 202-737-4215. *Pres* Andrew Robison; *Treas* Grace M Mayer.
For further information see National and Regional Organizations.

PUBLIC LIBRARY OF THE DISTRICT OF COLUMBIA,* Martin Luther King Memorial Library, 901 G St, NW, 20001. Tel: 202-727-1101. *Dir* Dr Hardy R Franklin; *Chief Art Division* Lois Kent Stiles.
Open Sat 9 AM - 5:30 PM; Sun 1 - 5 PM; Mon - Fri 9 AM - 9 PM; No admis. Estab 1896; Art Division, in Central Library, contains †reference and circulating books and periodicals on architecture, painting, sculpture, photography, graphic and applied arts; †an extensive pamphlet file includes all art subjects, with special emphasis on individual American artists and on more than 400 artists active in the area of the District of Columbia; †a circulating picture collection numbers over mounted reproductions 65,118 and †framed prints 290. †Films and filmstrips on art are in the Film Division of the library. Collections are used by individuals, clubs, colleges and universities; public, private and parochial schools, and miscellaneous organizations.
Exhibitions: Special exhibitions held occasionally.

SMITH-MASON GALLERY AND MUSEUM,* 1207 Rhode Island Ave, NW, 20005. Tel: 202-462-6323. *Dir* Helen S Mason; *Cur Graphics* James L Wells; *Cur Painting* Delilah W Pierce; *Cur Ceramics & Sculpture* Dr Leroy Gaskin

Open Tues - Fri Noon - 4 PM; Sat 10 AM - 5 PM; Sun 2 - 5 PM. No admis. Estab 1967 for the preservation and research of ethnology. Mem: Dues individual $10, sustaining $15, supporting $25, contributing $100, donor $250, Life 500.

Collections: Ethnology; sculpture; paintings; graphics; textiles; decorative arts.

Publications: Newsletter, annually; exhibit brochures.

Activities: Lectures; gallery talks; guided tours; films.

Library: Open to the public for research and reading on premises. Holdings: 300 vols.

SMITHSONIAN INSTITUTION, 1000 Jefferson Dr SW, 20560. Tel: 202-628-4422. Responsibility for administration of the trust is vested in the Board of Regents comprised of the Chief Justice of the United States, Chancellor of the Board of Regents, the Vice President of the United States, three members of the Senate, three members of the House of Representatives and nine citizen members. *Secy* S Dillon Ripley; *Under Secy* Robert A Brook; *Asst Secy for History & Art* Charles Blitzer; *Asst Secy for Public Service* Julian Euell; *Asst Secy for Museum Programs* Paul N Perrot.

Open Daily 10 AM - 5:30 PM; extended spring and summer hours determined yearly; cl Christmas. Estab 1846. James Smithson bequeathed his fortune to the United States to be used to found at Washington, under the name of the Smithsonian Institution, an establishment for the increase and diffusion of knowledge among men. To carry out the terms of the Smithson's will, the Institution performs fundamental research; perserves for study and reference about 65 million items of scientific, cultural, and historical interest; maintains exhibits representative of the arts, American history, aeronautics and space exploration, technology, and natural history; participates in the international exchange of learned publications; and engages in programs of education and national and international cooperative research and training. Average Annual Attendance: 20,000,000 (not limited to art bureaus). Board of Regents meets three times yearly, Jan, May and Sept.

The individual bureaus concerned with art under the Smithsonian Institution are as follows. For complete information see separate listing.

Archives of American Art Eighth & G Sts NW, 20560. (Administrative Headquarters) 41 E 65th St, New York, NY 10021.

Cooper-Hewitt Museum of Decorative Arts and Design, 9 E 90th St New York, NY 10028.

Freer Gallery of Art, 12th & Jefferson Dr SW, 20560.

Joseph H Hirshhorn Museum and Sculpture Garden, 900 Jefferson Dr SW, 20560.

John F Kennedy Center for the Performing Arts, 20566 (Administered under separate Board of Trustees).

National Air and Space Museum, Seventh & Independence Ave SW 20560.

National Collection of Fine Arts, Eighth & G St NW 20560 (includes the Renwick Gallery).

National Gallery of Art, Constitution Ave at Sixth St NW, 20565 (administered under separate Board of Trustees).

National Museum of History and Technology, Constitution Ave between 12th & 14th St NW, 20560.

National Portrait Gallery, Eighth & F St NW, 20560.

SOCIETY OF WASHINGTON PRINTMAKERS,*-c/o Prentiss Taylor, Pres, J 718 Arlington Towers, Arlington, Va 22209. Tel: 703-243-3286. *VPres* Isabella Walker; *Treas* Keiko Moore; *Recording Secy* Lila Asher; *Corresp Secy* Aline Feldman.

Estab 1934 as Society of Washington Etchers; name changed 1953. Mem: 60; dues $4; annual meeting in Fall.

Exhibitions: National Print Exhibitions, open to all printmakers; Members Exhibitions, alternating on a biennial basis. Purchase prizes presented to Library of Congress and Smithsonian Graphic Arts collections.

TEXTILE MUSEUM, 2320 S St NW, 20008. Tel: 202-667-0441. *Dir* Andrew Oliver, Jr; *Exec Asst* Mary Lee Berger-Hughes; *Cur Old World* Louise W Mackie; *Asst Cur New World* Ann P Rowe; *Asst Cur Old World* Patricia L Fiske; *Cur Emerita* Irene Emery; *Conservator* Clarissa Palmai; *Bookshop Mgr* Pinar Arcan; *Editor* Jane Brooks; *Museum Shop Mgr* Lilo Markrich.

Open Tues - Sat 10 AM - 5 PM. No admis. Estab 1925 for the acquisition, study and exhibition of rugs and textiles; the gallery contains eight rooms for exhibition, storage areas, museum shop, conservation laboratory, library and offices. Average Annual Attendance: 20,000. Mem: 1500; dues $20.

Income: Financed by endowment, membership and grants.

Collections: Oriental rugs from antiquity to the present as well as rugs and textiles from the Old and New Worlds with the general exception of Western Europe and the US other than Native Americans; collection contains approximately 9000 textiles and 700 rugs.

Exhibitions: (1976 - 77) Caucasian Rugs; Masterpieces in the Textile Museum from 3AD to 20th Century; Structures of Fabrics; Uzbek Textiles; Tribal Weavers of the Andes a Fanfare of 19th and 20th Century Rugs; White-Ground Turkish Rugs; Quilts; Molas; China Looms Resplendent; Ethnographic Textiles of the Western Hemisphere; History of Knitting; Spanish Silks and Carpets 13th to 17th centuries.

Publications: Newsletter, quarterly; The Textile Museum Journal, annually.

Activities: Dramatic programs; docent training; internships in conservation and museum studies; lectr open to the public, 40 vis lectr per yr; concerts; gallery talks; tours; original objects of art lent to other museums for special exhibitions; traveling exhibitions organized and circulated; museum shop and sales shop selling books, original art, patterns, yarn and floss, ethnic folk jewelry, woven and knitted articles.

—Arthur D Jenkins Library. Tel: 202-667-0442. *Librn* Katherine T Freshley.

Open Wed - Fri 10 AM - 5 PM. Established 1925 as a reference library dealing with ancient and ethnographic textiles and rugs of the world; photocopy service available.

Income: Financed by endowment, membership and gifts.

Holdings: Vols 7000; Per subs 30; Other—Clipping files; exhibition catalogs, pamphlets, photographs.

Special Collections: Oriental rugs; Peruvian; Indonesian; American Indian and Indian Textiles.

Activities: Gallery talks; library tours.

TRINITY COLLEGE LIBRARY, Michigan Ave & Franklin St NE, 20017. Tel: 202-269-2252. *Librn* Dorothy Beach; *Readers Services* Vivian Templin; *Acquisitions* Therese Marie Gaudreau; *Cataloger* Karen Leider; *Periodicals* Doris Gruber.

Open during school semesters, Mon - Thurs 9 AM - 11 PM; Fri 9 AM - 5 PM; Sat 10 AM - 5 PM; Sun 1- 11 PM. Estab 1897 as an undergraduate college library, serving the college community.

Income: $105,000 (financed by college budget). Purchases: $39,000 for all library materials.

Holdings: Vols 144,000; Per subs 684; AV—Microfilm, slides.

Special Subjects: Art collection in both books and slides is general in content, including works on painting, sculpture and architecture principally.

TRUXTUN-DECATUR NAVAL MUSEUM,* 1610 H St, NW 20006. Tel: 202-783-2573. *Pres* Vice Admiral W S DeLany, USN (Ret).

Open daily 10:30 - AM - 4 PM; cl national holidays. No admis. Estab 1950, the Museum is located in the carriage house adjoining the historic home of Stephen Decatur, who distinguished himself in the Tripolitan War. It is also named for Commodore Thomas Truxtun, another naval figure of that period. Sponsored by the Naval Historical Foundation, the exhibits cover the Merchant Marine, US Marine Corps, and Coast Guard in addition to the US Navy. Mem: Dues: $5 - $2000.

Collections: Documents; Navy memorabilia; nautical paintings; prints, photographs; ship models.

Exhibitions: Permanent and temporary exhibitions.

Publications: Newsletter, semi-annually; Naval Historical Foundation Report; historical pamphlets, semi-annually.

Activities: Lect; films; gift shop.

Library: Holdings—Vols 1000 rare books on Naval history; Other—Manuscripts.

UNITED STATES NAVAL MEMORIAL MUSEUM,* Navy Combat Art Gallery, Washington Naval Yard, 9th & M Sts, SE, 20390. Tel: 202-433-2651. *Dir* Capt Roger Pineau; *Chief Cur* Vice Admr Edwin B Hooper, USN (Ret); *Asst Comdr* W J Laux, Jr.

Open Mon - Fri 8 AM - 4 PM; cl holidays. No admis.

Collections: Watercolor prints; paintings; naval combat art.

UNITED STATES SENATE COMMISSION ON ART AND ANTIQUITIES, Room S-411 US Capitol Building, 20510. Tel: 202-224-2955. *Chmn* Sen Robert C Byrd; *VChmn* Sen Howard H Baker Jr; *Exec Secy* J S Kimmitt; *Cur* James R Ketchum.

Open daily 9 AM - 4:30 PM. No admis. Estab 1968 to accept, supervise, hold, place and protect all works of art, historical objects, and exhibits within the Senate wing of the US Capitol and Senate Office buildings. Average Annual Attendance: 1,000,000.

Income: Financed by US Senate appropriation.

Collections: Paintings, sculpture, historic furnishings and memorabilia; Old Senate and Old Supreme Court chambers restored to their appearances c 1850.

Exhibitions: The Senate in 1850; The First Presidential Election; Disputed Election of 1877.

Publications: Publications on restored Old Senate and Old Supreme Court chambers.
Library: A reference collection on fine and decorative arts; supplemented by US Senate Library.

WHITE HOUSE,* 1600 Pennsylvania Ave, NW, 20500. Tel: 202-456-1414. *Cur:* Clement E Conger; *Registrar:* Betty C Monkman.
Open winter Tues - Fri 10 AM - Noon; summer Tues - Sat 10 AM - Noon; cl Sun, Mon, most holidays. No admis.
Collections: 18th and 19th century period furniture; porcelain; glassware; portraits of Presidents, First Ladies and other notables; 18th, 19th and 20th century paintings and prints; sculpture.
Publications: The White House: An Historic Guide; The Presidents of the United States; The Living White House; The First Ladies.

WOODROW WILSON HOUSE, 2340 S St, NW, 20008. Tel: 202-387-4062. *Adminr* Earl James; *Asst Adminr* Robert Mawson; *Admin Asst* Vicki Sopher.
Open Mon - Fri 10 AM - 2 PM; Sat & Sun Noon - 4 PM. Admis adults $1.50, students & Sr citizens 50¢, Nat Trust Mem free. Estab 1968; owned by the National Trust for Historic Preservation, it works to foster interest and appreciation of the history and culture of the City. Wilson House is a 191 Georgian-Revival townhouse designed by Waddy B Wood, with formal garden. From 1921, it served as the retirement home of President Wilson and Mrs. Wilson. Average Annual Attendance: 10,000.
Income: Financed by endowment and membership.
Collections: Early 20th century furnishings, utensils, and clothing.
Exhibitions: Kalorama: From Country Estate to Urban Elegance; A 25¢ Discovery: The Architectural Drawings of Waddy Butler Wood; The War Against Freedom: Civil Liberties in Washington, DC during the First World War; Hornblower & Marshall, Architects.
Activities: Lect open to public, 60 vis lectr per yr; concerts; films; individual paintings and objects of art lent to qualified museums and non-profit corporations.

FLORIDA

BOCA RATON

FLORIDA ATLANTIC UNIVERSITY ART GALLERY,* Art Department, 33431. Tel: 305-395-5100, exten 2673. *Chmn Dept Art* Dorst; *Gallery Coordr* Mary C. Dorst.
Open Mon - Thurs 8 AM - 11 PM; Fri 8AM - 5PM; Sat 9 AM - 5 PM; Sun Noon - Midnight. No admis. Estab 1970 to provide exhibit space for faculty and students and to provide an opportunity to bring to the area exhibits which would expand the cultural experience of the viewers; gallery located in University Library.
Income: Financed by city and state appropriations and student activities fees.
Collections: Student work; slide collection.
Exhibitions: Faculty and former students; annual juried student show; work from area junior colleges; traveling exhibitions.
Activities: Lect open to public; workshops sponsored by Student Art Society; scholarships.

BRADENTON

ART LEAGUE OF MANATEE COUNTY,* Art Center, 209 Ninth St. W, 33505. Tel: 813-746-2862. *Dir* Mrs Roger Murray.
Open Sept - May, Mon - Fri 9 AM - 4:30 PM; Sat 9 AM - Noon; Sun 2 - 4 PM; June Mon - Fri 9 AM - Noon; cl July, Aug and holidays. No admis. Estab 1935. Average Annual Attendance: 25,000. Mem: 475; dues $5 and up; annual meeting Apr.
Exhibitions: Work by members, one-person shows and circulating exhibitions changing at three week intervals from Oct - May; members work June and Sept.
Activities: Art school instruction in painting, drawing, sculpture, copper enameling, clay techniques and variety of handcrafts; creative development for children; special art programs; gift shop; lect; films; gallery talks.
Library: Holdings—Vols 750.

CLEARWATER

FLORIDA GULF COAST ART CENTER, INC, 222 Ponce de Leon Blvd, 33516. Tel: 813-584-8634. *Managing Dir* Charles H B Latshaw; *Pres of the Board of Governors* Jay H Tiffin; *VPres* Lloyd Banks; *Treas* William Crown, III, *Secy* Mrs Alfred Hoffman; *Asst Secy* Jeanette Emrich.

Open Tues - Sat 10 AM - 4 PM; Sun 2 - 5 PM; cl Mon. No admis, donations accepted. Estab 1948 as a focal point for the arts. The gallery has carpeted walls with ceiling and spot lights to highlight displays. Average Annual Attendance: 10,000. Mem: 1000; dues individual $20, family $25; annual meeting Mar.
Income: Financed by membership.
Exhibitions: Exhibitions change every three weeks.
Publications: Monthly Bulletin.
Activities: Classes for adults and children; lectr open to the public; individual paintings and original objects of art lent; traveling exhibitions organized and circulated; sales shop selling original art.
Library: *Librn* Marion Davis. Open to members only.

CORAL GABLES

METROPOLITAN MUSEUM AND ART CENTERS, 1212 Anastasia Ave, 33134. Tel: 305-442-1448. *Dir* Dr Arnold L Lehman; *Asst Dir* Tom Schmitt; *Dir School* Juanita May; *Adminr* Dorothy Connors; *Registrar* Cynthia Sottile; *Educ Coordinator* Phyllis Reischer; *Pres Bd Trustees* Raymond Mathisen; *Chmn Bd Trustees* Joseph R Harrison; *Chmn Bd Governors* J Deering Danielson.
Open Mon - Thurs 10 AM - 5 PM; Sat - Sun 1 - 6 PM; Tues & Thurs 5 - 9:30 PM. No admis. Estab 1962 as a general museum of visual arts with emphasis on Latin America, 20th century sculpture and traveling exhibitions. Six gallery spaces devoted to both temporary and permanent exhibitions. Average Annual Attendance: 150,000. Mem: 5000; dues $15 - $5000; annual meeting Sept.
Income: $500,000 (financed by membership, contributions and grants).
Collections: Jacques Lipchitz Sculpture Center; Martinez-Canas Collection of Contemporary Latin American Painting; Fashion Group Collection of Historic Costumes; Pre-Columbian; oriental; contemporary American painting and graphics.
Exhibitions: John Marin Watercolors; Joseph Cornell Collages; Roy Lichtenstein (drawings and paintings); American Magic Realists; Silver from the Rio de la Plata; Third Miami International Graphics Biennial; CoBrA paintings and sculpture; Art De Deco; African Art from South Florida Collections; Amelia Paleaz: Retrospective; Image Before My Eyes: A Photographic History of Jewish Life in Poland; Contemporary Ceramics.
Publications: Newsletter, bimonthly, catalogs for exhibitions.
Activities: Classes for adults and children; docent training; programs for schools; lect open to public, 8 vis lectr per yr; gallery talks; tours; competitions; exten dept serving North Miami and Miami Beach; individual paintings and original objects of art lent to museums, libraries and educational institutions; traveling exhibitions organized and circulated; museum shop selling books, magazines, original art, reproductions, prints and slides; junior museum.
Library: Open to members only for reference. Holdings: Vols 2000; Per subs 6. Special Collections: Fern B Muskat Collection.

UNIVERSITY OF MIAMI, The Lowe Art Museum, 1301 Miller Dr, 33146. Tel: 305-284-3535. *Dir* John Baratte; *Asst to the Dir* Brian Dursum; *Registrar* Dorothy Downs.
Open Mon - Fri Noon - 5 PM; Sat 10 AM - 5 PM; Sun 2 - 5 PM. No admis. Estab 1952 to bring outstanding exhibitions and collections to the community and to the University; gallery maintained.
Income: Financed by university funds.
Collections: Samuel H Kress Collection; Alfred Barton Collection of Indian art collection; Oriental art collection; decorative arts.
Exhibitions: (1976-77) Chaim Gross Retrospective; Meissen; Costa Rican Pre-Columbian Pottery; Selections from Glass Collection; Nine Emerging Miami Artists; Recent Accessions; Printmaking, A History; Plains Indians Beadwork; Art of Oriental Bronze Metallurgist; Alfred Barton Collection of Southwest Textiles.
Activities: Classes for adults and children; lect open to the public and for members only, 2 vis lectr per yr; competitions; exten dept serving City of Miami; traveling exhibitions organized and circulated.
Library: For reference. Holdings: Vols 5000; Per subs 12; AV—Slides; Other—Exhibition catalogs, original art works, pamphlets, prints, sculpture.

DAYTONA BEACH

MUSEUM OF ARTS AND SCIENCES, Cuban Museum, Planetarium, 1040 Museum Blvd, 32014. Tel: 904-255-0285. *Pres Bd Trustees* Mrs George A Thompson; *First VPres Bd Trustees* Dr Charles J Wolfe; *Second VPres Bd Trustees* Mrs Wallace J Burt; *Recording Secy* Mrs J H Blickman; *Corresp Secy* Mrs Robert Grooms; *Treas* Mrs W R Gomon; *Asst Treas* Mrs Leila Gosney; *Dir* Gary Russell Libby.
Open Tues - Fri 9 AM - 5 PM; Sat Noon - 5 PM; Sun 1 - 5 PM; cl Mon. Admis individual 50¢; family $1.00,; museum members free. Estab 1955 to offer both educational and cultural services to the public. Large hexag-

onal main exhibition gallery, hall gallery and lobby gallery. Average Annual Attendance: 50,000. Mem: 1185; dues family $20; annual meeting Nov.
Income: $83,000 (financed by endowment, membership, city and county appropriations and donations).
Collections: Cuban Collection; Florida Contemporary Collection; decorative arts including silver and furniture; aboriginal art including Florida Indian; American Illustration: Norman Rockwell.
Exhibitions: Rockwell's America; Great American Illustrations; Indian Cultures Exhibit; Masterpieces of Modern Art.
Publications: Newsletter, bimonthly; catalogs, monthly.
Activities: Classes for adults and children; dramatic programs; docent training; lect open to public, 15 vis lectr per yr; gallery talks; concerts; tours; competitions; exten dept serving area schools; individual paintings and original objects of art lent to other museums and educational institutions; lending collection contains books, nature artifacts, original art works, original prints, paintings and sculpture; traveling exhibitions organized and circulated; sales shop selling books, magazines, reproductions, children and adult gifts.
Library: *Libr*n Marge Segerson. Open to members and school children. Holdings: Vols 20,000; Per subs 5. Special Collections: Cuban—Jose Marti Library.

DELAND

STETSON UNIVERSITY ART GALLERY, 32720. Tel: 904-734-4121, Exten 208. *Dir* Fred Messersmith.
Open Mon - Fri 9 AM - 4:30 PM. No admis. Estab 1964 as an educational gallery to augment studio teaching program; there is a large main gallery, 44 x 55 ft, with a lobby area 22 x 44 ft. Average Annual Attendance: 5000.
Income: University art budget. Purchases: $1000.
Collections: 20th century American prints, oils, watercolors.
Exhibitions: American Watercolor Traveling Show; various regional artists exhibitions.
Publications: Exhibition announcements, monthly.
Activities: Lect open to public, 3 vis lectr per yr; gallery talks; competitions.

FORT LAUDERDALE

FORT LAUDERDALE MUSEUM OF THE ARTS, 426 E Las Olas Blvd, 33301. Tel: 305-463-5184. *Pres* Elliott B Barnett; *Dir* George S Bolge.
Open Tues - Sat 10 AM - 4:30 PM; Sun Noon - 5 PM; cl Mon. No admis. Estab 1958 to bring art to the community and provide cultural facilities and programs. Library, reading room, exhibit space and classrooms. Average Annual Attendance: 14,000. Mem: 1000; dues $20; annual meeting Apr.
Income: $190,650. Purchases: $20,000.
Collections: American and European graphics; paintings and sculpture from late 19th century to present; American Indian ceramics, stone and basketry; West African Tribal Sculpture; Pre-Columbian ceramics and stone artifacts.
Exhibitions: Changing monthly exhibitions; Annual M Allen Hortt Memorial Competition.
Publications: Bulletin, quarterly; Calendar of Events, monthly; Annual Report; Exhibition catalogs.
Activities: Classes for adults and children; docent training; slide lecture program in schools by request; lect series; gallery talks; tours; films; competitions; individual paintings and original objects of art lent to other museums; sales desks.
Library: Holdings—Vols 1000; Others—Carnegie slides 3000.

GAINESVILLE

UNIVERSITY OF FLORIDA
—**University Gallery,** 32611. Tel: 904-392-0201. *Dir* Roy C Craven, Jr; *Secy* Marjorie Z Burdick.
Open Mon - Fri 9 AM - 5 PM; Sun 1 - 5 PM; cl Sat and holidays. No admis. Estab 1965 as an arts exhibition gallery, open 11 months of the year, showing monthly exhibitions with contemporary and historical content. Independent gallery building with small lecture hall, limited access and completely secure with temperature and humidity control, carpet-covered walls and adjustable track lighting; display area in excess of 3000 sq ft. Average Annual Attendance: 40,000. Mem: 200; dues individual $10, family $20, prof $100 and up; annual meeting May.
Income: $70,000 (financed by state appropriation). Purchases: $2,000.
Collections: †European and American prints, paintings and photographs; †Oriental (India) miniatures and sculptures; †Pre-Columbian and Latin American art (also folk art).

Exhibitions: Stuart R Purser Retrospective; San Blas Molas & Central American Ceramics; Concepts of Self in African Art; Folk Arts & Crafts of the Andes; Annual University of Florida Art Faculty (January).
Publications: Bulletin, infrequently; exhibition catalogs.
Activities: Docent training; lect open to public; exten dept serving area schools; lending collection contains cassettes, original art works, photographs and slides; traveling exhibitions organized and circulated.
—**Architecture and Fine Arts Library.** *Librn* Anna Weaver.
Holdings: Vols 30,000; Per subs several hundreds.
Special Subjects: Art and architecture.

JACKSONVILLE

CUMMER GALLERY OF ART,* DeEtte Holden Cummer Museum Foundation, 829 Riverside Ave, 32204. Tel; 904-356-6857. *Dir* Robert W. Schlageter; *Asst to Dir* Suzanne S. Burns.
Open Tues - Fri 10 AM - 4 PM; Sat Noon - 5 PM; Sun 2 - 5 PM; cl Mon and national holidays. No admis. Estab 1961, general art musueum, collecting and exhibiting fine arts of all periods, all cultures. Average Annual Attendance: 45,000.
Collections: †European and American painting, sculpture, graphic arts, tapestries and decorative arts; Oriental collection of jade, ivory, Netsuke, Inro and porcelains; collection of early Meissen porcelain is largest in United States.
Exhibitions: 6 - 8 special exhibitions annually.
Publications: Exhibition catalogs; Handbook of the Permanent Collections.
Activities: Lectures, concerts, gallery tours, gift shop.
Library: Open for reference. Holdings: Vols 4000; Other—Color slides 10,000.

JACKSONVILLE ART MUSEUM, 4160 Boulevard Center Dr. Tel: 904-398-8336. *Dir* Bruce H Dempsey.
Open Tues, Wed & Fri 10 AM - 4 PM; Thurs 10 AM - 10 PM; Sat & Sun 1 - 5 PM; cl Mon holidays and month of Aug. No admis. Estab 1947 as a center for the greater Jacksonville area. Average Annual Attendance: 65,000.
Income: Financed by Membership and city appropriation.
Collections: 20th century paintings and prints; Oriental porcelains and ceamics; Pre-Columbian; African.
Exhibitions: Florida Photographers; The American Landscape (photographs); Talent USA; Art of India; Elizabethan Portraiture; New Realism; The Florida Connection: Rosenquist and Rauschenberg; Helen Frankenthaler.
Publications: Monthly calendar; exhibition catalogs.
Activities: Classes for adults and children; docent training; art enrichment program; lect open to the public, 4 - 5 vis lectr per yr; concerts; gallery talks; tours; competitions; traveling exhibitions organized and circulated; museum shop selling books; magazines, original art, reproductions, prints.
Library: Open to teachers in Duval County Schools.

JACKSONVILLE MUSEUM OF ARTS AND SCIENCES, 1025 Gulf Life Drive, 32207. Tel: 904-396-7061. *Dir* Doris L Whitmore; *Admin Asst* Sally Taylor; *Asst to Dir* Thyra Dickson; *Cur Coll* Grace Eleazer.
Open Mon - Fri 9 AM - 5 PM; Sat 11 AM - 5 PM; Sun 1 - 5 PM; cl Mon and major holidays. Closed September. No admis. Estab 1941. Lobby and three floors contain exhibit areas, classrooms, and studios. Average Annual Attendance: 225,000. Mem: 825; dues vary.
Income: Financed by Membership, city appropriation, and grants.
Exhibitions: Ancient Egypt; Early Jacksonville (Cowford) during Revolution; On the banks of the St. Johns River; Florida Indians of the Everglades; Country Store.
Publications: Brochures, bi-monthly; annual report; Teacher's Guide, annually.
Activities: Classes for adults and children; dramatic programs; docent training; lect open to public; tours; Art in the Park; traveling exhibitions organized and circulated; museum shop and sales shop selling books, prints, museum-oriented items and toys for children.
Library: Open to staff, docents and volunteers for reference.

JACKSONVILLE PUBLIC LIBRARY,* Art and Music Dept, 122 N Ocean St, 32201. Tel: 904-633-6870. *Dir* Harry Brinton; *Art & Music Dept Librn* Jeff Driggers.
Open Mon - Fri 9 AM - 9 PM; Sat 9 AM - 6 PM. No admis. Estab 1905 to serve the public by giving them free access to books, films, phonograph recordings, pamphlets, periodicals, maps, plus informational services and free programming. Open area on the mezzanine of the building serves as a display area for local artists.
Income: Financed by city appropriation.

Holdings: (Art) Vols 555,000; AV—Motion pictures 1690, phonorecords 8060, slides 5100; Other—Framed art reproductions, photographs 3000, color reproductions 1000.
Publications: Annual Report.
Activities: Classes for adults; weekly film programs including presentation of 40 feature films per year.

KEY WEST

KEY WEST ART AND HISTORICAL SOCIETY, S Roosevelt Blvd, 33040. Tel: 305-296-3913. *Pres* Charles Munder; *VPres* Frederic Cole; *Secy* Ross McKee; *Exec Dir* Paul E Thompson.
Open Sun - Sat 9:30 AM - 5 PM. Admis $1.50 adults. Estab 1966 for the support and dissemination of the history and arts of Key West, the Florida Keys, State of Florida and the United States. The gallery is located in a restored 1861 brick fort; there are three larger, and four smaller galleries, all contiguous. These galleries have arched ceilings, are air conditioned and have moveable track lighting. Average Annual Attendance: 40,000. Mem: 1100; dues students $5, individual $15, couple $20; ann meeting first Wed in Apr.
Income: $55,000 (financed by membership). Purchases are meager.
Collections: Small collection with no plans of expansion.
Exhibitions: (1977-78) Local-regional artists exhibitions; membership exhibition; annual county schools exhibition; American Watercolor Society Exhibition.
Publications: Martello, infrequently.
Activities: Sales shop selling books, magazines, original art, prints, reproductions, slides and other gift-shop materials.
Library: There are approximately 250 historical items, such as ledgers, property abstracts, books on history, and others.

LAKELAND

FLORIDA SOUTHERN COLLEGE, Melvin Art Gallery, Ludd M. Spivey Fine Arts & Humanities Bldg, 33801. Tel: 813-682-9377. *Coordinator of Art/Gallery Dir* Dr Donna M Stoddard.
Open Mon - Fri 1 - 3:30 PM. No admis. Estab 1971 as a teaching gallery; Small gallery dedicated to Frank Lloyd Wright (architect for college), covers 2000 running sq ft.
Exhibitions: (1977) Interpretive Realism by R Wayne Waldron; Southern Print Makers; Crown Craftsmen of Duval County. (1978) Recent Paintings and Drawings by Downing Barnitz; Student Honors Exhibition; Phantasies in Watercolor by Calum Darren; Juried Show Number Seven (Lakeland Art Guild).

POLK PUBLIC MUSEUM, 800 E Palmetto, 33801. Tel: 813-688-7744. *Pres* Janet Tucker; *Secy* Rev Joseph Huntley; *Dir* James D Marler.
Open Tues - Fri 10 AM - 5 PM; Sat, Sun & holidays 1:30 - 4:30 PM; cl Mon. No admis. Estab 1966 to bring changing exhibits of art, history and science to community and to provide cultural enrichment to the area. Five galleries. Average Annual Attendance: 10,000. Mem: 398; dues $5 - $1000.
Income: Financed by membership.
Collections: Barnum Collection (outstanding regional artists); Ellis Verink photographs; 14th-19th century stoneware and pottery; various individual pieces of notable art and furniture.
Activities: Classes for adults and children; workshops; tours; concerts; dramatic programs; photograph collection; prints 100; lect open to public, 6 vis lectr per yr; Suitcase Museum Program.
Library: Open for reference. Holdings: Vols 500.

MAITLAND

MAITLAND ART CENTER RESEARCH STUDIO,* 231 W Packwood Ave, 32751. Tel: 305-645-2181. *Pres* Rae Bennett; *Secy* Mrs R Field; *Dir* Charles L Baker; *Cur Exhib* Roger F Dumas; *Cur Educ* Karen Neustadt.
Open Tues - Sat 10 AM - 4 PM; Sun 1 - 5 PM; cl Mon. No admis. Estab 1939 to promote exploration and education in the visual arts and contemporary crafts. Maintains gallery. Average Annual Attendance: 7500. Mem: 780; dues $10; annual meeting May.
Income: Over $50,000 (financed by membership; city and state appropriations). Purchases: Over $50,000.
Collections: Graphics-Paintings of Andre Smith (367); architectural work including 9-acre compound and memorial chapel designed by Smith.
Publications: Imagination, bimonthly.
Activities: Classes for adults and children; art training classes; lect open to public, 4 vis lectr per yr; gallery talks; tours; concerts; competitions; scholarships; book shop.

Library: Open for reference. Holdings: Vols 430 (notes, books, and records of Andre Smith).

MIAMI

DADE COUNTY ART MUSEUM, Vizcaya Museum and Gardens, 3251 S Miami Ave, 33129. Tel: 305-854-3531. *Dir* Carl J Weinhardt, Jr; *Asst Dir* James Loiacano *Cur Educ* Louise Drake; *Cur Coll* Susan W Reiling; *Conservator* Emilio Cianfioni.
Open daily 9:30 AM - 5:30 PM; cl Christmas. Admis Adults $3.50 house and gardens, $1.50 garden only; children $1. Estab 1952 to increase the general public's appreciation of the European decorative arts, architecture and landscape design through lectures and visits conducted by trained volunteer guides. Vizcaya is a house museum with a major collection of European decorative arts and elaborate formal gardens. The Villa formerly the home of James Deering, was completed in 1916 and contains approx 70 rooms. Average Annual Attendance: 225,000. Mem: 1500; dues $25 and up; annual meeting second Tue May.
Income: $880,000. (financed by admission fees).
Collections: Italian and French furniture of the 16th - 18th and early 19th centuries; notable specialized collections of carpets, tapestries, Roman antiquities and bronze mortars.
Publications: Vizcayan Newsletter (quarterly).
Activities: Docent training; lect open to the public, 6 vis lectr per yr; concerts individual paintings and original objects of art lent to accredited museum; sales museum shop selling original art, prints and slides.
Library: *Vol Librn* Mrs A Miller. Open to volunteers and students of the decorative arts for reference only. Holdings: Vols 1500; Per subs 10; Other—museum archival material. Special Subjects: Decorative arts; interiors and furniture.
Special Collections: Slide collection for reference and teaching.

MIAMI-DADE COMMUNITY COLLEGE, SOUTH CAMPUS, ART GALLERY, 11011 SW 104th St, 33176. Tel: 305-596-1281. *Dir Cur* Karen Valdes; *Chmn Art Dept* Margaret Pelton.
Open Mon - Fri 8 AM - 4 PM; Tues & Wed 6 - 8 PM. No admis. Estab 1970 as a teaching laboratory and public service.
Income: Financed by state appropriation. Purchases: $75,000.
Collections: Contemporary American prints, photographs, paintings, and sculpture, includes: Bolotowsky, Remington, Boice, Christo, Oldenburg, Judd, Pearlstein, Fine, Hockney, Beal, Hepworth.
Exhibitions: Bolotowsky; Bruce Boice; Mark Cohen; Willia T Williams; Five Washington Artists; Audrey Flack; Deborah Remington; Bob Thiele; Hap Tivey.
Activities: Lect open to public, 6 - 7 vis lectr per yr; gallery talks; individual paintings and original objects of art lent; lending collection contains original art works, original prints, paintings, photographs and sculpture; traveling exhibitions organized and circulated.

MIAMI-DADE PUBLIC LIBRARY, One Biscayne Blvd, 33132. Tel: 305-579-5001. *Dir* Edward F Sintz; *Asst Dir* Ben J Guilford II; *Supv Processing Center* Lillian Conesa; *Supv Traveling Libraries* Carol Gawron; *Public Relations Coordinator* Mrs Micki Carden; *Supv Branches* Eleanor McLaughlin; *Coordinator Work with Children and Young Adults* Anne Boegen; *Art Librn* Margarita Cano.
Open Mon - Fri 10 AM - 9 PM; Sat 10 AM - 6 PM; Sun 1 - 5 PM. Estab 1947 to provide the informational, educational and recreational needs of the community; Gallery maintained. Circ: 2,659,312.
Income: $10,400,150 (1977-78), (financed by special millage).
Holdings: Vols 1,238,352; Per subs 2900; AV—Microfiche, microfilm; motion pictures, phonorecords; Other—Clipping files, exhibition catalogs, framed reproductions, original art works, photographs, reproductions, sculpture.
Special Subjects: Latin American Art.
Special Collections: Latin American original graphics; Black American original graphics; Oriental Collection of original graphics.
Exhibitions: Cintas Fellows: Cintas Foundation Fellows Inernational Exhibit; New Dimensions: Works by Black American Artists; Re-Encuentro; Exhibit of Cuban Art.
Publications: Exhibit catalogs.
Activities: Lect open to the public; concerts; gallery talks; tours; competitions; exten dept; artmobile; traveling exhibitions organized and circulated.

MIAMI BEACH

BASS MUSEUM OF ART, 2100 Collins Ave, 33139. Tel: 305-673-7530. *Adminr* Phyllis A Gray; *Chmn of the Board* Dodd Southern.
Hours Tues - Sat 10 AM - 5 PM. No admis. Estab 1963 to provide a pleasant atmosphere for the viewing of the various art and artifacts that have been donated to the city; all of the art in the museum was donated by Mr John Bass. The museum is a two-story bldg of some seven gallery rooms. Average Annual Attendance: 21,000.

Income: $67,000 (financed by city appropriation).
Collections: Permanent collection of Old Master paintings, Renaissance sculpture, church vestments, and others.
Activities: Photographs and postcards for sale.

MIAMI BEACH PUBLIC LIBRARY, 2100 Collins Ave, 33139. *Chief Librn* Phyllis A Gray.
Open Mon - Wed 10 AM - 9 PM; Thurs - Sat 10 AM - 5:30 PM. Estab 1927 to serve the citizens of Miami Beach. Circ: 410,000. Maintains an art gallery. The Library Dept manages the Bass Museum of Art which is housed in the former library building.
Income: $515,000 (financed by city appropriation). Purchases: $40,000.
Holdings: Vols 180,500; Per subs 400; AV—Phonorecords; Other—Clipping files, pamphlets.

SAINT BERNARD FOUNDATION AND MONASTERY,* 16711 W Dixie Hwy, 33160. Tel: 305-945-1462. *Exec Dir* Rev Father Frank G Atlee, Jr.
Open Mon - Sat & holidays 10 AM - 4 PM; Sun, Ash Wednesday, Good Friday, Holy Saturday, Easter Noon - 4 PM; cl Xmas. Admis adults $1.50, children 6-12 75¢. Estab 1963 as a branch of the Diocese of Southeast Florida, a reconstruction of a monastery built in Segovia, Spain, in 1141, with original stones brought to the United States by William Randolph Hearst.
Collections: Historic and religious material; paintings; sculpture.
Activities: Guided tours; museum loan exhibitions; arts festivals; sales shop.

OCALA

CENTRAL FLORIDA COMMUNITY COLLEGE ART COLLECTION,* Box 1388, 3001 SW College Road, 32670. Tel: 904-237-2111. *Pres* Henry Goodlett; *Dir Div Fine Arts* O Joseph Fleming II.
Open Mon - Fri 8 AM - 9:30 PM. No admis. Estab 1967 as a service to the community. Gallery is the lobby to the auditorium. Average Annual Attendance: 5000.
Income: Financed by state appropriations.
Collections: Contemporary artists of varied media.
Exhibitions: Changing monthly shows, with one show for the summer.
Publications: Windfall.
Activities: Classes for adults; scholarships.
Library: Holdings—Vols 40,000.

ORLANDO

LOCH HAVEN ART CENTER, INC, 2416 N Mills Ave, 32803. Tel: 305-896-4231 & 896-4232. *Dir* Marena R Grant; *Cur Educ* William D Morrisey.
Open Tues - Sat 10 AM - 5 PM; Sun 2 - 5 PM. No admis. Estab 1926 to encourage the awareness of and participation in the visual arts. Accredited by the American Association of Museums. Average Annual Attendance: 120,000. Mem: 1800; annual dues vary; annual meeting May.
Income: Financed by membership, city appropriation and grants.
Collections: 20th Century American, pre-Columbian and African art.
Exhibitions: Major exhibitions in various media and styles.
Publications: Bulletin.
Activities: Classes for adults and children; docent training; film series, workshop, visiting artists; lect open to public, 3 - 5 vis lectr per yr; concerts; gallery talks; tours; exten dept serving central Florida; individual paintings and original objects of art lent to organizations within central Florida; lending collection contains original prints; traveling exhibitions organized and circulated; museum and sales shop selling books, original art, reproductions, prints, and cards.
Library: Holdings—Vols 200, Per subs 5.

ORMOND BEACH

TOMOKA STATE PARK MUSEUM, N Beach St, 32074. Tel: 904-677-9463. *Museum Guide:* Alice Strickland.
Open Wed - Sun 9 AM - 5 PM; cl Mon & Tues. Admis 25¢. Estab 1967.
Income: Financed by state appropriation.
Collections: Paintings and sculptures by Fred Dana Marsh; Indian artifacts.
Exhibitions: Exhibits on Florida geology, wildlife, Indian artifacts, Florida history, and paintings and sculptures by Fred Dana Marsh.
Publications: Richard Oswald: Tomoka State Park's Hero of the Revolution. (brochure).
Activities: Tours.

PALM BEACH

HENRY MORRISON FLAGLER MUSEUM, Whitehall Way (Mailing Add: Box 969, 33480). Tel: 305-655-2833. *Pres & Trustee:* Mrs Flagler Matthews; *Exec Dir* Charles B Simmons; *Asst to Dir* Nan Dennison.
Open Tues - Sun 10 AM - 5 PM; cl Mon. Admis Adults $2, children between 6 & 12 $1. Estab 1960 for preservation and interpretation of the Whitehall mansion, the 1901 residence built for Standard Oil partner and pioneer developer of Florida's east coast, Henry Morrison Flagler. Fifty room historic house with restored rooms and special collections, plus addition used for Junior League, Historical Society and special events and exhibits. Average Annual Attendance: 96,337. Mem: 550; dues $25; annual meeting Fri preceding first Sat in Feb.
Income: Financed by endowment, membership.
Collections: Original family furnishings, costumes; lace, silver, ceramics, and paintings.
Exhibitions: Various Smithsonian traveling exhibits; extensive exhibit on architect Addison Mizner; The White House in Miniature—costumes area exhibits such as the Gold Coast Needlearts Guild and Military Miniatures, plus exhibits by local artists.
Publications: The Henry Morrison Flagler Museum, 40 pages.
Activities: Docent training; lect open to public, 2 - 5 vis lectr per yr; gallery talks, tours; individual paintings and original objects of art lent by request, no fixed policy; lending collection contains 10 slides; museum shop selling books, slides and postcards.
Library: Only for reference and in conjunction with Historical Society; by appointment only. Special Collections: Florida history period 1880, archives.

SOCIETY OF THE FOUR ARTS, Four Arts Plaza, 33480. Tel: 305-655-7226. *Pres* Walter S Gubelmann; *VPres* Mrs James A dePeyster, Philip Hulitar, Mrs Robert A Magawan and Wiley R Reynolds; *Secy-Treas* William E P Doelger; *Dir* James M Brown; *Asst to Dir* Gabrielle Summerville; *Librn* Helen McKinney.
Open Dec to mid-Apr Mon - Sat 10 AM - 5 PM; Sun 2 - 5 PM. Admis to exhib galleries free. Estab 1936 to encourage an appreciation of the arts by presentation of exhibitions, lectures, concerts and films and the maintenance of a fine library and gardens. Five galleries for exhibitions, separate general library, gardens, and auditorium. Average Annual Attendance: 72,000 (galleries and library). Mem: 1500; dues single $95, double $150, sustaining $195, life $3000. Annual meeting Third Fri in Mar.
Income: $304,000 (financed by endowment, membership, city appropriation toward maintenance of library, and contributions).
Collections: Small collection (some 20 works).
Exhibitions: (1975-76) 37th Annual Exhibition of Contemporary American Paintings; At Home 1776-1976 American Furniture and Accessories; Golden Age of Ballet Design - Watercolors and Sculpture from the Spreckels Dance Collection lent by The Fine Arts Museums of San Francisco; Lyonel Feininger - Paintings lent by The Museum of Modern Art and Whitney Museum of American Art; (1976-77) 38th Annual Exhibition of Contemporary American Paintings; Imperial Robes and Bronzes of China lent by the Minneapolis Institute of Arts; The American Indian Paintings by George Catlin lent by the National Collection of Fine Arts and Indian Artifacts lent by the Lowe Gallery; Addison Mizner (1872-1933) Master Architect of Palm Beach (an exhibition in three parts held in conjunction with Norton Gallery and Flagler Museum); (1977-78) 39th Annual Exhibition of Contemporary American Paintings; German Expressionism - Oils, watercolors, drawings, prints, sculpture, from the Collection of Dr William R Valentiner; Milton Avery (1893-1965) retrospective exhibition of paintings and monotypes; Extraordinary People - portraits on paper of artists and writers lent by The Museum of Modern Art.
Publications: Calendar (Jan, Feb & Mar); Schedule of Events, annual.
Activities: Provides lectr open to the public when space permits; otherwise limited to members, 13 vis lectr per yr; competitions open to artists resident in United States; juror selects about 90 paintings for inclusion in annual exhibition; $5000 cash awards are given.
—**Library.** Tel: 305-655-2766. *Librn* Helen McKinney; *Cir Librn* Irene D Stevenson; *Children's Librn* Evelyn Rand.
Open Weekdays 10 AM - 5 PM; cl Sat May to Nov. Circ 38,000.
Income: $56,000 (financed by endowment, membership and city appropriation). Purchases: $6300.
Holdings: Vols 27,000; Per subs 56.
Special Collections: Addison Mizner Collection which consists of over 300 reference books and scrapbooks in Mizner's personal library.
Activities: Library tours.

PENSACOLA

HISTORIC PENSACOLA PRESERVATION BOARD, West Florida Museum of History, 205 E Zaragoza St, 32501. Tel: 904-434-1042. *Dir*

James W Moody, Jr; *Admin Asst* John C Azab; *Chief Cur* Russell Belous; *Architect* George Demmy; *Historian* Linda V Ellsworth; *Chmn Board of Trustees* Charles Cetti.
Open Mon - Sat 10 AM - 4:30 PM; Sun 1:30 - 4:30 PM. Donations accepted. Estab 1967 for collection, preservation, and interpretation of artifacts dealing with the history and culture of Pensacola and West Florida. Main gallery includes history of development of west Florida as well as area for temporary exhibits. Average Annual Attendance: 60,000.
Income: Approx 350,000 (financed by city, county, and state appropriation, sales and rentals.
Collections: (Art) Costumes; local artists; decorative arts.
Exhibitions: The Seat of American Invention, The World of Lilliput, and American Agriculture (SITES); Clockwork Music and Talking Machines.
Activities: Educ dept; docent training; sales shop selling books, reproductions and local crafts.
Library: Open to public for reference. Holdings: Vols 800; Per subs 15; slides and photographs. Special Subjects: Historic preservation, regional history, architecture, decorative arts.

PENSACOLA MUSEUM OF ART, formerly Pensacola Art Center, 407 S Jefferson St, 32501. Tel: 904-432-6247. *Dir* Brigitte Huybregts; *Secy* Edith Schmitz; *Pres* W Stewart Morrison; *Pres Elect* C Miner Harrell; *VPres* Mrs Raymond Dyson; *Treas* Joseph J Campus III.
Open Tues - Sat 10 AM - 5 PM; Sun 1 - 4 PM; cl Mon. No admis. Estab 1954 to further and disseminate information and instruction with regard to all of the Fine Arts and to increase knowledge and appreciation thereof. Historical building, old city jail built in 1908, 13,000 sq ft of exhibition area. Average Annual Attendance: 12,000. Mem: 550; dues $7.50 and up; annual meeting Oct.
Income: $62,000 (financed by membership, city and state appropriation, and private business).
Collections: Contemporary art.
Exhibitions: Traveling exhibitions; in-house organized exhibitions; changing displays of permanent collection.
Activities: Classes for adults and children; docent training; lect open to public; competitions; museum shop selling books, reproductions, crafts, and jewelry; junior museum.
Library: Harry Thornton Library. *Librn* Ona Butler. Open to members of Pensacola Art Association. Holdings: Vols 375. Special Subjects: Fine arts and related fields.

UNIVERSITY OF WEST FLORIDA ART GALLERY, 32504. Tel: 904-476-9500. *Dir* Duncan E Stewart; *Chmn* Robert L Armstrong.
Open Mon - Thurs 9:30 AM - 7:30 PM; Fri 9:30 AM - 4 PM; cl Sat & Sun. No admis. Estab 1975 to hold exhibitions which will relate to our role as a senior level university. The gallery includes a foyer gallery 10' x 40', and a main gallery of 1500 sq ft. It is fully air-conditioned and has carpeted walls with full facilities for construction and display. Average Annual Attendance: 3000.
Income: $3000 (financed by state appropriation).
Collections: Prints and photographs by a number of traditional and contemporary artists.
Activities: Lect open to public, 3 vis lectr per yr; gallery talks; tours; competitions; traveling exhibitions organized and circulated.

TT WENTWORTH, JR MUSEUM,* 8382 Palafox Highway (Mailing Add: PO Box 806, 32594). Tel: 904-438-3638. *Dir & Cur* T T Wentworth Jr; *Deputy Dir & Secy* T W Wentworth.
Open Sat - Sun 2 - 6 PM. No admis. Estab 1957 to conserve historical items and make them available to the public; art sections to encourage art and exhibit local art work. Annual meeting Aug.
Income: Financed by membership and founder's contributions.
Collections: Works of local and some nationally famous artists; Indian artifacts; coins; porcelain.
Exhibitions: Special yearly art exhibit of some distinguished local artist.

SAINT AUGUSTINE

FLORIDA ARTIST GROUP INC, 6 South St, 32084, Tel: 904-824-3187. *Pres* Reyna Youngerman; *VPres* John Sitton; *Secy* Susan Stairs Stevens; *Immediate Past Pres* Jean Wagner Troemel; *Mem Chmn* Stormy A Sandquist; *Treas* Marcelle Bear.
Estab 1949 for the stimulation of finer standards of the creative effort within the state of Florida. Mem: Approx 200, qualification for mem by invitation based on artistic merit; dues $15; annual meeting May.
Income: Approx $2800 (financed by membership).
Exhibitions: Florida is divided into 8 areas and each area sponsors exhibitions, either locally or lending to another area: (1976) Jacksonville Museum of Art, Fla; (1977) Metropolitan Museum of Art of Dade County, Miami, Fla; (1978) At Harmon Gallery, Naples, Fla.
Publications: Newsletter, 3 times per yr.

Activities: Lect open to both members and public; competitions, one annual competition open to members only, Genievieve Hamel, Robert Carson & Hilton Leech Memorial awards given; traveling exhibitions organized and circulated.

SAINT AUGUSTINE ART ASSOCIATION GALLERY,* 22 Marine St, 32084. Tel: 904-824-2310. *Pres* James E Long; *First VPres* William E Twamley; *Second VPres* Dr Joseph Veber; *Secy-Treas* Harold M Steele; *Corresp Secy* Dorothy O Smith.
Open Oct-May, Tues - Sat 1 - 5 PM; Sun 2 - 5 PM; cl Mon. No admis. Estab 1924, inc 1934, as a non-profit organization to further art appreciation and stimulate sales of members' work. Average Annual Attendance: 5000. Mem: 300; dues $6 and up; annual meeting Mar.
Collections: Work donated by area artists.
Exhibitions: Monthly exhibitions Oct - May with cash awards; New Talent Shows in Nov and Apr for those who have never before exhibited or won awards.
Activities: Art classes; demonstrations; discussions; lectures; promoting Alice Lawton Library of Art in public library building.

SAINT AUGUSTINE HISTORICAL SOCIETY
—**Oldest House and Museums,** 14 St Frances St, 32084. Tel: 904-829-9624. *Pres* Carleton Calkin; *VPres* Hubert W Carcaba; *Secy* W J Winter; *Treas* Charles Coomes; *Mgr* Virginia Solana.
Open Mon - Fri 9 AM - 5:30 PM; cl Christmas Day. Admis adults $1.00, students 50¢. Estab 1883 to preserve the Spanish heritage of the United States through exhibits in historic museum with collection of furnishings appropriate to the periods in St. Augustine history (1565 to date). The Oldest House was acquired in 1918; it is owned and operated by the St. Augustine Historical Society; it has been designated a National Historic Landmark by the Department of the Interior and is listed in the National Register of Historic sites and places. Average Annual Attendance: 105,000.
Income: Financed by admissions.
Collections: Period furnishings, archaeological material recovered from this area, both aboriginal and colonial.
—**Library,** 271 Charlotte St, 32084. Tel: 904-829-5512. *Mgr* J Carver Harris; *Admin Asst* Jacqueline Bearden.
Open Mon - Fri 9 AM - Noon and 1 - 5 PM; cl holidays. A research library.
Income: Financed by endowment and admissions from Oldest House.
Holdings: Vols 5500; Per subs 40; AV—Audio tapes, cassettes, kodachromes, microfilm, motion pictures, phonorecords and slides; Other—Clipping files, manuscripts, memorabilia, original art works, original documents, pamphlets, photographs, prints, reproductions and sculpture.
Special Subjects: Florida history (to 1821) with emphasis on early periods of St Augustine history to the present.
Special Collections: Paintings of early artists and of early St Augustine; 200 linear feet of maps, photographs, documents and photostats of Spanish archival materials as touching directly on St Augustine's history during the early Spanish, British and American periods (1565 to present).
Publications: East Florida Gazette, quarterly; El Escribano, annually.
Activities: Lect open to public, 4 vis lectr per yr.

SAINT PETERSBURG

MUSEUM OF FINE ARTS OF ST PETERSBURG, FLORIDA, INC, 255 Beach Dr N, 33701. Tel: 813-896-2667. *Dir* Lee Malone; *Asst Dir* Alan Du Bois; *Exec Secy* Mrs Robert S Baer; *Cur Educ* Mrs McDonnell Grady; *Mem & Museum Shop* Mrs Edgar Andruss; *Registrar* Mrs Thomas C Laughlin.
Open Tues - Sat 10 AM - 5 PM; Sun 1 - 5 PM; cl Mon. Admis by voluntary donation.
Estab 1961 to increase and diffuse knowledge and appreciation of art; to collect and preserve objects of artistic interest; to provide facilities for research and to offer popular instruction and opportunities for esthetic enjoyment of art. Nine galleries of works including American and European paintings, drawings, prints and photographs; French, American, Oriental sculpture; decorative arts; pre-Columbian art. Average Annual Attendance; 43,030. Mem: 2700; dues $5 and higher, annual meeting Apr or May.
Income: $315,000 (financed by endowment, membership, city and state appropriation). Purchases: $500
Collections: Paintings; sculpture; prints; drawings; photographs; decorative arts.
Exhibitions: (1976) New Vision, Florida Paintes, Art from Florida Corporations, Kent Bicentennial Portfolio, Latin American Horizons, Florida Photo Image, Marine Paints and Clipper Ship; (1977) Faberge, Boudin, Art of European Glass 1600-1800, Contemporary Crafts of Americas,

Contemporary French Photography, Stanton Macdonald-Wright, Edvard Munch, Ansel Adams, and Joseph Raffael; (1978) Photo Realism, Campbell Collection, Van Dongen, New Washington Painters.
Publications: Mosaic, quarterly newsletter; Pharos, schoarly magazine.
Activities: Classes for adults and children; docent training; films; lectures; Brownbagger Special Lunch; concerts; high school internship; videocassettes; 3 vis lectr per yr; gallery talks; tours; individual paintings and original objects of art lent to other museums; lending collection contains color reproductions, framed reproductions, motion pictures, original art works and prints, and photographs; traveling exhibitions organized and circulated; museum shop selling books, reproductions, prints, museum replicas, jewelry, pottery and crafts by local artisans.
—**Art Reference Library.** Tel: 813-896-2667. *Dir* Lee Malone; *Asst Dir* Alan Du Bois.
Open Tues - Sat 10 AM - 5 PM; Sun 1 - 5 PM; cl Mon. Estab 1962 to promote the appreciation of art. Circ 2700.
Income: Approx $284,000 (financed by endowment, membership, city appropriation and special gifts).
Holdings: Vols 5000; Per subs 30; AV—Audio tapes and slides; Other—Clipping files, exhibition catalogs, photographs, prints, and reproductions.
Special Collections: Photography.
Activities: Classes for adults and children; lect open to the public, 6 vis lectr per yr; concerts; gallery talks; exten serving public schools.

SARASOTA

JOHN AND MABLE RINGLING MUSEUM OF ART, 5401 Bayshore Road (Box 1838, 33578). Tel: 813-355-5101. *Dir* Richard S Carroll; *Adminr* Gerald Gartenberg; *Cur European Art* William H Wilson; *Cur Contemporary Art* Elayne H Varian; *Registrar* Elizabeth S Telford; *Librn* V L Schmidt; *Cur Ringling Museum of the Circus* John H Hurdle; *Head Educ and State Service* John P Daniels; *Chief Publ Information* Robert K Ardren; *Comptroller* George D Porter.
Open Mon - Fri 9 AM - 10 PM; Sat 9 AM - 5 PM; Sun 11 AM - 6 PM. Admis $3.50, children under 12 free; Museum of Art free on Sat. Estab 1946. Bequeathed to the State of Florida by John Ringling and operated by the state; built in Italian villa style around sculpture garden on 38 landscaped acres; original 18th century theater from Asolo, near Venice, in adjacent building; Ringling Residence and Ringling Museum of the Circus on grounds. Dues individual $15, family $25.
Collections: †European painting, sculpture, drawings and prints from the 16th, 17th & 18th centuries; Baroque pictures, especially those of Peter Paul Rubens; archaeology of Cyprus; medals and 18th century decorative arts; †developing collection of 19th & 20th century painting, sculpture, drawings and prints.
Exhibitions: Baroque masterworks from the Ringling Collection; Art of the theater; Honor awards exhibition; Latin American horizons, 1976; Florida collects; Doris Leeper; Contemporary photography; America's architectural heritage; Thomas Eakins: A Family Album; The Circus in Art; Henry Moore: prints 1969-1974; Milton Avery retrospective; Giacometti, sculptor and draughtsman; Contemporary Tapestries.
Publications: Newsletter, quarterly.
Activities: Dramatic programs; docent training; lect series; concerts; tours; art carnival; crafts festival; medieval fair; classic and foreign film series; winter opera season; statewide programs of exhibitions and lectures.
—**Art Research Library.** *Librn* Valentine L Schmidt. Open to the public for reference.
Holdings: Vols 7000; Per subs 50; Other—Museum and gallery catalogs 20,000, auction sale catalogs 20,000, rare books.
Special Subjects: Art history; renaissance and baroque art; iconography; emblematics.

SARASOTA ART ASSOCIATION, * Civic Center, 707 N Tamiami Trail, 33577. Tel: 813-958-3175. *Pres* Lloyd Gladfelter; *Gallery Dir* Virginia Klemmer.
Open Oct - May, Mon - Fri 10 AM - 5 PM; Sat & Sun 1 - 4 PM. No admis. Estab 1926, inc 1940. Average Annual Attendance: 17,000. Mem: Over 1000; dues $5 - $500; annual meeting Spring.
Exhibitions: 10 to 12 exhibitions for members only during an 8-month period.
Publications: Bulletin, monthly; Yearbook.
Activities: Lect; demonstrations; competitions with cash awards.
Library: Open for art reference. Holdings: Vols 200.

STUART

MARTIN COUNTY HISTORICAL SOCIETY, Elliott Gallery, 825 NE Ocean Blvd, 33494. *Dir* Janet Hutchinson.

Open daily 1 - 5 PM. No admis to gallery, museum admis adults $1, children 7 - 13 50¢. Society estab 1955, gallery estab 1965. Gallery exhibiting contemporary artists of prominence. Average Annual Attendance: 50,000. Mem: 794.
Collections: Small collection of original art works and sculpture not on public display.
Exhibitions: Four exhibitions a year.
Publications: Progress Report, quarterly.
Activities: Dramatic programs; lectr open to the public; concerts; receptions; sales shop selling books.
Library: Open to members for reference. Holdings: Vols 500; Per subs 5.

TALLAHASSEE

FLORIDA STATE UNIVERSITY ART GALLERY, * Fine Arts Building, 32306. Tel: 904-644-6836 and 644-6474. *Chmn Dept Art* J L Draper.
Open Mon - Fri 10 AM - 4 PM; Sat - Sun 1 - 4 PM; cl school holidays. Estab 1950; has an art museum, lecture room and lounge. Average Annual Attendance: 60,000.
Income: Financed by state appropriations.
Collections: Graphics, sculpture, paintings.
Exhibitions: Temporary exhibitions of collections; traveling exhibitions.
Activities: Lectures; gallery talks; educ prog for graduate students.

LEMOYNE ART FOUNDATION, 125 N Gadsden St, 32301. Tel: 813-222-8800. *Dir* Nancy J McIntyre; *Asst Dir* Stephen Oakley; *Staff Asst* Erin McCawley Smith; *Bookkeeper* Charlene Williams.
Open Tues - Sat 10 AM - 5 PM; Sun 2 - 5 PM; cl Mon. No admis. Estab 1963 as a non-profit organization to serve as gallery for contemporary, quality art; class center; sponsor the visual arts in Tallahassee; an educational institution in the broadest sense. Located in McDougal-Meginnes House, built c 1840; five main galleries and gallery shop. Average Annual Attendance: 7000. Mem: 976; dues $15.
Income: $100,000 (financed by membership, sales, classes and fund raisers).
Collections: Karl Zerbe serigraphs; William Watson (Collection of ceramics).
Publications: Newsletter, monthly.
Activities: Classes for adults and children; lect open to public, 10 vis lectr per yr; gallery talks; tours; competitions; exten dept serving surrounding rural counties; individual paintings and original objects of art lent to businesses and members; lending collection contains original art works, paintings and sculpture; sales shop selling original art and prints.

TALLAHASSEE JUNIOR MUSEUM, 3945 Museum Dr, 32304. Tel: 904-576-1636. *Dir* Ann M Matthews; *Coordinator of Educ* John Madden; *Cur of Animals* Mike Jones.
Open Tues - Sat 9 AM - 5 PM; Sun 2 - 5 PM. Admis adults $1.50, children 3 - 16 years 50¢; members free. Estab 1957 to educate children and adults about natural history, native wildlife, North Florida history, art and culture; facilities include 1880's farm, historic buildings, exhibit and class buildings, 40 acres of nature trails, and animal habitats. Average Annual Attendance: 100,000. Mem: 1582, dues $10 - $100; annual meeting third Thurs in Jan.
Income: $188,000 (financed by membership, fund raisers and county school board appropriations).
Collections: Decorative Arts; Oriental items; figurines; Pre-Columbian Florida Indian pottery.
Exhibitions: Changing exhibit on science, crafts, art, clothing, and history. Permanent or semi-permanent (3 years) exhibits on local history and natural history.
Publications: Newsletter, monthly; school handbook, yearly; guidebook series.
Activities: Classes for adults and children; lect open to the public, 8-12 vis lectr per yr; concerts; tours; original objects of art lent to local school groups, and to civic organizations occasionally; lending collection contains boxed exhibits 150, on art, culture, history and science; sales shop selling books, and mainly science and history objects.
Library. 904-576-1636. Open to members; Holdings: Vols 300; Per subs 7. Special Collections: Ivan Gundrum Pre-Columbian Florida Indian Artifacts (reproductions) representing the Weeden Island culture 500-1500 AD.

TAMPA

LATIN QUARTER ART GALLERY, * Ybor City Chamber of Commerce, 1509 Eighth Ave, 33605. Tel: 813-248-3712. *Pres* Arthur M Dosal; *Exec Dir* Oscar Aguayo.

Open Mon - Fri 9 AM - 5 PM; cl weekends. No admis. Estab 1968 to give artists facilities to display their works and the general public opportunity to see original works by contemporary artists. Mem: 339; dues $10 and up.
Income: $3500 (financed by sales and Ybor City Chamber of Commerce funds).
Publications: Monthly memo to artists.

HENRY B PLANT MUSEUM,* 401 W Kennedy Blvd, 33606. Tel: 813-256-8861. *Dir* Patricia Newton Moller.
Open Jan - July & Sept - Dec, Tues - Sat 10 AM - 4 PM; Sun 2 - 4 PM; cl Mon, Aug, most holidays. No admis. Estab 1933 in the old Tampa Bay Hotel built in 1891.
Income: Financed by city appropriation.
Collections: Prints; porcelains; paintings; bronzes; mirrors; carpets; early Chinese pottery.
Exhibitions: Temporary traveling exhibitions monthly.
Publications: The Henry B. Plant Museum, booklet; Collection of the Henry B. Plant Museum, catalog.
Activities: Lectures; gallery talks; tours; educational program; biannual twelve-week antiques survey courses; monthly public antiques evaluations.

TAMPA BAY ART CENTER, 320 North Blvd, 33606. Tel: 813-253-5346. *Dir* James M Bell; *Asst Dir* Julie M Saul; *Prog Coordinator* Bob Hellier; *Exec Secy* Linda Suarez; *Board Pres* L Edwin Hardman.
Open Tues - Fri 10 AM - 5 PM; Sat 10 AM - 3 PM; Sun 1 - 5 PM; cl Mon. No admis. Estab 1924 to provide high quality changing monthly exhibits. Average Annual Attendance: 15,000; Mem: 1100; dues vary.
Income: Financed by endowment, membership, city appropriation, grants—state & federal.
Collections: Pre-Columbian artifacts; various paintings, including a Renoir; sculpture by C Paul Jennewein.
Exhibitions: (1976-78) Ernest Trova, Jack Youngerman, Richard Brown Baker; Great American Quilt Show; Belgian Gunmaking and American History; Super Photo Realism; Robert Motherwell; Hamburg Realist Painters, Barry LeVa, Mel Bochner, Vito Acconci; World Print Competition.
Publications: Newsletter, bimonthly.
Activities: Classes for adults and children; docent training; films; lect series open to public, 8 vis lectr per yr; gallery talks; tours; competitions; members show, every 2 yrs; sales shop selling books, original art, reproductions and gift items.

UNIVERSITY OF SOUTH FLORIDA, College of Fine Arts/Galleries Program, 4202 E Fowler Ave, 33620. Tel: 813-974-2375. *Dir Fine Arts Events* John Coker; *Exhib Coordinator* Jerry Bassett; *Research & Development Coordinator* Margaret Miller; *Asst Exhib Coordinator* Roy Trapp; *Asst Cur* Michelle Juristo.
Open Mon - Fri 1 PM & 2 - 5 PM; Sat 10 AM - 1 PM & 2 - 4 PM; cl Sun. No admis. Estab 1961 to provide visual art exhibitions covering a broad range of media, subject matter, time periods for the university community and general public. Fine Arts Gallery - Student Services Center; Teaching Gallery - Fine Arts Bldg, 110; Theatre Gallery - Theatre Bldg. Average Annual Attendance: Approx 33,000.
Income: Financed by state appropriation and grants.
Collections: †Contemporary Works on Paper; †Contemporary Photography; †African Art, Pre-Columbian Artifacts, Folk and Ethnic Arts; painting, sculpture, ceramics; Student Study Collections (graphics, photography, ceramics, painting and sculpture); Art Bank Collection of free-loan traveling exhibitions (approx 60 small package exhib).
Exhibitions: (1976-78) Major exhibitions consist of contemporary painting, photography, sculpture, pre-Columbian art, African art; faculty and student group and one-person shows; Annual Juried Student Exhibition.
Publications: Exhibition catalogs.
Activities: Lect open to public, approx 4 vis lectr per yr; gallery talks; tours; competitions; exten dept serving state art orgnizations; individual paintings and original objects of art lent to institutions within the state of Florida and major institutions outside of the state by special requests; lending collection contains original art works and prints, paintings, photographs, sculpture, pre-Columbian art, African art and folk and ethnic art through the Art Bank Program; traveling exhibitions organized and circulated; shop selling prints, permanent collection and exhibition installations.
Library: Librn Mary Lou Harkness. Open to students and public. Special Subjects: Historical and contemporary. Special Collections: Rare art books.

TEQUESTA

LIGHTHOUSE GALLERY, INC,* 100 Waterway Rd, 33458. Tel: 305-746-3101. *Pres* Marvin Potts; *Secy* Augusta Wells; *Admin Dir* Elizabeth Long.

Open Tues - Sat 10 AM - 4 PM; Sun 2 - 5 PM; cl Mon. No admis. Estab 1964 to create public interest in all forms of the fine arts. Mem: 500; dues $25 and up; annual meeting Apr.
Exhibitions: Temporary and traveling exhibitions.
Publications: Calendar of events, monthly.
Activities: Classes for adults and children; lect open to public; competitions.
Library: Small library of art books and art magazines.

WEST PALM BEACH

NORTON GALLERY AND SCHOOL OF ART, 1451 S Olive Ave, 33401. Tel: 305-832-5194. *Dir* Richard A Madigan; *Pres* Dorothy Rautboard; *Asst Dir* Flan¢ders Holland; *Treas* R Brant Synder; *Cur* Cara Montgomery; *Asst to Dir* Alice Sturrock; *Registrar* Kaye Fish; *Mem Secy* Theresa Hickman; *Pub Relations Dir* Sue Whitman; *Supt* C Phelps Merrell.
Open Tues - Fri 10 AM - 5 PM. Admis Voluntary-mandatory donation required, $1 per person suggested. Estab 1978 for nonmembers to participate in aid to museum. The Norton Gallery of Art was founded in 1940, dedicated in 1941 for the education and enjoyment of the public; additions were made in 1946, 49, 52 and 66. Acquisitions and gifts are continually being made to the museum. Bldg and major collections were given by Ralph Hubbard Norton and Elizabeth Calhoun Norton. The Gallery, designed by the Palm Beach architects, Wyeth, King and Johnson, opened to the public in 1941, with an original collection of one hundred paintings; Mr Norton continued to acquire works of art for the museum until his death in 1953, when the remainder of his private collection was given to the museum. Average Annual Attendance: 71,515. Mem: 1600; dues family $35 & $50; annual meeting Apr.
Income: Financed by endowment, membership, city appropriation.
Collections: The Norton Collection of paintings and sculpture includes European and American oils and watercolors; late 19th and early 20th century French paintings and sculpture; The Chinese Collection includes Buddhist sculpture, ritual bronzes, archaic jades, tomb statuettes, porcelain and pottery.
Exhibitions: Annual members' exhibition; students' work; regular schedule of special exhibitions.
Publications: Monthly calendar.
Activities: Classes for adults and children; dramatic programs; docent training; lect for members only; concerts; gallery talks; tours; individual paintings and original objects of art lent to museums around the world; museum shop.
Library: Holdings—Vols 2000.

WHITE SPRINGS

STEPHEN FOSTER CENTER, PO Box 265, 32096. Tel: 904-397-2192. *Dir* John A Robertson; *Asst Dir* James McDuffee; *Staff Asst* Barbara Beauchamp; *Florida Folklife Coordr* Margaret Ann Bulger; *Cur* James T Doswell, III.
Open Daily 8:30 AM - 5:30 PM. Admis adults $2, children $1. Estab 1939 as a memorial to Stephen Collins Foster. The museum contains eight dioramas of Foster's best known songs, the north wing is a collection of minstrel materials, south wing contains 19th century furniture and musical instruments; the tower contains collection of bells and pianos. Average Annual Attendance: 100,000.
Income: $380,000 (financed by state appropriation and receipts).
Collections: (Art) Gardiner Collection of dolls.
Exhibitions: (1976-1978) Minstrel exhibit.
Publications: Florida Folk Arts Directory, annual.
Activities: Concerts, tours; sales shop selling, prints, slides and souvenirs.
Library: Librn Margaret Ann Bulger. Open to the public for reference only. Holdings: Vols 275; Per Subs 12; Other—Tapes.

WINTER PARK

ROLLINS COLLEGE, George D and Harriet W Cornell Fine Arts Center Museum, Holt Ave, 32751. Tel: 305-646-2526. *Dir* Dr Fred W Hicks; *Adminr* Joan B Wavell.
Open Tues - Fri 10 AM - 5 PM; Sat & Sun 1 - 5 PM; cl Mon. No admis. Estab 1925 when art collection was started. New Fine Arts Center completed in 1976 and dedicated and opened on Jan 29, 1978. Rollins College is a liberal arts college and the Cornell Fine Arts Center is part of this process. The museum houses the college permanent collection and provides a focus for the arts in central Florida. The museum consists of the Jeannette Genius McKean, the Yust and Knapp Galleries. Average Annual Attendance: 10,000.
Income: $50,000 (financed by endowment).

Collections: American paintings and portraits; European paintings from the 15th to 20th centuries, prints, and bronzes; Smith Watch Key Collection of 1200 watch keys; decorative arts.

GEORGIA

ATHENS

ATHENS ART ASSOCIATION,* Unitarian Universalist Fellowship Church, 834 Prince Ave, 30601.
Open until 8 PM. Estab 1919 to amplify art opportunities in Athens and develop appreciation in art interests and talents. Mem: 95; dues $5.
Exhibitions: Held at Athens Regional Library; monthly exhibitions of members work held in about 10 different locations.
Activities: Special interest classes; two sidewalk sales per year, one art purchase and donation to City Library of art books; monthly meetings with program

UNIVERSITY OF GEORGIA
—**Georgia Museum of Art,** Jackson St, 30602. Tel: 404-542-3254. *Dir* William D Paul, Jr; *Cur* Ethel Moore; *Cur Graphic Arts* Richard Schneiderman; *Registrar* Janice Stanland; *Preparator* Ronald Lukasiewicz.
Open Mon - Fri 8 AM - 5 PM; Sat 9 AM - Noon; Sun 2 - 5 PM. No admis. Estab 1945. Open to the public 1948 as a fine arts museum; five exhibition galleries. Mem: 250; dues $10 - $500; annual meeting May.
Income: Financed through university.
Collections: American paintings, †drawings; †European and American graphics, 15th century to the present.
Exhibitions: (1976-78) Decorative Arts of the Georgia Piedmont; Selections from the Permanent Collection; Tunisian Mosaics; Lithographs by John Steuart Curry; Eighteen Contemporary Artists; Paintings, Drawings and Lithographs by Jean Charlot; Open to New Ideas: A Collection of New Art for Jimmy Carter; Ben Shahn: A Retrospective 1898-1969; The Sculptor's Eye: The African Art Collection of Mr & Mrs Chaim Gross; MFA Thesis Exhibition; Landscape Etching in the Nineteenth Century; Photographs by Robert Demachy; Danish Expressions in Textiles; The Cuzco Circle; Treasure of Cyprus; Wright Morris: Structures and Artifacts—Photographs 1933-54; Lithographs by Richard Hunt; From Type to Landscape: Design, Projects and Proposals by Herbert Bayer, 1923-73; Photographs by Moholy-Nagy; Edvard Munch: The Major Graphics; Gregory Gillespie; Pol Bury; George Grosz: Works in Oil; Jiri Kolar: Transformations; The Human Form: Sculpture, Prints and Drawings by Fritz Wotruba; Jasper Johns: Prints 1970-1977; Michelangelo Pistoletto: On-Site Works.
Publications: Bulletin, biannual; exhibition catalogs.
Activities: Docent training; volunteer docents program; lect open to the public 3 - 5 vis lectr per yr; tours; individual paintings and original objects of art lent to other museums and galleries; traveling exhibitions organized and circulated.
—**Library.**
Holdings: Vols (art) 40,000.
Special Subjects: Art and art history.

ATLANTA

ATLANTA ART WORKERS COALITION, Suite 214, 972 Peachtree St, NE, 30309. Tel: 404-876-4096. *Pres* Santo Bruno; *VPres* Abby Drue; *Secy* Victoria Bugbeel. *Dir Activities* Julia A Fenton; *Gallery Cur* Dan Talley.
Open Mon - Fri Noon - 4 PM. No admis. Maintains an art gallery. Average Annual Attendance: 1500. Mem: 150; dues $15.
Income: Financed by membership, city and state appropriations, NEA, and gifts.
Exhibitions: Group Show by Members; Small Works (members); Just Such a Pineapple (Stan Sharshall); Works by New Members; Northeast/Southeast Exchange Exhibitions with RAW Gallery, Hartford, Conn; Darryl Vance & Elisa Tenenbaum; Deadbolt Stick Figure Extension (John Sanders); Hand Made Paper (Ruth Laxson); Maria Artemis Sawyer—Recent Work; Chattahoochee Weavers Guild; Elizabeth Lide and Chester Old; Vito Acconci.
Publications: Newspaper, bimonthly.
Activities: Lect open to public, 4 vis lectr per yr; concerts; gallery talks; traveling exhibitions organized and circulated; sales shop selling books and magazines.
Library: *Librn* Art Vandenberg. Open to general public for reference.

ATLANTA COLLEGE OF ART LIBRARY, 1280 Peachtree St NE, 30309. Tel: 404-892-3600, exten 210. *Dir* Gary R Sipe; *AV Cur* Sarah Daniels.
Open Mon - Thurs 9 AM - 8 PM; Fri 9 AM - 5 PM; Sat 11 AM - 2 PM. Circ: 7900. Small exhibition space in the library for art.
Income: $44,600. Purchases: $14,000.

Holdings: Vols 12,000; Per subs 170; AV—Phonorecords, slides, video tapes; Other—Exhibition catalogs.
Special Subjects: Art of the 20th century, especially contemporary developments.
Special Collections: Artists' books.
Exhibitions: Various student shows.

ATLANTA MUSEUM,* 537-39 Peachtree St, NE, 30308. Tel: 404-872-8233. *Dir* J H Elliott, Jr.
Open Mon - Fri 9 AM - 4:30 PM; cl Sat, Sun & holidays. Admis adults $1, children 50¢, special group rates. Estab 1938.
Collections: (Art) Early Chinese art; glass; porcelains; bronzes; furniture; paintings; sculpture; decorative arts; Indian artifacts; Confederate money.
Activities: Lectures; guided tours. Sales shop selling gifts, antiques, silver; porcelain; paintings, glass, furniture, rugs and china.

ATLANTA PUBLIC LIBRARY,* Fine Arts Department, 10 Pryor St SW, 30303. Tel: 404-688-4636. *Librn* Ella Gaines Yates; *Head Fine Arts Dept* Julie M Compton.
Open weekdays 9 AM - 9 PM; Sat 9 AM - 6 PM; Sun 2 - 6 PM. Fine Arts Department estab 1950 to provide materials in the fine arts; some exhibit space maintained.
Income: Financed by city and state appropriation.
Holdings: Volumes, reference and circulating, on art, theater, music, drama; AV—Cassettes, motion pictures 1100; phonorecords; Other—Framed prints 1400.
Activities: Classes for adults; lect open to the public.

GEORGIA INSTITUTE OF TECHNOLOGY, College of Architecture Library, 225 North Ave NW, 30332. Tel: 404-894-4877. *Librn* Frances K Drew; *Library Asst* Linda L Mackay.
Open Mon - Thurs 8 AM - 9:30 PM; Fri 8 AM - 5 PM; Sun 2 - 9:30 PM; cl Sat. Estab 1908 to give good library service to the College of Architecture. Circ: 89,000.
Income: $55,000 (financed by state appropriation). Purchase: $16,000.
Holdings: Vols 10,140; Per subs 138; AV—Microfiche, slides; Other—Exhibition catalogs, pamphlets.
Special Collections: Ecole des Beaux Arts publications; art nouveau.

HIGH MUSEUM OF ART, 1280 Peachtree St, NE, 30309. Tel: 404-892-3600. *Dir* Gudmund Vigtel; *Cur Educ* Paula Hancock; *Cur Decorative Arts* Katherine G Farnham; *Chmn Bd Trustees* L L Gellerstedt Jr; *Pres Bd of Sponsors* Jack Spalding.
Open Mon - Sat 10 AM - 5 PM; Sun Noon - 5 PM. No admis. Estab 1965 to make the best in the visual arts available to the Atlanta public in exhibitions and supporting programs. The Museum building, 50,000 sq ft, was completed in 1955. The Atlanta Memorial Arts Center was built around it in 1968. Average Annual Attendance: 300,000. Mem: 9700; dues $15 and up.
Income: $805,000 (financed by endowment, membership, city and state appropriations, grants, and operating income).
Collections: American paintings, sculpture, graphics; European paintings, sculpture, graphics; African objects; Oriental, Pre-Columbian, European and American decorative arts; Kress Collection of paintings and sculpture from the 14th-18th centuries; Uhry Collection of prints after 1850; Havery Collection; photography.
Exhibitions: Changing monthly exhibits: Bauhaus Color; Contemporary Art in Atlanta Collections; Currier & Ives Lithographs; Robert Coggins Collection of American Painting; Two Centuries of Black American Art; Edward Ross—A Retrospective; Prints: Bochner, LeWitt, Mangold, Marden, Martin, Renouf, Rockburne, Ryman; Rodin's Studies for the Burghers of Calais; Four Centuries of Masterpieces; Art from Zaire; John Safer Sculpture.
Publications: Calendar of Events, monthly.
Activities: Classes for children; docent training; lect open to public, 20 vis lectr per yr; gallery talks; tours; exten dept serving city of Atlanta; artmobile; individual paintings and original objects of art lent to Georgia Art Bus; traveling exhibitions organized and circulated; museum shop selling books, magazines, reproductions; slides and gift items; junior museum.
Library: Library of Atlanta College of Art. *Librn* Gary Sipe. Open to College students, staff, and Museum members. Holdings: Vols 12,000; Per subs 170; Other—Video tapes, slides 25,000.

AUGUSTA

AUGUSTA RICHMOND COUNTY MUSEUM,* 540 Telfair St, 30901. Tel 404-722-8454. *Dir* Clemens de Balliou; *Asst to Dir* Ellen L Schwarzbek.
Open Tues - Sat 1 - 5 PM; Sun 2 - 5 PM; cl Labor Day, Dec 20 - Jan 2. No admis. Estab 1927; owns 1850 historic house at 456 Telfair St.
Collections: (Art) Paintings; graphics; sculpture; decorative arts; archaeology; historial material.

Activities: Lectures; guided tours; training programs for professional museum personnel; traveling exhibitions.

GERTRUDE HERBERT INSTITUTE OF ART, 506 Telfair St, 30901. Tel: 404-722-5495. *Dir* Clemens de Baillou.
Open Tues - Fri 10 AM - Noon & 1 - 4 PM; Sat 4 - 6 PM; groups by special arrangement; cl Sun, Mon, Christmas and New Year's. Estab 1937. Mem: 250.
Income: $10,000.
Collections: European Renaissance and modern paintings, sculpture, graphics.
Exhibitions: Monthly exhibitions, circulating exhibitions; one-person and group exhibitions.
Activities: Art Classes; lectures; films.
Library: Small art library.

COLUMBUS

COLUMBUS MUSEUM OF ARTS & CRAFTS, INC,* 1251 Wynnton Rd, 31906. Tel: 404-323-3617. *Chmn Bd* Jack A Bell; *Secy Bd & Museum Dir* C Clay Aldridge.
Open Tues - Sat 10 AM - 5 PM; Sun 2 - 5 PM; cl Mon, Thanksgiving, Christmas, New Year's. No admis. Estab 1953 to build a permanent collection, to encourage work by Georgia and Southern artists and to establish loan shows and traveling exhibitions in all fields of art. Mem: dues $10 and up; annual meeting Jan. Average Annual Attendance: 56,000.
Income: $125,000. Purchases: $15,000.
Collections: †Early masters; †American art; †Georgia artists; †sculpture and prints; †Indian section with extensive collection of ethnological and archaeological material relating to local Indians; permanent collection includes portraits, landscapes and other paintings by English, Flemish, Dutch, Italian, early and contemporary American painters and others; †Oriental ivory collection; African sculpture; †Persian rugs; †extensive American and foreign doll collection; needlework gallery, fans, costumes and jewelry.
Exhibitions: Morton Youth Wing with permanent and changing exhibits.
Publications: Newsletter, monthly.
Activities: Art workshops for adults and children; gallery talks; tours; lectures; traveling exhibitions organized and circulated; active Museum Guild.
Library: Special Subjects: All phases of art, Indian history.

DALTON

CREATIVE ARTS GUILD, The Old Firehouse on Pentz St, 30720. Tel: 404-278-0168. *Pres* Ted Smith, *VPres* George Spence; *Secy* Susan Reams; *Dir* Bernice Spigel.
Open Mon - Fri 9 AM - 5 PM; Sat & Sun 1 - 3 PM. No admis. Estab 1963 to recognize, stimulate and popularize the arts. The gallery is maintained on the main floor of the Old Firehouse. Average Annual Attendance: Approx 2000. Mem: 500; dues individual $10, family $15; annual meeting Dec.
Income: $80,000 (financed by membership, commissions, fund raising events).
Exhibitions: Changing monthly exhibitions include shows of original art, crafts, sculpture, photography and graphics.
Publications: Bulletins to members, monthly.
Activities: Classes for adults and children; dramatic programs; visual and performing arts programs for schools; concerts; gallery talks; competitions with awards; artmobile, individual paintings lent; traveling exhibitions organized and circulated.

DECATUR

AGNES SCOTT COLLEGE, Dalton Gallery, College Ave & Candler St, 30030. Tel: 404-373-2571. *Cur* Leland Staven.
Open Mon - Fri 9 AM - 9 PM; Sat 9 AM - 5 PM; Sun 2 - 5 PM. No admis. Estab 1965 to enhance art program. Gallery consists of 4 rooms, 300 running ft of wall space, light beige walls and rug, Dana Fine Arts Bldg designed by John Portman.
Income: Financed by endowment.
Collections: Harry L Dalton; Clifford M Clarke; Steffen Thomas.
Exhibitions: Western Carolina Invitational Fibre Exhibition; Student Art Exhibition; Art Faculty Exhibition; Georgia Designer Craftsmen.
Activities: Lectures open to public.

FORT BENNING

NATIONAL INFANTRY MUSEUM, Bldg 396, Baltzell Ave, 31905. Tel: 404-545-2958. *Cur* Dick Dewayne Grube; *Registrar* C Clay Aldridge; *Exhibits Specialist* James Lett.

Open Tues - Fri 10 AM - 4:30 PM; Sat - Sun 12:30 - 4:30 PM. No admis. Estab 1959 to honor the infantryman and his two centuries of proud history. Contains 50,000 sq ft; Hall of Flags, Gallery of Military Art, Benning Room, West Gallery: 1750 - 1865, Center Galleries 1870 - 1970, Medal of Honor Hall and Airborne Diorama. Average Annual Attendance: 150,000. Mem: 9000; dues $20.
Income: $100,000 (financed by state appropriation and federal funds).
Collections: (Art) Presidential documents and memorabilia; military related art; 1896 Vintage Sutler's Store.
Exhibitions: Minority Art and the Military; Hail to the Chief; Mobil Museum: Two Centuries of Proud History.
Activities: Lectr open to the public; artmobile.
Library: Open to students. Holdings: Vols 6000; Per subs 25; Other—Photographs 250,000.

JEKYLL ISLAND

JEKYLL ISLAND MUSEUM,* 329 Riverview Dr, 31520. Tel: 912-635-2378. *Dir Restoration* RK Beedle; *Mgr State Park Authority* Robert C Anderson.
Open Mon - Sat 9 AM - 5 PM; Sun Noon - 5 PM. Admis adults $1.50, children 75¢. The museum is located in the former cottage of William Rockefeller.
Collections: Portraits; Tiffany stained glass window; furniture.

MACON

MUSEUM OF ARTS AND SCIENCES, INC,* 4182 Forsyth Rd, 31204. Tel: 912-477-3232. *Dir* Douglas R Noble.
Open Mon - Fri 9 AM - 5 PM; Sat 11 AM - 5 PM; Sun 2 - 5 PM; cl national holidays.
Collections: European and American paintings, prints, drawings and sculpture; historical material.
Exhibitions: Traveling art exhibits in Main Exhibit Hall.
Activities: Classes for adults and children; arts festivals; guided tours; lectures; movies; special events.

SAVANNAH

KIAH MUSEUM, 505 W 36th St, 31401. Tel: 912-236-8544. *Asst Cur* Nancy H Walker.
Open Tues and Thurs 11 AM - 5 PM. No admis. Estab 1959 to expose this type of culture to the masses; to teach the relationship of art to everyday life.
Collections: Marie Dressler Collection; 18th, 19th & 20th century furniture; Howard J Morrison Jr Osteological Exhibit; Civil War period collection; Indian artifacts; fine arts exhibit of all art work of students and adult artists from 18 countries; Harmon Foundation Collection of African wood carvings: hobby collection; folk art.
Activities: Docent training; gallery talks; tours; individual paintings and original objects of art lent to schools.
Library: Florence S Simpkins. Open to adults and students for reference. Special Subjects: Art. Special Collections: John Speight Simpkins.

SHIPS OF THE SEA MUSEUM, 503 E River St, 31401. Tel: 912-232-1511. *Dir* Pinny Crouch; *Asst Dir* Palmer Golson; *Mus Asst* Mary Ed Kennard, Chris Walker and Judy Henze.
Open Mon - Sat 10 AM - 5 PM; Sun 1 - 5 PM; cl Mon & Tues Sept - Feb. Admis adults $1.50; children 75¢; group rates available. Estab 1966 to bring a greater awareness to the general public of the great part in history ships have played. Four floors of ship models and items which pertain to the sea, an outstanding exhibit of ships-in-a-bottle and scrimshaw. Average Annual Attendance: 36,000.
Income: Financed privately.
Collections: Ships models, figureheads, scrimshaw, porcelains, etc.
Activities: Classes for children; lect open to public; sales shop selling books, magazines and slides.
Library: *Librn* Palmer Golson. Open to the public. Holdings: Vols 300. Special Subjects; All categories pertaining to the sea and ships.

TELFAIR ACADEMY OF ARTS & SCIENCES, INC, 121 Barnard St, (Mailing Add: PO Box 10081, 31401). Tel: 912-232-1177. *Dir* Alexander V J Gaudieri; *Cur of Coll* Feay Shellman; *Cur of Educ* Dorothy Radford; *Asst Cur* Glenda Nahoom; *Registrar* Deborah Helmken.
Open Tues - Sat 10 AM - 4:30 PM; Sun 2 - 5 PM; cl Mon. Admis $1.75; students $1, children under 12 50¢; free on Sun. Estab 1875 to preserve, exhibit and interpret the works of art forming the collections; to preserve and interpret our two National Historic Landmark edifices, the Telfair Academy and the Owens-Thomas House; to enlighten and to educate all groups through art related programs and services; to enrich the quality of life through offering a total cultural resource for the entire region; and to maintain a standard of the highest order throughout the museum. Museum housed in 1817 American Regency Mansion (with 1880s addition of Rotunda & Sculpture Galleries) which has been designated a National

Historic Landmark; designed by the famous English architect, William Jay, this is one of the two finest houses in Georgia. Average Annual Attendance: 24,000. Mem: 1675; dues junior citizen $5, senior citizen $5, individual $15, family $25; annual meeting spring.
Income: Financed by endowment, membership, city and state appropriation, and banks and corporate foundations, and federal government.
Collections: Decorative arts and period rooms; collections of 18th and 19th century American portraiture; American Impressionism, Ash Can Realism, 19th and 20th century French and German painting; prints; Kahlil Gibran's paintings and drawings.
Exhibitions: (1976-77) Myrtle Jones Retrospective; Frederick Baldwin (photography); Romaine Brooks: Thief of Souls; Ann Osteen (paintings); Walter Greer (paintings); Savannah Art Association Show; American Naval Prints Exhibition; Gina Gilmore Exhibition; Public School Show; Frederick Freer (paintings); Mills B Lane IV Book Exhibition; Claire Van Vliet Exhibition; Ogden Pleissner Exhibition; Shingleton Weavings Exhibition; Eliot Clark Exhibition; Ray Ellis Exhibition; August Georgia Folk Art Exhibition; Francois Jacquemin Exhibition; Know What you See Exhibition (conservation).
Activities: Classes for children; docent training; special tours (participatory); lect open to the public, 5 vis lectr per yr; concerts; gallery talks; extension dept serving public schools and Retired Citizens Centers; lending collection contains motion pictures, slides 1500; museum shop selling books, magazines, original art, reproductions, prints, slides, jewelry, small sculpture, pottery, decorative items; Junior Museum (3-room gallery within the museum) called The Gallery of Interpretation.
Library: *Librn* Kay Kole. For reference, open to scholars mainly, but also public. Holdings: Vols 1200.

VALDOSTA

VALDOSTA STATE COLLEGE ART GALLERY,* N Patterson St, 31601. Tel: 912-247-3319 and 247-3330. *Head Art Dept* Irene Dodd.
Open Mon - Fri 9 AM - Noon & 1 - 5 PM. No admis. Estab to expose both art and general education students to a variety of visual expressions. Gallery is an open rectangular room with approx 122 running feet of exhibition space. Average Annual Attendance: 8000.
Income: Financed by state appropriations.
Exhibitions: Approx 10 - 12 exhibitions per year.
Activities: Lectures at times; tours to museums in New York, Washington, Boston, etc.

HAWAII

HONOLULU

ASSOCIATION OF HONOLULU ARTISTS, PO Box 10202, 96816. *Pres* Ernest Brickman; *VPres* Joyce Mary Ott; *Secy* Helen Iaea; *Second VPres* Christine Evans; *Treas* Michael Kiyuan; *Asst Treas* Lilly R Abbott; *Corresponding Secy* Edna Loo.
Estab 1934 to promote congeniality and stimulate growth by presenting programs and to contribute to the cultural life of the State of Hawaii. Average Annual Attendance: 1000. Mem: 350; dues $12; monthly meeting third Tues each month.
Income: $4200 (financed by membership).
Exhibitions: (1976-78) Aloha Show; April Kahala Mall Show.
Publications: Paint Rag, monthly.
Actvities: Lect open to the public, 12 vis lectr per yr; demonstrations; competitions with cash, plaques and rossettes; schol.

CONTEMPORARY ARTS CENTER OF HAWAII, 605 Kapiolani Blvd, 96813. Tel: 808-525-8047. *Dir* Laila Roster; *Asst Dir* Mary Mitsuda; *Chrm of the Bd* Thurston Twigg-Smith.
Open Mon - Fri 8 AM - 5 PM; Sat 8 AM - noon; cl Sun. No admis. Estab 1960 to provide a showcase for artists living and working in the Hawaiian Islands; the gallery occupies 1800 sq ft of space in the center of the newspaper building. Average Annual Attendance: 25,000
Income: Approx $10,000 (financed by endowment). Purchases: $20,000.
Collections: Permanent Collection hangs throughout the building, and is continually augmented by purchase from ongoing exhibitions.
Exhibitions: (1976) Frank Beaver (ceramist); Lawrence Calcagno (painter); Allyn Bromley (sculptor); Lois Ryan (painter); Ron Kowalke (painter retrospective showing); Tradition American Style (group); Jean Williams (weaver); John Thomas (painter); John Wisnosky (painter); Barbara Engle (printmaker and painter). (1977) Juliette May Fraser (murals); Wendy Kim Chee (soft sculpture); Youth Art Week (children's art); Ken Bushnell (painter and printmaker); Pat Swenson (weaver and Randy Hokushin (ceramist); Mary Bonic (painter); Dennis Hanshew (painter); Erica Karawina (stained glass murals); Yvonne Cheng (batik); John Kjargaard (painter); Men Look at Women theme show (65 male artists). (1978) Russell Davidson (painter); Frank Salmoiraghi (photographer); Hiroki Morinoue (paintings from Japan); Honolulu Printmakers Invitational Print Show; Francis Haar and family

(photographers); group show of works on paper; Gilbert/Marcus (production and performance art); Les Biller (painter); Marcia Morse (printmaker); Lam Oi Char (Chinese Brush painter); works of Balinese artists.
Activities: Individual paintings and original objects of art lent; lending collection contains slides of complete exhibitions as well as permanent collection.

FOUNDRY,* 899 Waimanu St, 96813. Tel: 808-533-2609. *Pres & Dir* Alan M Leitner; *Secy Admin* Alice S Leitner; *Mgr* Christine Evans; *Chmn of Artists-in-Residence* William Evans.
Open Mon - Sat 10 AM - 5 PM. No admis. Estab 1969 as an art center with central exhibition gallery open to public in rustic environment of old Hawaii. Workshops and artist studios surrounding gallery allow public to view artists at work in a creative environment. Art Center cultivates a community education of the arts, provides an interchange of knowledge.
Income: $50,000 (financed partially by city and state appropriations, partially self-supporting).
Exhibitions: Monthly exhibits open to public with shows of graduate art thesis; art organizations; one-person shows; educational shows.
Publications: Exhibit bulletins, monthly.
Activities: Artists-in-residence program; classes for adults and children; concerts; lect open to public, 4 vis lectr per yr; gallery talks; tours; traveling exhibitions organized and circulated; junior museum; book shop.

HAWAII STATE LIBRARY, Fine Arts—Audiovisual Section, 478 S King St, 96813. Tel: 808-548-2340 Fine Arts, 808-548-5913 Audiovisual. *Head Fine Arts-AV Section* Marion N Vaught; *Head AV Unit* Mary Lu Kipilii; *Librn Fine Arts* Grace Hess; *Art Specialist* Chitra Stuiver.
Open Tues - Thurs 9 AM - 8 PM; Mon, Wed, Fri and Sat 9 AM - 5 PM. No admis. Estab 1930 as central reference and circulating collection for both city and county of Honolulu and for the state of Hawaii.
Holdings: Vols 13,000; AV—Films, filmstrips, motion pictures; Other—Photographs, reproductions 34,000.
Special Collections: Books on all of the fine arts including handcrafts, photography and costume; many major journals, approximately 68,000 pictures covering a wide range of subjects including reproductions of famous paintings.
Exhibitions: Various local artists exhibited in the courtyard area; special displays in the lobby.
Activities: Approx 8000 art items lent yearly.

HONOLULU ACADEMY OF ARTS,* 900 S Beretania St, 96814. Tel: 808-538-3693. *Dir* James W Foster; *Asst Dir* Selden Washington; *Special Asst to Dir* Ben Hyams; *Sr Cur & Cur Graphic Arts & Studio Prog* Joseph Feher; *Cur Asian Art & Keeper of Ukiyo-e Center* Howard A Link; *Cur Asian Art* Marshall P Wu; *Consultant for Western Art* Gertrude Rosenthal; *Cur Exten Services* Ruth Tamura; *Cur Gallery Prog* Roger Dell; *Cur Prog Development* James H Furstenberg; *Cur Art Center* Violet A Scott; *Keeper AV Center* Broné Jameikis; *Keeper, Lending Coll* Barbara F Hoogs.
Open Tues - Sat 10 AM - 4:30 PM; Sun 2 - 5 PM; cl Mon and major holidays. No admis. Estab 1927 as the only art museum of a broad general nature in the Pacific; to provide Hawaii's people of many races with works of art representing their composite cultural heritage from both East and West. Main building is a Registered National Historic Place. Average Annual Attendance: 124,000. Mem: 4500; dues $8 and up.
Income: $1,000,000. Purchased: $360,000.
Collections: Chinese painting, sculpture, ceramics, bronze, lacquerware, furniture; Japanese painting including screens, sculpture, prints, ceramics and folk arts; Korean ceramics; Islamic ceramics; ancient Mediterranean and Medieval Christian art; European and American painting, prints, sculpture and decorative arts, including the Kress Collection of Italian Renaissance painting; Western and Oriental textiles; traditional arts of Africa, Oceania and the Americas.
Exhibitions: Approx 35 temporary exhibitions annually.
Publications: Catalogs of special exhibitions; art books and pamphlets; Honolulu Academy of Arts Journal, biennially.
Activities: Classes for children; lectures; films; guided tours; gallery talks; arts festivals; workshops; lending collection contains paintings, prints, textiles, reproductions, photographs, slides and miscellaneous objects (about 21,000); exten dept serving neighbor islands; resident artist program; research in Asian art; book and gift shop.
Library: *Librn* Anne T Seaman. Holdings: Vols 23,000. Special Subjects: Chinese and Japanese art; history of art.

SCHOFIELD BARRACKS, Tropic Lightning Historical Center, 25th Infantry Division Headquarters, 96857. Tel: 808-655-0438/4844. The Center retains military personnel as Curators. Currently *Cur Spec/5* Steve H Kongshaug.

Open Wed - Sun 10 AM - 4 PM. No admis. Estab 1958 to preserve the military historical background in Hawaii. The Friends of the Tropic Lightning Historical Center render assistance for acquiring and displaying new exhibits; the 25th Inf Div Hq is charged with management and final directives. Average Annual Attendance: 13,000 - 15,000.
Income: Financed by military appropriations.
Collections: Military weapons past and present (many captured in combat), flags, banners, manuals, military art, photograph collections of early military installations on Oahu.
Exhibitions: Continual revision as new acquisitions become available.

TENNENT ART FOUNDATION GALLERY,* 203 Prospect St, 96813. Tel: 808-531-1987. *Dir* Hon-Chew Hee.
Open Tues - Sat 10 AM - Noon; Sun 2 - 4 PM; cl Mon. Admis adults $1, students 50¢; children under 12 25¢. Estab 1954, dedicated to aesthetic portrayal of Hawaiian people and to house works of Madge Tennant. Gallery on slopes of Punchbowl below National Cemetery of Pacific. Average Annual Attendance: 800. Mem: 100; dues $3.
Income: Financed by trust.
Publications: Prospectus, monthly newsletter.
Activities: Lectures; gallery talks; tours; individual paintings lent to schools; artmobile; training program for professional museum workers.
Library: Open for reference. Holdings: Vols 300.

UNIVERSITY OF HAWAII AT MANOA ART GALLERY, 2535 The Mall, 96822. Tel: 808-948-6888. *Dir* Tom Klobe; *Chmn Dept Art* John Wisnosky.
Open Mon - Fri 10 AM - 4 PM; Sun Noon - 4 PM; cl Sat. No admis. Estab 1976 to present a program of local, national and international exhibitions. The gallery is seen as a major teaching tool for all areas of specialization. It is located in the center of the new art building and is designed as a versatile space with a flexible installation system that allows all types of art to be displayed according to their own requirements. Average Annual Attendance: 25,000.
Exhibitions: Selection I (Hawaii collections); Han and T'ang Murals; Young American Printmakers (Pratt Traveling Exhibition); Faculty Exhibitions; The Art of Korea; Student Exhibitions; Dennis Rowan (printmaker).
Publications: Exhibition catalogs.
Activities: Classes for adults; lect open to public; gallery talks; traveling exhibitions organized and circulated.

KAILUA

WINDWARD ARTISTS GUILD, PO Box 851, 96734. *Pres* Faye Bryant; *VPres* Dagmar Kau; *Secy* Marilyn Davidson; *Treas* Shirley Hasenyager.
Estab 1961 to promote art and art appreciation in Hawaii; gallery is not maintained. Mem: 100; qualifications for membership—must live on the windward side of the island of Oahu; dues $10; meetings six times per yr.
Income: Financed by membership, private donations and state education grants.
Exhibitions: Easter Art Festival annually; Guild Members Show; Annual Windward Young Artists Show.
Publications: Windward Artists Guild Bulletin, monthly.
Activities: Classes for adults; art demonstrations in schools; lect open to the public, 5 vis lectr per yr; competitions with cash awards; schol.

LAHAINA

LAHAINA ARTS SOCIETY,* 649 Wharf St, 96761. Tel: 808-661-0111. *Pres* Daniel Vezzani; *Secy* Robert Kelsey; *Mgr* Janet Allan.
Open daily 10 AM - 4 PM. No admis. Estab 1964 as a nonprofit organization interested in perpetuating native culture, art and beauty by providing stimulating art instruction, lectures and art exhibits. Gallery located in old Lahaina Courthouse, Main Gallery is on ground floor, Old Jail Gallery is in the basement. Average Annual Attendance: 25,000. Mem: 310; dues single $10; family $15; annual meeting Sept.
Income: $12,000 (financed by membership and annual fundraising event, Beaux Arts Ball).
Exhibitions: Exhibits change each month; one or two-person shows are in Old Jail Gallery; group, special or theme exhibits in Main Gallery; Honolulu Academy of Arts annual traveling exhibit held each year.
Publications: Newsletter, monthly.
Activities: Classes for adults and children; lect open to public, 4 vis lectr per yr; gallery talks; competitions; scholarships.
Library: Open for reference. Holdings: Vols 100.

LAIE

POLYNESIAN CULTURAL CENTER,* 96762. Tel: 808-293-9291. *Dir* Vernon R Hardisty.

Open Mon - Sat 10:30 AM - 7 PM; cl Thanksgiving & Xmas. Admis adults $3, children $1.50. Estab in 1963 by the Church of Jesus Christ of Latter Day Saints as an authentic Polynesian village.
Collections: Paintings; sculpture; graphics; decorative arts; ethnic material.
Publications: Polynesia in a Day, magazine.
Activities: Lectures; guided tours; films. Sales shop selling Polynesian artifacts and souvenirs.

LIHUE

KAUAI MUSEUM, PO Box 248, 96766. Tel: 808-245-6931. *Pres* Dora Jane Cole; *Secy* Mary Mildred Jones; *Dir* Robert A Gahran; *Researcher* Katherine Stauder; *Manager Museum Shop* Hazel Ward Gahran.
Open Mon - Fri 9:30 AM - 4:30 PM; Sat 9 AM - 1 PM; cl Sun. Admis Adults $2, children thru age 17 no admission when accompanied by an adult. Estab 1960 to provide the history through the permanent exhibit, the story of Kauai and through art exhibits; ethnic cultural exhibits in the Wilcox Building to give the community an opportunity to learn more of ethnic backgrounds. Average Annual Attendance: 23,000. Mem: 500; dues $5, $10, $25, $50 & $100; annual meeting Nov.
Exhibitions: The First Americans: The First American Indian Exhibit in Hawaii; Annual Artists of Hawaii Exhibit; Pacific Northwest Indian Exhibit (watercolors by Wai Hang Lai); Watercolors by Hubert Buel; Hawaiian Quilts; Watercolors and Prints of Emily Ehlinger; Oils by John Young; Filipino Cultural Heritage Exhibit Featuring the Badillo Collection; Attempted Russian Expansion of Kauai, 1815 - 1817; Annual Elementary and Senior Division School Art Exhibit; Capt James Cook Bicentennial Exhibit.
Publications: Hawaiian Quilting on Kauai; Early Kauai Hospitality.
Library: For reference only. Holdings: Vols 2600. Other—Reference print, photograph collection. Special Subjects: Kauai history.

KAUAI REGIONAL LIBRARY, 4344 Hardy St, 96766. Tel: 808-245-3617. *Dist Adminr* Donna Marie Garcia.
Open Mon - Wed 8 AM - 8 PM; Thur - Fri 8 AM - 4:30 PM; Sat 8 AM - Noon. Estab 1922 to serve the public of Kauai through a network of a regional library, three community libraries, community/school library, reading room in community center and a bookmobile service. These libraries provide exhibition space for a variety of art works and individual art shows as well as participate in joint art exhibits with the local schools, community college and museum. Part of the Hawaii State Library System. Circ: 400,000. The gallery provides display and exhibit area for one-man and group art shows.
Income: $457,090 (financed by city appropriation).
Holdings: Vols 147,000 (includes all volumes in all public libraries); AV—Audio tapes, cassettes, film strips, phonorecords, video tapes; Other—Clipping files, pamphlets, mounted picture files.
Special Collections: Curator for art in State Buildings Collection for the island of Kauai funded through the statewide program by the State Foundation on Culture and the Arts. This collection is a revolving collection available for all state buildings and public schools.
Exhibitions: Series of small one-man exhibits; average thirteen per year.
Activities: Dramatic programs; lectr open to the pub, 4 - 8 vis lectr per yr; library tours.

WAILUKU

MAUI HISTORICAL SOCIETY, Hale Hoikeike, 2375A Main St (Mailing Add: PO Box 1018, 96793). Tel: 808-2443-3326. *Pres* Steve Parker; *VPres* Ben Baldwin; *Secy* Patricia Leffingwell; *Mus Dir* Virginia Wirtz.
Open Mon - Sat 10 AM - 3:30 PM. Admis Adults $2; students 50¢. Estab 1957 to preserve the history of Hawaii, particularly Maui County; housed in former residence of Edward Bailey (1814-1903). Average Annual Attendance: 5000. Mem: 400; dues individual $5, couple $7.50; annual meeting Mar.
Income: $25,000 (financed by membership and gift shop purchases).
Collections: (Art) Prehistoric Hawaiian Artifacts; landscape paintings (1860-1900); paintings of Hawaiian scenes by Edward Bailey.
Publications: LaHaina Historical Guide; La Perouse on Maui; Hale Hoikeike—A House and Its People.
Activities: Lectr open to the public, 5 vis lectr per yr; sales shop selling books, slides, postcards, notepaper, jewelry and souvenirs.

IDAHO

BOISE

BOISE GALLERY OF ART,* c/o Julia Davis Park, Box 1505, 83701. Tel: 208-345-8330. *Dir* Allen Dodworth; *Asst Dir* Beth Sellars; *Admin Asst* Bee Clark; *Cur Exhib* Bill Campton.
Open Tues - Sun 10 AM - 5 PM; Wed 5 - 9 PM; cl Mon and holidays. Estab 1931, inc 1961, gallery opened 1936. Average Annual Attendance: 80,000.
Income: Approx $90,000.
Collections: American, European and Oriental collections of painting, sculpture and the minor arts; collection of works by Idaho artists.
Exhibitions: 20 - 24 exhibitions annually of painting, sculpture, photography, graphics, architecture, crafts; annual exhibition for Idaho artists.
Publications: Bulletin; Annual Report; catalogs of exhibitions, occasionally.
Activities: Classes in art and art appreciation; docent tours; lect open to public; concerts; films; arts festival; Beaux Arts Societe (fundraising auxiliary); gallery shop.
Library: 4000 items.

CALDWELL

COLLEGE OF IDAHO,* Jewett Exhibition Center, 83605. Tel: *Dir Collection & Gallery* Max Peter; *Exhibits Chmn* Steven Drucker.
Open Tues - Thurs 10 AM - 4 PM; Fri 10 AM - Noon; Sun 2 -5 PM; cl academic holidays. No admis. Estab 1962 to give the College an art exhibition program.
Collections: Prints.
Exhibitions: Temporary and traveling exhibitions on an inter-museum loan basis.
Publications: Exhibit brochures.
Activities: Lectures; gallery talks; guided tours.

MOSCOW

UNIVERSITY OF IDAHO MUSEUM, FOC-W, 83843. Tel: 208-885-6480. *Dir* G Ellis Burcaw.
Open Mon - Fri 9 AM - 4 PM (when University is in session). No admis. Estab 1963 mainly as a training laboratory for students in museum training courses, but also to serve the University and the community by providing exhibits in a variety of fields. One room on the second floor of the Faculty Office Complex West is used as a gallery; exhibits also in the lobby and in the Administration Building. Average Annual Attendance: 1500.
Income: $35,000 (financed by state appropriation and through the University).
Collections: West African masks and figurines; Arab objects from North Africa and the Near East; American Indian and Eskimo objects; fine arts collection.
Exhibitions: Color and the Graphic Arts; Contemporary Botanical Prints; Quick Before They're Gone (historic architecture); People of the Cedar; Norwegian Viking Art; Know What You See; Norwegian Dolls.

OROFINO

CLEARWATER ART ASSOCIATION, PO Box 1482, 83544. *Pres* Jean A Wilfong; *VPres* Barbara Fitzsimmons: *Secy* Leah Lumper; *Treas* Mrs Arthur Johnson.
Estab 1957 to develop art in the local area. Mem: 55; dues $2; meetings quarterly.
Income: $200-$600 (financed by membership).
Activities: Classes for adults; competitions with awards; schol.

POCATELLO

IDAHO STATE UNIVERSITY, John B Davis Gallery of Fine Art, 83209. Tel: 208-236-2361. Dir Lorne Obermayr.
Open Mon - Fri Noon - 5 PM. No admis. Estab 1956 to exhibit art; gallery contains 130 running ft of space with 8 ft ceilings. Average Annual Attendance: 2600.
Income: $2600 (financed by city appropriation). Purchases: $350.
Collection: †Permanent collection.
Exhibitions: (1977 - 78) Tony Martin (ceramics); YWCA Art Membership; ISU Art Faculty; Al Kober (sculptor); Paul Missall (photo-realist); Watercolor West; ISU Undergraduate Show; MFA Thesis (Barry Hogrefe).

TWIN FALLS

COLLEGE OF SOUTHERN IDAHO ART GALLERY,* Box 1238, 83301. Tel: 208-733-9554. *Chmn Art Dept* La Var Steel; *Gallery Dir* Kent Jeppesen.
Open Mon - Sat 8 AM - 5 PM; cl Sun. No admis. Estab 1967 as a college gallery for student and public enjoyment. Fine arts building and auditorium. Average Annual Attendance: 15,000.
Income: Financed by community college and local support. Purchases: $1000.
Collections: Permanent collection.
Exhibitions: Alexander Napote; various Waam Shows; Arthur Okamura; others.
Activities: Classes for adults and children; concerts; dramatic programs; lect open to public; scholarships.
Library: Holdings—Vols 100,000.

ILLINOIS

BISHOP HILL

BISHOP HILL HISTORIC SITE, PO Box O, 61419. Tel: 309-927-3520. *Historian* Ronald E Nelson; *Site Supt* Edward J Hepner; *Asst Supt* James Likes.
Open daily 9 AM - 5 PM; cl Thanksgiving, Christmas and New Years. No admis. Estab 1946 to interpret history of Bishop Hill Colony. Average Annual Attendance: 60,000.
Income: Financed by state appropriation. Purchases: $25,000.
Collections: Primitive paintings; artifacts pertaining to Bishop Hill Colony 1846-1861.
Activities: Lect open to public.

BLOOMINGTON

ILLINOIS WESLEYAN UNIVERSITY MERWIN GALLERY,* Alice Millar Center for the Fine Arts, 210 E University St, 61701. Tel: 309-556-3077. *Dir School of Art* John Mulvaney.
Open Tues - Sun 1 - 4 PM & 7 - 9 PM; cl Mon. Estab 1945.
Income: Financed by endowment, and membership.
Collections: Approx 190 paintings, prints and drawings including works by Whistler, Max Beckmann, Larry Rivers, Philip Guston, Helen Frankenthaler, John Ible, Baskin and Oliviera.
Exhibitions: School of Art Faculty Exhibition; Annual Illinois High School Art Exhibition; School of Art Student Exhibition; traveling exhibitions.
Publications: Exhibition posters and gallery schedule, monthly.
Activities: Concerts; dramatic programs; lect open to public, 5 vis lectr per yr; tours; competitions; traveling exhibitions organized and circulated; original objects of art lent, on campus only.
—**Slide Library.** Holdings: Slides 30,000.

McLEAN COUNTY ART ASSOCIATION, 210 E Washington St, 61701. Tel: 309-827-8621. *Pres* Adrienne Ives; *Secy* Nancy Merwin; *Dir McLean County Arts Center* Terry M Bush; *Art Dir* Gerald Simac; *Outreach Proj Dir* John Holechek.
Open Mon-Fri 9 AM - 5 PM; Sat 10 AM - 4 PM. No admis. Estab 1922 to enhance the arts in McLean County by providing display gallery, and sales and rental gallery to aid local professional artists. Gallery is 2500 sq ft, hosts local shows and traveling exhibits. Mem: 406; dues students $5, single $10, family $15. annual meeting First Fri of May.
Income: $57,000 (financed by membership, art and book sales).
Collections: Variety of media.
Exhibitions: (1977-78) Graphic Artists of Illinois; Edward McCullough Retrospective; Fired Works and Fibers; Japanese Print Collection of Illinois State Museum; 51st Annual Amateur Competition and Exhibition; Oriental Rug Show drawn from local collectors; mini-shows on a monthly basis in sales and rental gallery.
Activities: Classes for adults and children; Outreach Project providing art instruction to low income individuals, lect open to public, 8 vis lectr per yr; gallery talks; tours; competitions. Merwin Medal for best in show, first through third in each category; sales shop selling books, magazines, original art; operates both a used book store and art sales gallery.

CARBONDALE

SOUTHERN ILLINOIS UNIVERSITY MUSEUM AND ART GALLERIES, Faner Hall, Room 2469, 62901. Tel: 618-453-5388. *Acting Dir* Darrell W Harrison; *Cur Art* Evert A Johnson; *Cur Educ and Exhib* Eugene P Moehring; *Cur Coll* William L Johnson; *Program Coordinator* Geraldine Kelley; *Museum Preparator* Richard A Perry; *Museum Researcher* Allan Harasimowicz.

Open Mon - Fri 10 AM - 3 PM; Sun 1:30 - 4:30 PM. No admis. Estab 1874 to reflect the history and cultures of southern Illinois and promote the understanding of the area; to provide area schools and the University with support through educational outreach programs; to promote the fine arts in an unrestricted manner through exhibitions and provide support to the School of Art MFA program through exhibition of MFA graduate students. Two art galleries totaling 3500 square feet and one semi-permanent exhibit hall featuring exhibits on southern Illinois. Average Annual Attendance: 30,000.
Collections: Ethnographic material of history and natural history. †Large art collection made up entirely of original works of art in all mediums; Melanesian cultural material; small collections from Nepal, Vietnam, Mexico, China, South America, and Afghanistan; Plains Indian material as well as West Coast and Southwest Indian.
Exhibitions: Handmade: A Time Remembered; Iron, Solid Wrought/USA; National Invitational Drawings; Faculty and MFA Thesis Exhibits.
Activities: Classes for adults and children; dramatic programs; docent training; lect open to public; tours; competitions; exten dept serving lower 30 counties in southern Illinois; individual paintings and original objects of art lent to University Depts; lending collection contains original art works 1500; traveling exhibitions organized and circulated; museum shop selling books, original art, reproductions, and unusual gift items.

CHAMPAIGN

UNIVERSITY OF ILLINOIS, Krannert Art Museum, 500 Peabody Dr, 61820. Tel: 217-333-1860. *Dir* Muriel B Christison; *Research Cur* Laurie McCarthy; *Director and Asst to Dir* Fred Fisher; *Registrar* Brenda Huft; *Consultant for Conservation* Alfred Jakstas; *Business Secy* Mary DeLong; *Consultant for Decorative Arts* Carl C Dauterman; *Preparator* James Ducey; *Asst Preparator* Gerald Guthrie.
Open Mon - Sat 9 AM - 5 PM; Sun 2 - 5 PM. No admis. Estab 1961 to house and administer the art collections of University of Illinois, to support teaching and research program, and to serve as an area art museum. Average Annual Attendance: 190,000, Mem: 600; dues $15 and up.
Income: $350,000 (financed by endowment, membership, state appropriation). Purchases: $50,000.
Collections: Trees Collection and Krannert Collection of Old Masters; †Oriental Arts—Class of 1908; Moore Collection of European and American decorative Arts; †ancient Near Eastern classical and medieval art; Olsen Collection of Pre-Columbian art; †American paintings, sculpture, prints and drawings.
Exhibitions: (1976-78) Contemporary American Painting and Sculpture; Vollard; Chinese Paintings; Henry Moore Prints; Cleve Gray; Sol LeWitt; Atelier 17 100 Master Photographs; International Print Exhibition; New Urban Monuments; Dean Brown; Painters of the Seventies; Drawings from Four Collections.
Publications: Krannert Art Museum Bulletin, semi-annually; catalogs, occasionally.
Activities: Classes for children; docent training; lect open to public, 5 - 10 vis lectr per yr; tours; original objects of art lent to museums and university galleries.

CHARLESTON

EASTERN ILLINOIS UNIVERSITY,* Paul Turner Sargent Gallery, Lincoln & 7th Sts, 61920. Tel: 217-581-3410. *Dir* Rodney Buffington.
Open Mon - Fri 8 AM - Noon & 1 - 4 PM; cl school holidays. No admis. Estab 1948 as an exhibition gallery.
Income: Financed by state appropriation and through the University.
Exhibitions: Temporary and traveling exhibitions, each for a 3-week period, including paintings, ceramics, photography, sculpture, jewelry, prints and textiles.
Publications: Exhibition catalogs.

CHICAGO

ART INSTITUTE OF CHICAGO, Michigan Ave at Adams St, 60603. Tel: 312-443-3600. *Chmn Board of Trustees* James W Alsdorf; *Pres* E Laurence Chalmers, Jr; *VPres Admin Affairs* Robert E Marrs; *VPres Develop & Public Relations* Larry Ter Molen; *VPres Acad Affairs* Donald J Irving; *Secy* Louise Lutz; *Asst Secy* Linda Starks; *Cur American Art* Milo M Naeve; *Cur Earlier Painting & Sculpture & Classical Art* J Patrice Marandel; *Conservator* Alfred Jakstas; *Assoc Conservator* Timothy Lenon; *Cur European Decorative Arts* John Keefe; *Cur Oriental Art* Jack Sewell; *Assoc Cur Oriental Art* Osamu Ueda; *Dir Museum Photography* Howard Kraywinkel; *Assoc Cur Photography* David Travis; *Cur Primitive Art* Evan Maurer; *Cur Prints & Drawings* Harold Joachim; *Assoc Cur Prints & Drawings* Anselmo Carini; *Cur Textiles* Christa C Mayer Thurman; *Cur 20th Century Painting & Sculpture* A James Speyer; *Assoc Cur 20th Century Painting & Sculpture* Anne Rorimer; *Museum Registrar* Wallace Bradway; *Dir Museum Educ* Barbara Wriston; *Dir Libraries* Daphne Roloff; *Dir Public Relations* Helen M

Lethert; *Dir Publications* Margaret Blasage; *Dir Annual Programs* Edith B Gaines.
Open Mon - Wed & Fri 10:30 AM - 4:30 PM; Thurs 10:30 AM - 8 PM; Sat 10 AM - 5 PM; Sun & holidays Noon - 5 PM; cl Christmas. No admis Thurs. Estab and inc 1879. Average Annual Attendance: 1,621,255. Mem: 54,700; dues single member $20, family $30.
Income: $13,646,058. Purchases: $1,041,745.
Collections: Paintings, sculpture, arts of the Far East, prints, drawings, photographs, decorative arts, primitive art. The painting collection reviews the great period of Western art, with an especially fine sequence of French Impressionists and Post-Impressionists. The print collection illustrates the history of printmaking from the 15th - 20th centuries with important examples of all periods. It is particularly rich in French works of the 19th century including Meryon, Redon, Millet, Gauguin and Toulouse-Lautrec. In drawings, there has been emphasis on 18th and 19th century France. Outstanding in the collection of earlier drawings is the group given by Mrs Tiffany Blake and those given by Mrs Joseph Regenstein. The photography collection, begun in 1949, was organized as a department in 1959. *Glore Print Study Room* is open to the public Monday through Friday afternoons. The *Oriental Department* displays the arts of China from the pre-Han through the early Ch'ing dynasties; sculpture, painting, jade, lacquer, textiles, ceramics and the Lucy Maud Buckingham Collection of Chinese bronzes. The Russell Tyson Collection is particularly strong in Chinese and Korean ceramics, with notable examples of Chinese furniture, Japanese sculpture and painting of the great periods are represented, and wood block printing is extensively surveyed in the Clarence Buckingham Collection of Japanese prints; the Gookin and Ryerson Collection of illustrated books; Arenberg gift of modern Japanese prints. A special assemblage of Turkish and Greek Island embroideries is the gift of Burton Y Berry; other donors have made possible the creation of a new gallery devoted to Indian sculpture and miniatures. *European Decorative Arts Department* contains notable groups of English pottery, including the Frank W Funsaulus Collection of Wedgwood, the Amelia Blanxius Collection of English pottery and porcelain, and English and French furniture and silver. The *American Arts Department* contains examples of American decorative arts as well as paintings. The Buckingham Medieval Collection and Thorne Miniature Rooms are on permanent view. Textiles are displayed in the Agnes Allerton Textile Galleries, which include a study room and new conservation facilities. The collection of primitive art consists of African, Oceanic and ancient American objects; The newly opened *Columbus Drive* facilities include the reconstructed Trading Room from the Chicago Stock Exchange.
Exhibitions: (1976-77) Jacques Villon; Ensor; Art Noveau in Belgium and France, 1885-1915; 77th Exhibition by Artists of Chicago and Vicinity; The Antiquarian Society: The First Hundred Years; The Julian Levy Collection: Starting with Atget; The Native American Heritage; The Dutch Republic in the Days of John Adams; The Age of Franklin and Jefferson; American Institute of Architect Awards, 1976; Frederic Bazille and Early Impressionism.
Publications: Bulletin; Museum Studies; catalogs; Annual Report.
Activities: Museum education programs for adults including lectures, films and discussions; Junior Museum exhibitions, programs, games and library; Art Rental and Sales Gallery; museum store and Kenneth Sawyer Goodman Memorial Theatre.
—Ryerson and Burnham Libraries.
Reference collections in art and architecture.
Holdings: Vols 120,000; (including school contribution); Other—pamphlets 64,000, slides 192,000.
—Woman's Board. *Pres* Mrs Silas S Cathcart.
Estab 1952 to supplement the Board of Trustees in advancing the growth of the Institute and extending its activities and usefulness as a cultural and educational institution. Mem: 78; annual meeting May.
—The Auxiliary Board. *Pres* David C Hilliard.
Estab 1973 to promote interest in programs and activities of the Art Institute among younger men and women. Mem 58; dues $25; annual meeting June.
—Antiquarian Society. *Pres* Mrs Harold T Martin.
Estab 1877. Mem 475 by invitation; annual meeting Nov.
Activities: Lectures and seminars for members; tours; trips. Makes gift of decorative arts to the Institute.
—Print and Drawing Club. *Pres* Edward A Bergman.
Estab and inc 1922 to study prints and drawings and their purchase for the institute. Mem: 190; dues $25.
—Society for Contemporary Art. *Pres* Dirk Lohan.
Estab and inc 1940 to assist the Institute in acquisition of contemporary works. Mem: 190; annual meeting May.
Activities: Lectures, seminars and annual exhibition at the Institute.
—Orientals. *Secy-Treas* Jack Sewell.
Estab 1925 to promote interest in the Institute's collection of Oriental art. Mem: 50; dues $10 and $25.
—Textile Society. *Acting Pres* Mrs Don S Reuben.
Estab 1978 to promote appreciation of textiles through lectures, raising of funds, special publications and exhibitions for the Department of textiles.

—**Old Masters Society.** *Pres* Mrs John A Bross, Jr.
Estab 1977 to promote interest in the Department of Earlier Painting through lectures and fund raising for acquisitions. Mem: Dues $35 and $100.

—**Junior Museum.** Tel: 312-443-3680. *Dir Junior Museum* L Raasch.
Open Mon - Wed & Fri 10:30 AM - 4 PM; Thurs 10:30 AM - 7 PM; Sat 10 AM - 4:30 PM; Sun & holidays Noon - 4:30 PM. Admis discretionary, Thurs free. Estab 1964. A facility including auditorium, lunchroom, galleries, offices and library. One main gallery with exhibits changing every 2-3 years and two corridor galleries changed every six months; plus Picnic Room for children's work. Average Annual Attendance: 150,000.
Income: Financed by endowment.
Exhibitions: America and the Artist; Joy; Tracing Holiday Symbols, Visual Arts Collection; Children's Work from Lincoln School, Chicago; Student drawings from Sauk School; The Changing Image of America; Pictures from the Drawing Box; Arts in the Park; Another Roadside Attraction; Tapestries by Children of Harrania Village, Egypt; Young Artist's Studio.
Publications: Volunteer Directory America and the Artist; The Lion's Pride; Heritage HIke I, II, III; Kaleidoscope, I Spy Games; Round Up; Needlework Patterns Meet Monet; Forms in Space.
Activities: Docent training; lect open to public; traveling exhibitions organized and circulated; museum shop selling books, reproductions, prints and slides.
Little Library of the Junior Museum. Volunteer staff. Open for reference. Holdings: Vols 1500.

ARTEMISIA FUND AND GALLERY, * 9 W Hubbard St, 60610. Tel: 312-751-2016. Gallery open Tues - Sat 10 AM - 5 PM. No admis. Estab 1973 as a non-profit women's cooperative to exhibit members' work, to provide an alternative to commercial galleries, to encourage the development of art created by women, and to offer the community an opportunity to understand and appreciate the artist and art as valuable to society. Photography Gallery. Mem: Dues mem $10, sponsor $25, patron $50, benefactor $100 or more.
Activities: Regular exhibitions by members; monthly visits to artists studios organized by artists for artists; monthly video programs of both video art and documentary video; evening programs and mini-seminars.
—**Learning Resource Center.**
Open to school groups, organizations and the public, the Learning Resource Center houses a collection of video and audio tapes of locally and nationally known artists, with emphasis on women. A video monitor and replay equipment makes the tapes available for viewing during regularly scheduled hours (4 - 5 PM Tues - Sat) or at other times by appointment. A slide collection is also available for viewing.

ARTS CLUB OF CHICAGO, 109 E Ontario St, 60611. Tel: 312-787-3997. *Pres* Mrs Alfred P Shaw; *First VPres* Mrs Roger Barrett; *Secy* Franklin D Trueblood; *Admin Asst* Patricia M Scheidt.
Open 10 AM - 5:30 PM. Exhibitions free to public. Estab 1916 to maintain club rooms for members and provide galleries for changing exhibitions. Gallery has 200 running ft of wall space. Average Annual Attendance: 15,000; Mem: 1150; dues lay mem $250, professionals $75. annual meeting Nov.
Income: Financed by membership. Purchases: Occasional purchases from bequests.
Exhibitions: (1976-77) Ben Nicholson, paintings; Horst Antes, paintings; Archipenko, polychrome sculpture; Ulfert Wilke, paintings; Leon Berkowitz, paintings.
Publications: Exhibition catalog.
Activities: Lectures; concerts; dramatic programs; traveling exhibitions organized and circulated.
Library: Reference library; Holdings; Vols 1600.

ASSOCIATION OF MEDICAL ILLUSTRATORS, 6650 Northwest Hwy, Suite 112, 60631. Tel: 312-763-7350. *Pres* Gottfried Goldenberg; *VPres* Martin Finch; *Corresp Secy* Phyllis Wood; *Assoc Dir* Larry Offriecht; *Chmn Public Relations* William Winn.
For further information see National and Regional Organizations.

CHICAGO ARCHITECTURE FOUNDATION
—**Glessner House,** 1800 S Prairie Ave, 60616. Tel: 312-326-1393. *Pres Bd of Trustees* Marian A Despres; *Dir* Edward F Sullivan; *Educ Coordr* Jethro M Hurt III; *Coordr Pub Information* Mary Sue Mohnke.
Open: Guided tours: Tues, Thurs & Sat 10 AM - 3 PM; Sun, May 1 - Aug 31, 11 AM - 4 PM, Sept 1 - Apr 30, 1 - 4 PM. Admis adults $2, students & senior citizens $1, members free, group rates available. Estab 1966 for the restoration of the main floor of this architecturally significant residence, and for the promotion of good architecture in general. Designed by world-famous Henry Hobson Richardson, often known as the "Father of Modern Architecture," Glessner House was completed in 1886. Its period furnishings give visitors an excellent idea of what Vic-

torian life was like on this street once known as "Millionaires' Row." Average Annual Attendance: 5000. Mem: 1800; dues students & seniors $10, individual $20, family $30; annual meeting June.
Income: Financed by membership, tours, and rentals of house.
Collections: †House furnishings.
Publications: Chicago Architecture Foundation Members' Newsletter, bimonthly.
Activities: Classes for adults and children; docent training; public service; 3 vis lectrs per yr; tours; original objects of art lent to galleries mounting exhibitions on architecture; lending collection contains architectural ornaments; sales shop selling books, posters, stationery, small gift items.
—**ArchiCenter,** 310 S Michigan Ave, Second Floor, 60604. Tel: 312-782-1776. *Mgr* Alice Sinkevitch.
Open Mon - Sat 9 AM - 5 PM. No admis. Estab 1976 to make people more aware of our built environment through exhibits, lectures, films and tours. Approximately 2500 sq ft of exhibit space offers a permanent exhibit chronicling Chicago's contributions to the modern building arts. Average Annual Attendance: 40,000.
Income: Financed by membership, book shop and federal grant.
Exhibitions: Great Moments in Architecture: The Work of David Macaulay; Women in American Architecture: A Historical and Contemporary Perspective; The Work of Abel Faidy, Recycled Chicago, AIA Honor Awards (Chicago Chap); Walter Burley Griffin; Bridges and Tunnels; Wicker Park: Back from the Brink.
Activities: 30 vis lectrs per yr; sales shop selling books, magazines, slides, small gift items, stationery and posters.

CHICAGO ART DEALERS ASSOCIATION, 646 N Michigan Ave, 60611. Tel: 312-642-2900. *Pres* William van Straaten; *Secy* Donald Young; *Asst Secy* Jo-Anne Dobrick; *Treas* Rebecca Blattberg; *Asst Treas* Neva Krohn.
East to educate and inform and to make continuing contributions to the cultural life of the community. Mem: 29. Members include persons, firms and corporations engaged in the sale of art works in the Chicago area; dues $125.
Income: Financed by membership.
Publications: Guide to Chicago Art Galleries, brochure.
Activities: Lectures.

CHICAGO HISTORICAL SOCIETY, Clark St at North Ave, 60614. Tel: 312-642-4600. *Pres* Theodore Tieken; *VPres* Stewart S Dixon; *Secy* Bryan S Reid Jr; *Dir* Harold K Skramstad Jr; *Cur Painting & Sculpture* Joseph B Zywicki; *Cur Decorative Arts* Sharon Darling; *Cur Costume* Elizabeth Jachimowicz; *Editor* Fannia Weingartner; *Chief Educ Prog* Sarajane Wells.
Open Mon - Sat 9:30 AM - 4:30 PM; Sun & holidays 12:30 - 5 PM; Library open Tues - Sat 9 AM - 5 PM. Admis adults $1, children (6-17) 50¢, sr citizens 25¢, Mon free. Estab 1856 to maintain a museum and library of American history with special emphasis on the Chicago region. Average Annual Attendance: 200,000. Mem 4500; dues $20; annual meeting Oct.
Income: $1,500,000 (financed by endowment, membership, city and state appropriations and public donations).
Collections: Lincoln collection; pioneer life; Civil War; Chicago decorative arts; graphics; manuscripts.
Exhibitions: Remember the Ladies; Chicago: Creating New Traditions; Chicago Metalsmiths; Six Chicago Brides; continuing program of craft demonstrations and exhibits from the Collections.
Publications: Chicago History, quarterly; Calendar of Events, quarterly; books and catalogs.
Activities: Classes for adults and children; lect open to public, 8-10 vis lectr per yr; gallery talks; tours; sales shop selling books, magazines, prints, reproductions, slides.
—**Library.**
Open Tues - Sat 9:30 AM - 4:30 PM.
Holdings: Vols 120,000; AV—Microfilm 8000; Other—Newspapers and periodicals 24,000, maps 10,000, printed ephemera 35,000, broadsides 14,000, prints 50,000, photographs 50,000, reels 8000, manuscripts 4,000,000.

CHICAGO PUBLIC LIBRARY, Art Section, Fine Arts Division, 425 N Michigan Ave, 60611. Tel: 312-269-2886. *Chief Librn* David L Reich; *Chief Fine Arts Division* Marjorie R Adkins; *Asst to Chief* Rosalinda Hack; *Head Art Section* Patricia Keane.
Open Mon - Thurs 9 AM - 9 PM; Fri 9 AM - 6 PM; Sat 9 AM - 5 PM. Estab 1897. The gallery is under the auspices of the Cultural Center of the Chicago Public Library.
Income: Financed by city and state appropriation.
Holdings: Vols 45,000; periodicals, indexes and pamphlets in the subject areas of fine and applied art, dance, film and theater arts, costume archi-

tecture, photography and decorative arts. Other divisions and sections of the library hold music, crafts, audiovisual and other related art materials.
Special Collections: Picture collection of over one million items of secondary source material covering all subject areas; exhibition catalogs beginning 1973, primarily English language catalogs; Folk Dance collection of 26 loose leaf volumes.
Activities: Lect open to the public; concerts; dramatic programs; general participation in interlibrary loan through the regular channels, each application is individually considered; Audiovisual material is handled by the audiovisual section. Materials are restricted to use by Chicago area residents.

CONTEMPORARY ART WORKSHOP, 542 W Grant Place, 60614.
Tel: 312-525-9624. *Dir* John Kearney; *Admin Dir* Lynn Kearney.
Open daily 9 AM - 5:30 PM; Sat Noon - 5 PM. No admis. Estab 1951 as an art center, a Workshop-Alternative Space for artists; it is the oldest artist-run art workshop in the country; studios for approximately 26 artists and Not for Profit Gallery for exhibition of developing and established artists from Chicago, and from across the country. Average Annual Attendance: 4000.
Income: $75,000 (financed by contributions, foundations, Illinois Arts Council and earnings by the workshop fees).
Exhibitions: John Kearney; Paul Zakoian; Julian Harr; Susan Berman; Suzanne Seed; Robert McCauley; Carol Bendell; Jacqueline Ruttinger; Norbert Brown; Walter Fydryck; Irmfriede Hogan; Suzanne Peters; Gail Sherman Kritlow; Mark Krastoff; Robert Appel.
Publications: Mailing piece sent out with each show or event.
Activities: Classes for adults and children; lect open to the public; gallery selling artwork shown in gallery and studios.

DU SABLE MUSEUM OF AFRICAN AMERICAN HISTORY,* 740
E 56th Pl, 60637. Tel: 312-947-0600. *Dir* Margaret T Burroughs; *Cur* Charles G Burroughs; *Res Dir* Eugene P Feldman.
Open Tues - Fri 10 AM - 5 PM; Sat & Sun 1 - 5 PM; cl Mon, last two weeks of Aug. & National holidays. Admis adults 50¢, children & students 25¢, groups by appointment. Estab 1961 as history and art museum to tell the story of African American history. Mem: Dues general $15, life $100.
Collections: Historical archives; paintings; sculpture; prints; photographs.
Publications: Heritage Calendar, annually; books of poems, children's stories, African and Afro-American history.
Activities: Lectures; guided tours; traveling exhibitions. Sales shop selling curios, sculpture, prints, books and artifacts.

FIELD MUSEUM OF NATURAL HISTORY, Roosevelt Rd at Lake
Shore Dr, 60605. Tel: 312-922-9410. *Pres & Dir* E Leland Webber; *Asst Dir Admin* Norman W Nelson; *Asst Dir Science & Educ* Lorin I Nevling; *Chmn Anthropology* Phillip Lewis; *Chmn Board* William G Swarthchild, Jr; *VChmn Program Planning & Evaluation* John S Runnells; *VChmn Resource Planning & Development* Bowen Blair; *VChmn Public Affairs* James J O'Connor; *VChmn Facilities Planning* John W Sullivan; *VChmn Internal Affairs* James H Ransom; *Treas* Edward Dyron Smith.
Open winter daily 9 AM - 4 PM; Fri 9 AM - 9 PM; summer 9 AM - 6 PM; spring & fall 9 AM - 5 PM. Admis adults $1.50, families $3.50, students 50¢, senior citizens 35¢. Estab 1893 to preserve, to increase and to dissemiate knowledge of natural history; to enhance in individuals the knowledge of and delight in natural history; 22 anthropological exhibitions halls including a Hall of Primitive Art. Average Annual Attendance: 1,200,000. Mem: 74,621, dues $15.
Income: $8,000,000 (financed by endowment, membership, city and state appropriation and federal and earned funds).
Collections: Anthropological collections totaling over one third million specimens, including approx 100,000 art objects from North and South America, Oceania, Africa, Asia and prehistoric Europe.
Exhibitions: Treasures of Tutankhamun; Chinese Folk Art; Peru's Golden Treasures; Basketry of the Northwest Coast Indians; Field Museum Gamelan; I Wear the Morning Star; Between Friends/Entre Amis; 19th Century Alaskan Eskimo Art.
Publications: Bulletin, monthly; Fieldiana (serial).
Activities: Classes for adults and children; lect open to the public, 25 vis lectr per yr;; concerts; gallery talks; tours; extension dept serving Chicago area; original objects of art lent to qualified museum or other scholarly institutions; traveling exhibitions organized and circulated; museum shop selling books, magazines, prints, slides.
—**Library.** *Librn* W Peyton Fawcett.
Holdings: Vols 190,000; Per subs 2000.

LOYOLA UNIVERSITY OF CHICAGO, Martin D'Arcy Gallery of
Art, 6525 N Sheridan Rd, 60626. Tel: 312-274-3000, exten 786, *Dir* Donald F Rowe.
Open Mon - Fri 1 - 4 PM; Tues & Thurs 6:30 - 9:30 PM; Sun 1 - 4 PM. No admis. Estab 1969 to display the permanent university collection of Medieval, Renaissance, and Baroque decorative arts and paintings. One

gallery set up as a large living room with comfortable seating, classical music, fresh flowers, view of Lake Michigan—and the art objects all around. Average Annual Attendance: 10,000.
Income: Financed by gifts. Purchases: $200,000.
Collections: †Bronze; †gold; †enamel; †ivory; †silver; †wax; †textiles; †sculpture; paintings.
Publications: Annual Report.
Activities: Gallery talks; tours on request; paintings and original objects of art lent to qualified museums; lending collection contains original art works, paintings and sculpture.
Library: Open to university students and scholars. Holdings: Vols 15,000; Per subs 40.

MUSEUM OF CONTEMPORARY ART, 237 E Ontario St, 60611.
Tel: 312-943-7755. *Dir* John H Neff; *Pres* Lewis Mamlow; *Bus Mgr* Elizabeth G Miller; *Treas* John Cartland; *Cur* Judith Russi Kirshner; *Secy* Donald Ludgin.
Open Mon - Sat 10 AM - 5 PM; Thurs 10 AM - 8 PM; Sun 12 AM - 5 PM. Admis adults $1, students, children and sr citizens 50¢. Estab 1967 as a forum for the contemporary arts in Chicago. Average Annual Attendance: 80,000; Mem: 4300.
Income: Approx $800,000 (financed by endowment, membership, National Endowment for the Arts and National Endowment for Humanities).
Collections: †Permanent collection is mainly contemporary, constantly growing through contributions and purchases.
Exhibitions: (1976) 100 Years of Architecture in Chicago; (1976) Peter Blume Retrospective; (1977) Richard Lindner Retrospective; (1977) Claes Oldenburg, Mouse Museum; (1978) Frida Kahlo.
Publications: Calendar, bimonthly.
Activities: Classes for children; dramatic programs; docent training; tours; museum shop selling books, magazines, original art, reproductions.
Library: Under supervision of education department, for reference only.

NORTHEASTERN ILLINOIS UNIVERSITY, North River Commu-
nity Gallery, 3307 W Bryn Mawr, 60659. Tel: 312-583-4050, exten 591; *Gallery Coordr* Frank J Fritzmann; *Secy* Marilee Lintz; *Dept Chmn* Russell Roller.
Open weekdays 1 - 5 PM. No admis. Estab Feb 1973 for the purpose of providing a link between the University and the local community on a cultural and aesthetic level, to bring the best local and Midwest artists here; gallery is located in a relatively small storefront, on a commercial street, three blocks from the University. Average Annual Attendance: 500 - 900.
Income: Financed by Department of Art funds and personnel.
Exhibitions: (1976) Juith Stein (photography); Art Alumni Show; Student Show; Juliet Rago (paintings); Werner/Lossman (inflatable sculpture, watercolor); Recycled Chicago; Midwest Printmakers. (1977) Bross/Macaulay (photography); 3D Sculpture; Daisy Chan (photography); Bev Harrington (watercolors); Student Show; Faculty Show; Poets/Artists; Tyler/Glover (batik, collage); McCauley (drawings); Alumni Show; Maxine Wishnick (hard edge). (1978) Jeanne Reilly (constructions); Mildred Armato (prints); Student Show; John Weber (paintings); Peter Hoell (sculpture).
Publications: Flyers mailed for each show.
Activities: Competitions.

PALETTE AND CHISEL ACADEMY OF FINE ARTS,* 1012 N
Dearborn St, 60610. Tel: 312-337-9889. *Pres* Cyril Mills; *Secy* Elsie T Lowe.
Open daily 2 - 5 PM; Tues & Thurs 7 - 9 PM. No admis. Estab and inc 1895; owns building containing galleries, classrooms, studios, library. Mem: 100; dues $84; annual meeting Jan.
Collections: Oil paintings by members.
Exhibitions: Annual juried exhibition of members' work in oils; annual juried exhibition of members' work in watercolors; annual juried exhibition of members' work, mixed media; regular exhibit of members' work; special and one-person shows.
Activities: Lectures; educational events; competitions with awards.

POLISH MUSEUM OF AMERICA, 984 N Milwaukee Ave, 60622.
Dir Donald Bilinski; *Secy* Barbara Stasiuk; *Guides* Henry Cygan & Mrs Schnitter; *Asst Librn* Sabina Logisz & Wanda Willing; *Editor* Doroth Michno.
Open daily 1 - 4 PM. No admis. Estab 1937 to gather and preserve items and records pertaining to Polish culture as well as Polish-American culture. A specialized Museum and Gallery containing works of Polish artists, and Polish-American artists. Average Annual Attendance: 7000.
Income: Financed by donations.
Collections: Works of Polish artists, Polish-American artists and works on a Polish subject; originals dating to beginning of 20th century, a few older pieces; Pulaski at Savannah (Batowski).

Exhibitions: One-person exhibits: Habura, Zebrowski, Wilkon and Kossakowski.
Publications: Polish Museum Quarterly.
Activities: Traveling exhibitions organized and circulated; museum shop.
—**Research Library.**
Holdings: Vols 25,000; Per subs 100.
Special Subjects: Poland and works by Polish-American authors.
Special Collections: Music, Haiman.

SPERTUS COLLEGE OF JUDAICA, Spertus Museum of Judaica, 618 S Michigan Ave, 60605. Tel: 312-922-9012, exten 68. *Dir* Arthur M Feldman; *Cur* Grace Cohen Grossman; *Asst to Dir* Judith Benjamin; *Registrar* Mary Larkin Dannerth; *Designer* Darcie Cohen Fohrman; *Asst to Cur* Meta Smith; *Technician* Gary Petri.
Open Mon - Thurs 10 AM - 5 PM; Fri & Sun 10 AM - 3 PM. Admis adults $1, children, students and sr citizens, 50¢, Fri free. Estab 1967 for interpreting and preserving the 3500-year-old heritage embodied in Jewish history. The museum houses a distinguished collection of Judaica from many parts of the world, containing exquisitely designed ceremonial objects of gold, silver, bronze and ivory; a pertinent collection of sculpture, paintings and graphic art; and ethographic materials spanning centuries of Jewish experience; a permanent holocaust memorial; and special changing exhibitions throughout the year. Average Annual Attendance: 13,000; Mem: 150; dues $15, $25, $50, $100.
Income: $50,000 (subsidized by college).
Collections: Judaica, paintings, ceremonial silver, textiles, archaeology.
Exhibitions: (1976-78) Jewish Artists of the 20th Century; Archaeology from The Land of the Bible; Yemenite Jewry; Ludwig Wolpert, Faith and Form: Synagogue Architecture in Illinois, Ben Shahn, Selected Acquisitions, Abraham Rattner: Loop Synagogue Stained Glass, 12 From the Soviet Underground, Miron Sima: Woodcuts.
Publications: Yearly Calendar of Events; Catalog of Collection; special publications with exhibits.
Activities: Educ dept; docent training; exten dept serving the faculty; original objects of art lent to the faculty for study purposes; lending collection contains 24 film strips, 12 motion pictures, 1500 slides, and archaeological replicas; traveling exhibitions organized and circulated; museum shop selling books, original art, reproductions, slides and jewelry.
—**Helen Asher & Norman Asher Library of Spertus College.** Tel: 312-922-9012. *Librn/Dir* Richard Marcus. Reference library open to students and members.
Holdings: Vols 70,000, art 5000; Per subs 560.
Special Subjects: Judaica art.
Special Collections: Badona Spertus Library of Art and Judaica.

UNIVERSITY OF CHICAGO
—**Bergman Gallery,*** 5811 S Ellis, 60637. Tel: 312-753-4137. *Dir* Louis Natenshow; *Dir of Photographic Exhib* Joel Snyder; *Asst to Dir & Registrar* Lisa Urbinato.
Open Tues - Fri 10:30 AM - 5 PM; Sat Noon - 5 PM; during academic year only, cl during summer. Estab 1968 as an exhibition gallery founded entirely by the College of the University of Chicago, which provides changing shows of artistic and educational interest to the University community in all aspects of the visual arts. Average Annual Attendance: 5000.
Publications: Catalogs.
Activities: Have adjacent studio facilities used for visual studies of photography; lect open to the public; various gallery talks; some courses through the University extension are given in conjunction with the Berman Gallery; material available to the public, fees vary; original objects of art lent only in traveling exhibitions; traveling exhibitions organized and circulated.
—**Lorado Taft Midway Studios,*** 6016 Ingleside Ave, 60637. Tel: 312-752-7708. *Dir* Harold Haydon.
Open Mon - Fri 9 AM - 5 PM; Sat Noon - 5 PM; cl Sun. Studios of Lorado Taft and Associates, a Registered National Historic Landmark; Now University of Chicago, Department of Art.
Exhibitions: Exhibit of maquettes and portraits by Lorado Taft; exhibitions of student work in painting, sculpture, graphics and ceramics held in the Court Gallery;
Activities: Tours arranged.
—**David and Alfred Smart Gallery,** 5550 S Greenwood Ave, 60637. Tel: 312-753-2121. *Dir* Prof Edward A Maser; *Cur of Coll* Katharine Lee Keefe; *Registrar* Leon R Upshaw; *Admin Secy* Mavis Takeuchi; *Mem & Pub Relations* Pamela Leaderman.
Open Tues - Sat 10 AM - 4 PM; Sun Noon - 4 PM; cl Mon. No admis. Estab Oct 1974 to assist the teaching program of the Art Department of the University by maintaining a permanent collection and presenting exhibitions of scholarly and general interest; designed by E L Barnes exhibit space covers 7000 sq ft and contains also conservation room, print and drawing study room, sculpture garden, storage and preparator's workroom. Average Annual Attendance: 12,000. Mem: 225; dues individual $15; annual meeting spring.

Income: Financed by membership and university funding.
Collections: †Ancient, †Medieval, †Renaissance, †Baroque, †Oriental, and Modern European and †American paintings, sculpture and decorative arts.
Exhibitions: (1976-78). The Documentary Photograph as a Work of Art; The Cleveland Tuti-name Manuscript and the Origins of Mughal Painting; The Trained Eye: The Art Historian as Photographer; the Oliver Statler Collection of contemporary Japanese prints; Artists View the Law in the 20th Century; Hsieh Shih-ch'en; German and Austrian Painting of the 18th Century.
Publications: Gallery newsletter, three times a year.
Activities: Museum training course for personnel; lect open to the public, 6 vis lectr per yr; tours; individual paintings and original objects of art lent to museums for special exhibitions; lending collection contains original art works 1000, original prints 500; paintings 100, sculpture 50; sales shop selling catalogs of exhibitions.
—**Oriental Institute,** 1155 E 58th St, 60637. *Dir* John A Brinkman; *Cur* John Carswell; *Asst Cur* David Nasgowitz.
Open Tues - Sat 10 AM - 4 PM; Sun Noon - 4 PM; cl Mon. No admis. Estab 1919 as a Museum of Antiquities excavated from Egypt, Mesopotamia, Assyria, Syria, Palestine, Persia, Anatolia, and Nubia, dating from 7000 years ago until the 10th century AD. Average Annual Attendance: 83,804. Mem: 2000; dues $15.
Income: $146,369 (financed by membership and through University).
Collections: Ancient Near Eastern antiquities from prehistoric times to the beginning of the present era plus some Islamic artifacts; Egypt: colossal statue of King Tut, mummies, Assyrian bullman (40 tons); Mesopotamian temple interior, house interior, jewelry; Persian bull; column & capital from Persepolis; Megiddo ivories and horned altar.
Exhibitions: Mesopotamia; The Magic of Egyptian Art; Treasures of Tutankhamen; A Photographer's World.
Publications: News and Notes, monthly; annual report.
Activities: Classes for adults; dramatic programs; lect open to public, 5 vis lectr per yr; gallery talks; tours; original objects of art lent to museums and institutions of higher learning; museum shop selling books, reproductions, prints, slides and near Eastern jewelry.
—**Research Archives.** *Librn* Richard Zettler. Open to staff, students and members for reference.
Holdings: Vols 9989; Per subs 74; Other—Pamphlets 5715.
Special Subjects: The ancient Near East.
—**Art Library,** Goodspeed Hall 401, 5845 S Ellis, 60637. Tel: 312-753-3439. *Asst-in-charge of Art Library* Scott O Stapleton.
Open Mon - Thurs 8:30 AM - 9 PM; Fri & Sat 9 AM - 5 PM; Sun 1 - 5 PM; hours vary in summer quarter.
Holdings: Vols 53,000 (on history of art excepting Classical, Near Eastern and city planning which are housed in the Regenstein Library); Other—Pamphlet 5000, auction sales catalogs 6000.
Also, Union Catalog of Art Books in Chicago, listing the art titles in the following libraries: Chicago Public, Art Institute of Chicago Libraries, University of Illinois Chicago Circle Campus, Field Museum, Newberry, Northwestern University Library (Evanston) and the various divisions of the University of Chicago Libraries.
—**Art Slide Collection,*** Tel: 312-753-3896. *Cur* Olivera Mihailovic.
Open Mon - Fri 8:30 AM - 4 PM; cl Sat & Sun. Estab 1938.
For reference.
Holdings: AV—Slides, black & white 75,000, colored 50,000. Annual additions: 6000 slides, not available for loan.
—**Max Epstein Archive,*** Tel: 312-753-2887. *Cur* Ruth R Philbrick.
Open Mon - Fri 9 AM - 5 PM; cl Sat & Sun. Estab 1938. For reference.
Holdings: Other—Mounted photographs of works of art 400,000, also original material in history of prints. Annual additions: 8000 catalogued and mounted photographs.
—**The Renaissance Society,*** Goodspeed Hall 108, 5845 S Ellis, 60637. Tel: 312-753-2886. *Pres* Edward A Maser; *Exhib Dir* Jean Goldman.
Open Mon - Fri 10 AM - 5 PM; Sat 1 - 5 PM during exhibitions. Estab 1915. Mem: 500; dues student Univ Chicago $5, $7 and up; annual meeting May.
Exhibitions: Changing exhibitions, about six per academic year; Annual Art for Young Collectors Sales Exhibition Nov - Dec.
Activities: Lectures, gallery talks.

CLINTON

FINE ARTS CENTER OF CLINTON,* 119 W Macon St, 61727. Tel: 217-935-5055. *Pres* Mrs John Warner, III; *Dir* Robin McNeil; *Secy-Treas* John Warner, III.
Open Sept - June 1, Mon - Fri 10 AM - Noon & 1 - 5 PM; Sun for exhib only; June 1 - Sept, Mon - Thurs 10 AM - Noon & 1 - 5 PM; cl holidays. Admis adults 50¢; children and members free. Estab 1960 in memory of John Smoot DeQuoin whose conviction it was that almost everyone is

born with a latent talent and that developing that talent could be most rewarding. Average Annual Attendance: 550 students, 1000 visitors.
Income: Financed by tuition fees and supported by Mr and Mrs J Warner, III.
Collections: Contemporary art—Aaron Bohrod, Emil Gruppe, Tom Polston et al.
Exhibitions: Watercolors.
Publications: Bulletin of Center activities, annually.
Activities: Classes for adults and children; concerts; competitions.

DANVILLE

VERMILION COUNTY MUSEUM SOCIETY,* 116 N Gilbert St, 61832. Tel: 217-442-2922. *Dir* Zella Brown Laury.
Open Thurs - Sat 10 AM - 5 PM; Wed 10 AM - 9 PM; Sun & holidays 1 - 5 PM; cl Mon, Tues, Thanksgiving & Xmas. Admis adults $1, students 25¢, school & scout groups and children under 12 no admis. Estab 1964 in 1855 doctor's residence and carriage house. Mem: Dues student $4, individual $5, family $10, organization $10, contributing $25, patron $50, Life $150.
Collections: Paintings; sculpture; graphics; decorative arts; costumes; historical material.
Exhibitions: Frequent temporary and traveling exhibitions.
Publications: Heritage, quarterly magazine.
Activities: Lectures; guided tours; arts festivals. Gift Shop.
Library: Open to the public and for inter-library loan. Holdings: 300 vols.

DECATUR

MILLIKIN UNIVERSITY,* Kirkland Gallery, Kirkland Fine Arts Center, 62522. Tel: 217-423-3661. *Dir* Marvin L Klaven.
Open Mon - Thurs Noon - 8 PM; Fri - Sun Noon - 5 PM; cl during vacation. No admis. Estab 1970. Mem: dues $5 - $1000.
Collections: Painting; drawings; sculpture; prints; watercolors; weaving.
Exhibitions: Monthly traveling exhibitions.
Publications: Center Activities, annual bulletin.
Activities: Classes for adults and children; guided tours; lectures; gallery talks.

DE KALB

NORTHERN ILLINOIS UNIVERSITY, Gallery 200, Art Department, 60115. *Chmn Dept* Robert L Even.
Open daily 8:30 AM - Noon & 1 - 5 PM. No admis. Estab 1898. One large gallery for general exhibitions; one small gallery for graduate student shows.
Income: Financed by state appropriation.
Collections: Mel Pfaelzer Collection (prints, surrealist).
Exhibitions: Changing exhibits in both galleries.
Publications: Show catalogs, twice a year.
Activities: Lect open to public, 75 vis lectr per yr; gallery talks; tours; competitions; exten dept serving Northern Illinois; individual paintings and original objects of art lent within the University.

ELGIN

ELGIN ACADEMY,* Laura Davidson Sears Fine Arts Gallery,† 350 Park St, 60120. *Headmaster* Robert Haggemann; *Fine Arts Chmn* D Scott Irving.
Open during drama presentations. Academy founded 1839, chartered 1856 for the purpose of educational art and theater. One room gallery is dedicated primarily to 20th century local artists.
Collections: Gilbert Stuart's George Washington; sculpture; furniture; Victorian silverplated items; decorative articles.
Activities: Classes in ceramics, architectural design, painting, drawing and sculpture; photograph collection; 500-1000 prints; dramatic programs. Librry.

ELMHURST

LIZZADRO MUSEUM OF LAPIDARY ART, 220 Cottage Hill Ave, 60126. Tel: 312-833-1616. *Dir* John S Lizzadro; *Exec Secy* Judith Greene.
Open Tues - Fri & Sun 1 - 5 PM; Sat 10 AM - 5 PM; cl Mon. Admis adults 50¢; ages 13-18 25¢; under 13 free; no charge on Fri. Estab 1962 to promote interest in the lapidary arts and the study and collecting of minerals and fossils. Main exhibit area contains hardstone carvings, gemstone materials, minerals; lower level contains educational exhibits. Average Annual Attendance: 45,000. Mem: 600; dues $15.
Income: Financed by endowment.
Collections: Hardstone carvings.
Exhibitions: Educational exhibits.

Publications: Museum publication, semi-annual.
Activities: Lect open to public, 6 vis lectr per yr; tours; traveling exhibitions organized and circulated; museum shop selling books, magazines, slides, minerals, fossils and carvings.
Library: Open for research. Holdings: Vols 750; Per subs 3.

ELSAH

PRINCIPIA COLLEGE, School of Nations Museum,* 62028. Tel: 618-466-2131, exten 334. *Cur* Mary Elizabeth Wheeler.
Open Mon - Fri 8:30 AM - Noon & 1:30 - 4:30 PM.
Collections: American Indian collection including baskets, blankets, pottery, leather, quill work, bead work, and silver; Asian Art Collection includes textiles, ceramics, arts and crafts from Japan, China, and Southeast Asia; European collections include glass, patch and snuff boxes, wood, metals, textiles; dolls represent customs and costumes of the countries and regions of the world.
Exhibitions: Changing exhibits on campus locations; permanent exhibits in School of Nations lower floor.
Activities: Special programs offered throughout the year; museology courses offered; youth museum.

EVANSTON

EVANSTON ART CENTER, 2603 Sheridan Road, 60201. Tel: 312-475-5300. *Pres* Gail Struve; *VPres* Jeanine Grossman; *Secy* Mary Breen; *Treas* Stewart McMullen; *Dir* Steven Klindt; *Office Mgr* Caryl Carver.
Open Mon - Sat 10 AM - 4 PM; Mon - Fri 7 - 10 PM; Sun 2 - 5 PM. No admis. Estab 1929 as a community visual arts center with exhibits, instruction, and programs; Wieghardt Memorial Gallery, West Gallery for prints and drawings, Photography Gallery. Average Annual Attendance: 6000. Mem: 2000; dues $15; annual meeting April.
Income: Financed by membership.
Exhibitions: Faculty exhibition; Signs and Measures, Marks of Man (photography); Recent Drawings by John Almquist; Fred Annes (sculpture); The Chicago Photographer; Young Printmakers; Sculpture by Ruth Aizuss Migdal; Flora (photography); Thelma Heagstedt (drawings); Steve Saunders (photography); Alan Stecker (paintings); The Vessel as Metaphor (ceramics); Harold Allen's Egypt (photography); Proposals for Lake Sculptures (drawings and maquettes).
Publications: Concentrics, monthly.
Activities: Classes for adults and children; lect, 6 vis lectr per yr; sales shop.

MIDWEST ART HISTORY SOCIETY, Dept of Art History, Northwestern University, 60201. Tel: 312-492-3741. *Pres* James D Breckenridge; *VPres & Secy* Edward J Olszewski.
For further information see National and Regional Organizations.

NORTHWESTERN UNIVERSITY LIBRARY, Art Collection, 60201. Tel: 312-492-7484. *Cur Special Coll* R Russell Maylone; *Art Coll Supv* Joan Perlman.
Open Mon - Fri 8:30 AM - 5 PM; Sat 8:30 AM - Noon. (Use during other hours limited to staff, faculty, and students. Hours vary during summer). No admis. Estab 1970 as a separate collection. It serves curriculum and research needs of the Art and Art History departments.
Income: Financed through the University.
Holdings: Vols 35,221.
Special Subjects: History of art.

FREEPORT

HIGHLAND AREA ARTS COUNCIL, Freeport Art Museum, 511 S Liberty, 61032. Tel: 815-235-9755. *Cur & Dir* Vincent Tolpo; *Asst Cur* Linda Prestwich.
Open Wed - Sun 10 AM - 5 PM. No admis. Estab 1975 to house W T Rawleigh Art Collection and to promote the arts in the region. Nine galleries, 30 x 24 ft with 12-foot ceilings, auditorium, two classrooms and a lounge. Average Annual Attendance: 10,000. Mem: 400; dues $20; annual meeting Jan.
Income: $140,000 (financed by endowment, membership, city and state appropriations, and other grants). Purchases: $4500.
Collections: †Oil paintings; †prints; sculpture; American Indian pottery; art nouveau pottery; primitive art and basketry; textiles.
Exhibitions: Phealzer Collection from Northern Illinois University; Professional Artists of Northwest Illinois; the best of the W T Rawleigh collection; Pottery and Vessels through the Centuries; Aaron Bohrod retrospective; numerous one-person shows.
Publications: Newsletter, monthly.
Activities: Classes for adults and children; dramatic programs; docent training; film festival; lect open to public, 6 vis lectr per yr; concerts; gallery talks; tours; competitions; exten dept serving Ogle, Carroll, Jo Daviess Counties; individual paintings and original objects of art lent to bona fide galleries with full insurance; lending collection contains original

art works, paintings, sculpture; traveling exhibitions organized and circulated.
Library: Open to members for research and reference. *Librn* Linda Prestwich. Holdings: Vols 200; Per subs 10; Other—US Govt materials.

GALESBURG

GALESBURG CIVIC ART CENTER, 114 E Main, 61401. Tel: 309-342-7415. *Pres* Patti Flint; *VPres* Jan West; *Treas* Rose Sampson; *Secy* Margie Renfroe; *Gallery Dir* Kevin Dean.
Open Tues - Fri 11:30 AM - 4:30 PM; Sat 10:30 AM - 3 PM. No admis. Estab 1965 as a non-profit organization for the furtherance of art. The main gallery has about 80 running feet of wall space for he hanging of exhibits. The sales-rental gallery runs on a 30% commission basis and is open to professional artists as a place to sell their work under a consignment agreement. Average Annual Attendance: 2500; Mem: 300; dues begin at $6.
Income: Financed by membership and grants.
Collections: Some paintings and sculpture.
Exhibitions: Illinois Woman Artists; Members Show; Three Area Artists; Woldemar Winkler; Galex Competition; Grank Berkenkotter; Jim Davis; Philip Amos; Bob Paulson; High School Invitational.
Publications: Newsletter.
Activities: Classes for adults and children; lect open to public, 4 vis lectr per yr; gallery talks; tours; competitions; individual paintings and original objects of art lent to schools, library, activity centers; lending collection contains original art works; museum shop selling magazines, original art.

GREENVILLE

GREENVILLE COLLEGE, Richard W Bock Sculpture Collection, 62246. Tel: 618-664-1840, exten 321. *Dir & Cur* Donald P Hallmark.
Open Mon, Wed, & Fri 1 - 5 PM; Sun 2 - 5 PM; cl August & holidays. Admis adults 50¢, students & senior citizens 25¢. Estab 1975 to display an extensive collection of the life work of the American sculptor in a restored home of the mid-19th Century period; five large rooms and two hallways approx. 320 running feet of exhibition space. Average Annual Attendance: 5000.
Income: $8000 (financed by future endowment, college appropriation, gifts and donations).
Collections: Late 19th and early 20th century sculpture, drawing, and painting; Japanese prints; late 19th and early 20th century posters; furniture and furnishings of the 1850-1875 era.
Exhibitions: (1976-78) The Work of Richard W Bock; Bronze Casts from the Bock Collection; The Columbian Exposition at Chicago (medallions and sculpture).
Publications: General museum brochures.
Activities: Lect open to the public, 1-2 vis lectr per yr; gallery talks; individual paintings and original objects of art lent to museums only; lending collection contains original art works 5000, paintings 25, photographs 100, sculpture 350, drawings 150; traveling exhibitions organized and circulated; museum shop selling books, magazines.
Research Library: Librn Donald P Hallmark. Tel: 618-664-1840. Open to researchers for reference only. Holdings: Vols 750 - 1000. Special Subjects: Frank Lloyd Wright; the Prairie School of Architecture; Richard W Bock.

JACKSONVILLE

ART ASSOCIATION OF JACKSONVILLE, David Strawn Art Gallery, 331 W College, 62650. Tel: 217-245-5075. *Dir* Peter S Cohan; *Asst Dir* Ann Liljengren Cohan; *Pres Art Assoc* Dorothy Floreth.
Open (Sept - May) Tues - Sun 2 - 5 PM; Fri 7 - 9 PM; cl Mon. No admis. Estab 1873, endowed 1915, to serve the community by offering monthly shows of visual arts and weekly classes in a variety of media. The two main rooms house the monthly exhibitions and a third large room houses a collection of pre-Columbian pottery. The Gallery is in a large building, previously a private home. Average Annual Attendance: 1200. Mem: 285; dues $3 and up; annual meeting June.
Income: Financed by endowment and membership.
Collections: Pre-Columbian pottery; pottery discovered in the Mississippi Valley.
Exhibitions: Paintings by Susan Sensemann; Watercolors by Jack Madura; Paintings & Drawings by Noreen Ten Eyck; Sculpture by Four Midwestern Artists; Ceramics by Bob Dixon; Batiks by Kristine Lindahl Northcutt; Recent Works by Peter & Ann Cohan.
Activities: Classes for adults and children; lect open to public, 2 vis lectr per yr; concerts.

LAKE FOREST

LAKE FOREST LIBRARY, 360 E Deerpath, 60045. Tel: 312-234-0636. *Acting Librn* Sydney S Mellinger; *Reference Librn* Nancy G Wallens; *Circ Head* Kathryn Summa.
Open Mon - Fri 9 AM - 9 PM; Sat 9 AM - 5 PM. Estab 1898 to make accessible to the residents of the city, books and other resources and services for education, information and recreation. Circ: 175,000. Maintains an art gallery with sculptures and minimasters (framed art prints).
Income: $250,000 (financed by city and state appropriations). Purchases: $30,000.
Library: Holdings—Vols 77,000; Per subs 215; AV—Phonorecords; Other—Clipping files, framed reproductions, pamphlets, reproductions and sculpture. Special Subjects: Art and gardening. Special Collections: Painting and folk art.

MACOMB

WESTERN ILLINOIS UNIVERSITY ART GALLERY,* Garwood Hall, 61455. Tel: 309-298-1549. *Dir* Marie Czach.
Open Mon - Fri 8 AM - 4:30 PM, and by appointment. Estab as an adjunct to Art Department and as a community service for the University and its constituency. Average Annual Attendance: 10,000.
Income: Financed by state appropriation.
Collections: American Indian pottery; contemporary painting; sculpture; crafts; †graphics; †Old Master prints; glass; jewelry; ceramics.
Exhibitions: Over 30 exhibitions per year including Annual National Print and Drawing Show; traveling exhibitions; one and two-person shows of contemporary artists; faculty and student exchange exhibitions.
Activities: Arts Development Office, serving West Central Illinois schools, banks, churches; lectures open to public, 4-6 vis lectr per yr; original objects of art lent; scholarships and tuition waivers; traveling exhibitions organized and circulated.

MONMOUTH

MONMOUTH COLLEGE, Boone Oriental Library and Fine Arts Collection, 61462.
A substantial private collection has been made available to the college by its owners, Commander and Mrs G E Boone. The collection is designed for study and display and is located near the Monmouth campus.
Holdings: Vols several thousand.
Special Collections: Art objects 1000.
Activities: Regularly scheduled classroom lecture courses; guest artists; films; gallery critiques; special exhibitions.

MOUNT VERNON

MITCHELL MUSEUM, Richview Rd (Mailing Add: Box 923, 62864). Tel: 618-242-1236. *Pres* Jerome Glassman; *Secy* Ruby Miller; *Exec VPres* Kenneth R Miller.
Open Tues - Sun 1 - 5 PM; cl Mon. No admis. Estab 1973 to present exhibitions of paintings, sculpture, graphic arts, architecture and design representing contemporary art trends; to provide continued learning and expanded education; Main Gallery, Hall Gallery and Lecture Gallery. Average Annual Attendance: 40,000. Mem: 650; dues $25; annual meeting Nov.
Income: Financed by endowment and membership.
Collections: Paintings by late 19th and early 20th century American artists; some drawings and small sculptures; silver; small stone, wood and ivory carvings; vases; Jade; cut glass; small bronzes.
Exhibitions: Changing exhibits.
Publications: Newsletter, quarterly; Calendar of Events, quarterly.
Activities: Classes for adults and children; dramatic programs; docent training; lect open to public, 10 vis lectr per yr; concerts; gallery talks; tours; competitions; individual paintings and original objects of art lent to museums and universities; sales shop selling books, magazines, reproductions, prints and slides.
Library: Dir K R Miller. Open to the public for reference. Holdings: Vols 500; Per subs 12; Other—Photographs.

NORMAL

ILLINOIS STATE UNIVERSITY
—**University Museum,** 61761. Tel: 309-829-6331. *Dir* Roslyn A Walker-Oni; *Secy & Registrar* Arlene A Boggs; *Exhibits Designer* David L Kuntz; *Cur International Coll of Child Art* Dr Barry E Moore; *Curatorial Asst* Jean Shepherd; *Curatorial Asst* Virginia M Wright; *Cur Graphic Reproduction Coll* William V White.
Ewing Museum of Nations Open Apr - Sept, Tues & Thurs 2 - 5 PM; Sun 1 - 5 PM; Oct - Mar Sat & Sun 1 - 5 PM; Eyestone School Museum, Apr - Sept Tues & Thurs 2 - 5 PM; Sun 1 - 5 PM Oct - Mar Sun 1 - 5 PM; Stevenson Memorial Room Apr 1 - Sept Mon - Fri 10 AM - 5 PM, Sun 1 - 5 PM, Oct - Mar Sun 1 - 5 PM; University Historical Mu-

seum all year Mon -. Fri 10 AM - 5 PM, Sun 1 - 5 PM; Estab 1872, reestab 1945 to collect, preserve and interpret museum objects directly related to academic programs of the university and the public schools; to support research related to exhibit collections; and to maintain general interest collections; six museums which house temporary and permanent exhibits on loan and from the permanent collection. Average Annual Attendance: 20,000.

Income: Financed by state appropriation.

Collections: (Art) †African art; †Pre-Columbian art of Middle America; South Pacific art; †international dolls; native American art; decorative arts; International Collection of Child Art; Southeast Asian Artifacts; Adlai E Stevenson memorabilia.

Exhibitions: (1976-78) Art of Mexico Before Columbus; Food and Culture in Northern Thailand; Masks of Upper Volta; Recent Acquisitions; Mascaras, Dance Masks of Mexico and Guatemala; Art and Community: A Senufo Example; Dennis Collection of Egyptian Antiquities.

Publications: Annual Report; exhibit brochures and catalogs.

Activities: Lectr open to the public; gallery talks; tours; original objects of art lent to local and county schools and local exhibits; lending collection contains cassettes, original art works, sculpture and slides; traveling exhibitions organized and circulated.

Library: Librn Arlene A Boggs. Open to scholars students and staff. Holdings: Vols 201; Per subs 22. Special Subjects: Native American Art; African art and history; Pre-Columbian folk art; decorative arts.

—Center for the Visual Arts Gallery, Beaufort St, 61761. Tel: 309-436-5487. *Dir* Tom R Toperzer; *Asst Dir* Barry D Weet; *Registrar* Janet L Bertagnolli.

Open Tues 9 AM - 10 PM; Wed - Fri 9 AM - 4:30 PM; Sat & Sun 1 - 4:45 PM. No admis. Estab 1974 to provide changing exhibits of the visual arts for the students and community at large; also display student art work; the main Gallery I contains rotating exhibitions; Galleries II and III display student work, graduate exhibitions and studio area shows. Average Annual Attendance: 50,000.

Income: Under $100,000.

Collections: †20th century graphics.

Exhibitions: (1978) Graphic Art of Max Klinger, Prints from 1870-1909; The Sensuous Line; Indian Drawings of the 17th, 18th and 19th Century; Illinois Sculptor's: Exhibition II.

Activities: Individual paintings and original objects of art lent for other exhibitions; lending collection contains original art works, original prints, paintings, photographs and sculpture; traveling exhibitions organized and circulated.

PEORIA

BRADLEY UNIVERSITY GALLERY, Division of Art, 61625. Tel: 309-676-7611, exten 498. *Dir* W A S Hatch.

Open daily 9 AM - 4 PM. No admis. Estab 1950 as a teaching gallery to students and community; exhibition space 45 x 25 ft. Average Annual Attendance: 2000.

Income: Financed by University.

Exhibitions: Bradley National Print and Drawing Exhibition; James Butler; Artemesia Gallery Group Show; Robert McCauley.

Activities: Classes for adults; lectr open to the public, 10 vis lectr per yr; gallery talks; tours; competitions.

LAKEVIEW CENTER FOR THE ARTS AND SCIENCES,* 1125 W Lake Ave, 61614. *Exec Dir* William Loebel; *Cur Coll* Virginia Najmi.

Open Tues - Sat 9 AM - 5 PM; Sun 1 - 6 PM; Wed 7 - 9 PM; cl Mon. Estab 196 new building opened 1965, organized to provide enjoyment and education by reflecting the historical, cultural and industrial life of the Central Illinois area. Average Annual Attendance: 150,000. Mem: dues $5 - $1000.

Income: $220,000.

Collections: Archaeological; paintings and graphics.

Exhibitions: Monthly exhibitions dealing with the arts and sciences.

Publications: Bulletin, bimonthly.

Activities: Art classes; demonstrations; lectures; concerts.

PEORIA ART GUILD, 1831 N Knoxville, 61603. Tel: 309-685-7522. *Pres* Esther Cohen; *VPres* Barbara Drake; *Secy* Janis Herring; *Treas* Ann Mathis; *Personnel Coordinator* P Atterberry; *Sales & Rental Chmn* R Howard Courtney.

Open Tues - Sat 10 AM - 4 PM; Sun 1 - 4 PM; cl Mon. No admis. Estab 1878 to encourage development of the arts. Average Annual Attendance: 5000. Mem: 500; dues $10 - $15.

Income: Financed by membership and Illinois Arts Council.

Collections: Winning works from the Bradley Print and Drawing Exhibition; framed and unframed two-dimensional work, ceramics, sculpture, jewelry and weaving.

Exhibitions: One-person shows; group theme shows.

Activities: Classes for adults and children; workshops; lect open to public; gallery talks; competitions with cash and purchase awards; scholarships; individual paintings and original objects of art lent to members of the community; lending collection contains original art works 700.

QUINCY

QUINCY ART CENTER,* 1515 Jersey St, 62301. Tel: 217-223-5900. *Dir* William C Landwehr.

Open Tues - Sun 2 - 5 PM; cl Mon, legal holidays and during the summer months. Estab 1923, inc 1951, to foster public awareness and understanding of the visual arts. Average Annual Attendance: 6000. Mem 400; dues individual $6, family $10, annual patron $25, life member $250; annual meeting June.

Collections: †Painting, sculpture, graphics and crafts by contemporary American and European artists.

Exhibitions: Quincy's Annual Art Show held in Nov and open to artists living within a 200-mile radius of Quincy.

Publications: Calendar, quarterly; catalogues of temporary exhibitions.

Activities: Classes for adults and children; lectures; films; gallery talks; concerts; tours; inter-museum loan; traveling exhibitions organized and circulated.

Library: Holdings—Vols 350 (includes periodicals and art books).

QUINCY COLLEGE ART GALLERY,* 1831 College Ave, 62301. Tel: 217-222-8020. *Gallery Dir* Robert Lee Mejer.

Open 8 AM - 10 PM. No admis. Estab 1968 as a cultural enrichment and artistic exposure for the community. Exhibitions held in the library foyer and the foundation room. Average Annual Attendance: 5000.

Income: Financed through the College.

Collections: 19th century Oriental and European prints; 20th century American prints and drawings; permanent collection of student and faculty works.

Publications: Gallery calendars, annually; brochures 3-5 times yearly.

Activities: Classes for adults; lect open to public, 2-3 vis lectr per yr; individual paintings and original objects of art lent; lending collection contains Kodachromes 20,000, photograph collection; scholarships; traveling exhibitions organized and circulated; book shop.

Library: Holdings—Vols 6800.

QUINCY SOCIETY OF FINE ARTS,* 1624 Maine St, 62301. Tel: 217-222-3432. *Pres* George M Irwin; *Secy* Mrs William Raufer.

Open Mon - Fri 9 AM - Midnight; Tues 5 PM - 1 AM. Estab 1948 as a community arts council to coordinate and stimulate the visual and performing arts in Quincy and Adams County. Mem: 12 art organizations.

Income: Financed by endowment, membership and contribution.

Publications: Cultural calendars, quarterly; pamphlets and catalogs, occasionally.

Activities: Workshops for adults and students in visual and performing arts.

ROCKFORD

ROCKFORD ART ASSOCIATION, Burpee Art Museum, 737 N Main St, 61103. Tel: 815-965-3131. *Pres* Mrs J R Bender; *VPres* Mrs Allen Pang; *Secy* Mrs Clark Galloway; *Dir* William A McGonagle; *Exec Secy* Mrs Roger Harlan; *Admin Asst, Librn & Archivist* Bruce Kruger; *Technical Asst* Chuck Ludeke.

Open Tues - Fri Noon - 5 PM; Sat - Sun 1 - 5 PM; cl Mon and holidays. No admis.

Estab 1914 to promote and cultivate an active interest in all fields of fine and applied art, past and present, in the surrounding area. The main building is an Italian style villa which was redecorated and renovated to house six rooms for exhibition space; an auditorium was added later. Average Annual Attendance: 4000. Mem: 400; dues young adult & sr citizens $5, individual $20, others up to benefactor $1000.

Income: Financed by membership and state appropriation.

Collections: Permanent collection Early American oil paintings, graphics, sculpture, photography, ceramics, glassware, textiles, watercolors and mixed media.

Exhibitions: Traveling exhibitions; Annual Rockford and Vicinity Show; Annual Young Artist's Exhibition; numerous one-person and group shows.

Publications: Newsletter, quarterly; exhibition brochures and catalogs.

Activities: Classes for adults and children; lect open to public, 6 vis lectr per yr; gallery talks; tours; competitions with cash awards; scholarships.

Library: Katherine Pearman Memorial Library. *Librn* Bruce Kruger. Open to the public and members by appointment, for reference. Holdings: Vols 500; Per subs 15. Special Subjects: The visual arts.

SPRINGFIELD

ILLINOIS STATE LIBRARY,* Centennial Bldg, 62756.Tel: 217-782-2994. *Dir* Kathryn J Gesterfield; *Head Audiovisual Section* Mrs Garnetta Cook.
Open weekdays 8 AM - 4:30 PM; cl Sat & Sun. Estab 1839, Art Service 1916.
Collections: Extensive collection of †art books and †magazines in general library; reference services are available to patrons of Illinois public libraries on inter-library loan requested through library systems; †vertical file prints 54,800 covering painting, sculpture, architecture; theatre, maps, and other items; †framed art prints 500; collection of original lithographs, etchings, and block prints.
Exhibitions: Framed art prints continuously displayed within the library.

ILLINOIS STATE MUSEUM OF NATURAL HISTORY AND ART, Spring & Edwards St, 62706. Tel: 217-782-7125. *Dir* R Bruce McMillan; *Asst Dir* Basil C Hedrick; *Cur Art* Robert J Evans; *Cur Decorative Arts* Susan Pickel; *Exhib & Graphic Designer* Steven Mercer.
Open Mon - Sat 8:30 AM - 5 PM; Sun 1:30 - 5 PM. No admis. Estab 1877 as museum of natural history, art added in 1928. Collection and display of items related or of interest to Illinois and its citizens; art program is specialized to Illinois to a great degree. Three changing exhibit galleries of approx 400 running feet of display. Permanent collection galleries of fine and decorative arts, and a gallery for ethnographic arts. Average Annual Attendance: 300,000. Mem: 900; dues $10 - $300.
Income: $1,400,000 (financed by state appropriation). Purchases: (art) $7000.
Collections: Paintings, sculpture, graphics and photography by American artists, emphasis on Illinois; folk and decorative art including pottery, textiles, glass, clocks and furniture.
Exhibitions: Approx 14 exhibitions each year featuring paintings, sculpture, graphics, crafts and photography.
Publications: Living Museum (also in Braille), bimonthly; Exhibit and Collection catalogs.
Activities: Docent training; lect open to public and members; tours; competitions; exten dept; original objects of art lent to museums and art galleries; traveling exhibitions organized and circulated; museum shop selling books, reproductions and other miscellaneous items.
—**Library.** Tel: 217-782-6623. *Librn* Orvetta Robinson; *Library Asst* Ronald Sauberli.
Open Mon - Fri 8:30 AM - 5 PM. Estab to provide informational materials and services to meet the requirements of the Museum Staff in fields pertinent to the purpose and work of the Museum. Circ: 100 per month.
Income: Financed by state appropriation. Purchases: $2600.
Holdings: Vols 10,000; Per subs 150; AV—Phonorecords; Other—Clipping files and manuscripts.
Special Subjects: Anthropology, art and natural sciences.
Special Collections: Anthropology and ornithology.

SPRINGFIELD ART ASSOCIATION OF EDWARDS PLACE, 700 N Fourth, 62702. Tel: 217-523-2631. *Pres* Phyllis Gilbert; *VPres* Kay Spencer; *Secy* Agnes Hayner; *Exec dir* William Bealmer.
Open Daily 2 - 4 PM; cl Mon. No admis. Estab 1913 to foster appreciation of art, to instruct people in art and to expose people to quality art; 12 - 15 exhibitions are scheduled yearly with 2 - 3 juries exhibitions; also work borrowed from museums and artists nationwide. Average Annual Attendance: Statistics not kept; evening opening for exhibitions 3 - 500. Mem: 3000; dues $20 - $2000; annual meeting May.
Income: $90,000 (financed by membership and grants, interests, tuition, and benefits).
Collections: †Prints; †paintings; †pottery; †textiles; Oriental and Japanese artifacts and textiles; Mexican; early American Paintings; furniture; African sculpture; †Contemporary American Indian.
Exhibitions: (1976-77) Prints and Paintings by John Wisnosky; Photography by Larry Gregory; Third Invitational Fibers and Fabric; Seven Potters; First National Watercolor Exhibition; Sculpture by John Walsh; Prints and Paintings by Fritz Scholder; Baskets-Old and New; Paintings by Five Artists; Student Show; Twelve Printmakers; (1977-78) Paintings by Harry Pattison; Sculpture by Abbott Pattison; SAA Collection; Town and Country Art Show; Prints (John Asquith) Harrania Tapestry Exhibition; Weaving (Jack Arends) Second Invitational Watercolor Show; Pottery (Ann Krestensen); A Tribute to Hands; Photography (Elaine Perleman); Fourth Invitational Fiber and Fabric Show; Art in Boxes (David Bower); Prints (R C Gorman); Paintings (Kevin Red Star) two student exhibitions; Five Midwest Painters; Roten Print Sale.
Publications: Newsletters, membership brochures, membership roster, 12 - 15 per yr.
Activities: Classes for adults and children; docent training; art outreach program in school in community funded through CETA; lectr open to the public; gallery talks; tours; competitions with cash awards of $50 - $100; individual paintings and original objects of art lent to businesses for dis-

plays; lending collection contains framed reproductions 300, original art works, original prints and paintings 1500, sculpture, pottery, furniture, textiles, craft items; sales shop selling original art.
Library: Michael Victor II Library. Vol staff. Open to members. Holdings: Vols 400; Per subs 12.

URBANA

UNIVERSITY OF ILLINOIS AT URBANA-CHAMPAIGN, World Heritage Museum, 484 Lincoln Hall, 61801. *Dir* Georgette Meredith; *Exhib Designer* Theodore Odenweller; *Cur Ancient Near Eastern Coll* Shin T Kang; *Cur Classical Archaeology* Hubert L Allen; *Cur Numismatics* James Dengate.
Open Mon - Fri 9 AM - 5 PM (when University is in session). No admis. Estab 1912. The Museum has Egyptian Room, Minoan and Mycenaean Room, Greek and Roman Rooms, The Hall of Writing, The European Wing, Oriental Room, Glassware Room, Ethnographic Section, Temporary Display Area, and Illinois Indian Room.
Average Annual Attendance: 10,500.
Income: Financed by city appropriation.
Activities: Conducted tours for classes and public groups.

WINNETKA

NORTH SHORE ART LEAGUE,* Winnetka Community House, 620 Lincoln, 60093. Tel: 312-446-2870. *Pres* Abby Block; *First VPres* Marianne Hartnett; *Treas* John M Butler, Jr; *Recording Secy* Paula Fisher; *Corresp Secy* Mildred Feinberg.
Open Mon - Sat 9 AM - 6 PM. Estab 1924, inc 1954, to promote interest in creative art through education, exhibition opportunities, scholarship and art programs. Mem: 800+; dues $15; annual meeting May.
Exhibitions: New Horizons in Painting and Sculpture Shows, juried for entry, nonmember; Old Orchard Art Festival, juried for entry, nonmember; print and drawing show is shown first at studio, then moves to another location, such as the University of Illinois Circle Campus; annual Members Show; Student Show; Faculty Show; annual Members' Fair, juried in all media, location may change from year to year; annual Midwest Crafts Festival, juried, open to members and nonmembers, at the Old Orchard Shopping Center in Skokie.
Publications: Art League News, ten issues yearly.

INDIANA

ANDERSON

ANDERSON FINE ARTS CENTER, Alford House, 226 W Historical Eighth St, 46016. Tel: 317-649-1248. *Exec Dir* Joseph B Schnek; *Admin Secy* Deborah McBratney; *Cur Asst CETA* Patricia Dayton; *Pres Bd Trustees* Kendall Zinszer.
Open Tues - Sat 10 AM - 5 PM; Sun 2 - 5 PM; cl Mon, August and holidays. No admis. Estab 1966 to serve the community by promoting and encouraging interest in the fine arts through exhibitions, programs and education activities and the development of a permanent collection; three galleries contain 1705 sq ft; also a small sales and rental gallery. Average Annual Attendance: 30,000 Mem: 700; dues from student $5 to benefactor $5000; annual meeting first Fri in May.
Income: $40,000 (financed by membership) Purchases: $2000.
Collections: Primarily Indiana, †Mid-West and †American art; small number of works by European artists.
Exhibitions: Anderson Society of Artists; Anderson Art League; Student Art Competition; Madison County Photography; Anderson Area Annual; variety of regional and national one-man shows, traveling exhibitions, special exhibitions organized by AFAC state and the Anderson Winter Show.
Publications: Calendar of Events, quarterly; various exhibitions catalogs.
Activities: Classes for adults and children; dramatic programs; docent training; monthly film series; lectr open to the public, 4 - 6 vis lectr per yr; concerts; tours; competitions; individual paintings and original objects of art lent to other art museums; lending collection contains books 300, Kodachromes 400, motion pictures, original art works 100, slides 400; traveling exhibitions organized and circulated; museum and sales shop selling books, original art, reproductions, prints and original crafts, children's gifts, postcards, and gift items.
Library: Librn Deborah McBratney. Open to members for lending and to the public for reference. Holdings: Vols 300; Per subs 11; Other—Catalogs.

BLOOMINGTON

INDIANA UNIVERSITY ART MUSEUM, Fine Arts 007, 46401. Tel: 812-339-5445. *Dir* Thomas T Solley; *Cur* Dr Wolf Rudolph; *Assoc Cur* Adelheid Gealt; *Registrar* Linda Baden.
Open Tues - Sat 9 AM - 5 PM; cl Sun - Mon. No admis. Estab 1962 to serve as a teaching adjunct to the Fine Arts Dept and as a cultural resource for the university community and the public at large. Average Annual Attendance: 35,000.
Income: $326,000 (financed by state appropriation and gifts). Purchases: $120,000.
Collections: †Ancient to modern, Far Eastern and primitive, prints and drawings.
Exhibitions: Italian Majolica from Midwestern Collections; German and Austrian Expressionism, 1900-1920.
Activities: Lect open to public; gallery talks; tours; original art objects lent to museums; lending collection contains kodachromes 175,000, lantern slides 40,000 and photographs 45,000; sales shop selling books.
—**Fine Arts Library.** *Fine Arts Librn* Betty Jo Irvine.
Open to students, faculty, Indiana residents and interlibrary loan.
Holdings: Vols 48,000; Per subs 268; Other—Microfilms 228.
Special Subjects: African art, ancient art and archaeology, medieval architecture, renaissance painting, 19th & 20th century painting and sculpture.
Special Collections: Eliosofon Collection of photographs on Africa.

CRAWFORDSVILLE

HENRY S LANE HOME, 212 S Water St, 47933. Tel 317-362-3416.
Pres John Bowerman; *Treas* Maude Arthur.
Open (summer) 1:30 - 4:30 PM; (winter) 1 - 4 PM. Admis adults 75¢; children under twelve 15¢. Estab 1933 as a museum. Average Annual Attendance: 1000. Mem: 250; dues $4.50, $7.00 and $10.00.
Income: Financed by membership, city and county appropriation.
Collections: Antique furniture, china and artifacts.

EVANSVILLE

EVANSVILLE MUSEUM OF ARTS AND SCIENCE, 411 SE Riverside Dr, 47713. Tel: 812-425-2406. *Dir* John W Streetman III; *Dir Emeritus* Siegfried R Weng; *Cur Exhib* Mark Schnepper; *Research Cur* Frances Patton Martin; *Pres Bd Dir* Alexa Jamison.
Open Tues - Sat 10 AM - 5 PM; Sun Noon - 5 PM; cl Mon. No admis. Estab 1926 to maintain and perpetuate a living museum to influence and inspire the taste and cultural growth of the community. To provide facilities for the collection, preservation and exhibition of objects and data and programs related to the arts, history, science and technology. Lower Level: 19th century village of homes, shops, offices and town hall, arms and armor gallery, science and technology gallery; Main Level: River Room Gallery, furnished Gothic Room with linenfold paneling; Sculpture Gallery; Galleries for Dutch & Flemish Art, American Art and English Portraits; Gallery for arts and crafts of Egypt, the Orient, Black Africa and the American Indian; Gallery for monthly exhibits; Upper Level: Planetarium and corridor display area. Average Annual Attendance: 100,000. Mem: 896; dues collegiate $5, adult $8, family $15, participating $25, contributing $50, patron $100 and donor $250; annual meeting third Tues in May.
Income: $174,000 (financed by membership, city and state appropriations).
Collections: †American Art; †18th & 19th century American Crafts; American paintings; American and European graphics; European paintings; sculpture from BC to contemporary; oriental art; arts and crafts of Black Africa, Egypt, Oceania and the American Indian; Victorian decorative arts; history archives.
Exhibitions: American Graphics of the 1920's and 30's; Mid-States Craft Exhibition; Gund Collection of American Western Art; Industrial Arts Exhibition; Five Sense Store; Sculpture from the Museum Collection; Illusions: Art, Science and Nature. The Other Face; Mid-States Art Exhibition; High School Art Show; Arts of the 1920's; The Mother and the Child; American Masters of Photography; The Indian as Craftsman; Artists Invitational Show; Magic under the Dome; The Conservation Miracle; Jane Morton Norton, Paintings.
Publications: Bulletin, monthly; catalogs of exhibitions.
Activities: Classes for adults and children; dramatic programs; docent training; lect open to public; concerts; gallery talks; tours; competitions; exten dept serving area schools; individual paintings and original objects of art lent to institutions; lending collection contains nature artifacts, original art works, original prints, paintings, photographs and sculpture; traveling exhibitions organized and circulated; museum shop selling books, original art, reproductions; prints, jewelry, and pottery.
—**Henry B Walker, Jr Memorial Art Library.** Tel: 812-425-2406.

Open Tues - Fri 10 AM - 5 PM. Estab to provide books, periodicals and archives for research in the art, history and science fields to staff, museum members and other interested individuals.
Income: $700 (financed by City-County Appropriation, museum sales and donations). Purchases: $700.
Holdings: Vols 3500; Per subs 49. AV—Audio tapes, lantern slides, slides; Other—Clipping files, exhibition catalogs, manuscripts, memorabilia, original art works, original documents, pamphlets, photographs, prints, sculpture.
Special Subjects: Art and artists.

UNIVERSITY OF EVANSVILLE, Krannert Gallery, Box 329, 47702.
Chmn Art Department Les Miley; *Gallery Coordr* Bill Richmond.
Open Mon - Sat 9 AM - 5 PM. No admis. Estab 1969-70 to bring to the University and public communities exhibitions which reflect the contemporary arts, ranging from crafts through painting and sculpture; public access gallery 1800 sq ft—unit is one part of the College of Fine Arts.
Income: Financed by Department of Art funds.
Collections: 20th century art primarily centered around paintings and prints acquired through purchase awards and private gifts.
Activities: Individual paintings and original objects of art lent to university community.

FORT WAYNE

FORT WAYNE FINE ARTS FOUNDATION,* 324 Penn Ave, 46805. Tel: 219-484-9661. *Pres* Darrell W Huntley; *Secy* Jean Greenlee; *Exec Dir* John V McKenna; *Mgr Community Arts Center* Mary Brant.
Estab 1955, dedicated to the development and support of the community artist in every arts discipline. Exhibits in Ft Wayne Arts Museum and Community Arts Center. Institutional membership organization. Annual United Arts Fund Drive.
Income: Financed by city and county allocation.
Collections: Permanent collection at Art Museum.
Publications: Fine Arts Calendar; Newsletter, quarterly.
Activities: Classes for adults and children; dramatic programs; concerts; competitions; schol; develop programs between colleges, universities and community schools; Fort Wayne School of Fine Arts works with Indiana-Purdue University on community arts council adult programs.

FORT WAYNE MUSEUM OF ART, 1202 W Wayne St, 46804. Tel: 219-422-6467. *Dir* John Krushenick.
Open Tues - Sun 1 - 5 PM; Sat 10 AM - 5 PM; cl Mon. No admis. Estab 1921 to heighten visual perception of fine arts and perception of other disciplines; two buildings—Main Building, Young People's Wing, sculpture garden. Average Annual Attendance: 30,000. Mem: 1200; dues $15 and up; annual meeting Apr.
Income: Financed by endowment, membership, fine arts foundation and grants.
Collections: Paintings, prints, sculpture and minor arts; Thieme Collection of paintings; Hamilton Collection of paintings and sculpture; Fairbanks Collection of paintings and prints; Weatherhead Collection of contemporary paintings and prints; William Moser Collection of African art; Dorsky and Tannenbaum Collections of contemporary graphics.
Exhibitions: Sunshine-Plastics-Water Solar Energy Sculpture (Wtz, Erdman, Toman, Romano); Hue and Far Cry of Color (Noland, Rosenquist, Olitski, Krushenick, Tworkor, Ron Davis, Joan Mitchell, Alam Alma Thomas and others); History of the Harley Davidson Motorcycle; Ovvrez La Fenetre-Contemporary New York. Painters Window Theme Bent Air; Regional Annuals Tri Kappa (Indiana, Ohio and Mich University faculties).
Publications: Calendar, bi-monthly; posters; catalogs; fact sheets.
Activities: Educ dept; docent training; lect open to the public; competitions; traveling exhibition organized and circulated; museum and sales shop selling books, original art, ceramics and other gift items; junior museum in Young People's Wing.
Library: Open to staff and docents for reference.

PUBLIC LIBRARY OF FORT WAYNE AND ALLEN COUNTY, 900 Webster St, 46802. Tel: 219-424-7241. *Dir* Fred J Reynolds; *Asst Dir* Robert H Vegeler; *Head Fine Arts Dept* Helen Colchin; *Financial Secy* Mrs Richard Belschner.
Open Mon - Fri 9 AM - 9 PM; Sat 9 AM - 6 PM. Estab 1968 to provide a reference collection of the highest quality and completeness for the community and its colleges, and a place where local artists and musicians could exhibit their works and perform; and to provide a circulating collection of art prints, slides and musical scores sufficient to meet the demand; gallery is reserved for painting, sculpture, graphics, ceramics and other art crafts; photography exhibits are held in the lobby area.
Income: $100,000 (financed by city appropriation).

Holdings: Vols 11,813; Per subs 157; AV—Cassettes; phonorecords 19,313; slides 7195, video tapes; Other—Clipping files, exhibition catalogs; framed reproductions, framed prints 11,465, mounted pictures 14,194, pamphlets 2962, reproductions.
Activities: Concerts.

GARY

GREATER GARY ARTS COUNCIL, 504 Broadway, Suite 1037, 46402. Tel: 219-885-8444. *Pres* Nathan J Cooley; *First VPres* Richard Hagelberg; *Second VPres* Dr Garrett Cope; *Secy* Susan Kent; *Treas* Maxine Young; *Exec Dir* John H Cleveland Jr.
Open 9 AM - 5 PM. Estab 1967 to sponsor and encourage cultural and educational activities in the city of Gary and Lake County. Average Annual Attendance: 20,000. Mem: 500; dues individual $5; head of family $5; student $2.50.
Income: $34,000 (financed by endowment, membership, city and state appropriations).
Publications: Greater Gary Arts Council's Artsgram, quarterly.
Activities: Classes for children; sponsored several arts projects and are now planning a Community Multi-Arts program which will feature instructions in music, art, theatre, and creative writing; competitions with awards; scholarships.

INDIANAPOLIS

HOOSIER SALON PATRONS ASSOCIATION, INC, Hoosier Salon Art Gallery,* 951 N Delaware, 46202. Tel: 317-632-1736. *Pres* Mrs Gordon Hughes; *Secy* Mrs Robert E Gates; *First VPres* Mrs Ardath Burkhart; *Treas* Corbin Patric; *Exec Dir* Kristin E Blum.
Main gallery open Tues - Fri 9:30 AM - 4:30 PM; Sat 11 AM - 4 PM; cl Sun & Mon. Estab 1925 to promote work of Indiana artists. Mem dues: artist $5, member $10 and up; annual meeting June.
Collections: Paintings; sculpture; prints.
Exhibitions: Annual Hoosier Salon in Jan, then on tour; over $5500 in prize money; Student Show, juried exhibit for undergraduate Indiana University students in April; over $200 in prize money.
Publications: Annual Salon Catalog; History of the Hoosier Salon; Hoosier Salon Newsletter, three times a year.
Activities: Gallery talks; loan service to members.

INDIANA CENTRAL UNIVERSITY, Leah Ransburg Art Gallery, 1400 E Hanna Ave, 46227. Tel: 317-788-3253. *Dir* Gerald G. Boyce.
Open daily 9:30 AM - 4 PM. No admis. Estab 1964 to serve the campus and community. Average Annual Attendance: 25,000 - 30,000.
Income: Financed by institution support. Purchases: $15,000.
Collections: †Krannert Memorial Collection; †Art Department collection.
Publications: Announcements; annual catalog/bulletin.

INDIANA STATE MUSEUM, 202 N Alabama St, 46204. Tel: 317-633-4948. *Dir* Carl H Armstrong: *Asst Dir* Thomas Gross; *Cur Coll* Diane Alpert; *Cur Exhib* David McLary; *Exhib Design Coordinator* Paul Deigl; *Cur Educ* Kathleen Cooper; *Pub Relations Coordinator* Shirley Boltz; *Grants & Memorial Liaison* Gregg Jackson.
Open daily 9 AM - 5 PM. No admis. Estab 1869 for collections; current museum building opened 1967 to collect, preserve and interpret the natural and cultural history of the State. Numerous galleries: Woodland Habitat; Indiana Wildlife; Earth Science; Pioneer Lifestyles and Fashions; Hoosier Artists; Modes of Travel; and Abraham Lincoln. Average Annual Attendance: 110,000. Mem: 1300; dues $5.00 and up; annual meeting Apr.
Income: Financed by state appropriation.
Exhibitions: George Rogers Clark Bicentennial Exhibit; three Indiana art shows annually.
Publications: History-on-the-Move, bimonthly.
Activities: Docent training; in-school programs; lect open to public, 4 vis lectr per yr; sales shop selling books, reproductions and prints.
Library: Open to staff for reference. Holdings: Vols 1000.

INDIANA UNIVERSITY—PURDUE UNIVERSITY AT INDIANAPOLIS, Herron School of Art.
—**Art Gallery,** 1701 N Pennsylvania St, 46202. Tel: 317-923-3651. *Dean* Arthur H Weber; *Asst Dean & Dir Admissions* Ralph R Thomas; *Asst to Dean, Business Affairs* Karl E Ralph.
Open Mon - Thurs 9 AM - 7 PM; Fri 9 AM - 5 PM. No admis. Estab 1877. The primary mission is to educate those students seeking professional careers in fine arts, visual communication and the teaching of art. Emphasis is placed on studio instruction provided by practicing professional artists, designers, and educators. The Gallery is located in the Museum Building and is part of the original John Herron Art Institute.
Income: Financed by state appropriation.
Exhibitions: Student and faculty shows; some traveling exhibits.

Activities: Classes for adults and children; exten dept serving Indianapolis and surrounding communities.
—**Library.** *Head Librn* Maudine B Williams; *Asst Librn* vacant.
Open Mon, Tues, Thurs 8 AM - 7 PM; Wed 8 AM - 9 PM; Fri 8 AM - 5 PM; cl Sat & Sun. Estab 1970 as a visual resource center for the support of the curriculum of the Herron School of Art. Circ: 38,101.
Income: Financed by state appropriation. Purchases: $8000.
Holdings: Vols 9000: Per subs 152; AV—Film strips, lantern slides, phonorecords and slides; Other—Clipping files, photographs, prints and reproductions.
Special Subjects: Art history, art education, visual communication, painting, sculpture, printmaking and photography.

INDIANAPOLIS MARION COUNTY PUBLIC LIBRARY, 40 E St Clair St, 46204. Tel: 317-635-5662. *Dir* Raymond Gnat.
Open Mon - Fri 9 AM - 9 PM; Sat 9 AM - 5 PM; Sun 1 - 5 PM. Estab 1873. Circ: 3,838,248.
Income: $5,460,000 (financed by state appropriation and county property tax).
Purchases: 1,800,000.
Holdings: Vols 1,254,535; AV—Microfilm, motion pictures, phonorecords; Other—Clipping files, exhibition catalogs, pamphlets, prints.
Activities: Lect open to public; concerts; tours; competitions.

INDIANAPOLIS MUSEUM OF ART, 1200 W 38th St, 46208. Tel: 317-923-1331. *Chmn Board of Trustees* Harrison Eiteljorg; *Pres Board of Trustees* Clarence W Long; *Dir* Robert A Yassin; *Assoc Cur Painting & Sculpture* Ellen Lee; *Cur Ethnographic Art & Textiles* Peggy S Gilfoy; *Superviser Educ Programs & Services* Peggy S Gilfoy; *Cur Oriental Art* Dr Yutaka Mino; *Assoc Cur Decorative Arts* Catherine Beth Lippert; *Asst Cur Painting & Sculpture* Diane G Lazarus; *Conservator* Martin J Radecki; *Dir Public Relations* Albert O Louer.
Open Tues - Sun 11 AM - 5 PM; cl Mon and Christmas. No admis.
Estab 1883 to maintain a museum, the grounds, pavilions, and other facilities for the display of art of all kinds; a library for the collection of books, manuscripts, periodicals, photographs and other similar data or facilities relating to art of all kinds; to promote interest in art of all kinds by lectures, exhibitions, publications, programs and general sponsorship of art and artists in the City of Indianapolis and State of Indiana; to cooperate with national state and city government and civic, educational and artistic groups and foundations. Maintains three galleries Krannert, Clowes and Lilly Pavilions. Average Annual Attendance: 500,000. Mem: 12,000; dues student $12.50, individual $15; family/double $25; sustaining $50; reciprocal $100.
Collections: †Oriental—bronzes, ceramics, jade, paintings; classical through contemporary including J M W Turner watercolors; †17th century European paintings; †18th century English portraiture; †19 - 20th century American and European paintings; †Indiana paintings; Western American Art; †Ethnographic art—North and South America, Africa, Oceania; †decorative arts—including watch collection; 18-19th century European porcelain and furniture; American period rooms; costumes and textiles; †drawings and prints—Renaissance through contemporary.
Exhibitions: (1976-78) Chinese Textiles and costumes; Indiana Coverlets; Harrison Eiteljorg Collection of Western American Art; African Decorative Arts; Impact of Art Deco; Painting and Sculpture Today, 1976, 78; Master Prints from the Permanent Collection; Mirages and Memory: 200 Years of Indiana Art; Biennial Indiana Artists' Exhibition; Sheffield Plated Silver; Perceptions of the Spirit in 20th century American Art; Kogo; Japanese Incense Boxes; Beverly Pepper Sculpture 1971-77; Paintings by Paxton; Enrico Baj.
Publications: Catalogs of permanent collection; brochures; newsletters and calendars of events, bimonthly.
Activities: Classes for adults and children; dramatic programs; docent training; lect open to the public and for members only; concerts; gallery talks; tours; competitions; Alliance Art Rental Gallery rents paintings to members and sells to members and public; traveling exhibitions organized and circulated; museum shop and sales shop selling books, magazines, original art, reproductions, prints, slides.
—**Stout Reference Library.** *Librn* Martha G Blocker; *Research Asst* Frank N Owing, Jr; *Cataloger* Julie C Su; *Research Assoc* Mary L Marley.
Open Tues - Fri 11 AM - 5 PM; Sat & Sun 1 - 4 PM; Estab 1908 as reference facility for all members and nonmembers who come to the museum.
Income: $12,000 (financed by membership). Purchases: $12,000.
Holdings: Vols 20,000; Per subs 75; Other—Clipping Files, exhibitions catalogs.
Special Subjects: Painting, architecture, sculpture, decorative arts, especially porcelain and glass.
Special Collections: Vertical file material on Indiana artists.
Publications: Newsletter, bimonthly; Indianapolis Museum of Art Bulletin, irregularly; exhibition catalogs are needed.
—**Slide Collection.** Tel: 317-923-1331, exten 35. *Head* Carolyn J Metz.

Open Tues - Sat 1 - 5 PM. Estab 1972 to provide visuals on the history of art and to document/record the museum programs and activities. Circ: 30,000.
Income: Financed by endowment and museum budget. Purchases: $6000.
Holdings: AV—Slides 60,000.
Special Subjects: History of art.
Special Collections: exhibits and installation documentation of programs.
—**Clowes Fund Collection,*** Clowes Pavilion. Tel: 317-923-1331. *Cur* Allen W Clowes; *Research Cur* A Ian Fraser.
Open Tues - Sun 11 AM - 5 PM; cl Mon. No admis. Estab 1958 to display paintings of the Old Masters from the collection of the late Dr G H A Clowes. Average Annual Attendance: 62,000. Mem: Board meeting Feb.
Income: Financed by endowment.
Collections: Italian Renaissance: Duccio, Fra Angelico, Bellini, Luini, Tintoretto, and others Spanish—El Greco, Goya and others; Northern Renaissance—17th and 18th century Dutch, Hals, Rembrandt and others. French—Clouet, Corneille de Lyon; English—Reynolds, Constable and others; Flemish—Breughel, Bosch and others.
Branches:
—**Downtown Gallery,** American Fletcher National Bank, 101 Monument Circle.
—**Indianapolis Museum of Art at Columbus Ind,** Fifth and Franklin Sts. Usually exhibitions from the permanent collection quarterly.

MARIAN COLLEGE, Art Department, Allison Mansion, 3200 Cold Spring Rd, 46222. Tel: 317-924-3291. *Prof Emeritus of Art* Sister Mary Jane Peine.
Open Sun 2 - 4 PM. No admis, donations accepted. Estab 1970 in the National Register of Historical Places, Allison Mansion houses the Art Department of Marian College, a four-year Liberal Arts College; the interior of the mansion is a work of art with its magnificent treatment of walls of hand carved marble and wood - oak, white mahogany and walnut. The grand stairway in the main hall leads to the balcony overlooking the hall, all hand carved walnut. A private collection of 17th Century paintings complement its beauty.

MORRIS-BUTLER MUSEUM OF HIGH VICTORIAN DECORATIVE ARTS,* 1204 N Park Ave, 46202. Tel: 317-636-5409. *Supvr* Barbara E Carson
Open Thurs, Sat & Sun 1 - 5 PM; Mon - Wed & Fri 9 AM - 11 PM by appointment; cl Aug. Admis adults $1, children under 12 50¢. Estab 1960.
Collections: Victorian sculpture; flint glass; paintings by early Indiana artists; furniture.
Activities: Classes for children; lectures; gallery talks; guided tours; temporary traveling exhibitions; school loan service of permanent collection.

LAFAYETTE

LAFAYETTE ART CENTER, 101 S Ninth St, 47901. Tel: 317-742-1128. *Pres* Nan Schwetman; *VPres* Marvin Wildfeuer; *Secy* Pat Grams; *Dir* Sharon A Theobald.
Open daily 1 - 5 PM; cl Mon. No admis. Estab 1909 to encourage and stimulate art and to present exhibitions of works of local, regional and national artists and groups as well as representative works of American and foreign artists; size of gallery is 24 x 60. Average Annual Attendance: 3000; Mem: 1300; dues student and senior citizen $5, individual $7.50, family $10; annual meeting Oct.
Income: Financed by endowment and membership.
Collections: Permanent collection of over 250 works of art obtained through purchase or donation since 1909.
Exhibitions: Monthly exhibitions.
Publications: Monthly newsletter.
Activities: Classes for adults and children; docent training; lectr open to the public, 5 vis lectr per yr; concerts; gallery talks; tours; competitions with awards; schol; individual paintings and original objects of art lent to members; lending collection contains books, original art works, original prints and paintings; traveling exhibitions organized and circulated; sales shop selling books, original art, prints, reproductions.
Library: Open to member.

TIPPECANOE COUNTY HISTORICAL MUSEUM, 909 South St, 47901. Tel: 317-742-8411. *Dir* John M Harris; *Asst Dir* Carol N Waddell; *Cur of Coll* Mildred Paarlberg; *Cur of Educ* Paula Woods; *Cur of Genealogy* Lyda Hilt.
Open daily 1 - 5 PM, cl Mon. No admis. Estab 1925 to collect, preserve, research and interpret the history of Tippecanoe County and the immediate surrounding area; housed in a Victorian house (1851-52), there are exhibits of various phases of county history in nine rooms. Average Annual Attendance: 20,000. Mem: 1000; dues $4 - $25; annual meeting Jan.
Income: $145,000 (financed by endowment, membership, county and state appropriation, sales and programs).

Collections: Broad range, incorporating any object relative to county history.
Exhibitions: Fixed exhibits include Pioneer Development: miniature rooms; porcelains; paintings. Changing exhibits include Schools in Tippecanoe County; Photo exhibit of Historic Architecture.
Publications: Weatenotes, nine times a year.
Activities: Classes for adults and children; docent training; lect open to the public; tours; individual paintings and original objects of art lent to other museums; sales shop selling books, reproductions, original crafts on consignment.
—**Alameda McCollough Library.** *Librn Historical Section* Carol Waddell; *Librn Genealogical Section* Lyda Hilt.
Open to serious researchers for reference only.
Holdings: Vols 2000; Per subs 15; Other—Maps, photographs.

MUNCIE

BALL STATE UNIVERSITY.
—**Art Gallery,** 47306. Tel: 317-285-5242. *Dir* William E Story; *Asst to Dir* Dolores Terhune; *Secy* Betty Magill.
Open Mon - Fri 9 AM - 4:30 PM & 7 - 9 PM; Sat & Sun 1:30 - 4:30 PM; cl legal & school holidays and evenings June - Aug. Estab 1936 as a university and community art museum with special emphasis on the art department. Eight large galleries, sculpture court, mezzanine and reception lounge. Average Annual Attendance: 36,000.
Collections: Italian Renaissance art and furniture; 19th & 20th century American paintings, prints, and drawings; Kraft-Ball Collection of Roman and Syrian glass.
Exhibitions: Artist in Indiana—Then and Now (a series of twelve exhibitions); Indiana Pressed Glass of the Gas-boom Era; Annual Drawing and Small Sculpture Show.
Publications: Newsletter, occasionally.
Activities: Lect open to public, 2-3 vis lectr per year; concerts; gallery talks; competitions; individual paintings and original objects of art lent to other art galleries and museums, and to offices and special buildings on campus; traveling exhibitions organized and circulated.
—**Architecture Library,** College of Architecture & Planning., McKinley at Neely, 47306. Tel: 317-285-4760. *Librn* Marjorie Hake Joyner; *Clerical Asst* Barbara Ballinger.
Open (Academic year) Mon 8 AM - 8 PM; Tues - Thurs 8 AM - 10 PM; Fri 8 AM - 8 PM; Sat 9 AM - 5 PM; Sun 2 - 10 PM; (summer) Mon - Fri 8 AM - 5 PM. Estab 1965 to provide materials necessary to support the academic programs of the college of Architecture & Planning. Circ: 25,000.
Income: Financed through University.
Holdings: Vols 18,000; Per subs 180; AV—Microfilm and slides; Other—Clipping files, pamphlets, manufacturers' catalogs, architectural drawings; maps and student theses.
Special Subjects: Architectural history.

NASHVILLE

BROWN COUNTY ART GALLERY ASSOCIATION, INC, 1 Artist Drive, (Mailing Add: PO Box 443, 47448). Tel: 812-988-4609. *Pres* Phyllis Whitworth; *VPres* Ida Gordon; *Exec Secy* R Dale Cassiday,
Open Mid-Feb - Mid-Dec, 10 AM - 5 PM. Admis adults 25¢. Estab 1926 to unite artists and laymen in fellowship; to create a greater incentive for development of art and its presentation to the public; to establish an art gallery for exhibition of work of members of the Association. Average Annual Attendance: 35,000. Mem: 47 artists; 750 supporting members; dues from individual $5 - life $500; annual meeting Oct.
Income: Financed by city appropriation and Trust.
Collections: 75 oil paintings and pastels by the late Glen Cooper Henshaw.
Exhibitions: 3 exhibits each year by the Artist members.
Activities: Competitions with awards.

NOTRE DAME

SAINT MARY'S COLLEGE
—**Moreau Gallery Three,** Art Department, 46556. Tel: 219-284-4074. *Chmn, Ceramics & Sculpture* H James Paradis; *Gallery Dir* Michele Fricke.
Open Mon - Fri 9 - 11 AM & 12:30 - 3 PM; Sat - Sun 12:30 - 4 PM; cl Mon. Estab 1956 for education and community-related exhibits. Gallery presently occupies three rooms; all exhibits rotate. Average Annual Attendance: 6000.
Collections: Cotter Collection; Dunbarton Collection of prints; Norman LaLiberte; various media.
Exhibitions: Dee Shapiro (painting); Bruce & Susan Carter (drawings and fibers); Javier Padilla (painting); Lou Krueger (photo silkscreen); High School Art Exhibition (various media); Faculty & Student Show (various media).

Activities: Classes for adults; dramatic programs; lect open to public; tours; concerts.
Publications: Catalogs, occasionally.
—Alumnae Centennial Library. *Head Librn* Sister Bernice Hollenhorst; *head Cataloguer* Sister Marjorie Jones; *Reference Librn* Robert Hohl; *Periodicals Librn* Anne Johnson.
Open Mon - Fri 7:45 AM - 11 PM; Sat 9 AM - 11 PM; Sun 1 - 11 PM. Estab 1855.
Income: Financed through the University.
Holdings: (Art) Vols 5600; Per subs 32; AV—Audio tapes, cassettes, film strips, kodachromes, microfilm, motion pictures, phonorecords, reels, slides.

UNIVERSITY OF NOTRE DAME
—Art Gallery, 46556. Tel: 219-283-7361. *Dir* Dr Dean A Porter; *Cur* Stephen B Spiro; *Educ Coordr* Marilyn Holscher; *Asst to Cur* Susan Bastian; *Secy* Gail Jones; *Preparator* Gregory Denby.
Open Mon - Fri 10 AM - 4:45 PM; Thur 7 AM - 9 PM; Sat & Sun 1 - 5 PM. No admis. University estab 1842; Wightman Memorial Art gallery estab 1917; O'Shaughnessy Hall Art Gallery estab 1951; to educate through the visual arts; during a four year period it is the objective to expose students to all areas of art including geographic, period and media; galleries consist of one large 80 x 30 ft gallery and four 28 x 28 ft galleries; in 1979, it is planned to expand to an additional 40,000 sq ft of exhibition space, Average Annual Attendance: 40,000.
Income: $120,000 (financed by endowment and university appropriation). Purchaes: $15,000.
Collections: Baroque painting—Northern and Italian; †18th and 19th century American, American, English and French paintings & drawings; †15th century - contemporary prints; †photographs; Kress Study Collection; contemporary paintings; Western sculpture-medieval-modern; Oriental porcelains and sculpture; African art; American Indian and pre-Columbian art.
Exhibitions: (1976-77) American Indian Art, Landscape into Art; Mirages of Memory: 200 Years of Art in Indiana (photographs by W Eugene Smith and Eugene Atget, graphics by Milton Avery); German Expressionist Prints and Drawings; Pre-Columbian Textiles, African Traditional Art; Faculty and Student Shows.
Publications: Exhibition catalogs, three - five times a year.
Activities: Educ dept; docent training; lect open to the public, 5 - 9 vis lectr per yr; gallery talks; tours; individual paintings and original objects of art lent to qualified institutions; traveling exhibitions organized and circulated; sales shop selling books, catalogs and note cards.
—Catalog Library. *Librn* Pamela Szabo.
Open to students and faculty for reference only.
Holdings: Vols 20,190; Per subs 30; Other—Exhibition, auction and sales catalobs.
—Architecture Library. Tel: 219-283-6654. *Librn* Geri Decker; *Library Asst* Charles Early.
Open Mon - Thurs 8 AM - 10 PM; Fri 8 AM - 5 PM; Sat 9 AM - 5 PM; Sun 1 - 10 PM; Vacations Mon - Fri 8 AM - 5 PM. Estab 1890 as a branch of the university library. Circ: 15,000.
Income: $34,500 (financed by university). Purchases: $8000.
Holdings: Vols 13,000; Per subs 100; AV—Motion pictures; phonorecords; slides; Other—Clipping files.
Special Subjects: Art, architecture; engineering, planning environment.
Special Collections: Rare folio books on architecture.
Exhibitions: Art of Robert Schultz; Models of Major Buildings; Models of Student Booths for School Mardi Gras; Student Thesis Projects.

RICHMOND

ART ASSOCIATION OF RICHMOND, McGuire Memorial Hall, Whitewater Blvd, 47374. Tel: 317-966-0256. *Pres* Hugh N Ronald; *VPres* Dr William Christopher; *Secy* Dr Denney G French; *Dir* Mrs James Lemon.
Open Mon - Fri 9 AM - 4 PM; Sun 2 - 5 PM; cl Sat and school holidays. No admis. Estab 1898 to promote creative ability, art appreciation and art in public schools. Maintains an art gallery with four exhibit rooms: 2 rooms for permanent collection and 2 rooms for current exhibits. Average Annual Attendance: 10,000. Mem: 600; dues from student $1.00 - $1000; annual meeting second Wed in Oct.
Income: Financed by membership and city appropriation.
Collections: Regional and state art.
Exhibitions: Two annual competitions; annual photography exhibit; crafts and prints; high school art.
Publications: Newsletter, quarterly.
Activities: Docent training; Lect open to public, 2 vis lectr per yr; gallery talks; tours; competitions with merit and purchase awards; scholarships; individual paintings and original objects of art lent to businesses and schools; lending collection contains books, original art works, original prints and photographs; traveling exhibitions organized and circulated; sales shop selling original art.

Library: Open to members. Holdings: Vols 200; Per subs 3. Special Subjects: Art museums, art techniques.

EARLHAM COLLEGE, Leeds Gallery, National Road W, 47374. Tel: 317-962-6561. *Pres College* Franklin Wallin; *Chmn Art Dept* Bernard Derr.
Open daily 8 AM - Noon. No admis. Estab 1847 as a liberal arts college; Leeds Gallery estab 1970.
Income: $2500. Purchases: $500 - $800.
Collections: Regional artists; Marcus Mote, Bundy (John Ellwood), George Baker; prints by internationally known artists of 19th & 20th centuries.
Exhibitions: One-man shows, mostly regional; some traveling shows.
Activities: Dramatic programs; lect open to public, 5-6 vis lectr per yr; concerts; individual paintings and original objects of art lent; traveling exhibitions organized and circulated; sales shop selling books.
Library: Holdings—Vols 220,000; Other—Photographs. Special Subjects: Art.

SOUTH BEND

ART CENTER, INC, 120 S St Joseph St, 46601. Tel: 219-284-9102. *Dir* John H Surovek; *Cur* Thomas B Schorgl; *Secy* Mrs Juanita N Williams.
Open Mon - Fri 9 AM - 5 PM; Sat & Sun - Noon - 5 PM. Admis varies 50¢ - $10. Estab 1948 for museum exhibitions, lectures and workshops and classes. The center is located in a three story building designed by Philip Johnson. Two galleries one the Upper Level Gallery and the Warner Art Gallery located on the street floor. Average Annual Attendance: 7541. Mem: 1090; dues student and senior citizen $10, individual $20, family $35.
Income: Financed by membership, city and state appropriation. Purchases: $294,900.
Collections: European and American paintings, drawings, prints and objects †20th century American art.
Exhibitions: (1977-79) 20th Century American and European Masters; Norman Rockwell Exhibition; Photographic Exhibition; Robert Indiana Retrospective; Students of the Art Center Exhibit; Northern Indiana Artists and St Joseph Watercolor Society Exhibit; Prints from the Permanent Collection; Hungarian Art Nouveau Exhibit; Max Klinger Master Printmaker; Area High School Exhibit; Jerome K Muller Collection of Cartoons; Charles Burchfield; Charles Rand Penny Collection.
Publications: Newsletter, monthly.
Activities: Classes for adults and children, docent training; workshops; lectr open to the public; gallery talks; tours; competitions with awards. schol; art lent through museum sales shop; museum shop selling books, original art, prints, art objects, jewelry, pottery, woven goods.
Library: Open to members.

TERRE HAUTE

INDIANA STATE UNIVERSITY,* Turman Gallery, 47809. Tel: 812-232-6311. *Chmn Art Dept* Elmer Porter.
Open Mon - Fri 8 AM - 5 PM; cl last two weeks Aug. No admis. School estab 1870.
Collections: Paintings and sculpture.
Exhibitions: Regular traveling exhibitions for short periods during school terms; student and faculty exhibitions.
Activities: Classes for children; lectures.

SHELDON SWOPE ART GALLERY, 25 S Seventh St, 47807. Tel: 812-238-1676. *Dir* James D Bowne; *Registrar* Collene Coleman; *Pres Emeritus* Mary F Hulman; *Pres Bd Mgrs* Hermine M Haslem; *Secy Bd Mgrs* Ewing H Miller; *Treas Bd Mgrs* Alan C Rankin.
Open Tues - Sat noon - 5 PM; Sun 2 - 5 PM; cl Mon. No admis. Estab 1942 to present publicly and free of charge fine works of art. Average Annual Attendance: 12,000. Mem: 750; dues individual $12; annual meeting Third Wed in Sept.
Income: $72,000 (financed by membership, city appropriation and trust fund).
Collection: Extensive American realism collections; Hudson River School; extensive print collections; African; Oriental; Old Masters; dolls; glass; artifacts.
Exhibitions: (1977-78) Greentown Glass, Contemporary Art from Permanent Collection; Image of Art Deco; Four Tales of the Arabian Knights; Marc Chagall; Annual Collector's Choice Exhibition; 34th Annual Wabash Valley Exhibition; Bob Evans: Metal; Hatch, Lattanzio, Trezise: Three Views Through the Lens; Rookwood and Other American Art Pottery.
Publications: Membership newsletter, bimonthly.

Activities: Classes for children; dramatic programs; docent training; lectr open to the public, 15 vis lectr per yr; concerts; gallery talks; tours; competitions; artmobile; individual paintings and original objects of art lent to other museums, banks, country clubs and retirement homes; sales shop selling books, magazines, original art, reproductions and prints.
Library: Open to the public. Holdings: Vols 1800; Per subs 24.

UPLAND

TAYLOR UNIVERSITY, Chronicle/Tribune Art Gallery, Art Dept, 46989. Tel: 317-998-2051. *Dir* Dr Ray E Bullock.
Open Mon - Sat 11 AM - 4 PM and Mon, Wed and Fri 7 - 9 PM; cl Sun. No admis. Estab 1972 as an educational gallery.
Activities: Classes for children; competitions.

VALPARAISO

VALPARAISO UNIVERSITY, Sloan Galleries of American Paintings & Henry F Moellering Memorial Library, 46383. Tel: 219-464-5365 or 464-5364. *Chmn Sloan Comt* Dr Jack Hiller; *Cur* Richard Brauer.
Open Mon - Fri 8 AM - 10 PM; Sat 9 AM - 5 PM; Sun 1 - 10 PM. No admis. Estab 1953 to present significant art to the student and citizen community for their education in the values of art. A 600 sq ft area off the check-out room of the library; similar gallery spaces are available in the Christ College Building and in the Union.
Income: $14,000 (financed by endowment). Purchases: $10,000.
Collections: †Sloan Collection—19th & 20th century American Landscape Paintings, Prints and drawings; VU Collection—Art on Biblical themes.
Exhibitions: Search for an American Image; Elder and Zehr Sculpture; Contemporary Art in Worship; Student Art Exhibit; German Biblical Wall Murals; Works on Paper; Toy Icons, Bird Icons (prints); Indiana Printmakers; Art for Religion; Sorell Paintings; Kortland Graphics Retrospective; Porter County Young Artists; Industrial Design in Porter County; Frank Dudley Paintings; Currier & Ives: Printmakers to America; Rubbings of English Brass Carvings; Revival! Photographs by Eleanor Dickinson; Photography of George Stimby.
Activities: Lect open to public; gallery talks; individual paintings and original objects of art lent to museums and art centers.

WEST LAFAYETTE

PURDUE UNIVERSITY, Gallery I, Gallery II and Union Gallery, Creative Arts Building #1, 47907. *Head Dept Creative Arts* Ralph Beelke; *Chmn Art & Design* William McGill; *Gallery Dir* Mona Berg; *Chmn Faculty Gallery Comt* Richard Paul.
Open Gallery I, Mon - Fri 8 AM - 5 PM; Gallery II, Mon - Fri 10 AM - 5 PM; Union Gallery, Mon - Fri 9:30 AM - 4:30 PM; Sun 12:30 - 4:30 PM. Gallery I and Gallery II are primarily educational facilities devoted to exhibitions of student and faculty work, and exhibitions related to programs in the Department of Creative Arts. Union Gallery serves the University and the community. Average Annual Attendance: 15,000.
Income: Financed through the University. Purchases: $1500.
Collections: Contemporary paintings, prints, sculpture.
Exhibitions: Faculty and student work; contemporary artists; traveling exhibitions; works borrowed from private collectors and other institutions; Expressive Images—Germany/Mexico; Critic's Choice—works by Ellen Lanyon, Jim Nutt and Ed Paschke—chosen by Art Critic, Franz Schulze; Max 60, Biennial Small Print Show; Surface Design '78; Paintings 8 Artists.
Publications: Exhibition catalogs.
Activities: Lect open to public, 2-4 lectr per yr; competitions; individual paintings and original objects of art lent to University Administrative offices; lending collection contains original prints, paintings, sculpture; traveling exhibitions organized and circulated.

IOWA

AMES

OCTAGON CENTER FOR THE ARTS, 232½ Main, 50010. Tel: 515-323-5331. *Pres* William Tysseling; *VPres* Robin Murray and James Sinatra; *Secy* Carol Wall; *Dir* Martha Benson; *Dir Educ* David Williamson.
Open Mon 1 - 9 PM; Tues - Fri 1 - 5 PM; Sat 10 AM - 5 PM; Sun 2 - 5 PM; Sun 2 - 5 PM. Estab 1966. The Octagon is an art center that provides year-round classes for all ages, exhibitions of the work of outstanding artists from throughout the world and special programs in the visual and performing arts. The gallery shows approx 8 exhibitions each year. Most exhibitions are designed and organized by the art center and some are toured. Some exhibitions are drawn from agencies, such as SITES and other national outlets. Average Annual Attendance: 25,000. Mem: 500, open to anyone who is interested in supporting or participating in the arts; dues $8 - $1000; annual meeting second Sun in Oct.
Income: $80,000 (financed by membership, city and state appropriations, class fees and fund raising).
Exhibitions: (1977) Folk Art of Guatemala; (1978) Drawings USA/77; The Clay and Fiber Show; A Time of Malfeasance; Pottery of Mary Weisgram; Batiks by Vickie Roth; Recent Work: Dean Daas and Sarah Grant; Iowa Photography Invitational.
Publications: Newsletter, monthly.
Activities: Classes for adults and children; dramatic programs; special workshops and symposia; lect open to public, 5 vis lectr per yr; gallery talks; tours; competitions, an annual regional juried show, awards given in each category and best in show; lending collection of 500 lantern slides; traveling exhibitions organized and circulated; sales shop selling books, magazines, original art, prints, reproductions.
Library: Open to members only for reference; Holdings: Vols 200.

ANAMOSA

PAINT 'N' PALETTE CLUB, RR 3 (Mailing Add: 204 N Huber St, 52202). Tel: 319-462-2601, 462-2680. *Pres* Mildred B Brown; *VPres* Betty Christophersen; *Secy* Malinda Derga; *Exec Dirs* Dr Gerald F Brown and Wilbur Evarts.
Open June 1 - Oct 15; Sun 1 - 5 PM; other times by appointment. No admis (donations accepted). Estab 1955 to maintain Antioch School (the school attended by Grant Wood, a famous Iowa artist), to provide a studio and gallery for local artists, and for public enjoyment. A log cabin art gallery on the grounds of the Grant Wood Memorial Park contains the work of some local and visiting artists. Average Annual Attendance: 2000 - 3000. Mem: 32, members must have art experience; dues $10.
Income: $700 - $800 (financed by endowment and donations).
Collections: Prints of Grant Wood, Iowa's most famous artist.
Exhibitions: (1976-77) Annual Grant Wood Art Festival; 22nd Annual Paint 'n' Palette Outdoor Art Show.
Activities: Occasional classes for adults and children; films; lect open to public, 6 or 7 vis lectr per yr; tours; competitions; sales shop selling magazines, original art, prints, reproductions, memorial plates and coins, postcards, used books.

BURLINGTON

ARTS FOR LIVING CENTER, Seventh & Washington St (Mailing Add: PO Box 5, 52601). Tel: 319-754-8069. *Dir* Shirley Bliven; *Pres* Jerry Rigdon; *Pres Elect* Roger Hill; *VPres* Betty Guy; *Treas* Kay Ditto; *Secy* Ellen Francis; *Corresponding Secy* Betty Read.
Open Tues - Sat 1 - 5 PM; special openings Sun 2 - 5 PM; cl Mon and all major holidays, with the exception of Thanksgiving. No admis. Purchased church building, built in 1868, in 1974; the building has been placed on the National Register of Historic Places. Arts for Living Center is operated by Art Guild, which was established in Sept 1966, Mem: 302; dues student $3.50 up to benefactor $1000; meeting first Thurs monthly.
Income: Financed by membership and donations.
Publications: Newsletter, once/twice monthly.
Activities: Classes for adults and children; lect open to the public; competitions; traveling exhibitions organized and circulated; sales shop selling original art, reproductions, prints.

CEDAR FALLS

UNIVERSITY OF NORTHERN IOWA GALLERY OF ART, 27th St at Hudson Road, 50613. Tel: 319-273-6114. *Dir* Sanford Sivitz Shaman.
Open Tues 10 AM - 9 PM; Wed - Sat 10 AM - 3 PM; Sun 1 - 5 PM; cl Mon. No admis. Estab 1978 to bring to the University and the community at large, the finest quality of art from all over the world. One main gallery with 365 running feet; two upstairs galleries, each with 100 running feet, a photographic exhibition corridor.
Income: Financed by state appropriation.
Collections: 20th century American & European Art.
Exhibitions: Contemporary Chicago Painter; Annual Faculty Show; Annual Student Competitive; Thesis Exhibitions; Michael Mazur; Evidence; Contemporary American Drawing; de Kooning 1969-78; Allan Kaprow; Contemporary Chicago Sculptors; Northwest Eccentric Art.
Publications: Exhibition catalogs.
Activities: Lect open to public, 20 vis lectr per yr; concerts; gallery talks; tours; competition.

CEDAR RAPIDS

CEDAR RAPIDS ART CENTER, 324 Third St SE, 52401. Tel: 319-366-7503. *Pres* D William Coppock; *VPres* Daniel S Perkins; *Secy* Mrs Kenneth Bastian; *Dir* Stan Wiederspan; *Asst Dir* Fred Easker.

Open Mon - Sat 10 AM - 5 PM, Thurs until 8 PM; Sun 2 - 5 PM. Estab art association, 1905, art center, 1966. An art gallery is maintained. Mem: 750; dues single $10, family $15, supporting $25.
Income: Financed by endowment, membership, city and state appropriations.
Collections: Largest concentrated collection of Grant Wood art in existence; plus a modest print collection.
Exhibitions: Rotating exhibitions.
Publications: Newsletter, monthly.
Activities: Classes for adults and children; dramatic programs; docent training; competitions; individual paintings and original objects of art lent on request; sales shop selling books, magazines, original art, prints, reproductions, and other merchandise.
—**Stamats Library.** *Librn* Mrs Gale Gregory. Open to public and members for lending and reference.

COE COLLEGE ART GALLERIES, 1221 First Ave NE, 52402. Tel: 319-398-1669. *Chmn Art Dept* Charles Stroh; *Gallery Dir* Shirley Donaldson.
Open Mon - Fri 7 - 9 PM; Sat 10 AM - Noon; Sun 2 - 4 PM. No admis. Estab 1942 to exhibit traveling exhibitions and local exhibits. Two galleries: both 60 x 18 ft with 125 running ft of exhibit space. Average Annual Attendance: 5000.
Income: $3,500 (financed through College).
Collections: Coe Collection of art works; Marvin Cone Collection of oils; Conger Metcalf Collection of paintings; Marvin Cone Alumni Collection of art works.
Exhibitions: Circulating exhibits; rental print exhibitions; one-person and group shows of regional nature.
Publications: College catalog, yearly; exhibit brochures, 6 - 8 per year.
Activities: Lect open to public, 5 - 6 vis lectr per yr; gallery talks; tours; competitions; individual paintings and original objects of art lent to colleges, and local galleries; lending collection contains framed reproductions, original art works, original prints, paintings, sculpture, and slides; traveling exhibitions organized and circulated.

MOUNT MERCY COLLEGE, McAuley Gallery, 1330 Elmhurst Dr NE, 52402. Tel: 319-363-8213. *Dir* Jane E Gilmor.
Open 8 AM - 5 PM & 7 - 9 PM. No admis. Estab to show work by a variety of fine artists. The shows are used by the art department as teaching aids. They provide cultural exposure to the entire campus. One room 22 x 30 ft; one wall is glass overlooking a small courtyard. Average Annual Attendance: 900.
Income: Financed through the College. Purchases: $200.
Collections: Small print collection.
Exhibitions: Frank Berkenkotter (lithographs, relief sculptures); Women Artists Soft Art and Fiber Show; Kirkwood Community College Art Faculty Exhibit (paintings, prints, ceramics); Second Annual High School Art Exhibit; Dick Stevens (colorgraphs, straight photographs); Coe College Art Faculty and Student Exchange Show; Marge Hirano (drawings); Group Silkscreen Exhibit; Carl Homstad (etchings and woodcuts); Senior Thesis Exhibit.

CHEROKEE

SANFORD MUSEUM AND PLANETARIUM, 117 E Willow St, 51012. Tel: 712-225-3922. *Dir* Robert W Hoge; *Asst Dir* Lennis Moore; *Admin Asst* Linda Burkhart.
Open Mon - Fri 9 AM - 5 PM; Sat & Sun 2 - 5 PM. No admis. Estab 1951 for collection, preservation and interpretation of historical, archaeological and biological specimens from the region; educational programs; community involvement. Contains Natural History Hall (archaeology, paleontology, geology, biology), combination auditorium, art display wall area and local history hall, temporary exhibitions gallery, and Sanford Room (historical period room). Average Annual Attendance: 15,000.
Mem: 150; dues $7.50 - $100; annual meeting-banquet, Apr or May.
Income: Approx $35,000 (financed by endowment and donations). Purchases: Under $100.
Collections: Archaeological materials from local cultures; archaeological and ethnographic materials from other regions; vertebrate and invertebrate paleontological specimens, mostly from the region; historical collections, mostly from the county, but including Civil War memorabilia; mounted local faunal specimens; mounted African big game animals.
Exhibitions: (1976-78) Tatangka Wotin Ni Sa: the Buffalo People (Plains Indian cultures); First Hundred Years (American Historical—Bicentennial); Children of the Blizzard (Inuit culture); Interweave (materials, techniques and history of textiles); Surprising Saurians (life and times of dinosaurs).
Publications: Northwest Chapter of Iowa Archaeological Society Newsletter, bimonthly.
Activities: Classes for adults and children; dramatic programs; lect open to public, 3 vis lectr per yr; concerts; gallery talks; tours; individual paintings and original objects of art lent to responsible parties and institutions, at the discretion of the director; traveling exhibitions organized and circulated; museum shop selling books, reproductions, natural science and historical souvenirs and jewelry.
—**Sanford Museum Library.** *Mus Dir* Robert W Hoge. Open to public upon approval of the director for reference only.
Holdings: Vols 2000; Per subs 10; Other—Records, slides, films, tapes, photographs, archives collection.
Special Subjects: Herrick quilt collection materials; Herrick Cross collection materials; archaeological materials.
Special Collections: Herrick Cross Collection; Herrick Quilt Collection; Brown-Fisher-Yates Collection; Vandercook-Green Collection; Kirkpatrick Collection; Sanford Collection.

CLINTON

CLINTON ART ASSOCIATION GALLERY, 708 25th Ave N (Mailing Add: PO Box 132, 52732). Tel: 319-242-9635. *Pres* vacant; *VPres* vacant; *Secy* Linda Huber; *Dir* Hortense Blake.
Open Sat & Sun 1 - 5 PM; cl Christmas and New Years. No admis. Estab 1968 to bring visual art to the community; small gallery is housed in an abandoned building of an army hospital complex and is loaned to the association by the Clinton Park and Recreation Board. Average Annual Attendance: 15,000. Mem: 400; dues single membership $5; annual meeting first Tues in May.
Income: $3000 (financed by membership and through grants from the Iowa Arts Council).
Publications: Newsletter every two months.
Activities: Classes for adults and children in watercolor, oil, rosemaling, macrame, photography and pottery making; docent training; lectr open to the public, 3 - 5 vis lectr per yr; gallery talks; tours; individual paintings lent by members to businesses; lending collection contains books, lantern slides and slides; sales shop selling original art and prints.
Library: Very small library in connection with gallery open to members.

DAVENPORT

DAVENPORT MUNICIPAL ART GALLERY, 1737 W 12th St, 52804. Tel: 319-326-7804. *Dir* L G Hoffman; *Admin Secy* Marielow Lee; *Arts Specialist* Ray Bouslough; *Dir Educ* Alex Vance; *Cur Registrar* Mitch Cohen; *Youth Coordr* Patrick Sweeney.
Open Tues - Sat 10 AM - 4:30 PM; Sun 1 - 4:30 PM. No admis; Estab 1925 as a museum of art and custodian of public collection; education center for the visual arts; consists of three levels including a spacious main exhibition display area; upper and lower level galleries are art reference library, six multipurpose art studies, gift shop, mechanical shop and storage area; 400 seat auditorium; children's gallery; studio workshop; registrar center and an outdoor studio-plaza on the lower level. Average Annual Attendance 131,000. Mem: 1009; dues $10 and up; annual meeting Apr.
Income: $512,000 (financed by city appropriation). Purchases $40,000.
Collections: Spanish/Colonial; Grant Wood; Haitian; 19th and 20th century American art; European art including English, French, German and Italian.
Exhibitions: Henry Moore Prints; David Hostetler: The American Woman; The Amanas Yesterday; Great Ideas of Western Man; New Talent: Caracas, Dilg, Patrick, Jones and Parker; 14th Annual Mid-Mississippi.
Publication: Bulletin, quarterly; catalogs.
Activities: Classes for adults and children; docent training; lect open to the public; concerts; gallery talks; tours; competitions; artmobile; traveling exhibitions organized and circulated; sales shop selling original art. Junior museum called Arterarium.
—**Art Reference Library.** *Librn* Gladys Hitchings.
Open for reference.
Holdings: Vols 6000; Per subs 17.
Special Subjects: General visual arts.

PUTNAM MUSEUM*, 1717 W 12th St, 52804. Tel: 319-324-1933. *Dir* Joseph L Cartwright; *Cur Exhibits* Jacqueline Denison; *Cur Prints & Documents* Betty Keen; *Registrar* Carol Hunt; *Cur of Educ* Peter Petersen.
Open Mon - Sat 9 AM - 5 PM; Sun 1 - 5 PM; cl National holidays. Admis adults 75¢, children 25¢; no admis Sat 9 AM - Noon. Estab 1867 as Academy of Science. Average Annual Attendance: 100,000. Mem: 2500; dues individual $10, joint $15; annual meeting May.
Income: Approximately $200,000.
Collections: (Art) Ethnology; archaeology; anthropology; prints, watercolors, drawings, and primitive art; manuscript collections.
Exhibitions: Permanent, temporary and traveling exhibitions.
Activities: Formally organized education programs for adults and children; films; lectures; gallery talks.
Library: Holdings—Vols 50,000 in science, art and history.

DECORAH

VESTERHEIM, The Norwegian-American Museum, 502 W Water St, 52101. Tel: 319-382-9682. *Dir* Marion John Nelson; *Cur* Darrell Henning; *Dir in Charge of Acad Relations* John Christianson; *Textiles Cur* Lila Nelson; *Admin Asst* Betty Seegmiller.
Open May - Oct 9 AM - 5 PM daily; Nov - Apr weekdays 10 AM - 4 PM, Sat & Sun 10 AM - 5 PM. Admis adults, $2, children 75 cents (summer); adults $1.50, children 75 cents (winter). Estab 1877 to engage in all activities necessary for the collection, preservation, and exhibition of all artifacts which will throw light on the life of people in the United States of Norwegian birth and descent, both in their home environment in Norway and in their settlements in America. Numerous historic bldgs, including two from Norway, make up the vast complex of Vesterheim. Average Annual Attendance: 30,000. Mem: 4000; dues $5; annual meeting Oct.
Income: $125,000 (financed by endowment, membership, donations).
Collections: Extensive collections combine those of Luther College and the Museum Corporation; through house furnishings, costumes, tools and implements, church furniture, toys, and the like, the Museum tells the story of the Norwegian immigrant.
Exhibitions: National Rosemaling Exhibition.
Publications: Newsletter, quarterly; Norwegian Tracks, quarterly; Rosemaling Letter, quarterly; Pioneer Cook Book, Time-Honored Norwegian Recipes, Norrona Sketchbook, Vesterheim: Samplings from the Collection.
Activities: Classes for adults; competitions; museum shop selling books, original art, prints, slides, related gift items, woodenware, artists supplies for rosemaling.
Library: Reference library open to public. Holdings: Vols 800. Special Subjects: Norwegian history, culture, crafts, genealogy.

DES MOINES

DES MOINES ART CENTER, Greenwood Park, 50312. Tel: 515-277-4405. *Dir* James T Demetrion; *Asst Dir* Peggy Patrick; *Dir of Educ* Georgeann Kudron; *Pres, Bd of Trustees* James E Cooney; *VPres & Treas* Robert Lubetkin.
Open Tues - Sat 11 AM - 5 PM; Sun noon - 5 PM; cl Mon. No Admis.
Estab 1948 for the purpose of displaying, conserving and interpreting art; Large sculpture galleries in I M Pei-designed addition opened in 1968; main gallery covers 36 x 117 ft area. Average Annual Attendance: 175,000. Mem: 3700; dues $20 up.
Income: $652,000 (financed by endowment, membership, city and state appropriation).
Collections: †American and European sculpture and painting of the past 200 years.
Exhibitions: Heritage of American Art; Maurice Prendergast Retrospective; Sculptures by Duane Hanson; Paintings by Wayne Thiebaud; Prints by Peter Milton; The American Farm: A Photographic History; Iowa Artists Exhibition.
Publications: Bulletin, bimonthly; Annual report; catalogs of exhibitions.
Activities: Classes for adults and children; docent training; lect open to members only, 6 vis lectr per yr; concerts; gallery talks; tours; competitions, traveling exhibitions organized and circulated; museum shop selling books, original art, prints and postcards; Junior Museum.
—**Library.** *Librn* Margaret Buckley. Open to the public for reference only.
Holdings: Vols 6482; Per subs 21; Other—Exhibition catalogs.

DUBUQUE

DUBUQUE ART ASSOCIATION,* *Pres* Mrs Edward Schuster.
—**Flora Park Barn Gallery,** Flora Park, 52001. Tel: 319-556-9485.
—**Old Jail Gallery,** Sixth & Central Ave, 52001. Tel: 319-556-9718.
Barn Gallery open daily 3 - 5 PM, week nights 7 - 9 PM; Jail Gallery open daily 2 - 5 PM. Estab 1910, inc 1956. Mem: 400; dues $5 and up; annual meeting May.
Collections: Paintings, drawings, prints, sculptures.
Activities: Classes for all ages; lectures, gallery talks; films; slides; bus tours; monthly programs; Beaux Arts Ball; Dubuqueland Area Annual Competition Show.

FAIRFIELD

FAIRFIELD PUBLIC LIBRARY AND MUSEUM,* Fairfield Art Association, Court & Washington, 52556. Tel: 515-472-3236. *Pres* Mrs Gary L Cameron; *Librn* James Rabis; *Chmn Mus Comt* Ben Taylor; *Chmn Art Gallery* Dr Paul Selz.
Library open 11 AM - 8:30 PM; museum 11 AM - 6 PM; art gallery 6 - 8:30 PM.
Income: Library and museum financed by endowment and city appropriation; Art Association financed by endowment and membership.

Collections: (Art Gallery) Indian art; †paintings; †graphics.
Activities: Art Association offers classes for adults and children; lect open to the public; competitions.

FORT DODGE

BLANDEN ART GALLERY, 920 Third Ave S, 50501. Tel: 515-573-2316. *Pres Board of Trustees* Robert A Loomis; *Dir* M Jessica Rowe; *Asst Dir* Cheryl Ann Parker; *Accountant & Receptionist* Helen Brouhard; *Secy* Sue Duvall; *Mem:* Catherine Deardorf; *Receptionist* Lauretta Nelson.
Open Tues - Sun 1 - 5 PM; cl Mon. No admis. Estab 1932, the Gallery was a gift to the city from Charles G Blanden as a memorial to his wife. Houses works of art in permanent collections. Neo-Italian Renaissance architecture. Average Annual Attendance: 8000 - 10,000. dues $3 - $100; annual meeting July.
Income: Approx $45,000 (financed by membership, city and state appropriations, and charitable foundation).
Collections: Works by Miro, Hofmann, Chagall, Calder, Matta, Moore, Kandinsky, Klee, Beckmann, Feininger, Prendergast; as well as oriental prints, posters and regional artist's painting, prints and sculpture; works by well-known Iowa artists; †20th century abstract and expressionist work.
Publications: Bimonthly bulletin; Annual report.
Activities: Classes for adults and children; dramatic programs; docent training; film series; lect open to public, 12 vis lectr per yr; concerts; gallery talks; tours; competitions; individual paintings and original objects of art lent to other accredited museums; sales shop selling books, original art, reproductions, prints, cards, museum replicas, imported jewelry.
Library: Open to public for reference only. Holdings: Vols 893; Per subs 10.

INDIANOLA

SIMPSON COLLEGE ART GALLERY, 50125. Tel: 515-961-6251. *Head Art Dept* Gaile Gallatin.
Estab 1860 as a four-year liberal arts college.
Collections: Small permanent collection; creche figures from 18th century Italy.
Exhibitions: Visiting exhibits from Iowa Arts Council; student shows.
Activities: Lect open to public, 2 vis lectr per yr; concerts.

IOWA CITY

UNIVERSITY OF IOWA
—**Museum of Art,** Riverside Dr, 52242. Tel: 319-353-3266. *Dir* Jan K Muhlert; *Cur Coll* Joann Moser; *Registrar* Hugo Ruiz-Avila; *Prog Coordinator* Elizabeth Broudy; *Installation Coordinator* David Dennis.
Open Mon - Sat 10 AM - 5 PM; Sun 1 - 5 PM, cl Thanksgiving, Christmas & New Year's Day. No admis. Estab 1969 to collect, exhibit and preserve for the future works of art from different cultures; to make these objects as accessible as possible to people of all ages in the state of Iowa; to assist the public, through educational programs and publications, in interpreting these works of art and expanding their appreciation of art in general; 48,000 sq ft in 16 galleries, including a central sculpture court. Average Annual Attendance: 50,000. Mem: Friends of the Museum 780; dues student $5, individual $15, family $25; annual meeting no set date.
Income: Financed by membership, state appropriation and private donations.
Collections: 19th and 20th century European and American painting and sculpture; prints; drawings; photography; African and Pre-Columbian art; silver; Oriental jade; Chinese and Tibetan bronzes.
Exhibitions: About 14 changing exhibitions each year, both permanent collection and traveling exhibitions. Silver and jade; the Elliott Collection of 20th Century European painting; a selection of African art and the Lasansky prints are on permanent display.
Publications: Bulletin (small magazine) and Calendar (brochure), biannually; about 3 exhibition catalogs per year.
Activities: Docent training; lect open to the public, 8 vis lectr per yr; concerts; gallery talks; tours; individual paintings and original objects of art lent to other museums; traveling exhibitions organized and circulated; sales area selling posters, postcards and catalogs.
—**Art Library.** Tel: 319-353-4440. *Librn* Harlan L Sifford.
Open Mon - Fri 8 AM - 5 PM; Mon - Thurs 7 - 10 PM; Sat & Sun 1 - 4 PM. Estab 1937 to support the University programs, community and state needs. Circ: 32,000.
Income: Financed by city appropriation. Purchases: $65,000.
Holdings: Vols 50,000; Per subs 230; AV—Microfiche, microfilm; Other—Clipping files, exhibition catalogs, memorabilia, pamphlets.

KEOKUK

KEOKUK ART CENTER,* Box 871, 52632. *Pres* Mrs Richard Gammon; *Secy* Mrs Richard Logton; *VPres* Richard Stebbings; *Treas* Delbert Chapman; *Prog Dir* Bruce Busey.
Open Mon - Sat 9 AM - 5 PM. No admis. Estab 1954 to promote art in tri-state area; Gallery maintained in Keokuk Public Library, 210 N Fifth St. Average Annual Attendance: 2000. Mem dues individual $5, family $8; annual meeting first Mon in May.
Income: $1500 (financed by membership).
Collections: Paintings; sculpture.
Exhibitions: One per month, runs for three weeks, all media.
Publications: Newsletter, quarterly.
Activities: Classes for adults and children; lect open to the public; gallery talks; individual paints and original objects of art lent; competitions.

LeMARS

WESTMAR COLLEGE, Weidler Art Gallery, 51031. Tel: 319-546-7081, exten 231. *Dir* Gary Bowling.
Open daily 8 AM - 9:30 PM; inactive during summer. No admis. Estab 1973, the purpose of the gallery is to provide a forum for cultivating the sensitivity of our student body and the community to a variety of visual arts through a regular schedule of art exhibits; gallery covers 2000 sq ft floor space, 170 linear feet of display space, with track lighting. Average Annual Attendance: 7500.
Income: Financed by endowment, college appropriation and private gifts.
Publications: Westmar College Fine Arts Schedule of Events, fall of each academic year.
Activities: Lect open to the public, 1-3 vis lectr per yr; tours by arrangement.
Mock Library: Librn Robert Yontz. Open to students. Holdings: Vols 1600; Per subs 9; Other—Art slides 7000.

MARSHALLTOWN

CENTRAL IOWA ART ASSOCIATION, INC,* Fisher Community Center, 50158. Tel: 515-753-9013. *Pres* Mrs Stanley Doerr; *Secy* Mrs LeRoy Ackerson.
Open 1 - 4 PM. Inc 1959. Average Annual Attendance: 30,000. Mem: 600; dues student $5, individual $7.50; annual meeting May.
Collections: Fisher Collection—Utrillo, Cassatt, Sisley, Vuillard, Monet, Degas, Signac, Le Gourge, Vlaminck and Monticelli; sculpture—Christian Petersen, Romenilli, Bourdelle; ceramic study collection—Gilhooly, Arneson, Nagle, Kottler, Babu, Geraedts, Boxem, Leach, and traditional Japanese wares.
Activities: Classes for adults and children in ceramics, sculpture, jewelry, painting; gallery talks; monthly exhibits, beginning the first Sun of the month and are open weekdays thereafter.
Art reference library.

MASON CITY

CHARLES H MacNIDER MUSEUM, 303 Second St SE, 50401. Tel: 515-423-9563. *Dir* Richard E Leet; *Dir Educ & Spec Prog* Glyde J Wheeler.
Open Tues & Thurs 10 AM - 9 PM; Wed, Fri, Sat 10 AM - 5 PM; cl Mon & holidays. No admis. Estab 1964, opened 1966 to provide experience in the arts through development of a permanent collection, through scheduling of temporary exhibitions, through the offering of classes and art instruction, through special programs in film, music and other areas of the performing arts. The museum was established in an English-Tudor style of brick and tile. It is located in a scenic setting, 2½ blocks from the main thoroughfare of Mason City. Gallery lighting and neutral backgrounds provide a good environment for exhibitions. Average Annual Attendance: Over 28,000. Mem: 730; dues from contributions $3 - $100 or more.
Income: $108,000 (financed by membership, city appropriation). Purchases: Varies.
Collections: Permanent collection being developed with an emphasis on American art, with some representation of Iowa art; contains paintings, prints, pottery; artists represented include: Oliveira, Dove, Davies, Levine, Francis, Healy, Prior, Lasansky, Burchfield, Graves, Burford, Metcalf, Wood, Maurer, Benton, and Baziotes.
Exhibitions: Monthly art exhibitions of regional, national, and international scope have featured; New Orleans Jazz Funerals: Photos by Tuchet; Weathervanes, Carvings and Quilts, from the Chase-Manhattan Bank; The Art of the Puppet: Bil Baird; Beads, American Indian Art from the Museum of the American Indian; John Flannagan, Sculpture and Works on Paper; The Cartoon Show; The Annual Iowa Crafts Competition ($800 in awards); and Annual Area Competitive Show ($350 in awards).

Publications: Monthly newsletter and occasional small exhibit fliers or catalogs.
Activities: Classes for adults and children; docent training; seminars and workshops; lect open to public, 2 - 4 vis lectr per yr; concerts; gallery talks; tours; competitions; individual paintings and original objects of art lent to other museums and art centers; museum shop selling original art.
Library: Reference library within the structure of the Museum. Materials available for use on premises. Holdings: Vols 500, Per subs 24; Other—Slide library for use in classes. Special Subjects: American art.

MASON CITY PUBLIC LIBRARY, 225 Second St SE, 50401. Tel: 515-423-7552. *Dir* Bruce Anderson; *Reference* Gladys Kehm; *Children's Room* Patricia Wargula; *Young Adult* Ruth Upton and Rosalind Weers.
Open Mon - Fri 9 AM - 9 PM; Sat 9 AM - 5 PM; Sun 3 - 5 PM. Estab 1869 to service the public in providing reading material and information. Circ: 164,986. Gallery maintained in auditorium.
Income: $258,185 (financed by city and county appropriation and Federal Reserve Sharing). Purchases $28,719.
Holdings: Vols 123,573, titles 350; AV—Cassettes, film strips, microfilm, motion pictures, phonorecords; Other—Clipping files, framed reproductions, original art works, original documents, pamphlets, prints.
Special Collections: Permanent collection of regional artists.
Exhibitions: (1976) New Reproductions; Ron Lyker (batik); Junior High School Watercolors; Wildflowers (serigraphs and photographs); Bob Nandell (photography); Evelyn Fatagati (children's book illustrator); Northern Iowa Artist League; Natural Things (Hanna); Paintings & Sculpture (Hof, Gabrielson, Jones and Root); Mondahl (mixed media); (1977) Elementary Art Teachers Exhibition; Acrylic Watercolor (Bergland); High School Students Exhibition; New Reproductions; Newman High School Students; Gauley (weaving, stitchery, watercolor, drawing); Udelhoffer; Paulson (acrylic abstract); Northern Iowa Artists League; Frish (mixed media miniatures); Bowman (textiles); Iowa Arts Council (Amana photography); (1978) Permanent Collection; Runion (watercolor); Youth Art Month; New Reproductions: Timmeracle (graphics); Chicken Coop Gang; Losterbour (watercolor); Schuler (painting); Northern Iowa Artists League; Polster (stitchery); Burington (painting); Hanes & Wagnor (mixed media).

MOUNT VERNON

CORNELL COLLEGE, Armstrong Gallery, 52314. Tel: 319-895-8811. *Dir Gallery* and *Chmn Dept of Art* Hank Lifson.
Open Mon - Fri 7:30 AM - 4:30 PM. Estab to display artist' work.
Income: Financed by Cornell College.
Collections: Thomas Nast Drawings and Prints; Sonnenschein Collection of 57 European Drawings of the 15th - 17th Century.
Exhibitions: Five exhibits each year, plus 10 - 20 student thesis shows each year.
Activities: Lect open to public, 1 vis lectr per yr.

MUSCATINE

LAURA MUSSER ART GALLERY AND MUSEUM,* 1314 Mulberry Ave, 52761. Tel: 316-263-8282. *Dir* Clifford J Larson.
Open Tues & Thurs 2 - 5 PM & 7 - 9 PM; Wed, Fri - Sun & holidays 2 - 5 PM; cl. National holidays. No admis. Estab 1965. Mem: Dues single $5, family $10, sustaining $25, life $200.
Income: Financed by city appropriation.
Collections: Historical and military material; paintings; graphics; decorative arts.
Publications: Newsletter, quarterly; catalogs.
Activities: Classes for children and adults; lectures; gallery talks; guided tours; concerts; films; temporary traveling exhibitions. Sales shop.
Library: Open to the public. Holdings: 300 vols; local, state and national history and art reference.

ORANGE CITY

NORTHWESTERN COLLEGE, Ramaker Library Art Gallery, 101 Seventh St SW, 51041. Tel: 712-737-4904. *Exhib Coordinator* John Kaericher.
Open Mon - Fri 8 AM - 5 PM. No admis. Estab 1968 to promote the visual arts in northwest Iowa and to function as a learning resource for the college and community. College art gallery for traveling exhibitions, student shows and faculty shows. Local artists are sometimes invited. Average Annual Attendance: Approx 2000.
Collections: Appro 75 original works of art: etchings, woodcuts, serigraphs, lithographs, mezzotints, paintings, sculpture and ceramics by modern and old masters of Western World and Japan.
Exhibitions: Contemporary American Artists Series; student and faculty shows.

Activities: Classes for adults, gallery run by college art department; lect open to public, 2 - 3 vis lectr per yr; gallery talks; competitions; individual prints and original objects of art lent to schools and libraries.
—**Library:** *Librn* Arthur Hielkema.

SIOUX CITY

BRIAR CLIFF COLLEGE, Gallery 147, 3303 Rebecca St, 51104. Tel: 712-279-5321, exten 452. *Chmn Dept Art* William Wells.
Open all week 9 AM - 5 PM. Estab 1971 as a working gallery for students and staff. One room gallery.
Exhibitions: Student work.
Activities: Educ dept.
Library: Librn Sister Mary Joanice. Open to students.

SIOUX CITY ART CENTER, 513 Nebraska St, 51101. Tel: 712-279-6272. *Pres* Dr Al Blenderman; *VPres* Robert Anderson; *Secy* Renee Weisser; *Dir* Peggy Parris; *Asst Dir* Bruce Bienemann; *Educ Coordinator* Dianne Mumm; *Cur* Ernest Ricehill, Jr.
Open Tues - Sat 10 AM - 5 PM; Sun 1 - 5 PM; cl Mon and holidays. No admis. Estab 1938 to provide art experiences to the general public. Gallery is 3 floors of exhibitions consisting of mainly artists from the Midwest-Regional area; includes a photogallery. Average Annual Attendance: 25,000 - 30,000. Mem: 509; dues $5 - $250; monthly meetings.
Income: Financed by membership, city and state appropriation.
Collections: Permanent collection of over 400 works consists of mainly regional artists.
Activities: Classes for adults and children; docent training; lect open to public, 6 vis lectr per yr; gallery talks; tours; competitions, Annual Fall Show with Purchase Award; schol; traveling exhibitions organized and circulated; sales shop selling original art.

WATERLOO

WATERLOO ART ASSOCIATION, 420 W 11th St, 56702. Tel: 319-232-1984. *Pres* James L Smith; *VPres* Ginny Nutt; *Secy* Sue Davis; *Gallery Dir* Edna Reeck; *Dir Exhib* Doris Frandsen.
Open Wed 10 AM - 4:30 PM; Sat & Sun 2 - 4 PM. No admis. Estab 1960 to encourage area artists and provide for the exhibition of their work; gallery is maintained in a rented building providing three gallery rooms, workshop, art supply sales room and storage. Average Annual Attendance: 1200. Mem: 175; dues $10; annual meeting last Tues Jan.
Income: $4000 (financed by membership).
Collections: Small collection of work by former members.
Exhibitions: Monthly exhibits by area professionals; Black Hawk County Art Show; Amateur Iowa Artists Regional Show.
Publications: Bulletin published six times per yr.
Activities: Lectr open to the public, 2 vis lectr per yr; gallery talks; competitions; sales and rental gallery for members; sales shop selling original art and art supplies.

WATERLOO MUNICIPAL GALLERIES,* 225 Cedar St, 50704. Tel: 319-291-4491. *Gallery Dir* Clarence Alling.
Open Mon - Fri 9 AM - 5 PM; Sat 9 - Noon; Sun 2 - 5 PM. No admis. Estab 1957 to provide an art forum for the Waterloo area. Average Annual Attendance: 35,000; Junior Museum attendance: 16,000. Mem: 500; dues single $3 and up; annual meeting second Thurs of Jan.
Collections: Small new collection of contemporary American painting, prints and sculpture.
Exhibitions: Monthly exhibitions of regional painting, sculpture, prints and fine crafts.
Activities: Classes for adults and children in the Waterloo area; dramatic programs; lect open to the public; gallery talks; competitions; Junior museum.

WEST BRANCH

HERBERT HOOVER PRESIDENTIAL LIBRARY, 234 S Downey, 52358. Tel: 319-338-0581. *Dir* Thomas T Thalken; *Asst Dir* Robert S Wood.
Open (May - Labor Day) Mon - Sat 9 AM - 6 PM; Sun 10 AM - 6 PM; (Sept - Apr) Mon - Sat 9 AM - 5 PM; Sun 2 - 5 PM. Estab 1962 as a research center to service the papers of Herbert Hoover and other related manuscript collections, and as a museum presenting the life and accomplishments of Herbert Hoover.
Income: $309,000 (financed by federal appropriation).
Holdings: Vols 22,000; Per subs 67; AV—Audiotapes, microfilm, motion pictures, phonorecords, slides; Other—Clipping files, manuscripts, memorabilia, original documents, pamphlets, still photographs.

KANSAS

ABILENE

DWIGHT D EISENHOWER PRESIDENTIAL LIBRARY, 67410. Tel: 913-263-4751. *Dir* Dr John E Wickman; *Museum Cur* William K Jones.
Open daily 9 AM - 5 PM; cl Thanksgiving, Christmas Day, New Year's Day. Admis adults and children over 16, 50¢, children accompanied by parents, free. Estab 1962 as library, in 1954 as museum. Attendance: Center, 400,000.
Income: Financed by Federal Government appropriation.
Holdings: Vols 23,000 reference; Other—Prints 75,000 reference.
Special Collections: Research Library and Museum contains papers of Dwight D Eisenhower and his associates, together with items of historical interest connected with the Eisenhower Family. Mementos and gifts of General Dwight D Eisenhower both before, during, and after his term as President of the United States.

COLBY

COLBY COMMUNITY COLLEGE, Northwest Kansas Cultural Arts Center, 1255 S Range, 67701. Tel: 913-462-3984. *Mgr Cultural Arts Center* Brian Foster.
Open Mon - Fri 8 AM - 5 PM; other for special showings. Large gallery, and small gallery, glass display cases. Average Annual Attendance: 1000.
Income: Financed by endowment.
Collections: Permanent collections of student two-dimensional work.
Exhibitions: (1976-78) National Watercolor Exhibit; Photography—13 state traveling exhibit from Kansas University; Annual High School Show (300-piece exhibit); Rocky Mountain Weavers Guild Annual local artists exhibits; Annual Graduate Show; Annual Children's Exhibit; Annual Women's Show.
Activities: Lect open to the public, 2 vis lectr per yr; gallery talks; tours; competitions; individual paintings lent.

ELLSWORTH

ROGERS HOUSE MUSEUM GALLERY, Snake Row, 67439. Tel: 914-472-3255. *Dir* Charles B Rogers.
Open Mon - Sat 10 AM - 5 PM; Sun & holidays 1 - 5 PM; cl Xmas. Admis adults 50¢, children 6-12 25¢. Estab 1968 in an historic cowboy hotel.
Collections: Original paintings; prints; miscellaneous art.
Publications: The Great West, Quill of the Kansan (books).
Activities: Temporary exhibitions; sales shop selling original paintings and prints.

HARPER

HARPER ART ASSOCIATION, INC, E 12th St, 67058.
Open by appointment. Estab 1961; gallery located in renovated Santa Fe depot; artwork of local scope. Mem: 20; dues $5; annual meeting second Sat in April.
Income: Financed by membership.
Collection: Permanent collection of past and present members' work.

HAYS

FORT HAYS STATE UNIVERSITY, Visual Arts Center, 67601. Tel: 913-628-4247. *Dir of Exhib* Zoran Stevanov; *Chmn Dept Art* John C Thorns, Jr.
Open Mon - Fri 8 AM - 5 PM; weekends on special occasions. No admis. Estab 1953 to provide constant changing exhibitions for the benefit of students and faculty and other interested people in an education situation. A new gallery is being constructed with 2200 sq ft, plus adequate storage.
Income: Financed by city appropriation. Purchases: Approx $2000.
Collections: Regionalist Collection (1930's); †Contemporary Prints; Vyvyan Blackford Collection; †National Exhibition of Small Paintings, Prints and Drawings.
Exhibitions: (1977-78) Mary Bates, Sculptor; Pratt Art Institute, Graphics Collograph; Sabatical Exhibition, Joanne Harwick; Dale Hartley, Ceramics; Graduate Thesis Exhibitions; Annual Faculty Exhibition; Kansas Third National Small Paintings, Drawing and Print Exhibition; Annual Undergraduate Exhibition; Annual High School Exhibition and Art Conference.
Publications: Exhibitions brochures; Art Calendar, annually.

Activities: Lectr open to public, 4 vis lectr per yr; gallery talks; tours; competitions; exten dept serving western Kansas; individual paintings and original objects of art lent to individuals, organizations, and institutions; lending collection of original art works and prints, paintings, sculpture, and slides; traveling exhibitions organized and circulated.

HUTCHINSON

HUTCHINSON ART ASSOCIATION,* c/o *Secy-Treas* Mrs Laura Barr, 321 E First St, 67501. Tel: 316-662-6242. *Pres* Shirley Schmidt; *VPres* Jan Dronberger; *Exhibit Chmn* Marvel Senti.
Estab 1949 to bring exhibitions to the city of Hutchinson and maintain a permanent collection in the public schools. Mem: 125; dues $5 and up.
Collections: Permanent collection of watercolors, prints, and oils circulated in the public schools.
Exhibitions: Include an all-member show as well as annual Art Fair, with prize awards of $3500, held in the Hutchinson Public Library.

INDEPENDENCE

LADIES LIBRARY AND ART ASSOCIATION, Independence Museum, 123 N Eighth, 67301. Tel: 316-331-3515. *Pres* Mrs Ben Morris; *Chmn Bd Trustees* Mrs Clifford M Funston; *Secy Bd Drs* Mrs Kirke C Veeder.
Open Wed, Sat & Sun 1 - 5 PM. Admis 25¢. Inc 1882 to provide library facilities and to secure an art collection for the community. The museum has a large gallery which contains original paintings; Indian art and artifacts; Mexican Room; late 1800 and early 1900 costume room; country store; War and Peace Room; presently establishing an historical oil room with the assistance of Arco Pipeline Company. Mem: 150; dues $5 - $25; meetings monthly Oct - May.
Income: Financed by membership, bequests, gifts, art exhibits, and various projects.
Collections: Oriental Collection; William Inge Memorabilia Collection.
Exhibitions: Various artists and craftsmen exhibits; Annual Art Exhibit; Photography Shows; Annual Arts and Crafts Fair.
Activities: Competitions with money awards.

LAWRENCE

UNIVERSITY OF KANSAS, Helen Foresman Spencer Museum of Art, 1301 Mississippi, 66045. Tel: 913-864-4710. *Dir* Dr Charles C Eldredge; *Asst Dir Admin* Douglas Tilghman; *Cur Western Art* William J Hennessey; *Cur Prints & Drawings* Dr Elizabeth Broun; *Cur Photography* Thomas Southall; *Dir Mus Educ* Dolores Brooking; *Research Cur* Dr Marilyn Stokstad.
Open Tues - Sat 10 AM - 4 PM; Sun 1:30 - 4 PM; cl Mon. No admis. Dedicated in Spooner Hall 1928, Spencer dedicated 1978. The Museum has traditionally served as laboratory for the visual arts, supporting curricular instruction in the arts. Primary emphasis is placed on acquisitions and publications, with a regular schedule of changing exhibitions. The Museum has a two level Central Court, seven galleries devoted to the permanent collections, and three galleries for temporary exhibitions, altogether affording 29,000 sq ft. Mem: 600; dues $25.
Income: Financed by endowment, membership, state appropriation and grants.
Collections: †Medieval art; †17th and 18th century art, especially German; †American paintings, †graphics, †ancient art; †19th century European and American art; †Oriental art; †20th century European and American art.
Exhibitions: Photographs by Robert Demachy; Recent Painting by Robert Green and Robert Sudlow; Western Textiles from the University of Kansas Museum of Art; The Art of Buddhism; The Max Kade Collection; Sallie Casey Thayer and Her Collection; Artists Look at Art; Prints from the Collection; The Hidden World of Misericords; Photographs from the Collection Obaku; Zen Painting and Calligraphy.
Publications: The Register of the Museum of Art, annually; Calendar, bimonthly.
Activities: Classes for children; dramatic programs; docent training; traveling art museum; lect open to public, 24 vis lectr per yr; concerts; gallery talks; tours; individual paintings and original objects of art lent for display in public university offices; lending collection contains 100 original prints, 50 paintings; traveling exhibitions organized and circulated; museum shop selling books, magazines, and postcards.
—**Art Library.** *Librn* Martha Kehde. Open to faculty, students, and public.
Holdings: Vols 30,000; Per subs 700.
Special Subjects: Comprehensive collection of art history volumes.

LINDSBORG

BETHANY COLLEGE
—**Birger Sandzen Memorial Gallery,** 401 N First St, 67456. Tel: 913-227-2220. *Co-Dir* Dr C P Greenough III; *Co-Dir* Carl William Peterson.
Open Wed - Sun 1 - 5 PM, cl Mon & Tues. Admis adults 50¢, grade school and high school students 25¢. Estab 1957 to permanently exhibit the paintings and prints by the late Birger Sandzen, teacher at Bethany College for 52 years; ten exhibition areas. Average Annual Attendance: 7000 - 9000. Mem: 350; dues $5 - $100; annual meeting April for Bd of Directors.
Income: Financed by admission fees and sales.
Collections: Sandzen, Poor, Raymer.
Exhibitions: (1976-77) Chinese textiles, paintings and embroideries; Figure drawings by Tomasch; lithographs by Dorothy Scott; Southwest Indian Art; paintings by U Hoel; ceramics by Lori Sargent; watercolors by Donna Brigman, acrylics by Laura Barr; block prints by Annie Lee Ross; oils by Oscar Gunnarson; toy bank loan collection; painting by R. Smith; Molas private collection; Bethany Art Faculty; Audubon prints; blown glass; sculpture by Kent Ullberg.
Publications: The Graphic Work of Birger Sandzen.
Activities: Lect open to the public; concerts; gallery talks; tours; lending collection contains books, color reproductions; sales shop selling books, reproductions.
Library: For reference only.
—**Mingenback Art Center.** *Head Dept* Daniel Mason.
Collections: Oil paintings, watercolors, prints, etchings, wood engravings, lithographs, ceramics and sculpture. Material is used as general education reference not for public display.

MANHATTAN

KANSAS STATE UNIVERSITY, Paul Weigel Library, College of Architecture and Design, 66506. Tel: 913-532-5968. *Dir* Dorothy Leonard; *Asst Dir* Patricia Weisenburger.
Hours: Mon - Thurs 8 AM - 10 PM; Fri 8 AM - 5 PM; Sat 10 AM - 2 PM; Sun 2 - 10 PM. Estab 1917. Circ: 31,300.
Income: $12,500 (financed by state appropriation and gifts).
Holdings: Vols 23,200; Per subs 190; AV—Motion pictures.
Special Subjects: Related to courses in the College of Architecture & Design: Pre Design Professions, Architecture, Interior Architecture, Landscape Architecture, Community and Regional Planning.

MCPHERSON

MCPHERSON COLLEGE, Friendship Hall, 1600 E Euclid, 67460. Tel: 316-241-0731. *Chmn Art Dept* Mary Ann Robinson.
Open Mon - Fri 8 AM - 10 PM. No admis. Estab 1960 to present works of art to the college students and to the community. A long gallery which is entrance to an auditorium, has four showcases and 11 panels 4 x 16 ft. Average Annual Attendance: 2500.
Income: Financed through College.
Collections: Original prints, watercolors, oils.

TOPEKA

ARTS COUNCIL OF TOPEKA, 215 E Seventh St, 66603. Tel: 913-295-3808. *Pres* Marlyn Burch; *Exec Dir* Don Lambert.
Open Mon - Fri 9 AM - 5 PM. Estab 1959; this is an umbrella organization serving more than 70 organization members and 300 individual members in promoting the arts in Topeka. Mem: 370; dues $10, annual meeting Mar.
Income: Financed by membership and city appropriation.
Publications: Newsletter, monthly.
Activities: Resource fair; competitions, art contest to select prints to be reproduced and given to new members.

TOPEKA ART GUILD,* 4640 West Dr, 66606. Tel: 913-272-9660. *Pres* Charles L Marshall; *Cur* Harry B Nelson.
Open weekdays 9 AM - 5 PM; Sun 3 - 5 PM. No admis. Estab 1916, inc 1936. Mem: 250; dues $2 and up; annual meeting May.
Collections: About 17,000 prints and photographs which are circulated to schools and organization in the State.
Exhibitions: Changing exhibits every two or three weeks through the school year.
Activities: Lect; demonstrations.

TOPEKA PUBLIC LIBRARY, 1515 W Tenth St, 66604. Tel: 913-233-2040, exten 330. *Dir* James C Marvin; *Asst Dir* Tom J Muth; *Fine Arts Chmn* Robert H Daw; *Circ Dept Head* Alene Giesy; *Adult Serv Dept Head* Jim Rhodes; *Childrens Dept Head* Sheila Radell; *Exten Head* Dick Brown; *Tech Serv Head* Helen Spencer.

Open Mon - Fri 9 AM - 9 PM; Sat 9 AM - 6 PM; Sun in winter 2 - 6 PM. Estab 1870 to serve the city and the Northeast Kansas Library System residents with public information, both educational and recreational; to be one of the areas cultural centers through services from the unique Fine Arts Dept and Gallery of Fine Arts within the library. Circ: 784,091.

Income: $653,000 (financed by endowment, city appropriation). Purchases: $72,713.

Holdings: Vols 267,782; Per subs 497; AV—Cassettes, film strips, microfiche, microfilm, motion pictures, phonorecords, reels, slides; Other—Clipping files, exhibition catalogs, framed reproductions, manuscripts, memorabilia, original art works and documents, pamphlets, photographs, prints, reproductions, sculpture, postcards, chamber music.

Special Subjects: Fine Arts Department, largest collection of books in the area; Topeka Room of Topeka artists and authors.

Special Collections: Rare book room.

Activities: Lectures open to public; concerts; gallery talks; library tours; competitions; exten dept.

—**Gallery of Fine Arts.** Tel: 913-233-2040, exten 33. *Dir* Larry D Peters; Head of *Maintenance Dept* Michael Kasson.

Open Mon - Fri 9 AM - 9 PM; Sat 9 AM - 6 PM; Sun in winter 2 - 6 PM. No admis. Estab 1886 to provide exhibitions for the public and to collect and conserve works of art for future public viewing.

Income: $3000 (financed by city appropriation). Purchases: $1645.

Collections: †Art glass; †pottery; †paintings; limited prints; West African art.

Exhibitions: (1976) Africa! Creative Expression in Rural West Africa; American Rural Folk Art; Early American Furniture: 1690-1790; (1977) Robert Russell Paintings; Topeka Crafts Exhibition; Frank Howell Paintings; Helen and Norma Eppink Paintings; Space Art from the USSR; (1978) Recent Acquisitions; Ukiyo-e Pictures of the Floating World.

Activities: Lect open to public, 1 - 3 vis lectr per yr; concerts; gallery talks; tours; competitions, juried crafts exhibition, media: jewelry, pottery, weaving and textiles, glass work, enamels and wood; lending collection contains cassettes 150, color reproductions 9000, film strips 50, framed reproductions 1500, motion pictures 200, original art works 700, original prints 300, paintings 100, phonorecords 3734, sculpture 10, slides 12,000.

WASHBURN UNIVERSITY,* Mulvane Art Center, 17th & Jewell, 66621. *Dir & Head Art Dept* R J Hunt; *Asst Dir* Edward Navone.

Open 9 AM - 5 PM; Sun 2 - 5 PM; cl Sat & holidays. Estab 1924; building gift of Margaret Mulvane; provides three galleries, studios and classrooms for Department of Art. Average Annual Attendance: 20,000. Mem: 750; dues $7.50 and up.

Income: Approximately $60,000. Purchases: Approximately $2000.

Collections: International paintings, sculpture, prints and ceramics.

Exhibitions: Continuous program of exhibitions; students' exhibition in May.

Publications: Exhibition brochures.

Activities: Classes for adults and children; popular art lectures in Topeka by staff and visiting artists; frequent gallery programs; films open to the community without charge.

Library: Holdings—Vols 3000 on art.

WICHITA

KANSAS WATERCOLOR SOCIETY,* 1545 Willow Rd, 67208. Tel: 316-686-1621. *Pres* Kean Tilford; *Secy* Jean Shelito.

Estab 1968 to promote watercolor in Kansas. Mem: 66; initiation dues; annual meeting fall.

Income: Financed by membership and entry fees.

Exhibitions: Traveling exhibitions, and two traveling shows in Kansas.

Activities: Lect open to the public; workshop; materials lent; watercolor; competitions; traveling exhibitions organized and circulated; schol.

WICHITA ART ASSOCIATION, INC,* 9112 E Central, 67206. Tel: 316-686-6687. *Chmn of Board* Olive Ann Beech; *Pres* Gladys Wiedemann; *Dir & Cur* John R Rouse; *Secy* Oliver Witterman; *Treas* John T Sheffield.

Galleries open Tues - Sun 1 - 5 PM; cl Mon, August & National holidays. No admis. Estab 1920, inc April 1932. Average Annual Attendance: 25,000. Mem: 1000; dues $25 and up, annual meeting May.

Collections: Prints and drawings, paintings, sculpture, decorative arts and crafts.

Exhibitions: National Graphic Arts and Decorative Art-Ceramics exhibitions alternate biennially, with $2500 prizes given for Decorative Arts; traveling exhibitions change each month; one-man shows; special programs.

Publications: Newsletter, monthly.

Activities: Lectures; concerts; gallery talks; workshops; films; demonstrations; Sales gallery.

Art Reference Library: Holdings—Vols 2500.

WICHITA ART MUSEUM, 619 Stackman Dr, 67203. Tel: 316-268-4621. *Dir* Howard E Wooden; *Cur of Coll-Exhib* Jeffrey Abt; *Admin Asst* Mary Lee Archer; *Financial Officer* Alma Gilley; *Registr* Barbara Odevseff.

Open Tues - Sat 10 AM - 4 PM; Sun 1 - 5 PM; Tues 7 - 9 PM; cl Mon and holidays. No admis. Estab 1935 to house and exhibit art works belonging to permanent collection; to present exhibits of loaned art works, to ensure care and maintain the safety of works through security, environmental controls and appropriate curatorial functions and to interpret collections and exhibitions through formal and educational presentations; new facility designed by Edward Larrabee Barnes opened Oct, 1977. Average Annual Attendance: 60,000 - 75,000. Mem: 2115, dues $2 - $1000; annual meeting May.

Income: Approx $395,000 (financed by endowment, membership, city appropriation, restricted gifts for art acquisition).

Collections: Roland P Murdock Collection of American Art; M C Naftzger Collection of Charles M Russell Paintings, Drawings and Sculpture; Gwen Houston Naftzger Collection of Boehm and Doughty Porcelain Birds; Kurdian Collection of Pre-Columbian Mexican Art; L S and Ida L Naftzger Collection of Prints and Drawings; Florence Naftzger Evans Collection of Porcelain and Faience.

Exhibitions: 5,000 Years of Art from the Metropolitan Museum of Art; Annual Kansas Watercolor Society Competition; Kansas Artists' Biennial; Paintings and Drawings by Mary Joan Waid.

Publications: Monthly Newsletter; Catalog of Roland P Murdock Collection; exhibition brochures.

Activities: Classes for children; dramatic programs; lect open to public; concerts; gallery talks; tours; competitions; individual paintings and original objects of art lent; museum and sales shop selling books, magazines, original art, reproductions, prints, slides; also a sales-rental gallery.

Library: Open to staff, docents, and public upon special arrangement for reference only. Holdings: Vols 2000; Per subs 15 - 20.

WICHITA PUBLIC LIBRARY, 223 S Main, 67202. Tel: 316-265-5281. *Head Librn* Ford A Rockwell; *Asst Librn* Gary D Hime; *Circulation Dept Head* Virginia Dillon; *Reference Dept Head* Viola Tidemann; *Acquisitions Dept Head* Bonnie Rupe; *Art & Music Dept Head* Wilma Brooks, *Children's Room Dept Head* Barbara Fischer; *Business & Technical Dept Head* William Hoffman; *State-Wide Film Service* Sondra Koontz; *Talking Books for the Blind* Betty Spriggs.

Open Mon - Thurs 8:30 AM - 9 PM; Fri & Sat 8:30 AM - 5:30 PM; Sun 1 - 5 PM. Estab 1876 and grown to be informational center and large free public library to improve the community with educational, cultural and recreational benefits through books, recordings, films, art works and other materials. Circ: 1,100,000.

Income: $1,400,000 (from local taxes)

Holdings: AV—Microfilms 5627, motion pictures (16mm) 1450, phonorecords 12,579 and liturgical music 925; Other—Framed reproductions, genealogy.

Collections: Driscoll Piracy Collection; John F Kennedy Collection; Harry Mueller Philately Book Collection; Kansas Book Collection.

Exhibitions: Annuals. Kansas Scholastic Art Awards Show; Wichita Area Girl Scout Exhibit; Best News Photographs Exhibit; Wichita Women Artists; Senior High School Students Spring Exhibit; plus numerous other exhibits throughout the year.

Activities: Nine branch libraries; Mail-A-Book to county residents; free service to everyone; puppet shows put on by Children's Department; noon-time programs of speakers through fall and winter; tours.

WICHITA STATE UNIVERSITY

—**Edwin A Ulrich Museum of Art,** McKnight Art Center, (Mailing Add: Box 46, 67208). Tel: 316-689-3664. *Dir* Dr Martin H Bush; *Cur* Gary Hood; *Asst Cur* Robert Workman.

Open Wed 9:30 AM - 8 PM; Thurs & Fri 9:30 AM - 5 PM; Sat, Sun & holidays 1 - 5 PM. No admis. Estab 1974 to provide exhibitions of major artists for the benefit of the university and community by accepting and putting together traveling shows; and to build and exhibit a permanent collection of outstanding quality. A 6000 sq ft main gallery has movable walls which can be changed to accommodate different exhibitions.

Income: Financed by endowment.

Collections: Ulrich Collection of American art includes paintings by Frederick J Waugh, sculpture by Trova; European, African, Pre-Columbian and American art with particular emphasis on the 20th century—painting, drawings and prints, sculptures, pottery and watercolors; outstanding collection of sculpture located on the University campus.

Exhibitions: Cynthia Polsky (paintings); Douglas Abdell (sculpture); Lotte Jacobi (photographs); Arman (painting and sculpture); John Stuart Curry (prints); Andre Naggar (photographs); Lowell Nesbitt (paintings); Alberto Giacometti (sculptures, drawings and prints); Edward S Curtis:

The North American Indian (photographs); Thomas Hart Benton (drawings and prints); Milton Avery (paintings); Andre Kertesz and France (photographs); New Guinea Art; Van Deren Coke (photographs); Balcomb Breene (paintings); Yousuf Karsh (photographs); Alice Neel (paintings); Carol Anthony (sculptures and paintings); Felix Mann (photographs); John Cage; Serve Louvat and Jean de Bire (photographs).
Activities: Lect open to public, 12 vis lectr per yr; concerts; gallery talks; tours by arrangement; traveling exhibitions organized and circulated; sales shop selling books.
—**Library.** Tel: 316-689-3586. *Dir* Jasper G Schad.
Open Mon - Fri 8 AM - 10 PM; Sat 9 AM - 8 PM; Sun 1 - 10 PM. Circ: 210,340.
Income: Financed through the University.
Holdings: Vols 550,984; Per subs 3191; AV—Audio tapes, cassettes, film strips, microfiche, microfilm, motion picture, phonorecords, reels, slides, video tapes; Other—Exhibition catalogs, manuscripts, original documents, pamphlets, photographs.
Publications: Annual Report.

WINFIELD

SOUTHWESTERN COLLEGE, Memorial Library, 100 College, 67156. Tel: 316-221-4150, exten 25 (after 5 PM & weekends 316-221-3400). *Dir* Daniel L Nutter.
Open school year Mon - thurs 8 AM - 10 PM; Fri & Sat 9 AM - 4 PM; Sun 1 - 10 PM; summer Mon - Fri only, 8 AM - 4 PM. Estab 1885 as a four-year Liberal Arts College. Gallery not maintained. Circulation 30,000.
Income: $65,000 (financed by college budget). Purchases: $40,000.
Holdings: Vols 100,000; Per subs 500; AV—Cassettes, microfiche, microfilm.
Special Collections: Arthur Covey Collection of paintings, mural sketches, etchings, lithographs, drawings and watercolors.
Exhibitions: Arthur Covey Centennial Exhibit.
Activities: Tours.

KENTUCKY

ANCHORAGE

LOUISVILLE SCHOOL OF ART GALLERY, 100 Park Road, 42023. Tel: 502-245-8836. *Dir* Bruce Yenawine; *Assoc Dir* Diana Arcadipone; *Registrar* Carolyn Stephenson.
Open 9 AM - 5 PM. Estab 1909 to enrich human life and to provide for the transmission of knowledge and technique, encourage original research and inquiry, and promote personal growth and experience. Located in an old, elaborately decorated space, it offers exhibitions of local and nationally-known artists.
Income: Financed by endowment, tuition, and fees.
Publications: Newsletter, infrequently.
Activities: Classes for adults and children; summer workshops; lect open to public, 12-15 vis lect per yr; gallery talks; tours; competitions; artmobile; traveling exhibitions organized and circulated.
Library: Librn Kent Metcalf. Open to students. Holdings: Vols 8000; Per subs 40. Special Subjects: Fine arts.
—**Art Center Association,** 1622 Stary Ave, 40223. Tel: 502-583-6300. *Pres* Junius Prince, III; *VPres* Mrs Edwin Middleton; *Treas* J Stuart Mitchell; *Secy* Mrs Robert S Dean, Jr.
Estab 1942 by merger of Louisville Art Center, founded 1929 and the Louisville Art Association, founded 1909, to promote art and art education in Louisville. Mem: 750; dues $10 and up; annual meeting June.
Collections: Permanent collection of international art.
Exhibitions: 11 contemporary art exhibits in the School Gallery; children's shows; Christmas sale.
Publications: Announcements, catalogs, school newspapers.
Activities: Gallery talks; lect series; movies; demonstration and annual auction.

BEREA

BEREA COLLEGE, Art Department Gallery, 40404. Tel: 606-986-9341, exten 292-3-4. *Chmn Art Dept* Lester F Pross.
Open Mon - Fri 8 AM - 5 PM. No admis. Estab 1935 for educational purposes. Three gallery areas; exhibitions change monthly; loan and rental shows, regional artists, work from Berea College collections.
Income: Financed by college budget.
Collections: Doris Ulmann photographs; Kress Study Collection of Renaissance art; prints, textiles, paintings, sculpture, ceramics; Asian art.
Exhibitions: (1976-78) From the College Collections; Concept Art; Ulmann Photos; student shows; Far Eastern Fabrics; Photos with a Diana camera; Harania (Egyptian children's tapestries); prints by Katherine Cawein; Alcoa Collection of Contemporary Painting; Naked Clay (American Indian ceramics), staff shows.

Activities: Educ dept; lect open to public, 3 - 4 vis lectr per yr; gallery talks; competitions, regional drawing, textiles; individual paintings and original objects of art lent to other colleges, museums, and galleries; lending collection contains 400 framed reproductions.
—**Art Department Library.** Tel: 606-986-9341. *Chmn Art Dept* Lester F Pross.
Open Mon - Fri 8 AM - 5 PM. Estab 1935. Reference library only.
Income: Financed by college budget. Purchases: c $1000 annually.
Holdings: Vols 2500; Per subs c 30; AV—Film strips; Kodachromes, lantern slides, phonorecords, slides; Other—Clipping files, exhibition catalogs, framed reproductions, manuscripts, memorabilia, original art works, pamphlets, photographs, prints, reproductions, sculpture.

KENTUCKY GUILD OF ARTISTS AND CRAFTSMEN, INC, 213 Chestnut St (Mailing Add: PO Box 291, 40403). Tel: 606-986-3192. *Pres* Edward Dienes; *VPres* Trudy Thompson; *Secy* Maggie Rifai; *Exec Dir* Garry Barker; *Admin Asst* Maggie Rifai; *Educ Dir* Andrew Combs-Smith.
Open Mon - Sat 8 AM - 4 PM. No admis. Estab 1961 for the pursuit of excellence in the arts and crafts and to encourage the public appreciation thereof. Maintains an art gallery. Mem: 500, must be Kentucky residents and be juried for exhibiting status; dues individual $7.50; annual meeting Nov.
Income: $250,000 (financed by endowment and state appropriation, sales and admissions).
Exhibitions: Two annual Fairs include a Members' Exhibit.
Publications: The Guild Record, 7 times a year.
Activities: Classes for adults; docent training; workshops; lect open to public; competitions; traveling exhibitions organized and circulated; sales shop selling original art, prints, slides and crafts.

BOWLING GREEN

WESTERN KENTUCKY UNIVERSITY
—**Kentucky Museum,** 42101. Tel: 502-745-2592. *Cur Coll* Bruce MacLeish; *Cur Exhib* Ira Kohn; *Educ Officer* Anne Johnston; *Registrar* Patricia MacLeish.
Open Tues - Sat 11 AM - 4 PM. No admis. Estab 1939 to serve as a laboratory and resources center for the study and preservation of materials relating to the history and heritage of the people of Kentucky; small temporary gallery is located in the Garrett Conference Center; museum currently in expansion to 80,000 sq ft. Average Annual Attendance: 20,000.
Income: Financed by state appropriation and University.
Collections: Textiles, furniture, art; archaeological specimens.
Exhibitions: Centenary Parlor 1976-1978; Quilts; Labor Saving Devices; Ivan Wilson Watercolors.
Activities: Dramatic programs; lect open to the pub; gallery talks; tours; competitions.
—**Kentucky Library.** *Librn* Riley Handy.
Open to the public for reference.
Holdings: Vols 30,000; Per subs 35; Other—Clipping files, maps, broadsides, postcards, photographs, manuscripts.
Special Collections: Gerard Collection of Bowling Green Photographs; Neal Collection of Utopian materials; Ellis Collection of steamboat pictures; McGregor Collection of rare books.
—**Ivan Wilson Center for Fine Arts Gallery,** Room 200. *Dir* John Warren Oakes.
Open Mon - Fri 8:30 AM - 4 PM; Wed 5:30 - 8:30 PM; Sat 2 - 9 PM; Sun 2 - 5 PM. No admis. Estab 1973 for art exhibitions relating to university instruction and regional cultural needs. Average Annual Attendance: 12,000.
Income: Financed by city appropriation.
Exhibitions: Twenty-Five years of Prints by Adja Yunkers; Recent Work: WKU Art Faculty; Walter Stomps: Recent Work; Neil Peterie: Sabbatical Work; First National College Student Print Invitations; Photo 77 Graphic; The Transforming Eye Photography by Clarence John Laughlin; Selected Art Students; Prints by Peter Milton; WKU Senior Art Exhibits; Sam Hunt and Robert Love; 10th Annual High School Art Competition; 18th Annual Student Art Competition; Selected WKU Seniors Art Exhibit.

FRANKFORT

KENTUCKY HISTORICAL SOCIETY MUSEUM, Broadway & Lewis Sts (Mailing Add: PO Box H, 40602). *Dir* Gen William R Buster; *Cur, Old Capitol* Willia Long; *Cur Museum* Elizabeth Perkins; *Registrar* Charles Pittenger.
Open Mon - Sat 9 AM - 4 PM; Sun & holidays 1 - 5 PM. No admis. Estab 1836 as a general history and art museum emphasizing the history, culture and decorative arts of the Commonwealth of Kentucky and its people. The Old Capitol Galleries located in the Old State House consist of two rooms totaling 2740 sq ft which are used by the Museum to display its fine arts exhibitions, painting, silver, furniture and sculpture.

Average Annual Attendance: 90,000. Mem: 9000; dues from individual $10 to life $100.
Income: $160,000 (financed by state appropriation).
Collections: Kentucky and American silver, paintings, textiles, quilts and coverlets and china.
Exhibitions: Mr Audubon and Mr Bien: An early phase in American Chromolithography; Pageant of the Bluegrass: Painting in Kentucky Collections 1400-1914; Contemporary Kentucky Cabinetmakers.
Activities: Lect open to public, 3-5 vis lectr per yr; concerts; traveling exhibitions organized and circulated; museum shop selling books, prints, slides and gift items.

LIBERTY HALL MUSEUM,* 218 Wilkinson St, 40601. Tel: 502-277-2560. *Chmn* Mrs Lawrence Brewer; *Cur* Mrs R H Coleman.
Open Tues - Sat 10 AM - 5 PM; Sun 2 - 5 PM; cl Mon and holidays. Admis adults $1.50, children and students 50¢. Estab 1937 as an historic museum, a Georgian house built in 1796, named Historic Landmark in 1972.
Collections: 18th century furniture; china; silver; portraits.
Activities: Guided tours.
Library: Open to the public during scheduled hours. Holdings: 6000 vols.
—**Orlando Brown House,** 202 Wilkinson St, 40601. Tel: 502-875-4952. *Chmn* Mrs Charles W Metcalf; *Cur* Mrs Joseph Taylor.
Open Tues - Sat 10 AM - 5 PM; Sun 2 - 5 PM; cl Mon and holidays. Admis adults $1.50, children 50¢. Estab 1956, built in 1835 by architect Gilbert Shryock.
Collections: Original furnishings; Paul Sawyier paintings.
Activities: Guided tours.
Library: Open to the public. Holdings: 500 vols history and genealogy.

LEXINGTON

TRANSYLVANIA COLLEGE,* Moxlan Gallery, Mitchell Fine Arts Center, 40508. Tel: 606-255-6861. *Prof* John R Bryden.
Financed by endowment, the Moxlan Gallery holds approximately 6 exhibitions a year during sessions when students are on campus.

UNIVERSITY OF KENTUCKY
—**Art Museum,** 213 Kinkead Hall, 40506. Tel: 606-258-5716. *Dir* Priscilla Colt; *Registrar* Jacqueline High; *Preparator* Christopher Meatyard; *Admin Asst* Lynn Stowell.
Estab 1975 to collect, preserve, exhibit and interpret world art for the benefit of the University community and the region. Building under construction: 20,000 sq ft of galleries and work space.
Income: $66,124 (financed by state appropriations and gifts). Purchases: $34,200.
Collections: †Graphics; †African; †Pre-Columbian; †19th & 20th Century paintings and sculpture; †Far Eastern.
Exhibitions: The Robert B Mayer Memorial Loan Collection and Recent Gifts of 20th Century Art; The Art of Paul Sawyier; Art Department Faculty Show; Robert Tharsing Show; Directions for a University Art Collection: Part I & II; From Color to Chiaroscuro; Graphics 1957-1976: A Tribute to Richard B Freeman.
Publications: Art Museum Notes, quarterly.
—**Art Library,** M I King Library, North. *Librn* Karin Sandvik.
Open to students and the general public.
Holdings: Vols 18,644; Per subs 149.

LOUISVILLE

FILSON CLUB,* 118 W Breckinridge St, 40203. Tel: 502-582-3727. *Pres* J Alexander Stewart; *Secy & Cur* Mss James R Bentley; *Asst to Pres* Richard L Hagy; *Dir of Museum Planning* Lois Price; *Editor History Quarterly* Nelson L Dawson.
Open Oct - June Mon - Fri 9 AM - 5 PM; Sat 9 AM - Noon; July - Sept Mon - Fri 9 AM - 5 PM; cl National holidays. No admis. Estab 1884 to collect, preserve and publish historical material, especially pertaining to Kentucky. Mem: 2200; dues $15, life $300; monthly meetings Oct - June.
Collections: †Books and manuscripts, family heirlooms, large collection of portraits of Kentuckians.
Publications: Filson Club History Quarterly; Series 1 and Series 2 Publications (38 volumes).
Reference and Research Library: *Librn* Martin F Schmidt. Holdings: Vols 38,000; Other—Photographs.

JUNIOR ART GALLERY, 301 York St, 40203. Tel: 502-583-7062. *Exec Dir* Roberta L Williams.
Open Mon - Sat 9 AM - 5 PM; cl Sun and holidays. No admis.
Estab 1950 to develop understanding and appreciation of man's effort to communicate visually. The Gallery attempts to achieve this goal through exhibitions, workshops for adults and children, and special events. The Gallery is housed in the Louisville Free Public Library. There is a 1500 sq ft exhibition area. Five or six exhibitions a year of work by professional artists. Each exhibition is planned around a theme and in context

for special interest to school-age children as well as adults. Average Annual Attendance: 27,000. Mem: 81; dues $10.
Income: $64,500 (financed by membership, united arts fund, grants).
Collections: Small permanent collection consists of drawings, paintings, prints, sculptures, ceramics, photographs, textiles and other miscellaneous items.
Exhibitions: (1976) Third Dimension; New York Soho Contract 76; The Artist and the Idea; Down on the Farm; Quilt; A Change of Face; (1977) Made in Metal; Please Touch, II; The Fine Art of Fun; Between the Covers of Cricket Magazine; Made to Wear; (1977-78) Silkscreen on Linen; (1978) Printmaking.
Activities: Classes for adults and children; dramatic programs; docent training; lect open to public; gallery talks; tours; exten dept, staff member visits schools in area planning a visit to the Gallery; lending collection contains 6000 slides.

SOUTHERN BAPTIST SEMINARY,* Eisenberg Museum, 2825 Lexington Rd, 40206. Tel: 502-897-4011. *Cur* Dr E J Vardaman.
Open Mon - Sat 9:30 AM - 10 PM; cl Sun & National holidays. No admis. Estab 1961.
Collections: Religious materials from Caesarea, Machaerus; numismatics; archeology; glass; textiles; sculpture.
Publications: Biblical Museum, bulletin.
Activities: Guided tours; films.
Library: Open to the public and for inter-museum loan. Holdings: 200,000 vols. Other—Manuscripts.

J B SPEED ART MUSEUM, 2035 S Third St (Mailing Add: PO Box 8345, 40208). Tel: 502-637-1925. *Pres Bd Governors* Gen Dillman A Rash; *Dir & Cur* Addison Franklin Page; *Cur Asst & Registrar* Mary E Carver; *Communications Officer* Reva Crumpler; *Technician* William E Kruetzman.
Open Tues - Sat 10 AM - 4 PM; Thurs 10 AM - 10 PM; Sun 2 - 6 PM. No admis. Estab 1925 for the collection and exhibition of works of art of all periods and cultures, supported by a full special exhibition program and educational activities. Galleries are arranged to present painting, sculpture and decorative arts of all periods and cultures; special facilities for prints and drawings. Average Annual Attendance: 108,000. Mem: 2800; dues $15; annual meeting Jan.
Income: $350,000 (financed by endowment). Purchases: $2,000,000.
Collections: Comprehensive permanent collection.
Exhibitions: Retrospective of Paintings by Sam Gilliam; Matthew Boulton Silver; An Auditory Environment by Joe Moss; An Exhibition for Corporate Collecting; British Watercolors, A Golden Age 1750-1850; French 19th Century Landscape Watercolors; Ruskin and Venice.
Publications: Calendar, monthly; Bulletin, semiannually.
Activities: Classes for children; docent training; lect open to public, 10-12 vis lectr per yr; concerts; gallery talks; tours; competitions; individual paintings and original objects of art lent to members; lending collection contains paintings (200); museum shop selling books, original art, reproductions.
—**Art Reference Library.** *Librn* Frances Whitfield.
Open to public.
Holdings: Vols 12,000; Per subs 25; Other—Picture files.

UNIVERSITY OF LOUISVILLE
—**Allen R Hite Art Institute,** Belknap Campus, 40208. Tel: 502-588-6794. *Dir* Dario A Covi; *Secy* Dorothy Jared; *Art Librn* Gail R Gilbert.
Open by appointment. Estab 1935 for education and enrichment. Exhibition Gallery in preparation, expected opening Sept 1978.
Income: Financed by endowment, and state appropriation.
Collections: Paintings 100; †prints 650; drawings.
Publications: Exhibition catalogs, ocasionally.
Activities: Lect open to public; individual paintings lent to University offices.
—**Margaret M Bridwell Art Library.** Tel: 502-588-6741. *Head, Art Library* Gail R Gilbert; *Asst to Art Librn* Kathleen Moore.
Open Mon - Thurs 8 AM - 10 PM; Fri 8 AM - 5 PM; Sat 9 AM - 5 PM; Sun 2 - 10 PM. Estab 1956 to support the educational program of the art dept.
Income: Financed by endowment and state appropriation. Purchases: $33,200.
Holdings: Vols 32,000; Per subs 200; AV—Microfiche, microfilm, and phonorecords; Other—Clipping files, exhibition catalogs, manuscripts, original documents and prints.
Special Subjects: American Art and Architecture; Photography; German Gothic Sculpture.
Special Collections: Posters; original Christmas cards; original prints.
—**University of Louisville Photographic Archives.** *Cur* James C Anderson; *Asst Cur* David Horvath.
Open Mon - Fri 8:30 AM - Noon & 1 - 5 PM. Estab 1967 to collect, preserve, organize photographs and related materials; primary emphasis on documentary photography.
Income: Financed through the University.

Holdings: Vols 500; AV—Microfilm; Other—Clipping files, exhibition catalogs, and photographs.
Activities: Classes for adults and children; lect open to public; traveling exhibitions organized and circulated.
—Slide Collection. Tel: 502-588-5917. *Cur Slides* Ann S Coates; *Asst to Cur* Eileen Toutant.
Open Mon - Fri 8:30 - 4:30. Estab 1930's to provide comprehensive collection of slides for use in the University instructional program. 200,000 catalogued slides illustrating history of Western art. Circ: 30,000.
Holdings: AV—Kodacromes, slides; Other—Clipping files.
Special Subjects: Painting, architecture, sculpture, photography and design; furniture; pottery and porcelain.
Special Collections: Manuscript of Medieval Life; American Studies; Calligraphy.

MOREHEAD

MOREHEAD STATE UNIVERSITY, Claypool-Young Art Gallery,* 40351. Tel: 606-783-3232. *Head Dept Art* Dr Bill R Booth; *Secy* Brenda Whitt.
Open Mon - Fri 7 AM - 11 PM; Sat & Sun 1 - 4 PM. Estab 1922 to provide undergraduate and graduate programs in studio and art education; the department maintains an exhibition gallery for traveling exhibitions, faculty, and student work. The Claypool-Young Art Gallery is tri-level with 2344 sq ft of exhibition space.
Income: $4000 (financed by appropriation).
Collections: Establishing a permanent collection which to date consists principally of prints by major contemporary figures; several works added each year through purchase or bequest. Additions to lending collection include, The Maria Rilke Suite of lithographs by Ben Shahn consisting of 23 pieces; the Laus Pictorum Suite by Leonard Baskin, consisting of 14 pieces; and three lithographs by Thomas Hart Benton: Jesse James, Frankie and Johnny, and Huck Finn.
Exhibitions: A large number of one-man exhibitions along with invitational shows and group exhibits.
Activities: Lect open to the public, 5 vis lectr per yr; concerts; gallery talks; tours; competitions; individual paintings lent to schools; lending collection contains 200 items, prints, photographs; traveling exhibitions organized and circulated; student and faculty exhibitions to schools and libraries.
Library: Holdings—Vols 5000.

MURRAY

MURRAY STATE UNIVERSITY, Clara M Eagle Gallery, Price Doyle Fine Arts Center, 42071. Tel: 502-762-3784. *Chmn* Robert W Head; *Gallery Dir* Richard G. Jackson.
Open Mon - Fri 7:30 AM - 9 PM; Sat 10 AM - 4 PM; Sun 1 - 4 PM. No admis. Estab 1970, as an educational gallery, part of curriculum of Art Department; and to house the permanent collection of University. Two floors—first floor 100 x 40 ft Main Gallery; second floor divided into three small galleries that may be used as one or three. Average Annual Attendance: 100,000.
Income: Financed by state appropriation and grants.
Collections: Collection of Clara M Eagle Gallery; Harry L Jackson Print Collection; Asian Collection (given by Asian Cultural Exchange Foundation).
Exhibitions: Graphic Design Invitational; Metalsmithing and Jewelry Invitational; Local Light; Photography Made in Kentucky; Ivan Wilson (water colors); Dale Leys (drawings) Marvin Jones (prints); Phylis Alvec (weavings); Brent Kington and students in forged Ironwork; Bill Ranson (graphic design); Know What You See—A Smithsonian show on the Preservation and Restoration of Paintings; Ed Mayer (sculpture); Third Annual Magic Silver Show; Nore Winter (architect); Annual Juried Student Exhibition.
Publications: Posters and brochures for individual shows.
Activities: Classes for adults and children; films, visiting artists; lect open to public, 8 vis lectr per yr; gallery talks; tours; competitions; exten dept serving Jackson Purchase Area of Kentucky; individual paintings and original objects of art lent; traveling exhibitions organized and circulated.

PADUCAH

PADUCAH ART GUILD, 200 Broadway (Mailing Add: PO Box 634, 42001). Tel: 502-442-2453. *Pres* Jane Bright; *VPres* Ivva Istas; *Secy* Deane Scheffler; *Exhibit Chmn* Bob Evans; *Treas* Nancy Bottoms.
Open Tues - Sat Noon - 4 PM; Sun 1 - 5 PM. No admis. Estab 1957 to exhibit quality exhibitions of various art media. The gallery maintains 200 ft of wall space. Average Annual Attendance: 9000. Mem: 250-300; dues $10; meetings monthly first Mon.
Income: $11,000 (financed by membership and state appropriation).

Exhibitions: Exhibitions of the works of local and regional artists; traveling exhibitions.
Publications: Paducah Art Guild, (newsletter), monthly.
Activities: Classes for children; docent training, workshops; lectr open to the public, 5 vis lectr per yr; gallery talks; tours; awards given at annual juried crafts exhibit.

WILMORE

ASBURY COLLEGE, Student Center Gallery, Lexington Ave, 40390. Tel: 606-858-3511. *Head Art Dept* Ruby Medlock.
Open 1 - 9 PM. No admis. Estab 1976 for the purpose of exhibiting the works of national, local, and student artists. Carpeted walls, and tract lighting in a 20 x 20 ft space. Average Annual Attendance: 2000.
Publications: Newsletter.
Activities: Classes for children; dramatic programs; lect open to public, 6 vis lectr per yr; gallery talks; competitions.

LOUISIANA

ALEXANDRIA

CENTRAL LOUISIANA ART ASSOCIATION, INC,* PO Box 5791, 71301. *Pres* Mrs Cedric Lowery; *First VPres* Mrs Ward T Jones; *Second VPres* Mrs William J Defee; *Secy-Treas* Mr & Mrs Windsor P Thomas Jr; *Dir* Mrs Leonard Fuhrer.
Estab 1937 to foster art appreciation and to encourage development of artists; inc 1969. Average Annual Attendance: 15,000. Mem: 400, available in student, general, family, participating, contributing, sustaining, and patron status; annual meeting April.
Income: Purchases—Approximately $5500.
Exhibitions: Traveling exhibitions from American Federation of Arts, Smithsonian Institute, Artists Collections and Art Galleries.
Activities: Docent program; lectures and films; art workshops; members shows annually and Young People's shows.

BATON ROUGE

JAY R BROUSSARD MEMORIAL GALLERIES, Old State Capitol, Corner North Blvd & River Rd (Mailing Addr: PO Box 44247, 70804). Tel: 504-389-6291. *Dir* Albert B Head; *Exhib Coordinator* Charles Ford.
Open Mon - Sat 10 AM - 4:30 PM; Sun 1 - 5 PM. No admis. Estab 1938 to promote contemporary art throughout the State. Average Annual Attendance: 85,000.
Income: $30,000 (financed by state appropriation). Purchases: $2,000.
Exhibitions: Annual competitions; Photography (in Spring); Professional Artists (in Fall); Amateur Artist (in Spring); International Watercolor Exhibition.
Publications: Exhibition catalogs.

LOUISIANA ARTS AND SCIENCE CENTER, 100 S River Rd (Mailing Add: PO Box 3373, 70821). Tel: 504-344-9463. *Pres Bd Trustees* Lee Griffin; *Dir* Mrs Allan R Brent; *Asst to Dir* Harold Arbour; *Mus Cur* Edith Kleinpeter.
Open Tues - Sat 10 AM - 5 PM; Sun 1 - 5 PM; cl Mon. Admis Planetarium only: children 50¢, adults $1. Estab 1960. General museum—art, history, and science. Average Annual Attendance: 200,000; dues $2 - $250.
Income: Financed by membership, city appropriation and donations.
Collections: †Ivan Mestrovic sculpture; Francois Brochet sculpture; Eskimo soapstone carvings and graphics; †Lynn Lennon, Richard Balzer, Turner Browne photography collections; Tibetan Religious Art; Graphics; North American Indian Crafts.
Exhibitions: (1976-77) Pitseolak: A Retrospective; One with the Earth; Russian Space Art.
Publications: Happenings, Heavenly Facts, quarterly; Planetarium Schedule Brochure; Newsletter.
Activities: Educ dept, docent training; school tours; lect for members only and in-service workshops for teachers, 3 vis lectr per yr; sales shop selling reproductions, handicrafts, local pottery, Eskimo carvings.
Library: Small reference library open to staff only.

LOUISIANA STATE UNIVERSITY
—Anglo-American Art Museum, 114 Memorial Tower, 70803. Tel: 504-388-4003. *Pres* Frank W Wurzlow, Jr; *Secy* John C Fisher; *Dir* Oscar G Richard; *Cur* H Parrott Bacot.
Open Mon - Fri 8 AM - Noon & 12:30 - 4:30 PM; Sat 9 AM - Noon & 1 - 4 PM; Sun 1 - 4 PM. No admis. Estab 1959 to serve as a constant reminder of the major cultural heritage the United States received from the British People. Two temporary galleries house loan exhibitions and local art work. Average Annual Attendance: 25,000. Mem: 400; dues $10 - $25; meeting twice year.

Income: Financed by endowment, membership.
Collections: †Collection of English and American decorative arts, paintings and drawings and watercolors; largest public collection of early New Orleans made silver; largest collection of early Baton Rouge subjects; largest collection of graphic works of Hogarth and Caroline Durieux.
Exhibitions: (1976-78) Historic and American Glass; Masterpieces of Colonial and Early Republic Period American Art; Anglo American Decorative Arts in the French Taste; William and Ellsworth Woodward; Gross Silver Collection; Caroline Durieux Show; Hudson River Valley School and Its Influence; Harold Young Photography Show; Jacob Epstein Sculpture.
Publications: Newsletter; catalogs—Louisiana Folk Art, Louisiana Landscape, Southern Furniture and Silver: The Federal Period 1788-1830, Nineteenth Century Natchez Made Silver, Sail and Stream in Louisiana Waters and Paintings, Prints and Drawing in the Anglo-American Art Museum.
Activities: Lect, 2 vis lectr per yr; gallery talks; tours; competitions; traveling exhibitions organized and circulated; sales shop.
Library: For reference. Holdings; Vols 600; Per subs 7. Special Subjects: Anglo-American decorative arts, paintings and drawings.
—**Union Art Gallery,** PO Box BU, 70803. Tel: 504-388-5117. *Art Dir* Judith R Stahl.
Open daily 9 AM - 9 PM. Estab 1964, designed for exhibitions for university and community interests; gallery is centrally located on the main floor of the LSU Union, with 1725 sq ft. Average Annual Attendance: 55,000.
Publications: Brochures for local exhibitions, quarterly.
Activities: Lect open to the public, 2 vis lectr per yr; free art films.
Library: Photography collection.
—**Department of Fine Arts.**Tel: 504-388-5402. *Head Dept* Walter E Rutkowski.
Open Daily 8 AM - 5 PM. No admis. Estab 1934 for special exhibitions planned by faculty committee. Circulates exhibitions of student's arts consisting of 30 to 40 works by Louisiana State University students. Department collection of contemporary graphic works, prints and drawings. Average Annual Attendance: 10,000.
Activities: Lectures; gallery talks.

JENNINGS

ZIGLER MUSEUM, 411 Clara St, 70546. Tel: 318-824-0114. *Chmn Bd Trustees* Mrs. C A Storer; *Pres Bd Trustees* Joe V Black; *Dir* Donn C Allison; *Cur for Promotions & Public Relations* Mrs Donn C Allison.
Open Tues - Fri 10 AM - Noon & 2 - 5 PM; Sat & Sun 2 - 5 PM; cl Mon. No admis. Estab 1963 to create an art gallery and cultural center for Southwest Louisiana. West Wing has permanent collection of American and European paintings and sculptures; East Wing contains nine dioramas of Southwest Louisiana wild life. Central Galleries are reserved for a new art exhibit each month. Average Annual Attendance: 12,000.
Income: $37,500 (financed by endowment). Purchases: $35,000.
Collections: Art by Reynolds, Pearce, Pissarro, Robert Wood, Constable, Crane, Sloan, Gay, Chierici, Whistler, Vergne, Frank Smith, Heldner, Gustave Wolff, George Inness, George Inness Jr, Bierstadt and more; Sculpture by Charles Parks and Euphemia Glover.
Exhibitions: Twenty-four Louisiana Artists.
Publications: Flyer, monthly.
Activities: Docent training; lect open to public.

LAFAYETTE

UNIVERSITY OF SOUTHWESTERN LOUISIANA
—**Art Center for Southwestern Louisiana,** PO Drawer 4-4290, University of Southwestern Louisiana Station, 70504. Tel: 318-232-1169. *Dir* Frances Love *Dir Foundation* M L Moore; *Pres Foundation* J Rayburn Bertrand; *Special Projects* Claudia Trevithick; *Secy* Marguerite Landry.
Open Mon - Fri 10 AM - 5 PM; Sun 2 - 5 PM; cl Sat. No admis. Estab 1968 as an art museum, for education and entertainment. First floor: permanent collection. Average Annual Attendance: 25,000. Mem: 1500; dues $25 - $400.
Collections: Paintings by 19th & 20th century American artists; †Hand engraved silver, bronze, and copper intaglios; †American slag glass; †ceramics and sculpture.
Exhibitions: America Through European Eyes: the Graphic Image; Haiti: Voodoo Art; Victorian Decorative Arts in Louisiana (1837-1901).
Publications: Newsletter, every other month; major catalogs, 1 or 2 a year.
Activities: Classes for adults and children; docent training; lect open to public, 25-50 vis lectr per yr; concerts; gallery talks; tours; competitions; exten dept serving Lafayette parish schools; individual paintings and original objects of art lent; traveling exhibitions organized and circulated; museum shop selling books, original art, prints, catalogs and postcards.

—**Union Art Gallery,** PO Box 4-2611, 70504. Tel: 318-233-3850, exten 779. *Dir Student Union* Glenn Menaro; *Dir Programming* Julie Calzand; *Program Advisors* Martha Hoover & Earnie Dannials; *Craftshop Dir* Michael Flaherty.
Open Mon - Fri 10 AM - 4 PM, and by appointment. No admis. Estab 1970 to expose the area and the campus to new ideas through the arts. The Gallery has 1500 sq ft of floor area and 153 running feet of wall space. Average Annual Attendance: 12,000.
Exhibitions: Lee J Sonniel; Dutch Kepler; Allan Jones; Annual Faculty Show; Bi-Annual student show; Tom Secrest; Herman M Hire; Charles Richardson; Gene Koss; David Wortman; Julie Pacaro; David Fox; The Graphics Group.
Publications: Gallery schedule, each semester.
Activities: Classes for adults and children; lect open to public; sales shop selling books, magazines and reproductions; junior museum.
Library: Dupre Library, St Mary St. Open to the public.

LAKE CHARLES

IMPERIAL CALCASIEU MUSEUM, 204 W Sallier St, 70601. Tel: 318-439-3797. *Dir* Amy S Boyd; *Staff Member* Bonnie Mae Smith; *Staff Member* Elizabeth Schidler.
Open Mon - Fri 10 AM - Noon & 2 - 5 PM; Sun 2 - 5 PM. No admis. Estab March 1963 by the Junior League of Lake Charles and housed in City Hall. After several moves in location, it is now housed in a building of Louisiana Colonial architecture which incorporates in its structure old bricks, beams, balustrades, and columns taken from demolished old homes. In December 1966 administration was assumed by The Fine Arts Center and Museum of Old Imperial Calcasieu Museum, Inc, with a name change in 1971. Site of the building was chosen for its historic value, having been owned by the Charles Sallier family, the first white settler on the lake, and the town named for him. The museum depicts the early history of the area. Average Annual Attendance: 10,000.
Income: Financed by membership.
Exhibitions: Special exhibitions four times a year, with smaller exhibits by other organizations at times; exhibits depict typical rooms of early era.
Activities: Classes for children; tours; lending collection contains original prints; shop selling books and museum stationery.
Gibson Library: Open to the public.

MONROE

TWIN CITY ART FOUNDATION,* Masur Museum of Art, 1400 S Grand St, 71201. Tel: 318-387-3525. *Chmn* Fred Westrom; *Secy* Jean Taylor; *Dir* U Schmidt; *Secy* Carolyn McGough.
Open Tues - Thurs 10 AM - 6 PM; Fri 1 - 4 PM; Sat & Sun 2 - 5 PM. No admis. Estab 1963 to encourage art in all media, to enrich the cultural climate of this area; gallery has 500 running ft hanging space. Average Annual Attendance: 5000. Mem: 250; dues $10, $25, $100.
Income: $46,000 (financed by membership and appropriations). Purchases $3000.
Collections: †Contemporary art all media, approximately 100 works.
Publications: Brochures of shows, monthly.
Activities: Classes for adults and children; lect open to the public, 4 vis lectr per yr; tours; competitions; presentation of programs to the public.
Library: Holdings—Vols 30.

NEW IBERIA

SHADOWS-ON-THE-TECHE,* 117 E Main St (Mailing Add: PO Box 254, 70560). Tel: 318-369-6446. *Adminr & Property Council & Staff of National Trust Interpretors* Letitia Galbraith; *Coordr Interpretive Programs* Carole T Scanlon.
Open daily 9 AM - 4:30 PM, cl Christmas. Admis adults $1.50, senior citizens 50¢, group rates available. The Shadows is a property of the National Trust for Historic Preservation. Preserved as a historic house museum; operated as a community preservation center, it is a National Historic Landmark. Average Annual Attendance: 25,000.
A townhouse on the Bayou Teche, it faces the main street of modern New Iberia, but is surrounded by three acres of landscaped gardens shaded by live oaks. Built in 1831, the Shadows represents a Louisiana adaptation of classical revival architecture. Fashionable balls and masquerades as well as everyday activities are reflected in the possessions of five generations of the Weeks family on display in the house. The property fell into ruin after the Civil War but was restored during the 1920's by Weeks Hall, great grandson of the builder. Mr Hall revived the spark of antebellum hospitality at the Shadows, entertaining such celebrities as W C Fields, Mae West, and H L Mencken. Mr Hall bequeathed the Shadows to the National Trust in 1958.
The house contains furnishings typical of those owned by a planter's family between 1830 and 1865. Collection includes two fine paintings by Louisiana itinerant artist Adrian Persac (1857-72) as well as paintings by the donor, Weeks Hall.

Property serves as a focal point for advancement of historic preservation. It develops new relationships among cultural community preservation groups and National Trust members in its area. Responds to community preservation needs by acting as a link between community and appropriate regional or headquarters offices of National Trust.
Activities: Interpretive programs which are related to the Shadows particular historic preservation program; community produced programs include Sugar Cane Festival and sidewalk art show; Members Day during National Historic Preservation Week, in early May.

NEW ORLEANS

HISTORIC NEW ORLEANS COLLECTION, Kemper and Leila Williams Foundation, 533 Royal St, 70130. Tel: 504-523-7146. *Chmn Bd* Benjamin W Yancey; *Dir* Stanton M Frazar; *Asst Dir* Dr Robert D Bush; *Chief Cur* Mrs Ralph V Platou; *Assoc Cur* John Mahe; *Asst Cur* Rosanne McCaffrey; *Asst to Cur* John Lawrence; *Registrar* Charlotte Chatlain; *Asst Registrar* Lisette Carriere; *Dir Documents* Ellen Leaman.
Open Tues - Sat 10 AM - 4:30 PM. No admis to Gallery; admis to Williams Residence and ten gallery tour by guide $1. Building constructed in 1927 by Jean Francois Merieult; recently renovated by Koch and Wilson to accommodate the 11 galleries which house a collection of paintings, prints, documents, books and artifacts relating to the history of Louisiana from the time of its settlement, gathered over a number of years by the late L Kemper Williams and his wife; the foundation was established with private funds to keep it intact. Average Annual Attendance: 50,000.
Income: Financed by endowment.
Collections: †Prints, maps, drawings, photographs, paintings and three-dimensional objects. Alfred R and William Waud drawings of Civil War and post-War; James Gallier, Sr and Jr, architectural drawings (1830-1870); Morris Henry Hobbs prints (c 1940); B Lafon drawings of fortifications; 1814; B Simon lithographs of 19th century businesses.
Exhibitions: Caroline Durieux Retrospective (20th century print master); Mardi Gras Indians (video presentation); Morgan Whitney (early 20th century photographer and collector); New Orleans sculpture and monuments; John Chase, political cartoonist; To Market, To Market (New Orleans' markets and street vendors); Boyd Cruise Retrospective (New Orleans watercolorist); Americanization of New Orleans, 1830-50; Degrees of Discovery (cartography).
Publications: Monograph series; exhibition catalogs and brochures.
Activities: Docent training; lect open to public; tours; competitions; individual paintings and original objects of art lent to museums, institutions, foundations, libraries and research centers; lending collection contains books 5500, motion pictures 70, original prints 2000, paintings 200, photographs 8000, sculpture 100, rare pamphlets 4500, and maps 400; traveling exhibitions organized and circulated; sales shop selling books, original art, reproductions and prints.
—**Library.** *Librn* Kenneth T Urquhart.
Open to researchers.
Holdings: Vols 5500; Per subs 100; Other—Rare pamphlets 4500.
Special Collections: Archives Division: unique textural sources on New Orleans and Louisiana history and culture, with broadsides, newspapers, sheet music and libretti.

LAMPE GALLERY OF FINE ART, Lampe School of Art, 3920 Old Gentilly Rd, 70126. Tel: 504-949-6387. *Co-Owners* Frederick and June Lampe.
Open Mon, Tues, Thurs, Fri 10 AM - 5:30 PM; Sat 10 AM - 3 PM; cl Wed. No admis. Estab 1968 to teach art and art appreciation. Restoration of old paintings. Collectors works such as L Icart; engravings; Calder; Renoir; European paintings; features June Lampe originals. Mem: 100; dues $20 to $30 monthly.
Collections: L Icart; Clementine Hunter; June Lampe.
Exhibitions: L Icart Etchings; Permanent Gallery for June Lampe.
Activities: Classes for adults and children; tours; museum shop selling original art, reproductions, prints, museum replicas in sculpture, jewelry.

LOUISIANA HISTORICAL ASSOCIATION, Confederate Museum, 929 Camp St, 70130. Tel: 405-523-4522. *Pres* Hubert Humphreys; *Chmn Memorial Hall Committee* Maj Henry Morris; *VChmn Memorial Hall Committee* Bernard E Eble; *Cur* Belinda Reuther.
Open Mon - Sat 10 AM - 4 PM. Admis adults $1, children 50¢. Estab 1891 to collect and display articles, memorabilia and records from Louisiana history and particularly the era surrounding the Civil War. The gallery is maintained in a one story brick building; one main hall paneled in Cypress, one side hall containing paintings of Civil War figures and display cases containing artifacts. Average Annual Attendance: 13,000. Mem: 2000; dues $8; annual meeting Mar.
Income: Financed by membership and admissions.
Publications: Louisiana Historical Association Newsletter; Louisiana History, quarterly.

Activities: Lect open to the public; competitions; sales shop selling books, reproductions and novelties.

LOUISIANA STATE MUSEUM, 751 Chartres St, 70118. Tel: 504-581-4321. *Dir* Robert R Macdonald; *Adminr* Freida Morford; *Chief Cur* Vaughn Glasgow; *Chief Cur* John R Kemp.
Open Tues - Sun 8:30 AM - 5 PM. Admis adults $1; students 50¢, children under 12 free. Estab 1906 to collect, preserve and interpret historical documents relative to the history of Louisiana. Eight historical buildings in the French Quarter, four of which are open to the public; they contain both permanent installations and changing exhibition galleries. Average Annual Attendance: 250,000.
Income: $1,200,000 (financed by city appropriation).
Collections: †Paintings; †photographs; †furniture; †decorative arts; †costumes and textiles; †industrial artifacts; †prints; †books; †archival collections; †maps.
Exhibitions: Louisiana from Colony to State, 1699-1812; Savoir Faire: French Tastes in Louisiana; Louisiana Images; 1880-1920; France Views America; Louisiana's Black Heritage.
Activities: Classes for children; docent training; lect open to public, 6 vis lectr per yr; tours; competitions; individual paintings and original objects of art lent to institutions; traveling exhibitions organized and circulated; sales shop selling books, original art, reproductions and prints.
Library: Louisiana Historical Center Library. *Librn* Rose Lambert. Open to the public for reference. Holdings: Vols 30,000; Other—Pamphlets, newspapers.

NEW ORLEANS MUSEUM OF ART, Isaac Delgado Museum, Stern Auditorium, Wisner Education Wing, Lelong Ave, City Park (Mailing Add: PO Box 19123, 70179). Tel: 504-488-2631. *Pres* Mrs Richard B Kaufmann; *First VPres* J Thomas Lewis; *Second VPres* Mrs Frederick Muller Jr; *Secy* Richard A Peneguy; *Treas* Prescott N Dunbar; *Dir* E John Bullard; *Sr Cur Coll* William Fagaly; *Cur Decorative Arts* Pamela P Bardo; *Registrar* Charles Mo; *Research Cur* Joan G Caldwell; *Sr Cur Educ* Annabelle Hebert; *Cur Educ* Ann Henderson; *Asst Cur Educ* David Swoyer; *Asst Cur Educ* Alice Yelen; *Cur Prints* Valerie Loupe; *Cur Photography* Tina Freeman; *Adminr* Barbara Neiswender.
Open Tues, Wed, Fri - Sun 10 AM - 5 PM; Thurs 1 - 9 PM; cl Mon. Admis adults (18-65) $1.00, children (12-18) 50¢; Thursday free. Estab 1911; building given to city by Isaac Delgado, maintained by municipal funds to provide a stimulus to a broader cultural life for the entire community. Stern Auditorium, Ella West Freeman wing for changing exhibitions; Wisner Education wing for learning experiences; Delgado Building for permanent display; Hyams Room for Barbizon and late 19th century Salon Painting. Average Annual Attendance: 150,000. Mem: 10,000; dues $15-$1000; annual meeting Nov.
Income: Financed by membership, city appropriation and federal grants.
Collections: †Old Master paintings of various schools; Samuel H Kress Collection of Renaissance masterpieces; †Pre-Columbian masterworks; †Latin American colonial painting and sculpture; Stern-Davis Collection of Peruvian colonial painting; †19th & 20th century American art; 19th & 20th century Louisiana painting and furniture; †Victor Kiam Collection of Fauve and Surrealist paintings; Japanese painting of the Edo period; †African art; †photography; †graphics; Latter-Schlesinger Collection of portrait miniatures.
Exhibitions: The America of Currier & Ives; Sculpture: American Directions, 1945-1975; Edvard Munch; Artists Biennial Winners; Modern Argentine Drawings; Nanga and Zenga Paintings; Five from Louisiana; Navajo Weavings; Sheila Isham; Judaica; Artists Biennial; Treasures of Tutankhamen.
Publications: Arts Quarterly; catalogs of exhibitions.
Activities: Classes for children; docent training; lect open to public, 20 vis lectr per yr; concerts; gallery talks; tours; competitions; individual paintings and original objects of art lent to museums; traveling exhibitions organized and circulated; museum shop selling books, original art, reproductions, prints, cards, toys and jewelry.
—**Felix J Dreyfous Library.** *Librn* Darla H Rushing.
Open to staff and members; to general public by appointment.
Holdings: Vols 5000; Per subs 53; Other—Slide Collection.

NEW ORLEANS PUBLIC LIBRARY, Art, Music and Recreation Division, 219 Loyola Ave, 70140. Tel: 504-586-4938. *Head Librn* Marilyn Wilkins; *Librn* Bess Loyd; *Library Assocs* Joe Clark and Pat Green.
Open Mon - Fri 9 AM - 9 PM; Sat 9 AM - 5 PM. Estab 1896. There is a collection of some 738 prints for circulation. The Community Relations Division of the library is in charge of the exhibit area used for exhibiting a wide scope of art shows. Circ: 1,305,513.
Income: $2,677,701 (financed by city appropriation). Purchases: $2,610,701.
Holdings: Vols 795,165; Per subs 1356; AV—Cassettes, motion pictures, phonorecords, extensive picture file; Other—Clipping files, framed reproductions, original art works.

Special Collections: Historical sheet music collection; historical golden age record collection.
Exhibitions: Community Relations Division of the New Orleans Public Library handles exhibits on the bridge area.
Publications: Library programming published monthly in Irons in the Fire, put out by Community Relations Division of Library.
Activities: Classes for adults and children; dramatic programs; lect open to public; concerts; tours; competitions.

TULANE UNIVERSITY
—**Newcomb Art Department Exhibition Gallery,** 60 Newcomb Pl, 70118. Tel: 504-865-4631. *Chmn Art Dept* Pat Trivigno.
Open daily 9 AM - 4:30 PM.
Exhibitions: Exhibitions as an integral part of the Art Department Program.
—**Architecture Library,** Division of Howard Tilton Library. *Librn* Elizabeth Gaudit Lockett.
Holdings: Vols 2500; other—Slides 3000, prints, photographs.
Special Collections: Extensive file of pictorial material, including architectural photographs relating to New Orleans; a small working reference library of architectural material is maintained in Stanely Thomas Hall, the School of Architecture quarters.

UNIVERSITY OF NEW ORLEANS FINE ARTS GALLERY,* Lake Front Dr, 70122. Tel: 504-288-3161, exten 493. *Chmn Fine Arts* Peggy P McDowell; *Secy* Molly Matthews; *Gallery Dir* Doyle J Gertjejansen.
Open Mon - Fri 8 AM - 4:30 PM. No admis. Estab August 1974 to expose the students and community to historic and contemporary visual arts; gallery consists of 1800 sq ft, 112 lineal ft of wall space, 20 ft ceilings, natural and artificial lighting.
Income: Financed by state appropriation.

PORT ALLEN

WEST BATON ROUGE MUSEUM, 845 N Jefferson Ave, 70767. Tel: 504-383-2392. *Pres & Dir Art Exhib* Evelyn B Terrill; *Chmn Empire Bedroom Coll* Mrs P Chauvin Wilkinson; *Cur* Mrs Michael Cutshaw; *Custodian* Mrs George Lefebre; *Asst Custodian* Dorothy Landry; *Exhib Chmn* Mrs John Hill.
Open Tues - Sat 10 AM - 4:30 PM. No admis. Estab 1968, Museum opened 1970, to foster interest in history, particularly that of West Baton Rouge Parish, to encourage research, collection, and preservation of material illustrating past and present activities of the parish, to operate one or more museums, to receive gifts and donations, to accept exhibits and historical materials on loan. One room housing a collection of American Empire (c 1840) bed room furniture; a large room housing a parish relief map, and parish memorabilia, two old printing presses; a room 31 x 40 ft for art exhibits. Average Annual Attendance: 6000. Mem: 275; dues $5; annual meeting January.
Income: $25,000 (financed by membership and gifts).
Collections: †Empire bedroom furnishings; †art collection of parish artists; †parish artifacts; †Newcomb pottery; †needlework; old duck decoys.
Exhibitions: Antique Louisiana Silver; Children's Exhibit of Old Dolls and Trains; Old Louisiana Duck Decoys; Carnival Glass; George Rodrigue's Cajun Paintings; Newcomb Pottery; Professional Artists's Competition; America through European Eyes: The Graphic Image; Stained Glass Ornaments; Sculptures of West Feliciana Pioneers; Multi Media Show.
Publications: Écoutez, twice a year.
Activities: Gallery talks; tours; competitions; sales shop selling books, postcards, needlework.

SHREVEPORT

LOUISIANA STATE EXHIBIT MUSEUM,* 3015 Greenwood Rd, 71109. Tel: 318-635-2323. *Dir* Heber E Long.
Open 9 AM - 5 PM; Sun 1 - 5 PM. No admis. Estab 1939 to display permanent and temporary exhibitions demonstrating the state's history, resources and natural beauty; art gallery maintained. Average Annual Attendance: 600,000.
Income: Financed by state appropriation.
Collections: Murals; dioramas; historical relics; archaeology; glass; china; coins; Indian artifacts.
Exhibitions: About 15 a year by local and regional art groups and artists; also ceramic and china painting shows.
Publications: History of Art; brochures.
Activities: Art workshops; films; concerts.

R W NORTON ART GALLERY, 4747 Creswell Ave (Mailing Add: PO Box 6760, 71106). Tel: 318-865-4201. *Pres of the Bd* Mrs Richard W Norton, Jr; *Secy-Registr* Jerry M Bloomer; *Bldg & Grounds Supt* Frank Todaro; *VPres of the Bd* A W Coon.

Open Tues - Sun 1 - 5 PM; cl Mon & holidays. No admis. Estab 1946, opened 1966. Founded to present aspects of the development of American and European art and culture through exhibition and interpretation of fine works of art and literature, both from the Gallery's own collections and from those of other institutions and individuals. Average Annual Attendance: 25,000.
Collections: Large collections of paintings and sculpture by Western American artists Frederic Remington and Charles M Russell; paintings and sculpture relating to early American history; †paintings by 19th century American artists of the Hudson River School; portraits of famous Confederate leaders; American miniatures and Colonial silver; European paintings, sculpture, 16th century Flemish tapestries, and large collection of Wedgwood pottery.
Exhibitions: (1976) Carolyn Wyeth Retrospective; Portrait Miniatures in Early American History: 1750-1840; The Destiny of the Red Man by A A Weinman; Stow Wengenroth: Artist-Lithographer; American Sculpture: a Tenth Anniversary Exhibition; 9th Annual Christmas Exhibition; (1977) Felix Kelly; Sculpture by Jacob Epstein; Paintings of the Old West by Frank McCarthy; The Esmark Collection of Currier & Ives; 10th Annual Christmas Exhibition; (1978) The Gross Collection of Irish, English & Continental Silver; English Delftware from the Morgan Collection; 11th Annual Christmas Exhibition.
Publications: Announcements of special exhibitions; catalogs (32 through 1978).
Activities: Educ dept; docent training; lectures open to public; gallery talks; tours; museum shop selling magazines, slides, exhibition catalogs; catalogs of permanent collection.
—**Library.** Tel: 318-865-4201. *Librn* Jerry M Bloomer; *Asst Librn* Eva W Moses.
Open Wed & Sat 1 - 5 PM. Estab 1946 to acquire and make available for public use on the premises, important books, exhibition catalogs, etc relating to the visual arts, literature, American history, and genealogy, as well as other standard reference and bibliographic works for reference only.
Income: Financed by endowment. Purchases: $10,700.
Holdings: Vols 6000; Per subs 125; AV—Microfilm, slides; Other—Clipping files, exhibition catalogs, manuscripts, memorabilia, original documents, pamphlets, photographs.
Special Subjects: Fine arts, literature, history, and bibliography; rare books and atlases; ornithological works by J J Audubon (elephant folio edition of Birds of America) and John Gould (complete set).
Special Collections: James M Owens Memorial Collection of Early Americana (725 volumes on Colonial history, particularly on Virginia).

MAINE

AUGUSTA

UNIVERSITY OF MAINE AT AUGUSTA GALLERY, University Heights, 04330. Tel: 207-622-7131. *Dir* Patricia McGraw Anderson.
Open Mon - Thurs 9 AM - 9 PM; Fri 9 AM - 5 PM. No admis. Estab 1970 to provide changing exhibitions of the visual arts for the university students and faculty and for the larger Augusta/Kennebec Valley community; the principal exhibition area is a two level combination lounge and gallery. Average Annual Attendance: 9000.
Income: Financed by university budget.
Collections: Paintings, drawings, prints and sculpture by students and faculty.
Exhibitions: (1977-78) Winslow Horner Graphics; Portrait of Augusta by Craig Stevens (contemporary photography); Paul Martin Paintings and Drawings; Six Maine Women Printmakers; Annual Student Show; Union of Maine Visual Artists' Juried Exhibition.
Activities: Lect open to the public, 2 - 3 vis lectr per yr; gallery talks; tours.

BATH

BATH MARINE MUSEUM, 963 Washington St, 04530. Tel: 207-443-6311. *Pres* Ralph L Snow; *Asst Cur* Marnee Lilly; *Asst Cur Exhib* Nathan Lipfert.
Open daily 10 AM - 5 PM (mid-May - mid-Oct). Admis adults $3.00 - $3.75; under 16 $1.00 - $1.25; under 6 free. Estab 1964 for the preservation of Maine's maritime heritage. Average Annual Attendance: 30,000. Mem: 1100; dues $10 and up; annual meeting Oct.
Income: $250,000 (financed by membership, gifts and grants).
Collections: Ships portraits and seascapes.
Publications: Long Reach Log, quarterly.
Activities: Docent training; lect open to public; individual paintings and original objects of art lent; museum shop selling books, reproductions, prints and related novelties.
—**Library/Archives.** *Cur Emeritus* Harold Brown.

Holdings: Vols 5000; Per subs 5; AV—Kodachromes and slides; Other—Clipping files, memorabilia, original art works, original documents, pamphlets, photographs.
Special Subjects: Maine maritime history, especially shipbuilding.
Special Collections: Photographs of vessels built in Bath; marine paintings; ship models; navigational instruments; shipbuilding tools.
Exhibitions: Permanent and changing exhibits concerned with Maine's maritime history.

BLUE HILL

PARSON FISHER HOUSE, Jonathan Fisher Memorial, Inc, 04614. Tel: 207-374-2780. *Pres* William P Hinckley.
Open Tues & Fri 2 - 5 PM; Sat 10 AM - Noon (summer only). Admis 50¢. Estab 1954 to preserve the home and memorabilia of Jonathan Fisher. The house was designed and built by him in 1815. Average Annual Attendance: 300. Mem: 320; dues $2; annual meeting August.
Income: Financed by endowment and membership.
Collections: Paintings, manuscripts, furniture and articles made by Fisher.

BOOTHBAY HARBOR

BOOTHBAY REGION ART GALLERY, Brick House, Oak St, 04538. Tel: 207-633-2703. *Pres* Lina Burley; *VPres* Ruth Gardner; *Secy* Ruth Potter; *Treas* William Burley.
Open Mon - Sat 11 AM - 5 PM; Sun 2 - 5 PM (July 1 through Sept 15). Admis 25¢. Estab 1966. Originated to help develop an art curriculum in the local schools, presently functions to bring art of the region's artists to enrich the culture of the community. Located in historic Brick House, built in 1807; two exhibition rooms on the first floor, and two on the second, one of which features prints, drawings and small watercolors. Average Annual Attendance: 3000. Mem: 475; dues $1 - $25; annual meeting Oct.
Income: Financed by membership.
Exhibitions: Summer shows by regional artists.
Activities: Classes for adults.

BRUNSWICK

BOWDOIN COLLEGE, Museum of Art & Peary-MacMillan Arctic Museum, 04011. Tel: 207-725-8731, exten 275. *Dir* Katharine J Watson; *Admin Asst to Dir* Lynn C Yanok; *Cur* Margaret B Clunie; *Secy to Dir* Brenda Pelletier; *Museum Receptionist & Shop Mgr* Mary Poppe.
Open Tues - Fri 10 AM - 4 PM; Sat 10 AM - 5 PM; Sun 2 - 5 PM; cl Mon & holidays. No admis. Estab Museum of Art 1894, Peary-MacMillan Arctic Museum 1967. The Walker Art Building, designed by McKim, Mead and White, houses a collection begun in 1811 by the bequest of James Bowdoin III. There are eight galleries housing the permanent collection and one for temporary exhibitions. Average Annual Attendance: 50,000. Mem: 800.
Collections: Colonial and Federal portraits by Smibert, Feke, Copley, and Stuart; Old Master prints and drawings; the Warren Collection of classical antiquities; the Winslow Homer Collection and memorabilia; the Molinari Collection of coins, medals and plaquettes; 19th & 20th century works by Thomas Eakins, Martin Johnson Heade, George Inness, Robert Henri, John Sloan and Leonard Baskin.
Exhibitions: The Ancient Collection; Spirit of the New Landscape; Daniel Putnam Brinley: The Impressionist Years.
Publications: Contemporary Photographers: The Persistence of Vision; Colonial and Federal Portraits at Bowdoin College; Ernest Haskell (1876-1925); Howard Warshaw: A Decade of Murals; Medals and Plaquettes from the Molinari Collection; Photographs: John McKee; Recent Figure Sculpture; many more.
Activities: Docent training; concerts; gallery talks; tours; individual paintings and original objects of art lent to qualified institutions; museum shop selling books, magazines, original art, reproductions, prints, slides and jewelry.

CAMDEN

GALLERY OF STELL AND SHEVIS,* 82 Elm St, 04843. Tel: 207-236-4290. *Dir* William A Shevis; *Asst Dir* Stell Shevis.
Open June 15 - Oct 15 Mon - Sat & holidays 10 AM - 5 PM. No admis.
Collections: Folk arts; prints; sculpture; paintings.
Activities: Temporary exhibitions; sales shop selling handcrafts and folk art.

DEER ISLE

HAYSTACK MOUNTAIN SCHOOL OF CRAFTS GALLERY,* 04627. Tel: 207-348-2816. *Chmn of Board* Jack Lenor Larsen; *Pres* Charles R Gailis; *Secy* Ethel Clifford; *Dir* Francis S Merritt; *Treas* Roger W Harding.
Open Sat & Sun, June - Sept. Estab 1950, for research and instruction in crafts and related extension services of exhibitions, consultation and conferences; gallery maintained for continuous summer exhibition of important American and other national craftsmen. Average Annual Attendance: 2500.
Income: $100,000 (financed by tuition income plus annual donations).
Collections: †American ceramics and †jewelry.
Publications: Annual brochure.
Activities: Educational department, 12-week summer session in ceramics, graphics, glass, jewelry, weaving and photography; lectures; gallery talks; national extension dept; original objects of art lent; crafts and slide material to schools, galleries and museums; lending collection contains Kodachromes 1000; traveling exhibitions organized and circulated; schol.
Reference library: Holdings—Vols 500; Other—Kodachrome 1000.

ELLSWORTH

COLONEL BLACK MANSION, 04605. Tel: 207-667-8671. *Pres* Col Haskell Cleaves; *Secy* Mrs Morton C Whitcomb.
Open June 1 - Oct 15 Mon - Sat 10 AM - 5 PM; cl Sun. Admis $1. Historical mansion operated by the Hancock County Trustees of Public Reservations. Average Annual Attendance: 5500. Mem: 225; annual meeting second Tues August.
Collections: Authentic period furniture, china, glass and decorative objects in their fine original setting.
Activities: Guided tours.

HALLOWELL

KENNEBEC VALLEY ART ASSOCIATION, Harlow Gallery, 160 Water St, (Mailing Add: PO Box 213, 04347). *Pres* Florence Daly; *Exhibit Chmn* Adele Nichols; *VPres* Dr Meyer Emanuel; *Treas* Madge Ames.
Open Tues - Sat 1 - 5 PM; Sun 2 - 4 PM; cl Mon. No admis. Estab 1963 to foster an interest in and appreciation of fine art. Single gallery on ground level, having central entrance and two old storefront windows which provide window display space, peg board covering walls, with two large display screens providing extra display area. Average Annual Attendance: 600 - 700. Mem: Approx 100; dues $5; annual meeting first Mon January.
Income: $5000 (financed by membership and donations).
Exhibitions: (1976-78) Needle Arts Show; Francis Hamabe (paintings); Members Show; Invitational Show I, Invitational Show II; Roderick Dew/Ellsworth Greene (pen and ink drawings); Hanks Family Show (paintings and drawings); Allen Lehtis (paintings) and Mariel Lehtis (sculpture); Members Christmas Sale; Metal Arts Show; Mixed Media Show; Scarlett (paintings); J Thomas Higgins/Peter Weil (paintings and relief sculpture); Members Open Show; Summer Invitational I and II, Michael Willis/Robert Deis (drawings, prints and sculpture); John Ireland Collins (painter) and Nancy McGuire (sculpture); Richard Wiggins Johnson (watercolors); Members Christmas Show; Wood Arts Exhibit; Faculty Members of the Haystack School on Deer Isle Show; Hal Polin (polychrome wood block prints) and Naima Rauam (oil paintings); Dan Cake (mixed media).
Publications: Newsletter, monthly.
Activities: Lect open to the public, 6-8 vis lectr per yr; museum shop selling original art.

KENNEBUNK

BRICK STORE MUSEUM, 117 Main St (Mailing Add: PO Box 177, 04043). Tel: 207-985-4802. *Dir* David C Thurheimer; *Dir Asst & Registrar* Sandy Armentrout; *Pres Bd* Frank Harrison.
Open Tues - Sat 10 AM - 4:30 PM. Admis by donation. Estab 1936 to collect and preserve all matters of historical value; perform all acts, services, and labors that may tend to preserve historical facts and material and make available for use, benefit and pleasure of the public. One gallery with a permanent marine exhibit; one gallery with exhibits of early 20th century home-life, and a gallery of changing exhibits. Average Annual Attendance: 5000. Mem: 400; dues $7 - $32; annual meeting June.
Income: Financed by endowment and membership.
Collections: Marine artifacts; art; local history; American primitive art and traditional crafts.
Exhibitions: Instructors Craft Exhibit; Edith C Barry Art Exhibit.
Publications: Newsletter, quarterly.

Activities: Classes for children; dramatic programs; docent training; lect open to public; concerts; gallery talks; tours; exten dept serving Kennebunk, Kennebunkport, and York County; individual paintings and original objects of art lent; sales shop selling books, prints, cards and gifts.
—**Edith C Barry Library.** *Museum Dir* David Thurheimer.
Open to public for reference.
Holdings: Vols 3000; Per subs 10; Other—Documents 10,000.
Special Subjects: Marine history; history of the Kennebunks.

LEWISTON

BATES COLLEGE,* Treat Gallery, 04240. Tel: 207-783-6535. *Cur* Synnove Haughom.
Open Mon - Fri 1 - 5, 7 - 8 PM; Sun 2 - 5 PM; open mornings by appointment; cl major holidays. No admis. Estab 1955 in honor of Mr and Mrs George W Treat to acquaint the student body and the community with the works of recognized artists. Average Annual Attendance: 6800.
Collections: Marsden Hartley drawings (99) and paintings (2); Sylvan Lehman Joseph Collection of prints including one Rembrandt and 19 Cassatts; 4 Thompson family portraits (ancestors of George W Treat); 17th and 18th century English, Dutch, French and Italian landscapes and portraits; 19th and 20th century American and European paintings and prints; one Zorach sculpture; Freeman Hinckley (former Bates College trustee) Collection of Chinese objects.
Exhibitions: Changed monthly.
Activities: Lectures.

MACHIAS

UNIVERSITY OF MAINE AT MACHIAS ART GALLERY,* 04654. Tel: 207-255-3313. *Chmn Cultural Affairs* Chenoweth Hall.
Open 8 AM - 8 PM. No admis. Estab 1968. Average Annual Attendance: 1200.
Income: Financed by city and state appropriation.
Collections: John and Norma Marin Collection.
Exhibitions: Traveling exhibitions and one-man shows.
Activities: Extension department serves Washington County; material available to residents and summer visitors; material lent, books, records, prints, slides; traveling exhibitions organized and circulated to Calais Technical Institute; individual paintings and original objects of art lent; lending collection contains color reproductions 100, lantern slides 2000, Kodachromes 6000, film strips 30; lectures; 12 vis lectr per yr; classes for adults.
Library: Lending and reference library. Holdings: Vols 1640; Other—prints 156.

OGUNQUIT

MUSEUM OF ART OF OGUNQUIT, Shore Rd (Mailing Add: Box 815, 03907). Tel: 207-646-8827. *Dir* Henry Strater; *Cur* Peter R Mawn; *Asst Dir* John Dirks.
Open (July through Labor Day, 10 wks only) Mon - Sat 10:30 AM - 5 PM; Sun 1:30 - 5 PM. No admis. Estab 1951, gallery has 3 large rooms in a cinder-block bldg overlooking a grove of cedar trees and a rocky cove on the coast of southern Maine. Average Annual Attendance: 16,000. Mem: 200; dues individual $15; couple $25; annual meeting Aug.
Income: Financed by endowment, membership.
Collections: Paintings and sculpture by Americans of Our Times (1920 on); restricted to North American artists of that period.
Exhibitions: (1976) Part of Permanent Collection plus sculpture by Bernard Langlais and 100 Years of American Watercolor; (1977) Permanent Collection plus Drawings by Henry Strater and Watercolors by DeWitt Hardy; (1978) Permanent Collection plus Sculpture by Clark Fitz-Gerald.
Publications: Exhibition catalog, annually.
Activities: Individual paintings and original objects of art lent (restricted list only, available for short periods to museums and galleries); some color postcard reproductions of permanent collection are sold.

OGUNQUIT ART ASSOCIATION, The Barn Gallery, Bourne's Lane, 03907. Tel: 207-646-5370. *Pres* Betty Bryden-Wills; *VPres* Frederick Lynch; *Secy* Jayne Dwyer; *Cur* Betsy Knight.
Open Mon - Sat 10 AM - 5 PM & 8 - 10 PM; Sun 2 - 5 PM (mid-June - Mid-Sept). No admis. Estab 1928 as a charitable, educational institution, including two main galleries, Collector's Gallery of unframed works, and J Scott Smart outdoor sculpture court. Average Annual Attendance: 15,000. Mem: 60, summer residents in Ogunquit area; dues $15; meetings June & Aug.
Collections: Hamilton Easter Field Art Foundation Collection.
Exhibitions: Exhibitions during the summer.

Activities: Classes for adults and children; workshops; films and demonstrations; art auction; lect open to public; concerts; gallery talks.

ORONO

UNIVERSITY OF MAINE AT ORONO, Art Collection, Carnegie Hall, 04473. Tel: 207-581-7165. *Univ Pres* Howard Neville; *Cur* Vincent A Hartgen.
Open Mon - Fri 8 AM - 4:30 PM. Estab 1946 to add to the cultural life of the university student, to be a service to Maine artists, and to promote interest in good and important art, both historic and modern. There are seven galleries, four of which are in Carnegie Hall, the other three in campus buildings. Average Annual Attendance: 15,000. Mem: 180; dues $25, $50, $100.
Income: $40,000 (financed by membership and state appropriation). Purchases: $1000.
Collections: By purchase and gifts, the University Collection has grown to a stature which makes it a nucleus in the state for outstanding contemporary art, in all media. It includes more than 3000 original works of art.
Exhibitions: Full schedule of exhibitions of all media by outstanding American and European artists; conducts an Art Program of Exhibitions in Annual Art Festivals and year-round exhibitions; maintains Artists of Maine Gallery to show examples of Maine art at all times.
Publications: Occasional catalogs and exhibition notes.
Activities: Individual paintings and original objects of art lent, lending collection contains 1800 original prints and drawings, 925 paintings, 330 manuscripts, photos, sculptures, and ceramics; traveling exhibitions organized and circulated to Maine Schools.
—**Fogler Library.** *Dir Libraries* Dr James C MacCampbell.
Holdings: Vols 515,000; Per subs 3800.
Regional depository for northern New England for US Government publications and a file of maps of the Army Map Service. Selective depository for Canadian government publications.

PEMAQUID POINT

PEMAQUID GROUP OF ARTISTS, Lighthouse Park (Mailing Add: c/o Gene Klebe, Route 130, Bristol, 04539). Tel: 207-677-3672. *VPres* Ernest Thompson & Maurice Day; *Secy* Florence Thompson; *Treas* Cynthia Brackett; *Gallery Hostess* Frances Curtis; *Asst* Jeanette Andrus & Helen Strauss.
Open Mon - Sat 10 AM - 5 PM; Sun 1 - 5 PM. Admis 25¢. Estab 1929 to exhibit and sell paintings, sculpture, carvings by members. Maintain an art gallery, open July 1 through Labor Day. Average Annual Attendance: 8000. Mem: 35, must be residents of the Pemaquid Peninsula; dues $5; annual meeting the day after Labor Day.
Exhibitions: Summer members exhibition.
Activities: Scholarships; sales shop selling original art.

POLAND SPRING

SHAKER MUSEUM, Sabbathday Lake, 04274. Tel: 207-926-4597. *Dir* Theodore E Johnson; *Cur Graphic Arts & Photography* David W Serette; *Cur Manuscripts* R Mildred Barker; *Archivist* Frances A Carr.
Open May 30 - Labor Day. Tues - Sat 10 AM - 4:30 PM; cl Sun & Mon. Admis adults $2.00, children (6-12) $1.00, under 6 free with adult. Estab 1931, inc 1971, to preserve for educational and cultural purposes Shaker artifacts, publications, manuscripts and works of art, to provide facilities for educational and cultural activities in connection with the preservation of the Shaker tradition, to provide a place of study and research for students of history and religion.
Collections: Shaker †textiles, †metal and wooden ware, †furniture, †community industries, †paintings and drawings by Shaker artists, †manuscripts.
Publications: The Shaker Quarterly.
Activities: Classes for adults; lect open to public; gallery talks; tours; museum shop selling books, prints and slides.
—**Shaker Library.** *Librn* Theodore E Johnson.
Open to qualified scholars by appointment.
Holdings: Vols 14,631; Titles 12,435; Per subs 32; Microfilm—Reels (353); Other—Prints (317), photographs, manuscripts, and ephemera.
Special Subjects: Art, music & technology, early American technology, American communal societies.

PORTLAND

MAINE HISTORICAL SOCIETY,* 485 Congress St, 04111. Tel: 207-774-1822. *Dir* Gerald E Morris.
Open June - Sept Mon - Fri 10 AM - 5 PM; cl. State & Federal holidays. No admis. Estab 1822, a society that owns and operates a branch museum established in a 1785 historic house, Wadsworth-Longfellow House. Mem: Dues $15-$250.

Collections: Maine historic artifacts; paintings; prints; photographs; glass; pottery; textiles; furniture.
Publications: Maine Historical Society, quarterly; tri-annual monograph.
Activities: Classes for local college students; archival training course; temporary exhibitions.
Library: Librn Esta J Astor; *Cataloger* Virginia Gronberg; *Cur Manuscripts* Thomas L Gaffney. Holdings: 60,000 vols; 1,000,000 manuscripts.

PORTLAND SOCIETY OF ART, Museum of Art, 111 High St, 04101. Tel: 207-775-6148. *Dir* John Holverson.
Open Tues - Sat 10 AM - 5 PM; Sun 2 - 5 PM; cl Mon & holidays. Admis to Galleries free (voluntary donation), to McLellan-Sweat House adults $1, children & students 50¢. Estab 1882 as a non-profit educational institution based on the visual arts and critical excellence. The Museum includes the McLellan-Sweat House, built in 1800 and Galleries built in 1911. The McLellan-Sweat House is furnished in the style of the Federal period and is a superb example of an early 19th century, three-story mansion, it is a Registered National Historic Landmark. The Museum Galleries, designed by John Calvin Stevens, 1911, consist of five galleries surrounding a central rotunda. Average Annual Attendance: 15,000. Mem: 1200; dues $15-$1000; annual meeting May.
Income: $150,000 (financed by endowment, membership, state appropriation, Federal funds, public support, fund-raising and grants. Purchases: $7500.
Collections: 19th century American paintings, expecially from the Portland and Maine region; contemporary prints; American decorative arts, particularly of the Federal period; neo-classic American sculpture; European paintings; Portland pattern glass (1863-1873).
Exhibitions: Collection of Contemporary Prints by Living American Artists; Ellen and Chris Huntington Collection; 58 Maine Paintings; Multiple Fields: William Manning; Images of Woman; The Revolutionary McLellans; Marsden Hartley; Andrew Wyeth in Maine; Paul Dougherty; American Glass.
Publications: Bulletin, monthly; exhibition catalogs, occasionally.
Activities: Dramatic programs; docent training; lect open to public, 6-10 vis lectr per yr; gallery talks; tours; competitions; individual paintings and original objects of art lent to museums; participation in State of Maine prog for Wider Availability; museum shop selling books, original art, reproductions, prints, posters, cards, jewelry, and gifts.
Library: Open to visiting scholars, students and members by appintment.

VICTORIA SOCIETY OF MAINE WOMEN, Victoria Mansion, Morse-Libby Mansion, 109 Danforth St, 04101. Tel: 207-772-4841. *Pres* Kathleen Coyne; *VPres* Mrs Howard F Detmer; *Secy* Mrs Ellis Leach; *Historian-Librn-Registr* Roger D Calderwood.
Open (Mid-June to Labor Day) Tues - Sat 10 AM - 4 PM; cl Sun, Mon & holidays. Admis adults $1, children under 12 50¢. Estab 1943 to display Italian Villa, Victorian Period, built by Henry Austin of New Haven, Connecticut in 1859-1863. Average Annual Attendance: 4000. Mem: 398. Annual meeting June.
Income: Financed by membership, tours and special activities.
Collections: Original interior-exterior and original furnishings, gifts and loans of the Victorian Period.
Activities: Lectures open to the public; tours; individual paintings lent; a lending collection contains books.

WESTBROOK COLLEGE, Joan Whitney Payson Gallery of Art, 716 Stevens Ave, 04103. Tel: 207-797-9546. *Dir* Martin Dibner; *Asst to Dir* Gael May McKibben; *Cur Asst* Thaddeus Macy.
Open Tues - Fri 10 AM - 4 PM; Sat & Sun 1 - 5 PM; cl Mon & holidays. No admis. Estab May 1977 for cultural exhibits and events; Payson Gallery is a tri-level cube 32 x 32 ft.
Income: Financed by college operating budget.
Collections: Impressionist paintings: Post-Impressionist; American masters of the 19th and 20th Century.
Exhibitions: There will be a major Milton Avery exhibit during the summer of '78. During that time the permanent collection will be down. There are also regularly changing sculpture exhibits and small exhibits in the Lower Gallery.
Activities: Individual paintings lent to art museums; lending collection contains paintings; museum shop selling catalogs and postcards.

ROCKLAND

WILLIAM A FARNSWORTH LIBRARY AND ART MUSEUM, 19 Elm St (Mailing Add: Box 466, 04841). Tel: 207-596-6457. *Dir* Marius B Peladeau; *Cur* Sandra Gordon Olson; *Admin Asst* Christine J Seelig; *Registr* Mary Wasgett.
Open Tues - Sat 10 AM - 5 PM; Sun 1 - 5 PM; Mon (June through Aug) 10 AM - 5 PM. Admis by donations. Estab 1948 to house, conserve, and exhibit American art, especially Maine artists. Two large open space galleries, one small gallery on the second floor and a permanent marine room exhibit downstairs. Average Annual Attendance: 47,000. Mem: 950; dues $10, $25, $50. Annual Meeting July.
Collections: American art and American decorative arts; European fine arts and decorative árts.
Publications: Annual report; Newsletter, monthly; catalog.
Activities: Classes for adults; lect open to public, 4 vis lectr per yr; concerts; gallery talks; competitions, Annual Open Show, Childrens Art Show; individual paintings and original objects of art lent to other museums and galleries; traveling exhibitions organized and circulated; museum shop selling books, original art, reproductions, prints, slides, limited edition gift items.
—William A Farnsworth Library. *Librn* Pamela Posey.
Open to public for reference only.
Holdings: Vols 3500; Per subs 24; Other—rare books.

ROCKPORT

MAINE COAST ARTISTS, Russell Ave (Mailing Add: Box 147, 04856). Tel: 207-236-2875. *Dir* Flora B Donham.
Open Tues - Sat 10 AM - 5 PM; Sun 1 - 6 PM; cl Mon. No admis. Estab 1958 to show the works of nationally and internationally known artists who paint in Maine, full time or part-time. Gallery building was a very old, large livery stable overlooking Rockport Harbor. Average Annual Attendance: Approx 8000. Sponsors 250; dues sponsorships, $15 and up.
Income: $15,000 (financed by sponsors, auction and sales).
Exhibitions: (1976-77) Artists from Vinalhaven and Recent Talent, The Skowhegan School.
Activities: Classes for children; lect open to public, 6 - 8 vis lectr per yr; traveling exhibitions organized and circulated.

SACO

YORK INSTITUTE MUSEUM,* 375 Main St, 04072. Tel: 207-282-3031. *Exec Dir* Barbara Bond; *Cur* Audrey Milne.
Open winter Wed - Sat 1 - 4 PM; summer Wed - Sun 1 - 4 PM; cl. two weeks in June, legal holidays. No admis. Estab 1867. Mem: Dues: single $5, family $10, contributing $25, life $100, perpetual $1000.
Collections: Colonial decorative arts; paintings; sculpture; glass; historical material.
Activities: Guided tours; temporary exhibitions; inter-museum loan.
Library: Historical books, early newspapers and manuscripts for use on the premises.

SEARSPORT

PENOBSCOT MARINE MUSEUM, Church St, 04974. Tel: 207-548-6634. *Dir* C Gardner Lane Jr; *Secy* Marilyn Kenney.
Open Memorial Day weekend through Oct 15, Mon - Sat 9:30 AM - 5 PM; Sun 1 - 5 PM. Admis adults $2.00; ages 13-17 $1.00; ages 7-12 50¢; under 7 free; Sr citizens $1.00. Estab 1936 as a memorial to the maritime record of present and former residents of the State of Maine in shipbuilding, shipping and all maritime affairs. Six buildings, including the Old Town Hall (1845); Capt Merithew House (1816); Fowler-True-Ross House and Barn (1820); Nickels-Colcord-Duncan House (c 1880); Small Craft Exhibit; Special Exhibits Building. Average Annual Attendance: 7500. Mem: 300; dues $10 and up; annual meeting July.
Income: Financed by endowment, membership and admissions.
Collections: †Ships models; †paintings; small craft; marine hardware; Oriental exports.
Exhibits: Offshore Oil Drilling.
Publications: Annual Report; newsletter, when appropriate.
Activities: Classes for children; individual paintings and original objects of art lent to other institutions.
Library: Open for reference to researchers. Holdings: Vols 3000; Per subs 10; Other—Nautical charts, photographs.

SPRINGVALE

NASSON COLLEGE, Anderson Learning Center, Bradeen St, 04083. Tel: 207-324-5340. *Dir* Robert J Berkley; *Cur* George Burk.
Open Mon - Fri 8:30 AM - 1 PM; Sat 9 AM - 5 PM; Sun 1 - 10 PM. Estab 1969. The Gallery provides facilities for the study of humanities and a location for the display of the college's permanent art study collection. Maintains an art gallery with exhibition and lecture area and an adjoining outdoor sculpture court.
Income: Financed by endowment and through college.
Holdings: Vols 120,000; Per subs 900; AV—Audio tapes, film strips, lantern slides, microfiche, microfilm, motion pictures, phonorecords, slides and video tapes; Other—Clipping files, exhibition catalogs, framed reproductions, memorabilia.
Special Collections: 20th century paintings, sculpture, graphic works and photographs.

Exhibitions: Seven exhibitions of prominent artists per year; historical exhibitions and student shows.
Publications: Posters for each exhibit.

WATERVILLE

COLBY MUSEUM OF ART,* 04901. Tel: 207-873-1131, exten 221. *Dir* Hugh J Gourley III.
Open Mon - Sat 10 AM - Noon & 1 - 4:30 PM; cl major holidays. No admis. Estab 1959 to serve as an adjunct to the Colby College Art Program and to be a museum center for Central Maine. Friends of Art at Colby, mem 625; dues $10 and higher.
Collections: The American Heritage Collection (about 85 American folk art objects), presented to Colby College by Mr and Mrs Ellerton Jette; The Helen Warren and Willard Howe Cummings Collection of American art; The Pulsifer Collection of Winslow Homer (13 paintings and drawings); the John Marin Collection of 25 works by Marin; American art of the 18th, 19th and 20th centuries; Pre-Columbian Mexico; Etruscan art; Jette Collection of American painting of the Impressionist Period; Adelaide Pearson Collection; Bernat Collection of Oriental ceramics and bronzes; William J Pollock Collection of American Indian art.
Publications: Quarterly newsletter.
Library: For reference only. Holdings: Vols 1500.

THOMAS COLLEGE,* W River Rd, 04354. Tel: 207-873-0771. *Pres* John L Thomas; *Dir* Dr Donald F Brown.
Open Mon - Fri 8 AM - 5 PM. No admis. Estab 1968 for presentation of instructional shows for student audience. Average Annual Attendance: 1500.
Exhibitions: 1 or 2 exhibitions a month during school year of Maine artists only. Included are Lois Dodd, Bernard Langlais, David Ellis, John Beuregard, and Harry Stump.
Library: For reference only. Holdings: Over 100 in slide collection.

WISCASSET

LINCOLN COUNTY CULTURAL AND HISTORICAL ASSOCIATION, 04578. *Pres* Woodbury Brackett; *Admin Asst* Gerry M Bradley.
Inc 1954 to preserve buildings of historic interest. Presents 200 years of Maine's crafts and skills including the work of craftsmen who spend part of the year in Maine. Presents the works of contemporary professional artists, working in Maine, by means of two juried summer exhibitions. Average Annual Attendance: 8000. Mem: 1000; dues $10 and up; annual meeting July. The Association maintains three museums and one art gallery.
Income: Approx $10,000.
Collections: Prison equipment and ephamera; hand tools; textiles; furniture; household articles.
Exhibitions: Lincoln County Museum, permanent exhibit on the history of punishment; changing exhibits on 200 years of Maine crafts and skills.
Publications: Newsletter and occasional monographs.
Activities: School programs and tours; slide shows; lectures; concerts.
Library: Open for reference. Special Subjects: local history and penology.
—**Lincoln County Museum**
Open June 1 - Sept 15, daily 10 AM - 5 PM; Sun 12:30 - 5 PM; Winter, Sat 10 AM - 5 PM; Sun 12:30 - 5 PM; weekdays by appointment.
—**Lincoln County Fire Museum**
Open June 1 - Labor Day, 10 AM - 5 PM
—**Maine Art Gallery,** Old Academy, Warren St (Mailing Add: PO Box 815, 04578). Tel: 207-882-7511. *Chmn & Dir* Roger Johnson; *Treas* William Burley; *Secy* Warren Spaulding.
Open, weekdays daily 10 AM - 5 PM; Sun 1 - 5 PM; Winter, Sat 10 AM - 4 PM; Sun 1 - 4 PM. No admis, donations appreciated. Estab 1958 as a cooperative, non-profit gallery created by the Artist Members of Lincoln County Cultural & Historical Association to exhibit the work of artists living or working in Maine. Occupies a red brick federal two-storey building built in 1807 as a free Academy. The building is now on National Historical Register. Average Annual Attendance: 6000. Annual meeting Sept.
Income: Financed by patrons.
Exhibitions: Summer Exhibition—a juried show in two parts of 5 weeks each featuring approx 100 painters and sculptors living or working in Maine. Winter series of one-person invited exhibitions.
—**Pownalborough Court House** (1761, Dresden)
Open June 26 - Sept 4.

YORK

OLD GAOL MUSEUM, York St and Lindsay Road, 03909. Tel: 207-363-3872. *Dir & Cur Coll* Eldridge H Pendleton; *Chmn Committee* Mrs Frank Hancock; *Asst Cur* Daniel E Sevigny; *Secy* Mrs Thomas Fawcett.

Open Mon - Sat 9:30 AM - 5 PM; Sun 1:30 - 5 PM. Admis $1.50. Estab 1900 as a local history museum to maintain, care for and develop historical collections of a regional nature and to promote historic research and historically educational programs. The museum consists of the oldest jail in the United States and an 18th century tavern arranged as period rooms. Two exhibition rooms house traveling shows and temporary exhibitions of an historical nature. Average Annual Attendance: 10,000. Mem: 600; dues $3; annual meeting Aug.
Income: $45,000 (financed by endowment).
Collections: Regional collection of American furniture and decorative arts, rare books and manuscripts.
Publications: Old Gaol Newsletter, quarterly.
Activities: Classes for adults and children; dramatic programs; lect for members, 8 vis lectr per yr; tours; lending collection contains original art works 4,000, original prints, paintings, sculpture; slides 500; museum shop selling books, reproductions, slides.
—**Library,** Box 188, 03909.
Open daily 10 AM - Noon & 1 - 4 PM. For reference only.
Holdings: Vols 3300; Other—Clipping files, manuscripts, memorabilia, original documents, pamphlets, photographs, prints.
Special Subjects: Decorative arts, local history and genealogy.

SOCIETY FOR PRESERVATION OF HISTORIC LANDMARKS, 03909. Tel: 207-363-3200. *Pres* Edward A Bragdon Jr; *VPres* Edwin E Kimball; *Secy* Nora Clements.
Society estab 1941 to operate buildings of historic interest. Mem: 150; dues $2; annual meeting Aug.
—**Elizabeth Perkins House**
Open June 16 - Sept 4, Mon - Sat 9:30 AM - 5 PM; Sun 1:30 - 5 PM. Admis adults $1. A Colonial house as lived in by a Victorian family; built 1730; contains 18th and 19th century furniture, china, and prints. Average Annual Attendance: 2300.
—**Old School House**
Open May 27 - Sept 30, Mon - Sat 9:30 AM - 5 PM; Sun 1:30 - 5 PM. Original school built in 1745; figures of the schoolmaster and children are in period costumes. Average Annual Attendance 11,500.
—**Jefferds Tavern**
Open May 30 through Sept 30, Mon - Sat 9:30 AM - 5 PM; Sun 1:30 - 5 PM. Admis adults $1. An ancient hostelry built before the Revolution by Capt Samuel Jefferds.
—**John Hancock Warehouse**
Open May 27 - Sept 30, Mon - Sat 9:30 AM - 5 PM; Sun 1:30 - 5 PM. Admis adults 50¢. Owned by signer of the Declaration of Independence at the time of his death; listed in the National Register of Historic Places; exhibits of old tools and antique ship models. Average Annual Attendance: 4500.
—**Marshall Store**
Open Mon - Sat 9:30 AM - 5 PM; Sun 1 - 5 PM. No admis. Built by George A Marshall in 1870, now a museum store featuring handcrafts by area craftsmen.

MARYLAND

ANNAPOLIS

HAMMOND-HARWOOD HOUSE, 19 Maryland Ave, 21401. Tel: 301-269-1714. *Admin* Barbara A Brand.
Open Nov - March Tues - Sat 10 AM - 4 PM; Sun 1 - 4 PM; Apr - Oct Tues - Sat 10 AM - 5 PM; Sun 2 - 5 PM. Admis adults $2, students $1, children 50¢. Estab 1938 to preserve the Hammond-Harwood House (1774), a National Historic Landmark, and to educate the public in the arts and architecture of Maryland in the 18th century. Average Annual Attendance: 19,000. Mem: 1800; dues varied; meeting May and Nov.
Income: Financed by endowment, membership, attendance and sales.
Collections: Paintings by C W Peale; prints; English and American furnishings especially Maryland; Chinese porcelain; glassware and silver.
Publications: Maryland's Way (Hammond-Harwood House cookbook); historic booklet on HHH.
Activities: Dramatic programs; docent training; lect open to the public; individual paintings and original objects of art lent to bonafide museums within reasonable transporting distance; sales shop selling books, slides postcards, and notepaper.

UNITED STATES NAVAL ACADEMY MUSEUM, 21402. Tel: 301-267-2108. *Dir* Dr William W Jeffries; *Sr Cur* James W Cheevers; *Cur of Ship Models; Cur of Prints* Alexandra Welsh; *Sr Exhibits Specialist* Archie M Wild.
Open Tues - Sat 9 AM - 5 PM; Sun 11 AM - 5 PM; cl Mon. No Admis.

Estab 1845 as Naval School Lyceum for the purpose of collecting, preserving and exhibiting objects related to American naval history; Museum contains two large galleries totaling 9000 sq ft, with other exhibits in other areas of the campus. Average Annual Attendance: Approx 600,000.
Income: Financed by Federal Government appropriations. Purchases: $5549 (1977).
Collections: †Paintings, drawings, prints, sculpture of naval portraits and events; ship models; naval uniforms, †weapons; medals; silver; ceramicwares; manuscripts; other memorabilia.
Exhibitions: (1976) (Art) American Colonial Wars at Sea (prints, ship models and medals); Selections 1776-1876 from Permanent Collection; Navy Girls (paintings, drawings and prints). (1977) Selections from Permanent Collection; The Art of Henry Reuterdahl: A Retrospective Exhibition. (1978) American Naval Prints.
Publications: Collection catalogs and special exhibition brochures, periodically.
Activities: Lectures and tours upon request; individual paintings and original objects of art lent to other museums and related institutions for special, temporary exhibitions; traveling exhibitions organized and circulated.
Library. For reference only. Open to students, scholars and public with notice. Holdings: Vols 2600, Per subs 24.

BALTIMORE

BALTIMORE MARITIME MUSEUM,* Pier 4, Pratt St, 21202. Tel: 301-837-1776. *Exec Dir* Donald F Stewart.
Open Mon - Sat 10 AM - 5 PM; Sun noon - 5 PM; cl Good Friday, Christmas. Admis adults $1.50, children 75¢, under 6 no charge. Estab 1921 in a working lightship.
Collections: Shipbuilding memorabilia; models; records; prints; paintings; scrimshaw; sailor art; woodcarving; flags and trophies; 1770-1945 ship lantern display relics of famous ships.
Activities: Guided tours; winter festival; sales shop.

BALTIMORE MUSEUM OF ART, Art Museum Dr, 21218. Tel: 301-396-7101. *Dir* Tom L Freudenheim; *Asst Dir of Art* Brenda Richardson; *Asst Dir for Admin* Ann Boyce Harper; *Chmn Curatorial Div & Cur Decorative Arts* William Voss Elder III; *Cur Prints and Drawings* Victor Carlson; *Asst Cur Decorative Arts* M B Munford; *Asst Cur Prints and Drawings* Jay Fisher; *Assoc Cur Painting and Sculpture* Sona Johnston; *Chrm Educ Div* Judith Sobol.
Open Tues - Sat 11 AM - 5 PM; Thurs eve 7 - 10 PM; Sun 1 - 5 PM; cl Mon & New Year's. No admis. Estab 1914 to house and preserve art works; to program art exhibitions and programs and to offer educational programs and events; the building was designed by John Russell Pope in 1929 and houses permanent and temporary galleries and Antioch Court. Average Annual Attendance: 250,000. Mem: 5000; dues $15 - $100.
Income: $1,602,000 (financed by endowment, membership, city and state appropriation and Federal and county funds).
Collections: Blanche Adler Collection of graphic art; Antioch Mosaics; Ellen H Bayard Collection of 18th and 19th century American paintings, European ceramics, Chinese export porcelain, Irish glass, 19th century European jewelry, and American and English silver; Thomas E. Benesch Memorial Collection of drawings by contemporary American and European artists; Harry A Bernstein Memorial Collection of contemporary American paintings; Cone Collection of 19th and 20th century French paintings, sculpture, drawings and prints, Near Eastern and European textiles, laces, Spanish and French 18th century jewelry, furniture and other decorative arts; Elise Agnus Daingerfield Collection of 18th century English, French and American paintings with emphasis on portraiture; Hanson Rawlings Duval Jr Memorial Collection of 19th century Baltimore architectural elements, American furniture, paintings, metalwork and European and Chinese ceramics; White Collection of Early Maryland Silver of outstanding examples of 18th and 19th century work of Maryland silversmiths; Abram Eisenberg Collection of paintings primarily of 19th century French origin; Jacob Epstein Collection of Old Master paintings; Edward Joseph Callagher III Memorial Collection of paintings by American artists executed between 1921 and 1955; T Harrison Garrett Collection of graphic art from the 15th through 19th century; Nelson and Juanita Greif Gutman Memorial Collection of 20th century paintings, sculpture and drawings; Mary Frick Jacobs Collections of 15th - 18th century European paintings, tapestries, furniture and objets d'art; Charles and Elsa Hutzler Memorial Collection of contemporary sculpture; George A Lucas Collection of 19th century paintings, drawings, prints and bronzes; Saidie A May Collection of 20th century paintings, sculpture and graphics, Ancient, Medieval and Renaissance sculpture, textiles; McLanahan Memorial Collection of furnishings for and installation of 1720 bedchamber; Samuel and Tobie Miller Memorial Collection of contemporary painting and sculpture; Julius Levy Memorial Fund Collection of Oriental Art; J G D'Arch Paul Collection of 18th century American furniture; Peabody Institute Collection of 19th and 20th century American paintings; General Lawrason Riggs Collection of

Old Master prints and Chinese ceramics; White Collection of ceramics, furniture, needlework, glass and decorative art books; William Woodward Collection of 18th and 19th century paintings of English sporting life; Wurtzburger Collection of Art from Africa, the Americas and the Pacific; Janet and Alan Wurtzburger Collection of 20th century sculpture by European masters with emphasis on the human figure.
Exhibitions: Exhibitions covering the fields of painting, sculpture, decorative arts, prints, drawings and photography.
Publications: Calendar, monthly; exhibition catalogs.
Activities: Classes for children; docent training; lect open to the public; concerts; gallery talks; tours; competitions exten dept serving Museum in the Mall, Columbia, Maryland; traveling exhibitions organized and circulated; museum shop selling books, original art, reproductions, prints, slides.
—Library: Tel: 301-396-7101. *Librn* Joan Robison.
Open by appointment for reference only.
Holdings: Vols 25,000; Per subs 62.
Special Subjects: American decorative arts; 19th and 20th century French art.

COMMUNITY COLLEGE OF BALTIMORE ART GALLERY, 2901 Liberty Heights Ave, 21215. Tel: 301-396-7980. *Gallery Dir* Bennard B Perlman.
Open Sun 2 - 5 PM; Mon - Fri 10 AM - 4 PM. No admis. Estab 1965 to bring to the Baltimore and college communities exhibitions of note by regional artists, and to serve as a showplace for the artistic productions of the college art students and faculty. Consists of one large gallery area, approx 120 running ft, well-lighted through the use of both natural light through sky domes and cove lighting which provides an even wash to the walls.
Income: Financed through the college.
Collections: Graphics from the 16th century to the present; paintings by notable American artists and regional ones.
Exhibitions: The Inner Harbor (an invitational theme show); Teachers as Artists; annual art faculty, art student, and one-person faculty exhibits.
Activities: Lect open to public; gallery talks.

JOHNS HOPKINS UNIVERSITY
—Archaeological Collection, Charles & 34th St, 21218. *Cur* Dr Ellen Reeder Williams.
Open Mon - Wed 11 AM - 3 PM. Estab 1876; small exhibit space in Gilman Hall.
Collections: Egyptian through Roman material 3500 BC to 500 AD.
—Evergreen House,* 4545 N Charles St, 21210.
Open Mon - Fri 2 - 5 PM. The former house of John W Garrett which he bequeathed to the University.
Collections: Fine arts, rare book library, paintings left by Mrs Garrett to the Evergreen House Foundation.
Exhibitions: Changing exhibitions.
—Milton S Eisenhower Library Galleries,* Quadrangle Level, 21218. *Assoc Librn* Alan R Taylor.
Open Mon - Fri 9 Am - 5 PM.
Exhibitions: Changing exhibitions of paintings, sculpture and photography by Baltimore artists.
—Welch Medical Library,* Johns Hopkins Medical School, 1900 E Monument St, 21205.
Collection: Portraits of medical men, medical artifacts, rare book library.
Exhibitions: Changing exhibitions.

MARYLAND HISTORICAL SOCIETY MUSEUM, 201 W Monument St, 21201. Tel: 301-685-3750, exten 70, 71 & 72. *Pres* Leonard C Crewe, Jr; *Recording Secy* Mrs Frederick W Lafferty; *Dir* Mrs Romaine S Somerville; *Gallery Adminr* E Hartley Eager; *Asst Gallery Cur* Stiles T Colwill.
Open Tues - Sat 11 AM - 4 PM; Sun 1 - 5 PM; No admis. Estab 1844 to collect, display and interpret the history of the State of Maryland. Average Annual Attendance: 43,000. Mem: 5000; dues; annual meeting Oct.
Income: Financed by endowment, membership, city and state appropriations.
Collections: Paintings; both portrait and landscape; silver; porcelain and pottery; crystal and glassware; metalwork; textiles and costumes; architectural drawings; ethnic artifacts, all of Maryland origin or provenance.
Exhibitions: Continually changing exhibitions reflecting the history and culture of the state.
Publications: Maryland Historical Society Magazine, quarterly; News and Notes; bimonthly.
Activities: Lect open to the public; gallery talks; tours; individual paintings and original objects of art lent to other organizations; sales shop selling books, magazines, prints and reproductions.
—Library, *Librn* A Hester Rich.
Open Tues - Sat 9 PM - 4 PM. Estab 1844 to provide resources for the study of Maryland history, genealogy and resources.

Holdings: Vols 80,000; Per subs 245. AV—Lantern slides, microfilm, slides; Other—Clipping.files, exhibitions catalogs, manuscripts 3,000,000, pamphlets, photographs, prints.
Special Collections: Robert G Merrick Collection of prints.
Activities: Lect open to the public.

MARYLAND INSTITUTE COLLEGE OF ART, Decker Gallery, 1300 Mt Royal Ave, 21239. Tel: 301-669-9200. *Pres* Dr Theodore Klitzke; *Dir* Joseph S Czestochowski.
Open Mon - Fri 10 AM - 4 PM & 6 - 10 PM; Sat 10 AM - 4 PM; Sun 1 - 4 PM. Exhibiting since 1826. Average Annual Attendance: 10,000.
Income: Financed by endowment and student tuition.
Collections: Maryland Institute-George A Lucas Collection donated in 1909 comprising over 400 paintings and drawings by Corot, Daumier, Greuze, Manet, Pissarro, Delacrox, Millet and Whistler, bronzes by Antoine Barye and a collection of 17,000 graphics.
Exhibitions: Alphonse Mucha; Selections from The Lucas Collection.
Publications: Two major publications per year, several small catalogs, handouts of the works in the Lucas Collection.
Activities: Dramatic programs; lect open to the public; concerts; gallery talks; tours; original objects of art lent; traveling exhibitions organized and circulated; sales shop selling books.
Library: Holdings—Vols 32,000.

MORGAN STATE UNIVERSITY GALLERY OF ART,* Cold Spring Lane & Hillen Rd, 21212. Tel: 301-893-3030. *Dir* James E Lewis; *Cur* Achameleh Debela.
Open daily 10 AM - 5 PM. No admis. Estab 1950. Average Annual Attendance: 5000.
Income: $5500.
Collections: European, New Guinea, African, American; sculpture, paintings; prints.
Exhibitions: Temporary and traveling exhibitions; exhibitions from the collection.
Publications: Catalogs, monthly.
Activities: Lectures open to the public, visiting lecturers; traveling exhibitions organized and circulated; 500 Kodachromes for lending.
Holdings: Vols 1200; photograph collection.

MOUNT CLARE MANSION, Carroll Park, 21230. Tel: 301-837-3262.
Chmn House Comt Mrs Samuel H Shriver; *Cur* Mrs Thomas G Young III; *Adminr* Charles Wineberg.
Open Tues - Sat 11 AM - 4 PM; Sun 1 - 4 PM. Admis adults $1, children (under 12) 25¢. Estab 1917 to demonstrate how wealthy colonial and Federal period families lived. Rooms of the house furnished with 18th & early 19th century decorative arts, much of which belonged to the Carroll family who built the house in 1754. Average Annual Attendance: 4500. Mem 500; dues $30; meetings May & Nov.
Collections: 18th and early 19th century English and American furniture; Irish crystal; Oriental export porcelain; other English and American decorative arts; English silver; American paintings.
Publications: Brochure on Mount Clare; booklet on the house.
Activities: Docent training; lect for members only, 3 vis lectr per yr; tours; competitions; individual paintings and original objects of art lent to local museums on occasion; sales shop selling books, prints, slides and gifts.
Library: Open to members and the public. Holdings: Vols 800. Special Subjects: Decorative Arts. Special Collections: Part of the library of Charles Carroll, Barrister-at-Law, builder of the house, 1754.

MUNICIPAL ART SOCIETY OF BALTIMORE CITY,* c/o *Pres* Beverley C Compton Jr, 135 E Baltimore St, 21202. Tel: 301-727-1700. *Treas* Alan P Hoblitzell.
Estab 1899, the Society contributes primarily to the painting of murals in public buildings and the adornment of public places with statuary. Mem: 150, dues $15.
Income: $5000.
Activities: Conducts series of lectures on art by outstanding critics. Offers an annual traveling scholarship at the Rinehart School of Sculpture conducted at the Maryland Institute.

PEALE MUSEUM, Municipal Museum, 225 Holliday St, 21202. Tel: 301-396-3523. *Pres* George D Hubbard; *VPres* Mrs Martin L Millspaugh; *Treas* H Chace Davis, Jr; *Dir* Wilbur H Hunter; *Asst Dir* Barry Dressel.
Open Tues - Fri 10:30 AM - 4:30 PM; Sat & Sun 2 - 5 PM. No admis. Estab 1931 as the museum of the life and history of Baltimore. Built in 1814 as Rembrandt Peale's Baltimore Museum and Gallery of Fine Arts, a national historical landmark. Also operates the Carroll Mansion, historic house built in 1812. Average Annual Attendance: 15,000. Mem: 450; dues $10 - $100.
Income: $175,000 (financed by endowment, membership, city appropriation). Purchases: $5000 - $10,000.

Collections: Paintings by members of the Peale family; prints of Baltimore; photographs of Baltimore furniture of the 18th and 19th century, especially the A Aubrey Bodine Collection; paintings by contemporary Baltimore artists.
Exhibitions: Baltimore in the Revolutionary Generation; Prints of Baltimore; Paintings of Florence H Austrian; Photographs of John Dubas.
Activities: Lect open to public, 1 - 2 vis lectr per yr; lending collection contains 350 photographs; museum shop selling books, reproductions, prints, slides.
Library: Open to staff for reference only. Holdings: Vols 2000. Special Subjects: History of Baltimore.

ENOCH PRATT FREE LIBRARY OF BALTIMORE CITY, Fine Arts Dept, 400 Cathedral St, 21201. Tel: 301-396-5490. *Dir* Ernest Siegel; *Chief Public Relations Div* Howard W Hubbard; *Head Fine Arts Dept* James K Dickson.
Open Mon - Thurs 9 AM - 9 PM; Fri - Sat 9 AM - 5 PM; Oct - May Sun 1 - 5 PM. Estab 1882 to provide materials, primarily circulating on the visual arts and music.
Income: Financed by city and state appropriation. Purchases: $25,000.
Holdings: Books; Per subs; AV—Film strips, motion pictures, phonorecords, slides; Other—Framed reproductions, reproductions.
Activities: Lect open to the public; concerts.
—**George Peabody Branch,*** 17 E Mt Vernon Place, 21202. Tel: 301-396-5540. *Head* Evelyn L Hart.
Open Mon - Sat 9 AM - 5 PM; cl Sun. Exhibition space in display windows, interior display cases corridors and special departments.
Holdings: Other—Framed prints 157, unframed pictures 405,000.
Publications: Booklets periodically.
Activities: Lectures and film showings.

STAR-SPANGLED BANNER FLAG HOUSE ASSOCIATION, 844 E Pratt St, 21202. *Pres* Herbert E Witz; *VPres* Hugh Benet Jr, S Vannort Chapman, and George A Conner; *Treas* John H Ensor; *Secy* Mrs Turner Moore; *Dir* Mrs Hugh Martin.
Open Tues - Sat 10 AM - 4 PM; Sun 2 - 4:30 PM. Admis adults $1. Estab 1927 for the care and maintenance of 1793 home of Mary Pickersgill maker of 15 star, 15 stripe flag used at Fort McHenry during Battle of Baltimore, War of 1812, which inspired Francis Scott Key to pen his famous poem, now our National Anthem. Also to conduct an educational program for public and private schools. Museum houses artifacts, portraits, and library. 1793 house furnished and decorated in Federal period to look as it did when Mary Pickersgill was in residence. Average Annual Attendance: 18,000. Mem: 750; dues vary; annual meeting Apr.
Collections: Original antiques of Federal period; flag collection.
Exhibitions: Old and historic Flag Exhibit.
Publications: The Star (newsletter), quarterly.
Activities: Classes for adults and children; lect open to public; tours; traveling exhibitions organized and circulated; sales shop selling books and souvenirs.
Library: Open to public for reference. Holdings: Vols 300.

UNITED METHODIST HISTORICAL SOCIETY, Lovely Lane Museum, 2200 St Paul St, 21218. Tel: 301-889-4458. *Pres* William Louis Piel; *Exec Secy* Edwin Schell.
Open Mon - Fri 4 - 10 PM; Sun after church; groups by appointment. No admis. Estab 1855; a religious collection specialising in Methodism. The main museum room contains permanent exhibits; three other galleries are devoted largely to rotating exhibits. Average Annual Attendance: 5,000. Mem: 581; dues $3 - $100; annual meeting May.
Income: $22,334 (financed by membership, and religious denomination).
Collections: Church edifices, photographs, statuary, medallions and emblems, furniture, and quilts.
Exhibitions: Warmth of Friendship: A Quilt for the preacher; The Military Chaplaincy through 200 years; 100 Years of Child Care; Usual and Unusual; Literary and Other Remains.
Publications: Third Century Methodism, quarterly; annual report.
Activities: Docent training; lect open to public, 1 vis lectr per yr; gallery talks; tours; competitions; sales shop selling books, prints, and cards.
Library: *Librn* Edwin Schell; *Asst Librn* Betty Ammons. Open to general public for reference. Holdings: Vols 4500; Per subs 30; Other—Archives, manuscripts. Special Subjects: Methodist history. Special Collections: Methodist history, Methodist polity, Methodist hymnody, biography.

WALTERS ART GALLERY, 600 N Charles St, 21201. Tel: 301-547-9000. *Pres Bd of Trustees* Francis D Murnaghan; *Dir* Richard H Randall Jr; *Asst Dir* William R Johnston; *Administrative Officer* Edward P McCracken; *Cur Renaissance and Baroque Art* Edgar Peters Bowron; *Cur of Egyptian and Ancient Near Eastern Art* Jeanny Vorys Canby; *Cur of Greek and Roman Art* Diana M Buitron; *Cur of Manuscripts and Rare Books* Lilian M C Randall; *Dir of Educ* Theodore L Low; *Editor of Publs* Anne Garside; *Dir of Conservation Dept* Terry Drayman Weisser; *Registrar* Leopoldine Arz; *Dir of Public Relations* May Ann Daily; *Sales Mgr* Irene Butterbaugh.

Open Mon 1 - 5 PM; Tues - Sat 11 AM - 5 PM; Sun and legal holidays 2 - 5 PM; cl New Year's Day, Fourth of July, Thanksgiving, Christmas Eve, Christmas. No admis. Estab 1931 by the will of Henry Walters and opened in 1934 as an art museum; a neoclassic museum of 1905 with a contemporary wing of five floors, opened in 1974, covering 126,000 sq ft of exhibition space with auditorium, library, and conservation laboratory. Average Annual Attendance: 166,000. Mem: 3000; dues $15 - $500.
Income: $1,200,000 (financed by endowment, membership, city and state appropriation and grants).
Collections: The Collection covers the entire history of art from Egyptian times to the beginning of the 20th century; it includes important groups of Roman Sculpture, Etruscan, Byzantine and medieval art; Sevres porcelains; Near Eastern Art; and 2000 European paintings.
Exhibitions: (1976) Greek and Roman Metalware; Maryland Heritage; European Art at the time of the Revolution; Chinese Export Porcelains from Maryland Collections; The Animal Fair; Masters of Italian Painting from 1300 - 1800. (1977) Antique Coffee Pots; Lustre Pottery; Printed Books before 1500; Controversies in Taste: The Paintings of Alfred Stevens.
Publications: Bulletin, monthly Oct through May; Journal, annually.
Activities: Classes for adults and children; docent training; instant tours; lect open to the public, 12 vis lectr per yr; concerts; gallery talks; tours; individual paintings and original objects of art lent; lending collection contains original art works 25,000; paintings 2000, sculpture 2500; museum shop selling books, reproductions, slides, Christmas cards, notepaper.
—Library. Tel: 301-547-9000 exten 20. *Librn* Muriel Gers.
Open Mon 1 - 5 PM; Tues - Fri 11 AM - 5 PM; by appointment only.
Holdings: Vols 75,000 reference; Per subs 500 reference.
Special Subjects: History of art from prehistoric times to the end of the 19th century, with emphasis on mss illumination and decorative arts.

BARNESVILLE

ARABIAN HORSE MUSEUM,* Box 307, 20703. Tel: 301-972-0568. *Exec Secy* Margaret Dietz.
Open Tues - Fri 9 AM - 5 PM; Sat, Sun & holidays 1 - 5 PM; cl Mon, Thanksgiving, Xmas and New Year's. No admis. Estab 1957.
Collections: Paintings; sculpture; photographs; horse equipment and trophies.
Activities: Guided tours; films; temporary exhibitions; sales shop.
Library: Open to the public for reference. Holdings: 800 vols; manuscripts. Special Subjects: Horses; stud farm catalogs and histories; fictional works on horses.

CHESTERTOWN

HISTORICAL SOCIETY OF KENT COUNTY, Church Alley (Mailing Add: PO Box 665, 21620). *Pres* Mrs Harrison Bristoll Jr; *VPres* William Cooper; *Secy* Mrs Henry A Bruening.
Open by appointment only. Estab 1936 to foster an appreciation of our Colonial heritage; to encourage restoration; to enlighten and to entertain. Headquarters are in an early 18th century town house, beautifully restored and furnished. Mem: 435; dues single $7; family $10; annual meeting Apr.
Income: Financed by membership, and a Candlelight Tour.
Collections: Furniture, some silver, pictures.
Exhibitions: Annual Decorative Arts Forum.
Activities: Lect for members and guests, 4 vis lectr per yr; tours by appointment.

COLLEGE PARK

UNIVERSITY OF MARYLAND, College Park, Art Gallery, 20742. Tel: 301-454-2717. *Dir* Eleanor Green; *Assoc Dir* William Hommel; *Dept Chmn* George Levitine; *Registr* Kate Miller.
Open Mon - Fri 9 AM - 4:30 PM; Sat & Sun 1 - 5 PM; check for summer hours. No admis. Estab 1966 for exhibitions related to the programs of the Department of Art of the University and to serve the Museum Training Program of the Department. Located in Art-Sociology Bldg; large exhibition space in front, smaller gallery in back. Average Annual Attendance: 20,000.
Collections: Small collection of 20th century paintings, sculpture and prints, mostly works executed on the WPA Federal Art Project and the Department of the Treasury, Section of Painting and Sculpture; small collection of West African sculpture.
Exhibitions: Pat Steir; Hugo Weber, a Retrospective; Annual Graduate Thesis Exhibitions; Maurice Prendergast: Art of Impulse and Color; Robert Irwin; Hundertwasser; Richard Diebenkorn Monotypes; Hand Colored Prints; Herman Maril; Kay Sage; Maniere Dawson: a Retrospec-

tive Exhibition of Painting; John Storrs: a Retrospective Exhibition of Sculpture; William Eggleston; Pen to Press; Delacroix to Cezanne: Nineteenth Century French Watercolor Landscapes.
Publications: Catalogs for exhibitions.
Activities: Lect open to public, 8 vis lectr per yr; traveling exhibitions organized and circulated; museum shop selling exhibition catalogs.

EASTON

ACADEMY OF THE ARTS, Box 605, 21601. Tel: 301-822-0455. *Pres* E Sam Hemming; *VPres* Esther Henry; *Treas* Louis Carter; *Secy* Be Holt; *Cur* Linnea Hall.
Open Mon - Fri 10 AM - 4 PM. No admis. Estab 1958 to enrich the lives of the people in the community with the arts through exposure and instruction; there are two galleries. Average Annual Attendance: 6000. Mem: 900; dues $12; annual meeting May.
Income: Financed by endowment, membership, city and state appropriation.
Collections: Art indicative of the area but not limited to that.
Exhibitions: (1976-77) Juried Show; Clay and Fiber show; L. Seyffert (one-man show); eight-man show; school shows, Christmas show, Members show, Needle Arts, and two photography shows.
Publications: Newsletter, quarterly.
Activities: Classes for adults and children; dramatic programs; docent training; music lessons; lect open to the public; concerts; gallery talks; tours; competitions; exten dept serving tri-county area; individual paintings lent to different organizations locally and to other galleries; lending collection contains books 200, original art works, original prints, paintings, photographs.
Library: Open to members only. Holdings: Vols 200, Per subs 3-5. Special Collections: Print collection.

FORT GEORGE MEADE

FORT MEADE MUSEUM, Griffin Ave, Bldg 4674, 20755. Tel: 301-667-6966. *Cur* David C Cole.
Open Wed - Sat 11 AM - 4 PM; Sun 1 - 4 PM; cl Mon, Tues and holidays. No admis. Estab 1963 to collect, preserve, study and display military artifacts relating to the United States Army, Fort Meade and the surrounding region. The gallery is a small post museum with a single display gallery. Average Annual Attendance: 7500.
Income: Financed by federal and military funds.
Collections: Military art mostly World War II.
Activities: Lect open to the public; gallery talks; tours.

FRIENDSVILLE

MUSEUM WITHOUT WALLS, RCEDA INC,* PO Box 45, Morris Ave, 21531. Tel: 301-746-5712. *Exec Dir* RCEDA Inc William F Robinson; *Mus Dir* Richard Kibbey; *Cur Exhibitions* Frank DuVal; *Assoc Cur* Lynda Waggoner; *Technical Dir* Randall Overdorff; *Asst Cur* B David Gaither.
Open 8:30 AM - 4 PM. No admis. Estab Sept 1971 to circulate 30 to 40 traveling exhibitions primarily through school systems in New York State, Pennsylvania, Maryland, Florida and a few other states. Each exhibition is accompanied by an artist-in-residence-lecturer; small gallery for temporary exhibitions for local patrons. Average Annual Attendance: 500,000.
Income: $1,500,000 (financed by endowment, city and state appropriation and earned income). Purchases: $30,000.
Collections: Contemporary monumental stone sculpture and small bronzes, wood sculpture; †20th century paintings; †etchings, engravings, lithographs, silkscreens, woodcuts, Renaissance to contemporary: †photographs.
Activities: Classes for adults and children; dramatic programs; lect open to the public, 6-8 vis lectr per yr, 5 full-time lectrs; concerts; gallery talks; development of workshops, festivals for community center, libraries and colleges; schol; individual paintings and original objects of art lent; lending collection contains lantern slides 5000, photographs 400.
Library: Holdings—Vols 2000; Other —Photographs 400.

FROSTBURG

FROSTBURG STATE COLLEGE, Fine Arts Gallery I, 21532. Tel: 301-689-4274. *Gallery Dir* Dustin P Davis.
Open Mon - Fri Noon - 5 PM; Sun 2 - 5 PM. No admis. Estab 1968 for educational purposes.
Income: Financed by state appropriation.
Collections: Folk art; prints.
Exhibitions: Regional quilt exhibition; 22 Polish textile artists; Works on Paper; Patrick Kelly.

Activities: Lect open to public, 5 vis lectr per yr; gallery talk; competitions.

HAGERSTOWN

WASHINGTON COUNTY MUSEUM OF FINE ARTS, City Park (Mailing Add: PO Box 423, 21740). Tel: 301-739-5727. *Pres, Bd of Trustees* Richard G Wantz; *Dir* H Paul Kotun; *Cur* Robert E Preszler; *Secy* Rita E Kershner.
Open Tues - Sat 10 AM - 5 PM; Sun 1 - 6 PM, cl Mon. No admis. Estab 1929 and opened to the public in 1931 for the purpose of preserving, protecting, promoting, displaying and educating through the arts; the Museum consists of the William H Singer Memorial Gallery; Sculpture Court, Concert Gallery, two general galleries, and the Youth Gallery. Average Annual Attendance: 60,000. Mem: 800; dues individual $10, family $25; annual meeting April and Oct.
Income: $116,000 (financed by membership, city and state appropriation, and county government).
Collections: European, †American sculpture, †prints and drawings; Oriental jades; †contemporary painting, drawing, prints and sculpture; American pressed glass; antique laces; illuminated manuscripts.
Exhibitions: First Snow (illustrations by Vo-Dinh); Early American Pressed Glass; Colonial Interiors (Bicentennial Exhibition); Paintings by Edward Fenimore, Alice Neal, Si Ling King; Fiber Art by Thurid Clark; Spirit of Independence (Kent Bicentennial Portfolio); Tramp Art (a form of American Folk Art); Royal Watercolor Society; Scouting through the Eyes of Norman Rockwell; African Sculpture; Americans Abroad; Charles Carroll of Carrollton; Americana (carvings) by Wilhelm Schimmel and John Bell (ceramics); Cambodian Art from Angkor Wat; Public School Art; Photographs by Marvin and Ginger Marcus; Hagerstown Art Club Annual Exhibition; Annual Photographic Salon; Annual Exhibition of Cumberland Valley Artists; Museum's Permanent Collection: Prints, Landscapes, Portraits, Drawings, Contemporary work, Sculpture, Oriental Objects.
Publications: Bulletin, monthly; Annual reports; catalogs of major exhibitions.
Activities: Classes for adults and children; dramatic programs; docent training; lect open to the public, 4 vis lectr per yr; concerts; gallery talks; tours; competitions; exten dept serving Pennsylvania, Virginia, WVirginia, western Maryland; individual paintings and original objects of art lent to other museums, galleries, as per Museum Policy regarding security; traveling exhibitions organized and circulated; sales shop selling books, magazines, original art, reproductions, prints, slides and original art objects and hand crafted items.
Library. Open to the public for reference only. Holdings: Vols 5000, Per subs 14.

MONKTON

BREEZEWOOD FOUNDATION MUSEUM AND GARDEN, 3722 Hess Road, 21111. Tel: 301-771-4485. *Pres* A B Griswold; *Secy* Ann Watters; *Treas* Mary Boehm.
Ope First Sun of each month from May - Oct, 2 - 6 PM. Admis $2. Estab 1956 to exhibit Breezewood's collection of sculpture and other art from Southeast Asia. One large room and two small ones. Average Annual Attendance: 600.
Income: Financed by endowment and privately.
Collections: Sculpture and art from Southeast Asia; Buddhist art from India.

ROCKVILLE

CITY OF ROCKVILLE MUNICIPAL ART GALLERY,* Civic Center Mansion, 603 Edmonston Dr, 20851. Tel: 301-424-3184. *Dir* Bernard R Loiselle; *Civic Center Supvr* Jane Loiselle.
Open Mon - Fri 1 - 5 PM; Sun 2 - 5 PM. No admis. Estab 1959. Average Annual Attendance: 7500.
Income: Financed by city appropriation.
Collections: Small permanent collection.
Exhibitions: Twelve shows per year, one a youth show.
Activities: Classes for adults.

SAINT MICHAELS

CHESAPEAKE BAY MARITIME MUSEUM, Navy Point (Mailing Add: PO Box 636, 21663). *Dir* R J Holt; *Cur* B A G Fuller.
Open Oct - May, Tues - Sun 10 AM - 4 PM; cl Mon; May - Oct, 10 AM - 5 PM. Admis adults $2, children 75¢. Estab 1968 as a waterside museum dedicated to preserving the martime history of the Chesapeake Bay. Twelve buildings on approximately five acres of waterfront property including Hooper's Strait Lighthouse, 1879. Average Annual Attendance: 60,000. Mem: 3000, dues $10 - $25.
Income: Financed by membership and admissions.

Collections: Vessels—Rosie Parks, 1955, Edna E Lockwood, 1839, Sadie, 1914, W A Johns, 1880, Minnie G; ship models; paintings.
Publications: Weather Gauge (newsletter), quarterly.
Activities: Educ dept; docent training; museum shop selling books, reproductions, prints.
Library: Small library for research only by appointment with curator.

TOWSON

GOUCHER COLLEGE, Kraushaar Auditorium Lobby Gallery, Department of Visual Arts, Dulaney Valley Rd, 21204. Tel: 301-825-3300, exten 310. *Chmn Dept Visual Arts* Hilton Brown; *Keeper of the Goucher Coll* Gretel Chapman.
Open Mon - Fri 9 AM - 5 PM during the academic calendar and on evenings and weekends of public events. No admis. Estab 1964 to display temporary and continuously changing exhibitions of contemporary and historically important visual arts. Gallery space located in the lobby of the Kraushaar Auditorium; 150 running feet of wall space. Average Annual Attendance: 15,000.
Income: Financed privately.
Collections: Ceramics; paintings; prints; drawings; coins; sculpture; textiles; Elizabeth Morris Collection, textiles containing over 200 objects representing textiles from Egypt, Peru, Java, China, Japan, Europe and America.
Exhibitions: Paintings by Hilton Brown; Photographs by Barbara Young; Paintings by Lisa Lawrence; Fiberworks by Sharon Rose; Artworks by Jane Kelly Morais; Ceramics from the Goucher Collection; Women Artists in Baltimore.
Activities: Lect open to public, 3 vis lectr per yr; gallery talks; individual paintings and original objects of art lent to museums and university galleries.

TOWSON STATE UNIVERSITY
—**Art Gallery,** York Road, 21204. Tel: 301-321-2808. *Dir* Christopher Bartlett.
Open Mon - Fri 11 AM - 4 PM; Tues & Thurs 6 - 9 PM; Sat & Sun 1 - 5 PM. No admis. Estab 1973 to provide primarily contemporary art exhibitions for students, faculty and the wider community. Situated in the seven million dollar fine arts building of Towson State and designated The Fine Arts Center for the State, the gallery is 60 x 30 ft and 15 ft high. Average Annual Attendance: 7500.
Income: Financed by state appropriation, donations and gifts.
Exhibitions: Leonard Baskin (new graphics and watercolors); Art Department Faculty; Tyler School of Art Faculty (painting, drawing, sculpture); John Mitchell (plastics and prints); New Directions in Fabric Design (national invitational); Art Department Student Show; Naive Art in Yugoslavia; Chinese Brush Painting by Chao-Hwa Tung.
Publications: Exhibition posters; catalogs of selected shows, 2 per year.
Activities: Lect open to public, 10 vis lectr per yr; artmobile.
—**Roberts Room,** Fine Arts Bldg, 21204. Tel: 301-321-2807. *Cur* Harriet McNamee.
Open during academic year Mon - Fri 10 AM - Noon and 2 - 4 PM; summers Mon - Fri 10 AM - Noon and 1 - 3 PM. No admis. Estab 1972 to provide an area to display the Asian art collections of the University and for the benefit of both the university community and the public. The gallery is located on the second floor of the Fine Arts building. Average Annual Attendance: 3000.
Income: $33,800 (financed by state appropriation and university budget).

WESTMINSTER

WESTERN MARYLAND COLLEGE, Gallery One, Department of Art, 21157. *Chmn Art Dept* Wasyl Palijczuk; *Gallery Dir* Roy Fender.
Open Mon - Fri 10 AM - 4 PM. No admis. Estab to expose students to original works by artists.

MASSACHUSETTS

AMHERST

AMHERST COLLEGE, Mead Art Building, 01002. Tel: 413-542-2335. *Dir* Frank Trapp; *Cur* Judith Barter.
Open Mon - Fri 10 AM - 4:30 PM; Sat & Sun 7 AM - 5 PM (shorter hours during the summer). No admis. Estab 1949. Average Annual Attendance: 35,000.
Collections: †American art; †English art; †Ancient art; Western European and Oriental collections.
Exhibitions: Changing exhibitions for college curriculum needs; War á la Mode; American Painters of the Arctic; American Folk Art.
Publications: Catalogs for major exhibitions.
Library: Art library. Holdings: Vols 20,000.

JONES LIBRARY, INC, 43 Amity St, 01002. Tel: 413-256-0246. *Dir* Anne M Turner; *Asst Dir* Sondra M Radosh; *Ref Librn* Pauline M Peterson; *Adult Serv Librn* Catherine B Gaoon; *Cur* Philip N Cronenwett.
Open Mon & Fri 9 AM - 5:30 PM; Tues - Thurs 9 AM - 9:30 PM; Sat 10 AM - 5:30 PM; Special Coll Mon - Fri 9 AM - 5 PM only. Estab 1919 as a public library. Circ: 210,000. Gallery has monthly exhibits by local artists.
Income: Financed by endowment and city appropriation.
Holdings: Vols 93,827; Per subs 295; AV—Audiotapes, cassettes, Kodachromes, lantern slides, microfilm, phonorecords, slides; Other—Clipping files, framed reproductions, manuscripts, memorabilia, original art works and documents, pamphlets, photographs, prints, reproductions, sculpture.
Special Subjects: Local history and Amherst authors.
Special Collections: Emily Dickinson, Harlan Fiske Stone, Robert Frost, Ray Stannard Baker, Sidney Waugh.
Activities: Lectures open to public; concerts; gallery talks; library tours.

UNIVERSITY OF MASSACHUSETTS, AMHERST
—University Gallery, Fine Arts Center, 01003. Tel: 413-545-3670. *Dir* Hugh M Davies; *Gallery Manager* Peter J Bena; *Registrar* Betsy Siersma.
Open Tues - Fri 11:30 AM - 4:30 PM; Sat & Sun 2 - 5 PM during school year. No admis. Estab 1961, main gallery 60 x 60 ft, East, West and Lower Galleries 20 x 60 ft each. Average Annual Attendance: 10,000. Mem: 150; dues $5 - $10.
Collections: †20th century American works on paper including drawings, prints and photographs.
Exhibitions: Critical Perspectives on American Art; Artist and Fabricator Large Scale Sculpture, Sol LeWitt, Larry Bell, John Wittenbecher, Richard Feischner and Steven Antonakos; 19th Century Drawings and Watercolors.
Publications: Exhibitions catalogs.
Activities: Lect open to the public, 6 vis lectr per yr; concerts; gallery talks; tours; individual paintings and original objects of art lent to other institutions; lending collection contains original art works, original prints, photographs, sculpture; traveling exhibitions organized and circulated.
—Art Collection,* Art Department, Bartlett Hall, 01002. Tel: 413-545-1902. *Chmn Art Dept* George Wardlaw; *Dir University Coll* Walter Kamys.
Estab 1963 to form best possible collection of contemporary American drawings.
Collection: Contemporary American drawings, paintings and sculpture.
—Art Slide Library. *Cur* Dorothy Perkins.
Open Mon - Fri 8 AM - 4 PM.
Holdings: Vols 24,500; AV—Slides 65,000.

ANDOVER

PHILLIPS ACADEMY, Addison Gallery of American Art, PO Box 48, 01810. Tel: 617-475-7515. *Dir* Christopher C Cook; *Cur Photography* James L Sheldon.
Open Tues - Sat 10 AM - 5 PM; Sun 2:30 - 5 PM. No admis. Estab 1931 in memory of Mrs Keturah Addison Cobb, to enrich permanently the lives of the students by helping to cultivate and foster in them a love for the beautiful. The gift also included a number of important American paintings, prints and sculpture. Average Annual Attendance: 35,000.
Income: Financed by endowment.
Collections: 18th, 19th and 20th century paintings, sculpture, drawings, prints; contemporary photographs, film and videotapes.
Exhibitions: Three Views of the North American Landscape: photographs by Bruce Davidson, Jerry Uelsmann, and NASA; Paintings by James Fasanella; Photographs by Clarence John Laughlin; Merrimack Valley Artists: Works and Video.
Activities: Art therapy for adults and children; lect open to public, 8-10 vis lectr per yr; concerts; individual paintings and original objects of art lent to museums.
Library: A small reference library.

ATTLEBORO

ATTLEBORO MUSEUM, INC, 199 County St, 02703. Tel: 617-222-2466. *Dir* Vera L Cross; *Bd of Trustees* Pasquale Masiello, Mrs Edwin Dunlop, August Schaeffer, Pierre Lonsbury, Mrs Donald Richardson, Charles Calverley, William Bott, Mrs Anthony Nyzio, Raymond Guillette, Lester Larson, Mrs Ariel Hall and Mrs Harold Washburn.
Open Tues - Fri 12:30 - 4 PM; Sat & Sun 2 - 5 PM; cl Mon & holidays. No admis. Estab 1927 to exhibit the works of current artists, as well as the art works of the museum's own collection. There are preview openings for members and guests, plus several competitive exhibits with awards and an outdoor art festival. Three galleries with changing monthly exhibits of paintings, drawings and prints, as well as glass cases for jewelry and

crafts. All three galleries are carpeted with grass cloth walls and excellent track lighting. Average Annual Attendance: Approx 7200. Mem: Approx 300; dues individual $6, family $10. Annual meeting May.
Income: Financed by membership, gifts. Purchases: $400.
Collections: Paintings and prints.
Exhibitions: (1977) Three Women Painters, Jane Chermayoff, Gracia Dayton and Nancy Eddy; The Hallidays, paintings by Allan and Dori Halliday; Guest Exhibition; (1978) Area Artist Exhibition; Young Talent I; Young Talent II; Art as a Visual Language; Competitive Painting Exhibition; Mirtala, one-woman show of the sculpture of sculpture and poet, Mirtala Bentov; Art in the Park; Members Summer Show.
Publications: Yearly Program Booklet; School Brochures; Newsletter, monthly.
Activities: Classes for adults and children; lect open to public; concerts; gallery talks; competitions, painting and photography; original objects of art lent; original art sold.

BEVERLY

BEVERLY HISTORICAL SOCIETY,* 117 Cabot St, 01915. Tel: 617-922-1186. *Pres* Robert Lovett; *Treas* Ray Standley; *Chmn Balch House* Roger Hanners; *Chmn Hale House* Esther Herrick.
Open throughout the year Wed, Thurs & Fri 10 AM - 4 PM; July & Aug daily 10 AM - 4 PM; Balch House open June through Sept, daily 10 AM - 4 PM; cl Sun, other times by appointment; Hale House open June 15 - Sept 15, daily 10:30 AM - 4 PM, cl Sun & Mon; other times by appointment. Admis adults $1, children 25¢. Estab and inc 1891, to investigate, record and perpetuate local history. Occupies house built by John Cabot in 1781. The Balch House built in 1636 by John Balch contains old furniture. The Hale House was built in 1694 by the first minister, John Hale. Mem: 380; dues single $5, life $250; annual meeting Oct.
Collections: An extensive collection of objects pertaining to the sea, instruments, ship models, shells, tapa cloth, ship portraits; portraits by Gilbert Stuart of early merchants and seamen; large collection of glass, porcelain, pewter, embroideries, colonial and Revolutionary documents.

BOSTON

ANCIENT AND HONORABLE ARTILLERY COMPANY OF MASSACHUSETTS,* Faneuil Hall, 02109. Tel: 617-227-1638. *Cur* Sidney M Abbott.
Open Mon - Fri 10 AM - 4 PM; cl Sat, Sun, holidays & two weeks in Oct. No admis. Estab 1638.
Collections: Military historical material; paintings; portraits.
Activities: Guided tours.
Library: Open to individuals by request for research. Holdings: 100 vols.

ART INSTITUTE OF BOSTON, MacIvor Reddie Gallery, 700 Beacon St, 02215. Tel: 617-262-1223. *Pres* William H Willis, Jr; *Chmn Gallery Comt* Nathan Goldstein.
Open Mon - Fri 9 AM - 5 PM; Mon - Thurs 6 - 9 PM. No admis. Estab 1969 to show work by young New England artists, all disciplines, and work by well known artists from any locale, especially in less exhibited disciplines such as graphic design, and to show work by students and faculty of the institute. 3000 sq ft of gallery. Average Annual Attendance: 2500.
Exhibitions: (1976-78) 31 selected shows, Complete Graphic Works of Hundertwasser; The Illustrators Workshop; Illustrations of LeRoy Nieman.
Activities: Classes for adults; lect open to public, 5 vis lectr per yr; gallery talks; competitions, local and regional, usually student oriented; exten dept serving metro Boston; individual paintings and original objects of art lent to other galleries.

BOSTON ARCHITECTURAL CENTER, 320 Newbury St, 02115. Tel: 617-536-9018. *Chmn* Peter Blake; *Dir Admin* Elsie Hurst; *Dean* Archangelo Cascieri; *Pres Bd Dir* Herbert Glassman.
Open Mon - Thurs 9 AM - 11 PM; Fri - Sun 9 AM - 5 PM. No admis. Estab 1883 for education of architects and designers. Small exhibition space on first floor. Average Annual Attendance: 2000. Mem: 300; dues $25; annual meeting June.
Exhibitions: Signs and Lights.
Activities: Classes for adults; lect open to public, 16 vis lectr per yr; competitions; exten dept serving professional architects; traveling exhibitions organized and circulated.
—Library. *Librn* Susan Lewis. Open to the public for reference.
Holdings: Vols 10,000; Per subs 140; Other—Slides 25,000.
Special Subjects: Architectural preservation, solar energy, architectural history.
—Memorial Library. Open by appointment only.
Holdings: Vols 2000.

Special Collections: 18th, 19th and early 20th century architectural books from the collections of practicing architects.

BOSTON ART COMMISSION OF THE CITY OF BOSTON, 334 Boylston St, 02116. *Chmn* Marvin E Goody.
Estab 1898 to accept and maintain the art collection owned by the City of Boston. Mem: 5, one representative from each organization: American Institute of Architects, Massachusetts Institute of Technology, Boston Public Library, Copley Society, and Boston Museum of Fine Arts; meetings approx once monthly.
Income: $3335 (financed by city appropriation).
Collections: City of Boston art collection, including sculpture, statuary, paintings, and fountains.
Publications: Catalog and guide to the art work owned by the City of Boston, in preparation.

BOSTON ATHENAEUM, 10½ Beacon St, 02108. Tel: 617-227-0270. *Dir & Librn* Rodney Armstrong; *Art Librn* David McKibbin; *Art Department Librn* Jack Jackson and Donald C Kelley; *Print Department Librn* Charles E Mason, Jr and Pauela Pamela Hayle.
Open Mon - Fri 9 AM - 5:30 PM; Sat 9 AM - 4 PM; cl Sun also Sat June 1 - Sept 1. Gallery serves New England living artists in the fine arts and crafts.
Income: $750,000 (financed by endowment and membership). Purchases: $75,000.
Holdings: Vols 500,000; Per subs 600; AV—Microfilm; Other—Clipping files, exhibitions catalogs, manuscripts, original art works, original documents, pamphlets, photographs, prints and sculpture.
Activities: Lect open to the public, 6 vis lectr per yr; concerts; gallery talks; tours; competitions.

BOSTON PRINTMAKERS, c/o Sylvia Rantz, Secy-Treas, 299 High Rock St, Needham, 02192. Tel: 617-444-2692. *Pres* Tim Hamill.
Estab 1947 to aid printmakers in exhibiting their work; to bring quality work to the public. Average Annual Attendance: 15,000. Mem: 150 (all printmakers, subject to a slide review); dues $15; annual meeting June.
Income: Financed by membership, entry fees, and commission on sales. Purchases: $5,000.
Exhibitions: Boston Center for the Arts; DeCordova Museum; Members' Exhibits at Duxbury Art Complex.
Activities: Lect; gallery talks; competitions with awards and prizes; traveling exhibitions organized and circulated.

BOSTON PUBLIC LIBRARY,* Copley Square, 02117. Tel: 617-536-5400. *Dir & Librn* Philip J McNiff.
—**Central Library.** Building contains mural decorations by Pierre Puvis de Chavannes, Edwin A Abbey, John Elliott, and John Singer Sargent; bronze doors by Daniel Chester French; sculptures by Frederick Mac-Monnies, Louis St. Gaudens, Bela Pratt, Francis Derwent Wood; illustrations by Howard Pyle; paintings by Duplessis and Copley; and bust of John Deferrari by Joseph A Coletti.
—**Fine Arts.** *Cur of Fine Arts* G Florence Connolly.
Open Mon - Fri 9 AM - 9 PM; Sat 9 AM - 6 PM; Sun 2 - 6 PM in winter, cl in summer.
Holdings: Vols 73,000; Other—Pictures 410,000.
—**Albert H Wiggin Gallery (Prints).** *Keeper of Prints* Sinclair H Hitchings.
Open Mon - Fri 9 AM - 9 PM; Sat - 6 PM; Sun 2 - 6 PM in winter, cl in summer. Study Room Mon - Fri 9 AM - 5 PM; cl Sat & Sun.
Holdings: Vols 1554; Other—Prints 49,400, photographs, drawings and watercolors, oil paintings 23, fore-edge paintings 258, porcelain figurines of 13 Cries of London.
Exhibitions: Eight or nine per year.

ISABELLA STEWART GARDNER MUSEUM, 280 The Fenway (Mailing Add: 2 Palace Rd, 02115). Tel: 617-566-1401. *Dir* Rollin van N Hadley; *Asst Dir* Linda V Hewitt; *Cur* Deborah Gribbon; *Conservator* Jack Soultanian; *Textile Conservator* Yvonne Cox.
Open (Sept - June) Tues 1 - 9:30 PM; Wed - Sun 1 - 5:30 PM; (July & Aug) Tues - Sun 1 - 5:30 PM; cl Mon. Admis adults $1, lesser amounts acceptable. Estab 1903, the museum houses Isabella Stewart Gardner's various collections. Museum building is styled after a 16th century Venetian villa; all galleries open onto a central, glass-roofed courtyard, filled with flowers that are changed with the seasons of the year. Average Annual Attendance: 170,000.
Income: Financed by endowment and door fee.
Collections: Permanent collections: Italian Renaissance, Dutch and Flemish 17th century, 19th century American and French paintings; rare books and manuscripts, dating from the 15th century; Oriental and Islamic sculpture, glass, ceramics; Japanese screens; Gothic and Italian Renaissance, Roman and classical sculpture.
Publications: Fenway Court (annual report).
Activities: Sales shop selling books, reproductions, prints, slides.

Library: Librn Susan Sinclair. Open to scholars who need to work with museum archives. Holdings: Vols 500; Per subs 6.

GIBSON SOCIETY, INC, 137 Beacon St, 02116. Tel: 617-267-6338. *Pres* Stephen T Hibbard; *Custodians* Mr and Mrs David Sweeney.
Open Tues - Sun 2 - 5 PM; cl Mon and holidays. Admis $1. Estab 1957 as a Victorian House museum. Average Annual Attendance: 1500.
Collections: Decorative arts; paintings; sculpture; Victorian period furniture.
Activities: Guided tours; sales shop selling books and postcards.

GUILD OF BOSTON ARTISTS,* 162 Newbury St, 02116. Tel: 617-536-7660. *Pres* Robert Douglas Hunter; *VPres* Charles A Mahoney; *Secy* Ruth Wynn; *Cur* Phyllis Church Maloney.
Open Tues - Sat 10:30 AM - 5:30 PM; cl Sun & July & Aug. No admis. Estab and inc 1914; cooperative organization; Guild owns building; one gallery with continuous exhibitions in which each member is entitled to show one work; second gallery devoted to one-man shows, each member by turn at regular intervals. Mem: Active 65-80, associates under 100; annual meeting April.
Exhibitions: Three yearly general exhibitions by entire active membership.

INSTITUTE OF CONTEMPORARY ART, 955 Boylston St, 02115. Tel: 617-266-5152. *Dir* Stephen S Prokopoff; *Business Mgr* Lindsay Shearer; *Development Dir* Thomas Kelley; *Cur* Elisabeth Sussman & Michael Leja; *Communications* Lyn Jackson.
Open Tues - Sat 10 AM - 5 PM; Wed 10 AM - 9 PM; Sun Noon - 5 PM. Admis adults $1.00, students & sr citizens 50¢. Estab 1936 to organize, document, and exhibit works of contemporary masters of new and innovative talents and of artists who have been overlooked. A full range of contemporary working methods including photography and film, the crafts and performance are shown. Two floors of gallery space (4000 sq ft), third floor offices and auditorium; located in 19th century renovated police station. Average Annual Attendance: 55,000. Mem: 2000; dues $20 and up; annual meeting Jan.
Income: $350,000 (financed by membership, city and state appropriations, gifts and grants. Purchases: $350,000.
Exhibitions: Skyscraper Style: Art Deco New York; Boston 200 Bicentennial; Calders Flying Colors; Oldenburg: 6 Themes; Catharine Murphy; Lucas Samaras: Photo Transformations; David von Schlegel; Skowhegan: A Retrospective 1946-1976; Tonia Aminoff's Recent Work; Marie Cosindas: Polaroid Photographs, 1960-1976; America 1976; America the Third Century; Prints: Buchner, Lewitt, Mangold, Marden, Martin, Renouf.
Publications: Newsletter, bimonthly; exhibition catalogs.
Activities: Classes for children; dramatic programs; docent training; lect open to public, 20 vis lectr per yr; concerts; gallery talks, tours; traveling exhibitions organized and circulated; museum shop selling books, catalogs and cards.

MASSACHUSETTS HISTORICAL SOCIETY,* 1154 Boylston St, 02215. Tel: 617-536-1608. *Dir* Stephen T Riley.
Open Mon - Fri 9 AM - 4:45 PM; cl Sat, Sun & holidays. No admis. Estab 1791.
Collections: Archives; historical material; paintings; sculpture.
Publications: Annual brochure; various books; irregular leaflets.
Activities: Lectures; temporary exhibitions.
Library: Librn John D Cushing. Holdings: 300,000 vols; manuscripts.

MUSEUM OF FINE ARTS,* 465 Huntington Ave, 02115. Tel: 617-267-9300. *Dir* Merrill C Rueppel; *Asst Dir Admin* Arthur D Larson; *Registrar* Linda Thomas; *Cur Asiatic Art* Jan Fontein; *Conservator Asiatic Art* Yashiro Iguchi; *Cur American Decorative Arts* Johnathan Fairbanks; *Cur European Decorative Arts & Sculpture* Robert C Moeller; *Cur Contemporary Art* Kenworth Moffett; *Cur Textiles* Larry Salmon; *Cur Prints & Drawings* Eleanor A Sayre; *Cur Egyptian Art* William Kelly Simpson; *Cur Classical Art* Cornelius C Vermeule.
Open daily 10 AM - 5 PM; Tues Eve until 9 PM; cl New Year's Day, July 4, Thanksgiving and Christmas. Admis adults $2.50, students and senior citizens $1.50; free Sun 10 AM - 1 PM; children under 16 free; 65 and over free Mon 10 AM - 12 PM. Estab and inc 1870; present building opened 1909. Average Annual Attendance: 650,000. Mem: 13,000, dues $10 - $1000.
Income: c $3,500,000. Purchases $1,000,000.
Collections: Outstanding Chinese, Japanese and Indian art; exceptional †Egyptian, †Greek and †Roman art; †master paintings of Europe and America; †superb print collection from 15th century to present; also †sculpture, †decorative and minor arts including period rooms, porcelains, †silver, †tapestries, †textiles, †costumes and †musical instruments.
Exhibitions: Specially organized exhibitions are continually on view in addition to exhibitions of the permanent collections.
Publications: Bulletin, quarterly; Calendar of Events, monthly.

Activities: Department of Public Education offers lectures, seminars and films for adults and school groups; lectures, exhibitions and slides for schools; special activities for young people in creative and visual arts such as Children's Room and High School Scholarship Class; art classes for adults and children; television programs in cooperation with WGBH-TV; study and performance of Early Music.
—**Library:** *Librn:* Kathy Berg.
Holdings: Vols 180,000; AV—Slides 70,000; Other—Clippings, pamphlets.

SOCIETY FOR THE PRESERVATION OF NEW ENGLAND ANTIQUITIES,* Otis House, 141 Cambridge St, 02114. Tel: 617-227-3956. *Pres* Mrs Gemmell Jainschigg; *Exec Dir* Abbott L Cummings; *Admin of Membership & Pub Affairs* Ellen F Deward; *Arch Conservator* Morgan W Phillips; *Cur Coll* Richard C Nylander; *Interpreter of Properties & Coll* Roy A Petre; *Asst to Exec Dir* Richard P Thompson; *Dir of Properties & Coll* Frederick E Eayrs Jr; *Properties Adminr* Lynne M Spencer; *Registrar* Christina H Nelson; *Dir of Development* Stanley M Smith; *Dir Consulting Services* David M Hart; *Arch Historian* Frederic C Detwiller; *Architect* Maximilian L Ferro; *Dir of Field Service* William B Hart; *Preservation Planner* Kathryn Welch.
Open Mon - Fri 10 AM - 4 PM; cl Sat, Sun & Holidays. Admis nonmembers $1. Estab and inc 1910, the Otis House serves as both headquarters and museum for the Society: Society owns over 60 historic houses throughout New England, which are open to the public. Mem: 3650; dues $10 and up; annual meeting May.
Publications: Old Time New England, biannual bulletin.
Activities: Guided tours of the newly restored period rooms are given at 10, 11, 1, 2 & 3, Mon - Fri.
Library contains study collections of New England architecture in the form of fragments 5000, measured drawings 3000, photographs 200,000, and pattern books 200; other collections include textiles and wallpaper.

BREWSTER

DRUMMER BOY MUSEUM,* Route 6A, 02631. Tel: 617-896-3823. *Mgrs* Lewis A & Bette McGowan.
Open May 15 - Oct 12 daily 9:30 AM - 6 PM. Admis adults $2, children 12-16 $1, 6-12 75¢, children under 6 free; special group rates. Estab 1961.
Collections: (Art) Mural paintings; historical material.
Activities: Guided tours; sales shop.

BROCKTON

BROCKTON ART CENTER, Fuller Memorial, Oak St, 02401. Tel: 617-588-6000. *Dir* Marilyn Hoffman; *Cur* Richard Minutillo; *Dir Public Affairs* Philip O'Brien; *Business Mgr* Kate Fielder; *Educ Coordr* Laureen Tucker; *Museum Technician* Patrick Bell; *Dir Art Workshops* Beverly Edwards.
Open Tues - Sat 1 - 5 PM; Sun 1 - 6 PM. Admis Donations. Estab 1969 to provide a variety of art exhibitions, performing arts and education programs of regional and national interest. The Center houses six galleries; one gallery is reserved for important works of art on loan from the Museum of Fine Arts, Boston. Average Annual Attendance: 28,000. Mem: 1500; dues $20.
Income: $784,000 (financed by endowment, membership, state appropriation and grants).
Collections: 19th century American and European paintings; contemporary American art; Early American and Sandwich glass.
Exhibitions: Temporary exhibits of 19th century American contemporary crafts; regional and national contemporary exhibits; biennial of Boston painting and sculpture.
Publications: Newsletter and Calendar of Events 4 time per yr.
Activities: Classes for adults and children; dramatic programs; docent training; special programs for children; lectr open to the public, 4 vis lectr per yr; gallery talks; tours; competitions; individual paintings and original objects of art lect to accredited museums of the American Association of Museums; lending collection contains paintings and slides; traveling exhibitions organized and circulated; museum shop selling original art, reproductions and contemporary crafts.
Library: Open to members, staff and students. Holdings: Vols 1200; Per subs 8.

BROCKTON PUBLIC LIBRARY SYSTEM,* Municipal Gallery, 304 Main St, 02401. Tel: 617-587-2516. *Libr Dir* Ernest J Webby.
Open Mon - Fri 9 AM - 9 PM; Sat 9 AM - 6 PM; cl Sun. No admis. Special room for monthly art exhibitions. Average Annual Attendance: 20,000.
Holdings: Vols 5000 on fine and applied art.
Collections: W C Bryant Collection of 19th and 20th century American paintings, chiefly by New England artists; loan collection of 20th century painters from the Woman's Club of Brockton; gifts of 20th century paintings which includes four paintings by Hendricks Hallett and an oil

painting by Mme Elisabeth Weber-Fulop; mounted photographs of Renaissance art and watercolors by F Mortimer Lamb.
Exhibitions: Monthly exhibitions by local and nationally known artists.

BROOKLINE

BROOKLINE PUBLIC LIBRARY, 361 Washington St, 02146. Tel: 617-734-0100. *Town Librn* Theresa A Carroll; *Asst Town Librn* Dalija Karoblis; *Supv Loan Dept* Barbara Kohl; *Head Technical Services* Irene Wilkinson; *Reference Supv* Lois Van Hoesen; *Art & Music Librn* Judith Jackson.
Open (Sept - June) Mon - Thurs 9 AM - 9 PM; Fri - Sat 9 AM - 6 PM; Sun 1 - 4 PM; (July - Aug) Mon - Thurs 9 AM - 9 PM, Fri 9 AM - 6 PM. Estab 1857 to provide information, books, records, pictures, etc. for the use of the community. Circ: 550,000.
Income: $1,086,198 (financed by city appropriation). Purchases: $168,500.
Holdings: Vols 300,000; Per subs 700; AV—Cassettes, microfilm, phonorecords 9000; Other—Clipping files, exhibitions catalogs 1000, pamphlets, photographs, prints and catalogued maps.
Special Collections: Reference collection of pictures and photographs of Brookline.
Publications: Booklists, sporadically.
Activities: Lect open to public, 6 vis lect per yr; concerts; tours; film programs; competitions.
—**Brookline Art Society**
Estab 1950. Dues $20.
Exhibitions: Rotating exhibits by individual members, local artists, and photographers; annual juried show.
Publications: Newsletter, monthly.
Activities: Workshops, programs open to public.

CAMBRIDGE

CAMBRIDGE ART ASSOCIATION,* 23 Garden St, 02138. Tel: 617-876-0246. *Exec Dir* Edward Cooper.
Open Tues - Sat 10:30 AM - 5 PM; Wed until 9 PM; Sun 2 - 6 PM; cl Sun in July, cl in Aug. No admis. Estab 1944 to exhibit, rent and sell members' work and to encourage an interest in fine arts and crafts in the community. Mem: 700; dues students $5, friends $15, artists $20; annual meeting June.
Exhibitions: Members' juried exhibitions in Main Gallery every two weeks, some invited shows and a foreign exhibition each year. Invited shows in Rental Gallery and Craft Gallery. Prize award approximately $1000 annually.
Publications: Bulletin, monthly.
Activities: Classes for adults, lectures and demonstrations; exhibit and sale of books by members; rental services of art works; spring auction; print box.

HARVARD UNIVERSITY
—**Busch-Reisinger Museum,** 29 Kirkland St, 02138. Tel: 617-495-2317. *Asst Cur* Charles W Haxthausen; *Staff Asst* Karen Davidson.
Open Mon - Sat 9 AM - 4:45 PM; cl Sun & holidays. No admis. Estab 1901 to collect and preserve art objects and artifacts of central and northern Europe which are of high quality and/or historically and culturally significant. This collection serves the teaching program of the Department of Fine Arts, outside scholars and the general public. The galleries are divided into three historical architectural styles which contain art of roughly the same period: Romanesque, Gothic and Renaissance. In addition, there are galleries for German Expressionist art. Average Annual Attendance: 39,000. Mem: 175; dues $20; annual meeting in the Fall.
Income: $115,000 (financed by endowment, membership).
Collections: Works of art of the Middle Ages, Renaissance and Modern Times; extensive collection of Expressionist and Bauhaus works; Bauhaus and Lyonel Feininger Archives; reproductions of works of Germanic art of the Middle Ages and Renaissance.
Exhibitions: Color of the Middle Ages (Facsimiles of Illuminated Manuscripts); Graphic Art in Germany Today; German and Netherlandish Art from the time of Durer and Breugel, German Expressionist Arts; Graphic Works of Max Beckmann; Graphic Art from the Romantic Age; The Works of Paul Klee; Prints, Drawings and Sculpture of Kathe Kollwitz.
Publications: Newsletter, quarterly.
Activities: Tours, by appointment; lect open to public; concerts; gallery talks; individual paintings (8000) and original objects of art (4000) lent to museums having special exhibitions; traveling exhibitions organized and circulated.
—**Carpenter Center for the Visual Arts,** 19 Prescott St, 02138. Tel: 617-495-3251. *Dir* Robert G Gardner; *Resident Artist & Acting Dir* Dimitri Hadzi; *Chmn, Dept Visual & Environmental Studies* Lou Bakanowsky.
Hours vary. No admis. Estab 1963 as an undergraduate department in visual and environmental studies;

Income: Financed by endowment.

Activities: Traveling exhibitions organized and circulated; individual paintings lent to other Harvard departments or houses.

Publications: Exhibition catalogs.

—Harvard Semitic Museum, 6 Divinity Ave, 02138. Tel: 617-495-4631. *Dir* Frank Moore Cross Jr; *Cur* Dr Carney E S Gavin.

Open by appointment only. No admis. Estab 1889 to promote sound knowledge of Semitic languages and history; an archaeological research museum, no permanent exhibition space. Average Annual Attendance: 500. Mem: 150; dues $20.

Income: Financed by endowment, membership and Federal research grants and contracts.

Collections: †Historic photographs, E E Hale Egyptian Collection; Excavated material from Nuzi and various other Palestinian and near Eastern sites; Phoenician glass; Islamic metal, weapons, garments (Ottoman Empire).

Publications: Harvard Semitic Series.

Activities: Classes for adults and children; docent training; lect open to public, 5 vis lectr per yr; tours; exten dept serving Harvard University; original objects of art lent to universities and museums; sells reproductions, prints, rubbings, jewelry and cards.

—William Hayes Fogg Art Museum, 32 Quincy St, 02138. Tel: 617-495-2387. *Dir* Seymour Slive; *Asst Dir* Suzannah Doeringer; *Financial Officer* Martha Coburn; *Archivist* Phoebe Peebles; *Chief Conservator* Arthur Beale; *Assoc Conservator* Greta Andersen & Marjorie Cohn; *Science Assoc* Leon Stodulski; *Cur Drawings* Konrad Oberhuber; *Asst Cur Drawings* Eunice Williams.

Open Mon - Fri 9 AM - 5 PM; Sat 10 AM - 5 PM; Sun 2 - 5 PM. No admis. Estab 1895, present structure opened 1927. The Museum serves both as a public museum and as a laboratory for Harvard's Department of Fine Arts, which trains art historians and museum professionals. The Center for Conservation and Technical Studies operates a training program for conservators and technical specialists. Average Annual Attendance: 72,000. Mem: 1200; dues $30.

Income: Financed by endowment, membership and federal grants.

Collections: Egyptian antiquities; sculpture from Persepolis; Greek and Roman sculpture and vases; ancient coins; Oriental sculpture, jades, bronzes, ceramics, paintings and prints; Romanesque and Gothic sculpture; European and American sculpture; European and American painting; Maurice Wertheim Collection of Impressionist and Post-Impressionist Art; watercolors; drawings; prints; contemporary art; photographs; English and American silver; Wedgwood.

Exhibitions: America 1976; Studies in Connoisseurship: Chinese Paintings from the Arthur M Sackler Collection; Degas Bronzes; Fogg Master Paintings; Wash and Gouache: Watercolor at Harvard; Daniel Chester French Retrospective; Drawings from the Collection of John and Alice Steiner; Giovanni Battista Piranesi: Drawings and Prints from the Sackler Collection; Stuart Davis: Art and Art Theory; Photographs from the Julien Levy Collection.

Publications: Annual report; newsletter, 4 - 5 times a year.

Activities: Lect open to public, 30 vis lectr per yr; concerts; gallery talks; tours; individual paintings and original objects of art lent to exhibitions; traveling exhibitions organized and circulated; museum shop selling books, reproductions, and prints.

—Fine Arts Library. Tel: 617-495-3373. *Librn* Wolfgang Freitag; *Acquisitions Librn* James Hodgson; *Cur Visual Coll* Helene Roberts; *Chief Cataloguer* open.

Open to Harvard community Mon - Thurs 9 AM - 10 PM; Fri 9 AM - 7 PM. Estab 1895 to support the teaching department of fine arts and the research needs of the curatorial department of the Fogg Art Museum and an international community of scholars in art history. Circ: 116,000.

Income: $460,000 (financed by endowment). Purchases: $98,000.

Holdings: Vols 160,000; Per Subs 1000; AV—Lantern slides, microfiche, microfilm and slides; Other—Clipping files, exhibition catalogs, pamphlets and photographs.

Special Subjects: All areas of art history with emphasis on Italian primitives, Italian renaissance, master drawings, Romanesque sculpture, architectural history, history of photography, art & architecture of Eastern Europe; Dutch 17th century; conservation and restoration of works of art.

Special Collections: Rübel Asiatic Research Bureau: library collection on the arts of the Far East; 25,000 catalogued auction sales catalogs; the Knoedler Library Microfiche; Foto Marburg Collection; DIAL index; Index of Jewish art; manuscript archives of American artists and art scholars.

Publications: Fine Arts Library Catalog; Catalog of Auction Sales Catalogs, and First Supplement.

MASSACHUSETTS INSTITUTE OF TECHNOLOGY*

—Hayden Gallery, Room 14W-111, 02139. Tel: 617-253-4400. *Pres* Jerome B Wiesner; *Chmn Comt Visual Arts* Wayne Andersen; *Projects Coordr* Marjory Supovitz; *Gallery Mgr* Steven Ringle; *Cur Hart Nautical Museum* William A Baker.

Open Mon - Sat 10 Am - 4 PM; cl Sun & holidays. No admis. Estab 1950. Average Annual Attendance: 36,000.

Collections: 20th century painting, sculpture, drawings, and graphics; the Catherine N Stratton Collection of graphics; archival quality photographs; the Allen Forbes Collection of whaling prints and the Arthur H Clark Collection of marine prints housed in the Hart Nautical Museum.

Exhibitions: Eight exhibitions per year.

Activities: Gallery talks, openings with the artists present; special events related to the specific exhibitions; films.

—Rotch Library of Architecture and Planning,* 77 Massachusetts Ave, 02138. Tel: 617-253-7052. *Librn* Margaret DePopolo; *Acquisitions Librn* Florence Doksansky; *Processing Librn* Micheline Jedrey; *Reference Librn* Ann Longfellow; *Slide Librn* Lenis Williams.

Open Mon - Thurs 9 AM - 11 PM; Fri 9 AM - 8 PM: Sat 10 AM - 6 PM; Sun 1 - 11 PM; special hours when school not in session. Estab 1868, to serve the students and faculty of the School of Architecture and Planning and other members of the MIT community.

Collections: †Books, journals, pamphlets, slides, photographs, microfiche; major subject areas are architectural design and history of architecture; history of art (19th and 20th century painting and sculpture); urban studies; regional, economic and social planning.

Publications: Selected Rotch Library Acquisitions, irregular.

—Reference Library.

Holdings: Vols 91,000; AV—Slides 117,000; Other—Pamphlets 30,750, photographs, prints 41,000. Borrowing privileges restricted to members of MIT community and purchasers of library cards.

CONCORD

CONCORD ANTIQUARIAN SOCIETY MUSEUM, 200 Lexington Rd (Mailing Add: Box 146, 01742). Tel: 617-369-9609. *Pres* Morgan K Smith; *VPres* Dr Rob Roy McGregor and John Hamilton; *Corresp Secy* Mrs Gregory Neal; *Secy* Robert Minton; *Treas* William A Lawrence; *Asst Treas* Mrs Murray Swindell; *Acting Dir* Mrs William F A Strike; *Adminr* Mrs Thomas G Doig.

Open Mon - Sat 10 AM - 4:30 PM; Sun 2 - 4:30 PM. Admis adults $1.50, children through 15, 75¢. Estab 1886 to collect and preserve objects of antiquarian interest to Concord and towns originally a part of Concord; to interpret life in Colonial America, range of American arts, role of Concord in the American Revolution, and contributions of Concord authors—Thoreau, Emerson, Alcotts, and Hawthorne—to American literature. 15 Period rooms showing life in Concord from 1685 to 1840; Ralph Waldo Emerson study. Average Annual Attendance: 20,000. Mem: 725; dues $15 and up; annual meeting Feb or Mar.

Income: $50,000 (financed by membership, admission).

Publications: Newsletter, quarterly; The Flavour of Concord, cookbook; Concord: Climate for Freedom by Ruth Wheeler.

Activities: Classes for adults and children; docent training; lect open to public, 6 vis lectr per yr; tours; individual paintings and original objects of art lent to other museums; museum shop selling books, magazines, reproductions, slides, gift items.

Library: Open to members only for lending reference. Special Subjects: Decorative arts.

CONCORD ART ASSOCIATION, 15 Lexington Rd, 01742. *Pres* Alice Moulton; *VPres* Loring Coleman; *Secy* Frances P Mellen; *Cur* Frances P Mellen.

Open Tues - Sat 11 AM - 4:30 PM; Sun 2 - 4:30 PM. Admis 50¢. Estab 1916 for the encouragement of quality art by New England artists. Average Annual Attendance: 10,000. Mem: 500; Acceptance in three CAA juried shows for artist membership; dues $15 & $20.

Income: Financed by membership.

Collections: Bronze sculptures; miniatures; colonial glass.

Exhibitions: Changing exhibits.

Publications: Exhibition notices.

Activities: Lect open to public, 4-6 vis lectr per yr; tours; sales gallery selling original art, prints and reproductions.

DEDHAM

DEDHAM HISTORICAL SOCIETY,* 612 High St, 02026. Tel: 617-326-1385. *Pres* Courtenay P Worthington; *Librn* Muriel N Peters.

Open daily 2 - 5 PM; cl Sun, cl Sat during July and Aug. Estab 1859, inc 1862 to preserve local material of historical importance; to provide data for historical research and to maintain a library of genealogies and histories. Average Annual Attendance: 2500. Mem: 394, dues individual $5, family $8, life $150; annual meeting first Tues in Mar.

Collections: Relics pertaining to Dedham history or Dedham families: 17th century furniture; china; silver; pewter; oil paintings and portraits; Indian relics.

Publications: Dedham Pottery, book: A Brief Guide to Dedham Village, pamphlet.

Holdings: Vols 7000, Histories and Vital Records of Dedham and other New England towns; Genealogical material; manuscripts.

DEERFIELD

DEERFIELD ACADEMY, Hilson Gallery, Department of Fine Arts, 01342. Tel: 413-772-0241, exten 221. *Dir* Robert Moorhead; *Gallery Assoc* Dan Hodermarsky.
Open Tues - Sun 2 - 4 PM; cl Mon. No admis. Estab 1955 to exhibit the work of regional artists, and members of the Deerfield community; to serve as a focus for visiting lecturers, concerts, and similar events; to be a logical extension of the academic program of the Fine Arts Department; to enrich the Academy. A single large exhibition space with its own entrance and central fireplace. Average Annual Attendance: 750-1500.
Income: Financed through Academy.
Exhibitions: Charles Steckler, theatre design; Kenneth Verzyl, drawings; Stephen Maniatty, paintings; Richard Hooke, prints; Robert Moorehead, paintings; Stoneleigh-Burnham School Art Faculty; Martha Junkins, paintings; Ron Michaud & Hanlyn Davies, prints; Dan Hodermarsky, paintings; Gabe Cooney, photographs.
Publications: Term schedule, three times a year.

DUXBURY

ART COMPLEX MUSEUM AT DUXBURY, 189 Alden St (Mailing Add: PO Box 1411, 02332). Tel: 617-934-6634. *Museum Dir* Charles A Weyerhaeuser; *Assoc Dir* Lilian E Bengtz; *Dir Publ Affairs* Lanci Valentine; *Librn* Genevieve Tribble.
Open Fri - Sun 2 - 5 PM. No admis. Estab 1971 to exhibit art; gallery 40 x 60 ft; entrance also used for exhibition purposes. Average Annual Attendance: 8000.
Collections: Shaker furniture; American, European and Oriental art.
Exhibitions: Bicentennial Exhibition in 1976; Boston Printmakers; various local artists, RB Beaman, Margaret Fitzhugh Browne, and others.
Publications: The Lithographs of Ture Bengtz (book).
Activities: Lect open to public, 2-3 vis lectr per yr; concerts; gallery talks; tours.
Library: Librn Genevieve M Tribble. Open to the public for reference. Holdings: Vols 1900. Special Subjects: Asiatic art.

FALL RIVER

GREATER FALL RIVER ART ASSOCIATION,* 80 Belmont St, 02720. Tel: 617-673-7212. *Pres* Michael Hurley, *VPres* Mrs Sumner Waring; *VPres* Mrs William Mullen; *VPres* Mrs Roger Buffington; *Clerk* Mrs Andrew Weelock; *Corresp Secy* Mrs George Aronis; *Treas* Anna Fuller; *Dir* Mrs Edward A Doyle.
Open Sept - June daily 1 - 4 PM. Estab 1955 for the cultural enrichment of the community; seven rooms of large Victorian house are used for art exhibitions. Average Annual Attendance: 10,000. Mem: 310, dues $6, $10, $25; annual meeting third Mon in June.
Income: $800 after expenses (financed by membership).
Purchases: $100.
Collections: †Graphics, †ceramics, slides of paintings of the Fall River School.
Exhibitions: Three or four one-man shows annually, Members Show; National Competitive Exhibition, Classes Exhibition; Fall River Collects Art, semi-annually; Annual Traditional Open Show-New England Artists.
Publications: Bulletin, monthly.
Activities: Classes for adults and children; let open to the public, 8 vis lectr per yr; competitions; schol; extension dept serving Greater Fall River organizations; individual paintings and original objects of art lent; lending collection contains lantern slides 53, original art works, paintings 50; gift shop of original graphics, ceramics.

FITCHBURG

FITCHBURG ART MUSEUM, Merriam Parkway, 01420. Tel: 617-345-4207. *Pres* P Warren Keating; *VPres* Andre A Gelinas; *Secy* Gale Fenn; *Treas* Myrtle Parcher; *Dir* Peter Timms; *Registrar* Aliki Katsaros.
Open Tues - Sat 9 AM - 5 PM; Sun 2 - 5 PM. No admis. Estab 1925. Two large galleries and entrance hall on the first floor; two large galleries with connecting hall gallery on the second. Average Annual Attendance: 10,000. Mem: 700; dues $10 - $500; annual meeting Dec.
Income: $70,000 (financed by endowment, membership, and city appropriation).
Collections: †Paintings; †drawings, †prints; American & English silver.
Exhibitions: Finnish Icons; American Graphic Art of 30's; Lalique Glass; Armin Landeck Prints; Otto Piene Paintings; Minor White Photography; American and English Decorated Tinware, 19th century.
Publications: Catalogs and events notices.

Activities: Classes for adults and children; gallery talks; individual paintings and original objects of art lent to museums, private schools, institutions; museum shop selling reproductions, handcrafted gifts, Alva reproductions.

FRAMINGHAM

DANFORTH MUSEUM, 123 Union Ave, 01701. Tel: 617-620-0050. *Dir* Joy L Gordon; *Pres Bd Trustees* Paul G Marks; *Treas* Paul Rosenberg.
Open Wed - Sun 1 - 4:30 PM. No admis. Estab 1974 to provide fine arts and art-related activities to people of all ages in the South Middlesex area; six galleries including special hands-on children's area, all on one floor. Average Annual Attendance: 75,000.
Income: Financed by membership.
Collections: †Old master and contemporary prints; turn-of-the-century American landscapes.
Exhibitions: Mary Cassatt Prints; Hannes Beckmann: Paintings at Dartmouth 1971-75; The Art of Diplomacy: Official Gifts to President John F Kennedy; Art as an Expressive Medium; Fibre Forms; Freedom of the Mind: Aspects of the art of the 18th century; American Landscape Painting; The Drawings of George Grosz; American Impressionist Painting; The Ancient Mediterranean World.
Publications: Newsletter, twice a year; calendar of events, monthly; Museum school brochure, quarterly.
Activities: Classes for adults and children; docent training; lect open to public, 9 vis lectr per yr; concerts; gallery talks; tours; museum shop selling books, original art, prints, ceramics, and glass; junior museum.
Library: Librn Susan Sheridan. Open to members and to public by permission for reference. Holdings: Vols 500.

GARDNER

MOUNT WACHUSETT COMMUNITY COLLEGE ART GALLERIES, Green St. 01440. Tel: 617-632-6600, exten 180. *Coordinator Dept Art* Jean C Tandy; *Dir Fine Arts Galleries* Gene Cauthen; *Dir College Art Gallery* William Gruters.
Open Mon - Fri 11 AM - 1 PM; Fine Arts Gallery open Mon 8 - 9:30 PM; No admis. Estab 1971 to supply resources for a two-year art curriculum; develop an art collection.
Income: Financed by city and state appropriations.
Collections: †Approx 75 works; framed color art posters and reproductions.
Exhibitions: Local, Boston, and former students' works; annual student competition of painting, sculpture, drawing, and crafts.
Activities: Dramatic program; lect open to public, 10 vis lectr per yr; concerts; gallery talks; tours; competitions; art club; evening and summer studio courses; workshops; visual arts film series.
—**Library.** *Head Librn* Mason Parker; *Asst Librn* Linda Oldach.
Open 8 AM Mon - Thurs 8 AM - 9:30 PM; Fri 8 AM - 5 PM; Sun 2 - 6 PM (when school is in session). Estab 1964. Circ: 12,998.
Income: $30,000 (financed by state appropriation). Purchases: $30,000.
Holdings: Vols 51,137; Per subs 256; AV—Cassettes, film strips, microfiche, microfilm, phonorecords, reels, slides; Other—Memorabilia, pamphlets.
Activities: Periodic exhibitions.

GLOUCESTER

CAPE ANN HISTORICAL ASSOCIATION,* 27 Pleasant St, 01930. Tel: 617-283-0455. *Asst Cur* Caroline E Benham.
Open Tues - Sat 11 AM - 4 PM; cl Sun, Mon & holidays. Admis adults $1, children no charge if accompanied by adult. Inc 1876 for the preservation of ancient houses, one built c 1650, one in 1750 and one in 1803. Average Annual Attendance: 5000. Mem: 425, dues $5 and up; annual meeting May.
Collections: Paintings and drawings by Fitz-Hugh Lane, antique furniture, porcelain, glass, silver, jewelry, ship models, mementos of the Revolutionary period.
Activities: Occasional classes, lectures, exhibitions.
Reference Library: Holdings—Vols 500.

HAMMOND MUSEUM, INC, Hammond Castle, 80 Hesperus Ave, 01930. Tel: 617-283-2080 & 283-2081. *Dir* Philip E Miller.
Open for guided tours (Spring - Summer - Fall) daily 10 AM - 4 PM; (Winter) Tues - Fri 10 AM - 3 PM; Sat & Sun 10 AM - 4 PM; cl Mon except holidays; cl during Jan; also on Thanksgiving Day, New Year's Day and Christmas Day. Admis adults $2, children 12 yrs and under $1; group rates available. Built 1928 by famous inventor, John Hays Hammond, Jr. A frequent traveler abroad, Mr Hammond combined elements of Roman, Medieval and Renaissance periods in his attempt to recreate an atmosphere of European beauty. Inc 1938 for the public exhibition of authentic works of art and architecture and specimens of antiquarian value to encourage and promote better education in the fine arts, with

particular reference to purity of design and style. Average Annual Attendance: 67,442. Mem: 126; dues $15 - $1000.
Income: Financed by tours, concerts, membership, grants.
Collections: Rare collection of European artifacts; Roman, Medieval and Renaissance Periods.
Publications: Newsletter; Visitor Reference Directory.
Activities: Organ concerts; special exhibits; gift shop.

NORTH SHORE ARTS ASSOCIATION, INC,* Rear, 197 E Main St, 01930. *Pres* Ronald Brake; *VPres* James Hooley; *Treas* Roger Curtis.
Open 10 AM - 5:30 PM; Sun 2:30 - 5:30 PM; July, Aug & Sept. No admis. Estab and inc 1922; Association owns gallery. Average Annual Attendance: 4000. Mem: 300; dues associate $5, patron $10, artist $15; annual meeting Aug.
Exhibitions: Summer exhibition of members' work; jury, prizes.
Activities: Art classes in painting and drawing from life; lectures; demonstrations; Artists-at-Work day in gallery in July and August with artists demonstrating all media; Silent Auction.

GREAT BARRINGTON

SIMON'S ROCK EARLY COLLEGE, Alford Rd, 01230. Tel: 413-528-0771. *Chmn Art Dept* Eunice Agar. Estab 1964 as a liberal arts college.
Exhibitions: Tom Magruder (ceramics); Peter DeWitt (drawings); William Jackson (drawings and photographs); Charles Woodard (stained glass); Eunice Agar (drawings and paintings); Ellen Eyman (photoprints); Marthe Hess (drawings); Franklin Jones (paintings); Famke Zonneveld (watercolors, prints, wall hangings); Wayne Ensrud (paintings); Andrea Biggs (paintings); Ann Jon (sculpture); student shows.
Activities: Gallery talks; tours.
Library: *Librn* Karen Carney. Holdings: Vols 35,000; Per subs 370.

HARVARD

FRUITLANDS MUSEUMS, Prospect Hill, 01451. *Dir* W H Harrison.
Open May 30 - Sept 30, Tues - Sun 1 - 5 PM; cl Mon. Admis adults $2, children 50¢. Estab 1914, inc 1930, by Clara Endicott Sears. Fruitlands was the scene of Bronson Alcott's experiment in community life. House contains furniture, household articles, pictures, books and valuable manuscript collection of Alcott family and Transcendental group. Average Annual Attendance: 18,000.
Old Shaker House contains relics, handicrafts and displays illustrating life of the Shakers.
American Indian museum contains ethnological exhibits; specimens of Indian lore, art, culture and dioramas illustrating historical events of the Indians of the region; sculpture by Philip Sears.
Picture Gallery contains portraits by itinerant artists and landscapes by Hudson River School.
Library: Holdings—Vols 10,000; Other—Manuscripts and publications relative to museum collections—Transcendental Movement, Shakers, American Indian North of Mexico, American art history.

HAVERHILL

HAVERHILL PUBLIC LIBRARY, 99 Main St, 01830. Tel: 617-373-1586. *Librn* Virginia Bilmazes Bernard; *Cur* Howard W Curtis.
Open Mon - Fri 9 AM - 9 PM; Sat 9 AM - 5:30 PM. No admis. Estab 1873; maintains an exhibition gallery.
Collections: 19th & 20th century prints, including Picasso, Kollwitz, Renoir, Whistler, Toulouse-Lautrec, Sloan, Degas, Cassatt, Daumier, Legros, Matisse, Chagall, Dufy, and others; mid-19th century photographs, work by Frith, Beato and Robertson, Naya, Bourne, O'Sullivan, Gardner, and others; illuminated manuscripts; small group of paintings, including William S Haseltine, Joseph A Ames, Thomas Hill, Harrison Plummer, Winfield Scott Thomas, Henry Bacon, Sidney M Chase.
†Non-circulating arts book collection of 8000 volumes on the fine and applied arts.
Exhibitions: Monthly exhibition program of regional artists and traveling shows.
Activities: Periodic film, videotape, and slide presentations; instruction in photography, film-making, and videotape production.

HOLYOKE

CITY OF HOLYOKE MUSEUM-WISTARIAHURST, 238 Cabot St, 01040. Tel: 413-536-6771. *Chmn Holyoke Historical Commission* Tom Wilhelmi; *Museum Dir* Marie S Quirk
Open Tues - Sat 1 - 5 PM; cl Sun, Mon, holidays & July. No admis. Sponsored by the City of Holyoke under the jurisdiction of the Holyoke Historical Commission. Mem dues: junior $3, active $5, regular $10, family $25, contributing $50, cooperating $100, sustaining $500, benefactor $1000.

Income: $77,000 (financed by city appropriation).
Collections: †Paintings; †antique furniture; historical dioramas; period rooms; silver; †glass and china; †Oriental art.
Activities: Classes for children; dramatic programs; special art shows; concerts; gallery talks; sponsors films and lectures; special exhibits and festivals of ethnic culture featured periodically; special programs and illustrated lectures planned for visiting school classes; sales shop selling booklets and items relating to exhibitions.
—Youth Museum.
Open Mon - Sat 1 - 5 PM; Sun 2 - 5 PM. Opened May 3, 1964 in Carriage House on Wisteriahurst estate; sponsored by the City of Holyoke, under jurisdiction of Holyoke Historical Commission. Average Annual Attendance: 18,000.
Exhibitions: (Art) Scrimshaw, an Early Folkart. North American Indian Hall opened May 1973 on the second floor; twelve exhibits encompassing Northeast, Southeast, Plains, Southwest, Northwest Coast and California Indian tribes.
Activities: Art classes for children; lect on arts and crafts; guided tours including film and slides on Indians; individual paintings and original objects of art lent, traveling exhibitions organized and circulated; Museum in a Box for local schools.

LINCOLN

DECORDOVA AND DANA MUSEUM AND PARK, Sandy Pond Road, 01773. Tel: 617-259-8355. *Exec Dir* Frederick P Walkey; *Asst Dir* Ann Russell; *Cur* Edith Tonelli; *Dir DeCordova School* Merric Blocker.
Open Tues - Fri 10 AM - 5 PM; Sat Noon - 5 PM; Sun 1:30 - 5 PM. Admis adults $1.50, under 21 50¢. Estab 1948 to offer a variety of exhibitions, build an important collection of contemporary art and to support living New England artist, in its collecting and exhibitions. 4500 sq ft broken into five galleries. Average Annual Attendance: 60,000. Mem: 3200; dues $35 - $500.
Income: $900,000 (financed by endowment, and membership). Purchases: 30,000.
Collections: †Works of living New England artists.
Exhibitions: Patron's Choice: New England Artists Under 36; Homer to Hopper: Sixty Years of American Watercolors; An American Dream: The Art of Free Enterprise; Boston Printmakers National; Francisco Zuniga: Sculpture and Drawing; By the People, For the People: New England; New England in Winter; Peter Milton (prints); Barbara Bustetter Falk (paintings); Donald Stoltenberg (collagraphs).
Publications: Exhibition catalogs; newsletter.
Activities: Classes for adults and children; docent training; lect open to public, 6 vis lectr per yr; tours; competitions; paintings and original objects of art lent to corporate membership; traveling exhibitions organized and circulated.
—DeCordova Museum Library. *Librn* Bea Warren.
Open Mon - Fri 9 AM - 5 PM. Open to members only.
Holdings: Vols 1600; Per subs 17; AV—Slides, slide tapes; Other—Exhibition catalogs.
Special Subjects: Fine arts and crafts.

LOWELL

LOWELL ART ASSOCIATION, Whistler House and Parker Gallery, 243 Worthen St, 01852. Tel: 716-452-7641. *Pres* Donald F Pattershall; *VPres* John A Goodwin; *Corresp Secy* Anastasia Porter; *Recording Secy* Arlene Redmond; *Whistler House Dir* Amy Woodfall.
Open Whistler House 1:30 - 5 PM; Parker Gallery 2:30 - 4:30; Tues - Sun except July & Aug. No admis. Estab 1878 to preserve the birthplace of James McNeil Whistler; to promote the arts in all its phases; and to maintain a center for the cultural benefit of all the citizens of the community. Mem: 200; dues $10 - $100.
Income: Financed by endowment and membership.
Exhibitions: (1977-78) Oils, Pastels, Watercolors, Ruth Costello; Metal Sculpture, Dr Robert Kaldeck; Drawings and Paintings, Bernard Petruzziello; Oil Paintings, Joanne Ferretti; 19th and Early 20th Century Portraits of Lowell Personalities; Paintings from the Permanent Collection; Oils, Raymond Doyle and Sally Fox; Members and Independent Artists Show; Oils, Paintings, Pasquale D'Orsi; Oils, Watercolors, Joan Avakian; Whistler House Students Show.
Publications: Brochures.
Activities: Classes for adults and children; lectures open to the public.
Library: Open to the public for reference only.

MALDEN

MALDEN PUBLIC LIBRARY, 36 Salem St, 02148. Tel: 617-324-0218. *Librn* Dina G Malgeri; *Art Librn* Frederica de Beurs; *Chmn Art Comt, Bd Trustees* Francis C Wilson.

Open Mon - Thurs 9 AM - 9 PM; Fri & Sat 9 AM - 6 PM; cl Sun & holidays; cl Sat during summer months. Estab 1879, inc 1885, as a public library and art gallery. Circ: 161,221. Maintains an art gallery with three galleries.
Income: $432,763 (financed by endowment, city and state appropriations). Purchases: $428,763.
Holdings: Vols 190,319; Per subs 350; AV—Audio tapes, cassettes, film strips, microfilm, motion pictures, phonorecords and slides.
Other—Clipping files, exhibition catalogs, framed reproductions, manuscripts, memorabilia, original art works, pamphlets, photographs, prints, reproductions and sculpture.
Publications: Annual Report; Thirty Paintings in the Malden Collection, (art catalog).
Activities: Lect open to public; concerts; gallery talks; library tours; competitions.

MARBLEHEAD

MARBLEHEAD ARTS ASSOCIATION, INC, 8 Hooper St, 01945. Tel: 617-631-2608. *Pres* Mary Conant; *VPres* William E McKeon; *Secy* Capt R Tate Simpson; *Exec Secy* Mrs James Clivengood.
Open Tues - Sun 1 - 4 PM; cl Mon. Admis $1. Estab 1922. Owns and occupies the historic King Hooper Mansion (1728) which contains fine paneling, ballroom, gallery, and garden by Shurclif. Maintains an art gallery. Average Annual Attendance: 3000. Mem: 400; dues $12 and up; annual meeting June.
Exhibitions: Continuous exhibitions of members' work and invited guest exhibitors.
Activities: Lect open to the public; tours; sponsors Friends of Contemporary Prints, yearly exhibitions; concerts.

MARBLEHEAD HISTORICAL SOCIETY, 161 Washington St, 01945. Tel: 617-631-1069. *Exec Secy* John Merrow, Jr.
Open May 15 - Oct 15 9:30 AM - 4 PM; cl Sun. Admis $1.50. Estab 1898, inc 1902 for the preservation of Lee Mansion and historical material and records of Marblehead. Average Annual Attendance: 3000.
Income: Financed by endowment, membership, and admissions.
Collections: (Art) furniture, china and glass; collection of portraits; pictures of ships; documents.
Activities: Lectures open to the public; tours; sales shop selling books, prints, reproductions.
Library: Open to qualified visitors for reference only.

MARION

MARION ART CENTER, Main St, 02739. Tel: 617-748-1266. *Pres* Sarah R Brown; *Secy* Rita Cain; *Exec Secy* Nina Campbell; *Asst Secy* Alice Phinney.
Open Tues - Sun 1 - 5 PM. Estab 1957 to provide theater and visual arts exhibitions for the community and to provide studio classes for adults and children. Gallery is 70 ft of wall space, 280 sq ft floor space; indirect lighting; entrance off Main St. Average Annual Attendance: 1200. Mem: 300, dues single $7.50, family $12.50; annual meeting second Tues in July.
Publications: Monthly invitations to opening; annual membership folder.
Activities: Classes for adults and children; dramatic programs; lect open to the public, 5 vis lectr per yr; concerts; competitions; schol; original objects of art lent; rental of paintings and prints, available to anyone for a fee of $10 - $20 per two-month period.

MEDFORD

TUFTS UNIVERSITY, Gallery Eleven, Cohen Arts Center, Fine Arts Department, Talbot Ave, 02155. *Gallery Mgr* Patricia Rogers Pelnar.
Open Fall & Spring Semesters, Mon - Fri 9:30 AM - 4:30 PM. No admis. Estab 1955 to display works of art by University students and faculty and special exhibitions of traditional and experimental works in all visual art media. Average Annual Attendance: 5,000.
Income: Financed through the Fine Arts Department.
Exhibitions: 14 shows annually, including theses exhibits of candidates for the MFA degree offered by Tufts in affiliation with the School of the Boston Museum of Fine Arts; one-person and group shows of contemporary art; The Tufts Quilt Show; Javanese Shadow Puppets from the World Music Collection of Wesleyan University.

NANTUCKET

ARTISTS ASSOCIATION OF NANTUCKET, Kenneth Taylor Gallery, 02554. Tel: 617-228-0722. *Pres* Douglas Frazier.
Open daily 9 AM - 10 PM (June - Oct 15). No admis. Estab 1944 to provide gallery space to approx 240 exhibiting artist members, to promote the arts; to provide arts and crafts workshops year round. Maintains an art gallery; two galleries: The Kenneth Taylor Gallery, 2 floors in historic building, and The Little Gallery, one small floor for one-person

shows. Average Annual Attendance: 50,000-75,000. Mem: 450; artists members are juried; patron and assoc mem are open to all; dues artist $20, patron $25 - $500; annual meeting Aug.
Income: $12,000-$15,000 (financed by membership, fund raising and commissions).
Collections: Permanent collection on loan to hospital and town buildings.
Exhibitions: Changing one-person and group member shows during summer; occasional off-season shows.
Publications: Newsletter, 3 times per yr.
Activities: Classes for adults and children; workshops; lect open to public, 3-4 vis lectr per yr; gallery talks; competitions with awards given; scholarships; individual paintings and original objects of art lent to local hospital and public offices.

NEW BEDFORD

NEW BEDFORD FREE PUBLIC LIBRARY, 613 Pleasant St (Mailing Add: PO Box C-902, 02741). Tel: 617-999-6291. *Dir* Laurence H Solomon; Dept Head Reference Thelma Paine; *Dept Head Genealogy & Whaling Coll* Bruce Barnes; *Dept Head AV* Thomas Grandmaison; *Dept Head Tech Serv* Pauline Bolduc.
Open Mon - Thurs 9 AM - 9 PM; Fri & Sat 9 AM - 5 PM; cl Sun & holidays. Estab 1852. Circ: 478,828.
Income: $738,005 (financed by endowment, city and state appropriation). Purchases: $162,694.
Holdings: Vols 361,478; Per subs 281; AV—Cassettes, film strips, microfilm, motion pictures, phonorecords, slides, videotapes, AV hardware; Other—49 framed reproductions, 480 juvenile photographs:
Special Subjects: Whaling; New Bedford artists.
Special Collections: Paintings by Albert Bierstadt, F D Millet, Clifford Ashley, William Wall.
Activities: Schol offered.

NEW BEDFORD WHALING MUSEUM, 18 Johnny Cake Hill, 02740. Tel: 617-997-0046. *Dir* Richard C Kugler; *Sr Cur* Philip F Purrington; *Cur Coll* Elton W Hall; *Cur Ethnology* John R Bockstoce.
Open Mon - Sat 9 AM - 5 PM; Sun 1 - 5 PM; cl Mon Oct - May. Admis adults $1.50, children 6 - 14 75 cents. Estab 1903 to interest and educate the public in the history of the whaling industry and the greater New Bedford area. Average Annual Attendance: 100,000. Mem: 1400; dues $10 - $500; annual meeting May.
Income: $196,850 (financed by endowment, membership). Purchases $12,000.
Collections: †New Bedford artists; †whaling arts and crafts; †scrimshaw; †furniture and domestic arts; Whaleship Lagoda (½ scale model); Russell-Purrington Panorama of a Whaling Voyage; paintings and prints; ship models; domestic crafts.
Exhibitions: (1976) Images of Childhood in 19th Century New Bedford; (1977) Steam Whaling in the Western Arctic; (1978) William Allen Wall: an artist of New Bedford.
Publications: Bulletin from Johnny Cake Hill, quarterly; exhibition catalogs.
Activities: Classes for children; docent training; lect open to public, 6 vis lectr per yr; tours; individual paintings and original objects of art lent to other museums; traveling exhibitions organized and circulated; museum shop selling books, reproductions, prints.
—Old Dartmouth Historical Society and Whaling Museum Library. Tel: 617-997-0046. *Dir* Richard C Kugler; *Sr Cur* Philip F Purrington. For use within library only.
Holdings: Vols 15,000; Per subs 12; manuscripts.
Special Subjects: History of whaling industry; Charles F Batchelder whaling collection; Andrew Snow logbook collection; Charles A Goodwin collection.

SWAIN SCHOOL OF DESIGN, William W Crapo Gallery, 19 Hawthorn St, 02740. Tel: 617-999-4436. *Pres* Dr Jean S Lozinski; *Gallery Dir* Merle Sanderson.
Open Mon - Fri 10 AM - 4 PM; cl Sat, Sun & holidays. Estab 1881.
Exhibitions: Monthly exhibitions.
Activities: Lectures, gallery talks.
—Library. 140 Orchard St, 02740. Tel: 617-999-5900. *Dir* Angela M Sciotti.
Open Mon - Fri 8:30 AM - 4:30 PM. Estab 1967 as a reference and research library supporting fine arts curriculum. Circ: 800 - 1000 vols per month.
Income: $7000 financed by endowment and government grant).
Holdings: Vols 12,000; Per subs 45; AV—Slides 15,000; Other—Clipping files, exhibition catalogs.
Special Subjects: Fine arts, art history; design.
Special Collections: New Bedford Area Artists File.

Exhibitions: Arthur Hoener: Works in Color; Kathrine and Michael McCoy: Visiting Artists; Photographics: New England Photographers; Richard Hunt; Leland Bell; James Rosenquist; Massimo Vignelli; Mary Gregory; David Hockney; John Matt.
Publications: Catalogs.

NEWBURYPORT

HISTORICAL SOCIETY OF OLD NEWBURY,* 98 High St, 01950. Tel: 617-462-2681. *Cur* Wilhelmina V Lunt.
Open May - Oct Tues - Sat 10 AM - 4 PM; Sun 2 - 5 PM; cl Nov - Apr except by appointment. Admis adults $1, children under 16 50¢, special group rates. Estab 1877. Mem. Dues student $2, individual $5, sustaining $10, couple $8, family $10, life $200.
Collections: Paintings; miniatures; glass; silver; china; dolls; furniture; paperweights; needlework; sampler collection; other historical material.
Activities: Lectures; guided tours; temporary exhibitions.
Holdings: Vols 5000; manuscripts; deeds; documents.

NORTH ANDOVER

MERRIMACK VALLEY TEXTILE MUSEUM, 800 Massachusetts Ave, 01845. Tel: 617-686-0191. *Pres* Samuel S Rogers; *Secy* Clifford E Elias; *Dir* Thomas W Leavitt; *Cur* Laurence F Gross; *Librn* Helena Wright; *Supv Educ Services* Paul Hudon; *Museum Conservator* Robert A Hauser; *Textile Conservator* Michael Bogle; *Asst Cur Textiles* Katherine R Koob.
Open Tues - Fri 9 AM - 4 PM; Sat & Sun 1 - 5 PM. Admis Tues-Sat age 16-65 $1.00, others 50¢; Sun ages 16-65 $2.00, others $1.00. Estab 1960 to preserve artifacts, documents and pictorial descriptions of the American textile industry and related developments abroad. Two permanent exhibit galleries: Homespun to Factory Made: Woolen Textiles in America, 1776-1876. Average Annual Attendance: 6000.
Income: Financed by endowment.
Collections: (art) †textile collection; prints and photographs.
Publications: Catalog of permanent exhibit; Occasional reports.
Activities: Classes for adults; docent training; tours; competitions; lending collection contains slides; traveling exhibits; sales desk selling books, prints and postcards.
—**Library.** *Librn* Helena Wright; *Asst Librn* Eartha Dengler.
Open Tues - Fri 9 AM - 4 PM. Estab 1960 to preserve library materials relating to the American textile industry and related development abroad.
Income: Financed by endowment.
Holdings: Vols 35,000; Per subs 30; AV—Microfilm and motion pictures; Other—Exhibition catalogs, manuscripts, original art works, original documents, pamphlets, photographs and prints.
Special Subjects: History of textile industry; textile mill architecture; textile design, and manufacturing.
Publications: Checklist of prints and manuscripts.

NORTHAMPTON

FORBES LIBRARY, 20 West St, 01060. Tel: 413-584-8550. *Dir* Stanley Greenberg; *Art & Music Librn* Daniel J Lombardo.
Open Mon - Sat 9 AM - 9 PM; Sun & holidays 2 - 6 PM; cl Memorial Day, July 4, Thanksgiving, Christmas, & New Years Day. Estab 1894 to serve a residential and academic community as a general public library and a research facility. Circ: 292,950. Gallery and exhibit cases for regional artists, photographers, and craftspeople.
Income: $328,050 (financed by endowment, city and state appropriation, federal funds). Purchases: $59,931.
Holdings: Vols 312,674; Per subs 312; AV—Cassettes, film strips, lantern slides, microfilm, motion pictures, phonorecords, reels, slides; Other—Clipping files, exhibition catalogs, framed reproductions, manuscripts, memorabilia; original art works and documents, pamphlets, photographs, prints, reproductions, sculpture.
Special Subjects: Art and music.
Special Collections: Official White House Portraits of President Calvin Coolidge and Grace Anna Coolidge; The Holland House Collection of English Miniatures; Connecticut Valley History; Early American Children's Literature; Genealogical Records; Lyman Collection of Japanese Wood Block Prints and Japanese Books; Library of Charles E Forbes; Walter E Corbin Collection of Photographic Prints and Slides; The Coolidge Collection.
Exhibitions: Monthly exhibits of works by regional artists, photographers, and craftspeople.
Activities: Lect open to public, 12 vis lectr per yr; concerts; library tours; weekly film and lecture program.

SMITH COLLEGE MUSEUM OF ART,* Fine Arts Center, 01060. Tel: 413-584-2700, exten 236, 740. *Dir* Charles Chetham; *Assoc Dir & Cur* Betsy Burns Jones; *Asst Cur Prints* Colles Baxter.

Open Tues - Sat 11 AM - 4:30 PM; Sun 2 - 4:30 PM; cl Mon & academic holidays; summer by appointment. Average Annual Attendance: 20,000.
Collections: Paintings including works by Rembrandt, Ingres, Gauguin, Juan Griz, Seurat, Picasso, Monet, de Kooning and others; prints; drawings; Orientalis; Mexican sculpture; especially strong in 18th century European paintings.
—**Hillyer Art Library,** Elm St, 01063. Tel: 413-584-2700, exten 743. *Art Librn* Karen H Harvey.
Open Mon - Thurs 8 AM - 11 PM; Fri & Sat 8 AM - 10 PM; Sun 2 - 10 PM. Estab 1900 to support courses offered by the Art Department of Smith College.
Income: Financed by endowment.
Holdings: Vols 35,000; Per subs 204; Other—Photographs.

NORTON

WHEATON COLLEGE
—**Watson Gallery,** E Main St, 02766. Tel: 617-285-7722, exten 428. *Dir* Dr Ann H Murray; *Cur Asst* Susan Werner.
Open Mon - Tues & Thurs; Fri 1 - 5 PM; Wed 10 AM - Noon & 2 - 4 PM. No admis. Gallery program since 1930, Watson Gallery estab 1960, to provide a wide range of contemporary one person and group shows as well as exhibitions from the permanent collections of paintings and graphics. Gallery is of fireproof steel-frame, concrete, glass and brick construction; there are no windows. Average Annual Attendance: 3000 - 5000.
Income: Financed by College budget. Purchases: $200 - $500.
Collections: Paintings; †drawings; †prints; †sculpture; glass and other decorative arts; Roman ancient coin collection.
Exhibitions: Wheaton: A Visual History; Bruce Helander: Recent Work; Nancy Helfant: Hard Shadows; Rochelle Levy: Paintings; Japanese Ukiyo-E Prints; Twentieth Century Prints; Lois Grabois: Work from 1975-77; Charlotte Shoemaker: Wall Pieces—Floor Pieces; Peter Berg: Installation; Peter Lipsitt: Work in Progress; Student Exhibition.
Publications: Gallery Notes, semi-annually.
Activities: Lect open to the public, 5 - 8 vis lectr per yr; concerts; gallery talks; tours; individual paintings and original objects of art lent to college and other museums and galleries; traveling exhibitions organized and circulated.
—**Fine Arts Library,*** Watson Hall, 02766. *Librn* Gertrude Martin.
Holdings: Vols & Folios 13,500; Per subs 67; AV—Slides 40,000, scores 2700, phonorecords 1900; Other—Photographs and reproductions 12,000.
Special Collections: Shippee Memorial Collection of framed reproductions and original prints.

PAXTON

ANNA MARIA COLLEGE, St Luke's Gallery, Moll Art Center, Sunset Lane, 01612. Tel: 617-757-4586. *Chmn Art Dept* David T Green.
Open 9 AM - 4 PM. No admis. Estab 1968 as an outlet for the art student and professional artist, and to raise the artistic awareness of the general community. Main Gallery is 35 x 15 ft with about 300 sq ft of wall space with additional areas adjoining the gallery. Average Annual Attendance: 2000.
Collections: Small assortment of sculpture, paintings, furniture.
Exhibitions: Annual Senior Art Exhibit; local artists, faculty and students shows.

PITTSFIELD

BERKSHIRE ATHENAEUM, Music and Arts Department, 1 Wendell Ave, 01201. Tel: 413-442-1559, exten 26. *Librn* Robert G Newman; *Asst Librn* Larry Price; *Supervisor Music and Arts Dept* Jean Bousquet; *First Asst Music and Arts Dept* Mary Ann Knight.
Open Mon - Fri 9 AM - 9 PM; Sat 9 AM - 6 PM; summer Mon, Wed, Fri 9 AM - 9 PM; Tues & Thurs 9 AM - 6 PM; Sat 9 AM - 5 PM. Estab 1872, music and arts Dept 1937 to develop an awareness in the Berkshire community of the gifted artists who live and work among us and to increase an aesthetic sensitivity to the arts.
Income: Financed by endowment, city and state appropriation.
Holdings: Vols 5000; AV—Cassettes, motion pictures, phonorecords; Other—Art prints.
Exhibitions: (1976-77) Collages by Lorraine Lauzon; The Poor Man's Silver; Folk Crafts for World Friendship by Florence Temko; Illuminated Manuscripts by Florence Brooks; An Old-Fashioned Love Story; Crane & Co—Historical Paper Exhibit; Weavings by Kate Pincus; Early Lighting Devices; Blown Glass by Thomas Greenleaf Photography by Walter H Scott; Pottery by Richard Bennett; The Great Barrington Pottery; Cloisonne Jewelry by Toni Strassler; (1977-78) Children in the Shaker Community; Ceramics by Pam Herd; Christmas Angels; Paper Sculpture by David Sears; Photography by Paul Rocheleau; Prints and Drawings by Barbara Finn-Eustace; Bygones—Amusements and Occupations of Children; South Mountain's Young Audiences Concerts 1955-1978;

Handwoven Works by Sharon Steinberg; Stoneware Pottery by Allan Steinberg; An Artist's View of Childhood by Leonard Weber; Musical Instruments by Thom Lipiczky.
Activities: Classes for children; dramatic programs; children's dept series; lect open to the public; outreach program for the elderly.

BERKSHIRE MUSEUM, 39 South St, 01201. Tel: 413-443-6721. *Dir* Stuart C Henry; *Cur Science* Bartlett Hendricks; *Head Junior Dept* Thomas G Smith; *Financial Secy* Samuel A Spratlin; *Secy-Registrar* Mrs Theodore W Hall; *Mem Secy* Mrs Avery H Conway; *Bldg Supt* Joseph A Trasatti.
Open Tues - Sat 10 AM - 5 PM; Sun 2 - 5 PM; cl Mon. No admis. Estab 1903 as a museum of art, science and history. Mem: 1620; dues single $7.50, family $15, sustaining $25 and up; annual meeting Feb.
Income: Financed by endowment, memberships, and gifts.
Collections: Old Masters (Patinir, Pons, de Hooch, Van Dyck, Reynolds, Raeburn, Lawrence and others); Chinese objects and two rooms from Aston Magna (home of Albrt Spaulding); Paul M Hahn Collection of 18th century English and American silver; original works and casts of famous Greek and Roman sculpture; grave reliefs from Palmyra; Egyptian, Babylonian and Near East arts; American paintings of the Hudson River School (Inness, Moran, Blakelock, Martin, Wyant, Moran, Church, Knight and other; Giant Redwood Trees of California (Albert Bierstadt); †contemporary sculptures; early American and European abstracts; two Norman Rockwell paintings.
Exhibitions: Changing monthly exhibits.
Publications: Schedule of events, quarterly.
Activities: Classes for adults and children; lect open to public, 12 vis lectr per yr; museum shop selling gifts; junior museum.
—**Pittsfield Art League.** Tel: 413-442-6373. *Pres* Olive Murphy; *VPres* William Conover; *Secy* Lawton Huban; *Treas* Suzanne Brown.
Estab 1924 to encourage the development of talent and apreciation of the fine arts. Mem: 120; dues $6; annual meeting May.
Income: Financed by membership.
Exhibitions: Annual November exhibition.
Publications: Highlights, spring and fall.
Activities: Competitions with awards.

SHAKER COMMUNITY, INC, US Rte 20 (Mailing Add: PO Box 898, 01201). Tel: 413-443-0188. *Pres* Mrs Lawrence K Miller; *Dir* John Harlow Ott; *Cur Coll* June Sprigg; *Cur Educ Serv* Cheryl Anderson.
Open June 1 - Oct 15, 9:30 AM - 5 PM daily. Admis adult's $3, children 6 - 12 $1, children under 6 free. Estab 1960 for the preservation and restoration of Hancock Shaker Village and the interpretation of Shaker art, architecture and culture. Period rooms throughout village; exhibition gallery of Shaker inspirational drawings and graphic materials. Average Annual Attendance: 50,000. Mem: 1000; dues individual $10.
Income: Financed by membership, donations.
Collections: Shaker furniture, architecture and industrial material; Shaker inspirational drawings.
Exhibitions: (1977) Shaker Villages in Massachusetts: Boston State House; (1978) Simple Gifts, William Benton Museum of Art.
Publications: Newsletter, biannually; Specialized Publications.
Activities: Classes for adults and children; workshops, seminars; lect open to public, 6 vis lectr per yr; concerts; tours; original objects of art lent to accredited museums; lending collection contains 1 film strip, 4 motion pictures, 250 photographs, 40 slides; museum shop selling books, magazines, reproductions, prints, slides.
—**Hancock Shaker Village Library.** Tel: 413-443-0188. *Dir* John Harlow Ott.
Reference library open to students and scholars by appointment.
Holdings: Vols 1000; Other—Photographic and graphic collections, manuscripts, maps.
Special Subjects: Shaker agriculture, horticulture, utopian studies.

PLYMOUTH

PLYMOUTH ANTIQUARIAN SOCIETY, 27 North St, 02360. Tel: 617-746-0012. *Pres* Mrs Gordon L Howland; *VPres* Mrs John Creeden; *Secy* Dorothy Reed; *Cur* Carla Crawley; *Chmn Spooner House* Mrs Quentin Maver; *Chmn Harlow House* Mrs Donald Hansen; *Chmn Antiquarian House* Mrs Willard Richards.
Open 10 AM - 5 PM. Admis adults $1, children 25¢. Estab 1919 to maintain and preserve the three museums—Harlow Old Fort House (1677), Spooner House (1747) and Antiquarian House (1809). Average Annual Attendance: 200. Mem: 450; dues $5; annual meeting first Thurs Nov.
Income: $38,779 (financed by membership).
Collections: (art) Antique dolls.
Activities: Classes for children; lect open to the public; sales shop at Harlow House selling hand woven items.

PROVINCETOWN

PROVINCETOWN ART ASSOCIATION AND MUSEUM, 460 Commercial St, 02657. Tel: 617-487-1750. *Pres* Larry Richmond; *VPres* Ciriaco Cozzi; *Secy* Candy Jeringan; *Dir* Sally Lindover; *Coordr* Carole Schmidt; *Archivist* Ben Brooks; *Cur* Bob Rodger.
Open daily 11 AM - 2 PM & 7 - 11 PM. Estab 1914 to promote and cultivate the practice and appreciation of all branches of the fine arts, to hold temporary exhibitions, forums, and concerts for the artists themselves and the public. A gallery is maintained. Mem: 600; dues vary.
Income: Financed by membership.
Exhibitions: (1978) Alvin Ross; Permanent Collection; Bruce McKain; Member Open; Works on Paper (members juried); Conceptual; Member Juried; Lower Cape Collectors; Days Studio; Members Miniatures.
Publications: Newsletter, bimonthly.
Activities: Classes for adults; lect open to public; concerts; gallery talks; lending collection contains books, cassettes, Kodachromes, photographs; sales shop selling books, original art, prints, reproductions, slides, postcards, note cards.
Library: Librn Ben Brooks. Open to members only. Holdings: Vols 500; Other—catalogs. Special Subjects: Provincetown artists. Special Collections: Memorabilia of W H W Bicknell.

QUINCY

ADAMS NATIONAL HISTORIC SITE, 135 Adams St, (Mailing Add: PO Box 531, 02171). Tel: 617-773-1177. *Supt* Wilhelmina S Harris.
Open daily (April 19 - Nov 10) 9 AM - 5 PM. Admis adult 50¢; children under 16 admitted free if accompanied by an adult. Estab 1946. The site consists of a house, part of which dates to 1731, a library containing approx 12,000 books (most of which belonged to John Quincy Adams), a carriage house, a woodshed, and grounds which were once owned and enjoyed by four generations of the Adams family. Average Annual Attendance: 20,000.
Income: Financed by Federal Government.
Collections: The house and library is furnished with original furnishings belonging to the four generations of Adamses who lived in the house between 1788 and 1937.
Activities: Lect (one week each spring); tours.

ROCKPORT

ROCKPORT ART ASSOCIATION, Old Tavern, 12 Main St, 01966. Tel: 617-546-6604. *Pres* Martin R Ahearn; *VPres* John Wentworth; *Secy* Eelanor Harper; *Cur* John W Pettibone; *Mgr Tavern Door Card Shop* Mary M Ahearn; *Membership Secy* Marie Smith.
Open Mon - Sat 9:30 AM - 4:30 PM; Sun 1 - 5 PM. No admis. Estab 1921 as a non-profit educational organization established for the advancement of art; three galleries are maintained in the Old Tavern Building; two large summer galleries adjacent to the main structure. Average Annual Attendance: 65,000. Mem: 1000; dues artists $35; annual meeting second Thurs in August.
Income: Financed by endowment and membership.
Collections: Small collection of works by former and current association artist members.
Exhibitions: (1976-78) Biweekly one-artist shows; monthly group shows year-round; four summer exhibitions each year; small changing exhibit of members is available for viewing during regular business hours.
Publications: Exhibition catalogs; Rockport Sketchbook; Rockport Artist Book (1970).
Activities: Classes for adults and children; sketch groups with models provided; summer series of weekly artist demonstrations; lectr open to the public, 35 vis lectr per yr; concerts; gallery talks; tours; competitions with awards given; schol; individual paintings and original objects of art lent to colleges, art schools, and hospitals for short term exhibition; lending collection contains original art works 200, original prints 400, paintings 100 and sculptures 75; sales shop selling books, cards and notes by artist members.
Library: In the process of organizing open for reference to members and friends of the association. Holdings: Vols 200. Special Subjects: Fine arts especially painting.

ROXBURY

MUSEUM OF THE NATIONAL CENTER OF AFRO-AMERICAN ARTISTS, 300 Walnut Ave, 02119 (Mailing Add: 122 Elm Hill Ave, Dorchester, MA 02121). Tel: 617-442-8820. *Dir* Edmund B Gaither; *Asst Dir-Registr* Harriet F Kennedy.
Open Tues - Fri 12 AM - 7 PM; Sat & Sun 12 AM - 4 PM; cl Mon.
Estab 1970 to collect, exhibit and promote black American and West Indian art, financed as part of the NCAAA. Gallery is 7000 sq ft divided into Permanent Afro-American Suite, Special Exhibition Suite, local gallery, and African Suite. Average Annual Attendance: 12,000. Dues $20.

Income: $101,000 (financed by support from parent organization and private funding). Purchases: $2500.
Collections: 19th and 20th century printing and drawings by Afro-American artists; 20th century painting by Afro-American artists; African art and artifacts.
Exhibitions: Photographs by Lawrence Skyes; Annual Invitational Show; Nigerian Fabrics and Sculptures; Jubilee: Afro-American Artists on Afro-America.
Publications: Annual report; Newsletter, quarterly.
Activities: Dramatic programs; 2 vis lectr per yr; concerts; gallery talks; tours; lending collection contains 1800 slides; traveling exhibitions organized and circulated.

SALEM

ESSEX INSTITUTE, 132 Essex St, 01970. Tel: 617-744-3390. *Dir* Bryant F Tolles Jr; *Asst to Dir* Katherine W Richardson; *Cur* Anne Farnam; *Librn* Robinson Murray Jr.
Open Mon (June 1 - Oct 15), Tues - Fri 9 AM - 4:30 PM Sun 1 - 5 PM. Admis adults $1.00, children 50¢. Estab 1848. The Institute's collections of artifacts and historic houses represent the richness of Salem's and Essex County's material culture from the early 17th into the 20th centuries. The Museum is housed in Plummer Hall (1857); it is an excellent example of Victorian Italian Revival architecture. On the first floor is the John A McCarthy Gallery devoted to changing displays and loan exhibitions. The second floor has a portrait gallery, and the main gallery containing three early period rooms; special collections and a print room used for small exhibitions are also here. Average Annual Attendance: 100,000. Mem: 1200; dues from active $15 to life $250; annual meeting April.
Income: $432,621 (financed by endowment, membership, gifts, and admissions).
Collections: Clocks, ceramics, dolls and toys, glassware, buttons, silver and pewter, architectural fragments, sculpture, furniture and paintings, all associated with the civil history of Essex County and adjacent areas since the early 17th century.
Exhibitions: New England Appearances; Recent Acquisitions; Arts and Crafts made in New England; Presidential Politicking of the Past; Crazy Quilts; Weaving Demonstration.
Publications: Historical Collections, quarterly; newsletter, quarterly; occasional books.
Activities: Classes for adults and children; docent training; lect open to public, 6 vis lectr per yr; gallery talks; tours; paintings and original objects of art lent to museums and institutions.
—James Duncan Phillips Library
Open to the public for reference. Mon - Fri 9 AM - 4:30 PM.
Holdings: Vols 400,000; Other—Manuscripts, diaries, letters, account books, newspapers, periodicals, broadsides, genealogies, pamphlets, printed sermons, city directories and log books.
Special Collections: Frederick T Ward China Collection treats the history of China and Chinese-American relations to the early 20th century.
—Gardner-Pingree House
Open Tues - Sat 10 AM - 4 PM; Sun 1 - 4:30 PM (June 1 - Oct 15). Admis adults $1, children and sr citizens 50¢. Built in 1804-1805, it illustrates the Federal Style of Salem master-builder and carver, Samuel McIntire; furnished in that period.
—Crowninshield-Bentley House
Open Tues - Sat 10 AM - 4 PM; Sun 1 - 4:30 PM (June 1 - Oct 15). Admis adults $1, children and sr citizens 50¢. Built in 1727, added to and remodeled after 1800, illustrates the styles of interior architecture and furnishings of much of the 18th century in Salem.
—John Ward House
Open Tues - Sat 10 AM - 4 PM; Sun 1 - 4:30 PM (June 1 - Oct 15). Admis $1, children and sr citizens 50¢. Built 1684, restored 1910-1912 under direction of George Francis Dow, architectural historian; furnished in the manner of the time. The rear lean-to contains a later apothecary's shop, a weaving room with operable loom, and a small "cent" shop.
—Andrew-Safford House, 13 Washington Square
Open Thurs 2 - 4:30 PM Admis $1. Built 1818-1819, purchased by Institute 1947, presents a vivid image of early 19th century urban life. It is the residence of the Institute's director.
—Peirce-Nichols House, 80 Federal St
Open Tues - Sat 2 - 4:30 PM Admis $1. Built in 1782 by Samuel McIntire; some original furnishings and a counting house.
—Assembly House, 138 Federal St
Open Tues - Fri 2 - 4:30 PM. Admis $1. Built in 1782 as a hall for social assemblies; remodeled in 1796 by Samuel McIntire as a home residence. The interior features a Victorian sitting room and an unusual Chinese parlor.
—Lye-Tapley Shoe Shop (1830) and Vaughan Doll House
Open Tues - Sat 10 AM - 4 PM; Sun 1 - 4:30 PM (June 1 - Oct 15). Accommodate special collections.

PEABODY MUSEUM OF SALEM, East India Square, 01970. Tel: 617-745-1876. *Dir* Ernest S Dodge; *Asst Dir* Peter Fetchko; *Cur Maritime Hist* Philip C F Smith; *Cur Natural Hist* Sarah P Ingalls; *Dir Educ* Sarah Fraser Robbins; *Asst Treas* Priscilla W Papin.
Open Mon - Sat 9 AM - 5 PM; Sun & holidays 1 - 5 PM. Admis adults $1.50, children 75 cents. Estab 1799 for the conservation of American maritime history, art objects; ethnology of non-European peoples; natural history of Essex County. Gallery is a conglomeration of old and new bldgs, 45,000 sq ft of exhib space, 95,000 sq ft total. Average Annual Attendance: 100,000; Mem: 1800; dues $20, $30, $100; annual meeting Sept.
Income: $200,000 (financed by endowment, membership).
Collections: American Maritime History (paintings, objects); Ethnology of Pacific Islands and Far East; Natural History of Essex County, Massachusetts.
Publications: The American Neptune, quarterly journal of maritime history.
Activities: Classes for adults and children; docent training; lect open to public, 4 vis lectr per yr; gallery talks; tours; museum shop selling books, reproductions, prints.
—Phillips Library. Tel: 617-745-1876. *Librn* Barbara B Edkins.
Open Mon - Fri 9 AM - 4:30 PM. Staff library, but open to qualified researchers.
Income: Financed by endowment.
Holdings: Vols 100,000; Per subs 225.
Special Subjects: Ethnology of non-European peoples; maritime history of New England; voyages of discovery; natural history of Essex County.

SANDWICH

HERITAGE PLANTATION OF SANDWICH, Grove & Pine Sts, 02563. Tel: 617-888-3300. *Dir* Gene A Schott; *Cur Arts & Crafts* Ladd MacMillan; *Cur Military Hist* James Cervantes; *Cur Bot Sci* Jean Gillis; *Registr* Allota Lentel.
Open daily 10 AM - 5 PM, May 1 - Oct 15. Admis adults $2.50. Estab 1969 as a museum of Americana. Heritage Plantation is an educational trust. Three galleries house collections. Average Annual Attendance: 100,000. Mem: 1200; dues individual $15, family $25; annual meeting Apr.
Income: $400,000 (financed by endowment, membership, admissions).
Collections: †Scrimshaw; primitive paintings; folk art; †American Indian artifacts; all are American.
Exhibitions: (1976) Unsung Heroes of the American Revolution; (1977) Cape Cod as an Art Colony; (1978) Birds in American Art; Arms and Armor.
Publications: The Cupola, quarterly.
Activities: Classes for adults and children; lect for members only, 4 - 5 vis lectr per yr; concerts; gallery talks; tours; exten dept serving Cape Cod area; artmobile; individual paintings and original objects of art lent.
Library: Open to staff and members for reference only. Holdings: Vols 1000; Per subs 10. Special Subjects: Art; military history; antique automobiles.

SCITUATE

BOSTON WATERCOLOR SOCIETY, 748 First Parish Rd, 02066. Tel: 617-545-2025. *Pres* Charles A Mahoney; *VPres* Glenn MacNutt; *Secy* Fletcher P Adams.
Estab 1886 to advance watercolor proficiency. Mem: 85; dues $15; annual meeting Jan.
Income: Financed by membership.

SHARON

KENDALL WHALING MUSEUM, 27 Everett St (Mailing Add: Box 297, 02067). Tel: 617-784-5642. *Dir* Kenneth R Martin; *Res Assoc* Rebecca L Jackson; *Registr* Robert H Ellis, Jr.
Open Mon - Fri 1 - 4 PM; cl holidays. Admis adults $1, children under 14 50¢. Estab 1956 to collect, preserve, and interpret materials relating to the history of whaling and the natural history of the whale. Dutch-European gallery; Arctic gallery; Japanese gallery; scrimshaw exhibit; whale boat and whaling gear room; two large American galleries. Average Annual Attendance: 3700.
Income: Financed by endowment.
Collections: †Prints; †paintings; scrimshaw and other whalemen's folk art; †logbooks-journals; †films; ship models; whaling gear; †phonograph records; †books; †pamphlets; †documents.,
Exhibitions: Save the Whale; Modern Whaling.
Activities: Lect open to public, 4 vis lectr per yr; tours; individual paintings and original objects of art lent to other museums; museum shop selling books, original art, prints.

Library: Res Assoc Rebecca L Jackson. Reference library, by appointment only. Holdings: Vols 3000; Per subs 25; Other—Pamphlets 250, films 30.

SOUTH HADLEY

MOUNT HOLYOKE COLLEGE ART MUSEUM, 01075. Tel: 413-538-2245. *Dir* Grant Holcomb; *Chief Cur* Wendy Watson; *Admin Asst* Margery Roy.
Open Mon - Fri 11 AM - 5 PM; Sat - Sun 1 - 5 PM; summer Mon - Fri 1 - 4 PM. No admis. Estab 1875 to display permanent collection and temporary exhibitions. Building erected in 1971 to house the equipment and collections of the Department of Art of Mount Holyoke College. It contains lecture rooms, painting and sculpture studios, art library; art museum with five galleries houses the permanent collection. Mem: Dues $10 - $100; no meetings held.
Income: Financed by endowment, membership, state appropriations and college funds.
Collections: †Asian art, †European and American paintings, sculpture, prints and drawings; Egyptian, Greek, Roman; Pre-Columbian.
Exhibitions: (1976-77) Collegiate Collections: 1776-1876; Monsters, Gargoyles and Dragons: Animals in the Middle Ages; Schemes and Variations: Work by Emmett Williams; (1977-78) Marion Miller: Paintings and Drawings; Offset Prints; Editions from Artists-Research-Technology; American Art from the Mount Holyoke College Collection; Silence and Slow Time (work by Salvatore Romano, Clement Meadmore, Jake Berthot and Robin MacKenzie).
Publications: Mount Holyoke College Art Museum Newsletter, twice yearly.
Activities: Lect open to the public, 5 - 6 vis lectr per yr; individual paintings lent to exhibitions sponsored by museums.
—Art Library.
Open to college community only.
Holdings: Vols 15,000 Per subs 60; Other Slides 60,000.

SOUTH SUDBURY

LONGFELLOW'S WAYSIDE INN, Wayside Inn Road, off Route 20, 01776. Tel: 617-443-8846. *Innkeeper* Francis Koppeis; *Chmn Trustees* Lawrence Coolidge.
Open daily 9 AM - 9 PM; cl Christmas Day. Admis 50¢; no charge for dining room and overnight guests. Estab c 1702 as the oldest operating Inn in America, the ancient hostelry continues to provide hospitality to wayfarers from all over the world. 18th century period rooms include Old Barroom, Longfellow Parlor, Longfellow Bed Chamber, Old Kitchen, Drivers and Drovers Chambers. Historic buildings on the estate include Redstone School of Mary's Little Lamb fame, grist mill, and Martha Mary Chapel. Average Annual Attendance: 250,000.
Collections: Early American furniture and decorative arts; Howe family memorabilia; paintings; prints; photographs of the Inn.
Activities: Classes for adults; docent training; colonial crafts demonstrations and workshops; lect open to public, 10 vis lectr per yr; gallery talks; tours; sales shop selling books, original art, reproductions, prints and slides.

SPRINGFIELD

CONNECTICUT VALLEY HISTORICAL MUSEUM,* 194 State St, 01103. Tel: 413-732-3080. *Dir* Juliette Tomlinson; *Secy* Cecelia F Callazzo.
Open Tues - Sat 1 - 5 PM; Sun 2 - 5 PM; cl Mon. No admis. Estab 1871.
Income: $20,000.
Collections: China, glass, pewter, period rooms relating to Springfield and the Connecticut Valley.
Exhibitions: Special permanent exhibitions including pewter of the Connecticut Valley; American silver; Scalamandre textiles; James S Ellsworth, American miniature painter; painting and prints from Connecticut Valley collectors.
Library: Contains material relating to early Springfield, including the Account Books of John Pynchon, 1651-1713; photograph collection for lending and reference.

MUSEUM OF FINE ARTS,* 49 Chestnut St, 01103. Tel: 413-733-5857. *Dir Pub Relations* Lee Sheridan.
Open Tues - Sat 1 - 5 PM; Sun 2 - 5 PM; cl Mon & holidays. No admis. Estab 1933 as a unit of the Springfield Library and Museums Association through the bequests of Mr and Mrs James Philip Gray. Building contains 18 galleries, library theater, offices.

Collections: Prehistoric Chinese to 19th century; Persian miniatures from 10th - 20th century; Japanese woodblock prints, paintings and sculpture; Gothic to Renaissance; 17th, 18th, and 20th century Italian, Dutch, French and British; primitive to contemporary American paintings, sculpture and graphics, print collection from Old Masters to present.
Exhibitions: Special exhibitions, historic to contemporary, are continually on view in addition to permanent collection.
Activities: Education Department offers docent training, lectures, films, concerts, in-class-in-room public schools program coordinated with student tours, audiovisual programs.
Reference Library: Holdings: Vols 5000; AV—Slides.
Other—Permanent collection and other art masterpieces.

GEORGE WALTER VINCENT SMITH ART MUSEUM, 222 State St, 01103. Tel: 413-733-4214. *Chmn* Kathleen Morehead; *Dir* Richard Muhlberger; *Cur Educ* Kathy Bell; *Asst Cur Educ* March Wasilewski; *Registrar* Mary Linda; *Conservator* Emil G Schnorr.
Open Tues - Sat 1 - 5 PM; Sun 2 - 5 PM; cl Mon. No admis. Estab 1889 to preserve, protect, present, interpret, study and publish the collections of fine and decorative arts; arrange temporary exhibits; and offer studio classes for children and adults. Eleven galleries housing permanent collection and one gallery reserved for changing exhibitions. Average Annual Attendance: 35,000. Mem: 2000; dues $15 and up; annual meeting June.
Income: Financed by endowment, membership, city and state appropriations.
Collections: Oriental and Asiatic decorative arts; American and European paintings; plaster casts; near Eastern carpets.
Exhibitions: 19th century Still Life Paintings; Richard Black Exhibition; "Under 30" Photography; American paintings, watercolors and drawings from the 19th century; Two Massachusetts Artists: Ronald Allen Leax and Leon Shulman; Women on Women; Annual Springfield Art League National Exhibition; A Private Eye: 19th century American paintings, drawings and watercolors; Holiday Treasury of Stained Glass: the Leuchs collection; Classical Casts: Ancient and Renaissance Sculpture; annual student show.
Publications: Quadrangle Calendar; Annual Report; special exhibition catalogs.
Activities: Classes for adults and children; docent training; lect open to public; gallery talks, tours; competitions with cash awards; scholarships; individual paintings and original objects of art lent to museums.
—Research Library. Open to public by appointment.
Holdings: Vols 2700.
Special Subjects: Related to collections.

SPRINGFIELD ART LEAGUE,* 220 State St, 01103.
Estab 1918 to stimulate art expression and appreciation in Springfield. Mem dues $7, annual meeting April.
Exhibitions: Special non-juried show in Nov, open to all artists, to promote sale of work; Annual jury exhibition in April with cash awards.
Activities: Lectures; demonstrations; exhibits each year at the Smith Museum of Art.

SPRINGFIELD CITY LIBRARY,* 220 State St, 01103. Tel: 413-739-3871. *Pres* Ramona L Corriveau; *Dir* Francis P Keough; *Head Fine Arts Dept* Karen A Dorval.
Fine Arts Dept open Mon - Fri 9 AM - 9 PM; Sat 9 AM - 5 PM; cl holidays. No admis. Estab 1857, Fine Arts Department opened 1905. In addition to the City Library system, the Springfield Library and Museums Association owns and administers, as separate units, the George Walter Vincent Smith Museum, The Springfield Museum of Fine Art, the Science Museum, and the Connecticut Valley Historical Museum.
Income: $8000.
Exhibitions: Monthly exhibitions from the Library's collections and of work by local artists. Loan exhibitions.
—Art Department.
Holdings: Vols 17,500, Per subs 60; Other—Pictures 25,000 including American wood engravings and blockprints, photographs, color reproductions and a circulating collection of framed prints.

SPRINGFIELD COLLEGE, Babson Library Art Gallery, 263 Alden St, 01109. Tel: 413-787-2332. *Chmn Art Dept* William Blizard.
Open daily 8 AM - 11 PM. Estab 1975 to bring a wide range of quality exhibits in all areas of the visual arts to the Springfield College campus and surrounding community.
Income: Financed by Cultural Affairs Comt. Purchases: $1000.
Holdings: Vols 110,000; Per subs 200; AV—Cassettes, film strips, motion pictures and video tapes; Other—Original art works and prints.
Exhibitions: Twenty-one exhibits during the last three years, one-person shows, national works on paper.
Activities: Lect open to public, 6 vis lectr per yr; concerts; gallery talks; competitions.

STOCKBRIDGE

CHESTERWOOD,* Box 248, 01262. Tel: 413-298-3579. *Adminr* Paul H Ivory; *Curatorial Asst* Susan Frisch; *Admin Asst* Kathleen Opperman; *Coordr Interpretive Programs* Carole T Scanlon.
Open Memorial Day weekend through Oct 31, 10 AM - 5 PM; candle-light tours Wed evenings during July & Aug 8 - 10 PM; open May on appointment basis; cl end of Oct until May. Admis adult $1.75, senior citizens 80¢, children 75¢, group rates by arrangement; free to National Trust members. Average Annual Attendance: 15,000.
Chesterwood is a property of the National Trust for Historic Preservation. Preserved as a historic house, operated as a community preservation center. Chesterwood was the summer home and studio of sculptor Daniel Chester French (1850-1931). Here he worked for 6 months of the year over a period of 30 years. Henry Bacon designed the 30-foot stucco and frame cubical studio (1897), as well as the Colonial Revival mansion (1900). Margaret French Cresson donated the house to the National Trust in 1969. The collection includes sculpture, bronzes, plaster casts and paintings by Daniel Chester French, Mrs French and their contemporaries.
Property serves as focal point for advancement of historic preservation. It develops new relationships among cultural, community, community's present needs by action as a resource look between community, preservation groups, and Trust members in its area. Responds to community preservation needs by acting as a link between community and appropriate regional or headquarters offices of National Trust.
Provides interpretive programs which are related to Chesterwood's particular case study in historic preservation. Programs include pre-visit school material and tour program, National Trust summer intern program, college field experience program; special exhibits, participation in Daniel Chester French Retrospective - 1976-1977. Members Day during part of National Preservation Week early part of May. Preservation Shop.
Reference Library: Holdings—Vols 5000; Other—Manuscripts, photographs 2000.

STOCKBRIDGE HISTORICAL SOCIETY, INC,* Main St, 01262. Tel: 413-298-3822. *Dir* David H Wood; *Asst Dir* Mrs John T Batty.
Open daily 10 AM - 5 PM; cl Tues, Thanksgiving, Xmas and New Year's. Admis adults $1, children under 12 25¢, local residents no admis. Estab 1967 in The Old Corner House, an 1800 Georgian house located on the original property deeded to successive Mohican Indians under charter granted to town by Queen Anne in 1739.
Collections: Historical material; original sketches and paintings by Norman Rockwell.
Activities: Lectures; guided tours; temporary exhibitions; sales shop selling Norman Rockwell books and prints.

STOCKBRIDGE MISSION HOUSE ASSOCIATION,* Box 422, 01262. Tel: 413-298-3383. *Chmn* Andrew R Mack; *Secy* John Rogers; *Cur* Carol Patten.
Open Tues - Sat 10 AM - 5 PM; Sun 11 AM - 4 PM. Average Annual Attendance: 3000. Annual meeting June.
Built 1739, restored by Mabel Choate, 1928, as a memorial to her parents, Mr and Mrs Joseph H Choate. Originally the home of John Sergeant, first missionary to the Stockbridge Indians, it is now an Early American Museum containing household objects, portraits and decorations of the period, and Indian relics.

STURBRIDGE

OLD STURBRIDGE VILLAGE, 01566. Tel: 617-347-3362. *Pres* Alexander J Wall; *VPres* John E Auchmoody; *VPres* Charles T Hesse; *Dir Admin* Darwin Kelsey; *Dir Educ* Alberta Sebolt; *Dir Cur Dept* John O Curtis; *Dir Research & Libr* Roger Parks.
Open daily Mar - Nov 9:30 AM - 5:30 PM; Dec - Mar 10 AM - 4 PM; cl Christmas and New Year's Day. Admis adults $4, children $1.50; special group rates. Estab 1936 to perpetuate and interpret the New England social, economic and cultural heritage; authentically restored rural village consisting of 43 structures. Average Annual Attendance; 670,000.
Collections: Buildings; furnishings; †pottery; †glass; †iron; †tin; †textiles; †folk arts; †clocks; †New England rural paintings; decorative arts; pewter.
Publications: The New England Galaxy; The Rural Visitor quarterly; Guidebook; pamphlet series; annual report.
Activities; Classes for adults and children; internship program; craft demonstrations; lectures; films; concerts; tours.
—**Research Library.** Tel: 617-347-3362, exten 132. *Librn* Etta Falkner; *Asst Librn* Theresa Rini.
Open Mon - Fri 8:30 - 5 PM; estab 1946 to serve the museum staff; open to the public for reference only.
Income: Financed through museum. Purchases: $7500.
Holdings: Vols 23,675; Per subs 165; AV—Microfiche, microfilm, slides; Other—Manuscripts.

Special Subjects: New England 1790-1850 including law, technology and industry especially textile, agriculture, crafts, fine and decorative arts, music, local history.

TYRINGHAM ·

TYRINGHAM ART GALLERIES, Tyringham Road, 01264. Tel: 413-243-0654 or 243-3260. *Co-Dir* Ann Marie & Donald Davis.
Admis 25¢, children under 12 free. Estab 1953 to exhibit and sell paintings, prints, sculptures by recognized artists, including world masters. The building was designed as a sculpture studio by the late Sir Henry Kitson; on three levels, smaller studios on the second level are furnished with trap door facilities for lowering sculpture to the main level; two former silos are involved in the structure. Average Annual Attendance: 30,000.
Income: Financed privately.
Exhibitions: Frequent one-person shows by established artists from New York City.
Publications: Auction catalogs, occasionally.
Activities: Gallery talks; tours.

TYRINGHAM INSTITUTE, Jean Brown Archive, Shaker Seed House, 01264. Tel: 413-243-3216. *Dir* Mrs Leonard Brown.
Open Mon - Fri 2 - 5 PM. No admis. Estab 1971 as a study and research center for graduate scholars, art historians, and critics. Large gallery, with cabinets for books, portfolios, primary source material, newspaper clippings, photographs, and letters. Average Annual Attendance: 100 - 300.
Income: Privately financed.
Collections: Dada; Surrealism; Concrete Poetry; Happenings; Fluxus; Intermedia.
Activities: Lending collection contains original art works, original prints and photographs.
—**Library.** *Dir* Mrs Leonard Brown.
Open Mon - Fri 2 - 5 PM. Estab 1971 for reference only.
Income: Privately financed.
Holdings: Vols 30,000; AV—Cassettes 200, phonorecords; Other—Clipping files, exhibition catalogs, manuscripts, memorabilia, original art works, original documents, pamphlets, photographs, prints.

WALTHAM

AMERICAN JEWISH HISTORICAL SOCIETY, 2 Thornton Road, 02154. Tel: 617-891-8110. *Pres* David R Pokross; *Chmn Exec Council* Saul Viener; *Dir* Bernard Wax; *Librn-Editor* Dr Nathan M Kaganoff.
Open (summer) Mon - Fri 8:30 AM - 5 PM; (winter) Mon - Thurs 8:30 AM - 5 PM; Fri 8:30 AM - 2 PM; Sun 2 - 5 PM. No admis. Estab 1892 to collect, preserve, catalog and disseminate information relating to the American Jewish experience. Two galleries where exhibitions mounted: 15 x 50 ft. Average Annual Attendance: 3000. Mem: 3200; dues $20; annual meeting May.
Income: $200,000 (financed by endowment, membership, city appropriation, grants and donations).
Collections: Portraits; Yiddish theater posters; Yiddish motion pictures; manuscripts.
Exhibitions: Haym Salomon: A gentleman of precision and integrity; Jews in Colonial America.
Activities: Lect open to public, 3 vis lectr per yr; gallery talks; individual paintings and original objects of art lent to museums and historical societies; lending collection contains motion pictures and paintings.
—**Lee M Friedman Memorial Library.**
Open to qualified researchers for reference.
Holdings: Vols 60,000; Per subs 100; Other—Manuscripts; archives of individuals and institutions.
Special Subjects: Colonial American Jewry; synagogues, philanthropic institutions.
Special Collections: The archives consist of approximately four million items which relate to all areas of American Jewish history.

BRANDEIS UNIVERSITY, Rose Art Museum, 415 South St, 02154. Tel: 617-647-2404. *Dir* Carl I Belz; *Cur* Bonny B Saulnier; *Registr* Marjorie Groggins; *Preparator* Roger Kizik; *Staff Asst* Barbara Vetter.
Open Tues - Sun 1 - 5 PM; cl Mon and holidays. No admis. Estab 1961 for the organization of regionally and nationally recognized exhibits of contemporary painting and sculpture. An additional gallery is located in the Spingold Theatre Building. All galleries are used for changing exhibitions; there are no permanent exhibitions. Average Annual Attendance: 20,000.
Collections: The permanent collections consist of: contemporary art (Post-WW II); modern Art (1800 to WW II), including the Riverside Museum Collections and the Teresa Jackson Weill Collection; pre-modern art (before 1800); the Helen S Slosberg Collection of Oceanic

art; the Mr and Mrs Edward Rose Collection of early ceramics; Japanese prints; Tibetian art; Pre-Columbian art; African art; American Indian art.
Exhibitions: (1976-78) Jewish Arts Festival; 15 Printmakers from the Experimental Etching Studio; Next Generation (recent work in color photography); Two Hundred Years of American Synagogue Architecture; Mitchell Siporin: a Retrospective; Action and Reaction: Contemporary Trends in Painting and Sculpture; Stepping Out: Five Bostonians; 12 From the Soviet Underground; Naftali Bezem; Turn of the Century Posters; Brandeis Designers' Exhibition; 7 Seniors 77; From Women's Eyes; Art of the State; Contemporary Masters; Locations (sculpture); James Weeks: Paintings and Drawings from the Last 30 Years; Alex Katz in the 70s.
Publications: Exhibition catalogs.
Activities: Educ dept; docent training; lect open to public, 6 vis lectr per yr; gallery talks; tours; individual paintings and original objects of art lent to students and individuals within the university; lending collection contains original art works 550, original prints 300, paintings 250; traveling exhibitions organized and circulated.

WELLESLEY

WELLESLEY COLLEGE
—**Museum**, 02181. Tel: 617-235-0320, exten 314. *Dir* Ann Gabhart; *Asst Dir* Judith Fox; *Admin Asst, Friends of Art* Marjorie Dings.
Open Mon - Fri 8:30 AM - 5 PM; Sat 8:30 - Noon & 1 - 5 PM; Sun 2 - 5 PM; cl New Year's Day, Thanksgiving, Christmas, and June through August. No admis. Estab 1899. Dedicated to acquiring a collection of high quality art objects for the primary purpose of teaching art history from original works. Main gallery houses major exhibitions; Corridor Gallery, works on paper; Sculpture Court, permanent installation, sculpture, reliefs, works on wood panel. Average Annual Attendance: 8000. Mem: 450; dues $15.
Income: Financed by membership, through college, and gifts.
Collections: Old master paintings; prints and drawings; contemporary painting; classical, medieval and Renaissance sculpture; photography.
Exhibitions: Tower, and roof, and pinnacle. . .(The Architecture of College Hall); James Wilson Rayen: Recent and Revised, 1975-1978 (paintings and drawings); One Century: Wellesley Families Collect; American Landscape Paintings; Sculpture: metalworks, clayworks, paperworks, photoworks, by Alice Atkinson Lyndon; Undertones: Photographs by Georgia Litwak.
Publications: Wellesley College Friends of Art Newsletter, yearly.
Activities: Docent training; original objects of art lent to students; lending collection contains original prints; traveling exhibitions organized and circulated; sales desk selling catalogs, postcards and notecards.
—**Art Library.** *Librn* Katherine D Finkelpearl; *Asst* Susan Farlow.
Open to scholars by application. Established to serve the bibliographic needs of Wellesley College students and faculty. Circ: 22,000.
Income: Financed by Wellesley College appropriation. Purchases: $15,000.
Holdings: Vols 26,000; Per subs 75; AV—Kodachromes, and lantern slides; Other—Exhibition catalogs, pamphlets and photographs.
Special Subjects: American art and architecture, Western European art and architecture, Far Eastern art, Ancient art and architecture, photography.

WENHAM

WENHAM HISTORICAL ASSOCIATION AND MUSEUM, INC, 132 Main St, 01984. Tel: 617-468-2377. *Dir* Eleanor E Thompson; *Doll Cur* Mrs FJ Donoghue; *Office Admin* Lee Nelson; *Pres* Mrs Dean Cogswell; *Registrar & Asst Cur* Joyce Munier.
Open Mon - Fri 1 - 4 PM; Sun 2 - 5 PM; mornings by appointment. Admis adults $1, children (6-14) 25¢. Estab 1921 as Historical Society, inc 1953, to acquire, preserve, interpret, and exhibit collections of literary and historical interest, to provide an educational and cultural service and facilities. Three permanent galleries and one gallery for changing exhibits. Average Annual Attendance: 8,000. Mem: 650; Dues individual $5; family $10; annual meeting Apr.
Income: $32,000 (financed by endowment, membership, earned income).
Collections: Dolls and figurines; costumes and accessories 1800-1960; quilts; fans; needlework and embroideries, mostly 19th century.
Exhibitions: Model Trains; Conservation; Needlecraft; Color Photography; Portraits, Still Lifes, Landscapes of Doris Suminsby; Scottish Holidays; Needle Artists; Weavers; Prints and Drawing of Ethan Berry.
Publications: Newsletter; Annual Report.
Activities: Classes for children; lect open to public, 4 vis lectr per yr; gallery talks; traveling exhibitions organized and circulated; museum shop selling books, miniatures, original needlework and dolls.

Library: Timothy Pickering Library. *Librn* Lee Nelson. Open to members and the public for reference. Holdings: Vols 1000; Other—Local historical research material. Special Subjects: Headquarters of Massachusetts Society for Promoting Agriculture; Vols 300; many original papers and source material.

WESTFIELD

WESTFIELD ATHENAEUM, Jasper Rand Art Museum, 6 Elm St, 01085. Tel: 413-568-7833. *Pres* Milton B Reach; *Treas* Leslie A Chapin; *Dir* Franklin P Taplin; *Secy* Elizabeth G S Reed.
Open Mon, Tues, Thurs & Fri 9 AM - 9 PM; Wed 9 AM - 6 PM; Sat 9 AM - 5 PM; cl Sat in summer. No admis. Estab 1927 to provide exhibitions of art works by area artists and other prominent artists; gallery measures 25 x 30 x 17 ft, domed ceiling with free-standing glass cases and wall cases. Average Annual Attendance: 12,000. Mem: 250; dues none; annual meeting fourth Mon Oct.
Income: Financed by endowment, city appropriation.
Exhibitions: Original paintings of scenes along the General Knox Trail by Wallace Noel; paintings by eleven members of Springfield Art League; paintings of New England scenes by Joseph R Corish; Bicentennial plaques by Eugene Lederle; American Indian pottery made by the Indians of Arizona.
Activities: Classes for children.

WESTON

REGIS COLLEGE, L J Walters Jr Gallery, 235 Wellesley St, 02193. Tel: 617-893-1820, exten 237. *Dir* Sister Louisella Walters.
Open Mon - Fri 9 AM - 4:30 PM. No admis. Estab 1964 for education, for visiting exhibits, and for student use. One room, 20 x 30 ft. Average Annual Attendance: 1500.
Exhibitions: Local painters and sculptors; student exhibits.

WILLIAMSTOWN

STERLING AND FRANCINE CLARK ART INSTITUTE, 225 South St (Mailing Add: PO Box 8, 01267). Tel: 413-458-8109. *Dir* David S Brooke; *Assoc Dir* John H Brooks; *Cur Prints & Drawings* Rafael A Fernandez; *Asst Cur* David B Cass and Beth Carver Wees; *Registr* Martha Asher; *Comptroller* Joseph A Kershaw; *Admin Asst* Selma Sabin; *Photograph & Slide Librn* J Dustin Wees; *Supt* G Louis McManus; *Chief Conservator* Gerald R Hoepfner.
Open Tues - Sun 10 AM - 5 PM; cl Mon, New Year's Day, Thanksgiving & Christmas. No admis. Estab 1955 as a museum of fine arts with galleries, art research library and public events in auditorium. Average Annual Attendance: 100,000.
Income: Financed by endowment.
Collections: Italian, Flemish, Dutch and French Old Master paintings from the 14th-18th centuries; French 19th century paintings, including The Impressionists; selected 19th century American artists (Homer and Sargent); 19th century sculpture; Old Master prints and drawings; porcelains, antique silver.
Exhibitions: The Permanent Collection and Traveling Exhibitions.
Publications: Calendar of Events, quarterly.
Activities: Educ dept; docent training; lectures; concerts; movies; gallery talks; organized educational programs for children; graduate program for MA in art history in collaboration with Williams College; museum shop selling books, reproductions, prints, slides; postcards.
Library: *Librn* Michael Rinehart. Art research library for students and scholars, public upon application, for reference only. Special Subjects: Art history.

WILLIAMS COLLEGE, Museum of Art, Main St, 01267. Tel: 413-597-2429. *Dir* Franklin W Robinson; *Supt* George T Aitken; *Secy* Flora Bloedel.
Open Mon - Fri 9 AM - 5 PM; Sat 10 AM - Noon & 2 - 5 PM; Sun 2 - 5 PM; Sun 2 - 5 PM; cl during College holidays. No admis. Estab 1926 for the presentation of the permanent collection and temporary loan exhibitions for the benefit of the Williams College community and the general public. Central rotunda, built in 1846 by Thomas Tefft; other period galleries and loan exhibition gallery. Average Annual Attendance: 5000 plus college students.
Collections: European and American painting, sculpture, prints and drawings, from the Renaissance to the present; †Ancient, Medieval, Pre-Columbian, African and Oriental art.
Exhibitions: All media, centuries and countries with special emphasis on prints, drawings and photographs.
Publications: Exhibition catalogs, 3-4 per year.
Activities: Classes for children; lect open to public, 20 vis lectr per yr; concerts; gallery talks; tours; individual paintings and original objects of art lent to museums; traveling exhibitions organized and circulated; museum shop selling books.

—**Sawyer Library.**
Income: $10,400.
Holdings: Vols: 16,600; Per subs 86; AV—Slides 50,000; Other—Color reproductions 500.

WORCESTER

CLARK UNIVERSITY, Gallery, In the Little Center for Visual and Performing Arts, 950 Main St, 01610. Tel: 617-793-7260. *Dir* Donald W. Krueger; *Intern* Stuart Gerrstein; *Asst* Stacie Gerard.
Open Mon - Fri Noon - 6 PM; Sat & Sun 2 - 6 PM; cl University holidays. No admis. Estab 1977 primarily for one and two-person shows of young, unknown artists; to help artists get recognition. One gallery 40 x 50 ft with moveable panels. Average Annual Attendance: 1450 monthly.
Income: Financed through the University.
Exhibitions: Nine exhibitions a year of young artists.
Publications: Announcements of exhibitions.
Activities: Vis lectr; gallery talks.

CRAFT CENTER GALLERY, 25 Sagamore Rd, 01605. Tel: 617-753-8183. *Dir* Angelo Randazzo; *Exhib Coordr* John I Russell.
Open Mon - Sat 9 AM - 5 PM; Sun 2 - 5 PM. No admis. Estab 1952 for educational exhibits of historic and contemporary crafts. 40 x 60 professionally lighted and installed gallery with 4 major shows per year. Average Annual Attendance: 5000. Mem: 1100; dues $10 - $25.
Income: Financed by membership.
Exhibitions: The North American Basket 1790-1970; Objects for an Interior Environment, David Davison; Faculty Show 1976; Student Work 1976.
Publications: Exhibition catalogs.
Activities: Classes for adults and children; lect open to public, 12 vis lectr per yr; gallery talks; tours; lending collection contains books 200, Kodachromes 2000, photographs 300; traveling exhibitions organized and circulated; museum shop selling books, original art, reproductions, slides.

JOHN WOODMAN HIGGINS ARMORY, 100 Barber Ave, 01606. Tel: 617-853-6015. *Pres* Mrs M L Wilding-White; *Dir* Richard E Fors; *Cur* Albert J Gagne.
Open Tues - Fri 9 AM - 4 PM; Sat 10 AM - 3 PM; Sun 1 - 5 PM; cl Mon & national holidays. Admis charged. Estab 1928 to inspire present day students; the Museum is in a Gothic Hall with high vaulted ceilings. Average Annual Attendance: 35,000. Mem: 325; dues $10 & $25; annual meeting May.
Income: Financed by endowment, membership, and gift shop.
Collections: (Art) Art of the Stone Age, Bronze Age and Iron Age; artistic objects of the iron smith's craft; paintings; tapestries; stained glass; wood carvings.
Publications: Catalog of Armor; Booklet on Armor; Ventail Voice, quarterly.
Activities: Docent training; audio-visual talks for adults and children; independent study for college students; lectr open to the public; concerts; gallery talks; tours; museum and sales shop selling books, reproductions, prints, slides and gifts relating to arms and armor.
Library: Librn Erveen C Lundberg; *Dir* Richard E Fors. Open for reference on appointment only. Holdings: Vols 2000. Special subjects: Arms and armor.

WORCESTER ART MUSEUM, 55 Salisbury St, 01608. Tel: 617-799-4406. *Dir* Richard Stuart Teitz; *Cur Coll* Dagmar E Reutlinger; *Assoc Cur* James A Welu; *Registr & Cur Photography* Stephen B Jareckie; *Cur Prints & Drawings* Timothy A Riggs; *Cur Japanese Prints* Alice Mundt; *Adminr* W Arthur Gagne; *Conservator* Norman E Muller; *Develop Officer* John C Ewer; *Cur Educ* Merle S Harbach; *Assoc Cur Educ* Ellen R Berezin; *Dir Pub Relations* Gaye L Brown; *Mem Secy* Jean T Larkin.
Open Tues - Sat 10 AM - 5 PM; Sun 2 - 5 PM; cl Mon, New Years, July 4, Thanksgiving & Christmas. Admis members free; nonmember adults $1, children under 14 and adults over 65, 50¢, children under 5 accompanied by adult free. Estab Museum 1896, School 1898. The Museum and School were founded for the promotion of art and art education in Worcester; for the preservation and exhibition of works and objects of art and for instruction in the industrial, liberal, and fine arts. There are 42 galleries housed in a neoclassical bldg. The Higgins Education Wing, built in 1970, houses the Museum School and contains exhibition space for shows sponsored by the Education Department and the School. Average Annual Attendance: 100,000. Mem: 3500; dues $8 - $1000 and over; annual meeting Oct.
Income: $1,200,000 (financed by endowment, membership, admission fees, private corporate contributions, and government grants).
Collections: †Mosaics from Antioch; †Egyptian, Classical, Oriental, and Medieval sculpture; †12th century French chapter house; †Pre-Columbian Collection; †John Chandler Bancroft Collection of Japanese prints; †Italian paintings of the 13th-18th centuries; †French paintings of 16th-19th centuries; †Flemish 16th century paintings; †Dutch 17th century paintings; †American paintings of 18th-20th centuries and 18th century silver; †British paintings of 18th and 19th centuries.
Exhibitions: (1976) Naives and Visionaries; American Photography: 1840-1900; The Early Republic: Consolidation of Revolutionary Goals; (1976-77) The Second Fifty Years: American Art, 1826-1876; The Sculptor's Eye: The African Collection of Mr and Mrs Chaim Gross; (1977) Recent Acquisitions in Contemporary American Art; Wellsprings of a Nation; The Massachusetts Open; Zenga and Nanga: Paintings by Japanese Monks and Scholars; (1977-78) For Collectors: A Sales Exhibition of Works of Art; (1978) Two Decades of American Printmaking.
Publications: Worcester Art Museum Bulletin, triannually; Calendar of Events, quarterly.
Activities: Classes for adults and children; docent training; lectr open to public, 5 - 6 vis lectr per yr; concerts; gallery talks; tours; competitions, a juried competition for Massachusetts artists; museum shop selling books, reproductions, prints, jewelry, and others.
—**Library.** Tel: 617-799-4406, exten 30. *Librn* Hollee Haswell; *Asst* Maureen Killoran; *Slide Librn* Joan Gallant.
Open Tues - Fri 10 AM - 5 PM. Estab 1909 to provide resource material for the Museum Departments. Participate in Worcester Area Cooperating Libraries. Circ: Non-circulating collection only.
Purchases: Approx $7400.
Holdings: Vols 35,000; Per subs 90; AV—Slides 32,000; Other—Clipping files, exhibition catalogs, photographs.
Special Subjects: Fine arts; auction sale catalogs; museum exhibition catalogs.
Activities: Tours.

MICHIGAN

ADRIAN

SIENA HEIGHTS COLLEGE,* Little Gallery, Studio Angelico, 1257 Siena Heights Dr, 49221. Tel: 313-263-8736. *Dir* Jeannine Klemm.
Open Tues - Fri 1 - 9 PM, Sat & Sun 1 - 5 PM; cl Mon, Easter, Christmas and semester breaks. No admis. Estab 1919 as an arts center and institute.
Collections: Paintings; sculpture; graphics; decorative arts; art history; textiles; archaeology; paintings and sculpture on loan from the University of Michigan.
Activities: Classes for adults and children; lectures; guided tours; competitions; invitational artists shows; temporary exhibitions.

ALBION

ALBION COLLEGE, Bobbitt Visual Arts Center, 49224. Tel: 517-629-5511, exten 246. *Chmn Dept Visual Arts* Frank Machek.
Open Mon - Thurs 9 AM - 4:45 PM & 6:30 - 10 PM; Sat 10 AM - 1 PM; Sun 2 - 5 PM; cl Fri. No admis. Estab 1835 to offer art education at college level, general art exhibition program for campus community and public. Four galleries, one large, three small.
Income: Privately funded. Purchases: $2000 - $4000.
Collections: †Prints; glass; ceramics; African art.
Exhibitions: From The Print Collection; pieces from the Permanent Collection; various one-man and group shows.
Activities: Lect open to public, 2 - 4 vis lectr per yr; gallery talks; original objects of art lent to faculty and students.

ALPENA

JESSE BESSER MUSEUM, 491 Johnson St, 49707. Tel: 517-356-2202. *Dir* Dennis R Bodem; *Pres* Russel H Wilson; *VPres* Philip M ark; *Secy-Treas* William B Zeller.
Open Mon - Fri 9 AM - 5 PM; Sat 9 AM - 1 PM; Sun 1 - 5 PM; Thurs Eve 7 - 9 PM. Admis by donation. Estab association 1962, building open to public 1966, a museum of history, science, and art serving northeast Michigan. Museum has a planetarium and the Foucault Pendulum. Three galleries are utilized for shows, traveling exhibits, and changing exhibition of museum's collection of modern art and art prints. There are 104 running ft of wall space on lower level, 1250 sq ft and 1645 sq ft on upper level galleries. Average Annual Attendance: 50,000.
Income: $150,000 (financed by private charitable fund). Purchases: $5000 - $10,000.
Collections: †Modern art; †art prints; photography of Daniel Farber.
Activities: Classes for adults and children; docent training; lect open to public, 2 - 4 vis lectr per yr; gallery talks; tours; sales shop selling books.
Library: Open to public for reference only. Holdings: Vols 300; Per subs 10.

ANN ARBOR

UNIVERSITY OF MICHIGAN MUSEUM OF ART.
—**Alumni Memorial Hall,** 525 S State St, 48109. Tel: 313-764-0395. *Dir* Bret Waller; *Asst Dir & Cur* John Holmes; *Cur Coll* Nesta Spink;

Coordr Mus Practice Prog Marjorie Swain; *Registr* Jacquelynn Slee; *Coordr Pub Progs* Forrest McGill; *Admin Secy* Jo Lau.
Open (Sept-May) Mon - Sat 9 AM - 5 PM; Sun 1 - 5 PM; (June-Aug) daily 11 AM - 5 PM. No admis. Estab 1946, as a university art museum and museum for the Ann Arbor community. Average Annual Attendance: 55,000. Mem: 1500; dues individual $25.
Income: Financed by state appropriation.
Collections: Arts of the Western world from the 6th century AD to the present; Asian, Near Eastern, African and Oceanic, including †painting, †sculpture, †decorative art, †graphic arts, †contemporary art, ceramics and manuscripts.
Exhibitions: (1976-78) The Art of Wen Cheng-ming; One-Eye View; Karl Struss; A Flower for Every Season; Robert Motherwell, Selected Prints; Edvard Munch; Alexander Corazzo/Leroy Turner; The Borden Limner; Indian Art from Bickford Collection; School of Art Faculty; Pompeii as Source and Inspiration; Alfred Stevens; Western Influenced Japanese Art; Peter Campus Video Art; Chicago: The City and its Artists; French Watercolor Landscapes of the 19th Century.
Publications: Bulletin of the Museums of Art and Archaeology, annually.
Activities: Educ dept; docent training; 10 vis lectr per yr; gallery talks; tours; museum shop selling publications and posters, postcards.
—Kelsey Museum of Ancient and Mediaeval Archaeology, 434 S State St, 48109. Tel: 313-764-9304. *Dir* John G Pedley; *Asst Cur* Elaine K Gazda; *Asst Cur* John H Humphrey; *Asst Cur* Margaret C Root; *Asst Cur* Amy Rosenberg; *Registrar* Jill B Bace; *Technician* David W Slee.
Open Mon - Fri 9 AM - 4 PM; Sat - Sun 1 - 4 PM. No admis. Estab 1928. Four small galleries. Average Annual Attendance: 25,500.
Collections: Objects of the Graeco-Roman period from excavations conducted by the University of Michigan in Egypt and Iraq; Greece, Etruria, Rome and provinces—sculpture, inscriptions, pottery, bronzes, terracottas; Egyptian antiquities Dynastic through Roman; Roman and Islamic glass, bone and ivory objects, textiles, coins.
Exhibitions: Greek Vases from Boston; Roman Portraiture: Ancient and Modern Revivals; Seleucia-on-the-Tigris; The Gods of Egypt; Islamic Art from the University of Michigan Collections; The Monastery of St Catharine's on Mt Sinai; Karanis Culpture; Cathage.
Publications: Bulletin of the Museums of Art and Archaeology.
Activities: Lect open to the public, 10-12 vis lectr per yr; gallery talks; tours; sales shop selling books and exhibition catalogs.

BATTLE CREEK

BATTLE CREEK CIVIC ART CENTER,* 265 E Emmett St, 49017. Tel: 616-962-9511. *Pres* William Kitchen; *Dir* Darwin R Davis; *Asst to Dir* Sara Dandenault.
Open daily 9:30 AM - 4:30 PM; Sun 1 - 4 PM; cl Mon, August & legal holidays. No admis. Estab 1947 to offer classes for children and adults, and to plan monthly exhibitions of professional work. Mem: 500; dues $10 and up; annual meeting May or June.
Collections: Small permanent collection of prints and paintings.
Exhibitions: Exhibitions of photography, drafts, paintings, prints and drawings; student exhibits; group and one-man shows; Battle Creek 100, sponsored by Battle Creek Gas Co, $1000 purchase awards.
Activities: Classes in painting, photography, pottery, sculpture; educational and informative movies, lectures and demonstrations; illustrated talks on art appreciation for elementary schools in the area through trained volunteers; maintains gift and rental gallery for the public.
Library: Holdings—Art books, slides.

BIRMINGHAM

BIRMINGHAM-BLOOMFIELD ART ASSOCIATION, 1516 S Cranbrook Rd, 48009. Tel: 313-644-0866. *Pres* Victor L Klein; *VPres* James W Atkinson; *Secy* Mrs Harry Velick; *Exec Dir* Kenneth R Gross; *Asst Dir* Leslie Masters; *Office Mgr* Mrs Douglas Garrison; *Bus Mgr* Mrs Frances St Lawrence.
Open Mon - Thurs 9 AM - 10 PM; Fri 9 AM - 7 PM; Sat 9 AM - 5 PM; cl Sun. No admis. Estab 1956 to provide a community-wide, integrated studio-gallery art center. A sales and rental gallery is maintained. Average Annual Attendance: 10,000. Mem: 800; dues $20 and up; annual meeting June.
Income: $100,000 (financed by membership, tuitions and special events funding).
Collections: Very small collection of craft objects and prints by local artists.
Exhibitions: (1976-78) Basketry/Artistry (national basketry competitive); Birmingham Society of Women Painters; Michigan Oriental Art Society; Michigan Watercolor Society; Birmingham Sculptors Guild; Detroit Society of Women Painters; Michigan Crafts Council; BBAA Faculty and Student Shows; Public Schools Art; Local Collectors; Pratt Alumni; Prints and Plates; The Handwritten Word; Industrial, Functional Art and Design; For the Love of Art; Innovations in Paper (national competitive); Toys and Games (competitive).

Publications: Newsletter, 10 a yr.
Activities: Classes for adults and children; docent training; Picture Lady Program; Career Program; Teen Volunteer Service; lect open to public, 4 - 8 vis lectr per yr; tours; competitions, cash awards, ribbons, and certificates; schol; exten dept serving public schools; individual paintings and original objects of art lent to public on a rental basis; lending collection contains color reproductions, Kodachromes, original art works and prints, paintings, photographs, sculpture, slides; sales shop selling books, original art, prints, photographs, paintings, and crafts.

BIRMINGHAM GALLERY, INC,* 1025 Haynes St, 48011. Tel: 313-642-7455. *Pres* John W McKinney; *VPres* Douglas Webster.
Open Tues - Sat 10 AM - 6 PM. No admis. Estab 1968 for exhibition of contemporary sculpture, painting, graphics and crafts.
Exhibitions: One-man shows; Cranbrook Academy of Art Printmakers.
Publications: Catalogs and announcements, eight times a year.
Activities: Lect to private groups; gallery; rental collection of original prints.
Library: Holdings—Vols 1450.

BLOOMFIELD HILLS

CRANBROOK ACADEMY OF ART MUSEUM, 500 Lone Pine Rd, 48103. Tel: 313-645-3300. *Dir Museum* Roy Slade; *Cur Coll* Mary Riordan; *Admin Asst* Linda Dunne Parks; *Cur Exhib* Mary Ann Igna.
Open Tues - Sun 1 - 5 PM; cl Mon and major holidays. Admis adults $1, students & sr citizens 75¢, group rates available. Estab 1924 as part of Cranbrook Academy of Art. Average Annual Attendance: 60,000.
Collections: Sculpture by Carl Milles; ceramics by Maija Grotell; decorative arts by Eliel Saarinen; contemporary paintings, 19th century prints, study collection of textiles, and porcelains by Adelaide Robineau.
Exhibitions: Contemporary painting, sculpture, architecture, design and crafts; annual student exhibition.
Activities: Lect; tours; film prog.

DEARBORN

GREENFIELD VILLAGE AND HENRY FORD MUSEUM, 48121. Tel: 313-271-1620, for information 271-1976. *Chmn* William Clay Ford; *Pres* Dr Donald A Shelley; *VPres/Admin* Frank Caddy; *VPres/Research & Interpretation* Robert G Wheeler; *Dir Pub Relations* Robert Dawson; *Dir Special Events* Ronald Kanack; *Dir of Coll & Preservation* Kenneth Wilson.
Open weekdays 9 AM - 5 PM; holidays, weekends and July-Aug 9 AM - 6 PM. Separate admission charges to the Village and Museum-adults $2.75, children 6-12 $1.25. Estab 1929 as a general museum of American culture and history for educational purposes. Greenfield Village has over 100 historic buildings including homes of famous Americans and public and industrial buildings. Most buildings are furnished or equipped, and many were moved from their original sites to Dearborn. Average Annual Attendance: 2,000,000.
Income: Publicly supported through admissions and the Friends of Greenfield Village and Henry Ford Museum.
Collections: (Art) Decorative arts, folk art, crafts and home art.
Publications: The Herald, museum quarterly issued to mem; publications on exhibits and individual collections, issued as published.
Library: Holdings—Vols 30,000 plus rare book collections; Other—Manuscripts, photographs. Special Collections: Henry Ford Archives contain some 14 million documents.

DETROIT

DETROIT ARTISTS MARKET, 1452 Randolph St, 48226. Tel: 313-962-0337. *Chmn of the Bd* Mrs Foster Redding; *Corresp Secy* Mrs John N McNaughton; *Gallery Mgr* Margaret Conzelman.
Open Mon - Sat 10 AM - 5 PM; cl Sun. Estab 1932 to give the appreciative public a gallery in which to view and to buy the original work of professional artists and craftsmen who live and work in Detroit or within a 60-mile radius of the city. A large 4000 sq ft of open, spacious gallery space with a balcony. Average Annual Attendance: 40,000. Mem: 1000; dues $5, $10, $25; board meetings are held quarterly.
Income: Financed by membership, sales commissions.
Exhibitions: Changing exhibitions.
Publications: Yearly newsletter.

DETROIT INSTITUTE OF ARTS,* 5200 Woodward Ave, 48202. Tel: 313-833-7900. *Dir* Frederick J Cumings; *Adminr & Secy* William A Bostick; *Cur Emeritus Medieval Art* Francis W Robinson; *Cur American Art* Larry J Curry; *Cur Ancient, Oriental, African Art* William H Peck; *Cur European Art* Dewey F Mosby; *Cur European Decorative Arts* Sheila K Tabakoff; *Cur Graphic Arts* Ellen Sharp; *Cur Modern Art* John H Neff; *Chmn Educ* Richard Mühlberger; *Registrar* Charles H Elam; *Photographer* Joseph Klima Jr; *Chief Conservator* James L Greaves.

Open Wed - Sun 9:30 AM - 5:30 PM; cl Mon, Tues and holidays. Voluntary admis. Estab and inc 1885 as Detroit Museum of Art: chartered as municipal department 1919 and name changed; original organization continued as Founders Society Detroit Institute of Arts; present building opened 1927; South Wing addition completed 1966; North Wing addition opened 1971. Midwest area office of Archives of American Art. Average Annual Attendance: 900,000.

Collections: Representative examples of the arts from prehistory to the present time, including Egypt, Mesopotamia, Greece and Rome, the Orient, Europe, Africa, the South Seas, and the Americas. Comprehensive collection of textiles and of American decorative arts. Paul McPharlin Collection of puppetry, theatre and graphic arts; Grace Whitney Hoff Collection of fine bindings; Robert H Tannahill Bequest of Impressionist and Post-Impressionist paintings, traditional African objects, French silver; Elizabeth Parke Firestone Collection of 18th century French silver; William Randolph Hearst Collection of arms and armor and Flemish tapestries. Central court decorated with Diego Rivera frescoes (1932-33). Incorporated in American Wing galleries is Whitby Hall, furnished with important collection of furniture.

Exhibitions: Michigan Artists and Michigan Artist-Craftsmen (alternate years).

Activities: Art workshops; films; cooperative programs with metropolitan area schools, university groups and special interest groups; Detroit Youtheatre; Puppetry; Detroit Film Theatre; Brunch with Bach; Concert Series; lect and lect series; gallery talks; tours; two Museum shops.

—*Library:* *Librn* F Warren Peters. Research library of art, archaeology, architecture and allied subjects.

Holdings: Vols 50,000; AV—Slides 40,000; Other—Clipping files, auction sales catalogs, photographs.

Publications: Bulletin; Calendar of Events; handbooks and catalogs of various collections, and catalogs of special exhibitions.

—**Detroit Institute of Art Founders Society.** Tel: 313-833-7950. *Chmn of Board* Stanford C Stoddard; *Pres* Norman B Weston; *VPres* Mrs Gaylord W Gillis Jr; *Secy* Mrs Alan E Schwatz; *Treas* Alfred M Pelham; *Exec Dir* Frederick J Cummings; *Mgr* Frank A Morgan.

Estab and inc 1885; public membership philanthropic society contributing to the growth of the Detroit Institute of Arts; underwrites Educ Dept activities, publications, special exhibitions, and most purchases of works of art; sponsors rental collection of original work by Michigan artists and reproductions, museum shops and other special activities. Mem: 12,000, dues individual $25, family $40, patron $150, corporate $250, corporate contributor $1,000, corporate sponsor $5,000, corporate patron $10,000.

DETROIT PUBLIC LIBRARY, Fine Arts Department, 5201 Woodward Ave, 48202. Tel: 313-833-1467. *Library Dir* Jane Hale Morgan; *Chief Fine Arts Dept* Shirley B Solvick; *First Asst Fine Arts Dept* Patricia W McHugh; *Reference Librn* Ruth Barton, Winnifred Clark and Leonard Parent; *Clerk* Shirlie Moloney.

Open Mon, Tues, Thurs, Fri & Sat 9:30 AM - 5:30 PM; Wed 9 AM - 9 PM; Mid-Oct - Mid-May, Sun 1 - 5 PM. Estab 1921 to serve residents of Michigan with circulating and reference materials in all fields of art.

Income: Financed by city and state appropriation. Purchases: $25,000 for books.

Holdings: Vols 55,000; Serial subs 270; AV—Microfiche, microfilm; Other—Clipping files, exhibition catalogs, framed reproductions, pamphlets, photographs, reproductions.

Activities: Concerts; tours.

WAYNE STATE UNIVERSITY,* McGregor Memorial, Community Arts Gallery. 450 W Kirby at Cass, 48202. Tel: 313-577-2400. *Gallery Coordr* Richard J Bilaitis.

Open Mon Fri 9 AM - 9 PM; Sat· & Sun 1 - 5 PM. No admis. Estab 1956 as a facility for university and community oriented exhibitions and programs.

Collections: Small collection of American and European painting, sculpture and graphics.

Activities: Lectures for adults, students and the community; monthly exhibitions; concerts.

EAST LANSING

MICHIGAN STATE UNIVERSITY,* Kresge Art Center, 48824. Tel: 517-355-7610; Gallery 517-355-7631. *Chmn Dept of Art* Roger Funk; *Dir of Gallery* Joseph Ishikawa.

Open Mon - Fri 9 AM - 5 PM; Tues 7 - 9 PM; Sat & Sun 1 - 4 PM. No admis.

Collections: Permanent collection of paintings, †prints and †sculpture.

Exhibitions: Rental shows; staff and student shows making up a yearly calendar of about 10 exhibitions supplementing the permanent collection.

Publications: Exhibition calendar, annually; regular bulletin; occasional announcements of art lectures and films; catalogs.

FLINT

FLINT INSTITUTE OF ARTS, 1120 E Kearsley St, 48503. Tel: 313-234-1695. *Dir* Dr G Stuart Hodge; *Asst Dir* Thos Kayser; *Cur Coll* Ann Reitz; *Cur Educ* Gerna Rubenstein; *Pub Relations* Evelyn N Lee; *Museum Shop Mgr* Barbara Lippincott.

Open Tues - Sat 10 AM - 5 PM; Sun 1 - 5 PM; Tues (May - Oct) 7 - 9 PM. No admis. Estab 1928 as a community art museum serving the citizens of the area. Average Annual Attendance: 100,000. Mem: 2200; dues $12 and up; annual meeting third Thurs in June.

Income: Financed by endowment and membership.

Collections: Decorative arts; Oriental jades, ivories, bronzes, porcelain and paintings; French paperweights, paintings by Sargent, Dufy, Goya, Sisley, Renoir, Degas, Vuillard, Bonnard and Cassat; sculpture by Henry Moore.

Exhibitions: Art of Haute Couture; Oriental Rugs in Flint Collections; John Roger Groups.

Publications: Monthly information calendar for members; exhibition catalogs.

Activities: Classes for adults and children; docent training; lectr open to the public, 6-7 vis lectr per yr; concerts; gallery talks; tours; competitions; individual paintings and original objects of art lent to other museums; museum shop selling books, gift items, stationery, cards and jewelry.

Library: *Librn* Ann Reitz. Open to members and staff for reference. Holdings: Vols 1500; Per subs 15.

FLINT PUBLIC LIBRARY,* 1026 E Kearsley, 48502. Tel: 313-231-7111. *Asst Dir* John A Oliver; *Head Art, Music & Drama Dept* Forrest Alter.

Open Mon - Thurs 9 AM - 9 PM; Fri & Sat 9 AM - 6 PM. Art, Music and Drama Dept estab 1958; a division of Flint Board of Education.

Exhibitions: Continuous program of exhibition of department's materials and materials borrowed.

Holdings: Vols 31,000; Per subs 2171 in art, music and drama; Other—Clipping files on fine arts, exhibition catalogs, pictures, vertical file drawers 70, mounted reproductions, vertical file drawers 10.

GRAND RAPIDS

CALVIN COLLEGE CENTER ART GALLERY, 49506. Tel: 616-949-4000, exten 326. *Dir Exhib* Brenda Van Halsema; *Secy* Marlene Vanderhill.

Open Sept - May Mon - Fri 9 AM - 9 PM; Sat 10 AM - 4 PM. No admis. Estab 1974 to provide the art students, and the college community and the public at large with challenging visual monthly exhibitions; well lighted, air-conditioned 40 x 70 ft with 10 ft ceiling along the sides and 8 ft ceiling in the center. Average Annual Attendance: 12,000.

Income: Financed through private budget.

Collections: Dutch 17th and 19th century paintings and prints; Japanese prints; †contemporary paintings, prints, drawings, sculpture, weavings and ceramics.

Exhibitions: Various faculty and student exhibits; Currier and Ives; Dutch Masters from Michigan Collections; One Hundred Years of American Toys (SITES); International Photography Competition; Early Michigan Paintings; Fiber Invitational; Michigan Ceramics Invitation; Detroit-Area Printmakers.

Publications: Various exhibition brochures.

Activities: Classes for adults; lect open to the public; concerts; gallery talks; competitions.

—**Library,** 49506. *Librn* Marvin Monsma.

Open to students and the public.

Holdings: Vols 280,000; Per subs 1800; AV—Microfilm, microfiche, microcards; Other—Curriculum Center of demonstration teaching materials.

Special Collections: H H Meeter Calvinism Research Collection; Colonial Origins Collection of the Christian Reformed Church; Cayvan Collection of recordings; government documents.

GRAND RAPIDS ART MUSEUM, 230 E Fulton, 49503. Tel: 616-459-4676. *Dir* Fred A Myers.

Open Mon - Sat 10 AM - 5 PM; Sun 2 - 5 PM; cl National holidays & Mon in June, July & Aug. No admis. Estab 1910, inc 1913, to promote an active interest in the fine and applied arts; to establish and maintain an art collection; and to provide special art exhibits for the enjoyment and education of the public. The building is an 1844 Classical Revival house with additional wings added in 1928 and 1930. Seven galleries are used for exhibits. Average Annual Attendance: 65,000. Mem: 1300; dues $15; annual meeting May.

Income: $225,000 (financed by endowment, membership, state appropriation, and Federal grants. Purchases: $10,000.

Collections: Early American; †Contemporary American; German expressionists; early and contemporary French; Italian Renaissance; early and contemporary English art; †print collection covering a broad range of art historical periods.

Exhibitions: Renaissance Revival Victorian Furniture; Breverman; Sculpture by Steven Urry; Michigan Folk Art; American Artists: A New Decade; Themes in American Painting; Environmental Works of Suzanne LaChance; John C Cary Print Collections.
Publications: Newsletter, monthly; catalogs of major exhibitions.
Activities: Docent training; lect open to public, 15 vis lectr per yr; gallery talks; tours; competitions; artmobile; individual paintings and original objects of art lent to museums; lending collection contains books, color reproductions, framed reproductions, original art works, original prints, paintings, photographs, sculpture, and slides; traveling exhibitions organized and circulated; museum shop selling books, reproductions, jewelry, arts and crafts objects.
Library: McBride Art Reference Library. Open to all for reference, members may borrow books.
Holdings: Vols 1300.
Special Subjects: Volumes supplement permanent collection of art.

GRAND RAPIDS PUBLIC LIBRARY, Music and Art Department, Library Plaza NE, 49503. Tel: 616-456-4410. *Dir Library* Alberta Massingil; *Head Music & Art Dept* Lucija Skuja; *Music Librn* Helen Vanden Engel.
Open Mon - Thurs 9 AM - 9 PM; Fri & Sat 9:30 AM - 5:30 PM; cl Sun. Estab 1871 to provide information and library materials for people in Grand Rapids and Lakeland Library Federation area. Circ: 871,859 for total library.
Income: $1,626,592 for entire library (financed by city and state appropriation). Purchases: $1,606,381 for entire library.
Holdings: Vols 17,000; Per subs 44; AV—Cassettes, film strips, microfilm, motion pictures, phonorecords; Other—Clipping files, pamphlets, sculpture.
Special Collections: The Furniture Design Collection.
Activities: Tours.

HARTLAND

HARTLAND ART COUNCIL,* PO Box 127, 48029. Tel: 313-632-5200. *Pres* William P Nelson; *VPres* Bruce Sdunek; *Secy* Helen J Nelson; *Treas* Sandra Scherba.
Estab 1967 to promote arts in Hartland community; gallery space in local library and Hartland High School Media Center. Mem: 50, dues $3 - $100.
Income: $3000 - $4000 (financed by membership). Purchases: $1500 - $2000.
Collections: Approximately 50 works—paintings, sculptures and photographs. Collection enlarged each year through purchased awards from Hartland Art Show, funds donated by community and Hartland Foundation.
Exhibitions: Annual Art Show.
Activities: Lect open to the public; dramatic programs; concerts; competitions; schol; extension dept serving Michigan art councils and schools for a $25 fee; lending collection contains Kodachromes 200 and commentaries on winning works of art in Hartland art shows, photographs 20; traveling exhibitions organized and circulated.

JACKSON

ELLA SHARP MUSEUM,* 3225 Fourth St, 49203. Tel: 517-787-2320. *Dir* Millie Hadwin; *Cur Historical Educ* Lynn Loftis; *Cur Art Educ* Elise Cole; *Conservator* James Richardson.
Open Tues - Fri 10 AM - 5 PM; Sat and Sun 1:30 - 5 PM; cl Mon, Jan and major holidays. Admis to Sharp Home, Hillside, adults 50¢, children 25¢, no admis for school tours. Estab 1965 to serve the people of Jackson and to provide a place for cultural education in the community; a temporary gallery where a variety of exhibits are held; large and small gallery. Average Annual Attendance: 10,000. Mem: 1000; dues $3, $10, $15, $25, $50, $100, $500, $1000 and up; annual meeting May.
Income: Supported by endowment and membership.
Collections: Furniture from Victorian period; china; porcelain; coverlets and quilts; †oil paintings; †prints.
Exhibitions: Egypt; Influence of the Flower; Contemporary Graphics; Furniture.
Publications: Newsletter, quarterly; Annual Report; bulletins and catalogs; research material as requested.
Activities: Classes for adults and children; dramatic programs; lect open to the public, 7 vis lectr per yr; concerts; gallery talks; tours; competitions; schol; objects of art lent to schools; kits of museum artifacts; lending collection contains photographs; traveling exhibitions organized and circulated; book shop.
Library: Holdings—Vols 250; Other—Photographs 2000.

KALAMAZOO

KALAMAZOO INSTITUTE OF ARTS, Genevieve and Donald Gilmore Art Center, 314 S Park St, 49006. Tel: 616-349-7775. *Dir Art Center* Harry Greaver.
Open Tues - Fri 11 AM - 4:30; Sat 9 AM - 4 PM; Sun 1:30 - 4:30 PM; cl Mon; (Summer Hours) Tues - Fri 10 AM - 4 PM; Sat 9 AM - 4 PM; cl Sun, Aug & holidays. Admis adults 50¢, children 25¢, free on Sun. Inc 1924 to further interest in the arts, especially in the visual arts; new building opened in 1961. There is one large gallery, four small exhibition galleries, with exhibitions changed monthly. One or more galleries always devoted to pieces from the permanent collection. Average Annual Attendance: 75,000. Mem: 1400; dues $15; annual meeting June.
Income: $350,000 (financed by endowment, membership).
Collections: †20th century American art, †sculpture, †art on paper—drawings, watercolors, graphics, and photographs.
Exhibitions: Traveling exhibit program covers all aspects of visual arts; Kalamazoo Area Show; Bronson Park Art Fair.
Publications: Exhibition catalogs, issued irregularly.
Activities: Classes for adults and children; traveling exhibits to area schools; lect open to public, 5 vis lectr per yr; gallery talks; tours; competitions; individual paintings and original objects of art lent to other institutions; lending collection contains books 5000, lantern slides 8000; traveling exhibitions organized and circulated; museum shop selling books, reproductions, craft items, jewelry, cards.
—Library. Tel: 616-349-7775. *Head Librn* Helen Sheridan; *Asst Librn* Martha Franklin.
Open Tues - Fri 11 AM - 4:30 PM; Sat 9 AM - 9 PM; Sun 1:30 - 4:30 PM; cl Sun in July; cl Aug. Estab 1961 for reference for the KIA school faculty and staff; support of the KIA school program; information on visual arts available to public. Circ: Books to KIA members. Art works from the KIA permanent collection on display in library.
Income: Financed by endowment and membership.
Holdings: Vols 5250; Per subs 55; AV—Slides.
Special Subjects: American art, especially art of the 20th century; printmaking, history and technique; photography.
Activities: Lectures; tours.

LANSING

MICHIGAN DEPARTMENT OF EDUCATION STATE LIBRARY SERVICES, 735 E Michigan Ave (Mailing Add: PO Box 30007, 48909). Tel: 517-373-1593. *State Librn* Francis X Scannell; *Supv Fiscal Mgt & Technical Services* Donald Leaf; *Supv College & Univ Library Program* Dale Pretzer; *Supv Public Library Program* Raymond Mahoney; *Supv School Library & Media Program* Mary Ann Hanna; *Supv Instructional Technology Program* Charles Ruffing.
Open Mon - Fri 8 AM - 5:30 PM. Estab 1827 to serve the state legislature, the civil service employees, the public and school libraries in the state, libraries located in institutions of higher learning, special libraries, the general public and special interest groups (blind, physically handicapped, etc) who are residents of the state. Circ: 525,000.
Income: $2,900,000 (financed by state appropriation). Purchases: $300,000. Library·Holdings: Vols 1,700,000; Per subs 2100; AV—Audio tapes, cassettes, film strips, microfiche, microfilm, motion pictures, phonorecords and video tapes; Other—Clipping files and prints.
Special Collections: Small United Nations flags; mounted prints of classic art works. *Activities:* Lect; Library tours.

MARQUETTE

NORTHERN MICHIGAN UNIVERSITY, Lee Hall Gallery, 49855. Tel: 906-227-2194. *Exhibits Coordinator* John D Hubbard.
Open Mon - Fri 8 AM - 5 PM; Sat 1 - 4 PM. No admis. Estab 1975 to bring exhibits of the visual arts to the university, community and the upper peninsula of Michigan; gallery covers approximately 1500 sq ft of space, with security system and smoke detectors. Average Annual Attendance: 4000 - 6000.
Income: $6000 - $7000 (financed by university funds).
Collections: Student Collection; †Permanent Collection.
Exhibitions: Average of one to two major exhibits each month, with a reduction of exhibits during the summer months.
Publications: Exhibit announcement, monthly.
Activities: Lect open to the public, 3 - 4 vis lectr per yr; gallery talks; competitions; individual paintings and original objects of art lent currently only to university and local residents; lending collection contains original art works 300; traveling exhibitions organized and circulated.

MIDLAND

MIDLAND ART COUNCIL OF THE MIDLAND CENTER FOR THE ARTS, 1801 W St Andrews, 48640. Tel: 517-631-3250. *Pres* Ann Boehm; *VPres* Nan Punnet; *Secy* Jean Wolf; *Coordr* Gene Sorville; *Secy* Shirley King; *Supervisor Media Contact* Mary Dalton.
Open daily 1 - 5 PM; Thurs 7 - 9 PM. No admis. Estab 1956, exhibition space consists of three galleries, one 40 x 80 ft and two smaller 20 x 40 ft space; spot track lighting. Mem: 350; dues $15; meetings held in spring and fall.
Income: $40,000 (financed by endowment and membership).
Exhibitions: (1977-79) Gund Collection of Western Art; An American Inspiration Danish Modern and Shaker Design; Sotheby, Parke, Bernet Heirloom Discovery Days; Bag Show; Delta and Saginaw Valley Colleges Art Exhibition; Mid-Michigan Exhibition; Photographs From the Himalayas: Abode of the Snow; Annual Michigan Watercolor Exhibition; Ashcan School and American Urban Realism; Studio Class Instructors Exhibition; Prints from the Guggenheim; Puppets from the Detroit Institute of Arts; New Guinea Art; African Art; Tsutsumu, The Art of the Japanese Package; National Watercolor Society Exhibition; Annual Midland Public School Art; Studio Class Instructor and Student Exhibition; Coverlet Exhibition.
Publications: Monthly newsletter for members; calendar of events; yearly report.
Activities: Classes for adults and children; docent training; picture lady show me a picture program in public schools; lect open to the public; gallery talks; tours; competitions; traveling exhibitions organized and circulated; sales shop selling books; magazines, original art and reproductions.

MONROE

MONROE CITY-COUNTY FINE ARTS COUNCIL, 1555 S Raisinville Rd, 48161. Tel: 313-242-7300. *Pres* Dr Robert Merkel; *Secy* Hugh Baker; *Treas* Elsie Little.
Estab 1967 to promote the arts. Average Annual Attendance: 120; Mem: 50; dues $2.
Income: $1000 (financed by endowment, membership, city appropriation).
Activities: Competitions with awards; schol.

MOUNT CLEMENS

ART CENTER, 125 Macomb St, 48043. Tel: 313-469-8666. *Pres Bd of Trustees* Joanne Roskopp; *Dir* Catherine Guinn.
Open Tues - Sat 11 AM - 5 PM; Sun 1 - 4 PM; cl Mon. No admis. Estab 1970 to foster art appreciation and participation for people of Macomb County; the only public facility of its kind in county northeast of Detroit Metro area; center has two rooms, 17 x 27 ft, connected by lobby area in former Carnegie Library Bldg, Historical State Register. Average Annual Attendance: 1200. Mem: 500; dues individual $10; annual meeting June.
Income: $38,000 (April 76 - May 77), (financed by membership, city and state appropriation and fund raising).
Exhibitions: Annually: Several all-state open competitive exhibitions including painting and sculpture; crafts; two countrywide student shows, one is regional scholastic Art Awards show.
Publications: Newsletter, semi-monthly.
Activities: Classes for adults and children; tours; competitions; exten dept serving senior citizens; individual paintings lent; sales shop selling original art.

MUSKEGON

HACKLEY ART MUSEUM, 296 W Webster, 49440. Tel: 616-722-6954. *Dir* Shirley Reiff Howarth; *Prog Dir* Betty Linacre.
Open Mon - Sat 9 AM - 5 PM; Sun 2 - 5 PM. Estab 1912. The building contains seven galleries, sculpture court, auditorium and studio. Average Annual Attendance: 30,000. Mem: 250; dues $15.
Income: $100,000 (financed by membership and school board).
Collections: American paintings: Old Master prints; impressionist paintings; Eastern art; modern master prints.
Exhibitions: Steven Urry: Recent Sculpture; Marcel Breuer: Architect & Designer; Decorative Arts of West Africa; North American Indian: Photographs by Edward Curtis; Navajo Textiles.
Publications: Newsletter, monthly; Annual Report.
Activities: Classes for adults and children; docent training; lect open to public, 6 vis lectr per yr; gallery talks; traveling exhibitions organized and circulated; museum shop selling books, reproductions.
Library: Open for reference by appointment, and for staff use.
—**Friends of Art.**
Estab 1977 to support museum in its endeavors. Mem: 200; dues individual $15; family $25.
Activities: Film series, travel art tours.

OLIVET

OLIVET COLLEGE, Armstrong Museum of Art and Archaeology,* 49076. Tel: 616-749-7000. *Dir* William Whitney.
Estab 1960 to collect artifacts and display for educational purposes. Average Annual Attendance: 1200.
Purchases: Approximately $1000.
Collections: †Modern American prints; Mesopotamian, American Indian, Thailand and Philippine artifacts; primitive art; sculpture.
Exhibitions: Invitational shows; one-man shows; student shows; traveling shows.
Library: Holdings—Vols 70,000; Other—Prints 350.

ORCHARD LAKE

ORCHARD LAKE SCHOOLS, Galeria 48033. *Dir* Dr Walter M Zebrowski. Open first Sun of month 1 - 4 PM; by appointment any time. No Admis. Estab to house major Polish and Polish-American plastic artists. Average Annual Attendance: 7000.
Exhibitions: Major Michigan Artists Exhibit; Polish Singers at the Met (Pictorial exhibit).
Activities: Lect open to public; concerts; tours.

PONTIAC

PONTIAC CREATIVE ARTS CENTER, INC,* 47 Williams St, 48053. Tel: 313-333-7849. *Pres* Frederick Poole, *Secy* Yolanda Flores; *Exec Dir* Ian R Lyons.
Open Mon - Fri 10 AM - 4 PM. No admis. Estab 1968 to educate and uplift minority and culturally deprived people through the exposure of art; gallery maintained. Mem: 400, dues $5, $10, $100, $500, annual meeting March.
Income: $84,000 (financed by endowment, membership, city and state appropriation).
Activities: Classes for adults and children, dramatic programs; lect open to the public, 4 vis lectr per yr; gallery talks; competitions; schol; exhibitions.

PORT HURON

MUSEUM OF ARTS AND HISTORY, 1115 Sixth St, 48060. Tel: 313-982-0891. *Pres* Mrs N Fred Haynes; *Dir* Mark J Meister.
Open Wed - Sun 1 - 4:30 PM. No admis. Estab 1968 to preserve area historical and marine artifacts; exhibit living regional artists; exhibit significant shows of national and international interest. Two galleries for loaned exhititions and the permanent collection; decorative arts gallery; sales gallery. Average Annual Attendance: 14,000. Mem: 400; dues family $10.
Income: $38,000 (financed by membership, city and state appropriations).
Collections: (art) 19th century American painting, prints and decorative arts; Woodlands Indian artifacts; Civil War; Thomas Edison; marine artifacts.
Exhibitions: Michigan Folk Art; Early Michigan Painting; the Contemporary Poster; Lakeland Painters; The Black Presence in the Era of the American Revolution; Capitol City Traveling Exhibition; Annual Eastern Michigan International Art Exhibition.
Publications: Newsletter, quarterly.
Activities: Classes for adults and children; docent training; lect open to public, 6 vis lectr per yr; gallery talks; tours; competitions; museum shop selling books, magazines, original art.

ROCHESTER

OAKLAND UNIVERSITY, Meadow Brook Art Gallery, 48063. Tel: 313-377-3005. *Cur* Kiichi Usui; *Secy* Doris Des Jardins; *Dir Off Cult Affairs, Oakland Univ* Robert Dearth; *Pres Meadow Brook Gallery Assocs* Mrs David Handleman.
Open Tues - Fri 1 - 5 PM; Sat & Sun 2 - 6:30 PM; Eve 7:30 - 8:30 PM in conjunction with Meadow Brook Theater performances. No admis. Estab 1962 to provide a series of changing exhibitions and to develop an art collection to serve the university community and the greater community of southern Michigan. Average Annual Attendance: Approx 50,000. Mem: 300; dues $20 - $500.
Income: Financed by university budget.
Collections: Over 300 pieces of art of Africa, Oceania and Pre-Columbian Americas; changing exhibitions emphasize contemporary art and architecture, Oriental art.

Exhibitions: (1976-77) Creative Encounters: Gertrude Kasle Collection of Contemporary Art; Art in Architecture: survey of successful integration of art and architecture; (1977-78) Through Closed Doors: Western Influence on Japanese Art (1639-1853); Stages Revisited: exhibition of costumes, stage design, renderings and models from past 10 years of the Meadow Brook Theater productions.
Publications: Exhibition catalogs.
Activities: Educ Dept; lect open to public, 2 vis lectr per yr; individual paintings and original objects of art lent within the university; slide presentations produced in conjunction with the exhibition; traveling exhibitions organized and circulated.

SAGINAW

SAGINAW ART MUSEUM, 1126 N Michigan Ave, 48602. Tel: 517-754-2491. *Dir* Janie K Chester.
Open Tues - Sat 10 AM - 5 PM; Tues Eve 7 - 9 PM; Sun 1 - 5 PM; cl Mon. No admis. Estab 1948 to offer the cultural and educational services of an art museum to the regional community, and to foster a love and understanding of the visual arts. Historic Georgian Revival Mansion (Charles Adams Platt, architect); approx 2600 sq ft of gallery space; formal outdoor garden. Average Annual Attendance: 12,000. Mem: 520; dues $5 - $500; annual meeting May.
Income: $124,000 (financed by endowment, membership).
Collections: American sculpture and painting (especially John Rogers' sculpture); Oriental prints, decorative arts, and textiles; European painting, sculpture, and decorative arts, 1000 AD - present; †contemporary painting, †prints, and sculpture.
Publications: Monthly Bulletin; Annual Report.
Activities: Classes for adults and children; docent training; lect open to public, 6 vis lectr per yr; gallery talks; tours; competitions, 2 annually; individual paintings and original objects of art lent to other museums and small extension exhibitions in community; traveling exhibitions organized and circulated; museum shop selling books, original art, reproductions, prints.
Library: *Librn* Deborah Schell. Open to public for reference only. Holdings: Vols 1000; Per subs 8.

TRAVERSE CITY

NORTHWESTERN MICHIGAN COLLEGE, Mark Osterlin Library, 1701 E Front St, 49684. Tel: 616-946-5650, exten 541. *Library Dir* Bernard C Rink.
Open Mon - Thurs 8 AM - 10 PM; Fri & Sat 9 AM - 4 PM; Sun 1 - 5 PM. Estab 1961, the library is charged with providing the resources needed to fulfill the educational and cultural task of the college. Permanent sculpture and print display in lobby and throughout building whenever wall space permits.
Income: $225,000 (financed by state and county appropriation).
Purchases: $2000 - $5000.
Holdings: Vols 39,000; Per subs 400; AV—Audiotapes, cassettes, film strips, Kodachromes, microfilm, motion pictures, phonorecords, reels, slides, videotapes; Other—Prints, sculpture.
Special Subjects: Italian Renaissance art history.
Special Collections: Canadian Eskimo sculpture and prints collected and for sale.
Exhibitions: Annual Eskimo Sculpture and Print Exhibit.

YPSILANTI

EASTERN MICHIGAN UNIVERSITY, Sill Gallery, 48197. Tel: 313-487-1268. *Dept Head* Kingsley Calkins; *Gallery Dir* Beverly Shankwiler.
Open Mon - Fri 8 AM - 5 PM. No admis. Estab 1925, in present building since 1964, for educational purposes; an Art Dept gallery showing staff and student work an original exhibitions from a wide variety of sources. One large, well-lighted gallery with lobby and a satellite student-operated gallery.
Income: Financed by city appropriation. Purchases: $500.
Collections: A modest permanent collection.
Exhibitions: Faculty art; student art; international ceramics; international jewelry and metal; international textiles; G Mennen Williams African art; conceptual art; children's art; National Student Photography Exhibition.
Publications: Campus Life, bi-annual bulletin.
Activities: Classes for adults; lect open to public, 6 vis lectr per yr; gallery talks; concerts; competitions.
Library: Art Department Library. *Librn* Virginia Stein. Open to faculty and students for reference.

MINNESOTA

DULUTH

UNIVERSITY OF MINNESOTA, DULUTH, Tweed Museum of Art, 55812. Tel: 218-726-8222. *Dir* William G Boyce; *Cur* Robin Poynor; *Technician* Larry Guenwald.
Open Mon - Fri 8 AM - 4:30 PM; Sat & Sun 2 - 5 PM. No admis. Estab 1950 to serve both the University and the community as a center for exhibition of works of art and related activities. Six galleries within the Museum. Average Annual Attendance: 55,000. Mem: 820; dues $10 - $100.
Income: Financed by membership, state appropriation, and foundation. Purchases: $1500.
Collections: George P Tweed Memorial Art Collections of 500 paintings with emphasis on Barbizon School and 19th Century American; †Jonathan Sax Collection of 20th century American prints; †20th century American paintings and sculptures.
Exhibitions: Faculty Invitational; American Watercolor Society; Student Exhibition; Artists and Poets; Midwest Watercolor Society Exhibition; Needle-Arts Exhibition; The Agrarian Landscape in American and French Painting; Environmental Design: Native Wit; Press Photography in Minnesota; African Sculpture.
Activities: Docent training; lect open to public, 1-2 vis lectr per yr; concerts; gallery talks; tours; individual paintings and original objects of art lent to qualifying museums and institutions; lending collection contains original art works, original prints and paintings; traveling exhibitions organized and circulated; museum shop selling books, original art, reproductions, craft objects and cards.

MANKATO

MANKATO STATE UNIVERSITY, Nichols Gallery, 56001. Tel: 507-389-6413. *Gallery Dir* Harlan Bloomer.
Open Mon - Fri 8 AM - 4:30 PM. No admis. Estab 1960 to provide cultural enrichment in the visual arts to the campus and community through a program of exhibitons from local, regional, and national sources, and student exhibitions. 180 running feet of carpeted display area, track lighting, climate controlled.
Income: $3300 (financed by city appropriation).
Collections: American bookplates; prints; contemporary prints, drawings, paintings, sculpture, photographs, and crafts; student works in all media.

MINNEAPOLIS

AMERICAN SWEDISH INSTITUTE,* 2600 Park Ave, 55407. Tel: 612-871-4907. *Pres* Leonard F Ramberg; *Dir* Dr Wesley M Westerberg.
Open Tues - Sat 1 - 4 PM; Sun 1 - 5 PM; cl Mon & National holidays. Admis adults $1, students under 21 and senior citizens 25¢, children under 6 no admis. Estab and inc 1929. Building donated by Swan J Turnblad and contains in a home setting a fine collection of Swedish artifacts plus many items of general cultural interest pertaining to Scandinavia. The Grand Hall, paneled in African mahogany, is considered the finest installation on this continent. Throughout the gallery there are eleven porcelain tile fireplaces: nine of Swedish and two of German design. Average Annual Attendance: 50,000. Mem dues: student attending school, below the age of 21, $5, non-resident single, or husband and wife outside a fifty-mile radius of Twin Cities $10, regular (single) $10, regular (husband and wife) $15, sustaining (husband, wife and all children under age 21, living at home) $25, supporting $50, patron $100, life $1000.
Collections: Paintings, sculpture, tapestries, ceramics, china, glass, pioneer items and textiles.
Publications: Happenings (newsletter), monthly.
Activities: Classes in Swedish and Swedish folk dancing; special exhibitions; films; lect; concerts; summer language camp; Gift shop and Book store.

METROPOLITAN CULTURAL ARTS CENTER, 1530 Russell Ave N, 55411. Tel: 612-522-4111. *Bd Chmn* Robert Samples; *Exec Dir* Evelyn Fairbanks.
Open 9:30 AM - 9 PM. No admis. Estab 1967 to offer training in the arts to people who could not afford it otherwise and to bring people of different cultural backgrounds together to experience the arts. Theatre arm: Shoestring Playhouse. Average Annual Attendance: 400. Mem: 100; dues $10; annual meeting Sept.
Income: $50,000 (financed by endowment, membership, state appropriation and grants).
Publications: Newsletter, monthly.
Activities: Classes for adults and children; dramatic programs.

MINNEAPOLIS INSTITUTE OF ARTS, 2400 Third Ave S, 55404. Tel: 612-870-3046. *Dir* Samuel Sachs II; *Assoc Dir & Chmn Communications Div* Ruth Humleker; *Chmn Cur Div* Merribell Parsons; *Cur Prints & Drawings* John Ittmann; *Cur Paintings* Gregory H Hedberg; *Cur Decorative Arts* David McFadden; *Cur Photography* Carroll T Hartwell; *Cur Pre-Columbian Arts* Ellen Bradbury; *Cur Oriental Arts* Robert Jacobsen; *Chmn Educ Div* Timothy Fiske; *Conservator* James Horns; *Registrar* Marilyn Bjorkland; *Librn & Editor* Harold Peterson.
Open Tues, Wed, Fri & Sat 10 AM - 5 PM; Thurs 10 AM - 9 PM; Sun Noon - 5 PM; cl Mon. Admis adults $1, student 50¢, free to members, sr citizens, under 12, scheduled school groups. Estab 1883. The society was founded to foster the knowledge, understanding and practice of the arts; the first art gallery was opened 1889. The original museum building was constructed 1911-1915, designed by the McKim, Mead & White firm. South wing added 1926. The original building and addition featured classical elements of the day. The museum was expanded to twice the original size in 1972-74, incorporating modern themes designed by Kenzo Tange and URTEC of Tokyo. Average Annual Attendance: 350,000. Mem: 11,862; dues individual $15, household $25; annual meeting Oct.
Income: Financed by endowment, membership, county and state appropriations, and admissions.
Collections: The museum has a collection of 65,000 objects representing all schools and periods of art, including European and American paintings, sculpture, decorative arts, period rooms, photography, prints and drawings, Ancient, African, Oceanic, Oriental and native north and South American arts.
Exhibitions: The Heritage of American Art; I Wear the Morning Star: The Ghost Dance of the American Indian; American Master Drawings and Watercolors; Charles Biederman: A Retrospective, America 1976; Japanese Art: Selections from the Mary and Jackson Burke Collection; The Royal Pavilion at Brighton; New Treasures at the Institute; Millet's Gleaners: A Masterpiece from the Louvre; James Jacques Joseph Tissot: The Complete Prints.
Publications: Bulletin, semi-annually; members' magazine, monthly; exhibition catalogs.
Activities: Classes for adults and children; docent training; workshops; lect open to public, 15 vis lectr per yr; concerts; gallery talks; tours; artmobile; individual paintings and original objects of art lent to other professional arts organizations; traveling exhibitions organized and circulated; museum shop selling books, original art, reproductions, prints, slides and jewelry.
—**Art Reference Library.** *Librn* Harold Peterson.
Open Tues - Sat 10 AM - 5 PM; Sun Noon - 5 PM; cl Mon. Estab 1915 to provide a reference collection based around the museum's collection of works of art for use primarily of curatorial staff but to be available to students and museum visitors. Maintains an art gallery, Leslie Memorial Room; exhibitions of books and prints.
Holdings: Vols 25,000; Per subs 85.
Special Subjects: History of books and printing, decorative arts, prints, photography.
Special Collections: Leslie Collection: History of books and printing; Minnick Collection: Botanical, Floral, and fashion books.
Exhibitions: History of Printing and Typography; Albrecht Durer; Woodcuts and Engravings; New England Writers influence Minnesota; La Mode de Paris: 1908-1925; Frontispieces from The Minnick Collection; Artist as Book Illustrator; Private Presses; 19th century English Book Illustrators.
—**Friends of the Institute.** *Pres* Mary J Bowman.
Estab 1922 to broaden the influence of the Institute in the community and to provide volunteer support within the museum. Mem: 1900; annual meeting May.
Activities: Coordinates the docent program; museum shop; sales and rental gallery; speakers' bureau; information desk; special lect; exhibitions; fund-raising projects.

MINNEAPOLIS COLLEGE OF ART AND DESIGN LIBRARY AND MEDIA CENTER, 200 E 25th St, 55404. Tel: 612-870-3291. *Dir* Richard Kronstedt; *Asst Librn* Tina Theeke; *Slide Librn* Peggy Rudberg; *Media Center Technical Dir* Gary Dale; *Media Center Dir* vacant; *Catalog Librn* vacant.
Open Mon - Thurs 8 AM - 8 PM; Fri 8 AM - 5 PM; Sat 12:30 PM - 4:30 PM; summer 8:30 AM - 4:30 PM; slide library and media center have different hours. Estab 1960 to provide library and media services and materials in support of the curriculum of the College Circ: Approx 40,000 items, limited to students and staff.
Income: Financed by College. Purchases: Books $7800; Per $4700; AV $6700.
Holdings: Vols 45,000; Per subs 170; AV—Cassettes, film strips, motion pictures, phonorecords, slides, video tapes; Other—Clipping files, exhibition catalogs, pamphlets, reproductions.

MINNEAPOLIS PUBLIC LIBRARY AND INFORMATION CENTER, Art, Music and Film Dept, 300 Nicollet Hall, 55401. Tel: 611-372-6500. *Dir* Joseph Kimbrough; *Assoc Dir* Zella Shannon; *Head Art, Music Films Dept* Marlea R Warren; *Films Specialist* Elizabeth Bingaman.
Open Mon - Thurs 9 AM - 9 PM; Fri & Sat 9 AM - 5:30 PM; cl Sat June - Labor Day. No admis. Library estab 1889. Circ: 2,515,399.
Income: $6,396,000. Purchases: $5,712,672.
Holdings: Vols 39,500; Per subs 165; AV—Film strips, lantern slides, 16mm motion pictures, slides, video tapes, projected books, stereographs; Other—Clipping files, clipped pictures, exhibition catalogs, original art works, pamphlets.

MINNESOTA ARTISTS ASSOCIATION, c/o Al Olson, *Pres,* 3121 Pillsbury Ave, 55408. Tel: 612-825-0319. *VPres* Tom Hessel; *Secy* Yvonne Duda; *Treas* Mary Shoquist.
Chartered 1937 to make the citizens of Minnesota more aware of the role art plays in their lives and to promote the welfare of Minnesota Artists. Mem: 180; dues associate $10, active $10; monthly meetings Sept - May; annual election May.
Exhibitions: Members work in rotating shows; annual juried shows for members.
Publications: Newsletters, monthly Sept - May; current membership rosters.
Archives: Archives, biographical file, photographic file of members' works; volume of Bulletins on file at Minneapolis Public Library.

UNIVERSITY OF MINNESOTA
—**University Gallery,*** Northrop Memorial Auditorium, 55455. Tel: 612-373-3424, 373-3425. *Dir* Barbara J Shissler; *Acting Dir* Lyndel King; *Cur* Charles P Helsell; *Cur* Susan Brown, *Registrar* Linda M Djerf.
Open Mon - Fri 11 AM - 4 PM; Sun 2 - 5 PM; cl Sat and holidays. Estab 1933. The program of the University Gallery is planned to provide for the all-University function of meeting the broad objective of an all-University art museum, and for the in-service function of meeting the specific teaching and research needs of the Art History Department of the University of Minnesota. Average Annual Attendance: 50,000.
Collections: †Paintings, †drawings, †prints by American artists working in the first half of the 20th century and contains notable works by Avery, Dove, Feininger, MacDonald-Wright, Marin and O'Keeffe; sculpture collection of major works by contemporary artists includes sculpture by Baizerman, Bertoia, Richier, David Smith and others; print collection including works by artists of all schools and periods; collections on extended loan from Ione and Hudson Walker and Mrs B J O Nordfeldt include major holdings in Hartley, Maurer and Nordfeldt.
Exhibitions: The University Gallery stresses a program of frequently changing major loan exhibitions, held concurrently with smaller exhibitions organized for specific teaching purposes or of the permanent collections.
Activities: Two lending programs are provided for University of Minnesota students, faculty and staff—Office Loan Collection of framed paintings and prints for staff offices; Student Rental Collection of framed prints for student homes.
—**Coffman Union Gallery,*** Tel: 612-373-7604. *Coördr* Roselyn Rezac; *Chairperson* Elaine Ward; *Advisor* Marlene Vernon.
Open Daily 10 AM - 5 PM. No admis. Estab 1976 for campus and local artists.
Income: Financed by student fees.
Activities: lectures; films; demonstrations.
—**Art Library,** 12 Walter Library, 117 Pleasant St, SE, 55455. *Librn* Herbert Scherer; *Junior Libr Asst* Dennis Skrade.
Open Mon - Thurs 8 AM - 9 PM; Fri 8 AM - 5 PM; Sat & Sun 1 - 5 PM; summer Mon - Fri 8 AM - 4:30 PM. Estab 1950 to serve the needs of the students and faculty of the University. The general public is welcome to use materials in the library. Circ: 34,260.
Income: Financed by membership and state appropriation. Purchases: Books $13,734; Per $4205.
Holdings: Vols 51,736; Per subs 142; AV—Microfiche; Other—Exhibition catalogs 4701.
Special Subjects: Collection covers the fine arts including painting, sculpture, graphic arts, architecture and photography; particularly Scandinavian, Baroque and American art.
Activities: Lect for Friends of the Art Library; library tour upon request.

WALKER ART CENTER, Vineland Place, 55403. Tel: 612-377-7500. *Chmn Bd* Thomas M Crosby Jr; *Pres* Roger L Hale; *VPres* Mrs James K Wittenberg; *Dir* Martin Friedman; *Adminr* D C Borrman; *Cur* Graham WJ Beal; *Asst Cur* Lisa Lyons; *Editor* Mildred S Friedman; *Registrar* Carolyn Clark DeCato; *Asst Registrar* Gwen Bitz; *Coordinator Development* Robert Sain; *Coordinator Education* Linda Nyvall; *Coordinator Film* Melinda Ward; *Coordinator Performing Arts* Nigel Redden; *Public Information* Peter Georgas; *Graphic Designer* James E Johnson.
Open Tues - Sat 10 AM - 8 PM; Sun 11 AM - 5 PM; cl Mon. No admis. Estab 1879 by T B Walker, reorganized 1939 as Walker Art Center, Inc; building erected 1927; new museum building opened 1971. Emphasis is on contemporary art in both special exhibitions and permanent collection.

The Center consists of seven galleries, three sculpture terraces, the Center Bookshop and the Gallery 8 restaurant. Average Annual Attendance: 450,000. Mem: 4500; dues regular $20, student and sr citizens $12.50, non-resident $15; annual meeting Sept.
Income: $1,983,625 (financed by endowment, membership, state appropriation, grants, and book shop). Purchases: $2,001,148.
Collections: 19th Century American Landscape paintings by Church, Cole, Durand, Kensett, Inness, Ryder; †20th century paintings; †sculpture; †graphics; †photography.
Exhibitions: Nelson, Eames, Girard, Propst: The Design Process at Herman Miller; Robert Irwin; Sculpture Made in Place: Dill, Ginnever, Madsen; The River: Images of the Mississippi; Morris Louis: The Veil Cycle; Scale & Environment: 10 Sculptors; Architecture of James Stirling: Four Works; Press Photography: Minnesota Since 1930; Noguchi's Imaginary Landscapes; Gene Davis: Recent Paintings.
Publications: Exhibition catalogs; Design Quarterly; Calendar of Events, 11 issues a year; brochures.
Activities: Classes for adults and children; docent training; family workshops; lect open to public, 8 vis lectr per yr; concerts; gallery talks; tours; exten dept serving Minnesota and surrounding states; individual paintings and original objects of art lent to schools, community groups, corporation, museums; traveling exhibitions organized and circulated; museum shop selling books, magazines, posters, jewelry, and gift items.
—**Staff Reference Library.** *Lib Asst* Geraldine Owens.
Open to staff, museum personnel, librarians, and graduates for reference; to students by appointment.
Holdings: Vols 3000; Per subs 95; Other—catalogues 35,000; vertical files; slide tapes.
Special Subjects: Contemporary art; design; graphics; architecture.
Special Collections: One-person artists' catalogues dating back to 1940.

WOMEN'S ART REGISTRY OF MINNESOTA, 414 First Ave N, 55401. Tel: 312-338-2267, 332-5672. *Admin Coordr* Diane E Gorney; *Artist Advocate/Slide Tape Project* Joyce Lyon.
Open Mon - Wed & Fri 11 AM - 4 PM; Sat Noon - 5 PM; cl Sun. No admis. Estab 1975; maintains gallery. Average Annual Attendance: 4000. Mem: 186 associate members must be a woman artist in Minnesota; gallery members by jury; dues $8; annual meeting Feb.
Income: Financed by membership and small grants for projects.
Collections: Members work on display in one area.
Exhibitions: Members work plus special shows and theme shows; International Women Invite Women Exhibit.
Publications: WARM Newsletter.
Activities: Educ dept; workshops for public, events-poetry readings, performance, lectr open to the public, 4 vis lectr per yr; gallery talks; traveling exhibitions organized and circulated.
Library: Open to members and the public. Holdings: Vols 37; Per subs 10; AV—Cassettes; slides. Special Collections: Slide/tape packets of WPA.

MOORHEAD

PLAINS ART MUSEUM
—**Main Gallery,** 521 Main Ave, (Mailing Add: Box 37, 56560). Tel: 218-236-7171. *Dir & Secy Bd Dir* James O'Rourke; *Asst Dir* Susan Hunke; *Pres Bd Dir* Richard B Crockett; *VPres Bd Dir* Richard Moorhead; *Business Mgr* Steven W Illg; *Cur* Roger Sherman; *Registrar & Educ Dir* Kevin Brown; *Photographer & Publ* Owen K Osten; *Museum Shop and Volunteers* Susie Freeman.
Open Wed -Sun 9 AM - 5 PM. No admis. Estab 1965 to foster and promote a knowledge and love of art in the community, and to provide a repository for the artistic heritage of this area, to operate and maintain an art gallery and museum, to promote the extension and improvement of education in the arts, to provide facilities for the exhibition and conservation of the art in this area, both past and present. Former Moorhead Federal Building (1913), Oscar Wenderoth, architect, houses the museum. This stately federal style building has a vari-colored marble lobby, ionic columns and tall arched windows. Average Annual Attendance: 26,000. Mem: 1100; dues $10 - $1000; annual meeting June.
Income: Financed by membership and foundation grants. Purchases: $3000.
Collections: African, Oceanic, Pre-Columbian and North American Indian, Persian and Oriental art; Eskimo sculpture; 19th & 20th century prints and drawings; 19th century decorative arts; 20th century paintings from local, regional and national artists; photography.
Exhibitions: British Artists; Andre Kertesz and Charles Harbutt (photographs); Black Kingdoms, West African Art; 19th Red River Annual Exhibition.
Publications: Slaytons Pictorial, monthly.
Activities: Classes for adults; docent training; lect open to public, 12 vis lectr per yr; concerts; gallery talks; tours; exten dept serving North Dakota, South Dakota, Western Minnesota; individual paintings and original objects of art lent to art galleries, historical museums, colleges, and schools; lending collection contains original art works 2000, original

prints 500, paintings 400, photographs 300; museum shop selling books, magazines, original art, prints, and slides.
—**Rourke Art Gallery,** 523 S Fourth St, 56560. Tel: 218-236-7171. *Pres of Bd of Dir* Richard B Crockett; *Exec Dir & Secy of Bd* James O'Rourke; *Asst Dir* Susan Hunke; *Business Mgr* Steven Illg; *Cur* Roger Sherman; *Registrar* Kevin Brown; *Publs* Owen K Osten.
Open Wed - Sun Noon - 5 PM. No admis. Estab 1960 to foster and promote a knowledge and love of art in our community and to provide a repository for the artistic heritage of this area, to operate and maintain an art gallery and museum; former Martinson family home built 1884, remodeled 1920, renovations have preserved the period details and historical features; three floors for exhibitions. Average Annual Attendance: 16,000. Mem: 800; dues $10 - $1000; annual meeting June 18.
Income: Financed by membership and foundation grants. Purchases: $5000.
Collections: West African Art; North American Indian Art; Pre-Columbian Art; 19th Century Decorative Art; Persian Art.
Exhibitions: West African Textiles and Jewelry; Cameron Booth Paintings; San Francisco artists.
Publications: Slaytons Pictorial, monthly newsletter.
Activities: Classes for adults and children; docent training; lect open to public, 12 vis lectr per yr; concerts; gallery talks; tours; extension dept serving NDakota and SDakota, and Western Minnesota; individual paintings and original objects of art lent; lending collection contains original art 2000, original prints 500, paintings 400, photographs 300; museum shop selling books, magazines original art, prints, slides.

OWATONNA

OWATONNA ARTS CENTER, 435 Dunnel Dr (Mailing Add: PO Box 134, 55060). Tel: 507-451-4540. *Pres* Mary E Leach; *VPres* F Keen Young; *Treas* James Birdsall; *Cur* Silvan A Durben; *Performing Arts Chmn* Virginia Birdsall; *Bldg Mgr* John M Spencer; *Secy* Bea Spencer; *Acquisitions Committee* Norma Darby; *Sept Fest Chmn* Jean Zamboni.
Open Tues - Sat 1 - 5 PM; Sun 2 - 5 PM. No admis, excepting specials. Estab 1975 to preserve local professional artists work and promote the arts in the community; West Gallery (32 x 26 x 12 ft) and North Gallery (29 x 20 x 12 ft) provide an interesting walk through space, and a versatile space in which to display two and three dimensional work; the two Galleries can be combined by use of moveable panels. Average Annual Attendance: Approx 5000. Mem: 400; dues individual $5, family $10; annual meeting first Tues in Oct.
Income: $20,394 (financed by membership and fund raising activities). Purchases: $500.
Collections: Marianne Young World Costume Collection; painting-prints-sculpture by local professional artists; Costume Collection of garments and jewelry from 27 countries.
Exhibitions: Owatonna Camera Club; American Scene Urban and Rural Regionalists of the 30s and 40s; Manamore; Annual Steel County Show; Steve Delaitsch Painting; Work of Purcell & Elmslie, Architects; Anthony Jackovich, Painting; Owatonna Watercolorists; An Old-Fashioned Christmas.
Publications: Monthly newsletter to members only.
Activities: Classes for adults and children; lect open to the public, 2 vis lectr per yr; concerts monthly; tours; traveling exhibitions organized and circulated; sales shop selling books, original art.
Library: Open to members only, for reference; Holdings: Vols 180.

ROCHESTER

ROCHESTER ART CENTER, 320 E Center St, 55901. Tel: 507-282-8629. *Dir* Betty Jean Shigaki.
Open Tues - Sat 10 AM - 4 PM; Sun 1 - 5 PM; cl Mon. No admis. Estab 1947 as a center for contemporary arts and crafts of the Upper Midwest region, sponsoring an on-going program of exhibitions, educational classes, lectures, workshops and community services in the arts. The Upstairs Gallery of Contemporary Crafts; The Holland Gallery; the main exhibit space. Average Annual Attendance: 30,000. Mem: 330; dues $15 - $100; annual meeting Nov.
Income: $91,000 (financed by endowment, membership, city and state appropriations, fund raising, and tuition).
Collections: Local and regional artists works.
Exhibitions: 24-30 traveling exhibits per year in Contemporary Fine Arts and Crafts.
Publications: Newsletter, quarterly.
Activities: Classes for adults and children; lect open to public, 2 vis lectr per yr; concerts; gallery talks, tours; competitions; sales shop selling original art.
Library: Open to staff and members only. Holdings: Vols 500; Per subs 12.

SAINT CLOUD

ST CLOUD STATE UNIVERSITY
—Atwood Center Gallery Lounge, Atwood Center, 56301. Tel: 612-255-2202. *Program Dir* Patricia A Krueger.
Open Mon - Fri 7:30 AM - 11 PM; Sat 8 AM - 11 PM; Sun noon - 11 PM. No admis. Estab 1967, as a university student union facility; Gallery area is part of program, designed for maximum exposure, where students may relax or study while enjoying exhibits; space is flexible; also areas for music listening and small theater; additional exhibits displayed in prominent area. Average Annual Attendance: Records not kept.
Income: Financed by student enrollment fee assessment.
Exhibitions: 2 - 3 exhibitions generally monthly, many by students.
Activities: Classes for adults and children; dramatic programs; lect open to public, 10 - 20 vis lectr per yr; concerts.
—Kiehle Gallery, 56301. Tel: 612-255-4283. *Dir* Kingsly Dorholt.
Open Mon - Fri 8 AM - 4:30 PM. No admis. Estab 1974 to expose college community to ideas and attitudes in the field of visual arts and crafts; the gallery has 1600 sq ft of enclosed multi-use gallery floor space and 2500 sq ft outside sculpture court. Average Annual Attendance: 15,000.
Income: Financed by student fund appropriation.
Collection: Consists of works donated by recipients of Master of Arts degree in visual arts.
Activities: Lectr open to the public 5 vis lectr per yr; gallery talks; competitions; individual paintings and original objects of art lent to other departments on campus; lending collection contains original prints, paintings, photographs and sculpture; traveling exhibitions organized and circulated.

SAINT PAUL

HAMLINE UNIVERSITY GALLERIES, Dept of Art, 55104. *Cur Permanent Collection* Roslye Ultan, *Exhib Dir* James Conaway.
Open Mon - Fri 9 AM - 4:30 PM, cl. Sat & Sun. Estab 1943 to display outstanding works of art in all media for instruction of and appreciation by the public and students.
Income: Financed by the University.
Collections: Paintings, prints, drawings and sculpture.
Exhibitions: Continuous exhibitions; annual purchase award exhibits in painting and in graphic arts.
Library: Rental library of original modern works and reproductions; extensive color slide library of paintings, architecture, sculpture, minor arts and graphics.

MACALESTER COLLEGE GALLERIES,* 1600 Grand Ave, 55101. Tel: 612-647-6416. *Cur* Roxann Sorenson.
Open Mon - Fri 8 AM - 10 PM; cl Aug, National holidays & school vacations. No admis. Estab 1964 as a college facility to bring contemporary art exhibitions to the students, faculty and community.
Activities: Lectures; guided tours; gallery talks; temporary, traveling and student exhibitions; sales shop selling art books and supplies.
—Weyerhauser Library.
Holdings: Vols 200,000.
Special Subjects: Artists, art history.

MINNESOTA HISTORICAL SOCIETY, 690 Cedar St, 55101. Tel: 612-296-6126. *Pres* Paul L Parker; *Dir* Russell W Fridley; *Assoc Dir* Robert C Wheeler; *Deputy Dir* John J Wood; *Asst Dir* June Holmquist; *Asst to Dir for Libraries and Museum Coll* Lila J Goff.
Open Mon - Sat 8:30 AM - 5 PM. No admis. Estab 1849 to collect, preserve, and make available to the public the history of Minnesota. Mem: 6000.
Income: $5,600,000 (financed by endowment, membership and state appropriation). *Purchases:* $30,000.
Collections: †Books, †maps, newspapers, †manuscripts, archives, †photographs, †art works, and †museum artifacts relating to the history of Minnesota.
Exhibitions: The Clothes Off Our Backs.
Publications: Minnesota History, quarterly; Minnesota History News, 6 issues per yr.
Activities: Classes for adults; lect open to the public; tours; sales shop selling books, magazines, prints, reproductions.
Library: Chief Reference Librn Patricia Harpole. Open to the public; general reference, contains only a few works relating to art. Special Collections: Seth Eastman watercolors; Edwin Whitefield watercolors; Minnesota photographs; maps.

MINNESOTA MUSEUM OF ART
—Permanent Collection Gallery, 305 St Peter St, 55102. Tel: 612-224-7431. *Chmn Board of Trustees* Walter N Trenerry; *VChmn* Frank Marzitelli; *Pres* Malcolm E Lein; *Exec Dir* Sherman K Headley; *Corporate Secy/Treas/Operations* Ruth Moran; *Dir Gallery* Otto S Theuer; *Dir Program & Publications* Patricia Heikenen; *Dir Visitor Services & Asst Public Relations* Betty S Runyon; *Adjunct Cur Asian Art* Dr Robert J

Poor; *Dir Operations & Registrar Temporary Exhibit* Mary Theuer; *Dir Development* Lola Plaisted; *Registrar Permanent Coll* Leanne Klein; *Dir Membership* Laurene Tibbetts; *Exhib* Pam Owens.
Open Mon - Fri 10 AM - 5 PM, Admis by donation. Estab 1927 to act as trustee in preserving important works of art for the benefit of present and future generations, and to use its resources and collection actively as an educational force to enrich the community. The gallery is housed in a beautiful four-story art deco building built in 1931 by architect St Paulite Magnus Jemne whose artist wife did curving brass stair rail and inlays of brass in foyer floors; there is an auditorium with gold-leaf on walls for programs and a dining room amid art works on fourth floor. Average Annual Attendance: 18,000. Mem: 800; dues family $25, professional, student and nonresidents $15; annual meeting Nov.
Income: $650,000. (financed by endowment, membership, county appropriation and allocation from St Paul-Ramsey Arts & Science Council). Purchases: $40,000.
Collections: 20th century drawings, sculpture, paintings and prints; contemporary American, African and Northwest Coast Indian crafts; Asian sculpture, ceramics, paintings, prints, screens, drawings, textiles and furniture; American and European lace; Korean ceramics, paintings and furniture.
Exhibitions: (1976-78) Metamorphose/One & Metamporphose/Two; Enrico Donati Retrospective; Sosaku Hanga; Svensk Hemslojd/Swedish Handcrafts; Buddhist Bronzes; Drawings USA/77; Netruke/Snuff Bottles; Portfolio 50/American Drawings 1927-77; Lasansky/The Nazi Drawings; Prints by Stanley Hayter; Portfolio 50/Highlights From the Permanent Collection/50th Anniversery Exhibition; Eskimo Prints from Cape Dorset; Egyptian Children's Tapestries; Living Japanese Treasures.
Publications: Exhibition catalogs.
Activities: Lect open to the public, 10 vis lectr per yr; gallery talks; tours; competitions; community service program in which changing exhibitions of art works are lent to businesses and professional offices in the community for a specified fee; traveling exhibitions organized and circulated.
—Library. *Librn* Leanne Klein.
Open to members, students and staff for reference only.
Holdings: Vols 3000; Per subs 15; Other—Slides.
Special Subjects: Asian art, contemporary prints and drawings; Eskimo art; Northwest Coast Indian art, lace and textiles.
Special Collections: Edwin H Lundie Collection of architectural books and drawings.
—Community Gallery, 30 E Tenth St, 55101. Tel: 612-227-7613. *Educ Programs for Schools* Alvaro Cardona-Hine; *Youth & Adult Educ, After-school Art;* Nell McClure; *Photographer* Claire Braude; *Exhibit* Jeff Brandes.
Open Mon - Wed 9 AM - 5 PM; Thurs - Sat 9 AM - 9:30 PM; Sun 11 AM - 9:30 PM. No admis. Estab 1927 to preserve important works of art for the benefit of present and future generations. The gallery is located on the lower level of Arts & Science Center on approach to the capitol; studio for art classes occupy one corridor. Average Annual Attendance: 150,000.
Income: Financed with Permanent Collection Gallery.
Exhibitions: (1976-78) Arts Awareness/Color Environment; Arts of China; African Arts of Transformation; Pride & Heritage, The Folk Art of La Raza; Chicano Program for St Paul School Children Grades 6 - 9; Mid-Century American Crafts; Nelda Getty Jewelry and Prints; Society of Minnesota Sculptors/25th Anniversary Exhibition; Midwest Watercolor Society Exhibition; The Bruno Gifts; Two Decades; Collector's Dolls; Works by Clara Mairs.
Publications: Exhibition catalogs.
Activities: Classes for adults and children.

ST PAUL COUNCIL OF ARTS AND SCIENCES,* 30 E Tenth St, 55101. Tel: 612-227-8241. *Exec Dir* Marlow Burt.
Open Tues & Wed 9 AM - 5 PM; Thurs - Sat 9 AM - 9:30 PM; Sun 1 - 9:30 PM; cl Mon. Estab 1958, opened in 1964. Conducts annual united arts and science fund drive; cooperative promotion and other activities for the five member agencies including the Minnesota Museum of Art, Community Programs in the Arts and Sciences, Science Museum, Schubert Club, St Paul Chamber Orchestra and KSJN Radio Station. Administers the St Paul Arts and Science Center which houses the galleries, the member agencies and the Crawford Livingston Theatre. Average Annual Attendance for the building: 450,000.

ST PAUL PUBLIC LIBRARY, 90 W Fourth St, 55102. Tel: 612-224-3383. *Dir of Libraries* J Archer Eggen; *Supvr, Arts & AV Services* Delores A Sundbye.
Open Mon & Thurs 11:30 AM - 8 PM; Tues, Wed, Fri & Sat 9 AM - 5:30 PM. Estab 1857, gallery has changing exhibitions where various organizations may hold meetings. Circ: 92,642 in Arts & AV.
Income: Financed by city appropriation. Purchases: $10,000 for Arts and AV.
Holdings: Vols 16,000; Per subs: 50; AV—Cassettes, film strips, motion pictures, phonorecords, slides; Other—Clipping files, exhibition catalogs, framed reproductions, sculpture.

Special Collections: Complete collection of first edition Arundel prints.
Exhibitions: Open exhibits for local artists, school children, senior citizens, art therapy.
Activities: Lect open to the public; exhibitions organized and circulated.

SCHOOL OF THE ASSOCIATED ARTS GALLERIES, 344 Summit Ave, 55102. Tel: 612-224-3416. *Dir* Virginia Rahjd; *Dean* Ronald Swenson.
Open Mon - Fri 9 AM - 4 PM. No admis. Estab 1948. Our galleries were established as an adjunct to, and part of, the art education we offer our students. Average Annual Attendance: 400-500.
Income: Financed by endowment.
Exhibitions: Ten shows per year of the work of local artists, faculty, students, traveling shows, and work from our own collection. The emphasis is on Modern Art.
—Library.
Estab 1948 to have reference material for our own students. Not open to public. Maintains an art gallery.
Holdings: Vols 7500; Per subs 5; AV—Slides; Other—Original art works, pamphlets, photographs and reproductions.
Special Subjects: Art.

UNIVERSITY OF MINNESOTA, Student Center Galleries, 2017 Buford, 55108. Tel: 612-373-1046, 373-1051. *Dir* Paul W Larson; *Asst Dir for Programming* Timothy L McCarty; *Gallery Cur* Ron Dufault; *Activities Consultant* Ester Neely.
Open daily 8 AM - 10 PM; Sun Noon - 10 PM. No admis. Estab 1959 to bring art of great variety into the daily lives of students; two lounge galleries and one pedestrian gallery. Average Annual Attendance: 1,500,000. Mem: 5400; dues undefined part of $30; annual meeting last Thurs Sept.
Income: Part of gross income of $290,000 (financed by student fee).
Exhibitions: Twenty-seven exhibits in three galleries in 1976-77.
Publications: Annual Report and Activity Summary.
Activities: Classes for adults; dramatic programs; mini-courses in crafts; lect open to the public, 10 vis lectr per yr; concerts; gallery talks; tours; competitions; exten dept serving Minnesota.

WORTHINGTON

NOBLES COUNTY ART CENTER GALLERY, 416 12th St (Mailing Add: PO Box 281, 56187). Tel: 507-376-4431. *Pres of Bd of Dir* Mrs John McVeety; *Cur and Secy* Genevieve Peterson.
Open Mon - Sat 2 - 3:30 PM; Mon - Fri in summer. No admis. Estab 1961 to nourish the arts, and to bring the arts and cultures of other communities, nations and civilizations to Nobles County and the surrounding area so that its residents may become more universal in their thinking; room on lower level of building housing county library and information center; 25 x 51 ft. Average Annual Attendance: Approximately 1000. Mem: 150; dues family $5; annual meeting May.
Income: Financed by county appropriation.
Exhibitions: New one each month through the season, Sept - May; the work of area artists; two exhibits during summer months, each lasting six weeks.
Publications: Newsletter, monthly, from Sept through June.
Activities: Classes for adults; gallery talks; competitions; original artwork for sale during exhibitions.

MISSISSIPPI

CLEVELAND

DELTA STATE UNIVERSITY, Fielding L Wright Art Center, Box D-2, 38733. Tel: 601-843-2151. *Chmn Dept* Malcolm M Norwood; *Exhib Chmn* Terry K Simmons; *Chmn Art Educ* Dr Carolyn Stone.
Open Mon - Fri 8 AM - 5 PM; Sun 3 - 5 PM on opening shows; cl school holidays. No admis. Estab 1968 as an education gallery for the benefit of students, but serves the entire area for changing art shows; it is the only facility of this nature in the Mississippi Delta Region; three gallery areas—Gallery A carpeted 40 X 22 ft; main gallery area about the same and the third gallery can accommodate about 25 hangings depending on size. Average Annual Attendance: 2500-3000.
Income: Financed by state appropriation.
Collections: Marie Hull Collection; Whittington Memorial Collection; Delta State University permanent collection; Smith-Paterson Memorial Collection.
Exhibitions: (1976-78) Tom Speck, Paintings; African Art Show; Sculptor Fred Brownstein and Painter Stella Brownstein; Faculty Show; Annual High School Senior Competition and Student Show; DSU Seniors' Theses Show; First Former Student Show; Harvey S Harris Painter; Johnny Ward and LaVerne Krause Sculpture and Prints; Walter Anderson Retrospective Show.

Publications: Announcement of exhibitions, monthly during fall, winter and spring.
Activities: Classes for adults; lectr open to the public, 10 vis lectr per yr; gallery talks; tours; competitions; exten dept serving the Mississippi Delta Region; individual paintings and original objects of art lent to offices of campus, lending collection contains color reproductions, film strips, motion pictures, original art works, slides 6000; traveling exhibitions organized and circulated.

COLUMBUS

MISSISSIPPI UNIVERSITY FOR WOMEN, ART GALLERY AND MUSEUM, Fine Arts Bldg, 39701. *Dir of Gallery/Cur of Museum & Permanent Coll* Charles E Ambrose.
Open Mon - Fri 8 AM - 5 PM. No admis. Estab 1948.
Collections: †Paintings, drawings, prints; †permanent collection of Mississippi artists; †American art.
Exhibitions: Frequent special and circulating exhibitions. Selections from permanent collection periodically; international exhibition.
Activities: Children's art classes; visiting artists program; art films in connection with Department of Art and student art organizations; visiting foreign artists workshops.

JACKSON

CRAFTSMEN'S GUILD OF MISSISSIPPI, Mississippi Crafts Center, Natchez Trace Parkway at Ridgeland (Mailing Add: PO Box 22886, 39205). Tel: 601-354-8884. *Exec Dir* Dan Overly; *Educ Dir* Steve Rigell; *Admin Asst* Duncan Green.
Open daily 9 AM - 5 PM.
Activities: Mississippi School of Crafts and Design; summer program; classes for children; exhibits program; marketing assistance.

MISSISSIPPI ART ASSOCIATION,* Pascagoula & Lamar, 39201. Tel: 601-354-5521. *Pres* Mrs Davenport Mosby, Jr; *Dir* D Michael Ogden; *Educ Dir* Ray Parish; *Assoc Dir* Dan Matusiewicz.
Gallery open Tues - Sat 9 AM - 5 PM; Sun 2 - 5 PM; cl Mon. No admis. Organized 1911, inc 1926, new charter received 1953, for purpose of education, exhibition and acquisition. Mem: 2100; dues $5 and up; annual meeting May.
Collections: Paintings and prints, sculpture, tapestry, pottery; collections added to annually include Mississippi Collection, First National Bank and Mississippi Art Association Collection. All collections become the property of the Association for the permanent collections.
Exhibitions: Mississippi Competitive Exhibition; Collegiate Exhibition; annual membership exhibition in Dec; outstanding monthly exhibitions year-round; national exhibitions.
Publications: Newsletter, monthly; exhibition calendars.
Activities: Art classes for adults and children; art education and docent program; lectures and workshops; travel-lecture program; gallery exhibitions; sponsoring of visual arts exhibitions at Mississippi Arts Festival; Civic Arts Center Planetarium Development; speakers bureau; art activities for young people; billboard art; state-wide program assistance; lending collection contains slides; traveling exhibition program.

MISSISSIPPI DEPARTMENT OF ARCHIVES AND HISTORY, 100 State St: (Mailing Add: PO Box 571, 39205). Tel: 601-354-6218 and 354-6222. *Pres Bd Trustees* William F Winter; *Dir* Elbert R Hilliard; *Dir Old Capitol Museum* Patti Carr Black; *Dir Information and Educ* Charlotte Capers; *Dir Archives & Libr* Robert J Bailey; *Dir Historic Preservation* Dawn Maddox.
Open Mon 8 AM - 9 PM; Tues - Sat 8 AM - 5 PM; cl Sun. Estab 1902 for the care and custody of official archives; to collect material relating to the history of the State from the earliest times and to impart knowledge of the history and resources of the State. Maintains the State Historical Museum. Maintains an art gallery which includes a portrait gallery of distinguished Mississippians and holds monthly exhibitions, folk song and folk crafts programs.
Income: Financed by city appropriation.
Holdings: Vols 33,000; Per subs 250; AV—Audio tapes, cassettes, film strips, microfiche, microfilm, motion pictures, phonorecords, reels, slides and video tapes; Other—Clipping files, exhibition catalogs, manuscripts; original documents; pamphlets, photographs and prints.
Special Subjects: Mississippiana; archaeology; genealogy; Civil War.
Special Collections: Maps; photographs; newspapers, all pertaining to Mississippi.
Publications: Journal of Mississippi History, quarterly; Mississippi History Newsletter, monthly.
Activities: Folk song and folk crafts programs.

MISSISSIPPI MUSEUM OF ART, Pascagoula at Lamar Sts (Mailing Add: PO Box 1330, 39205). Tel: 601-354-3538. *Chmn Bd of Trustees* David Fowler; *Pres* Mrs Charles Hayes; *Dir* M J Czarniecki III; *Assoc Dir* Dan Matusiewicz; *Exec Secy* Ruth Carr; *Pub Relations Specialist*

Dora Carl; *Sales Gallery Mgr* Emily Sue Mabry; *Coordr of Educ* W Ray Parish; *Coordr of Exhib* John B Henry; *Registrar* Janie Nichols.

Open Mon, Wed, Fri, Sat 10 AM - 6 PM; Tues & Thurs 10 AM - 10 PM; Sun 1 - 5 PM. Admis donation suggested. Chartered in 1911, administered by nonprofit art association; museum opened April 22, 1978; East Exhibition Galleries 6400 sq ft; West Exhibition Galleries 2600 sq ft; Graphics Study Center houses exhibition area, study and storage rooms; Open Gallery includes special power, lighting and water requirements for technological media; Upper and Lower Atrium Galleries, and outdoor Sculpture Garden. Mem: 3000; dues student $5, individual $15, artist $20, family $20, patron $100, donor $250, benefactor $500, grand benefactor $1000.

Income: Under $500,000 (financed by endowment, membership).

Collections: Varied Western art collection, state, regional, national, and international artists; smaller Eastern art collection.

Exhibitions: (1978-80) Key Works and New Acquisitions to the permanent collection; With a Little Help from Our Friends; Holography: Through the Looking Glass; American Painting, 1930-1955 from Whitney Museum; Before it's too Late: The Photographs of Edward S Curtis; Chuck & Eloise Black: Film/Video; Video Art; The National Sculpture Exhibition; While There is Still Time:The Photographs of Roland Freeman; To Live upon Canvas, the portrait art of Thomas Cantwell Healy (1820-1889); Stella since 1970.

Publications: Newsletter, bi-monthly; selected exhibition catalogs.

Activities: Classes for adults and children; docent training; Outreach programs, Art Cart, and travel lecture program; lect open to the public, some for members only, 20 vis lectr per yr; tours; competitions; Art Lecture Van; corporate museum memberships entitle business to 6-month loans from permanent collection; museum shop selling books, reproductions, prints, and fine handmade items.

—**Media Study Center Library:** *Media Center Supv* Margaret Tucker.

For reference only, open to the general public.

Holdings: Vols 1600; Per subs 26.

Special Collections: Metropolitan Miniature Album; Walter Anderson Collection on Slides, Museum's permanent collection.

LAUREL

LAUREN ROGERS LIBRARY AND MUSEUM OF ART, Fifth Ave & Seventh St (Mailing Add: PO Box 1108, 39440). Tel: 601-428-4875. *Dir* Donald D Crawford; *Dir Emeritus* Nell Davis; *Asst Dir* Amorita Gordon; *Librn* Betty Mulloy.

Open Tues - Sat 10 AM - Noon, 1 - 5 PM; Sun 2 - 5 PM; cl Mon. No admis. Estab 1923 as a reference and research library and museum of art for public use and employment; five smaller galleries open off large American Gallery; these include European room, Contemporary room, Gardiner Basket collection, Western and Indian room, and temporary exhibit gallery. Average Annual Attendance: 7000 (museum). Mem dues $5 - $100.

Income: Financed by endowment.

Collections: †19th and 20th Century American artists; †Georgian silver; Indian basketry; European artists of the 19th Century.

Exhibitions: (1976-78) John McCrady; Alan Flattmann; Mississippi Craftsmen; American Impressionists; Cotton Comes Home; Wyatt Cooper; William R Dunlap; Frances De Bra Brown; Harold Young; Lin Emery; Clementine Hunter; Mildred Wilfe; Hugh O Williams; James Lamantia; Sophie Coors; Emmitt Thames; Impressionist Painters; Collegiate Art; Eloise Buckler and Byron Myrick; Mississippi Art Colony.

Publications: Quarterly Preview.

Activities: Classes for adults and children; docent training; lect open to the public, 2-3 vis lectr per yr; concerts; competitions; individual paintings lent to AAM Accredited museums or galleries.

—Library: For reference only.

Holdings: Vols 17,000.

Special Subjects: Art, genealogy, Mississippiana, Laurel history.

Special Collection: Edward S Curtis books and photogravure portfolios on American Indian.

MERIDIAN

MERIDIAN MUSEUM OF ART,* Box 5773, 25th Ave at Seventh St, 39301. Tel: 601-693-1501. *Pres* Dr William Thornton; *Secy* Betsy Weems; *Exec Dir* William Myers Watkins III; *Admin Asst* Rosanne Knight.

Open Tues - Sun 1 - 5 PM; cl Mon & holidays. Estab 1969 to give cultural enrichment and educational benefits to the people of East Mississippi, West Alabama, the South, and the United States; three galleries. Average Annual Attendance: 20,000. Mem: 600; dues $10 - $1000 and up; annual meeting second week in Dec.

Income: Financed by membership and appropriation.

Collections: Lithographs, paintings, oil and acrylic; ink drawings; photographs.

Exhibitions: Occasional traveling exhibitions; art workshops.

Publications: Gallery Review, (newsletter), quarterly.

Activities: Classes for adults and children; docent program; lect for members only (some open to public), 2 vis lectr per yr; gallery talks; tours and school tours; competitions.

Library: For reference. Holdings: Vols 200.

MISSISSIPPI ART COLONY, c/o Alex M Loeb, 2741 38 St, 39301. Tel: 601-482-2827. *Dir* Bess Dawson; *Pres* Alex M Loeb; *VPres* RB Jacoby; *Secy-Treas* Jean R Loeb.

Estab 1945 to hold workshops at least twice yearly, for painting instruction and occasionally other areas; to select show, with prizes awarded, which travels state of Mississippi between workshops. Mem: 40; dues $5; annual meetings Oct and May.

Income: Financed by membership.

Exhibitions: Seven exhibitions since 1970.

Publications: Bulletin, newsletter.

Activities: Traveling exhibitions organized and circulated.

OXFORD

UNIVERSITY OF MISSISSIPPI, University Museums, University Ave and Fifth St (Mailing Add: University, 38677). Tel: 601-232-7073. *Dir* Valerie V Braybrooke; *Registrar* Loren D Lillis; *Honorary Cur of Classics* Lucy Turnbull; *Honorary Cur Millington-Barnard Collection* A B Lewis.

Open Tues - Sat 10 AM - 4 PM; Sun 1 - 4 PM, cl Mon. No admis. Estab 1977 to collect, conserve, and exhibit objects related to history of the University of Mississippi and to the cultural and scientific heritage of the people of the state and region; Main Gallery contains 300 sq ft with 12 ft ceilings for permanent collections; the temporary wall-hung exhibits has 800 sq ft with 18 ft ceilings for temporary exhibits; Meeting room has 1100 sq ft for temporary wall-hung exhibits; each of the four galleries of the Mary Buie Museum contains 400 sq ft for permanent collection. Mem: 75; dues, student $10, individual $15, family $25, contributing $50, patron $100 up.

Income: $70,000 (financed by membership and state appropriation).

Collections: David Robinson Collection of Greek and Roman antiquities; Millington-Barnard Collection; antique dolls; Victorian memorabilia; Theora Hamblett Collection (paintings, glass, drawings).

Exhibitions: (1977) Sara Virginia Jones Print Collection; San Francisco Rock Posters; Jere Allen Drawings and Paintings; GlennRay Tutor Art and Poetry; Eudora Welty Photographs; Theora Hamblett Memorial Collection; Davis/Lester/Dunlap—Faulkner's Oxford; Mohamed/Miller/James Stitchery; (1978) Ron Bartlett Art and Poetry; Women Look at Women; Folk Structures: Black Architecture in Mississippi; Myatt/Rothermel/Francis—Three Sculptors; 25th National Exhibition of Prints; Mississippi Mud; Religious Architecture in Mississippi; Law Center Dedication Show; Concepts in African Art; Art Department Faculty Show; Impressions of Faulkner Country—Bill Baggett; (1979) White House News Photographers; Black Women, Black Presence; Abe Tahir Galleries Print Show; (1981) I Shall Save One Land Unvisited (southern photographers).

Publications: Newsletter, quarterly.

Library: Open to members, students, researchers for reference. Holdings: Vols: 600; Per subs 7. Special Subjects: Victorian decorative arts, American art, graphic arts, general art history, philosophy of art.

PASCAGOULA

SINGING RIVER ART ASSOCIATION, INC, L & N Railroad Depot Gallery, PO Box 262, 39567. *Pres* Captain W A Dobbs; *VPres* Mrs Wallace Calhoun; *Secy* Kathy Linton.

Open Mon - Sat 11 AM - 3 PM. No admis. Estab 1964 to promote and encourage interest in art and exhibition of art works; gallery exhibits members works in old railroad station restored as Bicentennial project 1976. Average Annual Attendance: 2000 - 3000. Mem: 125; dues $5 and up, $10, and contributions; monthly meetings second Thurs.

Income: Approximately $1100 (financed by membership, and commissions on sales).

Collections: Paintings by local prominent artists, some purchase prize winners, some by memorial gifts; some donations by artists.

Exhibitions: Exhibitions on a six-week rotating basis.

Publications: Members newsletter, monthly.

Activities: Classes for adults; lect open to the public; gallery talks; educational workshops; competitions; schol; lending collection contains cassettes, film strips, lantern slides 200, original art works, original prints, paintings, phonorecords, slides; sales shop selling original art, prints, reproductions.

Library: Open to members only for reference. Holdings: Vols 50.

RAYMOND

HINDS JUNIOR COLLEGE, Marie Hull Gallery, 39154. Tel: 601-857-5261, exten 274. *Dir* Bob A Dunaway.
Open weekdays 9 AM - 3 PM. No admis. Estab 1971 as a community service and cultural agent for the visual arts; main gallery measures 60 x 60 ft; an adjacent gallery 8 x 45 ft; reception area 15 x 25 ft. Average Annual Attendance 2500.
Income: Approximately $700 (financed by Art Department budget).
Collections: †Permanent collection of state artist, with 75 pieces in prints, paintings, sculpture.
Exhibitions: The gallery sponsors six exhibits during college session, September to May.
Activities: Lect open to the public; gallery talks; tours; competitions; individual paintings and original objects of art lent to faculty and staff offices on three campuses; lending collection contains original art works.

TOUGALOO

TOUGALOO COLLEGE
—**Art Collection,** 39174. Tel: 601-956-4941, exten 327. *Cur* Ronald Schnell; *Photographer* Bruce O'Hara; *Pres* Dr George A Owens; *Academic Dean* Dr Nathaniel Pollard.
Open Wed 2 - 5 PM; Sun 1 - 4 PM, and by appointment. No admis. Estab 1963 to service the community and the metropolitan Jackson area; located in Student Union Building and Library. Average Annual Attendance: 1000.
Income: Financed by endowment and department budget.
Collections: New York School (abstract, expressionism, surrealism, minimal art); †Afro-American; African; International Print Collection with emphasis on European art.
Exhibitions: AMISTAD II (originated at Fisk University, Nashville), local artists, our Afro-American Collection, African Collection, Faculty and Student Shows.
Publications: Catalog, 1968 and 1978.
Activities: Dramatic programs; lect open to the public, 1 - 2 vis lectr per yr; concerts; gallery talks; tours by appointment; extension dept; individual paintings and original objects of art lent to libraries, universities, museums; lending collection contains lantern slides 8000, original art works 500, original prints 300, paintings 100, sculpture 100, industrial designs and typography; traveling exhibitions organized and circulated.
—**Library.** *Librn* Juanetta Roach.
Open to students & faculty.
Holdings: Vols 80,000; Per subs 426.
Special Collections: Tracy Sugerman (wash drawings, civil rights studies 1964).

TUPELO

LEE COUNTY LIBRARY, 219 Madison, 38801. Tel: 601-844-2377. *Chmn Bd Trustees* Mrs. Gilmer Garmon; *Dir* Betty R Kemp; *Asst Dir* Ann Wallace; *Technical Services Librn* Barbara Anglin; *Children's Librn* Marion Cagle.
Open Mon - Thurs 9 AM - 8 PM; Fri & Sat 9 AM - 5 PM; cl Sun. Estab 1941 to provide books and other sources of information to serve the intellectual, recreational, and cultural needs of its users. Maintains art gallery. The Mezzanine Gallery and Helen Foster Auditorium are used as exhibit space for works by University Art students, local professional artists and traveling exhibitions.
Income: $256,556 (financed by city, state, and county appropriations).
Holdings: Vols 151,354; Per subs 147; AV—Cassettes, motion pictures and phonorecords; Other—Framed reproductions.
Special Collections: The Tupelo Gum Tree Festival purchase prizes, these include paintings and pottery.

UNIVERSITY

UNIVERSITY OF MISSISSIPPI, University Gallery, Fine Arts Center, 38677. Tel: 601-232-7193. *Chmn Dept Art* James T Quinn; *Chmn Gallery Comt* Jere H Allen; *Secy* Barbara J Berry.
Open daily 8:30 AM - Noon & 1 - 4:30 PM. No admis. Estab 1954 as a teaching gallery. Average Annual Attendance: 2000.
Income: Financed by state appropriation.
Collections: Former faculty and student work; some work bought from traveling exhibitions.
Publications: Gallery schedule, yearly.
Activities: Lect open to public, 1 - 2 vis lectr per yr; gallery talks; individual paintings and original objects of art lent to departments within the University Complex; lending collection contains original art works, original prints, paintings and sculpture.

MISSOURI

CAPE GIRARDEAU

SOUTHEAST MISSOURI STATE UNIVERSITY, Kent Library, 63701. Tel: 314-651-2230. *Dir & Reference Librn* Duane Ed Henricks.
Open daily. exhibition areas on second and third levels; Atrium gallery on fourth level.
Holdings: Vols 290,000; Per subs 2100; AV—Cassettes, film strips, microfiche, microfilm, motion pictures, phonorecords and video tapes.
Special Subjects: The Jake K Wells Mural, 800 sq ft, covers the West wall of the library foyer, one of the largest murals in Missouri, it depicts the nature and development of the Southeast region of the state.
Special Collections: The 800 volumes in the Charles L Harrison Collection of rare books include some of the finest examples of the book arts. Virtually all literary genres as well as books and manuscripts ranging from the 13th to the 20th century are included.
Exhibitions: Missouri Arts Council touring shows; faculty and student art shows; Missouri Photographers; American Institute of Graphic Arts 50 Books of the Year; Folger Shakespeare Library Exhibit; Antonio Frasconi woodcuts, Molas, Honore Daumier prints; Smithsonian Institution exhibit: Tallgrass Prairie.

COLUMBIA

DANIEL BOONE REGIONAL LIBRARY, 100 W Broadway (Mailing Add: PO Box 1267, 65205). Tel: 314-443-3161. *Dir* Gene Martin.
Open Mon - Thurs 9 AM - 9 PM; Fri 9 AM - 6 PM; Sat 9 AM - 5 PM; Sun 1 - 5 PM. Estab 1959.
Holdings: AV—Cassettes, film strips, microfilm, motion pictures, phonorecords and slides; Other—Framed reproductions, original art works, pamphlets, photographs and sculpture.
Exhibitions: Touring exhibits through the Missouri State Council on the Arts, exhibits by local artists through the year.

STATE HISTORICAL SOCIETY OF MISSOURI, Hitt and Lowry Sts, 65201. Tel: 314-443-3165. *Dir* Dr Richard S Brownlee; *Cur* Sidney Larson.
Open Mon - Fri 8 AM - 4:30 PM. No admis. Estab 1898 to collect, preserve, make accessible and publish materials pertaining to the history of Missouri and Western America. Average Annual Attendance: 800. Mem: 14,000; dues $2; annual meeting held in the fall.
Income: Financed by state appropriation.
Collections: Works by George C Bingham, Thomas H Benton, Karl Bodmer, Frank B Muderscher, Frederick Sylvester, William Knox, Carl Gentry, Fred Geary, Fred Shane, Charles Schwarts and Roscoe Misselhorn; contemporary artists collection containing work of over fifty outstanding Missouri related artists; original cartoon collection of works by Daniel Fitzpatrick, S J Ray, Bill Mauldin, Don Hessee and Tom Engelhardt.
Publications: Missouri Historical Review, quarterly.
—**Library.** *Librn* Richard S Brownlee.
Open to the public.
Holdings: Vols 420,000; Per subs 200.
Special Subjects: Missouri and the midwest.
Special Collections: J Christian Bay Collection; Mahan Memorial Mark Twain Collection; Eugene Field Collection; Bishop William Fletcher McMurray Collection; Francis A Sampson Collection of rare books.

STEPHENS COLLEGE,* Lewis James and Nellie Stratton Davis Art Gallery, 65201. Tel: 314-442-2211, exten 302. *Dir & Head Art Dept* Gardiner McCauley.
Open Sept 10 - May 10, Mon - Fri 8 AM - 5 PM. No admis. Estab 1964 to provide exhibitions of art for the general interest of the local community and for the education of the student body in general. Average Annual Attendance: 7000.
Income: Operating budget $3000 (financed by endowment). Purchases: $250.
Collections: Modern paintings; †modern graphics; primitive sculpture.
Activities: Lect open to the public, 6 vis lectr per yr; gallery talks; exhibitions.

UNIVERSITY OF MISSOURI, COLUMBIA
—**Museum of Art and Archaeology,** 1 Pickard Hall, 65201. Tel: 314-882-3591. *Dir* Osmund Overby; *Asst Dir* Ruth E Witt; *Cur Renaissance & Modern Art* Richard Baumann; *Cur Ancient Art* Jane C Biers; *Assoc Cur South Asian Art* Sarla Nagar; *Assoc Cur American & Contemporary Art & Registrar* Harold Nelson; *Assoc Cur Exhib* Jeffrey Wilcox.
Open Tues - Sun 1 - 5 PM; Mon 4 - 10 PM. No admis. Estab 1957 to exhibit a study collection for students in Art History and Archaeology; a comprehensive collection for the enjoyment of the general area of Missouri. Nine separate galleries, each devoted to specific collections. Average Annual Attendance: 16,000. Mem: 675; dues family $15.

Income: $166,000 (financed by membership, and state appropriation). Purchases: $35,000.

Collections: †Ancient Art—Egypt, Near and Middle East, Greek and Roman; †Old Masters, painting & sculpture; †Early Christian—Byzantine and Coptic; †Modern paintings and sculpture; Primitive—Oceanic, African, Pre-Columbian; Oriental—Chinese and Japanese; South Asian—Indian, Thai, Tibetan, Nepalese; †Prints and drawings.

Exhibitions: Changing exhibitions from permanent collections, mainly in the archaeological material of the Near East and in Prints and Drawings.

Publications: Muse, annually.

Activities: Docent training; lect open to public, 6 vis lectr per yr; tours; original objects of art lent to institutions; museum shop selling books, reproductions, prints, and slides.

—Museum of Art & Archaeology Library.
Open to the public.

Holdings: Vols 6000; Per subs 2; Other—Sales catalogs of three major auction houses; bulletins, exhibition catalogs and annual reports of other institutions; coin catalogs and journals in Near Eastern archaeology.

—Museum of Anthropology, 104 Swallow Hall, 65201. Tel: 314-882-3764. *Cur & Dir* Lawrence H Feldman; *Assoc Cur* Elsebet Rowlett; *Chmn Museum Committee* Richard Diehl.

Open Mon - Fri 9 AM - 4:30 PM. No admis. Estab 1900 to house ethnographic and archeological collections of the university. Average Annual Attendance: 10,000.

Income: $1000 (financed by state appropriation). Purchases: $500.

Collections: Collection of Guatemalan native costumes; collection of Eskimo artifacts from the late 1800s; collection of Southwestern pottery from the early 1900s; collection of African weapons and musical instruments.

Activities: Lectr open to the public; original objects of art lent to other institutions; lending collection contains books 200, nature artifacts and original art works 600; museum shop selling books, magazines, original art, African and Latin American native art.

—Fine Arts Gallery, Corner of Hitt and University, 65201. Tel: 314-882-3555. *Assoc Prof, Chmn Exhib Comt* Jerry O Berneche; *Chmn Art Dept* Don Bartlett.

Open Mon - Fri 9 AM - 3 PM; Sun 2:30 - 4:30 PM; cl Sat. No admis. Estab 1960 to augment the art student's education and provide the community with important exhibitions of art. Gallery is set between the drama department and the art department. The well-lit gallery is 40 x 80 ft and has about 200 ft of wall space. Average Annual Attendance: 17,000.

Income: Financed by state appropriation.

Exhibitions: Eight to ten exhibitions are held each year ranging from shows rented from the AFA and other major museums to shows of local students and faculty work.

Activities: Lect open to public; gallery talks; competitions with awards and merits given.

—Stanley Hall Gallery, Dept of Housing & Interior Design, 65211. Tel: 314-882-7224. *Dir* Gary L Hennigh; *Assoc* Dr C Bud Kaufamm.

Open Mon - Fri 8 AM - Noon & 1 - 5 PM. No admis. Estab 1960 to provide aesthetic and learning experiences for students and the public in the field of interior design and related arts.

Income: Financed by city appropriation.

Collections: Historic textiles.

Exhibitions: Crafts, painting, computer graphics, textile design, interior design, furniture design, weaving.

Activities: Classes for adults; 4 vis lectr per yr; gallery talks; exten dept serving state of Missouri.

INDEPENDENCE

JACKSON COUNTY HISTORICAL SOCIETY, 217 N Main St, 64050. Tel: 816-252-1892. *Pres* Phil K Weeks; *Secy* Susannah Gentry; *Coordr* Mrs Kenneth L Graham.

Mem: 2500; dues $5 - $100.

Income: Financed by membership.

Collections: Furnishing and interior decor at 1859 Jail Museum and John Wornall House; original portraits and other materials to 1830s; displays featuring pioneer life in the period of the westward expansion; selected memorabilia of Harry S Truman, 33rd President of the United States.

Exhibitions: Mid-19th century Christmas displays and fine early handmade quilts at both museums; 19th century toys and 200 Years of Presidental Election Campaign Materials on loan at 1859 Jail Museum.

Publications: Jackson County Historical Society Journal.

Activities: Classes for adults and children; lect open to the public, 3 vis lectr per yr.

Library: Limited primarily archival material for reference only.

—Research Library and Archives, Independence Square Courthouse, 64050. *Dir* Nancy Ehrlich.

Open Mon - Thurs 11 AM - 3 PM. Estab 1960.

Special Collections: Photograph collection for reference.

—1859 Jail Museum and Marshal's House, 217 N Main St, 64050. *Dir* Mrs Kenneth L Graham.

Open June, July & Aug, Mon - Sat 9 AM - 5 PM; Sun 1 - 5 PM; Sept - May, Tues - Sat 10 AM - 4 PM; Sun 1 - 5 PM. Admin 50¢, children under 12 free. Estab 1959. Average Annual Attendance: 25,000.

Activities: Elementary school tours emphasizing local and regional history; sales desk.

—John Wornall House, 61st Terrace & Wornall Rd, Kansas City, Mo, 64113. *Chmn* Ann Stapleton; *Dir* Lynne Robert Madeo.

Open Tues - Sat 10 AM - 4:30 PM; Sun 1 - 4:30. Admis adults $1, children 50¢. Estab 1972 to familiarize people with how a farm family lived during the 1850s in early Kansas City. Average Annual Attendance: 11,582. Mem: 40; dues $15 - $100; annual meeting Fall.

Income: $16,000 (financed by membership, tours and rentals).

Publications: 1858 Society Newsletter, semi-annually.

Activities: Classes for children; docent training; lectures; traveling exhibitions organized and circulated; museum shop selling books, slides, postcards, pewter, herbs, and other gift items.

HARRY S TRUMAN LIBRARY AND MUSEUM, 64050. Tel: 816-252-1400. *Dir* Benedict K Zobrist; *Asst Dir* George H Curtis.

Open Summer 9 AM - 7 PM; winter 9 AM - 5 PM. Estab 1957 to preserve and make available for study and exhibition the papers, objects and other materials relating to President Harry S Truman and his contemporaries. Gravesite of President Truman in the courtyard. Administered by the National Archives and Records Service of the Federal Government. Circ: 314,000.

Income: Financed by federal appropriation and federal trust fund.

Holdings: Vols 44,000; Per subs 117; AV—Audio tapes, cassettes, microfilm, motion pictures, phonorecords, slides; Other—Clipping files, framed reproductions, manuscripts, memorabilia, original art works, original documents, pamphlets, photographs, prints, sculpture.

Collections: Portraits of President Truman; Art Collection of President Truman; original cartoons; mural by Thomas Hart Benton, historical collections relating to the history of the US Presidency.

Exhibitions: 1948 Whistlestop Campaign; The New Truman Library; Thomas Hart Benton and His Mural: Independence and the Opening of the West; The National Archives and Presidential Libraries.

Publications: Historical materials in the Truman Library.

JEFFERSON CITY

MISSOURI STATE MUSEUM,* State Capitol, 65101. Tel: 314-751-2854. *Dir:* Gerald R Massie.

Open daily 8 AM - 5 PM; cl holidays. No admis. Estab 1920.

Income: Financed by state appropriation, affiliated with the Missouri State Division of Commerce & Industrial Development.

Collections: (Art) Murals by N C Wyeth, T H Benton, Berninghause; Indian artifacts; historical material.

Publications: Pamphlets.

Activities: Temporary exhibitions.

JOPLIN

SPIVA ART CENTER, INC, Newman & Duquesne Rds, Missouri Southern Fine Arts Bldg, 64801. Tel: 417-623-0183. *Pres* Mrs William Rainey; *VPres* Mrs John Duffy; *Secy* Mrs John Cragin; *Treas* Mrs Elroy Thomas; *Exec Secy* Priscilla Eberle; *Dir* Darral A Dishman.

Open Tues - Fri 10 AM - 4 PM; Sat 9 AM - Noon; Sun 2 - 5 PM; cl Mon & National holidays. No admis. Estab June 1959, inc 1969, as a nonprofit educational, social and cultural community center with the purpose of collecting, preserving and exhibiting works of art for encouragement and advancement of art education. Average Annual Attendance: 15,000. Mem: 650; dues $5 - $1000; annual meeting Mar.

Collections: 19th century paintings; New Guinea sculpture; Mary Gregory glass; American Indian prints; early American glass.

Exhibitions: Changing monthly exhibitions including one-man and group; May competitive exhibition.

Publications: Calendar; newsletter.

Activities: Classes in various phases of the visual arts for adults and children; film classic series; 2-week summer painting workshops; lectures; gallery tours; competitions; schol.

Library: Art books for reference.

KANSAS CITY

ART RESEARCH CENTER, 922 E 48th St, 64110. Tel: 816-531-2067. *Coordinator* Michael Stephens; *Educ Dir* Virginia Hillix; *Editor* Patricia Schubert; *Publ Information* Catherine Emily; *Cur* Dorothy Moss; *Asst Cur* Jan Tvedten-Doran; *Tech Dir* Jay Heuser.

Open Sun - Thurs 3 - 7 PM. No admis. Estab 1967 as an independent collective of artists, stressing multi-disciplinary activity and open experiment in the Constructive Arts. Maintains an art gallery at 922 E 48th St and three temporary gallery spaces at 4725 Troost. No commissions on sales. Average Annual Attendance 1000. Mem: 30; monthly meetings.
Income: $35,000 (financed by grants).
Exhibitions: Process exhibitions by: Virginia Hillix; Hartmouth Bohm; Elizabeth Willmott; Clark Rickert; Steve Baer; Frank Young; Jaya James Kern; Jay Heuser; Willi Otremba; Chas DiJulio; Jon Thogmartin; Tenth Anniversary Exhibition and Symposium; International exhibition: photographs, films, prints, concerts, symposia, visual poetry (80 artists from 15 countries). Process exhibitions are designed to show the working processes of a systematic and programmatic artist.
Publications: ARC Magazine, annually; BioMechanic International Journal, semiannually.
Activities: Classes for adults; lect open to public, 6 vis lectr per yr; concerts; gallery talks; sales shop selling books, magazines, and exhibition catalogs.
Library: Open to members and students. Holdings: Vols 500; Per subs 6. Special Subjets: art/science in art; photography; art and politics; structuralist activity. Special Collections: Constructivist catalogs, films (abstract) by contemporary filmakers; tapes of concert performances at ARC; slides of ARC outdoor performances, theatre performances, and work show at ARC exhibitions.

AVILA COLLEGE, Art Gallery, Whitfield Continuing Education Center, 11901 Wornall Rd, 64145. Tel: 816-942-8400. *Pres* Sister Olive Louise Dallavis; *Academic Dean* G Richard Scott; *Chmn Fine Arts* William Louis; *Art Coordinator* Myron Brody.
Open 10 AM - 4 PM. No admis. Estab 1978 to present the visual arts in a contemporary sense to the student community as well as the Greater Kansas City community. Gallery space 60 x 35 ft with carpeted floor and walls; an Artist-in-Residence studio; track lighting. Average Annual Attendance: 2000.
Income: Financed through school budget.
Exhibitions: Stephen Sidelinger (posters); Bruce Robinson (paintings); Martha Crow, Lynn Manos Huber, Judy Kennett, David Melby, Barbara Mueller, Hal Parker (drawings); Student Exhibition; Susan Cochran, Laura Foster, Lynn Smiser, Eileen Troxell (ceramics and fiber); Richard Gillespie (sculpture and drawings); Michael Burks (photographs).
Activities: Classes for adults; dramatic programs; lect open to public, 10 vis lectr per yr; concerts; gallery talks.

HALLMARK CARDS, INC, Creative Library, 25th & McGee, 64141. Tel: 816-274-5111. *Mgr Library Services* Sara E Wallace.
Open to Hallmark artists only. Estab to provide pictorial research. Financed by state appropriation.
Holdings: Vols 9000; Per subs 100; AV—Slides; Other—Clipping files.

KANSAS CITY ART INSTITUTE*, Charlotte Crosby Kemper Gallery, 4415 Warwick, 64111. Tel: 816-561-4852. *Chmn Bd of Governors* George E Powell; *VChmn Board & Chmn Membership Committee* Mrs Robert G Evans.
Open Mon - Fri 8:30 AM - 5 PM; Sat 8:30 AM - Noon. Estab 1963 to provide exhibitions of interest to the college and regional community.
Exhibitions: Changing exhibitions.
—Library, Box 10360, 64111. Tel: 816-561-4852, exten 24. *Dir* Verna B Riddle.
Open Mon - Thurs 8:30 AM - 10 PM; Fri 8:30 AM - 5 PM; Sun 1 - 6 PM.
Estab 1924 as a library for a private art college. Circ: 57,000.
Holdings: Vols 26,270; Per subs 1000; AV—Audio tapes, cassettes, film strips, lantern slides, motion pictures, phonorecords, slides, video tapes; Other—Clipping files, exhibition catalogs, pamphlets.
Special Subjects: Art and art history.
Publications: School Bulletin.
Activities: Lect open to the public, 4 - 6 vis lectr per yr.

KANSAS CITY PUBLIC LIBRARY,* Art & Music Dept, 311 E 12th St, 64106. Tel: 816-221-2685. *Librn* Harold R Jenkins; *Art & Music Dept Head* Robert M Ross.
Open Mon - Wed 8:30 AM - 9 PM; Thurs - Sat 8:30 AM - 5 PM; cl Sun. Estab 1873.
Income: $2,998,856. Purchases: (Art) $13,800.
Holdings: (Art) Vols 30,000; AV—16mm films 1300; Other—Color reproductions 12,500.

MUNICIPAL ART COMMISSION, City Hall, 415E 11th St, 64106. Tel: 816-274-1866. *Chmn* Mayor Charles B Wheeler Jr; *VChmn* Lynn Bauer; *Exec Dir* Patti Browne; *Secy* K E Coombs.
Created by Charter in 1925. Approves all works of art that are to become property of the city whether by purchase or gift. Approves design of buildings, bridges, and other structures to be erected upon city property.

Approves issuance of permits for construction of marquees projecting over streets or boulevards. City Council may dispense with approval by the Art Commission.

WILLIAM ROCKHILL NELSON GALLERY OF ART
—Atkins Museum of Fine Art, 4525 Oak St, 64111. Tel: 816-561-4000.
Dir Ralph T Coe; *Senior Cur* Ross E Taggart; *Cur Oriental Art* Marc F Wilson; *Assoc Cur Oriental Art* Jeanne Harris; *Registrar & Cur Prints* George L McKenna; *Superintendent of Bldg* Sherwood Songer; *Cur 20th Century Art* Ellen R Goheen; *Dir Emeritus* Laurence Sickman; *Exec Dir Society of Friends* Dr Nicholas Pickard; *Dir Educ* Larry Eikelberry; *Designer & Cur Installations* Michael Hagler.
Open Tues - Sat 10 AM - 5 PM; Sun 2 - 6 PM. Admis adults 50¢, children under 12 25¢; free Sun. Estab 1933 to enrich and enliven; present the arts of the ancient and modern world to the midwest and the country; develop activities relating to art education, the interpretation of the collections and their general enjoyment. Average Annual Attendance: 300,000. Mem: 7000; dues $15 - $25.
Income: Financed by endowment, membership and gifts.
Collections: †The finest Oriental furniture collection outside of the Orient; †impressionist painting; †contemporary works of art: †Burnap Collection of English pottery, Oriental ceramics, paintings, sculpture, bronze, Egyptian tomb sculpture, American painting, period rooms and furniture; sculpture garden; Cloisters.
Exhibitions: Sacred Circles: 2000 Years of North American Indian Art; various loan shows and displays of permanent exhibitions; Humann Sensuous Immortals.
Activities: Classes for adults and children; docent training; films; lectr open to the public; concerts; gallery talks; tours; competitions. Individual paintings and original objects of art lent to other museums, city institutions requesting display; traveling exhibitions organized and circulated; museum and sales shops selling books, magazines, reproductions, prints, slides; sales and rental gallery sells/rents original art; maintains junior museum.
—Kenneth and Helen Spencer Art Reference Library. Tel: 816-561-4000.
Librn Katherine Haskins; *Asst to the librn* Sarah E Taxman.
Open Tues - Fri by appointment only; for reference only.
Holdings: Vols 25,000; Per subs 75; AV—Slides; Other—Clipping files, exhibition catalogs, auction catalogs, international auction records.
Special Subjects: Oriental art.
Special Collections: Oriental Study houses collection of materials on Oriental art; Bender Library is comprised of book on prints and drawings.
—Friends of Art. Tel: 817-561-4000, exten 33. *Pres* Daniel M Dibble, *VPres* Fred Beihl; *Secy* Mrs Don McGrath; *Exec Secy* Glenna Youngstrom.
Open Tues - Fri 9 AM - 5 PM. Estab 1934 as a non-profit organization supporting the Nelson Gallery and serving as a membership department. Mem: 6890; dues $20 and above; annual meeting Nov.
Income: Financed by membership and contributions.
Publications: Membership communication.
—Junior Gallery and Creative Arts Center, 4525 Oak St, 64111. Tel: 816-561-4000. *Dir* vacant.
Open Tues - Sat 10 AM - 5 PM; Sun 2 - 6 PM. Estab 1960 to create a greater awareness of the world around us through art. Average Annual Attendance: 144,249.
Income: $58,254.61.
Activities: Creative art classes; adult sculpture, drawing, painting, Oriental brushwork and design classes; tours; workshops; docent training.
Library: Open for children and guides. Holdings: Vols 2710; Other—Reproductions.

MARYVILLE

NORTHWEST MISSOURI STATE UNIVERSITY, DeLuce Gallery, 64468. Tel: 816-582-7141, exten 273 & 178. *Cur & Chmn Dept Art* Robert Sunkel.
Open Mon - Fri 1 - 4 PM. No admis. Estab 1965 to provide exhibitions of contemporary works in all media as a part of the learning experiences in the visual arts; 150 running feet exhibition space, high security, humidity controlled air-conditioning, flexible lighting. Average Annual Attendance: 6000.
Income: Financed by city appropriation.
Collections: Percival DeLuce Memorial Collection consisting of American paintings, drawings, prints and decorative arts; some European furniture and prints.
Exhibitions: Regional artists; Photography Exhibit; Print Exhibition; Craft Multiples.
Activities: Lect open to public, 6 vis lectr per yr; gallery talks; lending collection contains original art works, original prints, paintings and drawings.

MEXICO

MEXICO-AUDRAIN COUNTY LIBRARY,* 305 W Jackson, 65265. Tel: 314-518-4939. *Pres* Mrs Ernest Gantt; *Secy* Rebecca Gibbs; *Dir* Eldon R Burgess; *Acquisitions Librn* Violet Lierheimer; *Reference Librn* Christal Brunner; *Children's Librn* Vicky Smith; *Bookmobile Librn* Nancy Archer.
Open winter hours, Mon - Thurs 9 AM - 9 PM; Fri & Sat 9 AM - 5:30 PM; Sun 1 - 4 PM. No admis. Estab 1912 to provide library services to the residents of Audrain County, Missouri; Exhibit room with different exhibits each month; children's department has a continuously changing exhibit.
Income: $180,970 (financed by city and county appropriations).
Purchases: $169,293.
Holdings: Vols 92,519; Per subs 86; AV—Film strips 1869, Koda-chromes 1200, motion pictures 48; phonorecords 2946, Other—Art print color reproductions 100, newspaper 10.
Exhibitions: Local Federated Women's Club sponsored a different exhibit each month during the fall, winter and spring, these included local artists, both adult and young people and recognized artists of the area; The Missouri Council of the Arts also provides traveling exhibits that we display.
Activities: Classes for children; story hour 45 minutes each Tues; individual paintings and original objects of art lent.

POINT LOOKOUT

SCHOOL OF THE OZARKS, Ralph Foster Museum, 65726. Tel: 417-334-6411, exten 407. *Chmn* C Wallace Walter; *Secy* Dr John L Moad; *VChmn* Ralph Foster; *Treas* Dr Howell Keeter; *Museum Dir* Marvin E Tong, Jr; *Admin Asst* Jennings W Bunn, Jr; *Cur of Monies* John P Butler; *Museum Construction Supv* Herbert L Thomason; *Secy to Dir* Mary Carson.
Open Mon - Sat 8 AM - 5 PM; Sun 1 - 5 PM. No admis. Estab 1931 to portray the broad sweep of human history, arts and crafts of the Ozarks region of Missouri, Arkansas and Oklahoma; gallery contains 77,000 sq ft of exhibit space; 8,000 sq ft devoted to Ozarks Hall of Fame, which includes art gallery. Average Annual Attendance: 237,000. Mem: 102; dues $10; annual meeting May.
Income: $120,000 (financed by endowment, membership, and contributions). *Purchases:* $10,000.
Collections: (Art) †Ozarks art and crafts; †Fine Art; monies of the world; natural history; †archaeology of North America.
Exhibitions: (1976-77) Selected Worlds of C E Bloom; Forsyth Art Guild annual exhibit of museum permanent collection; Western Outlaws and Lawmen.
Publications: Ralph Foster Museum Newsletter, periodically.
Activities: Docent training; lect open to public, 2 vis lectr per yr; gallery talks; exten dept serving college campus; individual paintings lent to depts on campus; lending collection contains original art works and paintings; museum shop and sales shop selling books, magazines, original art, reproductions, prints and craft items.
—Lois Brownell Research Library. *Librn* Ranae Williams.
Open to staff and qualified scholars for reference.
Holdings: Vols 5780; Per subs 25; Other—Vertical file.
Special Subjects: Fine Art; Oriental Art; American and European antiques; archaeology; anthropology, Natural History; cameos.

SAINT CHARLES

LINDENWOOD COLLEGES,* Harry D Hendren Gallery, Department of Art, 63301. Tel: 314-723-7152, exten 241 or 946-6912, exten 241. *Chmn* W Dean Eckert; *Secy* Nancy Follis.
Open Mon - Fri 9 AM - 10 PM; Sat 9 AM - 4 PM; Sun Noon - 4 PM. No admis. Estab 1969 as a college exhibition gallery; gallery is approximately 3600 sq ft with skylight and one wall of side light. Average Annual Attendance: 4000.
Income: Financed by endowment.
Collections: Contemporary American and Euroean prints in various media including works by Paul Jenkins, William Hayter, Picasso, Villon and others.
Activities: Classes for adults; lect open to the public, 5-6 vis lectr per yr; gallery talks; tours; original objects of art lent; lending collection contains photographs; schol; traveling exhibitions organized and circulated through the Missouri State Council on the Arts; book shop.
Library maintained.

SAINT JOSEPH

ALBRECHT ART MUSEUM, 2818 Frederick Blvd, 64506. Tel: 816-233-7003. *Dir* Jim Ray; *Secy-Registrar* Margo Prentiss.

Open Tues - Fri 10 AM - 4 PM; Sat & Sun 1 - 5 PM; cl Mon. Admis children 10¢, adults 50¢, free to members. Estab 1914 to increase public knowledge and appreciation of the arts. Average Annual Attendance: 12,000. Mem: 600; dues $15 up; annual meeting second Wed in April.
Income: $55,000 (financed by membership).
Collections: St Joseph Photographic Collection of architecture and stained glass windows; †Henry D Bradley Memorial Collection of prints; Forrest C Campbell Collection of prints; †Drawing America Collection; †Hax Memorial Collection; Eugene S Juda Jr; Memorial Collection of American Engravings; William Toben Memorial Collection.
Exhibitions: Stained Glass Windows of St Joseph; Drawing Missouri 1976; Thomas Hart Benton's Illustrations from Mark Twain.
Publications: Calendar of events, monthly.
Activities: Classes for adults and children, lect open to public; competitions.
Library. Open to museum members. Holdings: Vols 500; Per Subs 4.

ST JOSEPH MUSEUM, 11th and Charles, 64501. Tel: 816-232-8471. *Dir* Richard A Nolf; *Asst Dir & Cur Pony Express Stables* Don L Reynolds; *Exec Secy* June M Swift; *Registrar* Bonnie K Harlow; *Conservator and Cur Coll* Marilyn S Taylor.
Open May to mid-Sept, Mon - Sat 9 AM - 5 PM; Sun & holidays 2 - 5 PM; mid-Sept to May, Tues - Sat 1 - 5 PM; cl Mon, Christmas and New Year's Days. No admis. Estab 1926 to increase and diffuse knowledge and appreciation of history, art and the sciences and to aid the educational work that is being done by the schools of St Joseph and other educational organizations. Mini-gallery, usually for small, low security traveling exhibits. Average Annual Attendance: 100,000. Mem: 209; dues $5 and up; annual meeting Jan.
Income: $100,000 (financed by membership, and city appropriation).
Publications: The Happenings (newsletter), bimonthly.
Activities: Classes for children; craft program; lect open to public; museum shop selling books, reproductions, prints, slides, gift items.
—Library. *Librn* Lucile Rush.
Open during museum hours for research purposes only.
Holdings: Vols 5000; Per subs 40.

SAINT LOUIS

ACADEMY OF PROFESSIONAL ARTISTS, 4 Daniel Rd, 63124. *Exec Dir* Ruth Keller Schweiss.
Estab 1968 to provide for the aesthetic needs of a human community irrespective of any and all persuasions by the exhibition of visual works of fine art; art work displayed in variety of locations. Average Annual Attendance: 100,000 - 500,000. Mem: 82; dues $35; annual meeting Jan.
Income: Financed by membership and Arts & Education Council of St Louis.
Exhibitions: Fine art by the membership presented in public area, such as malls, banks, universities, government centers, etc.
Activities: Lect open to members; competitions.

ART AND EDUCATION COUNCIL OF GREATER SAINT LOUIS, 607 N Grand, 63103. Tel: 314-531-6450. *Chmn* Clarence C Barksdale; *Pres* Stanley M Richman; *VPres* Homer E Sayad; *Secy* Robert S Edwards; *Exec Dir* Richard F Tombaugh.
Estab 1963 to coordinate, promote and assist in the development of cultural and educational activities in the Greater St. Louis area; to offer generally, planning, coordinating, promotional and fund-raising service to eligible organizations and groups, thereby creating a valuable community-wide association. Mem: 118 agencies.
Publications: Calendar of Cultural Events, monthly.

CONCORDIA HISTORICAL INSTITUTE,* 801 DeMun Ave, 63105. Tel: 314-721-5934. *Dir* Dr August R Suelflow.
Open Mon - Fri 8 AM - 5 PM; Sat & Sun 2 - 5 PM; cl National holidays. No admis. Estab 1847, affiliated with the Missouri Synod of the Lutheran Church. Mem: Dues active $7, sustaining $10, patron $25, organization $50, corporation $200, Life $300.
Collections: Works by Lutheran artists; crafts; Reformation and Lutheran coins and medals; church archives and historical material.
Publications: Concordia Historical Institute, quarterly; Newsletter, triannually; booklets.
Activities: Lectures; guided tours; temporary and traveling exhibitions; sales shop selling new and used books.
Library: Ref & Res Asst Rev Marvin A Huggins. Open to the public. Holdings: 55,000 vols; per sub; manuscripts.

MISSOURI HISTORICAL SOCIETY, Jefferson Memorial Building, 63112. Tel: 314-361-1424. *Pres* J Terrell Vaughan; *Archivist* Mrs Ernst A Stadler; *Librn* Kathleen S Schoefie; *Cur* Andrew Van Der Tuin; *Cur Pictures* Gail Guidry; *Cur Educ* Linda Claire Kulla.

Open daily 9:30 AM - 4:45 PM (library and archives cl Sun & Mon). No admis. Estab 1866 to collect and preserve objects and information relating to the history of Missouri and the Louisana Purchase Territory. Average Annual Attendance: 400,000. Mem: 3000; dues from $25; annual meeting Sept.
Income: Financed by endowment, membership and special events.
Collections: (art) †manuscripts; †paintings; †prints; †photographs; †early Midwestern arts and crafts; †other museum objects.
Exhibitions: Special show of Lindbergh memorabilia; show of Curtis Indian photographs.
Publications: Bulletin, quarterly; newsletter, quarterly.
Activities: Classes for children; lect open to public, 3 - 5 vis lectr per yr; gallery talks; tours; sales shop selling books, prints, slides, souvenirs, china, antique items, miniatures and doll houses.
—Library. *Librn* Kathleen S Schoene.
Open to members for reference, non-members must pay a $3.00 fee daily.
Holdings: Vols 120,000; Per subs 250; Other—Sheet music, theatre programs, newspapers.
Special Subjects: The fur trade, Lewis and Clark expedition, Charles Lindbergh, the 1904 Louisiana Purchase Exposition, American Indians.
Special Collections: Missouri sheet music; St Louis theatre programs.

ST LOUIS ART MUSEUM, Forest Park, 63110. Tel: 314-721-0067. *Dir* James N Wood; *Controller* Alan Brimble.
Open Tues 2:30 - 9:30 PM; Wed - Sun 10 AM - 5 PM; cl Mon. No admis. Estab 1904, erected as Palace of Art for 1904 World's Fair; designed by Cass Gilbert in Beaux Art architecture; the main sculpture hall is fashioned after Roman Baths of Carcalla. Average Annual Attendance: 500,000. Mem: 6500; dues student $12.50, individual $20, participating $25, contributing $50, sustaining $100, associate $500, fellow $1000.
Income: $4,018,075 (financed by endowment, membership, county, grants, sales and contributions).
Collections: Holdings range from Egyptian to contemporary art. A new department of prints, drawings and photographs displays works from the Museum's 6000 holdings; outstanding art collection of works from Oceania, Africa, Pre-Columbian and American Indian objects; paintings emphasize Northern European works from the Renaissance to Rembrandt as well as colonial to contemporary American, French Impressionist and Post Impressionist and German Expressionist works; 20th century European sculpture, American and European decorative art; Chinese bronzes and porcelains.
Exhibitions: (1975-77) Tsutsumu: The Art of the Japanese Package; American Art: The Federal Period; Primitive Art Masterworks; Era of Explorations: The Rise of Landscape Photography in the American West, 1860-1885; European Paintings in the Seventies: New Work by Sixteen Artists; Selection 76; Television: The Malleable Medium; 100 Master Photographs; Missouri Photographers, 1976; American Art: The Westward Movement; German Expressionist Paintings and Watercolors; Video Show I; Masterpieces of American Painting from the Brooklyn Museum; Visions of Courtly India.
Publications: The St Louis Art Museum Bulletin, quarterly.
Activities: Classes for adults and children; docent training; lect; concerts; gallery talks; tours; individual paintings and original objects of art lent to other museums; traveling exhibitions organized and circulated.
—Richardson Memorial Library. Tel: 314-721-0067, exten 36 and 37. *Librn* Ann B Abid; *Cataloger* Kathryn E Lemon.
Open Tues 2:30 - 5 PM Jun - Aug; 2:30 - 9 PM Sept - May; Wed - Fri 10 AM - 5 PM. Estab 1915 to provide reference and bibliographical service to the museum staff and the adult public; to bibliographically support the collections owned by the museum.
Income: Financed by endowment and city appropriation.
Holdings: Vols 23,500; Per subs 300; AV—Lantern slides, microfiche, slides, mounted photographs and color reproductions; Other—Clipping files, exhibitions catalogs, pamphlets, photographs, reproductions.

ST LOUIS ARTISTS' GUILD, 227 E Lockwood, 63119. *Pres* James W Harmon; *VPres* Mrs Catherine Milovich; *Secy* Marilynne Bradley; *Exec Mgr* Paul A McHugh.
Open daily noon - 4 PM; Sun 1 - 5 PM; cl Tues. No admis. Estab for the purpose of exhibiting art. Average Annual Attendance: 5000. Mem: 500; qualifications for membership: Sponsored by two members; dues $35.
Income: Financed by membership.
Activities: Lect open to the public; competitions with awards.

ST LOUIS PUBLIC LIBRARY, Art Dept, 1301 Olive St, 63105. Tel: 314-241-2288. *Librn* vacant; *Chief, Art Dept* Martha Hilligoss.
Open Mon 9 AM - 9 PM; Tues - Sat 9 AM - 5 PM. Estab Art Dept in 1912.
Income: $13,000.
Holdings: Vols 44,000, AV—Cassettes, microfiche, microfilm, motion pictures, phonorecords, slides, video tapes; Other—Clipping files, exhibition catalogs, framed reproductions, pamphlets, prints, reproductions, sculpture.
Special Collections: Steedman Architectural Library.

WASHINGTON UNIVERSITY, Gallery of Art, Steinberg Hall, (Mailing Add: Box 1189, 63130). *Dir* Gerald D Bolas; *Asst Cur* Arline Leven; *Admin Secy* Lucy Ude.
Open Mon - Fri 9 AM - 5 PM; Sat & Sun 1 - 5 PM. No admis. Estab 1879, present building opened 1960, for the students of Washington University and the community at large. A modern building containing two floors of gallery space for exhibit of the permanent collection and special exhibitions. Also houses a library of art, archaeology, architecture, and design.
Collections: Emphasis on modern artists, including Miro, Ernst, Picasso, Leger, Moore; many Old Masters, 19th Century.
Exhibitions: Charles Eames; Iranian Locks; Leonard Baskin: Images of Man; Joe Goode: Recent Work; Larry Bell: The Iceberg and its Shadow; Hugh Ferriss Drawings: An Architect's Vision.
Activities: Lect open to public, 12 vis lectr per yr; traveling exhibitions organized and circulated.
—Art & Architecture Library. Tel: 314-889-5268. *Librn* Imre Meszaros; *Circulation Supr* Julie Arnott; *Library Records* Betty Daniel; *Reserve Supr* Madeleine Illies; *Serials and Rare Books* Paula Ferrario.
Open Mon - Thurs 8:30 AM - 11 PM; Fri 8:30 AM - 5 PM; Sat 11 AM - 6 PM; Sun 11 AM - 10 PM; cl nights and weekends during vacations and intersessions. Estab 1879 to support the academic programs of the three departments of the University: the School of Fine Arts, the School of Architecture, and the Department of Art & Archaeology. Circ: 67,602.
Income: $100,000 (financed through the University). Purchases: $50,000.
Holdings: Vols 60,000; Per subs 473; AV—Microfiche, microfilm; Other—Exhibition catalogs, pamphlets, and reproductions.
Special Subjects: Art, architecture, archaeology, building technology, landscape gardening, cities and towns: planning, numismatics, costume design.
Special Collections: Sorger Collection: 243 volumes of 19th century historic costume books with lithographs and hand-coloured fashion or costume plates, and 4 drawers of plates; Bryce Collection: 576 volumes of early books on Architectural history; Eames and Young Collection: 273 volumes of mostly nineteenth and a few pre-nineteenth entury imprints on architectural history; Baker Collection: 50 examples of fine binding; Rare Book Room; East Asian Art Collection; Exhibitions: Fashion Design of the 19th century; Eames & Young Architectural Library: Printed Books and Photo-Albums.
Activities: Library tours.

WEBSTER COLLEGE,* Loretto-Hilton Center Gallery, 130 Edgar Rd, 63119. Tel: 314-968-0500. *Dir* Jack Canepa.
Open Mon - Sat 10 AM - 4 PM; Sun 1:30 - 5 PM; closed Xmas. No admis. Estab 1966.
Collections: 20th century Midwestern paintings; sculpture; graphics; archaeology.
Publications: Monthly news releases; exhibition catalogs; books.
Activities: Classes for adults and children; lectures; gallery talks; guided tours; concerts; films; temporary and traveling exhibitions; competitions.
Library: Open to the public for researching on the premises. Holdings: 300 vols.
Special Subjects: Renaissance, Medieval, Far Eastern and 20th century paintings; sculpture; archaeology.

SPRINGFIELD

SOUTHWEST MISSOURI MUSEUM ASSOCIATES, INC., 1111 Brookside Dr, 65807. Tel: 417-866-2716, exten 2. *Pres* Mrs John White; *VPres* Mrs A T Driscoll; *Secy/Treas* Mrs Guy Callaway Jr; *Exec Secy* Mrs Pat Richardson.
Estab 1928 to inform and interest citizens in appreciation of art, and maintain an art museum as an essential public institution. Mem: 1435; dues non-resident $6, resident $10; annual meeting second Wed in May.
Income: $25,000 (financed by membership).
Publications: Calendar, monthly, in cooperation with Museum.
Activities: Sales shop selling prints, reproductions, stationery.

SOUTHWEST MISSOURI STATE UNIVERSITY, University Gallery, 901 S National, 65802. Tel: 417-836-5110. *Dir* Dianne Strickland.
Open Mon - Fri 8 AM - Midnight; Sat 8 AM - 5 PM; Sun 2 - Midnight. No admis. Estab 1963 to present exhibitions of interest and educational worth to the university community and general public.
Income: $4000 (financed by state appropriation).
Collections: †Contemporary and historical prints.
Exhibitions: Six-State Regional Photography Competition; student and faculty shows; temporary exhibitions.
Publications: Catalogs, 2 or 3 a yr.
Activities: Traveling exhibitions organized and circulated.

SPRINGFIELD ART MUSEUM, 1111 E Brookside Dr, 65807. Tel: 417-866-2716. *Dir* William C Landwehr; *Cur of Coll/Registrar* Greg G Thielen; *Cur of Education* Dudley C Murphy.
Open Mon - Sat 9 AM - 5 PM; Tues - Thurs 6:30 - 9:30 PM; Sun 1 - 5 PM; cl Mon. No admis. Estab 1928 to encourage appreciation and foster education of the visual arts; museum has three temporary exhibition galleries totaling approximately 6500 sq ft; new wing opened in 1975 contains 400-seat auditorium and sales gallery. Average Annual Attendance: 100,000. Mem: 1450; dues, $10; annual meeting second Wed in May.
Income: $200,000 (financed by membership, city and state appropriations). Purchases: $15,000 - $20,000.
Collections: †American and European prints of all periods with emphasis on the 20th Century; †American painting and sculpture of all periods; †American drawing and photography.
Exhibitions: Watercolor USA 1976; Thomas Hart Benton's Illustrations from Mark Twain; Six Missouri Artists; Jose Luis Cuevas: Drawings.
Publications: Annual Accessions catalog and temporary exhibition catalogs, Watercolor USA, annually.
Activities: Classes for adults and children; performing arts programs, lect open to public, 4 - 6 vis lectr per yr; concerts; gallery talks; tours; competitions; sales shop selling books, original art, prints.
—**Art Reference Library.** *Librn* Lin Davis.
Open to public.
Holdings: Vols 3500; Per Subs 35; Other—Slides.

WARRENSBURG

CENTRAL MISSOURI STATE UNIVERSITY, Grinstead Gallery, 74093. *Dir* Dr Kenneth R Meredith.
Open Mon - Fri 8 AM - 5 PM excluding holidays. No admis. Estab 1958 for the purpose of education through exhibition; small university oriented gallery located in the Art Department. Average Annual Attendance: 2000.
Income: Financed by state appropriation and university funding.
Activities: Lect open to the public, 2 vis lectr per yr; gallery talks; competitions; traveling exhibitions organized and circulated.

MONTANA

ANACONDA

COPPER VILLAGE MUSEUM AND ARTS CENTER, Eighth and Main St (Mailing Add: PO Box 29, 59711). Tel: 406-563-3604. *Dir* Elizabeth Rak Cortright; *Admin Asst* Florence Cortright; *Gallery Hostess* Mary Blaskovich; *Pres Bd of Dir* Mildred Avery; *VPres Bd of Dir* Lorraine Biggs.
Open Tues - Sun 1 - 5 PM; Wed 7 - 9 PM. No admis. Estab 1971 as Community Arts Center, gallery and local historical museum. Average Annual Attendance: 15,000. Mem: 300; dues $1 - $10; annual meeting Oct.
Income: Financed by endowment, membership and city appropriation.
Collections: Permanent collection.
Exhibitions: Monthly exhibits.
Activities: Classes for adults and children; traveling exhibitions organized and circulated; sales shop selling original art, reproductions, prints and pottery.
Library: Open to the public for reference. Holdings: Vols 30; Per sub 3. Special Subjects: Western History and Art.

BILLINGS

YELLOWSTONE ART CENTER, 401 North 27th St, 59101. Tel: 406-259-1869. *Pres of Bd* Larry Siegel; *Dir* Donna M. Forbes; *Cur* Jim Palmersheim.
Open Tues - Fri 11 AM - 5 PM (summer 10 AM - 4 PM); Sat & Sun Noon - 5 PM; Thurs 7 - 9 PM. No admis. Estab 1964 to offer a broad program of art exhibitions, both historical and contemporary, of the highest quality; to provide related educational programs; two large galleries and four smaller ones in a large brick structure. Average Annual Attendance: 25,000. Mem: 850; dues $10 and up; annual meeting third Wed in June.
Income: $90,000 (financed by membership and county appropriations).
Collections: Poindexter Collection of Abstract Expressionists; †Contemporary print collection. Mackay Collection of Olaf Wieghorst painting; Mary Mulloy Carmichael Collection of 20th Century French prints.
Exhibitions: Contemporary Norwegian Prints; Hogarth; Tom Berg-Bill Shepherd, Two Painters; Lorrilard Bicentennial Prints; Norwegian Stave Churches; 8th Annual Art Auction Exhibition; The Art and Illustration of 19th Century Montana; Montana Sculptors; Master Drawings; The Poindexter Collection, new additions; Max Beckman drypoints.

Publications: Newsletter, monthly; monthly exhibition announcements.
Activities: Classes for adults and children; docent training; lect open to public, 6 vis lectr per yr; gallery talks; tours; competitions; individual paintings and original art objects lent to museums and art centers; museum shop selling books, original art, reproductions, prints, jewelry and pottery.

BOZEMAN

KETTERER ART CENTER, 35 N Grand, 59715. *Dir* Ray Campeau; *Cur* Rand Honadel.
Open Tues - Sun 1 - 5:30 PM. No admis. Estab 1969 as a Fine Arts Center with a gallery and art school.
Income: Financed from sales of art and fees.
Exhibitions: Monthly shows.
Activities: Gallery talks; individual paintings lent; lending collection contains original art works, original prints, paintings and sculpture; traveling exhibitions organized and circulated; sales shop selling original art.

MONTANA STATE UNIVERSITY
—**Museum of the Rockies,** 59717. Tel: 406-994-2551. *Dir* Roy E Hoffman; *Construction Specialist* Jim Goosey; *Secy* Judy Weaver.
Open Mon - Fri 9 AM - 4:30 PM; Sat & Sun 1 - 4:30 PM. No admis. Estab 1958 to interpret the physical and social heritages of the Northern Rockies region; 45 panel 4 x 8 ft in a 15 ft wide corridor connecting two buildings. Mem: 500; dues $5 and up; annual meeting May.
Income: $65,000 (financed by membership state appropriation and university funds).
Collections: Cultural history and technology; archaeological and anthropology.
Publications: Newsletter, quarterly.
Activities: Docent training; school tours; competition; traveling exhibitions organized and circulates; museum and sales shop selling books, magazines, original art, reproductions, prints and arts and crafts.
—**Exit Gallery,*** Student Union Bldg, 59715. Tel: 406-994-4501.
Exhibitions: Co-sponsored by MSU Art Club and the Associated Students of Montana State University; traveling and local exhibitions, principally contemporary.
Activities: Adjunct programs—lectures, workshops for faculty, students and public, sponsored by the School of Art.

BROWNING

MUSEUM OF THE PLAINS INDIAN, US Highway 89 (Mailing Add: PO Box 400, 59417). Tel: 406-338-2230. *Acting Cur* Rosemary Ellison.
Open June - Sept, daily 9 AM - 5 PM; Oct - May, Mon - Fri 10 AM - 4:30 PM, cl New Year's Day, Thanksgiving Day and Christmas. No admis. Estab 1941 to promote the development of contemporary Native American arts, administered and operated by the Indian Arts and Crafts Board, US Dept of the Interior. Average Annual Attendance: 80,000.
Income: Financed by Federal appropriation and gifts.
Collections: Contemporary Native American arts and crafts; historic works by Plains Indian craftsmen.
Exhibitions: Permanent exhibit of historic Plains Indian arts; Contemporary Shoshone Arts and Crafts; Plains Indian Metalwork; continuing series of one-person exhibitions.
Publications: Continuing series of brochures for one-person shows.
Activities: Gallery talks; traveling exhibitions organized and circulated; sale shop selling books, original art.

BUTTE

COPPER KING MANSION,* 219 W Granite, 59701. Tel: 406-792-7580. *Dir* Ann Cote Smith; *Deputy Dir* Robert Ross Smith
Open May - Sept Mon - Sat 9 AM - 9 PM; Sun mornings; winter daily 9 AM - 6 PM. Admis adults $2, students $1.50, children $1; tours at discount. Estab 1966 in 1884 mansion built by Sen W A Clark.
Collections: Victorian furniture; glass (crystal and cut glass); silver; porcelains; paintings; sculpture.
Activities: Classes for adults and children; lectures; gallery talks; guided tours; films; temporary and traveling exhibitions; sales shop selling arts and craft items.

DILLON

WESTERN MONTANA COLLEGE ART GALLERY, 59725. Tel: 406-683-7232. *Dir* Jim Corr.
Open Mon - Fri 8 AM - 10 PM; Sat 2 - 4 PM; Sun 7 - 10 PM. No admis. Estab 1970 to display art works of various kinds, used as an eductional facility. Average Annual Attendance: 5,000.
Income: Financed through college funds.

Library: Librn Ken Cory. Open to public. Holdings: Vols 80,000; per subs 280.

GLASGOW

FORT PECK FINE ARTS COUNCIL, 59230. Tel: 406-228-4443. *Pres* Carl Dix; *VPres* Dorraine Worrall; *Secy* Marlene Zinner.
Estab 1970 to promote fine arts, theatre and other entertainment for eastern Montana. Spring dinner theatre and summer theatre with gallery-type showing in lobby, changes weekly. Average Annual Attendance: 15,000.
Income: $24,000.

GREAT FALLS

C M RUSSELL MUSEUM,* 1201 Fourth Ave, N, 59401. Tel: 406-452-7369. *Dir* Ray W Steele.
Open summer Mon - Sat 10 AM - 5 PM; Sun 1 - 5 PM; winter Tues - Sat 10 AM - 5 PM; Sun 1 - 5 PM. Estab 1953; includes Russell's original studio. Average Annual Attendance: 50,000. Mem dues: student $2, individual and family $15; associate $35; supporting $50, sustaining $100, sponsor $500.
Income: Operating budget $125,000.
Collections: Works by Charles M Russell and other Western works, historical and contemporary.
Exhibitions: Traveling exhibitions in contemporary arts; more than a dozen exhibitions are offered yearly along with related programs within the arts.
Activities: Creative dramatics; creative workshops; children's theatre; film program; Arts/Science Fair; annual C M Russell Auction; gift shop selling books, reproductions, jewelry.
Library: Western Americana, 500 items.

HELENA

ARCHIE BRAY FOUNDATION, 2915 Country Club, 59601. Tel: 406-442-2521. *Pres* David Shaner; *Treas* Ray Steele; *Secy* Branson Stevenson; *Res Dir* Kurt Weiser; *Materials Mgr* Chip Clawson.
Open Mon - Sat 9 AM - 5 PM. No admis. Estab 1951 to make available a fine place to work for all interested in the ceramic arts; maintains an art gallery.
Income: Self-supporting with occasional aid from National Endowment and State Art Council.
Collections: Works by Voulkos, Hamady, Leach, Ferguson, Shanery, McKinnel, Higby, Turner, Cushing and Rhodes.
Exhibitions: Resident potters and occasional shows of other outstanding potters.
Activities: Classes for adults and children; resident potter program; lect open to the public, 2 - 3 vis lectr per yr; lending collection of original art works 100; traveling exhibitions organized and circulated; sales shop selling original pottery.
Library: Open to resident potters and students. Holdings: Vols 300; Per subs 3.

MONTANA HISTORICAL SOCIETY, 225 N Roberts, 59601. Tel: 406-449-2694. *Pres* Toni Hagener; *VPres* Eric J Muhne; *Secy* James H Vandenbeck; *Dir* Kenneth L Korte; *Business Mgr* J Dennis Sheehy; *Exec Secy* Delores Brown.
Open daily 8 AM - 5 PM (Sept - May), 8 AM - 8 PM (June - Aug). No admis. Estab 1865 to collect, preserve and present articles relevant to History and Heritage of Montana and the Northwest; C M Russell Art Gallery—western artists; Poindexter Gallery—contemporary revolving art shows; Haynes Gallery—collection of exceptional western art. Average Annual Attendance: 200,000. Mem: 11,000; dues $10.
Income: $512,000 (financed by membership, state appropriation and donations). Purchases: $400,000 (goods for resale and collections).
Collections: MacKay Collection of C M Russell Art; †Haynes Collection of Art and Artifacts; Poindexter Collection of Contemporary Art.
Exhibitions: Monthly contemporary art shows; Haynes Gallery Opening; Annual Christmas Show and Sale.
Publications: Montana, Magazine of Western History, quarterly; Montana Post (newsletter), quarterly.
Activities: Classes for adults and children; docent training; lect open to public, 2 vis lectr per yr; gallery talks; special guided tours; individual painting and original objects of art are lent only with approval of Board of Trustees; traveling exhibitions organized and circulated; sales shop selling books, magazines, original art, prints, reproductions, slides, sculpture, pottery and bronzework.
—**Library.** Tel. 406-449-2694. *Art Cur* Mike McCourt; *Photographs* Lori Morrow.
For reference and research only.
Holdings: Vols 5,000; Per subs 100; Other—Historical journals and volumes of State History.

Special Subjects: Photographic collections, newspaper collections and Archival Department.

KALISPELL

HOCKADAY CENTER FOR THE ARTS,* Flathead Valley Art Association, Second Ave, E & Third St (Box 83), 59901. Tel: 406-755-5268. *Dir* Steve Lehmer; *Secy* Marsha Davis.
Open Tues - Sat Noon - 5 PM; cl Mon & holidays. No admis. Estab 1967 to encourage interest and participation in all art forms through a program of traveling exhibits, classes, films and recitals; Center is housed in the old Carnegie Library Building which has three galleries on the main floor and one downstairs. Average Annual Attendance: 9000. Mem: 250, dues individual $5, family $10, patron $25, benefactor $50; annual meeting third Mon in Nov.
Income: Financed by membership, city or state appropriation.
Collections: The main collection includes eight portrait studies by Hugh Hockaday, the center's late namesake, as well as several other of his works.
Exhibitions: Changed monthly; include a wide variety of art forms from Japanese posters to fabric sculpture by Dana Boussard; annual juried art competition with $450 in awards.
Publications: Bulletin, monthly to members.
Activities: Classes for adults and children; drama programs; pottery lab with full-time resident potter; darkroom facilities; lect open to the public, vis lectr; concerts.
Library: Holdings—Vols 100.

MISSOULA

UNIVERSITY OF MONTANA,* Gallery of Visual Arts, Turner Hall and University Center Art Gallery, 59801. Tel: 406-243-5416. *Dir* Dean Douglas; *Cur* Grove Hull; *Cur Asst* Michelle B Wurth.
Open Mon - Fri, summer and academic year, 10 AM - 5 PM; Sat & Sun, academic year, 2 - 5 PM. No admis. Estab 1970 to provide exhibit space for students and faculty of the Art Dept at the University of Montana and for periodical showings of the University's permanent art collection; to sponsor outside exhibitions in an effort to acquaint the community and the university with significant contemporary artists nationwide; to provide guest lecturers to the community; Gallery covers 60 x 40 ft exhibit space with spot and flood lighting, moveable panels and 14 ft ceilings. Average Annual Attendance: 10,000.
Income: $3000 (financed by city and state appropriation).
Collections: Dana Collection; Poindexter Collection.
Exhibitions: Faculty, student and traveling exhibitions are shown in both galleries as well as shows from the permanent collection.
Activities: Lect open to the public, 5 vis lectr per yr; competitions; schol; original objects of art lent; lending collection contains Kodachromes.

PRYOR

CHIEF PLENTY COUPS STATE MONUMENT,* Box 35, 59066. *Dir* Wes Woodgerd; *Deputy Dir* Fletcher Newby; *Cur* Harley R Sorrells.
Open Mon - Sat 9 AM - 6:30 PM; Sun Noon - 5 PM; Museum cl Wed & Thurs. No admis. Estab 1932.
Income: Financed by state appropriation; affiliated with Montana Fish and Game Dept.
Collections: Ethnographic materials of the Crow Indians; paintings; drawings; prehistoric artifacts.
Sales shop selling books, prints, sculpture, and handicrafts of the Crow Indians.

SIDNEY

J K RALSTON MUSEUM AND ART CENTER, 221 Fifth Ave S W (Mailing Add: PO Box 50, 59270). Tel 406-482-3500. *Chmn County Museum Bd* Dave Torrence; *Dir* Linda K Mann.
Open Tues - Fri & Sun 1 - 5 PM, cl Mon & Sat. No admis. Estab 1972 to preserve history of area and further interest in fine arts. Average Annual Attendance: 4,500. Mem: 200; dues $5; annual meeting March.
Income: Financed by County and State appropriations.
Exhibitions: Monthly exhibits of contemporary and Western art; Tipi Designs; Japanese Prints; Helen Siegel Prints; DinWitty Jack-in-Boxes; Cooke Photos; WPA Prints; Old Master Classical Prints; Local Art Competition; MIA Traveling Exhibit; Helgoe Drawings; Mcleod Oils; Juli Bush Weaving.
Activities: Classes for adults and children; dramatic programs; competitions; sales shop selling books, magazines, original art, reproductions, postcards, dolls, minerals and coins.

Library: Willo Ralston Library for Historical Research. *Librn* Gary Thogerson. Open to public for historical reference.

NEBRASKA

BROWNVILLE

BROWNVILLE FINE ARTS ASSOCIATION,* Carriage House Art Gallery, Main St, 68321. *Dir* Lola Vice; *Deputy Dir* Don Gappa.
Open Wed - Fri 1 - 5 PM; Sat & Sun 10 AM - 6 PM; cl Mon & Tues. Estab 1970 to promote the cultural activities of early and present Nebraska and to establish a place for new artists to work. Annual Average Attendance: 3000 to 10,000 at festivals. Mem: 400; dues $7.
Income: Financed by mem and festivals.
Activities: Fine Arts Day; Folk Life Festival; seminars; concerts; summer workshops for teenagers.

CHADRON

CHADRON STATE COLLEGE ARTS GALLERY, Tenth and Main Sts, 69337. Tel: 308-432-4451, exten 317. *Coordinator* Harry E Holmberg.
Open Mon - Fri 9 AM - noon, 1 - 4 PM. No admis. Estab 1967 to offer opportunities for students, faculty and local artists to present their works; to bring in shows to upgrade the cultural opportunities of students and general public; main gallery has space for traveling and larger shows; little gallery suffices for small shows. Average Annual Attendance: 5000.
Income: Financed by college budget, and state appropriation.
Exhibitions: Watercolor USA; Edges: Hard and Soft; Tony Martin: Ceramics and Crafts; Roten Galleries: Graphics Show; Greg Lafler: Handmade Jewelry; Photographs of the Farm Security Administration; Faculty Art Show; Bosworth, Rickenbach Exhibits; Student Art Show; Hands in Clay; Former Students Works; National Cone Box Traveling Show; Arts and Crafts Fair.

CHAPPELL

CHAPPELL MEMORIAL LIBRARY AND ART GALLERY, 289 Babcock, 69129. Tel: 308-874-2626. *Head Librn* Doris McFee; *Asst Librn* Gladys Smith.
Open Mon - Wed 2 - 5 PM, 7 - 9 PM; Sat 2 - 5 PM. Estab. in 1935, by gift of Mrs. Charles H Chappell.
Income: Financed by membership.
Holdings: Vols 10,390; Per subs 34.
Collections: Permanent personal collection of art works from many countries, a gift from Mrs. Charles H Chappell.
Activities: Gallery talks; library tours.

GERING

SCOTTS BLUFF NATIONAL MONUMENT,* Department of the Interior, National Park Service, Box 427, 69341. Tel: 308-436-4340. *Supt* Donald R Harper; *Supv Park Ranger* Lary D Barney; *Admin Officer* Linda Hahn.
Open day after Labor Day through May 29, 8 AM - 4:30 PM; May 30 through Labor Day 8 AM - 8:30 PM. No admis. Estab 1919 for commemoration of the Oregon Trail; gallery has three exhibit rooms; Oregon Trail Room, Landmark Room and William H Jackson Memorial Wing.
Income: Financed by Federal Government.
Collections: †Original watercolor paintings.
Library: For reference. Holdings: Vols 100.

HASTINGS

HASTINGS MUSEUM, 1330 N Burlington Ave, 68901. Tel: 402-463-7126. *Pres Bd Trustees* O J McDougal Jr; *Dir* Ed Bisaillon; *Cur Exhib* Burton R Nelson; *Museum Coordinator* Geraldine S Shuman; *Cur Astronomy* Rex Wright; *Exhib Spec* Jerome Dierfeldt.
Open Mon - Sat 8 AM - 5 PM; Sun 1 - 5 PM. Admis adults 75¢, children (6-11) 25¢, tots free. Estab 1926 for a program of service and exhibits to augment and stimulate the total educative program of schools and the general public. Animal displays in natural habitat settings. Average Annual Attendance: 45,000. Mem: 930; dues $200.
Income: Financed by city appropriation.
Collections: (art) Richards Coin Collection; American Indian exhibits and artifacts; glassware; furniture.
Publications: Yester News, bimonthly.
Activities: Sales shop selling books and selected gift items.
Library: Reference library for use at museum only.

LINCOLN

LINCOLN COMMUNITY ARTS COUNCIL,* Room 508 Lincoln Center Bldg, 68508. Tel: 402-477-5930. *Pres* Larry Lusk; *Secy* Mary Alice Snider; *Coordr* Patsy Davidson.
Open 8:45 AM - 4:45 PM. Estab 1967 to promote and encourage the community-at-large and all its arts organizations to grow, develop, use all the resources available, avoid over-lapping of energy, money, talent and to enrich the entire community; clearing house for arts activities scheduling. Mem: 100 members, 50 groups; dues prorated, meetings monthly.
Income: Financed by endowment, membership, city and state appropriation.
Publications: Newsletter; arts calendar, six per year.

NEBRASKA WESLEYAN UNIVERSITY, Elder Gallery, 50th and Huntington, 68504. Tel: 402-466-2371. *Dir* Betty Wallace.
Open Tues - Fri 10 AM - 4:30 PM; Sat & Sun 1 - 4:30 PM. No admis. Estab 1966 as a cultural addition to college and community. Average Annual Attendance: 10,000.
Income: Financed through College.
Collections: †Permanent collection of prints, paintings and sculpture; Campus collection.
Exhibitions: Tim Aldrup; Hastings College Permanent Collection; Fred Wells 10-state juried show; Chad Keel; Nebraska Art Educators; Nadine McHenry; Student Shows.
Activities: Classes for adults.

UNIVERSITY OF NEBRASKA-LINCOLN
—**Sheldon Memorial Art Gallery**, 68588. Tel: 402-472-2461. *Dir* Norman A Geske; *Asst to Dir* Jon Nelson; *Dir Educ Services* Mrs A Douglas Anderson; *Dir Sheldon Film Theater* Dan Ladely.
Open Tues 10 AM - 10 PM; Wed - Sat 10 AM - 5 PM; Sun 2 - 5 PM. No admis. Estab 1888 to exhibit the permanent collections owned by the University and to present temporary exhibitions on an annual basis. These activities to be accompanied by appropriate interpretive programs. The Sheldon Gallery is the gift of Frances and Bromley Sheldon. Opened in 1963, it is the work of Philip Johnson. Facilities, in addition to 25,000 sq ft of exhibition galleries, include an auditorium, a print study, members room and an outdoor sculpture garden. Average Annual Attendance: 110,000.
Income: Financed by endowment, state appropriation and Nebraska Art Association. Purchases: $30,000.
Collections: †Frank M Hall Collection of contemporary paintings, sculpture, prints, drawings, photographs, ceramics; †Nebraska Art Association Collection of American paintings and drawings; Bertha Schaefer Bequest.
Exhibitions: Bob Starck Photographs; Val Christensen Prints; 19th Century American Prints from Library of Congress; Reuben Tam Paintings; Bradley Walker Tomlin Paintings; Pat Rowan Sculpture; Dean Gillette Paintings; Harry Orlyk Paintings; Alice Cumbow Paintings; Edward Curtis Photographs; I-80 Sculptures; Metal Craftsmen; New Glory I; John Spence Photographs; George Baker Sculpture; Michael Smith Photographs; Russell Forrester Drawings; Robert Therien Paintings & Drawings; Duane Hanson Sculpture.
Publications: Exhibition catalogs, 2 per year.
Activities: Classes for adults; docent training; lect open to public; tours; competitions; individual paintings and original objects of art lent to campus offices; traveling exhibitions organized and circulated; museum shop selling books, original art, prints, jewelry and ceramics.
—**Nebraska Art Association.** *Pres* Mrs John H Ames; *VPres* Dr Philip Heckman, Mrs Hale McCown, Congdon E Paulson; *Secy* Mrs Clark W Faulkner.
Open Tues 10 AM - 10 PM; Wed - Sat 10 AM - 5 PM; Sun 2 - 5 PM; cl Mon. Estab 1888 as the Haydon Art Club, inc 1900, to study and prepare papers on art, to form a collection, to acquire a suitable art museum, to encourage young artists, to interest public school children and to attract industry and keep abreast of a growing city; a supportive organization to the Sheldon Memorial Art Gallery. Mem: 900; dues family $15; annual meeting May.
Income: $18,865 (financed by endowment, membership). Purchases: $15,000.
Collections: Paintings; drawings, prints, photographs, crafts, sculpture.
Publications: Calendar, 5 times a year; annual report; exhibition catalog, occasionally.
Activities: Scholarships, individual paintings and original objects of art lent to corporations.

McCOOK

HIGH PLAINS MUSEUM,* 423 Norris Ave, 69001. Tel: 308-345-3661. *Pres* Mrs Alan Redfern.

Open daily 1:30 - 4:30 PM; cl legal holidays. No admis. Estab 1966 to preserve the items pertaining to the local history and to interpret them to the public; museum is located in former Carnegie Library mission style building. Average Annual Attendance: 2000. Mem: 50; dues $2 - $25; annual meeting Jan.
Income: Financed by membership.
Collections: Paintings made on the barracks walls of prisoners of war camp near McCook; paintings donated by local artists.
Activities: Lect open to the public; temporary exhibitions; gallery talks; tours; Book shop.
Library: For reference. Holdings: Vols 500; Other—Photographs 200.

MINDEN

PIONEER VILLAGE, 58959. Tel: 308-832-1181. *Pres* Harold Warp; *Cur* Ruby Warp Nielsen.
Open daily. Admis adults $2, children 75¢, children under 6 free; special rates to groups.
Collections: (Art) Paintings; sculpture; graphics; folk art; historical materials.

OMAHA

CREIGHTON UNIVERSITY FINE ARTS GALLERY,* 2500 California St, 68178. Tel: 402-536-2509. *Dir* Bidez Embry Moore; *Chmn Fine & Performing Arts Dept* Donald A Doll.
New gallery facility opened 1973; gallery handles 10 exhibits per academic year; space provided for student thesis exhibits.
Collections: Graphics, paintings, drawings, sculpture, ceramics, photography and pottery.
Activities: Lect open to the public.

JOSLYN ART MUSEUM,* 2200 Dodge St, 68102. Tel: 402-342-3996. *Chief Cur* Ruth H Cloudman; *Cur Western Collections* Mildred Goosman; *Cur Exhib* Harrison C Taylor; *Registrar* Berneal Anderson; *Publicity & Programming* Joanne Evans.
Open Tues - Sat 10 AM - 5 PM; Sun 1 - 5 PM; cl Mon & holidays. Admis 50¢, children under 12 free with adult; free Sat AM. Joslyn Art Museum was inc May 3, 1928, under the laws of the State of Nebraska, opened Nov 29, 1931, a gift of Mrs Sarah H Joslyn in memory of her husband, George A Joslyn, Omaha businessman. Purpose of the Museum is to care for and expand the collections, offer exhibitions, promote education in and cultivation of the fine arts. The Museum, a marble building covering a two-block area, contains ten large galleries with small exhibit areas surrounding a large central court and 1200-seat Witherspoon Concert Hall on the main floor. The concert hall is used for programs by major community music and cultural organizations. The ground floor includes exhibit areas, library, studios, lecture hall, museum shop, rental and sales gallery and offices. Mem: 5000; dues student $5, individual $10, family $15, friend $25, associate $50, sustainer $100, sponsor $250, donor $500, patron $1000, benefactor $2500. The Museum is governed by the Board of Trustees, who are the voting members with the annual meeting the third Tues in Dec.
Collections: The Joslyn permanent collections are arranged chronologically. More than half the exhibit area on the main floor is devoted to period collections, starting with the Classical through the Renaissance, to European art of the 17th, 18th and 19th centuries, to the Impressionists, and contemporary American arts. The exhibits combine painting, sculpture, the decorative and graphic arts. New acquisitions are being added in all areas. Artists in the permanent collections include DiCredi, Titian, Veronese, El Greco, Ribera, Rembrandt, Goya, Reynolds, Raeburn, Corot, Stuart, Renoir, Monet, Henry, Grant Wood, Benton, Pollock and others. In the Court balcony are works by Karl Bodmer, Alred Jacob Miller, and George Catlin. The Bodmer Collection, owned by the Northern Natual Gas Company, Omaha, is housed at Joslyn and includes 400 watercolor sketches. The collections on the ground floor are devoted to the Great Plains Region, outlining development of art and design in the Middle West from earliest times to today, with emphasis on the 19th century. Native arts of the North American Indians are included in this Early West section.
Exhibitions: The Midwest Biennial Exhibition, a juried show open to artists in a 16-state area around Nebraska, is held in even-numbered years; it includes paintings, sculpture and graphics; additions to the Museum's permanent collection are purchased from the exhibition. Temporary exhibitions include traveling shows of national significance, Joslyn-organized shows, one-man and group shows in all media, student art.
Publications: Monthly calendar September through June; special exhibition catalogs; Annual Review; Guide to the Museum; brochures.
Activities: Creative and art appreciation classes for children pre-school through high school and adults, plus special workshops; monthly film programs; lectures and exhibition gallery talks; tours of the collections and special exhibitions; special tour program of the permanent collections and special exhibitions maintained for public school children.

—Art Reference Library: *Librn* Evelyn A Sedlacek.
Holdings: Vols 10,000; periodicals, AV—Slides 15,000; Other—Clipping files; pamphlets, circulating material of mounted pictures and folios.
Special Collections: Nebraska art and artists.

SOCIETY OF NORTH AMERICAN ARTISTS, INC, PO Box 37072, Millard Station, 68137. Tel: 402-895-4252. *Pres* Eugene H Grimm; *VPres* Gloria D Grimm; *Secy* Michele K Berry.
For further information see National and Regional Organizations.

UNIVERSITY OF NEBRASKA-OMAHA ART GALLERIES*
—New Gallery, Annex 22, 133 S Elmwood Rd, 68101. Tel: 402-554-2686. *Gallery Dir* Betty R Hiller; *Asst Dir* Ron Bishop; *Dean School of Fine Arts* Jerome Birdman.
Open weekdays 9 AM - 7:30 PM. No admis. Estab 1975 to heighten cultural and aesthetic awareness of the metropolitan and midlands area.
Income: Financed by state appropriation.
Exhibitions: (1976-77) Lorraine Rohman Collection; Contemporary Prints and Posters Exhibition; Video Art Exhibit; Rudy Pozzatti (one-person exhibit); Student Art Competition; Roten Gallery (print show and sale); Women Look at Women; Patrick Rowan (one-person exhibit); John Himmelfarb (one-person exhibit); Thesis Exhibition; UNO Faculty Exhibit; Nebraska Penal Complex Exhibition; Annual Student Juried Exhibition; Richard Brooker (one-person exhibit); African Exhibition; Student Art Competition; Annual UNO Invitational Exhibit Regional; UNO Collection; Warrington Colscott (one-person exhibit, Printmaker in Residence); Thesis Exhibition; Alumni Exhibition.
—Administration Gallery, Admin Bldg, Room 371, 68101. Tel: 402-554-2420.
Open weekdays 9 AM - 4 PM. No admis. Estab 1967 to heighten cultural and aesthetic awareness of the metropolitan and midlands area. Average Annual Attendance: 14,000.
Income: Financed by state appropriation. Purchases: $5000.
Activities at both locations: Lect open to public, 2 vis lectr per yr; photograph collection in the planning stage; gallery talks; tours; competitions; schol.

SEWARD

CONCORDIA COLLEGE, Koenig Art Gallery, 800 N Columbia Ave, 68434. Tel: 401-643-3651. *Dir* Richard Wiegmann.
Open weekdays 8 AM - 5 PM; Sun 2 - 5 PM. No admis. Estab 1959 to provide the college and community with a wide variety of original art; both monthly exhibitions and permanent collection serve primarily an educational need; spacious gallery has additional showcases.
Income: Financed by college and churchbody. Purchases: $6000.
Collections: †Contemporary Original Prints; ceramics.
Exhibitions: Graphic works by Albers, Rosenquist, Sloan and others added to Permanent Collection; temporary exhibitions shown monthly.
Activities: Gallery talks; original objects of art lent; lending collection of framed reproductions, original prints and paintings.

WAYNE

WAYNE STATE COLLEGE, Nordstrand Visual Arts Gallery, Fine Arts Center, 68787. *Div Chmn of Fine Arts* Dr Cornell Runestad.
Open Mon - Fri 9 AM - 5 PM. No admis. Estab January 1977 to provide art students with a space to display work; to enhance student's education by viewing incoming regional professional work; to enrich cultural atmosphere of college and community; small gallery, carpeted floors and walls, ceiling spotlights on tracts. Average Annual Attendance: 800.
Income: Financed by city and state appropriation, as well as Wayne State Foundation.
Collections: †Wayne State Foundation print collection.
Exhibitions: Lutheran Brotherhood; faculty exhibitions; student exhibitions.
Activities: Lect open to the public, 1-2 vis lectr per yr; competitions.

NEVADA

ELKO

NORTHEASTERN NEVADA MUSEUM, 1515 Idaho St (Mailing Add: PO Box 503, 89801). Tel: 702-738-3418. *Dir* Howard Hickson; *Registrar* Karen Walther; *Office Mgr* Carol Sanders; *Researcher* Claudia Riordan.
Open weekdays & Sat 9 AM - 5 PM; Sun 1 - 5 PM. No admis. Estab 1968; general museum concentrating on Northeastern Nevada; also area cultural center; art gallery is 30 x 40 ft. Average Annual Attendance: 55,000. Mem: 1350; dues $5 - $1000; annual meeting date varies.
Income: $85,000 (financed by private funding).
Publications: Historical, quarterly.

Activities: Classes for adults and children; lect open to public, 2 vis lectr per yr; gallery talks; competitions; exten dept serving Nevada; lending collection of film strips, slides (complete programs); traveling exhibitions organized and circulated; Museum Shop selling books and local Indian craft items.
Library: Open to public for reference. Holdings: Vols 1200; Per subs 5; Other—Extensive collection of newspapers, photographs and negative files. Special Subjects: Concentration on Northeastern Nevada history.

LAS VEGAS

CLARK COUNTY LIBRARY DISTRICT, 1401 E Flamingo Rd, 89109. Tel: 702-733-7810. *Dir* Charles W Hunsberger; *Admin* Nancy Hudson; *Admin* Joel McKee; *Admin* Jack Gardner; *Young People's Coordr* Nancy Cummings; *Programming Coordr* Lamar Marchese; *Reference* Vlasta Honsa; *Head of Circulation* Darlene Warfield; *Exten Serv Coordr* Ann Thompson; *Regional Serv Librn* Jeanne Owen; *Asst Program Coordr* Virginia Mulloy.
Open Mon - Thurs 9 AM - 9 PM; Fri & Sat 9 AM - 5 PM; Sun 10 AM - 6 PM. Estab Oct 1965 to provide information in all its varieties of form to people of all ages. Circ: 600,000. Gallery provides regularly rotating art exhibitions of regional and national repute as well as three solo local shows a year, and a regional mixed media competition every spring.
Income: $1,600,000 (financed by state and county appropriation). Purchases $120,000.
Holdings: Vols 200,000; Per subs 750; AV—Cassettes, film strips, microfiche, microfilm, motion pictures, phonorecords, reels; Other—Clipping files, framed reproductions, original art works, pamphlets, photographs, prints, sculpture.
Special Collections: Nevada materials.
Exhibitions: (1976-78) Contemporary Mexican Artists; Danish Expressions in Textiles (Smithsonian); Daniel Glasco (drawings); Art-A-Fair competition; Great American Slot Show (now touring with the Arizona Commission on the Arts & Humanities); First Edition Prints; New Blues/Cyanotypes; Southwest Invitational; Mick Reber (sculpture and acrylics); Plates & Platters; Nevada Watercolor Society; Navaho/Hopi Rugs and Baskets; Southwest Landscapes; Tom Askman (airbrush); Ukiyo-E (Japanese prints); Desertscapes/Textiles and Pottery; Jon Hudson (metal sculpture); Warhol Reconsidered.
Publications: Library program, bi-monthly; exhibition brochures, monthly; Coming Soon (cinema guide) irregular intervals.
Activities: Dramatic programs; issue-oriented forums, cinema series; lect open to the public; 12 vis lectr per yr; concerts; gallery talks; library tours; competitions; extension dept and regional service dept utilize the Bookmobiles to transport traveling exhibitions and to provide the Traveling Artist series; artists in various media travel through Southern Nevada giving demonstrations and lectures at each stop.

LAS VEGAS ART LEAGUE, Las Vegas Art Museum, 3333 W Washington, 89107. Tel: 702-648-1868. *Pres* Jerry Motto; *Secy* Mary Shaw; *Gallery Dir* Cookie Best.
Open winter daily Noon - 4 PM; summer daily 1 - 5 PM. No admis. Estab 1950 to offer fine arts to the citizens of Las Vegas, to offer artists a place to show, work and study, to offer good education in fine arts to adults and children of the community. Average Annual Attendance: 8000. Mem: 400; dues single $10, dual or family $12; annual meeting May.
Income: $24,000 (financed by membership). Purchases $1000 - $5000.
Collections: Present day artists, majority of which have been winners in annual national competition.
Exhibitions: One, two or three-man juried exhibits for members and nonmembers held monthly; local and out-of-town artists. National Art Roundup and Fall Roundup Exhibits with cash and purchase awards for each show.
Publications: Bulletin, monthly.
Activities: Classes for adults presented by leading artists and craftsmen; Junior Art League sponsors classes for youths; self-help workshops; competitions.

UNIVERSITY OF NEVADA, LAS VEGAS, ART GALLERY,* 4505 Maryland Parkway, 89109. Tel: 702-736-6111, exten 237. *Chmn Art Dept* Bill Leaf.
Open 8 AM - Noon, 1 - 5 PM. Gallery measures 55 x 30 ft. Average Annual Attendance: 5000. Mem: 50; dues $10.
Income: Financed by membership and appropriation.
Collections: Prints, †paintings, †sculpture, †ceramics and Oriental art.
Exhibitions: Regularly exhibits work by students and faculty; sponsors exhibits throughout the year by several nationally-renowned artists.
Activities: Classes for adults and children; dramatic programs; lect open to the public, 2 vis lectr per yr; concerts; gallery talks; tours; competitions; schol; lending collection contains Kodachromes 15,000; traveling exhibitions organized and circulated; book shop.
Library: Holdings—Vols 200,000.

RENO

NEVADA ART GALLERY,* 643 Ralston St, 89503. Tel: 702-322-5626. *Dir* Kenneth L Miller.
Open Sept - July Tues - Sun 1 - 4 PM; cl Aug & holidays. No admis. Estab 1931. Mem: individual $10, family $15, sustaining $25 and higher.
Collections: Paintings; sculpture; graphics; decorative arts; archaeology.
Exhibitions: Monthly exhibitions by local and Western artists.
Activities: Classes for adults and children; lectures; gallery talks; guided tours; competitions.
Library: Small collection of art history books available for research upon request.

SIERRA ARTS FOUNDATION, PO Box 2814, 89505. Tel: 702-329-1324. *Pres* George Aker; *VPres* Carol Mousel; *Secy* Charles D Glattley; *Exec Dir* Don R M Carter.
Estab as a service organization and management organization for arts; opeation of arts center (in design). Art gallery is to be completed in 1980.
Income: Financed by endowment, membership, city and state appropriations, and gifts.
Publications: Newsletter and calendar, bimonthly.
Activities: Educ dept; classes in elementary schools.

NEW HAMPSHIRE

CONCORD

LEAGUE OF NEW HAMPSHIRE CRAFTSMEN, 205 N Main St, 03301. Tel: 603-224-3375. *Pres* Ann Margolis; *VPres* Derek Marshall; *Secy* Samuel Azzaro; *Dir* Merle D Walker; *Business Mgr* Brian Curry; *Merchandiser* Peter Solomon; *Supv of Standards* Ruth Burt; *Education Coordinator* Evelyn Zimmerman.
Estab 1932 to encourage the economic development and education of the crafts; small gallery displaying traveling shows (SITES, ACC) and exhibits of members' works. Mem: 3500; dues $6; annual meeting in Oct.
Publications: Newsletter, six times per yr.
Activities: Classes for adults; advanced seminars for craftsmen; lect open to the public; tours; competitions with awards; schol; lending collection of books and slides.
Library: Open to members. Holdings: Vols 1000; Per subs 24. Special Subjects: Crafts.

NEW HAMPSHIRE HISTORICAL SOCIETY, 30 Park, 03301. Tel: 603-225-3381. *Pres* Richard F Upton; *VPres* Mrs Carl G Gesen, Charles E Clark; *Dir & Secy* John F Page; *Cur* James L Garvin, *Asst Librn* William N Copeley.
Open Mon - Tues - Thurs - Fri 9 AM - 4:30 PM; Wed 9 AM - 8 PM. No admis. Estab 1823 to collect, preserve and make available books, manuscripts and artifacts pertaining to the history of New Hampshire; art gallery maintained. Average Annual Attendance: 10,000. Mem: 1800; dues active $10, $15 family; annual meeting first Sat in May.
Income: $200,000 (financed by endowment, membership, state appropriation and grants). Purchases: $10,000.
Collections: Fine and decorative arts, artifacts made or used in New Hampshire such as collections of paintings, furniture, silver, glass, textiles and metals; historical memorabilia.
Exhibitions: Walter Ingalls, a 19th Century New Hampshire portrait painter; Zedekiah Belknap.
Publications: Newsletter, quarterly; Historical New Hampshire, quarterly magazine.
Activities: Classes for children; lect open to the public, 8 vis lectr per yr; gallery talks; tours; individual paintings lent for special exhibitions in other museums or historical societies; sales shop selling books and post cards.
—Library:
Open to the public for reference.
Holdings: Vols 75,000; Per Subs 75; Other—Local history and genealogy (New Hampshire and New England emphasis).

ST PAUL'S SCHOOL,* Art Center in Hargate, 03301. Tel: 603-225-3341, exten 58. *Head Art Dept* Thomas R Barrett; *Secy* Juanita White.
Open Tues - Sat 10 AM - 4:30 PM; during school year. June, Mon - Fri 1 - 4 PM. Estab 1967 to house the Art Department of St Paul's School, provide a cultural center for the school community as well as the central area of New Hampshire; secure gallery consisting of subdivided room approximately 60 x 40 ft. Average Annual Attendance: 6500. Friends of the Arts at St Paul's School, mem: 150, dues $10-$50.
Income: Financed by endowment.
Collections: Painting, sculpture, drawings, graphics, chiefly gifts to the school; collection represents varied periods and nationalities.

Activities: Classes for students; exhibitions by faculty and students; lect for mem only, 4 vis lectr per yr; gallery talks; tours; original objects of art lent.

Library: For use of students enrolled at St Paul's School. Holdings: Vols 150; Other—Reproductions 500, facsimiles of Old Master drawings from 14th - 19th century.

CORNISH

SAINT-GAUDENS NATIONAL HISTORIC SITE, off New Hampshire Route 12A (Mailing Add: RR2, Windsor, Vermont, 05089). *Supt* John H Dryfhout; *Maintenance Supv* B Allan Jansson.
Open daily 8:30 AM - 5 PM (end of May - Oct 31). Admis (16 and older) 50¢. Estab 1926, transferred to Federal Government 1965, to commemorate the home, studios, and works of Augustus Saint-Gaudens (1848-1907), one of America's foremost sculptors. The Home has three historically (1907) furnished rooms, studios and gardens displaying approximately half of the work of Augustus Saint-Gaudens. Sculptor-in-residence program. Average Annual Attendance: 11,000.
Income: Financed by state appropriation and National Park Service.
Collections: Historic furnishings and plaster, bronze, and marble works by Augustus Saint-Gaudens.
Exhibitions: Cornish, New Hampshire, The First Hundred Years 1763-1863; The Cornish Colony 1885-1935; Roger Palmer (paintings and drawings); Eric Gugler (architect, painter, sculptor).
Activities: Individual paintings and original objects of art lent to museums and societies; sales shop selling books, slides and souvenir medallions.
Library: Open for reference. Holdings: Vols 400; Per subs 6. Special Subjects: 19th and early 20th century Amrican Art.

DURHAM

UNIVERSITY OF NEW HAMPSHIRE ART GALLERIES,* Paul Creative Arts Center, 03824. Tel: 603-862-2190. *Dir* Susan C Faxon; *Chmn Dept of the Arts* Arthur Balderacchi.
Open Mon - Thurs 10 AM - 4 PM; Sat & Sun 1 - 5 PM; cl Fri & school holidays. No admis.
Collections: Small collection of contemporary art.
Exhibitions: Traveling exhibitions and regularly mounted exhibitions from the collection.
Publications: Exhibition catalogs; miscellaneous booklets.
Activities: Classes for adults and children; competitions; lectures.

EXETER

PHILLIPS EXETER ACADEMY,* Lamont Gallery, 03833. Tel: 603-772-4311, exten 324. *Prin* Stephen G Kurtz; *Dir* John Wharton; *Asst Dir* Bridget Paddock.
Open Tues - Sat 9 AM - 5 PM; Sun 2 - 5 PM; cl Mon. Estab 1953 to provide an Art Center and studios for art instruction. Dedicated to the memory of Thomas William Lamont II, lost in action in 1945.
Collections: 19th century English prints; 19th century American prints; portraits; †contemporary prints and paintings.
Exhibitions: Fifteen exhibitions per year; annual student exhibition with awards. (1976-77) Sculpture and ceramics by David Davison; Paintings by John Grillo; James Hendricks, John Towsend and George Wardlow; Photographs from the George Eastman Collection; Sculpture by Dan Gibbons; Structúres by Henry James.
Activities: Classes for Academy students; dramatic programs; films; lectures; concerts—all open to the public.

HANOVER

DARTMOUTH COLLEGE MUSEUM AND GALLERIES, Hopkins Center, 03755. Tel: 603-646-2808. *Dir* Jan van der Marck; *Cur* Arthur Blumenthal; *Registrar* Mary Jane Clark; *Exhib Coordinator* Malcolm Cochran; *Admin Asst* Nancy Tenney; *Asst to Exhib Coordinator* Jack Wilson.
Open Mon - Sat 11 AM - 4 PM and 7 - 10 PM; Sun 2 - 5 PM. No admis. Esab 1771. Situated in the Hopkins Center for the Visual and Performing Arts along with extensive facilities for theatre, music, studio, film and workshops. It houses anthropological collection in Wilson Hall; permanent collection in Carpenter Galleries; sculpture court; Barrows print room; lower Jewett corridor; Beaumont-May, Strauss, Jaffe-Friede Galleries.
Income: Financed by endowment. Purchases: $15,000.
Collections: American & European paintings, sculpture, drawings and prints; Far Eastern art; Far and near Eastern Art; anthropological artifacts; ethnic arts.

Exhibitions: Piranesi at Dartmouth; Jennifer Bartlett/Robert Filliou Rhapsody Telepathic Music; Curator's Choice: Dartmouth College Permanent Collection; Hundterwasser Graphics, and the Sign of the Leopard: Beaded Art of Cameroon.
Activities: Lect open to public, 4 vis lectr per yr; gallery talks; individual paintings and original objects of art lent; museum shop selling slides and small anthropological objects.
—**Sherman Art Library,** Carpenter Hall. *Librn* Molly O'Connor.

KEENE

KEENE STATE COLLEGE, Thorne-Sagendorph Art Gallery, Appian Way, 03431. Tel: 603-352-1909, exten 382. *Dir* Nancy Doll.
Open Sun - Fri 1 - 4:30 PM. No admis. Estab 1965 to provide a year-round calendar of continuing exhibitions, to sponsor related programs of artistic and educational interest, and to maintain small permanent collection displayed on campus; two adjacent galleries occupy space in a wing of Mason Library on campus. Average Annual Attendance: 6500. Mem: 400; dues $5.
Income: $5000 (financed by endowment, and state appropriation and $15,000 from annual College budget).
Collections: Paintings by Regional Artists; Artists of National Prominence; Paintings and Prints of Historical Interest included: George Rickey, Gregorio Prestopino, Milton Avery, Paul Pollaro, Sidney Twardowicz.
Exhibitions: Paintings by E E Cummings; Six American Sculptors; Palladium Prints; Burmese Instruments; Graphic Art of Sidney Chafetz; Works by Nicholas Isaak; Work in Fibers and Clay; Annual KSC Student Art Exhibition.
Publications: Small catalogs or brochures to accompany exhibitions.
Activities: Lect open to the public, 2 vis lectr per yr; concerts; gallery talks; tours; competitions; individual paintings lent to depts on campus, other museums and galleries; lending collection consists of original prints, paintings, and sculpture; traveling exhibitions organized and circulated.

MANCHESTER

CURRIER GALLERY OF ART, 192 Orange St, 03104. Tel: 603-669-6144. *Pres* Kimon S Zachos; *Treas* Ernest A Sweet Jr; *Clerk* Mrs Lawrence W Shirley; *Dir* Robert M Doty; *Cur* Melvin E Watts; *Asst Cur* James V Galgano; *Dir of Educ* Marian D Woodroff; *Supv The Currier Art Center* Robert Eshoo.
Open Tues - Sat 10 AM - 4 PM; Sun 2 - 5 PM; cl Mon and national holidays. No admis. Estab and inc 1915 by will of Mrs Hannah M and Gov Moody Currier, which included endowment. The building, opened in 1929, contains six galleries, library and auditorium. Currier Art Center is housed in an adjacent building acquired in 1938, and offers after school and Sat classes for children. Average Annual Attendance: 30,000. Mem: 700; dues $10 up; annual meeting in March.
Income: Financed by endowment.
Collections: †European Masters 13th to 20th Century; †American paintings and sculpture 18th Century to present; †fine American decorative art 17th to 19th Century including furniture, textiles, glass and silver.
Exhibitions: Special exhibitions of painting, sculpture, decorative and industrial art.
Publications: Bulletin, annually; exhibition catalogs, sporadically.
Library. Librn Maria K Graubart. Open to gallery staff, docents, and research students by appointment for reference only. Holdings: Vols 5000; Per subs 40.

MANCHESTER CITY LIBRARY,* 405 Pine St, 03104. Tel: 603-625-6485. *City Library Dir* John J Hallahan; *Fine Arts Librn* Ann Frank.
Open Mon - Thurs 9 AM - 9 PM; Fri 9 AM - 6 PM; Sat 9 AM - 5 PM; cl Sun.
Holdings: Vols 8500 on art; AV—16 mm films 105, film strips 95, Canadian travel films available to groups; Other—Mounted pictures, art magazines 20. Cooperative film collection available for loan; monthly film program to public, interlibrary loan; teletype.

MANCHESTER HISTORIC ASSOCIATION,* 129 Amherst St, 03104. Tel: 603-622-7531. *Pres* John R Reilly, Jr; *Dir & Cur Asst Dir & Librn* Elizabeth B Lessard.
Tues - Fri building open 9 AM - 4 PM; Sat 10 AM - 4 PM; cl Sun & Mon, National & state holidays, and Tues following Mon holidays. Inc 1896 to collect, preserve, and make known Manchester's historical heritage. Average Annual Attendance: 8000. Mem: 145; dues $3 - $100; annual meeting April.
Income: $22,000.
Collections: †Furniture, †glass, †pewter, †maps, †prints, †paintings, †ceramics, †costumes, †textiles, and †artifacts of all types; †Indian artifact collection of over 10,000 pieces found at Manchester sites; historical material.

Exhibitions: Permanent and changing exhibitions reflecting all aspects of Manchester history.
Publications: The Bulletin, bi-monthly newsletter; Annual Report; occasional catalogs; special bulletins each on an individual subject.
Activities: Spring and fall program series.
Library: Holdings—Other—Manuscript and printed material, photographs, prints, maps, early textile mill records and swatch sample books.

MANCHESTER INSTITUTE OF ARTS AND SCIENCES, 148 Concord St, 03104. Tel: 603-623-0313. *Exec Dir* James K Boatner; *Admin Asst* Helen Economou; *Cur Exhib* Richard C Frantz; *Registrar* Pamela Riel.
Open Mon - Thurs 9 AM - 9 PM; Fri & Sat 9 AM - 5 PM; cl Sunday; Gallery is free. Estab 1898, the Manchester Institute of Arts & Sciences is a private nonprofit educational institution established in order to promote, encourage, and stimulate education in the arts & sciences. Through credit and noncredit courses, performing arts programs and visual arts exhibitions, it is concerned with the enrichment of human life. Limited gallery space, devoted to a variety of exhibitions including historical as well as contemporary themes. Mem: 450; dues individual $15, family $25; annual meeting June.
Income: Financed by endowment, membership, state appropriation and grants.
Exhibitions: Glass: Blown, Stained & Tinted; Jacobi Place: Portrait of a Photographer; Made in New Hampshire: Art esthetic of New Hampshire's manufactured items.
Publications: Schedule of courses, exhibitions & programs, 3 or 4 times a year.
Activities: Classes for adults; lect open to public, 10 vis lectr per yr; concerts; traveling exhibitions organized and circulated.

NEW HAMPSHIRE ART ASSOCIATION, INC,* 24 W Bridge St, 03105. Tel: 603-622-0527. *Exec Dir* Grace Casey; *Pres* Jafar Shoja; *First VPres* Elaine Biganess Livingstone; *Second VPres* Calvin Libby; *Treas* Lucie Duhaime; *Corresp Secy* Alice Coyne; *Recording Secy* Virginia Hurt.
Sales and rental gallery open year-round, Tues - Fri 10 AM - 4 PM. Summer gallery in Strawbery Banke Historic Preservation Area, Portsmouth, NH. Estab 1940, inc 1962, as a non-profit organization. Mem: 300, dues $20; annual meeting June.
Exhibitions: Annuals at Currier Gallery of Art—Spring Annual which travels to museums and galleries in New Hampshire, Massachusetts, Maine; Summer Annual combined with New Hampshire League of Arts and Crafts at Mount Sunapee State Park, Sunapee, NH. Various one-man and group shows at gallery.

SAINT ANSELM'S COLLEGE, Chapel Arts Center, 03102. Tel: 603-669-1030, exten 328. *Assoc Dir* Joseph E Scannell & Beverly Zisla Welber; *Cur* Paul Sullivan; *Docent* Patricia Farrell.
Open Mon - Fri 9 AM - 5 PM. No admis. Large gallery—formerly college chapel with painted, barrel-vaulted ceiling, stained glass windows; one small gallery. Average Annual Attendance: 2000.
Income: Financed through College.
Collections: †Photographs; †prints; †New Hampshire artists and craftsmen.
Exhibitions: Victorian Architecture of Manchester; Flagging Tape; Harnessing the Sun (Solar Energy); Viewpoints: 15; The Warrior; Other Prophets; The Parthenon; Gothic Cathedral; Illuminated Manuscripts; Student Show.

NASHUA

ARTS AND SCIENCE CENTER,* 14 Court St, 03060. Tel: 603-883-1506. *Pres* Gerald Q Nash; *Chmn Exec Comt* J Herman Pouliot; *Exec Dir* Ronald D Deane; *Coordr Children's Museum* Nancy Fite.
Open Mon - Fri 10 AM - 5 PM; Thurs 10 AM - 9 PM; Sat 10 AM - 5 PM; Sun 1:30 - 5 PM. No admis. Inc 1961 to provide performances and exhibitions, lectures, film programs, musical performances and productions by theater arts groups. New facility opened Nov, 1973, includes two large exhibition galleries, rental and sales department, museum shop, theater with capacity of 250 for performances and productions, six classrooms, coffee shop, large meeting room, storage and office space. The Children's Museum, the only one of its kind in New Hampshire is designed to allow children to experience more through participation instead of observation. Special tours and programs for school and children's groups. There is a nominal admission fee. Average Annual Attendance: 30,000. Mem: 954; dues $5 - $1000; monthly meeting of the Board of Trustees held first Tues of each month, annual meeting of the Board and members held in May.
Publications: Newsletters; releases; invitations to openings.
Activities: Classes for preschool, primary, secondary and adults in arts, crafts, languages, lectr; films; schol.

PETERBOROUGH

SHARON ARTS CENTER, INC,* RFD 2, Box 361, 03458. Tel: 603-924-3582. *Pres* George Kendall; *Dir* Carl M Jackson.
Open daily 10 AM - 5 PM; Sun 1 - 5 PM; cl Dec 24 - May 1. Estab 1945 to promote appreciation of the arts and crafts in the Monadnock Area. Member of the League of New Hampshire Craftsmen. Exhibition gallery and shop. Mem dues: $7, $50 and up; annual meeting Sept.
Income: Financed by endowment and membership.
Activities: Arts and crafts classes conducted.

PLYMOUTH

PLYMOUTH STATE COLLEGE, Herbert H Lamson Library, 03264. *Dir Libr Services* Janice Gallinger; *Coordr Public Services* Robert V McDermand; *Slide Librn* William Kietzman; *Acquisitions Librn* Jane M Sasse; *Interlibrary Loan Librn* Michael J Flannery.
Open Mon - Thurs 8 AM - 11 PM; Fri 8 AM - 6 PM; Sat 10 AM - 6 PM; Sun 1 - 10 PM. Estab 1871 to serve the academic and personal needs of the college's students and faculty. Circ: 80,000. Maintains exhibition space — 18 ft exhibition wall.
Income: $450,000 (financed by state appropriation). Purchases: $169,000.
Holdings: Vols 185,000; Per subs 1100; AV—Audio tapes 5600, cassettes 1500, film strips 2600, microfiche 180,000 microfilm 7000, phonorecords 5500, slides 26,000; Other—Pamphlets.
Exhibitions: Herbert Waters; Elsa Beckman; Peter Hall; Frank Moulton; John Hatch.
Publications: Newsletter and new acquisitions list, bi-weekly; Handbook; brochures.
Activities: Lect open to the public; library tours.

PORTSMOUTH

JOHN PAUL JONES HOUSE, Middle & State St, (Mailing Add: 54 Court St, 03801). Tel: 603-436-8420. *Pres* Arnold J Grover; *VPres* Wyman P Boynton; *Secy* Mrs Harry Downing.
Open Mon - Sat 10 AM - 5 PM; cl Sun. Admis $1.50. Estab 1920 to identify and retain local history. The house was built in 1758 by Gregory Purcell, a merchant sea-captain. Purchased and restored in 1920 by the Portsmouth Historical Society. Average Annual Attendance: 7000. Mem: 245; dues $5; annual meeting April.
Income: Financed by membership and investment.
Collections: China, glass, silver, books, documents, furniture, portraits and costumes pertaining to the early history of Portsmouth.

NEW JERSEY

ATLANTIC CITY

PRINCETON ANTIQUES BOOKSERVICE, Art Marketing Reference Library, 2915-17 Atlantic Ave, 08401. Tel: 609-344-1943. *Pres* Robert E Ruffolo Jr, *Cur* Martha Ireland; *Adminr* Robert Eugene.
Open by appointment only. Estab 1974 for pricing documentation of books and antiques. Maintains an art gallery; collection of 19th century art.
Income: $25,000-$30,000 (financed by state appropriation). Purchases: $20,000.
Holdings: Vols 12,500; Per subs 20; AV—Slides; Other—Exhibition catalogs, original art works and prints.
Special Subjects: The function in US of art book market; price information history from 1900.
Special Collections: Post-card Photo Library Information Bank, 1900-1950, consisting 250,000 post-cards.

BLOOMFIELD

NEW JERSEY WATERCOLOR SOCIETY,* c/o Nessa Grainger, *Corresp Secy,* 554 Bloomfield Ave, 07003. Tel: 201-743-8700. *Pres* Don Voorhees, *VPres* Edwin Havas; *Secy* John Bermingham; *Treas* J Luigina. Mem: 110; dues $8.
Exhibitions: Annual Members Shows; Annual Open Juried Exhibitions—alternating between Morris Museum of Arts and Science, Morristown, NJ and the Monmouth Museum, Lincroft, NJ.
Publications: Newsletter, 4 times yearly.
Activities: Traveling exhibitions organized and circulated.

BURLINGTON

BURLINGTON COUNTY HISTORICAL SOCIETY, 457 High St, 08016. Tel: 609-386-4773. *Pres* Rodman Zwirner; *VPres* Susan Bradman; *Secy* Anita Parry; *Dir* Rebecca H Siman.

Open Wed 1 - 4 PM; Sun 2 - 4 PM. Admis by contribution. Estab 1923 to maintain collections relating to Burlington County history and residents; gallery not maintained. Average Annual Attendance: 2300. Mem: 350; dues $3, annual meeting May.
Income: Financed by endowment.
Collections: (Art) Sampler; quilts; china; glass.

CALDWELL

CALDWELL COLLEGE ART GALLERY, 07006. Tel: 201-228-4424. *Dir* Sister M Gerardine.
Open Mon - Fri 8:30 AM - 5 PM; weekends by appointment. No admis. Estab 1970 to provide students and area community with exposure to professional contemporary talent, to afford opportunities for qualified artists to have one-person shows.
Exhibitions: Matteo Jannicello; Markland Thakar; Edward Sokol; Robert Cariola; Esther Fuhrman; Margery Ryerson; Howard Conant; R T Kahn; Eileen Shreiber; Robert Phillips; Tela Banks; Jane Bearman; Ugo Giannini; Sister Mary Compassion; Marlene Lenker; Anne Steele Marsh; Simon Cohen; Frances McQuillan; William Gorman; Ina Golub; Annie Lenney; Ralph Stein; Carmen Cicero; James Kearns; Robert Henri; Sherman Edwards.
Activities: Educ dept in connection with the college art dept; lending collection of lantern slides, kodachromes 10,000, motion pictures, film strips and cartridges; lect open to public, 3 vis lectr per yr; scholarships.

CAMDEN

CAMPBELL MUSEUM, Campbell Place, 08101. Tel: 609-964-4000, exten 2200. *Pres* Ralph Collier; *Museum Asst* Bess Brock.
Open Mon - Fri 9:30 AM - 5 PM. No admis. Estab 1966 to assemble and exhibit a collection of soup equipage such as tureens, plates and ladles. Average Annual Attendance: 20,000.
Income: Financed by endowment.
Exhibitions: Soup Tureens 1976.
Publications: Catalog, every three years.
Activities: Traveling exhibitions organized and circulated.

RUTGERS UNIVERSITY, Stedman Art Gallery, Camden College of Arts & Sciences, Fine Arts Complex, 08102. Tel: 609-757-6350 and 757-6176. *Dir* Virginia Oberlin Steel.
Open Mon - Sat 11 AM - 4 PM. No admis. Estab 1975 to serve educational needs of Art Department, and to serve community of Southern New Jersey. The gallery is a large open space in the Fine Arts Complex. Average Annual Attendance: 7000.
Income: Financed by endowment, and state appropriation. Purchases: $6500.
Collections: Modern and contemporary art, including artists such as Paul Wunderlich, George Rouault, Abraham Rattner, Agnes Denes, Louis Sloan, Bruce Samuelson, Sir Jacob Epstein, Charles Schmidt, Burton Silverman, Ben Kamihira, Harvey Breverman, Jacob Landau, Sandra Lerner, Anne Chapman.
Exhibitions: Changing exhibitions of fine arts in wide range of media.
Publications: Catalog for a major exhibition, yearly.
Activities: Lect open to public, 6 vis lectr per yr; concerts; gallery talks; tours; competitions with purchase prizes.

CLINTON

CLINTON HISTORICAL MUSEUM VILLAGE, 56 Main St, 08826. Tel: 201-735-4101. *Dir* Gloria Lazor; *Cur* Claire Young.
Open Mon - Fri 1 - 5 PM; Sat & Sun Noon - 6 PM. Admis adults $1.75, seniors $1.00, children under 12 50¢, pre-schoolers free. Estab 1960 for the preservation and display of artifacts from the 18th and 19th century for educational and cultural purposes. Four-floor grist mill containing pottery shop, blacksmith shop, general store, log cabin and herb garden. Average Annual Attendance: 22,000. Mem: 250; dues $5 - $1000; annual meeting April.
Income: $85,000 (financed by membership and donations).
Collections: Artifacts pertaining to 18th and 19th centuries.
Publications: The Old Mill Wheel, newsletter, three times a year.
Activities: Classes for adults and children; docent training; harvest jubilee; dance; lect; lending collection of slides; sales shop selling books, slides and gift items.
Library: For historical reference. Holdings: Vols 500.

HUNTERDON ART CENTER, 7 Center St, 08809. Tel: 201-735-8415. *Pres* Larry Carlbon; *VPres* Helen Axel; *Secy* Richard Dieterly; *Dir Exhib* Susan McKelvy; *Office Adminr* Laurie Adams.
Open Tues - Fri 1 - 4 PM; Sat & Sun 1 - 5 PM; cl Mon; No admis. Estab 1951 as a non-profit organization to provide opportunity for adults and children to participate in the enjoyment of the arts and crafts in all forms. The first and second floors provide gallery space. The old stone mill has been remodeled retaining the original atmosphere with open broad wooden beams, white walls and plank flooring. Average Annual Attendance: 15,000. Mem: 2000; dues student $5, single $15, family $20, sustaining $25, patron $100; annual meeting April.
Income: Financed by membership, city and state appropriations, and federal funding. Purchases: $100.
Collections: †Print collection.
Exhibitions: National Print Exhibition; Annual Exhibit; Members Exhibition; Invitational group shows; Antique Show; Craft Exhibition; Folk Art Bazaar.
Publications: Newsletter, monthly.
Activities: Classes for adults and children; workshops; lect open to public; competitions; theatre productions; informal chamber music; films; museum shop selling prints, pottery, weavings, jewelry and books.

CONVENT STATION

COLLEGE OF SAINT ELIZABETH, Mahoney Library, 07961. Tel: 201-539-1600, exten 365. *Librn* Sister Marie Rousek.
Open weekdays 9 AM - 5 PM. Estab 1899 for academic purposes; gallery not maintained.
Income: Financed by private funds.
Holdings: Vols 130,000 (total, not art only); Per subs 1000; AV—Cassettes, film strips, microfiche, microfilm, phonorecords; Other—Exhibition catalogs, reproductions.
Special Subjects: Art; Science; Religion; Social Science; Women.
Special Collections: Rare Atlases and Bibles.
Exhibitions: (1976) Watercolors by Rita Keiper; Sculpture by Marie Welsh. (1977) Selected prints from the Vatican Exhibition of Contemporary American Spiritual Art; New Jersey's First Feminists.

EAST ORANGE

ART CENTRE OF NEW JERSEY, 16 Washington St, 07017. Tel: 201-674-8445. *Pres* Eve Breeden; *Treas* George Schwacha; *VPres* John Watson & Frances McQuillan; *Recording Secy* Cathy Cantlin.
Open daily. Estab 1924 as an art school and as a venue for art events, lectures, etc. Three galleries and one large work studio. Mem: 250; dues $10; annual meeting May.
Income: Financed by membership and art sales.
Exhibitions: Annual Regional and members exhibitions, as well as others.
Publications: Quarterly.
Activities: Classes for adults; docent training; workshops; lect open to public; gallery talks; competitions.

ELIZABETH

FREE PUBLIC LIBRARY OF ELIZABETH, NJ, 11 S Broad St, 07202. Tel: 201-354-6060. *Library Dir* Hazel Hulbert Elks; *Asst Dir* Roman Sawycky; *Sr Art Librn* Daisy Tamayo.
Open Mon - Fri 9 AM - 9 PM; cl Sun. No admis. Estab 1913, the art department functions within the area library system, it offers free service to patrons of Elizabeth and also to patrons of neighboring towns, Roselle Park, Kenilworth, Union and Cranford; special exhibit area displays paintings and miscellaneous objects d'art.
Income: Financed by city and state appropriations.
Collections: Fine Arts †Vols 15,000; †mounted pictures 200,000, illustrations and photographs on miscellaneous subjects for lending; †large art reproductions 800, some framed, all for lending; reference collection of Japanese prints by various artists.
Exhibitions: Works by local artists and photographers; other special exhibitions from time to time.
Activities: Dramatic programs; furnish information on history and current trends in art education; lect open to the public, 15 vis lectr per yr; concerts; extension dept servicing Elizabeth and towns of Union, Kenilworth, Roselle Park, Cranford, material available to patrons of these municipalities with no fees; individual prints lent to schools; lending collection contains film strips 400 and projection equipment, motion pictures 250.

HOPEWELL

HOPEWELL MUSEUM,* 28 E Broad St, 08525. Tel: 609-466-0103. *Pres* Dr Donald M Bergen; *Cur* Beverly Weidl; *Asst Cur* Betsy Errickson.
Open Mon, Wed & Sat 2 - 5 PM; cl National holidays. No admis, donations suggested. Estab 1922 as a museum of local history from early 1700 through 1900, to show what this community was like for almost 300 years. Average Annual Attendance: 2000.
Income: Financed by endowment, membership and donations.
Collections: Colonial parlor; Victorian parlor; Colonial furniture; antique china, glass, silver and pewter; early needlework; Indian handicrafts; photograph collection.

Publications: Hopewell Valley Heritage; Pioneers of Old Hopewell; maps.
Library: For reference. Holdings: Vols on local history.

JERSEY CITY

HUDSON COUNTY COURT HOUSE,* Board of Chosen Freeholders, 595 Newark Ave, 07306. Tel: 201-792-3737. *Dir* Hon Anne H O'Malley; *County Supv* Hon Edward F Clark Jr.
Mural Paintings: The Coming of the Dutch, The Coming of the English, In Old Dutch Days and decorations in Superior Court Room, by Howard Pyle; The Purchase of Pavonia and A Skirmish with the Indians, by Frank D Millet; Washington Watching the Assault on Fort Washington from Fort Lee and The First Trip of the Clermont (in the upper gallery of the Rotunda), by Charles Yardley Turner; dome decorations installed 1911, by Edwin Howland Blashfield.

JERSEY CITY MUSEUM ASSOCIATION, 472 Jersey Ave, 07302. Tel: 201-547-4513. *Pres* J Owen Grundy; *VPres* Theodore Conrad; *Secy* Adelaide Dear; *Treas* Arthur Hansen; *Trustee & Cur* Cynthia Sanford; *Asst Cur* Robert Ferguson.
Open Wed 4 - 8 PM; Fri & Sat 11 AM - 4:30 PM. No admis. Estab 1932 for the purpose of advancing interest in the Arts, Sciences and History. Maintains art gallery housing Will Collection. Average Annual Attendance: 10,000. Mem: 189; dues from Junior $1 to Benefactor $1000; meetings Nov, Jan and Mar.
Income: $1,000 (financed by endowment).
Collections: Will Collection of Paintings & Drawings (1850's - 1910) of Jersey City Scenes; modern and old paintings; sculpture; antiques; local historical pictures and artifacts; posters.
Publications: Year Book.
Activities: Educ dept; lect open to public, 4 - 5 vis lectr per yr; competitions.

JERSEY CITY PUBLIC LIBRARY, Fine Arts Department, 678 Newark Ave, 07306. Tel: 201-547-4546. *Dir* Ben Grimm; *Librn Fine Arts Dept* Alfred Trattner.
Open Mon 1 - 8 PM; Tues - Fri 10 AM - 6 PM; Sat 10 AM - 5 PM. Circ: 28,000. Maintains an art gallery of four movable panels totalling 250 sq ft.
Income: Financed by city appropriation. Purchases: $12,000.
Holdings: Vols 9,400; Per subs 40; AV—Cassettes, film strips, motion pictures, phonorecords, slides; Other—Framed reproductions, prints and reproductions.

JERSEY CITY STATE COLLEGE,* Courtney Art Gallery, Dept of Art, 2039 Kennedy Blvd, 07307. Tel: 201-547-3214. *Dir* Raymond Statlander.
Open Mon - Fri 10 AM - 5 PM. No admis. Estab 1969 to bring examples of professional work to the campus in each of the areas in which students are involved—painting, sculpture, film, photography, textiles, weaving, ceramics, graphic design; operated by students, and with the Jersey City Museum form a student internship training program. Average Annual Attendance: 5000.
Income: Financed by city or state appropriation, and Art Department.
Collections: Small collection of prints and paintings which are on loan to faculty and staff offices on campus.
Exhibitions: Recent Work Annual; Photography; Video; multi-media exhibitions in painting, sculpture, ceramics, crafts, animation, antiques and prints.
Activities: Lect open to the public, 5 vis lectr per yr; gallery talks; extension dept serving community organizations; individual paintings and original objects of art lent; lending collection contains color reproductions 500, film strips, Kodachromes 5000, motion pictures 30, photographs 200; traveling exhibitions organized and circulated.

PAINTERS AND SCULPTORS SOCIETY OF NEW JERSEY, INC,* c/o May Heiloms, *Hon Life Pres,* 340 W 28th St, New York, NY 10001. Tel: 212-924-2596.
Estab 1941. Average Annual Attendance: 10,000. Mem: 115; qualif for mem: new members by invitation only, through election by Mem Comt. Dues $15; meetings March and Nov.
Exhibitions: 1976 annual exhibitions held at National Arts Club Gallery, New York City; jury, prizes. Exhibition open to all artists nationally and internationally; nonmembers subject to jury of selection. Exhibitions usually one-third members and two-thirds nonmembers.

SAINT PETER'S COLLEGE ART GALLERY, Kennedy Blvd, 07306. Tel: 201-333-4400. *Dir* Oscar Magnan; *Dir Special Prog* Edward Reuther; *Secy* Antuanette Caruso.
Open Mon, Tue, Fri & Sat 11 AM - 4 PM; Wed & Thurs 11 AM - 9 PM. No admis. Estab 1971 to present the different art trends; good space with good lighting and alarm systems.

Income: Financed by the college.
Exhibitions: 40 Years of American Collage; The History of the Poster; Puerto Rican Prints; 3D/2D.
Activities: Classes for adults; docent training; lect open to public, 20 vis lectr per yr; concerts; gallery talks; tours; exten dept serving students.
Library: The College Library, Art Section. *Librn* Richard Tetrau. Open to students and faculty.

LAKEWOOD

GEORGIAN COURT COLLEGE, Gallery, Lakewood Ave, 08701. Tel: 201-364-2200, exten 48. *Dir* Sister M Christina Geis.
Open Mon - Fri 9 AM - 4 PM. No admis. Estab 1964 to offer art students the opportunity to view the works of professional artists, and also to exhibit student work. One large room with 100 running feet of wall area for flat work; the center area for sculpture. Average Annual Attendance: 1000.
Income: Financed through the college.
Exhibitions: Halina Rusak (paintings); Douglas McIlvain (sculpture); Frances McIlvain (watercolors); Monita Boesewetter (sculpture); Jane Geayer (paintings); Merri Vetrano (drawings & wall hangings); Sister M Christina (paintings); Lois Rapp (watercolors); Fenn Vogt (wall sculptures).

LAVALLETTE

FEDERATED ART ASSOCIATIONS OF NEW JERSEY, INC,* 31 Pershing Blvd, 08735. Tel: 201-793-0803. *Pres* Barbara L Jost; *Secy* Rose Reilly; *Exec Secy* Jane Whipple Green; *Judge and Jury Chmn* Mary Keim Tietze; *Parliamentarian* Lucy Worley.
Estab 1969 to provide communication and exchange of ideas among art associations. Mem: 2000 (35 clubs); dues per club $10; annual seminar, four sections meet separately in Oct, Nov, Feb and March.
Publications: Newsletter, four times a year; Dictionary of Art Organizations in New Jersey, annually in Sept.
Activities: Lect open to the public and other interested art clubs at section meetings; supply information to member groups on running state shows, selection of judges, program suggestions.

LINCROFT

MONMOUTH MUSEUM AND CULTURAL CENTER, Brookdale Community College, Newman Springs Road, 07738. Tel: 201-747-2302. *Dir* Dr Judith Van Baron; *Pres* Howard R Berger; *First VPres* Philip C Carling; *Second VPres* Jean Blair; *Prog Adminr* Susan Gmeiner.
Open Mon - Sat 10 AM - 4:30 PM; Sun 1 - 5 PM. Admis adults $1; children and sr citizens 50¢; free to Museum members and students. Estab 1963 to advance interest in art, science and nature in this area. The Museum houses two large galleries; an upper level gallery and the main gallery; an educational programs area and a conference area. Average Annual Attendance: 100,000. Mem: 1600; dues individual $9, family $15; annual meetings Jan.
Income: $250,000 (financed by membership, donations, and county funds).
Exhibitions: Monmouth County Collects; Blacks and the Westward Movement; Leonardo and his Inventions; Impact: Architecture; Made in Monmouth; Indian Art of the Americas; American Handcrafts; Hands on Nature.
Publications: newsletter, quarterly; calendar of events.
Activities: Classes for adults and children; docent training; lect open to public; artmobile; traveling trunks organized and circulated for use in schools; museum shop selling books and gift items.

LONG BRANCH

LONG BRANCH HISTORICAL MUSEUM, 1260 Ocean Ave, 07740. Tel: 201-229-0600; 201-222-9879. *Pres* Edgar N Dinkelspiel.
Open summers Wed - Sun 10 AM - 5 PM; cl Mon & Tues; other times by appointment. No admis. Estab 1953 as post Civil War historical museum. Average Annual Attendance: (at art shows) 10,000. Dues $1.00.
Income: Financed by Art Shows.
Exhibitions: Art Shows for several years.
Publications: Annual Art Show Book.

MADISON

DREW UNIVERSITY,* College Art Gallery, 07940. Tel: 201-377-3000, exten 320. *Dean* Robert Ackerman; *Chmn Art Dept* Martyvonne Dehoney.

Open weekdays 1 - 4 PM; Sat 9 AM - Noon, and by appointment. Estab 1968 to provide 8 or 9 exhibitions each school year to augment program of courses and to serve the community. Mailing list of about 700 persons, outside the campus. Mem: 60 consisting of Friends of the College Gallery and student members.
Income: Financed by university instructional budget, general budget and donations.
Collection: Study collection of serigraphs, lithographs and intaglio prints; pottery; large sculpture by Robert Mallary.
Exhibitions: One-person shows; Berger Collection of Prints; The Print-making Council of New Jersey Benefit Show; Aspects of Drawing; Student Show and others; some shows on loan from major New York galleries. During the shows, often a discussion session takes place with the artist(s) in the Gallery.
Library: For art history courses. Holdings: AV—Slides.

MILLBURN

PAPER MILL PLAYHOUSE,* Brookside Dr, 07041. Tel: 201-379-3636. *Dir* Frank Carrington; *Cur* Gene Carrington.
Gallery open during all performances, Sept. through July. Estab 1929, inc 1930, building purchased 1934; gallery above lobby was opened 1936.
Collections: Paintings and prints.
Exhibitions: Changing exhibitions throughout season include work by local groups and individual artists of standing.

MONTCLAIR

MONTCLAIR ART MUSEUM, 3 South Mountain Ave (Mailing Add: PO Box X, 07042). Tel: 201-746-5555. *Pres* S Barksdale Penick Jr; *Dir* Kathryn E Gamble; *Asst Dir* Robert J Koenig; *Cur* C O'Brien; *Coordinator Public Relations* Lillian Bristol; *Curatorial Registrar* Joan Lorenson; *Education Cur* Terry J Sherman; *Bursar* Adelaide R Birnie.
Open Tues - Sat 10 AM - 5 PM; Sun 2 - 5:30 PM. No admis. Estab 1914; five galleries of changing exhibitions; one gallery of permanent exhibition; student gallery. Average Annual Attendance: 38,000 - 40,000. Mem: 2500; dues general $20.
Income: Financed by endowment, membership.
Collections: †Chiefly American paintings, 18th - 20th Century; American costumes; The Lang Collection and Tomlin Collection of Chinese snuff bottles; the Rand Collection of American Indian art; the Sargent Collection of North American Indian necklaces; prints and drawings; The Whitney Silver Collection.
Exhibitions: Moses and Ida Soyer Collection; Vaclav Vytlacil Retrospective; Heritage of Freedom.
Publications: Bulletin, bi-monthly, 5 issues.
Activities: Classes for adults and children; docent training; workshops, coordinated programs with school groups; lect open to the public, 6-8 vis lectr per yr; concerts; gallery talks every Sunday; tours; museum shop selling books, reproductions, slides, handcrafted textiles, pottery, jewelry, objects for children.
—LeBrun Library: *Librn* Edith A Rights. Tel: 201-746-5555. Open Tues - Fri 10 AM - 5 PM; Sat 10 AM - 1 PM; cl July & August. Estab to support the scholarship of the curatorial staff of the museum, for reference only.
Income: Financed by endowment, membership.
Holdings: Vols 8000; Per subs 50; AV—Audio tapes, cassettes, microfiche, phonorecords, slides; Other—Clipping files, exhibition catalogs, reproductions.
Special Subjects: American Indian culture and crafts.
Special Collections: Bookplates, posters.
Publications: Montclair Art Museum Bulletin, bi-monthly, 5 issues.

MORRISTOWN

MORRIS MUSEUM OF ARTS AND SCIENCES,* Normandy Heights & Columbia Rds, 07960 (Mailing Add: PO Box 125, Convent, 07961) Tel: 201-538-0452. *Dir* Chester H Newkirk; *Asst Dir* Robert J Koenig; *Art Cur* Mary Chandor.
Open Mon - Sat 10 AM - 5 PM; Sun 2 - 5 PM. Summer, July and August, Tues - Sat 10 AM - 4 PM; cl major holidays. Admis adults $1, children 25¢, students & senior citizens 50¢, groups 25¢. Inc 1943. Average Annual Attendance: 135,000. Mem: 1300; dues students and senior citizens $5, individual $10, couple $15, family $25, organizations $25 and up, patron $50, benefactor $100; annual meeting third Wed in Jan.
Collections: American historic and foreign; decorative arts; North American Indians; dolls.
Activities: Dance, music and drama programs; art and nature workshops; audio-visual; lectures; gallery talks; tours; sales shop; Junior Museum (Five Sense Center).

Library: Holdings—Vols art and science 1000; AV—Art slides; reading room.

MOUNT HOLLY

HISTORIC BURLINGTON COUNTY PRISON MUSEUM,* 128 High St, 08060. Tel: 609-267-2104. *Cur* Harold R Hirshblond.
Open Tues - Sat 10 AM - Noon & 1 - 4 PM; cl National holidays. No admis. Estab 1966 in the old Burlington County Prison built in 1810. Mem: dues $2.
Collections: Paintings; sculpture; graphics; glass; Indian artifacts; historic military materials.
Activities: Lectures; guided tours; concerts; competitions; temporary and traveling exhibitions; sales shop.

NEW BRUNSWICK

RUTGERS UNIVERSITY
—Art Gallery, Voorhees Hall, Hamilton St, 08903. Tel: 201-932-7237. *Dir & Cur Prints* Phillip Dennis Cate; *Cur Painting & Sculpture* Jeffrey Wechsler; *Admin Asst Educ* Stephanie Grunberg.
Open Mon - Fri 10 AM - 4:30 PM; Sat & Sun noon - 5 PM. No admis. Estab 1966 to house Fine Arts Collection and present exhibitions through the school year. Average Annual Attendance: 40,000. Mem: 300; dues single $10, family $15, patron $25, endowment $100.
Income: Financed by state appropriation. Purchases: $10,000.
Collections: 15th and 17th century Italian; 17th century Dutch; 18th, 19th and 20th century American; 18th and 19th century English paintings; †19th and 20th century French and American prints.
Exhibitions: (1976) Photographic Process as Medium; Contemporary Latin American Artists; Miniature Woodcuts (Posada); The City of New Brunswick from the Revolution to the First World War (Bicentennial exhibition); Contemporary American Prints; Sam Gilliam; Edward Steichen: WWII; (1977) Surrealism and American Art: 1931-1947; Pre-Columbian Ceramics: the Harkna Collection; Twelve from Rutgers; (1978) Henry Reuterdal; Hungarian Art Nouveau; The Color Revolution: Color Lithography in France 1890-1900.
Publications: Exhibition catalogs, annually; Friends Newsletter.
Activities: Classes for adults and children; lect open to public; concerts; gallery talks; tours; traveling exhibitions organized and circulated.
—Art Library. Tel: 201-932-7739. *Librn* Ferris Olin.
Open Mon - Thurs 9 AM - 10 PM; Fri 9 AM - 5 PM; Sat Noon - 5 PM; Sun 1 - 11 PM during academic yr. Estab 1966 as a research library dealing specifically with art and related topics.
Holdings: Vols 30,000; Per subs 200; AV—Microfiche, microfilm; Other—Clipping files, exhibition catalogs, museum reports, pamphlets, sales catalogs and miscellaneous items related to art.
Special Subjects: Art history covering Ancient Egypt, Greek, Roman, Early Christian, Gothic, Renaissance, Baroque, Modern and Contemporary periods.
Special Collections: Stern Collection of Modern art; Cowdery Collection of American art.

NEWARK

NEW JERSEY HISTORICAL SOCIETY MUSEUM, 230 Broadway, 07104. Tel: 201-483-3939. *Chmn of the Bd* Milford A Vieser; *Pres* Robert A Beck; *Dir* Clifford L Lord; *Cur* Howard W Wiseman; *Registrar* Alan D Frazer.
Open Tue - Sat 10 AM - 4:15 PM. No admis. Estab 1845 to collect, preserve, exhibit and make available for study the materials pertaining to the history of New Jersey and its people. The gallery has six period rooms and lobby display cases on the main floor; three galleries on second floor totaling 3900 sq ft devoted to permanent or changing exhibitions. Average Annual Attendance: 10,000. Mem: 3600; dues adults $20 and up; annual meeting third Wed in April.
Income: Financed by endowment, membership gifts and grants. Purchases: $500.
Collections: New Jersey portraits, landscapes, prints and photographs; important technical drawings from 1790-1815; silver; toys; sculpture; silhouettes and miniatures; Indian relics; World War I posters; ceramics; glassware.
Exhibitions: (1976-78) The Small Bright World of Anna Linder; New Jersey Medicine in the Revolutionary Era; The Pulse of the People; A Collector's Legacy/Bequest of Edwin A Ely; A Self-Portrait/The New Jersey Historical Society, 1845-1977; The American Marines in the Revolution; Yearning to Breathe Free; Shooting Pictures by A B Frost; Alone with the Pigeons/Public Sculpture in New Jersey (photographs and graphics).
Publications: New Jersey History, quarterly; New Jersey Messenger, quarterly newsletter; The Cockpit; The Crossroads; exhibition catalogs.

Activities: Classes for children; docent training; school history clubs; lectr open to the public; tours; competitions; individual paintings and original objects of art lent to established institutions; traveling exhibitions organized and circulated; sales shop selling books, reproductions, prints and items for children.

—**Library.** Tel: 201-483-3939. *Asst Dir* Robert C Morris; *Reference Librn* Barbara S Irwin; *Keeper of Manuscripts* Don C Skemer; *Cataloger* Cynthia E Browne; *Conservator* Janet L Koch.

Open Tues - Sat 10 AM - 4:15 PM. Estab to collect and make available materials relating to the study of New Jersey History. For reference only.

Income: Financed by endowment, membership, gifts and grants. Purchases: $4000.

Holdings: Vols 55,000; AV—Audio Tapes, microfilm; Other—Clipping files, exhibition catalogs, original documents, pamphlets, maps, broadsides.

Special Collections: Rare books, manuscripts (over 1000 major groups); 18th and 19th century newspapers.

Publications: Library Acquisitions, quarterly.

NEWARK MUSEUM, 49 Washington St, (Mailing Add: PO Box 540, 07101). Tel: 201-733-6600. *Pres* Robert M Krementz; *Dir* Samuel C Miller; *Asst to Dir* Dorothy McNally; *Admin Asst* Wilmot T Bartle; *Business Mgr* Dominic A Lisanti; *Dir Educ* Sally O'C Townsend; *Junior Museum* Sheryl Bouler; *Lending Dept* Anne Vanderhoof; *Arts Workshop* Jean West; *Prog & Publ* Marjorie H Fredericks; *Pub Relations* Mary Sue Sweeney; *Cur Classical* Susan Auth; *Cur Coins & Fri Museum* Dorothy B Bartle; *Cur Decorative Arts* Phillip H Curtis; *Cur Oriental Coll* Valrae Reynolds; *Cur Ethnology* Anne Spencer; *Cur Painting & Sculpture* Fearn Thurlow.

Open daily Noon - 5 PM; holidays 1 - 5 PM; cl Thanksgiving Day, Christmas, New Years and July 4. No admis. Estab 1909 to exhibit articles of art, science, history and technology, and for the study of the arts and sciences. The building was the gift of Louis Bamberger, opened 1926; held in trust by the Museum Assoc for the City of Newark, which gave the site. The adjoining building purchased by Museum in 1937. Average Annual Attendance: 231,106. Mem: 3,470; dues $10 and up; annual meeting Jan.

Income: $1,800,000 (financed by city and state appropriations, county funds).

Collections: †American painting and sculpture of all periods with primitives well represented; †Tibetan, †Chinese, †Japanese, †Indian, †African, †South Pacific, †American Indian and †Islamic Art; †Mediterranean Antiquities, including Eugene Schaefer Collection of ancient glass; †decorative arts; †Pre-Columbian material; †crosses and crucifixes; †coins.

Exhibitions: Whaling Days in New Jersey; Tibet: A Lost World; Making Movies in New Jersey; Survival: Life and Art of the Alaskan Eskimo; As the Seasons Turn: Southwest Indian Easel Painting of the Early 20th Century and Related Traditional Art; Myth and Gospel, Art of Coptic Egypt; 2000 Years of Chinese Ceramics; Colonial and Federal Portraits from the Collection; The Two Worlds of Japanese Art; Murals Without Walls; Lee Garch; Abstract Artists from the Collection.

Publications: New Notes, monthly; The Newark Museum, quarterly; catalogs and bulletins on major exhibitions.

Activities: Classes for adults and children; dramatic programs; docent training; lect open to public, 15 - 20 vis lectr per yr; concerts; gallery talks; tours; competitions; exten dept serving community neighborhoods; individual paintings and original objects of art lent to museums; lending collection contains nature artifacts; museum shop selling books, magazines, original art, reproductions, prints, original craft items from around the world; junior museum.

—**Library.** Tel: 201-733-6640 and 733-6584. *Librn* Eleanor Townsend; *Library Asst* Helen Olsson.

Open Mon - Fri 9 AM - 5 PM. Estab 1926 to serve the Museum staff and to provide information on the collections.

Holdings: Vols 21,000; Per subs 143; AV—Kodachromes, lantern slides, slides; Other—Clipping files, exhibition catalogs, pamphlets, photographs.

Special Subjects: American art of all periods; decorative arts; Oriental art; Tibet; American Indian art; primitive art; general art subjects.

Special Collections: Tibet

Publications: Acquisitions list, bimonthly to staff.

—**Junior Museum.** *Supv* Sheryl B Bouler; *Asst Supv* Stephen Kneisel; *Art Asst* Naomi King; *Art Asst* Barbara Mauriello.

Open daily Noon - 5 PM. No admis. Estab 1926 to supply art and science programs designed to stimulate the individual child in exploration and discovery of self expression, and to teach the child effective use of the Museum as a whole, which may lead him or her to valuable lifetime interests. Average Annual Attendance: 16,733. Mem: 10,123; dues 10¢; annual meeting May.

Income: Financed through Newark Museum.

Collections: Art

Exhibitions: Changing exhibits; annual exhibition of children's work.

Activities: Art and science education resource information and workshops; after-school, Saturday, and summer workshops in art for children ages 3-18; pre-school art workshops Tues - Fri mornings; special holiday festivals for children; awards; field trips; parents art workshops; special education workshops for exceptional children and adults.

NEWARK PUBLIC LIBRARY, 5 Washington St (Mailing Add: Box 630, 07101). Tel: 201-733-7840. *Supv Art & Music Dept* William J Dane; *Prin Art Librarian* Joan E Burns.

Open Mon, Wed & Thurs 9 AM - 9 PM; Tues & Fri 9 AM - 6 PM; Sat 9 AM - 5 PM. Estab 1888 to provide materials on all aspects of the visual arts to the metropolitan area of New Jersey. Circ: 70,000. Maintains an art gallery: three separate galleries with a total of 375 running feet.

Income: Financed by city and state appropriations. Purchases: $18,000.

Holdings: Per subs 70,000; AV—Cassettes, microfiche, microfilm, and slides; Other—Clipping files, exhibition catalogs, manuscripts, original art works, original documents, pamphlets, photographs, prints, and reproductions.

Special Subjects: Fine prints; Japanese books and prints; history of fine printing.

Special Collections: Autographs; Posters (2500); picture collection (1,000,000 illustrations); art slides (15,000); R C Jenkinson Collection of fine printing (3100 items); fine print collection (12,000).

Exhibitions: Photography in Posters; Heritage of Italian Printing; American Art Magazines; Minna Citron: Prints in Series; Visuals for Black Studies; Folk Costume the World Over; The Hoboken Five; Posters from Paris 1955-1970; Caxton and His Followers; Oversize Art Books and Prints.

Publications: Calendar of events, bimonthly.

Activities: Lect open to public; concerts; gallery talks; library tours; traveling exhibitions organized and circulated.

NORTH BRUNSWICK

JOHNSTON NATIONAL SCOUTING MUSEUM, Rtes 1 and 130, 08902. Tel: 201-249-6000, exten 428. *Dir* Ilmar Pleer; *Cur* Joan Delle Cave.

Open Tues - Sat 9 AM - 4:30 PM; Sun 1 - 4:30 PM; cl Mon & holidays. No admis (donations encouraged). Estab 1960 to provide a learning experience for youth groups and the general public through the preservation and exhibition of the history of the Boy Scouts of America by maintaining a diversified collection of scouting memorabilia. There is a weather station, replica of a space capsule, replica of the liberty bell, and a theater for showing scout-related motion pictures, plus conservation and history subjects. Average Annual Attendance: 50,000.

Income: Financed by the Boy Scouts of America.

Collections: National and international scouting memorabilia including works by Baden-Powell, Daniel Beard, and Ernest T Seton; Tussaud wax sculpture of Baden-Powell; original art works; Norman Rockwell's scouting paintings.

Exhibitions: Norman Rockwell traveling exhibit; Sailing Ships; Christmas Around the World; Wood Carving; The Symbols of Christmas; Historical Highlights of the Boy Scouts of America 1910-1978; High Adventure and Historic Trails programs of the BSA.

Activities: Competitions; individual paintings and original objects of art lent to Scout councils, individual scout troops and cub packs, museums, and libraries; lending collection contains books, cassettes, color reproductions, framed reproductions, original art works, lantern slides, original prints, paintings, phonorecords, photographs, sculpture, uniform parts, patches, insignia and posters; sales shop selling books, magazines, original art, prints, slides, patches, neckerchiefs, cassettes and souvenirs.

Library: Johnston Memorial Library. Open to public for reference. Holdings: Vols 3000; Per subs 7; Other—encyclopedias, Braille magazines and handbooks.

Special Subjects: Scouting history, scouting fiction, biographies and autobiographies of prominent individuals, nature subjects, state travel and history books, science, military, Americana, religion, and Norman Rockwell.

Special Collections: Original books by Sir Robert Baden-Powell, Daniel Beard, Ernest Thompson Seton; autographed books presented by prominent individuals, back issues (to 1911) of scout related periodicals, handbooks.

NUTLEY

MINIATURE ART SOCIETY OF NEW JERSEY,* 200 Chestnut St, 07110. Tel: 201-661-2280. *Pres* John Barnwell; *VPres Publicity* Pat Longley; *VPres Programs* Marilyn Brill; *Secy* Vivian Noyes Fikus; *Treas* V Egan; *Recording Secy* Adele Landfear.

Mem: 100; dues $10, meeting first Wed each month.

Exhibitions: Annual National Show; four to five traveling shows a year.

Publications: Newsletter, four to five times a year.

Activities: Traveling exhibitions organized and circulated; competitions.

NUTLEY PUBLIC LIBRARY, 93 Booth Dr, 07110. Tel: 201-667-0405. *Dir* Richard P. Bernaudo; *Children's Services* Jean E Roberts; *Acquisitions and Young Adult Services* Yolanda Iocovantuno; *Reference* Ann L Eustance; *Technical Services* Mara E Pavars; *Adult Services* Jean V Piro.
Open Mon, Tues & Thurs 9 AM - 9 PM; Wed & Fri 9 AM - 5:30 PM; Sat 9 AM - 1 PM. Estab 1913 to provide library services; gallery not maintained. Circ: 143,000.
Income: $212,867 (financed by city and state appropriation). Purchases: $35,447.
Holdings: Vols 81,805; Per subs 212; AV—Audio tapes, cassettes, film strips, microfilm, phonorecords; Other—Clipping files, pamphlets, reproductions.
Special Collections: Nutley authors.
Activities: Classes for children; dramatic programs.

PARAMUS

BERGEN COMMUNITY MUSEUM, E Ridgewood & Farview Ave, 07652. Tel: 201-265-1248, 265-1255. *Dir* Carol Stahl; *Preparator* Charlotte Withington; *Secy* Gladys Choolijan; *Educ Liaison* Robyn-Lynn Gudehus.
Open Wed - Sat 1 - 5 PM; Sun 2 - 6 PM. No admis. Estab May 1956 to maintain a museum which will provide a creative and recreative center to stimulate youth and adult interest in arts, science, history and industry.
Income: Financed by membership, contributions and country appropriations.
Collections: Mainly works of New Jersey artists.
Publications: Calendar, bi-monthly.
Activities: Classes for children; lect open to the public, 10 vis lectr per yr; concerts; gallery talks; tours; individual paintings lent to county offices; museum shop selling books, souvenirs for children.

PATERSON

PASSAIC COUNTY HISTORICAL SOCIETY,* Lambert Castle, PO Box 1729, 07509. Tel: 201-523-9883. *Cur* Edward M Graf.
Open Wed - Fri 1 - 4:45 PM; cl Mon, Tues, Thanksgiving, Christmas and New Year's Day. No admis. Estab 1926, located in Lambert Castle built in 1892. Mem: Dues regular $5, sustaining $10, contributing $25.
Collections: Paintings; sculpture; primitive art; Indian art; textiles; coins; spoon collection; local historical material.
Publications: Castle Lite, bi-monthly newsletter; pamphlets.
Activities: Lectures; guided tours; temporary and traveling exhibitions sponsored; sales shop selling slides, postcards and souvenirs.
Library: Open to the public when museum is open. Holdings: Vols 5000.

PITTSTOWN

ASSOCIATED ARTISTS OF NEW JERSEY, RD #1, 08867. Tel: 201-735-5831. *Pres* Ruth Krieger; *VPres* Joseph Konopka; *Secy* Anne Steele Marsh.
Estab 1941 to hold one or two exhibitions a year, with informal meetings in summer. Mem: 50; members selected by invitation of Board; dues $7; annual meeting April/May.
Income: Financed by membership.

PLAINFIELD

PLAINFIELD PUBLIC LIBRARY, Eighth St at Park Ave, 07060. Tel: 201-757-1111. *Dir* L A Moore.
Open Mon - Fri 9 AM - 9 PM; Sat 9 AM - 5 PM. Estab 1881. Circ: 200,000. Maintains an art gallery with original artworks on permanent display, group shows as scheduled.
Income: $575,000 (financed by endowment, city and state appropriation, and Federal funds).
Holdings: Vols 190,000; Per subs 546; AV—Cassettes, film strips, Kodachromes, microfiche, microfilm, motion pictures, phonorecords, slides and video tapes; Other—Exhibition catalogs, original art works, photographs.
Special Collections: Lincoln Fine Arts Collection (books & periodicals); Arts of the United States (slides).
Exhibitions: Associated Artists of New Jersey; Invitational Exhibits; Annual National Print Exhibition; student work.
Activities: Dramatic programs; lect open to public, 3 - 4 vis lectr per yr; gallery talks; library tours.

PRINCETON

PRINCETON UNIVERSITY
—**Art Museum,** 08540. Tel: 609-452-3787. *Dir* Fred S Licht; *Asst Dir* Allen Rosenbaum; *Cur Coll* Frances F Jones; *Dir Publ* Virginia Wage-

man; *Dir Community Services* Mary Wisnovsky; *Registrar* Robert Lafond; *Custodian Prints & Drawings* Barbara T. Ross.
Open Tues - Sat 10 AM - 4 PM; Sun 1 - 5 PM (summer 2 - 4 PM; cl Mon & major holidays. No admis. Estab 1882 to make original works of art available to students in the Dept of Art & Archeology and also for the enjoyment of the University, community and general public. About 24,000 sq ft of gallery space for permanent, semi-permanent and changing installations. Average Annual Attendance: 90,000. Mem: 1200; dues $15 and up.
Income: Financed by endowment and University. Purchases: $150,000.
Collections: †Far Eastern, especially Chinese and Japanese, painting; †Chinese ritual bronze vessels; †pre-Columbian; †ancient Mediterranean; †mediaeval and later European; †British and American.
Exhibitions: Temporary exhibitions arranged for 1976-77, from museum collection and other loan exhibitions and miscellaneous exhibitions.
Publications: Record of the Art Museum, Princeton University, semi-annually; catalogs, occasionally.
Activities: Docent training; lect open to public and for member only; gallery talks and tours.
—**Index of Christian Art, McCormick Hall.** Tel: 609-452-3773. *Dir* Rosalie B Green.
Open Mon - Fri 9 AM - 5 PM; cl August and holidays. Estab 1917 as a division of the Dept of Art and Archaeology. It is a research and reference collection of cards and photographs designed to facilitate the study of Christian iconography in works of art before 1400. Duplicate copies exist in Washington, DC in the Dumbarton Oaks Research Center and in Los Angeles in the Library of the University of California. European copies in Rome in the Vatican Library and in Utrecht in the University.

RINGOES

RELIGIOUS AMERICANA MUSEUM, Van Lieu's Road, 08551. Tel: 201-782-0392. *Cur* Mrs Joseph J Domas; *Trustee* Clyde M McBride; *Secy* Joseph J Domas; two volunteer staff members.
Open Mon - Fri 10 AM - 4 PM; weekends to church groups by appointment. No admis. Estab 1971 as a corporation under New Jersey laws to preserve our nation's religious heritage in artifacts of the three major faiths. Main gallery 35 x 18 ft, two side galleries 25 x 16 ft. Average Annual Attendance: 200; annual meeting May.
Income: Financed by donations and lecture fees.
Collections: Over 450 artifacts, in 23 media, all made in America before 1900. Beadwork; books (pamphlets, broadsides, leaflets); bottles; ceramics; chalkware; cloth; costume; glass; horn; jewelry; metal (brass, copper, iron, pewter, silver, tin); music; needlework; painting; paperwork; parian; perforated cardboard; plaster; pottery; prints (woodcuts, engravings, lithographs); quilts; scrimshaw; shellwork; stone and wood.
Exhibitions: Beginnings (founders of sects); Issues (affecting all faiths); Regional; Folk Art.
Activities: Classes for children; lect open to public.
Library: Open to serious students only.

RINGWOOD

RINGWOOD MANOR HOUSE MUSEUM,* Sloatsburg Rd (Mailing Add: PO Box 1304, 07456). Tel: 201-962-7031. *Cur* Elbertus Prol.
Open May - Oct Tues - Fri 10 AM - 4 PM; Sat, Sun & holidays 10 AM - 5 PM. Admis adults 50¢, children free. Estab 1935.
Income: Financed by state appropriation.
Collections: Paintings; graphics; decorative arts; furniture; historical material.
Activities: Guided tours; sales shop.

RIVER VALE

RIVER VALE PUBLIC LIBRARY, 644 River Vale Road, 07675. Tel: 201-391-2323. *Dir* Dorothy Cornell; *Adult Services Librn* Beatrice Fazio.
Open Mon - Thurs 10 AM - 8 PM; Fri 10 AM - 5 PM; Sat 10 AM - 4 PM; cl Sat July & Aug.
Circ: 70,000. Exhibit space available.
Income: $90,000 (financed by city appropriation).
Holdings: Vols 30,000; Per subs 115; AV—Cassettes, phonorecords, slides; Other—Framed reproductions, prints, sculpture.
Special Collections: Fine arts—music and art, history, artists, techniques; theater history—Broadway, movies; beginning photography collection.
Exhibitions: Local artists exhibits.

SOUTH ORANGE

SETON HALL UNIVERSITY, Student Center Art Gallery, S Orange Ave, 07079. Tel: 201-762-9000, exten 675. *Dir* Petra ten-Doesschate Chu; *Cur Exhib* Barbara W Kaufman.
Open daily 9 AM - 10 PM; No admis. Estab 1963. Troast Memorial Gallery, estab 1974, houses permanent collection of contemporary American art; Wang Fang-Yu Collection of Oriental art was estab in 1977. Average Annual Attendance: 35,000.
Exhibitions: (1976-78) Chinese Brush Painting: I Chao Chu, Shiou-Ping Liae; Graphics: Louis Lozowick; Painting: Anthony Triano, Herbert Bierman; Watercolor: Edwin Havas, New Jersey Watercolor Society.
Activities: Lect open to the public; gallery talks.
Library: Holdings—Slides 10,000.

SPRINGFIELD

SPRINGFIELD HISTORICAL SOCIETY, 126 Morris Ave (Mailing Add: Box 124, 07081). *Pres* Madeline E Lancaster; *VPres* Howard Wiseman; *Secy* Mildred Leusen.
Open Sun 2 - 4 PM, except holidays and storm days. Admis 25¢. Estab 1953, the Society owns and maintains the historic Cannon Ball House, circa 1741, known as Hutchins Homestead, registered as State Historic Site in 1976, and National in 1977. Average Annual Attendance: 500. Mem: 185; dues $5; meeting four times a year.
Income: Financed by membership and small donations.
Collections: Pictures of Revolutionary soldiers and local history; †furnishings in the home.
Activities: Tours; sales shop selling maps, plates, postcards.

SUMMIT

SUMMIT ART CENTER, INC,* 68 Elm St, 07901. Tel: 201-273-9121. *Pres* Mrs Alex Aidekman; *Dir* Robert Reid.
Exhibits open daily 2 - 4 PM. Estab 1933. Mem: 2000; dues $15; annual meeting April.
Exhibitions: New exhibitions every 3-4 weeks; Annual Statewide Juried Show; one and two-man shows.
Activities: Art classes for adults and children; lectures; musical events.

TRENTON

FREE PUBLIC LIBRARY, Art and Music Department, 120 Academy St (Mailing Add: PO Box 2448, 08608). Tel: 609-392-7188, exten 26. *Dir* Veronica F Cary; *Head Art & Music Dept* James N Kisthardt.
Open Mon - Fri 9 AM - 9 PM; Sat 9 AM - 5 PM; cl Sun & holidays. Estab 1900.
Income: Financed by city appropriation.
Holdings: Vols 7000; Per subs 81; AV—Motion pictures, phonorecords; Other—Photographs.

MERCER COUNTY COMMUNITY COLLEGE LIBRARY,* 1200 Old Trenton Rd, 08690. Tel: 609-586-4800. *Dir* Frank G Butorac.
Open 9 AM - 5 PM. No admis. Estab 1891 to provide library services for the college; Triangle Gallery primarily for exhibiting student work; portion of the library main floor is devoted to permanent display cabinets, in addition display panels are used in the library for faculty exhibits; community exhibits and traveling exhibits, on a rotating basis.
Collections: Cybis Collection; ceramics collection; Kelsey Collection; painting by Wolf Kahn; Mexican art and handicrafts.
Exhibitions: Faculty, student and children's art exhibits as well as exhibits from the permanent collection.
Publications: College catalog, every two years.
Activities: Classes for adults and children; lect open to the public; gallery talks; extension dept; lending collection contains motion pictures 627.
Library: Holdings—Vols 48,000; Other—Photographs 200.

NEW JERSEY STATE MUSEUM, 205 W State St, 08625. Tel: 609-292-6300. *Dir* Leah P Sloshberg; *Asst Dir* Karen Cummins; *Cur Fine Arts* Zoltan Buki; *Cur Cultural History* Suzanne Corlette; *Cur Exhibits* Wallace Conway; *Cur Educ* Raymond Howe; *Cur Archaeology/Ethnology* Lorraine Williams.
Open Mon - Fri 9 AM - 4:45 PM; Sat, Sun & holidays 1 - 5 PM; cl Christmas, New Year's, Thanksgiving, Fourth of July. No admis. Estab 1891 (by legislation), to collect, exhibit and interpret fine arts, cultural history, archaeology/ethnology and science with a New Jersey focus: changing exhibit gallery, Hall of Natural Science, projected hall for permanent collection. Average Annual Attendance: 425,000. Mem: 1800 Friends; dues $25 and up; annual meeting Jan.
Income: $1,300,000 (financed by state appropriation). Purchases: $60,-000, plus $30,000 - $60,000 from Friends.
Collections: American fine and decorative arts of the 18th, 19th and 20th century; †New Jersey fine and decorative arts; American painting from 1910-1950 with special emphasis on the †Steiglitz circle, Regionalist, Abstract Artists.
Exhibitions: Pulse of the People—New Jersey in the Revolution, Steiglitz and the Photo-Secession; Daumier; Mercer (cars); Henry Mercer Tiles, Avant-Garde Today.
Publications: Catalogs, and irregular serials - Bulletins; Investigators; Reports.
Activities: Classes for children; dramatic programs; docent training; lect open to the public; competitions; outreach services include film and exhibit loans; individual paintings and original objects of art lent to other institutions; to Friends through ART LEASE; lending collection contains motion picture titles 1281, reels 2613, nature artifacts, original art works, original prints, paintings; traveling exhibitions organized and circulated; museum shop selling books, international folk crafts or items related to collection.
Library: Open to staff for reference only.

UNION

KEAN COLLEGE OF NEW JERSEY, College Gallery, Morris Avenue, 08063. Tel: 201-527-2307 or 527-2347. *Pres* Dr Nathan Weiss; *Chmn Art Dept* Dr Robert Coon; *Gallery Dir* Zara Cohan.
Open Mon - Fri 10 AM - 2 PM; by appointment at other times. No admis. Estab 1971 as a forum to present all art forms to students and the community through original exhibitions, catalogues, fine art, art history, and museum training. One gallery 22 x 34 ft. plus an alcove 8 x 18 ft on first floor of arts and humanities building. Average Annual Attendance: 3000.
Income: Financed by city appropriation.
Collections: American painting by J Stella, P Jenkins, L Baskin, W Homer, Audubon, W Gropper, Lamar Dodd.
Exhibitions: Mount, Homer and their contemporaries; Piranesi: Real and Imaginary; Local Limners; John Cotton Dana: Visionary; Three Women Graduate Thesis; Major Works Art Faculty; Good Design Interior Design Projects; Italian Renaissance Drawings.
Publications: Catalogues for exhibitions.
Activities: Dramatic programs; lect open to public; individual paintings lent to colleges, institutions, and departments on the campus; lending collection contains original art works, original prints, photographs, sculpture, and slides.
—**Nancy Thompson Library.** *Librn* Louis N Nagy.
Open to faculty, students and the public.
Holdings: Vols 211,000; Per subs 1800.

NEW MEXICO

ABIQUIU

GHOST RANCH VISITOR CENTER, Carson National Forest, Canjilon District (Mailing Add: General Delivery, 87510). *Dir* David C Suazo.
Open daily 8 AM - 4:30 PM. No admis. Estab 1959 as an outdoor interpretive project for the conservation of natural resources. Average Annual Attendance: 90,000.
Income: Financed by federal and private contributions.
Collections: Paintings and prints related to natural resources conservation; art objects.
Library: Limited number of reference books.

ALBUQUERQUE

ALBUQUERQUE ARTS COUNCIL, 5900 Domingo Road NE, 87108. Tel: 505-265-3271. *Exec Dir* Helen A Sidler; *Financial Secy* Frances Moody.
Open Mon - Fri 8 AM - 5 PM. No admis. Estab 1971 to stimulate and encourage cultural and educational activities. Mem: 450; three categories of membership: individual, art organizations and art related businesses, and business/industry; dues individual $10-, Arts $15-, business $50-; annual meeting November.
Income: $16,737 (financed by membership, state appropriation and grants).
Exhibitions: INTRODUCTIONS
Publications: Cultural Arts Calendar, bi-monthly.
Activities: Competitions with purchase awards; open workshops in various areas of concern to the arts community.

ALBUQUERQUE MUSEUM OF ART, HISTORY AND SCIENCE, Yale Blvd SE (Mailing Add: PO Box 1293, 87103). Tel: 505-766-7878. *Dir* Suzanne de Borhegyi; *Cur Art* Ellen Landis; *Cur Exhibits* Ruth

Gebel; *Cur Collections* Zana Grant; *Cur History* Byron Johnson; *Cur Educ* Patrick McCracken; *Public Information Officer* Ladonna Robson; *Admin Asst* Irene Kersting.

Open Tues - Fri 10 AM - 5 PM; Sat & Sun 1 - 5 PM. No admis. Estab 1967 as a city museum with the purpose of diffusing knowledge and appreciation of history, art and science, establishing and maintaining a museum and related reference library, of collecting and preserving objects of historic, artistic and scientific interest, of protecting historic sites, works of art and works of nature from needless destruction, of providing facilities for research and publication and of offering popular instruction and opportunities for aesthetic enjoyment. Four history galleries with long term exhibitions and two art galleries with exhibitions changing every 6 - 8 weeks. Average Annual Attendance: 35,000. Mem: 1075; dues from individual $5 - benefactor $1000; annual meeting November.

Income: Financed by city appropriation and Albuquerque Museum Foundation.

Collections: Decorative arts; fine arts and crafts; costumes; photography; objects and artifacts relevant to our cultural history from 20,000 BC to present.

Exhibitions: Art of the First Australians; Textiles New Mexico; Francoise Gilot; Crafts VII; Early 20th Century European; The Santero Experience; Ancient Roots/Ancient Visions; Albuquerque Artists I.

Publications: Las Noticias, monthly.

Activities: Classes for children; docent training; lect open to public and for members only, 7 vis lectr per yr; gallery talks; tours; competitions; extension department serving Albuquerque Public Schools; artmobile; sales shop selling books, magazines, reproductions, prints, Indian jewelry and local crafts.

Library: Open to staff, docents and volunteers for reference. Holdings: Vols 1500; Per subs 20. Special Subjects: New Mexico history, art and material culture.

ALBUQUERQUE PUBLIC LIBRARY,* Fine Arts Department, 423 Central NE, 87101. Tel: 505-766-5009. *Dir* Alan B Clark; *Head Fine Arts Dept* Hester Miller.

Open Mon - Thurs 9 AM - 9 PM; Fri - Sat 9 AM - 5:30 PM. Estab 1967 to provide study, research, and recreational materials in the arts for the people of the city, county, and state.

Income: $5000 (financed by city and state appropriations). Purchases: $5000.

Holdings: †Vols on non-performing arts 9000; Other—circulating †pictures 39,500; framed circulating original †graphics 37; framed circulating †reproductions 88; †slides 1863.

Activities: Individual paintings, reproductions and original graphics lent to schools.

CLASSICAL SCHOOL GALLERY, 614 Indian School Rd NW, 87102. Tel: 505-843-7749. *Pres* C M Flumiani.

Open daily 10 - 12 AM and 3 - 5 PM. No admis. Estab 1969 to foster the classical approach to the arts and art education; new 2500 sq ft building. Mem: 15; dues $200.

Income: Financed by endowment.

Collections: Italian masters.

Publications: Art & Life, quarterly.

Activities: Classes for adults; lect open to public; schol; book shop.

Library: Holdings—Vols 2000.

NEW MEXICO ART LEAGUE, Ken Roberts Gallery, 3401 Juan Tabo NE, 87111. Tel: 505-293-5034. *Pres* Mike Trimble; *VPres* Ken Roberts; *Secy* Sandra Quinlan; *Dir* Jean Rosenburg.

Open Mon - Sat 11 AM - 6 PM; Sun 12:30 - 5 PM. No admis. Estab 1929 to promote artists of New Mexico; art gallery. Mem: 400, must be New Mexico resident; dues $20; monthly meetings.

Income: Financed by membership and sales.

Collections: Best of show of National Small Painting Show.

Exhibitions: National Small Painting Show.

Publications: Newsletter, monthly; catalog of National Small Painting Show.

Activities: Classes for adults; lect open to public, 12 vis lectr per yr; competitions; sales shop selling original art and prints.

UNIVERSITY OF NEW MEXICO.

—**University Art Museum,** Fine Arts Center, 87131. Tel: 505-277-4001. *Dir* Van Deren Coke; *Asst Dir* Marian Pope; *Assoc Cur* Cleta H Downey; *Preparator* William Masterson; *Staff Asst* Kay Wille; *Receptionist* Sandra Edwards.

Open Tues - Fri 10 AM - 5 PM & 7 - 10 PM; Sun 1 - 5 PM. Admis 50¢. Estab 1963. An upper level gallery; a print and photograph room which is open to the public at certain hours. Mem: 200; dues $10 to $500; annual meeting May.

Collections: Contemporary American paintings, drawings, prints, photographs and sculpture with emphasis on artists who have worked in New Mexico; the Labhard Collection (photography); prints by American and European masters; 19th & 20th century lithographs.

Publications: Bulletin, yearly.

Activities: Lect open to public; inter-museum loans; traveling exhibitions organized and circulated; museum shop selling books, magazines, reproductions, cards and newspapers.

—**Jonson Gallery,** 1909 Las Lomas Road, NE, 87106. Tel: 505-243-4667. *Dir* Raymond Jonson; *Cur* Arthur H Johnson.

Open Tues - Sun Noon - 6 PM; cl Mon. No admis. Estab 1948 for the assemblage and preservation of a comprehensive collection of the works of Raymond Jonson; a depository for works of art by other artists and their preservation; the exhibition of works of art. The structure includes a main gallery, four storage rooms, two work shops, studio for Jonson, a museum room and living quarters for the director. Average Annual Attendance: 4000.

Income: Financed through University.

Collections: Jonson reserved retrospective collection; other artists' works by Jonson students.

Exhibitions: Casimir Mayshark; Frank McCulloch; Howard Cook; Catherine Fisher; Vernon Fimple; Raymond Jonson; Frank Walker; Ed Garman; Joseph A Chavez; Jeanette Styborski; David Gale; Gwen Peterson; Martha Slaymaker; RC Ellis; Women Contempo: Esther Sutin, Ann Upson, Harriet Sutton, Arlene Wackerbarth; Ray Jacobsen; Arthur Sussman; Betty J Pritchard; Peggy Hight-Robb.

Publications: Exhibition announcements.

Activities: Individual paintings and original objects of art lent to museums.

Library: Open to students and others doing research. Holdings: Vols 1000; Per subs 1. Special Collection: The Jonson Archives containing books and magazines relating to Raymond Jonson, his letters, his diaries, catalogs, clippings, photographs and slides of works.

—**Fine Arts Library.** Tel: 505-277-2901. *Fine Arts Librn* James Wright; *Asst Fine Arts Librn* Phyllis M Cohen.

Open Mon - Thurs 8 AM - Noon; Fri 8 AM - 9 PM; Sat 9 AM - 9 PM; Sun 10 AM - Noon. Estab 1963 to support teaching and research of the university. Circ: 148,720.

Income: Financed by state appropriation.

Holdings: Vols 62,000; Per subs 450; AV—Microfiche, microfilm and phonorecords; Other—Exhibition catalogs.

Special Subjects: Lithography, and photography.

Special Collections: Batchelder-McPharlin Puppetry Collection; Photographic Collection; Tamarind Archive; Archive of Southwestern Music; Robb Collection (Music manuscripts of J D Robb's compositions and articles by and about him).

DEMING

LUNA COUNTY MUSEUM,* 300 S Nickel Ave, 88030. Tel: 505-546-2382. *Cur* Mark Forster. Open Tues & Thurs 11 AM - 5 PM; Sat 10 AM - 5 PM. No admis. Estab 1969. Mem: Dues $2.

Collections: Paintings; folk art; Indian artifacts.

GALLUP

GALLUP MUSEUM OF INDIAN ARTS AND CRAFTS, 103 W 66th (PO Box 1395, 87301). Tel: 505-863-6849.

Open Mon - Fri 9 AM - 5 PM. No admis. Estab 1959 to acquaint visitors with the arts and crafts of the Navajo, Zuni and Hopi Indians. A small museum manned by the Chamber of Commerce Staff. Thirteen cases displaying Indian arts and crafts. Average Annual Attendance: 6,000.

Publications: Catalog of exhibits.

LAS VEGAS

NEW MEXICO HIGHLANDS UNIVERSITY ART GALLERY, National Ave, 87701. Tel: 505-425-7511. *Chmn of Fine Arts* Grady Greene.

Open Mon - Fri 8 AM - 5 PM. No admis. Estab 1956 to acquaint university and townspeople with art of the past and present; gallery averages 100 x 35 ft.

Income: Financed by state appropriation.

Collections: Very small, about eight pieces.

Publications: University general catalog, annually.

Activities: Classes for adults; dramatic programs; concerts; exten dept serving Northern New Mexico.

LOS ALAMOS

LOS ALAMOS ARTS COUNCIL,* c/o *Secy* Judy Gursky, 223 El Viento. Tel: 505-662-7384. *Pres* Jane Bennorth.

Estab 1967 for coordination of cultural activities in Los Alamos and environs. Gallery for permanent †collection and exhibits just beginning. Average Annual Attendance: 100 (small events), 7500 (Arts Festival), 4000 (Crafts Fair). Mem: 17 organizations, 200; dues $5, $8 and $20; meetings Sept and Mar.

Income: Under $2000 (financed by membership, city and state appropriations).

Publications: Los Alamos Arts Council Newsletter, monthly.

Activities: Sponsor various types of cultural activities, including an annual four-day arts festival in the summer, two Northern New Mexico Crafts Fairs, monthly cultural programs, monthly Morning Musicale, master classes in music, sack lunch musicales, student musicales, photography; plus serving as an advisory board to the county on matters concerning cultural activities and the maintenance of Fuller Lodge.

PORTALES

EASTERN NEW MEXICO UNIVERSITY, Art Gallery, Liberal Arts Bldg 101, 88130. Tel: 505-562-1011. *Dir* Chris Gikas.
Open 8 AM - 9 PM. No admis. Estab 1974 for exhibiting student artwork; gallery is room converted for student works.

Income: Financed by university funds.

Collections: Student works in Art Department Collection.

Activities: Individual paintings and original objects of art lent to the university.

ROSWELL

ROSWELL MUSEUM AND ART CENTER, 11th and Main Sts, 88201. Tel: 505-622-4700. *Pres Bd Trustees* Donald B Anderson; *VPres* Robert V Ely; *Secy* Martha Gillespie; *Treas* Ralph McIntyre; *Dir* Wendell Ott; *Asst Dir* William D Ebie; *Registrar & Cur* Wesley A Rusnell.
Open Mon - Sat 9 AM - 5 PM; Sun & holidays 1 - 5 PM. Estab 1937 to promote and cultivate the fine arts. The basis of the fine arts collection being paintings and sculptures with emphasis on the artistic heritage of the Southwest. Six galleries for art works; science display area; Robert H Goddard display area. Average Annual Attendance: 50,000. Mem: 600; dues $10 and up.

Income: $50,000 (financed by membership, city and county appropriation). Purchases: $5000 or $10,000.

Collections: †20th century Southwestern paintings & sculpture; †International graphics collection; Witter Bynner collection of Chinese paintings & jade; ethnological and archaeological collection of Southwestern Indian art; New Mexico regional natural history displays.

Exhibitions: Bicentennial Exhibition of art and Indian artifacts including the Robert O Anderson Indian Coll; various Artists-in-Residence Exhibits; Gund Collection of Western Art; Exhibitions of Recent Acquisitions; Hopi Kachina Exhibition and exhibit of Peter Paone's Paintings; Burt Barnes Paintings and Drawings; Photography exhibits: George Eastman House Collection, Rosamond Purcell.

Publications: Bulletin, quarterly; Exhibition catalogs.

Activities: Classes for adults and children; lect open to public, 2-3 vis lectr per yr; gallery talks; tours; individual paintings lent to museums; lending collections contains books, kodachromes, and motion pictures; traveling exhibitions organized and circulated; museum shop selling books, magazines, reproductions, prints, and Indian jewelry.

Holdings: Vols 1500; Per subs 6. Special Subjects: Southwestern Art.

SANTA FE

INSTITUTE OF AMERICAN INDIAN ARTS MUSEUM,* Cerillos Rd, 87501. Tel: 505-988-6281. *Dir* Charles Dailey; *Cur Functions* Manüelita Lovato.
Open Mon - Fri 9 AM - 5 PM; cl on weekends & holidays. No admis. Estab 1962 to instruct in all aspects of arts and crafts to Americas' native American peoples from all of United States; museum serves as a support to curriculum and as a repository for the only major collection of contemporary Indian arts and crafts, provides opportunity for study of museology as applies to Indian visitors' centers as well as study of the unique collection; traveling shows important for reservation areas; gallery approximately 4000 sq ft of exhibition area; revolving shows constantly featuring primarily student work and material from permanent collection. Average Annual Attendance: 15,000.

Income: $40,000 (affiliated with US Department of Interior, Bureau of Indian Affairs, and financed through federal government).

Collections: Only major collection of contemporary Indian arts and crafts in America. Not only is the traditional material collected, but also the most avant garde and experimental directions in Indian Art. Vital and comprehensive collection in fields of paintings, graphics, textiles, ceramics, sculpture, jewelry, photographs, printed textiles, costumes, ethnological materials such as drums and paraphernalia for general living.

Exhibitions: Yearly student sales exhibit held in June - Sept each year; photograph traveling show.

Activities: Assisting any Indian reservation in setting up their own visitor centers or museums in America; material available to Indian reservations, museum, cultural centers and universities, with fees, transportation and insurance provided; lect open to the public; competitions; schol; individual paintings and original objects of art lent; traveling exhibitions organized and circulated.

Library: Holdings—Vols 30,000, specializing in Indian related materials, arts books.

MUSEUM OF NEW MEXICO, 105 W Palace (Mailing Add: PO Box 2087, 87503). Tel: 505-827-2834. *Dir* George Ewing; *Assoc Dir* Michael Weber; *Dir Fine Arts Div* Donald O Strel.
Open daily 9 AM - 5 PM; cl Mon in winter. Estab 1909. It is a state institution and operates in four major fields of interest, Fine Arts, International Folk Art, History, and Anthropology, which are housed in four separate buildings. Average Annual Attendance: 800,000.

Income: Financed by state appropriation.

Collections: Over 185,000 items in collections.

Publications: El Palacio, quarterly; exhibition catalogs; annual report; monographs; pamphlets; books, magazines, and guides.

Activities: Educational kits with hands-on materials are sent to schools throughout the state; docent program serving 15,000 school children; traveling exhibitions organized and circulated.

Library: The Museum houses four separate research libraries on Folk Art, Fine Arts, History, and Anthropology. Holdings: Vols 24,000.

—Museum of Fine Arts. *Dir* Donald Strel; *Cur Coll* Edna Robertson; *Cur Exhib* Malin Wilson; *Librn* Louise Durston.
Open daily 9 AM - 4:45 PM; cl Mon in winter. No admis. Estab 1917 to serve as an exhibitions hall chiefly for New Mexican and Southwestern art. The building is of classic Southwestern design (adobe); attached auditorium used for performing arts presentations. Average Annual Attendance: 290,000.

Income: Financed by state appropriation.

Collections: Paintings, drawings, prints, sculpture, and photographs with the emphasis on New Mexican and regional art, including native American artists.

Exhibitions: Ansel Adams Southwest Photography; Southwest Fine Arts Biennial; Fred Kabotie: Hopi Artist; New Mexico Landscapes The Roswell Compound.

Activities: Classes for adults and children; docent training; lect open to public, 10 vis lectr per yr; concerts; gallery talks; tours; competitions; individual paintings and original objects of art lent to art museums; lending collection contains original prints, paintings, photographs, and sculpture; traveling exhibitions organized and circulated; museum shop selling books, magazines, reproductions, and slides.

Library: Fine Arts Library. Open to the public for reference. Holdings: Vols 2,000; Per subs 90; Other—Files on southwestern artists, catalogs of past museum shows. Special Subjects: Southwestern art.

—Museum of International Folk Art, Camino Lejo, 87503. Tel: 505-827-2544. *Dir* Dr Yvonne Lange; *Asst to Dir* Paul Winkler; *Cur Coll* Carol Steiro; *Cur Textiles* Nora Fisher; *Cur Spanish Colonial Coll* Christine Mather; *Cur* Judy Cohen & Charlene Cerny; *Conservator* Alan Vedder; *Librn* Judith Sellars.
Open daily 9 AM - 4:45 PM; cl Mon in winter. No admis. Estab 1950 to collect, exhibit and research objects related to folk culture and to encourage the art of the craftsman.

Income: Financed by endowment and state appropriation.

Collections: International folk art, with emphasis on Spanish Colonial and Hispanic-related culture; costumes and textiles; also worldwide toys, carvings, and ceramics.

Activities: Lends complete exhibits to libraries, community centers, school, universities and private organizations which have exhibition space; classes for adults and children; lect open to the public, 4 vis lectr per yr; gallery tours; concerts; dramatic programs; competitions; sales shop selling books.

Library: Open for reference and copying. Holdings: Vols 4000; Other—slides, prints, tape and manuscript collection of folk dramas of New Mexico.

—Palace of Governors. Tel: 505-827-2921.
Built in 1610.

Exhibitions: Southwestern History, Spanish-Colonial and Territorial Periods; The Palace Press, a working exhibit of frontier printing.

—Hall of the Southwestern Indian.

Collections: Contemporary Indian Civilizations of the Southwest.

—Laboratory of Anthropology, Camino Lejo. Tel: 505-827-3241.
Open Mon - Sat 8 AM - Noon & 1 - 5 PM. Estab 1936 as a research laboratory in archaeology and ethnology.

Collections: Materials from various Indian cultures of the Southwest: pottery, textiles, jewelry.

Exhibitions: Ceremonial paraphernalia; Indian silverwork.

SCHOOL OF AMERICAN RESEARCH, 660 Garcia St (Mailing Add: PO Box 2,188, 87501). Tel: 505-982-3583. *Dir* Douglas W Schwartz; *Cur Coll* Arthur H Wolf.
Open to members and special scholars by appointment. Estab 1907. Dedicated to advance studies in anthropology; supporting advanced seminars for post-doctoral scholars; archaeological research; anthropological publication and a public education program. Southwest Indian Arts Building

houses collections for research. Mem: 1250; dues individual $18, family $28.

Income: Financed by endowment, membership, special grants and individuals.

Collections: Southwest Indian pottery, textiles, basketry, silver jewelry, and paintings (about 5500 items).

Exhibitions: (1976-77) One-day exhibits by invitation only—Laura Gilpin Canyon de Chelly (photographs); John Gaw Meem (architectural photographs).

Publications: Explorations, yearly; Discovery, yearly; Publications of Advanced Seminar Series.

Activities: Lect for members only, 5 vis lectr per yr; resident scholar program.

—Library. Tel: 505-982-3583.

Open to scholars of the School of American Research, staff and members by appointment.

Holdings: Vols 6000; Per subs 27; Other—Government publications.

Special Subjects: Anthropological research.

WHEELWRIGHT MUSEUM (formerly Museum of Navajo Ceremonial Art), 704 Camino Lejo, (Mailing Add: PO Box 5153, 87502). *Dir* Steven H Tremper; *Admin Asst* Evalynne Rippel; *Cur* Susan McGreevy; *Dir Development* Carlton Colquitt; *Designer & Preparator* Joseph Chipmen.

Open Tues - Sat 10 AM - 5 PM; Sun 1 - 5 PM. No admis. Estab 1937 to preserve Navajo ceremonialism and promote the culture of the American Indian. Main gallery has changing exhibitions dealing with contemporary Indian themes; lower gallery is a recreation of a turn-of-the-century trading post and functions as a museum shop. Average Annual Attendance: 20,000. Mem: 1000; dues $10 and up; annual meeting.

Income: $243,000 (financed endowment, membership).

Collections: Sandpainting reproductions of various Navajo ceremonies; ritual material; masks; tapes; photographs; jewelry.

Exhibitions: Feasts and Ceremonies; American Indian Art Now.

Publications: Bulletins and books on Navajo culture.

Activities: Lect open to public, 15 vis lectr per yr; tours; individual paintings and original objects of art lent to museums; lending collection contains books, color reproductions, film strips, framed reproductions, kodachromes, nature artifacts, original art works, original prints, paintings and phonorecords; museum shop selling books, magazines, original art, reproductions, prints, slides and authentic American Indian Arts and Crafts.

Mary Cabot Wheelwright Research Library. Open to members for reference. Holdings: Vols 2000; Per subs 3000.

SOCORRO

SOCORRO ART LEAGUE, 1212 North Drive NW, 87801. Tel: 505-835-0651. *Pres & Cur* Betsy Dorr; *VPres & Prog Dir* Vivian Drewien; *Secy* Pat Basham.

Estab 1960 for the purpose of sponsoring art classes and study groups, presenting exhibitions and generally encouraging interest in art. Mem: 30; dues $5.

Income: $170 (financed by membership and commissions).

Exhibitions: Socorro Arts Fiesta; Socorro County Fair.

Activities: Workshops; lect open to public, 6 vis lectr per yr; competitions, ribbons and some cash awards given; gifts of framed reproductions made to public schools.

TAOS

KIT CARSON MEMORIAL FOUNDATION, INC., PO Box B, 87571. Open daily summer 7:30 AM - 7:30 PM (summer); 8 AM - 5 PM (winter); 8 AM - 6 PM (spring and autumn). Admis adults 50¢, youths (12-15) 25¢; children (6-11) 15¢; children under 6 free with parents; family rate $1.50. Estab 1949 to maintain and operate the home of Kit Carson and to perpetuate his name and deeds. The Kit Carson Home is now classified as a Registered National Historic Landmark. In 1962 the home of Ernest L Blumenschein was given to the Foundation by Miss Helen C Blumenschein; it is now classified as a Registered National Historic Landmark. In 1967 Mrs Rebecca S James gave the Foundation the Ferdinand Maxwell House and Property. The 6-room house is an excellent example of the New Mexican Territorial Period. In 1972, acquired the Hacienda de Don Antonio Severino Martinez, prominent Taos merchant and official during the Spanish Colonial Period. It is designated a Registered National Historic Landmark. Average Annual Attendance: 53,000. Mem: 230; dues contributing $10, participating $15, share $25, sustaining $50, subscribing $100, supporting $250, benefactor $500, sponsor $750, patron $1000; annual meeting March.

Income: $33,796. Purchases: $20,840.

Collections: †Kit Carson Home collection; †Historical and Archaeological Collection; Western Americana; pieces of art by members of the original Taos Society of Artists and other Taos Artists (1890-1930 period).

Activities: Tours for groups; lect.

Library: For reference. Holdings: Vols 3600; Other—Photographs and negatives, and maps.

TAOS ART ASSOCIATION, INC,* PO Box 198, 87571. Tel: 505-758-2052. *Pres* Emil Bisttram; *Secy* Johanna Jones; *Exec Dir* Sue McCleery, *Dir Stables Gallery* Thom Andriola.

Open daily 10 AM - 5 PM. No admis. Estab April 1952 as an art association composed of artists and businessmen to encourage the understanding of the arts, both plastic and performing; Stables Gallery. Average Annual Attendance: 15,000. Mem: 450; annual meeting April.

Income: Financed by membership.

Exhibitions: Annual Awards Show for Taos County, over $500 in prizes.

Publications: Monthly calendar of events to membership and with map to hotels.

Activities: Classes for adults and children; children's program in painting and theater; dramatic programs; lect open to the public; concerts; competitions; traveling exhibitions organized and circulated.

UNIVERSITY OF NEW MEXICO,* Harwood Foundation, Box 766, 87571. Tel: 505-758-3063. *Pres of Board* Dorothy Brandenburg; *Dir* Stephen R Brogden; *Acting Dir* Dixie M Gillette; *Dir Continuing Educ* Dr Rupert A Trujillo.

Open 10 AM - 5 PM; cl Sun and holidays. No admis. Buildings and contents given to the University of New Mexico by Elizabeth Case Harwood, 1936, to be maintained as an art, educational and cultural center; maintained by the university with all activities open to the public.

Collections: Old New Mexico Santos; Indian artifacts; †permanent collection of works by Taos artists; primitive New Mexico wood sculpture and tin ware; Persian miniatures.

Library: Holdings— Vols 20,000. Only public library in Taos County.

Special Collections: Southwest literature and art library; D H Lawrence first editions.

TOME

TOME PARISH MUSEUM,* PO Box 397, 87060. Tel: 505-865-7497. *Dir* R Auman; *Cur* George C Pearl.

Open daily daylight until dark. No admis. Estab 1966 as a religious museum.

Collections: Paintings; religious material.

NEW YORK

ALBANY

ALBANY INSTITUTE OF HISTORY AND ART,* 125 Washington Ave, 12210. Tel: 518-463-4478. *Pres* Herbert A Jones; *Dir* Norman S Rice.

Open Tues - Sat 10 AM - 4:45 PM; Sun 2 - 6 PM; cl Mon. No admis. Estab 1791, inc 1793 as the Society for the Promotion of Agriculture, Arts, and Manufacturers; 1829 as Albany Institute; 1900 as Albany Institute and Historical and Art Society. Present name adopted 1926. Average Annual Attendance: 80,000. Mem: 2000; dues $15 and up; annual meeting May.

Income: $350,000 (financed through University). Purchases: $25,000.

Collections: Art and historical material, chiefly related to artists and craftsmen of the region; †silver; †pewter; †furniture; †glass; †ceramics; †18th & 19th century painting and sculpture by artists of the Hudson River area; export ware; Chelsea, Bow china; English 18th century furnishings and paintings; †contemporary paintings and sculpture.

Exhibitions: American Decorative Arts Centered Around Albany; some area history; Annual Regional Exhibition by Artists of the Upper Hudson; changing exhibition program in contemporary design and fine arts.

Activities: Classes for adults and children; dramatic programs; lect open to public; exten dept serving area schools.

—McKinney Library. *Librn* James R Hobin; *Manuscripts Librn* Christine W Ward.

Open Mon - Fri 8:30 AM - 4 PM; Sat 9 AM - 1 PM. Estab 1793 to collect historical material concerning Albany and the Upper Hudson region, as well as books on fine and decorative art related to the Institute's holdings. A reference library.

Income: $5,800 (financed by endowment, membership, city and state appropriation, and federal grant).

Holdings: Vols 8,500; Per subs 35; Other—Clipping files, exhibition catalogs, manuscripts, original documents, pamphlets, photographs.

Special Subjects: Dutch in the Upper Hudson Valley, 17th and 18th century manuscripts; Albany social and political history, 18th and 19th century manuscripts; American painting and sculpture.
Special Collections: American Art Collections: Thomas Cole, Frederic Church, Erastus D Palmer, Sanford Gifford, Will H Low, John Q A Ward.

COLLEGE OF SAINT ROSE ART GALLERY, 432 Western Ave, 12203. Tel: 518-471-5111. *Dir* Sister Marion Charlene Honors.
Open Sun - Fri 2 - 5 PM; cl Sat. No admis. Estab 1969 to provide a facility that presents fine art both to the college community and to the public and provide a place for college art students to display their works.
Income: Financed by college funds.
Collections: Very small permanent collection consisting of paintings, prints, and a few pieces of sculpture.
Exhibitions: Traveling exhibitions, plus senior, faculty and student shows.

NEW YORK STATE LIBRARY, State Education Bldg, 12234. Tel: 518-474-5958. *State Librn/Assoc Commissioner for Libraries* Joseph Shubert; *Dir* Peter J Paulson; *Manuscripts & Spec Coll* Peter Christoph.
Open Mon - Fri 8:30 AM - 6 PM. No admis. Estab 1818.
Income: Book budget $925,854,
Collections: Over 35,000 titles in a collection of 4,800,000 items, especially strong in architecture, painting, sculpture, and music (texts). A picture collection of over 50,000 on New York State is maintained in the Manuscripts and Special Collections. Most materials available on interlibrary loan.
Exhibitions: Exhibit program involves mainly printed and manuscript materials.

SCHUYLER MANSION, 27 Clinton St, 12202. Tel: 518-474-3953. *Site Mgr* Paul Stambach; *Interpretive Progs Asst* Chris Averill; *Historic Site Assts* Mary Ellen Latcher and Joseph Grimaldi.
Open Wed - Sun 9 AM - 5 PM; cl Mon & Tues. No admis. Estab 1917 for the preservation and interpretation of the 18th century home of Philip Schuyler. Period rooms: informal parlour, formal parlour, dining room, study, ballroom, young ladies' bedroom, master bedroom, summer bedroom. Average Annual Attendance: 11,000.
Income: Financed by state appropriation.
Collections: 18th Century American and European antiquities.
Exhibitions: All permanent collections.
Activities: Educ dept; docent training; lect open to public, 5 vis lectr per yr; tours.

STATE EDUCATION DEPARTMENT, * State University of New York, State Educ Bldg, 12234. Tel: 518-474-2121. *Pres of Univ & Commissioner of Educ* Ewald B Nyquist; *Exec Deputy Commissioner of Educ* Gordon M Ambach; *Deputy Commissioner for Elementary, Secondary and Continuing Educ* Thomas D Sheldon; *Assoc Commissioner for Instructional Services* William L Bitner III; *Asst Commissioner for General Educ & Curricular Services* Vivienne Anderson; *Chief Bureau of Art Educ* Vincent J Popolizio; *Assoc in Art Educ* Ernest Andrew Mills; *Assoc in Art Educ* James V Gilliland; *Assoc in Art Educ* Robert L Reals.
The State Education Department through its various supervisors, determines the policy and directs the courses and the supervision and inspection of work in art in the elementary and secondary schools, including the junior and senior high schools. The Department also passes upon applications for licenses to teach art in the public schools, and upon college progams for teachers of the subject.

STATE UNIVERSITY OF NEW YORK AT ALBANY, University Art Gallery, 1400 Washington Ave, 12222. Tel: 518-457-3375. *Dir* Nancy Liddle; *Asst Dir* Marijo Fasulo; *Preparator* John Wisniewski; *Admin Asst* Phyllis Sosnick. Open Mon - Fri 9 AM - 5 PM; Sat & Sun 1 - 4 PM. No admis. Estab 1968, the purpose is threefold: to augment the teaching program of the Fine Arts Department, to present exhibitions of community interest, and to be of service to the University System, particularly Albany. Gallery has 6400 sq ft on first floor, 3200 sq ft on second floor. Medium security gallery, students as security personnel. Average Annual Attendance: 25,000.
Income: Financed by city appropriation.
Collections: †Paintings, †prints, †drawings and †sculpture of 20th century contemporary art; the collection is enlarged by donations and limited purchases.
Exhibitions: (1976) Sons and Others: Women Artists See Men; Warrington Colescott Prints; Marilyn Giersbach Paintings; Richard Callner Paintings; William Christenberry Photo; (1977) Jim Dine Prints; Contemporary Yugoslav Prints; Graphic Artists of New York; (1978) J Pindyck Miller; Aluminum Sculpture; Polly Hope, Stuffed Pictures.
Activities: Educ dept; docent training; student assistants; lect open to public, 5 vis lectr per yr; gallery talks; tours; individual paintings lent to offices on the university campus only; lending collection contains original art works 300, original prints 150, sculpture 75.

Special Collections: The University Art Gallery is custodian for the Student Art Council collection, a collection of contemporary art which is available on premises for study purposes.

ALFRED

NEW YORK STATE COLLEGE OF CERAMICS AT ALFRED UNIVERSITY, Scholes Library of Ceramics, Harder Hall, State St, 14802. Tel: 607-871-2494. *Dir & Head Serials Section* Robin R J Murray; *Head Readers Services* Martha A Mueller; *Head Technical Services* Bruce E Connolly; *Head Technical Reference* Paul T Culley; *Head Art Reference & AV Services* Susan R Strong.
Open Mon - Thurs 8:30 AM - 10:30 PM; Fri 8:30 AM - 4:40 PM; Sat 10 AM - 5 PM & 6:30 - 10:30 PM; Sun 1 - 5 PM & 6:30 - 10:30 PM. Estab 1947 to service art education to the Masters level in fine art and the PhD level in Engineering and science related to ceramics. Reference library. The College has a 2500 sq ft Art Gallery which is managed by the Art & Design Division.
Income: $254,124 (financed by endowment, city and state appropriation, and federal grant). Purchases: $77,252.
Holdings: (Art) Vols 5000; Per subs 150; AV—Cassettes, film strips, microfiche, microfilm, reels, slides; Other—Original art works, pamphlets.
Special Subjects: Pottery; glasswork; porcelain; fine art; murals.
Special Collections: Silverman Collection (glass).
Publications: Library Notes, bimonthly.
Activities: Tours.

AMENIA

AGES OF MAN FOUNDATION, Sheffield Road, 12501. Tel: 914-373-9380. *Pres* Dr Nathan Cabot Hale; *VPres* John Bell; *Secy* Alison B Hale.
Open 10 AM - 5 PM. Estab 1968 for the building and design of a sculpture chapel based on the thematic concepts of the Cycle of Life. Mem: 20 (must show a professional interest in the Cycle of Life concepts); dues $100; meetings May and Nov.
Income: Financed by membership and contributions.
Collections: Sculpture and architectural models of the chapel.
Publications: Project Report, yearly.
Activities: Art history; apprenticeship and journeyman instruction in Cycle of Life design; lect open to the public, 20 vis lectr per yr; gallery talks; original objects of art lent to museums, art associations, educational institutions; traveling exhibitions organized and circulated.

AMHERST

DAEMEN COLLEGE, Dun Scotus Gallery, 4380 Main St, 14226. Tel: 716-839-3600, exten 241. *Dir* Bruce Marzahn.
Open daily 9 AM - 5 PM. No admis. Estab to add dimension to the art program and afford liberal arts students opportunity to view art made by established artists as well as art students. Gallery area is part of main building protected by folding gate. Average Annual Attendance: 1000.
Income: Financed by College art department.
Activities: Lect open to public, 4 - 5 vis lectr per yr; competitions.

AMSTERDAM

WALTER ELWOOD MUSEUM AND ART GALLERY, * 300 Guy Park Ave, 12010. Tel: 518-843-3180, exten 287. *Coordr* Joseph Todak.
Open weekdays Sept 1 - June 31, 8:30 AM - 4 PM; July 1 - Aug 31, 8:30 AM - 3 PM; cl legal holidays. Founded 1940 by the late Walter Elwood; sponsored by the Board of Education. Average Annual Attendance: 10,000.
Collections: Early American, Victorian, and Indian material; paintings; prints; period rooms.
Activities: Guided tours, special topic tours; multi-media kits on request.

ANNANDALE-ON-HUDSON

BARD COLLEGE, * William Cooper Procter Art Center, 12504. Tel: 914-758-8494. *Dir* Matt Phillips; *Secy & Cur* Sandra Phillips.
Open 10 AM - 5 PM daily. Estab 1964 as an educational center; art center has a gallery, slide library and uses the college library for its teaching.
Collections: Assorted contemporary paintings and sculptures; photograph collection of 2000 prints.
Exhibitions: Two student exhibitions per year plus faculty and traveling exhibitions.
Publications: Catalogs, major one every two years.
Activities: Children's art classes; lect open to the public; gallery talks; schol.

AUBURN

CAYUGA MUSEUM OF HISTORY AND ART, 203 Genesee St, 13021. Tel: 315-253-8051. *Dir* Walter K Long; *Asst Dir* Anita Wheeler.
Open Tues - Fri 9 AM - 5 PM; cl Mon. No admis. Estab 1936 for research; Indian history. Average Annual Attendance: 40,000. Mem: 800; dues $10 - $50; annual meeting Jan.
Income: $40,000 (financed by endowment, membership, county and city appropriation).
Collections: †Sound on film; Herter textiles; Beardsley Filipino; †permanent paintings by Americans.
Exhibitions: Bicentennial, 12 Ethnic Group Shows.
Activities: Classes for adults and children; docent training; lect open to public, 6 vis lectr per yr; gallery talks; tours; competitions, individual paintings lent to schools, homes, and businesses; lending collection contains motion pictures, paintings, slides 5000; traveling exhibitions organized and circulated; museum shop selling original art, reproductions, small gifts.
Library: Open to researchers for reference. Holdings: Vols 15,000. Special Subjects: Indians; local history. Special Collection: Clarke Collection.

BAYSIDE

QUEENSBOROUGH COMMUNITY COLLEGE LIBRARY,* 56th Ave & Springfield Blvd, 11364. Tel: 212-631-6340. *Chief Librn* Prof Charles Pappalardo; *Music & Art Librn* Eleanor Eldot.
Open Mon - Thurs 8:30 AM - 10 PM; Fri 8:30 AM - 5 PM; Sat 9 AM - 2 PM. Estab 1961 to serve the students and faculty of the college.
Income: Budget $610,000. Purchases: $80,000.
Holdings: Book and periodical collection which includes material on painting, sculpture and architecture; reproductions of famous paintings on walls throughout the library and reproductions of artifacts and sculpture.
Special Collections: Print collection; extremely valuable vertical file collection.
Exhibitions: Exhibit cases are changed approximately every two months; exhibits include Black Art, Mosaics, Pop Art, Posters, Women in Art.
Publications: Queensborough Community College Library Newsletter, monthly.

BINGHAMTON

ROBERSON CENTER, 30 Front St, 13905. Tel: 607-772-0660. *Pres of the Board* Robert Aber; *VPres* Theodore Mulford; *Secy* Virginia Gouldin; *Treas* Floyd W Roper; *Dir* Keith Martin; *Asst Dir* Laura B Martin; *Controller* Arket Lewis; *Cur* Robert Aguglia; *Cur* Richard Barons; *Cur* Philip Carey; *Cur* Richard DeLuca; *Cur* Roselyn Tunis.
Open Mon - Fri 9 AM - 10:30 PM; Sat 9 AM - 5 PM; Sun Noon - 5 PM. No admis. Estab 1954. The Roberson Center is a complex of museums—Art Museum, Historical Museum and Science Museum; Roberson Center is Broome County's Arts and Science Council; it is an Education Center, a Performing Arts Center. The Roberson Mansion built in 1910 contains eight galleries; the Neutra built in 1968 contains 5 galleries. Average Annual Attendance: 300,000. Mem: 3000; dues $10 - $30.
Income: $780,500 (financed by endowment, membership, city and state appropriation, federal funds and foundations).
Collections: Paintings; prints; drawings; documents; photographs; decorative art; furniture.
Exhibitions: (1976-77) Traditional Crafts; American Cooking Hearth; The Black Presence in the Era of the American Revolution; Nature's Realm; Chemistry Then and Now; Selections from the Permanent Collection; Christmas Forest; Binghamton 1905; Scholastic Art Exhibition; Artifacts of Medicine; Afro-American History; Photo Exhibition Winners; Franck Taylor Browers; Artists of Broome County; Easter Egg Tree; Cycles: Uni, Bi, Tri; Victorian Fans and Portraits; Roberson Student Exhibition; Photographic Exhibition; Science Exhibitions.
Publications: Bulletin, monthly; catalogs, 3 major a year.
Activities: Classes for adults and children; dramatic programs; docent training; programs; sent to schools in ten counties; lect open to the public; competitions; individual paintings and original objects of art lent; traveling exhibitions organized and circulated; museum shop selling books, original art; reproductions, prints.
Broome County Historical Library: For reference only.

STATE UNIVERSITY OF NEW YORK AT BINGHAMTON, University Art Gallery, 13901. Tel: 607-798-2634. *Gallery Adminr* Jill Grossvogel; *Secy* Katherine Gleason; *Technician* Walter Luckert.
Open Mon - Sat 11 AM - 5 PM; Wed 7 - 10 PM; Sun 1 - 5 PM. Estab 1967.
Income: Financed by state appropriations and gifts.
Collections: †Teaching collection from Egyptian to contemporary art.

Exhibitions: Frans Kline; Women in the Arts; Don Demauro; David Shapiro; Images of the Plague; Mirror of Marvelous Rome (16th century engravings); German expressionist Drawings; Steven Barash; Linda Sokolowski.
Publications: Yearly publication of the University Art Gallery Bulletin, of which Number One appeared in the form of a concise catalog of the collections.
Activities: Lectures, musical programs; and tours for the special exhibit exhibitions are organized regularly.
Library: The Gallery Library is supplemented with the University Library and very adequate for research.

BLUE MOUNTAIN LAKE

ADIRONDACK LAKES CENTER FOR THE ARTS,* 12812. Tel: 518-352-7715. *Pres* L Robert Webb; *Treas* Edith Mitchell; *Secy* Abbie Verner; *Dir* James E Hutt.
Open year round. Estab 1967, the center offers an extensive art and craft instruction program. During July and August the Center's activities include classical, traditional and contemporary music programs, a film program, and coffeehouse performances. The Shop, featuring one-of-a-kind crafts, is open year round, 10 AM - 4 PM daily, except Sun. Mem dues: students $1, adults $3, family $8.
Income: Financed by memberships, contributions, and assistance from The New York State Council of the Arts.
Publications: Newsletter, bimonthly.
Library: For reference. Holdings: Vols 300, plus magazines..

ADIRONDACK MUSEUM OF THE ADIRONDACK HISTORICAL ASSOCIATION,* 12812. Tel: 518-352-7311. *Pres* H K Hockschild: *Dir* Craig A Gilborn.
Open June 15 - Oct 15 daily including Sun 10 AM - 5 PM; admis adults $3 children under 7 $1; special group rates. Estab 1955 to show the relationship of man to the Adirondacks. Average Annual Attendance: 90,000. Mem: Annual meeting Aug.
Collections: Paintings and prints.
Exhibitions: One special exhibition each year; has included printings by Winslow Homer, A F Tait, photographs by Eliot Porter.
—Library. Tel: 518-352-7312. *Librn* Marcia Smith.
Open Mon - Fri 9:30 AM - 4:30 PM by appointment. Estab to provide research materials for museums staff to document exhibits to preserve all printed and paper materials relating to the Adirondack and to assist historians, authors and others in the research of the Adirondack. For reference only.
Holdings: Vols 5000; Per subs 90 - 100; AV—Audio tapes, cassettes, Kodachromes, microfilm; motion pictures, slides; Other—Exhibition catalogs, manuscripts, pamphlets, photographs, maps.
Special Subjects: All Adirondackiana.
Special Collections: Buntline Collection of his writings; small collection of memorabilia.
Exhibitions: A One season rustic furniture show; Permanent Exhibition Woods and Waters.

BRIARCLIFF MANOR

PACE UNIVERSITY
—The Art Gallery, Elm Rd, 10510. Tel: 914-941-6400, exten 714. *Gallery Keeper* Beth A Treadway.
Open Mon - Fri 2 - 6 PM; Sat 2 - 5 PM: cl Sun. No admis. Estab 1978 to exhibit the works of nationally known professional artists and groups; to serve as a focal point for artistic activities within the university and the surrounding communities; the gallery is located on the ground floor of the Arts Building; it is modern, spacious and has a commanding view of the center of the campus.
Income: Financed by University.
Exhibitions: Brenda Bettinson and John Mulgrew; Vincent Ciniglid; Martha Holland; Andrea Kantor and Carol Morley.
Activities: Lect open to the public, 8 - 10 vis lectr per yr; gallery talks; tours.
—Library.
Open to the public for reference; to affiliates of Pace for circulation.
Holdings (art) Vols 7265; Per subs 34.

BRONX

BRONX MUSEUM OF THE ARTS,* 851 Grand Concourse, 10451. Tel: 212-681-6000. *Chmn Bd* Sol Shaviro; *Dir* Edward M Dweck.
Open 10 AM - 4:30 PM; Sun 1 - 5 PM; cl National holidays. No admis. Estab 1971 as a conduit for other museums of the city to bring their works to the community and for local artists to have their works viewed, making art available, free and easily accessible to the Bronx community; community Gallery for local artists. Mem: 75; dues initial fee $15; no annual meeting.

Income: Financed by membership, and city and state appropriations.
Activities: Classes for adults and children; multi-media art workshops for school children and the community; concerts.

HUNTINGTON FREE LIBRARY AND READING ROOM, Depository Library for the Museum of the American Indian, 9 Westchester Square, 10461. Tel: 212-829-7770. *Librn* Mary B Davis; *Asst Librn* Dorothy Cisneros; *Pres Board Trustees* Edward A Morgan.
Open Mon - Sat 9:30 - 4:30 PM by appointment. Estab 1891, the Reading Room was established as a library for the people of Westchester Square. Materials are for reference use only; they do not circulate.
Income: Financed by endowment.
Holdings: Vols 40,000; Per subs 80; AV—Microfiche, phonorecords; Other—Clipping files, exhibition catalogs, manuscripts, original documents, pamphlets.
Special Subjects: Indians of North, South and Central America.

SOCIETY OF ANIMAL ARTISTS, INC, 151 Carroll St, City Island 10464. Tel: 212-885-2181. *Pres* Paul Branson; *VPres* Albert Gilbert; *Secy* Patricia Allen Bott; *Treas* Beverly Bender; *Mem Jury* Douglas Allen, William F Bartlett, Louis DeDonato, Richard Ellis, Donald Miller and Douglas MacClintock.
For further information see National and Regional Organizations.

VAN CORTLANDT MUSEUM,* Van Cortlandt Park, W 246th St & Broadway, 10471. Tel: 212-543-3344. *Chmn* Mrs Norbert Hansen.
Open 10 AM - 4:30 PM; Sun 2 - 4:30 PM; cl Mon. Admis adult 50¢, children under 12 no admis; Fri & Sat free to all. Estab 1898. Average Annual Attendance: 30,000.
Collections: Furniture and objects relating to the Colonial period of American history; also Delftware, pottery and glass.
Activities: Classes for school children each day; slide programs for all visitors.

BRONXVILLE

BRONXVILLE PUBLIC LIBRARY, 201 Pondfield Rd, 10708. Tel: 914-337-7680. *Dir* Mrs Marion H Wade.
Open (Winter) Mon, Wed & Fri 9:30 AM - 5:30 PM; Tues, Thurs 9:30 AM - 9 PM; Sat 9:30 AM - 5 PM; (Summer) Mon, Wed, Thurs & Fri 9:30 AM - 5 PM; Tues 9:30 AM - 9 PM; Sat 9:30 AM - 1 PM. No admis.
Income: Financed by city and state appropriations.
Collections: Many American painters represented, such as Winslow Homer, Frederick Waugh, Childe Hassam, Bruce Crane and William Henry Howe; 25 Original Currier and Ives prints and a collection of Japanese art prints.
Exhibitions: Original paintings and prints on walls throughout. An exhibit room also, is for use by current artists, and changed monthly.

SARAH LAWRENCE COLLEGE LIBRARY, Glen Washington Rd, 10708. Tel: 914-337-0700. *Lbirn* Rose Anne Burstein; *Exhibits Librn* Carol Shaner; *Slide Librn* Renee Kent.
Open 9 AM - 5 PM. Estab 1974 to provide library facilities for students and members of the community; has a strong art history section. Reference materials are open to the public for use in the library; the slide collection is not open to the public, membership program. Gallery spaces used by faculty and other organizations.
Holdings: Vols (art) 15,000; Per subs 951; AV—Slides 45,000.
Exhibitions: Changing exhibitions.
Activities: Library tours on request.

BROOKLYN

BROOKLYN INSTITUTE OF ARTS AND SCIENCES,* 200 Eastern Pkwy, 11238, Tel: 212-783-6500. *Chmn of Board* Edward S Reid; *VChmn* Seth S Faison; *VPres* Robert A Levinson; *Secy* John J McAtee Jr *Treas* James Q Riordan; *V Chmn Admin* Thomas A Donnelly.
Estab 1823, re-inc 1890; organized into three departments: The Brooklyn Museum, Brooklyn Children's Museum, Brooklyn Botanic Garden. For information on exhibitions, educational activities, library and publications in the field of art see listing for The Brooklyn Museum. Average Annual Attendance: 2,500,000. Mem: 8000; annual meeting Jan.
Income: $6,000,000. Purchases: $3,000,000.

BROOKLYN MUSEUM, 188 Eastern Parkway, 11238. Tel: 212-638-5000. *Chmn Bd of Governors* Robert A Levinson; *Dir* Michael Botwinick; *Exec Asst* John R Lane; *Asst Dir for Operations* Robert Hayden; *Asst Dir Educ & Prog Development* David H Katzive; *Development Mgr* Edward Czerwinski; *Public Relations Mgr* Herbert Bronstein; *Chmn of Dept Egyptian & Classical Art, Keeper of the Wilbour Coll* Bernard V Bothmer; *Cur Egyptian & Classical Art* Richard Fazzini; *Asst Cur Egyptian & Classical Art* Robert Bianchi; *Cur & Dept Head Paintings & Sculpture* Sarah C Faunce; *Cur Paintings & Sculpture* Linda Ferber;

Asst Cur Paintings & Sculpture William James Roth; *Cur Oriental Art* Robert Moes; *Assoc Cur Oriental Art* Amy Poster; *Cur Costumes & Textiles* Elizabeth A Coleman; *Cur Decorative Arts* Dianne H Pilgrim; *Asst Cur Decorative Arts* Donald Peirce; *Asst Cur-in-Charge Middle Eastern Art & Archaeology* Madeline Noveck; *Assoc Cur African Oceanic & New World Cultures* Sylvia Williams; *Consult Cur Prints & Drawings* Gene Baro; *Asst Cur Prints & Drawings* Ripley Albright; *Conservator* Suzanne P Saçk; *Publications & Marketing Services Mgr* Brian Rushton; *Security Mgr* James Jackson; *Registrar* Barbara LaSalle; *Librn* Margaret Zorach; *Community Gallery Coordinator* Richard Waller; *Graphic Designer* Daniel Weidmann; *Personnel Mgr* Richard Johnson; *Assoc Cur Sculpture Garden* Barbara Millstein.
Open Wed - Sat 9 AM - 5 PM; Sun Noon - 5 PM; Holidays 1 - 5 PM; cl Mon & Tues. No admis. Estab 1823 as an art museum with educational facilities; five floors of galleries, 7th largest museum of art in the U.S. Average Annual Attendance: 575,000 (1977). Mem: 3600; dues $20.
Income: $3,242,408 (financed by endowment, membership, city and state appropriation).
Collections: †Major collections of Egyptian and Classical; Oriental, Middle Eastern and African art; art from the Americas and South Pacific; European and American paintings, sculpture, prints and drawings, textiles, decorative arts; American period rooms; Sculpture Garden of ornaments from demolished New York buildings.
Exhibitions: (1977) Anamorphoses: Games of Perception and Illusion; Gustave Caillebotte; Women in American Architecture; Lewis W Hines, 1874-1940; Two Centuries of Black American Art; Women Artists: 1550-1950; Chinese Peasant Paintings from Husien County; Lace: An Ornamental Art; American Painted Furniture: 1680-1880; Consuelo Kanaga; Mountains of the Mind; Nanga; Prints in Series; Idea into Image; Anni Albers; Artists Lives in American Prints and Drawings.
Publications: Calendar, monthly; handbooks; guides to collections; catalogs of major exhibitions; annual report.
Activities: Classes for adults and children; dramatic programs; docent training; lect open to the public, 150 vis lectr per yr; concerts; gallery talks; tours; individual paintings and original objects of art lent to other museums; traveling exhibitions organized and circulated; museum and sales shop selling books, original art, reproductions, prints, slides.
—**Art Reference Library.** Tel: 212-638-5000, exten 307-309. *Principal Librn* Margaret B Zorach.
Open Wed - Fri 1 - 5 PM. Estab 1823 to serve the staff of the museum and local researchers. Circ: 3000. Gallery not maintained.
Income: $22,000 (financed by city and state appropriation). Purchases: $15,000.
Holdings: Vols 90,000; Per subs 600; AV—Microfiche, slides; Other—Clipping files, exhibition catalogs, original art works, pamphlets.
Special Collections: Original designer sketches.
—**Wilbour Library of Egyptology.** Tel: 212-638-5000, exten 215. *Librn* Diane Guzman; *Asst Librn* Amy Frank Gutman.
Open Mon - Fri 10 AM - 5 PM, by appointment and for reference only. Estab 1916 for the purpose of the study of Ancient Egypt.
Income: Financed by endowment, and city appropriation. Purchases: $6000.
Holdings: Vols 18,000; Per subs 150; AV—Microfiche; Others—Exhibition catalogs, original documents, pamphlets.
Special Collections: Seyffarth papers.
Publications: Wilbour Monographs, and many other publications, as well as reading lists suitable for young readers.

BROOKLYN PUBLIC LIBRARY,* Grand Army Plaza, 11238. Tel: 212-636-3111. *Dir* Kenneth F Duchac; *Chief Art & Music Div* William R Johnson; *Chief AV Div* Kenneth Axthelm.
Open Mon - Thurs 9 AM - 8 PM; Fri & Sat 10 AM - 6 PM; Sun 1 - 5 PM (fall-spring, tentative). No admis. Estab 1892.
Income: Financed by city and state appropriation.
Exhibitions: Art works, photographs, crafts, historical and cultural displays.
Publications: Brooklyn Public Library Bulletin, bimonthly.
Activities: Classes for children; other programs; films; exhibitions in lobby and on second floor; Brooklyn Art Books for Children Citations, annual awards given jointly for children's books outstanding as works of literature and of art.
Holdings: Art & Music Division—Vols 116,350; Other—Picture files 60,000, framed prints 470; AV Division—Cassettes 225; film strips, motion pictures 2,000, phonorecords 15,000.
Special Collections: Costume Collection.

LONG ISLAND HISTORICAL SOCIETY, 128 Pierrepont St, 11201. Tel: 212-624-0890. *Pres* Dwight Demeritt Jr.
Open Tues - Sat 9 AM - 5 PM. Admis members free; non members $1 a day for library use. Estab 1863 to discover, procure, and preserve historical and genealogical materials concentrating on New York City, especially Brooklyn Borough, Long Island and the New England vicinity; the exhibition area is on the library floor. Average Annual Attendance: 6200. Mem: 1300, dues $15; annual meeting May.

Income: $150,000 (1977) (financed by endowment, membership, state appropriation, and grants). Purchases: $10,000.
Collections: (Art) Photographs, paintings, prints, and artifacts.
Exhibitions: Battle of Long Island; Conserving Brooklyn's Heritage; Old Brooklyn in Early Photographs (1865-1929).
Publications: Journal of Long Island History, biannual.
Activities: Lect open to the public, 10 vis lectr per yr; concerts; individual paintings and original objects of art lent to other institutions; lending collection contains original prints 6000, paintings 275, sculpture 20; sales shop selling books, prints.
Library. Librn Anne M Gordon; *Asst Librn* Elaine Bak. Open to members and the public for reference only. Holdings: Vols 150,000; Per subs 80.

NATIONAL CARTOONISTS SOCIETY, * 9 Ebony Court, 11229. Tel: 212-743-6510. *Pres* Bill Gallo; *Secy* Bill Kresse; *Scribe* Marge Duffy Devine.
For further information see National and Regional Organizations.

NEW MUSE COMMUNITY MUSEUM OF BROOKLYN, INC, 1530 Bedford Ave, 11216. Tel: 212-774-2900/2901. *Chmn Bd of Dir* Eduardo J Standard; *Secy Bd of Dir* Robert O Lovell; *Exec Dir* Andrew J Gill; *Exec Secy* Ima Zawadi, *Coordinator of Cultural Arts* Gaylord Hassan; *Coordinator of Music* Reginald Workman; *Coordinator of Exhibitions* Arthur Coppedge; *Coordinator of Public Relations* Mark Irving.
Open Tues - Fri 2 - 10 PM; Sat & Sun 1 - 5 PM. No admis (donations and contributions accepted). Estab 1973 to establish an African-American educational and cultural institution of high calibre in the Crown Heights and Bedford-Stuyvesant sections of Brooklyn; Gallery contains cultural and historic exhibitions; fine art exhibitions. Average Annual Attendance: 650,000. Mem: 150; dues $5 - $100; annual meeting Jan 31.
Income: $180,000 (financed by membership, city and state appropriation).
Collections: Small nucleus of Haitian, African and African-American artifacts.
Exhibitions: Black artists of Brooklyn; Bed-Stuy Camera Club; Children's Art Workshop; Malcolm X Photographs; Black Contribution to the Development of Brooklyn; permanent and semi-permanent exhibitions, three to six weeks durations.
Publications: Bulletins, announcing activities and workshops, monthly.
Activities: Classes for children; dramatic programs; music; lect open to public.

PRATT INSTITUTE LIBRARY, 11205. Tel: 212-636-3685. *Dir* Louis D Sass; *Art & Architecture Librn* Sydney Starr Keaveney and Ann Marie Bergholtz.
Open Mon - Thurs 9 AM - 9 PM; Fri & Sat 9 AM - 5 PM; Sun 12 AM - 6 PM. Estab 1887 for students, faculty, staff and alumni of Pratt Institute. The school has several galleries, the library has exhibitions in display cases.
Income: $80,000 (financed by endowment and tuition).
Holdings: Vols approx 26,000; AV—Audiotapes, cassettes, microfiche, microfilm, phonorecords, slides; Other—Clipping files, exhibition catalogs, pamphlets, reproductions.
Special Subjects: Art and architecture; library science.
Publications: Periodicals in the Library (computer printout).

SCHOOL ART LEAGUE OF NEW YORK CITY, * 131 Livingston St, 11201. Tel: 212-875-5381. *Pres* Charles M Robertson; *First VPres* Eleanor Greenan; *Second VPres* Sybil C Simon; *Treas* Reynolds Girdler Jr; *Secy* Arnold Roston; *Dir* Dorothy G Evans.
Estab 1909 to foster art education in the public schools of the City of New York, the League is co-sponsored by a Board of Trustees and the Board of Education of the City of New York. Its purpose is to enrich and enlarge the arts programs available to our young people in our city's schools. Interdisciplinary arts activities are offered as a supplement to existing arts programs through the use of New York City's cultural resources. Support is provided for innovative programs within the schools, and scholarships and grants are given to encourage gifted students. Mem: 3000; dues $5 and up. Public school pupils may join for $1 a school term. Junior mem: 22,000.
Activities: Classes; workshops, seminars, in-service training for teachers; visits to galleries, artists studios, private film showings and museum openings; annual awards, an average of 50 scholarships to professional art schools and colleges to graduates of the academic and vocational high schools; approximately 500 medals each year to graduates of elementary, academic, and vocational high schools; special awards to needy students doing graduate art work, through contributions from foundations, commercial firms and philanthropic institutions.

BUFFALO

ALBRIGHT-KNOX ART GALLERY, The Buffalo Fine Arts Academy, 1285 Elmwood Ave, 14222. Tel: 716-882-8700.
Chmn Seymour H Know; *Pres* Samuel D Magavern; *VPres* Mrs John T Elfvin; *VPres* Northrup R Knox; *VPres* Robert E Rich; *Secy* Roy W Doolittle Jr; *Treas* William J Magavern II; *Dir* Robert T Buck Jr; *Chief Cur* Steven A Nash; *Cur Educ* Charlotte Buel Johnson; *Cur* Douglas G Schultz; *Cur* Linda L Cathcart; *Registrar* Jane Nitterauer.
Open Tues - Sat 10 AM - 5 PM; Sun Noon - 5 PM; cl Thanksgiving, Christmas and New Year's Day. No admis, voluntary contribution. Estab 1862 as The Buffalo Fine Arts Academy, gallery opened in 1905, with a new wing added 1962. Average Annual Attendance: 236,463 (1976-77). Mem: 3484; dues $20, annual meeting Oct.
Income: $956,683.53 (financed by endowment and county appropriation).
Collections: †1500 paintings and drawings; †450 sculpture and constructions; †2500 prints ranging from 3000BC to the present with special emphasis on American and European contemporary art.
Exhibitions: American Folk Painting from the Collection of Mr & Mrs Peter Tillou; Robert Moran: Musical Graphics; Heritage and Horizon: American Painting, 1976-77; Gilbert and George: The General Jungle or Carrying on Sculpting; 36th Western New York Exhibition; The Hekimian Bequest: Views of Niagara Falls; Recent Photographs by Russell Drisch; Recent Acquisitions—Portrait Photographs of Artists; Cartoon Art: An Exhibition in Two Parts; Constructivism in Poland 1923-1948; 17 Contemporary Artists from Poland; Paul harits: Dream Displacement and Other Projects; Richard Diebenkorn: Paintings and Drawings, 1942-1976; Antoni Tapies: 33 Years of His Work; In Western New York; Joel Shapiro; The School of Paris: Drawings In France; Roger Welch: The O J Simpson Project; Les Levine: I am Not Blind; Rembrandt and Hals; Modern European Drawings from Permanent Collection; Charles Simonds Temenos; Cleve Gray Paintings, 1966-1977; Far Eastern Art in Upstate New York; Robert Rauschenberg; Buffalo Society of Artists/Patteran Artists; Rafael Ferrer: SUR; Alfred Jensen: Paintings and Diagrams From the Year 1957-1977.
Publications: Monthly (calendar); Annual Report; catalogs to accompany major exhibitions originating at Albright-Knox.
Activities: Classes for adults and children; docent training; community outreach program; lect open to the public; concerts; gallery talks, tours; original objects of art lent to members through Members Gallery rental and sales; lending collections contain paintings, photographs, sculptures; traveling exhibitions organized and circulated; gallery shop selling books, magazines, original art; reproductions, prints, slides, cards, stationery, toys, jewelry.
—Art Reference Library. Tel: 716-882-8700, exten 25. *Librn* Annette Masling; *Asst Librn* Margaret Cantrick.
Open Tues - Fri 2 - 5 PM; Sat 1 - 3 PM. Estab 1905 to support the staff research and to document the Gallery collection; also to serve the fine art and art historical people doing research in the Western New York area; exhibits are prepared in a small vestibule just outside the library; rare items in the library collection and print collection are displayed.
Holdings: Vols 16,500; Per subs 120; AV—Microfiche, video tapes; Other—Clipping files, manuscripts, memorabilia, original art works, original documents, pamphlets, photographs, prints.

BUFFALO AND ERIE COUNTY PUBLIC LIBRARY, Lafayette Square, 14223. Tel: 716-856-7525. *Dir* Paul M Rooney; *Deputy Dir Public Services* Winifred K Harper; *Deputy Dir Support Services* Donald Cloudsley.
Open Mon - Thurs 10 AM - 9 PM; Fri & Sat 9:30 AM - 5:30 PM. Estab 1954 through a merger of the Buffalo Public, Grosvenor, and Erie County Public Libraries; gallery not maintained. Circ: 4,647,000 (1977).
Income: $9.6 million (1978) (financed by county appropriation). Purchases: $20,000 (Art)
Holdings: Vols 33,000; Per subs 75; AV—Motion pictures; Other—Exhibition catalogs, manuscripts, original art works, photographs, prints.
Special Collections: Rare Book Room with emphasis on fine printing; Niagara Falls prints; original woodcut of J J Lankes; etchings by William J Schwanekamp; posters (mostly WW I); drawings by Fritz Eichenberg.
Publications: Buffalo and Erie County Public Library Bulletin, monthly.
Activities: Dramatic programs; gallery talks, tours.

BURCHFIELD CENTER, 1300 Elmwood Ave, 14222. Tel: 716-862-6011. *Chmn Advisory Comt* Dr E K Fretwell Jr; *Chmn Center Council* Peter Vogt; *Dir* Dr Edna M Lindemann; *Librn/Archivist/Registrar* Barbara L Lewczyk; *Education Prog Coord* Sylvia P Volk and Margaret Bauer.
Open Mon - Fri 10 AM - 5 PM; Sun 1 - 5 PM. No admis. Estab 1966 to develop a total center concept-Western New York Forum for American Art-a regional Center for the exhibition, study and encouragement of significant art expression in the Western New York area including building a permanent collection of works by Charles Burchfield and by other outstanding artists of Western New York, both living and historical; the museum facility is composed of a main gallery with four supplemental

galleries, plus Burchfield studio gallery. Average Annual Attendance: 40,000. Mem: 1600; dues $20; annual meeting varies.

Income: Financed by endowment, membership, SUNY and other sources.

Collections: †Works by Charles Burchfield; †Works by contemporary artists from the Western New York area; †Works by historical artists from the Western New York area.

Exhibitions: Burchfield Collection of the Burchfield Center; 81st Annual Buffalo Society of Artists Exhibition; Works by Living American Artists; Western New York; Cartoon Art; The Sites of a City: Charles Burchfield's Buffalo; 3rd Western New York Purchase Award Collegiate Drawing Exhibition; Edwin Dickinson Tribute Exhibition; The Roycroft Movement: A Spirit for Today?

Publications: Newsletter, occasionally.

Activities: Docent training; lect open to the public; concerts; tours; competitions; exten dept serving area schools and community organizations; original objects of art lent to students and teachers; lending collection contains books, cassettes, color reproductions, film strips, framed reproductions, original art works, slides, magazine articles, periodicals; traveling exhibitions organized and circulated; sales shop selling books, magazines, reproductions, wallpapers designed by Charles Burchfield.

Library. Tel: 716-862-6011. *Librn* Barbara L Lewczyk. Open to the public for reference only. Holdings: Vols 225; AV—Audio tapes, film strips, slides; Other—Clipping files, photographs. Special Subjects: The library's holdings consist primarily of books and exhibition catalogs on Charles Burchfield, artists from the Western New York area and other American artists; slides and photographs of works by Charles Burchfield and Western New York artists. Special Collections: Charles Burchfield's journals, his indices of his works, letters written by him and other Burchfield archival material; George William Eggers Archive consisting of over 1000 drawings and lithographs by the artist as well as his teaching materials.

STATE UNIVERSITY OF NEW YORK AT BUFFALO

—Gallery 219, University Union Activities Board, Arts Committee, (Mailing Add: Room 106 Talbert Hall, Amherst, New York 14260). Tel: 716-636-2957. *Chmn* Ken Brauchler; *Exec Secy* Mrs Pulvino.

Open daily. No admis. Estab to expose the campus to a wide variety of art, ranging from contemporary painting, sculpture, prints, photographic design, crafts, and media related arts; and to give student artists a place to show their works. A small gallery in Elliot Complex.

Income: $1,300 (financed by student fees).

Exhibitions: Local artists' shows; student shows; loan exhibitions.

Activities: Lect open to public, 4 vis lectr per yr; competitions.

—Lockwood Memorial Library, Art Department. Tel: 716-636-2000. *Art Librn* Florence S DaLuiso.

Open Mon - Thurs 9 AM - 9 PM; Fri 9 AM - 5 PM; Sat 1 - 5 PM; Sun 2 - 9 PM. Estab 1913 to support curriculum in the history of art and architecture, and in the fine arts.

Holdings: Vols 38,000; Other—Exhibition catalogs 10,000. Library has microfiche holdings on a reciprocal exchange basis, of the Albright-Knox Art Gallery catalog.

Exhibitions: Monthly exhibitions of bibliothecal interest.

CANAJOHARIE

CANAJOHARIE LIBRARY AND ART GALLERY, Erie Blvd, 13317. Tel: 518-673-2314. *Pres* Mrs William Crangle; *Cur* Edward Lipowicz; *Secy* Mrs James Dern.

Open Mon - Fri 10 AM - 5:15 PM; Thurs 10 AM - 9 PM; Sat 10 AM - 2 PM; cl Sun. No admis. Estab 1927 as a memorial to Senator James Arkell. Average Annual Attendance: 3,000 - 5,000. Annual meeting Jan.

Income: Financed by endowment and village grants.

Collections: †Paintings by American artists.

Exhibitions: From permanent collection, changed each month.

Activities: Gallery talks; tours; individual paintings and original objects of art lent to community residents and business institutions; lending collection contains paintings 300, and sculptures.

Library. Tel: 518-673-2314. *Librn* Kathy Munson. Holdings: Vols 21,000; Per subs 50.

CANTON

ST LAWRENCE UNIVERSITY, Griffiths Art Center, Romoda Dr, 13617. Tel: 315-379-6003. *Cur* Paul D Schweizer.

Open Mon - Fri 9 AM - 5 PM. No admis. Estab 1968, a teaching collection with emphasis on modern art, an extension of Dept of Fine Arts Studio Program. The center has two galleries, one devoted to permanent collection, the other to changing exhibitions.

Income: Financed by university funds.

Collections: Contemporary prints, paintings and photography; 19th century American art; modern sculpture; European graphics; Oriental art; African art.

Exhibitions: (1977-78) Annual Acquisitions; Clayton Fowler Retrospective; Richard Margolis Photographs; Painting Techniques; Southeast Missouri State Art Faculty; Contemporary Prints; Student Show.

Activities: Lect open to public, 4 vis lectr per yr; competitions; individual paintings and original objects of art lent to student loan program and museums; lending collection contains original art works and prints, paintings, photographs.

CAZENOVIA

CAZENOVIA COLLEGE, Chapman Art Center Gallery, 13035. Tel: 315-655-3466, exten 246. *Dir Art Prog* John Alstars.

Open Mon - Fri 1 - 4 PM & 7 - 9 PM; Sat & Sun 1 - 5 PM. No admis. Estab 1977 as a college gallery for students and community. Gallery is 1084 sq ft with track lighting, movable display panels. Average Annual Attendance: 1000.

Income: Financed through College.

Collections: A small permanent collection of work donated to college.

Exhibitions: Syracuse Area Artists; Syracuse Printmakers Guild; Marion Faller Exhibition; Don Cortese and Lee Dusell Exhibition; Peter Sobin and James Barton; Faculty Exhibition; Ferdinand Carter Exhibition; Cazenovia College Student Exhibition.

CHAPPAQUA

ART RESEARCH SERVICE,* 855 Hardscrabble Rd (Mailing Add: PO Box 95, 10514). Tel: 914-238-4039. *Pres* Dr H G Hesslein.

Open by appointment only. Estab 1962; research on the history of art done for museums, collectors, art dealers.

CHAUTAUQUA

CHAUTAUQUA GALLERY OF ART,* Chautauqua Art Association, Summer: Wythe Ave, Chautauqua, NY, 14722. Tel: 716-357-2771. Winter: 1192 Parkside Dr, Alliance, Ohio, 44601. Tel: 216-821-0468. *Dir* Dr Helen B Cleveland; *Secy* Marilyn Glendening; *Secy* Mrs Robert Bargar; *First VPres* George Weaver; *Gallery Asst* Petrina Neher; *Gallery Asst* Douglas Miller; *Gallery Asst* Conrad Brunner.

Open Mon - Sat 1 - 7:30 PM; Sun 12:30 - 2:30 PM, 4 - 7:30 PM. No admis. Estab 1948 to promote quality art, culture and appreciation of the arts. Average Annual Attendance: 12,000. Mem: 1200; dues $4; six annual meeting dates.

Income: Financed by membership.

Exhibitions: Approximately 68.

Publications: Art Gallery Magazine; publications in art magazine; national jury show program activities schedule.

Activities: Classes for adults and children; dramatic programs; art appreciation; lect open to the public, 24 vis lectr per yr; concerts; gallery talks; tours; competitions; schol; individual paintings lent to schools; lending collection contains paintings, art magazines; book shop; Junior museum.

CLINTON

HAMILTON COLLEGE,* Edward W Root Art Center, 13323. Tel: 315-859-7331. *Supv* Lettie Tourville.

Open Mon - Fri 8:30 AM - 10:30 PM; Sat 9 - 12 AM, 2 - 6 PM; Sun 2 - 10:30 PM. Estab 1958 to make available to Hamilton College students and to the entire community fine examples of art, music and literature. Housed in 1800 building. Average Annual Attendance: 15,000.

Income: Financed by Hamilton College appropriations.

Exhibitions: Seven exhibitions throughout the academic year arranged by the Joint Exhibitions Committee of Hamilton and Kirkland Colleges.

Activities: Lectures; concerts; gallery talks; tours.

Library: Books on art and related subjects.

—Bristol Campus Center.

Exhibitions: Fourteen per year, changing approximately every other week during the academic year. A wide variety of graphic forms is selected by Student Exhibition Committee.

Art Lending Library: 200 original prints, copies, and sculpture which can be rented by the semester by students for a nominal fee.

KIRKLAND ART CENTER, On-The-Park, 13323. Tel: 315-853-8871. *Dir* Bernardine T Lohden; *Secy* Sally Williams; *Artist In-Residence* Ruth Fairchild.

Open Tues - Fri 10 AM - 5 PM; Sat & Sun 2 - 4 PM; cl Mon; (July & Aug) Tues - Fri 1 - 5 PM. No admis. Estab 1960 to promote the arts in the town of Kirkland. The center has a large main gallery, small downstairs gallery. Average Annual Attendance: 15,000 - 17,000. Mem: 1100; dues adults $5; annual meeting June.

Income: $50,000 (financed by endowment, membership, state appropriation, fund raising events, thrift shop.

Exhibitions: Monthly exhibitions—varied; Group shows—painting, sculpture, graphics, photography, crafts, and others.

Publications: Newsletter, bimonthly.
Activities: Classes for adults and children; lectures open to public; gallery talks; competitions; sales shop selling books, original art, crafts and purchased items.

COOPERSTOWN

BRUSH AND PALETTE CLUB, PO Box 446, 13326. *Pres* Anna Roemer; *VPres* Celia McShane; *Secy* Katie Tacy; *Treas* Virginia Hawxhurst. Estab 1965 to encourage original arts and crafts work and foster general art appreciation and education. Arts and crafts gallery in local historical building. Mem: 100; dues $3; meetings May & Oct.
Income: $2420 (financed by membership and outdoor show).
Exhibitions: (1976-78) Annual Outdoor Arts and Crafts Show; Annual Fall Fine Arts Exhibition; Firehouse Arts and Crafts Gallery.
Publications: Information Bulletin, quarterly.
Activities: Classes for adults; sales shop selling original art.
Library: Cooperstown Art Association Workroom. *Librn* Dorothy V Smith. Open to members only for lending and reference. Holdings: Vols 12; Per subs 2. Special Subjects: Art history; arts and crafts techniques.

COOPERSTOWN ART ASSOCIATION, 22 Main St, 13326. Tel: 607-547-9777. *Pres* James Mullen; *VPres* John Sanford; *Secy* Olga Welch. Open Mon - Sat 10 AM - 4 PM, Sun 1 - 4 PM. Estab 1928 to provide a cultural program for the central part of New York State. An art gallery is maintained. Average Annual Attendance: 14,000. Mem: 1284; dues $7.50 and up.
Income: Financed by membership.
Collections: †Paintings, †sculpture and †crafts.
Exhibitions: (1978) 50th Anniversary Exhibition; Annual National Juried Exhibitions.
Publications: Newsletter, annual.
Activities: Classes for adults; competitions, over $3000 in prizes; individual paintings and original objects of art lent; leading collection contains paintings, sculpture.
Reference library.

HISTORICAL SOCIETY OF EARLY AMERICAN DECORATION, INC,* Fenimore House, 13326. Tel: 607-547-2533. *Pres* Mrs Edwin Rowell; *Corresp Secy* Mrs John C Miller; *Secy* Mrs E A Nibelink; *Cur* Mrs Spencer G Avery.
Exhibition Hall in Farmer's Museum of the New York State Historical Association open summer 9 AM - 5 PM; winter, Tues - Sat 9 AM - 5 PM; cl Sun AM & Mon. Admis fee; special educational group rate. Estab 1946 to perpetuate Early American decoration as an art, promote research in that field, record and preserve examples of the decorative arts, with emphasis on Americana; mantain exhibits and publish works on the subject of early American decoration and the history thereof; to elevate the standards of its reproduction and utilization. Average Annual Attendance: 136,000. Mem: 800; dues $15 and up; annual meeting May.
Collections: †Stenciled and painted tin of all kinds; †decorated chairs, painted chests.
Publications: The Decorator, twice a year; The Ornamented Chair; The Decorator Digest; The Ornamented Tray; An Illustrated Glossary of Decorated Antiques; also, reprinted from Antiques Magazine, 27 articles by Esther Stevens Brazer.
Activities: Lectures; two exhibitions each year other than in the permanent gallery 'at the Farmer's Museum; awards to members for outstanding craftsmanship at each exhibition.
Holdings: Vols 150; AV—Lantern slides; Other—Photograph collection, recordings of original antiques by Esther Stevens Brazer and Walter H Wright, for members use.

NEW YORK STATE HISTORICAL ASSOCIATION
—Fenimore House, Rte 80, Lake Rd (Mailing Add: PO Box 391, 13326). Tel: 607-547-2533. *Pres* Hugh M Flick; *VPres* John H G Pell; *Secy* Edward W Stack; *Assoc Dir & Chief Educ* Milo V Stewart; *Cur* Richard E Slavin III; *Registr & Cur Photographic Coll* Gerard F Reese.
Open (May - Oct) Tues - Sat 9 AM - 5 PM; cl Mon & Sun; (Nov & Apr) mornings only; cl in winter. Admis adults $2.75, juniors $1. Estab 1899 as a historical society whose purpose is to promote the study of New York State through a statewide educational program, the operation of two museums, and graduate programs offering master's degree in conjunction with the State University College at Oneonta. Fenimore House is an art museum with an extensive collection of art. Average Annual Attendance: 55,000. Mem: adults 2800, juniors 5000; dues $12; annual meeting July.
Collections: †American folk art, †portraits, landscapes, genre paintings of New York State, Browere life masks of famous Americans, memorabilia of James Fenimore Cooper.
Exhibitions: Photographs from the Smith and Telfer Photographic Collection of the New York State Historical Association.

Publications: New York History, quarterly journal; The Yorker, junior magazine; Newsletter, biannual; Director's Report, annual.
Activities: Classes for adults and children; docent training; seminars on American culture; junior program; conferences; lectures open to public; gallery talks; tours; individual paintings and original objects of art lent to selected museums.
—Farmers' Museum, Inc. Tel: 607-547-2533. *Dir & Chief Cur* Minor Wine Thomas Jr; *Cur* David L Parke, Jr; *Asst Cur* Virginia P Partridge. Open (May - Oct) Sat - Sun 9 AM - 5 PM; (Nov - Apr) cl Mon & Sun mornings. Admis adults $2.75, juniors $1. Estab 1943 as an outdoor folk museum of rural life in upstate New York, 1785-1860. Main buildings with collections and craft demonstrations; recreated Village Crossroads with 13 buildings brought in from nearby area; folk art. Average Annual Attendance: 120,000.
—Library. Tel: 607-547-2533. *Ed Assoc & Chief Library Serv* Wendell Tripp. Open to public for reference only.
Holdings: Vols 50,000; Per sub 150; Other—Manuscripts.
Special Subjects: New York State history, folk art, decorative arts, genealogy.

CORNING

CORNING MUSEUM OF GLASS, Centerway (Mailing Add: 5 Denison Parkway E, 14830). Tel: 607-937-5371. *Dir* Thomas S Buechner; *Deputy Dir Collections* Dwight P Lanmon; *Deputy Dir Admin* John H Martin; *Deputy Dir Communications* Antony E Snow; *Research Scientist* Robert H Brill; *Cur Ancient Glass* Sidney M Goldstein; *Cur American Glass* Jane Shadel Spillman; *Registrar* Priscilla B. Price.
Open all year daily 9 AM - 5 PM. No admis. Estab 1951 to present to the public the art, history, archaeology and early manufacture of glass; the gallery covers the period from ancient to contemporary; new museum facilities being constructed. Average Annual Attendance: 750,000.
Income: Financed by state appropriation.
Collections: Collection of over 15,000 objects representing all periods of glass history from 1500 BC to the present.
Exhibitions: Battson Collection of Paperweights; William Cullen Bryant Collection; Independence Pursued and Achieved; School Art Exhibitions (annual); Glass Art Society; Cut and Engraved Glass of Corning, 1868-1940; A Victorian Toyshop; The Great Paperweight Show; Glassmaking: America's First Industry (traveling).
Publications: Journal of Glass Studies, annually.
Activities: Classes for children; annual seminar on glass; lect open to the public, 20 vis lectr per yr; original objects of art lent to other museums for exhibits; lending collection contains books 20,000, slides 1000; traveling exhibitions organized and circulated; sales shop selling books, slides.
—Corning Museum of Glass Library, 5 Denison Parkway E, 14830. Tel: 607-937-5371. *Assoc Librn* Norma P H Jenkins.
Open Mon - Fri 9 AM - 5 PM. Estab 1951 for the purpose of providing extensive and comprehensive coverage of the art, archaeology, history and early manufacture of glass. The library is primarily for research reference only.
Holdings: Vols 20,000; AV—Microfiche, microfilm, motion pictures; Other—Clipping files, exhibition catalogs, original documents, pamphlets, photographs.
Special Subjects: Glass history; Ornamental Glass; Glass manufacturing and technology; Glassware; Glass painting and staining.
Special Collections: 350 manufacturers' trade catalogs on microfiche; incunabula related to glass; archival materials relating to glass manufacturers.

ROCKWELL-CORNING MUSEUM, Baron Steuben Pl, 14830. Tel: 607-937-5386. *Dir* Antony E Snow; *Asst Dir for Coll* Kristin A Amylon; *Asst Dir for Admin* P Jensen Monroe; *Educational Services* Cathy Leffel Birch; *Admin Asst* Carolyn Lovejoy; *Staff Photographer* Charles W Swain.
Open June - Sept, Mon - Sat 10 AM - 5 PM; Sun Noon - 5 PM; Oct - May, Tues - Sat 10 AM - 5 PM; Sun 1 - 5 PM, cl Mon. Admis adults $1, Senior & Students 50¢, Children 25¢. Estab 1976 to house and exhibit the collections of the Robert F Rockwell Foundation and Family; to serve the Corning community with the funding provided by the Corning Glass Works. Average Annual Attendance: 35,000.
Income: $40,000 (financed by state appropriation and grant from the Corning Glass Works. Purchases: $10,000.
Collections: Paintings; prints; etchings; bronzes; Pueblo Indian pottery; Navajo rugs; Plains Indian beadwork and artifacts; Carder Steuben glass (1903-1933).
Exhibitions: Currently on display is the best of Bob Rockwell's Western Art Collection. This temporary exhibition is one fifth of his holdings.
Publications: The Painters' West (Nov. 1976), (exhibition catalog); Newsletter, quarterly.
Activities: Classes for children; docent training; programs for 4th grade, junior high and high school students; lect open to the public and for members only, 2 vis lectr per yr; gallery talks; tours; artmobile; individual paintings and original objects of art lent to established museums by per-

mission of the Director and Mr. Rockwell; lending collection contains color reproductions, framed reproductions, original art works 350, original prints 200, Victorian toys, Carder Steuben Glass; traveling exhibitions organized and circulated; museum shop selling books, magazines, reproductions, prints, Indian jewelry, postcards, needlepoint, T-shirts.
Library. Tel: 607-937-5386. *Librn* Carolyn Lovejoy. Open to the public by prior arrangement for reference only. Holdings: Vols 75; Per subs 10.

CORTLAND

CORTLAND FREE LIBRARY, Art Gallery, 32 Church St, 13045. Tel: 607-753-1042 & 753-1043. *Library Dir* Warren S Eddy.
Open: Mon - Thurs 10 AM - 9 PM; Fri & Sat 10 AM - 5:30 PM; cl Sun. No admis. Estab 1938. Monthly exhibitions held.
Holdings: Vols 1300.

STATE UNIVERSITY NEW YORK COLLEGE AT CORTLAND, Art Slide Library, 13045. Tel: 607-753-4316. *Chmn* J Catherine Gibian; *Cur* Jo Schaffer.
Open Mon - Fri 8:30 AM - 5 PM; and by appointment. Estab 1967 to provide visual resources to faculty, students and community; art gallery is maintained under separate jurisdiction of art department.
Income: Financed by state appropriation. Purchases $1000.
Holdings: Vols 300; Per subs 10; AV—Lantern slides, slides; Other—Exhibition catalogs, photographs.

DOUGLASTON

NATIONAL ART LEAGUE, 44-21 Douglaston Parkway, 11360. Tel: 212-229-9495. *Pres* Leo Breslau.
Estab 1932, inc 1950, as Art League of Long Island, Inc. Mem: 200.
Exhibitions: Two annual major shows, one national; gallery exhibitions.
Publications: Bulletins; catalogs; brochures.
Activities: Art classes for adults and children in all media; lectures; demonstrations.

EAST HAMPTON

GUILD HALL OF EAST HAMPTON, INC, Museum Section, 158 Main St, 11937. Tel: 516-324-0806. *Chmn* Walter J Fried; *First VChmn* Mrs Condie Lamb; *Second VChmn* Deborah L Perry; *Secy* Mrs Dana Raymond; *Treas* Oscar Weinberger; *Dir* Enez Whipple; *Asst Dir & Publicity* Mildred Granitz; *Off Mgr-Secy* Billie Kalbacher; *Secy* Mary Frayher; *Asst Cur* Rae Ferren.
Open Mon - Sat 10 AM - 5 PM, Sun 2 - 5 PM (May - Sept); Tues - Sat 10 AM - 5 PM, cl Sun (Oct - Apr). No admis. Estab 1931, a cultural center for the visual and performing arts with a New York State Board of Regents Educational Charter. Three galleries and a sculpture garden. Emphasis on art collection and exhibitions is chiefly on the many artists who live or have lived in the area. Average Annual Attendance: 82,000. Mem: 1700; dues $25 - $1000; annual meeting Apr.
Income: $361,000 (financed by membership, state appropriation, benefits, events and fund drives). Purchases: $10,000.
Collections: Over 500 works: †paintings, †sculptures, †prints, mainly of work by Childe Hassam, Thomas Moran, Jackson Pollock, James Brooks, Ilya Golotowsky, Jimmy Ernst and other artists of the region.
Exhibitions: Boris Kroll, Master Weaver; Long Island Painters Awards Exhibition; Polish Heritage; Recycled Art; Point of View (Collection); 39th Annual Guild Hall Members Exhibition; Artists of the Region Annual Invitational; Drawings by Artists of the Region; Abraham Rattner, Selected Works 1953-1977; Rattner, Studies for the Stained Glass Window, Chicago Loop Synagogue; Joe Wilder, Recent Paintings; Peter Lipman-Wulf, Sculpture; Photography in the Hamptons, a Survey of Historical and Contemporary Camera Work; Robert Kaufmann, Retrospective; Phyllis Hirschberg Awards Exhibition; 14 traveling mini-exhibitions.
Publications: Guild Hall Newsletter, monthly.
Activities: Classes for adults; docent training; cooperative projects with area schools; lect open to public, 12 vis lectr per yr; concerts; gallery talks; tours; competitions; original objects of art lent to museums, libraries, schools, public buildings, lending collection contains cassettes, original art works and prints, paintings, photographs, sculpture, slides; traveling exhibitions organized and circulated; museum shop selling books, prints, hand crafts, posters.

ELMIRA

ARNOT ART MUSEUM, 235 Lake St, 14901. Tel: 607-734-3697. *Dir* Kenneth H Lindquist; *Educ Cur* Alan Lee Voorhees; *Cur of Coll* Allen C Smith.

Open Tues - Fri 10 AM - 5 PM; Sat & Sun 2 - 5 PM; cl Mon. No admis. Estab 1911 to serve the people of the community with a regular schedule of changing exhibits from the permanent collection and traveling shows, as well as providing other free cultural activities not ordinarily available in the area. Average Annual Attendance: 40,000. Mem: 650; dues $3 and higher; annual meeting May.
Collections: Flemish, Dutch, French, English, German, Italian, Spanish, and †American paintings; †contemporary prints; European and †American sculpture.
Exhibitions: Changed monthly; assembled from the permanent collection, rented from traveling exhibition services, or borrowed from private collectors or institutions. Regional exhibition for artists living in 60 mile radius of Elmira held annually, prizes $650; regional (60 mile radius of Elmira) craft exhibition annually, prizes.
Activities: Classes for adults and children; lectures open to pblic.

ELMIRA COLLEGE, Hamilton Art Gallery, Park Pl, 14901. *Dir* Mark S Schmidt.
Open Mon - Fri 1 - 4:30 PM. No admis. Gallery is located in Gothic Cathedral-like building with 100 x 35 ft space. Average Annual Attendance: 1000.
Income: Financed by School Budget.

FLUSHING

QUEENS COLLEGE OF THE CITY UNIVERSITY OF NEW YORK, Art Collection, Kissena Blvd and Long Island Expressway, 11367. Tel: 212-520-7243. *Chief Librn* Robert Muller; *Art Librn & Cur* Neal W Richmond; *Art Bibliographer* Gerd Huehsam.
Open Mon - Wed 9 AM - 8 PM; Tues & Thurs 9 AM - 6 PM; Fri 9 AM - 5 PM. No admis. Estab 1957 for a study collection for Queens College students. Permanent collection exhibited in Art Library reading room; loan shows in adjacent gallery and entrance corridor.
Income: Financed by state appropriation.
Collections: Ancient and antique glass; Renaissance and later bronzes; old master and WPA prints; Egyptian, Greek, Luistan antiquities; 16th-20th century paintings.
Exhibitions: Ancient and Antique Glass; Alice Neel Drawings, Joyce Kozloff (prints); Sylvia Sleigh (watercolors); Richard McDermott Miller (sculpture); Diana Kurz (drawings); Cheryl Heyman (dioramas).
Publications: Exhibition catalogs; brochures for shows.
Activities: Lending collection contains lantern slides 11,000.
—**Paul Klapper Library.**
Open to City University students for reference.
Holdings: Vols 22,000; Per subs 100.

QUEENS MUSEUM, New York City Bldg, Flushing Meadow Pk, 11368. Tel: 212-592-2405. *Dir* Janet Schneider; *Cur* Susan Bloom; *Museum Educator* Janet Katz; *Secy* Emmy Piombino; *Financial Secy* Barbara Sperber; *Technician Film/Video* Alan Law.
Open Tues - Sat 10 AM - 5 PM; Sun 1 - 5 PM; cl Mon. No admis, contributions requested. Estab March 1972 to provide quality art and related programs for residents of Queens and New York City; Large gallery with changing exhibitions, permanent exhibition. Average Annual Attendance: 100,000. Mem: 300.
Income: $245,000 (financed by endowment, membership, city and state appropriation).
Exhibitions: Permanent exhibition, The Panorama, a scale model of the Ciy of New York; (1976) Queens Artists; Urban Aesthetics; Visual Vibrations; Queens High School Artists; The Tulip and The Rose: Seeds of Queens History; Cows; Walter Rosenblum Retrospective; Iagel Tumarkin (sculpture). (1977) Queens Artists; Masters of the Brush: Chinese Painting and Calligraphy from the 16th - 19th Century; Life Ripening into Fullness/ Contemporary Chinese Paintings by Chung Hsiang Chao; American Sculpture: Folk and Modern; Casts: a Queens Museum project; Antarctica; Masked Rituals; Christmas Treasures. (1978) Queens Artists '78; Private Myths; Photography: Art & Artifacts.
Publications: Catalogs; newsletter, quarterly.
Activities: Classes for adults and children; docent training; lect open to the public, 25 vis lectr per yr; concerts; gallery talks; traveling exhibitions organized and circulated; museum shop selling gift items and catalogs.

FREDONIA

STATE UNIVERSITY OF NEW YORK COLLEGE AT FREDONIA, Michael C Rockefeller Arts Center Gallery, 14063. Tel: 716-673-3537. *Art Gallery Asst* Nancy Weekly.
Open Mon, Wed, Fri 9 - 10:30 AM, 1 - 10 PM; Tues & Thurs 2 - 3:30 PM, 6 - 9 PM; Sat 10 AM - 5 PM; Sun 4 - 9 PM; schedule subject to change each semester. No admis. Estab 1963 and relocated in 1969 to new quarters designed by I M Pei and Partners. The gallery serves as a focal point of the campus, uniting the college with the community. Average Annual Attendance: 20,000.

Income: Financed by state appropriation.

Collections: Primarily 20th century American art and architectural archival material, with an emphasis on †prints and †sculpture.

Exhibitions: Approx 10 per year. Highlights of 1977-78: Printed Quilts/Quilted Prints; International Miniature Print Exhibition; Ceramics by Holt and Milnes; Federation of Modern Painters and Sculptors; as well as student and faculty exhibitions.

Publications: Exhibition catalogs.

Activities: Lect open to public, 2 - 4 vis lectr per yr; gallery talks; tours; competitions; individual paintings and original objects of art lent to offices and public lobbies on campus; lending collection contains framed reproductions 100, original prints 50, paintings, photographs 400, sculpture; traveling exhibitions organized and circulated; small slide library.

GARDEN CITY

ADELPHI UNIVERSITY, Fine Arts Library, 11530. Tel: 516-294-8700, exten 7353. *Head Fine Arts Library* Erica Doctorow; *Fine Arts Librn* Grace Temple; *Music Librn* Gary Cantrell.

Open Mon - Thurs 8:30 AM - 10 PM; Fri & Sat 9 AM - 5 PM; Sun 1 - 5 PM. The Fine Arts Library builds print and nonprint collections and provides reference service in fine and applied arts, music and related performing arts. Maintains an art gallery.

Income: Financed by state appropriation and through the University.

Holdings: Vols 20,000; Per subs 100; AV—Cassettes, microfiche, microfilm, phonorecords, slides, video cassettes; Other—Exhibition catalogs, manuscripts, memorabilia, original art works, original documents, pamphlets, photographs, prints, sculpture.

Special Subjects: Art and music.

Special Collections: William Blake; Americana; Cuala Press; Expatriate Writers.

Exhibitions: Eighty-five Golden Florins; The Book Beautiful in Ireland; The First Blast of the Trumpet; William Blake: the Painter as Poet (NEA grant); Aspects of Book Collecting; Professors in Print, Perspective and Performance.

Publications: Exhibition catalogs, irregularly.

Activities: Lect open to public; library tours; exhibitions organized.

GENESEO

STATE UNIVERSITY OF NEW YORK COLLEGE AT GENESEO, Fine Arts Gallery, 14454. Tel: 716-245-5801 & 245-5802. *Coordr Fine Arts Activities* Bertha V B Lederer; *Secy* Dora J Scorsone.

Open 2 - 5 PM for exhibitions. No admis. Estab 1967; general purpose gallery serving college and community; shows are mostly originated here. Average Annual Attendance: 6000.

Income: Financed by state appropriation.

Collections: Paintings; graphics; sculpture; ceramics; furniture.

Exhibitions: (1968) Hudson River School; (1973) Horses and Hounds of the Genesee Valley; (1974) Early Arts in the Genesee Valley, 18th and 19th Centuries; (1975) Early Architecture of the Genesee Valley, Drawings by Carl F Schmidt, Photographs by Roger B Smith; (1976) Art and History; (1977) Up and Down the River.

Publications: Exhibition catalogs.

Activities: Lect open to public, 3 - 4 vis lectr per yr; concerts; lending collection contains books 400 - 600.

GLENS FALLS

HYDE COLLECTION, 161 Warren St, 12801. Tel: 518-792-1761. The Hyde Collection Trust, Owners: *Interim Adminr* Henry Musser; *Cur* James Kettlewell.

Open Tues, Wed, Fri, Sat & Sun 2 - 5 PM; cl Mon & Thurs. No admis. Estab 1952. Volunteer Council of about 100 members as guards, guides, office help and public relations committees. Average Annual Attendance: 15,000.

Collections: Sculpture, tapestries, furniture; paintings by El Greco, Rembrandt, Rubens, Botticelli, Tintoretto, Renoir, Picasso, Homer, and others; drawings by da Vinci, Degas, Tiepolo, Matisse, Lorraine, and others.

Exhibitions: Artists of Lake George 1776-1976, summer 1976; 10 additional temporary exhibitions throughout the year.

Publications: Rembrandt's Christ; The Art of Henry Ossawa Tanner; The Sculpture of John Rogers; David Smith of Bolton Landing; Rockwell Kent (1882-1971); American Quilts - European and American Samplers; Elihu Vedder; Annual Report.

Activities: Classes for adults; lectures; concerts.

Library: Holdings—Vols 300; color reproductions; Kodachromes 800.

GOSHEN

HALL OF FAME OF THE TROTTER, 240 Main St, 10924. Tel: 914-294-6330. *Dir* Philip A Pines; *Registr* Jean E Musgrave; *Graphics Designer* Janet S Hack; *Asst Secy & Treas* John A Fraser; *Staff Asst* Walter Latzko.

Open Mon - Sat 10 AM - 5 PM; Sun & holidays 1:30 - 5 PM. No admis. Estab 1951 to preserve the artifacts of harness racing. There are two galleries; one usually has the museum's permanent collection; the smaller one is used for visiting art shows. Average Annual Attendance: 27,000 - 35,000. Mem: 1200; dues $15, $30, $100; annual meeting July.

Income: Financed by endowment, membership.

Collections: Large collection of lithographs by Currier and Ives pertaining to harness racing, plus other leading printers of the 19th century; wood carvings, bronzes, dioramas and statuary.

Exhibitions: (1976-78) Visiting art shows for nine months of the year.

Publications: Newsletter, bimonthly.

Activities: Classes for children; lectures open to public; concerts; tours; museum shop selling books, prints, slides.

Library: Open to public for reference only.

GREENVALE

C W POST CENTER, LONG ISLAND UNIVERSITY, Art Gallery, 11548. Tel: 516-299-2788 & 299-2789. *Dir* Joan Vita Miller; *Secy* Annette Demow.

Open Mon - Fri 10 AM - 5 PM; Sat & Sun 1 - 5 PM. No admis. Estab 1973; a university gallery which has great appeal to the surrounding North Shore community as well as the student body. The gallery is located in a multimillion dollar student complex; it occupies a space of approx 46 x 92 ft. Varied exhibitions change monthly. Average Annual Attendance: 40,000 - 50,000.

Income: Financed by university budget, grants and donations.

Collections: Contemporary graphics, including works by Rauschenberg, Max Ernst, Pearlstein, Mark di Suvero, and Salvador Dali.

Exhibitions: (1976) An Exploration of Photography 1839-1976; Roger Shimomura; (1977) Art Arts of China; Marsden Hartley; (1978) The Unconquered Spirit: American Indian Painting and Objects 1937-1977; Naive Art in Yugoslavia.

Publications: Catalogs: Louise Nevelson, The Arts of China, Marsden Hartley.

Activities: Docent training; lect open to public, 4 vis lectr per yr; concerts; gallery talks; individual paintings lent; lending collection contains original prints 200, paintings 100; traveling exhibitions organized and circulated; sales shop selling books, magazines, reproductions.

HAMILTON

COLGATE UNIVERSITY, Picker Art Gallery, Charles A Dana Arts Center, 13346. Tel: 315-824-1000, exten 632. *Dir-Cur* Edward Bryant; *Secy-Registr* Linda Murray.

Open Mon - Fri 10 AM - 5 PM; Sat & Sun 1 - 5 PM; cl during school recesses and intersessions. No admis. Estab 1966; an educative adjunct to study in the fine arts and to the liberal arts curriculum. The gallery was designed by architect Paul Rudolph. Average Annual Attendance: Approx 10,000. Mem: 110; dues $5 and up; annual meeting in the Spring.

Income: Financed by the university.

Collections: Luis de Hoyos Collection of Guerrero stone sculpture; Herman Collection of Oriental art; paintings; sculptures; prints; photographs; posters.

Exhibitions: One-person shows: Adal, Frank Lincoln Viner, Lynn Itzkowitz, Leslie Krims, Neil Spitzer, Steven Barbash, Tom Doyle, Rene Gelpi, Marty Greenbaum, John Koch, Douglas Holloley, and James Loveless; Thomas Nast: President Maker; 10 in situ; New Deal for Art (GANYS); Luis de Hoyos Collection; Folk Art of Central New York State.

Publications: Catalogs.

Activities: Lect open to public, 10 vis lectr per yr; gallery talks; individual paintings and original objects of art lent to members of Friends of the Visual Arts; lending collection contains original art works and prints, paintings, sculpture.

HEMPSTEAD

HOFSTRA UNIVERSITY, Emily Lowe Gallery, Hempstead Turnpike, 11550. Tel: 516-560-3275 & 560-3276. *Dir* Kevin E Consey; *Secy* Emma Knutsen.

Open Mon - Thurs 10 AM - 5 PM; Tues & Wed 10 AM - 9 PM; Sun 1 - 5 PM. No admis. Estab 1963; a university museum that serves the needs of its student body and the surrounding Nassau County community. Average Annual Attendance: 22,000 - 25,000. Mem: 220; dues $15 - $50.

Income: Financed by endowment, membership, foundation, and university.

Collections: African, pre-Columbian, New Guinea, Japanese and Indian art; †American prints; 17th and 18th century European painting; contemporary prints.
Exhibitions: (1976) Election: Political Drawings and Illustrations; Fourteen from Hofstra; (1977) American Quiltmakers; Art off the Picture Press: Tyler Graphics, Ltd; Children's Arts from Leningrad; Our America; Art Faculty Works 77; (1978) The Art of Boxing.
Publications: Exhibition catalogs.
Activities: Classes for children; lect open to public, 2 - 3 vis lectr per yr; gallery talks; tours; individual paintings and original objects of art lent; traveling exhibitions organized and circulated.

HEWLETT

HEWLETT-WOODMERE PUBLIC LIBRARY, 1125 Broadway, 11557. Tel: 516-374-1967. *Dir* William H Menear; *Chief of Public Services* Rebecca Rockmuller; *Art Librn* (vacant).
Open Mon - Thurs 9 AM - 9 PM; Fri 9 AM - 6 PM; Sat 9 AM - 5 PM; Sun 1 - 5 PM. Estab 1947 as a Co-Center (of the 54 member Nassau County Library system) for Art and Music; gallery maintained. Circ: 265,630.
Income: $820,000 (financed by state appropriation and school district). Purchases $110,000.
Holdings: Vols 118, 589; Per subs 473; AV—Film strips; Kodachromes, motion pictures, phonorecords, reels, slides; Other—Clipping files, exhibition catalogs, framed reproductions, pamphlets, photographs, prints, reproductions.
Special Subjects: Art; music; architecture; photography; film; dance; theatre, crafts and antiques.
Publications: Index to Art Reproductions in Books (Metuchen, NJ: Scarecrow Press, 1974).
Activities: Classes for adults and children; lect open to the public; concerts; gallery talks; tours.

HUDSON

OLANA HISTORIC SITE, New York State Dept of Parks and Recreation, RD 2 (Off Rt 9-G), 12534. Tel: 518-828-0135. *Historic Site Mgr* Alan Dages; *Interpretive Programs Asst* Linda McLean; *Pres Governor's Bd* Thomas Quinn.
Open Wed - Sun 9 AM - 5 PM, Memorial Day weekend to Oct 31. Admis 50¢. Estab 1870-74, and opened as a museum June 1967 to promote interest in and disseminate information of the life, works, and times of Frederick Edwin Church, landscape painter of the Hudson River School; the building is a Persian-style castle overlooking the Hudson River. Average Annual Attendance: 30,000 - 70,000. Mem: 150; dues $10, annual meeting May or June.
Income: Financed by state appropriation.
Collections: Paintings by Church, and many other artists; oil sketches, drawings, and photographs by Church; extensive 19th Century furniture collection; decorative arts; textile collection from all over the world.
Publications: The Crayon, journal, quarterly, produced by Friends of Olana.
Activities: Classes for children; dramatic programs; docent training; special events; concerts; individual paintings and original objects of art lent to other institutions who qualify; slides and postcards available.
Archives. Open to public with approval of Site Manager, for reference only. Special Collections: Family papers, photographs, books, correspondence, diaries, receipts.

HUNTINGTON

HECKSCHER MUSEUM, Prime Ave 11743. Tel: 516-421-1000, exten 244, 245. *Chmn Bd Trustees* Miner D Crary, Jr; *Dir* Katherine Lochridge; *Asst Dir* Ruth Solomon; *Registr* William Titus; *Mem & Progs Coordr* Dorothy Spencer.
Open Tues - Fri 10 AM - 5 PM; Sat, Sun & holidays 1 - 6 PM; cl Mon. No admis. Estab 1920, inc 1957 for the maintenance, preservation and operation of the museum building together with the preservation, exhibition and display of all objects and works of art therein. Four galleries, each 20 x 40 ft (two used for changing exhibitions and two for permanent collection) with 15 ft ceilings. Track incandescent and diffused ultraviolet-free fluorescent lighting. Security staff. Average Annual Attendance: 46,000. Mem: 525; dues $10 and up; annual meeting June.
Income: Approx $250,000 (financed by endowment, membership, town appropriation, grants).
Collections: Paintings, sculpture, drawings and prints by 16th-20th century artists, primarily American with some European. Major works by the Moran family, George Grosz, Thomas Eakins, Lucas Cranach the Elder are included.
Exhibitions: (1976-77) Heritage of Freedom: A Salute to America's Foreign-Born Artists; Lockwood de Forest; George Grosz, Works in Oil; A Private Eye: Fifty 19th Century American Paintings, Drawings and Watercolors from the Stebbins Collection; The Seeing Eye: Neutron Activa-

tion Autoradiography; Artists of Suffolk County is an annual invited exhibition; New Directions in Sculpture; Recorders of History. Huntington Township Art League sponsors annual Long Island Artists Exhibition. Regional artists are featured in Little Shows.
Publications: Heckscher News, quarterly newsletter.
Activities: Lect open to public, 9 - 12 vis lectr per yr; gallery talks; tours; individual paintings and original objects of art lent to art institutions and galleries; lending collection contains original art works 290, paintings 260, sculpture, antique work tools; shop selling magazines, reproductions, slides.
Library: Open to researchers by appointment for reference only. Holdings: Vols 1000; Per subs 15.

HYDE PARK

FRANKLIN D ROOSEVELT LIBRARY AND MUSEUM, Albany Post Rd, 12538. Tel: 914-229-8114. *Dir* William R Emerson; *Acting Cur Museum* Marguerite B Hubbard.
Open daily 9 AM - 5 PM; cl Christmas Day and New Year's Day. Admis $1.50 for combination ticket to the Roosevelt Home, Library/Museum and Vanderbilt Mansion; children, school groups and senior citizens no admis. Estab 1941. Average Annual Attendance: 225,000.
Collections: Papers of President and Mrs. Roosevelt and of various members of his administrations; Museum displays illustrative of their lives, careers, and special interests, including personal items; gifts from heads of state, friends, and admirers; and items collected by President Roosevelt including paintings, prints, ship models, documents and relics on the history of the United States Navy as well as other marine items; prints and paintings and documents on the Hudson Valley.
Publications: The Franklin D Roosevelt Library and Museum for visitors; Historical Materials in the Franklin D Roosevelt Library for researchers.
Activities: Sales shop selling books, reproductions, prints and slides.
—**Library.** *Librn* Joseph W Marshall.
Open to scholars for reference.
Holdings: Vols 38,000; Per subs 45; Other—Unbound per 62,000, pamphlets, newspapers, maps, broadsides.
Special Subjects: Life and career of Franklin and Eleanor Roosevelt; the New Deal, History of the US Navy and the Hudson River Valley.

EDWIN A ULRICH MUSEUM, "Wave Crest" on-the-Hudson, Albany Post Rd, 12538. Tel: 914-229-7107. *Dir* Edwin A Ulrich.
Open May - Oct Thurs - Mon 11 AM - 4 PM. Admis $1.50. Estab 1956 to exhibit three generations of the Waugh family of painters, 1813 - 1973; this is a museum, not a gallery, with exhibits of the fine art and works of the Waugh family. Average Annual Attendance: 500.
Income: Financed by owner and *Dir* Edwin A Ulrich.
Collections: Paintings by Samuel Bell Waugh, 1813-1884; Fred J Waugh, 1860-1940; Coulton Waugh, 1896-1973.
Exhibitions: (1977-78) Exhibit of 30 Fine Art pieces displayed at Cayuga Museum of History and Art, Auburn, New York.
Activities: Lect open to the public, only on Waugh; individual paintings lent to other recognized museums; lending collection contains Kodachromes 300; sales shop selling books, reproductions, slides.
Library: Tel: 914-229-7107. *Librn* Edwin A Ulrich. Open to museum visitors. Holdings: Vols 50; Per subs 2.

ITHACA

CORNELL UNIVERSITY, Herbert F Johnson Museum of Art, 14853. Tel: 607-256-6464. *Dir* Thomas W Leavitt; *Cur Asian Art* Martie Young; *Adj Cur Modern Art* Robert Hobbs; *Asst Cur* Elizabeth C Evans; *Coordr Educ & Cur Crafts* Nancy S Press; *Registr* Jill Aszling; *Supt* Donald Feint; *Adminr* Nancy Scoones; *Admin Aide* Jill Chambers-Hartz; *Pub Progs Coordr* Kitty Campbell.
Open Tues - Sat 10 AM - 5 PM; Wed 10 AM - 9 PM; Sun 11 AM - 5 PM; cl Mon. No admis. Estab 1973, replacing the Andrew Dickson White Museum of Art, originally founded in 1953 as Cornell University's Art Museum to serve students, the Tompkins County community and the Finger Lakes region. The collection and galleries are housed in an I M Pei designed building on Cornell University campus overlooking downtown Ithaca and Lake Cayuga. Average Annual Attendance: 93,000. Mem: 1050; dues $5 - $100,000 or more.
Income: $400,000 (financed by endowment, membership, state appropriation, grants and university funds). Purchases: $100,000.
Collections: European and American paintings, drawings, sculpture, graphic arts, photographs; Asian art; and arts of primitive societies.
Exhibitions: Photo/Synthesis; The Handwrought Object: 1776-1976; Far Eastern Art in Upstate New York; New York State Artists Series I-IV; Kay Sage; The Selective Eye: Photographs by Benjamin Hertzberg; Ed-

win Dickinson; New Aspects of Self in American Photography; Landscape: New Views; Abstract Expressionism: The Formative Years; Cornell Then, Sculpture Now.
Publications: Seasonal calendars, 3 times a yr; exhibition catalogs, approx 10 a yr.
Activities: Classes for adults and children; lect open to public, 5 - 10 vis lectr per yr; gallery talks; tours; individual paintings and original objects of art lent to selected loans upon official permission; lending collection available only to Cornell University community, contains paintings 544, sculpture, drawings 110; traveling exhibitions organized and circulated; museum shop selling slides, exhibition catalogs, postcards, notecards.
Library: Non-circulating for staff, students and scholars (in-house use only). Holdings: Vols approx 3600; Per subs 26; sales and auction catalogs, vertical and artist files.

JAMAICA

EXHIBITIONISTS, INC, 92-20 Union Hall St, 11432. Tel: 212-658-4926. *Pub Relations* Pat Hammerman & Carol Crawford; *Treas* Peter Engelbrect; *Membership* Marilyn Moskowitz.
Open Tues - Sat Noon - 5 PM. No admis. Estab 1976. It is a gallery organized, controlled and operated by a group of artists for their mutual benefit. The gallery is an architect-designed space with a large display window. Average Annual Attendance: 7500. Mem: 16; dues $25 per month.
Income: Financed by membership, grants, and fund raising events.
Exhibitions: Choose a Sculpture for Jamaica: a Documentation and Exhibition of Jamaica's Wall Murals; In Celebration; Expo Cuba (an Exhibition of Cuban Posters) members' work; Louis Kunsch (paintings).
Activities: Lect open to public, 2 vis lectr per yr; concerts; gallery talks; individual paintings and original objects of art lent to patron; lending collection contains original art works, original prints, paintings, photographs, sculpture.

QUEENS BOROUGH PUBLIC LIBRARY,* 89-11 Merrick Blvd, 11432. Tel: 212-739-1900. *Dir* Milton S Byam; *Head Art & Music Div* Dorothea Wu.
Open Mon - Fri 10 AM - 9 PM; Sat 10 AM - 5:30 PM; Sun 1 - 5 PM, except June to Sept. Estab 1896; Art & Music Division estab 1933.
Holdings: Vols 40,000 on art and music for home loan; Per subs 14,000; Other—Picture collection 1,500,000, classified by subject, mounted for circulation.

SAINT JOHN'S UNIVERSITY, Art Gallery, Chung-Cheng Cultural Center, Sun Yat Sen Hall, Grand Central and Utopia Parkways, 11439. Tel: 212-969-8000, exten 582. *Dir Chung-Cheng Cultural Center* Dr Paul K T Sih; *Cur Chung-Cheng Art Gallery* Abraham P Ho.
Open Mon - Sun 10 AM - 8 PM. No admis. Estab Oct 1977 to make available Oriental art objects to the public, and to expose the metropolitan area to the Oriental culture through various exhibits and activities; gallery displays contemporary as well as ancient objects, mainly Oriental with a few western subjects. Average Annual Attendance: 50,000.
Income: Financed by endowment and private contributions.
Collections: †Harry C Goebel Collection containing 595 pieces of rare and beautiful art objects dating from the 7th to 19th century—jades; ivory carvings; netsuke; sword guards; porcelains; lacquerware and paintings from Japan and China. †Permanent collection contains 600 pieces of Chinese porcelain, paintings and calligraphy, dating from 7th to 20th century.
Exhibitions: (1976) Brushwork of Ch'ing Master, 17th - 19th Century. (1977) Chinese Artists in New York. (1978) 15th Annual Sumi-e Society National Exhibition; Leory Neiman: Sports Art.
Publications: Chinese Artists in New York.
Activities: Classes for adults; films and demonstrations; lect open to the public, 5 vis lectr per yr; gallery talks; tours; lending collection contains original art works 200; original prints; paintings 200; traveling exhibitions organized and circulated.
—*Library,* Asian Collection, St Augustine Hall. *Librn:* Hou-Ran Ferng. Open to the public for reference only.
Holdings: Vols 50,000; Per subs 100.
Special Collections: Japan Foundation Collection includes 200 volumes on various Japanese art subjects; Series of Chinese Arts (Mei Shu Ts'ung Shu) Vols. 1-30; Collected Works of Chinese and Japanese Calligraphy (Shodo Zenshu) Vols. 1-28.

STORE FRONT MUSEUM,* 162-02 Liberty Ave, 11433. Tel: 212-523-5199. *Dir & Cur* Tom Lloyd; *Asst Dir* Janet DeSisso.
Open Mon - Fri 10:30 AM - 5 PM; Sat, Sun & holidays Noon - 3 PM. No admis. Estab 1970 to preserve Black art and history, and for use as a cultural center.
Collections: Paintings; sculpture; drawings; tribal African art.

Activities: Classes for adults and children; training programs for professional museum workers; lectures; gallery talks; guided tours; concerts; competitions; hobby workshops; TV programs; temporary and traveling exhibitions; artmobile.
Library: Open to the public; material also for inter-museum loan. Holdings: Vols. 500. Special Subjects: Black history and culture.

JAMESTOWN

JAMES PRENDERGAST LIBRARY ASSOCIATION, 509 Cherry St, 14701. Tel: 716-484-7135. *Dir* Murray L Bob.
Open Mon - Fri 9 AM - 9 PM; Sat 9 AM - 6 PM; Sun 1 - 4 PM (shorter hours in summer). Estab 1891 as part of Library. Maintains art gallery.
Income: $381,131.
Holdings: (art) Vols 5000; Other—Records, films, art prints, art slides, sculpture reproductions.
Exhibitions: Traveling exhibitions; local one-person and group shows.

KATONAH

JOHN JAY HOMESTEAD, Jay St, (Mailing Add: PO Box AH, 10536). Tel: 914-232-5651. *Cur of History* Lino S Lipinsky de Orlov.
Open Wed - Sun 9 AM - 5 PM. No admis. Estab 1958 as a New York State Historic Site, the home of the first Chief Justice John Jay and six following generations, and contains period furnishings, historic portraits, and library. Average Annual Attendance: 28,000.
Income: Financed by state appropriation.
Activities: Classes for children; docent training; lect open to the public; tours.
Library. Open by appointment.

KATONAH GALLERY, 28 Bedford Rd, 10536. Tel: 914-4988 & 232-4343. *Pres* Mrs Arthur Himmel; *VPres* Mrs John McCain; *Secy* Mrs Mott Schmidt; *Treas* Richard Weinland; *Adminr* Mrs Paul Baren.
Open Tues - Thurs 2 - 5 PM; Fri & Sat 10 AM - 5 PM; Sun 1 - 5 PM; cl Mon. No admis. Estab 1953 to present exhibitions by local artists; programs for schools; films, lectures, demonstrations, workshops. Located on the ground floor of the Katonah Village Library, the Katonah Gallery consists of 1800 sq ft of exhibition space with a meeting room of 1200 sq ft. Average Annual Attendance: 25,000. Mem: Approx 875; dues $10 - $500.
Income: Approx $117,000 (Financed by membership, contributions, grants).
Exhibitions: American Painting 1900-1976; Hopi Clay-Hopi Ceremony; Olga Hirshhorn Collection: Member Artists 76; Graphics from the Tyler Workshop; Change and Permanence in Egyptian Sculpture; Drawings by Marlene Gerberick and Muslins by Winn Smith; Milton Avery: The Late Years; Ukiyo-e: Japanese Woodblock Prints 1680-1850; Works on Paper; Potography: Four Stylistic Approaches; Medieval Images; Edward Giobbi: Ten American Masters of Watercolor.
Publications: Exhibition catalogs.
Activities: Educ dept; docent training; teacher workshops; programs for schools; lect open to public, 5 - 10 vis lectr per yr; gallery talks; concerts; tours; competitions; individual paintings and original objects of art lent; lending collection contains motion pictures, photographs, slides 1800; traveling exhibitions organized and circulated; sales shop selling books, reproductions, prints, jewelry, postcards, notepaper.
Library: Open to gallery personnel. Not cataloged.

KINGSTON

PALISADES INTERSTATE PARK COMMISSION, Senate House State Historic Site, 296 Fair St, 12401. Tel: 914-338-2786. *Historic Site Mgr* James A Ryan; *Historic Site Asst* Suzanne E Lown.
Open Wed - Sun 9 AM - 5 PM; cl Mon & Tues. No admis. Estab 1887. The site is one of 38 New York State historic sites. The Senate House is the place where the first New York State Senate met in 1777; furnished as 18th century middle-class dwelling. The Museum has exhibits of paintings by John Vanderlyn, an early 19th century American artist, and the New York Senate, plus changing exhibits area. Loughran House has a changing exhibits area. Average Annual Attendance: 30,000.
Collections: 18th and 19th century decorative arts; 18th and 19th century paintings and other works of art, particularly those by John and Pieter Vanderlyn, Ammi Phillips, James Bard, Joseph Tubby, Jervis McEntee.
Exhibitions: Vanderlyn the Artist (permanent); At the Risk of our Lives and Fortunes, about the first New York State Senate (permanent); (1976) Kingston Through a Lens (architectural photography); (1977) Images of Women; (1978) Currier and Ives in the Hudson Valley; Courthouses of New York State.
Activities: Classes for children; lect open to public, 4 - 6 vis lectr per yr; concerts; junior museum, The Yorkers Workshop.

Library: Librn John Landau. Open to scholars, students, researchers for reference. Holdings: Vols 2500, collection of 40,000 17th, 18th and 19th century manuscripts, mostly about Ulster County. Special Collections: Collection of letters relating to the artist John Vanderlyn.

LAKE PLACID

LAKE PLACID SCHOOL OF ART GALLERY, Saranac Ave, 12946. Tel: 518-523-2591. *Dir* Brian Gromley; *Dean* Students Lesley Cadman; *Mgr Dir Center for Music, Drama & Art* Barry Hoffman; *Pres Bd* James Roger, III, *VPres Bd* Carolyn Hopkins.
Open 9 AM - 6 PM. Estab 1972 to serve as an art resource center for the north country region through school classes and programs; the gallery offers 12-15 exhibitions a year; approximately half are invitational to artists of national prominence other shows are group shows from national organizations. Average Annual Attendance: 6000.
Income: Financed by foundation funds and tuition.
Activities: Lectr open to the public, 16 vis lectr per yr; concerts; gallery talks; competitions.
—**Fine Arts Library.** Tel: 518-523-2592 or 523-2593, exten 31. *Library Asst* Suellen Linn; *Library Asst* Sarah Adams; *Library Asst* Liz Rapalee; *Part-time Library Asst* Mary Ann Ricketson.
Open Tues, Wed & Fri 9 AM - 5 PM; Mon & Thurs 9 AM - 10 PM; Sat Noon - 5 PM; Sat and Eve hours only when school is in session. Estab 1975 to support the staff and students of the Lake Placid School of Art and the surrounding area. Circ 1416.
Income: $62,000 (financed by endowment, membership). Purchases: $9,000.
Holdings: Vols 7500; Per subs 130; AV—Phonorecords, slides 6000; Other—Clipping files, exhibition catalogs, memorabilia, original art works, sculpture.
Special Collections: Victor Herbert Memorial Collection; Stedman Glass Negative Collection.
Activities: Tours.

LONG BEACH

LONG BEACH ART ASSOCIATION, 111 W Park Ave, 11561. Tel: 516-432-7201.
Founded in 1952 by a group of interested residents determined to form an organization to promote art activity and appreciation with emphasis on quality; sponsored by the Long Beach Public Library.
Exhibitions: Three Membership Shows annually; Material awards shows; May Open Juried Show; July Outdoor Show and Sale, co-sponsored by the City of Long Beach; Artists-of-the-Month Shows.
Publications: Brochures on exhibitions.
Activities: Lect; demonstrations; discussions; workshops.

LONG BEACH PUBLIC LIBRARY, 111 W Park Ave, 11561. Tel: 516-432-7201. *Dir* Sylvia Eisen; *Asst Dir* George Trepp; *Adult Serv* Norman Kupferman; *Children's Librn* Margaret Ptasinski; *Circulation* Katherine Fanata.
Open Mon, Wed, Thurs 9 AM - 9 PM; Tues & Fri 9 AM - 6 PM; Sat 9 AM - 5 PM; Sun 1 - 5 PM. Estab 1928 to serve the community with information and services, including recreational, cultural and informational materials. Circ: 263,126. The Long Beach Art Association in cooperation with the library presents monthly exhibits of all types of media in a room 32 ft x 22 ft with seating capacity of 50.
Income: $497,171 (financed by school taxes). Purchases: $497,171.
Holdings: Vols 106,549; Per subs 290; AV—Cassettes, film strips, microfiche, microfilm, motion pictures, phonorecords; Other—Memorabilia; pamphlets, photographs.
Special Collections: Local history, 300 photographs of Long Beach.
Exhibitions: Mostly local talent, membership shows, juried exhibitions, politician myth and reality; Telma Hillman's spectra sculpture.
Publications: Monthly newsletter.
Activities: Dramatic programs; lect open to public, 18 - 20 vis lectr per yr; concerts; gallery talks.

MOUNT VERNON

MOUNT VERNON PUBLIC LIBRARY,* 28 S First Ave, 10550. Tel: 914-668-1840. *Library Dir* Emanuel Dondy.
Open Mon - Fri 9 AM - 9 PM; Sat 9 AM - 6 PM; Sun 1 - 5 PM; cl Sat & Sun during July and Aug. No admis. Doric Hall, murals by Edward Gay, NA; Exhibition Room, frescoes by Louise Brann Soverns; Norman Wells Print Alcove, estab 1941.
Exhibitions: Semi-annual shows by Mount Vernon Art Association. Others, changing monthly, cover a wide range of subjects; one-man shows of painting and sculpture; woodcarving; metalwork; silver; porcelains; costume dolls; fans; stamps.

Holdings: Vols 4000 on art, specifically architecture, ceramics, costumes, decoration, design, painting, photography and prints. Lending collection of pictures on many subjects for practical purposes, as well as framed prints and sculptures.

MOUNTAINVILLE

STORM KING ART CENTER,* 10953. Tel: 914-534-3115. *Pres* H Peter Stern; *Cur* David Collens.
Open April - Oct Tues - Sun 1 - 5:30 PM; cl Mon. Estab 1959. Average Annual Attendance: 25,000.
Collections: 200 acre sculpture garden with over 125 large scale outdoor contemporary sculptures including 13 works by David Smith; works by Hepworth, Moore, Caro, Snelson, Lewitt, Stankiewicz, Rickey, Ferber, Calder, Grosvenor, Von Schlegell, Bill, Myers, Ginnever, and others.
Exhibitions: Permanent sculpture collection, plus over 100 loan sculptures in special Sculpture in the Fields exhibitions; changing exhibitions in the galleries of prints, paintings and sculpture.
Activities: Lect by artists; lect series on contemporary painting and sculpture; gallery and garden tours.
Holdings: Vols 1000, art from 1850; exhibition catalog file of one-man shows since 1960; all art periodicals since 1965.

NEW PALTZ

STATE UNIVERSITY OF NEW YORK AT NEW PALTZ, College Art Gallery, Smiley Art Bldg, 12561. Tel: 914-257-2439. *Interim Gallery Coordr* James Eager; *Admin Asst* Nancy Campbell; *Asst Gallery Coordr* Irene Lester.
Open Mon - Fri 10 AM - 4 PM. No admis. The exhibitions program is intended primarily as support for the courses in studio art and art history, theatre and music offered by the faculty of fine and performing arts. Functioning in this way, the gallery displays material in traditional media, ranging from the antique to contemporary. There are two adjoining galleries, South Gallery 59 x 56 ft.; North Gallery 42 x 23 ft. Average Annual Attendance: 15,000 - 20,000.
Collections: Painting, principally 20th century American; prints, primitive, African and New Guinea; pre-Columbian; Oriental prints, sculpture, artifacts, photographs, folk art, posters.
Exhibitions: (1976) Sons and Others: Women Artists see Men for IWY; Chinese Art from Permanent Collection; One-Man Show (Sedestrom); Hudson River Valley Design of 18th and 19th century; BFA, MFA and Student Annual; (1977) Funny?; One-Man Show (Peterson); Whistler Prints, One-Man Show (Martin); Photojournalism; BFA/MFA and Student Annual; Intercollegiate: Selection 77 (New York State); Wolfgang Roth: Theatre Design; Cragsmoor Artist' Vision of Nature (19th Century American Oils); Contemporary Prints from the Collection of Richard Brown Baker; Pre-Columbian Show from Permanent Collection; Harley Gaber (installation of recent tape music, original); (1978) CAPS Photography; West of the Rockies: 19th century Western Landscape Photography; New Aspects of Self, Contemporary Photographers; Student Annual; BFA/MFA Shows; Landscape in Far Eastern Art; National Student Invitational, Painting and Drawing/78.
Activities: Lectures open to public; concerts; gallery talks; competitions; individual paintings and original objects of art lent to museums and galleries; lending collection contains artifacts, original prints 412, paintings 145, photographs, sculpture, folk art, textiles, drawings, posters.

NEW ROCHELLE

NEW ROCHELLE PUBLIC LIBRARY,* 662 Main St, 10805. Tel: 914-632-7878. *Dir* Eugene L Mittelgluck; *Fine Arts Librn* Mrs Willie R Carrington.
Art Gallery and Library open Mon - Thurs 9 AM - 9 PM; Fri 9 AM - 6 PM; Sat 9 AM - 6 PM; cl Sun & holidays, also on Sat during July & Aug. Estab 1893.
Exhibitions: Art Gallery shows work of members of New Rochelle Art Association; changing exhibitions Oct through May; case displays.
Activities: Illustrated lect and demonstrations at Association meetings; lending collection contains framed prints, and art slides.
Fine Arts Library: Holdings—Vols 7800; Other—Prints 500,000 of clipping and picture file for circulation, mounted and unmounted. Headquarters for audiovisual service for Westchester Library System, serving 38 libraries.
—**New Rochelle Art Association*.** Tel: 914-632-7878. *Pres* Len Gorelick. Estab 1912. Mem: 200; dues $10; monthly meeting.
Exhibitions and lectures.

NEW YORK

ALLIED ARTISTS OF AMERICA, INC, 1083 Fifth Ave, 10028. *Pres* Dale Meyers; *VPres* William Gorman; *Treas* Moses Worthman; *Corresponding Secy* Diana Kan.
For further information see National and Regional Organizations.

AMERICAN ABSTRACT ARTISTS, 218 W 20th St, 10011. *Pres* Leo Rabkin; *Secy* Ruth Eckstein; *Treas* Esphyr Slobodkina; *Exhib Chmn* Nick Kazak.
For further information see National and Regional Organizations.

AMERICAN ACADEMY AND INSTITUTE OF ARTS AND LETTERS, 633 E 155th St, 10032. Tel: 212-368-5900. *Pres* Jacques Barzun; *VPres Art* John Heliker; *Treas* William Schuman; *Secy Acad* John Cheever; *Secy Institute* Ralph Ellison; *Exec Dir* Margaret M Mills.
Merger of the American Academy of Arts and Letters and the National Institute of Arts and Letters. For further information see National and Regional Organizations.

AMERICAN ACADEMY IN ROME,* 41 E 65th St, 10021. Tel: 212-535-4250. *Pres* Henry T Rowell, *Secy* Walker O Cain; *Treas* William H Hohnstone; *Dir* Henry A Millon; *Head, Classical School* Frank E Brown; *Exec Secy* Martha Peitzke Wilson.
Estab 1884, inc by Congress 1905; consolidated with School of Classical Studies 1913; Dept of Musical Composition estab 1921; Annual meeting Oct; Board in Jan.
Fellowships in architecture, landscape architecture, environmental design, classical studies, post-classical humanistic studies, history of art, musical composition, painting and sculpture, are open to citizens of the United States for two years beginning October first with the option of accepting a single year. In total, approximately 15 fellowships are awarded each year. Though there is no age limit, the Academy aims to give the awards to young persons of outstanding promise, when candidates apply. Stipend and travel allowances $4600; free residence, studio or study, library and other facilities at the Academy. Applications must be received at the New York office before January first of each year.
Address in Rome, Via Angelo Masina 5, 00153.

AMERICAN ACADEMY OF ARTS AND LETTERS, 633 E 155th St, 10032. Tel: 212-368-5900. Merged with National Institute of Arts and Letters. For further information see American Academy and Institute of Arts and Letters, National and Regional Organizations.

AMERICAN ARTISTS PROFESSIONAL LEAGUE, INC,* 215 Park Ave S, 10003. Tel: 212-475-6650. *Pres* Frank C Wright; *Secy* Mary Keim Tietze.
For further information see National and Regional Organizations.

AMERICAN COUNCIL FOR THE ARTS (formerly Associated Councils of the Arts), 570 Seventh Ave, 10018. Tel: 212-354-6655. *Pres* Michael Newton; *VPres* Nancy Bush; *Secy* Anne Bartley; *Conf Dir & Publns Dir* Raymond Baron.
For further information see National and Regional Organizations.

AMERICAN COUNCIL FOR THE ARTS IN EDUCATION, 115 E 92nd St, 10028. Tel: 212-831-8110. *Pres* Eldon Winkler; *VPres* Robert Glidden; *Secy-Treas* Gerry J Martin.
For further information see National and Regional Organizations.

THE AMERICAN FEDERATION OF ARTS, 41 E 65th St, 10021. *Pres Board of Trustees* Bayard Ewing; *VPres* Arthur D Emil; *Secy* Francis E Brennan; *Dir* Wilder Green; *Asst Dir & Dir Exhib* Jane S Tai; *Coordr Loans* Konrad G Kuchel; *Exhib Coordr* Susanna D'Alton; *Registrar* Melissa Meigham; *Dir Film Prog* Steven Aronson; *Dir Membership* Margot Linton; *Graphic Designer* Michael Shroyer; *Coordr Museum Publications Distribution Serv* Alice S Zimt; *Controller* Stanley W Berger.
For further information see National and Regional Organizations.

AMERICAN FINE ARTS SOCIETY,* 215 W 57th St, 10019. Tel: 212-247-4510. *Pres* Stewart Klonis; *Secy* Arthur J Foster.
Inc 1889; estab to provide facilities for art activities as owner of the American Fine Arts Society Building. Annual meeting Jan. Sponsors lectures by prominent persons in the art world.

AMERICAN INSTITUTE OF GRAPHIC ARTS, 1059 Third Ave, 10021. Tel: 212-752-0813. *Pres* Richard Danne; *Exec Dir* Caroline Hightower.
For further information see National and Regional Organizations.

AMERICAN INTERNATIONAL SCULPTORS SYMPOSIUMS, INC, 799 Greenwich St, 10014. Tel: 212-242-3374. *Pres & Exec Dir* Verna Gillia; *VPres* Bradford Graves; *Secy* Benay Rubenstein.
For further information see National and Regional Organizations.

AMERICAN MUSEUM OF NATURAL HISTORY, Central Park West at 79th St, 10024. Tel: 212-873-1300. *Pres* Robert G Goelet; *Dir* Dr Thomas D Nicholson.

Open Mon - Fri 10 AM - 4:45 PM; Sun & holidays 11 AM - 5 PM, Wed until 9 PM; cl Thanksgiving and Christmas. Admis by contribution (suggested, adults $1.50, children 75¢). Estab and inc 186. A museum for the study and exhibition of all aspects of natural history; includes ceremonial objects, artifacts, clothing, weapons and architecture of primitive peoples and earlier civilizations. Mem: Average Annual Attendance: 2,500,000. Mem: 350,000.
Exhibitions: Permanent exhibition of Museum's renowned habitat dioramas of mammals, birds, forest and ocean life, examples are the Hall of Small Mammals of North America, the Hall of Primates, the Hall of Man in Africa, the Lindsley Hall of Earth History, the Hall of Mexico and Central America, the Hall of Minerals and Gems.
Activities: Adult evening lecture series; gallery talks; slide lecturers and films. Library: Holdings—Vols 350,000.
—**New York Theodore Roosevelt Memorial**
Collections: Equestrian statue of Theodore Roosevelt by the late James Earle Fraser located at the entrance; mural painting by William Andrew Mackay in the hall.

AMERICAN NUMISMATIC SOCIETY, Broadway at 155th St, 10032. Tel: 212-234-3130. *Pres* Harry W Bass, Jr; *VPres* Harry W Fowler; *Dir & Secy* Leslie A Elam; *Chief Cur* Margaret Thompson.
For further information see National and Regional Organizations.

AMERICAN SOCIETY OF CONTEMPORARY ARTISTS,* c/o Rose Hart Betensky, Pres, 66 Hayloft Place, Roselyn Heights, NY^s 11577.
For further information see National and Regional Organizations.

AMERICAN SOCIETY OF INTERIOR DESIGNERS, 730 Fifth Ave, 10019. Tel: 212-586-7111. *Pres* Irving D Schwartz; *VPres* Rita St Clair; *Secy* Bruce Stodola; *Exec Dir* John J Mead; *Dir Mem & Chapter Services* Ed Gips; *Dir Educ* Russell Radley.
For further information see National and Regional Organizations.

AMERICAN WATERCOLOR SOCIETY, 1083 Fifth Ave, 10028. Tel: 212-876-6622. *Pres* Mario Cooper; *VPres* Samuel Leitman; *Second VPres* William Strosahl; *Secy* Maxwell Desser; *Treas* Elsie Ject-Key; *Recording Secy* Mina Kocherthaler.
For further information see National and Regional Organizations.

ARCHAEOLOGICAL INSTITUTE OF AMERICA, 260 W Broadway, 10013. Tel: 212-925-7333. *Pres* Robert H Dyson, Jr; *VPres* Claireve Grandjouan; *Gen Secy* Elizabeth A. Whitehead; *Acting Managing Dir* R John Carpenter; *Exec Assts* Carol Smallman and James G Hamilton, Jr.
For further information see National and Regional Organizations.

ARCHITECTURAL LEAGUE OF NEW YORK,* 41 E 65th St, 10021. Tel: 212-628-4500. *Pres* Robert A M Stern; *Admin Dir* Marita O'Hare; *Treas* Walter Rooney; *Secy* Liz Show.
Open weekdays 10 AM - 5 PM. Admis seminars $2.50, mem free. Estab 1881 to promote art and architecture; serves as a forum for new and experimental ideas in the arts. Sponsors Archive of Women in Architecture. Mem: 500; dues students $15, $40 (under 35 yrs), $75 (over 35 yrs), annual meeting April.
Exhibitions: Annual Juried Exhibition of Architectural Renderings.
Publications: Newsletter, quarterly; Membership directory; art tour map of New York City.
Activities: Lectures; slide lectures; walking tours; competitions; awards.

ARCHIVES OF AMERICAN ART, Smithsonian Institution, 41 E 65th St, 10021. Tel: 212-825-5722. *Chmn* Mrs Otto L Spaeth; *Pres* De I F Burton; *Secy* Mrs Dana M Raymond; *Dir* William E Woolfenden; *Archivist* Garnett McCoy; *Cur Manuscripts* Arthur Breton.
The Archives preserves its original documents at the National Collection of Fine Arts in Washington DC with microfilm copies in the following regional centers:
New York Area Office, 41 E 65th St, New York, NY 10021. Tel: 212-628-1251. *Dir* William McNaught.
Midwest Area Office, 5200 Woodward Ave, Detroit MI 48202. Tel: 313-833-2199. *Dir* Dennis Barrie.
North East Area Office, 87 Mt Vernon St, Boston, MA 02108. Tel: 617-523-2460. *Dir* Robert Brown.
West Coast Area Office, M H De Young Museum, Golden Gate Park, San Francisco CA 94121. *Dir* Paul Karlstrom.
For further Information see Washington, DC.

ART COMMISSION OF THE CITY OF NEW YORK, City Hall, 10007. Tel: 212-566-5525. *Pres* Muriel R Silberstein; *VPres* Whitney North Seymour, Jr; *Secy* Secy Elias Wilentz; *Exec Secy* Donald J Gormley; *Supv Stenographer* Irene Andrejko.
Open 10 AM - 4 PM. No admis. Estab 1898 to review designs for city buildings and the works of art proposed for their embellishment. Portraits are installed in Governors Room and other areas in City Hall. Mem: 11.

West Coast Area Office, M H De Young Museum, Golden Gate Park, San Francisco CA 94121. *Dir* Paul Karlstrom.
For further Information see Washington, DC.

ART COMMISSION OF THE CITY OF NEW YORK, City Hall, 10007. Tel: 212-566-5525. *Pres* Muriel R Silberstein; *VPres* Whitney North Seymour, Jr; *Secy* Secy Elias Wilentz; *Exec Secy* Donald J Gormley; *Supv Stenographer* Irene Andrejko.
Open 10 AM - 4 PM. No admis. Estab 1898 to review designs for city buildings and the works of art proposed for their embellishment. Portraits are installed in Governors Room and other areas in City Hall. Mem: 11.
Income: Financed by membership.
Collections: 100 portraits of historic figures, state, city and national.
Publications: City Hall, Art and Architecture.
Activities: Lending collection contains 100 paintings, sculpture.
—**Associates of the Art Commission, Inc,** City Hall, 10007. Tel: 212-566-5525. *Pres* David Levine; *VPres* Francis D Rogers; *Secy* Allyn Cox.
Estab 1913 to advise and counsel Art Commission as requested. Mem: 35; dues $35; annual meeting Jan.
Income: $1000 (financed by membership).

ART DEALERS ASSOCIATION OF AMERICA, INC, 575 Madison Ave, 10022. Tel: 212-644-7150. *Pres* Leo Castelli; *VPres* Norman Hirschl & William Acquavella; *Secy* Gilbert S Edelson; *Admin VPres & Counsel* Ralph F Colin.
For further information see National and Regional Organizations.

ART DIRECTORS CLUB, INC, 488 Madison Ave, 10022. Tel: 212-838-8140. *Pres* David Davidian; *VPres* William Taubin; *Secy* Robert Reed; *Exec Dir* Diane Herzman.
For further information see National and Regional Organizations.

ART INFORMATION CENTER, INC, 189 Lexington Ave, 10016. Tel; 212-725-0335. *Dir* Betty Chamberlain; *Asst Dirs* May Asher, Stanley William Hayter, Jacob Lawrence and Andrew C Ritchie.
Open Mon - Fri 2 - 5:30 PM by appointment; mid-Sept - mid-June.
Organized 1959, inc 1963; free tax-deductible clearing house of contemporary fine arts. Maintains †files of living artists with their gallery affiliations (c 40,000 artists); files of galleries, their rosters of artists and catalogs of current and recent shows (c 450 in New York, 300 in other US cities, 50 in foreign cities); †files of slides of work by unaffiliated artists (c 750 artists and 8-12 slides each) for use by dealers looking for new talent. The Center helps to channel the many artists in New York, and those coming to New York, seeking New York outlets for their work. It aids new galleries to start, helps artists to find out where they can learn special disciplines and skills. Furnishes information on many aspects of contemporary art to museums, art schools, collectors and the public. All documentation kept constantly up-to-date.

ART STUDENTS LEAGUE OF NEW YORK, 215 W 57th St, 10019. Tel: 212-257-4510. *Pres* Frank E Field; *Recording Secy* Adela S Lintelmann; *Exec Dir* Stewart Klonis.
Estab 1875 to maintain art school and membership activities. Average Annual Attendance: 2400. Mem: 5000; dues $5; annual meeting Dec. Maintains an art gallery.
Exhibitions: Exhibitions by members, students and instructors.
Activities: Lect; scholarships (210 annually); maintains school.
Publications: Art Students League News, monthly.
Library: Reference library for students and members.

ARTIST-CRAFTSMEN OF NEW YORK, INC,* 130 E 28th St, 10016. Tel: 212-679-8154. *Pres* R Leigh Glover; *First VPres* Joan Zimet; *Second VPres* Donald O Mauros; *Treas* Muriel Barnes; *Recording Secy* Nell Znamierowski; *Corresp Secy* Mary Walker Phillips.
Estab 1958 as successor to New York Society of Craftsmen and New York Society of Ceramic Arts. Affiliated with American Craftsmen's Council. Mem: 300; qualif for mem: by submission of work by artist/craftsman member to membership jury with emphasis laid upon professional standards of craftsmanship and the quality of work; non-craftsman may become associate or contributing member on election by the Board of Governors; annual meeting in March with six membership meetings a year.
Exhibitions: Exhibitions and demonstrations are arranged for the purpose of broadening public interest in and knowledge of crafts and developing standards of taste in design and workmanship. Annual exhibition in New York City; periodic exhibitions at National Design Center and other New York City locations; purpose is to promote interest in quality craftsmanship.
Publications: Newsletter, four to six times a year.

ARTISTS EQUITY ASSOCIATION OF NEW YORK, INC, 1780 Broadway, 10019. Tel: 212-245-6376. *Pres* Alton S Tobey; *VPres* Domenico Facci, Mark Freeman, Hortense Kassoy and Joseph Rothman; *Recording Secy* Bea Begman; *Corresp Secy* Bernard Kassoy; *Exec Secy* Eve Wilen.
Open 10 AM - 5 PM. Estab 1947 to advance the cultural, legislative, economic and professional interest of painters, sculptors, printmakers, and others in the field of visual arts. Mem: Over 1000; dues $20; meetings Oct, Dec, Feb, Apr.
Publications: Artists Equity Association of New York, Inc, quarterly.
Activities: Various committees concerned with aims. Administrators of the Artists Welfare Fund, Inc. Donations are tax-deductible.

ARTISTS' FELLOWSHIP, INC,* 3 E 89th St, 10028. Tel: 212-369-4880. *Pres* Furman J Finok; *VPres* Gerard A Knipscher; *Recording Secy* Martin Hannon; *Corresp Secy* J B Adams; *Treas* Elliot Liskin; *Historian* Russell Rypsam.
Estab 1859, reorganized 1889 as Artists' Aid Society, inc 1925 as Artists' Fellowship, Inc. Its purpose is to aid artists in need because of death, illness or financial reverses. Controls an endowed bed in Presbyterian Hospital. Awards the Gari Melchers Gold Medal for distinguished service to the arts, and the Benjamin West Clinedinst Memorial Medal for outstanding achievement in the arts. Mem: 125; annual meeting Dec.

ARTISTS GUILD INC OF NEW YORK, 25 West 36th St, 10018. Tel: 212-239-1348. *Chmn* John Josephs; *Pres* Dean Powell; *Secy* Joan De Katch; *Treas* Thomas Connolly.
For further information see National and Regional Organizations.

ARTISTS SPACE, 105 Hudson St, 10013. Tel: 212-226-3970. *Exec Dir* Helene Winer; *Assoc Dir Services* Susan Wyatt; *Assoc Dir Gallery* Ragland Watkins.
Open Sept - June Tues - Sat 11 AM - 6 PM. No admis. Estab 1972, is a non-profit organization formed to respond to the diverse needs of the artists community in New York. The gallery is devoted exclusively to the exhibition of serious new art that is not given adequate exposure in galleries and museums and, by virtue of its unfamiliarity, transitory form, unconventional media or controversial content, is not readily accommodated by these traditional outlets. Exhibition space includes three gallery spaces for regular exhibitions, project rooms for special installations and a hall gallery for photographic exhibitions. Average Annual Attendance: 10,000.
Income: $125,000 (financed by National Endowment for the Arts; NY State Council, New York City Dept of Cultural Affairs and corporate and foundation funds).
Exhibitions: Audio Works; Pictures; Traditions/Five Painters; Artists Performance Series; Artists Super 8 Film Exposition; Artists Film Series; New Art Auction; Bands.
Publications: Exhibition catalogs.
Activities: Lectures; internship programs
—**Unaffiliated Slide File,** c/o Committee for the Visual Arts, 105 Hudson St, 10013. *Dir* Susan Wyatt.
Open to dealers, critics, curators, artists for reference.
Holdings: Slides registry.
Special Collections: Resumes for 1000 resident artists in the State of New York who are not represented by a gallery.

ARTISTS TECHNICAL INSTITUTE INC, 207 W 106th St, 10025. Tel: 212-749-7819. *Pres* Herb Aach; *VPres & Secy* Bena F Mayer; *Treas* Edward J Garber; *Dir* Ralph Mayer.
Estab 1959 for the publication of results of scientific laboratory investigations of the materials of creative painting and sculpture.
Income: Financed by appropriations and grants from NEA and private donations.
Publications: Journal, quarterly.
Activities: Publication of audio-visual materials.

ASIA SOCIETY, INC, Asia House Gallery, 112 E 64th St, 10021. Tel: 212-751-4210. *Chmn Bd of Trustees, Asia Soc, Inc* George W Ball; *Pres, Asia Soc, Inc* Phillips Talbot; *Exec VPres, Asia Soc, Inc,* Lionel Landry; *Dir, Asia House Gallery* Allen Wardwell; *Asst Dir, Asia House Gallery* Sarah Bradley.
Open during exhibitions: Daily 10 AM - 5 PM; Thurs until 8:30 PM; Sun 1 - 5 PM. No admis. The Asia Soc is a nonprofit organization; inc 1957 to further greater understanding and mutual appreciation between the US and the peoples of Asia; Asia House Gallery was inaugurated 1960 to acquaint Americans with the historic art of Asia. Average Annual Attendance: 56,341. Mem: 2400; dues $15 and up; annual meeting May.
Income: Financed by membership, contributions and grants.
Collections: No permanent collection, loans obtained from the US and foreign collections for special exhibitions.

Activities: Three or more lectures for members given by guest specialists in connection with each exhibition and recorded lectures by the gallery director available to visitors. Film, dance, musical and additional lecture programs presented by other Asia Society departments. Loan exhibitions originated. Sales shop selling exhibition catalogs.

ASSOCIATION OF ART MUSEUM DIRECTORS,* PO Box 620, Lenox Hill Station, 10021. Tel: 212-249-5236. *Exec Secy* Millicent Hall Gaudieri.
For further information see National and Regional Organizations.

ASSOCIATION OF JUNIOR LEAGUES, INC, 825 Third Ave, 10022. Tel: 212-355-4380. *Pres* Alice Weber; *VPres* Margaret Grapham; *Exec Dir* Dean Londa.
For further information see National and Regional Organizations.

AUDUBON ARTISTS, INC, 1083 Fifth Ave, 10028. Tel: 212-369-4880. *Pres* Mark Freeman, 307 E 37th St, 10016; *VPres* Howard Mandel; *Secy* Mervin Honig.
For further information see National and Regional Organizations.

W BRAUN COMPANY, Wolf and Mary Braun Fund, 260 Fifth Ave, 10001. Tel: 212-MU9-6600. *Chmn* Bertram Reibel; *Coordr Young Designers Competition* Nelsine Montanino. Sponsors the annual Young Designers Competition. It is available to all credited schools in the United States and Canada. Jurors represent major companies. Winners receive United States Savings Bonds, also exposure of designs and employment opportunities.

CARAVAN OF EAST AND WEST, INC, Caravan House Galleries, 132 E 65th St, 10021. Tel: 212-744-4793. *Gallery Dir* John Lally; *Asst Dir* Franca P Lally.
Open Tues - Sat 11:30 AM - 5:30 PM; cl Sun & Mon. No admis. Estab 1929 as a nonprofit foundation, chartered to help artists expose their work to the general public. In addition chartered to help communication between peoples of the world. Founded the first Pen Pal Journal. Caravan House has two galleries designed to show two separate artists at the same time. Located in a town house with a gallery downstairs and one upstairs. Average Annual Attendance: 14,000. Mem: 367; dues $10; annual meeting Apr.
Income: $100,000 (financed by endowment, membership).
Exhibitions: Two exhibits every month January to May, September to December.
Publications: Pen Friend Guide, Biannually.
Activities: Classes for adults; lect open to public, 12 vis lectr per yr; concerts; gallery talks.

CATHEDRAL MUSEUM,* Cartwright Foundation for Religious Art, Cathedral Church of St John the Divine, Amsterdam Ave at 112th St, 10025. Tel: 212-678-6888. *Dean* James Morton; *Museum Dir* Rev Richard Mann.
Exhibitions: Annual exhibitions planned to demonstrate contemporary art that expresses religious values, the first being the Cartwright Exhibition mounted in 1977 including more than 45 paintings and sculptures by 26 American and European artists; works by Mark Rothko, Audrey Flack, Richard Pousette-Dart, Giacomo Manzu, Gyorgy Kepes, Morris Graves, Mark Tobey and Alfonso Ossorio are included.

CENTER FOR INTER-AMERICAN RELATIONS ART GALLERY, 680 Park Ave, 10021. Tel: 212-249-8950. *Dir Visual Arts Prog* James Wolfe: *Asst Dir* Sharon L Schultz; *Educ Coordinator* Mara Gardner; *Installation Designer* J Esteban Perez.
Open daily Noon - 6 PM; cl Mon (during exhibitions). Admis suggested contribution $1. Estab Sept 1967 as a major program element of the Center; to enlarge knowledge and appreciation in the United States of the art and cultural heritage of other areas in the Western Hemisphere; three galleries, 5 - 6 loan exhibitions a year of Latin American and Canadian art. Average Annual Attendance: 10,000. Mem: 880; dues student $25, program $100, Regular $250.
Income: $102,500 (financed by endowment, membership).
Collections: Limited collection of contemporary Latin American paintings, drawings and prints; 19th Century Mexican, Colonial and Pre-Columbian objects on permanent loan; 17th and 18th Century French, English, Italian and Spanish furniture and decorative arts as house furnishings.
Exhibitions: Pioneer Photographers of Brazil; Aztec Stone Sculpture; Lines of Vision: Recent Latin American Drawings; Americas: The Decorative Arts of Latin America in the Era of the Revolution; Warp-patterned Weaves of the Andes; Abstract Currents in Ecuadorian Art: Ron Martin and Henry Saxe: Two Contemporary Artists from Canada.
Publications: Exhibition catalogs.

Activities: Classes for adults and children; lect open to the public, 20-25 vis lectr per yr; gallery talks; traveling exhibitions organized and circulated; sales shop selling books.

CHINA INSTITUTE IN AMERICA, China House Gallery, 125 E 65th St, 10021. Tel: 212-744-8181. *Chmn Art Comt* Gordon B Washburn; *Pres & Dir* F Richard Hsu; *Asst Dir* Amy V McEwen.
Open Mon - Fri 10 AM - 5 PM; Sat 11 AM - 5 PM; Sun 2 - 5 PM, during July exhibitions only. No admis. Estab 1966 to present two different exhibitions of classical Chinese art per year; to promote a knowledge of Chinese culture; one-room gallery. Average Annual Attendance: 12,000. Mem: 800; dues $50.
Income: $30,000 (financed by membership and government grants and sponsors).
Exhibitions: Chinese Folk Art; Early Chinese Miniatures; I-Hsing Ware; Embroidery of Imperial China; Origins of Chinese Ceramics; Art of the Han Dynasty.
Publications: Exhibition catalogs, two per year.
Activities: Classes for adults; lect open to the public, 10 vis lectr per yr; gallery talks.

CITY COLLEGE OF THE CITY OF NEW YORK
—Eisner Hall Art Gallery, 133 St & Convent Ave, 10031. Tel: 212-690-4201. *Chmn Art Department* Marvin Jules.
Open by appointment. No admis. Estab 1960, contains modest collection of paintings and prints acquired by gifts for use of art student and faculty; gallery is located in two areas in the lobby of Eisner Hall.
Collections: Paintings of Renaissance, Baroque and 19th century America; selection of prints from Renaissance to 20th century.
Activities: Individual paintings and original objects of art lent to other museums and galleries; lending collection contains original prints and paintings.
—Morris Raphael Cohen Library, Arts Division, 135th St & Convent Ave, 10031. Tel: 212-690-4268. *Librn* Mary M Cope.
Open Mon - Thurs 10 AM - 6 PM; Fri 10 AM - 5 PM. Estab as a college library in 1847 and an art division in 1958 to support the education goals of the college; it is open to students, faculty and staff only and as reference to others.
Income: Financed by city and state appropriation.
Holdings: Vols 21,000; Per subs 53; Other—Clippings files, pamphlets.

COLLEGE ART ASSOCIATION OF AMERICA, 16 E 52nd St, 10022. Tel: 212-755-3532. *Pres* Marilyn Stokstad; *VPres* Joshua C Taylor; *Secy* Lucy Freeman Sandler; *Exec Secy* Rose R Weil.
For further information see National and Regional Organizations.

COLUMBIA UNIVERSITY, Avery Architectural and Fine Arts Library, 117th St W of Amsterdam Ave, 10027. Tel: 212-280-3501. *Avery Librn* Adolf K Placzek.
Open Mon - Thurs 9 AM - 11 PM; Fri 9 AM - 5 PM; Sat 10 AM - 6 PM; Sun 2 - 10 PM. Estab 1890 for reference only.
Holdings: Vols 175,000; Per subs 1000; AV—Microfiche, microfilm; Other—Clipping files, exhibition catalogs, original documents.
Special Subjects: History of architecture.
Special Collections: Over 10,000 original architectural drawings, mainly American.
Publications: Catalog of Avery Memorial Architectural Library and Avery Index to Architectural Periodicals by G K Hall of Boston, and supplements.

COOPER-HEWITT MUSEUM, Smithsonian Institution National Museum of Design, 2 E 91st St, 10028. Tel: 212-860-6868. *Dir* Lisa Taylor; *Cur Coll* Christian Rohlfing; *Adminr* John Dobkin; *Cur Drawings and Prints;* Elaine Evans Dee; *Cur of Architecture and Design* Richard B Oliver; *Cur Textiles* Milton Sonday; *Exhib Coordr* Dorothy Twining Globus.
Open Tues 10 AM - 9 PM; Wed - Sat 10 AM - 5 PM; Sun Noon - 5 PM; cl Mon and major holidays. Admis Wed - Sun $1, no admis Tues. Founded 1895 as the Cooper Union Museum. The Cooper-Hewitt Museum is the Smithsonian Institution's National Museum of Design, is based on large and varied collections of decorative arts, architecture and a library strong in those field. Its purpose is to serve the needs of scholars, craftsmen, students, designers and everyone who deals with man's living world. Exhibitions are based on the Museum's vast collections or loan shows, illustrative of some phase of design, make available the best examples of man's creative genius from the past and from the present. Its emphasis on education is expanded by special courses and seminars related to design in all forms and of all periods. The Main galleries occupy the first and second floors; exhibiting related to the collections and some aspects of design; the Contemporary Design Gallery has changing exhibitions relating to architecture and design. Average Annual Attendance: Several hundred thousand. Mem: 5000; dues $25 - $1000.
Income: Financed by membership and partly Smithsonian Institution.

Collections: Contains several hundred thousand items including collections of original drawings and designs for architecture and the decorative arts; 15th - 20th century prints; textiles; lace; furniture and woodwork; ceramics; glass; drawings and paintings by Frederic Church, Winslow Homer, Thomas Moran and other 19th century American artists.
Exhibitions: (1976-78) Man Transforms; The Royal Pavilion at Brighton; Architectural Drawings from 19th Century Berlin; Henry C Mercer (tiles); Andrea Palladio; 200 Years of Architectural Drawing; The Carnegie Mansion; Palaces for the People; Drawing Toward a More Modern Architecture; Winslow Homer; More than Meets the Eye; To Celebrate the Moment; The Subway; Place, Product, Packaging; Museum of Drawers; Look Again.
Publications: Newsletter four times a year.
Activities: Classes for adults and children; tours, seminars; lect open to the public; concerts; tours; individual pait paintings and original objects of art lent to other museums and cultural institutions; museum and sales shop selling books, reproductions, prints, slides, posters, postcards, catalogs.
—**Doris and Henry Dreyfuss Study Center,** Tel: 212-860-6887. *Librn* Robert C Kaufman; *Libr Technician* Margaret Luchars; *Co-Supervisor Picture Libr* Sheila Smith; *Co-Supervisor Picture Libr* Jacqueline Rea.
Open Mon - Fri 9 AM - 5:30 PM by appointment. Estab 1896 to serve the museum staff in all of its programs and to serve the design field and the design public. For reference only.
Income: Financed by federal appropriation.
Holdings: Vols 26,000; Per subs 18; AV—Pictures and photographs 1,500,000; Other—Exhibition catalogs; manuscripts, memorabilia, original documents, photographs, prints, reproductions located in the archives.
Special Subjects: Color; decorative arts; interior design; industrial design; materials of design; advertising and graphic design.
Special Collections: Henry Dreyfuss Archive; Donald Deskey Arach Archive; Ladislav Sutnar Arac Archive.

LOVIS CORINTH MEMORIAL FOUNDATION, INC, 55 Liberty St, 10005. Tel: 212-964-4424. *Dir & VPres* H Borchardt; *Treas* M Weinstein; *Secy* Thomas Corinth; *Art Ed* M Klopfer.
Open by appointment. No admis. Estab 1969-70 as a tax-exempt, nonprofit, educational Membership Corporation, organized to dispense information about German art as represented by the painter Lovis Corinth to the inquiring public at large. The foundation provides access to Lovis Corinth collections by appointment. Loans of Lovis Corinth works arranged for: Lovis Corinth Exhibition, Art Museum Cologne, 1976; German and Austrian Expressionism, Indiana University Art Museum, Bloomington, Ind, 1977. Members must be over 21 years of age and interested in pursuing the purposes for which the organization was founded. Dues $120; annual meeting Oct.
Income: Financed by membership.
Publications: Bulletin, published on special occasions; collaborating in the publishing of the Lovis Corinth Documentary.
Activities: The foundation provides access to a Lovis Corinth archive by appointment.

COUNCIL OF AMERICAN ARTIST SOCIETIES,* 215 Park Ave S, 10003. Tel: 212-475-6650. *Pres* Frank C Wright; *First VPres* Donald DeLue; *VPres, Treas & Gen Counsel* John S Dole; *Recording Secy* Florence Whitehill.
For further information see National and Regional Organizations.

EL MUSEO DEL BARRIO,* 1230 Fifth Ave, Suite F, 10029. Tel: 212-831-7272. *Dir* Hiram S Maristany; *Asst Dir* Laura Moreno; *Cur* Cruz Anibal Ramos; *Gallery Coordr* Gilberto Hernandez.
Open Mon, Tues & Thurs 10 AM - 5 PM; Wed 10 AM - 7 PM; Fri 10 AM - 3 PM; Sun Noon - 5 PM; cl Sat. No admis. Estab 1969, operated by the Friends of the Museum of the Barrio, located in the center of the Puerto Rican community.
Collections: Paintings and prints by Puerto Rican artists; crafts from Puerto Rico.
Exhibitions: Temporary and traveling exhibitions; work toured through community in mobile unit.
Publications: Quimbamba, bilingual educational quarterly; books and magazines.
Activities: Classes for adults and children; workshops in painting, graphics, etching, ceramics, woodcarving and dance; lectures; guided tours; films. Museum shop offering Puerto Rican handicrafts, books and magazines, and calendars depicting Puerto Rican historical events.

ELECTRONIC ARTS INTERMIX, INC, 84 Fifth Ave Room 403, 10011. Tel: 212-989-2316, 989-2317. *Pres* Howard Wise; *Admin Dir* Marianne A Cocchini; *Technical Dir* David Pentecost; *Distribution Manager* Ann Volkes.

Open daily 9:30 - 5:30. Estab as a non-profit corporation to assist artists seeking to explore the potentials of the electronic media, particularly television as a means of personal expression. It also operated a distribution service for artists' videotape programs to institutions such as universities, art schools, public libraries.
Income: Financed by Federal and state funds.
Publications: Electronic Arts Intermix Videocassette Catalog, annual.

FASHION INSTITUTE OF TECHNOLOGY, Galleries, 277 W 27th St, 10001. Tel: 212-760-7760. *Dir* Marty Bronson; *Asst to the Dir* Mary Ellen Palaszczuk.
Open Tues & Wed 10 AM - 8 PM; Thur - Sat 10 AM - 5 PM; cl Sun, Mon and holidays. No admis. Estab May 1975 to bring to the student body and the community at large a variety of exhibitions in the applied and fine arts; the gallery contains 11,500 sq ft of space divided into 4 galleries. The gallery on the main floor is used for small exhibits while the three galleries located in the lower level are used for major exhibitions. Average Annual Attendance: 50,000.
Income: Financed by endowment and grants.
Collections: Largest working costume and textile collection in the world.
Exhibitions: (1976-78) Paul Paret, King of Fashion; Galanos—25 Years; The Look; Facades by Bill Cunningham; The Larsen Influence, Jack Lenor Larsens First 25 years.
Publications: Facades by Bill Cunningham (book); Poiret (book).
Activities: Classes for adults; docent training; lect open to the public 2 vis lectr per yr; gallery talks; tours; exten dept serving the museum personnel; individual paintings and original objects of art lent to major museums and art institutions; traveling exhibitions organized and circulated.
—**Library/Media Services.** Tel: 212-760-7695.
Dir John F Touhey; *Art Reference Librn* Marjorie Miller; *Bus Reference Librn & ILL* Sweetman Smith; *Gen Reference Librn* Helen Rubin; *Media Specialist* Lionel White.
Open Mon - Fri 9 AM - 10 PM; Sat & Sun Noon - 5 PM. Estab 1950 to provide instructional and educational resources for faculty and students of Fashion Institute of Technology or other institutions serving similar purposes. Limited to students and faculty of Fashion Institute of Technology.
Income: Financed by endowment and grants.
Holdings: Vols 49,000; Per subs 554; AV—Audiotapes, cassettes, film strips, microfilm, motion pictures, phonorecords, reels, slides, videotapes; Other—Clipping files, exhibition catalogs, photographs, prints.
Special Collections: Original Fashion Sketches; Textile Collection—15th century to present; Costume Collection—mid-17th century to present.
Publications: Library/Media Newsletter, quarterly.
Activities: Lectures; library tours.

FEDERATION OF MODERN PAINTERS AND SCULPTORS, 340 W 72nd St, 10023. Tel: 212-362-4608. *Pres* Ahmet Gursoy; *VPres* Theo Hios, Barbara Krashes & Louise Nevelson; *Secy* Elisabeth Model.
For further information see National and Regional Organizations.

FINE ARTS FEDERATION OF NEW YORK,* 44 W Ninth St, Room 20, 10011. Tel: 212-982-7272. *Pres* Margot Gayle; *Secy* Minor Bishop, 131 E 36th St, 10016. Tel: 212-684-4880. *Treas* Bradford Greene.
Estab 1895, inc 1897, to secure united action by the art societies of New York in all matters affecting their common interests, and to foster and protect the artistic interests of the community. Members of the Art Commission of the City of New York are appointed by the Mayor from nominations provided to him by the Federation. Mem: 7000 consisting of six delegates from each of the 20 constituent organizations making up the Federation; dues each representative $7 (making $42 for each society); annual meeting April.

FRANKLIN FURNACE ARCHIVE, INC, 122 Franklin St, 10013. Tel: 212-925-4671. *Exec Dir* Martha Wilson.
A non-profit corporation dedicated to the cataloging, exhibitions and preservation of book-like works by artists.
Holdings: Titles 2000; Per subs 100; AV—Audio tapes, slides, videotapes.
Special Collections: Books, periodical, pamphlets and ephemera produced by artists as artworks.
Activities: Intern training program.

FRENCH INSTITUTE, Alliance Francaise Library, 22 E 60th St, 10022. Tel: 212-355-6100. *Librn* Fred J Gitner.
Open Mon - Thurs 10 AM - 8 PM; Fri 10 AM - 6 PM; Sat 10 AM - 1:30 PM. Estab 1911 to encourage the study of French language and culture. Circ 23,500. Maintains art gallery.
Income: Financed by endowment and membership.
Holdings: Vols 35,000; Per subs 60; AV—Cassettes.
Special Subjects: French art, civilization, history, language and literature.

Special Collections: Books relating to Paris (especially books publ 1880-1930); Art (decorative arts, architecture; painting and costume).
Exhibitions: Hommage à Gustave Eiffel (photography); America in the 18th century: A French view (prints & drawings); Lucien Aigner: Images of France in the 30's (photos); The Golden Age of the Picture Postcard.
Publications: Acquisitions list, quarterly.
Activities: Lect open to public, 50 vis lectr per yr; concerts; classes for adults in French.

FRICK ART REFERENCE LIBRARY, 10 E 71st St, 10021. Tel: 212-288-8700. *Librn* Helen Sanger; *Asst Librn & Indexer of Photographs* Marie C Keith; *Cataloguer* Blanche V Houston; *Reference Librn* Paula L Pumplim.
Open Mon - Fri 10 AM - 4 PM; Sat 10 AM - Noon; cl Sun, holidays & month of August. Estab 1920 as a reference library to serve adults and graduate students interested in the history of European and American painting, drawing, sculpture, illuminated manuscripts. For reference only.
Holdings: Vols & bound per 81,340; Other—Exhibition catalogs & pamphlets 63,226, photographs 450,000; sales catalogs 49,923.

FRICK COLLECTION, 1 E 70th St, 10021. Tel: 212-288-0700. *Pres* Henry Clay Frick II; *Secy* Martha F Symington; *Cur* Edgar Munhall; *Research Cur* Bernice Davidson; *Bus Adminr* David M Collins; *Mgr Sales & Info* Martha Hackley; *Supt* William Fleming.
Open (Sept - May) Tues - Sat 10 AM - 6 PM; (June - Aug) Wed - Sat 10 AM - 6 Pm; Sun 1 - 6 PM; cl Jan 1, July 4, Thanksgiving, Dec 24 & 25. Admis adults $1, students & sr citizens 50¢, children under 10 not admitted. Estab 1920; opened to public 1935 as a gallery of art. The Frick Collection is housed in the former residence of Henry Clay Frick (1849-1919), the Pittsburgh Coke and Steel industrialist. The edifice was built in 1913-1914, alterations and additions were made 1931-1935 and a further extension and garden were completed in 1977. The rooms are in the style of English and French interiors of the 18th century. Average Annual Attendance: 228,027. Mem: 200 Fellows; dues $250 minimum contribution.
Income: $2,000,000 (financed by endowment, membership, admissions).
Collections: 14th-19th century paintings, with fine examples of Western European masters and suites of Boucher and Fragonard decorations; 16th-19th century drawings and prints; 15th-18th century sculpture, of which Renaissance bronzes are most numerous; 16th century Limoges enamels; 17th-18th century Chinese and French porcelains; Renaissance and French 18th century furniture.
Publications: The Frick Collection, An Illustrated Catalog, Vols I & II, Paintings (1968), Vols III & IV, Sculpture (1970), Vol VII, Porcelains (1974), Vol VIII, Enamels, Rugs, Silver (1977); Bellini Monograph (1964); Masterpieces of The Frick Collection (1970); Handbook of Paintings (1971).
Activities: Lect open to public, 3 vis lectr per yr; concerts; museum shop selling books, prints, slides, postcards, greeting cards.

GALERIA VENEZUELA, 7 E 51st St, 10022. Administered by the Consulate-General of Venezuela in New York City.
Estab 1945 to exhibit the work of prominent Venezuelan artists, painter, sculptors, printmakers, photographers, graphic artists. Large exhibit on ground floor.
Exhibitions: One-person shows by: Carlos Cruz-Diez; Luis Guevara Moreno; Oswaldo Vigas; Bogarin; Bellorin; J J Castro; Marius Sznajderman; Mitos; Ephraim Guevara; Exhibits of Guajiro Tapestries by Tere and Luis Montiel.

GALLERY OF PREHISTORIC PAINTINGS, 20 E 12th St, 10003. Tel: 212-674-5389. *Dir* Douglas Mazonowicz; *Co-Dir* Susan Dryfoos; *Cur* Sharon Citrin.
Open Mon - Fri 9 AM - 5 PM; Sat 9 AM - Noon; other times by appointment. No admis. Estab 1975 to make available to the public the art works of prehistoric peoples, particularly the cave paintings of France, Spain and the Sahara Desert; large display area. Average Annual Attendance: 10,000.
Income: Financed by private funds.
Collections: Serigraph reproduction editions of Cave Art of France and Spain; Rock Art of Eastern Spain; Rock Art of the Sahara; Early American Indian Rock Art.
Exhibitions: Three traveling collections circulating the US: Paleolithic Cave Paintings of France and Spain; Rock Art of Eastern Spain; Rock Paintings of the Tassili, Sahara.
Publications: Newsletter, quarterly.
Activities: Classes for adults and children; Cave Art-in-Schools Program; lect open to the public; gallery talks; tours; lending collection contains books 2000, cassettes, framed reproductions, kodachromes 1000, motion pictures, original prints, photographs 1000, slides 2000; traveling exhibitions organized and circulated; sales shop selling books, magazines, reproductions, prints, postcards.

Library. Tel: 212-674-5389. Open to the public for reference only. Holdings: Vols 200; Per subs 15. Special Subjects: General Works on Prehistory: Cave Art of France and Spain, Rock Art of Eastern Spain, American Indian, Sahara, India, Hawaii, southern Africa, Canada, Australia, South America, New Zealand, Russia, Etruscan Tomb paintings.

GRAND CENTRAL ART GALLERIES, INC, Biltmore Hotel, 43rd St & Madison Ave, 10017. Tel: 212-867-3344. *Pres Bd of Trustees* Jack S Parker; *Gallery Mgr* James Cox; *Sales Mgr* John Evans; *Public Affairs Dir* Ms Jeremyn Davern.
Open Mon - Fri 10 AM - 6 PM. No admis. Estab 1922 to promote, exhibit, and sell America's finest representational artists, and to do so through the operation of large, well-appointed New York showrooms. A professional staff and a national board of trustees assure this operation of the nonprofit organization. The organization has a series of well-appointed showrooms. The gallery has world-wide packing and shipping capabilities, and several departments dealing with portraits, commissions, graphics, sculpture, etc. Mem: 100 patron members; dues $500; annual meeting: The Founders Festival.
Income: Financed by membership, commissions.
Collections: †Eric Sloan, and a continually changing display of several active artist members.
Exhibitions: (1976-78) A full exhibition schedule of changing themes and artist groupings, including Marine Art, Western, Air and Space, Watercolor, Founders' Festival, Illustrators, Wildlife; special showings for Helen Hoffman, Gary Carter, Eric Sloane, Tom Nicholas, and several others.
Publications: The Illuminator, quarterly.
Activities: Individual paintings lent; traveling exhibitions organized and circulated; shop selling books, prints.

GROLIER CLUB, 47 E 60th St, 10022. Tel: 212-838-6690. *Pres* H W Liebert; *Secy* F S Streeter; *Librn* Robert Nikirk.
Open Mon - Fri 10 AM - 5 PM; Sat 10 AM - 3 PM; cl Sun. Estab 1884, devoted to the arts of the book. Owns building. Mem: 625.
Purchases: $15,000.
Holdings: Vols 65,000; Other—Prints 5000.
Special Subjects: Bibliography.
Special Collections: Bookseller and auction catalogs from 17th century.

JOHN SIMON GUGGENHEIM MEMORIAL FOUNDATION, 90 Park Ave, 10016. Tel: 212-687-4470. *Pres* Gordan B Ray; *VPres* James F Mathias; *Secy* Stephen L Schlesinger; *Treas* Robert P Bergin.
Estab and inc 1925, offers fellowships to further the development of scholars and artists by assisting them to engage in research in any field of knowledge and artistic creation in any of the fine arts, including music, under the freest possible conditions and irrespective of race, color or creed.

SOLOMON R GUGGENHEIM MUSEUM, 1071 Fifth Ave, 10028. Tel: 212-860-1313. *Dir* Thomas M Messer; *Deputy Dir* Henry Berg; *Exec Asst* Susan L Halper; *Secy to the Dir* Vanessa Jalet; *Auditor* Agnes R Connolly; *Cur* Louise Averill Svendsen; *Cur Exhib* Diane Waldman; *Cur Special Exhib* Margit Rowell; *Research Cur* Angelica Rudenstine; *Asst Cur* Linda Shearer; *Archivist* Ward Jackson; *Conservator* Orrin Riley; *Technical Adminr* David Roger; *Preparator* Saul Fuerstein; *Photographer* Robert E Mates; *Public Affairs Officer* Mimi Poser; *Public Affairs Coordr* Mark A Rosenthal; *Membership Dept Head* Miriam Emden; *Development Officer* Jane E Heffner; *Development Assoc* Carolyn Porcelli.
Open Wed - Sun 11 AM - 5 PM; Tues 11 AM - 8 PM; cl Mon except holidays, and Christmas. Admis. Students $1.50 with validated ID cards, visitors over 62 75¢; group rates for students when accompanied by a teacher, children under seven free; Tues eve free. Estab 1937 as a nonprofit organization which is maintained by the Solomon R Guggenheim Foundation; founded for the promotion and encouragement of art and education in art; to foster an appreciation of art by acquainting museum visitors with significant paintings and sculpture of our time; the gallery was designed by architect Frank Lloyd Wright. Average Annual Attendance: 380,000. Mem: 500; dues $25 - $250.
Income: $2,244,607 (financed by endowment, membership and state and federal appropriations).
Collections: Reflects the creative accomplishments in modern art from the time of the Impressionists to the constantly changing experimental art of today. The collection of nearly four thousand works, augmented by the Justin K Thannhauser Collection of 75 Impressionists and Post-Impressionist masterpieces including the largest group of paintings by Vasily Kandinsky; one of the largest and most comprehensive collection of paintings by Paul Klee; Largest number of sculptures by Constantin Brancusi in any New York museum; paintings by Chagall, Delaunay, Lager, Marc, Picasso, Bacon, Bennard, Braque, Cezanne, Malevitch, Modigliani, Moore, Reusseau and Seurat, with concentration of works by Dubuffet, Miro and Mondrian among the Europeans; and such Americans as Davis, de Kooning, Diebenkorn, Frankenthaler, Gottlieb, Guston, Johns, Lichtenstein, Louis, Agnes Martin, Motherwell, Nevelson, Nogu-

chi, Pollack, David Smith, Stuart and Warhol; works of younger artists includes Andre, Christensen, Hamilton, Hesse, Norman, Mangold, Nauman, G Richter and Serra; Paintings, drawings, sculpture and print collections are being enlarged by gifts and purchases.
Exhibitions: Aristide Maillol: 1861-1944; Jiri Kolar; James Ensor; Kenneth Noland—A Retrospective; Lucio Fontana 1899-1968: A Retrospective; Willen de Kooning; small group and one man shows and periodic selections from the Museums permanent collection; International Talent Exhibitions held periodically; American Talent Exhibitions held every three - four years sponsored by private foundation.
Publications: Calendar of Events, quarterly; catalogs and newsletter with exhibitions; books.
Activities: Docent training; lect open to the public, 6 - 10 vis lectr per yr; concerts; gallery talks; individual paintings and original objects of art lent to other museum and galleries; lending collection contains original art works, original prints, paintings, photographs 4000, sculpture, and slides 50,000; traveling exhibitions organized and circulated; museum shop selling books, reproductions, slides, post cards, catalogs, newsletters and lithographs.
—**Library.** *Librn* Mary Joan Hall.
Open to museum associates and scholars by appointment only for reference.
Holdings: Vols 20,000; Per subs 40; Other—Vertical file of artists, galleries and museums.
Special Subjects: Modern art since the Impressionists.
Special Collections: Rebay Library.

GUILD OF BOOK WORKERS, 1059 Third Ave, 10021. Tel: 212-752-0813. *Pres* Mary C Schlosser; *VPres* Jeanne F Lewisohn; *Secy* Grady E Jensen.
For further information see National and Regional Organizations.

HEYE FOUNDATION, Museum of the American Indian, Broadway at 155th St, 10032. Tel: 212-283-2420, *Adminr* Alexander F Draper; *Senior Cur* William F Stiles; *Cur Exhibits* Thomas Martin; *Cur North America U* Vincent Wilcox; *Cur South & Middle America* Anna C Roosevelt; *Registrar* G Lynette Miller; *Conservator* Phillis Dillon.
Open Tues - Sun 1 - 5 PM; cl Mon & holidays and the month of Aug. No admis. Estab 1916; building opened 1922. Average Annual Attendance: 75,000. Mem: 1000; dues student $10, regular $15, family $25, sustaining $50, contributing $100, associate $250, patron $1000, benefactor $5000.
Collections: World's largest collection of art and culture of the Indians of North, Central and South America, West Indies and the Eskimo. Outstanding collections of pre-Columbian art and historical materials; decorative arts; numismatic.
Exhibitions: Temporary and permanent exhibitions of all phases of Indian life; regular special and annual shows; research facilities available to qualified scholars; special exhibits feature American Indian art.
Publications: Annual book; annual monograph; Indian News.
Activities: Gallery talks; tours; lending service to schools.

HISPANIC SOCIETY OF AMERICA, Broadway Between 155th and 156th Sts, 10032. Tel: 212-WA6-2234. *Pres* A Hyatt May; *Dir* Theodore S Beardsley, Jr; *Cur Mus Paintings & Metalwork* Priscilla E Muller; *Cur Archaeology* Vivian A Hibbs; *Cur Costume* Ruth M Anderson; *Cur Decorative Arts* Dorothy A Kostuck; *Cur Iconography* Lydia A Dufour; *Cur Emer Sculpture* Beatrice G Proske; *Cur Textiles* Florence L May.
Open Tues - Sat 10 AM - 4:30 PM; Sun 1 - 4 PM. No admis. Estab 1904 by Archer Milton Huntingon as a free public museum and library devoted to the culture of Hispanic peoples. Gallery exhibits are representative of the cultures of Iberian Peninsula from prehistory to the present. Average Annual Attendance: 35,000. Mem: 100 plus 300 corresponding members; membership by election.
Income: Financed by endowment.
Collections: †Paintings; †sculpture; †decorative arts of the Iberian peoples; costumes; customs; †photographic reference files.
Exhibitions: Gifts to the Collection.
Publications: Works by members of the staff and the Society on Spanish art, history, literature, bibliography, with special emphasis on the collections of the Society.
Activities: Individual paintings and original objects of art lent; sales shop selling books, reproductions and slides.
—**Library.** *Cur Librn* Jean R Longland; *Asst Cur* Shirley A Victor; *Cur Manuscripts & Rare Books* Martha M de Narvaez.
Open Tues - Fri 1 - 4:30 PM; Sat 10:30 AM - 4:30 PM. Estab 1904 to present the culture of the Spanish and Portuguese speaking peoples. For reference only.
Income: Financed by endowment.
Holdings: Vols 150,000; AV—Audio tapes, cassettes, film strips, Kodachromes, lantern slides, microfiche, microfilm, phonorecords, slides; Other—Clipping files, exhibition catalogs, manuscripts 200,000, original documents, pamphlets, photographs, prints, reproductions.

Special Subjects: History, art, literature and general culture of the Spanish and Portuguese-speaking countries.
Special Collections: Books printed before 1701 approx 150,000, incunabula 250.
Activities: Library tours on request.

INSTITUTE FOR ART & URBAN RESOURCES,* 108 Leonard, 10013. Tel: 212-233-1096. A non-profit Manhattan group, whose specialty is matching artists with unused city spaces, establishing artists' compounds with low-rent studios, exhibitions in galleries on the premises, and special-project rooms in which artists can work out experimental ideas. For instance, Project Studios One at 21- 01 46th Rd was rehabilitated from an abandoned 19th century schoolhouse in Long Island City, with spaces for over 50 artists; studios are opened from time to time to the public.

INTERNATIONAL CENTER OF MEDIEVAL ART, INC, The Cloisters, Fort Tryon Park, 10040. Tel: 212-923-3700. *Pres* Carl F Barnes Jr; *VPres* Walter Cahn; *Secy* Barbara Dirlam; *Treas* Carl D Sheppard.
Estab 1963 as The International Center of Romanesque Art, Inc. The International Center of Medieval Art was founded to promote greater knowledge of the arts of the Middle Ages, and to contribute to and make available the results of new research. Mem: 775; dues student $10, active (individual, institutional) $18; contributing $100, benefactor $1000; annual meeting Jan/Feb, (in conjunction with College Art Association of America).
Publications: Gesta (illustrated journal devoted to medieval art history), two issues per year.
Activities: Organize and sponsor public lectures, exhibitions and symposia; financial support given to excavations of important medieval sites at Spoleto, Caen, and the Abbey of Psalmodi; sponsor sessions at the annual Conferences of The Medieval Institute of Western Michigan University, Kalamazoo.

INTERNATIONAL CENTER OF PHOTOGRAPHY, 1130 Fifth Ave, 10028. Tel: 212-860-1777. *Exec Dir* Cornell Capa; *Adminr* Ann Donerty; *Dir Exhib* William Ewing; *Mem Secy* Phyllis Levine; *Dir Publ Relations* Barbara Shapiro; *Dir Educ* Via Wynroth.
Open Tues - Sun 11 AM - 5 PM. Admis adults $1; students 50¢, sr citizens voluntary contributions. Estab 1974 to encourage and assist photographers of all ages and nationalities who are vitally concerned with their world and times, to find and help new talents, to uncover and preserve forgotten archives and to present such work to the public. Four exhibition galleries showing a changing exhibition program of photographic expression and experimentation by over 350 photographers. Average Annual Attendance: 70,000. Mem: 1900; dues $25 and up.
Income: Financed by city and state appropriation, grants.
Exhibitions: Weegee the Famous; Wedding; Julien Levy Collection; Andreas Feininger Retrospective; The End of the Game by Peter Beard.
Publications: Centernews, 3 times a year; monographs.
Activities: Classes for adults and children; docent training; workshops; lect open to public, 75 vis lectr per yr; gallery talks; tours; museum shop selling books, magazines, original art, reproductions, prints, postcards.

INTERNATIONAL FOUNDATION FOR ART RESEARCH, INC, 24 E 81st St, 10028. Tel: 212-879-1780. *Pres* Edwin L Weisl, Jr; *Exec Dir* Elizabeth B Burns; *Dir Art Theft Archive* Bonnie Burnham.
For further information see National and Regional Organizations.

JAPAN SOCIETY, INC,
—**Japan House Gallery,** 333 E 47th St, 10017. Tel: 212-832-1155. *Exec Dir Japan Society* David LacEachron; *Dir Gallery* Rand Castile.
Open Mon - Thurs 11 AM - 5 PM; Fri 11 AM - 7:30 PM. No admis to members; contribution for nonmembers. Estab 1907, bi-cultural membership organizations to deepen understanding and friendship between Japan and the United States. Average Annual Attendance: 50,000 - 100,000. Mem: 3000 individual; dues $10, $25, $40, $100; annual meeting Oct.
Income: Financed by membership, grants and donations.
Exhibitions: Whose Sleeves ... Kimono from the Kenabo Collection; Shinto Arts; The Tokugawa Collection of No Robes and Masks; Utamaro and Hiroshige prints from the James A Michener Collection.
Publications: Japan Society Newsletter, monthly; exhibition catalogs.
Activities: Classes for adults; docent training; concerts; gallery talks; tours.
—**Library.** *Librn* Tomie Mochizuki. Tel: 212-832-1155.
Open Mon - Fri Noon - 5 PM. Estab 1971.
Income: Financed by membership. Purchases $6500.
Holdings: Vols 6500; Per subs 113; Other—Clipping files, pamphlets.

JEWISH MUSEUM, 1109 Fifth Ave, 10028. Tel: 212-860-1888. *Dir* Joy G Ungerleider; *Adminr* Henry J Korn; *Chief Cur* Susan Goodman; *Asst Cur Judaica* Cissy Grossman; *Mgr Membership* Ruth Dolkart; *Dir Pub Relations* Joan M Hartman; *Educ Dir* Janice Rous.

Open Mon - Thurs 12 noon - 5 PM; Sun 11 AM - 6 PM. Admis adults $1.75, children (6-16) and students with ID card $1, sr citizens pay-as-you-wish, members free. Estab 1904 to preserve and present the Jewish cultural tradition. Three exhibition floors devoted to the display of ceremonial objects in the permanent collections, special exhibitions from the permanent collections and photographs and contemporary art on loan. Average Annual Attendance: 85,000. Mem: 2000; dues $10 - $250 and up.

Income: $800,000 (financed by membership, grants, individual contributions, organizations.

Collections: Jewish ceremonial objects; textiles; paintings; graphics; contemporary art; the world's most comprehensive collection of Jewish ceremonial art, the largest collection in the United States, the third largest collection in the world.

Exhibitions: (1976-78) Image Before My Eyes (photographs, Jews in Poland); Jewish Experience in the Art of the Twentieth Century; Passover: Matzah Making; Birds of the Heaven, Beasts of the Field: The Bible as Source (Gail Rubin); And There Was Light (Abraham Rattner); Ben Shahn: A Retrospective 1898-1969; Chaim Gross: A Retrospective Exhibition; Fabric of Jewish Life; Israel Kaleidoscope.

Publications: Quarterly calendar; program brochures; exhibition catalogs; posters and other graphics.

Activities: Classes for children; docent training; lect open to public, 4 or more vis lectr per yr; traveling exhibitions organized and circulated; museum shop selling books, magazines, original art, reproductions, prints, slides, needlecrafts, posters, catalogs, postcards.

Library: Reference library open to staff only. Special Subjects: Judaica. Special Collections: Harry G Friedman Collection of ceremonial objects; Samuel Friedenberg Collection of plaques and medals; Rose and Benjamin Mintz Collection of Eastern European art; Harry J Stein-Samuel Friedenberg Collection of coins from the Holy Land.

LINCOLN CENTER FOR THE PERFORMING ARTS, INC, Amsterdam, Plaza, and Main Galleries, 1865 Broadway, 10023. Tel: 212-765-5100. *Chmn of the Board* Amyas Ames; *Managing Dir* John W Mazzola.

Open daily 10 AM - Midnight. Admis varies. First building open 1962, Center complete 1969 to present the performing arts to the broadest cross-section of the community. Average Annual Attendance: Paid audiences 26,000; tours 90,000; one million attend free performances in the parks and on the plaza. Mem: Has guilds or associations that support the Center or a constituent; dues $15-$1000.

Income: $71,000,000 (financed by endowment, membership, city, state and federal appropriations). Purchases: $76,000,000.

Collections: Painting; sculpture; portraits by such artists as Jasper Johns; Jacques Lipchitz, Elie Nadelman, Seymour Lipton, Auguste Rodin, Henry Moore, Alexander Calder, Marc Chagall, Aristide Maillol, Raoul Dufy, David Smith, Louise Nevelson and Jaacov Agam.

Exhibitions: Exhibits of the collection change frequently.

Publications: Calendar of Events; newsletter or magazines.

Activities: Dramatic programs; lectures for subscribers; concerts; tours; schol; lending collection of photographs.

LOTOS CLUB, 5 E 66th St, 10021. Tel: 212-737-7100. *Pres* J Roger Friedman; *1st VPres* George Repper; *2nd VPres* Silas R Mountsier III; *Secy* Seymour Udell; *Mgr* Emmanuel Roux.

Not open to public. Estab 1870 as a cultural center. Mem: 500; dues $750.

Income: $600,000 (financed by membership).

Exhibitions: Antique Quilts; Posters of World War I and II; Exhibit of Member's Paintings; Howard Chandler Christy Oil and Watercolors.

Publications: Lotos Leaf, monthly.

Activities: Round tables; receptions; state dinners; lect for members only, 20 vis lectr per yr; concerts; individual paintings and original objects of art lent to museums.

METROPOLITAN MUSEUM OF ART, Main Building, Fifth Ave at 82nd St, 10028. Tel: General Information 212-736-2211, Museum Offices 212-879-5500. *Pres* William B MacOmber, Jr; *Dir* Philippe de Montebello; *VPres Public Affairs* Richard Dougherty; *VPres Finance* Daniel Herrick; *VPres Operations* Richard Morsches; *VPres Architecture & Planning* Arthur Rosenblatt; *VPres, Secy & Counsel* Ashton Hawkins; *Chmn Board Trustees* Douglas Dillon; *Treas* Ann R Leven; *Chmn Special Projects* Karl Katz; *Mgr Personnel* John T Conger; *Cur American Paintings & Sculpture* John K Howat; *Cur in Charge American Decorative Arts* Berry B Tracy; *Cur American Decorative Art* Morrison H Heckscher; *Cur in Charge Ancient Near Eastern Art* Vaughn E Crawford; *Cur Ancient Near Eastern Art* Prudence Oliver Harper; *Cur Arms & Armor* Helmut Nickel; *Cur Drawings* Jacob Bean; *Cur Egyptian Art* Christine Lilyquist; *Lila Acheson Wallace Cur Egyptology* Henry G Fischer; *Cur European Paintings* Elizabeth E Gardner; *Special Consultant for Far Eastern Affairs* Wen Fong; *Research Fellow Far Eastern Art* Martin Lerner; *Chmn Greek & Roman Art* Dietrich von Bothmer; *Consultative Chmn Islamic Art* Richard Ettinghausen; *Cur Robert Lehman Collection* George Szabo; *Cur in Charge Medieval Art* Carmen

Gomez-Moreno; *Assoc Cur in Charge Musical Instruments* Laurence Libin; *Chmn Primitive Art* Douglas Newton; *Cur Primitive Art* Julie Jones; *Cur Prints & Photographs* Janet S Byrne; *Cur in Charge Prints & Photographs* Colta Feller Ives; *Cur 20th Century Art* Hess Thomas; *Chmn Sculpture & Decorative Arts* Olga Raggio; *Cur Sculpture & Decorative Arts* Yvonne Hackenbroch; *Cur Western European Arts* James Parker; *Conservator Paintings* John Brealey; *Conservator Prints & Drawings* Merritt Safford; *Special Asst Urban Affairs* Catherine Chance; *Museum Educ in Charge* Donald Reynolds; *Special Asst to the Dir* John Buchanan; *Assoc Cur Central Catalog* Marica Vilcek; *Program Mgr Concerts & Lectures* Hilde Limondjian; *Mgr Data Processing* Jerry Mirelli; *Mgr Development & Promotion* Inge Heckel; *Mgr Public Information* Jack Frizzelle; *Publisher* Radford D Kelleher; *Editor Bulletin* Joan Holt; *Editor-in-Chief* Leon Wilson; *Admin Design* Stuart Silver; *Mgr Photograph Studio* Mark Cooper; *Mgr Purchasing* Theodore Ward; *Mgr Office Service* Charles F Webberly; *In Charge Community Program* Herbert Scott-Gibson.

Open Tues 10 AM - 8:45 PM; Wed - Sat 10 AM - 4:45 PM; Sun 11 AM-4:45 PM; cl Mon. Admis pay-what-you-wish suggested contribution $2. Estab 1870 to encourage and develop the study of the fine arts, and the application of arts to manufacture and practical life, of advancing the general knowledge of kindred subjects and to that end of furnishing popular instruction and recreation. Average Annual Attendance: 3,000,000. Mem: 49,500; dues student $15, individual $35, participating $50, sustaining $100, contributing $250, donor $500, sponsor $1000, patron $2500.

Income: $32,600,555 (financed by endowment, membership, city and state appropriations).

Collections: Comprehensive collections spanning the ancient civilizations of Egypt, the ancient near East, the Far East, Greece and Rome; Western European paintings, sculpture and decorative arts; American paintings and sculpture and decorative arts; Egyptian, Greek and Roman, Islamic, Ancient Near East and European paintings; medieval art; Arms and Armor; Lehman Collection; musical instruments; primitive art; Far East; 20th century art.

Exhibitions: Tricolour: 17th Century Dutch, 18th Century English and 19th Century French Drawings from the Robert Lehman Collection; Five Paintings from the Bavarian State Paintings Collections; Portraits by Stuart and Sully; Contemporary American Prints; Gifts from the Singer Collection; Liberty or Death; Egyptian Reinstallation Phase I; Two Worlds of Andrew Wyeth: Kuerners and Olsons; Titian and his Circle; Roman Artists of the Seventeenth Century: Drawings and Prints; Daniel Chester French: An American Sculptor; Blue and White; Early Japanese Export Porcelain; Annual Baroque Christmas Tree and Creche Display; Annual Cloisters Christmas Display; Original Silent Night Manuscript; The Glory of Russian Costume; Maurice Prendergast's Large Boston Public Garden Sketchbook; Gustave Dore: Dark Tales and Drolleries; Nadar, Photographer; Degas in the Metropolitan; Andrew Wyeth: Drawings and Watercolors; A Faun Teased by Children; Paris/New York, American Cinematheque; Fifteenth-Century Woodcuts and Other Relief Prints; Rubens in Prints; Russian and Soviet Painting; Irving Penn: Street Material; The Wrightsman Galleries; Thracian Treasures from Bulgaria; Childe Hassam; The Putto with a Dolphin.

Publications: Bulletin, quarterly; The Journal, annually.

Activities: Classes for children; docent training; films; lectr open to the public and occasionally for members only; concerts; gallery talks; tours; extension department serving community programs for Greater New York City area; individual paintings and original objects of art lent to other institutions; lending collection contains color reproductions and original art works; traveling exhibitions organized and circulated; museum shop selling books, reproductions, prints, slides and post cards.

—**Thomas J Watson Library,** Tel: 212-879-5500, exten 221 & 222. *Chief Librn* Elizabeth R Usher; *Museum Librn* Dobrila-Donya Schimansky.

Open Tues - Fri 10 AM - 4:45 PM; cl holidays and month of Aug. Estab 1881 for the use of the curatorial, educational and other staff. Privileges are extended to qualified researchers and graduate students with appropriate identification. Circ: 208,500.

Income: Financed by endowment.

Holdings: Vols 212,000; Per subs 1200; AV—Microfiche, microfilm; Other—Clipping files, exhibition catalogs, memorabilia, original documents, pamphlets.

Special Subjects: Painting; sculpture; ancient and modert art, archaeology, industrial arts.

Special Collections: Art Auction Catalogs.

Exhibitions: Outstanding Art Books of the Year Annual.

—**Photograph and Slide Library.** Tel: 212-879-5500, exten 230 & 260. *Chief Librn* Margaret P Nolan.

Open Tues - Fri 10 AM - 4:45 PM. Estab 1907 to provide a circulation (rental) library of slides covering the history of art; to provide color transparencies and photographs of the collections of the Metropolitan Museum of Art for publication purposes; to maintain a reference collection of photographs and mounted color prints covering the history of art. Circ: 170,000.

Holdings: AV—Color 2 x 2 slides, lantern slides, slides; Other—Photographs, prints.
Special Subjects: Collections of the Metropolitan Museum of Art, particularly complete coverage of western decorative arts.
Special Collections: William Keighley Slide Collection covering France, Italy, Spain, Germany, Austria and Asia Minor; architecture and other arts of various periods.
—Robert Goldwater Library of Primitive Art, Tel: 212-879-5500. *Museum Librn* Allan D Chapman.
Estab 1957. For reference only.
Holdings: Vols 20,000; Per subs 125; AV—Microfiche, microfilm, black and white photographs of primitive art for study only 100,000.
Special Subjects: Primitive, African, Oceanic, American Indian, Pre-Columbian and Eskimo art; anthropology; ethnology; archaeology.
Publications: Primitive Art Bibliographies, irregular.
—Robert Lehman Collection Library. Tel: 212-879-5500, exten 656. *Asst Cur Research* Victoria S Galban.
Open by appointment only.
Income: $10,000 (financed by endowment).
Holdings: Vols 8000; Bound Per 758; Other—Clipping files, exhibition catalogs, manuscripts, original documents, pamphlets, photographs, reproductions.
Special Subjects: Western European arts from the 13th - 20th centuries with special emphasis on the art of Siena, Old Master drawings, and Renaissance decorative arts.
Special Collections: Archives containing books, manuscripts, reproductions and correspondence; photograph collection.
—Irene Lewisohn Costume Reference Library. Tel: 212-879-5500, exten 628. *Assoc Museum Librn* K Gordon Stone.
Open Tues - Fri 10 AM - 1 PM & 2 - 4:30 PM. Estab 1946 to study costume history, fashion and theatre design and any subject related to the subject of dress. Non circulating.
Income: Financed by bequest.
Holdings: Vols 30,200; Per subs 32; AV—Fashion plates, original fashion sketches; Other—Clipping files; memorabilia; photographs; prints.
Special Subjects: Costume.
Special Collection: Mainbocher fashion sketches by Douglas Pollard from 1940-1970.
—Junior Museum, Fifth Ave at 82nd St, 10028. Tel: 212-879-5500. Museum Educator Roberta Paine; *Assoc Museum Educator* Elizabeth Flinn; *Asst* Meera Thompson.
Open Tues - Sat 10 AM - 4:45 PM; Sun & holidays 11 AM - 4:45 PM; cl Mon & holidays. Estab 1941 as a department of The Metropolitan Museum of Art, and opened in 1957 as the new Junior Museum with greatly expanded exhibition area, and auditorium seating 279. Average Annual Attendance: Approx 300,000.
Collections: Junior Museum draws upon the collections of the Metropolitan Museum of Art.
Exhibitions: (Major) Archaeology-Exploring the Past, 1966-1968, and the Artist's Workshop-Tools and Techniques, 1968-. Changing exhibitions of children's work, (Minor).
Activities: School programs, auditorium programs, studio hours, treasure hunts, sales desk.
—Library. Tel: 212-TR9-5500, exten 350.
Open Tues - Sat 10 AM - 4:45 PM; Sun Noon - 4:45 PM; cl holidays. Estab 1941 for children; an art research library within the Junior Museum. Non circulating.
Income: Financed by state appropriation; private funds. Purchases: $400 for books.
Holdings: Vols 5200; Per subs 4.
Special Subjects: Art history; archaeology; applied arts and crafts; mythology; history; juvenile picture books; illustrations; children's books.
Publications: A Selection of Art Books for Young People in the Junior Museum Library, annually.
—The Cloisters, Fort Tryon Park, 10040. Tel: 212-923-3700. *Asst to the Dir* Timothy Husband; *Cur in Charge* Jack L Schrader; *Cur* Jane Hayward; *Assoc Cur* Bonnie Young.
Open Tues - Sat 10:45 AM - 4:45 PM; Sun & holidays Oct - Apr 1 - 4:45 PM; May - Sept Noon - 4:45 PM. Estab 1938 to display in an appropriate setting works of art and architecture of the middle ages. Medieval French cloisters incorporated into the building, as well as the chapter house, a chapel, and Romanesque apse; also Medieval herb garden. Average Annual Attendance: 130,000-200,000.
Collections: Frescoes, polychromed statues, stained glass, tapestries, paintings, ivories, precious metalwork, and other French and Spanish architectural elements.
Publications: The Cloisters Guidebook.
Activities: Classes for adults and children; dramatic programs; lectr open to the public; concerts; original objects of art lent to other museums; museum shop selling books, reproductions and slides.
—Cloisters Library. Tel: 212-923-3700, exten 54. *Librn* Suse C Childs; *Libr Asst* Daniel Schoonover.

Open Tues - Fri 10 AM - 1 PM; & 2 - 4:45 PM. Estab 1938 to be used as a small highly specialized reference library for the curatorial staff at the Cloisters; scholars and accredited graduate students are also welcome. Non circulating.
Income: Financed by endowment. Purchases: $12,000.
Holdings: Vols 5750; per subs 46; AV—Slides; Other—Exhibition catalogs, original documents, photographs.
Special Collections: George Grey Barnard Archive.

PIERPONT MORGAN LIBRARY, 29 E 36th St, 10016. Tel: 212-685-0008. *Pres* H S Morgan; *Secy* Haliburton Fales; *Dir* Charles Ryskamp; *Asst Dir* Francis S Mason, Jr; *Research Fellow for Texts Emeritus* Curt F Buhler; *Cur Printed Books and Bindings* Paul Needham; *Cur Mediaeval and Renaissance Manuscripts* Dr John H Plummer; *Assoc Cur Mediaeval & Renaissance Manuscripts* William M Voelkle; *Cur Drawings and Prints* Felice Stampfle; *Assoc Cur Drawings and Prints* Cara D Denison; *Cur Autograph Manuscripts and Later Printed Books* Herbert Cahoon; *Honorary Cur Seals and Tablets* Edith Porada; *Cur of Gilbert & Sullivan Coll* Reginald Allen; *Cur Early Children's Books* Gerald Gottlieb; *Conservator* Alexander J Yow; *Reference Librn* Evelyn Semler; *Registrar* David W Wright.
Open Tues - Sat 1:30 AM - 5 PM; Sun 1 - 5 PM; cl Sun during July; cl month of Aug; reading room open Mon - Fri. Estab 1924 by endowment, collection placed in custody of a Board of Trustees for research and exhibition purposes. Gallery has changing exhibitions with of various types of printed materials as well as Old Master drawings.
Income: $770,000 (financed by endowment and membership). Purchases: $1,050,000.
Holdings: Vols 45,000; Per subs 170; AV—Slides; Other—Manuscripts, original art works, original documents.
Special Collections: Illuminated manuscripts; autograph manuscripts; letters and documents; printed books from 1450; bookbindings; original drawing from 14th - 19th centuries; Rembrandt etchings; modern calligraphy; mezzotints; art objects; musical manuscripts; later printed books; early children's books; ancient written records including seals, cuneiform tablets and papyri.
Exhibitions: (1976-78) American Literary Autographs; Rembrandt Etchings; Dutch Drawings of the 17th Century; Literary Association Books; Oxford University Press; French and English Flower Books; The Spanish Forger; Drawings of Fantastic Creatures.
Publications: Report to the Fellows, biennial; books, catalogs, facsimiles.
Activities: Lect open to the public, 8 vis lectr per yr; concerts; schol.

MORRIS-JUMEL MANSION, W 160th St & Edgecombe Ave, 10032. Tel: 212-WA3-8008. *Pres* Mrs J Frank Wood; *Dir* Jane Sullivan Crowley.
Open Tues - Sun 10 AM - 4 PM. Admis 50¢. Estab 1903 as an Historic House Museum. There are 12 rooms furnished in three periods of American history. Average Annual Attendance: 20,000. Mem: 400; dues $10 - $500; annual meeting May.
Income: Financed by membership and fund raising.
Collections: Art; furniture of 18th and 19th centuries.
Publications: Morris-Jumel News, quarterly.
Activities: Educ dept; docent training; lect open to public, 4 vis lectr per yr; concerts; tours for adults and children; traveling exhibitions organized and circulated; sales shop selling books, postcards.

MUNICIPAL ART SOCIETY OF NEW YORK,* 30 Rockefeller Plaza, 10020. Tel: 212-586-4761. *Pres* Brendan Gill; *Secy* Gordon Hyatt; *Exec Dir* Kent Barwick.
Estab 1892, inc 1898. The Society is the one organization in New York through which the layman, professional and the business firm can work together to encourage high standards for public art, architecture, planning, landscaping and preservation in the five boroughs. Mem: 1200; dues $15 and up; annual meeting May.

MUSEUM OF AMERICAN FOLK ART, 49 W 53rd St, 10019. Tel: 212-581-2475. *Chmn* Ralph Esmerian; *Pres* Barbara Johnson; *VPres* Mrs. Ronald Lauder and Mrs. Richard Taylor; *Treas* Lewis Cabot, *Secy* Kenneth Page; *Dir* Dr Robert Bishop; *Asst Dir* Patricia L Coblentz.
Open Tues - Sun 10:30 AM - 5:30 PM; cl Mon. Admis $1. Estab 1961, the Museum's primary purpose is to present outstanding exhibitions on specific topics of folk art. Organized by prominent authorities on folk art and dedicated collectors, this unique Museum has become a focal point for the many people who want to explore the folk art traditions in their art, design, and way of life. The gallery has 950 sq ft of floor space; total length of gallery, 76½ ft; width of gallery, 20 ft; height of ceilings, 14 ft. Average Annual Attendance: 40,000. Mem: 1800; dues $20 and up; annual meeting Sept.
Income: $200,000 (financed by membership, state appropriation, personal donations).
Collections: Paintings; sculpture; prints and drawings; textiles; furniture; miscellaneous decorative arts.

Exhibitions: (1976-78) The Image of the Cat in Folk Art; Paper of New York State; Crib and Doll Quilts; Masterpieces of New York State Folk Painting; Best of Friends to Bruce Johnson; Folk and Funk: The Folk Art World of Andy Warhol; The All American Dog: Man's Best Friend in Folk Art; Masterpieces from the Permanent Collection and Recent Accessions and Promised Gifts; Folk Art: The Heart of America; Great American Samplers.

Publications: The Clarion, quarterly magazine.

Activities: Classes for adults and children; docent training; lect open to public, 6 vis lectr per yr; individual paintings and original objects of art lent to sister institutions in the United States; traveling exhibitions organized and circulated.

Library: Not open to public. Holdings: Vols 300.

MUSEUM OF CONTEMPORARY CRAFTS OF THE AMERICAN CRAFTS COUNCIL, 29 W 53rd St, 10019. Tel: 212-997-8989. *Dir* Paul Smith.

Open Tues - Sat 11 AM - 6 PM; Sun 1 - 6 PM; cl Mon. Admis $1, children 7-14 25¢, citizens 25¢. Estab 1956 by the American Crafts Council (see National and Regional Organizations). Average Annual Attendance: 58,000.

Collections: Contemporary American crafts.

Exhibitions: (1976) Homage to the Bag; The American Indian and the American Flag; The New American Quilt; Selections from Objects USA, The Johnson Collection of Contemporary Crafts; Celebration 20; mezzanine exhibition; The Dyer's Art: Ikat, Batik and Plangi. (1977) Solid Wrought/USA; Grass; The Object as Poet; Young Americans: Fiber, Wood, Plastic, Leather. (1978) New Stained Glass; The Great American Foot.

Activities: Lect open to the public, 6 vis lectrs per yr.

MUSEUM OF MODERN ART,* 11 W 53rd St, 10019. Tel: 212-956-6100. *Chmn of Board* William S Paley; *VChmn* Gardner Cowles; *VChmn* David Rockefeller; *Pres* Mrs John D Rockefeller, III; *VPres* J Frederick Byers, III; *VPres* Mrs Cliss Parkinson; *Treas* Neal J Farrell; *Dir Museum* Richard E Oldenburg; *Dir Admin* Richard Koch; *Dir Painting & Sculpture Coll* William Rubin; *Dir Drawings* William S Lieberman; *Dir Prints & Illustrated Books* Riva Castleman; *Dir Dept Architecture & Design* Arthur Drexler; Dir Dept Photography John Szarkowski; *Dir Dept Film* Edward (Ted) S Perry; *Coordr Exhib* Richard Palmer; *Dir International Program* Waldo Rasmussen; *Special Asst for Educ* William Burback; *Dir Dept Publication* Carl Morse; *Librn* Inga Forslund; *Dir Mem & Development* John Limpert; *Dir Public Information* Elizabeth Shaw.

Open Mon, Tues, Fri, Sat & Sun 11 AM - 6 PM; Thurs 11 AM - 9 PM; cl Wed and Christmas; Admis adults $2, students $1.25, children and senior citizens 75¢; Tues pay-what-you-wish. Estab 1929 to help people enjoy, understand and use the visual arts of our time. New gallery addition to be designed by Cesar Pelli. Nonprofit education organization. Average Annual Attendance: 1,000,000. Mem: 28,000; dues $25 and up (student $15).

Income: Financed by admissions, membership, sales of publications and other services and contributions.

Collections: Painting and sculptures 3000; drawings 2600; prints 10,000; illustrated books 800; posters and graphics 3000; photographs 14,000; architectural drawings 400; architectural models 60; design objects 2500; films 4500; film stills 3,000,000.

Exhibitions: (1976) Andre Masson; The Taxi Project; William Eggleston; The Architecture of Luis Barragan; Narrative Prints; The Wild Beasts: Fauvism and its Affinities; Morgan Russell; Projects: William Wiley; Cubism and its Affinities; Projects Video VIII; Photography for Collectors; Museum Collections—Architecture and Design, Drawings and Prints, Photography and Painting and Sculpture; (1977) European Master Paintings from Swiss Collections: Post Impressionism to World War II; Prints: Acquisitions, 1973-76; Recent Lithographs by R Buckminster Fuller; Posters by Painters; selections in a variety of mediums based on various artists use of maps, including Christo, Jasper Johns and William Wiley.

Publications: Book on exhibitions, artists, monographs and catalogs.

Activities: Film showings, international in scope, illustrating the historic and esthetic development of the motion picture; lectr; symposia; concerts; art lending service; national circulating exhibitions; circulating film programs; bookstore selling publications, reproductions, postcards, note and seasonal cards, posters, slides, calendars and gift items.

Library: Holdings—Titles 30,000 in 16 languages on the modern visual arts; Other—Photographs 100,000.

MUSEUM OF THE CITY OF NEW YORK, 1220 Fifth Ave, 10029. Tel: 212-534-1672. *Dir* Joseph Veach Noble; *Senior Cur* Albert K Baragwanath; *Controller* Lawrence R Wirth; *Public Affairs* Monika Dillon.

Open Tues - Sat 10 AM - 5 PM; Sun & holidays 1 - 5 PM; cl Mon. No admis. Estab 1923 to preserve the cultural accomplishments of our City's ancestors and to meet the needs and interests of everyone living in the City today. Average Annual Attendance: 800,000. Mem: 2583; dues $15 and up.

Collections: Print collection, decorative arts collection, costume collection, theatre and music collection, toy collection.

Exhibitions: (1976-78) Best Bib & Tucker, Costume History of New York Dining and Galas; Frozen Motion, Photographic Dance Images of Marcus Blechman; Alcoholism; In Loving Memory, Gravestone Rubbings.

Publications: Annual Report; Bulletin, fall and spring.

Activities: Dramatic programs; Please Touch Demonstration; concerts; tours; individual paintings and original objects of art lent to affiliated institutions; sales shop selling books, reproductions, slides.

NATIONAL ACADEMY OF DESIGN,* 1083 Fifth Ave, 10028. Tel: 212-369-4880. *Secy* Umberto Romano; *Dir* Alice G Melrose.

Open during exhibitions 1 - 5 PM. Estab 1825, inc 1828, painters, sculptors, graphic artists, architects, and aquarellists interested in cultivation and extension of the arts of design, education of art students, and presentation of exhibitions of work of living artists: Academy owns building, opened 1942. Mem: 425; no dues; annual meeting March. Maintains National Academy School of Fine Arts at 5 E 89th St.

Collections: Permanent collection includes portrait of and a work by every Academician from S F B Morse, the first President, to the present day.

Exhibitions: Annual juried exhibitions with awards, open to non-members. Other societies hold their exhibitions in the Academy's building.

Publications: Exhibition catalog, annually.

NATIONAL ART MUSEUM OF SPORTS,* 4 Pennsylvania Plaza, 10001. Tel: 212-244-4127. *Pres* James F Keresey; *Exec Secy* Carolyn Johnes.

Open Mon - Fri 9:30 AM - 5:30 PM; holidays 10 AM - 5:30 PM; cl Christmas & New Year's Day. Admis adults 50¢, children 25¢. Estab 1959 as an art museum covering sports subjects. Mem: Dues individual $10, sustaining $25, general $100, sponsor $5000.

Income: Financed by the State University of New York and governed by the Board of Regents.

Collections: Paintings, sculpture and prints of sporting subjects.

Publications: News from the Museum, quarterly newsletter.

Activities: Guided tours; permanent, temporary and traveling exhibitions; rental gallery.

NATIONAL ASSOCIATION OF WOMEN ARTISTS, INC, 41 Union Square, 10003. Tel: 212-675-1616. *Pres* Elizabeth Horman.

For further information see National and Regional Organizations.

NATIONAL COUNCIL FOR ARTS AND EDUCATION, 743 Fifth Ave, 10022. Tel: 212-759-5800. *Chairperson* Henry Fonda; *Exec Dir* Frances Richard.

For further information see National and Regional Organizations.

NATIONAL INSTITUTE FOR ARCHITECTURAL EDUCATION,* 139 E 52nd St, 10022. Tel: 212-759-9154. *Chmn Bd Trustees* Hugh N Romney; *VChmn* Byron Bell; *Secy* Herman C Litwack; *Treas* Sidney L Katz; *Dir Educ* Howard H Juster; *Exec Secy* Lilian Marus.

For further information see National and Regional Organizations.

NATIONAL INSTITUTE OF ARTS AND LETTERS, 633 E 155th St, 10032. Tel: 212-368-5900. Merged with American Academy of Arts and Letters. For further information see American Academy and Institute of Arts and Letters, National and Regional Organizations.

NATIONAL PARK SERVICE, Federal Hall National Memorial, 26 Wall St, 10005. Tel: 212-264-8711. *Supt* Duane Pearson; *Cur* David Kahn.

Open (Oct - May) Mon - Fri 9 AM - 4:30; (June - Sept) daily 9AM - 4:30 PM. No admis. Estab 1955 as a national memorial to commemorate site of Federal Hall, first capitol of the United States, where Washington was inaugurated as our first President in 1789, and where the Bill of Rights was adopted. Exhibits on George Washington Inauguration, Bill of Rights, John Peter Zenger. Average Annual Attendance: 100,000.

Income: Financed by federal funds.

Collections: †Washingtoniana.

Activities: Classes for children; docent training; program for school groups; concerts; sales shop selling books, reproductions.

Library: Open to staff only. Holdings: Vols 1000. Special Subjects: Washington; American Colonial and Federal History; New York City History; National Parks.

NATIONAL SCULPTURE SOCIETY, 777 Third Ave, 10017. Tel: 212-838-5218. *Pres* Charles Parks; *VPres* John Terken; *Secy* Marilyn Newmark; *Exec Dir* Claire A Stein.
For further information see National and Regional Organizations.

NATIONAL SOCIETY OF MURAL PAINTERS, INC,* 41 E 65th St, 10021. Tel 212-988-7700. *Secy* Lloyd L Goff.
For further information see National and Regional Organizations.

NATIONAL SOCIETY OF PAINTERS IN CASEIN AND ACRYLIC, INC, 1083 Fifth Ave, 10028. Tel: 212-686-2659. *Pres* Mark Freeman, 307 E 37th St, 10016; *VPres* Mina Kocherthaler & Walter Scott; *Secy* Lily Shuff, 155 W 68th St, 10023.
For further information see National and Regional Organizations.

NEW MUSEUM, 65 Fifth Ave, 10003. Tel: 212-741-8962. *Dir* Marcia Tucker; *Dir Planning & Development* Dieter Morris Kearse; *Adminr* Maureen Reilly.
Open Mon - Fri Noon - 6 PM; Wed Noon - 8 PM; Sat Noon - 5 PM; cl Sun. Estab 1977 to present to the public new, provocative art that does not yet have wide public exposure or critical acceptance. The gallery space is 2500 sq ft which has been given to us by the New School for Social Research on an extended basis. Average Annual Attendance: 60,000. Mem: 400; dues $15 and up.
Income: Financed by endowment, membership, state appropriation and federal grant.
Exhibitions: Early Work by Five Contemporary Artists: "Bad" Painting; Alfred Jensen; New York/New York.
Publications: Newsletter, quarterly; exhibition catalogs.
Activities: Lect open to public; gallery talks.

NEW SCHOOL FOR SOCIAL RESEARCH ART CENTER,* 65 Fifth Ave, 10003. Tel: 212-741-7914. *Art Workshops Dir* Julian Levi; *Dir Art Center* Paul Mocsanyi.
A university for adults estab 1919, to advance education of both the scholar and the layman, with work centering in the social sciences and the humanities. Includes large non-credit program; Graduate Faculty of Political and Social Science, Center for New York City Affairs and undergraduate New School College. In 1970 the Parsons School of Design affiliated with The New School. Occupies six buildings, dedicated 1931, 1956, 1959, 1969, and 1972. Mural decorations by Thomas Hart Benton, Jose Clemente Orozco, Camilo Egas, Michael Cadoret and Gonzalo Fonseca. Average Annual Attendance: 17,000.
Collections: †Sculpture including works by Lipchitz, Hadzi, Noguchi, Penalba, Baskin, Zogbaum, Konzal, Lipton, King, Gross, Trajan and others. Paintings by Rattner, Carlo Dolci, Cleve Gray, Youngoman.
Publications: Monthly Bulletin; Social Research, quarterly.
—**Collectors Institute of the New School,** 65 Fifth Ave, 10003. Tel: 212-741-7914. *Dir* Paul Mocsanyi.
Open to members only. Estab to teach connoisseurship in many fields of art ancient and modern, as well as the ways and means of collecting. Mem dues: $600.

NEW YORK CHAMBER OF COMMERCE AND INDUSTRY, 65 Liberty St, 10005. Tel: 212-766-1300. *Exec VPres* Thomas N Stainbach.
Open 9:30 - 11:30 AM & 2 - 4:30 PM, by applying at office. No admis. Estab 1768. Mem: 1800; annual meeting May.
Collections: Portraits of business leaders of the United States from the late 18th century to the present.
Library: *Librn* Miss A Randolfi. Holdings: Vols 10,000.

NEW YORK HISTORICAL SOCIETY, 170 Central Park West, 10024. Tel: 212-873-3400. *Pres* Robert G Goelet; *VPres* R McAllister Lloyd; *Secy* Mrs Robert J Malone; *Dir* James J Heslin; *Librn* James Gregory; *Cur Museum* Richard J Koke; *Cur Painting & Sculpture* Mary Black.
Open Tues - Fri 11 AM - 5 PM; Sat 10 AM - 5 PM; Sun 1 - 5 PM. No admis. Estab 1804 to collect and preserve material relating to the history of New York City and State. Maintains art gallery. Average Annual Attendance: 400,000. Mem: 2500; dues research member $10, annual member $25, sustaining member $50, corporate member $250.
Income: $750,000 (financed by endowment, membership).
Collections: American portraits; American landscape and genre paintings; European paintings prior to 1850.
Publications: The New York Historical Society Quarterly, quarterly.
Activities: Lect for members only, 5 vis lectr per yr; concerts; gallery talks; tours; individual paintings and original objects of art lent to museums; lending collection contains paintings 8000; photographs 500,000; sculpture 2500; sales shop selling books, magazines and prints.
Library: Open Tues - Sat 10 AM - 5 PM; for reference to members and (for a fee) to general public. Holdings: Vols 600,000.

NEW YORK PUBLIC LIBRARY, Astor, Lennox and Tilden Foundations, Fifth Ave & 42nd St, 10018. Tel: 212-790-6262. *Pres* Richard C Couper; *Dir* John M Cory.
Estab 1895. Holdings for entire library contain over 5,607,863 vols.
—-**Prints Division,** Room 308. *Keeper of Prints* Elizabeth E Ruth.
Estab 1899. Admis by application to Research Libraries.
Holdings: Vols 13,000; Other—Prints 160,000.
Special Subjects: Original fine prints of the past six centuries with special emphasis on 19th century French and American, contemporary American and European; graphic artists and catalogs of their works; prints, techniques and illustrated books.
Special Collections: Phelps Stokes Collection of American views; Eno Collection of New York City Views; British and American caricatures; McAlpin Collection of George Washington portraits; Beverly Chew bequest of Milton and Pope portraits; bookplates including Radin Collection of Western European bookplates; Smith Collection of Japanese prints.
—**Spencer Collection,** Room 324. Tel: 790-6110. *Cur* Joseph T Rankin.
Holdings: Vols 8000.
Special Subjects: Rare illustrated and illuminated manuscripts and books in fine bindings, in all languages of all countries and of all periods constituting the development of book illustration and the book arts of the world.
—**Art and Architecture.** Tel: 790-6205. *Chief* Donald F Anderle.
Holdings: 100,000; Other—Clipping files, exhibition catalogs, sales catalogs.
Special Subjects: Painting, sculpture, architectural design and history of the decorative arts of all countries from prehistoric times to the present; special emphasis on scholarly works in history, post-Columbian American art, Oriental art; costume, interior decoration, design, textiles, ceramics, glass, folk arts, silversmithing, jewelry and furniture.
Special Collections: Private and public collection catalogs; individual artists and architects.
—**Schomburg Center for Research in Black Culture,** 103 W 135th St 10030. Tel: 862-4000. *Chief* Jean B Huston.
A reference library devoted to material by and about Black people throughout the world.
Holdings: Vols 70,000; AV—Microfilm, film, phonorecords. Other—Clipping files, maps, playbills, programs, photographs, prints, broadsides.
Special Subjects: Black people throughout the world with major emphasis on Afro-American, Africa and Caribbean; Nucleus of collected rarities of Arthur A Schomburg, a Puerto Rican of African descent.
Special Collections: Largest collection in the country of books on black culture and art; permanent collection of African art.
—**Picture Collection,*** Room 73. *Cur* Lenore Cowan.
Open Mon, Wed & Fri 10 AM - 5:45 PM; Tues & Thurs Noon - 7:45 PM; cl Sat, Sun & holidays. Estab 1915.
Special Collections: Approximately 2,250,000 classified pictures encyclopedic in subject copy may be borrowed by those who live, work or study in New York State except for exhibition or classroom use.
—**Donnell Library Center Art Library,*** 20 W 53rd St, 10019. *Librn* Rebecca Siekevitz.
Open Mon - Thurs 9:30 AM - 8:30 PM; Fri & Sat 9:30 AM - 5:30 PM; cl Sun & holidays.
Holdings: Vols 15,800; Per subs 80; Other—Vertical files of catalogs and clippings on contemporary artists and art movements.
—**Shelby Cullom Davis Museum of the Performing Arts and: The Library and Museum of the Performing Arts, at Lincoln Center,** 111 Amsterdam Ave, 10024. Tel: 212-799-2200. *Head Library & Museum of the Performing Arts* Dr Robert Henderson; *Dir Shelby Cullom Davis Museum of the Performing Arts* Don Vlack.
Open Mon & Thurs 10 AM - 8 PM; Tues & Wed 10 AM - 6 PM; Fri & Sat Noon - 6 PM. No admis. Estab 1964 to present exhibitions of high quality pertaining directly with the performing arts. The main gallery 140 x 40 x 20 ft has large glass space designed by Saarinen; Astor Gallery at the rear of Vivian Beaumont Theatre measures 80 x 30 x 30 ft; Amsterdam Gallery 30 x 50 x 10 ft; small plaza gallery 20 x 20 x 20 ft.
Income: Financed by endowment and city appropriation.
Collections: Maintained by the curators of the various departments—95% of the material is of an archival nature and physically flat, photographs, letters and documents, original costumes and scene designs, memorabilia.
Exhibitions: Asian Dance Images—The Spencer Collection; Reginald Marsh—The Art of Popular Entertainment; Senegalese Ballet; Richard Tucker—Life and Work; Mr Edison and his Wonderful Talking Machine; Kurt Weill and Loite Lenya; Dance Photographs of Frank Loesser—Broadway; Michael Truppin.
Activities: Sales shop selling, books, magazines, reproductions, prints, slides and various material related to the performing arts.

NEW YORK SOCIETY OF ARCHITECTS, 101 Park Ave, 10017. Tel: 212-683-2244. *Pres* Robert Friedlander; *VPres* Paul DiNatale and William R Sachs; *Secy* Samuel Horn; *Exec Dir* Margot A Henkel.

Open 10:30 AM - 5 PM. Inc 1906. An art gallery is maintained. Mem: 450; dues $82.50; meetings: 3rd Wed of the month.
Income: $32,000 (financed by dues and sale of New York City Building Code Manual).
Publications: Monthly bulletin.
Activities: Matthew W DelGaudio Award for Excellence in Design to Architectural Students given.

NEW YORK UNIVERSITY.
—**New York University Art Collection,** 100 Washington Square E, 10003. Tel: 212-598-3479. *Cur* Ruth Bowman; *Asst Cur Educ* Joy Gordon; *Chmn Art Collection Comt* Howard Conant.
Estab 1958, the Collection is installed throughout the University as an environmental collection, in lounge areas of the student centers and dormitories, in seminar rooms, and in faculty and administrative offices.
Income: Financed by gifts and University appropriation.
Collections: Approx 2500 paintings, sculptures, drawings, prints and photographs primarily 20th century, acquired almost entirely through donations from artists, alumni and friends of the University, approved by the Art Collection Committee.
Exhibitions: Special exhibitions coordinated for classes and seminars within the University; loan shows to other universities and museums.
Activities: Gallery talks; panel discussions; lect.
—**Grey Art Gallery and Study Center,** 33 Washington Place. Tel: 212-598-7603. *Dir* Robert R Littman; *Asst to Dir* Cynthia Nachmani; *Registrar-Cur* Gary Reynolds; *Prog Coordr* Helen Carr; *Gallery Mgr* James Clearwater.
Open Tues - Fri 10 AM - 5 PM; Wed 10 AM - 8:30 PM; Sat 1 - 5 PM. No admis. Estab 1975. University art museum, serving public as well as university community. Gallery space of approx 4,000 sq ft used for changing exhibitions.
Collections: American and European 20th century paintings, watercolors, and prints. Ben and Abby Grey Foundation Collection of contemporary Asian and Middle Eastern art.
Exhibitions: Inaugural Exhibition, Part II; Circa 1776; Tanavoli Sculpture; Avedisian/Hennessey; Drawings and Collages from the NYU Art Collection; Panoramic Photography; New Deal for Art; Wilmarth/Sandman; Changes of Perspective: 1880-1925; Photographs from the Sam Wagstaff Collection; Decorative Arts of Frank Lloyd Wright.
Publications: Exhibition catalogs.
Activities: Individual paintings and original objects of art lent to other cultural institutions; traveling exhibitions organized and circulated; sales shop selling exhibition catalogs.
—**The Stephen Chan Library of Fine Arts,** 1 East 78th St, 10021. *Dir* Evelyn K Samuel; *Cataloger* Francis G Bondurant.
Open to the public upon application to the Librarian. Estab to provide scholarly materials for graduate studies in art history and archaeology.
Holdings: Vols 80,000; Per subs 450; AV—Microfiche, microfilm, slides.

92ND STREET YMHA-YWHA, Weill Art Gallery, 1395 Lexington Ave, 10028. Tel: 427 212-427-6000, exten 722. *Exec Dir* Reynold Levy; *Assoc Exec Dir Admin* Sidney Zachter; *Educ Dir* Omus Hirshbein; *Asst Educ Dir* Sima Mittman.
Open Mon - Sat 8 - 10 PM; Sun 2 - 4 PM & 8 - 10 PM. No admis. Large room with facilities to mount on wall panels; no partitions; track lighting; windows; no humidity control system; minimal security. Average Annual Attendance: 100,000.
Income: Financed by state appropriation and NEA.
Exhibitions: Lingering Images: Yiddish Culture in Poland 1864-1930; A Disappearing Community: Jewish Life on New York's Lower East Side; Carl Van Vechten: A Photographic Legacy; Pottery Exhibit: Eliza D'Arrigo.
Publications: The Y Bulletin, bimonthly.
Activities: Classes for adults and children; dramatic programs; lect open to the public, 100 vis lectr per yr; concerts.

ONCE GALLERY, INC,* Automation House, 49 E 68th St, 10021. Tel: 212-628-1010. *Pres* Alfred S Goldfield; *Dir* Clare Fisher.
Open 10 AM - 5 PM; cl Sun & major holidays. No admis. A nonprofit nonmembership service organization inc May 1974, opened Nov 1974, to provide first one-person exhibits for artists who have not shown in New York City at no cost to artists. Governed by Board of Directors and Advisory Board of prominent persons in the arts. Average Annual Attendance: 3500.
Income: Financed by corporations, foundations, private donors.
Exhibitions: Exhibitors chosen by panel pf professional curators.
Publications: Catalog of each exhibit.
Activities: Planned panel discussions; symposiums; lectures.

PARSONS SCHOOL OF DESIGN, Adam L Gimbel Library, 2 W 13th St (Mailing Add: 66 Fifth Ave, 10011). Tel: 212-741-8914/8915. *Head Librn* Christiane C Collins; *Reference Librn/Cataloguer* Marelyn Johnson.
Open Mon - Thurs 9 AM - 9 PM; Fri 9 AM - 6 PM. Estab as a school in 1896, with the Adam L Gimbel Library moving to its present location in 1974 as a support to the curriculum of the school; there are monthly exhibitions within the library.
Holdings: Vols 28,000; Per subs 125; AV—Mounted picture plates 30,000; Other—Clipping files, exhibition catalogs, memorabilia; original art works, prints.
Special Subjects: Architecture, painting, sculpture, costume, graphics, furniture, fashion, city planning, environmental design, typography.

PEN AND BRUSH, INC, 16 E Tenth St, 10003. Tel 212-475-3669. *Pres* Margaret Sussman; *First VPres* Helen Slottman; *Recording Secy* Harriet M Hagerty; *Corresp Secy* Arthur Ray Nichols; *Exec Secy* Camilla Belding; *Treas* Jennie M Phalen.
Open 1 - 5 PM except holidays during exhibitions. Estab 1893, inc 1912; clubhouse purchased 1923, contains rooms, dining room and exhibition galleries. Ann meeting Feb; mem about 250 professional women writers, artists, sculptors, and craftsmen.
Exhibitions: Ten annual exhibitions of members' work; occasional one-man shows.
Activities: Lectures and workshops.
Library: Holdings—Vols 1500, fiction, nonfiction by members, plus reference and current best sellers.

PRINTED MATTER INC, 7 Lispenard St, 10013. Tel: 212-925-0324. *Gen Mgr* Ingrid Sishy.
Open Tues - Sat 10 AM - 6 PM. Estab 1976 for the distribution and publishing of artists' books; direct sale from store as well as mail distribution network. Average Annual Attendance: 10,000.
Exhibitions: Permanent exhibition of all artists' books in stock; largest inventory of artists' books anywhere, with continually changing window shows of artists' books.
Publications: Catalog, annually.
Activities: Artists' books lent for exhibitions; sales shop selling books, magazines, slides and related artists' records.

PRINTMAKING WORKSHOP,* 114 W 17th St, 10011. Tel: 212-989-6125, 242-9884. *Dir* Robert Blackburn; *Mgr* Madeleine-Claude Jobrack. *Workshop Foreman* Anthony Kirk.
Open weekdays 8 AM - 11 PM; weekends 9 AM - 5 PM. Estab 1949 as a workshop space for artists to print etchings and lithographs; night classes and edition printing; gallery maintained with 2000 contemporary prints for sale and exhibition rental. Mem: 800; dues vary.
Income: Financed by endowment, membership, city and state appropriation.
Activities: Classes for adults; classes in graphic arts; lect open to the public; original objects of art lent; schol; material available to local areas with mobile print programs; traveling exhibitions organized and circulated.

NICHOLAS ROERICH MUSEUM, 319 W 107th St, 10025. Tel: 212-864-7752. *Pres* Katherine Campbell Stibbe; *Secy* Elina Yussupoff; *Exec VPres* Sina Fosdick; *VPres* Robert Leser, Dorothy Blalock, Dr D Fogel, Svetoslav Roerich, Edgar Lansbury and Ingeborg Fritschi.
Open daily 2 - 5 PM; cl Sat & holidays. No admis. Estab 1958 to show a permanent collection of paintings by Nicholas Roerich, internationally known artist, to promote his ideals as a great thinker, writer, humanitarian, scientist, and explorer, and to promote his Pact and Banner of Peace. There is a gallery in which works of contemporary artists are shown. Average Annual Attendance: 5000; dues, assoc $10, contributing $25, sustaining $50.
Income: Financed by membership and donations.
Collections: Paintings by Nicholas Roerich.
Exhibitions: Exhibition of Paintings and Drawings by Dagmara Igals; Exhibition of Gouache Paintings by Edward Lopez; Exhibition of Paintings by Charles W Haddock; Exhibition of Paintings by Ella K Morgenlander.
Activities: Lect open to public, 3 vis lectr per yr; concerts; gallery talks; tours; museum shop selling books, reproductions, prints, slides.
Library: Pamphlets and publications being cataloged for reference; colored reproductions; postcards.

SALMAGUNDI CLUB,* 47 Fifth Ave, 10003. Tel: 212-255-7740. *Chmn of Bd* Martin Hannon; *Corresp Secy* Ruth R Reininghaus.
For further information see National and Regional Organizations.

SCALAMANDRE MUSEUM OF TEXTILES,* 950 Third Ave, 10022. Tel: 212-361-8500. *Founder & Pres* Franco Scalamandre; *Dir* Serena Hartian.

Open 9 AM - 5 PM; cl Sat, Sun and National holidays. Estab 1947 to encourage interest in textile design for decoration.
Collections: 2000 old documentary pieces of textile; reproductions of old textiles; contemporary textiles showing modern motifs in textured weaves of today.
Activities: Lectures given on History of Textile Design, including the Classification of Textiles, both Period and Modern; permanent display of textiles used in †Historic Restorations; traveling exhibits in the various periods of decorative art for circulation throughout the United States to museums only; 15 small Student Exhibits for art schools, colleges (must be requested by faculty member).

SCHOOL OF VISUAL ARTS LIBRARY, 380 Second Ave (Mailing Add: 209 E 23rd St, 10010). Tel: 212-679-7350, exten 67. *Chief Librn* Zuki Landau; *Cataloger* Rosemary Pandolfi; *Slide Cur* Cynthia Roberts.
Open Mon - Thurs 9 AM - 7:30 PM; Fri 9 AM - 5 PM. Estab 1962 to serve needs of School of Visual Arts students and faculty. Small gallery space for student work.
Income: Financed by tuition.
Holdings: Vols 18,000; Per subs 135; AV—Cassettes, phonorecords, slides; Other—Clipping files, exhibition catalogs, pamphlets.
Special Subjects: Art history, painting, sculpture, film, photography, media arts.
Publications: Library Handbook; Monthly Accessions Lists.
Activities: Poetry readings are held.

SCULPTORS GUILD, INCORPORATED, 10 E 53rd St, 10022. Tel: 212-752-2160. *Pres* Roy Gussow; *Exec VPres* Renata M Schwebel; *VPres Exhib* (vacant); *VPres Mem* Luise Kaish; *VPres Programs* Sidney Simon; *Treas* Chaim Gross; *Secy* Legh Myers.
Open varies, phone for information. No admis. Estab 1937 as a nonprofit organization to maintain a high standard in presenting works expressing all aspects of the constantly evolving and varying sculptural scene; the Sculptors Guild does not try to mold public taste but tries to present a wide variety of excellent contemporary sculpture. Mem: Approx 100; dues $25; annual meeting May.
Exhibitions: Bi-annual exhibition (Oct-Nov) held at Lever House, NY; exhibitions elsewhere as well; over the years the Guild has also presented a series of large outdoor exhibitions in central NYC locations.
Publications: Sculpture, fully illustrated catalog of yearly exhibition.
Activities: Lect; initiates educational programs connected with sculpture; maintains office for public, with files on members' works; competitions; assembles traveling exhibitions of sculpture.

SCULPTURE CENTER,* 167 E 69th St, 10021. Tel: 212-737-9870. *Dir* Janak K Khendry; *Pres* Marjorie Fields; *Treas* Frank R Donahue; *Secy* Barbara Lekberg.
Gallery open Tues - Sat 11 AM - 5 PM. No admis. Estab 1929 as Clay Club of New York to further the interest of student and professional sculptors. Inc in 1944 as Sculpture Center, a nonprofit organization, for the cultivation of the art of sculpture and to provide facilities for work. Moved into new building 1950 at which time the present name was adopted. Approximately 55 professional sculptors represented in the gallery. Average Annual Attendance: 35,000.
Publications: Over 50,000 catalogs printed every year.
Activities: Monthly lectures on art by famous sculptors, museum directors, art historians; visits to sculptors studios in New York area; maintains school and studios for beginners, advanced and professional sculptors; gallery presents one-man, group and feature sculpture exhibitions; traveling sculpture exhibitions.
Library: Holdings—Vols 200.

SOCIETY OF AMERICAN GRAPHIC ARTISTS, 1083 Fifth Ave, 10028. Tel: 212-289-1507. *Pres* Stanley Kaplan; *VPres* Robert Conover; *VPres* Jan Gelb; *Treas* Helen Gerardia; *Corresp Secy* Bernice B Hunter; Recording Secy Christine Engler.
For further information see National and Regional Organizations.

SOCIETY OF ILLUSTRATORS, 128 E 63rd St, 10021. Tel: 212-838-2560. *Pres* Charles McVicker; *Exec Dir* Arpi Ermoyan.
For further information see National and Regional Organizations.

SOHO CENTER FOR VISUAL ARTISTS, 110-114 Prince St, 10012. Tel. 212-226-1993, 226-1995. *Founder & Pres* Larry Aldrich.
Open Tues - Fri 12 AM - 5 PM; Sat 11 AM - 5 PM; cl Aug. No admis. Estab 1974, a nonprofit activity sponsored by the Aldrich Museum of Contemporary Art and the Mobil Foundation. An Exhibition Center was established for the purpose of showing the work of new artists who are not represented by a commercial gallery. No commission is taken on sales of works and no fees charged to artists selected for presentation. Changing monthly exhibitions. Average Annual Attendance: 50,000.

Library: A reference library. Holdings: Vols 2000; Per subs 40. Books, pamphlets and periodicals specially selected for the working artist. Free to all artists who register.

SOUTH STREET SEAPORT MUSEUM, 203 Front St, 10038. Tel: 212-766-9020. *Pres* John B Hightower; *VPres* Anthony Newman; *VPres* Christopher Lowery; *VPres* William Shreiner.
Open daily 11 AM - 6 PM. Admis voluntary contribution. Estab 1967 to preserve the maritime history and traditions of the Port of New York. Several gallery spaces: The Seaport Gallery for art exhibits; the model ship gallery; the printing press gallery at Bowne & Co., Stationers; the museum orientation center. Mem: 9,000; dues individual $10, family $15; annual meeting May.
Income: Financed by membership and corporate grants.
Collections: The core of the collection is the buildings and ships themselves and the neighborhood they define; a small permanent collection of marine art and artifacts; Palmer Collection of ship models.
Exhibitions: John DePol: The Wood Engraver's Art; In Celebration of Fish: 19th Century prints of fish and fishing scenes, highlighting the Fulton Fish Market.
Publications: South Street Reporter, quarterly; South Street Packet, bimonthly.
Activities: Classes for adults and children; walking tours of area; lect open to public, 10-15 vis lectr per yr; concerts; individual paintings and original objects of art lent to institutions with adequate insurance and security; lending collection contains original prints 200, paintings, ship models; museum shop selling books, magazines, original art, reproductions, prints, slides.
Library: Librn Norman J Brouwer. Open for reference to the public. Holdings: Vols 3500; Per subs 20; Other—Photo and negative collection.

STUDIO MUSEUM IN HARLEM, 2033 Fifth Ave, 10035. Tel: 212-427-5959. *Exec Dir* Mary S Campbell; *Deputy Dir* William Day; *Develop Dir* T Peter Davis; *Cur of Photography* Reginald McGee; *Cur* Gylbert Coker; *Dir of Educ* Robin Jones; *Coordinator of Spec Prog* David Jackson; *Business Mgr* Anthony McGee; *Exec Secy* Barbara Tate; *Preparator/Registrar* Brenton Greenwood; *Asst Cur of Photography* Coreen Simpson.
Open Tues - Fri 10 AM - 6 PM; Wed 10 AM - 9 PM; Sat & Sun 1 - 6 PM. No admis. Estab 1968 to exhibit the works of contemporary Black American Artists, mount historical and informative exhibitions, and provide culturally educational programs and activities for the general public; 4500 sq ft of exhibition space. Average Annual Attendance: 100,000. Mem: 400; dues $10 - $1000.
Income: Financed by membership, city and state appropriation, and corporate funding.
Collections: James Van Der Zee Collection of photography; 200 works of art by Afro-American artists including sculpture, painting and works on paper.
Exhibitions: (1976-78) Geraldine McCoullough (sculpture); Milton Sherrell (sculpture); Paul Collins (paintings); Willis Bing Davis (paintings); Freida High (paintings); Murray De Pillars (paintings); California Group Show; Prisons, USA; Black Photographers Annual; WPA-Black Artists, New York/Chicago; Al Smith, Jr, Richard Yarde, Al Loving, Randy Williams.
Publications: The Studio Museum in Harlem Bulletin, quarterly.
Activities: Classes for adults and children; Artist in Residence, Cooperative School program; lect open to the public, 5 vis lectr per yr; concerts; gallery talks; tours; museum shop selling books, magazines, original art, reproductions, prints, postcards and pottery.

FREDERICK THOMPSON FOUNDATION, INC, 441 E 20th St, 10010. Tel: 212-533-6631. *Pres* Mrs Humbert Cofrances; *Exec Dir* Mrs Frederick Thompson.
Open Sat and by appointment. Estab 1956, inc 1962, to provide a center where there may be study, discussion and the production of creative arts. A program of activities planned to create a sense of appreciation of art and particularly the art of painting. Average Annual Attendance: Over 5000; annual meeting Oct; board meets quarterly.
Collections: Over 300 paintings by Frederick Thompson, all excellent examples of Trompe L'Oeil technique.
Exhibitions: Lincoln Center Museum of the Performing Arts, New York.
Activities: Loan collection of color plates from American and European museums on Giotto, Raphael, Hals, Vermeer, Rembrandt, Chardin, Copley, Homer, Cezanne, Eakins and van Gogh; slide and film shows; essays by Frederick Thompson on the above masters available upon request. Programs with color slides and tapes free to New York City residents for presentations. Instructional outlines also available.

LOUIS COMFORT TIFFANY FOUNDATION, 1083 Fifth Ave, 10028. *Pres* Lewis Iselin; *VPres* Paul Smith; *Secy* Gerard Jones; *Asst to Pres* Elizabeth Stevens. Estab 1918 to give grants to painters and sculptors and in the crafts. Annual meeting May.
Income: Financed by endowment.

Activities: Open competition for painters and sculptors every two years; 20 grants of $5000 each are given.

TRAPHAGEN SCHOOL OF FASHION, Museum Collection, 257 Park Ave S, 10010. Tel: 212-673-0300. *Cur Museum Coll* Florita Raupt.
Open to public by appointment only. No admis. Estab 1923 to record fashion changes through the centuries; to use the collection as another means of teaching History of Costume; to use the items as inspiration for new design ideas. Exhibition area in Reception Hall. Trunk showings in Museum Workroom are also given.
Collections: Collection includes over 1000 period and ethnic costumes, plus fashion accessories; extensive African and American Indian costumes and jewelry; bride and bridegroom folk costumes around the world; four doll collections, including children of the 19th and 20th centuries; famous women in history; famous women in the theatre; ethnic dolls in native costume.
Exhibitions: Period Bridal Gowns; Children of the 19th and 20th Centuries; Beaded Chemises of the Twenties; Antique Laces; Gloves and Fans; Undercover Fashions 1840-1910.
Activities: Educ dept; docent training, trunk showings for students or guests on tour or designers by appointment.
—Library. Tel: 212-673-0300. *Librn* Anne Terwilliger.
Open to public by appointment. Estab 1923 to stimulate inquiry into new areas of fashion and allied fields; to give students of fashion design, illustration, or interior design the opportunity to explore related subjects in depth.
Holdings: Vols 16,000; Per subs 10; AV—Slides; Other—Clipping files, memorabilia, pamphlets.
Special Subjects: Fashion design, fashion illustration, interior design and decoration.
Special Collections: Bound volumes of early fashion magazines including: Les Modes and Usages du temps de Marie Antoinnette (1787-1792), 2 vols; Journal des Dames et Modes (1798-1840); Journal des Demoiselles (1870-1907; Graham's Magazine; Ladies' Companion; La Art et La Mode (1880-1915); Les Medes (1903-1936); Studio and Illustration Magazine of Fine and Applied Arts, 41 vols.
Activities: Library tours.

UNION OF AMERICAN HEBREW CONGREGATIONS,* Synagogue Art and Architectural Library, 838 Fifth Ave, 10021. Tel: 212-249-0100. *Dir* Myron E Schoen.
Open Mon - Fri 9:30 AM - 5 PM; cl Sat & Sun. Estab 1957.
Collections: Ceremonial objects and works of Jewish artists.
Publications: An American Synagogue for Today and Tomorrow (book); Contemporary Synagogue Art (book).
Activities: Slide rental service.
Library: For use on the premises only. Holdings: Vols 200. Special Subjects: Synagogue architecture, ceremonial objects and art.

UNITED STATES COMMITTEE OF THE INTERNATIONAL ASSOCIATION OF ART, INC, c/o Dorothy Paris, VPres, 33 W 67th St, 10023. Tel: 212-787-7063.
For further information see National and Regional Organizations.

UNIVERSITY CLUB LIBRARY,* 1 W 54th St, 10019. Tel: 212-247-2100. *Dir* Fred McKechnie; *Gen Asst* R Smith.
Open to members only 9:30 AM - 5 PM weekdays. Estab 1865 for the promotion of the arts and culture in post university men. For members reference only. Art is hung in all areas of the building. Average Annual Attendance: 7000. Mem: 4250; dues $600; annual meeting March. 17.
Income: Financed by endowment and membership.
Holdings: Vols 135,000.
Special Collections: Art; Architecture; fine binding; photograph collection.
Publications: Library & Club Bulletin, Nov - May.
Activities: Dramatic programs; lect for members only; concerts; gallery talks; tours.

VISUAL ARTISTS AND GALLERIES ASSOCIATION, INC, One World Trade Center, Suite 1535, 10048. Tel: 212-466-1390. *Exec Dir* Dorothy M Weber; *Artist Trustees* Wil Barnet, Ernst Beadle, Romare Bearden, Robert Motherwell, James Rosenquist & Estate of Ben Shahn; *Gallery Trustees* Leo Castelli, Sylvan Cole, Lawrence A Fleishman, Meredith Long & Alex Rosenberg.
For further information see National and Regional Organizations.

WHITNEY MUSEUM OF AMERICAN ART, 945 Madison Ave, 10021. Tel: 212-794-0600. *Dir* Thomas N Armstrong, III; *Adminr* Palmer Wald; *Development Officer* Walter Poleshock; *Cur* Patterson Sims; *Cur* Barbara Haskell; *Cur* Gail Levin; *Cur* Richard Marshall; *Cur* Jennifer Russell; *Cur* Patricia Hills; *Cur* Paul Cummings.

Open Tues 11 AM - 9 PM; Wed - Sat 11 AM - 6 PM; Sun Noon - 6 PM. Admis $1.50, no admis Tues 6 - 9 PM. Estab 1930, inc 1931 by Gertrude Vanderbilt Whitney for the advancement of contemporary American art; Museum open 1931; moved to 54th Street in 1954; new building opened in 1966.
Income: Financed by endowment.
Collections: Paintings, sculpture; drawings, prints. Work is mainly 20th century American artists.
Exhibitions: (1977-78) Selected Paintings from the Promised Gift of Mrs Percy Uris; Foirades/Fizzles; Jasper Johns; American Art: 1920-1945; American Art-Union; Synchromism and American Color Abstractions, 1910-1925; Duane Hanson; Saul Steinberg; American Art 1950 to the present; H C Westermann; Art about Art; 100 American Drawings and Works on Paper; Bloedel Bequest.
Activities: Courses Seminars with Artists; films; lectures held each Saturday.
Library: Open to advanced students and scholars for reference by appointment with the librarian.
—Downtown Branch, Uris Building; 55 Water St, 10041.
Operated by students participating in the Education Department Independent Study Program.
Open Mon - Fri 11 AM - 3 PM. No admis.
Income: Supported by the lower Manhattan business community and the National Endowment for the Arts.
Activities: Gallery talks.
—Friends of the Whitney Museum of American Art.
Mem: Approx 700; dues junior members $100 for persons up to age 30, individual or couple $250, members of the Whitney and Corporate members $1000.
Since their founding in 1956, the Friends have contributed a large number of important works of art to the permanent collection as well as supporting other parts of the Museum's program.

CATHARINE LORILLARD WOLFE ART CLUB, INC, 802 Broadway, 10003. Tel: 212-254-2000. *Pres* Carey Boone Nelson; *First VPres* Cecilia Cardman, *Treas* Sybil D'Orsi, *Recording Secy* Patricia Sprouls; *Corresp Secy* Jacquie-Louise Gray.
Estab 1896, inc 1963, to further fine, representational American art, and is a club of professional women painters and sculptors. Mem: 200, membership accepted on an international basis subject to jury; dues $10; monthly meetings.
Exhibitions: Two annuals; one open; one members.
Activities: Lect; programs; schol; annual Metropolitan Museum benefit for travel grant and research in USA.

WOMEN IN THE ARTS FOUNDATION, INC., 435 Broome St, 10013. Tel: 212-988-1476. *Pres* Alice Phillips; *VPres* Evelyn Eisgrau; *Secy* Elsa Goldsmith; *Treas* Dina Baker; *Mem Chair* Freda Pond; *Action Chair* Joyce Weinstein; *Public Appearance Chairs* Lisa Shainswit and Jackie Skiles; *Publicity Chair* Carol Hamoy; *Slide Registry Chair* Ruth Jacobsen; *Program Chair* Jean Zaleski; *Museum Liaison Chairs* Tanya Duana and Aldona Sabalis; *In-House Gallery Chairs* Barbara Crawford and Christine Griffin; *Funding Chairs* Ann Kronenberg and Ellen Baum; *Area Liaison* Annette Nachumi; *Newsletter Editor* Catherine de Bary.
Open Tues & Sat 2 - 5 PM. Estab 1971 for the purpose of overcoming discrimination against women artists both in government and the private sector; gallery is located in the Soho district of New York City, and exhibits the work of women artists, both established and unknown. Average Annual Attendance: 1000. Mem: 300, qualifications open to women who are professional artists, or who are interested in the arts; dues $23; meeting second Wed monthly.
Income: $12,000 (financed by endowment, membership).
Exhibitions: Artists Choice; Eleven Women Artists; Paintings and Sculpture at Fort Lee; Four Artists at WIA.
Publications: Women in the Arts, bulletin/newsletter, monthly.
Activities: Classes for adults; public education as to the problems and discrimination faced by women artists; lect open to the public, 10 vis lectr per yr; individual paintings and original objects of art lent to museum and university art galleries for special exhibitions; lending collection contains slides 1500; original art works for exhibitions are obtained from member artists; traveling exhibitions organized and circulated; sales shop selling catalogs of own exhibitions.

WOMEN'S SLIDE REGISTRY,* 105 Hudson, 10013. Tel: 212-216-3970. Slide Registry Comt: Mary Miss; Michelle Stuart; Sandy Gellis; Paula Tavins; Jean Feinberg.
The Women's Slide Registry was formed in 1970 by the Ad Hoc Women Artists' Committee to make available a collection of slides by women artists. Open for viewing to everyone, no charge, but is aimed at specialists in the visual arts; there are three registries, all artists are represented by one slide in each. A folder containing additional slides, a biography and related materials is also available for viewing at Artists Space. The registry, which is nonprofit, is used solely as a source of information and by directors seeking artists for shows.

Activities: Two duplicate traveling registries which are rented to colleges, lecturers, etc for a fee of $25 plus postage.

NORTH SALEM

HAMMOND MUSEUM, Museum of the Humanities, Deveau Rd, 10560. Tel: 914-669-5033. *Dir* Natalie Hays Hammond; *Assoc Dir* Elizabeth H Taylor.
Open May - Dec, Wed - Sun 11 AM - 5 PM. Admis to the Museum adults $1.50, children $1; to the Gardens adults $1.50, children $1. Inc in 1957 as a non-profit, educational institution; absolute charter from New York State Board of Regents, 1962. A Museum of the Humanities, it presents changing exhibitions of international scope and varied historic periods and topics, supplemented by programs of related special events. The Oriental Stroll Gardens, comprising 15 individual gardens on 3½ acres, include a lake, a reflecting pool, a dry landscape, a waterfall, and a Zen Garden. Average Annual Attendance: 35,000. Mem: 1800; Qualif for mem: Open to all who are in sympathy with its aims and purposes.
Activities: Dramatic programs; lect open to the public; concerts; documentary films; museum shop; Terrace Restaurant, luncheon by reservation, open May - Oct.

NORTHPORT

NORTHPORT-EAST NORTHPORT PUBLIC LIBRARY, 151 Laurel Ave, 11768. Tel: 516-261-6930. *Dir* Victoria Wallace; *Asst Dir* Frances Ingram.
Open Mon - Fri 9 AM - 9 PM; Sat 9 AM - 5 PM; Sun 1 - 5 PM, Oct - May. Estab 1914. Circ: 476,240.
Income: $765,159 (financed by state appropriation, local tax levy). Purchases: $100,300 book budget.
Holdings: Vols 150,853; Per subs 550; AV—Cassettes, microfiche, microfilm, phonorecords; Other—Exhibition catalogs, framed reproductions.
Special Subjects: Art: 6500 ‛volumes; 64 art and photographic periodicals.
Special Collections: Art exhibition and auction catalogs, 1400; Rex Brasher, Birds and Trees of North America.
Exhibitions: Freda Johnston (etching and marine algae collages); Annelle Low (acrylics); March Westerling (mixed media - oils); Christopher Dreger and Angelo Marino (oil paintings); Wayne Smokey René-Creager O'Briene and Arthur Kaliski (photography); Linda Runko (watercolors and photography); Howard Lucas (watercolors and charcoal drawings); Jean Gentile (oils and acrylics); Paula Kuehn (oil painting and pastels); Elizabeth Sandblom (watercolors); Hayes Ingram (wood carvings); Elizabeth Cranendonk (oils, watercolors and collages); Rhoda Needlman (pastels); Jean Gravlin, Jack Danley and Doris Davis Price (oil paintings); Ann Santelli (abstracts).

OGDENSBURG

REMINGTON ART MUSEUM, 303 Washington St, 13669. Tel: 315-393-2425. *Dir* Mildred Dillenbeck; *Secy Receptionist* Ruth Hunter; *Secy Receptionist* Beverly Walker.
Open Mon - Sat 10 AM - 5 PM; Sun 1 - 5 PM; cl Sun in winter. Admis adults $1; students 12 and over 50¢. Estab 1923 to house and exhibit the major works of art of Frederic Remington. The museum is in the converted Parish Mansion which was built in 1809-10; the newly constructed Addie Priest Newell Galleries display the major Remington artifacts. Remington's last studio has been reconstructed with most of the original furnishings. Average Annual Attendance: 12-14 thousand.
Income: Financed by endowment and city appropriation.
Collections: Remington artifacts, paintings, bronzes, oils and watercolors; Parish Collection of Belter furniture; Sharp Collection of period glass, china, silver, and cameos; the Haskell Collection of 19th century American and European paintings; studies in plaster by Edwin Willard Deming; sculpture by Sally James Farnham.
Activities: Tours; sales shop selling prints, slides, post cards, plates, spoons and rings.
Library: Remington's own personal library for viewing purposes only.

OLD CHATHAM

SHAKER MUSEUM, Shaker Museum Rd, 12136. Tel: 518-794-9105. *Dir* Peter Laskouski; *Admin Asst* Claire Wheeler; *Cur* Ruth Roberts; *Educ Coordinator* Jean Anderson.
Open May - Oct daily 10 AM - 5:30 PM. Admis adults $2.50, youths & sr citizens $1.50, children 75¢. Estab 1950 as a non-profit educational organization to promote interest in and understanding of the Shaker cultural heritage. The exhibits are housed in a complex of eight buildings. Average Annual Attendance: 20,000. Mem: 100; dues $15.
Income: $90,000 (financed by endowment, membership and state appropriation). Purchases: $3000.

Collections: The products of Shaker genius as well as the means of production. Exhibitions: Intro to Shaker History; Shaker Architecture.
Publications: Newsletter.
Activities: Classes for adults and children; lect open to public; gallery talks; tours; traveling exhibitions organized and circulated; museum shop selling books, magazines, original art, reproductions, prints and slides.
Library: Emma B King Library. Open to qualified persons by appointment. Special Collections: Manuscripts and records; photographic and map archive.

OLD WESTBURY

NEW YORK INSTITUTE OF TECHNOLOGY,* Wheatley Rd, 11568. Tel: 516-686-7542. *Chmn Fine Arts Dept* Dr F T Lassiter.
Open Mon - Fri 9 AM - 5 PM. Estab 1964; gallery maintained for many exhibits held during the year.
Exhibitions: Annual faculty shows and student shows; some traveling exhibitions.
Activities: Custom silk-screen printmaking for artists, galleries, publishers, etc. Also serves as an atelier.

ONEONTA

HARTWICK COLLEGE FINE ARTS MUSEUM,* Anderson Center for the Arts, 13820. Tel: 607-432-4220. *Cur* Kathryn Henkel.
Open Mon - Fri 10 AM - 4 PM, or by appointment; cl last half of Dec. No admis. Estab 1928, college collection and exhibitions for benefit of faculty, students, and community.
Collections: Paintings; sculpture, prints, drawings and minor arts, majority of which are 19th and 20th century works; Van Ess Collection of Renaissance and Baroque art; Collection of North American, Mexican and South American Indian art and artifacts available for exhibition from Yager Museum on campus.
Exhibitions: Changing exhibitions to meet curriculum needs.
Activities: Classes in museum studies; lectures; guided tours; films.
Library: Small collection of books on the history of the American Indian can be used on the premises upon request.

STATE UNIVERSITY OF NEW YORK COLLEGE AT ONEONTA,* Fine Arts Center, 13820. Tel: 607-431-2550. *Chmn Art Dept* James M Mullen.
Estab 1972 to offer students, staff and visitors an opportunity to view current as well as past artistic styles and works; an Art Gallery and Sculpture Court are major features of the Art Wing.
Income: Financed by city and state appropriation.
Activities: Lect open to the public, 8 vis lectr per yr; extensive exhibition program.

OSWEGO

STATE UNIVERSITY OF NEW YORK AT OSWEGO, Tyler Art Gallery, 13126. Tel: 315-341-2113. *Dir* Coy Ludwig, *Asst Dir* Marjorie Panadero; *Secy* Barbara Beckwith.
Open Mon - Fri 9:30 AM - 4:30 PM; Sat & Sun 12:30 - 4:30 PM; Sept through May, sometimes during summer. No admis. Estab 1968 as a teaching gallery; located in Tyler Hall, as part of fine arts complex (art, music, theater departments, studios, performance areas); two galleries show a combined total of 20 exhibitions per school year. Average Annual Attendance: 34,000.
Income: $7000 (financed by university funds).
Collections: Contemporary American prints and paintings; Grant Arnold Collection of lithographs.
Exhibitions: (1976-78) Oswego County Architecture; Frontrunners of Contemporary Chinese Painting; Outside City Limits; Third Oswego Ceramics Invitational; Traditions in American Basketry; Invitational Sculpture Exhibition; Recent Abstract Paintings; New Deal for Art.
Publications: Catalogs for exhibitions, occasionally.
Activities: Lect open to the public, 2 vis lectr per yr; individual paintings and original objects of art lent to members of faculty and administration, and for offices; traveling exhibitions organized and circulated.

PORT CHESTER

PORT CHESTER PUBLIC LIBRARY, 1 Haselo Ave, 10573. *Dir* Vivian Conan; *Reference Librn* Carol Woodger; *Art Dir* Winifred DeVeau.
Open Mon 9 AM - 9 PM; Tues & Wed 9 AM - 8 PM; Thurs - Sat 9 AM - 5 PM. Estab 1876 to circulate books, records, magazines, etc to the general public; to provide reference services. Circ: 108,969. Maintains an art gallery. A small gallery with about ten shows per year; mostly local artists.
Income: $220,500 (financed by endowment, city and state appropriation). Purchases: $33,689.

Holdings: Vols 93,911; Per subs 215; AV—Film strips, microfilm, phono-records, slides; Other—Framed reproductions, pamphlets, prints.
Exhibitions: Water colors, oils, panel acrylics.
Activities: Lect open to public, 4 vis lect per yr; concerts.

POTSDAM

POTSDAM PUBLIC MUSEUM, Civic Center, 13676. Tel: 315-265-6910. *Pres of Bd* Mrs A D Palmer; *Secy* Mrs F A Ramsdell; *Dir-Cur* Katharine F Wyant; *Asst Cur* Klara Lovass-Nagy; *Registr* Sharon Dresye.
Open Tues - Sat 2 - 5 PM; cl Mon & Sun. No admis. Estab 1940 as an educational institution acting as a cultural and historical center for the Village of Potsdam and surrounding area. Educational services taken to area schools. The Museum occupies a sandstone bldg, formerly a Universalist Church built in 1876. Average Annual Attendance: 5000. Annual meeting Nov.
Income: Approx $29,000 (financed by city and state appropriation).
Collections: Burnap Collection of English pottery; pressed glass and art glass of the 19th and early 20th century; costumes of the 19th and 20th centuries; Mandarin Chinese hangings, china and costumes; photograph collection and artifacts and material on local history.
Exhibitions: From Old China; History of Lighting; Faberge-Style Decorated Eggs; Local History; Ironstone China; Cranberry Glass; Charles Edison Fund Exhibit; New York State Forces Exhibit; Wedding Party; Wrapping Up (coats and capes).
Publications: Newsletter, ten times per yr.
Activities: Classes for adults and children; programs for schools craft days; lect open to public, 8 vis lectr per yr; concerts; tours.
Library: Reference library. Holdings: Vols 300. Special Subjects: Antiques; local history; early American crafts.

STATE UNIVERSITY OF NEW YORK COLLEGE AT POTSDAM ART GALLERY,* Brainerd Hall, Pierrepont Ave, 13676. Tel: 315-268-5041. *Art Dept Chmn* Dr Roger W Lipsey; *Gallery Dir* Benedict Goldsmith; *Secy* Carol Belshaw.
Open weekdays 1 - 5 PM, 7 - 9 PM; Sat & Sun 1 - 5 PM. No admis. Estab 1967 to serve college and community as a teaching gallery. Gallery associated with Art Department. Average Annual Attendance: 18,000.
Income: Operating budget $15,000 (financed by state appropriation).
Collections: Roland Gibson Collection, contemporary Japanese, Italian and American art—painting, sculpture and prints; †contemporary prints collection; †contemporary drawing collection; †contemporary painting collection; †contemporary sculpture collection.
Exhibitions: Six-major exhibitions per year plus student and faculty exhibitions.
Activities: Beginning photograph collection; William King, Artist-in-Residence; lect open to the public, 6 vis lectr per yr; concerts; gallery talks; tours; original objects of art lent; traveling exhibitions organized and circulated.

POUGHKEEPSIE

VASSAR COLLEGE ART GALLERY, Raymond Ave, 12601. Tel: 914-452-7000, exten 2645. *Art Dir* Peter Morrin; *Cur* Mary Jo McNamara; *Secy* Allegra Knight; *Friends of the Art Gallery (Exec Dir)* Mary Busch; *Cur Asst* Ann LaPides.
Open Mon - Sat 9 AM - 5 PM; Sun 1 - 5 PM. No admis. Estab 1864 as a college gallery collecting Eastern and Western art of all periods. The gallery has 6000 sq ft of exhibition space in 1915 Gothic style building. Average Annual Attendance: 9000. Mem: 450, dues $15 - $1000; annual meeting Apr.
Income: Financed by endowment, membership. Purchases: $15,000.
Collections: Charles M Pratt gift of Far Eastern ceramics and jades and Italian paintings; Matthew Vassar Collection of American paintings of Hudson River School and 19th century English architectural watercolors; Mary Thaw Thompson Collection of 17th century French engravings including works of Nanteuil, Morin; Dexter M Ferry Collection of paintings and etchings; Felix M Warbur Collection of mediaeval sculpture and of graphics including 54 by Durer and 68 by Rembrandt; Olga Hasbrouck Collection of Chinese ceramics; †European paintings, sculptures and drawings ranging from the Renaissance to the 20th century, including Bacchiacca, Valentin de Boullogne, Cézanne, Salvator Rosa, Claesz, Robert, Corot, Courbet, Delacroix, Tiepolo, Van Gogh, Munch, Klee, Bourdelle, Laurent, Kolbe, Gabo, Calder, Moore; †20th century American and European paintings including Bacon, Nicholson, Rothko, de Kooning, Hartley, Weber, Ryder; graphics ranging from Rembrandt to Rouault, Picasso, Matisse and Braque. The Classical Collection, which was established 1938, includes Greek vases; Egyptian, Etruscan and Mycenaean objects ranging from a mummy to tiny bronzes; Roman glass; marble portraits; jewelry; other archaeological finds.
Exhibitions: Woodstock, An American Art Cology; Promised Gifts 77; 17th Century Dutch Landscape Drawings and Prints; Alton Pickens.

Publications: Gallery, biannually.
Activities: Lect open to public, 3 - 4 vis lectr per yr; gallery talks; tours; individual paintings and original objects of art lent to other museums.
—**Art Library.** Tel: 914-452-7000. *Librn* Janis Ekdahl.
Open Mon - Thurs 8:30 AM - midnight; Fri 8:30 AM - 10 PM; Sat 9 AM - 10 PM; Sun 10 AM - 12 PM; cl summers. Estab 1937. Circ: To students and faculty only.
Holdings: Vols 31,000; Per subs 180.

PURCHASE

MANHATTANVILLE COLLEGE, Brownson Art Gallery, 10577. Tel: 914-946-9600, exten 331. *Pres* Dr Barbara Knowles Debs; *Dean of Faculty* Dr Marlene Fisher.
Open during academic year and summer session. Brownson Art Gallery is west room of Reid Hall.
Income: Financed by endowment and tuition.
Publications: Magazine, bimonthly; catalogs.
Activities: Classes for adults; dramatic programs; concerts; gallery talks; tours.
Library: Manhattanville Library. *Librn* Catherine Tashjean. Holdings: Vols 200,000; Per subs 800.

STATE UNIVERSITY OF NEW YORK COLLEGE AT PURCHASE, Roy R Neuberger Museum, 10577. Tel: 914-253-5087. *Dir* Jeffrey Hoffeld; *Asst Cur* Simon Zalkind; *Museum Mgr* John Cassidy; *Chmn Friends of the Newberger Museum* Leonard Yaseen; *Pres* Margot Linton.
Open Tues - Sat 11 AM - 5 PM; Sun 1 - 5 PM; cl Mon. No admis. Estab 1971, opened May 1974 to serve college and community. Mem: Dues regular $25; contributing $100, patron $500.
Collections: Roy R Neuberger Collection of 19th and 20th century American art. Other gifts and long term loans include: Rickey Collection of constructivist art; Hans Richter Collection of American and European artists, including Richter's own art; Eliot P Hirshberg Collection of African art; Cleve Gray's Threnody, a sequence of 14 paintings.
Activities: Film showings; lectures and symposia, Yaseen lecture series; guided tours.
Library: Holdings—Vols 112,000, with special strength in the performing and visual arts; AV—Art slides 20,000; Other—Photographs.

ROCHESTER

AMERICAN BAPTIST HISTORICAL SOCIETY,* 1106 S Goodman St, 14620. Tel: 716-473-1740. *Dir & Librn* James D Leachman.
Open Mon - Fri 9 AM - 4 PM; cl Sat, Sun & holidays. No admis. Estab 1853, a religious Museum, affiliated with American Baptist Convention.
Collections: Paintings; pewter; silver; religious historical material.
Publications: Foundations, quarterly.
Library: Available to the public under staff supervision. Holdings: Vols 55,000. Other—Manuscripts. Special Collections: Baptistiana; records; archives.

INTERNATIONAL MUSEUM OF PHOTOGRAPHY AT GEORGE EASTMAN HOUSE, 900 East Ave, 14607. Tel: 716-271-3361. *Chmn* Dr Wesley T Hanson; *Dir* Robert J Doherty; *Asst Dir* Andrew Eskind; *Dir Film* Dr John Kuiper; *Cur* William Jenkins and Robert Sobieszek; *Equipment* Philip Condax.
Open Tues - Sun 10 AM - 4:30 PM; cl Mon. Admis adults $1.50.
Estab 1949 for photography exhibitions, research, and education. Average Annual Attendance: 125,000. Mem: 1200; dues $20.
Income: Financed by membership, grants, and earned income.
Collections: 19th century photography; 20th century photography; equipment (photographic); film.
Exhibitions: (1977) History of Fashion Photography; Alvin Langdon Coburn.
Publications: Image, quarterly.
Activities: Classes for children; docent training; teacher workshops, school exhibition program; lectures open to public; concerts; gallery talks; tours; exten dept; original objects of art lent to corporations, other institutions; lending collection contains photographs 1500; traveling exhibitions organized and circulated; museum shop selling books, original art, reproductions, prints.
—**Archives.** Tel: 716-271-3361, exten 235, 236. *Dir* Martha E Jenks; *Asst* Susan Stromei.
Open Tues - Fri 1:30 - 4:45 PM. Estab 1949 to act as a research center for staff and students, scholars and curators of photography; houses prints and photographs of the museum collection.
Income: Financed by trust endowment, admission, traveling exhibitions, loan shows. Purchases: $15,000 library budget.

Holdings: Vols 30,000; Per subs 1200; AV—Audiotapes, Kodachromes, microfiche, microfilm, phonorecords, slides, autochromes; Other—Clipping files, exhibition catalogs, manuscripts, memorabilia, original documents, pamphlets, photographs, prints, reproductions.
Special Subjects: History and aesthetics of photography.
Special Collections: Lewis W Hine; Alvin Langdon Coburn; Nikolas Muray; Edward Muybridge.
Exhibitions: (1976-77) Southworth and Harves: The Spirit of Fact; Robert Hieneckin; History of Fashion Photography, French Daguerreotype, Alvin Langdon Coburn; Image of Industry.

ROCHESTER HISTORICAL SOCIETY, 485 East Ave, 14607. Tel: 716-271-2705. *Pres* Elizabeth G Holahan; *First VPres* Stuart Bolder; *Second VPres* William E Diez; *Secy* Helen Brooks; *Cur* Mary R Shannon.
Open Mon - Fri 10 AM - 4 PM; Admis adults $1, senior citizens and students 50¢. Estab 1888 to collect and protect books, manuscripts, paintings, and artifacts pertinent to Rochester history. A fine collection of oils are hung throughout the house on a rotating basis. Average Annual Attendance: 1000. Mem: 300; dues $10 - $500; annual meeting May.
Income: Financed by membership.

UNIVERSITY OF ROCHESTER
—**Memorial Art Gallery,** 490 University Ave, 14607. Tel: 716-275-3081.
Pres Bd of Mgrs William B Webber; *Dir* John A Mahey; *Asst Dir Cur Services* Bruce W Chambers; *Asst Dir* Langdon F Clay; *Adminr* Bernice L Meyer; *Develop Officer* Christine D Hyer; *Head Public Relations* Margaret Bond; *Head Membership* Margaret Bennett; *Superintendent* Robert Young.
Open Tues 2 - 9 PM; Wed - Sat 10 Am - 5 PM; Sun 1 - 5 PM; cl Mon. Admis adults $1, children 25¢, senior citizens 50¢; No admis Tues 5 - 9 PM and to members, students and children accompanied by adult. Estab 1913 as a university art museum and public art museum for the Rochester area involved in a broad variety of community programs. The building is built in an Italian renaissance style, a new wing built in 1968 reflects a contemporary style. Average Annual Attendance: 200,000. Mem: 8000; dues $25 and up.
Income: $950,000 (financed by endowment, membership, city and state appropriation and grants and earned income).
Collections: Covers all major periods and cultural areas from Assyria and predynastic Egypt to the present—paintings, sculpture, prints, drawings, decorative arts. Special strengths are medieval, Renaissance and 17th century art, 19th and early 20th century French paintings, American tribal arts, folk art and contemporary prints.
Exhibitions: The Genesee Country; Charles Rand Penney Collection; Contemporary Images in Watercolor; Tunisian Mosaica; Robert P Coggins Collection of American Painting; Far Eastern Art in Upstate New York; The Chicago Connection; Chinese Painting from the Sackler Collection; Charles Burchfield: The Charles Rand Penney Collection; Annual Regional Finger Lakes and Clothesline Exhibitions.
Publications: Gallery Notes, nine times yr; bulletin, annual, exhibition catalogs.
Activities: Classes for adults and children; docent training; lect open to the public, 30 vis lectr per yr; concerts; gallery talks; tours; exten dept serving Rochester area and nine county surrounding areas; individual paintings lent and original objects of art lent to cultural institutions; lending collection contains books, cassettes, color reproductions, framed reproductions, kodachromes, motion pictures, original art works, original prints, paintings, photographs, sculpture, slides. Traveling exhibitions organized and circulated; museum and sales shop selling books, magazines, original art, reproductions, and prints.
—**Memorial Art Gallery Library.** Tel: 716-275-4765. *Librn* Mrs Thomas Besbit; *Libr Clerk* Grace Field.
Open Tues 2 - 4 PM; Wed - Sat 10 AM - 4 PM; Sun 1 - 5 PM; Cl Mon and July and Aug. Research library for use of the staff and gallery members. For reference only.
Income: Financed by endowment, membership and city appropriation.
Holdings: 12,000; Per subs 65.
—**Fine Arts Library/Gallery,** River Campus, 14627. Tel: 716-275-4476.
Librn Stephanie Frontz.
Open Mon - Thurs 9 AM - 10 PM; Fri 9 AM - 8 PM; Sat 12 - 5 PM; Sun 2 - 10 PM. Estab to support academic programs of Fine Arts Department and other academic departments within the university. Circ: Mostly books, no periodicals. Small gallery is maintained by Fine Arts Department.
Income: Approx $10,000 (financed by private funds). Purchases: Approx $10,000.
Holdings: Vols 32,000; Per subs 220; Other—Exhibition catalogs.

ROSLYN HEIGHTS

PROFESSIONAL ARTISTS GUILD, 69 Shelter Lane (Mailing Add: PO Box 11, 11577). Tel: 516-621-4792. *Pres* Anne Orling; *VPres* Rhoda Sherbell; *Secy* Lucille Orzack; *Treas* Sunya Levy.
For further information see National and Regional Organizations.

SAINT BONAVENTURE

SAINT BONAVENTURE UNIVERSITY ART COLLECTION, 14778. Tel: 716-375-2323, exten 6. *Art Cur* Fr Irenaeus Herscher; *Asst Art Cur* Bro John Capozzi.
Open Mon - Thurs 8 AM - Midnight; Fri 8 AM - 5 PM; Sat 8 AM - 8 PM; Sun 10 AM - Midnight. No admis. Estab 1856 to provide artistic surroundings for students. Average Annual Attendance: Approx 3500.
Income: Financed by university budget.
Collections: 200 paintings; 100 porcelains and American Indian pottery; 50 ivories, jades, miniatures; 4 cloissonnes.
Exhibitions: Rotating exhibitions.
Publications: Art Catalog of Collection, in process.
Activities: Museum shop selling reproductions.
—**Friedsam Memorial Library.** Tel: 716-375-2323. *Librn* John Macik; *Art Cur* Fr Irenaeus Herscher. Open to the public.
Holdings: Vols 180,000; Per subs 3000; Other—Microfiche, microfilm, microcard.
Special Subjects: Franciscana, Art, Science, Philosophy and Theology Collections.
Special Collections: Fine Arts; Library of American Civilization (20,000 vols on microfiche); Vatican Library Microfilms; NY Times Collection complete on microfilm (1851-1978); Short Title Catalog (1475-1640).

SANBORN

NIAGARA COUNTY COMMUNITY COLLEGE ART GALLERY, 3111 Saunders Settlement Rd, 14132. Tel: 716-731-3271, exten 159. *Gallery Dir* Dorothy H Westhafer.
Open hours vary from semester to semester, generally, Mon, Tues, Thurs 10 AM - 3 PM; Wed 10 AM - 8 PM; occasional Sun hours. Estab 1973 for varied exhibits that will be of interest to students and the community. There are two galleries with 270 sq ft of area and approx 250 running ft. Average Annual Attendance: 7500.
Income: $3500 (financed by college).
Collections: Student work, prints (contemporary); Rochester Institute of Technology School for American Craftsman pieces.
Exhibitions: Art in the Market (art skills in western New York business and industry); Charles R Penney Western New York Collection; Correspondence of Reality and Abstraction (4 CAPS winners); Fantasy 78 (prints, paintings, weaving, furniture, metal, ceramics, glass, assemblage); Student and Art Teacher Shows; Smithsonian, Pratt and other traveling shows.
Publications: Catalogs.
Activities: Classes for adults; dramatic programs; art interns; lectures open to public; tours.
Library: College has a library and art slide collection.

SARATOGA SPRINGS

NATIONAL MUSEUM OF RACING, INC, Union Ave, 12866. Tel: 518-584-0400. *Chmn* John W Hanes; *Pres* Charles E Mather II; *VPres* Walter M Jeffords, Jr, Whitney Tower and R Frederick Woolworth; *Secy-Treas* Paul R Rouillard; *Dir* Elaine E Mann.
Open all year 9:30 AM - 5 PM; Sat 12 noon - 5 PM (except Jan, Feb & Mar); Sun 12 noon - 5 PM (June 15 - Sept 15); August Racing Season 9:30 AM - 7 PM every day. No admis, children under 12 must be accompanied by parents. Estab 1950 as a museum for the collection, preservation and exhibition of all kinds of articles associated with the origin, history and development of horse racing; there are 10 galleries of sporting art. The handsome Georgian-Colonial design brick structure houses one of the world's greatest collections of equine art along with trophies, sculptures and memorabilia of the sport from its earliest days. Average Annual Attendance: Approx 45,000. Annual meeting Aug.
Income: Financed by state appropriation, and annual appeal.
Collections: Oil paintings of thoroughbred horses, trophies, racing silks, bronzes, prints, racing memorabilia.
Exhibitions: Special exhibits annually during summer months, loans from private collectors of sporting art.
Publications: Catalog; Hall of Fame booklets.
Activities: Lect open to public, 2 - 4 vis lectr per yr; gallery talks; exten dept serving Northeast; original objects of art lent on special occasions; museum shop selling books, reproductions, prints, jewelry, figurines, and other items.

Library: Reference library open to researchers, students and authors by appointment. Limited holdings. Special Subjects: Thoroughbred racing—horses.

SKIDMORE COLLEGE, Hathorn Gallery, North Broadway, 12866. Tel: 518-584-5000, exten 370. *Dir* David Miller.
Open Mon - Fri 9 AM - 5:30 PM; Sat & Sun Noon - 5:30 PM; cl during Skidmore vacations. No admis. Estab 1927. Hathorn Gallery's purpose is educational enrichment of the college and community. The exhibitions are intended to bring awareness of both contemporary and historical trends in art. In the fall of 1978 the gallery will be located in Skidmore's new Art Building. Average Annual Attendance: 6,000.
Income: Financed through College.
Collections: American and European prints; Saratoga Springs Historical Collection.
Exhibitions: Student and Faculty Shows; Drawings by students NASA Oakleigh Collection; Navajo Art & Ceremony; Watercolors, historical and contemporary; 20th Century Printmaker's portfolio; Crafts Invitational.
Publications: Exhibition catalogs, occasionally.
Activities: Lect open to public, 5-6 vis lectr per yr; gallery talks; traveling exhibitions organized and circulated.
Library: Art Section of The Lucy Scribner Library. *Art Librn* Jane Graves.

SCHENECTADY

SCHENECTADY COUNTY HISTORICAL SOCIETY,* 32 Washington Ave, 12305. Tel: 518-374-0263. *Pres* William E Fasake; *Cur* Elsa Church & Jean Thorkildsen.
Open Mon - Fri 12:30 - 5 PM; Sat 1 - 5 PM; Sun 2 - 5 PM; cl National holidays. No admis. Estab 1906, located within area of original Schenectady stockade by the Dutch in 1661. Mem: Dues regular $5, patron $10, organization $25, Life $50.
Collections: Paintings; decorative arts; photographs; Indian artifacts; historical material.
Publications: Newsletter, monthly.
Activities: Lectures; guided tours; films; temporary exhibitions from other museums. Sales shop selling books and postcards.
Library: Holdings—Vols 2500.

SCHENECTADY MUSEUM, Nott Terrace Heights, 12308. Tel: 518-372-3386. *Pres* Prof Joseph Finkelstein; *VPres* Joseph Flora; *Secy* Mrs Robert L Fullman; *Treas* Joseph A Matocha; *Acting Dir & Cur Art Coll & Exhibits* Mark Winetrout; *Cur Costumes* Marjorie B Foote; *Assoc Cur Educ* Sarah R Mason; *Dir Development* Virginia Strull.
Open Tues - Fri 10 Am - 4:30 PM; Sat & Sun Noon - 5 PM. Founded 1934, chartered by the New York State Regents in 1937 to increase and diffuse knowledge in appreciation of art, history, industry, and science by providing collections, exhibits, lectures, and other programs. Average Annual Attendance: 68,000. Mem: 2200; dues $5, $12.50, $15, $25, $50, $100, $250, $500 and up.
Income: $190,000.
Collections: (Art) 19th and 20th century costumes and textiles; North American Indian art, African art, decorative arts; 19th and 20th century art.
Exhibitions: Artists of the Mohawk-Hudson Region; Regional Crafts Show, purchases and awards $600; temporary exhibits of costumes and textiles and art.
Publications: Calendar, monthly; Annual Report.
Activities: Art and craft classes: planetarium programs for school pupils and public; amateur radio station; annual indoor plant show, Haunted House; Festival of Nations; Crafts Fair; Rock Festival; lecture and movie series; guided tours for school pupils; bus tours to other museums, historic sites, and cultural events; European and Central American tours; loan materials and exhibits for area schools, colleges, and libraries; Sales and Rental gallery; gift shop.
Library: Reference and technical. Holdings: Vols 5000.

SKANEATELES

SKANEATELES LIBRARY ASSOCIATION,* 49 E Genesee St, 13152. Tel: 315-685-5135. *Pres* Frederick G Martin; *Secy* Mrs J W Thorne.
Open 10 Am - 5:30 PM; cl Sun. Estab 1877.
Collections: Paintings by American artists and etchings by American and foreign artists. 200 paintings by John D Barrow in separate wing.
Exhibitions: Occasional special exhibitions.
Library: *Librn* Mrs Samuel Townsend; *Asst Librn* Mrs Edward D Ramage. Holdings: Vols 25,000.

SOUTHAMPTON

PARRISH ART MUSEUM, 25 Jobs Lane, 11968. Tel: 516-283-2118. *Dir* Jean M Weber; *Cur* Helen Harrison; *Cur Chase Coll & Archives*

Ronald G Pisano; *Registr* Penelope Henry; *Educ Dir* Anke tom Dieck Jackson; *Pres* Franklin O Canfield; *First VPres* Garrick C Stephenson; *Treas* Mark J Millard; *Secy* Edward P Sharretts, Jr.
Open Tues - Sat 10 AM - 5 PM; Sun 2 - 5 PM; cl Mon. No Admis.
Estab 1896 to exhibit, care for and research permanent collections and loaned works of art, emphasis on American 19th and 20th century paintings. Art workshops for children and adults, community programs, film, concert lecture series. Three main galleries, 4288 sq ft, 355 running ft. Average Annual Attendance: 50,000. Mem: 1100; dues $10 - $1000; annual meeting Dec.
Income: Approx $170,000 (financed by endowment, membership).
Collections: Samuel Parrish Collection of Italian Renaissance panel paintings; †American paintings, 19th and 20th century; Dunnigan Collection of 19th century etchings; Carney Collection of Chinese ceramics; Oriental decorative arts; D Doughty porcelains; Phillips Collection of 17th-18th century portraits; Japanese woodblock prints and stencils.
Exhibitions: Viewpoint: The American Land; Eisenstadt, First Fifty Years; Fabrications; Options; Clay; G Ruger Donoho Retrospective; Abraham Rattner, Henry Miller: Our America; Fairfield Porter's Maine; Lion Rugs from Fars; 24th Annual Juried; 20th Century American Paintings; plus others.
Publications: Exhibition catalogs (c 10 annually); Newsletter (quarterly).
Activities: Classes for adults and children; dramatic programs; films; lect open to public, 3 vis lectr per yr; concerts; competitions; exten dept serving area schools; lending collection contains color reproductions 100, film strips, original art works, original prints 200; traveling exhibitions organized and circulated; museum shop selling books, magazines, reproductions, prints, craft items.
—Aline B Saarinen Library. Tel: 516-283-2118. *Librn* Penelope Henry. Reference library open to public.
Holdings: Vols 4000; Per subs 6; Other—Exhibition catalogs.
Special Subjects: Architecture, Oriental art, American painting.
Special Collections: William Merritt Chase Archives; original documents, photographs, memorabilia, research materials pertaining to the life and work of Chase (1849-1916).

STATEN ISLAND

JACQUES MARCHAIS CENTER OF TIBETAN ARTS, INC,* 338 Lighthouse Ave, 10306. Tel: 212-987-3478. *Dir* Ruth Sprute; *Cur* Rosemary Tung.
Open April 1 - Nov 30, Sat & Sun 2 - 5 PM; June, July & Aug open Tues & Thurs 2 - 5 PM. Admis 50¢. Estab 1946 for maintenance of library and museum in Buddhist philosophy, art and religion, with particular emphasis on Tibetan Buddhism. Buildings planned for and collection amassed by Mrs. Harry Klauber (known professionally as Jacques Marchais) who ran an Oriental art gallery from 1938 until her death in 1948. She never left the United States but, through agents and dealers, built her collection upon original bronzes, a gift from her grandfather. The Center is a memorial to her by her husband. Buildings are facsimile of a Tibetan lamasery, located in a garden setting. Average Annual Attendance: 4000.
Income: Financed by contributions, admissions, some county, state and federal appropriations, and gift shop sales.
Collections: Jacques Marchais permanent collection of Tibetan and Buddhist Art.
Activities: Lect open to the public, 6 vis lectr per yr; special lectures and tours are available by appointment; gift shop selling reproductions and woodblock prints, incense, prayer flags.
Library: *Librn* Sigred Sidrow. For reference only. Holdings: Vols 1100; Other—Photographs.

STATEN ISLAND FERRY MARITIME MUSEUM, St George Ferry Terminal Bldg, 10301. *Captain & Historian* Theodore Costa; *Registrar* Edith Nilsen; *Deputy Dir* Patricia Green.
Open Mon - Fri 8 AM - 3 PM; Summer, Sat - Tues 9:30 AM - 3 PM; Wed - Fri 8 Am - 3 PM. No admis. Estab July 1976 to collect and preserve history of ferries and educate the public of their true historic value.
Income: Financed by city appropriation.
Collections: Permanent historical exhibitions of ferry boat models, a working pilot house, and engineer's gages and signals; also a series of highly detailed, finely worked color pen and ink drawings of the floating derrick, City of New York, circa 1876; also artists' renderings of boats of the future-a sleek 6000 passenger ferryboat that the city will soon contract for, and a smaller ferryboat that is still under development.
Library. *Librn* Gerda Bernhardt. Open to the public for reference. Special Subjects: History of Ferry Boats and New York Harbor.

STATEN ISLAND INSTITUTE OF ARTS AND SCIENCES,* 75 Stuyvesant Place, St George, 10301. Tel: 212-727-1135. *Pres* Terence H Benbow; *Dir* George O Pratt; *Cur of Art* Barry Leo Delaney; *Editor & Librn* Gail K Schneider; *Museum Lectr* Freda Mulcahy Esterly; *Asst to Dir* Elsie Verkuil.
Open Tues - Sat 10 AM - 5 PM; Sun and holidays 2 - 5 PM; cl Mon, Thanksgiving, Christmas, New Year's, Fourth of July, Labor Day. No admis. Estab 1881, inc 1906. Average Annual Attendance: 105,000. Mem: 900; dues $10 and up.
Collections: (Art) †American paintings of the 19th and 20th centuries; †prints, small sculptures; Oriental, Greek, Roman and primitive art objects.
Exhibitions: (Art) Exhibitions in decorative arts; design exhibitions in various media; major loan shows of paintings and prints; special exhibitions of graphic arts and of photography.
Publications: The New Bulletin (indexed), monthly except for the summer; Proceedings, 3 times a year; catalogs; Annual Reports.
Activities: Fall and spring terms of adult classes; lectures on art and science; complete program of lectures, art and natural history, for school children with annual registration of 30,000; four Weissglass awards totaling $400 presented each year.
Library: Reference collection of 30,000 publications in science, art history, history, and genealogy; a choice collection of Staten Island newspapers from 1834-1934 on microfilm (reader in Library); letters, documents, journals, files of clippings, and old photographs relating to the history of Staten Island and the metropolitan region; The George W Curtis Collection of books, manuscripts, and memorabilia.

STONE RIDGE

ULSTER COUNTY COMMUNITY COLLEGE, Visual Arts Gallery, 12484. Tel: 914-687-7621, exten 76. *Coordinator* Allan L Cohan; *Asst Coordinator* John A Locke III.
Open Mon - Fri 10 AM - 4 PM, Fall and Spring semesters; Noon - 3 PM, Summer. No admis. Estab 1963 as a center for creative activity, the gallery functions as an adjunct to the college's cultural and academic program; 40 x 28 ft enclosed space in John Vanderlyn Hall on campus. Average Annual Attendance: 3000 - 4000.
Income: Financed by college funds. Purchases $750.
Collections: Contemporary drawings, paintings, prints, photographs, and sculpture.
Exhibitions: (1976-78) Regularly changing exhibitions, every 4-6 weeks; Image of the Kaaterskill Region: Hudson River School; The Bible in Graphic Arts (from the Jewish Museum, New York City); Leonard Baskin: American Indian Prints; The Cragsmoor School (19th and 20th century paintings).
Publications: Flyers announcing each exhibit, every four to six weeks.
Activities: Lect open to the public, 2-3 vis lectr per yr; concerts.

STONY BROOK

MUSEUMS AT STONY BROOK, Rte 25A, 11790. Tel: 516-751-0066. *Dir* Susan Stitt; *Adminr* Nicholas Langhart; *Pub Info Officer* Marian Leifsen.
Open Wed - Sun 10 AM - 5 PM; cl Mon & Tues. Admis (Apr - Nov) adults $2, students & sr citizens $1.50, children $1; (Dec - Apr 15) adults 75¢, children 50¢. Estab 1942 as a nonprofit educational institution whose purpose is to collect and preserve objects of historic and artistic interest. The museums consist of the Carriage Museum, the Art Museum, period buildings, and museum store. The Carriage Museum is closed from mid-Nov to Apr. A History Museum is to open in 1979. Average Annual Attendance: 47,000. Mem: 660; dues $10 - $50.
Income: $490,000 (financed by endowment, membership, admis, student fees and tuition, private contributions, grants, and store).
Collections: (Art) Paintings, drawings and memorabilia of artist William Sidney Mount; decoys; miniature rooms.
Exhibitions: Changing exhibitions in Art Museum.
Publications: Annual Report; Quarterly Newsletter; exhibition catalogs.
Activities: Classes for adults and children; docent training; lect open to public, 12 vis lectr per yr; gallery talks; tours; individual paintings and original objects of art lent to other museums; museum shop selling books, reproductions, prints, children's folk toys and early American housewares.
—Kate Strong Historical Library. Tel: 516-751-0066. *Librn* Michiko Taylor. Reference library open to researchers by appointment.
Holdings: Vols 1500; Per subs 15; Other—Trade catalogs, carriage; archival—manuscript and photographs.
Special Collections: Archives: Papers of William Sidney Mount (1807-1868) and Family; Daniel Williamson and John M Williamson, Stony Brook - 19th century; William Cooper, shipbuilder 19th century, Sag Harbor; Photos: Israel Green Hawkins, Edward P Buffet, Hal B Fullerton.

STATE UNIVERSITY OF NEW YORK AT STONY BROOK ART GALLERY, 11794. Tel: 516-246-7071. *Dir* Lawrence Alloway; *Asst to the Dir* Elizabeth S Boudreau.
Open Mon - Fri Noon - 5 PM. No admis. Estab 1967 to serve both the campus and the community by exhibitions of professional artists; two galleries connected; one gallery 42 x 74 ft with 22 ft ceiling; second space 22 x 60 ft with 12 ft ceilings. Average Annual Attendance: 500 students per show.
Income: Financed by city and state appropriation.
Exhibitions: (1978) Leon Golub: Gigantomachies and Mercenaries; Women from New York; Janet Fish: Painting and Pastels.
Activities: Lectures.

SYRACUSE

ERNEST STEVENSON BIRD LIBRARY,* Waverly Ave, 13210. Tel: 315-423-2440. *Dept Head* Donald C Seibert; *Architecture Librn* Barbara A Opar; *Slide Librn* Ramona Roters; *Art Librn* Jeannette T Sullivan.
Open weekdays 8 AM - 11 PM; Sat 10 AM - 5 PM; Sun Noon - 10 PM. Estab to serve faculty and students teaching and studying in the fine arts field. Located in Syracuse University Library.
Purchases: $36,000 for books and periodicals.
Holdings: Vols 38,000; AV—Slides 110; Other—Exhibition catalogs 5000, picture file 26,000.

EVERSON MUSEUM OF ART,* 401 Harrison St, 13202. Tel: 315-474-6064. *Dir* James Harithas; *Asst Dir Exhib* Sandra Trop-Blumberg; *Cur Educ* Barbara Beckos; *Mem Chmn* Letty Murray; *Registrar* Rob Harper; *Assoc Cur Video Arts* Richard Simmons; *Cur Coll* Peg Weiss; *Pres* Mrs Robert N Small; *First VPres* Richard Montmeat; *Second VPres* Mrs John W Chapman; *Secy* Mrs Robert C Hosmer Jr; *Treas* Edward Green.
Open Tues - Sun Noon - 5 PM; Sat 10 AM - 5 PM; cl Mon & major holidays. No admis. Estab and inc 1896. Average Annual Attendance: 300,000. Mem: 2700; dues individual $15 and up, corporate $100 and up; annual meeting May.
Income: $579,350. Purchases: $30,000.
Collections: Contemporary American painting and sculpture; traditional American painting; Cloud Wampler Collection of Oriental art; 17th, 18th & 19th century English porcelain; contemporary American ceramics; African collection.
Exhibitions: A blend of special holdings in a wide range of creative expressions in American art dating from 1792 to 1973; moreover the exhibition is a noteworthy one in the step which it represents in encouraging cooperation on a very basic level between neighboring institutions which share many similar qualities and attitudes.
Activities: Adult studio courses in drawing, printmaking and introduction to art media; children's art classes Sat mornings and weekdays during summer; docents for all exhibitions; annual lecture series; guest lecturers related to exhibitions; traveling education exhibitions to schools; sales gallery featuring work of local professional artists and craftsmen, contemporary posters and graphic works; luncheon restaurant open to public.
Library: Art reference: Holdings: Vols 4000; AV—Slides, video tapes.

SYRACUSE UNIVERSITY

—Joe and Emily Lowe Art Gallery, College Place, 13210. Tel: 315-423-2380. *Dir* Joseph A Scala; *Cur* Jason D Wong; *Secy* Carol S Dana; *Technical Asst* Gary McLoughlin.
Open Tues - Thurs & Sat - Sun Noon - 6 PM; Fri Noon - 9 PM; cl Mon. No admis. Estab 1952 to present art exhibitions to inform University and communities of Central Upstate New York areas of international heritage of art, of new advances in contemporary art with emphasis on the discovery of regional values, outstanding local art including faculty and student work. A professional Museum Training Program complements our exhibition program. 5000 sq ft of space normally divided into separate galleries by movable walls. Average Annual Attendance: 30,000.
Income: Financed through University.
Exhibitions: Images of Women in Japanese Prints; The Mural Art of Ben Shahn; Korean Ceramics; Critics' Choice: a loan exhibition of contemporary paintings from the New York Gallery Season 1976-77; Unity in Diversity: Faculty Art; Record Album Art: The Recording Artist; Master of Fine Arts; Margaret Bourke White: The Deco Lens; The Woman in American Art; Le Corbusier Architectural Drawings; Undergraduate Selected Show.
Publications: Exhibition catalogs, each show.
Activities: Private tours on request; traveling exhibitions organized and circulated.
—Art Collection, Sims Hall. Tel: 315-423-4097. *Dir* Dr Alfred T Collette; *Cur Coll* Domenic J Iacono; *Cur Prints* Maryann Calo; *Senior Clerk* William Boylan.

The Art Collection is housed in a temperature and humidity-controlled area of Sims Hall, adjacent to the Art Gallery. Used primarily for storage and care of the Collection, this facility also includes a teaching-display area to accommodate classes and individuals involved in research.
Collections: Paintings: 20th century American works with an emphasis on the Depression and War years, 19th century European Salon paintings; Prints: surveys the history of print-making and is well represented by American artists; Decorative Arts: Korean, Japanese and American ceramics, pre-Columbian and contemporary Peruvian ceramics, Scandinavian designs in metal, wood and clay; Ruth Reeves Collection of Asian-Indian Folk Art; Andrei Nitecki Collection of West African Tribal Art.

TARRYTOWN

LYNDHURST,* 635 S Broadway, 10591. Tel: 202-638-5200. *Admin & Property Council & staff of National Trust Interpretors* William C Taggert; *Coordr Interpretive Programs* Carole T Scanlon.
Open May 1 - Oct 31 10 AM - 5 PM & legal holidays; Nov 1 - April 30 10 AM - 4 PM; cl Christmas & New Year's. Admis adults $2.25, senior citizens $1.25, group rates by arrangement; free to National Trust members. Average Annual Attendnce: 51,000. A property of the National Trust for Historic Preservation, preserved as a historic house museum operated as a community preservation center. It is a National Historic Landmark. Lyndhurst is a Gothic Revival castle designed in 1838 for General William Paulding by Alexander Jackson Davis, one of America's most influential 19th century architects. Commissioned by second owner, George Merritt, to enlarge the house, Davis in 1865 continued the Gothic Revival style in the additions. It was purchased in 1880 by Jay Gould and willed to his daughter, Helen. Later acquired by another daughter, Anna, Duchess of Talleyrand-Perigord, Lyndhurst was left to the National Trust in 1964. The property is located on spacious grounds along the Hudson River. Visitors are free to explore the magnificent park which is being restored to an 1873 site plan. Other highlights include a carriage house stocked with period vehicles, stables and the remains of what was once one of the world's private greenhouses. Highly important collection of Gothic furniture designed by architect A J Davis in the 1830's and again in the 1870's. Other fine 19th century furnishings and paintings. Windows attributed to L C Tiffany. The preservation of Lyndhurst is a composite of the contributions of the three families who lived in it. Property serves as a focal point for advancement of historic preservation. Through it are developed new relationships among cultural, community, preservation groups and National Trust members in its area. Responds to community preservation needs by acting as a link between community and appropriate regional or headquarters offices of National Trust. Provides interpretive programs which are related to Lyndhurst's particular case study in historic preservation. The National Trust Restoration Workshop, located in a portion of the stable complex, carries out restoration craft services for National Trust properties. Many special programs are produced at Lyndhurst in cooperation with community groups such as outdoor summer concerts, antique and auto shows and Christmas programs. A set of 10 x 8 in measured drawings of Lyndhurst taken by Historic American Buildings Survey is available in Preservation Shop.

SLEEPY HOLLOW RESTORATIONS, INC,* Box 245, 10591. Tel: 914-631-8200. *Pres* Dana S Creel; *Exec Dir* John W Harbour Jr; *Deputy Dir Admin* Saverio Procario.
Open 10 AM - 5 PM; cl Thanksgiving Day, Christmas and New Year's. Admis to Sunnyside, Philipsburg Manor and Van Cortlandt Manor adults $2.25 each property, juniors 6 - 14 $1.50 each property. Three-visit tickets valid one year adults $5.75, juniors $3.75. Groups of 20 or more must make reservations in advance. Average Annual Attendance: 200,000.
Chartered 1951 as a nonprofit educational foundation. Owns and operates historic properties which are Sunnyside in Tarrytown, the home of author Washington Irving; Philipsburg Manor in North Tarrytown, a Dutch-American gristmill-farm site of the early 1700s; Van Cortlandt Manor in Croton-on-Hudson, a manorial estate of the Revolutionary War period.
Collections: 17th, 18th and 19th century decorative arts; memorabilia of Washington Irving and of the Van Cortlandt Family.
Publications: The Van Cortlandts of Croton: York State Patriots; The Loyalist Americans; America's Wooden Age; Life of George Washington; Life Along the Hudson; The Mill at Philipsburg Manor; Rip Van Winkle and The Legend of Sleepy Hollow; Washington Irving's Sunnyside; Philipsburg Manor: A Guidebook; The Knickerbocker Tradition; The Worlds of Washington Irving; Six Presidents from the Empire State; Aspects of Early New York Society and Politics; Washington Irving: A Tribute; The Family Collections at Van Cortlandt Manor; plus prints and documents including Declaration of Independence, Howe Map and A Portfolio of Sleepy Hollow Prints.
Activities: Demonstrations of 17th and 18th century arts and crafts; organized education programs; exhibition of collections; lectures; guided tours.

Library: Specialized reference library with particular emphasis on 17th, 18th and 19th century living in the Hudson River Valley. Films: Lords of the Manor: The Story of Philipsburg; The Mill at Philipsburg Manor.

TICONDEROGA

FORT TICONDEROGA MUSEUM, 12883. Tel: 518-585-2821. *Pres* John H G Pell; *Cur* Jane M Lape; *Genl Mgr* Wayne J Morgan.
Open daily 8 AM - 6 PM. Admis $3. Estab 1909 to preserve and present the Colonial and Revolutionary history of Fort Ticonderoga; the museum is the restored barracks of the Colonial fort. Average Annual Attendance: 200,000.
Income: Financed by state appropriation and admission fee.
Collections: Paintings, manuscripts, artifacts.
Exhibitions: Exhibitions are held in mid-May - mid-Oct.
Publications: Bulletin of the Fort Ticonderoga Museum.
Activities: Classes for adults; individual paintings and original objects of art lent to qualified museums; sales shop selling books, reproductions, slides.
Library. *Librn* Jane M Lape. Open by appointment for reference only. Holdings: Vols 5000.

TROY

INTER-SOCIETY COLOR COUNCIL, c/o Dr Fred W Billmeyer, Jr, Secy, Rensselaer Polytechnic Institute, 12181. Tel: 518-270-6458. *Pres* Franc Grom; *VPres* William D Schaeffer; *Treas* S Leonard Davidson.
For further information see National and Regional Organizations.

RENSSELAER COUNTY HISTORICAL SOCIETY, 59 Second St, 12180. Tel: 518-272-7232. *Pres* Edward D Nicoll; *VPres* George W Singiser; *Secy* Mrs John P Jaffarian; *Dir* Breffny A Walsh; *Cur* Esther Thyssen; *Secy* Sandra Reizen.
Open Tues - Sat 10 AM - 4 PM; Admis donation for adults $1. Estab 1927 to promote historical research and to collect and exhibit materials of all kinds related to the history of the Rensselaer County area including books, papers, fine and decorative arts. An historic house museum with 11 period rooms. Average Annual Attendance: 10,000. Mem: 550; dues $2 - $1000; annual meeting Sept.
Income: Approx $60,000 (financed by endowment, membership).
Collections: Elijah Galusha 19th century furniture; portraits; silver; ceramics; costumes, quilts and coverlets; paintings by local artists including Joseph Hidley, Abel Buel Moore, and C G Beauregard.
Exhibitions: (1976) Troy Stoves; Costumes from the Collection; Santos for Christmas.
Publications: Monthly Newsletter.
Activities: Lect open to public, 8 vis lectr per yr; internships; lending collection contains cassettes, motion pictures, slides; traveling exhibitions organized and circulated; sales shop selling books, prints and gifts.
Library: Decorative arts library and library of local history. Holdings: Vols 1000; Per subs 3; Other—Photographs, lantern slides of local history.

RENSSELAER NEWMAN FOUNDATION CHAPEL AND CULTURAL CENTER, 2125 Burdett Ave, 12180. Tel: 518-272-7793. *Pres* John I Millett; *Secy* Rev Thomas Phelan and Peggy Howe; *Dir* George Garrelts.
Open 8 AM - 11 PM. Estab 1968 to provide religion and culture for members of Rensselaer Polytechnic Institute and Troy area, a broadly ecumenical service; supported by contributions. Gallery. Average Annual Attendance: 100,000.
Income: $110,000.
Collections: Medieval sculpture; contemporary paintings, sculpture and needlework; liturgical vestments and artifacts.
Exhibitions: Laliberté banners; Picasso traveling exhibition; New York State Council on the Arts; Smithsonian Institution Traveling Exhibition; local one-man shows.
Publications: Sun and Balance, 3 times a year.
Activities: Lect open to public, 10 vis lectr per yr; concerts; dramatic programs; classes for adults and children.

RUSSELL SAGE COLLEGE, New Gallery, Schacht Fine Arts Center, 12180. Tel: 518-270-2248. *Gallery Dir* Ruth Healey.
Open Mon - Fri 9 AM - 5 PM; Sun 2 - 5 PM. No admis. Estab 1970 for exhibition of contemporary art for college and public. The gallery is one room; 150 running ft. Average Annual Attendance: 3000.
Income: Financed by the college.
Collections: Paintings (contemporary); drawings (contemporary); sculpture of New Guinea and Africa.
Exhibitions: Paintings, drawings, sculpture from New York City galleries and area artists; faculty and student shows.

Activities: Gallery talks; original objects of art lent on campus; lending collection contains original prints, paintings 100; sculpture.

UTICA

MOHAWK VALLEY MUSEUM, 620 Memorial Parkway, 13501. Tel: 315-724-2075. *Dir* Dr Eino Kivisalu; *Educ Asst* Emily Meyers; *Secy, Receptionist, Bookkeeper* Harriette Tilley.
Open Tues - Sat 10 AM - 5 PM; Sun 12 AM - 5 PM; cl Mon. No admis. Estab 1966 to supplement school curricula in history, natural history and science. A classroom contains mini exhibits where children learn by operating pulleys, hydraulic lift, sand pendulum, bee hive to explore internally. Average Annual Attendance: 30,000. Mem: 570; dues family $8.
Income: $40,000 (financed by membership and state appropriation).
Collections: Major collection of dolls.
Exhibitions: (Permanent) Iroquois Exhibit; History of the Mohawk Valley in Dioramas; Colonial Craftsmen Exhibit.
Publications: Mohawk Valley Museum Newsletter, monthly.
Activities: A state certified educational institution; classroom demonstrations; school tours; museum shop.

MUNSON-WILLIAMS-PROCTOR INSTITUTE, Museum of Art, 310 Genesee St, 13502. Tel: 315-797-0000. *Pres* Paul J Farinella; *Dir* Edward H Dwight; *Asst to Dir* Joseph S Trovato; *Cur Decorative Arts* Carol Gordon.
Open Tues - Sat 10 AM - 5 PM; Sun 1 - 5 PM; cl Mon. No admis. Estab 1919 through an endowment, granted a provisional charter by The Board of Regents of the University of the State of New York, changed to an absolute charter in 1941, and amended in 1948 to empower the Institute to provide instruction at the college level in the field of fine arts. The Institute became active in 1935 with the purpose of establishing and maintaining a gallery and collection of art; to give instruction; and to have an auxiliary library. It consists of a School of Art estab 1941; a Museum of Art opened in 1960; Fountain Elms, a house-museum restored in 1960; a Meetinghouse opened in 1963. Average Annual Attendance: 200,000. Mem: 4,500; dues $7.50.
Income: FInanced by endowment and private contributions.
Collections: †18th, 19th and 20th century American paintings, sculpture, and decorative arts; Greek, Persian and pre-Columbian art; †arts of Central New York; †contemporary European paintings and sculpture; †drawings and prints; †Archives of Central New York architecture.
Exhibitions: Made in Utica; American Textiles; Willard Leroy Metcalf; The Last Empire: Victorian Photographs of India; Drawings and Prints by David Itchkawich; Seven Artists and Craftsmen of Central New York; Henry Moore: Prints, 1969-1974; Far Eastern Art in Upstate New York; The Figure in 20th Century American Art; Sculpture Space; Utica Art Festival.
Publications: Bulletin, monthly.
Activities: Educ dept; docent training; lect open to public, 5 vis lectr per yr; concerts; tours; competitions; sales shop selling books, original art, reproductions, prints, slides.
—**Library.** Art reference library. *Librn* Florence Herbst.
Open to members and the public.
Holdings: Vols 12,500; Per subs 50; Other—Exhibition catalogs, slides, pamphlets.

WATERTOWN

ROSWELL P FLOWER MEMORIAL LIBRARY, 229 Washington St, 13601. Tel: 315-788-2352. *Dir* Anthony F Cozzie.
Open (Sept - June) Mon - Fri 8:30 AM - 8:30 PM; Sat 9 AM - 5 PM; (July & Aug) Mon - Thurs 8:30 AM - 5:30 PM; Fri 8:30 AM - 8:30 PM; cl Sat. Estab 1904. Circ: 168,221. The art gallery contains murals, paintings and sculptures scattered throughout the building.
Income: $336,452 (financed by city appropriation). Purchases: $1400.
Holdings: Vols 83,000; Per subs 211; AV—Microfiche, microfilm, motion pictures, phonorecords; Other—Framed reproductions.
Special Subjects: Many of the murals and paintings are of local history or local interest.
Special Collections: New York State material and genealogy.
Exhibitions: Local Artists Guild; North Country Artist Guild.
Publications: Focus, every other month.
Activities: Lectures open to public; concerts; library tours.

WEST POINT

UNITED STATES MILITARY ACADEMY, West Point Museum, 10996. Tel: 914-938-2203. *Dir Museum* Richard E Kuehne; *Cur Arms & Armor* Robert W Fisch; *Cur Design* Ray W Moniz; *Cur History:* Michael J McAfee; *Cur Art* Michael E Moss; *Museum Specialist* Walter J Nock.

Open 10:30 AM - 4:15 PM. No admis. Estab 1854, supplementing the academic, cultural and military instruction of cadets; collections open to the public. Average Annual Attendance: Approx 370,000.
Income: Approx $100,000. Purchases: Approx $5000.
Collections: Sully portrait collection; Rindisbacher watercolors; †military paintings and prints; †military artifacts including weapons, flags, uniforms, medals, etc; paintings and prints of West Point.
Exhibitions: (1976) Retrospective Exhibition of Robert W Weir; Robert Weir: Artist and Teacher of West Point and Robert W Weir of West Point: Illustrator, Teacher and Poet; (1977) Japanese Samurai Swords from the David E J Pepin Collection; (1977) Rudy Wedow: Illustrator at War: 43 Drawings by a World War II Combat Artist.
Publications: West Point Museum Bulletin, quarterly.
Library: Small reference library of military subjects; photograph collection of 2500 items for lending or reference.

WESTFIELD

PATTERSON LIBRARY, 40 S Portage St, 14787. Tel: 716-326-2154. *Pres* Cecily Moot Johnson; *Library Dir* Charles Thompson; *Art Dir* Joseph Koshute; *Arts Coordinator* Ann Rogers.
Open Mon - Sat 9:30 AM - 5 PM; Mon, Wed & Thurs Eve 7 - 9 PM. Estab 1896 to provide opportunity for education and recreation through the use of literature, music, films, paintings and other art forms; Octagon Gallery has 1115 sq ft with 11 ft ceilings while Members Gallery is 70 ft long with 8 ft high display wall of burlap-covered plywood. Cir: 100,000.
Income: $80,000 (financed by endowment, city and state appropriation). Purchases $12,500.
Holdings: Vols 30,000; Per subs 160; AV—Audio tapes, cassettes, film strips, motion pictures, phonorecords, slides; Other—Framed reproductions, memorabilia, original art works, pamphlets, photographs, sculpture.
Special Subjects: 300 species of seashells; 100 specimens of mounted birds; 50 WW I posters; 5000 glass plate negatives of local history.
Exhibitions: Traveling exhibits; paintings, sculpture and photography from western New York, Ohio, and Pennsylvania artists.
Activities: Classes for adults and children; lect open to the public; concerts; gallery talks; tours; traveling exhibitions organized and circulated.

WHITE PLAINS

HUDSON VALLEY ART ASSOCIATION, c/o Rayma M Spaulding, *Pres,* 15 Minivale Rd, Stamford, CT, 06907. Tel: 914-478-1097. *Treas* Perry Alley; *Secy* Joan Rudman.
Estab 1928, inc 1933, to perpetuate the artistic traditions of American artists such as made famous the Hudson River School of Painting through exhibitions of painting and sculpture with public support. Mem: 300; membership by invitation; dues $10, special exhibits extra; annual meeting May.
Exhibitions: Annual juried exhibition each May, open to all artists of the US who work in realistic tradition, to compete for money awards and gold medals of honor; other exhibits from time to time.
Activities: Free demonstrations; exhibitions; lectures.

YONKERS

HUDSON RIVER MUSEUM, 511 Warburton Ave, Trevor Park-on-Hudson, 10701. Tel: 914-963-4550. *Dir* Richard Koshalek; *Adminr* Reed Manville; *Cur Exhib* Catherine Conn; *Cur duc* Richard Carlson; *Develop Dir* Julie Lazar; *Pub Info Dir* Jane Cohn; *Registr* Judy Matson.
Open Wed - Sat 10 AM - 5 PM; Sun 1 - 5 PM. No admis. Estab 1924 as a general museum of art, history and science. Victorian Mansion, Glenview, 300 seat auditorium. Average Annual Attendance: 150,000. Mem: 1600; dues vary.
Income: Financed by membership, city and state appropriations, corporations, foundations.
Collections: Contemporary art and architecture; 19th century American painting, sculpture, decorative arts and photography.
Exhibitions: American Art for 10e Biennale de Paris, Warburton Ave; The Architecture of a Neighborhood, John Mason; Recent Work, Lee Friedlander; Selected Photographs, Ronald Bladen; Outdoor Sculpture Proposals, The Gilded Age in Westchester, Eastlake Influenced American Furniture.
Publications: Bimonthly calendar of events; occasional exhibition catalogs.
Activities: Classes for adults and children; docent training; lectures open to public; competitions; exten dept serving Westchester County; artmobile; art lent to other museums for exhibition purposes; lending collection contains original art works, paintings, photographs, sculpture; traveling exhibitions organized and circulated; museum shop selling books, inexpensive items for children.
Library: For staff use only. Holdings: Vols 3000.

PHILIPSE MANOR HALL STATE HISTORIC SITE, 29 Warburton Ave (Mailing Add: PO Box 496, 10702). Tel: 914-965-4027. *Historic Site Mgr* Mary Dougal; *Historic Site Asst* Tracy Van Riper.
Open Wed - Sun 9 AM - 5 PM. No admis. Estab 1908 to preserve Georgian manor house owned by the Frederick Philipse family-to interpret Philipse Manor Hall's architecture, significance as the home of an American Loyalist and its importance as a example of 17th and 18th Century Anglo-Dutch patterns in landholding and development; the State Historic Site is part of the New York State Office of Parks and Recreation; the Hall houses contemporary style exhibits of history, art and architecture hung against a backdrop of fine 18th and 19th Century architectural carvings.
Income: Financed by state appropriation.
Collections: Cochran Portrait Collection of Famous Americans.
Activities: Classes for children; lect open to the public, 3 vis lectr per yr; concerts, tours, demonstrations; films.

YONKERS PUBLIC LIBRARY, Fine Arts Dept, 1500 Central Park Ave, 10710. Tel: 914-337-1500, exten 21. *Librn III & Head Dept* Marta Schwarz; *Librn II* Alan Beggs; *Librn I* Beverly Katopis.
Open Mon, Wed & Fri 9 AM - 9 PM; Tues, Thurs & Sat 9 AM - 5 PM. Estab 1962 to serve the general public with a special interest in the arts, especially the decorative and applied arts, the fine arts and the performing arts. Circ: Printed material approx 23,000; recorded material approx 49,000.
Income: $20,500. (financed by city appropriation). Purchases: $34,000.
Holdings: Vols 11,702; Per 48; AV—Cassettes, phonorecords, slides; Other—Clipping files, pamphlets.
Special Collections: William Wood Struthers Collection of historical recordings some 2000 78RPM records most of which were pressed between 1903 and 1925; cassette copies of this collection are available to the public; Lennox Collection of classical music.
—Will Library.
Exhibitions: Exhibits work by local artists and craftsmen.

NORTH CAROLINA

ASHEVILLE

ASHEVILLE ART MUSEUM, Civic Center Complex, Haywood St, 28801. Tel: 704-253-3227. *Dir* Mary Alice Young; *Asst Dir & Exhib Cur* George Harrison; *Admin Asst* Lynda Nichols; *Educations Cur* Sara Sagar; *Registrar* Mrs David Marder.
Open Tues - Fri 10 AM - 5 PM; Sat & Sun 1 - 5 PM, cl Mon. No admis. Estab 1948 to provide educational services to the western North Carolina area through exhibitions, three galleries with movable walls. Average Annual Attendance: 45,000. Mem: 1000; dues family $20; annual meeting in July.
Income: Financed by endowment, membership, city appropriation, State Arts Council and auxiliary.
Collections: †Traditional and contemporary crafts and works indigenous to the area; Pisgah pottery and Oriental art on loan.
Exhibitions: (1976-1978) Selections from the North Carolina Museum of Art; Southern Highland Handicraft Guild; Cherokee Sculpture; Black Mountain College Retrospective; American Paintings, Arts and Crafts Festival; Southern Association of Sculptors; Area college and university facilities; Letts Treasurers (dolls); Original Oriental Art; The Mineral World: A Blow-Up (photography). Norman-Schulman—Ceramics, Landscapes from Contemporary Swiss Artists; Watercolor Society of North Carolina; Nancy Witt—Contemporary Paintings.
Publications: Asherville Art Museum Newsletter, every 6-8 weeks.
Activities: Classes for adults and children; docent training; lect open to the public, 8-10 vis lectr per yr; competitions; individual paintings and original objects of art lent to other art or nonprofit organizations; museum and sales shop selling magazines, original art, reproductions; cards, jewelry, craft items.

PACK MEMORIAL PUBLIC LIBRARY,* Haywood St, 28801. Tel: 704-252-8701. *Dir* Kenneth Brown; *Community Activities Dir* John Bridges.
Open Mon - Fri 9 AM - 9 PM; Sat 9 AM - 6 PM; cl Sun. No admis. Estab 1879. Exhibition Room shows monthly topical displays of general interest and literary exhibitions assembled from the library's holdings. Average Annual Attendance: (Main Library Program) 7000.
Circulating collection of 16mm sound films and LP records; circulating and reference collection of general books on art. Monthly presentations of outstanding films Oct through Apr sponsored by Friends of the Library. Weekly films during summer. Series of popular art lectures in fall. Some recitals on Sunday afternoons jointly sponsored by library and Friends of the Library.

SOUTHERN HIGHLAND HANDICRAFT GUILD, 15 Reddick Rd (Mailing Add: PO Box 9545, 28805). Tel: 704-298-7928. *Pres* Gerald Edmundson; *VPres* Sandra Blain; *Secy* Carol R Smith; *Dir* Robert W Gray; *Asst Dir/Educ* James Gentry.
Open Mon - Fri 9 AM - 5 PM; No admis. Estab 1930 to encourage wider appreciation of mountain crafts; raise and maintain standards of design and craftsmanship, and encourage individual expression. Mem: 621; qualifications for mem: Depends on approval of applicant's work by Standards Committee and Bd of Trustees, and is open to eligible craftsmen from the Southern Appalachian Mt Region; dues single $6, group $20; annual meeting April.
Income: Financed by membership and merchandising.
Publications: Highland Highlights, newsletter, monthly.
Activities: Craft wokshops, seminars, library of books, slides and movies; lect; schol; traveling exhibitions organized and circulated; sales shop selling handcrafts.

BELHAVEN

FANNIE MEBANE RALPH LIBRARY AND GALLERY,* 27810. Tel: 919-943-2993. *Pres* Mrs J W Lloyd; *Secy* Miss Loyce Brinson; *Art Dir* Mrs W E Bateman, Jr.
Open Mon, Wed & Fri 2 - 5 PM. No admis. Estab 1914, permanent building 1952, to serve the public and to furnish material for research and to enrich the cultural life of the community with exhibitions of art. Quarterly meetings; dues.
Collections: †Old Master prints; Metropolitan miniatures; James Walker serigraphs; Ethel Parrot Hughes tempera; Effie Raye Bateman portraits, woodcuts, seascapes and abstracts. There are lent for exhibitions on request.
Activities: Special lecture tours for local school groups; paintings and art objects lent to schools; exhibitions of noncompetitive shows (philanthropic project of Effie Raye Bateman in conjunction with Library Association); library for reference and lending.

CHAPEL HILL

SOUTHEASTERN COLLEGE ART CONFERENCE, Box 1022, 27514. Tel: 919-933-6981. *Pres* Virginia Rembert; *VPres* Martha B Caldwell; *Secy* Anne W Thomas; *Staff Asst* Marion Kay Smith.
For further information see National and Regional Organizations.

UNIVERSITY OF NORTH CAROLINA AT CHAPEL HILL
—William Hayes Ackland Memorial Art Center, Columbia & Franklin Sts, 27514. Tel: 919-933-3039. *Dir* Joseph C Sloane; *Asst Dir* Innis H Shoemaker; *Cur* John M Wisdon.
Open Tues - Sat 10 AM - 5 PM; Sun 2 - 6 PM, cl Mon and one week in Aug. No admis. Estab 1958 as an art museum which serves the members of the university community as well as the public; the museum houses a permanent collection in two galleries and foyer, a period room, a prints and drawings gallery, and an exhibition gallery. Average Annual Attendance 40,000. Mem: 225; dues $25.
Income: $400,000 (financed by endowment, membership, and state appropriation). Purchases: $150,000.
Collections: †Collection of paintings, sculpture, prints and drawings covering the history of primarily Western art from ancient Egypt to the present day; decorative arts.
Exhibitions: The American Situation (photography); (1976) Small Sculptures in Bronze from the Classical World; (1977) Contemporary Ceramic Sculpture; 7th National Student Printmakers Exhibition.
Publications: Newsletter, fall and spring.
Activities: Docent training; lect open to the public; gallery talks; tours; competitions; individual paintings and original objects of art lent to temporary exhibitions at approved borrowing institutions; traveling exhibitions organized and circulated; books and catalogs available for sale.
—Art Library. Tel: 919-933-3039. *Art Librn* Philip Rees; *Library Asst* Michele Patterson.
Open Mon - Thurs 8 AM - 11 PM; Fri 8 AM - 5 PM; Sat 8:30 AM - 5 PM; Sun 2 - 11 PM.
Income: Financed by state appropriation. Purchases: $31,000.
Holdings: Vols 35,000; Per subs 185; AV—Microfiche, microfilm; Other—Pamphlets.

CHARLOTTE

CHARLOTTE NATURE MUSEUM,* 1658 Sterling Rd, 28209. Tel: 704-333-0506. *Dir* Russell I Peithman; *Cur Exhib* Navar Elliot; *Cur Educ* John Karn.
Open Mon - Sat 9 AM - 5 PM; Sun 2 - 5 PM; cl holidays. No admis. Inc 1947 to develop an appreciation of man and nature. Average Annual Attendance: 405,000. Mem: 1000; dues $10 - $500; annual meeting May.
Income: $228,000. Purchases: $4000.

Collections: †Primitive Art—Oceania, South America, Alaskan Eskimo, Africa; †Pre-Columbian—Mayan, Peruvian, North America.
Activities: Art workshops in nature sketching and museum methods; lectures on African kingdoms, ancient civilizations.
Library: Nature and Anthropology.

MINT MUSEUM OF ART, 501 Hempstead Pl (Mailing Add: PO Box 6011, 28207). Tel: 704-334-9723. *Dir* Milton J Bloch; *Cur of Exhib* Jerald Melberg; *Cur of Coll* Steven Musgrove.
Open Tues - Fri 10 AM - 5 PM; Sat & Sun 2 - 5 PM. No admis. Estab 1936 as an art museum in what was the first branch of the US mint erected in 1837; museum houses three changing galleries, a permanent gallery, Delhom Decorative Arts gallery, two Charlotte Gold rooms, and a sales and rental gallery. Average Annual Attendance: 150,000. Mem: 1850; annual meeting Jan.
Income: Financed by endowment, membership, and city appropriation.
Collections: Largest public collection of art in the region. Changing contemporary and historical exhibitions with over 5000 pieces including paintings, sculpture and decorative arts with emphasis on Renaissance, Baroque, 18th Century English, 19th and 20th Century European and American paintings, and pre-Columbian art.
Publications: Mint Museum newsletter and calendar of events, six times a yr.
Activities: Classes for adults; docent training; lect open to the public, 25 vis lectr per yr; concerts; gallery talks; tours; competitions; original objects of art lent to other museums; museum shop selling books, original art, prints, gifts, museum replicas, jewelry, cards.
Library. *Librn* Sara Wolf. Open to members for reference only. Holdings: Vols 5000.

PUBLIC LIBRARY OF CHARLOTTE AND MECKLENBURG COUNTY, 310 N Tryon St, 28202. Tel: 704-374-2725. *Dir* Arial A Stephens; *Assoc Dir* Judith Sutton; *Art Librn* Carolyn Hunter.
Open Mon - Fri 9 AM - 9 PM; Sat 9 AM - 6 PM; Sun 2 - 6 PM; cl Sun June - August. Estab 1903 to provide free public library service to citizens of Mecklenburg County; gallery contains 90 linear feet of wall space.
Income: $2,320,061 (financed by state and county appropriation). Purchases: $377,733.
Holdings: Vols 655,231; AV—Cassettes, film strips 308, phonorecords 16,018, motion pictures 1137 (16mm), slides 9261; Other—Prints 262, sculpture, maps 6507.
Exhibitions: Local artists exhibit for one month.
Activities: Individual paintings lent to residents.

DALLAS

GASTON COUNTY ART AND HISTORY MUSEUM, 131 N Gaston St (Mailing Add: PO Box 429, 28304). Tel: 704-922-8361. *Pres* Lucy Penegar; *VPres* Alan Stout; *Treas* Robert Ragan; *Secy* Kathryn Royster; *Dir* Alan D Waufle; *Cur of Education* Melissa Jones; *Chief Art Instructor* Larry Young.
Open Tues - Fri 10 AM - 5 PM; Sat 10 AM - 2 PM; Sun 2 - 5 PM. No admis. Estab November 1975, opened July 1976 to promote the fine arts and local history in Gaston County, through classes, workshops and exhibitions; to preserve Historic Dallas Square; and promote the history of the textile industry; the museum is located in 1848 Greek Revival Courthouse; the Hands on Gallery includes sculpture and weavings which may be touched; the two small galleries are on local history, with the major gallery for changing and traveling exhibitions. Average Annual Attendance: 10,000. Mem: 400; dues $10 - $35; annual meeting November, with monthly meetings the first Thurs in Feb, May, August, and Nov.
Income: $35,000 (financed by membership and county appropriation). Purchases: $2,000.
Collections: †Contemporary sculpture; †paintings by NCarolina artists living and dead; †textile history; †documents, photographs, and objects of local history.
Exhibitions: (1976-78) Toys of Switzerland; 19th Century Transportation; NCarolina artists; Carroll Saunders; McConnell Collection; Hobson Pittman (watercolors); Annual Crafts Show; Annual Spring Art Show; Victorian Needlework; Quilts and Coverlets of Gaston County; Barbara Harmeyer and Larry Merenstein; Annual County High School Art Exhibit.
Publications: Museum Newsletter, quarterly.
Activities: Classes for adults and children; docent training; puppet performances; lect open to the public, 4 vis lectr per yr; competitions; traveling exhibitions organized and circulated; museum shop selling books, slides, stationery, jewelry, maps, decorative art objects.
Library: Tel: 704-922-8361. Open to the public for reference only. Holdings: Vols 50, Per subs 10.

DAVIDSON

DAVIDSON COLLEGE ART GALLERY, Box 2495, 28036. Tel: 704-892-2000. *Dir* Herb Jackson.
Open Mon - Fri 10 AM - 5 PM; Sat & Sun 2 - 5 PM. No admis. Estab 1952 to provide exhibitions of educational importance; gallery covers 4000 sq ft. Average Annual Attendance: 6000.
Income: Financed by college budget.
Collections: Primary emphasis in graphics.
Activities: Lect open to the public, 6 vis lectr per yr; gallery talks.
Library: *Librn* Dr Leland Park. Open to students and visitors.

DURHAM

DUKE UNIVERSITY MUSEUM OF ART, 6877 College Station, 27708. Tel: 919-684-5135. *Dir* W K Stars; *Staff Asst* Judith S Markwordt; *Cur Pre-Columbian Coll* Paul A Clifford; *Cur Classical Coll* Dr. Keith Stanley; *Hon Cur Medieval Coll* Dr Elizabeth Sunderland.
Open Mon - Fri 9 AM - 5 PM; Sat 10 AM - 1 PM; Sun 2 - 5 PM. No admis. Estab 1969 as a study museum with the collections being used and studied by various university depts, as well as the public school system and surrounding communities; the museum is located on the East Campus in a renovated two-story Georgian building; gallery space includes part of the first floor and entire second floor with the space divided into eight major gallery areas. Average Annual Attendance: 8000-10,000.
Income: Financed by University.
Collections: Medieval sculpture and decorative art; Oriental jade and porcelain: †Pre-Columbian; African; Classical; textiles (Peruvian, Navajo); paintings; graphics.
Publications: Exhibition catalogs, 1-2 per yr; Friends of the Museum Newsletter, quarterly.
Activities: Dramatic programs; lect open to the public, 2-4 lectr per yr; gallery talks; tours; individual paintings and original objects of art lent to other museums which are equipped with proper security and insurance.
—**Union Graphic Arts Committee,*** Box KM, Duke Station, 27706. Tel: 919-684-2911. *Pres* Tina I Finkel.
Open 8:30 AM - Noon. No admis. Estab to bring to the university community exhibits of every type of graphic arts, to bring artists to campus for workshops. Galleries, large room in Union and wall and shelf space in Booklovers Room in East Campus Library. Mem: 15; monthly meetings.
Income: Financed by endowment and 10% commission on exhibit works sold.
Exhibitions: Professional and local artists, approx twice monthly.
Activities: Classses for adults; lect open to the public, 1 vis lectr per yr; competitions.

NORTH CAROLINA CENTRAL UNIVERSITY, Museum of Art, Fayetteville St, 27707. Tel: 919-683-6211. *Dir* Norman E Pendergraft; *Secy-Registrar* Brenda Gray; *Guard-Preparator* Betty Jean Brown.
Open Tues - Fri 9 AM - 4 PM; Sun 2 - 4 PM. No admis. Estab 1971 as a predominantly black teaching institution with a collection of contemporary art, many Afro-American reflecting diversity in style, technique, medium and subject; three galleries on housing the permanent Collection, and two for changing shows. Average Annual Attendance: 4000.
Income: Financed by state appropriation. Purchases: $174,359 from private donations and grants.
Collections: African and Oceanic; †Contemporary American with a focus on minority artists; †Contemporary, non-American.
Exhibitions: (1976-1977) NCCU Artists: The Past 50 Years; Tools of the Print Maker and Selections from NCCU Collection of Prints; Recent Acquisitions; Reginald Gammon, Painter and Robert Kennedy, Sculptor; Heralds of Life: Artis, Bearden and Burke.
Publications: Exhibition catalog.
Activities: Lectr open to the public; gallery talks; tours.

GREENSBORO

GREEN HILL ART GALLERY, 712 Summit Ave, 27405. Tel: 919-273-6696. *Pres Bd Dir* Mrs Edward N Booker; *VPres* Mrs Edwin D Seagraves; *Secy* Mrs Charles D Walters; *Treas* John R Beaman Jr; *Dir* Hope S Beaman.
Open Mon - Fri 9 AM - 5 PM; cl Sat, Sun & holidays. No admis. Estab and inc 1974 as a non-profit institution offering a variety of visual arts programs to serve the public, artists, and educational organizations of North Carolina. Dues from student $5 to Patron $100 up.
Income: Financed by membership, United Arts Council of Greensboro, state appropriation, and NEA.
Exhibitions: State-wide juried exhibitions; over 30 monthly exhibits of North Carolina artists—Horace Farlow, Joe Cox, Herb Jackson, Noyes Capehart, Mary Todd Shaw, Ann Kessler Shields, Charles Joyner, Nona Short.

Activities: Information service; artists' registry; group tours; lecture series; docent training; competition with cash and purchase awards.

UNIVERSITY OF NORTH CAROLINA AT GREENSBORO, Weatherspoon Art Gallery, Walker Ave at McIver St, 27412. Tel: 919-379-5770. *Cur* James E Tucker; *Dir* Gilbert F Carpenter; *Secy* Gretchen Williams.
Open Tues - Fri 10 AM - 5 PM; Sat & Sun 2 - 6 PM; cl Mon, University holiday periods, and between academic sessions. No admis. Estab 1942 as a teaching arm of the University department of art; the gallery houses modern art for the Greensboro and Piedmont area; the main gallery is large and can exhibit large shows, or several small shows at once; the outer lobby gallery is used mainly for student shows; a sculpture court contains permanently-installed modern sculptures. Average Annual Attendance: No records kept. Mem: 500; dues $5 up; annual meeting April or May.
Income: $9200 (financed by university budget). Purchases: $60,000.
Collections: 20th Century American and European paintings, sculpture, drawings, and prints; smaller collection of Oriental scrolls, prints, snuff bottles.
Exhibitions: (1976) Jack Moebes-Photography; William Christenberry-Photography; Susanne Suba-Illustrations for Children's Books; Post-WW II Figurative Styles in American Art; Art from the Comics; Morton D May Gifts to the Permanent Collection; Art on Paper 1976; (1977) A M Sachs Gallery Artists; MFA Thesis Exhibition; Robert B Mayer Memorial Loan; Walter Barker—Small Works from the Years 1947-1977; Selected Recent Acquisitions; Scholastic Art Awards: Gold Key Winners; Painterly Representation; Drawings by Isabel Bishop; Matisse Graphics and Bronzes from the Cone Collection; Spring Loan Exhibition; Prints in the Permanent Collection; West African Strip-weaving; The Art of Islamic Women; Contemporary Printmakers of the Americas; Mark David Gottsegen-Landscape Paintings; Virginia Budny-Small Sculptures; The Five Winston-Salem Printmakers; Selections from the Permanent Collection; Von Stephen Eisenhardt-Recent Paintings and Drawings; Small Sculpture; Judaic Ceremonial Art; Art on Paper 1977; (1978) Yearning to Breathe Free; Immigrants in Search of the American Dream; MFA Thesis Exhibition; The Architecture of North Carolina; Selections from the Permanent Collection; Marianne Gurley-Recent Works; Howard Pyle Drawings; Bernard Chaet-Paintings; Scholastic Art Awards; Balcomb Greene Retrospective Exhibition; Silent Auction; Robert B Mayer Memorial Loan; Spring Loan Exhibition; UNC-G Art Faculty Exhibition; Annual Student Exhibition.
Publications: Weatherspoon Gallery Assoc Bulletin, annually.
Activities: Lect open to the public, 6-8 vis lectr per yr; gallery talks; tours; individual paintings and original objects of art lent to other museums, and local corporate and individual benefactors contributing $1000 or more per yr; lending collection consists of original art works, original prints, paintings, photographs, sculpture and videotapes; traveling exhibitions organized and circulated; postcard reproductions sold at reception desk.

GREENVILLE

EAST CAROLINA UNIVERSITY, Wellington B Gray Gallery, School of Art, 27834. Tel: 919-757-6665. *Acting Dean* Tran Gordley; *Gallery Dir* Aaron Karp.
Open Mon - Fri 9 AM - 5 PM. No admis. Estab 1977 as a teaching gallery offering students visual experiences on campus; the gallery is a large, modern facility. Average Annual Attendance: New, no figures.
Income: Financed by state appropriation.
Collections: Contemporary American art.
Exhibitions: Crafts Exhibition; Samia Halby, (drawings); Graduate Thesis Exhibition; Faculty Exhibition; Annual Student Show; Permanent Collection includes Norma Gray gift.
Activities: Educ Dept.

GREENVILLE ART CENTER,* 802 S Evans St, 27834. Tel: 919-758-1946. *Dir* Edith G Bradley Walker.
Open Sept - June Mon - Sat 9 AM - 5 PM. Estab 1939, inc 1960 to foster public interest in art and to form a permanent collection. Sponsored by East Carolina Art Society. Average Annual Attendance: 19,000. Mem: 600; dues $10 and higher; annual meeting Feb.
Income: $12,000 for operation, plus Foundation income for acquisition of art.
Collections: †Sculpture, crafts, †graphics; †contemporary paintings; watercolors.
Exhibitions: Changing exhibitions from national traveling exhibition sources; exhibitions of local artists' work.
Publications: Newsletter, monthly.
Activities: Lectures, demonstrations; art classes for adults and children; musicals, poetry readings; lending collection of photographs.
Library: Holdings—(Art) Vols 200; Per subs 150.

HICKORY

HICKORY MUSEUM OF ART, INC, Third St & First Ave, NW (Mailing Add: PO Box 2572, 28601). Tel: 704-327-8576. *Pres* Boyd L George; *VPres* Henry Absher; *Secy* Virginia Slack; *Treas* Neill W Clark; *Dir* Mildred M Coe; *Asst to Dir* Thelma M Abee.
Open Mon - Fri 10 AM - 5 PM; Sun 3 - 5 PM. No admis. Estab 1944 to collect and foster American art and serves the western Piedmont area as an exhibiting and training art center; one large gallery is used mainly for traveling exhibitions; eight small galleries are used for permanent collections. Average Annual Attendance: 10,000. Mem: 600; dues $10-$150 by donations; meetings second Tues of each quarter.
Income: $20,000 (financed by membership and donations).
Collections: Very fine collection of 19th and 20th century American paintings; small European collection; †American paintings.
Exhibitions: Twelve National, Regional and Local Exhibitions per yr.
Activities: Classes for adults and children; docent training; periodic art classes; lect open to public and Museum Guild for members only; gallery talks; tours; competitions; exten dept; individual paintings lent to museums only.

LAKE JUNALUSKA

UNITED METHODIST CHURCH COMMISSION ON ARCHIVES AND HISTORY, 49 Lakeshore Dr (Mailing Add: Box 488, 28745). Tel: 704-456-9433. *Exec Secy* Dr John H Ness, Jr; *Admin Asst* Louis Queen.
Open Mon - Fri 9 AM - 5 PM; summer Sat 8:30 AM - 4:30 PM; Sun 1 - 5 PM; cl holidays; Sept - May cl. Sat & Sun. No admis. Estab 1885 as a religious history museum.
Collections: John Wesley busts; paintings of church leaders and historic buildings; religious church materials.
Publications: Methodist History, quarterly; Historian's Digest, bimonthly.
Activities: Guided tours in summer; sales shop selling books, plates, cards, slides and prints.
Library: Holdings—Vols 40,000.

NEW BERN

TRYON PALACE RESTORATION COMPLEX, 613 Pollock St, 28560. Tel: 919-638-5109. *Dir* Donald R Taylor; *Chmn* Mrs John A Kellenberger; *Cur Educ* Dabney M Coddington; *Educ Specialist* Julia B Claypool; *Registrar* Mrs Robert A Ipock; *Maintenance* James A Thomas; *Horticulturist* W H Rea.
Open Tues - Sat 9:30 AM - 4 PM; Sun 1:30 - 4 PM; cl Mon. Admis adults $2, children $1. Estab 1959, historic house museums (Tryon Palace, Stevenson House, John Wright Stanley House) with fine portraits, paintings, Federal and Empire antiques, furnishings, silver, porcelain and objet d'art. Average Annual Attendance: 47,500. Meetings Apr & Oct.
Collections (art): Paintings by Richard Wilson, Thomas Gainsborough, Claude Lorrain, School of Sir Godfrey Kneller, E Van Stuven, Matthew William Peters, Charles Phillips, Richard Paton, David Martin, Jan Siberechts, Alan Ramsay, Nathaniel Dance; graphics.
Publications: Seven books, many leaflets.
Activities: Audio-visual orientation program; annual symposium on 18th century decorative arts; lect open to public; lending collection contains slides; Mirror of the Past, 28-minute color and sound film; tours; museum shop.
Library: Open for use with permission. Holdings: Vols 3000; Other—Photographs.

RALEIGH

NORTH CAROLINA ART SOCIETY,* 107 E Morgan St, 27601. *Pres* Mrs Isaac V Manly; *VPres* Mrs Charles M Reeves; *Secy-Treas* Charles Lee Smith; *Exec Secy* Mrs Christopher R Webster.
Estab 1927 to formulate programs to promote public appreciation of visual art, to encourage talent, to disseminate information on art through publications, to encourage private acquisition of works of art and to support the State Art Museum's programs by membership. Mem: 3000; dues $5 (student) and higher; annual meeting Dec.
Income: $25,000; art purchases (Phifer Fund) - $3000 NC Artists' Exhibition; $50,000 (Phifer Fund) annually for work of art for State Art Museum.
The Art Society's collection has been given to the North Carolina Museum of Art and all purchases are given either to that or other art centers .n the state.
Exhibitions: Annual North Carolina Artists' Exhibition held at North Carolina Museum of Art, financed, including medal awards and purchases, by the Art Society.

NORTH CAROLINA MUSEUM OF ART, Department of Cultural Resources, State of North Carolina, 107 E Morgan St, 27611. Tel: 919-733-7568. *Dir* Moussa M Domit; *Educ Services* Michael W Brantley; *Coll Care & Preparation* Benjamin F Williams; *Coll Research & Publ* Gay M Hertzman; *Prog Research & Coordination* Dorothy B Rennie.
Open Tues - Sat 10 AM - 5 PM; Sun 2 - 6 PM; cl Mon & holidays. No admis. Estab 1947, open to public 1956, to acquire, preserve, and exhibit works of art for the education and enjoyment of the people of the State, and to conduct programs of education, research, and publications designed to encourage interest in, and an appreciation of art, on the part of the people. Average Annual Attendance: 90,000.
Income: Financed by state appropriation.
Collections: European and American painting, sculpture, and decorative arts; ancient art; Pre-Columbian. African and North American Indian art; Samuel H Kress Collection; Mary Duke Biddle Gallery for the Blind.
Exhibitions: Original Bireline: A Retrospective of the Work of George Bireline; 200 Years of the Visual Arts in North Carolina; Audubon's Birds of America; Correspondence, An Exhibition of the Letters of Ray Johnson; Annual Artists Exhibition; John J McCurdy: A Memorial Exhibition; A Survey of Zairean Art.
Publications: Bulletin, irregular; Calendar, monthly.
Activities: Classes for children; docent training; lect open to public, 10 vis lectr per yr; concerts; gallery talks; tours; competitions; exten dept serving North Carolina; individual paintings and original object of art lent to museums; traveling exhibitions organized and circulated; museum shop selling books.
—**Library.** *Librn* Dr Anna Dvorak.
Open to the public for reference.
Holdings—Vols 13,000; Per subs 46; Other—Photographs 18,900, slides 13,700, transparencies 1370.

NORTH CAROLINA STATE UNIVERSITY, Harrye Lyons Design Library, 209 Brooks Hall, 27650. *Librn* Maryellen LoPresti; *Asst Librn* Margaret R Barile; *Asst Librn* Gloria W Close; *Asst Librn* Lynn P Crisp.
Open Mon - Thurs 8:30 AM - 9:30 PM; Fri 8:30 AM - 5 PM; Sat 9 AM - 1 PM; Sun 1 - 5 PM. Estab 1946 to serve the reading, study, reference and research needs of the faculty, students and staff of the School of Design and the University campus, as well as off-campus borrowers. Circ: 42,366.
Income: Financed by membership, city appropriation, and private funds. Purchases $16,000.
Holdings: Vols 18,384; AV—Cassettes, film strips, microfiche, microfilm, motion pictures, slides, video tapes; Other—Clipping files, exhibition catalogs, pamphlets, photographs, prints, reproductions.
Special Subjects: Books and periodicals on urban design, product design, industrial design, landscape design, art and architecture. Slides 35,498 focus primarily on the history of art and architecture, painting and sculpture; vertical file materials 2761; trade literature items 3356.
Special Collections: Maps and plans 1154; bibliographies 300 compiled by the Design Library staff, and a print collection 370; John L Skinner Collection (etchings of the Raphael Loggia); file on measured drawings of North Carolina historic sites.
Publications: Index to the School of Design, student publication book Vols 1-25.

ROCKY MOUNT

ROCKY MOUNT ARTS AND CRAFTS CENTER,* Old Nashville Rd, PO Box 4031, 27801. Tel: 919-977-2111, exten 257. *Dir* Julia Jordan; *Dir Theatre* William A Rawls.
Open Mon - Fri 9 AM - 1 PM and 2 - 5 PM; Sun 3.- 5 PM; cl Sat except for classes. No admis. Estab 1957 to promote the development of the creative arts in the community through education, participation, and appreciation.of music, dance, painting, drama, etc, and to provide facilities and guidance for developing talents and enriching lives through artistic expression and appreciation. Average Annual Attendance: 25,000. Mem: approx 600; dues $5 and higher.
Income: Financed by membership and sponsored by the City Recreation Department.
Exhibitions: Permanent collection and traveling shows change each month. Outdoor Art Exhibition in the Spring, part of the Arts Festival.
Activities: Conducts art classes; maintains small lending library; lectures, concerts, year-round theatre program, classes for adults and children.

SALISBURY

SUPPLEMENTARY EDUCATIONAL CENTER, ART GALLERY, 314 N Ellis St, 28144. Tel: 704-637-0219. *Art Specialist* Rosemary Johnson.
Open usually during school hours. No admis. Estab 1968 to exhibit art work of public schools, supplemented by exhibits of local artists from time to time during the school year. Our primary purpose is to supplement art education activities in the public schools. Our Specialist, Ms Johnson, visits classrooms, and classes visit the gallery for workshops and

to see exhibitions of school art. The Center is comprised, of two areas, one approximately 24 x 65 ft; the other 15 x 70 ft; with an adjoining classroom for instruction and demonstrations. Average Annual Attendance: 3500.
Income: Financed by membership, state and county appropriation, and from local foundations.
Activities: Classes for adults and children.

WILMINGTON

ST JOHN'S ART GALLERY, 114 Orange St, 28401. Tel: 919-763-0281. *Dir* Alan Aiches.
Open Tues - Sat 10 AM - 5 PM. No admis. Estab 1962 to promote interest in the fine and applied arts, to establish and maintain an art collection; and to provide exhibitions for the enjoyment of creative ability and artistic achievement; the gallery is a non-profit educational and cultural center serving southeastern North Carolina. Average Annual Attendance: 15,000. Mem: 700; dues $15-$100; annual meeting first Tues in June.
Income: Financed by membership, city, county and state appropriation.
Collections: Collection of paintings; scent bottles; Jugtown pottery.
Exhibitions: Monthly exhibition including artwork from regional artists, and loans from North Carolina Museum of Art.
Publications: Bulletin, monthly.
Activities: Classes for adults and children; docent training; lect open to the public, 2 vis lectr per yr; concerts; gallery talks; tours; sales shop selling original art.
Library: Open to members by appointment. Holdings: Vols 250; Per subs 3.

USS NORTH CAROLINA BATTLESHIP MEMORIAL,* Cape Fear River on Eagles Island (Mailing Add: PO Box 417, 28401). Tel: 919-762-1829. *Dir* Capt C B Jennings; *Asst Dir* Lt Comdr Charles Peek.
Open daily 8 AM - 6 PM. Admis adults $1.26, children 6-11 50¢. Estab 1961 as an historic ship museum.
Income: Financed by state appropriation.
Collections: World War II and US Navy paintings; float plane.
Activities: Tours; summer exhibitions.

WILSON

ATLANTIC CHRISTIAN COLLEGE, Case Art Gallery, 27893. Tel: 919-237-3161. *Museum Dir* Edward Brown.
Open Mon - Fri 10 AM - 4:30 PM; Sat 1:30 - 3:30 PM. Estab 1967 to provide art exposure for our students and community; gallery 50 x 50 ft. Average Annual Attendance: 1000.
Income: Financed by college budget. Purchases: $500.
Collections: Recent drawings, prints, painting, ceramics, sculpture.
Exhibitions: Joe Cox (paintings); area ceramic exhibit; visiting artists exhibit; high school competition; NCarolina Museum Exhibition; Art Students' Exhibit.
Publications: Exhibition notices for individual shows.
Activities: Classes for adults; docent training; lect open to the public, 3 vis lectr per yr; gallery talks; competitions; lending collections contains cassettes, original art works 750, original prints, sculpture, slides 4000.

WINSTON-SALEM

ARTS COUNCIL, INC,* 610 Coliseum Dr, 27106. Tel: 919-722-2585. *Pres* Elizabeth M Booke; *Exec Dir* Milton Rhodes; *Assoc Dir* Allan H Cowen.
Open weekdays 9 AM - 5 PM. Estab 1949, The Arts Council is a housing, coordinating, promoting, and fund raising organization for 39 member groups, including Associated Artists, Arts and Crafts Association, the Winston-Salem Symphony Association, The Little Theatre, South Eastern Center for Contemporary Art, and Childrens' Theatre.
Housing facilities include a theatre, rehearsal rooms, art and craft studios and an exhibition gallery. Ann meeting May; mem 15,000; member groups are autonomous of Art Council, but management counsel, promotion and funds are provided for various arts programs.
Income: FInanced by endowment, city and state appropriation and fund drives.

ASSOCIATED ARTISTS OF WINSTON-SALEM, 601 Coliseum Dr, 27106. Tel: 919-723-9075. *Pres* Agnes David; *VPres* Miriam Grymes; *Secy* Sarah Bolling.
Gallery is not maintained; the Association rents the walls of the Gallery from the Arts Council. Mem: 300; qualification for mem: associate member non-exhibiting member by committee screening; dues $7.
Income: $5,000 (financed by membership and other funds).
Exhibitions: Five juried shows, five two-man shows.
Publications: Newsletter, monthly.

Activities: Classes for adults; lect open to the public; gallery talks; competitions.

MUSEUM OF EARLY SOUTHERN DECORATIVE ARTS, Old Salem, Inc, 924 S Main St, (Mailing Add: Drawer F, Salem Station, 27108). Tel: 919-722-6148. *Dir* Thomas A Gray; *Sr Research Fellow* Frank L Horton; *Research Fellow* Bradford L Rauschenberg; *Educ Coordinator* Jan G Hind; *Registrar* Rosemary E Estes.
Open Mon - Sat 10:30 AM - 5 PM; Sun 1:30 - 4:30 PM. Admis adult $2, $1 student. Estab 1965 to bring to light the arts and antiquities produced in Maryland, Virginia, Kentucky, Tennessee, North and South Carolina, and Georgia through the first two decades of the 19th Century; three galleries are furnished with southern decorative arts or imported objects used in the South, and fifteen period settings from southern houses dating from 1680 to 1821. Average Annual Attendance: 21,000. Mem: 650; dues $15 - $500; annual meeting April.
Income: $225,000 (financed by endowment, membership, state appropriation, and other funds). Purchases: Approx $50,000.
Collections: †Southern decorative arts in general, and specifically furniture, paintings, silver, ceramics, metalwares, and woodwork of southern origin.
Exhibitions: (1976-1978) Ongoing Research in Southern Decorative Arts.
Publications: Journal of Southern Decorative Arts, semiannually.
Activities: Classes for adults and children; docent training; graduate Summer Institute; lect open to the public, 5 lectr per yr; gallery talks; exten dept serving eight Southern States; individual paintings and original objects of art lent to other museums or cultural institutions, and with special permission from staff, are available for special exhibits; sales shop selling books, slides.
—**Library.** *Librn* Bradford L Rauschenberg. Open to serious collectors, students, or MESDA staff for reference only.
Holdings: Vols 8000; Per subs 30.
Special Subjects: County Histories of Southern States; Southern Decorative Arts.

NORTH CAROLINA MUSEUMS COUNCIL (Mailing Add: Drawer F, Salem Station, 27108). Tel: 919-723-3688.
Estab 1964 to stimulate interest, support and understanding of museums, and to provide a medium of cooperation and communication among museums and museum personnel. Mem: 250; dues individual $5; annual meeting spring and fall.
Income: Financed by membership.
Publications: NCMC newsletter, summer and winter.

REYNOLDA HOUSE, INC, Reynolda Village, Reynolda Rd (Mailing Add: PO Box 11765, 27106). Tel: 919-725-5325. *Exec Dir* Nicholas B Bragg; *Cur of Educ* Melrose Tapscott; *Admin Asst* Wendy Felker; *Development Asst* Peggy LaRochelle; *Secy* Marge Wagstaff.
Open Tues - Sat 9:30 AM - 4:30 PM; Sun 1:30 - 4:30 PM; cl Mon; cl during Jan. Admis $2 adults, $1 senior citizens, 75 cents students.
Estab 1964 to offer a learning experience through a correlation of art, music and literature using the house and the Collection of American Art as resources; the gallery is located in the 40 rooms of the former R J Reynolds mansion. Average Annual Attendance: 37,500. Mem: 600; annual meeting of Bd of Dir in May and Nov.
Income: $230,000 (financed by endowment, Friends' contributions, local and state government grants for specific programs, as well as foundation grants). Purchases: $10,000.
Collections: †Permanent collection of paintings and prints on permanent loan; costume collection: Doughty Bird Collection.
Exhibitions: A collection of paintings from the Weatherspoon Art Gallery at The University of North Carolina, Greensboro emphasizing the period from 1900-1930.
Publications: Annual Report; Calendar of Events, twice annually; Poetry publication; The Recollections of A D Reynolds.
Activities: Classes for adults and children; dramatic programs; docent training; lect open to public, 20 vis lectr per yr; concerts; gallery talks; tours; exten dept serving the Reynolds Homestead in southern Virginia; individual paintings and original objects of art lent to specific museums with reciprocity agreement; lending collection contains original prints, paintings; slides of paintings are sold.
Library. *Librn* Anna Cooper. Open to public. Holdings: Vols 1000; Per subs 30.

SOUTHEASTERN CENTER FOR CONTEMPORARY ART, 750 Marguerite Dr, 27106. Tel: 919-725-1904. *Pres* Noel L Dunn; *Dir* Ted Potter; *Asst to Dir* McChesney S Dunn; *Business Mgr* Lucy P Wilson; *Cur* Mackey Bane.
Open Tues - Sat 10 AM - 5 PM; Sun 2 - 5 PM; cl Mon. No admis. Estab 1956 to identify and exhibit the southeast's major artists of exceptional talent; to present educational programs for children and adults, and to

bring the viewing public in direct contact with artists and their art. Nine indoor and outdoor exhibition areas. Average Annual Attendance: 80,000. Mem: 1500; dues varying categories; annual meeting June.
Income: Financed by endowment, membership, and state appropriation.
Exhibitions: Approx 40 changing exhibitions annually.
Publications: Newsletter, quarterly.
Activities: Classes for adults and children; docent training; workshops; lect open to public, 12 vis lectr per yr; concerts; gallery talks; tours; competitions; traveling exhibitions organized and circulated; Center shop selling books, magazines, original art, gifts, paper products, crafts.

NORTH DAKOTA

DEVILS LAKE

LAKE REGION ART ASSOCIATION,* PO Box 11, 58301. *Co-Chairwoman* Dikka Ballentine; *Co-Chairwoman* Ann Schroeder; *Secy* Mrs L E Campbell.
Estab 1957 to further art appreciation and provide exhibits from throughout the State of North Dakota; encourage art and art appreciation to young and old alike. State Art Gallery, open Memorial Day - Labor Day; admis free. Meeting dates, monthly, Sept - May; mem 60; dues $2.
Income: Financed by endowment and membership.
Exhibitions: Annual Spring Art Show.
Activities: Lectures open to the public; scholarships.

DICKINSON

DICKINSON STATE COLLEGE, Mind's Eye Gallery, Department of Art, 58601. Tel: 701-227-2312. *Dir* Jame Beaudoin; *Gallery Supervisor* Den Navrat.
Open daily during academic year, regular library hours. No admis. Estab 1972 as a visual arts gallery presenting monthly exhibits representing the work of local, national, and international artists. The gallery is a secure, large room approx 60 x 20 ft, with a 20 ft ceiling and approx 180 running feet of carpeted display space. Average Annual Attendance: 10,000.
Income: $8,000 (financed by endowment, state appropriation, Badlands Art Assoc). Purchases: Variable, to $1000.
Collections: Zoe Beiler paintings; †contemporary graphics.
Exhibitions: Monthly rental exhibits.
Publications: Exhibit announcements.
Activities: Docent training; lect open to public, 2-4 vis lectr per yr; gallery talks; traveling exhibitions organized and circulated.
—**Stoxen Library.** *Librn* Bernnett Reinke.
Open to college students.
Holdings: (Art) Vols 3,000; Per subs 10.

FORT RANSOM

SHEYENNE VALLEY ARTS AND CRAFTS ASSOCIATION, Bjarne Ness Gallery, (Mailing Add: PO Box 52, 50833). *Pres* Wayne Hankel; *VPres* Helen Bjone; *Exec Secy* Mrs Bjarne Ness; *Recording Secy* Mrs Ed Monson.
Open Sat, Sun & holidays 1 - 6 PM. No admis, donations accepted. Estab 1971 to preserve and care for the Bjarne Ness Gallery and to sponsor and promote interest in arts and crafts by conducting seminars, workshops, and an annual festival. The Gallery is the former studio of the late Bjarne Ness. Average Annual Attendance: 2400. Mem: 205; dues single $3, couple $5; annual meeting Nov.
Income: Financed by membership, and grants.
Collections: Paintings of Bjarne Ness.
Exhibitions: One or two members' shows; Annual Arts and Crafts Festival.
Activities: Classes for adults; gallery talks; individual paintings lent to banks, libraries, cafes.
Library: Bjarne Ness Gallery Library. Open to members for reference. Holdings: Vols 100. Special Subjects: Arts and crafts.

GRAND FORKS

UNIVERSITY OF NORTH DAKOTA ART GALLERIES, University Ave (Mailing Add: Box 8136, University Station, 58202). *Dir and Head Cur* Laurel J Reuter; *Asst Dir* Pat Gimbel.
Open Mon - Thurs 10 AM - 9 PM; Fri 10 AM - 5 PM; Sat & Sun 1 - 5 PM. No admis. Estab 1971 as an exhibition gallery, historical as well as contemporary arts and crafts; galleries are also involved in educational and humanities projects; galleries occupy three large sections on third floor of University Center, offices adjacent; mobile gallery housed in trailer. Average Annual Attendance: 18,000.
Income: Financed by endowment, state appropriation and grants.

Exhibitions: (1976-78) North Dakota Annual; Annual Student Show; Kathie Killowitz; prints; Samaras; Homage to the Bag; Experimental Printmaking; Soldner raku; Art of Fiber; Bay Area Artists; Ihle Retrospective; J Nutt; Gladys Nilson; New American Quilt; Midgette (murals) & Luis Jimenez (sculpture); Sol Lewitt; Anreson; Masterson (porcelain); Manisphere annual; The American Farm (photographic history); I Wear the Morning Star; Ghost Dance Objects: Munoz (fiber sculpture); Donald Roller Wilson.
Publications: John Ihle Retrospective, Indian Images, (catalogs); Jiri Anderle, Printmaker (exhibition catalog).
Activities: (Classes organized by Crafts Center in conjunction with Galleries) Classes for adults and children; general arts/crafts classes; lect open to the public, 12-15 vis lectr per yr; gallery talks; artmobile; individual paintings lent to offices on the University campus; traveling exhibitions organized and circulated.
Special Collections: Gallery serves as proprietor for Art Students Collective collection, bought out of annual juries exhibitions of student work.

MINOT

MINOT ART GALLERY, Minot Art Association, State Fair Grounds (Mailing Add: PO Box 325, 58701). Tel: 701-838-4445. *Gallery Dir* Galen R Willert; *Pres* Mary Ann Broshahan; *VPres* Dougals Hultberg; *Secy* Ardis Hamilton Huss.
Open Tues - Sun 1 - 5 PM. Admin adults 50¢; children 14 and under 10¢. Estab 1970 to promote means and opportunities for the education of the public with respect to the study and culture of the fine arts. Average Annual Attendance: 10,000. Mem: 235; dues from student $5 - life member $500+; annual meeting April.
Income: $23,000 (financed by endowment, membership, and contributions). Purchases: $500.
Collections: Prints, paintings, macrame, pottery, sculpture—done by local and national artists.
Exhibitions: One-person exhibits; traveling art exhibits; artfests; art competitions; change monthly.
Publications: Calendar of Exhibits, 5 times a year; newsletter, occasionally.
Activities: Classes for adults and children; lect open to public, 3 vis lectr per yr; concerts; gallery talks; tours; competitions; individual paintings and original objects of art lent to local businesses, schools, and libraries; lending collection contains original art works, original prints, paintings; traveling exhibitions organized and circulated; junior museum.
—**Downtown Minot Art Gallery,** Balcony Floor, Ellisons "The Fair", 120 Main St.
Estab 1975.
Exhibitions: Weavings (Evelyn Souther); North Dakota Impressions: Color Photography by Dave McGlauchlin; Acrylic Paintings (Ruth Houff); Artwork by Art Students at Magic City Campus; Acrylic and Watercolor Paintings (Betsy Jones).

VALLEY CITY

FINE ARTS CLUB, 2nd Crossing Gallery, (Mailing Add: Valley City State College, PO Box 1319, 58072. Tel: 701-845-2690. *Dir* Mrs. Riley Rogers.
Open Mon - Fri 1 - 4 PM; Mon & Wed 7 - 9 PM; Sun 2 - 4 PM; cl Aug. No admis. Estab 1973 to provide local, state, national and international shows for people in this area. Small but professional gallery consists of a room 28 x 40 ft with track lighting and movable standards. Average Annual Attendance: 3500. Mem: 130; dues $15 and up.
Income: $12,000 (financed by endowment and membership).
Collections: †The Fine Arts Club has 19 pieces; †2nd Crossing Gallery has 25 pieces.
Exhibitions: 11 or 12 exhibitions a year of material from American Federation of Arts, Smithsonian, Western Association of Art Museums, local and State shows.
Publications: Calendar, annually.
Activities: Competitions with cash awards; individual painting and original objects of art lent to various offices on campus.

WILLISTON

WILLIAMS COUNTY HISTORICAL SOCIETY, Frontier Museum, 58801. *Pres* Fred Rathert.
Open May - Labor Day Mon - Sat 7 - 9 PM; Sun & holidays 2 - 8 PM; cl Labor Day - Apr. Admis adults $1, students 50¢, children 9 and under free; special rates to groups. Mem: Dues annual $3, patron $10, sustaining $25, life $100.
Collections: Paintings; sculpture; prints; decorative arts; coins; textiles; historical material and buildings.
Activities: Lectures; guided tours; tapes; sales shop.
Library: Small collection of historical and biographical publications.

OHIO

AKRON

AKRON ART INSTITUTE, 69 E Market St, 44308. Tel: 216-376-9185. *Dir* John Coplans; *Asst Dir Development* Gregory Allgire Smith; *Cur Educ* Marcianne Herr.
Open Tues - Fri Noon - 5 PM. Sat 9 AM - 5 PM; Sun 1 - 5 PM. No admis. Estab 1921 as a museum to exhibit and collect art. Total of four galleries: two house the permanent collection and two for changing exhibitions. Average Annual Attendance: 75,000. Mem: 1200; dues $20; annual meeting May.
Income: $300,000 (financed by membership, city appropriation and grants). Purchases: $50,000.
Collections: Early 20th century American art.
Exhibitions: Claes Oldenburg: The Inverted Q; Charles Burchfield: The Ohio Years; Rips in Reality; Folk Art of Ohio; Project: New Urban Monuments; Stephen Greene: A Decade of Painting; Contemporary American Watercolors.
Publications: Calendar, monthly; exhibition catalogs.
Activities: Classes for adults and children; docent training; lect open to public, 6-8 lectr per yr; gallery talks; concerts; tours; artmobile; individual paintings and original objects of art lent to city agencies; lending collection contains film strips, original art works, original prints, paintings and slides; traveling exhibitions organized and circulated; museum shop selling books, original art.
—**Martha Stecher Reed Art Library.** *Librn* Marjorie Harvey.
Open for reference.
Holdings: Vols 5000; Per subs 50.
Special Subjects: Oriental and contemporary art.
Special Collections: Edwin Shaw volumes, to accompany collection of American Impressionistic art.

STAN HYWET HALL FOUNDATION, INC, 714 N Portage Path, 44303. Tel: 216-836-5533. *Chmn of the Bd* Robert S Pflueger; *VChmn* Raymond Wernig; *Pres* David C Corbin; *VPres* John L Tormey; *VPres* Robert L Reeves; *Secy* Mrs Nelson V Seeger; *Asst Secy* Mrs Albert J Brewster III; *Treas* Howard Milford; *Asst Treas* Frank W Steere Jr.
Open Sat 10 AM - 4 PM; Sun 1 - 4 PM; cl Mon & major national holidays. Admis adults $3, children 6 - 12 years 50¢. Inc May 25, 1956, Stan Hywet Hall is a house museum, serving as a civic and cultural center. All restoration and preservation work is carefully researched to retain the original concept of the property, which represents a way of life that is gone forever; the mansion, focal point of the estate, is a 65-room Tudor Revival manor house, furnished with priceless antiques and works of art dating from the 14th century. The property is the former home of Frank A Seiberling, Akron rubber industrialist, completed in 1915. There are 70 acres of formal gardens, meadows, woods, and lagoons. Average Annual Attendance: 130,000. Mem: 2835; dues $20 and up, annual meeting third Sun March.
Income: $600,000 (financed by endowment, membership, admissions, gifts, grants, rentals, special events).
Collections: Books, paintings, sculpture, antique furniture, tapestries, rugs, silver, porcelain, china, crystal.
Publications: Stan Hywet Hall Newsletter, monthly.
Activities: Classes for children; dramatic programs; docent training; lect open to the public, 20 vis lectr per yr; concerts; gallery talks; tours; competitions; lending collection contains photographs, slides, and slide show with soundtrack, available with operator; sales shop selling books, original art, slides and wide variety of gift items.
Library. Currently being developed, with reference materials relative to Stan Hywet Hall and Gardens.

UNIVERSITY OF AKRON
—**University Galleries,** Akron, 44325. Tel: 216-375-7012. *Gallery Dir* Donald E Harvey; *Art Dept Chmn* Warren A Wolf.
Open Mon - Fri 10 AM - 4 PM; Wed 6 - 9 PM. Estab Nov. 1, 1974 to exhibit the work of important contemporary artists working in all regions of the United States, as well as to provide a showcase for the work of artists working within the university community; two galleries: Emily H Davis Art Gallery, 1500 sq ft with 150 running ft of wall space; Guzzetta Hall Atrium Gallery, 120 running ft of wall space. Average Annual Attendance: 7500 - 9000.
Income: Financed by university funds.
Exhibitions: (1976-77) John Baldessari; Agnes Denes; Artists Books, Prints and Photographs; Works in Clay; Sand by Karen Shirley; Ralph Eugene Meatyard (photographs). (1977-78) Joan Brown (paintings); Works from the Bertha Urdang Gallery; Edward Curtis (photogravures); David Hockney (photographs); Stephen Shore (photographs); Gretna Campbell (paintings).

Publications: Catalogs and artists' books in conjunction with exhibitions.
Activities: Lect open to the public, 6-8 vis lectr per yr; gallery talks; traveling exhibitions organized and circulated.
—**Bierce Library.*** Tel: 216-375-7495. *Librn* H Paul Schrank, Jr.
Open Mon - Fri 7:30 AM - 12 AM; Sat 9 AM - 5 PM; Sun 2 PM - 12 AM. Estab 1870.
Holdings: (Art) Vols 9000.

ASHLAND

ASHLAND COLLEGE ARTS AND HUMANITIES GALLERY,* College Ave, 44805. Tel: 419-289-4005. *Chmn* Leon F Schenker; *Dir Exhib* Carl M Allen.
Open Tues - Sun 1 - 4 PM; Tues 7- 10 PM. No admis. Estab 1969-70. Gallery maintained for continuous exhibitions, with accent on contemporary works, some historical, occidental and Oriental.
Income: Base amount $2500, plus occasional assists. Purchases: $500 - $20,000.
Activities: Original objects of art lent to Akron Art Institute and Cleveland Museum of Art; lectures open to public; 2 - 3 gallery talks; tours; concerts, dramatic programs, classes for children; scholarships; regular tours to leading art museums.

ATHENS

OHIO UNIVERSITY, Anthony G Trisolini Memorial Gallery, 48 E Union St, 45701. Tel: 614-594-5664. *Dir* Henry H Lin; *Asst to Dir* Barbara F Mantel; *Graduate Asst* Lyneulle Wyatt.
Open Tues - Sat Noon - 4 PM. No admis. Estab 1974 to provide cultural exposure to the university community and to the residents of the surrounding region; four rooms with carpeted walls and floors. Average Annual Attendance: 6,000-7,000.
Income: Financed by state appropriation. Purchases: $5000.
Collections: †Contemporary prints, some paintings, photographs and sculpture.
Exhibitions: How Do I See the USA?; 18th Century String Instruments; Masters of the 19th Century (painting); Bridges and Tunnels; Clarence H White, Sr Photography; George Segal (sculpture and prints); Arne Jacobsen Furniture.
Publications: Scholarly exhibition catalogs, two or three times a year.
Activities: Lect open to public; traveling exhibitions organized and circulated; museum shop selling original art, prints and crafts.
—**Seigfred Gallery, School of Art,** Seigfred Hall 528, 45701. Tel: 614-594-5667. *Dir* Erik Forrest; *Gallery Dir* Mary Manusos.
Open Mon - Fri 10 AM - 4 PM. No admis. The gallery is used for faculty exhibitions, student exhibitions and visiting artist shows.
—**Fine Arts Library,*** Tel: 614-594-5065. *Art Librn* Anne Brazton; *Asst Art Librn* Timothy Daum.
Open Mon - Fri 8 AM - 12 AM; Sat & Sun 1 PM - 12 AM.
Income: Financed by state appropriations.
Holdings: Vols 30,000; Other—Photographs 7500 prints, exhibition catalogs 3500.
Special Collections: Research collection in history of photography; small collection of original photographs for study purposes.

BEACHWOOD

SALVADOR DALI MUSEUM, 24050 Commerce Park Road, 44122. Tel: 216-464-0372. *Pres* A Reynolds Morse; *Dir* Joan Kropf; *Asst Mgr* Betsey Johnson.
Open Tues - Sat 10 AM - Noon and 1 - 4 PM, appointments necessary. No admis. Estab 1971 to share the private Dali collection of Mr. and Mrs. A Reynolds Morse with the public. The collection is housed in a private office building in a Commerce Park. Average Annual Attendance: 16,000.
Income: Financed by private collector.
Collections: †55 oils and 3 large Masterworks by Dali make up a retrospective of his work from 1914 to the present; numerous drawings and watercolors; continually changing graphic exhibits.
Exhibitions: Les Diners de Gala and Dalivision (Graphic); Archaeological Reminiscence of Millet's Angelus; Anamorphoses by Dali (graphic); Dali's Surrealist Fruits and Flowers (Graphic show); Anthropomorphic Echo; Classical Series; Erotic Art by Dali; Broken Bridge of the Dream; Hiram College Graphic Exhibit.
Publications: Dali. . .A Panorama of his Art; Guide to Works by Dali in Public Museums; Dali Adventure; Dali/Picasso; Poetic Homage to Gala-Dali; Dali Primer; Dali Draftmanship; Introduction to Dali.
Activities: Lect open public; gallery talks; tours; lending collection contains color reproductions; museum shop selling books, magazines, original art, reproductions, prints, slides, postcards, collector plates and jewelery.

Library: Use restricted at present; contains references to Dali in books, periodicals and newspapers. Special Collections: Films and tapes on or by Dali.

BEREA

BALDWIN-WALLACE COLLEGE ART GALLERY,* 95 E Bagley Rd, 44017. Tel: 216-826-2152. *Head Dept Art* Dean Drahos; *Dir Art Gallery* Helen A Leon; *Conservator* Terry Speer.
Open Sun - Fri 2 - 5 PM. No admis. The Art Gallery is considered to be a part of the art program of the department of art; its purpose is that of a teaching museum for the students of the college and the general public. Average Annual Attendance: 2500.
Income: Financed through budgetary support of the college.
Collections: Approx †200 paintings and sculptures by Midwest artists of the 20th century; approx †1900 drawings and prints from 16th-20th century, with a concentration in 19th-20th century examples.
Exhibitions: Traveling and student exhibitions.
Publications: Exhibition catalogs are published for important exhibitions, 1-2 per year.
Activities: Individual paintings lent to schools; 20 items lent in an average year; photograph collection begun in 1972, 10 prints; lectures open to the public; 4 gallery talks; 10 tours; competitions.

BOWLING GREEN

BOWLING GREEN STATE UNIVERSITY, Fine Arts Gallery, School of Art, 43403. Tel: 419-372-2787. *Dir of Gallery* Ralph Warren.
Open Mon - Fri 8:30 AM - 5 PM; Sun 2 - 5 PM. Estab 1964 to provide enrichment to School of Art program by furnishing research materials, exhibitions and related events; to provide for the growth of public sensitivity to the visual arts; gallery is a multi-level facility located in the Fine Arts building with approximately 1500 running feet of exhibition space. Average Annual Attendance: 7500.
Income: Financed by city and state appropriation, and foundation.
Exhibitions: (1976-77) National Blacksmiths: Contemporary Decorative Ironwork; Christian Mischke (graphics); Virginia Myers (graphics); Ohio Designer Craftsmen; Richard Hunt (sculpture).

CANTON

CANTON ART INSTITUTE,* 1001 Market Ave N, 44702. Tel: 216-453-7666. *Pres* E Lang D'Atri; *VPres* Mrs Kenneth Adams; *Treas* Paul Basner; *Secy* John P Van Abel; *Dir* Jesse G Wright, Jr; *Asst to Dir* Joseph R Hertzi; *Admin Asst* Shirley A Hawk.
Open Sept - July 15, Tues - Sat 10 AM - 5 PM; Tues, Wed & Thurs 7 - 9 PM; Sun 2 - 5 PM. Summer, July 15 - Aug 16, Tues - Sat Noon - 4 PM; Sun 2 - 5 PM. Estab 1935, inc 1941. Average Annual Attendance: 75,000. Mem: 1680; dues $10 and higher; annual meeting Apr.
Collections: American, Italian, and Spanish paintings; 18th and 19th century English and American portraiture; 20th century regional art; graphics; sculpture; decorative arts; costumes; art objects.
Exhibitions: Approx 40 to 50 traveling or collected exhibitions of painting, sculpture, commercial and industrial arts annually.
Activities: Guided tours; lectures; films; gallery talks; arts festivals; formally organized education programs for children and adults; sales shop.
Library: Art Library. Holdings: Vols 4000.

CINCINNATI

CINCINNATI ART CLUB,* 1021 Parkside Place, 45205. Tel: 513-762-9484. *Pres* Gene P Hinckley; *Secy* Robert B Schoellkopf; *Treas* Joseph O Emmett.
Estab 1890, inc 1923. New Gallery completed. Small collection of paintings by American artists. Average Annual Attendance: 3500. Mem: Approx 250; dues active $45, assoc $35.
Exhibitions: Exhibition of members' work changed monthly. Open to the public each Sunday afternoon Sept to May. Annual Club Shows Sept, Jan, and Christmas Art Bazaar. Sales $6000-$7000 annually.
Activities: Lectures and demonstrations by important artists each month (Sept to May); a Forum open to the public each month.
Library: Small library of books on art.

CINCINNATI ART MUSEUM, Eden Park, 45202. Tel: 513-721-5204. *Dir* Millard F Rogers; *Asst Dir* Betty L Zimmerman; *Business Mgr* Robert J Petersen; *Sr Cur & Cur Decorative Arts* Dr Carol Macht; *Cur Costumes, Textiles, Tribal Arts* Carolyn R Shine; *Cur Prints, Drawings & Photographs* Kristin L Spangenberg; *Assoc Cur Ancient, Near and Far Eastern Arts* Daniel S Walker; *Assoc Cur Painting* Denny T Carter; *Conservator* Elisabeth Batchelor; *Registrar* Anita Ellis.
Open Tues - Sat 10 AM - 5 PM; Sun 1 - 5 PM; cl Mon & holidays. Admis adults $1; ages 12-18 50¢; free to members, scheduled tours through grade 12, children under 12; free to all on Sat. Estab 1881 to collect, exhibit, conserve and interpret works of art from all periods and

civilizations (range of 5,000 years of major civilizations of the world). The exhibition galleries cover an area of approx 4 acres, occupying two floors, with a few exhibition galleries, assembly areas and social center on ground level; altogether some 118 galleries given over to permanent collections, with additional galleries set aside for temporary exhibitions. Average Annual Attendance: 210,000. Mem: 3,600; dues $25 and up; annual meeting March.

Income: $1,000,000 (financed by endowment, membership, city appropriation, Cincinnati Fine Arts Fund, museum shop earnings, federal, state and private grants).

Collections: †Paintings (European and American); †Greek, Roman, Egyptian, Near and Far Eastern Arts; †Decorative arts and period rooms from around the world; †world costumes, textiles and tribal arts; †world sculpture; †world prints, drawings and photographs; ancient musical instruments.

Exhibitions: Jean Arp—sculptures, reliefs, works on paper; Prints and Drawings by William Wiley; Oriental Rugs in Cincinnati Collections; Richard Diebenkorn—Paintings and Drawings; Cincinnati Invitational Exhibition: Photographs and Watercolors; The Art of Dominick Labino—A Decade of Glass Craftsmanship; The Sculptor's Eye—African Art Collection of Mr and Mrs Chaim Gross; The Printed Word—Printmakers as Satirists and Critics.

Publications: Annual Report; catalogues for exhibitions; Handbook.

Activities: Classes for adults and children; docent training; seminars; lect open to public, 8 vis lectr per yr; gallery talks; tours; competitions; exten dept serving Greater Cincinnati; individual paintings and original objects of art lent to established art institutions meeting aesthetic and security standards approved by Director and Board of Trustees, by arrangement not later than 9 months in advance; museum shop selling books, original art, reproductions, prints, slides, postcards and others.

—**Library.** Tel: 513-721-5204, exten 51 & 52. *Librn* Patricia P Rutledge; *Asst Librn/Museum Archivist* Carole Schwartz; *Reference Librn* Grace S Keam.

Open Tues - Fri 10 AM - 4:45 PM.

Holdings: Vols 40,692; Per subs 98; Other—Clipping files, exhibition catalogs, pamphlets, reproductions.

Special Collections: Files on Cincinnati artists, art in Cincinnati, the Cincinnati Art Museum, and the Art Academy of Cincinnati.

CINCINNATI INSTITUTE OF FINE ARTS,* 2649 Erie Ave, 45208. Tel: 513-871-3325. *Pres* Morley P Thompson; *Secy* James M E Mixter; *Exec Dir* Paul George Sittenfeld.

Estab and inc 1927 to provide for the continuance and growth of education and culture in the various fields of fine arts in the metropolitan community of Cincinnati. Ann meeting Oct. Management of endowments and coordination of financial policies of Cincinnati Symphony Orchestra, Cincinnati Art Museum, Cincinnati Opera, Taft Museum (q.v.) Manages the Fine Arts Fund of Cincinnati, conducting an annual campaign for public support in behalf of the four participating institutions named above.

CONTEMPORARY ARTS CENTER, 115 E Fifth St, 45202. Tel: 513-721-0390. *Chmn* Alfred A Moore; *Pres* Mrs. John H Wulsin; *VPres* Phillip C Long; *Treas* Stuart A Schloss, Jr; *Secy* K R B Niehoff; *Dir* Robert Stearns; *Asst to Dir* Jean-Marie Baines; *Cur* Ruth K Meyer; *Public Information Mgr* P Matthew McClain; *Educ Asst* Carolyn R Brown.

Open Tues - Sat 10 AM - 5 PM; Sun Noon - 5 PM; cl Mon. Admis adults 50¢, students & seniors 25¢. Estab 1939, operates under the kunsthalle model: frequent changes of major visual arts exhibitions of leading contemporary art. Other programs: regional artists, temporary arts events (live music, performance, dance, video and film). Maintains an art gallery, 12,000 sq ft in two main galleries and a cruciform gallery with a dome above. Used together or separately with flexibility of arrangement by means of track-hung walls. Meeting/Dining area accommodates 200 for meals, 400 for lectures, films, etc. Average Annual Attendance: 15,000 - 20, 000. Mem: 1000; dues from $10 - $100.

Income: $225,000 (financed by endowment, membership, city and state appropriations).

Exhibitions: Dorothy & Herbert Vogel Coll; Jack Tworkov; WCET-Bob Cosgrove; 14 Cincinnati Artists; Jackie Winsor Sculpture; Photography and Light Hauling; Aka Pereyma Sculpture; Jennifer Bartlett: Rhapsody; Selections from the Permanent Collection of The Vent Haven Museum; Duane Michals Photographs; Artists and Friends: Dan Flavin and Michael Venezia; Tsutsumu: The Art of the Japanese package; Confluences; Donald Judd 15 Plywood Boxes; John Pearson Paintings; Earth, Moon, Mars, Jupiter: Video from Interplanetary Space: Painting 75/76/77; Laszlo Veszpremi; Project: New Urban Monuments; Proposals for Sawyer Point Park, Cincinnati; Patricia Renick Triceracopter; See Here: Cincinnati Art Directors Annual Show; Carl Andre Sculpture 1959-1977; Charles Curro Recent Drawings; Patrick Ireland Rope Drawings; Performance: The Photography of Sandy Underwood.

Publications: Catalogs of exhibitions.

Activities: Programs for adults and children; docent training; lect, 6 vis lectr per yr; concerts; gallery talks; tours; lending collection contains slides and videotapes; traveling exhibitions organized and circulated.

Library: Open to members and others by appointment for reference. Holdings: Per subs 10; Other—Exhibition catalogs and related publications.

EDGECLIFF COLLEGE,* Emery Gallery, 2220 Victory Parkway, 45206. Tel: 513-961-3770. *Pres* Sister Margaret Molitor; *Dir* Dorothy M Kiel.

Open 1 - 5 PM daily. No admis. Estab 1967 to present to students and the public at large outstanding artists of local, national and international fame.

Income: Privately financed.

Exhibitions: Art Students of Edgecliff College; traveling exhibitions.

Activities: Individual paintings lent to schools; lectures open to public; classes for adults and children; scholarships; book shop.

TAFT MUSEUM, 316 Pike St, 45202. Tel: 513-241-0343. *Pres* Morley P Thompson; *Chmn* John W Warrington; *Dir* Katherine Hanna; *Designer* Jan Weigel; *Art Historian/Promotion* Marsha K Semmel.

Open Mon - Sat 10 AM - 5 PM; Sun & Holidays 2 - 5 PM; cl Thanksgiving and Christmas. No admis. Estab 1927 a gift of Mr. and Mrs. Charles P Taft's art collection to the Cincinnati Institute of Fine Arts including the house and an endowment fund for maintenance. Active control was taken in 1931; Museum opened in 1932. The historic house, built in 1820, is one of the finest examples of Federal architecture in this country. It has been designated a National Landmark. Its interior is decorated in the period. An architectural green, formal garden was opened in 1949. Average Annual Attendance: 60,000. Annual meeting Oct.

Income: $250,000 (financed by endowment and annual Fine Arts Fund drive).

Collections: 150 paintings including works by Rembrandt, Hals, Turner, Goya, Corot, Gainsborough, Raeburn and other Masters; 200 notable Chinese porcelains K'ang Hsi and Ch'ien Lung; 120 French Renaissance enamels; Renaissance jewelry and 18th century watches from many countries; furnishings include antique toiles and satins and a notable collection of Duncan Phyfe furniture.

Exhibitions: John Marin; Look Again (trompe l'oeil); Sounds of Sculpture; Harry Bertola, Francois and Bernard Baschet; Yüan Paintings; Puppets; Best of Fifty; Riding High; René Magritte; Jesse Allen.

Publications: Catalog Taft Art collection; Booklet on history of House and Art Collection; special exhibition catalogs; announcements special events.

Activities: Docent training; lect open to public, 10 vis lectr per yr; gallery talks; tours; individual paintings lent to special museum exhibitions; museum shop selling reproductions, prints, slides, needlework and tiles.

Library: Open to scholars for reference. Holdings: Vols 1000. Special Subjects: Books and portfolios relating to Taft Collection.

UNIVERSITY OF CINCINNATI
—**Tangeman University Center Art Gallery,** * 403 Tangeman, 45221. Tel: 513-475-3462. *Co-Dir & Conservator* Gilbert Young: *Co-Dir & Cur* Elizabeth B Sittenfeld.

Open Mon - Fri 8 AM - 5 PM. No admis. Estab 1967 to preserve and maintain the University's art collection; to maintain Tangeman University Center Art Gallery, open to public seven days a week, 12 AM - 5 PM. Average Annual Attendance: 10,000.

Collections: Persian miniatures; Japanese woodblock prints; Indian basketry; some 250 paintings by European artists executed in the 1950's, donated by Mr and Mrs Julius Fleischmann. Over 2000 paintings hung in offices across the campus; the collection is strongest in early Cincinnati art.

Exhibitions: The usual painting exhibitions by area artists, highlighted by a variety of exhibitions.

Activities: Small traveling exhibitions organized and circulated; individual paintings and original objects of art lent, 10 items lent in an average year; lectures open to public, 2 vis lectrs per yr; numerous gallery talks.

—**Design, Architecture and Art Library.** * Tel: 513-475-3238. *Acting Librn* Suzanne Yoder.

Estab to serve the teaching and research needs of the College of Design, Architecture & Art.

Income: Approx $45,000 (financed by appropriations). Purchases: Approx $20,000.

Holdings: Vols and per approx 28,000.

CLEVELAND

CLEVELAND INSTITUTE OF ART, 11141 East Blvd, University Circle, 44106. Tel 216-421-4322. *Pres* Joseph McCullough.

Open Mon - Fri 9 AM - 4 PM; Tues - Wed 7 - 9 PM; Sat 9 AM - Noon; Sun 2 - 5 PM. No admis. Estab 1882 as a five-year, fully accredited professional college of art; maintains an art gallery with extensive galleries.

Exhibitions: (1976) Modern Argentine Drawings; (1977) Annual Faculty Exhibition; Student Independent Exhibition; Student Summer Exhibition; Distinguished Alumnus Exhibition: Fred Gutzeit; Paul Travis: Works on Paper; Annual Faculty Exhibition; (1978) Student Independent Exhibition; One-Man Faculty Exhibition (Moe Brooker); Student Summer Exhibition; Distinguished Alumnae Exhibition (Shirley Aley Campbell and Janet Roush Taylor); Invitational Crafts at CIA: A NOVA Show; One-Man Faculty Exhibit (Robert Jergens); (1979) Student Independent Exhibition; Annual Faculty Exhibition.
Publications: Posters to accompany each exhibit; Link (alumni magazine) quarterly.
Activities: Classes for adults and children: lect open to public.
—**Jessica Gund Memorial Library** *Lib Dir* Karen Tschudy; *Asst-Librn* Kenneth P Goldberg; *Cataloger* Vivian Gladden; *Media Center Librn* Kim Kopatz.
Open Mon - Thurs 9 AM - 9:30 PM; Fri 9 AM - 5 PM; Sat 9 AM - 4:30 PM; cl Sun. Estab 1882 to select, house and distribute library material in all media that will support the Institute's studio and academic areas of instruction.
Holdings: Vols 30,050; Per subs 236; AV—Cassettes, lantern slides, microfiche, microfilm, motion pictures and slides; Other—Clipping files, exhibition catalogs, memorabilia, original art works, original documents, pamphlets, photographs, prints, and reproductions.
Special Subjects: Art, humanities, natural science, social and behavioral sciences, anthropology, Russian Studies, 20th century literature.
Special Collections: Posters & graphics, mounted pictures, nature study, archival collection of clippings and exhibition notices, late 19th and early 20th century textiles and a mounted natural history collection.
Activities: Library tours.
—**Cleveland Art Association.** *Pres* Mrs Robert Little; *Secy* Joseph McCullough.
Estab and inc 1916, re-incorporated 1950 as a non-profit organization. Mem: 200; dues $25; annual meeting Nov.
Income: $6000. Purchases: $5200.
Activities: †Collection of pictures by local artists may be borrowed by members; endowment fund for scholarships in Cleveland Institute of Art; donated funds to the Institute for student prizes, awards and special projects aimed in general at the promotion of local artists' work. Donates work by Cleveland artists to the Cleveland Museum.

CLEVELAND MUSEUM OF ART,* 11150 East Blvd, 44106. Tel: 216-421-7340. *Pres* Lewis C Williams; *Dir & Chief Cur Oriental Art* Sherman E Lee; *Gen Mgr* A Beverly Barksdale; *Admin Asst to Dir* Ursula Korneitchouk; *Cur Modern Art* Edward B Henning; *Assoc Cur Paintings* William S Talbot; *Assoc Cur Paintings* Ann T Lurie; *Cur Prints & Drawings* Louise S Richards; *Cur Textiles* Dorothy G Shephard; *Cur Chinese Art* Wai-Kam Ho; *Cur Indian Art* Stanislaw Czuma; *Asst in East Indian Art & Museum Designer* William E Ward; *Asst Cur in Charge Ancient Art* Arielle P Kozloff; *Research Cur Egyptian Art* John D Cooney; *Cur Decorative Arts (Medieval & Renaissance)* William D Wixom; *Cur Decorative Arts (Post-Renaissance)* Henry Hawley; *Cur Educ* Gabriel P Weisberg; *Cur Musical Arts* Karel Paukert; *Ed Museum Publ* Merald E Wrolsted; *Mgr Pub Relations & Mem* Frances Stamper; *Registr* Delbert R Gutridge.
Open Tues, Thurs, Fri 10 AM - 6 PM; Wed 10 AM - 10 PM; Sat 9 AM - 5 PM; Sun 1 - 6 PM; cl Mon & nat holidays. No admis. Estab and inc 1913. Building opened 1916, New Wing 1958, New Education Wing 1970. Average Annual Attendance: 500,000. Mem: approx 9700; dues $15 and higher; annual meeting Nov.
Income: $6,582,300. Purchases: $2,839,600.
Collections: European and American paintings of all periods and styles, especially strong in works of 17th and 19th centuries; European and American Decorative arts of all periods, notably medieval and 18th century; Oriental art, including important collections of Chinese and Japanese painting and ceramics, and Indian sculpture; drawings and prints; Classical and Egyptian art; Near Eastern art; textiles. Included are the †Holden, †J H Wade, †John L Severance, Elisabeth Severance Prentiss, Grace Rainey Rogers, †Mr and Mrs William H Marlatt, and †Leonard C Hanna, Jr, Collections.
Exhibitions: Annual exhibition, May Show—work by artists and craftsmen of the Western Reserve, awards by jury. Annual exhibition, Year in Review, all acquisitions made during the year, in Fall or early Winter.
Publications: Bulletin 10 times a year; News & Calendar 6 times a year; book-catalogs of special exhibitions; Monographs and Evolution in the Arts: And Other Theories of Culture History; Chinese Art Under the Mongols: The Yuan Dynasty (1279-1368); The Many Ways of Seeing; Fabergé and His Contemporaries; African Tribal Images; Lyonel Feiniger: a Definitive Catalogue of His Graphic Works.
Activities: Lectures, concerts, study courses; gallery talks; classes; films; special exhibits for children; extension exhibitions in schools and other groups.
Library: *Head Librn* Daphne Cross Roloff; *Assoc Librn* Judith Frost. Holdings: Vols over 83,000; Other—Slides over 152,000.

—**Print Club of Cleveland.** Tel: 216-421-7340. *Pres* Wesley C Williams; *VPres* Elizabeth Shearer; *Secy* John C Bonebrake.
Estab 1919 to stimulate interest in prints and drawings through education, collecting and commissioning of new works and enhancement of the museum's collection by gifts and purchases. Mem: 250 (residence in the Western Reserve and membership in the Cleveland Museum of Art. Demonstration of a serious interest in the world of prints); dues $75 and higher; annual meeting Jan.
Income: Financed by membership.
Publications: The Print Club of Cleveland 1919-1969. Available at Museum Sales Desk, $10 plus postage.
Activities: Lectures open to the public.

CLEVELAND PUBLIC LIBRARY, 325 Superior Ave, 44114. Tel: 216-623-2800, Fine Arts Dept 216-623-2848. *Head of Fine Arts Dept* Joan Hoagland; *Dir* Ervin J Gaines.
Open Mon 9 AM - 8:30 PM; Tues - Sat 9 AM - 6 PM; cl Sun. Estab 1869. Circ: 2,730,706 (1977).
Income: $16,418,025. (1977) (financed by state and county appropriation).
Holdings: Vols 200,000; Per subs 6395; AV—Cassettes, film strips, microfiche, microfilm, motion pictures, phonorecords, slides; Other—Clipping files, exhibition catalogs, manuscripts, original art works, original documents, pamphlets, photographs.
Special Subjects: Architecture; costume; art history; primitive and oriental art; history, theory and literature of music; musical scores; decorative arts.
Special Collections: Schweinfurth Architecture Collection; Hubbell Architecture Collection; J G White Collection of folklore, orientalia and chess.
Activities: Lect open to the public; tours.

COOPER SCHOOL OF ART,* Cooper Gallery, 2341 Carnegie Ave SE, 44115. Tel: 216-241-1486. *Dir* Joseph C Hruby; *Pres* Donald H Wright; *Secy* Howard Hammerlund.
Open 8 AM - 4:30 PM; Mon, Tues & Thurs 6 - 10 PM; Sat 9 AM - 2 PM. No admis. Estab 1936 as a private art school with emphasis in communicating visual arts and photography.
Income: Financed by tuition and fees.
Exhibitions: Local and regional professional artists showing in one-man or small group exhibits; 8 exhibits plus faculty and student shows.
Activities: High school and adult avocational art programs; extension material available to high school art instructors; traveling exhibitions organized and circulated; individual paintings and original objects of art lent; 5000 lantern slides in lending collection; lectures for students only, 30 vis lectrs per yr; 12 gallery talks; 50 tours; classes for adults and children; competitions; scholarships. Book shop.
Library: For lending and reference. Holdings: Vols 3000; Other—Slides 15,000.

DEZIGN HOUSE III, 1701 E Twelfth St, 44114. *Dir* Ramon J Elias; *Assoc* Margery M Elias.
Open only to clients.
Estab 1962 for the encouragement of original art. Private gallery.
Collections: Original American and European.
—**Library.** Estab 1953 for private research. Maintains an art gallery containing a private collection.
Holdings: Vols 4000; Per subs 20.

TEMPLE MUSEUM OF JEWISH RELIGIOUS ART AND MUSIC,* University Circle & Silver Park, 44106. Tel: 216-791-7755. *Dir* Rabbi Daniel Jeremy Silver.
Open Mon - Fri 9 AM - 5 PM; Sun 10 AM - Noon; cl Jewish & legal holidays & summer weekends. No admis. Estab 1950; branch museum on Shaker Blvd, Beachwood.
Collections: Paintings; sculpture; prints; decorative arts; ceremonial art; archaeology.
Library: Small library of art books and manuscripts available for research.

WESTERN RESERVE HISTORICAL SOCIETY, 10825 East Blvd, 44106. Tel: 216-721-5722. *Exec Dir* Meredith Colket; *Dir History Museum* Jairus B Barnes; *Librn* Kermit Pike; *Dir Auto Museum* Kenneth Gooding; *Dir Hale Farm & Village and House Museums* Siegfried Buerling.
Open Tues - Fri 10 AM - 5 PM; Sun 2 - 5 PM. Admis adults $1.50, children 50¢. Estab 1867 to collect and preserve items of historical interest to Western Reserve such as antique furniture and cars. Average Annual Attendance: 50,000. Mem: 2938; dues $15 and up; annual meeting May.
Income: $657,000 (financed by endowment, membership, city and state appropriations, and special grants).
Collections: Period room.
Exhibitions: Changing exhibits.

Publications: Western Reserve Historical Society News, bimonthly.
Activities: Classes for adults and children; docent training; lect open to public; gallery talks; tours; competitions; individual paintings and objects of art lent to institutions; traveling exhibitions organized and circulated; sales shop selling books, magazines and original art.

WOMEN'S CITY CLUB OF CLEVELAND, 320 Superior Ave NE, 44114. Tel: 216-696-3760. *Pres* Mrs. Frank Kosich; *VPres* Mrs. Allen Deutsch; *Secy* Mrs. Arthur W Shantz; *Exec Dir* Norma Huey; *Asst Dir* Dorothy Fell.
Open Mon - Fri 9 AM - 5 PM (closes at 4:30 during July & Aug). No admis. Estab 1916 to promote a broad acquaintance, provide a central meeting place, maintain an open forum and promote the welfare of the City of Cleveland. Maintains an art gallery featuring monthly exhibitions by local professional artists. Average Annual Attendance: 25,000. Mem: 900; dues Junior member $50, Resident Member $100.
Income: Financed by membership.
Exhibitions: Continuous exhibitions changing every four to six weeks.
Publications: Bulletin, monthly.
Activities: Classes for adults; art appreciation classes; lect open to public; gallery talks; presents Cleveland Arts Prize of cash and certificate.

COLUMBUS

AMERICAN CERAMIC SOCIETY, 65 Ceramic Dr, 43214. Tel: 614-268-8645. *Pres* Lyle A Holmes; *VPres* John B Wachtman, Jr, *Exec Dir* Frank P Reid.
For further information see National and Regional Organizations.

CAPITAL UNIVERSITY, Schumacher Gallery, 2199 E Main St, 43209. Tel: 614-236-7108. *Dir* Prof Richard G Bauer; *Secy* Janet E Popp.
Open Mon - Fri 1 - 5 PM; Sun 2 - 4 PM; Eves by appointment; cl Sat. No admis. Estab 1966 to provide students with the best available in the visual arts; to serve community via the permanent collection; monthly travelling shows, and community programming; the gallery consists of 16,000 sq ft, including a community reception room, lecture hall seating 60, lecture space seating 250, fabrication room, vault, offices and six display galleries. Average Annual Attendance: 6000 - 7000.
Income: Financed by endowment.
Collections: 16th - 17th century Flemish paintings; †prints; 19th century paintings; Oceanic collection of tribal arts and artifacts; †20th century American paintings, sculpture, graphics; †Ohio painters.
Exhibitions: Nine visiting shows (individual and group) per year, plus selected works from permanent collection. Annual group exhibits: Central Ohio Watercolor Society; Bexley Area Art Guild; Ohio Liturgical Art Guild; Senior Student Show; Art Faculty Show.
Activities: Classes for adults and children; lect open to the public, 4 vis lectr per yr; concerts; gallery talks; tours; competitions; individual paintings and original objects of art lent on special request only.
Library. Tel: 614-236-7108. *Dir* Dr Albert Maag. Open to students, faculty, staff, and for reference only to the public. Holdings: Vols 2000; Per subs 7.

COLUMBUS GALLERY OF FINE ARTS, 480 E Broad St, 43215. Tel: 614-221-6801. *Pres* Mrs Richard M Ross; *Dir* Budd Harris Bishop; *Cur Coll* Steven W Rosen; *Development Dir* James V Buchanan; *Registrar and Curator Decorative Arts* Katherine W Paris.
Open Tues, Thurs, Fri & Sun 11 AM - 5 PM; Wed 11 AM - 8:30 PM; Sat 10 AM - 5 PM; cl Mon & holidays. Admis adults $150, children, senior citizens and students 50¢. Estab 1878 to administer gifts, to promote the fine arts and obtains grounds and erect buildings and to establish and maintain a Gallery of Fine Arts; original building constructed in 1931 in an Italianate palatial style, contemporary style New Wing added in 1974; objects of the collection date from Mesopotamian votive cones c 2225 BC to contemporary multi-media works. Average Annual Attendance: 150,000. Mem: 4000; dues $25.
Income: Financed by endowment, membership, city and state appropriations).
Collections: Ferdinand Howald Collection of modern French, and modern American, especially 20th century; Frederick W Schumacher Collection of Renaissance, Baroque, 19th and 20th century American and European paintings; Lillie Gill Derby Collection of Old Masters leading collection of paintings, especially English and Dutch portraiture; Nevelson O'Keeffe purchases.
Exhibitions: (1976-78) Conserving Our Cultural Heritage; American Impressionism Rediscovered; Beaux Arts Designer/Craftsman, Richard Anuszkiewicz in Retrospect; Masters of the Camera; Steiglitz, Stechen and Their Successors; Athletes by Warhol; Jamie Wyeth: Recent Paintings.
Publications: Exhibition catalogs and books about the permanent collection.

Activities: Classes for adults and children; dramatic programs; docent training; film series; lectr open to the public; concerts; gallery talks; tours; artmobile; individual paintings and original objects of art lent to gallery members; lending collection is not part of permanent collection and contains framed reproductions, original art works, original prints, paintings and sculpture; traveling exhibitions organized and circulated; museum shop selling books, magazines, slides and original contemporary crafts by Ohio artists.
Library: Open to staff and volunteers for reference only. Holdings: Vols 8000.

OHIO HISTORICAL SOCIETY, 1982 Velma Ave, 43211. Tel: 614-466-4663. *Dir* Thomas H Smith; *Assoc Dir* Charles C Pratt; *Asst Dir* Michael J Devine; *Acting Head Educ Div* Amos Loveday; *Head Archaeology* Martha Otto; *Head History* Tom Hartig.
Open Mon - Sat 9 AM - 5 PM; Sun 10 AM - 5 PM. No admis. Estab 1885, date on which Ohio Historical Society was chartered, to promote a knowledge of history, natural history, and archaeology, especially of Ohio; to collect and maintain artifacts, books, and archives, relating to Ohio's history; main gallery covers over one acre of floor space and includes exhibits on history, natural history, archaeology and furniture; several audio-visual theatres and a natural history demonstration laboratory. Average Annual Attendance: 500,000. Mem: 10,500; dues individual $10, family $15; annual meeting Sept.
Income: $4,500,000 (financed by endowment, membership, state appropriation and contributions). Purchases: $100,000.
Collections: (Art) †Artifacts; †paintings; †glassware; ceramics, †furniture; †clothing; archaeology.
Exhibitions: Ohio in the Centennial Year, 1876; Images for Everyone; The First 50 Years of American Photography; Ohio in the American Revolution; History of American Currency; traveling exhibits.
Publications: Museum Echoes, newsletter, monthly; Ohio History, scholarly journal, quarterly.
Activities: Docent training; lectures; individual paintings and original objects of art lent; lending collection contains film strips; traveling exhibitions organized and circulated; sales shop selling books, magazines, reproductions; prints; slides and other souvenir items, post cards, jewelry.
Archives and Library. Tel: 614-466-4663. *Head Librn* Anita Lunn; *Head of Archives/Manuscripts* Dennis East. Open to the public for reference only. Holdings: Vols 100,000; Per subs 400; AV—Oral history interviews; motion picture films 5500; Other—Maps 3000. Special Collections: Rare books; Ohio newspapers; Coonskin Library; Ohio government documents; papers of early Ohio political leaders; maps; broadsides; posters; lithographs.

OHIO STATE UNIVERSITY, Fine Arts Library, 1813 N High St, 43210. Tel: 614-422-6184. *Head Fine Arts Library* Jacqueline D Sisson.
Open Mon - Thurs 8 AM - 10 PM; Fri 8 AM - 5 PM; Sat 10 AM - 4 PM; Sun 2 - 10 PM. Estab 1930's, to support the academic programs of the university including faculty research; gallery not maintained. Circ: 109,289.
Income: $34,755 (financed by state appropriation).
Holdings: Vols 56,984; Per subs 353; AV—Microfiche, microfilm; Other—Exhibition catalogs, photographs from Decimal Index of the Art of the Low Countries.
Special Subjects: Medieval and Renaissance; Slavic publications with special emphasis on Byzantine painting; Archival materials on microfiche such as Victoria and Albert museum collection.
Activities: Lect for members only.

COSHOCTON

JOHNSON-HUMRICKHOUSE MEMORIAL MUSEUM,* Sycamore & Third Sts, 43812. Tel: 614-622-3155. *Dir* Mary M Shaw.
Open Tues - Sat 1 - 4:30 PM; Sun and holidays 2 - 5 PM; cl Mon except Memorial Day, July 4, Labor Day. No admis. Estab 1931, gift of two pioneer residents; occupies a school building erected in 1853; managed by Library Board.
Collections: American Indian baskets and bead work; Eskimo artifacts; material from Coshocton County Mound Builders; Chinese and Japanese porcelains, prints, embroideries, lacquers, cloisonne, jade, ivory, amber, wood carvings, bronze, brass, copper and pewter ware; European prints, pewter, porcelains, glass and laces; Aztec, Toltec and Mayan pottery heads. In 1947 acquired Miller-Preston bequest of furnishings and implements used by Coshocton County pioneer families.
Exhibitions: Traveling exhibitions; permanent collection exhibitions changed periodically.
Activities: Program, in close cooperation with city, parochial and county schools, includes gallery talks, lectures.
Library: Technical books for research supplied by City Library on permanent loan.

CUYAHOGA FALLS

RICHARD GALLERY AND ALMOND TEA GALLERY,* Divisions of Studios of Jack Richard, 2250 Front St, 44221. *Dir* Jack Richard; *Agent* Fran Nancarrow.
Open weekdays 9 AM - 5:30 PM; Sat 9:30 AM - 12:30 PM; no admis. Estab Almond Tea Gallery 1964, Richard Gallery 1960, for exhibition of local, regional and national works of art.
Income: Financed privately.
Collections: Brackman; Grell; Gleitsmann; Terry Richard; Ball; Cornwell; Loomis; and others.
Exhibitions: Maria von Trapp; Mitsuka Sakata; Susan Shoemaker; Brackman; Grumbacher Palette Collection; Akron Society of Artists; Dalton Collection of Japanese Art; Fletcher Collection of Indian Art; African Art; Pottery; Antique Glassware; Longnecker Collection.
Activities: Traveling exhibitions organized and circulated; individual paintings and original objects of art lent; lending collection of 300 paintings and prints; 300 items lent in average year; 10 active borrowers; photograph collection of 5000 prints; lect open to the public, 3 vis lectrs per yr; 20 gallery talks; 20-25 tours; competitions; scholarships. Book shop. Frame shop. Art supplies.
Library: Holdings—Vols 1000 for reference and some lending; Other—Clipping files 50,000 for reference.

DAYTON

DAYTON ART INSTITUTE, Forest and Riverview Aves (Mailing Add: PO Box 941, 45401). Tel: 513-223-5277. *Dir* Bruce H Evans; *Chief Cur* Kenneth L Mathis; *Asst Cur* Kathy K Foley; *Registrar & Asst Cur Asian Art* Rhonda Cooper; *Chmn Educ Dept* Honore S David; *Dir Development* Marie D Ferguson; *Pub Relations* Linda Steen.
Open Tues - Fri Noon - 5 PM; Sat 9 AM - 5 PM; Sun Noon - 5 PM. No admis. Estab 1929 for the public benefit. American Wing, Print Gallery, New Acquisitions Gallery, Special Exhibitions Gallery, Oriental Gallery, Contemporary Gallery, European 16th-18th Century Gallery, Medieval Gallery, Ancient Gallery. Average Annual Attendance: 30,000. Mem: 2000; dues $20 - $1000; annual meeting April.
Collections: †American Collection and Oriental Collection; European art from medieval to present.
Exhibitions: Art from Zaire; Delacroix and the French Romantic Print; Chinese Export Porcelain from the Reeves Collection; Edward Weston's Gifts to his Sister; German Expressionist Drawings from the Collection of D Thomas Bergen; Rodin's Burghers of Calais: Sculptural Studies; Artists; Authors, and Others: Drawings by David Levine; Not Normally on View; Paintings by George Cope; Soho: On the Market; Courtesans of the Floating World; All-Ohio Painting, Sculpture, Graphics and Photography Biennial 1979; The Dyer's Art: Ikat, Batik, Plangi.
Publications: Bulletin; annual report.
Activities: Classes for adults and children; docent training; lect open to public, 3-6 per yr; gallery talks; tours; individual paintings lent to members; traveling exhibitions organized and circulated; sales shop selling books, original art, toys and jewelry.
Library: Art Reference Library. *Librn* Helen Pinkney. Open to all.

WRIGHT STATE UNIVERSITY, Fine Arts Gallery, 45435. Tel: 513-873-2896 or 873-2397. *Dir* William H Spurlock, II; *Admin Asst* Kathleen J Letson.
Open Mon - Sat 10 AM - 4 PM; Wed & Thurs 5 - 7 PM. No admis. Estab 1974, devoted to exhibitions and research in contemporary art. A multi-leveled contemporary space with 1500 sq ft on each of two levels and 300 running feet of wall on each level. Available also for exhibition are areas outside on the University campus and selected sites in the greater Dayton area. Average Annual Attendance: 13,000.
Income: Financed through the University.
Collections: Small collection of works of contemporary art on paper.
Exhibitions: Installation or Project works by Vito Acconci, Barry Le Va, Cecile Abish, Patrick Ireland, Robert Irwin, Dennis Oppenheim, John Willenbecher; exhibitions of existing works by Rudolf Baranik, Richard Fisher, Michelle Stuart; regional artists and traveling exhibitions.
Publications: Artist's books and exhibition catalogs, 6 per year.
Activities: Lect open to public, 16 vis lectr per yr; gallery talks; individual paintings and objects of art lent to faculty and administrative areas; lending collection contains original art works; original prints; paintings; photographs and sculpture; traveling exhibitions organized and circulated; sales desk selling books.

DELAWARE

OHIO WESLEYAN UNIVERSITY, Department of Fine Arts, Humphreys Art Hall, 43015. Tel: 614-369-4431, exten 650. *Dir of Exhib* Marty J Kalb; *Chmn* Justin Kronewetter.
Open daily 9 AM - 4 PM; Sat 9 AM - Noon. No admis. Gallery estab 1915.

Collections: †Photography; †Prints.
Exhibitions: Monthly exhibitions in Lynn Mayhew Gallery; exhibitions of professional and student work; annual exhibition of contemporary photography. (1977-78) Eugene Jackson (prints); Craig Lucas (painting); Sharon Wybrants (painting); Barry Gunderson (sculpture); Jim Thornton (painting); Castilli (graphics, photography); Ban Kajitoni (ceramics); Robert Knipschild (painting); John Taylor (photography); Justin Kronewetter (photography).
Activities: Classes for children; art programs; vis artists workshops; lect open to the public, 10 vis lectr per yr; gallery talks; lending collection contains slides 40,000.
—**Beeghly Library,** Tel: 6145-369-4431, exten 650.
Open to the public.
Holdings: Vols 2200; Per subs 8.

FINDLAY

FINDLAY COLLEGE,* Egner Fine Arts Center, 1000 N Main St, 45840. Tel: 419-422-8313. *Dir* Douglas Salveson.
Open Mon - Fri 7 AM - 5 PM. Estab as a college art department, plus gallery.
Income: Financed by endowment.
Collections: †Primarily contemporary prints.
Exhibitions: 18 exhibitions of contemporary art and crafts and one retrospective exhibition during last three years.
Activities: Concerts, dramatic programs, classes for adults and children, competitions; scholarships. Book shop. Library.

GRANVILLE

DENISON UNIVERSITY ART GALLERY, 43023. Tel: 614-587-0810, exten 255. *Dir* Christopher Bunge; *Registrar* Letha Schetzsle; *Cur Burmese Art* Jane Terry Bailey.
Open Mon - Fri 10 AM - 4 PM; Sun 1 - 4 PM; cl Sat. No admis. Estab 1946 for educational purposes.
Income: Financed through University.
Collections: European and American drawings, paintings, prints and crafts; Burmese sculpture, manuscripts, paintings and crafts; Chinese ceramics, rubbings, sculpture and crafts; American Indian pottery and Central American arts and crafts.
Publications: Catalogs.
Activities: Lect open to public; individual paintings and original objects of art lent.
Library: Open to students and faculty only for reference.

KENT

KENT STATE UNIVERSITY
—**School of Art Gallery,** 44242. Tel: 216-672-7853. *Dir* James M Someroski.
Open Mon - Fri 8 AM - 5 PM; Sat 8 AM - Noon; cl school holidays. No admis. Estab 1950 as part of the instructional program at Kent State.
Collections: Paintings; sculpture; prints.
Exhibitions: Traveling exhibitions from museums; faculty and student one-man and group exhibitions; Annual Invitational Painting and Sculpture Show.
Publications: Catalogs.
Activities: Classes for students in museum preparation; gallery talks.
—**Architecture/Urban Studies Library.** Tel: 216-672-2854. *Librn* Edward J Hall, Jr; *Supvr* Judy Meyer.
Open 8 AM - 5 PM. Estab 1967.
Income: Financed by state appropriations.
Holdings: Vols 6435; Per subs 275, Per bound 1575; AV—Kodachromes 6400, microfilm 106; Other—Bibliographies 885; vertical files 52.
Publications: Urban Scene (newsletter), quarterly.

MANSFIELD

MANSFIELD ART CENTER,* Mansfield Fine Arts Guild, Inc, Inc, 700 Marion Ave, 44903. Tel: 419-756-1700. *Dir* H Daniel Butts III; *Exec Secy* Mrs Henry Van Horn.
Open Tues - Sun 12 AM - 5 PM; cl Mon & national holidays. No admis. Estab 1945, inc 1956, to maintain an art center in which exhibitions, lectures, gallery talks, special programs, symposia and series of classes for children and adults are provided for the North Central Ohio area; maintained by membership, commission on sales and classes. Gallery 5000 sq ft with flexible lighting, movable walls, props, etc to facilitate monthly exhibition changes. Average Annual Attendance: 15,000. Mem: 1050; dues $3 - $500; meetings Apr & Oct.
Income: $45,000.
Exhibitions: Changing exhibitions of member artists work, traveling shows & locally organized one-man, group and theme exhibitions changing monthly throughout the year.

Publications: Bimonthly newsletter and annual report.
Activities: Original objects of art lent through a rental gallery with minimal fees, 100 borrowers, 150-200 items per year; lectures open to public, an average of 6 vis lectrs per yr; film series; over 100 gallery talks mainly for school groups; classes for adults and children; competitions; scholarships.
Library: The library is basically a collection of monographs and studies of styles and periods for teacher and student reference. Holdings: Vols 750.

MARIETTA

CAMPUS MARTIUS MUSEUM AND OHIO RIVER MUSEUM, 601 Second St, 45750. Tel: 614-373-3750. *Mgr* John B Briley; *Asst Mgr* Juanita Etter.
Open daily 9:30 AM - 5 PM; cl New Year's Day, Thanksgiving and Christmas. Admis adults, 3 and over $1.50, children 6-12 75¢, children 5 and under free. Estab 1920 as part of the Ohio Historical Society to collect, exhibit and interpret historical items, including art and manuscripts, pertaining to Ohio's history and, particularly, to that of Marietta, the Northwest Territory (Ohio portion) and the Ohio River. Campus Martius Museum has 2500 sq ft of exhibition space on two floors plus a two-story home, a portion of the original fort of 1788-91, entirely enclosed within the building. The Ohio River Museum has approximately1500 sq ft of exhibit space in three separate buildings connected by walkway. Average Annual Attendance: 90,000.
Income: Financed by endowment, membership, state appropriation, other grants and fund raising.
Collections: (Art) Ohio River landscapes; early Ohio paintings, prints, and photographs; Ohio Company & Marietta materials; early family items from Putnam, Blennerhassett and other families; steamboat and riverboat models; 19th century Ohio decorative arts.
Exhibitions: Ohio Longrifle Exhibit; People on the River; Ohio University Photography Exhibit.
Activities: Classes for adults and children; museum tours; original objects of art lent to other museums for exhibitions; sales shop selling books, reproductions, prints, slides, crafts, and souvenir items.
Library: Open to the public for reference. Holdings: Vols 2000; Per subs 6.

MARIETTA COLLEGE,* Grover M Hermann Fine Arts Center, 45750. Tel: 614-374-5173. *Chmn Art Dept* M Jeanne Tasse.
Open Mon - Fri 8 AM - 11 PM; Sat 8 AM - 5 PM; Sun 1 - 11 PM. No admis. Center estab 1965. Gallery maintained. Average Annual Attendance: 20,000.
Collections: Permanent collection of contemporary American painters, sculptors and craftspeople; significant collection of African and pre-Columbian art.
Exhibitions: (Annual) Mainstreams, Marietta College International Competition; Marietta College Crafts National.
Publications: Marietta College Crafts Directory, semiannually.
Activities: Traveling exhibitions organized and circulated; lectures open to public; competitions. Book shop. Library.

MASSILLON

MASSILLON MUSEUM, 212 Lincoln Way, E, 44646. Tel: 216-833-4061. *Chmn* Robert E Dawson; *VChmn* Mrs. Howard Cooper; *Secy* Mrs. Richard Gessner; *Clerk-Treas* Raymond Ruwadi; *Dir* Mary M Merwin.
Open Tues - Sat 9:30 AM - 5 PM; Sun 2 - 5 PM. No admis. Estab 1933 as a museum of art and history with a representative collection of the fine arts and crafts with emphasis on the Ohio area; a representative historical collection of the people in Massillon area will be maintained. Average Annual Attendance: 17,000. Mem 1254; dues $5 and higher.
Income: Financed by state and county appropriations. Purchases: $928.
Collections: †Paintings, prints and drawings; †Crafts—ceramics, glass, jewelry; china; ivories; costumes; many others.
Exhibitions: Monthly exhibitions.
Publications: Pamphlet of activities and exhibitions, twice yearly.
Activities: Classes for adults and children; docent training; tours; competitions; individual paintings and original objects of art lent to qualified museums or like institutions for exhibition; sales shop selling crafts, toys, jewelry.

MIDDLETOWN

MIDDLETOWN FINE ARTS CENTER,* 116 S Main St, 45042. Tel: 513-424-2416. *Dir* Edward Burroughs.
Open Mon - Fri 9:30 AM - 3 PM; Sat 9 - 12 AM; Mon & Thurs eve 7:30 - 9:30 PM. Estab 1957 to provide facilities, program, and instruction, for the development of interests and skills in the visual arts, for students of all ages from Middletown and its surrounding communities; endowment through funds donated to Arts in Middletown (our funding agency). Annual meeting Mar.
Exhibitions: Annual Student Show; annual Area Art Show; sponsored the showing of the Mead Corporation's Collection; joint sponsorship of many varied shows with the Miami University, Middletown.
Activities: Classes in painting, ceramics, enameling on copper, calligraphy, design, silk screen and others from time to time; lect open to public, 3-4 vis lectrs per yr; gallery talks or tours occasionally, 3-4 per year; competitions.
Library: Holdings—Vols 472 for lending and reference.

NORTH CANTON

NORTH CANTON PUBLIC LIBRARY,* Little Art Gallery, 185 N Main St, 44720. Tel: 216-499-4712. *Pres* Mrs R T Warburton; *Secy* Mrs Ed Hill; *Dir* Mrs John L Zumkehr.
Open during regular library hours Mon - Fri 10 AM - 9 PM; Sat 10 AM - 5 PM. No admis. Estab 1936 to encourage and promote appreciation and education of fine art, graphic arts, commercial art and other related subjects; recognizes and encourages local artists by promoting exhibitions of their work. Average Annual Attendance: 5000.
Income: Budget $1200 (financed by city and state appropriation). Purchases: $500
Collections: †Original works by contemporary artists.
Exhibitions: Monthly shows featuring the works of many northeastern Ohio artists, some of them nationally known; competitive May show each year with cash awards totaling $270; art from the classrooms of the North Canton Public Schools (April); shows featuring our collection of famous reproductions of religious subjects as well as secular.
Activities: 1109 color reproductions in lending collection; 446 circulations in 1974; lectures open to the public; 2 gallery talks and tours per year; classes for adults and children; competitions.

OBERLIN

INTERMUSEUM CONSERVATION ASSOCIATION, Allen Art Bldg, 44074. Tel: 216-775-7331. *Pres* Bret Waller; *VPres* Budd Bishop; *Secy-Treas & Dir* Marigene H Butler; *Admin Asst-Art Historian* Ricardo Barreto; *Chief Conservator* Philip Vance; *Painting Conservators* Leni Potoff, Carol Mancusi-Ungaro, Mervin Richard; *Paper Conservator* vacant; *Secy-Acct* Ruth E Spitler.
For further information see National and Regional Organizations.

OBERLIN COLLEGE, Allen Memorial Art Museum, Main & Lorain Sts, 44074. Tel: 216-775-8665. *Dir* Richard E Spear; *Cur* Chloe H Young; *Cur Modern Art* Stephen C McGough; *Honorary Cur Modern Art* Ellen H Johnson.
Open during school year Tues 11 AM - 5 PM; Wed - Fri 11 AM - 5 PM; Sat & Sun 2 - 5 PM; cl Mon; during vacations, summer and Jan term Wed - Sun 2 - 5 PM; cl Mon & Tues. No admis. Estab 1917 to serve teaching needs of Oberlin College Art Dept and other departments of the College and the College community. Original building designed by Cass Gilbert; new addition opened Jan 1977, designed by Venturi & Rauch. Average Annual Attendance: 27,000. Mem 650; dues student $5, - $30.
Income: Financed by endowment and membership.
Collections: †Sculpture, †painting, †graphics, †decorative arts, from early Egyptian period to present day.
Exhibitions: Frequent traveling exhibitions and specially assembled exhibitions; Oberlin Artists; The Stamp of Whistler.
Publications: Allen Memorial Art Museum Bulletin.
Activities: Gallery tours on request; lect open to public; competitions; individual paintings and original objects of art are lent to other institutions for special exhibitions; lending collection contains original art works 250 for lending to students on a semester basis; traveling exhibitions organized and circulated; sales desk selling reproductions, slides and museum publications.
—**Clarence Ward Art Library,** Allen Art Bldg, Tel: 216-775-8635. *Art Librn* Christina Huemer.
Open Mon - Thurs 8 AM - 5:30 PM and 7 - 11 PM; Fri 8 AM - 5:30 PM and 7 - 10 PM; Sat 9 AM - 5 PM; Sun 1 - 5 PM and 7 - 10 PM (abbreviated hours during vacation periods). Estab 1917 to serve the library needs of the Art Department, the Allen Memorial Art Museum and the Oberlin College community in the visual arts. Circ: 10,000.
Holdings: Vols 35,000; Per subs 200; AV—Microfilm; Other—Clipping files, exhibition catalogs, pamphlets and reproductions.
Special Collections: Jefferson Collection of early architectural books.
Activities: Library tours by appointment.

OXFORD

MIAMI UNIVERSITY ART CENTER,* Rowan Hall, 45056. Tel: 513-529-2232. *Coordr Mus Art Coll* Sterling Cook; *Asst in Charge of Folk Art* Bonnie Masson.
Open daily 1 - 5 PM, when exhibitions are up. Estab 1972 to care for and exhibit university art collections, to arrange for a variety of exhibitions from other sources, and for the educational and cultural enrichment for the university and community. Gallery is approx 180 ft of wall space. Average Annual Attendance: 8000.
Income: Financed by endowment and state appropriation. Purchases: $2000 - $70,000.
Collections: †Paintings; †prints; †sculpture; decorative arts; †folk art, largely Middle European, Middle Eastern, Mexican, Central and South American.
Exhibitions: 6-8 exhibitions per year.
Publications: Brochures and/or small catalogs for exhibits, approx 6-8 per year.
Activities: Lect open to public, 4 vis lectrs per yr; gallery talks; tours. Items from folk art collections lent to university and local public schools; lending collection contains Kodachromes 2500, motion pictures and photograph collection of 1500 prints.
Library: Holdings—Vols 200 for reference only.

SPRINGFIELD

CLARK COUNTY HISTORICAL SOCIETY, Memorial Hall, 45504. Tel: 513-324-0657. *Pres* George B Raup; *Secy* Linda Davis; *Exec Dir & Cur Museum* George H Berkhofer.
Open Tues - Thurs 9 AM - 4 PM; Sat 9 AM - 1 PM. Estab 1897 for collection and preservation of Clark County history and historical artifacts. Mem: 600; dues individual $6.00; family $7.50; annual meeting Nov.
Income: $7500 (financed by appropriation). Purchases: $7500.
Collections: Books, paintings and items of everyday life; oil paintings, mostly mid-late 19th century, of prominent Springfielders, plus some European landscapes.
Publications: Newsletter, monthly.
Activities: Monthly meetings and lect open to public; books for sale; restoration project: The David Crabill House (1826), located at Lake Lagonda in Buck Creek State Park.
Library: Open to public. Holdings: Vols several thousand. Special Collections: Photograph collection; Early newspapers back to 1830's.

SPRINGFIELD ART CENTER, 107 Cliff Park Road, 45501. Tel: 513-325-4673. *Chmn Bd* Ralph H Wetherbee, Jr; *Pres* Mrs. Joseph C Shouvlin; *VPres* Roger Kadel; *Secy* George McCleary; *Dir* Patricia Catron.
Open Tues - Fri 9 AM - 5 PM; Sat 9 AM - 3 PM; Sun 2 - 4 PM; cl Mon. No admis. Estab 1951 for educational and cultural purposes, particularly the encouragement of the appreciation, study of, participation in and enjoyment of the fine arts. Average Annual Attendance: 25,000. Mem: 1000; dues individual $15, family $25, sustaining $35, benefactor $100; meetings third Tues in June.
Income: $85,000 (financed by endowment, membership, and tuition fees).
Collections: 19th & 20th Century artists (mostly American, some French).
Exhibitions: Monthly exhibits.
Publications: Newsletter, monthly.
Activities: Classes for adults and children; lect open to public, 3 - 4 vis lectr per yr; tours; sales shop selling original art.
Library: For reference. Holdings: Vols 1500; Per subs 12. Special Subjects: Photography.

TOLEDO

BLAIR MUSEUM OF LITHOPHANES AND CARVED WAXES, 2032 Robinwood Ave (Mailing Add: 2243 Ashland Ave, 43620). Tel: 419-243-4115. *Cur* Laurel G Blair.
Open by appointment at any time, for groups of 10 - 20.
Admis $2. Estab 1965 for the purpose of displaying lithophanes and carved waxes—the only museum of its kind in the world; there are five galleries. Average Annual Attendance: 2000. Mem: 145; dues $10.
Income: $30,000 (financed by membership and sales to members).
Collections: Wax collection is being enlarged as the lithophane collection is the world's largest, with 2300 examples; only 1000 can be shown at once.
Publications: Bulletin, bi-monthly.
Activities: Lect open to the public.
Library. For reference only. Holdings: Vols 100; Per subs 30.

SPECTRUM, FRIENDS OF FINE ART, INC, 5304 Elmer Dr, 43615. Tel: 419-531-7769. *Pres* Helen Hawley; *VPres* Line Bloom-Draper; *Corresp Secy* Colleen Langenderfer; *Rec Secy* Odessa W Rowan; *Treas* Lana Discepolo.
Open Tues - Sun 1 - 5 PM; cl Mon. No admis. Estab 1976 to encourage and support public appreciation of Fine Art and to organize and promote related activities; promote mutual understanding and cooperation among artists, artist groups and the public; promote beautification of Toledo through use of art work; Clubhouse (2 galleries, sales room and office) part of Crosby Village Green in Crosby Gardens; large garage adjacent soon to be remodeled into Art Education Center. Average Annual Attendance: 1500 - 2000. Mem: 350; dues student $7, adult $15 - $25; annual meeting May.
Income: Approximately $6000 - $7000 (financed by membership and fund-raising events).
Exhibitions: Membership Show, Edison Co-juried, Spectrum touring Show (six locations); Spots Exhibitions; Summer Fiesta; Sauders Museum; Photographic Exhibition; Promenade Park; Scarab Show.
Publications; Spectrum (newsletter), monthly.
Activities: Classes for adults and children; lect open to the public, 4-5 vis lectr per yr; competitions; traveling exhibitions organized and circulated; sales shop selling original art.

TOLEDO ARTISTS' CLUB, 1456 Sylvania Ave, 43612. Tel: 419-478-5222. *Pres* Helen A Grude; *First VPres* Ernest Spring; *Second VPres* Dale Keiser; *Secy* Helen Packard; *Treas* Lowell Skilliter.
Open Mon - Fri 1 - 5 PM. Estab 1943, the clubhouse is currently in process of relocating. Temporary forwarding address is 3560 Maxwell Rd, Toledo, OH 43606. Mem: 500; dues $15 (variable).
Income: Financed by memberships and exhibitions.
Exhibitions: Approximately 100 paintings in monthly exhibits.
Publications: Newsletter, monthly.
Activities: Classes for adults and children; lect open to the public; competitions; gallery sales of original art.

TOLEDO FEDERATION OF ART SOCIETIES, PO Box 5588, 43613. Tel: 419-255-8000. *Pres* Dale Keiser; *First VPres* Edith Franklin; *Second VPres* Sharon Breay; *Recording Secy* Beryl Preketes; *Treas* Christine Turnbull; *Corresp Secy* Peggy Snug.
Estab 1917 to arrange for annual area exhibition. Mem: 13 area clubs; dues $10; meetings first Sat after first Fri (Sept - May).
Income: Financed by membership, city appropriation, fund drive and Ohio Arts Council Grant. Purchases: Varies yearly.
Collections: Permanent collection acquired by purchase award at annual exhibit.
Activities: Annual exhibition organized; competitions with cash awards, purchase and special awards, and medal; individual paintings and original objects of art lent to civic organizations; lending collection contains original art works, original prints, paintings and sculpture.

TOLEDO MUSEUM OF ART,* Monroe St at Scottwood Ave, 43609 (Mailing Add: Box 1013, 43697). Tel: 419-255-8000. *Pres* Marvin S Kobacker; *Dir* Otto Wittmann; *Assoc Dir* Roger Mandle; *Asst Dir Educ* Charles F Gunther; *Registr* Patricia Whitesides; *Chief Cur* William Hutton; *Cur Contemp Art* Robert F Phillips; *Cur Ancient Art* Kurt T Luckner; *Assoc Cur European Paintings* William J Chiego; *Asst Cur Decorative Arts* Roger M Berkowitz; *Supvr Music* Joyce Young; *Supt* George F Hartman, Jr.
Open 9 AM - 5 PM; Sun & Mon 1 - 5 PM; cl major legal holidays. No admis. Estab and·inc 1901; building erected 1912, additions 1926 and 1933. Average Annual Attendance: 463,000. Mem: 6000; dues $15 and higher.
Collections: †Edward Drummond Libbey and Arthur J Secor collection paintings; †Maurice A Scott galleries of American paintings; †George W Stevens collection of books and manuscripts; †sculpture; †prints; †ancient and modern glass; †stained glass; †ceramics; †Oriental, †Egyptian, †Assyrian and †classical antiquities; †medieval art; †contemporary art in Glass Gallery.
Exhibitions: Annual exhibitions of the work of Toledo area artists and several traveling exhibitions schueduled each year.
Publications: Quarterly Museum News; monthly Calendar Guide to the Collections; Art in Glass.
Activities: Lectures; concerts; classes; talks for public school groups; conducts Museum School of Design (See Schools).
—Library. *Librn* Anne O Reese.
Holdings: Vols 30,000 for reference; Other—Slides 40,000.

VERMILION

GREAT LAKES HISTORICAL SOCIETY, 480 Main St, 44089. Tel: 216-967-3467. *Pres* Alexander C Meakin; *VPres* Douglas S Keith; *Secy* T A Sykora; *Business Mgr* Arthur N O'Hara.

Open daily 11 AM - 5 PM (summer 6 PM). Admis adults $1, children 50¢. Estab 1944 to promote interest in discovering and preserving material about the Great Lakes and surrounding areas. Maintains art gallery as part of maritime history museum. Average Annual Attendance: 25,000. Mem: 2700; dues from $12 - $500; meetings May and Oct.

Income: $100,000 (financed by endowment, membership and sales from Museum Store).

Collections: Unparalleled collection of ship models, marine relics, paintings and photographs dealing with history of the Great Lakes; also a collection of marine engines and navigational instruments. The Inter-Lake Yachting Asn Room houses eighty years of yachting history on the Great Lakes.

Exhibitions: Willard Collection (Spirit of '76); Maritime History in Art (James Clary).

Publications: Inland Seas, quarterly; Chadburn (newsletter), quarterly.

Activities: Educ dept; lect open to public, 5 vis lectr per yr; tours; competitions, a model boat show is held annually for exhibition and competition of craftsmanship in models of Great Lakes vessels. Starting 1978 competition held in Jan in conjunction with Mid-America Boat Show in Cleveland. Special awards for Best of Show, also plaque in field of restoration of antique boat; sales shop selling books, magazines, original art, prints, slides and gifts.

WILLOUGHBY

FINE ARTS ASSOCIATION,* School of Fine Arts, 38660 Mentor Ave, 44094. Tel: 216-951-7500. *Pres* Brian Sherwin; *Secy* Mrs Ronald Chapnick; *Exec Dir* James J Savage; *Visual Arts Coordr* Doris Foster.
Open weekdays 9 AM - 9 PM; Sat & performance times 9 AM - 5 PM. No admis. Estab 1957 to bring arts education to all people regardless of their ability to pay, race or social standing. Gallery maintained. Average Annual Attendance; 20,000. Mem: 1152; dues $15 and up; annual meeting Apr.

Income: Financed by membership and donations.

Exhibitions: Monthly exhibitions, theme, one-man and group; annual juried exhibit for area artists.

Activities: Art classes; in-school programs; lect open to public, 10-15 vis lectrs per yr; three-county area served by Extension Department; material available to schools and organizations; gallery talks; tours; concerts, dramatic programs, classes for adults and children, competitions; scholarships.

Library: Holdings—Vols 5000 for reference only.

WOOSTER

COLLEGE OF WOOSTER ART-CENTER MUSEUM, University St, 44691. Tel: 216-264-1234, exten 388. *Dir* Dr Arnold Lewis; *Asst Mus Dir* Phyllis Blair Clark.
Open Mon - Sat 9 AM - Noon & 1 - 5 PM; Sun 2 - 5 PM. No admis. Estab 1944 to provide an opportunity for students, faculty and the local community to view original works of art. Gallery formerly College Library, main floor has large open areas and upper balcony more intimate exhibition space. Average Annual Attendance: 5000.

Income: $7000 (financed through College).

Collections: Paintings, prints, sculpture, tapestries, Chinese bronzes and porcelains.

Exhibitions: Monthly exhibitions from the collection and traveling exhibitions; Invitational Functional Ceramics Exhibition.

Activities: Lect open to public, 10 - 15 vis lectr per yr; gallery talks.

Library: The Andrews Library. *Dir* Robert Golter.

YELLOW SPRINGS

ANTIOCH COLLEGE, Noyes, Read & Gray Galleries, 45387. Tel: 513-767-4061, exten 464. *Chmn Art Dept* Allan Jones.
Open Mon - Fri 1 - 4 PM. No admis. Estab 1972. Noyes Gallery to offer works to students and the community that both challenge and broaden their definitions of Art; Gray Gallery, a small photo gallery; Read Gallery, primarily a student gallery. Average Annual Attendance: 3000.

Exhibitions: Sid Chafetz—30 Years in Ohio; Ohio University Graduates Print Exhibit; Area Invitational; John Ritters Kamp—Sculpture/Drawings/Paintings; plus others.

Activities: Lect open to public, 6 - 10 vis lectr per yr; traveling exhibitions organized and circulated.

YOUNGSTOWN

BUTLER INSTITUTE OF AMERICAN ART, 524 Wick Ave, 44502. Tel: 216-743-1711. *Dir & Pres* Joseph G Butler; *Assoc Dir* Clyde Singer; *Cur* Dr Eric C Hulmer; *Educ Dir* Alice Goldcamp.

Open Tues - Sat 11 AM - 4 PM; Sun Noon - 4 PM; cl Mon. No admis. Estab 1919, and is the first museum building to be devoted entirely to American Art. Average Annual Attendance: 80,000. Mem: 700 (Friends of American Art, art auxiliary organization).

Income: Financed by endowment.

Collections: American paintings dating from 1750 to present: †Oils, †watercolors, †drawings; †sculpture and ceramics; prints; †paintings and drawings of the American Indian; †32 paintings of Clipper ships from Sail to Steam; seven ship scale models.

Exhibitions: Annual Midyear Show; Ohio Ceramic Annual. Other exhibitions include Polish Arts Club Show; Area Artists Annual; Youngstown State University Annual; numerous traveling exhibitions.

Publications: Catalog of Permanent Collection with numerous reproductions issued Sept 1951; Supplements issued 1954, 1959, 1960, 1966 and 1969.

Activities: Classes for children; lect open to the public; concerts; gallery talks; tours; individual paintings and original objects of art lent to qualified museums, institutions; lending collection contains color reproductions, original art works, original prints, paintings, photographs, sculpture, slides; traveling exhibitions organized and circulated; sales shop selling books, original art, reproductions, slides.

Library: Open to the public for reference only. Holdings: Vols 400; Per subs 15.

YOUNGSTOWN STATE UNIVERSITY, Kilcawley Center Art Gallery, 410 Wick Ave, 44555. Tel: 216-742-3575. *Prog Dir* M Kevin Fahey Jr; *Art Gallery Coordinator* Sherri Lynn Hill.
Open Mon - Thurs 10 AM - 8 PM; Fri 10 AM - 3 PM. Estab April 10, 1974 to provide the university and the community with a diversified art program; gallery is 100 running ft. Average Annual Attendance: 10,000.

Income: Financed by university appropriation. Purchases: $1000.

Collections: †Kilcawley Collection includes works by Alan Davie, Jim Dine, Don Eddy, Robert Indiana, Alfred Leslie, Andy Warhol, Robert Rauschenberg.

Exhibitions: (1976-78) Alfred Leslie, Jasper Johns, Nelson Stevens, Bing Davis, John Downs, Student & Faculty Shows.

Activities: Lect open to the public, 4 vis lectr per yr; gallery talks; individual paintings lent to anyone on exchange.

ZANESVILLE

ZANESVILLE ART CENTER, 620 Military Road, 43701. Tel: 614-452-0741. *Dir* Dr Charles Dietz; *Secy & Registrar* Mrs Joseph Howell; *Pres Bd Trustees* Walker Huffman; *Pres Bd Dir* Mrs Peter Fomenko; *Cur Oriental Art* Mrs Willis Bailey; *Cur Glass* William Brown.
Open daily 1 - 5 PM; cl Fri and holidays. No admis. Estab 1936 to provide a public center for the arts and crafts, permanent collections and temporary exhibitions, classes in art and crafts, library of art volumes and a meeting place for art and civic groups. There are eleven galleries for old and modern Master paintings, sculpture, prints, ceramics, glass, photography, children's art and gift art. Average Annual Attendance: 25,000. Mem: 300; dues $10 and up.

Income: Financed by endowment, membership.

Collections: †American, European and †Oriental paintings, sculptures, ceramics, prints, drawings, and crafts; †Midwestern and †Zanesville ceramics and glass; †children's art.

Exhibitions: Paintings and Prints—Bevlin Simson; Paintings and Collages—Lyn Kierns; Paintings, Drawings, Prints, Collages—Madaline Pepper; Ceramics and Glass—John Gilmore; Paintings and Collages—Carol Owen; Prints, Joyce White; Photographs (Ken Frick); Needlepoint Show, Dorothy Van Voorhis; Art Association Show; Art and Crafts Exhibition.

Publications: Bulletin, monthly.

Activities: Classes for adults and children; lect open to public, 5 vis lectr per yr; concerts; gallery talks; tours; competitions; individual paintings lent to public institutions; sales shop selling original art, prints.

—**Library.** *Librn* Mrs Joseph Howell.
Open to members of the public library.

Holdings: Vols 4500; Per subs 10; Other—Slides, color reproductions, film strips.

Special Collections: Midwestern & Zanesville glass.

OKLAHOMA

ANADARKO

NATIONAL HALL OF FAME FOR FAMOUS AMERICAN INDIANS, Hiway 62, E of Anadarko (Mailing Add: Box 808, 73005, Attn Paul T Stonum). Tel: 405-247-3000, 247-5795. *Pres* Allie Reynolds; *Exec VPres/Dir* Paul T Stonum; *Treas* Lorraine Cox; *Secy* Sally Stonum.

Open during daylight hours, seven days a week. No admis. Estab 1952 to honor famous American Indians who have contributed to the culture of America, including statesmen, innovators, sportsmen, warriors, to teach the youth of our country that there is reward for greatness; an Outdoor Museum in a landscaped area containing bronze sculptured portraits of Honorees; also bronze statues, tributes to two animals important in Indian culture. Average Annual Attendance: 10,000. Mem: Approx 1000; dues individual $5, family $10, life $100; annual meeting Aug.
Income: Financed by membership, city and state appropriation, and donation. Purchases: $2500 - $5000.
Collections: †Bronze busts; Indian paintings.
Exhibitions: Dedication ceremonies for Hiawatha, Mohawk.
Publication: Brochure.
Activities: Seminars of American Indian Culture.

SOUTHERN PLAINS INDIAN MUSEUM, US Hwy 62 (Mailing Add: PO Box 749, 73005). Tel: 405-247-6221. Cur Rosemary Ellison.
Open (June - Sept) Mon - Sat 9 AM - 5 PM; Sun 1 - 5 PM; (Oct - May) Tues - Sat 9 AM - 5 PM; Sun 1 - 5 PM; cl New Year's Day, Thanksgiving and Christmas. No admis. Estab 1947-48 to promote the development of contemporary native American arts and crafts of the United States. Administered and operated by the Indian Arts and Crafts Board, US Department of the Interior. There are changing exhibitions of works by contemporary native American artists and craftsmen of the United States; permanent exhibit of historic Plains Indian arts. Average Annual Attendance: 80,000.
Income: Financed by federal appropriation. Purchases: Primarily dependent upon gifts.
Collections: Contemporary Native American arts and crafts of the United States; Historic works by Southern Plains Indian craftsmen.
Exhibitions: Contemporary Southern Plains Indian Metalwork; Painted Tipis by Contemporary Plains Indian Artists; continuing series of one-person exhibitions.
Publications: One-person exhibition brochure series, monthly.
Activities: Gallery talks; traveling exhibitions organized and circulated.

ARDMORE

CHARLES B GODDARD CENTER FOR THE VISUAL & PERFORMING ARTS, First & D St SW, 73401. Tel: 405-226-0909. *Pres* Mrs Leon Daube; *Secy* Richard Colvert; *Managing Dir* Laurence London; *Treas* Jerome Westheimer; *Dir* Robert Batis and James E Thompson; *Office Secy* Sue Bacon.
Open Mon - Fri 9:30 AM - 4 PM; Sat 11 AM - 4 PM. No admis. Estab March 1970 to bring fine art programs in the related fields of music, art and films to local community at minimum cost; gallery to bring traveling exhibitions to Ardmore. Average Annual Attendance: 35,000. Mem: 450; dues $12 - $1000; monthly Advisory Board meeting, and semi-annual Primary Board meeting.
Income: $62,000 (financed by endowment).
Collections: Portraits, paintings and drawings.
Exhibitions: American Watercolor Society; Museum of New Mexico Exhibit; Gigliotti-Valli Batiks; Local Art Teachers Exhibit; Delahunty Gallery Exhibit; Ada Four Art Exhibit & Joanne; WPA Exhibit from Smithsonian; 9th Annual Ardmore Art Exhibit; Texas Watercolor Society.
Publications: Outlook, monthly.
Activities: Classes for adults and children; dancing; art; pottery; piano; adult ballroom dancing; ladies exercise and movement classes; lect open to the public; concerts; books for sale.

BARTLESVILLE

WOOLAROC MUSEUM, State Highway 123 (Mailing Add: Route 3, 74003). Tel: 918-336-6747. *Dir* Robert R Lansdown; *Cur Art* Lucinda Simmons; *Cur Exhib* Francis Letchworth.
Open daily 10 AM - 5 PM; cl Christmas. No admis. Estab 1929 to house art and artifacts of the Southwest. Museum dedicated by Frank Phillips. Gallery has two levels, five rooms upstairs and two rooms downstairs. Average Annual Attendance: Over 250,000.
Income: Financed by endowment.
Collections: American Indian artifacts; paintings; drawings; graphics; sculpture; Oriental art; Frank Phillip's personal items; prehistoric artifacts.
Activities: Lect open to public; gallery talks; tours; lending collection contains transparencies to be used to illustrate educational publications; museum shop selling books, original art, reproductions, prints, slides, Indian-made jewelry and pottery, postcards.
Library: Reference library open to employees only. Holdings: Vols 718.

CLAREMORE

WILL ROGERS MEMORIAL AND MUSEUM, W Will Rogers Blvd (Mailing Add: PO Box 157, 74017). Tel: 918-341-0719. *Cur* Dr Reba Neighbors Collins; *Mgr* Delmar L Collins; *Tour Guide* Greg Malek; *Secy* Patricia A Lowe.
Open Daily 8 AM - 5 PM. No admis. Estab 1938 to perpetuate the name, works, and spirit of Will Rogers. There are three main galleries, diorama room, foyer and gardens. The large Jo Davidson statue of Will Rogers dominates the foyer; the north gallery includes photographs and paintings of Will Rogers and his ancestors (including a family tree, explaining his Indian heritage), and many other personal items; east gallery has saddle collection and other Western things; Jo Mora dioramas. Average Annual Attendance: 500,000.
Income: Approx $100,000 (financed by state appropriation).
Collections: Jo Mora Dioramas (13); Count Tamburini oil of Will Rogers; paintings of Will's parents by local artists; mural by Ray Piercey; original of Will Rogers by Leyendecker; Borein etchings; collection of paintings by various artists commissioned by a calendar company with originals donated to Memorial; large equestrian statue (outdoors) by Electra Wagoner Biggs; bust by Electra Wagoner Biggs.
Exhibitions: (1979) Traveling exhibits are planned, plus possibly a traveling museum.
Publications: Brochures and materials for students.
Activities: Curator gives many lectures, shows Will Rogers films; many school tours come to the Memorial; assist with publishing project of Will Rogers works at Oklahoma State University; lending collection contains motion pictures, photographs 50, slides 144, 20 minute documentary of Will Rogers available to nonprofit organizations; museum shop selling books, magazines, reproductions of original photographs in sepiatone; slides.
Library: *Cur-Librn* Dr Reba Collins. Reference library for research by appointment only. Holdings: Vols 600, plus thousands of original writings. Special Subjects: Will Rogers, includes items on vaudeville, films, politics, travel, and aviation. Special Collections: Will Rogers letters, original writings for his books and newspaper columns; thousands of photographs, clippings, and others. About 40 films are in the library vault.

ENID

PHILLIPS UNIVERSITY,* Grace Phillips Johnson Art Gallery, University Station, 73701. Tel: 405-237-4433. *Cur* William T Henning, Jr.
Open Tues - Fri 10 AM - 5 PM; Sat, Sun & holidays 2 - 5 PM; cl National holidays. No admis. Estab 1966.
Collections: Paintings; sculpture; prints; decorative arts; historical material of the University.
Exhibitions: Varying traveling exhibitions, and exhibitions from the collection.
Activities: Lectures; gallery talks; guided tours; competitions.

GOODWELL

NO MAN'S LAND HISTORICAL SOCIETY, Sewell St, 73939. Tel: 405-349-2670. *Pres* Lona Neff Graham; *VPres* Henry C Hitch, Jr; *Mus Dir* Dr Harold S Kachel; *Cur & Secy* Joan Overton Kachel.
Open Tues - Fri 9 AM - 5 PM; Sat & Sun 1 - 5 PM; cl Mon & holidays. No admis. Estab 1934 to procure appropriate museum material with special regard to portraying the history of No Man's Land (Oklahoma Panhandle) and the immediate adjacent regions. The gallery is 14 ft x 40 ft (560 sq ft). Average Annual Attendance: 4000. Mem: 59; dues individual $5, organization $10, life $100.
Income: Financed by state appropriation and donations.
Collections: Oils by Pearl Robison Burrows Burns.
Exhibitions: Nine exhibits of art each year by local artists; six exhibits of other forms of art (sculpture, crafts, etc) by local craftsmen each year.
Activities: Lect open to public, 2 vis lectr per yr; gallery talks; tours.

LANGSTON

LANGSTON UNIVERSITY ART GALLERY, 73050. Tel: 918-466-2231. *Chmn* Wallace Owens.
Open Mon - Fri 8 AM - 5 PM. No admis. Estab 1959 to exhibit pertinent works of art, both contemporary and traditional, to serve as a teaching tool for students. Average Annual Attendance: 6000.
Income: Financed by state appropriation.
Collections: Award purchases.
Activities: Classes for adults; lect, 2 vis lectr per yr; gallery talks; tours.

LAWTON

INSTITUTE OF THE GREAT PLAINS, Museum of the Great Plains, 601 Ferris (Mailing Add: PO Box 68, 73501). Tel: 405-353-5675. *Dir* Steve Wilson; *Cur Anthropology* Towana Spivey; *Cur Exhibits* Raymond Watkins; *Cur Educ* Maryruth Prose; *Archaeologist* John Northcutt;

Registr Bette Franken; *Exhibits Technician* Gale Brown; *Bldg Supt* Adam Leday.
Open Mon - Fri 8 AM - 5 PM; Sat 10 AM - 5:30 PM; Sun 1:30 - 5:30 PM. No admis. Estab 1961 to collect, preserve, interpret, and exhibit items of the cultural history of man in the Great Plains of North America. Galleries of the Museum of the Great Plains express a regional concept of interpreting the relationship of man to a semiarid Plains environment. History, archaeology, and ethnological exhibits. Average Annual Attendance: 90,000. Mem: 800; dues $7.50.
Income: Financed by endowment, city and state appropriations.
Collections: Archaeological, ethnological, historical, and natural science collections relating to man's inhabitance of the Great Plains.
Exhibitions: Lawton Jr Service League Annual Juried Art Show.
Publications: Great Plains Journal, quarterly; Contributions to the Museum of the Great Plains 1-7, irregular; Museum Newsletter, irregular.
Activities: Classes for children; dramatic programs; docent training; lect open to public, 6 vis lectr per yr; gallery talks; museum shop selling books, magazines, original art, reproductions, prints.
—**Research Library,** Sixth & Ferris, 73502. Tel: 405-353-5676. *Cur Special Coll* Donnice Cochenour.
Open Mon - Fri 8 AM - 5 PM. Estab 1961 to provide research materials for the 10-state Great Plains region. Circ: Only to staff.
Income: Financed by endowment, city and state appropriations.
Holdings: Vols 15,000; Per subs 100; AV—Microfilm; Other—Photographs. Special Subjects: Archaeology, anthropology, history of the trans-Mississippi West, specifically the 10-state Great Plains Region.
Special Collections: Photographic collections; archives.

MUSKOGEE

BACONE COLLEGE MUSEUM, Ataloa Lodge, 74401. Tel: 918-683-4581, exten 220. *Dir Development* Gary W Wagner; *Admin Asst* Roseanna Spinks.
Open Mon - Fri 8 AM - Noon & 1 - 4:30 PM. No admis. Estab to enhance Indian culture by having a collection of artifacts (including bead work, pottery, weaving, and basketry) from various Indian tribes. One large room. Average Annual Attendance: 1000.
Income: Financed through Bacone College.
Collections: Indian crafts and artifacts: silverwork, weapons, blankets, dolls, beadwork, pottery, weaving, and basketry.
Activities: Tours.

FIVE CIVILIZED TRIBES MUSEUM, Agency Hill, Honor Heights Drive, 74401. Tel: 918-683-1701. *Pres* John T Griffin Jr; *Secy* Charlene Adair; *Dir* Mrs Spencer Denton.
Open Mon - Sat 10 AM - 5 PM; Sun 1 - 5 PM. Admis adults 50¢; student 25¢; group rates available. Estab 1966 to exhibit artifacts, relics, history, and traditional Indian art of the Cherokee, Chickasaw, Choctaw, Creek, and Seminole Indian Tribes. Average Annual Attendance: 33,000. Mem: 1242; dues $5-$300; annual meetings April and October.
Income: $48,000 (financed by membership, and admissions).
Collections: †Traditional Indian art by known artists of Five Tribes heritage; †Books, manuscripts, documents and letters pertaining to history of Five Civilized Tribes and Indian Territory.
Exhibitions: Competitive Art Show; Students Competitive Show; Annual Judged Exhibition and Sale of beadwork, pottery, basketry and silver.
Publications: Newsletter, bimonthly.
Activities: Competitions; museum shop selling books, magazines, original art, reproductions, prints, beadwork, pottery, basketry and other handmade items.
—**Library.** *Chmn* Frances R Brown; *Dir* Mrs Spencer Denton.
Open Mon - Sat 10 AM - 5 PM; Sun 1 - 5 PM. Estab 1966 to preserve history, culture, traditions, legends, etc of Five Civilized Tribes (Cherokee, Creek, Choctaw, Chickasaw, and Seminole tribes). Maintains an art gallery.
Income: Financed by Museum.
Holdings: Vols 3500; Per subs 5; AV—Cassettes, lantern slides; Other—Clipping files, exhibitions catalogs, framed reproductions, manuscripts, memorabilia, original art works, original documents, pamphlets, photographs, prints, reproductions, sculpture.

NORMAN

UNIVERSITY OF OKLAHOMA
—**Museum of Art,** 410 W Boyd St, 73019. Tel: 405-325-3272. *Dir* Sam Olkinetzky; *Asst Dir* Edwin J Deighton; *Mus Secy* Mary Cook.
Open Tues - Fri 10 AM - 4 PM; Sat 10 AM - 1 PM; Sun 1 - 4 PM; cl Mon & holidays. Estab 1936 to provide cultural enrichment for the people of Oklahoma; to collect, preserve, exhibit and provide research in art of all significant periods. Approx 15,000 sq ft for permanent and tempo-

rary exhibitions on two indoor levels; 30 ft high, carpeted walls in 3 galleries; 2 galleries 120 sq ft each. Average Annual Attendance: 50,000. Mem: 100; dues $15 - $100; meetings Sept & Jan.
Income: Financed by university allocation.
Collections: †American all media; †crafts; European all media; African sculpture; †photography.
Exhibitions: (1977-78) Six Painters: Southwest; Oklahoma Designer Craftsmen; Egyptian Tapestries; African Sculpture.
Publications: Calendar of Activities; posters; announcements.
Activities: Docent training; lectures open to public; concerts; gallery talks; tours; competitions; individual paintings and original objects of art lent to other museums and galleries; lending collection contains original art works and prints, paintings 5000; museum shop selling books, magazines, original art, slides.
—**Art Library,** 550 Parrington Oval, Room 203 Jacobson Hall, 73019. Tel: 405-325-2841. *Art Librn* Paul D Bobo.
Open Mon - Fri 9 AM - 5 PM; Sat 10 AM - 1 PM; Mon - Thurs 6:30 - 9 PM. Estab to provide instructional support to the academic community of the university and general service to the people of the state. Circ: 6900.
Income: Financed by state appropriation.
Holdings: Vols 10,000; Per subs 55; AV—Microfiche, microfilm.

OKLAHOMA CITY

NATIONAL COWBOY HALL OF FAME AND WESTERN HERITAGE CENTER, 1700 NE 63rd St, 73111. Tel: 405-478-2250. *Exec Dir* Dean Krakel; *Managing Dir* Rich Muno; *Cur* Robert Davidson; *Educ Dir* Esther Long; *Pub Relations Dir* Marsi Thompson.
Open daily 9:30 AM - 5:30 PM; summer 8:30 AM - 6 PM. Admis adults $2, children $1, group rates available for 10 or more persons; cl New Year's Day, Thanksgiving & Christmas Day. Estab 1965 as a memorial shrine to great Westerners; Rodeo Hall of Fame; Hall of Fame of Great Western Performers. Mem: 5000; dues $25 and up; annual meeting Apr.
Income: Financed by membership.
Collections: Western Art, James Earle and Laura G Fraser Studio Collection; Albert K Mitchell Russell-Remington Collection; C M Russell bronzes; contemporary Western Art; Taos Collection; Fechin Collection; Schreyvogel Collection; Albert Bierstadt; Thomas Moran.
Exhibitions: National Academy of Western Art Exhibition; Ansel Adams Photography; Laura Gilpin Photography; temporary and traveling exhibitions.
Publications: Persimmon Hill Magazine, quarterly.
Activities: Docent guided tours, docent training, yearly seminar; competitions; with awards; traveling exhibitions organized and circulated.
Library: Open for reference. Holdings: Vols 7000; Per subs 75.

NATIVE AMERICAN PAINTING REFERENCE LIBRARY, Box 32504, 73132. *Dir* Arthur Silberman.
A privately funded institution committed to the premise that Indian painting is a valuable part of the American cultural heritage. It is a repository for any kind of information having a bearing on the history and development of native American paintings.
Holdings: Books, brochures, clipping files, photographs, correspondence catalogues, auction records, interview tapes.
Special Collections: Slides of paintings in private and public museums.
Activities: Traveling exhibitions organized and circulated.

OKLAHOMA ART CENTER, * Plaza Circle-Fair Park, 3113 Pershing Blvd, 73107. Tel: 405-946-4477. *Pres* Robert E Lee; *VPres* William Hulsey; *VPres* Jerome M Westheimer; *Treas* Charles Buchwald; *Dir* George F Kuebler; *Asst to Dir* Mary Catherine Connery.
Open Tues - Sat 10 AM - 5 PM; Sun 1 - 5 PM; cl holidays. No admis. Estab 1936, inc 1946 to encourage regional art activity and to present an educational program for adults and children. Average Annual Attendance: 50,000. Mem: 2500; dues $15 and higher.
Collections: †Contemporary prints, drawings, watercolors; †historical survey of prints and drawings; †American masters paintings; †American contemporary paintings and sculpture (including Washington Gallery of Modern Art complete collection and Eight State purchase awards).
Exhibitions: Annual Eight State Exhibition of Painting and Sculpture; National Exhibition of Prints and Drawings; Oklahoma Designer-Craftsmen Exhibition; Young Talent in Oklahoma (juried high school show with awards of seven $150 one-year college scholarships).
Activities: A program of changing national loan exhibitions; gallery tours; art films; circulating OAC collection exhibitions; lectures by guest speakers; gallery talks; family art events; Book Store; Sales & Rental Gallery.
Library: Holdings—Vols approx 1500, magazines and files back to 1936.
—**Arts Place II,** 115 Park Ave, 73116. Tel: 405-232-1787. *Mgr* June C Parsons; *Educ Dir* Betty Barnett; *Prog Dir* Peter Dolese.

Open Mon - Fri 10 AM - 4 PM. No admis. Estab 1977 to promote the visual and performing arts; providing these experiences to downtown, offering fine arts and crafts for sale and rental for offices and houses. Exhibition Gallery, Performing Arts Area, Sales and Rental Gallery.
Income: $10,000 (financed by membership and donations).
Exhibitions: One-man 2-5-man exhibitions plus permanent collection from OAC featured every three weeks in main gallery, 59 artists are offered in sales and rental gallery, drawing primarily from the various university art professors over the state.
Publications: OAC Bulletin; monthly mailer listing exhibitions and performances.
Activities: Classes for adults and children; dramatic programs; docent training; lect open to public, 12-15 vis lectrs per yr; concerts; gallery talks; tours; competitions; artmobile; individual paintings and original objects of art lent; lending collection contains cassettes, film strips, motion pictures, original art works and prints, paintings, photographs, sculpture; traveling exhibitions organized and circulated; sales shop selling books, magazines, original art, reproductions, prints.

OKLAHOMA HISTORICAL SOCIETY,* Division of Museums, Historical Bldg. Tel: 405-521-2491. *Pres Bd Trustees* George H Shirk; *Exec Dir & Ex-Officio Secy* Jack Wettengel; *Educ* Bruce E Joseph; *Historic Sites Dir* C E Metcalf; *Indian Archives* Martha Blaine; *Newspaper Archives* Mary Moran; *Publications* Dr Kenny Franks; *Mus Dir* R W Jones; *Cur Coll* Joe L Todd; *Exhib Technician* Roy T Pope; *Exhib Technician* John R Hill; *Registr* Inez Orr.
Open Mon - Fri 8 AM - 9 PM; Sat 8 AM - 6 PM; Sun 1:30 - 4:30 PM. No admis. Estab 1893 to provide an overview of the history of the State of Oklahoma, presented in graphic and three-dimensional forms, through the use of artifacts with which the history was made, to tell the story in chronological order, pointing out the highlights of history. Gallery has a feature of the month program to place focus on prominent Oklahoma artists whose works deal with historical interests. Average Annual Attendance: 50,000. Mem: 2000, dues $5; annual meeting Apr.
Income: $1.2 million (financed by state appropriations and membership, society depends on donations for additions to its collections).
Collections: (art) anthropological; archaeological; costumes; ethnological; folk; history; Indian; numismatic; specialized collections at historic sites and museums over the state.
Exhibitions: Chronologically progressive display areas of the main museum (depicting pre-history, Plains Indian history, the Five Civilized Tribes' occupancy of Indian territory, the land openings of the late 19th and early 20th centuries, statehood, and progress since statehood) are permanent; feature of the month program.
Publications: Mistletoe Leaves, monthly newsletter; The Chronicles of Oklahoma, scholastic quarterly; and various brochures and reprints.
Activities: Guided tours for school groups and other groups; junior historian clubs; special presentations and study programs for children and adults; other interpretative programs; lect open to the public, approx 40 vis lectrs per yr; approx 500 gallery talks; approx 2200 tours. Book shop.
Library: Dir Research Library Alene Simpson. For reference only. Holdings: Vols approx 40,000; photograph collection.

OKLAHOMA MUSEUM OF ART, 7316 Nichols Rd, 73120. Tel: 405-840-2759. *Pres* S T Fee; *Secy* Mrs James Randolph; *Dir* James K Reeve; *Bus Mgr* J Howard Christy; *Dir Educ* Cynthia Longley; *Mem Secy* Mrs Vernon Bradley.
Open Tues - Sat 10 AM - 5 PM; Sun 1 - 5 PM; cl Mon & major holidays. Admis adults $1, young people under 18 free, members free. Estab 1960, reorganized 1975, the Museum is committed to those ideals which hold that the great traditional values of art not only provide the soundest basis for continuing artistic expression, but offer a stability against which the merits of contemporary art can be weighed. The Museum sponsors exhibitions and offers studio and lecture art classes which familiarize the visitor and student with all art idioms; Twelve galleries are used for permanent collection and monthly changing temporary loan shows. Average Annual Attendance: (1977) 19,450. Mem: 1600, dues $15 - $1000; annual meeting Jan.
Income: $100,000 (financed by membership and private contributions).
Collections: †17th-20th century European and American paintings, tapestries, furniture, prints and drawings; major works include paintings by Courbet, Boudin, Delacroix, Lawrence and Blakelock; the museum is expanding collections through purchase and gifts to include works in all media.
Exhibitions: Works by major historic and contemporary artists presented in one-man and group shows on monthly-six week basis; annual competitive juried shows include Statewide High School Drawing Show, Members' Juried Annual, Annual Artists Salon; recent major shows include The Sculpture of Jacob Epstein, Japanese Painted Screens and Scrolls, Imperial Chinese Decorative Arts, The Birds and Beasts of Audubon, Masters of the Landscape: 1650-1900, and 100 Years of Native American Painting.
Publications: Monthly Calendar; exhibition catalogs; postcards; reproductions of art work.

Activities: Studio training for adults and children; fine arts and crafts fairs; lecture series; docent program; volunteer program; fund-raising benefits; concerts and dramatic presentation; air and bus tours; film series; gallery talks; competitions; scholarships; museum gift shop; sales-rental gallery.
Library: Reference library; small slide library. Holdings: Vols 500.

OMNIPLEX (formerly Oklahoma Science and Arts Foundation, Inc.), Kirkpatrick Center, 2100 NE 52nd, 73111. Tel: 405-424-5561. *Pres Bd of Trustees* Max L Knotts; *Acting Dir/Dir of Operations* William M Sudouth; *Dir of Educ/Asst Dir* Sherman Kent; *Coordr of Exhib* Donald Binkley; *Coordr of Promotion/Publicity/Membership and Special Events; Coordr of Vol* Dayna Hadley.
Open Mon - Sun 9 AM - 5 PM, including holidays. Admis Museum adult $1, children 50¢; Planetarium adult $1, children 6-12 years 50¢, under 6 free. Estab 1958 to focus on the inter-relationships between science, arts and the humanities; to supplement educational facilities offered in the public schools in the areas of arts and sciences. Average Annual Attendance: Projected 1,000,000. Mem: 900; dues $25 minimum.
Income: Financed by membership, private donations, Allied Arts Foundation, admission fees, class tuition.
Collections: (Art) George M Sutton Collection of Ornithology; Kirkpatrick Collection of ivory; Gerrer Collection of ancient artifacts.
Exhibitions: Traveling exhibitions every 6-10 weeks, ie, David Scharf Collection of Electron Microscope Photos; Kirlian photography; Myths, Legends and Lore; art pieces based on constellations; Transportation in Switzerland.
Publications: Newsletter, weekly.
Activities: Classes for adults and children; docent training; lect open to the public; tours; museum shop selling books, prints.
—**Florence O Wilson Library.** Tel: 405-424-5561. *Librn* Nancy Kempf. Open to the public for reference only.

OKMULGEE

CREEK COUNCIL HOUSE AND MUSEUM, Council Square, 74447. Tel: 918-756-2324. *Dir* Phyllis Warnock; *Pres* Joehugh Mansfield.
Open Tues - Sat 9 AM - 5 PM. No admis. Estab 1867, first Council House built, present Council House erected in 1878, to collect and preserve artifacts from the Creek History. Five rooms downstairs containing artifacts, four rooms upstairs showing art work, early time of Okmulgee, rooms of House of Warriors and House of Kings. Average Annual Attendance: 4000.
Income: Financed by membership and city appropriation.
Activities: Guided tours; sales shop selling books, magazines, reproductions.
Library: Creek Indian Memorial Association Library. Open to students for reference. Holdings: Vols 150; Per subs 15.

PONCA CITY

PONCA CITY ART ASSOCIATION,* Box 1394, 819 E Central, 74601. Tel: 405-765-9746. *Pres* Bob Westmoreland; *Secy* Arzella Walz.
Open Wed - Sun 1 - 5 PM. No admis. Estab 1947 to encourage creative arts, to furnish place and sponsor art classes, sponsor art exhibits and workshops. Mem: 600; dues $5 family; annual meeting first Tues in Apr.
Income: $10,000 (financed by membership and flea market).
Collections: Permanent fine arts collection, additions by purchases and donations.
Exhibitions: Eight per year.
Publications: Association Bulletin, quarterly.
Activities: Education Committee has spring and fall classes, lectures, workshops in all media, competitions, scholarships, annual fine arts festival, prizes and purchase awards.

PONCA CITY CULTURAL CENTER AND INDIAN MUSEUM, 1000 E Grand Ave, 74601. Tel: Center 405-765-5268, Museum 762-6123. *Cur* Delia F Castor; *Asst* Thelma Reeves.
Open weekdays, except Tues, 10 AM - 5 PM; Sun 1 - 5 PM. No admis. The Indian Museum was estab in 1936. Emphasis is placed on materials from the five neighboring tribes—The Ponca, Kaw, Otoe, Osage and Tonkawa—whose artistic use of beading, finger-weaving and ribbon-work is demonstrated in displays throughout the museum. The Cultural Center was dedicated in 1968. The purpose of the Center is to foster and preserve the culture of Ponca City and the surrounding area. The Center is housed in the former home of Ernest Whitworth Marland, oil man, one of Ponca City's most illustrious citizens and benefactor to the community at large. The Center houses four separate museums and two libraries. Average Annual Attendance: 22,553.
Income: Financed by city appropriation and donations.
Collections: Indian artifacts, Kansa, Osage; archaeology.

Exhibitions: Smithsonian; Indian Images and Pottery and Baskets; Exxon Local Arts and Crafts; Skin Paintings, and Other Sculpture and Paintings by Cliff Clay; one-man show of paintings and pottery by Clyde Otipoby.
Publications: Brochure
Activities: Tours; lessons in finger weaving; sales shop selling books, original art, reproductions, prints, Indian arts and crafts.
Library: *Cur* Delia F Castor. Holdings: Vols 200; Per subs 15. Special Subjects: Indian history and crafts; ranch and other local history; paintings, portraits, landscapes, skin painting, antiques; Indian clothing; photographs.

SHAWNEE

ST GREGORY'S ABBEY AND COLLEGE, The Mabee-Gerrer Museum, 1900 W MacArthur Dr, 74801. Tel: 405-9870 or 273-9878. *Dir* Robert G Dodson; *Chief Conservator* Martin Wiesendanger; *Assoc Conservators* Margaret Wiesendanger and John Walch; *Staff Asst* Justin Jones.
Open daily 2 - 4 PM; cl Sat. No admis. Estab 1915 to contribute to the cultural growth and appreciation of the general public of Oklahoma as well as of the student body of St Gregory's College. A new 15,000 sq ft gallery is presently under construction. All collections are being enlarged by purchases and by gifts. Average Annual Attendance: Approx 50,000. Dues $25.
Income: Financed by endowment, membership and foundation funds.
Collections: †Oil paintings by American and European artists; †etchings, †engravings, †serigraphs and †lithographs; †artifacts from ancient civilizations: Egyptian, Roman, Grecian, Babylonian, pre-Columbian north, south and central American Indian, and South Pacific.
Activities: Classes for adults and children; docent training; lect open to public; gallery talks; tours; competitions; individual paintings and original objects of art lent to other museums and galleries; lending collection contains nature artifacts, original art works and prints, paintings, sculpture; sales shop selling books, magazines, original art, reproductions, prints, replicas.
Library: Reference library open to art students and researchers. Holdings: Vols 1000; Per subs 10.

STILLWATER

OKLAHOMA STATE UNIVERSITY, Gardiner Art Gallery, Department of Art, Gardiner Hall, Morrill & Knoblock Sts, 74074. Tel: 405-624-6016. *Dir* B J Smith.
Open Mon - Fri 8 AM - 5 PM; Sat 9 - 12 AM; Sun 2 - 5 PM. No admis. Estab 1970 (formerly Whitehurst Hall Art Gallery) as a visual and educational extension of the department's classes and as a cultural service to the community and area. One gallery located on the ground floor in the East wing of the building. 170 running ft of wall space, 16 ft ceiling. Average Annual Attendance: 5000.
Income: Financed by College of A & S.
Collections: Fifty plus prints, mostly post World War II.
Exhibitions: Exhibitions changed every 3 - 4 weeks year round; faculty, student, invitational and traveling shows.
Publications: Exhibition schedule, biannually.

TAHLEQUAH

CHEROKEE NATIONAL HISTORICAL SOCIETY, INC, PO Box 515, 74464. Tel: 918-456-6007. *Pres* Ross O Swimmer; *Exec VPres* M A Hagerstrand; *Secy* James C Leake; *Office Mgr* Earl E Squyres.
Open Mon - Fri 10 AM - 5 PM. Estab 1963 to commemorate and portray the history, traditions and lore of a great Indian tribe, and to assist in improving local economic conditions. Maintains an art gallery—primarily Cherokee art. Average Annual Attendance: 30,000 (museum); 100,000 (complex). Mem: 1500; dues $5.
Income: Financed by membership, state appropriation, and admissions.
Publications: The Column, quarterly.
Activities: Lect open to public; competitions with cash awards; scholarships; sales shop selling books, prints, slides.
—Cherokee National Museum Library.
Open Mon - Fri 8 AM - 5 PM. Estab 1976 to preserve remnants of Cherokee history and to educate the general public about that cultural heritage; a repository of Indian art and documents. Maintains an art gallery with work by artists of several different tribes; heavy emphasis given to the Cherokee experience.
Income: Financed by membership and admissions.
Holdings: Vols 1000; Per subs 10; AV—Kodachromes, microfilm, reels, slides; Other—Clipping files, manuscripts, memorabilia, original art works, original documents, pamphlets, photographs, prints, sculpture; archival materials in excess of 500 cu ft.
Special Subjects: Cherokee history.

Special Collections: Original newspapers relating to Cherokees, dating from 1762 to present.
Exhibitions: Annual Trail of Tears Art Show—Indian artists interpretation of the Trail of Tears theme; Cherokee Artists Exhibition; rotating exhibitions.

TULSA

THOMAS GILCREASE INSTITUTE OF AMERICAN HISTORY AND ART,* 2500 W Newton St (Mailing Add: RR 6, 74127). Tel: 918-581-5311. *Chmn of the Bd* Cecille Bales; *Dir* William R Best; *Cur Anthropology* Daniel M McPike; *Cur Art* Carolyn Tannehill Bradshaw; *Cur History* Gerald P Edwards.
Museum open Mon - Sat 9 AM - 5 PM; Sun & holidays 1 - 5 PM; cl Christmas. Library open for research, cl weekends and holidays. No admis. Estab by the late Thomas Gilcrease as a private institution; acquired by the City of Tulsa 1954 (governed by a Board of Directors and City Park Board); building addition completed 1963. Average Annual Attendance: 80,000. Mem: 1600; dues $15 and up.
Collections: American art from Colonial period to present, with emphasis on art of historical significance, sculpture, painting, graphics. Much of the work shown is of documentary nature, with considerable emphasis on the American Indian and the opening of the West. Art collections include 4000 paintings by 400 American artists; artifact collections include 10,000 objects from Mid-Americas, and North America, and include both prehistoric and historic materials from most of the Indian cultures of these areas.
Exhibitions: A special or rotating exhibit during fall-winter-spring seasons; special exhibitions periodically; public school art exhibit.
Publications: The American Scene, quarterly; The Curator, bimonthly; The Gazette, bimonthly.
Activities: Film program and lectures on art and history; gallery tours; lectures to school groups outside the museum.
Library: Contains 65,000 books and documents, many rare books and manuscripts of the American discovery period, as well as materials concerning the Five Civilized Tribes.
Book Shop: Books, magazines, pamphlets, covering such subjects as the American Indian, art and history, and Western artists in the collection; slides and reproductions from Gilcrease collections; artifacts and jewelry handcrafted by Indian artists.

GREEN COUNTRY ART CENTER, 1825 E 15th St, 74104. Tel: 918-932-4259. *Pres* Eloise J Schellstede; *VPres & Dir* Richard L Schellstede.
Open 11 AM - 5:30 PM. No admis. Estab 1970 to promote the fine arts and the artists. There is a gallery for continuing exhibit of fine art, and for special exhibitions.
Income: Financed by endowment.
Collections: Oil paintings; watercolors, acrylics; graphics; sculptures; outstanding works are being added to the collection.
Exhibitions: Bicentennial, Western, area group showings.
Publications: Newsletter, 4 - 6 times per yr.
Activities: Classes for adults; lect open to public; gallery talks; sales shop selling original art, prints, reproductions.
Library: *Librn* Richard L Schellstede. Open to art students for reference only. Special Subjects: Fine art, history, animals, birds, flowers.

PHILBROOK ART CENTER, 2727 S Rockford Rd, 74114. Tel: 918-742-2459. *Dir & Pres* Alexander Stoia; *Educ Dir* Marcia Manhart; *Gallery Supervisor* Raymond Watkins; *Dir* Jay Wright; *Asst Dir* Marcia Manhart; *Cur Indian Coll* Ben Stone; *Registrar* Christine Knop; *Preparator of Exhib* Charles Taylor.
Open 10 AM - 5 PM; Sun 1 - 5 PM. Admis adults $1.50; students with ID 75¢; children under 15 free. Estab 1939 as an art center for exhibiting art of all historical periods including the present; encourages regional art activity and art education. Average Annual Attendance: 100,000. Mem: dues $18 and up; annual meeting Apr.
Income: Financed by endowment, membership and earned income.
Collections: European, Early American and contemporary American oils, watercolors and prints; American Indian paintings; sculpture; period furniture; Indian pottery, baskets, six period rooms; Samuel H Kress Collection of Italian Renaissance paintings and sculpture; Laura A Clubb Collection of paintings; Clark Field Collection of American Indian baskets and pottery; Roberta Campbell Lawson Collection of Indian costumes and artifacts; American Indian murals and paintings; Gussman Collection of African sculpture.
Exhibitions: Regular changing exhibition program of exhibits; Oklahoma Artists Annual with awards; American Indian Annual open to artists of Indian descent; annual Collectors Choice exhibit.
Activities: Classes for adults and children; gallery talks; Junior Studio, mornings, June and July; Ruskin Rental and Sales Gallery, paintings for rent.

—**Library.** (Mailing Add: PO Box 52510, 74152). Tel: 918-749-7941. *Librn & Asst to Registrar* Thomas Elton Young.
Open Mon - Fri 10 AM - 5 PM. Estab 1939. Initially set up as a browsing room, within the past few years it has, and still is going through a transformation into a library designed to serve as a reference/resource center for the Curatorial staff, teaching faculty, volunteer element and their education, as well as the membership-at-large.
Income: $12,000 (financed through Philbrook Art Center). Purchases: $800.
Holdings: Vols 4,000; Per subs 40; AV—Slides; Other—Clipping files, exhibition catalogs.
Special Collections: Roberta Campbell Lawson Library of source material on Indians.
Publications: Calendar of events, bimonthly.

WORLD MUSEUM/ART CENTRE, Osborn Foundation, 1400 E Skelly Dr (Mailing Add: Box 7572, 74105). *Founders* T L and Daisy Osborn; *Manager* James R Bolley.
Open daily 8 AM - 4:30 PM; summer 8 AM - 8 PM. Admis adults $2.50, students $1.75, children (6-12) $1; under 6 free. Estab 1972 to house the ever-increasing art collection of the Osborn Foundation. It is devoted to preserving for future generations, great works of art from many Ages of Man. Over 60,000 sq ft of corridors and galleries. Average Annual Attendance: 70,000.
Collections: Bronze, marble and porcelain works by noted sculptors of the last two centuries; primitive sculptures; Chinese and Oriental expositions; European and American furniture; large collection of crafts: Stone Age weapons, tools, drums, masks, grotesque aboriginal statuary; primitive bark paintings; totem poles; collection of musical instruments; clocks of distinction; oil paintings; prints; etchings; engravings.

WOODWARD

PLAINS INDIANS & PIONEER HISTORICAL FOUNDATION, Pioneer Museum & Art Center, 2009 Williams Ave (Mailing Add: Box 1167, 73801). Tel: 405-256-6136. *Cur* Elena Ruttman; *Art Dir* Mrs C E Williams.
Open Mon - Sat Noon - 5 PM; Sun 2 - 5 PM. No admis. Estab 1957 to preserve local history and for the purpose of supporting the art movement. Average Annual Attendance; Approx 15,000. Mem: 450; dues $5; annual meeting Nov.
Income: Financed by membership and trust fund.
Collections: Collections pertain to early day artifacts as well as Indian material.
Exhibitions: Minerals; Cut glass; Bisque dolls; Plate collection; twelve different art exhibits.
Publications: Woodward County Pioneer Families, before 1915, book published in 1975.

OREGON

ASHLAND

SOUTHERN OREGON COLLEGE,* Stevenson Union Art Gallery, 97520. Tel: 503-482-6461. *Dir Stevenson Union* Mrs Marythea Grebner; *Asst Dir Activities* Edith L Morrill.
Open Mon - Thurs 9 AM - 9 PM; Fri 9 AM - 5 PM. No admis. Estab 1966 to provide members of the Southern Oregon College community and the greater Ashland area an opportunity to experience a well rounded selection of art and crafts. Average Annual Attendance: 4000.
Income: Financed by student fees.
Collections: †Small permanent collection of prints, paintings by local artists and a sculpture by Bruce West.
Exhibitions: Works of professional artists, paintings, sculpture, weaving, photography, ceramics, graphic design, are shown.
Activities: Special lectures; artist workshops; short programs for educational television; exhibiting artists lecture to art classes when possible; lect open to the public, 3 vis lectrs per yr; 8 gallery talks yearly.

ASTORIA

COLUMBIA RIVER MARITIME MUSEUM,* 16th & Exchange Sts, 97103. Tel: 503-325-2323. *Dir* Rolf Klep; *Cur* Michael Naab.
Open May - Sept daily 10:30 AM - 5 PM; Oct - Apr Tues - Sun 10:30 AM - 5 PM. Admis adults 50¢, children 10¢. Estab 1962 as a maritime museum.
Collections: Maritime paintings, prints and photography; ship models and sailing memorabilia.
Library: Library for use on the premises. Holdings: Vols 1000.

COOS BAY

COOS ART MUSEUM, 515 Market Ave, 97420. Tel: 503-267-3901. *Dir* Maggie Karl; *Pres* Josie Reid; *VPres* Paul Lagregren; *Treas* Nina Grunwaldt; *Secy* Jean Day.
Open Tues - Sun 1 - 4 PM. No admis. Estab 1966 to bring contemporary art to southwestern Oregon, and to have classes in related art subjects; there are two large spacious galleries with a wide entrance hall. Average Annual Attendance: 10,000. Mem: 800; dues single $10, family $15; annual meeting first Sat of the yr.
Income: $5315 (Financed by membership).
Collections: †Contemporary American Printmakers; †sculpture; †paintings; †photographs.
Exhibitions: Monthly exhibits; three juried shows a yr; one Photography show; Crafts, functional; Sculpture, Painting, and nonfunctional Pottery, Weaving.
Publications: Bulletins, monthly.
Activities: Classes for adults and children; dramatic programs; film festivals; lect open to the public, 2 - 3 vis lectr per yr; concerts; tours; competitions; individual paintings and original objects of art lent to members; museum and sales shops selling books, original art, prints, photographs, pottery, stained glass, blown glass.

COQUILLE

COQUILLE VALLEY ART ASSOCIATION, Fairview Rte, Box 625, 97423. Tel: 503-396-3294. *Pres* Wilma Ryan; *VPres* Darlene Castleman; *Secy* Marilyn Dahlen; *Treas* Evelyn Hunnicutt; *Board Member/Teacher* Vicki McKean-Smith; *Teacher* Betsey Hammond; *Librn* Sharon Orchard.
Open Tues - Sun 1 - 4 PM, cl Mon. Estab 1950 to teach art and art appreciation; Gallery maintained on main floor of Art Association-owned old refurbished schoolhouse.
Income: Financed by membership.
Exhibitions: Exhibits by local members, as well as by others from throughout the state.
Activities: Classes for adults and children; lect open to the public, 2 - 3 vis lectr per yr; traveling exhibitions organized and circulated.
Library: The library is presently being set up, and information on holdings will be available later in the yr.

CORVALLIS

OREGON STATE UNIVERSITY

—**Horner Museum,** Gill Coliseum, 26th near Western, 97331. Tel: 503-754-2951. *Dir* Lucy Skjelstad; *Asst Dir* Wallace Weltzin.
Open Tues - Fri 10 AM - 5 PM; Sat 10 AM - 2 PM; Sun 2 - 5 PM. No admis. Estab 1877 to collect, preserve and display the history and natural history of Oregon. Average Annual Attendance: 8000. Mem: 80; dues individual $10.
Income: Financed by state appropriation and donations.
Collections: Oriental rugs; dolls; Indian materials, especially baskets; historic clothing, some Oriental art, quilts.
Activities: Lect, 2 - 3 vis lectr per yr; tours; sales shop selling books.
—**Fairbanks Gallery.** Tel: 503-754-4745. *Dir* Dr Phyllis A Yes; *Asst Dir* John Rock.
Open 8 AM - 5:30 PM. No admis. Estab 1933 to display work of contemporary American artists. One gallery space 20 x 50 ft.
Income: Financed by state appropriation and grants.
Exhibitions: Annual Faculty and Student Exhibition: Miriam Schapiro; Paul Clinton; Lee Chesney; Lukman Glasgow; Herb Lubalin; Bill Rades.
Publications: Posters and flyers announcing shows.
Activities: Lect, 5 vis lectr per yr; gallery talks; exten dept serving Oregon; traveling exhibitions organized and circulated.
—**Memorial Union Art Gallery.** Tel: 503-754-2416. *Secy & Dir* George F Stevens.
Open daily 8 AM - 10 PM. Estab 1928. Average Annual Attendance: 50,000. Mem: 15,000; annual meeting May.
Income: $70,000.
Collections: The William Henry Price Memorial Collection of Oil paintings.
Publications: Calendar and exhibition pamphlets.
Activities: Educ prog; exten dept serving the State; traveling exhibitions organized and circulated; individual paintings lent to schools; material available to responsible galleries for fees; lect.
Library: Special Collection—Color reproductions.

EUGENE

MAUDE I KERNS ART CENTER, Henry Korn Gallery, 1910 E 15th Ave, 97403. Tel: 503-345-1126. *Dir* Carol Wood; *Pres* Paul Raffin; *Secy* Pat Houghton.

Open daily 11 AM - 5 PM. No admis. Estab 1955, the Center is a non-profit educational organization dedicated to promoting quality in the Arts and Crafts through classes, exhibitions, workshops, community projects, and special events; the Center houses the Henry Korn Gallery, the main gallery featuring monthly shows of contemporary artists; the Mezzanine Gallery, suited to photographs, prints, drawings and smaller works of art; Rental/Sales Gallery, featuring an Artist of the Month as well as a stock of a variety of art works available. Average Annual Attendance: 8000. Mem: 900; dues teen/child $5, individual $10, couple $15, family $20, sponsor $25 or more; annual meeting second Mon in April.
Income: $100,000 (financed by endowment, membership, CETA).
Collections: Sculpture and painting of Oregon artists.
Exhibitions: (1978) Nexus: Marie Lyman, Suzanna Kuo, Alice Van Leone; Mel Vincent (watercolors); Brent Jenkins (sculpture); Tom Blodgett (drawings); Harold Hoy (sculpture); Pete Shoemaker (photographs); Earthworks; Paul Buckner (sculpture) and Kay Buckner (paintings); Paul Schneider (pottery); David Cotter (Kinetic sculpture); Tom Hughes (stained glass); Glen Povey (weaving); Ecesis: A Collaborative Show; Christmas Show.
Publications: Membership newsletter, monthly.
Activities: Classes for adults and children; dramatic programs; docent training; lect open to the public and for members only on request, 12 vis lectr per yr; concerts; gallery talks; tours; competitions; sales shop selling original art.

UNIVERSITY OF OREGON

—**Museum of Art,** 97403. Tel: 203-686-3027. *Dir* Richard C Paulin; *Designer/Preparator* Tommy L Griffin; *Supervisor, Visual Art Resources* Michael Whitenack; *Admin Asst* Norine M Arens; *Registrar* Barbara Zentner.
Open Tues - Sun Noon - 5 PM; cl Monday and university holidays. No admis. Estab 1930 to promote among university students and faculty and the general public an active and continuing interest in the visual arts of both Western and Oriental cultures. Average Annual Attendance: 90,000. Mem: 425; dues $15-$250; annual meeting Apr.
Income: $201,000 (financed by state appropriation and private donations).
Collections: Oriental art representing the cultures of China, Japan, Cambodia, Korea, Mongolia, Tibet, Russia, and American and British works executed in the traditional Oriental manner; Greater Pacific Basin collection; contemporary Northwest collection; African.
Exhibitions: The Travel Sketches of Louis I Kahn; The Gund Collection of Western Art; Prints by Jacob Kainen; Canadian Landscapes; The Performing Arts as a Visual Experience.
Activities: Docent training; exten dept serving Oregon and Washington; museum shop selling books, magazines, original art, reproductions, prints, slides and gift items.
—**Erb Memorial Union Art Gallery,** 13th & University Sts. Tel: 503-686-4373. *Dir* Adell McMillan; *Prog Consultant* Frank Geltner; *Craft Center Coordr* Thomas Urban.
Open Mon - Sat 7:30 AM - 11:30 PM; Sun Noon - 11:30 PM. No admis. Estab 1950 to provide art in various forms and programs for enrichment of university community. Periodic art exhibitions on portable display boards in various rooms; display in the art gallery of selections from the permanent collection.
Income: Financed by student fees. Purchases: $100-$2000.
Collections: †Pacific Northwest Art (purchases made annually from exhibitions by Pacific Northwest artists).
Activities: Classes for adults; craft workshops.
—**School of Architecture and Allied Arts Library,** Lawrence Hall. Tel: 503-686-3637. *Librn* Reyburn R McCready; *Librn* Alan C Miller; *Slide Cur* Carmi Weingrod.
Open Mon - Thurs 8 AM - 10 PM; Fri 8 AM - 5 PM; Sat 1 - 5 PM; Sun 2 - 10 PM. Estab 1919 to provide resources for the courses, degree programs, and research of the departments in the School of Architecture and Allied Arts and related Institute for Community Art Studies and Center for Environmental Research. Circ: 58,882.
Income: Financed by city appropriation.
Holdings: Vols 23,000; Per subs 250; AV—Slides 140,000; Other—Exhibition catalogs; pamphlets, photographs 45,000.

HILLSBORO

HILLSBORO PUBLIC LIBRARY, 775 SE Tenth, 97123. Tel: 503-648-6669. *City Librn* Debra Brodie; *Asst City Librn* Gregory Cutting; *Library Asst* Diane Gatke; *Children's Librn* Ginny Cooper; *Children's Librn* Carol Wakefield.
Open Mon - Thurs 9:30 AM - 8:30 PM; Fri & Sat 9:30 AM - 5:30 PM. Estab 1914 as a library, for information, and for referral service; gallery not maintained. Circ: 143,981 (1977-78).
Income: $143,585 (1977-78), (financed by city appropriation). Purchases: $27,500 capital outlay.

Holdings: Vols 43,000; Per subs 75; AV—Cassettes, microfilm, phonorecords; slides; Other—Clipping files, pamphlets, reproductions.
Special Collections: Oregon history.
Exhibitions: Monthly art exhibits.
Activities: Classes for adults; dramatic programs; lect open to the public, 6 vis lectr per yr; concerts, tours.

JACKSONVILLE

SOUTHERN OREGON HISTORICAL SOCIETY, Jacksonville Museum, 206 N Fifth St, 97530. (Mailing Add: PO Box 480, 97530). Tel: 503-899-1847. *Dir* C William Burk; *Cur Coll* Donald Draisner; *Exhib Cur* Renee Bush; *Programs Dir* Lyyn Lango; *Historian/Newsletter Editor* Marjorie Edens; *Photographer* Ann Warrington; *Restoration Coordr* Ruth Preston.
Open Tues - Sat 9 AM - 5 PM; Sun Noon - 5 PM; Summer also Mon 9 AM - 5 PM. No admis. Estab 1950 to collect and exhibit materials showing the history of Southern Oregon. Peter Britt Gallery—Jackson County History, Indian artifacts; Regina Dorland Robinson Gallery—Costume gallery; Historic houses—Cornelius C Beekman house c 1871, Catholic Rectory c 1875, and Cool-Beekman-Armstrong house c 1860. Average Annual Attendance: 90,000. Mem: 525; dues $5 and up; annual meeting June.
Income: Financed by membership and county tax.
Exhibitions: (1976) Peter Britt: Photographer of a Frontier; (1977) Handweaving; Oregon Old-Time Fiddlers; Aviation: A Brief Look Back; Quilts; Photographing the Frontier (SITES); (1978) Handweaving.
Publications: Newsletter 6 times year.
Activities: Classes for children; docent training; film program; lect open to the public; sales shop selling books.
Library: Librn Richard H Engeman. Open to public for reference only. Holdings: Vols 1500; Per subs 40; other—Manuscripts, ephemera; photographs; art on paper. Special Subjects: Local history, historic preservation, museum techniques.

KLAMATH FALLS

FAVELL MUSEUM OF WESTERN ART & INDIAN ARTIFACTS, 125 W Main (Mailing Add: PO Box 165, 97601). Tel: 503-882-9996. *Pres* Gene H Favell; *VPres & Treas* Winifred L Favell; *Admin* Charles Mitchell; *Asst Admin* Mrs Charles Mitchell.
Open Mon - Sat 9:30 AM - 5:30 PM; Sun 1 - 5:30 PM; cl Mon; Jan 1 - Apr 1. Admis adults $1.50, youth 6 - 16 years 75¢. Estab April 15, 1972 to preserve western heritage represented by Indian artifacts and contemporary Western art; Sales gallery featuring contemporary western artists combined with art and artifact displays. Average Annual Attendance: 15,000 - 20,000. Annual meeting May.
Income: $100,000 - $150,000 (financed by owners).
Collections: (Art) †Contemporary Western art; †Western Indian Artifacts—pottery, stonework, baskets, bead and quillwork.
Activities: Museum shop selling books, original art, reproductions, prints, slides, jewelry, artifacts.

KLAMATH ART ASSOCIATION,* PO Box 955, 97601. *Pres* Warren Kerr; *VPres* James Leard; *Treas* Don Ross; *Chmn Exhib* Nina Pence; *Secy* Beth Grigg.
Gallery, 120 River St, open Mon - Sat 1 - 4 PM, Sun 2 - 5 PM & special occasions. No admis. Association estab 1948 to provide art training for local residents; Gallery estab 1960 to provide display and teaching space for the Association's activities. Annual Average Attendance: 5000. Mem: over 200; dues $7 and higher; annual meeting Sept.
Income: $7000 (financed by membership, gallery sales, tuition).
Collections: Paintings, ceramics, weaving; owned by members.
Exhibitions: 12 annually, one membership show, one juried show and remainder varies.
Activities: Annual arts festival, mid-Sept. Classes in painting, drawing, ceramics, weaving. Children's summer art classes. Visiting lectures; workshops.

KLAMATH COUNTY MUSEUM, 1451 Main St, 97601. Tel: 503-882-2501, exten 208. *Dir* Harry V Drew; *Archivist* Charles Wells.
Open Tues - Sat 9 AM - 5 PM; Sun 1 - 5 PM; cl Mon. No admis. Estab 1953 to tell the story of the Klamath Country and to preserve and exhibit related material. Average Annual Attendance: 18,000. Dues $5; monthly meetings.
Income: Financed by county appropriation.
Collections: Wildlife; Indian artifacts; Pioneer artifacts; four original Rembrandt etchings.
Publications: Museum Research Papers, every 2 years.
Activities: Lect open to public; traveling exhibitions organized and circulated; museum shop selling books.
—**Research Library.**
Open to the public for reference by appointment.

Holdings: Vols 12,000.
Special Subjects: Klamath County, Oregon; Northern California history.
Special Collections: Modoc Indian War books, documents and manuscripts.

MEDFORD

ROGUE VALLEY ART ASSOCIATION,* PO Box 763, 40 S Bartlett, 97501. Tel: 502-772-8118. *Pres* Phil Patterson; *Gallery Coordr* Jill R Day.
Open Mon - Sat 9 AM - 4 PM; cl Sun & national holidays. No admis. Estab 1960 to provide the surrounding area with changing exhibits in what is going on in the world of art; supported by membership. Maintains the Rogue Gallery, Auxiliary Board initiated in 1971. Average Annual Attendance: 8000. Mem: 330; dues $2 - $25; annual meeting Apr.
Income: (1974) $17,500.
Exhibitions: New exhibit each month.
Publications: Newsletter, approx 4 annually.
Activities: Summer art education for children 7 - 18, scholarships offered; adult education classes throughout year have included calligraphy, drawing and workshops in stained glass and printmaking; tours and artist lectures.

MONMOUTH

OREGON COLLEGE OF EDUCATION, Gallery 107, 97361. Tel: 503-838-1220. *Comt Chmn* Peter G Stone; *Comt Mem* John Casey; *Comt Mem* Leo J Kirk *Comt Mem* Donald Hoskisson.
Open Mon - Fri 8 AM - 5 PM during scheduled exhibits. No admis. Estab to bring work of contemporary and traditional artists and craftsman to the community and the college for study and familiarity. Average Annual Attendance: 3000.
Income: $1000 (financed by state appropriation).
Exhibitions: Mike McGuire (paintings); Painting, Fiber, Mixed media ("2+1=3"); Harrison Branch (photography); Jerry Eshelman (etchings); Annual Oregon High School Invitational; Christmas Juried Invitational Show; Fibers by BettyJo Swanson; Four Portland Serigraphers; Oregon College of Education Faculty Show.
Collections: Contemporary Northwest Ceramics.
Activities: Educational Department conducts tours for public schools, encounters in the gallery; material available to Oregon schools; lect open to the public, 3 - 5 vis lectr per yr; gallery talks; tours, original objects of art lent; lending collection contains lantern slides 500; slides 8000.
Library maintained.

PORTLAND

BASSIST INSTITUTE, 923 Southwest Taylor St, 97205. Tel: 503-228-6528. *Pres* Donald H Bassist; *Secy* Ernest Buhlinger.
Open 9 AM - 5 PM. No admis. Estab 1964 to provide practical instruction in retail merchandising, interior design, display, fashion design, advertising and promotion, fashion history and textiles. Average Annual Attendance: 5000.
Collections: Definitive collection of fashion and costume history books, also notable collection in furniture and interior decorations fields.
Activities: Lect open to the public; scholarships; lending collection of 150 motion pictures; book shop.
—Library. *Librn* Norma Bassist.
Open 9 AM - 5 PM. Estab 1964 to provide practical instruction in retail merchandising, interior design, and apparel design. Graduates are granted an Associate in Arts Degree upon completion of a 2-year program.
Holdings: Vols 8,000; Per subs 90; AV—Motion pictures, slides; Other—Clipping files.
Special Subjects: Costume history; fashion industry and biography; retail; textiles; architecture; art; furniture history; interior decoration; apparel design and construction.

CONTEMPORARY CRAFTS ASSOCIATION AND GALLERY, 3934 SW Corbett Ave. 97201. Tel: 503-223-2654. *Pres of Bd of Dir* Melody Teppola; *VPres* Anne Crumpacker, *Secy* Steven Hughes; *Dir* Lukman Glasgow; *Secy/Bookkeeper* Barbara Weber; *Asst to the Dir* Elyse Hallahan.
Open Mon - Fri 11 AM - 5 PM; Sat 11 AM - 4 PM; Sun 1 - 4 PM. No admis. Estab 1938 to promote, exhibit and sell contemporary crafts; the gallery is maintained also as a consignment outlet, and holds exhibits monthly. Average Annual Attendance: 30,000. Mem: 1400; dues $5 - $100 depending on classification.
Income: $114,000 (financed by membership).
Collections: †Craft objects including ceramics, textiles, wood, glass collected over a 40-year period.
Exhibitions: (1978) Jane Marquis (stained glass); Alan Kluber (ceramics); Keith Jones (constructions).

Publications: Contemporary Crafts News, quarterly.
Activities: Craftsmen-in-the-Schools program; lect open to the public, 5 vis lectr per yr; gallery talks; tours; lending collection contains books 430, cassettes 15, slides 2000; sales shop selling books, magazines, original art.
Library: *Librn* Bea Parisi. Open to members. Holdings: Vols 430; Per subs 260.

METROPOLITAN ARTS COMMISSION,* 430 SW Morrison, 97204. Tel: 503-248-4569. *Chmn* Henry Stanley; *VChmn* Robert Jones; *Exec Dir* Emily Carpenter; *Staff Secy* Liz Thorsten.
Office open 8 AM - 5 PM. Estab Feb 1973 to promote and encourage programs to further the development and public awareness of and interest in the visual and performing arts.
Income: Financed by city and county appropriation.
Publication: Newsletter, quarterly.

MULTNOMAH COUNTY LIBRARY, Henry Failing Art & Music Department, 801 SW Tenth Ave, 97205. Tel: 503-223-7201 *Librn* James H Burghardt; *Head Art & Music Dept* Barbara J Kern.
Open Mon - Thurs 9 AM - 9 PM; Fri & Sat 9 AM - 5:30 PM. Estab 1864 as a public library serice to Multnomah County.
Holdings: Titles 23,000; AV—Phonorecords 18,233, slides 12,000; Other—Framed Reproductions 700, Picture clippings 2,000,000.

OREGON HISTORICAL SOCIETY,* 1230 SW Park Ave, 97205. Tel: 503-222-1741. *Dir* Thomas Vaughan; *Assoc Dir* Millard McClung; *Museum Adminr* Robert Stark.
Open Mon - Sat 10 AM - 4:45 PM. No admis. Estab 1873, inc 1898, to collect, preserve, exhibit and publish materials pertaining to the Oregon Country. Average Annual Attendance: 125,000. Mem: 5500; dues $10; annual meeting Nov.
Income: Financed by endowment, membership, state appropriation.
Collections: Approx 60,000 museum objects, approx 20,000 sq ft of exhibit space.
Exhibitions: James Madison Alden, Yankee Artist of the Pacific Coast, 1854-1860; The Genius of Ivan Collins: Wagons in Miniature; Indians of the Oregon Country; Darius Kinsey, Photographer, documents Northwest Logging Industry; A Sense of Proportion—Oregon architects; Last View of The First North Americans—Edward Curtis photographs of North American Indians.
Publications: Oregon Historical Quarterly; books; maps; pamphlets; newsletter.
Activities: Lectures, field trips. films, exhibits; educational prog for all ages; maintain historic 1856 Bybee Howell House, Sauvie Island.
—Library. *Chief Librn* Louis Flannery; *Managing Editor* Priscilla Knuth.
Open Mon - Sat 10 AM - 5 PM.
Holdings: Vols 50,000; AV—Cassettes, film strips, lantern slides, microfiche, microfilm, motion pictures, phonorecords, slides, video tapes; Other—Clipping files, exhibition catalogs, framed reproductions, manuscripts, memorabilia, original art works, original documents, pamphlets, photographs, prints, reproductions, sculpture.
Special Subjects: Pacific Northwest history and Oregon history; Westward movement; Pacific maritime history; local, urban affairs and labor history; Russian exploration and activity in the north Pacific Rim from the 17th century to date. Special Collection: 3000 separate manuscript collections containing 15,000,000 pieces; 1,000,000 historic photographs; 10,000 maps; local television news and documentary film.

PORTLAND ART ASSOCIATION, Portland Art Museum, Museum Art School, 1219 SW Park Ave, 97225. Tel: 503-226-2811. *Dir* Donald Jenkins; *Acting Dean* Harry Widman; *Cur* William Chiego; *Cur of Educ* Pauline Eyerly; *Editor* Robert Peirce; *Development Officer* Carl Lantz; *Bus Mgr* E Scott Clodfelter; *Registrar* Kathryn Gates; *Asst Cur* Rachel Rosenfield; *Exec Asst to Dir* Evelyn Lamon; *Head, Membership Dept* Jan Liss.
Open Tues, Wed, Thurs, Sat & Sun noon - 5 PM; Fri noon - 10 PM, cl Mon. Admis $1 adults, 50¢ students, free to children under 12, senior citizens and members. Estab 1892 to make a collection of works of art and to erect and maintain a suitable building in which the same may be studied and exhibited, and to develop and encourage the study of art. Average Annual Attendance: 180,000. Mem: 6000; dues individual $15; annual meeting Nov.
Income: $1,666,650 (financed by endowment, membership, gifts, donations and grants). Purchases: $61,835.
Collections: Lewis Collection of Classical antiquities: ancient Chinese sculptures, bronzes and ceramics; Mary Andrews Ladd Collection of Japanese prints; Oriental painted screens and lacquers; Persian and Hindu miniatures; William S Ladd Collection of Pre-Columbian art; Rasmussen Collection of Northwest Coast Indian and Eskimo arts; Samuel H Kress Collection of Renaissance paintings and sculptures; Alice B Nunn Collection of English silver; contemporary paintings, sculptures, drawings and prints; contemporary ceramics; Gebauer Collection of

Cameroon (west African) art; Lawther Collection of Ethiopian crosses; Hirsch Collection of Oriental rugs; Gordon and Vivian Gilkey Collection of graphic arts.

Exhibitions: (1976) A Tribute to C S Price; Art Advocates: George Johanson: 18 People in 14 Paintings; Masterworks in Wood: China and Japan; American Photography Past into Present; (1977) Oregon Group Exhibition: Mixed Media and Techniques; Imogen: Imogen Cunningham Photographs (1910-1973); Indians in Washington, DC; Photographs (1858, 1890); Artists in Oregon 1977; Museum Art School Thesis Projects; Duane Hanson; Delacroix and the French Romantic Print.

Publications: Calendar, monthly; annual report; exhibition catalogs.

Activities: Classes for adults; docent training; Chamberlain training; films; lect open to the public, 15 vis lectr per yr; concerts; gallery talks; tours; exten dept serving Area III, Portland Public Schools; traveling exhibitions organized and circulated; museum shop selling books, magazines, original art, reproductions, jewelry and postcards.

—**Library.** Tel: 503-226-2811, exten 36. *Librn* Mary Ann Mees; *Asst Librn* Emily Evans; *Slide Librn* James H Hicks.
Open Tues - Fri 9 AM - 5 PM; cl Mon; special schedules for holidays. Estab 1892 to provide a reference collection for MAS as supportive materials for the Museum collection. Circ: Museum Art School students only.

Income: $10,000 (financed by endowment). Purchases: $10,000.

Holdings: Vols 8500; Per subs 62; AV—Motion pictures, slides; Other—Exhibition catalogs, photographs.

PORTLAND CENTER FOR THE VISUAL ARTS, 117 NW Fifth Ave, 97209. Tel: 503-222-7107. *Exec Dir* Mary L Beebe; *Dir Special Events* Donna J Milrany; *Bus Mgr* Jane E Craford; *Pres* Mike Russo; *VPres* Mel Katz; *Secy/Treas* Ivan Gold.
Open Tues - Sat Noon - 6 PM. No admis. Estab 1972 to bring a wide cross-section of nationally recognized contemporary art to Oregon; the gallery covers 6200 sq ft, in one large space and has adjustable partitions. Average Annual Attendance: 13,200. Mem: 701; dues $6 - $240; annual meeting in fall.

Income: $94,086 (financed by membership, city and state appropriation, and NEA grants).

Exhibitions: (1976) Lucy Lippard; In Touch: Nature, Ritual and Sensous Art; Cynthia Lubar/Chris Knowles; Annual Meeting and Fourth Birthday celebration; Billy Al Bengston; Barbara Dilley; Jackie Winsor; (1977) Guy de Cointet/Mary Ann Duganne; Robert Mangold; Eclectic Union Theater; Tom Johnson; David Antin; Tom Marioni; Robert Morris; Robert Smithson; David Mahler; Terry Riley; Robert Hudson; Soho Hustle; Trisha Brown & Co; Northwest artists group show; Martha Wilson; Dance Workshop; Solo Film & Dance; The Great Art Gambol III; Deborah Remington; Nam June Paik; Katrina Krimsky; Doug Ohlson; (1978) John Baldessari; Alice Aycock; Brenda Miller; Louis Bunce; Lynn Hershman; John Gibson; Ingram Marshall; Portland Symphonic Choir new music; Norma Jean Deak; Morton Subotnick; Meridith Monk; Bob Gardiner; Thara Memory; Charlemagne Palestine; Laurie Anderson.

Activities: Lect open to the public, 24 vis lectr per yr; concerts; gallery talks; traveling exhibitions organized and circulated.

Library: *Librn* Mary Beebe. Open to the public for reference only. Holdings: Vols 7; Per subs 6; Other—Catalogs, approx. 200, of contemporary art exhibitions, limited edition magazines. Special Subjects: Contemporary art: Music, dance, performance, visual art.

PORTLAND CHILDREN'S MUSEUM,* 3037 SW Second Ave, 97201. Tel: 503-227-1505. *Dir* Dianne Kornberg.
Open June 1 - Sept 30 Mon - Fri 10 AM - 5:30 PM; Oct 1 - May 30 Mon - Fri 10 AM - 6 PM; Sat 10 AM - 3 PM. Estab 1949; sponsored by Portland Bureau of Parks and Recreation. Average Annual Attendance: (Museum and lectures) 65,000.

Collections: Natural history, art gallery, toys, dollhouses, miniatures; children's art.

Activities: Art classes in painting, photography, filmmaking, jewelry, graphics, pottery, calligraphy, weaving for children 4-18; lectures and tours on selected art and natural history subjects.

PORTLAND STATE UNIVERSITY, White Gallery, PO Box 751, 97207. Tel: 503-229-4078. *Dir* Kim Bradley.
Open Mon - Fri 8 AM - 10 PM; Saturday 9 AM - 7 PM. No admis. Estab 1970 as a student operated gallery exhibiting works by professional artists representing a wide range of media, style and geographical distribution; the Gallery is basically a wide long hall in the Student Union. Mem: 350.

Income: $4200 (financed by city and state appropriations, and student incidental fees).

Collections: The permanent collection mainly consists of work by local professionals, with a few nationally recognized artists.

Exhibitions: (1976-78) Betty Dodson; Cathleen McCuistion; Pat Steir; John Rock; International Poster Show; Anne Veraldi/Christopher Simons; Sean Licka/Dennis Evans performance; Paul Miller/Liza Jones

(group textiles); Barry Johnson; Catherine Wilson; Michael Bowley; Ray, Barnes; five local photographers; Brenda Miller; Paul Davis; Lynda Benglis (talk), Esther Podemski; Dick Rezac.

Activities: Lect open to the public, 12 vis lectr per yr; gallery talks; individual paintings and original objects of art lent to other schools or museums; lending collection contains original prints, paintings and sculpture.

REED COLLEGE ART GALLERY, 3202 SE Woodstock Blvd, 97202. Tel: 503-771-1112. *Dir Gallery Program* Prof Charles S. Rhyne; *Pres, Art Assoc* Mrs Paul Feldenheimer; *Supv, Installations* Prof Scott Sonniksen; *Dir, Campus Events* Joan White.
Open Sat & Sun Noon - 5 PM, or by appointment. No admis. Estab 1962 to bring to the college and the community shows of significant contemporary art not previously available in the Northwest. Many shows relate to advanced art courses at the college and to important exhibitions at the Portland Art Museum, the PCVA or other Northwest institutions. Mem: 55 Art Associates; dues $100.

Income: $15,000 (financed by endowment, membership, state appropriation, individual donations and NEA grants).

Collections: †20th Century prints; †drawings; †paintings and sculpture; †pre-20th Century prints.

Exhibitions: (1976-77) Andrew Leicester (landscape sculpture); Lee Kelly (outdoor sculpture for the public); John Walker (paintings and drawings); Richard Anuskiewicz (paintings and prints); John Seery (recent paintings); William Eggleston (color photographs); (1977-78) Cart Morris/Hilda Morris (works from the permanent collection); David Bottini (recent sculpture); John Pearson (paintings, prints and drawings); Willard Midgette (Indians); contemporary German prints; Miriam Schapiro (Anatomy of a Kimono); (1978-79) Francoise Grossen (fiber as sculpture); Scott Sonniksen (recent paintings and drawings); Garery Winogrand (public relations).

Publications: Poster with introductory write-up on back published for each show.

Activities: Lect open to public, 4 - 6 vis lectr per yr; gallery talks; individual paintings and original objects of art lent to other museums only, for major exhibitions; traveling exhibitions organized and circulated cooperatively with other institutions.

—**Eric V. Hauser Memorial Library.** *Librn* Luella Pollock; *Chmn Art Dept* Prof Charles S Rhyne.
Open Mon - Fri 8 AM - 2:30 AM; Sat 8 AM - Midnight; Sun Noon - Midnight. Estab 1912 to support class work and research of Reed faculty and students.

Income: Financed by endowment, student tuition and individual donations. Purchases: $155,000.

Holdings: Vols 260,000; Per subs 1560; AV—(Reference only) Lantern slides, microfiche, microfilm, motion pictures, phonorecords; Other—(Reference only) Exhibition catalogs, framed reproductions, memorabilia, original documents, prints.

SCHOOL OF THE ARTS AND CRAFTS SOCIETY OF PORTLAND, Hoffman Gallery, 616 NW 18th Ave, 97209. Tel: 503-228-4741. *Dir* Bridgett Beattie McCarthy.
Open Mon - Thurs 8 AM - 10 PM; Fri & Sat 9 AM - 4 PM, cl Sun. Estab in 1906 to promote quality handcrafts. The Julia E. Hoffman Gallery is a small well designed area occupying part of the building's first floor. It presents thoughtfully planned and well installed exhibitions of work both by contemporary artists and craftsmen and by traditional, folk and primitive cultures. It aspires to exemplify the highest standards of design and workmanship, to set goals and provide stimulation of ideas for students, to elevate the capacity for judgment and appreciation in all viewers. It adheres to no bias toward the avant garde or the traditional, but seeks instead to call attention to quality, in whatever mode it comes; Main gallery is L shaped with 500 sq ft of floor space; white walls for hanging shows. Average Annual Attendance: 4000. Mem: 1200; dues $8 - 100; annual meeting May.

Income: $196,000 (financed by membership, city and state appropriation and school tuitions).

Exhibitions: Cynthia and Edwina Bringle (pottery and weaving); Kristen Anderson (enamelings); Ray Atkeson (photography); Handmade Stones; Julia Hoffman (photography); Sandra Haefker (sculpture and drawings).

Publications: Catalog, quarterly; gallery announcements, monthly; newsletter; descriptive brochure.

Activities: Lect open to the public, gallery talks.

Library: Holdings—Vols 600 for reference: periodicals and slides.

UNIVERSITY OF PORTLAND, Wilson W Clark Memorial Library, 5000 N Willamette Blvd, 97203. Tel: 503-283-7111. *Dir* Rev Joseph P Browne; *Reference Librn* Jane Wahl; *Technical Services Librn* Janice F Starr; *Special Services Librn* Mary K Devlin.
Open Sun 1 - 11 PM; Mon - Thurs 8 AM - 11 PM; Fri 8 AM - 5 PM; Sat 9 AM - 4 PM. Estab 1901 to support the University curriculum. Circ: 50,000. Maintains an art gallery with a rotating exhibit.

Income: Financed through the University.

Holdings: Vols 170,000; Per subs 1250; AV—Microfiche; microfilm, phonorecords.
Exhibitions: Women Painters of the West; Jean Sorenson; Margaret Martin; Dorothy Carnine Scott; California Society of Printmakers; Watercolor Society of Oregon; John Christianson; John Petrucelli; Evelyn Porter; Betty Waldo Parish; Revingon Arthur; National Society of Painters in Casein; Joseph Corish.

WEST HILLS UNITARIAN FELLOWSHIP, 8470 S W Oleson Rd, 97223. Tel: 503-246-3351. *Pres* Ralph Pratt; *VPres* Edward Weinstein; *Secy* Rachael Kester; *Office Admin* Jill Prislin; *Fine Arts Chmn* Doll Gardner.
Open Mon - Fri 9 AM - 1 PM; No admis. Estab 1970 to give professional artists one or two-man shows in a lovely gallery space, and to expose the congregation and public to fine visual art; the entire sanctuary wall space is like a large gallery and the building is light, airy with a woodsy backdrop. Average Annual Attendance: 10,000.
Income: $30,000 (financed by membership).
Collections: Paintings, wall sculptures by local artists.
Exhibitions: Paul Missal (paintings); Sylvia Wheeler (prints and watercolors); Ted Waltz (prints and wall constructions); Byron Gardner (drawings); Manuel Izquierdo (prints); Rachael Kester (wall hangings); Marian Kolisch & Kathy Davis (photos); Judy Cooke and Robert Hanson (paintings and drawings); Robert Powne (photos); Vicki Clarke (drawings); Group Show; 20 Poets and Painters; Candace Coleman & Tanya Durham Hilber (weaving and quilted wall hangings); Bonnie Laing-Malcolmson & Jackie Johnson (paintings); Jaki Svaren/Bettye Lou Bennett/Enga Dubay (calligraphy); Steven Green (photos).
Publications: Newsletter, monthly; bulletin, weekly.
Activities: Classes for adults and children; dramatic programs; lect open to the public, 8 vis lectr per yr; concerts; sales shop selling books.

SALEM

SALEM ART ASSOCIATION,* Bush House, Bush Barn Art Center, 600 Mission St SE, 97301. Tel: 503-363-4714, 581-2228. *Pres* Tom Hallman; *VPres* Helen Ward; *Exec Dir* Mrs William Lindburg; *Exec Secy* Maxine E Cooper.
Bush Barn open year around, Tues - Fri 9:30 AM - 5 PM; Sat & Sun 1 - 5 PM. No admis. Bush House open Sept through May, Tues - Sun 2 - 5 PM; June, July, Aug, Tues - Sat 12 AM - 5 PM; Sun 2 - 5 PM. Admis adults 75¢, students 25¢, children (under 12) 10¢; Wed free during winter only. Inc. 1938, Museum opened 1953; Bush Barn Art Center opened 1965 to preserve the best of the past and encourage the arts of the present. Average Annual Attendance: 25,000. Mem: 1000; dues $10 and higher; annual meeting May.
Exhibitions: Changed monthly.

WILLAMETTE UNIVERSITY, George Putnam University Center, 900 State St, 97301. Tel: 503-370-6267. *Dir* Sally Howell.
Open Mon - Sun 8 AM - 11 PM. No admis. Estab 1970 to enrich the atmosphere of the University Center and to acquaint students, faculty and staff with various forms of art. Two separate areas are used: one area is a paneled wall; the other area is comprised of free standing art panels with surface area of approx 54 x 54 in. Total panels surface area is 18. Average Annual Attendance: 45,000.
Income: Financed through the University.
Exhibitions: Robert Hess; sculptures; several exhibits from Visual Arts Resources (Univ of Oregon); Betty LaDuke; China exhibit; several local artists and photographers.
Activities: Lect; gallery talks.

SPRINGFIELD

EMERALD EMPIRE ARTS ASSOCIATION,* 421 North A, 97477. Tel: 503-726-8595. *Pres* Mrs Frank Light; *Secy* Michele Thorp; Nellie Mae Ayres; Ethel Lyngholm; Bob Forehand; Willis Washburn.
Estab 1957 to advance art in our community and to build up funds for a workshop and gallery. Mem: 150-170, dues $5; monthly meetings third Tues.
Publications: Monthly Art League Bulletin.
Activities: Classes for adults and children; 10 week classes each year plus 2 - 3 workshops, area served is Willamette Valley, material available to anyone; exhibitions twice a year at local shopping center; lect open to the public; gallery talks; tours; competitions; individual paintings and original objects of art lent; traveling exhibitions organized and circulated; book shop.
Library: Holdings—Vols 150.

THE DALLES

THE DALLES ART ASSOCIATION - THE DALLES ART CENTER,* Fourth & Washington, 97058. Tel: 503-296-4759. *Pres* Jeanne Hillis; *Secy* Muriel Harrison; *VPres* Ray Hotka; *Exhibit Chmn* Carl Kramer.
Open Thurs, Fri & Sat 1 - 4 PM. No admis. Estab 1959 for presentation of community arts activities. Gallery maintained. Average Annual Attendance: 3000. Mem: 60; dues $10; annual meeting 1st Mon in June.
Income: Financed by membership.
Exhibitions: State services exhibits, member and guest exhibits.
Publications: Monthly bulletn.
Activities: Traveling exhibitions organized and circulated; individual paintings lent to schools; lect open to public, 4 vis lectrs per yr; 4 gallery talks; classes for adults and children; competitions. Junior Art Club with 15 members.

PENNSYLVANIA

ALLENTOWN

ALLENTOWN ART MUSEUM, Fifth and Court Sts (Mailing Add: PO Box 117, 18105). Tel: 215-432-4333. *Pres Bd Trustees* Bernard Berman; *Dir* Richard N Gregg; *Cur* Peter F Blume; *Cur Educ* Mimi Miey; *Comptroller* Barbara Strohl; *Registrar* Patricia Delluva; *Mem Secy* Valerie Heins; *Sales Desk Mgr* Gloria Hvazda; *Bldg Supt* David Miller.
Open Tues - Sat 10 AM - 5 PM; Sun 1 - 5 PM; cl Mon. No admis. Estab 1939 to acquire, protect, display and interpret the visual arts from the past and present, world wide. Building and land cover three quarters of a city block; 28,000 sq ft wing was added in 1975 to more than double the space. Average Annual Attendance: 100,000. Mem: 3600; dues from student $7.50 to benefactor $500.
Income: $435,000 (financed by endowment, membership, city and state appropriations, and contributions). Purchases: $13,125.
Collections: Samuel H Kress Memorial Collection of European paintings & sculpture, c 1350-1750 (Bugiardini, Hals, de Heem, Rembrandt, Ruisdael, Steen and others); †American 18th, 19th & 20th century paintings, sculptures and prints; Frank Lloyd Wright period room, 1912; †Textile study room; Chinese porcelains; English and American silver.
Exhibitions: American Flag in the Art of our Country; French Masterpieces of the 19th Century; Howard Chandler Christy: Artist/Illustrator of Style; Stitches in Time plus others.
Publications: Calendar of Events, monthly; catalogs of major exhibitions.
Activities: Docent training; lect open to public; gallery talks; tours; competitions; individual paintings lent to museums; lending collection contains original art works, original prints, paintings and textiles; traveling exhibitions organized and circulated; museum shop selling books, original art, reproductions, prints, slides, cards and catalogs.
—Mack Trucks Art Reference Library, *Librn* Richard N Gregg.
Open to staff, volunteers and members for reference.
Holdings: Vols 7000; Per subs 25.
Special Subjects: Related to permanent art collection.

MUHLENBERG COLLEGE CENTER FOR THE ARTS,* 24th & Chew Sts, 18104. Tel: *Dir* Monroe A Denton, Jr; *Asst Dir* David M Seamans.
Open daily during school term. No admis. Estab 1976. Building designed by architect Philip Johnson; focal point of its design and function is a 220 ft glass-covered galleria which bisects the structure; main level contains theatre/auditorium complex, lecture/recital hall, galleries/classrooms, offices, slide library and studios; the upper level contains the Music and English Departments.
Collection: †Small contemporary art collection has been started.
Exhibitions: Monthly traveling exhibitions and shows by students and faculty.

AUDUBON

AUDUBON WILDLIFE SANCTUARY, Mill Grove, Box 25, 19407. Tel: 215-666-5593. *Cur/Dir* Edward W Graham.
Open daily 10 AM - 5 PM; cl Mon. No admis. Estab 1951 to display the major artwork of John James Audubon, artist-naturalist, who made Mill Grove his first home in America, 1804-1806; this is a National Historic Site and features two original artworks by Audubon, plus examples of all his major publications. Average Annual Attendance: 25,000 - 30,000.
Income: Financed by county appropriation.
Collections: Birds of America (double elephant folio, 4 vols, Audubon & Havell); Quadrupeds of North America (Imperial size, 2 vols, Audubon & Bachman); Birds of America (first ed, Octavo, 7 vols, Audubon, Lithos by Bowen); Quadrupeds of North America (Octavo, 3 vols, Audubon, Lithos by Bowen).

BETHLEHEM

LEHIGH UNIVERSITY GALLERIES, Fine Arts Bldg, Chandler-Ullmann Hall, Room 17, 18015. Tel: 215-691-7000, exten 736. *Dir Exhib & Coll* Ricardo Viera; *Asst to the Dir* Judith Goldworm.
Estab to bring diverse media and understanding to the Lehigh students and general public of the Lehigh Valley area. Collection is maintained in the following two galleries.
  DuBois Gallery: Open Mon - Fri 9 AM - 10 PM; Sat 9 AM - Noon; cl Sun. No admis. Four floors of approx 250 running ft of wall hanging space per floor. Average Annual Attendance: 10,000.
  Ralph Wilson Gallery: Open 9 AM - 5 PM, Sat 9 - Noon; Sun 2 - 5 PM. Three rooms of exhibition space. Average Annual Attendance: 5000.
Income: Financed by endowment and gifts.
Collections: Ralph Wilson Collection of paintings and graphics; photography collection; Grace Collection of paintings; Kempsmith Collection of sculpture and graphics; Berman Collection, Adler Collection and Driebe Collection of paintings; Baker Collection of porcelain.
Exhibitions: Approximately six exhibits per academic year in each gallery.
Publications: Calendar, twice a year; exhibition catalogs.
Activities: Classes for adults; lect open to the public, 6 vis lectr per yr; gallery talks; individual paintings and original objects of art lent to other schools and galleries.

BLOOMSBURG

BLOOMSBURG STATE COLLEGE, Haas Gallery of Art, 17815. Tel: 717-389-2607. *Chmn Dept of Art* Dr Percival R Roberts III; *Dir Haas Gallery of Art* Karl A Beamer.
Open Mon - Fri 9 AM - 5 PM. No admis. Estab 1966 as an educational and cultural extension of the College's Department of Art; gallery covers 2350 sq ft with track lighting and three dome skylights. Average Annual Attendance: 10,000.
Income: Financed by city appropriation and grants.
Collection: Permanent Collection includes over 300 works.
Exhibitions: One-man exhibitions of Jim Myford (welded aluminum, and cast aluminum).
Publications: Exhibition catalogs and brochures, monthly.
Activities: Lect open to the public, 6-8 vis lectr per yr; gallery talks; tours.
—**Andruss Library.** Tel: 717-389-2607. *Librn* William V Ryan.
Holdings: Vols 500,000; Per subs 200,000.
Special Collections: Fine Arts books and Prints.

BOALSBURG

COLUMBUS CHAPEL, BOAL MANSION AND MUSEUM, Rte 322. 16827. Tel: 814-466-6210. *Dir* Mathilde Boal Lee; *Dir* Christopher G Lee; *Cur* Lillian Major.
Open June - Labor Day 10 AM - 5 PM; May, Sept & Oct 2 - 5 PM. Admis adults $1.75; students $1.00; children 50¢. Estab 1952 as a nonprofit educational organization devoted to preservation of this historic homestead built in 1789. Average Annual Attendance: 3,000.
Income: Financed by admissions.
Collections: Chapel contains 16th & 17th century Spanish, Italian and Flemish art; mansion contains 18th and 19th century French, Spanish, Italian, Flemish and American art; weapons: American, French and German (1780-1920); furniture, china and glassware.
Activities: Sales shop selling books, slides and postcards.

BRYN MAWR

BRYN MAWR COLLEGE, Art and Archaeology Library, Thomas Library, 19010. Tel: 215-LA 5-1000, exten 248. *Head* Eileen Markson; *Library Asst* Babette Bauerle.
Open during academic year Mon - Fri 9 AM - 12 PM; Sat 9 AM - 5 PM; Sun 2 - 12 PM. Summer Mon - Fri 9 AM - 5 PM; Wed Eve until 10 PM; cl weekends. Estab 1931 to serve the needs of the general college program, and the undergraduate majors and graduate students through the PhD degree in both history of art and Classical and Near Eastern archaeology; gallery not maintained. For reference only.
Income: Financed by college funds.
Holdings: Vols 40,000; Per subs 400.
Special Subjects: Italian Renaissance; Italian Baroque; Impressionism; Greek architecture and sculpture; Near Eastern archaeology; Aegean archaeology.

BUCK HILL FALLS

BUCK HILL ART ASSOCIATION, 18323. *Pres* Elizabeth Dickson; *VPres* Mrs J Vincent Hackett; *Secy* Mrs Henry Hood.

Open 10 AM - 5 PM. No admis. Estab 1931 to further appreciation of art. Average Annual Attendance: 1,850. Mem: 125.
Income: $8,000 (financed by endowment and membership). Purchases: $500.
Collections: Contemporary American artists.
Exhibitions: Gallery temporarily closed and exhibitions suspended until 1979.
Activities: Lect open to public, 2 vis lectr per yr; sales shop selling original art, and prints.

CHADDS FORD

BRANDYWINE RIVER MUSEUM, PO Box 141, 19317. Tel: 215-388-7601. *Dir* James H Duff; *Business Mgr* Charles Burns; *Dir Public Relations* John Sheppard; *Cur Coll* Ann Barton Brown; *Assoc Cur* Joan H Gorman; *Registrar* Gene E Harris; *Coordinator Visitor Services* Cynthia Repplier; *Bookstore Mgr* Sue Coleburn.
Open daily 9:30 AM - 4:30 PM; cl Christmas. Admis adults $1.75; sr citizens $1.00; students and children 75¢. Estab 1971, devoted to the preservation, documentation and interpretation of art history in the Brandywine Valley, the history of American illustration and the relationship of regional art to the natural environment. Three main galleries housed in renovated 1864 grist mill with contemporary additions for public services, storage, offices and bookstore. Average Annual Attendance: 175,000. Mem: 2400; dues $15 - $100.
Income: Purchases—$24,000.
Collections: †Art of the Brandywine Valley from early and mid-19th century; †American Illustration; regional artists of the 20th century, painting, drawing and sculpture, including a major Andrew Wyeth Collection.
Exhibitions: The Art of American Illustration; Peter Hurd: a Retrospective; Horace Pippin; Beyond Necessity: Art in the Folk Tradition; Faces of Old Kris: Santa Claus in American Art; George Cope; The Art of the Carousel.
Publications: The Catalyst, quarterly; exhibition catalogs.
Activities: Classes for children; dramatic programs; tours for adults; individual paintings and original objects of art lent to other museums for exhibition purposes; traveling exhibitions organized and circulated; museum shop selling books, reproductions, slides, postcards and catalogs.
—**Library.** *Librn* Mary Bassett.
Open daily 9 AM - 5 PM, for reference to staff and volunteers; by appointment to the public.
Holdings: Vols 3,000; Per subs 20; Other—Artists' memorabilia, including photographs, letters and other records.
Special Subjects: The history of American illustration in books and periodicals.
Special Collections: N C Wyeth memorabilia; Howard Pyle's published work.

CHESTER

DESHONG MEMORIAL ART GALLERIES, 11th St & Edgmont Ave, 19013. *Sr Trustee* J Edward Clyde.
Open Mon - Fri 3 - 8 PM; Sat 9 - 12 AM. Estab 1913.
Income: Financed by endowment.
Collections: 18th and 19th century Oriental art objects; 19th century European landscape and genré pictures.

DOYLESTOWN

BUCKS COUNTY HISTORICAL SOCIETY MERCER MUSEUM, Pine & Ashland Sts, 18901. Tel: 215-345-0210. *Exec Dir* Gary D Schuman; *Chief Cur* Lynne F Poirier; *Pres Bucks County Historical Society* William F Heefner.
Open Tues - Sun 10 AM - 5 PM, Mar - Dec. Admis adults $2; family $4.50, students $1. Estab 1880. Inside this poured, re-inforced concrete building, four galleries wrap around a towering central court where different hand crafts are exhibited inside small cubicles. Additional artifacts hang from ceilings, walls and railings. A six story tower on each end completes the building. Average Annual Attendance: 40,000. Mem: 2400; dues $10 and up; annual meeting Nov.
Income: $150,000 (financed by endowment, membership, state appropriation, and admissions).
Collections: Over 40,000 artifacts representing more than 40 early American crafts, their tools and finished products; the history and growth of our country as seen through the work of the human hand; large American folk art collection.
Exhibitions: A new orientation exhibit introducing Henry Mercer, his collections and buildings is permanently housed in the new Entrance Pavilion, supported by grant from NEH.
Publications: Journal, semi-annually; newsletter, monthly.
Activities: Classes for adults and children; lect open to public, 6-7 vis lectr per yr; museum shop selling books, magazines, reproductions, prints.

—**The Spruance Library.** *Librn* Terry A McNealy.
Open to the public for reference.
Holdings: Vols 44,000; Per subs 50; Other—Genealogical records, newspapers, deeds, contracts.
Special Subjects: Genealogy and history.

DUNCANSVILLE

LEE ATKYNS STUDIO-GALLERY, Box 120, Rte 2, 16635. Tel: 814-695-0186. *Dir* Lee Atkyns.
Open by appointment. No admis. Estab 1950, original gallery was in Washington, DC, present studio-gallery opened in 1975 in what was once an abandoned chapel, the old cemetery adjacent has been converted into a flower garden.
Income: Financed personally.
Collections: Paintings by Lee Atkyns of "Liberated Lines" series (1971 -) showing the derivative trends through the years from 1947 to present. Landscapes, abstractions and "Music Expressionist" paintings.
Activities: Individual paintings lent to galleries.

ERIE

ERIE ART CENTER, 338 West Sixth St, 16507. Tel: 814-459-5477. *Pres* Michael Carr; *VPres* Marvin Gold; *Secy* Mary Becht; *Treas* Fred Reed; *Exec Dir* John Vanco.
Open Tues - Sun 1 - 5 PM. No admis. Estab 1898 for the advancement of visual arts. Galleries located in historic building. Average Annual Attendance: 4800. Mem: 617, dues individual $10, family $15; annual meeting second Monday in April.
Income: $124,000 (financed by membership). Purchases: Minimal.
Collections: Contemporary graphics, photographs, paintings, sculpture and some historical paintings and graphics.
Exhibitions: James Steffan/Robert Schroeck—Paintings; Paintings by Martin Lemelman; Selections from Edinboro State Collection; Northwestern Pennsylvania Artists Association; Photographs by Tom Caravaglia; Adele Becker/Anita Johnson—Paintings; Vincent Smith—one-man show; Photographs by Wolfgang Christian & Ceramics by Bob Milnes; Annual Spring Show; Four-Woman show: Shelle Lichtenwalter Barron, Mary Rosiak, Susan Stone, Mary Brigit Williams; Charles & Lisa Lindsay Daugherty—Paintings & Sculpture.
Publications: Flyers for shows, monthly.
Activities: Classes for adults and children; docent training; gallery talks; tours; competitions; individual paintings and original objects of art lent to public buildings, community centers, colleges, etc; lending collection contains original art works 205; traveling exhibitions organized and circulated; sales shop selling framing.

ERIE DISTRICT LIBRARY CENTER,* 3 S Perry Square, PO Box 1631, 16507. Tel: 814-452-2333. *Dir* Kenneth G Sivulich.
Open, Winter Mon - Fri 9:30 AM - 9 PM, Sat 9 AM - 5:30 PM, cl Sun; Summer Mon & Fri 9:30 AM - 9 PM, Tues, Wed & Thurs 9:30 AM - 6 PM, Sat 9 AM - 5:30 PM, cl Sun. No admis. Estab 1899 to provide public library services to the community. Gallery contains original paintings, drawings, prints and reproductions of paintings and sculpture.
Income: financed by city and state appropriations.
Exhibitions: Local artists.
Activities: Material available to all adult patrons, no fees; material lent includes original paintings, prints, drawings, painting and sculpture reproductions; lending collection contains 700 color reproductions; 6000 items lent in an average year; photograph collection.

FRANKLIN CENTER

FRANKLIN MINT CORPORATION MUSEUM, 19091. Tel: 215-459-6348. *Museum Dir & VPres Collector Relations of Franklin Mint* William F Krieg; *Supvr Guest Relations* Pam Pentland.
Open Mon - Fri 9 AM - 5 PM, except holidays. No admis. Estab 1973 to make available to the general public, a location where the collectibles created by The Franklin Mint can be viewed. Average Annual Attendance: 100,000.
Income: Financed by Franklin Mint funding.
Collections: Porcelain and crystal art; silver and gold coins struck by The Franklin Mint; medallic collections recognizing the genius of Michelangelo, DaVinci and Rembrandt; leather bound books ornamented in 22kt gold. A 15-screen sight-and-sound show is shown, 23 minutes in length, accented by the skillful use of narratives and music.
Activities: Sales shop selling jewelry, medals, greeting cards and collectibles.

GLENSIDE

BEAVER COLLEGE, Eugene Richard Fuller Gallery of Art, Church and Limekiln Pike, 19038. *Chmn Dept Fine Arts* Jack Davis.

Open 1 - 5 PM except during school holidays. No admis. Estab 1969 to show contemporary art generally. One large gallery 20 x 50 ft. Average Annual Attendance: 5000.
Income: Purchases $500.
Collections: A few prints and drawings.
Exhibitions: Faculty Exhibition; Annual Eastern Pennsylvania Drawing Show; Robert Morris; Drawings; Alex Katz: Heads.
Publications: Brochures for major exhibitions, 3 per year.
Activities: Gallery talks; competitions.

GREENSBURG

WESTMORELAND COUNTY MUSEUM OF ART, 221 N Main St, 15601. Tel: 412-837-1500. *Dir* Dr Paul A Chew; *Exec Secy* Regina L Narad; *Mem Secy* Mary K Hollahan.
Open Tues - Sat 10 AM - 5 PM; Sun 1 - 5 PM; cl Mon & holidays. No admis. Estab 1949 to create, establish and maintain a memorial foundation of a public, charitable, cultural, literary and educational nature and, in conjunction therewith, to maintain a public art museum. The museum houses two large galleries and one small gallery for changing exhibitions, two English 18th century pine-panelled rooms, and a suite of Victorian period rooms. Average Annual Attendance: 17,600. Mem: 859; dues $10 - $1000.
Income: Financed by endowment.
Collections: †American Art (paintings, drawings, sculpture, and decorative arts); †antique toys; Continental and British paintings; American prints; British drawings; European prints.
Exhibitions: John J McDonough Collection: A Panorama of American Painting; Nancy Dudchenko (ceramic wall constructions); Boris Dudchenko & Jan Zandhuis (glass and metal sculptures); Julio Larraz; 19th & Early 20th Century Regional Painters; 18th & 19th Century Regional Folk Art; Three Centuries of American Painting; Biblical Etchings (Marvin Hayes); David Hanna; Jim Myford; Jack Massey; Ray DeFazio; Polish Textile Artists.
Publications: Calendar of Events, twice a year; catalog of permanent collection.
Activities: Dramatic programs; lect open to public, 6 vis lectr per yr; concerts; gallery talks; tours; individual paintings lent to museums; lending collection contains original prints, paintings and sculpture; museum shop selling books, original art, reproductions, slides and cards.
—**Art Reference Library.**
Open to the public for reference.
Holdings: Vols 5500; Per subs 40.
Special Subjects: American painting, sculpture, architecture, prints, drawings and decorative arts.

GREENVILLE

THIEL COLLEGE, Sampson Art Gallery, College Ave, 16125. Tel: 412-588-7700, exten 415. *Dir of Permanent Coll* Ronald Pivovar; Richard Hayes; *Student Dir* Matthew Cunningham.
Open Sun - Thurs 1 - 4 PM & 7 - 9 PM; Fri & Sat 1 - 4 PM. No admis. Estab 1971 to provide students, faculty, college staff and the community with a gallery featuring a variety of exhibitions, and give students an opportunity to show their work; gallery has white walls, track floodlighting system, linoleum tile floor, and one window wall. Average Annual Attendance: 1000.
Exhibitions: (1977-78) Drawings & Prints by Bill Davis; Sculpture by Michael McConnell; Carl & Wilda Sundberg (watercolors).
Activities: Lect open to the public, 6 vis lectr per yr; gallery talks.

HARRISBURG

PENNSYLVANIA DEPARTMENT OF EDUCATION, Division of General Education-Arts in Education Program, (Mailing Add: Box 911, 17126). Tel: 717-787-7814. *Chief* Clyde M McGeary; *Sr Prog Adviser* Joseph McCarthy; *Prog Adviser* Robert Revicki; *Prog Adviser* Bernice Gottschalk Roehner; *Dir Governor's School for the Arts* Arthur Gatty; *Dir Aesthetic Educ Prog* Robert Snyder.
The Arts in Education Program provides leadership and consultative and evaluative services to all Pennsylvania schools in arts program development. Infusion of arts processes into differentiated curriculums for all students is a particular thrust. The program offers model programs at several sites, ongoing staff development programs, assistance in designing aesthetic learning environments and consultation in identifying and employing regional and community resources for arts education.

PENNSYLVANIA HISTORICAL AND MUSEUM COMMISSION,* William Penn Memorial Museum & Archives Bldg, 17120. Tel: 717-787-3362. *Exec Dir* William J Wewer; *Dir Bur of Mus* Michael J Ripton; *Dir Bur Archives & Hist* Harry E Whipkey.
State Museum, State Archives, Historical Commission and Historical Properties combined into one agency in 1945.

Income: $5,000,000 for entire Commission.
Activities: Guided tours in William Penn Memorial Museum, Pennsylvania Farm Museum of Landis Valley, and at most historical properties. Special exhibitions at William Penn Memorial Museum. Craft and Harvest Days at Farm Museum.
—**William Penn Memorial Museum** (formerly State Museum), Harrisburg. *Dir* J Duncan Campbell.
Museum open Mon - Sat 9 AM - 5 PM; Sun 1 - 5 PM. Offices Mon - Fri 8:30 AM - 5 PM.
Collections: (Fine Arts Gallery) China; glass; silver; textiles; period rooms; decorative arts; folk art; archaeology; anthropology; Indian artifacts.
Publications: Books, brochures.
Activities: Classes for children; lectures; guided tours; art competitions; exhibitions from outer-museum loan.
Library: Open to the public for use on premises only. Holdings: Vols 40,000. Special Subjects: History, art, folk art, archaeology.

HAVERFORD

MAIN LINE CENTER OF THE ARTS, Old Buck Rd & Lancaster Ave, 19041. Tel: 215-LA5-0272. *Admin Dir* Eleanor Daitzman; *Pres* Robert Wesson; *VPres* Dan Goldman; *Secy* Joan Smith; *Treas* Maria Raday.
Open Mon - Fri 10 AM - 12 Noon & 1 - 4 PM. No admis. Estab 1937 to develop and encourage the fine arts. Three large, well lit galleries, completely modernized to accommodate over one hundred painting and sculptures, etc. Average Annual Attendance: Several thousand. Mem: 800; dues child $8, adult $15, family $18; meetings once a month except Aug.
Income: Financed by membership and fund raising.
Exhibitions: Craft Show; Membership Shows; One-man and group Graphic Shows; Porcelain Show.
Publications: Brochures, 3 times a year.
Activities: Classes for children; dramatic programs; lect open to public and for members only, 12 vis lectr per yr; gallery talks; concerts; tours; competitions; individual paintings and original objects of art lent to libraries, schools, hospitals, etc; lending collection contains original art works, original prints and sculpture; traveling exhibitions organized and circulated.

INDIANA

INDIANA UNIVERSITY OF PENNSYLVANIA, Kipp Gallery, 15701. Tel: 412-357-2530. *Chmn Exhib* Ned O Wert.
Open Mon - Fri 9 AM - 4:30; Sat & Sun by appointment to groups. No admis. Estab 1970 to make available a professional gallery program to Western Pennsylvania and to the university community. Versatile space with portable wall system, track lighting, secure, humidity controlled. Average Annual Attendance: 10,000.
Income: Financed by Student Coop Assn.
Exhibitions: Milton Glaser; National Drawing Invitational; Toys from Switzerland; Hunt Botanical Collection; one-person & group shows; Richard Brown Baker Print Collection.
Activities: Lect open to public, 3 - 5 vis lectr per yr; gallery talks; tours; traveling exhibitions organized and circulated; sales shop selling original art and prints.

JENKINTOWN

ALVERTHORPE GALLERY, 511 Meetinghouse Rd, 19046. Tel: 215-884-0466. *In Charge Coll Prints & Rare Books* Lessing J Rosenwald; *Cur* Ruth E Fine.
Open Mon - Fri by appointment. No admis. Estab 1939 for the study of prints and rare books relating to the history of the graphic arts.
Collections: Drawings; prints and rare books 15th-20th centuries; Blake Collection.
Activities: Works lent on limited basis to institutions meeting established qualifications; photograph service for purchase.
Library: Holdings—Vols 3000.

KUTZTOWN

KUTZTOWN STATE COLLEGE
—**Sharadin Art Gallery,*** 19530. Tel: 215-683-3511, exten 342. *Gallery Coordr* Eldon Katter.
Open Mon - Fri 10 AM - 4 PM; Sat 10 AM - Noon, 2 - 5 PM; Sun 2 - 5 PM. No admis. Estab 1956 to make the best of the contemporary arts available to the town and gown communities.
Income: Financed by city and state appropriations. Purchases: $5000.
Collections: Approx 400 works in prints, drawings and paintings.
Publications: Brochure listing a gallery season's collection of shows.

Activities: Lectures open to the public; 2 gallery talks per year; temporary, traveling, faculty and student exhibitions.
—**Rohrbach Library,** 19530. Tel: 215-683-3511, exten 301. *Col Librn* John K Amrhein.
Open Mon - Thurs 7:45 AM - 11 PM; Fri 7:45 AM - 5 PM; Sat 9 AM - 5 PM; Sun 2 - 11 PM. Estab 1866. Circ 90,000.
Holdings: Vols 270,000 for lending, Per subs 2000 for reference; AV—Audiotapes, cassettes, film strips, microfiche, microfilm, motion pictures, phonorecords, reels, slides; Other—Exhibition catalogs, pamphlets.
Special Subjects: Russian art, history of art; art education.

LANCASTER

COMMUNITY GALLERY OF LANCASTER COUNTY, 13 West Grant St, 17603. *Dir* Genevieve D Libhart; *Pres* Helen Woolworth.
Open Tues & Fri 9 AM - 4 PM; other days Noon - 4 PM. No admis. Estab 1965 to present the best quality in art exhibits. Average Annual Attendance: 10,000. Mem: 450; dues; various categories; annual meeting first Sunday in April.
Income: $23,000 (financed by membership and county commissioners).
Exhibitions: Leavitt Collection; Robert Indiana; Luigi Rist; Eric Sloane; Henri Cartier Bresson; New Guinea Art; Personages; William Accorsi; local and regional artists.
Activities: Docent training; lect for children and members; gallery talks.

LANCASTER COUNTY ART ASSOCIATION,* Art Center, 22 E Vine St, 17602. Tel: 717-392-9258. *Pres* John G Gates.
Estab 1936, inc 1950. Mem: 320; dues $10; annual meeting 2nd Tues in May.
Collections: Currently being enlarged by purchases.
Exhibitions: Monthly exhibitions; Spring and Fall Member & Student Shows; three 3-man shows, and others.
Activities: Demonstrations, lectures, classes, programs, tours; 6 vis lectrs per yr; 2 gallery talks; free classes for Retired Citizens Association; sponsors Lancaster County day tour of fine homes and gardens annually as a project to raise funds for community projects. Sponsors traveling exhibitions.
Library: Technical only. Association supplies funds to the Public Library for purchase of art books and publications.

PENNSYLVANIA FARM MUSEUM OF LANDIS VALLEY, 2451 Kissel Hill Road, 17601. Tel: 717-569-0401. *Dir* Carroll J Hopf; *Cur Crafts & Educ* John B Brooks; *Preparator:* Vernon S Gunnion.
Open Mon - Sat 9 AM - 4:30 PM; Sun 12 Noon - 4:30 PM. Admis adults $1, over 65 free, under 12 free, school groups free. Estab 1925 to collect, preserve and interpret Pennsylvania rural life and culture, c 1750 to c 1900; farm implements, crafts, tools, domestic furnishings and folk art. Outdoor museum with 25 exhibit buildings including restored 18th and 19th century structures. Average Annual Attendance: 100,000. Mem: 1125; dues $3 and up; annual meeting: third Tues in Oct.
Income: $645,000 (financed by state appropriation). Purchases: $6000.
Collections: (Art) Folk art, including ceramics, textiles, furniture and metals.
Publications: Newsletter, monthly.
Activities: Classes for adults and children; docent training; lect open to public, 4 vis lectr per yr; occasional loans made from permanent collection; sales shop selling books, craft items, reproductions and slides.
Library: Open to staff, scholars, etc by appointment, for reference. Holdings: Vols 12,000; Per subs 25. Special Subjects: Agricultural history, crafts, decorative arts and folk art.

LEWISBURG

BUCKNELL UNIVERSITY, Ellen Clarke Bertrand Library, 17837. Tel: 717-524-3056. *Librn* George M Jenks; *Chief Pub Services* Ronald B Daniels; *Chief Technical Services* Helena G Rivoire.
Open Mon - Fri 8:30 AM - 11 PM; Sat 9 AM - 5 PM; Sun 1 - 11 PM. Estab 1846 to serve students and faculty of university. Circ: 131,374. Maintains art gallery, a study collection of twenty paintings and one sculpture of the Renaissance given by the Samuel H Kress Foundation.
Income: $900,000 (financed by endowment, tuition and gifts). Purchases: $325,000.
Holdings: Vols 380,000; Per subs 2,076; AV—Cassettes, microfiche, microfilm, phonorecords; Other—Manuscripts, memorabilia, original art works, pamphlets and prints.

LORETTO

SOUTHERN ALLEGHENIES MUSEUM OF ART, Saint Francis College Mall (Mailing Add: PO Box 8, 15940). *Dir* Michael M Strueber; *Admin Secy* Sophia Burkey; *Security/Maintainance* Tom Sokolowski; *Community Outreach Coordinator* Lynn David Wolpert.

Open Wed, Thurs, & Fri 10 AM - 5 PM; Sat & Sun 1:30 - 5:30 PM. No admis. Estab and dedicated June 1976 to facilitate interest, understanding and the appreciation of the visual arts of the past, present and future through the exhibition of our permanent as well as temporary collections; an extremely versatile main gallery, 50 x 77 ft with ten moveable cases that are 3 x 4 x 7½ ft high; print gallery upstairs. Average Annual Attendance: 10,000. Mem: 100, dues variable.
Income: Financed by membership, business, corporate and foundation grants.
Collections: †American paintings, sculpture, drawings, prints, and ceramics.
Exhibitions: (1976-78) Inaugural; Kelly Collection; World Premier of the Virginia Steel Scott Collection; Linda Rohrbach; Altman and Cronauer; Richard Treaster; 1st Painting Invitational; Juried Pennsylvania Sculpture; Dines and Emil Carlsen Retrospective; Ralph Woehrman; 33rd Annual Pittsburgh Watercolor Society's Exhibition; Christopher Pekoc; 2nd Annual Painting Invitational (artists from Cleveland, Pittsburgh and Washington, DC); Botanical Art (contemporary); Stuart Frost; Penna Decorative and Functional Arts, 1700-1865; Henry Koerner; 3rd Annual Painting Invitational; Pittsburgh Glass Exhibition; five Weavers and Print Exhibition; four Sculptors and Print Exhibition.
Activities: Classes for adults, dramatic programs; luncheons; theatre; dance; lect open to the public; concerts, tours; individual paintings and original objects of art lent; lending collection contains books, original prints, paintings, sculpture, drawings.

MEADVILLE

ALLEGHENY COLLEGE, Bowman, Megahan, and Penelec Galleries, 16335. Tel: 814-724-3371. *Gallery Dir* Martha A Holt.
Open Tues - Fri 12:30 - 5 PM; Fri Eve 7 - 9 PM; Sat 1:30 - 5 PM; Sun 2 - 4 PM; cl Mon. No admis. Estab 1971 as one of the major exhibition spaces in northwest Pennsylvania, the galleries present exhibits ranging from works of contemporary artists to displays relevant to other fields of study; galleries are housed in three spacious rooms, white walls, stone floor, 13 ft ceilings. Average Annual Attendance: 8000.
Income: Financed by college funds.
Collections: Samuel Pees Collection of contemporary painting; General David M Shoup Collection of Korean pottery.
Exhibitions: (1977-78) Northwest Biennial Craft Show; Development of the Figure Concept in Graphic Artwork by children from different Countries; Batiks from the Pees Collection of Indonesian Art; Confluences, an architectural show; Northwest Pennsylvania Artists' Association Show; Japanese Prints; Marie Kelly (prints and paper sculpture); Jerry Uelsmann (photographs); Mars Show (photographs of Viking I and II explorations); Photography Invitational; Student Show.
Activities: Lect open to the public; gallery talks; tours; individual paintings and original objects of art lent to local organizations.
Library: Lawrence Lee Pelliter Library. *Librn* Margaret Moser. Open to students and faculty.

MERION

BUTEN MUSEUM OF WEDGWOOD, 246 North Bowman Ave, 19066. Tel: 215-664-9069. *Pres* Mrs Harry M Buten; *Dir* David Buten; *Asst to Dir* Patricia Pelehach; *Mem Secy* Sally Krohn; *Assoc Dir* Mrs. Samuel Laver.
Open Tues - Thurs 2 - 5 PM; Sat 10 AM - 1 PM; cl Sun, Mon & Fri. Admis adults $1, sr citizens 50¢. Estab 1957 for study and exhibition of Wedgwood ceramics. Mem: 2000; dues $20; meetings first Sun of month (Sept to May).
Income: Financed by membership.
Collections: Over 10,000 examples of Wedgwood ware made from 1759 to the present.
Publications: Bulletin, 7 - 9 times per yr; Monographs in Wedgwood Studies, annually.
Activities: Lect open to public, 5 vis lectr per yr; gallery talks; original objects of art lent to other museums and colleges; lending collection contains kodachromes and original art works; museum shop selling books and original art..
Library: *Librn* Mrs S Arthur Levy. Open to scholars by appointment for reference. Holdings: Vols 1600. Special Subjects: English ceramics, especially Wedgwood ware.

NAZARETH

MORAVIAN HISTORICAL SOCIETY, Whitefield House Museum, 210 E Center St, 18064. Tel: 215-759-0292. *Pres* Rev H Williams; *Secy* Mary Henry Stites; *Cur* E B Clewell.
Open Tues, Fri & Sat 2 - 5 PM; 2nd & 4th Sun of each month 2 - 5 PM; other times by appointment. No admis, donations requested. Built in 1740 by George Whitefield, famous preacher, and bought by the Moravians in 1741 and continued in use by various segments of the Church, until its present occupation as a missionary home and the seat of the

Moravian Historical Society which was organized on April 13, 1857 to elucidate the history of the Moravian Church in America; not, however, to the exclusion of the general history of the Moravian Church; the museum houses many unique and distinctive items pertaining to early Moraviana and colonial life. Average Annual Attendance: 1500. Mem: 400; dues $3 - $100; annual meeting second Thurs in Oct.
Income: Financed by endowment, membership and donation.
Collections: (Art) John Valentine Haidt Collection of Paintings, which comprises the only known collection of extant religious paintings of the early American era, 1754-1770; musical instruments; pottery and Stiegel glass; handwrought and cast bells; clothing and textiles; Indian and foreign mission artifacts; rare books, manuscripts; also changing exhibits.
Publications: Transactions, bi-annual.
Activities: Classes for adults and children; dramatic programs; docent training.

NEW BRIGHTON

MERRICK ART GALLERY, Fifth Ave and Eleventh St (Mailing Add: PO Box 312, 15066). Tel: 412-846-1130. *Trustee* Robert S Merrick; *Dir* Charles Moore; *Educ Dir* Dona Boots.
Open Tues - Sat 10 AM - 5 PM; Sun 1 - 5 PM; cl Mon; reduced hours during summer. No admis. Estab 1880 to preserve and interpret .the collection of paintings and other objects owned by Edward Dempster Merrick, the founder. Also to foster local art through classes and one-man shows. All galleries are on the second floors of two parallel buildings with a connecting bridge; there are three small rooms and one large one. Three rooms have clerestory monitors overhead. Mem: 275; dues $10, $15 and $25; annual meeting February.
Income: Financed by endowment, membership.
Collections: Most paintings date from the 19th century. American artists—W T Richards, Paul Weber, Emil Bott, E Poole, Birge Harrison, A F King, Thomas Sully, Thomas Hill, W L Sonntag, Edward and Thomas Moran, F K M Rehn, Worthington Whittredge. European artists—Richard Westall, Pierre Paul Prud'hon, Franz Xavier Winterhalter, Hans Makart, Gustave Courbet.
Exhibitions: History Through Industry, a Bicentennial Exhibit; Oriental Carpets; Panoramic Painting of the Military Career of Garibaldi, painted during the 1850's by Robert Burford; The Drawings of Edward B Lee, Sr; shows by local artists.
Publications: Newsletter, six times per yr.
Activities: Classes for adults and children; docent training; outdoor summer art fairs; lect open to public, 1 - 2 vis lectr per yr; gallery talks; concerts; tours.
Library: Open to any person for reference. Special Subjects: Old and rare books, many about art.

NEW CASTLE

HOYT INSTITUTE OF FINE ARTS, * 124 E Leasure Ave, 16105. Tel: 412-658-9418. *Pres Bd of Trustees* John L Wilson; *Exec Dir* William Craig McBurney.
Open Tues - Sat 9 AM - 4 PM. No admis. Estab 1968 to encourage the development of the arts within the community. Average Annual Attendance: 27,000. Mem: 440 including honorary; dues $5, $10, and $25.
Income: Financed by endowment and membership.
Collections: Local artists.
Publications: Newsletter to members, semiannually.
Activities: Lectures open to public; concerts; dramatic programs; classes for adults and children; competitions; scholarships.

NEW WILMINGTON

WESTMINSTER COLLEGE ART GALLERY, * 16142. Tel: 412-946-8761. *Dir* Robert Godfrey.
Open Mon - Sat 10 AM - 7 PM; Sun 2 - 7 PM. No admis. Estab 1854 to organize and present 9 exhibitions per season, to organize traveling exhibitions, publish art catalogs of national interest; visiting artists program. Average Annual Attendance: 15,000.
Income: Over $2000 (financed by endowment).
Collections: †20th century prints and drawings; 19th and 20th century paintings.
Exhibitions: Student, faculty and loan exhibitions.
Publications: Westminster College Art Gallery, annually; occasional catalogs.
Activities: Traveling exhibitions organized and circulated; lect open to public, 4 vis lectrs per yr; gallery talks.

NEWTOWN

BUCKS COUNTY COMMUNITY COLLEGE, Hicks Art Center, Fine Arts Department, Swamp Rd, 18940. Tel: 215-968-5861. *Chairperson* Bruce Katsiff.

Open Mon - Fri 8 AM - 10 PM; Sat 9 AM - 5 PM. No admis. Estab 1970 to bring outside artists to the community; gallery covers 960 sq ft. Average Annual Attendance: 5000.
Income: Financed by city and state appropriation.
Exhibitions: Margerie Lee Miller (printmaker); Margrit Fischer (drawings); William Hodder (glass); Three Philadelphia Photographers.
Activities: Lect open to the public, 8 vis lectr per yr; competitions; artmobile.

PHILADELPHIA

AMERICAN COLOR PRINT SOCIETY,* c/o Philadelphia College of Art, Broad and Pine Sts, 19102. Tel: 215-893-3100. *Pres* Richard Hood; *Treas* Bernard A Kohn; *Secy* Ethel V Ashton; *VPres* Mildred Dillon; *VPres* Stella Drabkin.
Estab 1939 to exhibit and sell color prints. Mem: 150; dues $5 and up; annual meeting Oct.
Exhibitions: (Annuals) National juried exhibition held at Print Club, Philadelphia, in March; 6 annual prizes, 3 of which are Purchase Prizes with the prints becoming a part of the American Color Print Society's Collection housed in the Philadelphia Museum of Art; printmaking demonstrations at the Print Club in March.
Activities: Society has published a presentation print each year, until 1960, in an edition of 50 which have been given to the associate members; sponsors annual members exhibition of all media color prints.

AMERICAN SWEDISH HISTORICAL FOUNDATIONS, Museum, 1900 Pattison Ave, 19145. Tel: 215-389-1776. *Pres* Claes Bothen; *Cur Coll* Charles L Seeburger.
Open Tues - Sat Noon - 4 PM; cl Sun, Mon & holidays. Admis adults $1.00, students 50¢. Average Annual Attendance: 10,000. Mem: 1200; dues $10 and up; annual meeting June.
Collections: †History and culture of Americans of Swedish descent.
Exhibitions: Temporary exhibitions of paintings, arts and crafts by Swedish and Swedish-American artists.
Publications: Newsletter.
Activities: Group tours by appointment; Lucia Fest, Valsborgs, massoafton; lect; slide/film strip shows.
Library: General reference. Holdings: Vols 12,500. Special Subjects: Rambo Research of genealogical and colonial material, Jenny Lind, Fredrika Bremer, and John Ericsson.

ATHENAEUM OF PHILADELPHIA, 219 S Sixth St, 19106. Tel: 215-925-2688. *Secy & Librn* Dr Roger W Moss Jr; *Program Coordr* Eileen Magee; *Architectural Librn* Sandra Tatman; *Circulation Librn* Mrs David Sorbe.
Open Mon - Fri 9 AM - 5 PM. No admis. Estab 1814 to collect, preserve and make available original sources on American cultural history, 1814-1914; all fine and decorative arts arranged in room settings. Average Annual Attendance: 10,000. Mem: 1000; annual meeting first Mon in Feb.
Income: $170,000 (financed by endowment, membership). Purchases: $20,000.
Collections: (Art) †Permanent study collection of American decorative Arts, 1810-1850; †French in America.
Exhibitions: John Notman, Architect.
Publications: Bookshelf, ten; Annotations, four; Annual Report, one; and 3-5 Mongraphs each yr.
Activities: Lect open to the public, 6-10 vis lectr per yr; concerts; tours; sales shop selling books, prints, slides.
—Library.
Open to all qualified applicants for reference only.
Holdings: Vols 100,000; Per subs 75; Other—Photographs 50,000, manuscripts, architectural drawings and related materials.
Special Collections: Early Travel and Exploration; fiction and literary periodicals; transportation; military history; 1812-47.

CLIVEDEN,* 6401 Germantown Ave, 19144. Tel: 215-848-1777. *Adminr & Property Council & Staff of National Trust Interpretors* Raymond V Shepherd, Jr; *Coordr Interpretive Progs* Carole T Scanlon.
Open year round 10 AM - 4 PM; cl Christmas Day. Admis adults $1.25, senior citizens 60¢, group tours by arrangement, free to National Trust members.
Cliveden is a property of the National Trust for Historic Preservation. Preserved as an historic museum operated as a community preservation center, it is a National Historic Landmark. Cliveden was built in 1763-67 as the country house of Benjamin Chew, a distinguished Philadelphia lawyer and political leader. Surrounded by six acres of centuries-old trees, it has continued to be used through seven generations.
Chew family furnishings include extremely important Philadelphia pieces made by such prominent cabinetmakers as Thomas Affleck, Jonathan Goste Lowe, and Daniel Wood. There is also some Penn family furniture,

as well as paintings by Smibert, Wollaston, Pine and Henry. Chew papers include over 100,000 manuscript pages plus 3000 volumes and the law library of Chief Justice Benjamin Chew.
Property serves as a focal point for advancement of historic preservation. It develops new relationships among cultural, community, and preservation groups, and Trust members in its area. Responds to community preservation needs by acting as a link between community and appropriate regional or headquarters offices of National Trust. Adaptive use, is a preservation project of 1976-77. Interpretive programs are provided which relate to Cliveden's particular care study in historic preservation. Special Christmas program, Members Day during National Historic Preservation Week early May. Set of 16 in x 8 in measured drawings, taken by Historic American Building Survey, available from Cliveden's Preservation Shop.

DREXEL UNIVERSITY ART GALLERY AND MUSEUM COLLECTION,* Chestnut & 32nd Sts, 19104. Tel: 215-895-2424. *Cur* Geraldine Peterson Staub.
Open 9 AM - 5 PM; Sat 9 AM - 1 PM; cl Sun. No admis. Estab 1891; Picture Gallery 1902.
Collections: Museum collection includes examples of decorative arts of India, China, Japan and Europe; hand printed India cottons, European textiles; Sevres and other ceramics. Randell Hall Gallery contains the John D Lankenau and the Anthony J Drexel Collections of German and French paintings of the 19th century.

FAIRMOUNT PARK ART ASSOCIATION, 25th St & The Parkway (Mailing Add: Box 7646, 19101). *Pres* C Clark Zantzinger, Jr; *VPres* Theodore T Newbold & Henry W Sawyer III; *Exec Secy* Eileen H Wilson. Estab 1872 for the purpose of buying sculpture which is then given to the City of Philadelphia. Mem: 350; dues $15 - $100 annual meeting April.
Income: $120,000 (financed by membership and city appropriation).
Publications: Annual Report.

FREE LIBRARY OF PHILADELPHIA, Art Department, Logan Square, 19103. Tel: 215-686-5403. *Dir Library* Keith Doms; *Head Art Dept* Miriam L Lesley.
Open Mon - Thurs 9 AM - 9 PM; Fri 9 AM - 6 PM; Sat 9 AM - 5 PM; Sun 1 - 5 PM. Estab 1891, art department estab 1896, to serve the citizens of the City of Philadelphia. Circ: 39,000.
Income: Financed by endowment, city and state appropriations. Purchases: $30,540.
Holdings: Vols 150,000; Per subs 193; AV—Microfiche, microfilm; Other—Clipping files, exhibition catalogs, memorabilia, pamphlets.
Special Collections: Index of exhibition catalogs of The Pennsylvania Academy of the Fine Arts 1870 to date; 368 original measured drawings of colonial Philadelphia buildings, Philadelphia Chapter, American Institute of Architects; 18th and 19th century architectural pattern books; John Frederick Lewis Collection of books on fine prints and printmaking.
—Print and Picture Department,* Room 211. Tel: 215-686-5405. *Head* Robert F Looney.
Open 9 AM - 5 PM; cl Sun; also cl Sat June - Sept. Estab 1954 by combining the Print Department and the Picture Collection.
Special print collections (non-circulating): †John Frederick Lewis Collection of portrait prints (211,000); Hampton L Carson Collection of Napoleonic prints (3400); Americana (1200); †Philadelphiana (8000); †graphic arts (2000); †greeting and tradesmen's cards (27,000). Circulating picture collection of pictures in all media, universal in subject coverage (500,000). Print exhibitions, library-owned and traveling. Original drawings—Rosenthal Collection, American (847); Bendiner Collection, International (102). Samuel Castner Collection of Philadelphia—scrapbooks, 46 volumes; prints, drawings, photographs, clippings.
—Rare Book Department, Third Floor. Tel: 215-686-5416. *Rare Book Librn* Howell J Heaney.
Open Mon - Sat 9 AM - 5 PM. Estab 1949.
Special Collections: Cuneiform tablets and seals, 2800 Babylonian and Sumerian (John Frederick Lewis Collection); †Mediaeval and Renaissance manuscripts, 250 volumes, 2000 individual leaves—mostly with miniatures (Lewis Collection); †Oriental manuscripts, 155 volumes (Lewis Collection); Oriental miniatures, 1250, mostly Mughal, Rajput and Persian (Lewis Collection); †Angling prints, 1000 from 17th-20th century (Evan Randolph Collection); †prints of Philadelphia, 400 from 1800-1950 (Randolph Collection); †Howard Pyle and His School, books and original drawings (Thornton Oakley Collection); †Legal prints, 8000 (Hampton L Carson Collection); †Pennsylvania German Fraktur, 1000 (Borneman and Yoder Collections); †Horn books, 150 (Elisabeth Ball Collection); †original drawings, paintings, prints, and other illustrative material relating to the works of Dickens, Goldsmith and Thackeray; early American prints and engravings. †Arthur Rackham (Grace Clark Haskell Collection); †Kate Greenaway; †Beatrix Potter. Early American

children's books (15,000) including Rosenbach Collection (1682-1836); American Sunday-School Union Historical Collections; 300 caricatures, prints and drawings (Alfred Bendiner Collection).

HISTORICAL SOCIETY OF PENNSYLVANIA, 1300 Locust St, 19107. Tel: 215-732-6200. *Pres* Harold D Saylor; *VPres* Thomas C Cochran, E P Richardson, Caroline Robbins and Henry R Pemberton; *Secy* Harold H Lewis; *Dir* James E Mooney; *Chief Mss* Peter J Parker; *Head Librn* John H Platt; *Asst Treas* Sarah B Pomerantz.
Open Mon 1 - 9 PM; Tues - Fri 9 AM - 5 PM. Admis to Library & MSS Dept $1.00, to Museum free. Estab 1824 to collect and preserve records relating primarily to Pennsylvania history, also collects various artifacts and paintings of persons relevant to Pennsylvania history. Maintains art gallery with four exhibit rooms, two contain changing exhibits from the collections and two serve as meeting rooms and contain numerous early American paintings and furniture. Mem: 3250; dues $15; meetings four per year.
Income: Financed by endowment and membership.
Collections: Unmatched collection of papers, prints, paintings, furniture, household and personal effects from pre-Revolution through 1800; more than 800 paintings and miniatures by early American artists Stuart, Sully, Copley, Peale, Wright, Birch, Inman, Neagle and others; more than 14 million manuscripts.
Publications: The Pennsylvania Magazine of History and Biography, quarterly.
Activities: Lect for members, 4 vis lectr per yr; individual paintings and original art objects lent primarily to other museums.

INDEPENDENCE NATIONAL HISTORICAL PARK, 313 Walnut St, 19106. Tel: 215-597-7132. *Supt* Hobart G Cawood; *Asst Supt* Bernard Goodman; *Interpretive Specialist* Martin I Yoelson; *Chief Cur* John C Milley.
Open daily 9 AM - 5 PM. No admis. Estab 1948 to preserve and protect for the American people, historical structures, properties, and other resources of outstanding national significance, and associated with the Revolution and growth of the Nation. Average Annual Attendance: 3,500,000. Mem: 1600; dues $15; annual meeting May.
Income: Financed by membership and federal grant.
Collections: Historic buildings and sites; archeological specimens; original documents relating to America's Revolutionary and Federal periods; 18th century American period furnishings; decorative arts; American portraits from 1728-1830.
Publications: Friends of Independence NHP Newsletter.
Activities: Classes for children; docent training; lect for members; gallery talks; tours; individual paintings and original objects or art lent to qualified professional institutions; museum shop selling books, magazines, reproductions, prints, slides.
—*Library,* 120 S Third St, 19106. *Librn-Archivist* Sondra D Gutkind.
Open to public by appointment.
Holdings: Vols 5500; Per subs 23; Other—microfilm 540 reels, photographs, slides 35,000, video-tapes, research notecard file 150,000 items, films, pamphlets.
Special Subjects: American history 1750-1830 History and decorative arts of Philadelphia and Pennsylvania for the 18th century.
Special Collections: 18th century insurance surveys; Judge Edwin O Lewis papers; Independence Hall Association papers; D Knickerbocker Boyd papers.

LA SALLE COLLEGE ART GALLERY, 20th & Olney Ave, 19141. Tel: 215-951-1221. *Cur* Thomas Ridington; *Asst Cur* Caroline Wistar.
Open Mon - Fri 10:30 AM - 3:30 PM; Tues 6:30 - 8:45 PM. No admis. Estab 1975 for educational purposes and to house the collection begun 1965 as support for art history program and as a service to community. Gallery has several large spaces set up to suggest various centuries and to contain paintings of the period.
Income: Financed by endowment.
Collections: 15th and 16th century paintings, drawings, watercolors and prints; Western art, European and American, with a few pieces of sculpture and decorative art.
Exhibitions: Two special exhibitions are held each semester: Selections of Graphic Art by the social satirist Gavarni (French 1804-1866); Bible Illustrations from the 16th and 17th centuries.
Publications: Exhibition catalogs.
Activities: Concerts; gallery talks; tours by appointment with gallery staff.
Library: Open to visitors for reference only. Special Collections: Rare Bible collection 15th - 20th century; portrait collection; books illustrated with portrait prints.

LIBRARY COMPANY OF PHILADELPHIA, 1314 Locust St, 19107. Tel: 215-K16-3181. *Librn* Edwin Wolf II; *Asst Librn* Gordon Marshall; *Cur of Printed Books* Marie Korey; *Cur of Prints* Kenneth Finkel.

Open Mon - Fri 9 AM - 4:45 PM. No admis. Estab 1731 for the purpose of scholarly research. Average Annual Attendance: 2000. Mem: 540; dues $8; annual meeting first Mon May.
Income: Financed by endowment, membership, city appropriation, and federal grants.
Collections: (Art) Primarily a collection of Americana; †American Printing; †Philadelphia prints, watercolors, drawings and photography.
Exhibitions: (1976) A Rising People (in cooperation with the Historical Society and the American Philosophical Society). (1977) A Flock of Beautiful Birds. (1978) A Pride of Acquisition, 1953-1978.
Publications: Occasional Miscellany, 2-4 times per year; Annual Report, annually.

MOORE COLLEGE OF ART GALLERY, 20th and Race Sts, 19104. Tel: 215-568-4515. *Gallery Dir* Helen Williams Drutt.
Open Mon - Fri 9 AM - 4:30 PM. No admis. Estab 1831 to offer the Philadelphia community and its students the opportunity to view contemporary artwork that is usually not available locally; gallery is housed in moderate exhibition space with flexible panels to accommodate current exhibit. Average Annual Attendance: Approximately 5000.
Income: Financed by endowment.
Collections: Limited permanent collection items which are displayed in other parts of the college.
Exhibitions: (1976-78) John Sloan/Robert Henri: Their Philadelphia Years 1886-1904; Annual Alumnae Exhibition; Collection in Progress; 200 or so Selections from the Milton Brutten & Helen Herrick Collection; Alan Shields; Robert Hudson Retrospective.
Publications: Catalogs for major exhibitions; bulletins, irregularly.
Activities: Classes for adults and children; lect open to the public, 16 vis lectr per yr; traveling exhibitions organized and circulated.
—*Library:* *Librn* Marjorie Bilk. For reference only.
Open Mon - Thurs 8 AM - 9:30 PM; Fri 8 AM - 5 PM; Sat 8:30 AM - 1 PM. Estab to serve Moore students.
Income: Purchases—$26,000.
Holdings: Vols 32,000; Per subs 200; AV—Slides; Other—Clipping files, exhibition catalogs.

MUSEUM OF THE PHILADELPHIA CIVIC CENTER, Civic Center Blvd at 34th St, 19104. Tel: 215-561-5100, exten 21-201. *Chmn Bd* William G Chadwick; *Exec Dir* John Pierron; *Asst Dir Museum* Ronald L Barber; *Chief Cur* Robert Nobel; *Registrar* Robert Carter; *Design Dir* Zenon L Fesczak; *Cur Educ* Albina D DeMeio; *Promotion & Publicity Specilist* Henry Spector.
Open Tues - Sat 9 AM - 5 PM; Sun 1 - 5 PM; cl Mon & legal holidays. No admis. Estab 1894 to present exhibitions of contemporary local, national and international art, craft, photography and design. Average Annual Attendance: 200,000.
Income: Financed by city appropriation.
Collections: Oriental and African crafts; New Caledonian ethnographic material; Southeastern Siberian ethnographic collection; Philippine ethnographic collection; Latin American crafts.
Exhibitions: Changing exhibitions of contemporary local, national and international art, craft, photography and design.
Activities: Classes for children; lect for scheduled school class only; suitcase exhibits on foreign countries loaned to schools.

VIOLET OAKLEY MEMORIAL FOUNDATION, INC., 627 St George's Road, 19119. Tel: 215-CH7-0633. *Pres & Cur* Edith Emerson; *VPres* Wm Jeffrey Hudson; *Secy* Lisa Ulrich; *Treas* Nelson Ogden; *Asst Treas* Theodore Ulrich.
Open by appointment. Estab 1961-62 to preserve the Violet Oakley Collection; maintains art gallery in her large studio. Dues $15, non-resident $10; annual meeting May.
Income: Financed by membership.
Collections: Violet Oakley Collection.
Exhibitions: June exhibition by members and friends.
Activities: Lect for members and guests; musical recitals; loan exhibitions.
Library: For reference. Holdings: Private library of Violet Oakley and E Emerson combined.

PENNSYLVANIA ACADEMY OF THE FINE ARTS, Broad & Cherry Sts, 19102. Tel: 215-972-7600. *Dir* Richard J Boyle; *Cur* Frank H Goodyear Jr; *Admin* Robert Stubbs; *Pres & Chmn of Bd* Henry S McNeil.
Open Tues - Sat 10 AM - 5 PM; Sun 1 - 5 PM. Admis adults $1, children under 12 years, students, senior citizens 50¢. Estab 1805 by C W Peale, Thos Sully, Benj West, et al, to cultivate the health and development of the fine arts in America. The Academy building, opened in 1876, was restored for the American Bicentennial. Considered the masterpiece of its architect, Philadelphian Frank Furness, its style is called, alternately, polychrome picturesque and High or Gothic Victorian. It was designated a Registered National Historic Landmark in 1975. Adjunct

building: Peale House, 1811 Chestnut St, 19103; Dining facility: Peale Club, 1819 Chestnut St, 19103. Average Annual Attendance: 90,000. Mem: 3100; dues $15 and up.
Income: Financed by endowment, membership, city and state appropriation, contributions and federal grants.
Collections: The collections excel in 18th and 19th century American paintings, sculpture, drawings and prints. Allston, West, the Peale family, Stuart, Sully, Rush and Neagle are represented in important works and/or quantities.
Exhibitions: (1977) Eight Contemporary American Realists. (1978) The Last Three Years: A Selection of Recent Acquisitions; The Travel Sketches of Louis I Kahn; as well as exhibitions of works by contemporary artists, Jo Hanson, David Pease, Dennis Will, Edith Neff, Eileen Goodman, Valerie Jaudon, Don Lantzy, Deryl Mackie, David Fertig, John Dowell, Phil Simkin, Martha Erlebacher.
Publications: In This Academy, (newsletter), quarterly.
Activities: Dramatic programs; lect open to the public; concerts; tours; traveling exhibitions organized and circulated; museum shop selling books, magazines, reproductions; prints, slides, and miscellaneous items related to Collection.
—*Library.* Tel: 215-972-7611. *Librn* Marietta P Bushnell.
Open Mon - Fri 9 AM - 4:30 PM, during school term, to students and by appt to the public. Estab 1805, the Library serves students of painting, sculpture and printmaking, and is intended as a source of visual inspiration. It is not a research library and therefore has little material on aesthetics or the history of art.
Income: Financed by school funds.
Holdings: Vols 5000; Per subs 30; Other—Clipping files, exhibition catalogs.
—**Fellowship of the Pennsylvania Academy of the Fine Arts,*** The Peale House, 1811 Chestnut St, 19103. Tel: 215-299-5083. *Pres* Dorothy Pere; *Secy* Lucy Glick; *Treas* L A D Montgomery.
Estab 1897 to provide opportunities for creative incentive and sharing in responsibilities for the development of facilities and activities in the field of art for its members and to maintain relations with the students of the Pennsylvania Academy of the Fine Arts. Mem: 700; dues $6, nonresident $3, meetings held Sept, Oct, Feb & May.
Income: Approx $3000.
Collections: Paintings and sculpture.
Exhibitions: Annual exhibition of oils, sculpture, watercolors and graphics partly invitational and partly juried, with awards; annual prizes awarded at exhibitions $1050.
Activities: Classes; lectures; films; individual paintings and objects of art lent.

PHILADELPHIA ART ALLIANCE,* 251 S 18th St, 19103. Tel: 215-K15-4302. *Chmn of the Bd* Raymond S Green; *Pres* George A D'Angelo; *VPres in Charge Art* Raphael Sabatini; *Dir* Irene Korsyn.
Open Mon - Fri †0:30 AM - 5 PM; Sat & Sun 1 - 5 PM. No admis. A unique, educational and cultural organization founded in 1915, catering to all the arts; music, drama, painting, sculpture, prints, design, literary arts, illustration, architecture. Galleries open free to members, guests and the public; restaurant for members and their guests. Average Annual Attendance: 100,000. Mem: approx 2400 individuals and organizations; dues from $50; annual meeting Mar.
Publications: The Art Alliance Bulletin, published 9 times a year, Oct - May; Philadelphia Art Alliance Press publishes 3 or 4 art-related volumes annually.

PHILADELPHIA ART COMMISSION, 1329 City Hall Annex, 19107. Tel: 215-686-4470. *Pres* F Eugene Dixon, Jr; *Exec Dir* Beverly T Volk.
Open 8:30 AM - 5 PM. No admis. Estab 1911 under Philadelphia Home Rule Charter as the Art Jury, later retitled Art Commission. An Art Ordinance passed in 1959 provides for art work in city buildings and on city owned property. The Art Commission reviews architectural designs and art work covering all media for municipal locations or other locations in which municipal funds are expended. The Art Commission's files are open to inspection by anyone since the information contained therein qualifies as public information. As indicated, the material deals solely with art proposals and architectural designs. Designs cover all buildings, major highways, and bridges. The Commission meets twice monthly to review plans and proposals. Mem: 9; between 20 and 24 meetings annually.
Income: Financed by city appropriation.

PHILADELPHIA COLLEGE OF ART, Broad & Spruce Sts, 19102. Tel: 215-893-3100. *Pres* Thomas F Schutte; *Dean of Faculty* Nathan Knobler; *Dir Exhib* Janet Kardon.
Open Mon - Fri 9 AM - 5 PM. No admis. Estab 1876 to prepare artists and designers for careers in business, industry, education and the fine arts. Gallery's varied exhibition program serves to stimulate its own community as well as the general public. The work of younger but innovative, recognized artists is featured.
Income: Financed by endowment and city appropriation.

Exhibitions: Artists' Sets and Costumes; Duane Michals Photographs; Seventies Painting; Projects for PCA (Siah Armajani, Alice Aycock, Patrick Ireland, Robert Irwin, Charles Simonds, George Trakas).
Publications: Alumni Magazine, twice yearly; a general newspaper, twice monthly; catalogues accompany each gallery exhibition.
—*Library.* Tel: 215-893-3126. *Library Dir* Hazel Gustow; *Gallery Dir* Janet Kardon; *Readers' Services Librn* Martha Hall.
Open Mon - Thurs 8:15 AM - 1 PM; Fri 8:15 AM - 8 PM; Sat 9 AM - 1 PM; (shorter hours during the summer). Estab 1876 to assist the art community in general and cooperative actively with other libraries. Circ: 41,000.
Holdings: Vols 40,000; Per subs 270; AV—Audio tapes, cassettes, microfiche, microfilm, motion pictures, phonorecords, slides; Other—Clipping files, exhibition catalogs, pamphlets, photograph, reproductions.
Special Subjects: Visual arts, particularly contemporary.

PHILADELPHIA MARITIME MUSEUM, 321 Chestunut St, 19106. Tel: 215-WA5-5439. *Pres* J Welles Henderson; *Dir* Richard K Page; *Asst Dir* Howard J Taylor; *Registrar* John Groff; *Teacher* William Ward.
Open Mon - Sat 9 AM - 5 PM; Sun 1 - 5 PM. No admis, small donation requested. Estab 1960 to preserve and interpret the maritime heritage of the Bay and River Delaware, and the Port of Philadelphia; Gallery 1, Man and the Sea, general maritime history; Gallery 2, Man under the Sea, history of underwater technology; Gallery 3, Waterway of History, history of Bay and River Delaware and Port of Philadelphia; Gallery 4, changing exhibits. Average Annual Attendance: 40,000. Mem: 900; dues $10 minimum; annual meeting May.
Income: $800,000 (financed by endowment, membership and private and corporate gifts). Purchases: $40,000.
Collections: (Art) †Paintings by major American marine artists; †17th - 20th century maritime prints; small craft; sailing vessel, 177 ft Gazela Primeiro, built 1883.
Exhibitions: Defense of the Delaware-1777, from the collection and loans history of British invasion and occupation of Pennsylvania in 1777. (1978) An exhibit of the works of George Bonfield (19th Century Marine Painter).
Publications: Spindrift, (newsletter), quarterly; annual report; books and catalogs, intermittently.
Activities: Classes for adults and children; lect for members only, 10 vis lect per yr; concerts; gallery talks; competitions; individual paintings and original objects of art lent to recognized non-profit museums with adequate facilities and pertinent need, six month only; lending collection contains books, kodachromes, lantern slides 150; motion pictures 10, original art works 50, original prints 900, paintings 80, photographs 1200; slides 1500; museum shop selling books, magazines, reproductions, prints, postcards, models and souvenirs.
Library. Tel: 215-WA5-5439. *Librn* Dorothy Mueller. Open to members and scholars for reference only. Holdings: Vols 5000; Per subs 20; Other—Rare books, manuscripts, maps. Special Subjects: Philadelphia and Delaware Valley history; Lloyds Register of Ships, 1880 to present; general maritime history and technology. Special Collections: Nautical artifacts and decorative arts (navigation instruments, China trade items).

PHILADELPHIA MUSEUM OF ART, 26th and Parkway (Mailing Add: Box 7646, 19101). Tel: 215-763-8100. *Pres* William P Wood; *Chmn* Henry P McIlhenny; *Acting Dir* Arnold Jolles; *Cur 20th Century Art* Anne d'Harnoncourt; *Cur Decorative Arts: Medieval & Renaissance* David T Dubon; *Advisor Decorative Arts* Henry P McIlhenny; *Cur American Art* Darrel Sewell; *Cur Paintings before 1900* Joseph Rishel; *Cur European Decorative Arts after 1700* Kathryn Kiesinger; *Cur Far Eastern Art* Jean Gordon Lee; *Cur Emer Indian Art* Stella Kramrisch; *Cur Prints, Drawings & Photographs* Kneeland McNulty; *Cur Emeritus Costume & Textiles* Elsie Siratz McGarvey; *Advisor Alfred Stieglitz Center* Michael Hoffman; *Conservator* Marigene Butler; *Chief Div Educ* Theodore Katz; *Registrar* Barbara Chandler; *Pub Relations Manager* Sandra Horrocks; *Museum Supt* Robert Lipsey; *Manager Museum Shop* Shelley Holdupp; *Publ Editor* George Marcus; *Park Houses* Leslie Moneta; *Head Dept Community Prog* Penny Bach; *Volunteer Guides Coordr* Caroline Thiermann Gladstone; *Annual Giving Coordr* Jane Copeland.
Open daily 9 AM - 5 PM. Admis adults $1.50; children 75¢, sr citizens, art students, under 5 free. Estab 1876 as an art museum and for art education, known as Pennsylvania Museum of Art, present name adopted 1938. Buildings owned by the City, opened 1928; wings 1931 and 1940; Fashion Galleries 1949, 1951 and 1953; Gallatin and Arensberg collections 1954; Far Eastern Wing 1957; Decorative Arts Galleries 1958; Charles Patterson Van Pelt Auditorium 1959; Napalese-Tibetan Gallery 1960; New Galleries of Italian and French Renaissance Art 1960; new American Wing and Kienbusch Armor Collection. Museum contains 250 Galleries. Average Annual Attendance: 600,000. Mem: 18,000; dues individual $20, family $30; annual meeting Oct.
Income: $5,906,548 (financed by endowment, membership, city and state appropriations, grants and bequests). Purchases: (Art) $137,669.

Collections: Cover the general history of European, American and Eastern Art since the beginning of the Christian era. Ensembles include Chinese palace hall; Chinese temple; Chinese scholar's study; Japanese temple; Japanese tea house; Indian temple; Sasanian units from Iran; Romanesque cloister and facade; Gothic chapel; French Renaissance choir screen; many period rooms, European and American. Sculpture, especially medieval Renaissance, French 18th century and work from India. Comprehensive collection of Old Masters (†Wilstach, Elkins. McFadden and John G Johnson Collections) and 19th & 20th century art (Gallatin, Arensberg, Tyson, White and Stern Collections). The American Art Galleries, newly installed contain architectural elements, Philadelphia furniture and silver; Tucker porecelain; Stiegel glass; Geesey Collection of Pennsylvania Dutch folk art; Barberini-Kress Foundation Tapestry Series, The History of Constantine the Great; The Nepalese-Tibetan Gallery collection; Italian and French Renaissance art collection includes architectural elements, furniture, bronzes and decorative arts from Edmund Foulc and other collections. In Eastern art, imported Persian, Chinese (Crozier collection), Nepalese and Tibetan art. Prints 100,000 items.
Exhibitions: Three centuries of American Art; Kienbusch Collection of Arms & Armor.
Publications: Bulletin, quarterly; newsletter, monthly; engagement calendar, annually; exhibitions catalogues.
Activities: Classes for adults and children; dramatic programs; docent training; lect open to public, 20 vis lectr per yr; concerts; gallery talks; tours; exten dept serving all Philadelphia communities; artmobile; traveling exhibitions organized and circulated; museum shop selling books, magazines, original art, reproductions, prints, slides, jewelry, needlework, and postcards; junior museum.
—Rodin Museum.
Open daily 9 AM - 5 PM; cl legal holidays. Admis by donation. Estab 1928 as an art museum of Rodin works. The largest collection of works by Auguste Rodin outside of Paris; including sculpture and drawings. Average Annual Attendance: 60,000.
Income: Financed through museum.
—Mount Pleasant, Fairmount Park.
Open daily except Wed; cl major holidays. Admis adults 50¢, children 25¢. Built 1761, an elaborate example of 18th century building and carving; a perfect model of Georgian symmetry. Some of the finest achievements of the master craftsmen in the Philadelphia area are well-preserved in the boldly ornate woodwork and Chippendale style furnishings.
Collections: Contents of the house from the Museum represent the elegant way of life in Philadelphia in the 1760's.
—Cedar Grove, Lansdowne Dr, Fairmount Park.
Open Wed - Mon 10 AM - 5 PM; cl Tues. Admis adults 50¢, children 25¢. A country farmhouse built in the 1740's for Elizabeth Coates Paschall. The house was enlarged in the 1790's and a piazza added in the 1840's. In 1926, Lydia Thompson Morris, fifth generation owner of Cedar Grove, had the house dismantled stone by stone and moved to Fairmount Park as her gift to the city.
Collections: The furniture was given with the house and reflects changes in styles through the 17th, 18th and 19th centuries.
—John Graver Johnson Collection, Parkway & 25th St, 19101. Tel: 215-PO3-8100, exten 249. *Cur* Joseph J Rishel.
Open daily 9 AM - 5 PM. Admis to Philadelphia Museum of Art $1.50. Upon his death in 1917, prominent Philadelphia lawyer, John Graver Johnson left his extensive collection intact to the people of Philadelphia; since 1933 the collection has been housed in the Philadelphia Museum of Art; administration and trusteeship of the collection is maintained separately from the other collections in the museum.
Collections: Early and later Italian Renaissance paintings; northern European schools of Flanders, Holland and Germany in the 15th, 16th and 17th century; French 19th century paintings.
Publications: Several catalogs for various parts of the collection including Catalog of Italian Paintings and Catalog of Flemish and Dutch Paintings.
Activities: Special lectures and related activities; occasional lending of collection to significant exhibitions.
Library. Tel: 215-PO-8100, exten 249. For reference only. Holdings: Vols 4500; Other—Rare sales catalogs.
—Samuel S Fleisher Art Memorial,* 719 Catharine St, 19147. Tel: 215-WA2-3456. *Chmn* Mrs Stuart F Louchheim; *Treas* George B Clothier; *Coordr* David H Katzive; *Adminr* Thora E Jacobson; *Dir Instruction* Louis P Hirshman.
Open during exhibitions Mon - Fri 10 AM - 4 PM, Mon - Thurs 7 - 9:30 PM; Sat 1 - 3 PM. No admis. Estab 1898 as a free art school and sanctuary (Museum of Religious Art), an Italian Romanesque Revival building. Gallery is primarily used for school-related exhibitions, also for special shows of contemporary artists.
Income: $160,000. Financed by endowment.
Collections: Medieval and Renaissance religious paintings and sculpture; 18 - 19th century Portuguese liturgical objects; 17 - 20th century Russian icons; 20th century paintings and prints; some sculpture.

Exhibitions: Annual student, faculty, adult and childrens' exhibitions.
Activities: Classes for adults and children; lect open to the public; concerts; gallery talks; original objects of art lent; traveling exhibitions organized and circulated.
—Marian Angell Boyer and Francis Boyer Library. Tel: 215-763-8100, exten 229. *Librn* Barbara Sevy; *Asst Librn* Merle Chamberlain.
Open Mon, Wed & Fri 10 AM - 4 PM. Estab 1876 as a research source for the Museum staff, and to serve the public three days per week. For reference only.
Income: $53,000 (financed by endowment and corporation funds). Purchases: $18,000.
Holdings: Vols 80,000; Per subs 350; AV—Slides; Other—Clipping files; exhibition catalogs, pamphlets.
Special Subjects: Decorative arts; 20th century art.
Special Collections: Art auction sales catalogues.
—Women's Committee. *Pres* Mrs Stanley Root.
Estab 1877, inc 1915; takes an active interest in the Museum. Mem: 40 active, 10 sustaining, and 2 honorary. Sponsors Art Sales and Rental; Park Houses; Volunteer Guides; Craft Show.

PHILADELPHIA SKETCH CLUB INC, 235 S Camac St, 19107. Tel: 215-545-9298. *Pres* Morris Goldsmith; *VPres* George Douris; *Secy & Exhib Chmn* John M Dooley Jr; *Treas* Frederick Decker.
Open Wed - Sun 1 - 5 PM. No admis. Estab 1860 for artistic practice, exhibitions, and education as well as social functions; Club owns building and maintains sky-lit gallery on the second floor, approx 30 x 60 ft. Average Annual Attendance: 3000. Mem: 100 qualifications. Be an artist, collector, or patron; dues $60; monthly meeting on first Fri.
Income: Financed by endowment, and membership.
Collections: Forty Thomas Anshutz portraits; Pernell citiscapes; deceased members collection.
Exhibitions: Ten exhibitions yearly; Annual Members Show (Guildmasters Presentation); Annual Children's Show; Small Oil (115th Annual); Annual Invitational.
Publications: The Portfolio, (bulletin), monthly.
Activities: Classes for adults and children from Sept - June; lect open to the public, 8 vis lectr per yr; gallery talks; competitions with cash prizes, purchase awards and certificates; individual paintings and original objects of art lent on a very limited basis; lending collection contains books, original art works, original prints, paintings.
Library. Open by special permission of Board. Holdings: Vols 1000.

PLASTIC CLUB, Art Club for Women, 247 South Comac St, 19107. Tel: 215-K15-9324. *Pres* Dorothy Gibson; *VPres* Barbara McIlvain; *Secy* Mary Lalli; *Treas* Sara Sharpe; *Finance* Mrs. Wallace Jones; *Program* Mrs. George Taylor; *Painting Workshop & Painting Class* Mrs John McGonigal & Mrs G Taylor.
Open Mon 10 AM - 3 PM; Tues 10 AM - 2 PM; Wed 10 AM - 3 PM. Estab 1897 to promote wider knowledge of art and to advance its interest among artists. Maintains art gallery in small club house. Mem: 70, must qualify for membership by submitting three framed paintings or two sculptures to be juried; annual meeting first Wed in May.
Income: Financed by membership and money-making projects.
Exhibitions: Monthly exhibitions of paintings by members.
Activities: Lect open to public and members; gallery talks; competitions with cash awards and medals; individual paintings lent to hospitals and public buildings; sales shop selling books, original art and small craft items.
Library: Open to members. Special Collections: Paintings of outstanding early members of club.

PRESBYTERIAN HISTORICAL SOCIETY, 425 Lombard St, 19147. Tel: 215-MA7-1852. *Pres* Dr R Douglas Brackenridge; *Mgr* William B Miller; *Records Researcher* Jane Ramsay; *Treas* H Woodward McDowell; *Research Historian* Gerald W Gillette; *Catalog Librn* Sheila A Hallowell.
Open Mon - Fri 9 AM - 5 PM. No admis. Estab May 1852 to collect and preserve official records and memorabilia of the United Presbyterian Church, its predecessors and affiliates; portraits displayed in the Reading Room, Mackie Room, Board Room and hallways. Six Calder statues representing American Presbyterian personalities who played a significant role in the history of the Church are displayed outside in front of the building. Average Annual Attendance: 1200. Mem: 1250; dues $7.50; annual meeting second Fri Oct.
Income: $226,000 (financed by membership and General Assembly).
Collections: (Art) Silver and pewter communionware; church plates; relics.
Publications: Journal of Presbyterian History, quarterly.
Activities: Tours.
—Library. Tel: 215-MA7-1852. *Librn* William B Miller.
Open to the public for reference.
Holdings: Vols 130,000; Per subs 800; Other—Manuscript Volumes 20,000; manuscripts 3,000,000.

Special Subjects: Church records; Church history; Pastoral records and works; Missionary correspondence and reports.
Special Collections: Shane Collection; Jackson Collection; Indians of North American Correspondence; Scotch-Irish Society Archives; National Council of Churches Collection; Westminster Book Collection; Early American and European Imprints.

PRINT CLUB, 1614 Latimer St, 19103. Tel: 215-735-6090. *Pres* Donald W McPhail; *VPres* Cynthia Lister, Ruth Fine & Richard Jaffe; *Secy* Lois Johnson; *Dir* Ofelia Garcia; *Asst to Dir* Blanche Moore.
Open Tues - Sat 10 AM - 5 PM. No admis. Estab 1915 as a non-profit, educational organization dedicated to the promotion of fine prints and the support and encouragement of printmakers and print collectors. Average Annual Attendance: Several thousand. Mem: 2000; dues artists $12.50, single $20, family $30, contributing $50; annual meeting in Feb.
Income: $70,000 (financed by endowment, membership and private and Govt grants for some activities).
Collections: Prints and bookplates and bindings collection held at the Philadelphia Museum of Art.
Exhibitions: New Directions in Printmaking, recent monoprints; Exhibit of important prints to be at Print Club Auction; Peter Milton—major retrospective; Members' Show; American Masterprints; Philadelphia teaches printmaking.
Publications: Newsletter, quarterly.
Activities: Workshops for artists; lect series for print collectors; lect open to public, 25 vis lectr per yr; gallery talks; competitions with various prizes and purchase awards; traveling exhibitions organized and circulated.
Library: Open to members for reference. Holdings: Vols unknown; Per subs 30 (in process of revision and extension). Special Subjects: Printmaking, history of prints, catalogs raisonnes, exhibitions, auction information.

PHILIP H & A S W ROSENBACH FOUNDATION MUSEUM,* 2010 DeLancey Pl, 19103. Tel: 215-732-1600. *Dir* Clive E Driver; *Cur Decorative Arts* Suzanne Bolan.
Open for guided tours daily 2 - 5 PM except Mon; group tours from 10 AM - 5 PM by appointment; Library open Mon - Fri to scholars 10 AM - 6 PM by appointment; cl Aug & nat holidays; cl weekends June & July. Estab 1948 as a nonprofit corporation. Admis adults $1.50, students 50¢, groups of 8 or more $1 per person; exhibit only 50¢.
Collections: 18th century English antiques and silver, paintings, prints and drawings, porcelain, rugs and objets d'art; rare books and manuscripts, consisting of British and American literature, Americana, and book illustration; 100,000 manuscripts; 25,000 boks; Marianne Moore Archive.
Exhibitions: Changing exhibitions of aspects of the collections.
Publications: Notable Acquisitions; The Art of Claud Lovat Fraser.

SOCIETY OF ARCHITECTURAL HISTORIANS, 1700 Walnut St, Room 716, 19103. Tel: 215-735-0224, 735-0246. *Pres* Adolf K Placzek; *First VPres* David Bebhard; *Second VPres* Damie Stillman; *Secy* David T Van Zanten; *Exec Secy* Rosann S Berry.
For further information see National and Regional Organizations.

TEMPLE UNIVERSITY, Tyler School of Art Library, Beech and Penrose Ave, 19126. Tel: 215-CA4-7575, exten 245. *Librn* Ivy Bayard.
Open Mon - Thurs 8:30 AM - 9 PM; Fri 8:30 AM - 6 PM; Sat & Sun 1 - 4 PM (shorter hours between sessions). Estab 1934 to provide library services to students and faculty. Circ: 22,590.
Income: $48,783 (financed by appropriation from main University Library). Purchases: $14,150.
Holdings: Vols 16,350; Per subs 75; AV—Cassettes, microfiche, microfilm and video tapes; Other—Exhibition catalogs, pamphlets and pictures.

UNIVERSITY OF PENNSYLVANIA, University Museum, 33rd and Spruce St, 19104. Tel: 215-386-7400. *Dir* Martin Biddle; *Secy of Museum* Ronald J Goff; *Keeper of Coll* Mary Elizabeth King; *Keeper of Publ Services* Alan M Cook; *Cur African Ethnology* Igor Kopytoff; *Cur Amer Section* William R Coe; *Cur Latin Amer Ethnology* Ruben E Reina; *Cur North Amer Ethnology* Anthony FC Wallace; *Assoc Cur in Charge Amer Historical Archaeology* John L Cotter; *Cur Biblical Archaeology Section* James B Pritchard; *Assoc Cur, Co-Dir, Egyptian Expedition* David O'Connor; *Assoc Cur European Archaeology* Bernard Wailes; *Assoc Cur Mediterranean Section* G Roger Edwards, Donald White and Keith De Vries; *Cur Near Eastern Section* Robert H Dyson, Jr, *Cur Tablet Coll* Ake W Sjoberg; *Cur Akkadian Language & Literature* Erle Leichty; *Cur Oceanian Section* William H Davenport; *Cur Oceanian Ethnology* Ward H Goodenough; *Assoc Cur Palaeolithic Archaeology* Jacques Bordaz; *Cur Physical Anthropology* Francis E Johnston and Solomon H Katz; *Asst Cur in Charge South and Southeast Asian Section* Chester F Gorman.

Open Tues - Sat 10 AM - 5 PM; Sun 1 - 5 PM; cl Mon. Admis $1.00. Estab 1897 to investigate the origins and varied developments of man's cultural achievements in all times and places; to preserve and maintain collections to document these achievements; and to present to the public results of these investigations by means of permanent exhibits and temporary exhibitions. Average Annual Attendance: 27,000. Mem: 3,188; dues from junior $5 to benefactor $1,000.
Income: $85,000 (financed by endowment, membership, state appropriation and university).
Collections: Archaeological and enthnographic displays relating to the Old and New World; the Classical civilization of the Mediterranean; Egypt; Mesopotamia; Iran; India; Southeast Asia and the Far East; North, Middle and South America; Oceania; Physical anthropology.
Exhibitions: American Indian Life 1776-1976; permanent galleries have exhibits from each of the broad geographical areas represented in collections. Changing exhibitions in the Nevil Gallery for the Blind and Sighted; temporary exhibitions composed of ethnological and archaeological specimens from the Museum's own collections and from other institutions.
Publications: Expedition Magazine, quarterly.
Activities: Classes for adults and children; docent training; lect open to public, 5 vis lect per yr; concerts; gallery talks; tours; exten dept serving Pennsylvania Commonwealth; original objects of art lent to libraries and instructional centers in the state; lending collection contains motion pictures, original art works 1000 and slides; traveling exhibitions organized and circulated; museum shop selling books, magazines, reproductions, slides, jewelry and craft items.
—John and Ada Lewis Memorial Library. *Librn* Jean Adelman.
Open to staff and students of the University and the public.
Holdings: Vols 63,000; Per subs 1,500.
Special Subjects: Archaeology and Anthropology, Classical Archaeology.
Special Collections: Brinton Collection.
—Institute of Contemporary Art, 34th & Walnut St, 19104. Tel: 215-243-7108. *Dir* Suzanne Delehanty; *Asst Dir* Michael A Quigley; *Cur Asst* Carla B Hultman.
Open Wed - Fri 10 AM - 5 PM; Sat & Sun Noon - 5 PM; Tues 10 AM - 7:30 PM. No admis. Estab 1963 to provide a continuing forum for the active presentation of advanced development in the visual arts; two large gallery spaces devoted to exhibiting contemporary art in all media. Average Annual Attendance: 80,000. Mem: 800; dues $20, $50, $125, $500 and up.
Income: Approx $180,000 (financed by endowment, membership and grants).
Exhibitions: George Segal: Environments; Made in Pennsylvania: A Selection of Amish Quilts; The Philadelphia Houston Exchange; Joan Jonas/Stage Sets; Charles Ross/The Substance of Light; Improbable Furniture; Paul Thek/Processions; Architecture: Seven Architects; Eight Abstract Painters.
Publications: Exhibition catalogs; calendar of events; annual newsletter.
Activities: Lect open to the public, 10 - 15 vis lectr per yr; concerts; gallery talks; tours; traveling exhibitions organized and circulated; sales shop selling original art and catalogs.
—Houston Hall. *Dir* Anthony S Codding.
Estab 1896 for the enhancement of social living, providing opportunity for self-expression, and experiences which are educational and relaxing. Includes an art gallery.
Activities: Art exhibits; film series; lectures; Cultural Theatre Series.

WILLET STAINED GLASS STUDIOS,* 10 E Moreland Ave, 19118. Tel: 215-247-5721. *Chmn* Henry Lee Willet; *Pres* E Crosby Willet; *VPres* Marguerite Gaudin; *VPres* Augusta W Willet; *Secy-Treas* William R Eagan.
Open Mon - Fri 8 AM - 4:30 PM by appointment. Estab 1890 as the largest stained glass studio in the United States.
Activities: Apprentice school; classes for hobbyists; tours; individual paintings and original objects of art lent; lending collection contains photographs, Kodachromes and motion pictures; lectures; traveling exhibitions organized and circulated.
—Willet Studio Library. *Librn* Helene H Weis.
Open Mon - Fri 8 AM - 4:30 PM. Estab 1898 as a resource for staff artists; limited use for students and general public.
Income: Financed by the company.
Holdings: Vols 1,000; Per subs 20; AV—Kodachromes; Other—Clipping files, exhibition catalogs; memorabilia, original art works, photographs.
Special Subjects: Stained glass; art; architecture; lives of saints; Christian symbolism; iconography; miscellaneous subjects for windows.
Special Collections: Original designs of this studio's work—photographs and slides of the same.

WOODMERE ART GALLERY,* 9201 Germantown Ave, 19118 Tel: 215-247-0476. *Chmn of the Bd* Carl Helmetag, Jr; *Pres* Dr John H Wolf; *Treas* Wallace S Martindale, Jr; *Secy* Mrs Michael Puchek; *Cur* Edith Emerson; *Dir & Chmn Exhib* Harry A Harris.

Open daily 10 AM - 5 PM; Sun 2 - 5 PM; cl holidays. No admis. Estab 1940; founded by Charles Knox Smith, in trust for benefit of the public. Original collection and building increased. A large addition in 1965 provides additional gallery and studio space. Average Annual Attendance: 14,000. Mem: 1500; dues $8 and higher; annual meeting Apr.
Collections: Smith Collection of European and American paintings; Oriental rugs, furniture, porcelains; European porcelains and furniture; European and American sculpture; contemporary American †paintings, †sculpture, and †graphics.
Exhibitions: 8 current exhibitions annually; prizes awarded in Members', Annual Juried and Special Exhibitions.
Activities: Classes for adults and children; Philadelphia Guild of Handweavers' classes; concerts, lectures, gallery tours.

PITTSBURGH

ART INSTITUTE OF PITTSBURGH GALLERY,* 536 Penn Ave, 15222. Tel: 412-263-6600. *Pres* John A Johns.
Open to public free of charge. Institute estab 1921 as an art school and proprietary trade school. Scholarships available. Library.
Exhibitions: Local art group shows; student and faculty members; local artists; technical art exhibits; loan exhibitions.
Publications: Catalog, brochures, school newspaper.

ARTS AND CRAFTS CENTER OF PITTSBURGH,* Mellon Park, Fifth & Shady Aves, 15232. Tel: 412-361-0873. *Pres* Donal Pierucci; *Exec Dir* Audrey Bethel.
Open Tues - Sat 10 AM - 5 PM; Sun 2 - 5 PM. Estab 1944, inc 1947. Headquarters for nonprofit organizations in the creative arts. 15 resident and 2 affiliated member groups (1600 individuals). Average Annual Attendance: 85,000. Annual meeting Jan; administered by board of resident group and community representatives; resident members pay per capita dues according to own memberships; affiliated members, group dues.
Income: Approx gross income $225,000; gross sales $75,000.
Exhibitions: Galleries maintained for monthly contemporary exhibitions, group and one-man shows. Special exhibitions: Artist of the Year, retrospective show honoring a Pittsburgh artist chosen by Board; Invitational one-man or group show.
Publications: Center brochure, class brochure 4 times a year.
Activities: Noncredit arts and crafts classes conducted for adults and children; Mart operated for outlet for members' work; rental facilities provided for outside groups for art programs; professional workshops offered to artists throughout state (3 per year).

ASSOCIATED ARTISTS OF PITTSBURGH ARTS AND CRAFTS CENTER, Fifth and Shady Aves, 15232. Tel: 412-361-4235. *Pres* Robert Qualters; *VPres* Anna Marie Sninsky; *Secy* David Nowicki; *Exec Secy* Sylvia M Solof.
Open to Tues - Sat 10 AM - 4 PM; Sun 2 - 5 PM; cl Mon. Estab 1910 to give exposure to member artists and for education of the area in the field of art. Maintains a small art gallery. Average Annual Attendance: 25,000. Mem 450 (must be juried into the group); dues $20.
Income: Financed by membership.
Exhibitions: One, two or group shows by members.
Activities: Lect open to public.

CARNEGIE INSTITUTE, Museum of Art, 4400 Forbes Ave, 15213. Tel: 412-622-3300. *Pres* James M Walton; *Chmn Museum of Art Committee* Richard M Scaife; *Dir* Leon A Arkus; *Cur Exhib* Paul F Binai; *Cur Film Section* William D Juson; *Cur Education* Anthony N Landreau; *Cur Antiquities Oriental and Decorative Arts* David T Owsley; *Cur Painting and Sculpture* Herdis Bull Teilman; *Registrar* Charles W Cathey; *Administrative Secy* Nancy Noyes; *Exec Secy* Helen J Goodman.
Open Tues - Sat 10 AM - 5 PM; Sun 10 AM - 6 PM; cl Mon and major holidays; Admis by suggested contribution adults $1, students and children 50¢, no admis Sat. Estab 1896, Inc 1926. Original building 1896-1907; Scaife Gallery for permanent collection opened 1974; Heinz Galleries for special exhibitions opened 1975 Ailsa Mellon Bruce Decorative Arts Galleries opened 1975. Average Annual Attendance: 750,000. Mem: 9500; dues $17.50 and up; annual meeting Founder-Patrons Day.
Income: Financed by endowment, membership, city and state appropriation and other funds.
Collections: American and European paintings and sculpture, especially Impressionist and Post-Impressionist; drawings; prints; watercolors; Japanese woodblock prints; antiquities; Oriental and decorative arts; Ailsa Mellon Bruce Collection; photographs; films.
Exhibitions: Three Rivers Art Festival; Associated Artists of Pittsburgh; series of one-man exhibitions by local artists; Heopolitan Presepe; Naive Art in Yugoslavia; The Design Process at Herman Miller; 150 Years of American Glass; Women Artists 1550-1950; Pittsburgh International Series; Pierre Alechinsky.

Publications: Carnegie Magazine 10 times year; catalog of permanent collection; exhibition catalogs; annual report; employee newsletter.
Activities: Classes for adults and children; dramatic programs; docent training; lect open to the public, 15 vis lectr per yr; concerts; gallery talks; tours; competitions; exten dept serving public schools; traveling exhibitions organized and circulated; museum shop selling books, magazines, original art, reproductions, prints, slides, textiles, jewelry, pottery, sculpture, china, postcards.
Library: Open to staff and museum docents for reference only.

CARNEGIE LIBRARY OF PITTSBURGH, Art Room, Music and Art Department, 4400 Forbes Ave, 15213. Tel: 412-622-3107. *Librn in Charge* Anne W Gordon; *Librn* A Catherine Tack; *Librn* Katherine Kepes.
Open Mon, Tues, Fri & Sat 9 AM - 9 PM; Wed & Thurs 9 AM - 5:30 PM; Sun 2 - 5 PM; cl Sat Eve and Sun, Memorial Day - Labor Day. Estab 1930 to provide reference and circulating materials on all aspects of art; gallery not maintained.
Income: Financed by city, state and county appropriation.
Holdings: Vols 40,000; Per subs 60; AV—Film strips, slides. Other—Clipping files, exhibition catalogs, pamphlets.
Special Collections: Architecture; Costume.

CARNEGIE-MELLON UNIVERSITY
—Forbes Street Gallery, 5200 Forbes Ave, 15213. Tel: 412-578-2081. Student positions: (1978-79) *Dir* Andy Epstein; *Asst Dir/Operations* Jean DeRensis; *Asst Dir/Public Relations* Lisa Lien.
Open Tues & Thurs 7 - 9 PM; Wed & Sun Noon - 4 PM. Estab 1969 to offer exhibition space to students, and an opportunity to learn about gallery management through practice; gallery is approximately 20 x 40 ft, plus small back room space; weekly student exhibits. Average Annual Attendance: 750.
Income: $1700 (financed by university funding).
—Hunt Library, 5000 Forbes Ave, 15213. Tel: 412-578-2000. *Fine Arts Librn* Helen A Lingelbach; *Dir of Univ Libraries* Ruth R Corrigan.
Open Mon - Thurs 8 AM - Noon; Fri 8 AM - 9 PM; Sat 9 AM - 9 PM; Sun 1 - 12 PM. Estab 1912, the Fine Arts Library is a part of Hunt Library housed on the fourth floor of the main Library building.
Holdings: Vols 26,000; Per subs 300; AV—Slides; Other—Clipping files, pamphlets, photographs, prints, reproductions.

CHATHAM COLLEGE ART GALLERY, Woodland Rd, 15232. Tel: 412-441-8200. *Co-Dir* Shirley Stark; *Co-Dir* Jerry Caplan; *Co-Dir* Joseph Shepler.
Open Tues - Sun 2 - 5 PM; Fri 7 - 9 PM. No admis. Estab 1960 as an art gallery in a small liberal arts college, serving both the college and community by mounting or renting exhibitions of high quality; Gallery is 26 x 20 f, located in Jennie King Mellon Library, and is fitted with track lighting. Average Annual Attendance: 1000.
Exhibitions: One month is reserved for exhibiting senior tutorials of studio art majors; Faculty Exhibition; Marilyn Bruya (paintings); Regis Brodie (ceramics); Marisol (drawings); Vienna Secession Prints.
Activities: Lect open to the public, 2 vis lectr per yr; gallery talks.

FRICK ART MUSEUM,* 7227 Reynolds St, 15208. Tel: 212-371-7766. *Dir* Virginia E Lewis; *Exec Secy* Mrs John F Connors; *Registrar* Mrs C W Cox.
Open Wed - Fri 10 AM - 4 PM; Sat 10 AM - 5 PM; Sun 1 - 5 PM; cl Aug. No admis. Estab 1970 as an art museum for public enjoyment and ecuation. Average Annual Attendance: 15,500.
Income: Financed by endowment.
Collections: †Italian, Flemish, French paintings from the early Renaissance through the 18th century; French 18th century period rooms; Italian and Flemish bronzes of the 15th, 16th and 17th centuries; 16th to 18th century Italian furniture; 18th century French furniture; Chinese 18th century porcelains; 18th century English and Irish silver; 18th century Russian silver; Sculpture, Houdon, Clodion; tapestries, French mille fleurs and Flemish 16th century.
Publications: Five Lectures by Dr W R Hovey; The Arts in Changing Societies: Reflections Inspired by Works of Art in the Frick Art Museum, Pittsburgh; Check List; Madame Jean Antoine Houdon (reprinted from the Art Bulletin); The Treasures of Frick Art Museum.
Activities: Lect open to the public, 3-5 vis lectrs per yr; 24 gallery talks; 50 tours; concerts; small working library.

GALLERIE OF IVY SCHOOL OF PROFESSIONAL ART, University Ave, 15214. Tel: 412-323-3200. *Dir* Morris B Kirshenbaum; *Exhib Asst* Rebecca Watkins.
Open Mon - Fri 9 AM - 4 PM; Sat 9 AM - 2:30 PM. No admis. Estab 1961 for exhibition of fine arts, group or one-person shows; student shows; applied arts (graphic design, photography, textiles, advertising art); approx 500 running feet of wall space, comprised of hall galleries connecting two small galleries.
Income: Financed by school budget.

Collections: Faculty and student works.
Activities: Educ dept.
Library: *Librn* Mary Boukamp. Open to students and faculty for reference.

PITTSBURGH PLAN FOR ART GALLERY, 407 S Craig St, 15213. Tel: 412-683-7600. *Pres* Sylvester Damianos; *VPres* James Winokur; *Secy* Eva W Weill; *Exec Dir* Rebecca Berman.
Open Tues - Sat 10 AM - 5 PM; Sun 1 - 5 PM; cl Mon. No admis. Estab 1955 as a non-profit organization under aegis of Education to Learn by Looking. Maintains an art gallery for rental and/or sale of artworks; two floors over 6,000 sq ft. Average Annual Attendance: 10,000. Mem: 567; dues artists free, public $10.
Income: Financed by membership, rental and sales fees.
Exhibitions: One-person and group shows every month (closed August).
Activities: Lect open to public; tours; individual paintings lent; lending collection contains original art works, original prints, paintings, sculptures and slides; traveling exhibitions organized and circulated.

UNIVERSITY OF PITTSBURGH
—**University Art Gallery,** 15260. Tel: 412-624-4121. *Dir* David G Wilkins.
Open Tues - Sat 10 AM - 4 PM; Thurs 4 - 7 PM; Sun 2 - 5 PM; cl Mon. No admis. Estab 1970 to provide exhibitions for the university community and the community at large and to provide students with gallery experience. 350 running feet in five areas. Average Annual Attendance: 4000.
Income: Financed through the University.
Collections: Drawings and prints.
Exhibitions: Confluences, the Architecture of Urban Design Associates; America Underfoot; Hovey Collection; Paintings by David Summers; Art in 19th Century Pittsburgh; Barnett Aden Collection; Paintings by Stefan Stirbu; Art Nouveau; Prints by Jacob Kainen.
Publications: Exhibition catalogs, three per yr.
Activities: Original objects of art lent; lending collection contains original art works 922, original prints 700, paintings, photographs 100, sculpture and drawings 100; traveling exhibitions organized and circulated.
—**Henry Clay Frick Fine Arts Library,** Henry Clay Frick Fine Arts Bldg, 15260. Tel: 412-624-4124. *Head Librn* Elizabeth C Booth; *Cataloguer* D Sherman Clarke; *Ref Librn* Barbara S Salthouse.
Open Mon - Thurs 9 AM - 10 PM; Fri & Sat 9 AM - 5 PM; Sun 2 - 5 PM. Estab 1927 to support teaching mission of departments of Fine Arts (History of Art) and Studio Arts at the University in undergraduate and graduate studies, and to serve the university and its community. Circ: Reference library only.
Income: Financed by endowment and through the University.
Holdings: Vols 50,000; Per subs 309; AV—Microfiche and microfilm; Other—Clipping files, exhibition catalogs, pamphlets and dealer's catalogs.
Special Subject: Western and Oriental art history; archaeology; architecture; sculpture; painting; manuscripts; fine printing; artistic photography.
Special Collections: Illuminated manuscript facsimiles.

POTTSTOWN

POTTSTOWN AREA ARTISTS' GUILD, PO Box 512, 19464. *Pres* Joan C Clark; *VPres* Cynthia Scherer; *Secy* David Westley.
Estab 1960 as a non-profit organization open to all who are interested in art in its many forms. It consists of both professional and non-professional artists and also many others who are interested in art. Mem: 154; dues $5.
Income: Financed by membership.
Exhibitions: Membership Show; Anvil Studio and Gallery; Ursinus College.
Publications: Sketch Pad, monthly.
Activities: Lect for members only, 9 vis lectr per yr; tours; competitions; traveling exhibitions organized and circulated locally.

READING

BERKS ART ALLIANCE,* Wyomissing Institute of Art Bldg, Trent & Belmont St, 19610. *Pres* Regina D Gouger; *VPres* Merri Woolley.
Estab 1941 to maintain active art center in Reading and Berks county. Mem: 150; dues $10; meetings 2nd Tues of odd months.
Exhibitions: Three annual membership shows, plus solo or two-persons shows of a two week period each, all open to public, free of charge.
Activities: Life drawing workshops; open painting session Thurs afternoon; sponsors one day painting class with visiting artist once a year; sponsors annual trip to American Watercolor Society show in New York.

READING PUBLIC MUSEUM AND ART GALLERY, 500 Museum Road, 19611. Tel: 215-373-1525. *Dir* Bruce L Dietrich; *Res Specialist* Mary R Rigg; *Exhib Designer* Robert E Stanley.

Open Mon - Fri 9 AM - 5 PM, Sat 9 AM - Noon; Sun 2 - 5 PM. No admis. Estab 1904 to promote knowledge, pleasure and cultivation of the arts and sciences. Ground floor: oil painting gallery; first floor: natural and social sciences exhibits; second floor: permanent and temporary art exhibitions. Average Annual Attendance: 100,000. Mem: 451; dues vary; annual meeting second Monday in May.
Income: $420,000 (financed by government).
Collections: Pennsylvania-German Room; Old Masters Gallery.
Exhibitions: Youth Art'Shows; The Sea; Benton Spruance; Reading and Berks Collects; Winter Winds; Print Show; Director's Choice.
Activities: Classes for children; docent training; lect open to public, 5 vis lectr per yr; concerts; tours; exten dept serving City of Reading; individual paintings and original objects of art lent to other Institutions; lending collection contains paintings 825 and sculpture 73; museum shop and sales shops selling books, reproductions, prints and slides.
—**Reading Public Museum Library.**
Open Mon - Fri 9 AM - 4 PM.
Holdings: Vols 3000; Per subs 30; Other—Exhibitions catalogs, manuscripts, memorabilia, original documents, pamphlets, prints and reproductions.
Special Subjects: Natural and social sciences, art (fine), anthropology.
Special Collections: Unger Geology Library; American Bureau of Ethnology Collection.

SCRANTON

EVERHART MUSEUM,* Nay Aug Park, 18510. Tel: 717-346-7186. *Chmn Trustees* Judge Otto P Robinson: *Dir & Cur Art* Carl E Ellis.
Open 10 AM - 5 PM; Sun 2 - 5 PM; cl Mon & holidays. No admis. Estab and inc 1908; gift to the city from Dr Isaiah F Everhart; building rebuilt 1928-29. Average Annual Attendance: 200,000. Mem: 1200; dues $7.50 and higher; annual meeting June.
Income: $67,150 (financed by endowment and city appropriations). Purchases: $2000.
Collections: †American folk art; Oriental art; African, Oceanic; †American Indian material; European and American painting, prints and sculpture; †natural history and science, birds, animals, reptiles and fishes of Pennsylvania; Dorflinger Glass (1852-1921).
Exhibitions: Monthly exhibitions.
Activities: Monthly membership lectures series (art and science); weekly classes in art and science for children and adults; guided tours; outside lectures; Annual Member Ball; artists-in-residence programs.
Library: Holdings—Vols approx 8500 for reference, art and history.

SWARTHMORE

SWARTHMORE COLLEGE, Friends Historical Library, 18081. Tel: 215-328-2625. *Dir* Dr J William Frost; *Asst Dir* Albert W Fowler; *Cur Peace Collection* Bernice B Nichols.
Open Mon - Fri 8:30 AM - 4:30 PM; Sat 9 AM - Noon; cl August and Sat when college not in session. Estab 1871 to preserve and make available to the public material by and about Quakers and their concerns, records of non-sectarian peace organizations and papers of peace movement leaders. Circ: 4106 items.
Income: $110,343 (financed by endowment and college). Purchases: $12,124.
Holdings: Vols 37,895; Per subs 438; AV—Audio tapes, cassettes, Kodachromes, lantern slides, microfilm, motion pictures, phonorecords, reels, slides, video tapes, maps, charts; Other—Clipping files, manuscripts, memorabilia, original art works, original documents, pamphlets, photographs, prints, sculpture, posters.
Special Subjects: Quaker history; history of the peace movement.
Special Collections: Quaker paintings; Quakers as subject in art; Meeting House Picture Collection; portraits; group pictures; residences; Swarthmore College pictures; other Quaker schools; silhouettes and sketches of individual Friends conveniently arranged for consultation; Swarthmore College Peace Collection consists primarily of archival material; records of non-sectarian peace organizations the United States and 59 foreign countries; papers of peace leaders including Jean Addams, Emily Greene Balch, Elihu Burritt, A J Muste, Wilhelm Sollmann and others; 1400 peace posters and war posters.

UNIVERSITY PARK

PENNSYLVANIA STATE UNIVERSITY
—**Museum of Art,** 16802. Tel: 814-865-7672. *Dir* William Hull; *Asst Dir* William D Davis; *Cur* Olga Preisner; *Registrar* John P Driscoll.
Open Tues - Sun Noon - 5 PM; cl Mon & legal holidays. No admis. Estab 1972 to promote a variety of visual experiences through a program of changing exhibitions; a window to the world for the university community. A three-story brick building with one large gallery on each floor which can be sub-divided with movable panels. Average Annual Attendance: 60,000.

Income: Financed by state appropriation.
Collections: American and European painting, drawing, graphics and sculpture with some emphasis on Pennsylvania artists; Oriental ceramics, painting and prints; limited material in Ancient, African and Near Eastern areas; Kehl and Nina Markley Collection of Ancient Peruvian Ceramics; Ralph C Marcove Collection of Oriental Art.
Exhibitions: Portraits USA; Prints by Pennsylvania Artists; Twenty-four British Potters; From Gothic to Baraoque; The Material Dominant (some current artists and their media); Ancient Glass, Vorticism and Abstract Art in the First Machine Age; Philip Grausman, Sculptor: Growing Forms; American Paintings from the Daniel J Terra Collection; Models and Moments, Paintings and Drawings by John Koch.
Publications: Calendar of Events, bi-monthly.
Activities: Docent training; lect open to public, 8 vis lectr per yr; concerts; gallery talks; tours; museum store selling books, magazines, original art, reproductions, prints and slides.
—**Pattee Library,** Arts Library, E 405, 16802. Tel: 814-865-6481. *Arts & Architecture Librn* Jean Smith; *Music Librarian* Carole Franklin.
Open Mon - Thurs 8 AM - Midnight; Sat 8 AM - 5 PM; Sun 1 PM - Midnight. Estab 1957 to support the academic programs of the College of Arts and Architecture and the Division of Art and Music Education; to provide information on the arts to interested members of the university and community.
Holdings: Vols 36,500; Per subs 517; AV—Cassettes, phonorecords; Other—Prints.

WASHINGTON

WASHINGTON & JEFFERSON COLLEGE, Commons Gallery, Lincoln St, 15301. Tel: 412-222-4400. *Chmn* Paul B Edwards.
Open daily 9 AM - 7 PM. No admis. Estab 1969 for the display of circulating art shows and the college collection; the gallery is modern, well lighted and large. Average Annual Attendance: 3000.
Financed by private funding. Purchases: $2000.
Washington & Jefferson College Permanent Collection.
Publications: Catalogs.

WAYNE

WAYNE ART CENTER, 413 Maplewood Ave, 19087. Tel: 215-688-3553. *Pres* Linda Rodgers; *VPres* Sandy Slaymaker and Mary Sims; *Secy* Beth Kempf; *Treas* Bruce Gillespie.
Open Mon - Fri 10 AM - 4 PM. No admis. Estab 1930 as a community art center. Two galleries offering rotating exhibits of work by local artists. Average Annual Attendance: 2000. Mem: 300; dues $15; annual meeting in May.
Income: $25,000 (financed by membership, grants, corporations and Pennsylvania Council on the Arts).
Activities: Classes for adults and children; lect for members, 6 vis lectr per yr; gallery talks; competitions.

WEST CHESTER

CHESTER COUNTY HISTORICAL SOCIETY, 225 N High St, 19380. Tel: 215-696-4755. *Pres* Hon John H Ware III; *Secy* Dr Robert E Carlson; *Treas* Richard C Cloud; *Exec Dir* Kurt E Brandenburg; *Secy* Mary L Evans; *Cur of Educ* J Richard Kyle; *Admin Asst* Ida McIntyre; *Librn* Rosemary B Philips; *Asst Librn* Kathleen A Frederick; *Cur* Ruth K Hagy; *Registrar/Conservator* Marilyn Norcini.
Main museum building closed during renovations; reopening Spring 1979. Admis adults $1; students 25¢. Estab April 14, 1893 for the "acquisition and preservation of property and information of historic value or interest to the people of Chester County." Average Annual Attendance: 7000. Mem: 1200; dues individual $15, family $25; annual meeting third Tues May.
Income: $124,000 (financed by endowment, membership).
Collections: Museum houses regional collections of furniture, from William & Mary through Victorian; pewter; ceramics; needlework; textiles; glassware.
Exhibitions: Handwoven coverlets.
Publications: Newsletter, monthly; Chester County History, occasionally.
Activities: Classes for adults and children; docent training; lect open to the public, 10 vis lectr per yr; tours; individual paintings and original objects of art lent to other museums; museum shop selling books, reproductions, prints.
—**Library.** Tel: 215-696-4755. *Librn* Rosemary B Philips.
Open to the public, admis $1; to members free. For reference only.
Holdings: Vols 20,000; Per subs 60. Other—Manuscripts 200,000.
Special Subjects: Chester County history, genealogy, artifacts.

WILKES-BARRE

WILKES COLLEGE, Sordoni Art Gallery, 150 S River St, 18703. Tel: 717-824-4651, exten 289. *Dir* J Philip Richards; *Exhib Coordinator* Cara Berryman.
Open Mon - Fri 1 - 5 PM; Sat 10 AM - 5 PM, Sun 1 - 5 PM. No admis. Estab 1973 to encourage art appreciation in the Wilkes-Barre and the Northeastern Pennsylvania areas. The Gallery has one room, 30 x 40 ft with adjustable flats used for hanging. Average Annual Attendance: 20,000. Monthly meetings.
Income: Financed by endowment.
Collections: 19th Century Academic European Paintings and Sculpture.
Exhibitions: Ronald Wing (paintings, drawings, etchings); Ned Nergleroth (oils); Ralph L Wilson Collection of American Art Lehigh Univ; Max Weber Forum Gallery, New York; Mark Cohen (photography); Franz Kafka; Wilkes College Art Alumni Exhibition (mixed media); Brooks Parker (sculpture); Rose O'Neill (kewpie dolls and drawings; Benton Spruance (graphics); John Hardy Fisbach Gallery, New York; Henry Casilli (ceramics and jewelry); Sally Elliot (soft sculpture); American Watercolor Society.
Publications: Gallery Briefs, bi-monthly.
Activities: Lect open to public, 6 vis lectr per yr; gallery talks; tours; competitions, scholastic art awards; individual paintings and original objects of art lent to other universities; lending collection contains paintings and sculpture.

WILLIAMSPORT

LYCOMING COLLEGE, Art Center Gallery, 17701. Tel: 717-326-1951. *Dir* Jon Bogle and Roger Shipley.
Open Mon & Wed 2 - 5 PM; Tues & Thurs 9 AM - 4 PM. No admis. Estab 1947 to bring quality art work to the students and faculty as well as to the interested community; gallery is comprised of three fully lighted and carpeted rooms. Average Annual Attendance: 1000.
Income: Financed by school budget.
Collections: Paintings and prints of 19th and 20th century artists.
Exhibitions: One-man Shows of regional and area artists and alumni of the Department; traveling exhibitions.
Activities: Gallery talks; tours; individual paintings lent; traveling exhibitions organized and circulated.

YORK

HISTORICAL SOCIETY OF YORK COUNTY,* 250 E Market St, 17403. Tel: 717-848-1587. *Exec Dir* Harry L Rinker; *Cur* James Gergat; *Cur Educ* Norwood Miller; *Librn* Robert Nawrocki; *Pres* Henry S McFall; *First VPres* G William Schaumann; *Secy* Byron H LeCates; *Treas* Marvin Sedam.
Open Mon - Sat 10 AM - 4 PM; Sun 1 - 5 PM; admis charged (gallery at museum is free). Estab 1895 to record, preserve, collect and interpret the history of York County and Pennsylvania, including music and art of the past and present. Restoration Properties: General Gates House (1751), Golden Plough Tavern (1741) and Log House (1812), 157 W Market; Bonham House (1870), 152 E Market. Average Annual Attendance: 30,000. Mem: 3500; dues $12 and higher; annual meeting Apr.
Income: $160,000.
Collections: Works by Lewis Miller and other local artists; †Fraktur and other Pennsylvania folk art; James Shettel Collection of theater and circus material.
Exhibitions: Five gallery shows per year featuring living artists; two major shows on some aspect of regional and national decorative or folk arts; three to four secondary shows featuring subject areas (eg, textiles, Fraktur, etc) from the collection.
Publications: Monthly Newsletter; Lewis Miller Sketches and Chronicles; Regional Aspects of American Folk Pottery; The Kentucky Rifle.
Activities: Guided tours; education program; lecturers; concerts; classes for adults and children; summer internship program. Gift shops.
Library: Holdings—Vols 15,000 for reference; Other—Photograph collection of 10,000 prints; large collection of genealogical manuscripts and records.

MARTIN MEMORIAL LIBRARY,* 159 E Market St, 17401. Tel: 717-843-3978. *Dir* Mary Catharine Weaver.
Open Mon - Fri 9 AM - 9 PM; Sat 9 AM - 5 PM. No admis. Estab 1935.
Income: $285,000. Purchases: $55,000.
Holdings: Vols 125,999; Other—Mounted pictures 12,481, pamphlets 16,874, recordings 7900, 16mm films 192.
Exhibitions: Frequent exhibitions of paintings, arts and crafts, manuscripts and books.
Publications: Bulletin, monthly; occasional bibliographies of special collections; Annual Reports; Martin Memorial Library Historical Series; Martin Memorial Library.
Activities: Lectures; concerts; programs for adults and children.

YORK ACADEMY OF ARTS, 625 E Philadelphia St, 17403. Tel: 717-848-1447. *Pres* William A Falkler; *Ed Dir* Florian Suitak; *Financial Aid Officer* David Gross.
Estab 1952 to promote education in commercial art, fine arts and interior design; work on display.
Activities: Education Department; classes for adults and children; sales shop selling art supplies.
Library: Open to students of the Academy only, lending purposes.

RHODE ISLAND

KINGSTON

SOUTH COUNTY ART ASSOCIATION, Helme House, 1319 Kingstown Rd, 02852. Tel: 401-783-2195. *Pres* Dr Conrad Hill; *VPres* Peg Gregory; *Recording Secy* Lynn Feiner; *Treas* Ann Aldrich.
Open Tues - Sun 2 - 5 PM during exhibitions; No admis. Estab August 1929 to promote an interest in art and to encourage artists, and to support in every way the aesthetic interests of the community. Mem: Approximately 350; applicants for membership must submit three paintings and be accepted by a committee; dues student $3, artist $7.50, lay member $10, sustaining $15; annual meeting Oct.
Collections: No large permanent collection; paintings by early members, usually not on display.
Exhibitions: Art Annual Open Show, juried with prizes totaling $250; Members Show; Regional Open Earthworks Show, juried with prizes totaling $250.
Publications: Newsletter, 3 - 4 annually.
Activities: Classes for adults and children; lect for members only; competitions with awards given; schol; original objects of art lent to other art associations; lending collection contains books, lantern slides, sculpture original art works, sculpture and slides.

UNIVERSITY OF RHODE ISLAND GALLERY, 02881. Tel: 401-792-2131. *Dir Exhib* Ronald J Onorato.
Open daily 2 - 4 PM; Mon - Fri 6 - 8 PM; cl Mon. No admis. Estab 1970 to expose campus and community to contemporary and historical art. Average Annual Attendance: 5000.
Income: Financed through University.
Collections: Contemporary artists in various media.
Exhibitions: Dennis Oppenheim; H C Westermann; Robert Cumming; Nicholas Africano; Dotty Attic.
Publications: Catalogues, occasionally; brochures for each exhibit.
Activities: Gallery talks.

NEWPORT

ART ASSOCIATION OF NEWPORT,* Howard Gardiner Cushing Memorial Gallery, 76 Bellevue Ave, 02840. Tel: 401-847-0179. *Pres* Bruce Howe; *VPres* Mrs W R Michael; *Exec Secy* Mrs Paul C Rogers; *Treas* Ralph O Udall; *Dir* Mrs James Silvia.
Open Mon - Sat 10 AM - 5 PM; Sun 2 - 5 PM; cl December 25 - Jan 1. No admis. Estab 1912, inc 1915 for the promotion of art, literature, music and science; owns building. Mem: 700; dues $5 and up; annual meeting June.
Income: $55,000.
Exhibitions: Annual exhibition, oils and small sculptures, watercolors, drawings, pastels, prints; open to American artists with jury selection; continuous special exhibitions.
Publications: Annual Report.
Activities: Lectures; maintains art school; choral society; schol; prints lent to schools; sales shop selling cards, notepaper, reproductions of jewelry.
Library: Open to the public. Holdings: Vols 290; Other—Pictures for rent.

NEWPORT HISTORICAL SOCIETY, 82 Touro St, 02840. Tel: 401-846-0813. *Pres* William A Sherman; *VPres* Dr William Reitzel; *Secy* Patrick O'N Hayes; *Exec Dir* Wilbur T Holmes.
Open Tues - Fri 9:30 AM - 4:30 PM; Sat 9:30 AM - Noon. No admis. Estab 1853 to collect and preserve items of historical interest pertaining to the City. Maintains an art gallery and small marine museum. Also owns and exhibits the first Seventh Day Baptist Church in America (1729; the Wanton-Lyman-Hazard House (1675), the first home to be restored in Newport; the Friends Meeting House (1699), site of the annual New England Quakers Meeting for over 200 years. Average Annual Attendance: 5000. Mem: 700; dues $15 and up; annual meeting May.
Income: Financed by endowment, membership, state appropriation and museum sales.
Collections: Colonial silver; pewter; china; glass; furniture; Newport scenes and portraits; dolls, toys and artifacts.

Publications: Newport History, quarterly.
Activities: Lect open to public, 4-6 vis lectr per yr; tours; original objects of art lent to museums.

REDWOOD LIBRARY AND ATHENAEUM, 50 Bellevue Ave, 02840. Tel: 401-847-0292. *Pres* Dr Donald B Fletcher; *Librn* Donald T Gibbs.
Open Mon - Sat 10 AM - 6 PM; 10 AM - 5 PM in August. Estab 1747 as a general library; art gallery maintained. Circ: 53,000.
Income: Financed by endowment, membership.
Holdings: Vols 136,000; Per subs 100; AV—Phonorecords.
Special Collections: Pictures, statues; portraits by Stuart, Sully, Feke, Healy, Rembrandt Peale, Charles Wilson Peale, and other early American painters; many paintings by Charles B King.
Activities: Library tours.

PROVIDENCE

BROWN UNIVERSITY
—**Bell Gallery,** 64 College St, 02912. Tel: 401-863-2421. *Cur* Nancy T Versaci.
Open Mon - Wed 11 AM - 4 PM; Sat, Sun & holidays 1 - 4 PM. No admis. Estab 1971 to present exhibitions of interest to the university and community; the gallery is modern, covers 2625 sq ft, 14 ft ceilings, and has track lighting. Average Annual Attendance: 12,000.
Income: Financed by endowment and university funds.
Collections: Substantial collection of Modern Masters (contemporary); Prints dating from the 15th - 20th century.
Exhibitions: (1976-78) Photovision 75; Classical Spirit in American Portraiture; RISD Faculty; Steven Welte; Homage to Franz Kune: Photographs by Aaron Siskind; Blankets/Cylinders; Golden Age of Illustration; five New York Artists; Appalachia; Graham, Gorky, Smith and Davis in the 30s.
Activities: Lect open to the public, 14 vis lectr per yr; individual paintings and original objects of art lent to museums and galleries; lending collection contains original prints 1200, paintings 50, sculpture 20.
—**Annmary Brown Memorial,** 21 Brown St (Mailing Add: Box 1905, 02912). Tel: 401-863-2429. *Cur* Samuel J Hough; *Research Asst* Catherine Denning.
Open 9 AM - 5 PM. Estab 1907 to offer representatives of schools of European and American painting; there are three galleries which house early printed books, to 1501AD; the art collection of the founder and his wife; and portraits of the Brown family.

PROVIDENCE ART CLUB, 11 Thomas St, 02903. Tel: 401-331-1114. *Pres* John Cutler; *VPres* Fred A Andrews Jr; *Secy* Maralyn Poland; *Gallery Secy* Marjory Dalenius.
Open daily 10 AM - 4 PM; Sun 3 - 5 PM. No admis. Estab 1880 for art culture, and to provide exhibition space for artists; gallery maintained in two rooms of an historic building built in 1790. Average Annual Attendance: 5000. Mem: 846, qualifications artists—work must pass a board of artists, non-artists—no qualifications; dues artist $100, non-artist $160; annual meeting first Wed June.
Income: Financed by endowment, membership.
Collections: Small permanent collection of paintings and sculpture.
Exhibitions: Eighteen shows a season of which two/three are open shows with a juror and prizes offered.
Publications: Newsletter for members.
Activities: Classes for adults; lect open to members and guests, 20 vis lectr per yr; gallery talks; competitions with awards given; schol; work in shows usually for sale.

PROVIDENCE ATHENAEUM, 251 Benefit St, 02903. Tel: 401-421-6970. *Pres* Edward O Handy Jr; *VPres* Robert Spink Davis; *Treas* Laurens W Goff; *Secy* Peter M Hewitt; *Exec Dir* Sylvia Moubayed.
Open Mon - Fri 8:30 AM - 5:30 PM; Sat 9:30 AM - 5:30 PM; cl Sun. No admis. Estab 1753 to provide cultural services, information, rare and current materials in an historic setting. Mem: 1304; dues $45; annual meeting fourth Mon Sept.
Income: $113,988.87 (financed by endowment, membership, state appropriation and gifts). Purchases $15,654.52.
Collections: Strength in the 19th century.
Exhibitions: Programs and/or exhibitions vary each month.
Publications: The Athenaeum Bulletin, three times a year; Annual Report.
Activities: Dramatic Programs; festivals, film programs; lect open to the public and some to members only; tours; individual paintings and original objects of art lent to bonafide institutions, libraries or societies; lending collection contains cassettes, color reproductions, motion pictures, original art works, original prints, paintings, phonorecords 313, sculpture; the center selling Audubon prints in limited edition, stationery, and to other museums.
—**Library.** Tel: 401-421-6970. *Exec Dir* Sylvia Moybayed.

Open to the public.
Holdings: Vols 151,084; Per subs 117; Other—Paintings, prints, objets d'art, rare folios, manuscripts.
Special Subjects: Art; Biography; Old fiction; Fiction; History.
Special Collection: 19th Century; Robert Burns Collection; Audubon; Old Fiction; Holder Border Bowen Collection.

PROVIDENCE PUBLIC LIBRARY, Art and Music Dept, 150 Empire St, 02906. Tel: 401-521-7722, exten 235. *Head* Susan R Waddington; *Asst* Linda M Daniels; *Asst* Margaret Chevian; *Asst* Anne Kirby.
Open Mon - Wed 8:30 AM - 9 PM; Thurs - Sat 8:30 AM - 5:30 PM. Summer hours vary. Estab 1878 to serve needs of public; art gallery is maintained in large exhibit hall.
Income: $1,650,000 (financed by endowment, city and state appropriation and Federal funds). Purchases: $3960.
Holdings: Vols 34,950; Per subs 85; AV—Phonorecords; AV Dept—Film strips, kits; Other—Clipping files, framed reproductions, original art works, posters.
Special Subjects: Architecture, jewelry, design, crafts.
Special Collections: Nickerson Architectural Collection.
Exhibitions: Rhode Island inventors and inventions; Paintings by members of the Providence Senior Citizens Center; America's Builders Sources; Fine printing and Rhode Island Small Presses; Rhode Island Bottles and Related Items; Wanskuck Handicrafts Club Exhibit; Professional Photographers of Rhode Island; Butterflies from the Collection of Mr/Mrs Frank Spino; Photography by Monika Cotugno and Paul Merluzzo; Artwork by students from Central High School; Group show by Robert Imhoff, Jeffrey Watson, Christina Hartley and Dan Gosch.

PROVIDENCE WATER COLOR CLUB,* 6 Thomas St, 02903. Tel: 617-272-9864. *Pres* Barbara Green; *VPres* Leslie Swuift; *Secy* A E S Peterson; *Treas* Robert Pomfret; *Asst Treas* Rose D Roman.
Open Tues - Fri 12:30 - 3:30 PM; Sun 3 - 5 PM; during exhibitions 1 - 3 PM; cl Mon. Estab 1898. Mem: 230; dues $15; annual meeting March.
Collections: Small collection of paintings and drawings by early members; prints and paintings by contemporary members.
Exhibitions: Annual exhibition of members' works; Annual Christmas Exhibition; Annual Print Show; Annual Open Juried National Show; six or more one-man exhibitions per year.
Activities: Lectures, slide lectures; demonstrations.

RHODE ISLAND COLLEGE ART CENTER GALLERY, 600 Mount Pleasant Ave, 02908. Tel: 401-456-8054 or 274-4900, exten 335. *Gallery Coordinator* Craig Coonrod; *Gallery Asst* Linda Baker; *Chmn Gallery Comt* Samuel Ames.
Open Mon - Fri 11 AM - 4 PM; Sun 1 - 5 PM (Sept - May). No admis. Estab 1977 to provide the Rhode Island community with a varied and progressive exposure to the visual arts, to offer to the college community, with its liberal arts perspective, access to top quality exhibits, artists, and workshops. One room, 25 x 60 ft, separated by supports; a 12 ft ceiling on one side and a 8 ft ceiling on the other; a total of 55 spots and floods on tracks. Walls are a light beige with a black floor. A large bank of windows fills one end of the gallery. Average Annual Attendance: 16,000.
Income: Financed by state appropriation.
Collections: Groundwork is presently being laid for the establishment of a permanent collection with annual purchases, and possible gifts.
Exhibitions: Sante Graziani: Painter; Four from Providence, four Black artists in the Rhode Island social landscape: Edward Bannister (painter), Elizabeth Prophet (sculptor); Wilmer Jennings (designer), Frank Alston (designer); Paul Rahilly: painter; Faculty Show; Juried Invitational Crafts Show; Shaker Furniture Exhibit.
Publications: Brochures, eight per year; catalogs, 2 or 3 per year.
Activities: Competitions.

RHODE ISLAND HISTORICAL SOCIETY,* 52 Power St, 02906. Tel: 401-331-8575. *Pres* Duncan Hunter Mauran; *Secy* Bradford Swan; *Dir* Albert T Klyberg; *Ed/Nathanael Greene Papers* Richard K Showman.
Admis adults $1.50, students 50¢. Estab 1822 to preserve, collect and interpret Rhode Island historical materials, including books, manuscripts, graphics, films, furniture and decorative arts. Mem: 2500, dues $15 and up, annual meeting Jan.
Income: Financed by endowment, membership and city and state appropriation.
Exhibitions: American Paintings in the Rhode Island Historical Society.
Publications: Rhode Island History, quarterly; The John Brown House Loan Exhibition of Rhode Island furniture; American Paintings in the Rhode Island Historical Society (catalog); Nathanael Greene Papers; occasional monographs; newsletter, bimonthly.
Activities: Classes for adults and children; children's tours, film programs; lect open to the public, 4-6 vis lectr per yr; concerts; gallery talks; tours; lending collection contains prints 10,000 for reference and copying; Book shop.
—**John Brown House (1786),** 52 Power St, 02906.

Open Tues - Fri 11 AM - 4 PM; weekends 2 - 4 PM. Estab 1942, carefully restored and furnished with fine examples of Rhode Island heritage. Average Annual Attendance: 5000.
Collections: †Pieces by Rhode Island cabinetmakers, some original to the house; †portraits; †china; †glass, †pewter, and †other decorative objects; Rhode Island furniture, silver, porcelain, paintings, textiles; Carrington Collection of Chinese export objects; McCrellis Collection of antique dolls; Greene Collection of children's tea sets and dishes.
—**Library,** 121 Hope St, 02906. *Librn* Nancy Peace.
Open Tues - Sat 9 AM - 5 PM; June, July and Aug Mon - Fri 9 AM - 5 PM. Admis $1 per day, $5 for four months. Estab as a research library housing an outstanding historical and genealogical collection. Average Annual Attendance: 9000.
Collections: †1000 manuscripts, dating from 17th century; †Rhode Island imprints, 1727-1800; †Rhode Island Broadsides; †Providence Postmaster Provisional Stamps; †Rhode Island post office covers; †genealogical sources; all state newspapers; maps; films, TV news films and movies; graphics; architectural drawings; photographs 20,000 and for reference volumes 200,000.
—**Aldrich House and Gardens,** 110 Benevolent St, 02906.
Garden open May - Sept Fri 1 - 4 PM. Aldrich was acquired in 1974 and is being developed as a museum of Rhode Island history.

RHODE ISLAND SCHOOL OF DESIGN, Museum of Art, 224 Benefit St, 02903. Tel: 401-331-3511, exten 270. *Dir* Dr Stephen E Ostrow; *Chmn Museum Council* Barnet Fain; *Chief Cur & Cur Prints & Drawings* Diana Johnson; *Cur Decorative Arts* Christopher Monkhouse; *Cur Educ* Cora Lee Gibbs; *Museum Shop Mgrs* Susan Handy & Alice Westervelt.
Open Tues, Wed, Fri, Sat 11 AM - 5 PM; Thurs 1 - 7 PM. Admis adults $1.00, children 5-18 25¢, children under 4 free. Estab 1877 to collect and exhibit art for general education of the public. Present buildings opened in 1897, 1906 and 1926. Average Annual Attendance: 80,000. Mem: 2500.
Income: Financed by endowment, membership, state and federal appropriation, private and corporate contributions.
Collections: Ancient, Oriental and ethnographic art; 15th thru 18th century European art; 19th & early 20th century French art from Romanticism thru Post-Cubism; American painting; English watercolors; contemporary graphic arts; Lucy Truman Aldrich Collection of European porcelains and Oriental textiles; Abby Aldrich Rockefeller Collection of Japanese bird and flower prints; Nancy Sayles Day Collection of modern Latin American art; The Albert Pilavin Collection of 20th century American art; Pendleton House Collection of 18th century American furniture and decorative arts. A costume center and a prints and drawings cabinet are open to the public by appointment.
Exhibitions: A Special Genius: Contemporary American Graphics; Image of America in Caricature & Cartoons; Art for Your Collection XIII; Transformations of the Court Style: Gothic Art in Europe 1270-1330; Faculty Exhibition; Graduate Student Exhibition; Faces & Portrait Photography; Harry Callahan Retrospective; Cleve Gray; Napoleon in Rhode Island; Spaces.
Publications: Museum Notes, annually; Calendar of Events, 5 per year.
Activities: Classes for adults and children; dramatic programs; docent training; field trips; lect open to public, 15-20 per yr; concerts; gallery talks; tours; exten dept serving schools in area; lending collection contains color reproductions, original art works and slides; traveling exhibitions organized and circulated; museum shop selling books, original art, reproductions, prints, jewelry, posters and postcards.
—**Library,** 2 College St, 02903. *Librn* Jeanne Borden.
Open to public for reference.
Holdings: Vols 55,500; Per subs 250; Other—Clippings, slides, mounted photographs and records.
Special Subjects: Fine arts and crafts.

SAUNDERSTOWN

GILBERT STUART BIRTHPLACE, Gilbert Stuart Rd, 02874. Tel: 401-294-3001. *Cur* Mrs Kenneth W Pettigrew; *Pres* Mrs Oliver Marion.
Open daily 11 AM - 5 PM; cl Fri. Admis $1 adults, 50¢ children under 12. Estab 1932 as a national historic landmark, the furnished birthplace of America's foremost portrait painter; the home was built 1751. Average Annual Attendance: 10,000. Mem: 180; dues $2 - $4; annual meeting June.
Income: Financed by endowment, membership and grants.
Activities: Guided tours of the home.

WARWICK

RHODE ISLAND JUNIOR COLLEGE ART DEPARTMENT GALLERY,* Knight Campus, 400 East Ave, 02886. Tel: 401-825-1000. *Chmn* Rita C Lepper.
Open Mon - Fri 8 AM - 4 PM. Estab 1960 to exhibit local artists.

Exhibitions: Exhibitions are changed monthly.

Activities: Lect open to the public; original objects of art lent; lending collections contains color reproductions 300, film strips 20, Kodachromes 10,000, motion pictures 12; clipping/small prints 200; book shop. Library maintained.

—**Providence Branch,** 235A Promenade St, Providence, 02908. Tel: 401-331-5500.

—**Blackstone Valley Campus,** Louisquisset Pike, Lincoln, 02865.

WARWICK ARTS FOUNDATION, Buttonwoods School, W Shore Rd, 02886. Tel: 401-738-2000, exten 197. *Pres* Donald Conlon; *VPres* John Pellegrino; *Secy* Sylvia Tocco; *Exec Dir* Ruby Shalansky.
Estab 1963 to foster the arts within the city of Warwick. Mem: 200; dues individual $3; annual meeting April.
Income: $5000 (financed by membership, city and state appropriation and Federal grants).
Exhibitions: Rotating Art Show in public buildings and banks in the city, using artwork of professional and nonprofessional artists in the area.
Publications: Artspaper; Warwick Arts Foundation Newsletter, 4 - 6 wks.
Activities: Programs for elderly, handicapped, students; lect open to the public; competition with cash awards; traveling exhibitions organized and circulated.

WESTERLY

WESTERLY PUBLIC LIBRARY, Broad St, 02891. Tel: 401-596-2877. *Dir* Ardis Holliday; *Asst Dir* Susan Collins; *Art Dir* Bruce Pelletier.
Open Mon - Thurs 9 AM - 9 PM; Fri 9 AM - 6 PM; Sat 9 AM - 5:30 PM. Estab 1892 as a memorial to soldiers of the Civil War, and to provide a library and activities center for the community; art gallery maintained, 30 x 54 ft, 16 ft ceiling, with incandescent track lighting. Circ: 130,000.
Income: Financed by endowment, city and state appropriation. Purchases: $40,000.
Holdings: Vols 108,000; Per subs 250; AV—Microfilm, phonorecords; Other—Framed reproductions, original art works.
Special Subjects: Local history and genealogy.
Special Collections: Local history photographs.
Exhibitions: Ten - twelve exhibitions scheduled per yr.
Activities: Lect open to the public; library tours.

SOUTH CAROLINA

CHARLESTON

CAROLINA ART ASSOCIATION, Gibbes Art Gallery, 135 Meeting, 29401. Tel: 803-722-2706. *Pres* Harold E Igoe, Jr; *VPres* Mrs B H Rutledge Moore; *Secy* John Henry Dick; *Dir* William H Coles; *Dir* William C Coleman; *Adminr* Mary M Muller; *Cur Coll* Martha R Severens; *Cur Educ* Paul C Figueroa; *Supervisor Art Sch* Barbara Karesh; *Asst Cur Coll* Jean C Stewart.
Open Tues - Sat 10 AM - 5 PM; Sun 2 - 5 PM; cl Mon and national holidays. No admis. Estab 1858 as an art gallery and museum; one million dollar expansion program was recently completed which doubled the size of the gallery facilities to 31,000 sq ft; old building built in 1905 was also renovated. Average Annual Attendance: 75,000. Mem: 2700; dues student $5, individual $15, family $25; annual meeting second Mon Oct.
Income: $200,000 (financed by endowment, membership, city and county appropriation).
Collections: Colonial and Federal portraits; †miniature portraits; Japanese woodblock prints; Oriental art objects; †contemporary American paintings and prints.
Exhibitions: Expressions of Nature in Art; Edgefield Pottery; South Carolina State Arts Commission Annual Exhibition; Impressions of Women: Etchings and Drypoints (Alfred Hutty); Constantine Manos Photos A Greek Portfolio; Recent American Etching: Spoleto Festival USA; Alice Ravenel Huger Smith: Visions of Lowcountry; An Artist Collects: Jasper Johns.
Publications: Bulletins, quarterly; books.
Activities: Classes for adults and children; docent training; lect open to the public, 3 vis lectr per yr; concerts; gallery talks; tours; individual paintings and original objects of art lent; traveling exhibitions organized and circulated; sales shop selling books, original art, prints, reproductions and jewelry and crafts.
—**Library.** *Librn* Betsy Jones.
Open to members and scholars for reference only.
Holdings: Vols 3000; Per subs 10.

CHARLESTON MUSEUM, 121 Rutledge Ave, 29401. Tel: 803-722-2996. *Pres* Arthur Wilcox; *Dir* Donald G Herold; *Cur Decorative Arts* J Kenneth Jones; *Registrar* Jan Hiester; *VPres* Robert L Clement, Jr; *Cur Natural History* Albert E Sanders; *Cur Historic Houses* Mrs Edward Webb; *Cur Anthropology* Allen Liss.
Open Mon - Sat 9 AM - 5 PM; Sun 9 AM - 5 PM. Admis adults $1; children 50¢. Estab 1773 as a museum and library to diffuse knowledge of history, decorative arts, art, natural history, anthropology and technology; also to preserve houses, monuments. It is the oldest museum in the United States. Average Annual Attendance: 225,000. Mem: 1500; dues $12.50 and up; annual meeting March.
Income: $265,000 (financed by endowment, membership, city and county appropriations, admissions and sales).
Collections: Textiles, ceramics, glass, furniture, decorative arts.
Exhibitions: Program discontinues until 1980 when new building will be finished.
Publications: Newsletter, occasionally.
Activities: Discontinued temporarily, until 1980.
—**Library.** Tel: 803-722-2996, exten 3. *Librn* K Sharon Bennett; *Libr Technician* Myrtle Brown.
Open Mon - Sun 9 AM - 5 PM. Estab 1773 as an educational institution, collects, preserves and uses artifacts of natural history, history, anthropology and decorative arts.
Income: $190,000 (financed by junior league).
Holdings: Vols 30,000; Per subs 100; AV—Phonorecords; Other—Clipping files, manuscripts, pamphlets.
—**Heward-Washington House,** 87 Church St.
Open daily 10 AM - 5 PM. Admis adults $1.75, students 50¢. Built 1772; home of Thomas Heyward, Jr; purchased by the Museum in 1929, furnished with Charleston-made furniture of the period. A National Historic Landmark.
—**Hunley Museum,** 50 Broad St.
Open daily 10 AM - 5 PM. No admis. Built about 1798 as a bank, restored in 1966; the museum is in the basement; it houses a display of Charleston Civil War naval history.
—**Joseph Manigault House,** 350 Meeting St.
Open daily 10 AM - 5 PM. Admis adults $1.75, students 50¢. Built 1803 as Adam style mansion designed by Gabriel Manigault; contains Charleston-made furniture of the period. A National Historic Landmark.

CLEMSON

CLEMSON UNIVERSITY
— **Rudolph E Lee Gallery,** College of Architecture, 29631. Tel: 803-656-3081, exten 2/30. *Coordr of Educ Media and Exhib* Tom Dimond.
Open Mon - Fri 9 AM - 4:30 PM; Sun 2 - 5 PM; cl Sat. No admis. Estab 1956 to provide cultural and educational resources; to collect, preserve, interpret and display items of historical, educational and cultural significance. Average Annual Attendance: 20,000.
Income: Financed by state appropriation.
Collections: Contemporary American paintings and graphics; †Clemson Architectural Foundation Collection.
Exhibitions: Ireland Regnier (paintings); Jack Perlmutter (graphics); Thonet Furniture Show; Scott Gilliam (sculpture); Peter Feldstein (photography); New Architecture: New England; The Egg and Art Show; Architectural Thesis Projects; MFA Show; Summer Art Show; The Work of Gustav Eiffel; Photographic Prints by South Carolina Photographers; Robert Hunter, Paintings and Serigraphs; Michael Mazur, Vision of a Draughtsman; Frank Ozerecko, Sculpture and Graphics; A Time of Malfeasance, Engravings by Virginia Myers; Fiber and Chairs; The Cartoon Show.
Publications: Exhibition Bulletin, annually; Posters on Exhibits, monthly.
Activities: Lect open to public, 12-15 vis lectr per yr; gallery talks; tours; exten dept serving southeast United States; individual paintings and original objects of art lent to museums, universities; lending collection contains original prints, paintings, sculpture; traveling exhibitions organized and circulated.
—**Emery A Gunnin Architectural Library.** *Librn* Mrs Dillman B Sorrells.
Open to the public for reference.
Holdings: Vols 10,000; Per subs 200; Other—Slides 38,000, art and architecture rare book room.
—**Fort Hill,*** 29631. Tel 803-656-2061. *Cur* Mrs Revelie Brannon.
Open Tues - Sat 10 AM - Noon & 1 - 5:30 PM; Sun 2 - 6 PM; cl holidays and Christmas week. No admis. An historic museum located in the home of John C Calhoun.
Collections: Flemish paintings; family portraits; period rooms and furnishings.
Activities: Lectures; guided tours; sales shop.
Publications: Fort Hill, brochure.

COLUMBIA

COLUMBIA MUSEUMS OF ART AND SCIENCE, Senate and Bull Sts (Mailing Add: 1112 Bull St, 29201). Tel: 803-799-2810. *Chmn Museum Commission* W Croft Jennings; *Pres* John L M Tobias; *VPres* Lee J Baker; *Dir* Walter M Hathaway; *Cur/Preparator* David H VanHook; *Cur/Registrar* F Edward Barnwell; *Admin Asst* Sarah A Cahill; *Dept of Educ* Cassandra Baker; *Controller* Fred Panasiuk.
Open Tues - Sat 10 AM - 5 PM; Sun 2 - 6 PM; cl Mon. No admis. Estab 1950 to extend and increase art understanding, to asist in the conservation of a valuable cultural heritage, and to recognize and assist contemporary art expression. Science Museum opened in 1960 to correlate youth activities in the field of natural history and physical sciences. Average Annual Attendance: 130,000. Mem: 2759; dues Single $15, Family $25 up; annual meeting in Jan.
Income: $367,000 (financed by membership, city, county and state appropriation).
Collections: Samuel H Kress Collection of Renaissance paintings; Seibels Collection; †Barringer Collection of contemporary art; Scotese Collection of graphics; Hammond Collection; Spanish Colonial Collection; Neuhoff Collection of English furniture; Erin Kohn Collection of dolls; †European and American paintings and decorative art; South Carolina Dispensary Bottles.
Exhibitions: (1976-77) Springs Mills Annual Juried Exhibit; Mosaics by Marjorie Kreilick; American Watercolor Show; Marietta Crafts National; Post Cubism by Francoise Jacquemin: Seibels, Bruce Annual Watercolor Competition; Artist Guild of Columbia Annual Juried Exhibit: Paintings by John Chumley; Textiles by Marie Lippens Berenstein; Private Collection of Jasper Johns; Survey of the French and English Paintings in the Permanent Collection.
Publications: Galaxy, members quarterly; annual report, and occasionally exhibition folders and catalogs.
Activities: Docent training; lect open to the public, 6 vis lectr per yr; concerts; gallery talks; tours; exten dept serving Metropolitan area; individual paintings and original objects of art lent to qualified galleries, historic houses, and approved city and state facilities; traveling exhibitions organized and circulated; museum shop selling original art, postcards and exhibition catalogs; junior museum maintained.
—**Columbia Science Museum,** 1519 Senate St, 29201. Tel: 803-799-2812.
Supvr Christopher H Craft; *Secy* Mary F Galloway.
Open Tues - Sat 10 AM - 5 PM; Sun 2 - 6 PM; cl Mon. Estab 1959 to present a coherent framework for the understanding of natural history. Average Annual Attendance: 55,364. Annual meeting last Thurs Jan.
Collections: (Art) Dr Robert Gibbes Collection of Shells; Kendall Collection of Pan American pots.
Publications: Galaxy, quarterly.
Activities: Docent trining; tours; lectr for school groups; sales shop selling books.
—**Library.** *Librn* F Edward Barnwell.
Open to members and scholars for reference only.
Holdings: Vols 5000; Per subs 14; AV—Slides; Other—Clipping files, exhibition catalogs, pamphlets.
Special Subjects: Reference relating to the permanent collection, plus general art sources.
Special Collections: A S Salley Collection of early South Carolina exhibition catalogs and books.
—**Columbia Art Association.** *Pres* John L M Tobias; *VPres* Lee J Baker; *Secy* Mrs Richard C Slocum.
Estab 1915; the association is the operating agent for the Museum.

GUILD OF SOUTH CAROLINA ARTISTS, * 1112 Bull St, 29201. *Pres* Dr Diane Chalmers Johnson; *Pres Elect* Edwin Ritts Jr; *VPres* Bette Lee Coburn; *Secy/Treas* Steven A Jordan; *Admin Asst* Sally Cahill.
Estab 1951 for the purpose of promoting the visual arts in South Carolina. Mem: 400; dues association $5, active $10, patron $25, commercial patron $50; annual meeting Nov 1.
Income: $8906.
Exhibitions: Annual exhibition, juried, by members; rotates from Columbia Museum of Art, Greenville County Museum of Art, Florence Museum of Art, and Gibbes Art Gallery in Charleston; host gallery receives purchase award ($1000 annual purchase award).
Publications: Brochure; newsletter; annual membership directory.
Activities: Workshops, programs; lect open to the public, 1-2 vis lectr per yr; competitions; photograph collection of award winner and work from annual exhibition.

SOUTH CAROLINA ARTS COMMISSION, 829 Richland St, 29201, Tel: 803-758-3442. *Chmn* Kenneth Brown; *Exec Dir* Rick George; *Dir Community Arts Div* David Furchgott; *Dir Arts Educ Div* Ms Scott Sanders; *Dir Public Information* Mary Teague.
Open 8:30 AM - 5 PM. Estab 1967 to promote and develop the arts in South Carolina.
Income: Financed by Federal funds.

Collections: †State Art Collection.
Exhibitions: (1978) Annual Exhibition at Columbia College.
Publications: Newsletter on Tapestry.
Activities: Docent training; Artists-in-the Schools programs; schol; art-mobile; traveling exhibitions organized and circulated.

UNIVERSITY OF SOUTH CAROLINA, McKissick Museums, 29208.
Dir & Archivist Dr Barry H Rosen; *Cur Historical Coll* George Terry; *Cur Art Gallery* Lynn Myers; *Educ Museums* Dr William Savage.
Open Mon - Fri 9 AM - 4 PM; Sun 1 - 5 PM; cl Sat. Estab 1976 to centralize and promote the University's museum collections for the benefit of the academic program of the university, and the community and the state. Average Annual Attendance: 24,000.
Income: Financed by state appropriation.
Collections: Bernard Baruch Collection: 18th Century Silver; J Harry Howard Gemstone Collection; Richard Mandell; Art Nouveau Collection; James F Byrnes Collection.
Activities: Dramatic programs; lect open to public, 5-6 vis lectr per yr; concerts; gallery talks; tours; competitions; traveling exhibitions organized and circulated; sales shop selling books, magazines.

FLORENCE

FLORENCE MUSEUM, 600 Spruce St, 29501. Tel: 803-662-3351. *Dir* Dr William A Burns; *Bd Pres* Andrew Kampiziones; *Treas* O S Aiken; *Secy* E Cart.
Open Tues - Sat 10 AM - 5 PM; Sun 2 - 5 PM; cl Mon. No admis. Estab 1936 as a general museum of art, natural science, and history of South Carolina, with emphasis on the region known as the Pee Dee, and to acquaint the public with fine art; twelve galleries exhibit artwork. Mem: 400, dues $15 - $1000; annual meeting third Thurs April.
Income: $40,000 (financed by membership, county appropriation, and donations).
Collections: Chinese, Japanese, Korean and African collections; works of local and regional artists; artifacts; works of local black artists, particularly William H Johnson.
Exhibitions: 24th Pee Dee Regional Art Exhibition; Flora Exotics; Janet Dreskin-Haig paintings; Nell LaFaye; Dixie Dugan; Charles Councell; Steve Gately; Batiks, prints and their Makers; Children's Art; 50th Annual Art Exhibition of Florence Art Assoc; Papal Coins; Southern Phenomena; SC State Artists; South Carolina Guild of Artists; Bicentennial Year in SC History Hall.
Activities: Classes for adults and children; docent training; puppet shows; lect open to the public; 6 vis lectr per yr; gallery talks; tours; competition with cash prizes; lending collection contains books 1500, photographs 500; traveling exhibitions organized and circulated.
—**Evans Research Library.**
Open to students, for reference only.
Holdings: Vols 2000.

GREENVILLE

BOB JONES UNIVERSITY, Museum and Art Gallery, 29614. Tel: 803-242-5100. *Chmn of the Bd* Bob Jones; *Dir* Joan C Davis; *Staff Supv* Janice Churdar; *Conservator* Kathy Pflug.
Open Tues - Sun 2 - 5 PM; cl Mon, Dec 20 - 25, New Year's Day and July 4. No admis. Estab 1951 to show how universal is the Word of God in its appeal to human hearts in every generation; the Bowen Collection of Biblical antiquities was presented to the University by Mr and Mrs Frank Bowen in 1932; the permanent sacred art collection was made by Dr Bob Jones, Chancellor of the University, and opened to the public in 1951; it is termed one of the most remarkable collection of famous religious paintings in the world. Average Annual Attendance: 29,000.
Income: Financed by University and gifts.
Collections: Bowen Collection of Biblical antiquities and illustrative material from Palestine, Syria, Lebanon, Egypt, and Jordan; †Bob Jones University Collection of Sacred art including only religious art by the Old Masters from the 13th - 19th centuries and numbering works by such artists as Botticelli, Tintoretto, Veronese, Solimena del Piombo, Rubens, van Leyden, Rembrandt, Titian, Benson, Cranach the Elder, G David, Ribera, Murillo, Zurbaran; furniture and sculpture. In 1963 Bob Jones University acquired for its War Memorial Chapel a series of important paintings on Revealed Religion by Benjamin West. These were originally executed for King George III to be placed in his new Chapel at Windsor Castle. Because of the illness of the King, plans for the construction of the Chapel were abandoned, and the completed paintings were returned to the painter. The posthumous sale of West's works in 1829 included a number of the pictures on Revealed Religion. Joseph Neeld, MP, was the successful bidder, and the pictures hung in his home until 1962. At that time they were offered for sale by Christie's of London. Six were acquired for the Bob Jones University with funds provided for that purpose by an anonymous friend of the University.
Publications: Catalogs; illustrated booklets.

Activities: Tours for school and adult groups by appointment; individual paintings lent to other galleries in the US and abroad; sales shop selling reproductions, prints, slides.
Library. Mark Library. *Librn* Dr L Gene Elliott. Open to the public. Holdings: Art Per subs 36.

GREENVILLE COUNTY MUSEUM OF ART, 420 College St, 29601. Tel: 803-271-7570. *Exec Dir* Jack A Morris Jr; *Chief Cur/Deputy Dir* Edwin Ritts Jr; *Assoc Dir of Educ* Sylvia L Marchant; *Asst Dir Museum School of Art* Sharon Whitley.
Open Mon - Sat 10 AM - 5 PM; Sun 1 - 5 PM. No admis. Estab 1958 for the collection and preservation of North American Art. Average Annual Attendance: 100,000. Mem: 10,000; dues graduated schedule; annual meeting June.
Income: Financed by membership, and county appropriation.
Collections: Limited to North American art, mainly contemporary.
Exhibitions: 1976 Textiles: Past and Prologue; (1977) American Art since 1945; (1978) sculptors and their Drawings from Collection of Hirshhorn Museum and Sculpture Garden; Andrew Wyeth in Southern Collections.
Publications: Museum Notes, three times per yr.
Activities: Classes for adults and children; docent training; lect open to the public, 3 vis lectr per yr; gallery talks; tours; competitions with cash awards; schol; traveling exhibitions organized and circulated; sales shop selling books, original art, prints, crafts.

GREENWOOD

MUSEUM, 567 Phoenix St (Mailing Add: PO Box 3131, 29646). Tel: 803-229-7093. *Pres* I G Wooten, *Secy* Dr R J Lund; *Treas* W DuBose Stuckey; *Cur* J W Durst.
Open Mon - Fri 9 AM - 5 PM; Sun 2 - 5 PM; cl Sat. No admis. Estab June 1967, for educational purposes. Average Annual Attendance: 7654. Mem: 150; dues $15; meeting Jan, March, May and Nov.
Income: $7500 (financed by endowment). Purchases: $2600.
Collections: Bone, wood and ivory carvings; crystals; chinaware; glassware; limited art works; photographs; Frank E Delano Gallery of African animal mounts, and rare African works of art by the now extinct Katanga Tribe.

MURRELLS INLET

BROOKGREEN GARDENS, 29576. Tel: 803-237-4218. *Pres* Joseph Veach Noble; *First VPres* A Hyatt Mayor; *Second VPres* Marshall M Fredericks; *Secy* Eric S Malm; *Treas* Robert R Coker; *Dir* Gurdon L Tarbox.
Open 9:30 AM - 4:45 PM. Admis $1.50 adults, 50¢ (6-12 years), under six free. Estab 1931 to exhibit the flora and fauna of South Carolina and to exhibit objects of art; the outdoor museum exhibits American sculpture, while smaller pieces are shown in the Small Sculpture Museum and indoor gallery. Average Annual Attendance: 160,000. Mem: 350; dues $25 - $1000; annual meeting in Oct.
Income: $350,000 (financed by endowment, membership, and admission). Purchases: $27,000.
Collections: †Representative collection of American sculpture, by 182 sculptors.
Publications: Brookgreen Bulletin, quarterly.
Activities: Competitions; museum shop selling books, reproductions, slides.
Library. *Librn* Gurdon L Tarbox Jr. For reference only to staff. Holdings: Vols 406; Per subs 72; Other—Pictures, maps, architectural and engineering drawings and plans, clippings. Special Subjects: American sculpture, natural history, horticulture, local history. Special Collections: Photographs and slides of sculpture and natural history.

ROCK HILL

MUSEUM OF YORK COUNTY, Route 4, Box 211, Mt. Gallant Rd, 29730. Tel: 803-366-4116. *Exec Dir* Charles W Hall: *Asst Dir* Chris Houmes; *Secy* Sue Sanders.
Open Mon - Sat 9 AM - 5 PM; Sun 1 - 5 PM. Admis 25¢ per person. Estab 1949 as a natural and physical science museum; the Art Gallery has monthly traveling shows. Average Annual Attendance: 186,000 (1977).
Income: Financed by county appropriation.
Publications: Naturezette, (newsletter), monthly.
Activities: Classes for adults and children; dramatic programs; lect open to the public; traveling exhibitions organized and circulated; museum shop selling books, prints.
Library. Open to the public.

WINTHROP COLLEGE GALLERY OF ART, 29733. *Dir* Edmund D Lewandowski.

Open Mon - Fri 8:30 AM - 5 PM; Sun 2 - 5 PM; cl Sat. No admis. Estab 1970 to present area viewers with a wide variety of exhibitions, local, regional, and national in scope; and to provide an opportunity for regional artists to exhibit. Two galleries 40 x 80 x 20 ft and 15 x 15 x 12 ft. Average Annual Attendance: 12,000-15,000.
Income: Financed by city appropriation.
Collections: Limited collections.
Exhibitions: South Carolina State Art Collection; Spring Mills Annual Traveling Exhibition; Annual Textile Invitational; South Carolina Architectures 1670-1970; Foundry Art; several one-person shows.
Activities: Classes for adults; lect open to public; gallery talks; traveling exhibitions organized and circulated; museum shop selling original art and prints.

SPARTANBURG

ARTS COUNCIL OF SPARTANBURG COUNTY, INC, 385 S Spring St, 29301. Tel: 803-583-2776. *Pres* Mrs Myles Whitlock Jr; *VPres* Leslie McMillan Jr; *Secy* Mrs Hubert Hendrix; *Exec Dir* Georgia K Allen; *Asst Exec Dir* Mrs Danny R Hughes; *Business Mgr* William C Taylor Jr.
Open Mon - Fri 9 AM - 5 PM; Sat 1 - 4 PM; Sun 3 - 5 PM. No admis. Estab 1968 to coordinate all cultural activities in the area; to promote its member organations; and maintain an Arts Center with changing and permanent exhibitions. Average Annual Attendance: 80,000-100,000.
Income: $170,000 (financed by state appropriation and private donations).
Collections: The Girl with the Red Hair by Robert Henri; twenty other paintings.
Exhibitions: The Sporting Scene; Predilections II; many changing exhibits.
Publications: Spartanburg Arts, bimonthly.
Activities: Classes for adults and children; dramatic programs; docent training; arts camp for children; drama festival; lect open to public; concerts; gallery talks; tours; scholarships; exten dept serving schools in county; sales shop selling original art, prints, original pottery, jewelry, hand-printed cards and stationery.
Library: Open to the public for reference. Holdings: Vols 50; Per subs 2. Special Subjects: Art history.

SPARTANBURG COUNTY ART ASSOCIATION, Gallery, 385 S Spring St, 29301. Tel: 803-582-7616. *Cur* Shelley E Churchill; *Pres* Mrs Daniel Kahrs; *Chmn* Mrs Jerry Cogan.
Open Mon - Fri 10 AM - 5 PM; Sat 2 - 4 PM; Sun 3 - 5 PM. No Admis. Estab 1969 to promote the works of contemporary artists in the southeastern United States; the gallery is located in the Spartanburg County Arts Center and contains both a permanent sales section and a changing exhibit area. Average Annual Attendance: 4000 - 5000. Mem: 300; dues $7 - $500.
Income: Financed by endowment, membership.
Collections: †Contemporary Southeastern artists.
Exhibitions: (1978-79) Anne Lattimore of Aiken; Marianna Hamilton of Myrtle Beach; Invitational Crafts by craftspeople from throughout the US; South Carolina Collections from the 19th Century; Jean McWhorter of Columbia; Pierre Humbert from Paris, France; Elaine Wagner and Jeanette Ritsch of Spartanburg; Invitational Graphics by artists from the SE region.
Publications: Newsletter, quarterly.
Activities: Classes for adults and children; docent training; lect open to the public, 2 vis lectr per yr; gallery talks; tours; competitions; sales shop selling books, original art.
Library. Holdings—Vols 150; Per subs 2. Special Subjects: Most books deal with the "how to's" of Art. Special Collections: Limited art historical volumes.

SUMTER

SUMTER GALLERY OF ART, 421 N Main St (Mailing Add: PO Box 1316, 29150). Tel: 803-775-0543. *Chmn Bd Dir* J Eugene Matthews; *Gallery Dir* Jane Walker.
Open Tues - Sun 3 - 6 PM. No admis. Estab 1970 to bring to area exhibits of works of recognized artists, to provide an outlet for local artists for showing and sale of their work, and to serve as a facility where visual art may become a part of life and education of the people, particularly children, of this community. The Gallery is the 1850 home of the late Miss Elizabeth White, well-known artist of Sumter, which was deeded to the gallery in 1977 under the terms of her will. Presently using hall and four downstairs rooms. Average Annual Attendance: 4500. Mem: 360; dues individual $8, family $10, patron $25; annual meeting May.
Income: $8,000 (financed by membership and earned income).
Collections: Approx sixty paintings, etchings and drawings of Elizabeth White given to the gallery by trustees of her estate.

Exhibitions: Individual and group exhibits of paintings, sculpture, collages, photography and crafts by recognized artists, primarily from Southeast; traveling exhibits; annual Young People's Exhibit.
Publications: Newsletter, monthly.
Activities: Classes for adults and children; lect open to public, 8 vis lect per yr; gallery talks; competitions, awards given; sales shop selling original art, prints.

SOUTH DAKOTA

ABERDEEN

DACOTAH PRAIRIE MUSEUM, 21 S Main St (Mailing Add: PO Box 395, 57401). Tel: 605-229-1608. *Dir* William E Busta; *Cur of Educ* Helen Bergh; *Asst to Dir* William Booker.
Open Mon - Fri 9 AM - 5 PM, Sat & Sun 1 - 4 PM. No admis. Estab 1969 to preserve the heritage of the peoples of the Dakotas; to maintain and develop exhibits that educate people about the heritage of the Dakotas; two galleries are devoted to art, the Lamont Gallery and the Heritage Gallery. Average Annual Attendance: 25,000. Mem: 200; dues $3; annual meeting third Sat Jan.
Income: $65,000 (financed by membership and county appropriation). Purchases $25,000.
Collections: (Art) Sioux and Arikara Indian artifacts; local and regional artists; photography.
Exhibitions: (1977) Jim Armstrong (recent watercolors); South Dakota Western Artists Association; Dave Huebner (ceramics); The Late Victorian Sense of Beauty; Palmer Eide Retrospective; Circus Posters; Africa-The Black Kingdoms; Fronts and Forms by Joe Kegler; Mark McGinnis (selected '77 paintings and drawings); FSA Photographs; Rosebud and Pine Ridge Photographs, 1922-1942; Contemporary Sioux Quilts.
Publications: Dacotah Prairie Times, ten times per year; Annual Report.
Activities: Classes for adults and children; lect open to the public, 3 vis lectr per yr; gallery talks; tours; individual paintings and original objects of art lent to other museums or art centers; some materials to schools; museum shop selling books, magazines, original art, reproductions.
—**Historical Research Center Library.** Tel: 605-229-1608. *Dir* William E Busta.
Open to members and individuals by request for reference only.
Holdings: Vol 5000; Per subs 7.

BROOKINGS

SOUTH DAKOTA STATE UNIVERSITY, South Dakota Memorial Art Center, Medary Ave at Harvey Dunn St, 57006. Tel: 605-688-5423. *Dir* Joseph Stuart; *Asst to Dir* Rex Gulbranson; *Cur Marghab Coll* Cora Sivers, *Secy* Marian Borstad.
Open Mon - Fri 8 AM - 5 PM; Sat 10 AM - 5 PM; Sun 1 - 5 PM. No admis. Estab 1969 as the state center for visual arts with various programs; the gallery was designed by Howard Parezo, AIA, Sioux Falls, and occupies 112 x 90 ft site; there are six galleries, and a 147-seat auditorium. Average Annual Attendance: 140,000. Mem: 2500 Friends; dues contributions; annual meeting April.
Income: $57,958 (financed by endowment, state appropriation, gifts and grants). Purchases: $2000.
Collections: Harvey Dunn paintings; Marghab linens; †art of South Dakota; †Northwestern art (Iowa, Minn, Neb, NDakota, SDakota); United States art; Ben Reifel Collection of Plains Indian Art.
Exhibitions: (1977-78) Myra Miller Paintings: South Dakota Biennial III; The Dyer's Art; Northwestern Artists; The Sensuous Line; South Dakota Collects II; Karl Bodmer Prints; Art of South Dakota; Charles Greener Paintings; Five West River Artists; Paul Manship Sculpture; American Graphic Art; South Dakota Works on Paper; Drawings USA; Northwestern Biennial IV; Oscar Howe Paintings.
Publications: Newsletter, monthly; bulletin, quarterly.
Activities: Docent training; lect open to the public, 4 vis lectr per yr; gallery talks; tours; competitions; exten dept serving SDakota; artmobile; individual paintings and original objects of art lent to SDakota museums, galleries, libraries, schools, banks; lending collection contains original prints, paintings 226, photographs, drawings; traveling exhibitions organized and circulated; museum shop selling books, original art reproductions, crafts.
—**Jeannette Lusk Library Collection.** *Librn* Evelyn Baumberger.
Open to the public for reference only.
Holdings: Vols 2000; Per subs 11; Other—Slides 1500 of South Dakota art. Special Subjects: Archives of South Dakota Art.

CUSTER

WESTERN WOODCARVINGS,* Hwy 16, Box 747, 57730. *Mgr* Charles A & Lillian E Schaffer.

Open May 15 - Oct 1 daily 9 AM - 5 PM; June, July & Aug 8 AM - 6 PM; other times for special events. Group rates available. Estab 1966 in general area of Black Hills near the place Custer's party found gold in 1874.
Collections: Niblack Collection of woodcarvings; work of wood sculptors.
Exhibitions: Temporary exhibitions of collection and current work.
Activities: Lectures; gallery talks; tours, competitions, studios for artist use.
Library: Small collection of books and reference material on sculpturing and woodcarving available for use on premises.

DEADWOOD

DEADWOOD GULCH ART GALLERY,* 665½ Historic Main St, 57732. Tel: 605-578-3636. *Pres* J D Sulentic; *Secy* Margaret Sulentic.
Open April - Dec 9 AM - 5 PM. No admis. Estab 1967 to display and sell works of art; the gallery is operated in conjunction with a Chinese Museum Tunnel Tour, for which a charge of 25¢ per person is made.
Collections: Paintings; Chinese art.
Activities: Book shop.

MITCHELL

OSCAR HOWE CULTURAL CENTER,* 119 W 3rd St, 57301. Tel: 605-996-4111. *Dir* William W Anderson.
Open Mon 1 - 5 PM, 7 - 9 PM; Wed - Sat 1 - 5 PM; Sun 2 - 5 PM; cl Tues & holidays. No admis. Estab 1972 in 1906 Carnegie Building. Mem: Dues individual $5, family $10, sponsor $25, business $50, patron $100.
Collections: Small collection of paintings by Sioux artists.
Activities: Lectures; gallery talks, guided tours; concerts; competitions; hobby workshops; rental gallery; sales shop selling handmade pottery, weaving, paintings and prints done by Sioux Indians.

RAPID CITY

DAKOTA ART GALLERY,* Dakota Artists Guild, Dahl Fine Arts Center, 713 Seventh St, 47701. Tel: 605-342-2144. *Dir* Thomas J Winn.
Open Mon - Sat 10 AM - 5 PM. Estab 1965 as Civic Art Gallery by Dakota Artists Guild. Average Annual Attendance: 5000 - 6000. Mem: Approximately 200; dues $10.
Income: Approximately $38,000 - $40,000 (financed by membership and public contributions).
Exhibitions: Continuing local exhibits and exhibits of national artists by invitation; all exhibits changed monthly.
Publications: Brochure; newsletter, monthly.
Activities: Classes of instruction; community art projects; lect open to the public, monthly meetings open to the public; gallery tours; schol.

SIOUX INDIAN MUSEUM, W Boulevard, between Main and St Joseph, (Mailing Add: Box 1504, 57709). Tel: 605-348-0557. *Cur* Rena McGhan.
Open June - Sept, Mon - Sat 9 AM - 5 PM; Sun 1 - 5 PM; Oct - May, Tues - Sat 10 AM - 5 PM; Sun 1 - 5 PM; cl New Year's Day, Thanksgiving, Christmas. No admis. Estab 1939 to promote the development of contemporary native American arts and crafts of the United States. Average Annual Attendance: 80,000.
Income: Financed by Federal appropriation.
Collections: Contemporary native American arts and crafts of the United States; Historic works by Sioux craftsmen.
Exhibitions: Contemporary Sioux Quillwork; Contemporary Sioux Quilts; continuing series of one-person exhibitions.
Publications: One-person exhibition brochure series, monthly.
Activities: Gallery talks; traveling exhibitions organized and circulated; sales shop selling books, original art.

SIOUX FALLS

CIVIC FINE ARTS ASSOCIATION, 235 W Tenth St, 57102. Tel: 605-336-1167. *Pres* Mrs H W Farrell; *VPres* Lawrence Piersol; *Secy* Mrs Robert Burnette; *Exec Dir* Raymond Shermoe; *Office Mgr* Beverly Friedhoff.
Open Tues - Sat 11:30 AM - 5 PM; Sun 2 - 5 PM; cl Mon. No admis. Estab 1961 as a contemporary museum; an art gallery is maintained. Average Annual Attendance: 80,000. Mem: 1500; dues $10.
Income: $50,000 (financed by endowment, membership, city appropriation and fund-raising projects).
Collections: Regional art; poster collection.
Exhibitions: Women Painters' Biennial; Drawings USA; Library of Congress-An American Album; Contemporary Sioux Quilts; Arts '76.
Publications: Newsletter; monthly.

Activities: Classes for adults and children; lect open to the public, 2 vis lectr per yr; tours, competitions with awards; schol; lending collection contains books 200; traveling exhibitions organized and circulated; sales shop selling books, magazines, original art, prints, reproductions, pottery and imports, cards.
Library: Open to members only.

SPEARFISH

BLACK HILLS ART CENTER,* Little Gallery, 57783. *Dir* Mrs Harry Henderson.
Open daily during school hours. Estab 1936 to encourage art expression and greater appreciation in the Black Hills area. Work of the Art Center is promoted jointly by Black Hills State College and by the local Chapter of Kappa Pi, National Honorary Art Fraternity, and by Spearfish Paint and Palette Club. Average Annual Attendance: 1500. Mem: 500, dues $5 and up.
Exhibitions: Local exhibits are quarterly; traveling exhibitions occasionally; annual exhibition for May 15 to June 15; Black Hills Art Exhibit in Student Union.
Activities: Classes for adults, and programs held each semester; summer workshop; summer Art Colony in August annually; traveling exhibitions.
Library: Holdings—Vols 200; Other—Books, films, reproductions are being added annually; Carnegie gift library contains prints 1000 and art books 150.

VERMILLION

UNIVERSITY OF SOUTH DAKOTA, W H Over Museum, 57069. Tel: 605-677-5228. *Dir* June Sampson; *Exhib Designer* Walter Voll; *Educ Prog Specialist* Allen Schroeder.
Open Mon - Fri 8 AM - 4:30 PM; Sat 10 AM - 4:30 PM; Sun 2 - 4:30 PM. No admis. Estab 1911 to collect, preserve and study the specimens and artifacts of the natural history of South Dakota and the cultural heritage of its people; to interpret these collections as well as the cultural similarities and diversity of people through exhibits, publications, and educational programs for the benefit of the public and the educational institutions of the state. Carl Norgren Hall of Natural History: habitat groups illustrating the region's flora and fauna. The Hall of Man: the major prehistoric cultures of the area and the historic Sioux culture shown in interpretive exhibits. The World of the Dakota Pioneer: the tools, homelife, and industry of the early European settlers. The changing Gallery: loan exhibits and special exhibits each quarter. Average Annual Attendance: 11,000. Mem: 140; dues $5; annual meeting Jan.
Income: $150,000 (financed by membership, state appropriation, federal grants). Purchases: $1000.
Collections: The David and Elizabeth Clark Memorial Collection of Dakota (Sioux) ethnological material; the Stanley J Morrow Collection of photographs.
Exhibitions: The Aquarius Plateau: A Photographic Tour; Early Dakota (Sioux) Paintings on Muslin; Contemporary Sioux quilts; William Over's Attic: Bits of the Museum's Past; Blackfeet Indian Tipis: Design and Legend; Stanley Morrow Photographs.
Publications: The South Dakota Museum, infrequently.
Activities: Classes for adults and children; lect open to public, 6 vis lectr per yr; gallery talks; traveling exhibitions organized and circulated; museum shop selling books, reproductions, slides and native American crafts.
Library: *Librn* June Sampson. Open to public for reference. Holdings: Vols 300; Per subs 6. Special Subjects: Ethnology, natural history, and museology.

YANKTON

YANKTON COLLEGE,* Durand Art Collection, James Lloyd Library, 57078. *Cur* Prof Jerome E Gallagher.
Estab 1909. Chiefly serves the Art Department, but open to students, faculty and townspeople.
Collections: Some original paintings, sculpture and prints.
Exhibitions: Frequently changed exhibitions.
Activities: Lectures for schools and clubs, and loan exhibits circulated.
Library: Comprehensive section on art history.

TENNESSEE

CHATTANOOGA

HOUSTON ANTIQUE MUSEUM,* 201 High St, 37403. Tel: 615-267-7176. *Dir & Cur* Mary E Baker.
Open Tues - Sat 10 Am - 4:30 PM; Sun 2 - 4:30 PM; cl Mon & holidays. Admis adults $1, children 50¢. Estab 1961, inc 1949, collection willed to Chattanooga by the late Mrs Houston. Average Annual Attendance: 10,000. Mem: 500; dues $5 - $100; annual meeting Apr.
Collections: Rare collection of glass—15,000 pitchers, 600 patterns of pressed glass, all types art glass, steins, Tiffany glass; Early American furniture; dolls.
Publications: The Fabulous Houston.
Activities: 6 lectures per year; lending library for members; slide program for elementary schools.
Library: Books on antiques.

HUNTER MUSEUM OF ART, 10 Bluff View, 37403. Tel: 615-267-0968. *Dir* Cleve K Scarborough; *Cur Educ* Carla M Michalove; *Coordinator of Exhib* J Bradley Burns; *Admin Asst* Kate B Lochte.
Open Tues - Sat 10 AM - 4:30 PM; Sun 1 - 4:30 PM; cl Mon. No admis. Estab 1924, chartered in 1951, to present a visual arts program of high quality, maintain a fine collection of American art, and to carry out a vigorous educational program in the community and the schools. The permanent collection of American Art is housed in the George Thomas Hunter Mansion constructed in 1904; a contemporary addition was opened in 1975 with 50,000 sq ft of space in four major gallery areas, a classroom wing and an auditorium. Average Annual Attendance: 38,000. Mem: 1603; dues student $5, individual $15; family $25.
Income: $300,000 (financed by city and state appropriations and contributions).
Collections: American paintings including works by Benton, Burchfield, Henri, Marsh, Bellows, Beirstadt, Hassam and others; Contemporary American Prints; sculpture by Snelson and Sugarman.
Exhibitions: National Exhibition of Prints; Navajo Blankets; Selected Prints of Robert Motherwell; North American Beadwork; Art from the Cameroon; Photographs of Roger Minick; Watercolors of Hubert Donati; Contemporary Photographers VI; Paintings by John Piper; Rodin Studies for the Burghers of Calais; Toys, Doll and Crib Quilts; Photographs by Jerry Uelsman; Tyler Graphics; Watercolors of Frank Baisden; SITES: Images of Urban Optimism; Prints of Phillip Pearlstein; American Impressionists; Photographs of Arnold Newman; Cavepaintings of France and Spain.
Publications: Bulletin, monthly; brochures and announcements.
Activities: Classes for adults and children; docent training; lect open to public, 5 vis lectr per yr; gallery talks; concerts; tours; competitions; individual paintings are lent to other museums; museum shop selling miscellaneous decorator items.
Library: Volunteer staff. Open to members and the public on an appointment basis. Holdings: Vols 1000; Per subs 25 - 30. Special Subjects: Focus on American Art.

UNIVERSITY OF TENNESSEE AT CHATTANOOGA ART GALLERY,* Baldwin St, 37401. Tel: 615-755-4177. *Dir* Jim L Collins.
Open Mon - Fri 9 Am - 5 PM; cl University holidays. No admis. Estab 1952.
Collections: Paintings; graphics; students work.
Activities: Gallery talks; loan program; temporary and traveling exhibitions.

CLARKSVILLE

AUSTIN PEAY STATE UNIVERSITY,**•Art Department, Margaret Fort Trahern Gallery, 37040. Tel: 615-648-7236. *Chmn Dept Art* Charles T Young; *Cur* Lewis B Burton.
Open workdays 9 AM - 3 PM. No admis. Estab 1962 as a university-community service to exhibit a variety of visual media from regional professionals and university art majors.
Income: Financed by university appropriations.
Collections: Regional artists, primarily watercolors, graphics and sculpture.
Exhibitions: Average 8-10 per year.
Publications: Announcements of shows and artist biographies, monthly.
Activities: Classes for adults and children; dramatic programs; lect open to the public, 20 vis lectr per yr; gallery talks; extension dept; competitions; schol
Library: Noncirculating department library. Holdings: AV—Kodachromes 17,000, color reproductions 100, lantern slides 300, motion pictures, film strips.

COOKEVILLE

CUMBERLAND ART SOCIETY, Cookeville Art Center, 186 S Walnut, 38501. Tel: 615-526-2424. *Pres* Reba Bacon; *VPres* Sally Crain.

Open Sun 2 - 5 PM; Tues - Fri 1:30 - 4 PM. No admis. Estab 1961 to promote arts in the community and area. A new building with adequate gallery and studio space. The gallery is carpeted and walls are finished with wallscape; track lighting. Average Annual Attendance: 3000. Mem: 100.
Income: $1500 (financed by membership, city and state appropriations).
Exhibitions: Changing exhibits, monthly.
Activities: Classes for children; lect open to public; exten dept.

JACKSON

UNION UNIVERSITY ART GUILD,* Highway 45 Bypass, 38301. Tel: 901-668-1818.
Open 8 - 10 AM. No admis. Estab 1973 to further art as a beneficial and needed factor of life; gallery maintained. Mem: 43; dues $2.
Income: Financed by membership.
Collections: Eli Prouty Collection; individual student collections.
Activities: Lectures for members only; one tour per year; concerts, dramatic programs, competitions.

JOHNSON CITY

EAST TENNESSEE STATE UNIVERSITY*
—**Carroll Reece Museum,** 37601. Tel: 615-929-4392, 929-4283. *Dir* Harvey A Dean; *Registrar* Helen Roseberry; *Mus Secy* Audaleen H McNutt.
Open Mon - Fri 12:45 - 4:45 PM; Sat - Sun 1 - 5 PM. No admis. Estab 1964 to enhance the cultural and educational advantages of the university and the people of upper east Tennessee. Average Annual Attendance: 28,000. Friends of the Reece Museum annual memberships; purpose of the group is to acquire paintings to be a part of the permanent collection. Dues student $1, regular $10-$100, benefactor $250.
Collections: Tennessee Frontier Room, a reconstructed scene of frontier life in the latter part of the 18th century and early 19th century; Reece Room, an exhibition of memorabilia of former United States Congressman from Tennessee, B Carroll Reece; Music from the Past, a collection of early musical instruments; Old Master and contemporary prints; contemporary paintings; Tennessee Craftsman Collection; Marks Collection of Pre-Columbia art; Colonel Hart Collection of military art; John Steele Collection of contemporary prints; historical material.
Exhibitions: Three galleries of traveling exhibitions, some rented and some organized by museum staff.
Activities: Musical concerts, film series, educational programs; meetings, receptions and other activities are carried on during the year.
Library: Located on campus as part of the university. Holdings: Vols approx 2500 of art literature.
—**Elizabeth Slocum Gallery,** Art Department, 37601. Tel: 615-929-4292, 929-4247. *Chmn Art Dept* W Radford Thomas; *Dir Exhib* George Moldovan.
Open daily 8 AM - 5 PM; Sat 9 - 12 AM. No admis. Estab to augment all the programs and areas of instruction within the Art Department and to foster interest in various modes of artistic expression in the campus at large.
Collections: A small teaching collection of prints, paintings, ceramics and weaving.
Exhibitions: Original and traveling exhibits.
Publications: Catalogs; posters.
Activities: Full art education program; classes for adults and children; scholarships and fellowships; frequent lectures, seminars and workshops.

KINGSPORT

KINGSPORT FINE ARTS CENTER,* Church Circle, 37660. Tel: 615-246-9351. *Pres* James Cochrane; *Secy* Marian Stras; *Dir* Katherine Thomas; *Secy* Debbie Watkins.
Open weekdays 9 AM - 5 PM; Sat Noon - 4 PM. No admis. Estab 1968 to promote and present all the arts to all the people in area; this includes performing arts, visual arts, and classes. Average Annual Attendance: 10,000. Mem: 548; dues $10 - $250; annual meeting May.
Income: $20,000 (financed by membership).
Publications: Newsletter, bimonthly.
Activities: Several gallery talks; 5-10 tours; concerts; dramatic programs; classes for adults and children; competitions; traveling exhibitions. Craft Shop.

KNOXVILLE

DULIN GALLERY OF ART, 3100 Kingston Pike, 37919. Tel: 615-525-6101. *Acting Dir* Mrs John R Ruggels, Jr; *Pres Bd Trustees* Ernest B Rodgers; *VPres* Thomas J Rentenbach; *Treas* Charles H Dean, Jr; *Secy* Mrs Robert S Young, Jr.

Open Tues - Sun 1 - 5 PM; cl Mon. Admis adults $1.00, children, students & members free. Estab 1961 to preserve, conserve and interpret works of art. It is a non-profit private corporation; the Gallery is located in the historic house designed in 1915 by John Russell Pope for H L Dulin and is listed in the National Registry. Average Annual Attendance: 15,000. Mem: 1052; dues $30.
Income: Financed by endowment and membership.
Collections: American paintings; a collection of prints and drawings from the last twelve National Print and Drawing Competitions.
Exhibitions: Annual National Print and Drawing Competition.
Publications: Bulletin, monthly; The H L Dulin Residence; The Thorn Miniature Rooms.
Activities: Classes for adults and children; docent training; lect open to public, 7 vis lectr per yr; tours; competitions; individual paintings lent to schools; lending collection contains framed reproductions 161; traveling exhibitions organized and circulated.
Library: Reference Library. Holdings: Vols 700.

UNIVERSITY OF TENNESSEE
—**Frank H McClung Museum,*** 1327 Circle Park Dr, 37916. Tel: 615-974-2144. *Dir* Alfred K Guthe; *Exhib Coordr* Joseph W Hopkins; *Cur Coll* Elaine A Evans.
Open Mon - Fri 9 AM - 5 PM. No admis. Estab 1961 to collect, maintain and interpret paintings, works of art, items of natural history and historical objects. Emphasis is placed on the Tennessee area. A major purpose is to provide research materials for students and faculty of the university. Average Annual Attendance: 35,000.
Income: Financed by city and state appropriations.
Collections: Lewis-Kneberg Collection (Tennessee archaeology); Frederick T Bonham Collection (18th-20th century furniture, art objects); Grace Moore Collection (memorabilia of her career 1920's - 1940's).
Activities: Lect open to public; gallery talks; tours; competitions; exten dept serving the Southeast; original objects of art lent; lending collection contains prints in photograph collection.
—**Eleanor Dean Audigier Art Collection,*** Hoskins Library, 1401 Cumberland Ave, 37916. Tel: 615-974-2122.
Open 15 hours a week. Estab 1934. Average Annual Attendance: 5,000.
Income: Financed by state appropriations.
Collections: The Audigier Collection contains over 800 art objects—19th century copies of Italian Renaissance paintings, sculpture, furniture and silver; 19th century cameos; Chinese, French and German porcelain; personal jewelry, ivory miniatures; Turkish and Arabic trays; Ancient Egyptian scarabs, shawbtis; Greco-Roman jars and lamps.
—**University of Tennessee Art Exhibitions,*** 306 University Center, 37916. *Dir* Kevin Majut.
—**University of Tennessee Exhibits Committee,** 305 University Center. Tel: 615-974-5455. *Dir* Erica Gruen.
Open Mon - Fri 7:30 AM - 10:30 PM; Sat 7 AM - 10 PM; Sun 1 - 8 PM. No admis. Estab to provide cultural arts for the students of the University. Two major galleries—Gallery Concourse (300 running ft) and Gallery II (60 running ft) for intimate shows. Average Annual Attendance: 20,000.
Income: $8,000 (financed by state appropriation and student activities fees). Purchases: $1,000.
Collections: †Dunford Collection; †Marion Heard Collection of Crafts.
Exhibitions: 20 exhibits per year—student shows, traveling shows.
Activities: Lect open to public, 3 vis lectr per yr.

MARYVILLE

MARYVILLE COLLEGE FINE ARTS CENTER GALLERY,* 37801. Tel: 615-982-6950. *Chmn Dept Fine Arts* Harry H Harter.
Open daily except Sun.
Ten to twelve traveling exhibitions during college year; art movies four times a year; gallery programs in connection with circulating exhibitions. Paintings of local and visiting artists exhibited twice a year. †Print Collection.

MEMPHIS

BROOKS MEMORIAL ART GALLERY, Overton Park, 38112. Tel: 901-726-4762. *Dir* Dr John J Whitlock; *Secy to Dir* Gail Chumley; *Cur Educ* Diana Prewitt; *Asst Cur Educ* Sandra Peace; *Registrar* Maurine F Newell.
Open Tues - Sat & holidays 10 AM - 5 PM; Sun 1 - 5 PM; cl Mon. No admis. Estab 1914 by gift from Mrs Samuel H Brooks to promote interest and development in cultural arts; to present a diversity of exhibitions; to assist people in their quest for knowledge and aesthetic experiences, as well as contributing to their mental health through art education. The original building was opened in 1916 with additions in 1955 and 1973. Average Annual Attendance: 129,000. Dues $10 and up. Annual meeting Sept.
Income: Financed by city appropriation.

Collections: Kress Collection of Italian paintings and sculptures, 13th-18th centuries; Dutch and Flemish paintings, 16th-18th centuries; English paintings, 17th-19th centuries; French paintings, 16th-19th centuries; American paintings and sculpture, 18th-20th centuries; †International Collection of paintings and sculptures, 19th & 20th centuries; Dr Louis Levy Collection of American prints; Eastern and Near-Eastern decorative arts Collection (Han, T'ang and Ching Dynasty Chinese), 19th century Japanese and 15th and 16th Dynasty and New Empire Egyptian; Mid-South Collection of 20th century paintings and sculptures; porcelain, glass and textile collection.
Exhibitions: Biennial Mississippi River Craft Show; changing exhibition program; Carroll Cloar Retrospective; The River; William Eggleston Photographs; Richard Hunt Sculptures; Art Today/Recent Media; Han & T'ang Murals; Faberge Exhibition; Abraham Rattner; American Art (1934-1956) from the Whitney Museum Collection; Memphis Architecture; Rhodesian Sculpture Exhibtion.
Publications: Newsletter, bimonthly.
Activities: Educ dept; lect open to public; concerts; gallery talks; tours; competitions; museum shop selling books, reproductions, museum replicas.
Library: Librn Letitia B Proctor. Open to the public for reference. Holdings: Vols 11,500.

DIXON GALLERY AND GARDENS, 4339 Park Ave, 38117. Tel: 901-761-5250. *Dir* Michael Milkovich; *Horticultural Dir* Edwin J Toth; *Cur of Educ* Reba Russell; *Business Mgr* Charlotte Snow; *Educ Asst* Laney Dunn.
Open Tues - Sat 11 AM - 5 PM; Sun 1 - 5 PM, cl Mon. Admis adult $1, children 5 - 12 years, students 50¢. Estab 1976 to provide community with opportunity to view original works of art and to enjoy the formal and informal gardens surrounding the gallery; ten exhibition galleries located in the downstairs area of the house, and in an addition completed in 1977. Seventeen acres of formal and informal gardens, a large camellia house and a small greenhouse are part of the premises. Average Annual Attendance: 15,300. Mem: 400; dues students $5, individual $15, family $25, supporting $50, donor $100, patron $500.
Income: Financed by endowment.
Collections: †French and American Impressionists, Post-Impressionists and related schools; †British portraits and landscapes of the 19th century; †French and English sculpture of the 19th and 20th century; †porcelain; works by Cals, Constable, Piette, Romney, Rouart, Tucker and Turner.
Exhibitions: (1976) Mary Cassatt and the American Impressionists; (1977-78) Impressionists in 1877; (1978) Collected in Memphis; Charles Francois Daubigny; Flowers in Art.
Publications: Newsletter, bi-monthly.
Activities: Classes for adults; docent training; film series; lect open to the public, 6 vis lectr per yr; concerts; gallery talks; tours; individual paintings and original objects of art lent to museums and galleries; lending collection contains original art works, original prints, paintings, sculpture, porcelain, silver, antique furniture.
—Library. Tel: 901-761-5250.
Open to the public during museum hours, for reference only.
Holdings: Vols 3500; Per subs 15; Other—1000 slides (used in connection with gallery and gardens programs).
Special Subjects: There is a garden educational program of lectures, short courses, guided walks and slide programs.
Special Collections: English 17th and 18th Century furniture and porcelain; antique garden statuary.

MEMPHIS ACADEMY OF ARTS,* Overton Park, 38112. Tel: 901-726-4085. *Pres* Dr Jameson J Jones; *Dir Emer* Edwin C Rust.
—Frank T Tobey Gallery.
Open Mon - Sat 9 AM - 5 PM; Sun 1 - 5 PM; cl summer Sat & Sun; cl school holidays. No admis. Estab 1936 as an adjunct educational program. The Standing Comt on Exhibitions arranges visiting shows.
Collections: Jacob Marks Memorial Collection; works by college graduates.
Exhibitions: One and two-man faculty shows; juried student shows; senior exhibition; summer student show; traveling exhibitions.
Publications: Exhibit catalogs.
Activities: Classes for adults and children, undergraduate college students; lecures; guided tours; films; competitions.
—G Pillow Lewis Memorial Library. *Librn* Robert Scarlett; *Asst Librn* Bette Ray Callow.
Open Mon - Fri 8 AM - 5 Pm; Sat 9 AM - Noon; Mon & Wed Eve until 10 PM.
Income: Approx $8500 (financed by city and county appropriations).
Holdings: Vols 15,000; Per subs 104; AV—Slides 22,000; Other—original prints, reproductions.

SOUTHWESTERN AT MEMPHIS, Jessie L Clough Art Memorial for Teaching, Burrow Library, 200 N Parkway, 38112. Tel: 901-274-1800, exten 365. *Cur* Etta Hanson.

Collection donated by the late Miss Floy K Hanson of her fine and valuable collection of oriental objects of art to be known as the Jessie L Clough Art Memorial for Teaching in memory of her first art teacher and friend Miss Clough.
Collections: Textiles; Japanese prints; brass; copper; precious metals; jewelry; pottery; woodcarvings.

MURFREESBORO

MIDDLE TENESSEE STATE UNIVERSITY, Photographic Gallery, 37132. Tel: 615-898-2491. *Cur* Harold L Baldwin.
Open Mon - Fri 8 AM - 4 PM; Sat 9 AM - 5 PM; Sun 1 - 6 PM. No admis. Estab 1969 for the exhibition of outstanding photographers and beginners. Gallery has 42 panels lighted individually. Average Annual Attendance: 8,000 - 10,000.
Income: Financed by endowment, membership and city appropriation. Purchases: $1800.
Collections: †Student collection; †professional collection.
Exhibitions: Annual student exhibition; John Weiss; Garry Winogrand; Richard Newman; Aneta Sperber; George Walker III; Holography Exhibition; Eric Kister; Richard Procopio; Jim McQuaid; Richard Avedon; Kathleen Fuller; Jim Robertson; Mark Orlove; Barbara Morgan; Richard McKown; Vincent Vallarino.
Publications: Lightyear, annually.
Activities: Classes for adults; exten dept serving the area; original objects of art lent to responsible organizations; lending collection contains photographs; traveling exhibitions organized and circulated.

NASHVILLE

FISK UNIVERSITY MUSEUM, 18th & Jackson Sts, 37203. Tel. 615-329-8685. *Dir* Earl J Hooks; *Cur* Robert Hall; *Asst to Cur* Pearl Cresswell.
Open Mon - Fri 9 AM - Noon & 1 - 5 PM; cl weekends, June, July & Aug. No admis. Estab 1949 as an education resource center for the Fisk and Nashville communities, and for the promotion of the arts. Van Vechten Gallery houses the library, temporary exhibits and art offices; Library Gallery houses the permanent collection and African Art. Average Annual Attendance: 4000.
Income: Financed through the University.
Collections: Alfred Stieglitz Collection of modern art; †Afro-American collection; †Traditional African art collection.
Exhibitions: Lev Mills (Prints); Ben Jones (mixed media); Wilhelmina Godfrey (textiles); Alumni Exhibit; Faculty Exhibits; William H Johnson (prints); Metropolitan Nashville Artists.
Publications: Fisk Art Report, yearly.
Activities: Lect open to public, 3 vis lectr per yr; gallery talks; tours; individual paintings and original objects of art lent to institutions, organizations, community groups; lending collection contains original prints, paintings; traveling exhibitions organized and circulated; sales shop selling reproductions and exhibition catalogs.
Library: Florine Stettheimer Library. Open to students for reference. Holdings: Vols 4500; Per subs 3.

GEORGE PEABODY COLLEGE FOR TEACHERS,* Cohen Memorial Museum of Art, Box 513, 37203. Tel: 615-372-8178. *Dir* Dr Walter Rutkowski; *Cur* Lucius B DuBose; *Secy* Patricia S Irwin.
Open Mon - Fri 9 AM - Noon & 1 - 4:30 PM. No admis. Galleries are used to exhibit student works, faculty works, and visiting artist's works; on occasion, permanent collection is exhibited. Average Annual Attendance: 3000.
Income: College funded.
Collections: Kress Study Collection of Renaissance paintings; Algernon Sydney Sullivan Collection of 19th century paintings; 18th and 19th century European painting and sculpture; contemporary American painting, prints and sculpture; English china and silver; lace, tapestries and antique furniture.
Exhibitions: 6 visiting artists; Middle Tennessee High School Art Exhibit; Peabody Senior Exhibition; 4 graduate exhibitions.
Activities: Lectures and traveling exhibitions from major museums open to the public.
Library: Open to the public. Holdings: Vols 2000; slide library for student and faculty use only.

TENNESSEE BOTANICAL GARDENS AND FINE ARTS CENTER, INC, Cheekwood, Cheek Road, 37205. Tel: 615-352-5310. *Exec Dir* Julia C Haworth; *Garden Dir* P Duncan Callicott; *Asst Garden Dir* Richard C Page; *Horticulturist* Randall E Lantz; *Dir Fine Arts Center* John Henry Nozynski; *Cur Educ* Roberta Mathews; *Registrar* Dianne Gannaway; *Exhibit Designer* David Moore; *Pres* Albert Werthan; *VPres* Dr Charles Wells; *Secy* Mrs George Green, Jr.

Open Tues - Sat 10 AM - 5 PM; Sun 1 - 5 PM; cl Mon. Admis adults $2, students 7-17 $1; children under 6 free. Estab 1957, the Fine Arts Center is in a Mansion; the Botanic Hall was built in 1971. Main galleries for major exhibitions; Mary Cheek Hill Gallery for smaller exhibitions; Nashville Artist Guild holds members shows; Permanent Collection Gallery. Mem: 5000; dues $20.
Income: Financed by membership and private donation.
Collections: American artists.
Publications: Newsletter, monthly; Trees of Christmas (book).
Activities: Classes for adults and children; dramatic programs; docent training; lect open to public and members, 6 - 10 vis lectr per yr; gallery talks; individual paintings and original objects of art lent to museums and corporations; lending collection contains original art works, paintings and sculpture; traveling exhibitions organized and circulated; sales shop selling books, original art, prints and film strips.
Library: Botanic Hall Library. Open to staff and members for reference. Holdings: Vols 5000; Per subs 45. Special Collections: Extensive snuff bottle collection.

TENNESSEE HISTORICAL SOCIETY,* 403 Seventh Ave, N, 37219. Tel: 615-741-2660. *Pres* Walter T Durham.
Open Mon - Sat 8 Am - 4:30 PM; cl National holidays. No admis. Estab 1849. Mem: Dues active $5, life $100.
Collections: Paintings, some contemporary.
Publications: Tennessee Historical Quarterly; History Imprints, eight times per year.
Activities: Guided tours; temporary exhibitions.
Library: Small collection of books and manuscripts.

TENNESSEE STATE MUSEUM, War Memorial Bldg, 37219. Tel: 615-741-2692. *Dir* Dr Ellsworth Brown, *Admin Asst* Dancy Jones; *Cur of Coll* Peter LaPaglia; *Chief Researcher* Dr James Kelly; *Chief of Exhibits* Charles Baker; *Cur of Educ* Lois Riggins; *Coordinator of Museum Information* Debby Dale Mason; *Coordinator of Tenn State Museum Association Inc* Marti Rosenberg; *Coordinator of Museum Development* John Buchanan; *Cur of Military History* William Baker.
Open Sun & Mon 1 - 5 PM; Tues - Sat 9 Am - 5 PM; cl Christmas, Easter, Thanksgiving, New Year's Day. No admis. Estab. 1937 to preserve and interpret the historical artifacts of Tennessee through museum exhibits and statewide outreach and educational programs. In summer of 1978, the present museum will start to be converted into a military branch of the main museum which opens in 1981, and will be in a multimillion dollar facility. Average Annual Attendance: 500,000.
Income: Financed by state appropriation.
Collections: The Tennessee State Museum holds in trust the collection of the Tennessee Historical Society as well as protraits and paintings of and by prominent Tennesseans. †There is also a large collection of military artifacts dating from the Revolutionary War through the Second World War.
Publications: Museum/Museum Association newsletter to be published in the late spring, quarterly.
Activities: Classes for adults and children, docent training; lect open to the public, exten dept serving statewide; Museum on Wheels (trailer) to travel across the state; museum shop selling books, Tennessee crafts, items relating to the collection.

VANDERBILT UNIVERSITY, Art Gallery, Department of Fine Arts, West End Ave at 23rd (Mailing Add: Box 1801-B, 37235). Tel: 615-322-2831. *Chmn* Prof F Hamilton Hazlehurst; *Gallery Dir* Prof Lamar Lynes.
Open Mon - Fri 1 - 4 PM; Sat & Sun 1 - 5 PM. No admis. Estab collection 1956, gallery 1961, to provide exhibitions for the University and Nashville communities, and original art works for study by Vanderbilt students; the gallery is included in a building of 1880 which is on the National Register of Historic Places. Mem: 300; dues $5 - $500.
Income: Financed by university resources.
Collections: Anna C Hoyt Collection of Old Master prints; Harold P. Stern Collectin of Oriental art; †the collection is representative of Western, Eastern, Ancient and Modern cultures.
Exhibitions: Howard Thomas - The Transitional Works, 1950-1954; Works by American Artists from the permanent Collection; Arts of Asia (from the Permanent Collection); American Twentieth Century Folk Art; Egypt to Expressionism (sculpture from the Permanent Collection); American Media - Roads to Experience; Drawings and Paintings by Barry Buxkamper; Two and Three Dimensional drawings by Margaret Koscielny; Prints from the Wichita Falls Museum; Paintings and Drawings by Werner Wildner; Selection from the Permanent Collection; Works by Lamar Lynes; Paperworks by Richard Duncan.
Activities: Lect open to members only.

WATKINS INSTITUTE,* Sixth Ave at Church St, 37219. Tel: 615-242-1851. *Dir* C H Sargent; *Art Dir* Anton Weiss; *Exec Secy* Dorris Stone.

Open 8 AM - 9:30 PM. No admis. Estab 1885 as an adult education center for art, home economics, business education, adult evening high school, and courses of a general nature.
Income: Rent from business property is source of income.
Collections: All-State artist collection (oldest collection of Tennessee art in the state); this is a purchase-award collection, oil, pastels, watercolors, graphics, and sculpture; several other collections of lesser value.
Exhibitions: Six or eight per year.
Publications: Quarterly catalog listing courses; art brochure.
Activities: Traveling exhibitions organized and circulated; individual paintings lent to schools; original objects of art lent; lect open to public, 6 or 8 vis lectrs per yr; classes for adults and children; competitions.
Library: Holdings—Vols 20,000.

OAK RIDGE

OAK RIDGE COMMUNITY ART CENTER, (Mailing Add: PO Box 105, 37830). Tel: 615-482-1182. *Dir* Jewel Stallions; *Pres* Kurt Kraus.
Open Mon - Fri 9 AM - 4 PM; Sat - Sun 2 - 5 PM. No admis. Estab 1952 to help fulfill the cultural needs of the community and encourage enjoyment and understanding of the arts. Mem: 700; dues individual $11, family $16.
Income: $30,000 (financed by membership).
Collections: The Mary and Alden Gomez Collection.
Publications: Bulletin, monthly.
Activities: Classes for adults and children; lect open to public; competitions; sales shop selling books, magazines, original art prints and slides.
Library: Librn Gen Stoughton. Open to members for reference.

SEWANEE

UNIVERSITY OF THE SOUTH GALLERY OF FINE ARTS,* Guerry Hall, 37375. Tel: 615-598-5917. *Dir* Dr Edward Carlos; *Asst Dir* Georgia Quimtard Joyner.
Open daily 2 - 5 PM except holidays and non-university sessions. Art Gallery estab 1938; monthly exhibitions during school year, 2 - 4 per month, changing shows; two lectures per year; tours regularly by request. Museum chambers estab 1972. Average Annual Attendance: 5000 - 6000.
Collections: Period rooms; paintings; prints; drawings; furniture and artifacts; sculpture; photography.

TULLAHOMA

TULLAHOMA FINE ARTS CENTER, 401 S Jackson, 37388. Tel: 615-455-9294. *Pres Bd* Jerry Spurlin; *Treas* Malde Ray; *Recording Secy* Rose Jordan; *Corresp Secy* Lois Heald; *Art Dir & Gen Mgr* Dana Lanier.
Open Tues & Thurs Noon - 4 PM; Wed 2 - 4 PM; Fri 9 AM - 1 PM; Sun 2 - 5 PM. No admis. Estab 1968 to increase the awareness of art in the community and to enrich the art experience of the individual member. Four gallery spaces; the building is a converted house. Mem: 200; dues $10; meetings each month.
Income: $5000 (financed by membership and fund-raising activities).
Collections: Just beginning a permanent collection of paintings and two-dimensional works by area artists.
Publications: Newsletter, monthly.
Activities: Classes for adults and children; lect open to public, 3 vis lectr per yr; concerts; competitions.

TEXAS

ABILENE

ABILENE FINE ARTS MUSEUM, Box 1858, 79604. Tel: 915-673-4587. *Pres* Eddie Boykin; *VPres* Eleanor Hoppe; *VPres* John Weeks; *Treas* Wes Shaver; *Dir* Chet Kwiecinski.
Open Tues - Fri 9 AM - 5 PM; Sat & Sun 1 - 5 PM, cl Mon. No admis. Estab 1937 as an art and history education institution; two galleries and gift shop, built in 1964, cover approximately 5000 sq ft. Average Annual Attendance: 25,000. Mem: 800; dues $15 and up; monthly 3rd Wed.
Income: $42,000 (financed by membership).
Collections: American paintings and prints.
Exhibitions: Regional and national exhibits; Blaffer Foundation Show of Modern Expressionism.
Publications: Newsletter, monthly.

Activities: Classes for adults and children; docent training; lect open to the public; gallery talks; tours; competitions; individual paintings and original objects of art lent to local civic and business organizations; lending collection contains paintings; sales shop selling original art, reproductions, prints.

McMURRY COLLEGE, Ryan Fine Arts Center, Sayles Blvd (Mailing Add: Box 8, 79605). Tel: 915-692-4130, exten 307. *Dept Chmn & Gallery Dir* Sherwood E Suter.
Open Mon - Fri 8 AM - 5 PM, cl Sat & Sun (open some Sun 2 - 5 PM for Opening Receptions). No admis. Estab 1970 when building was completed; large room overlooking larger sculpture garden. Average Annual Attendance: 2500.
Income: Financed by college art budget.
Collections: Artists represented include Picasso, Jack Levine, Adolph Dehn, Frelander.
Exhibitions: (1976-77) Senior Student Solo Shows; American Watercolor Society Traveling Shows; Clint Stokes (Ft. Worth watercolor painter); Boyd Graham (Abilene painter); West Texas Photographic Society.
Activities: Classes for adults; lect open to the public; gallery talks; competitions; individual paintings and original objects of art lent to college offices; lending collection contains color reproductions and slides.

AMARILLO

AMARILLO ART CENTER, 2200 S Van Buren (Mailing Add: PO Box 447, 79178). Tel: 806-372-8356. *Dir* Thomas A Livesay; *Cur of Art* Jerry M Daviee; *Cur of Educ* David Turner; *Bus Mgr* Emma Avara; *Admin Asst* Gail Gilbert, *Sales Gallery Mgr* Jennifer Clark Shields; *Asst Sales Gallery Mgr* Ursula Muntz.
Open Tues - Fri 10 AM - 5 PM; Sat & Sun 1 - 5 PM; Wed eve 7 - 9 PM. No admis. Estab 1972 for cultural enrichment and education in the visual arts; Gallery 100, 90 x 30 ft, atrium area 45 ft; Gallery 200 & 203, 90 x 32 ft, 11 ft ceiling; Gallery 305 & 307, each 32 x 28ft, 10 ft ceiling. Average Annual Attendance: 100,000.
Income: $177,000 (financed by membersip and college).
Collections: American Images, a collection of Farm Security Administration (FSA) photographs.
Exhibitions: (1976-1978) Gaston Lachaise; Charles Burchfield; The Amarillo Competition; Art between the Wars (1919 - 1940); The American Quilt (catalog); The Young Texas Artists Series (15 one-person exhibits cosponsored by the Texas Commission on the Arts & Humanities); the Thomas Cranfield Collection of Japanese Prints; Jewelry by Peter Carl Fabrege.
Publications: Calendar of Events, bimonthly; catalogs on exhibits, brochures, as needed.
Activities: Classes for adults; lect open to the public; 10 vis lectr per yr; gallery talks; tours; competitions; traveling exhibitions organized and circulated; museum shop selling books, magazines, original art, reproductions, prints.
Library: Open to the public, for reference only. Holdings: Vols 5000, Per subs 14.
—Amarillo Art Center Association. *Chmn of the Bd of Trustees,* Robert R Hucker; *VPres* George Quarterman; *Secy* Barbara Rudd.
Open Tues - Fri 10 AM - 5 PM; Sat & Sun 1 - 5 PM; Wed eve 7 - 9:30 PM. Estab 1972 to provide quality visual and performing arts to the Texas Panhandle. Mem: 1200; dues student $5, single $15, family $25, others $50 - $5000.
Income: Financed by endowment, membership and Amarillo College funds.
Activities: Classes for adults and children; docent training; Classes in Art Appreciation and Film Appreciation; lect open to the public, 10 vis lectr per yr; concerts; gallery talks; tours; individual paints and original objects of art lent to other institutions; traveling exhibitions organized and circulated.

ARLINGTON

UNIVERSITY OF TEXAS AT ARLINGTON, University Art Gallery. Fine Arts Building, 76019. Tel: 817-273-2891. *Dir* Max W Sullivan; *Secy/Registrar* Sherry R Dunaway.
Open Mon - Fri 9 AM - 4 PM; Sun 1 - 4 PM; cl Sat and major holidays. No admis. Estab 1975 on completion of Fine Arts Complex, the Gallery serves the entire university; exhibitions draw on all cultures and all periods; Main and Mezzanine Galleries are air cooled, carpeted, fabric wall covered with incandescent light. Average Annual Attendance: 1500.
Income: $43,000 (financed by state appropriation and private gifts).
Collections: Very small collection mainly American and Contemporary.
Exhibitions: (1976-77) Andy Anderson: Still Photography; Women in Art Exhibition and Festival; Prints and Drawings from the Fort Worth Art Museum Collection; Faculty Projects, School of Architecture; Lee Boltin: The Photographer of the Museum; Metal Sculptures from West Africa; Bruce Cunningham: Recent Paintings and Drawings; Contempo-

rary Crafts-Clay & Metal; The Sensuous Line; Sandra Rubin: Column Reflections; Palladio in America.
Activities: Docent training; undergraduate course on Museum Techniques; lect open to the public, 3 vis lect per yr; catalogs on sale.

AUSTIN

LAGUNA GLORIA ART MUSEUM, 3809 W 35th St (Mailing Add: PO Box 5568, 78763). Tel: 512-458-8192. *Dir* Laurence Miller; *Dir Prog* Judith Sims; *Dir Admin* Robert Lester.
Open Mon - Sat 10 AM - 5 PM; Thurs 10 AM - 9 PM; Sun 1 - 5 PM. No admis. Estab 1961 as a community art museum devoted to changing exhibitions of 20th century American art. Mediterranean-style villa converted into art museum; on 24 acres of landscaped grounds. Three galleries downstairs, one upstairs. Average Annual Attendance: 80,000. Mem: 600; dues $25 and up; annual meeting Oct.
Income: $425,000 (financed by endowment, membership, city and state appropriations, earned income).
Exhibitions: Varied exhibitions from national and regional sources; annual Arts and Crafts Fiesta in May.
Publications: Newsletter, quarterly; catalogs, occasionally.
Activities: Classes for adults and children; docent training; lect open to public, 8 vis lectr per yr; concerts; gallery talks; tours; competitions; exten dept serving Travis County; traveling exhibitions organized and circulated; museum shop selling prints, and area crafts.
Library: Open for reference to art school instructors, and staff.

ELIZABET NEY MUSEUM, 304 E 44th, 78751. Tel: 512-454-1762. *Dir* James Fisher; *Cur* Sarah Bolz; *Cur* Terence Keane; *Specialist* Willie Nunn.
Open Tues - Fri 11 AM - 4:30 PM, Sat - Sun 2 - 4:30 PM. No admis. Estab 1909 for the preservation and promotion of Elizabet Ney's works, studio and historical importance through relevant educational interpretation. Eclectic limestone "castle", one of four 19th century American sculpture studios to survive intact with its contents. Average Annual Attendance: 12,000.
Income: $48,0000 (financed by city appropriation).
Collections: Works of Elizabet Ney in the form of original plaster casts, supplemented by bronze and marble works and tools, furnishings and memorabilia.
Publications: Sursum (annotated letters of Elizabet Ney).
Activities: Classes for adults and children; lect open to public, 1 vis lectr per yr; concerts; gallery talks; tours; original objects of art lent to museums; museum shop selling books and stationary.
Library: Open to public for reference. Holdings: Vols 300. Special Subjects: Books relevant to Elizabet Ney and her time.

ST EDWARD'S UNIVERSITY,* Fine Arts Exhibit Program, 78704. Tel: 512-444-2624, exten 316. *Dir Fine Arts Exhibit Prog* Brother Hilarion Brezik.
Open weekdays 8 AM - 6 PM; Sun 1 - 5 PM. No admis. Estab 1961 to present for the university population and general public a monthly schedule of exhibits in the visual arts as a means of orientation toward established and current trends in art styles in terms of their historical-cultural significance and aesthetic value, through teaching exhibitions, art films, public and private collections from distributing and compiling agencies, museums, galleries, artists. Average Annual Attendance: 10,000.
Income: $4000-$6000. Purchases: $300-$400.
Exhibitions: Annual faculty and art student exhibitions.
Activities: Tours; lectures; one vis lectr per yr; classes; literature.
Library: Holdings—Vols over 2000 for lending and reference.

UNIVERSITY OF TEXAS AT AUSTIN, Art Library, 23rd at San Jacinto, 78712. Tel: 512-471-1636. *Librn* Joyce Hess.
Open Mon - Thurs 8 AM - 10 PM; Fri 8 AM - 5 PM; Sat 10 AM - 4 PM; Sun 2 - 6 PM. Estab 1948 to support teaching and research to the PhD level in art history, and to the master's level in art education and studio art. Circ: 136,455 (1976-77).
Income: Financed by state appropriation.
Holdings: Vols 36,500; Per subs 380; AV—Microfiche, microfilm; Other—Clipping files, exhibition catalogs, pamphlets, reproductions.
—Art Museum, 23rd & San Jacinto Sts, 78705. Tel: 512-471-7324. *Dir* Donald B Goodall; *Cur* Marian B Davis.
Open Mon - Sat 9 AM - 6 PM; Sun 1 - 5 PM; cl school holidays. No admis. Estab 1963.
Collections: Michener Collection of 20th century American paintings; Latin American paintings and drawings; prints; etchings; woodcuts; engravings; the Barbara Duncan Collection.
Publications: Bulletin for exhibitions; catalogs.
Activities: Classes for adults and children; lectures; gallery talks; guided tours; temporary and traveling exhibitions.

BANDERA

FRONTIER TIMES MUSEUM,* PO Box 313, 78003. Tel: 512-796-3864. *Pres* Sandra Doane Turk; *Cur & Mgr* Mrs E B Batto.
Open daily 10 - 12 AM, 1 - 4:30 PM; cl Mon; admis 25¢ ten yrs and over, children must be accompanied by an adult. Estab 1933 to preserve records, photographs, and artifacts of the American West with emphasis on those of the local Texas hill country area. Average Annual Attendance: 6500. Mem: 17; no dues; meetings 3 times a yr.
Income: $10,000 (financed by endowment).
Collections: F B Doane Collection of Western paintings; Louisa Gordon Collection of antiques, including bells from around the world; J Marvin Hunter Collection of photographs, artifacts, memorabilia of American West and the Texas hill country, and many rare items.
Exhibitions: Occasional one-man shows by Texas artists whose work coincides with the theme of the museum.
Activities: Photograph collection. Book shop.

BEAUMONT

BEAUMONT ART MUSEUM, 1111 Ninth St, 77702. Tel: 713-832-3432. *Pres* Patrick E Boyt; *First VPres* Ralph Leaf; *Second VPres* Charles V Hill; *Secy* Mrs Peter Wells; *Treas* Thomas A Page; *Dir* Betty W Hirsch; *Asst to the Dir* Mrs Harrison Baier; *Registrar* Yvonne Craig.
Open Tues - Fri 10 AM - 5 PM; Sat & Sun 2 - 5 PM; cl Mon and holidays. No admis. Estab 1950 as a non-profit community-owned institution chartered to serve the community-at-large through education, cultural enrichment and aesthetic enjoyment activities. The Museum has 2785 sq ft of exhibition space, three galleries downstairs devoted to temporary exhibitions which change monthly, and three galleries upstairs devoted to permanent collection. Average Annual Attendance: 40,000. Mem: 1200; dues $20 - $500; annual meeting May.
Income: $169,290 (1977-78) (financed by endowment, membership, city and state appropriation, Kaleidoscope and grants).
Collections: †20th century Texas and American painting, sculpture, graphics; 19th century decorative arts; Eskimo and Thai prehistoric artifacts; photography.
Exhibitions: Biennial Invitational Exhibition of Texas Artists; Southeast Texas Photography Competition; changing exhibitions monthly in painting, sculpture, graphics, decorative arts, and archaeology.
Publications: Newsletter, bi-monthly.
Activities: Classes for adults and children; extensive in-school education program with slide classes; monthly slide lectures for 8th grade American history classes; monthly seminars for high school classes; lect open to the public, and some for members only; gallery talks, tours; traveling exhibitions organized and circulated; museum shop selling books, original art, reproductions, original jewelry, pottery, handcrafted items.
Library: Tel: 713-832-3432. *Registrar* Yvonne Craig. Open to staff and docents for reference only. Holdings: Vols 800; Per subs 37; Other—Art history slides 6500.

BEAUMONT ARTS COUNCIL, 3360 Beard St, 77703. Tel: 713-892-0336. *Co-Chmn* Mrs Burton Doiron.
Estab 1969 to foster total esthetic involvement in the community and improved communications among cultural organizations. Annual meeting in spring and fall.
Activities: Sponsored forum for city election candidates to discuss their attitudes toward cultural environment.

BROWNSVILLE

BROWNSVILLE ART LEAGUE MUSEUM, Neale Dr, 78520. Tel: 512-542-0941.
Open Mon - Sat 9:30 AM - 4 PM; Sun 2 - 4 PM. No admis. Estab Jan 1977 for the preservation of valuable collection. Mem: 125.
Income: Financed by endowment.
Collections: Miscellaneous collection of fine art, all media.
Exhibitions: Arts and Crafts; International Art Show.
Publications: Brush Strokes, six times a year.
Activities: Classes for adults; individual paintings lent.
Library maintained.

BUCHANAN DAM

BUCHANAN ARTS AND CRAFTS INC, Highway 29, 78609. Tel: 512-793-2858. *Chmn of Board* Alice Reese; *Pres* Alma Howerts; *Treas* Neloise Cooper; *Secy* Bea Golladay.
Open Mon - Sat 10 AM - 5 PM; Sun 1 - 5 PM. No admis. Estab 1963 to increase interest in our community; own building, approx 1800 ft floor space. Average Attendance: Weekdays 10, Sun 20-30, at Art Shows 500-600. Mem: 52, assoc mem, 5; dues $25; meeting second Tues monthly.
Income: Financed by membership.

Exhibitions: Monthly exhibitions in Burnet First State Bank, Burnet, Texas; Blue Bonnet Trail Exhibit; Aqua Festival; Highland Lakes Arts & Crafts Trail in October.
Activities: Classes for adults; lect open to the public; sales shop selling original art.

CANYON

PANHANDLE-PLAINS HISTORICAL SOCIETY MUSEUM,* 2401 Fourth Ave, 79015. Tel: 806-655-2567. *Dir* Dr James A Hanson; *Asst Dir* Jack Downing; *Cur Art* Olive Vandruff Bugbee; *Cur Anthropology* B R Harrison; *Exhib Designer* Carol Cline.
Open weekdays 9 AM - 5 PM; Sun 2 - 6 PM; cl holidays. No admis. Estab 1921 to preserve history of the region, including all phases of history, fine arts and natural sciences. Average Annual Attendance: 125,000. Mem: 1000; dues $5 and higher; annual meeting May.
Collections: Over 1300 paintings by early and contemporary American painters.
Exhibitions: Exhibitions normally changed monthly.
Publications: Panhandle-Plains Historical Review, annually.
Library: *Archivist & Librn* Claire Kuehn. Reference library. Holdings: Vols 10,000; Other—Photograph collection of 2000 prints.

COMMERCE

EAST TEXAS STATE UNIVERSITY, Little Gallery, Art Department, 75428. Tel: 214-468-2216. *Dir* Charles McGough.
Open Mon - Fri 9 AM - 5 PM. No admis. Estab 1977 to house all student exhibitions; 9-month exhibition calendar of exchange and traveling shows; gallery 55 x 69 ft.
Income: Financed by state appropriation.
Collections: Collection of student work.
Activities: Lect open to the public, 30 vis lectr per yr; gallery talks; tours; competitions; individual paintings and original object of art lent to regional citizens; traveling exhibitions organized and circulated; sales shop selling original art.

CORPUS CHRISTI

ART MUSEUM OF SOUTH TEXAS, 1902 N Shoreline (Mailing Add: PO Box 1010, 78403). Tel: 512-884-3844. *Dir* Cathleen S Gallander; *Business Mgr* Linda B Walker.
Open Tues - Sat 10 AM - 5 PM; Sun 1 - 5 PM. Admis adults 50¢; children 25¢. Estab 1960 as a non-profit organization offering a wide range of programs to the South Texas community in an effort to fulfill its stated purpose to stimulate and encourage the fullest possible understanding and appreciation of the fine arts in all forms. A large central area, the Great Hall, and a small gallery. The sky-lighted Upper Gallery on the second floor level has over 1900 sq ft of space. Average Annual Attendance: 100,873. Mem: 1297; dues $25.
Income: $479,009 (financed by membership, city and state appropriations, school district). Purchases: $318,010.
Collections: Works on Paper (permanent drawing collection).
Exhibitions: 18th & 19th Century American Paintings; Texas Architectural Survey; Light Pieces by Boyd Mefford; Bill Wiman: One-man Show; Naives and Visionaries; Navajo Pictorial Weaving; Larry Bell: Iceberg and Its Shadow; Louis Eugene Boudin; Winslow Homer's Work in Black and White; Sculpture by Donald Judd; Antwerp Prints and Drawings; Les Lalannes; 100 Master Photographs; Corpus Christi Art Foundation Show; African Textiles; Goya: Los Desastres de la Guerra; Folk Arts and Crafts: The Deep South; Etchings by Rembrandt and His Followers.
Activities: Classes for adults and children; dramatic programs; lect open to public, 4 vis lectr per yr; gallery talks; tours; competitions traveling exhibitions organized and circulated; museum shop selling books, magazines, reproductions, prints.
Library: *Librn* Melinda M Mayer. Open to public for reference.

DEL MAR COLLEGE, Department of Art Gallery, Baldwin at Ayers, 78404. Tel: 512-881-6216. *Chmn* Joseph A Cain.
Open Mon - Fri 8 AM - 9:30 PM. No admis. Estab 1932 to teach art and provide exhibition showcase for college and community; gallery consists of over 200 running feet space, plus other smaller areas.
Income: Financed by city and state appropriation.
Collections: Purchases from Annual National Drawings and Small Sculpture Show; art donations.
Exhibitions: Regular schedule of local and traveling shows from Sept to May; National Drawings and Small Sculpture Show in May.

SOUTH TEXAS ARTMOBILE, PO Box 8183, 78412. Tel: 512-888-7352, 991-4347. *Dir* Maudmae E Eldridge; *Cur (Traveling with Artmobile)* Vacant.

Open during school hours, during school year. No admis. Estab January 1969 to take original works of art to the people throughout South Texas who would not have the opportunity to see art of this calibre; also where there are no musuems available. Average Annual Attendance: 35,000.
Income: Financed by Dougherty Carr Arts Foundation.
Collections: European period.
Exhibitions: (1976) Realist Tradition in American painting: Elliott, Bierstadt, Moran, Luks, Hirst, Dewing, Lawson, Levine, O'Keefe, Cook, Valerio Alo, McLean, Anonymous - Mary Jaquelin, Tea Time, Pansies. (1977-78) Charles C Curran (one-man show).
Publications: Handbook; Catalog of each exhibit, yearly.
Activities: Dramatic programs; docent training; slide lectures; lect open to the public; concerts; slides sold.
Library. Open to Artmobile staff only. Holdings: Vols 30; Per subs 6.

DALLAS

DALLAS HISTORICAL SOCIETY, Hall of State, Fair Park, (Mailing Add: PO Box 26038, 75226). Tel: 214-421-5136. *Dir* John W Crain; *Business Mgr* Jan Upton; *Cur of History* Lonn W Taylor; *Educ Coordinator* Cosy McLemore; *Asst to Dir* Kay Pledger.
Open Mon - Sat 9 AM - 5 PM. No admis. Estab 1922 to collect and preserve materials relative to the history of the Southwest, Texas and particularly Dallas. Average Annual Attendance: 120,000. Mem: 1050; annual meeting May.
Income: Financed by membership, city appropriation.
Exhibitions: Centennial Curiosities; Fifty-five Years: A Survey of the Dallas Historical Society's Collections; John Knott Cartoons; John H Reagan: A Photographic Essay; Photographs of Grimes County, Texas; The American Farm; Peter Mansbendel: A Swiss Woodcarver in Texas.
Publications: Dallas Historical Society Report (newsletter), quarterly.
Activities: Docent training; In-class programs, story time; lect open to the public, 4 vis lectr per yr; gallery talks; individual paintings and original objects of art lent to other museums only.
—**Research Center Library.** Tel: 214-421-5136. *Dir* John W Crain.
Open to the public for reference only.
Holdings: Vols 10,000; Other—Archives, pages 2,000,000.
Special Collections: Robert M Hayes Photographic Collection of Texas historic sites.

DALLAS MUSEUM OF FINE ARTS, Fair Park (Mailing Add: PO Box 26250, 75226). Tel: 214-421-4187. *Dir* Harry S Parker; *Asst Dir Admin* Eugene W Mitchell; *Cur* John Lunsford; *Cur Contemporary Art* Robert M Murdock; *Cur Exhib* Barney Delabano.
Open Mon - Sat 10 AM - 5 PM; Sun 1 - 5 PM; cl Mon. No admis. Estab 1903 to purchase and borrow works of art from all periods for the aesthetic enjoyment and education of the public. Fifteen galleries for permanent collection; five for temporary exhibition. Average Annual Attendance: 350,000. Mem: 4000; dues $25 - $1000; annual meeting May.
Income: $2,000,000 (financed by endowment, membership and city appropriation). Purchases: $1,000,000.
Collections: †Contemporary; †Pre-Columbian; †African; †American 19th century; †European 18th & 19th century.
Exhibitions: America: The Third Century; Irish Watercolors; Edvard Munch; Texas Painting and Sculpture Competition and Invitational; Santos; Renaissance Prints; Berlin/Hanover: The 1920's; Titian and the Venetian Woodcut; Two Centuries of Black American Art; Translations; Salvages and Pop-ups by Jess; The Face of Egypt; New Photographs and Prints; Calder's Universe.
Publications: Newsletter, bimonthly; annual report.
Activities: Classes for children; docent training; lect open to public, 10 vis lectr per yr; concerts; gallery talks; tours; competitions; exten dept serving Dallas County; artmobile; museum shop selling books, magazines; original art; reproductions, prints and slides.
—**Library.** *Librn* Fred Mitcham.
Open to the public for reference.
Holdings: Vols 14,000; Per subs 30; Other—Exhibition catalogs.

DALLAS PUBLIC LIBRARY, Fine Arts Division, 1954 Commerce St, 75201. Tel: 214-748-9071. *Div Head* George Henderson; *Art Librn* Chester Haddaway; *Theatre Librn* Robert Eason; *Music Librn* James Calhoun; *Recordings Librn* Donna Mendro.
Open Mon - Fri 9 AM - 9 PM; Sat 9 AM - 6 PM. Estab to furnish the citizens of Dallas materials and information concerning the arts.
Income: Approx $60,000 (financed by city appropriation).
Holdings: Vols 40,000; Per subs 500; AV—Phonorecords; Other—Clipping files, exhibition catalogs, framed reproductions, manuscripts, memorabilia, original art works, pamphlets, photographs, prints.
Special Collections: Margo Jones Theater Collection; Manuscript Archives (music); Lawrence Kelly Collection of Dallas Civic Opera Set and Costume Designs; W E Hill Collection (History of American Theater); original print collection.

Activities: Tours.
—**Dallas Print and Drawing Society,** 1954 Commerce St, 75201. Tel: 214-748-9071. *Pres* Jane Rose Sallis, *VPres* Mike L Hulme, *Secy* P Bush Elkin.
Estab 1935 to study history, techniques and to collect prints and drawings. Mem: 75; annual dues $10; meeting six times per yr.
Income: Approx $1000 (financed by membership and income from legacy). Purchases: $250 - $500.
Activities: Lect open to the public, 5 - 6 vis lectr per yr.

SOUTHERN METHODIST UNIVERSITY
—**University Gallery,** 75275. Tel: 214-692-2516. *Chmn Exhib Comt* William B Jordan.
Open Mon - Sat 10 AM - 5 PM; Sun 1 - 5 PM. No admis. The exhibitions scheduled in the gallery are primarily for the purpose of study and the committee selects them according to the needs of the classes. A one-room gallery with movable walls used for changing exhibitions. Average Annual Attendance: 10,000.
Income: Financed through the University.
Exhibitions: Jerry Bywaters Retrospective; Paintings from the Dallas Museum of Fine Arts Storage; Drawing Today in New York; Twelve Contemporary Painters; Andy Warhol 'Athletes'; Contemporary Prints from Dallas-Fort Worth Collections; Faculty Show and Graduate Student MFS Qualifying Exhibitions.
Library: Art Library. *Librn* Helen Lawrence. Open to the public for reference and research.
—**Meadows Museum.** *Dir* William B Jordan; *Asst to Dir* Irene Martin; *Cur Educ* Nancy Berry.
Open Mon - Sat 10 AM - 5 PM; Sun 1 - 5 PM. No admis. Estab 1965 to preserve and study the art of Spain. Average Annual Attendance: 15,000.
Income: Financed by endowment.
Collections: Spanish paintings from late Gothic to modern including works by Juan de Borgona, Velazquez, Murillo, Zurbaran, Ribera, Goya, Miro, Juan Gris, and Picasso.
Activities: Educ dept; docent training; scholarships; lect open to public.
Library: Meadows Collection Fine Arts Library. Open for reference to scholars.
Special Subjects: Spanish art.
—**Pollock Galleries,** * Owen Arts Center, 75222. Tel: 214-692-2489. *Dir* William A Robinson.
Open Mon - Sat 9 AM - 5 PM; Sun 1 - 5 PM. No admis. Estab 1965 to present monthly exhibitions of art in all media of interest to the University and to the community. Four large galleries. Average Annual Attendance: 110,000.
Income: Financed by special funds.
Collections: Contemporary American and European art.
Publications: Exhibition catalogs.
Activities: Lect open to public, 4 vis lectr per yr; gallery talks; tours; concerts; original objects of art lent; traveling exhibitions organized and circulated; sales shop selling exhibition catalogs.

DENTON

NORTH TEXAS STATE UNIVERSITY, Art Gallery, Mulberry and Ave A (Mailing Add: North Texas Box 5098, 76203). Tel: 817-788-2071. *Gallery Dir* C Kenneth Havis.
Open Mon - Fri Noon - 5 PM. No admis. Estab 1960 as a teaching gallery directed to students of North Texas State University and the Denton community; the gallery covers 193 running ft of exhibition wall space, approximately 10 ft high, which may be divided into smaller spaces by the use of semi-permanent portable walls; the floor is carpeted/terrazzo. Average Annual Attendance: 8000.
Income: $4000 (financed by state appropriation). Purchases: $1250.
Collections: Fashion collection; permanent collection; †permanent student collection; †Voertman Collection (student purchases).
Exhibitions: (1976-77) Faculty Exhibition; Jim Johnson and Rob Erdle (recent watercolors); Three Artists: Three Points of View (Janet Fish, Ree Morton, Deborah Remington); MFA Graduate Exhibition of Cecila Feld; NTSU Invitational Artists Biennial Winners at the New Orleans Museum of Fine Arts-C Kenneth Havis, James Hill, O W "Pappy" Kitchens, Michael Kostiuk, Russ Warren, Edward Whiteman; MFA Graduate Exhibition of Gail Spring (photography); Tom Glover (ceramics), Dianne Kirk (fibers); Annual Student and Faculty Artwork Christmas Sale; Northern Renaissance Prints from the Dallas Museum of Fine Arts; Luis Jimenez (sculptor); Design at North Texas State University Competitive Exhibition; Annual Voertman Awards, (1977-78) Prints from the Collection of the Wichita Falls Art Museum and Limited Edition Books and Broadsides by Sandi Fellman, John Risseeuw, Cathie Ruggie, Susan Wineberg, and Judy Youngblood; Master of Fine Arts Exhibition of Drawing and Painting by Catherine Hoge; Children's Art Exhibition; Exhibition by Andy Steinhauer, Lionell Glaze, and Dennis

O'Leary; MFA Exhibition; National Watercolor Society Traveling Exhibition; Nam June Paik (video); Design at North Texas State University competitive exhibition; Voertman Awards.
Publications: Exhibition announcements.
Activities: Lect open to the public, 4 - 8 vis lectr per yr; tours; competitions; individual paintings and original objects of art lent to the University offices.

TEXAS WOMAN'S UNIVERSITY ART GALLERIES, TWU Station, Box 22995, 72011. Tel: 817-382-8923. *Chmn, Dept of Art* Dr Donald E Smith; *Dir of Galleries* Mark S Smith.
Open 8:30 AM - 4:30 PM daily. No admis. Estab 1935 to exhibit art works for TWU students and the public at large; East and West Galleries contain over 1000 sq ft of exhibit area. Average Annual Attendance: 4000 - 5000.
Income: Financed by dept budget.
Collections: Japanese print collection; graphic art collection.
Exhibitions: Approx 20 exhibits per yr.
Activities: Classes for adults; workshops/travel to Europe/seminars, lect open to the public, 5 - 10 vis lectr per yr; gallery talks; tours; competitions.

EL PASO

EL PASO MUSEUM OF ART, 1211 Montana, 79902. Tel: 915-534-3800. *Dir* Leonard P Sipiora; *Senior Cur* William Rakocy; *Cur Educ* Patricia Davenport; *Asst Cur* Loretta Martin; *Cur Hist* Wanda Bell.
Open Tues - Sat 10 AM - 5 PM; Sun 1 - 5 PM; cl Mon. No admis. Estab 1960 as a cultural and educational institution; One gallery houses a permanent display of the Kress Collection; second gallery is used for monthly changing exhibits; Heritage Gallery has decorative arts from 18, 19th and 20th centuries. Average Annual Attendance: 80,000. Mem: 1036; meetings Jan, Mar, Apr, Sept, Nov.
Income: Financed by membership and city appropriation.
Collections: Kress Collection †Early American Impressionists; †Mexican colonials.
Exhibitions: Tenth Anniversary Members Guild Acquisitions Retablos; Reynolds Beal Show; Scholastic Art Awards; Ke Kaethe Kolwitz Graphics Show; Edvard Munch: Major Ra Graphics; Arthur Heinztleman Retrospective; Big Bend Photographs; The Glaser Collection; Bartolozzi: The Holbein Drawings; El Paso Art Association; Anschutz Collection of Western Paintings; Industry Paintings by Garrett Beneker; New Glory—Part II Flags; Sun Carnival Show—American Landscapes. Miller Collection of Retablos; Toys From Switzerland; Scholastic Arts Awards; Sissom; Winslow Homer; American Drawings 1976; El Paso Designer Craftsmen; Folk Woodcuts-Brazil; First Ladies of the White House; World Print Competition; McKee Foundation Collection of Western Art; A Decade of Gifts and Acquisitions; The Art of Edward Borein; A Blending of Cultures; The American Abstract Expressionist; Collection of the Sarah Campbell Blaffer Foundation.
Publications: Artline (newsletter), quarterly.
Activities: Classes for adults and children; dramatic programs; docent training; lect open to the public, 12 vis lectr per yr; concerts; gallery talks; tours; competitions; individual paintings and original objects of art lent to other museums on request; museum shop selling books, original art, reproductions, prints and replicas.
Library: Open to the public and members for reference only.
—**Cavalry Museum,** 12901 Gateway W, 79935.
Open daily 10 AM - 5 PM; cl Mon. Estab 1974 as a tribute to the mounted rider, who played a major role in the settling of the Southwest. The collections tell the story of the Indian, the conquistador, the vaquero, the cowboy and the United States Army Cavalryman.
Exhibitions: Moody Exhibition; Texas and Her Constitutions; Cisneros Drawings; Image of America in Caricature and Cartoon.
—**Wilderness Park Museum,** 2000 Trans Mountain Rd, 79924.
Estab 1977. Museum contains replica of Olla Cave and Mogollon cliff dwelling.
Collections: Five dioramas depict life styles and climate changes of Paleo Indians; the hunting and gathering era and the Jueco Tanks site.

UNIVERSITY OF TEXAS AT EL PASO,* Department of Art Galleries, 79968. Tel: 915-747-5181. *Chmn Dept* Clarke H Garnsey.
Department Studios and Galleries open Mon - Fri 8 AM - 5 PM. No admis. University estab 1916, Department of Art estab 1940.
Income: Financed by city and state appropriation.
Collections: Small Collection of prints from old and modern Masters, and growing collection of student works.
Exhibitions: Best of Show Exhibitions out of the Texas Fine Arts Association; annual student shows and faculty exhibitions.
Publications: Exhibition catalogs.

Activities: Classes for adults; lectures open to public; 2 - 4 gallery talks per year; 2 - 4 tours. Extension work is offered through the regular University Extension Service to anyone over high school age, variable fees.

FORT WORTH

AMON CARTER MUSEUM OF WESTERN ART, 3501 Camp Bowie Blvd (Mailing Add: PO Box 2365, 76101). Tel: 817-738-1933. *Pres* Ruth Carter Johnson; *Dir* Mitchell A Wilder; *Dir Educ* Dr John A Diffily; *Dir Publ & Cur History* Dr Ron Tyler; *Cur Paintings* Carol Clark; *Cur Photographic Coll* Marjorie Morey; *Registrar* Anne Adams.
Open Tues - Sat 10 AM - 5 PM; Sun & holidays 1 - 5:30 PM; cl Mon. No admis. Estab 1961 for the study and documentation of westering North America through permanent collections, exhibitions and publications. Main gallery plus ten smaller galleries. Average Annual Attendance: 110,000.
Income: Financed by endowment.
Collections: †American and Western American paintings and sculpture; †photographs; †print collection.
Exhibitions: The Face of Liberty, Founders of the United States; The Image of America in Caricature and Cartoon; The Bison in Art: A Graphic Chronicle of the American Bison; Ben Shahn, A Retrospective Exhibition.
Publications: Newsletter, nine times a year.
Activities: Docent training; produces films and TV cassettes; lect open to public, 12 vis lectr per yr; gallery talks; tours; individual paintings and original objects of art lent to museums; traveling exhibitions organized and circulated; museum shop selling books, magazines, reproductions, prints and slides.
—**Library.** *Librn* Nancy G Wynne.
Open to qualified researchers for reference.
Holdings: Vols 20,000; Per subs 132; Other—19th century newspapers on microfilm; Western Americana on microfilm.
Special Subjects: American history and art; American and Canadian history.
Special Collections: Exhibition catalogs (including the Knoedler Library on fiche).

FORT WORTH ART MUSEUM, 1309 Montgomery, 76107. Tel: 817-738-9215. *Dir* Jay Belloli; *Cur* Anne Livet; *Cur* Marge Goldwater; *Dir of Installations* Barry Whistler; *Registrar* Marcia Mendes.
Open Tues - Sat 10 AM - 5 PM; Sun 1 - 5 PM. No admis. Estab 1901 as a museum of 20th century art; five large galleries on the main floor. Average Annual Attendance: 92,000. Mem: 1200; dues $25, $100, $1000; annual meeting Oct.
Income: $673,816 (financed by membership, city and state appropriations, grants and acquisition trusts). Purchases $136,011.
Collections: 20th century paintings, sculpture, drawings and prints.
Exhibitions: (1976-78) North, East, West, South and Middle; Southwest/Tarrant County Annual 1976, 1977; Dan Flavin: Drawings, Diagrams and Prints from 1972 - 1975; Permanent Collection; A Tribute to Alvar Aalto; Robert Irwin; Continuing Responses; American Artists: A New Decade; The American Abstract Expressionist Collection of the Blaffer Foundation; A Television Exhibition: Rauschenberg, Tudor, Farber, Lucier; Texas Today: Three Exhibitions; Morris Louis: The Veil Cycle; America 1976; Dallas/Fort Worth Collectors; Rafael Ferrer: Valparaiso, Hotel Aubry; Los Angeles in the Seventies; Ed Ruscha and Allen Ruppersburg; The Record as Artwork; The Collection of Germano Celant; Danny Lyon; Photographs and Films; Stella Since 1970; Light on Fort Worth; The Modern Chair: Its Origins and Evolution.
Publications: Monthly calendar.
Activities: Classes for adults and children; docent training; lect open to the public, 10 - 20 vis lectr per yr; competitions; traveling exhibitions organized and circulated.
Library: Open to the public for reference only; specializing in 20th century art.

FORT WORTH PUBLIC LIBRARY,* Arts Department, 300 Taylor St, 76102. Tel: 817-335-4781, exten 34, *Dept Head* Miss Lirl Treuter; *Asst* Thomas K Threatt.
Open Mon - Fri 9 AM - 9 PM; Sat 9 AM - 6 PM; cl Sun. No admis. Estab 1902. Not a commercial gallery, but exhibit areas for framed and matted reproductions of paintings which are displayed and available for circulation to the public; also frequent small exhibits of original works and crafts.
Income: Financed by appropriation.
Holdings: Books; sheet music, music scores, tune cards, phonorecords; framed and matted reproductions of paintings; special files of clipped pictures, articles, pamphlets and programs.
Special Collections: Hal Coffman Collection of original cartoon art; Nancy Taylor Collection of bookplate; historic picture and photograph collection autographed by various celebrities.
Publications: Bibliographies and occasional catalogs.

Activities: Classes for adults; traveling exhibitions organized and circulated; 280 circulating reproductions; 150 photographs and 115 albums; also photograph collection for reference; competitions.

KIMBELL ART MUSEUM, Will Rogers Rd W (Mailing Add: PO Box 9440, 76107). Tel: 817-332-8451. *Pres* Kay Fortson; *Dir* Dr Richard F Brown; *Chief Cur* David M Robb, Jr; *Business Mgr* Andrew Resnick; *Conservator* Perry Huston.
Open Tues - Sat 10 AM - 5 PM; Sun 1 - 5 PM; Cl Mon, July 4, Thanksgiving, Christmas, New Years. No admis. Estab 1964, open to public 1972 for the collection, preservation, research, publication and public exhibition of art of all periods. Average Annual Attendance: 200,000.
Income: Financed by endowment.
Collections: Highly selective collection of European paintings, sculpture and graphic arts from Ancient to early 20th century; Asian sculpture, painting and ceramics; Pre-Columbian sculpture and ceramics; African sculpture.
Exhibitions: (1976) French Illustrated Books; The Wild Beast; Fauvism and its Affinities; (1977) The Last Empire; European Drawings from the Fitzwilliam Museum; 17th century Dutch Drawings from American Collections; The Tokugawa Collection: No Robes and Masks; Chinese Ceramics of Japanese Collections: Jazz (Henri Matisse); (1978) Silver for the Gods: 800 Years of Greek and Roman Silver; Louis I Kahn: Sketches for the Kimbell Art Museum.
Publications: Catalog of the collection; Light is the Theme; Handbook of the Collection.
Activities: Classes for children; docent training; lectr open to the public, 6 - 9 vis lectr per yr; concerts; gallery talks; tours; museum shop selling books, magazines and slides.
—**Library.** Tel: 817-332-8451. *Librn* Ilse S Rothrock.
Open by appointment to scholarly users for reference only.
Holdings: Vols 17,000; Per subs 90; Other—Slides 30,000.
Special Subjects: Art excepting American and Modern.

TEXAS CHRISTIAN UNIVERSITY, Student Center Gallery, Brown-Lupton Student Center, (Mailing Add: PO Box 292-80A, 76129). *Dir* Pat Crowley.
Open Mon - Sat 10 AM - 4 PM; Sun Noon - 4 PM. No admis. Estab to present the best art possible to the student body; to show faculty and student work; gallery consists of one large room, 30 x 40 ft, with additional moveable panels. Average Annual Attendance: 6000.
Income: $4800 (financed by college funds).
Exhibitions: Major Pop Artists of the 60s; Rafael Ferrer; Otis Jones: Recent Paintings and Works on Paper; David Conn: Recent Drawings and Multiples done with Crayons; Early Paintings of Jusepe de Ribera; Contemporary American Drawings; Art Students Annual Christmas Sale; Just before the War (photographs).
Publications: Only exhibition notes and mailers/posters.
Activities: Classes for adults; lect open to the public, 15 vis lectr per yr; gallery talks; competitions.

GALVESTON

ROSENBERG LIBRARY,* 2310 Sealy, 77550. Tel: 713-763-8854.
Librn John D Hyatt; *Public Services Dir* Frieda Sheel; *Cur Special Coll* Jane Kenamore; *Rare Bks Librn* Ruth Kelly.
Open Mon - Thurs 9 AM - 9 PM; Fri - Sat 9 AM - 6 PM; cl Sun & national holidays. No admis. Estab 1900 to provide library services to the people of Galveston, together with lectures, concerts, exhibitions. Library includes the Harris Art Gallery, The James M Lykes Maritime Gallery, The Hutchings Gallery, together with miscellaneous art and historical exhibit galleries and halls. Mem: 523; dues $5 - $100.
Income: $681,212 (financed by endowment, city and state appropriation). Purchases: $83,000.
Collections: 19th century American and European paintings and sculptures; Lalique crystal; 19th century Japanese art; †Texas art; †contemporary American graphics; †historical artifacts relating to Texas, 15th century to present; incunabula through fine contemporary printing.
Exhibitions: Average approx 18 exhibitions per year; numerous one-man shows.
Publications: The Rosenberg Library Bulletin, irregular, semiannual.
Activities: Classes for adults and children; lectures; gallery talks; concerts; dramatic programs; Extension Department serves Galveston County; material available to individuals and organizations; film, framed pictures and film strips; traveling exhibitions organized and circulated; original objects of art lent; lending collection contains color reproductions 18,444, motion pictures 810, film strips 310, framed pictures 487, sculptures 17; 1961 items lent in average year; photograph reference collection; 438,395 volume lending and reference library.

HOUSTON

ART LEAGUE OF HOUSTON, 1953 Montrose Blvd, 77006. Tel: 713-523-9530. *Pres* Michael Wood; *VPres* Roy Willoughby; *Secy* Marianne Hornbuckle; *Dir* Charlene Harris.
Open Mon - Fri 10 AM - 4 PM; Sat noon - 4 PM. No admis. Estab 1948 to promote public interest in art and the achievements of Houston area artists; gallery maintained for monthly exhibits. Average Annual Attendance: 10,000. Mem: 850; dues single $15; annual meeting May.
Income: $50,000 (financed by membership, state appropriation and fund-raising functions).
Exhibitions: Membership exhibits; Dimension Houston; Student Exhibits; Texas Fine Arts Asn Regional Citation Exhibit; "Fiber & Clay", Commercial and Vocational Art; "Paper Products".
Publications: Newsletter, monthly; Year Book and Membership Roster, annually.
Activities: Classes for adults; lect open to the public, 6 vis lectr per yr; competitions with approx $1100 cash award in area exhibit and $115 in membership shows.

CONTEMPORARY ARTS MUSEUM,* 5216 Montrose, 77006. Tel: 713-526-3129. *Dir* James Harithas; *Asst Dir* Mrs D L Prince; *Cur* Paul Schimmel; *Cur* Joanie Whitebird; *Cur* Vidal Briseno; *Cur Educ* Ann Bunn.
Open Tues - Sat 10 AM - 5 PM; Sun Noon - 6 PM; cl Mon. Estab 1948 to promote a better understanding of contemporary art. The 15,000 sq ft building was designed by Detroit architect Gunnar Birkerts; the parallelogram shaped structure consists of two floors. The upper level houses an 8000 sq ft gallery with a ceiling height of 20 ft. The lower level houses shipping and receiving, bookshop, research library, multipurpose room, staff offices and storage. Average Annual Attendance: 300,000. Mem: 2000; dues $10 students, others $25 and higher; annual meeting May.
Income: $250,000.
Collections: Damaged in the 1976 flood. New collection being developed of contemporary paintings, sculpture and constructions.
Exhibitions: Exhibitions covering contemporary art in all media—painting, sculpture, drawing, video, dance, theater, poetry and music, with an emphasis on Texas artists.
Activities: Wide ranging educational program including the prototypical Art After School, a program of art classes in selected elementary schools; docent programs; special events; book store.

HOUSTON PUBLIC LIBRARY, Fine Arts and Recreation Dept, 500 McKinney, 77002. Tel: 713-224-5441, exten 336, 337, 338. *Head, Fine Arts & Recreation* John Harvath Jr; *First Asst* C Harlan Schenk; *AV Librn* Alice Jacqmin; *Art Librn* Jane Truran; *Music Librn* Nicholas McCauley.
Open Mon - Fri 9 AM - 9 PM; Sat 9 AM - 6 PM; Sun 2 - 6 PM. Estab 1848 as a private library for the Houston Lyceum and opened to the public in 1895. Monthly exhibit, including art shows are spread throughout the Central Library building. Circ: Dept circ not counted at present, but estimated at 80,000 items per yr.
Income: Approx $90,000 (financed by endowment, city appropriation, Federal and State aid (LSA & LSCA), "Friends" of the Library).
Purchases: $90,000.
Holdings: Vols 62,000; Per subs 375, AV—Audio tapes, cassettes, film strips, kodachromes, microfiche, microfilm, phonorecords, slides; Other—Clipping files, exhibition catalogs, framed reproductions; pamphlets, reproductions, sculpture, exhibition posters, portrait file, sheet music collection, auction catalogs.
Special Subjects: Decorative Arts; Oriental Art.
Activities: Lect open to the public; tours.

MUSEUM OF FINE ARTS, HOUSTON, 1001 Bissonnet, (Mailing Add: PO Box 2826 77005). Tel: 713-526-1361. *Dir* William C Agee; *Pres Bd* Alexander K McLanahan; *Assoc Dir* David B Warren; *Chmn Bd* Harris Masterson; *Chief Cur* Kent Sobotik; *Adjunct Cur* Anne Tucker; *Assoc Cur* Katherine S Howe; *Cur The Bayou Bend Coll* Barry Greenlaw; *Dir Museum School of Art* Ken Jewesson; *Publicist* Anne Feltus; *Registrar* Edward Mayo; *Development Officer* Patrice Jones Day; *Activities Coordr* Linda Letzerich; *Docent Coordr* Marjorie S Thompson; *Admin Asst* Lisa Harrell.
Open Tues - Sat 10 AM - 5 PM; Sun Noon - 6 PM. No admis. Estab 1926 as an art museum containing works from prehistoric times to the present. Average Annual Attendance: 320,000. Mem: 13,000+; dues $25; annual meeting May.
Income: Financed by endowment, membership, city appropriation, and donations.
Collections: †American and European paintings, graphics, and sculpture; †Oriental art; †antiquities; †photography; †African, Oceanic, Pre-Columbian, and American Indian art objects; †Western Americana; †European and American decorative arts; †Medieval and Early Christian work; major collection of Impressionist and Post-Impressionist paintings.

Exhibitions: The Collection of John A and Audrey Jones Beck: Impressionist and Post Impressionist Paintings; Works on Paper: Recent Acquisitions; The Printed Book in the Baroque Period; Paul Revere Silver from the Bortman-Larus Foundation Collection; Two Hundred Years of Christmas in America; Anthony Caro; Russian Art and Culture: Selected Objects; Selections from the Primitive Collections; Master Paintings from the Hermitage and the State Russian Museum; The Gothic Revival Style in America, 1830-1870; Houston Post Spring Art Festival; American Scenes: Etchings and Lithographs by Childe Hassam; The Making of Worcester Porcelain; Photographs from the Wellesley College Collection; The History of Jacob: Flemish Renaissance Tapestries; Joan Miro—a tribute; The Photographic Book in Germany and France, 1930-1960; Andre Masson; Winslow Homer's America: Graphics from the Mavis P and Mary Wilson Kelsey Collection; Studio; Hans Hofmann; Japanese Ukiyo-E Prints; The Photograhic Process; Derriere le Miroir; Modern American Painting: Toward a New Perspective; Archaeology and Photography: Troy; SW Hayter Graphics from the Romansky Collection.
Publications: Bulletin, infrequently; calendar of events, bimonthly; catalogs of exhibitions.
Activities: Classes for adults and children; docent training; lect open to public, 20 vis lectr per yr; concerts; gallery talks; tours; traveling exhibitions organized and circulated; museum shop selling books, magazines, reproductions, prints, slides, postcards and others.
—**Library.** *Librn* Linda Nelson.
Open to the public for reference.
Holdings: Vols 10,000; Per subs 74; Other—Exhibition and sales catalogs.
Special Subjects: Art history and photography.

RICE UNIVERSITY, Institute for the Arts, Rice Museum, University at Stockton Sts (Mailing Add: 1892 Box 1892, 77001). *Dir* Mrs John de Menil; *Exec Adminr* Harris Rosenstein; *Production Mgr* Jesse Lopez; *Registrar* Patricia McQueen.
Open Tues - Sat 10 AM - 5 PM; Sun Noon - 6 PM; No admis. Estab to organize and present art exhibitions. Average Annual Attendance: 38,000.
Exhibitions: Art Nouveau, Belgium/France; Goya Prints; Magritte—Secret Infinities; Joseph Cornell Grass; Visions of Courtly India; Leger.
Activities: Docent training; lect open to public; traveling exhibitions organized and circulated.

UNIVERSITY OF HOUSTON, Sarah Campbell Blaffer Gallery, 114 Fine Arts Bldg, 77004. Tel: 713-749-1320. *Dir* William A Robinson; *Asst to Dir* Michael J Metyko; *Asst to Dir* Toni Beauchamp.
Open Tues, Wed, Fri & Sat, 10 AM - 6 PM; Thurs 10 AM - 8 PM; Sun 1 - 6 PM; cl Mon, during Exhibitions. Closed between exhibitions. No admis.
Estab 1973 as an educational Art Museum facility for University of Houston campuses and Houston community; the Main Gallery covers 1521 sq ft with 25 ft ceiling; adjacent galleries covers 3024 sq ft with 10 ft ceiling; the Mezzanine Gallery covers 1517 sq ft with 10 ft ceiling. Average Annual Attendance: 20,000.
Income: $65,000 - $100,000 (financed by state appropriation, grants and gifts).
Collections: European Old Masters and American abstract expressionists collected, under the auspices of the Blaffer Foundations; Charles and Katherine Fleetwood Collection of Pre-Columbian art.
Exhibitions: (1976-78) Edvard Munch (originating); American Abstract Expressionist Collection; 06 Art 76: French Bicentennial Loan; Photographs by F R B Rapho; Willem de Kooning (recent work); German Expressionism: Toward a New Humanism (originating); Louise Herreshoff; Houston Area Exhibition; Works on Paper by women artists; Harry Callahan Photographs: Faculty and Student Shows. Permanent collections are selectively displayed each year.
Publications: Catalogs with some exhibitions.
Activities: Lect open to the public, 1-5 vis lectr per yr; concerts; gallery talks; tours; competitions; traveling exhibitions organized and circulated; sales shop selling catalogs and posters of gallery exhibitions.

INGRAM

HILL COUNTRY ARTS FOUNDATION, Hwy 39 (Mailing Add: PO Box 176, 78025). Tel: 512-367-5121. *Pres* Mrs Byron W Dalrymple; *VPres* Michael E Sears; *Secy* Col W W Barnett Jr; *Chmn Art Dept* Mrs W J Jowdy; *Chmn Theater Dept* Andrew J Ritch.
Open varies seasonally. No admis except for special events. Estab 1959 to provide a place for creative activities in the area of visual arts and performing arts; and to provide classes in arts, crafts, drama and music; art gallery is maintained for members artwork. Average Annual Attendance: 30,000. Mem: 750; dues $15, $25, $50, $100, $250, $500 and up; annual meeting second Sat Aug.

Income: Financed by endowment, membership, benefit activities and donations.
Exhibitions: Young Artists Exhibit; Sixth Annual Juried Exhibit; Annual Craft Exhibit; Texas Fine Arts Exhibit; Photography Exhibit.
Publications: Newsletter, bi-monthly.
Activities: Classes for children; dramatic programs, art workshops; competitions with awards; schol; sales shop selling original art, prints, and original work by members, including crafts.
Alice Naylor Memorial Art Library. Tel: 512-367-5121. Open to members for reference only.

KINGSVILLE

TEXAS A&I UNIVERSITY ART GALLERY, Art Department, Santa Gertrudis, 78363. Tel: 512-592-2619. *Chmn* R Scherpereel.
Open 8 AM - Noon & 1 - 5 PM. No admis. Estab to exhibit art works of students, as well as visitors' exhibits and receptions. Average Annual Attendance: 3000.
Income: Financed by state appropriations.
Exhibitions: Fifteen exhibitions a year of students, instructors, and regional artists.

LONGVIEW

LONGVIEW MUSEUM AND ARTS CENTER, 102 W College, (Mailing Add: Box 562, 75601). Tel: 214-753-8103. *Dir* Joan Nachbaur Rathbum; *Secy* Holly Thompson.
Open Tues - Fri 9 AM - 5 PM; Sun 2 - 4 PM. No admis. Estab June 16, 1970 for the encouragement of art through a program of exhibition, education, participation of members of the community and the surrounding area; East Gallery 40 x 60 ft, large windows, overhead lights; West Gallery smaller but similar; galleries between are rooms that were once a private home. Mem dues single $20, family $35; meeting monthly Exec; quarterly Board of Trustees.
Income: Financed by membership and guild projects. Purchases: $1700 and up.
Collections: †Regional artists collection formed by purchases from Annual Invitational Exhibitions over the past 20 years.
Exhibitions: Annual Student Art Exhibition: Annual Invitational Exhibition; Citation Show of East Texas Fine Arts Association; Monthly exhibitions—Charles McGough, Marty Averett, Bill Biety, Frank Weyrich, Lucille Reid, Clyde Connell, Stephen Wilder, Jim Hill, Jerry Bywaters, Remington and Russell from Amon Carter, J Jay MeVic, Charles Greeley, C Umlauf, Vance Kirkland, Hartung & Defrese, R Russell, Beauboeuf & Brossard and James Martin/Artist-in-Residence.
Publications: Newsletter, monthly; Calendar for members; brochures for each exhibition.
Activities: Classes for adults and children; docent training; lect open to the public, 2 vis lectr per yr; tours; competitions; individual paintings and original objects of art lent to Courthouse, and church; lending collection contains film strips, original art works, original prints; paintings, photographs, sculpture, slides.
Library: *Chmn* Millicent Canter. Open to the public.

LUBBOCK

MUSEUM OF TEXAS TECH UNIVERSITY, Fourth St & Indiana (Mailing Add: PO Box 4499, 79409). Tel: 806-742-5151. *Acting Dir* Charles M McLaughlin.
Open Tues - Sat 10 AM - 5 PM; Sun 1 - 5 PM; cl Mon. No admis. Estab 1929 for teaching, research, and public service.
Income: Financed by state appropriations, West Texas Museum Association and Ranch Headquarters Association.
Collections: Art fields are primarily contemporary American in all media and Western American; permanent exhibitions in art, history and natural sciences. A 40 ft mural by Peter Rogers dominates the entrance lobby.
Exhibitions: Monthly changing exhibitions in temporary galleries.
Publications: Museum Digest; Museum Journal; Occasional Papers and Special Publications.
Activities: Traveling exhibitions organized and circulated; original objects of art lent; lect open to the public, over 2 vis lectrs per yr; over 2 tours. Book Shop.

MARSHALL

HARRISON COUNTY HISTORICAL MUSEUM,* Old Courthouse, Peter Whetstone Square, 75670. *Pres* James K Abney; *Dir* Inez H Hughes.
Open Mon - Fri & Sun 1:30 - 4:30 PM; cl Sat & holidays. Admis adults 50¢, students 25¢, children under 6 free. Estab 1965, housed in a 1901 Courthouse. Mem: Dues individual $5, life $150.

Collections: Portraits; paintings; porcelains; jewelry; silver; hand-painted china; cut and pressed glass; 400BC - 1970 ceramics; religious artifacts; historical material.
Activities: Guided tours; military records researched.
Library: Open to the public for reference. Holdings: Vols 300. Other—Manuscripts.

McALLEN

McALLEN INTERNATIONAL MUSEUM, 1900 Nolana (Mailing Add: PO Box 2495, 78501). Tel: 512-682-1564. *Exec Dir* Rudolph V Pharis, *Asst Dir* John R F Alger.
Open Tues - Sat 9 AM - 5 PM; Sun 2 - 5 PM; cl Mon. No admis. Estab 1969 to exhibit art, science and cultural history. Average Annual Attendance: 50,000. Mem: 350; dues $25 up.
Income: Financed by membership, city appropriation and other funds.
Collections: †Mexican Folk Art; †local, state and regional artists; †original prints.
Exhibitions: Continous traveling exhibits for one to two month duration; Western art; West African folk art; Pan American University Faculty Art Exhibition; Sculptures by Marie Lesher; American Bison.
Publications: Newsletter, monthly; bulletins and brochures periodically.
Activities: Classes for adults and children; docent training; art and craft demonstrations; lect open to the public, 6 vis lectr per yr; concerts; gallery talks; tours; museum shop selling books, reproductions, prints, slides, jewelry, museum related science kits.
Library: Open to staff, volunteers, and researchers for reference only. Holdings: Vols 2000; Per subs 10; Others—Photographs and slides. Special Subjects: Rio Grande Valley, Texas, Mexico.

MIDLAND

MUSEUM OF THE SOUTHWEST, 1705 W Missouri, 79701. Tel: 915-683-2882. *Dir* Samuel H Grove; *Secy* Mary Jane Warren; *Coordinator of Museum Services* Leila Seal; *Preparator* Randy Ray; *Custodian* Herbert Ray; *Clerical Asst* Diane Carlton.
Open Mon - Sat 10 AM - 5 PM; Sun 2 - 5 PM. No admis. Inc 1965 as a museum dedicated to history, natural science, and art of the American Southwest; there are four galleries. Average Annual Attendance: 17,190. Mem: 850; dues single $5, couple $10; Board meeting third Wed monthly.
Income: $117,000 (financed by endowment, membership).
Collections: Permanent art collection, Indian art exhibit, and Oriental fan collection.
Exhibitions: Bud Biggs (one-man show); Student Art Festival; Joe Grandee (one-man show); Doll exhibit; Southwest Annual Art Show; West Texas History Exhibit; Texas Watercolor Society Show; Lubbock Art Asn Bicentennial Exhibit; James Johnson (one-man show); 18th and 19th Century European Oil Paintings and Watercolors; Indian artifacts of the Southwest; Art and the Book; Contemporary Mexican Art; The Tinker Collection; Oaxacan Mexican Masks; Angelo Garzio Pottery, Bladan Stiha (one-man show); Warren Cullar (watercolors); Ronald Thomason (watercolors), Birds of Prey.
Publications: Museletter, monthly; bulletin concerning current exhibits, new and renewed members, and report.
Activities: Docent training; arts and crafts classes; lect open to the public; competitions; individual paintings and original objects of art lent on only limited conditions; museum shop selling books, magazines, reproductions, jewelry, novelties.
Library. Vol Librn Donna Grove. Holdings: Vols 400.

ODESSA

PRESIDENTIAL MUSEUM,* 622 N Lee, 79761. Tel: 915-332-7123. *Chmn* John Ben Shepperd; *Cur* Alzada Malone.
Open 9 - 12 AM & 1 - 5 PM. No admis. Estab 1965 to heighten appreciation of and respect for the responsibilities of the Office of The President, to dramatize in nonpartisan manner the background, accomplishments, trials, and human side of all the presidents of the United States, of Texas. Portraits of all presidents, wives and vice-presidents on one canvas in oil; gallery of vice-presidents, also-rans, and pets of presidents, as well as wood mosaics of all presidents. Average Annual Attendance: 40,000. Mem: 500; dues $25 and $100; annual meeting Feb.
Income: $20,000 (financed by membership). Purchases $18,500.
Collections: Portrait Galleries of Presidents, †also-rans, †pets of presidents; †acetate brush drawings of vice-presidents; wood mosaics of all presidents; †first lady dolls in inaugural gowns; presidents of Texas; †White House china; churches of presidents; †mothers and fathers of presidents; †personal items of presidents; †signatures, †birthplace replicas of the presidents; †hand-carved caricatures of the presidents; sculpture; coins.
Publications: Presidential Museum Newsletter, monthly.

Activities: Special programs for schools, teachers, and service groups, including tours and visual instruction; lectures open to public; special exhibitions.
Library: Holdings—Vols 3000 for reference; Other—Photograph collection, books only relating to the presidency, tape recordings.

ORANGE

STARK MUSEUM OF ART, 712 Green Ave (Mailing Add: PO Box 1897, 77630). Tel: 713-883-6661. *Chmn* Nelda C Stark; *VChmn* Eunice Benckenstein; *Secy-Treas* C V McKee Jr; *Registrar* Anna Jean Caffey.
Opening Nov 1978. Owned and operated by the Nelda C and H J Lutcher Stark Foundation, it was established to preserve and display the Stark collection of art, and promote interest in subjects relative to the same through exhibits, publications and educational programs. Five galleries containing exhibits.
Income: Financed by endowment.
Collections: Dorothy Doughty porcelain sculpture; Steuben crystal; American 19th and 20th century Western and Taos paintings and sculpture; Indian artifacts; Navaho rugs.

SAN ANGELO

ANGELO STATE UNIVERSITY,* Houston Harte University Center, Box 11027, 76901. Tel: 915-942-2062. *Dir Univ Center* Wes Davis; *Prog Consult* Joy Carol Sloan; *Chairperson Art Comt* Ms Arcie Cervantes.
Open Mon - Fri 9 AM - 4 PM; Wed 7 - 9:30 PM. No admis. Estab 1970 to provide entertainment and informal education for the students, faculty and staff. Gallery is maintained.
Income: $3000 (financed by city and state appropriation).
Collections: In Our Image, collection of 32 wax drawings done by Guy Rowe as basis for illustrating the book, In Our Image, written by Houston Harte.
Exhibitions: Historical artifacts, weaving, photography, sculpture, pottery, modern drawings; children's, students and faculty exhibitions.
Activities: Lect open to public, 2 vis lectrs per yr; 5 gallery talks; 1 tour; concerts; dramatic programs; competitions.

SAN ANGELO ART CLUB,* Kendall Art Gallery, 119 W First St (Mailing Add: Box 3362, 76901). *Pres* Roxye Bynum; *Secy* Rosa Gray; *Exhib Chmn* George Maxwell.
Gallery open year round, Sun, Wed & Sat 2 - 5 PM. Art Club estab 1928, Kendall Art Gallery estab 1949, to promote the fine arts in the City of San Angelo. Mem: Approx 100; dues $12, includes newsletter; annual meeting Aug.
Income and Purchases: $8000 for upkeep and prizes (Memorial Endowment Fund estab 1972 by friends of the gallery).
Collections: Paintings by Xavier Gonzales, Gladys Rockmore Davis, Bryon Browne, Frederick Waugh, Iver Rose and many others.
Publications: Splashes, gallery newsletter.
Activities: Classes in oil painting and other media; monthly exhibits from area artists; cooperative program with city under study. Special workshops arranged, approx 2 per year.

SAN ANTONIO

COPPINI ACADEMY OF FINE ARTS,* 115 Melrose Place, 78212. Tel: 512-824-8502. *Pres* Dr Warren Hester; *Corresp Secy* Margaret Jones; *Exhib Chmn* Erwin O Wesp.
Open Sat, Sun or by appointment 2 - 5 PM. No admis. Estab 1945 to foster a better acquaintance and understanding between artists and patrons; to encourage worthy accomplishment in the field of art and to serve as a means of public exhibition for active members works and other works of art. Upstairs gallery donated by founder Dr Pompeo Coppini to the academy for exhibition of works. Mem: 191; dues $2 - $100; annual meeting third Sun in Jan.
Income: Financed by membership.
Collections: Oil paintings by Rolla Taylor; sculpture by Waldine Tauch and Pompeo Coppini.
Exhibitions: Different artists and exhibits from Victoria, Houston, Clifton and Georgetown, Texas.
Publications: Coppini News Bulletin, monthly.
Activities: Gives educational programs and art demonstrations and sponsors workshops; photograph collection for exhibition and reference; lect open to the public; approx 5 tours; competitions; scholarships.

MARION KOOGLER McNAY ART INSTITUTE, 6000 N New Braunfels St, 78209. Tel: 512-824-5368. *Pres* Mrs Edgar Tobin; *Dir* John Palmer Leeper.
Open Tues - Sat 9 AM - 5 PM; Sun 2 - 5 PM, cl Mon. No admis. Inc 1950 for the encouragement and development of modern art. Mem: 400, dues $50; annual meeting May.
Income: $350,000 (financed by endowment). Purchases: $30,000.

Collections: Large collection of French 19th century painting, particularly Impressionist and Post-Impressionists including Gauguin, Cezanne, Matisse, Picasso; †American watercolors of distinction from Winslow Homer, to present; New Mexican arts and crafts; Dr and Mrs Frederic Oppenheimer Collection of Gothic and Mediaeval art; distinguished print collection; Sylvan and Mary Lang Collection of 19th and 20th century French and American art.
Publications: Exhibition catalogs; permanent collection catalogs.
Activities: Films; lect; concerts; gallery talks; tours; traveling exhibitions organized and circulated.
—Library. *Librn* Mrs John P Leeper.
Open Tues - Fri 9 AM - 5 PM. Estab 1970 an as adjunct to the museum. For reference only.
Income: $5000 (financed by endowment, gifts). Purchases $5000.
Holdings: Vols 8000; Per subs 18; Other—Clipping files, exhibition catalogs, pamphlets.
Special Subjects: General reference for visual arts.
Special Collections: 19th - 20th century Western visual arts; Far Eastern art, especially Japanese woodblock prints.
Activities: Library tours.

SAN ANTONIO ART LEAGUE,* 310 W Ashby, 78209. Tel: 512-732-6048. *Pres* Mrs E H CuBose; *Secy* Mrs Joseph Satel; *Exec Dir* Mrs Jack Casey; *Mus Consult* Charles Long.
Open Tues - Fri 10 AM - 4 PM; weekends 1 - 4 PM; cl Mon. No admis. Estab 1912 as a public art gallery for San Antonio, and for the promotion of a knowledge and interest in art by means of exhibitions. Mem: 1000; dues $10 - $100; meetings are 1st Tues of month, Oct - May.
Income: Approx $28,000 (financed by membership and fund raising projects). Purchases: $1500.
Collections: Paintings, sculpture, crafts and prints.
Exhibitions: San Antonio Artist of the Year, one-man show; Annual San Antonio Art League Artists exhibition, juried show for San Antonio and the surrounding area with approx $4000 in prizes. Traveling exhibitions; permanent collection on exhibit during summer.
Publications: Monthly calendar of events; exhibition catalogs, 3 per year.
Activities: Individual paintings lent to schools upon request; original objects of art lent; 50 items in an average year; lectures open to public; 3 gallery talks per year; 2 tours; competitions.
Library: Holdings—Vols 350 for reference.

SAN ANTONIO MUSEUM ASSOCIATION, INC, 3801 Broadway, 78029. Tel: 512-826-0647. *Pres* Nancy B Negley; *VPres* Robert H Seal; *VPres* Elizabeth Maddux; *Secy* Clifton Bolner; *Asst Secy* Mrs Frank Valdey; *Chmn of Bd of Trustees* A B Duncan; *Treas* Gordon George; *Exec Dir* Jack R McGregor; *Assoc Dir for Development* Mrs Adair Sutherland; *Sr Cur of History and Decorative Arts* Cecilia Steinfeldt; *Cur of Photography* David Simpson; *Cur of Transportation* Joseph Zawatski; *Community Relations Coordinator* Roberto Esparza; *Outreach Coordinator* Marcia Solon.
Open Mon - Fri 9 AM - 5 PM; Sat, Sun & holidays 10 AM - 6 PM. Admis by voluntary contribution. Estab 1922 to further education of and conservation of local and regional history, art science and technology. Average Annual Attendance: 300,000. Mem: 1500; dues individual $15; Bd meeting monthly.
Income: $1,246,000 (fiscal 1977) (financed by endowment, membership, city appropriation and other fund raising projects). Purchases: $121,000.
Collections: Modern and contemporary art. Collection of local history added as gifts are accepted.
Exhibitions: (1976-77) San Antonio Is . . . ; Abstract Expressionism; Silverworks from Rio De La Plata; Carr Foundation Special Exhibit; Four Texans - About Photography; Image of American Caricature and Cartoon; The Art of the Circus; Dean Brown Retrospective; The Campbell Collection; Tramp Art; The Great American Rodeo; Pioneer Photographs of Brazil; recent acquisitions in Photography; Star Spangled History; Cities on Stone; Traditional Costumes of Guatamala; The Cuzco Circle; Ford Thunderbirds; How tires are built; The American Farm; Motor Cyclorama; Scientific Siberia; Cisneros Drawings; Edvard Munch Retrospective; Iwonski in Texas; Beriant Collection of Navajo Rugs.
Publications: Calendar, monthly; Publication of books as time permits.
Activities: Lect open to the public, 2 - 3 vis lectr per yr; gallery talks; tours; a SAMAVan for community involvement; individual paintings and original objects of art lent if special occasion warrants; lending collection contains books 2000 - 3000; traveling exhibitions organized and circulated; sales shop selling books, prints, reproductions, slides and local crafts.
—Ellen Quillin Memorial Library. *Librn* Ms Billie Persons.
For reference only to the public with notification and appointment.
Holdings: Vols 2000 - 3000; Per subs 30.

SAN ANTONIO PUBLIC LIBRARY, Art, Music & Films Department, 203 S St Marys St, 78202. Tel: 512-223-6851, exten 34. *Librn III* Kathryn Ley; *Librn II* Robert Beebee; *Librn I* Raymond Villareal.

Open Mon - Fri 9 AM - 9 PM; Sat 9 AM - 6 PM. Estab to provide art reference and lending materials to the residents of Bexar County; art gallery maintained.
Income: $30,000 (financed by membership, and city appropriation). Purchases $30,000.
Holdings: AV—Cassettes, film strips, microfilm, motion pictures, phonorecords, slides; Other—Clipping files, pamphlets.
Exhibitions: Monthly exhibit of local artists work.
Activities: Lect open to the public, 2 vis lectr per yr.

SOUTHWEST CRAFT CENTER, 300 Augusta St, 78205. Tel: 512-224-2847. Gallery, 420 Paseo de La Villita, 78205. Tel: 515-222-0926. *Exec Dir* Mrs William Larsen; *Chmn of Board* Mrs Donald Saunders; *Pres* Mrs Thomas Berg.
Open daily 10 AM - 5 PM. Estab 1963, shop estab 1968, to keep crafts alive by giving craftsmen an outlet for their work, to educate the public in crafts by putting good crafts before them and also maintaining a school where these media can be taught. Average Annual Attendance: 100,000 at openings and events. Mem: students 1500, craftsmen 35; dues $10 and up; annual meeting May.
Income: Financed by endowment and membership.
Exhibitions: Approx 12 one-man and group craft shows; Student-Faculty Show.
Publications: Yearbook; opening invitations.
Activities: Classes for adults and children; crafts workshop programs with visiting artists; sales shop selling juried crafts of over 110 craftsmen.
Library: Reference library of craft books, slides and films.

SHERMAN

AUSTIN COLLEGE,* Ida Green Gallery, 75090. Tel: 214-892-9101, exten 218. *Dir* C R Neidhardt.
Open weekdays 9 AM - 5 PM. No admis. Estab 1972 to serve campus and community. Average Annual Attendance: 5000.
Income: Financed by endowment.
Collections: Minor collection of approx fifty prints.
Exhibitions: Monthly, September through May; one or two during summer.
Activities: Lect open to the public, 2 - 4 vis lectrs per yr; 6 - 10 tours.

SNYDER

DIAMOND M FOUNDATION MUSEUM,* Diamond M Building, 909 25th St (Mailing Add: PO Box 1149, 79549).
Open by appointment only. Estab 1950.
Collections: Paintings; original Currier and Ives lithographs; bronzes; jade; ivory; other pieces of art.

SUNSET

SUNSET TRADING POST OLD WEST MUSEUM,* Rte 1, 76270. Tel: 817-872-2027. *Cur* Jack N Glover.
Open daily 8 AM - 6 PM. Admis adults 50¢, children free. Estab. 1956.
Collections: Paintings; sculpture; prints and drawings; anthropology; archaeology; Indian artifacts; historical material.
Exhibitions: Temporary exhibitions from the collection and on loan from other museums.
Activities: Classes for adults and children; lectures; guided tours; sales shop.
Library: Indian and frontier books available for use on the premises. Holdings: Vols 500.

TYLER

TYLER MUSEUM OF ART, 1300 S Mahon Ave, 75701. Tel: 214-595-1001. *Dir* Ron Gleason; *Cur of Educ* Barbara Meyer; *Cur of Exhibitions* Michael Dillon; *Admin Asst* Judy Pirtle.
Open Tues - Sat 10 AM - 5 PM; Sun 1 - 5 PM. No admis. Estab 1971 as a museum of 19th and 20th century Art; two galleries are 40 x 60 ft, with 20 ft ceilings; one gallery covers 25 x 45 ft. Average Annual Attendance: 35,000. Mem: 650; dues $25 - $2000.
Income: $140,000 (financed by endowment, membership and Jr College/Auction).
Publications: Exhibition catalogs.
Activities: Classes for children; docent training; lect open to the public, 5 - 6 vis lectr per yr; concerts; gallery talks; tours; original objects of art lent; traveling exhibitions organized and circulated; sales shop selling books.
Library: Open to the public for reference only. Holdings: Vols 1000; Per subs 12; Other—Films.

WACO

ART CENTER, 1300 College Dr (Mailing Add: Box 5396, 76708). Tel: 817-752-4371. *Dir* Paul Rogers Harris; *Cur* Russell A Cargo.
Open Tues - Sat 10 AM - 5 PM; Sun 1 - 5 PM. No admis. Estab 1973 to provide a variety of exhibitions for appreciation and classes for participation; Former residence of William Cameron, it was renovated by Ford, Powell, and Carson of San Antonio, and contains one large main gallery and a small adjacent gallery; there is additional exhibition space on the second floor. Average Annual Attendance: 20,000. Mem: 900; dues $25.
Income: $100,000 (financed by endowment, membership and grants).
Collections: Small collection of contemporary regional art.
Exhibitions: (1977-78) Peruvian Colonial Paintings; Ten from Houston; The Art Center 1977 Competition; Lynn Lennon: Photographs; The Phillip Anschutz Collection of Western Art; Roger Winter: Paintings, Prints, Collages; Cowboys, Indians and Settlers; Richard Hunt Sculpture.
Publications: Newsletter; three catalogs per yr.
Activities: Classes for adults and children; docent training; docent tours regularly scheduled for fifth grade classes; lect open to the public, 2 - 3 vis lectr per yr; gallery talks; tours; competitions; exten dept serving ethnic minorities and low socio-economic groups; traveling exhibitions organized and circulated; museum shop selling books; reproductions, and gift items.
Library: Open to the public for reference only. Holdings: Vols 200.

BAYLOR UNIVERSITY

—Baylor Art Museum, 76703. Tel: 817-755-1867. *Dir* J B Smith; *Cur* Vernie Logan.
Open daily 8 AM - 5 PM; cl Sat & Sun. Estab 1967 as a teaching arm of the university to serve the area; gallery contains one large room with storage and preparation room. Average Annual Attendance: 500.
Income: Through the art department. Purchases: $2000 annually.
Collections: Local artists; prints; graphics; sculpture from Sepik River area, New Guinea.
Exhibitions: Exhibitions are held in University art gallery.
Activities: Lect open to public, 4 vis lectr per yr.
Library: Dept of Art reference library. *Librn* Vernie Logan. Restricted to scholars and advanced students. Holdings: Vols 200.
—Armstrong Browning Library, 700 Speight Ave (Mailing Add: PO Box 6336, 76706). Tel: 817-755-3566. *Dir* Dr Jack W Herring; *Librn* Betty A Coley; *Admin Asst* Rita S Humphrey; *Hostess* Nancy Dobbins.
Open Mon - Fri 9 AM - Noon and 2 - 4 PM; Sat 9 AM - Noon. Estab 1918 to provide a setting for the personal possessions of the Brownings and to have as complete as is possible a collection for the use of Browning scholars; gallery is maintained.
Income: $80.000 (financed by endowment and private university). Purchases: $12,000.
Holdings: Vols 10,000; Per subs 25; AV—Audio tapes, cassettes, film strips, microfilm, motion pictures, phono records, reels, slides; Other—Clippng files, manuscripts, memorabilia, original art works, original documents, pamphlets, photographs, prints, reproductions, sculpture.
Special Subjects: Robert and Elizabeth Barrett Browning and the Victorian Era of literature.
Special Collections: Meynell; Hagedorn; Shields; Kress Foundation Gallery Collection of portraits; portraits of Robert Browning and Elizabeth Barrett Browning; Pen Browning; portraits of donors; photograph collection of prints.
Publications: Baylor Browning Interests, irregular; Studies in Browning and His Circle, semiannual; Browning Music, 1973, music catalog; Armstrong Browning Library Newsletter, semiannual.
Activities: Lect open to the public, 2 vis lectr per yr; concerts; tours; schol.

FORT FISHER AND HOMER GARRISON MEMORIAL MUSEUM,* Interstate 35 West, Box 1370, 76703. Tel: 817-756-2211. *Cur* Gaines de Graffenried.
Open Mon - Sat 9 AM - 5 PM; Sun 11 AM - 5 PM. Admis adults $1, children 6-12 50¢, children under 6 free; special group rates.
Collection: Paintings and sculpture; Texas Ranger items; Western history.
Exhibitions: Temporary and traveling exhibitions.
Activities: Lectures; guided tours; research on Texas rangers; sales shop.

YOUTH CULTURAL CENTER,* 815 Columbus Ave, 76702. Tel: 817-752-9641. *Dir* Mrs George J Moen.
Open Tues - Wed 9 AM - Noon; other times by appointment. No admis. Estab 1963 by the public school district and Waco City Council PTA.
Collections: Paintings; sculpture; decorative arts; Indian artifacts; music; natural history.
Activities: Special education classes; docent program; lectures; tours; films; hobby workshops; school loan service.

WICHITA FALLS

WICHITA FALLS MUSEUM AND ART CENTER, Two Eureka Circle, 76308. Tel: 817-692-0923. *Dir* Larry Francell; *Cur of Educ* Kim Jayroe; *Registrar/Preparator* Gretchen Glick; *Exec Secy* Anne Jones.
Open Mon - Sat 8:30 AM - 4:30 PM; Sun 1 - 5 PM. No admis. Estab April 1967 for the purpose of serving the community; three galleries house art exhibits, science exhibits, and history exhibits. Average Annual Attendance: 60,000. Mem: 1500; dues $15 - $1000; annual meeting April.
Income: $130,000 (financed by endowment, membership, city appropriation and schools). Purchases: $10,000. (Art).
Collections: †American prints.
Exhibitions: (1977) Phillip Anschutz Collection of Western Art; Sara Campbell Blaffer American Expressionists; Mexican Folk Retablos. (1978) The American Quilt; American Art through Printmaking; The Way I See It (public school art).
Publications: Catalog of the Collection 1976; events calendar, Sept, Jan and May.
Activities: Classes for adults and children; docent training, lect open to the public, 2-5 vis lectr per yr; gallery talks; tours; lending collection contains original prints 150; traveling exhibitions organized and circulated; sales shop selling books, prints, crafts and jewelry.
Library. Tel: 817-692-0923. *Librn* Larry Francell. Open to the public for reference only. Holdings: Vols 1500; Per subs 15.

WIMBERLEY

PIONEER TOWN,* 7A Ranch Resort, Box 259, Rte 1, 78676. Tel: 512-847-2517. *Dir* Raymond L Czichos.
Open Memorial Day - Labor Day daily 9 AM - 10 PM; Labor Day - Memorial Day Sat & Sun afternoons. No admis. Estab 1956 as a village and art museum.
Collections: 300 works of repligraphic art of Charles Russell, Frederic Remington, Thomas Moran, Albert Beirstadt and work by many contemporary Western artists; sculpture and metalwork of the West.

UTAH

BRIGHAM CITY

BRIGHAM CITY MUSEUM-GALLERY, 24 N Third W, 84302. (Mailing Add: PO Box 583, 84302). Tel: 801-723-6769. *Dir* Frederick M Huchel; *Chmn Bd* Delone B Glover.
Open Mon - Sat 11 AM - 7 PM; cl Sun and holidays. No admis. Estab 1970 to promote and preserve artistic and cultural opportunities and appreciation of the history and accomplishments of local citizens, and to further promote understanding of the natural resources and wildlife of the area. An art gallery with permanent collections and rotating displays. Average Annual Attendance: 13,000.
Income: Financed by Brigham City Corporation and membership.
Collections; †Art; crystal and glass. 19th century clothing, artifacts, furniture, arms, transportation, expecially transcontinental railroad and the "Golden Spike" which was driven near here.
Exhibitions: Rotating monthly exhibits of art and varied collections.
Activities: Lect, 5 vis lectr per yr; concerts; gallery talks; competitions; sales shop selling souvenirs.
Library: John B Rentmeister Western Americana Library. Open for reference to any responsible researcher. Holdings: Vols 600; Per subs 2; Other — Documents, clippings and photographs. Special Subjects: Utah, Western History (Americana); LDS Church (Mormon) History; Northern Utah flora, fauna and natural history.

CEDAR CITY

SOUTHERN UTAH STATE COLLEGE, Braithwaite Fine Arts Gallery, 84720. *Cur* Thomas A Leek; *Asst to Cur* Karen K Gilg.
Open Mon - Fri 10 AM - 5 PM; Sat 1 - 6 PM. No admis. Estab 1976 to provide a quality visual arts forum for artists' work and the viewing public. The gallery has 2000 sq ft of space with 300 lineal ft of display surface; it is equipped with facilities for two and three-dimensional media. Electronic security system. Average Annual Attendance: 2500.
Income: Financed by city and state appropriations and private donations. Purchases: $4400.
Collections: 18th, 19th & 20th century American art; currently purchasing three-dimensional media.
Exhibitions: Small Metals (Carl E Riggs, Jr); Recent Paintings (Eric Brown); Annual Watercolor West; Annual Faculty Exhibition; Recent Art Gifts to College; Annual Printmaking West; Utah Open; Annual Student Exhibition.
Publications: Exhibition announcements, monthly.

Activities: Classes for adults; lect open to public, 4 vis lectr per yr; gallery talks; tours; competitions; artmobile; lending collection contains kodachromes 10,000, original art works 300, original prints 200, paintings 300 and slides 10,000.
Library: Librn A Thomas Challis. Open to registered students and by permission to public. Holdings: Vols. 80,000.

FILLMORE

TERRITORIAL STATEHOUSE,* 50 W Capital Ave, 84631. Tel: 801-743-5316. *Dir* Harold J Tippetts, *Asst Dir* Marvin G Jenson; *Ranger-in-Charge* C Max Martin.
Open June 1 - Sept 1 8 AM - 9 PM; all other months 9 AM - 5 PM. No admis. Estab 1930, dedicated by Gov George H Dern as a museum for pioneer relics; restored by the State and local Daughters of Utah Pioneers; run by State Parks, Division of Parks and Recreation.
Income: Financed by state appropriations.
Collections: Over fifty paintings, formerly in the Legislative Hall; seven pieces of sculpture, some silk screen prints, charcoal and pencil sketches, lithographs, and pioneer portraits in beautiful antique frames that in themselves are a work of art; more than 200 prints in photograph collection, used for reference.
Activities: Local art classes and schools make several tours each year; art classes come for sketching; motion pictures taken by schools and other organization, sometimes shown here as courtesy; lectures open to the public, 2 vis lectr per yr; gallery talks and tours.

KAYSVILLE

KAYSVILLE COMMUNITY ART LEAGUE,* LeConte Stewart Art Gallery, 611 Crestwood Rd, 84037. Tel: 801-376-4438. *Pres* Gerald Purdy; *Secy* Mrs Eldean Holliday.
Open Tues - Fri 3 - 5 PM; Sun & Mon 7 - 9 PM. No admis. Estab 1971 to administer affairs of gallery and provide source of funds for its maintenance; small gallery near community center remodeled from historical building. Average Annual Attendance: 1000. Mem: 655; dues $2; annual meeting upon call of president.
Income: Financed by membership.
Collections: Paintings, lithography and other work of LeConte Stewart.
Activities: Lect open to the public; gallery talks.

OGDEN

ECCLES COMMUNITY ART CENTER, 2580 Jefferson Ave, 84401. Tel: 802-392-6935. *Pres* John D Eccles; *VPres* Ted Collins; *Secy* Rebecca Gale; *Dir* Sandra H Havas.
Open Mon - Sat 10 AM - 5 PM; cl Sun. No admis. Estab 1959 to serve as a pivot and focal point for community cultural activities and to promote cultural growth. Maintains an art gallery with changing monthly exhibits. Average Annual Attendance: 25,000. Mem: 300; dues $5 - $100; annual meeting Nov.
Income: $25,000 (financed by membership, state appropriation and fund raising).
Exhibitions: Fred Martin; Watercolor West; Printmaking West.
Publications: Newsletter, bimonthly.
Activities: Classes for adults and children; dramatic programs; lect open to public, 12 vis lectr per yr; concerts; competitions with cash award.

PROVO

BRIGHAM YOUNG UNIVERSITY
—B R Larsen Gallery, Harris Fine Arts Center, F-303, 84602. Tel: 801-374-1211, exten 2881. *Dir* Dale T Fletcher; *Dir Art Acquisitions* Wesley M Burnside; *Preparator* J Clyff Allen; *Secy* Debra Palmer.
Open 8 AM - 10 PM. No admis. Estab 1963 to bring to the University students and faculty a wide range of new experiences in the visual arts; the gallery occupies large open space on the main floor of the Harris Fine Arts Center; partitions are put and arranged in different ways for display; there is approx 10,944 sq ft of space for hanging art. Average Annual Attendance: 150,000.
Income: Financed by university.
Collections: International collection of prints; Utah artists; 19th and 20th century American paintings; drawings, sculpture; Western art; Maynard Dixon Collection; Mahonri Young Collection of manuscripts; J Alden Weir Collection.
Exhibitions: Monthly exhibitions of one-man shows by invitation, student and faculty work and circulating exhibits and works from the permanent collection.
Activities: Lect open to the public; competitions with awards; individual paintings lent to offices on campus and church offices only; traveling exhibitions organized and circulated.
—Harold B Lee Library. Tel: 801-374-1211, exten 4005. *Dir Libraries* Donald K Nelson; *Mus and Art Librn* Beth R Webb.

Open Mon - Sat 7 AM - 11 PM. Estab 1875 to support the university curriculum.
Income: Financed by endowment, membership and church funds.
Holdings: Vols 29,634; Per subs 155; AV—Audio tapes, cassettes, film strips, microfiche, microfilm, motion pictures, phonorecords, slides, video tapes; Other—Exhibition catalogs, manuscripts, memorabilia, pamphlets, photographs, prints.
Special Collections: 15th and 16th century graphic art collection; Vought indexed and mounted art print collection; Edmund J Sullivan Collection of Oriental drawings and sketches; C R Savage Collection and George Anderson Collection of early Utah photographs.
Activities: Library tours.

SAINT GEORGE

DIXIE COLLEGE, Southwestern Utah Art Gallery, 84770. Tel: 801-673-4811, exten 297. *Personnel:* Gerald Olson; Roland Lee; Glen Blakley.
Open 8 AM - 6 PM. No admis. Estab 1960 to serve Southwestern Utah as a visual Art Exhibit Center; gallery is located in Fine Arts Center. Average Annual Attendance: 12,000.
Income: Financed by state appropriation.
Collections: Early Utah painters; contemporary Utah painters.
Exhibitions: Utah 77 Photos; Watercolor West; Utah Watercolor Society; The Great Salt Lake; Telford: Japanese Print Show; Dixie College Spring Invitational; Utah 76.
Activities: Classes for adults; dramatic programs; lect open to the public, with vis lectr; gallery talks.

SALT LAKE CITY

CHURCH OF JESUS CHRIST OF LATTER-DAY SAINTS,* Information Center and Museum, Temple Square, 84101. Tel: 801-531-2675. *Dir* Keith E Garner.
Open winter 8 AM - 6 PM, summer 6:30 AM - 9 PM. No admis. Museum estab 1869, Information Center 1904, to disseminate information and display historical memorabilia to the visiting public.
Income: Financed by Church.
Collections: Historical and religious paintings and museum objects.
Exhibitions: Continuous exhibitions.

SALT LAKE ART CENTER, S Temple at W Temple Sts (after Feb 1, 1979), (Mailing Add: 54 Finch Lane, 84102). Tel: 801-328-4201. *Pres* Paul Dougan; *Treas* Charles Boynton; *Dir* Allen Stevens Dodworth; *Business Mgr* Marti Smith; *Cur Educ* Mark Anderson; *Sales Shop Mgr* Marianne Johnson.
Open Tues - Fri 11 AM - 6 PM; Sat & Sun Noon - 5 PM; cl Mon. No admis. Estab 1931 to educate the community in the visual arts through exhibitions and classes. After Feb 1, 1979, one large gallery of 5800 sq ft, one small gallery of 1000 sq ft, sales shop and rental sales gallery 1400 sq ft. Average Annual Attendance: 15,000. Mem: 800; dues $10 - $1000; annual meeting Sept.
Income: $150,000 (financed by membership, city and state appropriations, earned income and gifts). Purchases $10,000.
Collections: †Utah artists; †American and European prints 19th & 20th century.
Exhibitions: New building schedule still indefinite.
Publications: Bulletin, bimonthly.
Activities: Classes for adults and children; workshops; lect open to public, 3 vis lectr per yr; concerts; gallery talks; tours; competitions; traveling exhibitions organized and circulated; sales shop selling books, original art, prints, slides and local crafts.

SALT LAKE CITY PUBLIC LIBRARY, Fine Arts Dept, 209 E Fifth South, 84111. Tel: 801-363-5733, exten 41. *Dir* J Dennis Day; *Head Fine Arts* Dept Glenda Rhodes; *Coordinator Atrium Gallery* Lori Arnall.
Open Mon - Fri 9 AM - 9 PM; Sat 9 AM - 6 PM; Sun 1 - 5 PM (Winter only). Estab 1898. Maintains an art gallery with monthly exhibitions.
Income: $1,599,345 (financed by endowment and city appropriation).
Holdings: AV—Cassettes, film strips, microfiche, phonorecords, slides; Other—Clipping files, exhibition catalogs, framed reproductions, original art works, pamphlets, reproductions.
Special Subjects: Contemporary art, dance and film.
Special Collections: Utah artists, art of western United States.
Exhibitions: Traveling exhibits from state-wide Museum on the Road Program, one-person and group shows such as Utah Watercolor Assoc; Mary Atwater Weavers' Guild.
Publications: Brochures accompanying individual shows.
Activities: Folk-Life Festival; concerts; gallery talks; tours.

UNIVERSITY OF UTAH, Utah Museum of Fine Arts, 101 Art & Architectural Center, 84112. Tel: 801-322-7332. *Dir* E F Sanguinetti; *Assoc Cur of the Coll* Thomas Southam; *Preparator/Gallery Supv* Douglas R Holladay; *Asst Cur of Educational Services* Ann Day; *Registrar*

Dan Burke; *Mem & Vol Coordinator* Jean Mueller; *Exec Secy* Josephine Theodore.
Open Mon - Fri 10 AM - 5 PM; Sat & Sun 2 - 5 PM. No admis. Estab 1951 as a museum of fine arts under the administration of the College of Fine Arts. The Museum's holdings include a wide variety of objects with an emphasis on 19th Century American and French landscape paintings. Average Annual Attendance: 75,000. Mem: 400; dues single $15, family $25.
Income: Financed by state appropriation.
Collections: Collections of French 18th century furnishings and tapestries; English 17th and 18th century furniture and pictures; contemporary graphic works; Egyptian antiquities; objects from Buddhist cultures; Italian Renaissance paintings and furniture; Winifred Kimball Hudnut Collection; Marion Sharp Robinson Collection; Bartlett Wicks Collection; Natacha Rambova Egyptian Collection; Trower and Michael Collections of English, American and Peruvian silver.
Exhibitions: American Painting of 1850; Graphic Styles of the American Eight; Indian Basket Designs of the Greater Southwest; Sol Lewitt; Recent work by avant-garde New York artist, Manuel Neri; recent sculpture and works on paper; Masterpieces of English watercolor from the Victoria & Albert Museum; Images of Women; 19th Century French Prints; Cities on Stone; Jo Hanson: Crab Orchard Cemetery.
Publications: Twice a year.
Activities: Classes for adults; docent training; lect open to the public, some for members only; concerts; gallery talks; tours; individual paintings and original objects of art lent; traveling exhibitions organized and circulated.
Library. Tel: 801-322-7332. Open to students and docents for reference only. Holdings: Vols 500; Per subs 25.

UTAH DIVISION OF STATE HISTORY, Suite 1000, Crane Bldg, 307 W 200 S, 84101. Tel: 801-533-5755. *Dir* Melvin T Smith.
Open Mon - Fri 8 AM - 5 PM. No admis. Estab 1897 to collect and preserve material relating to Utah's history, and publish data relating thereto; to stimulate research, maintain history library, and mark and preserve historic sites; gallery not maintained. Historical organization with limited art holdings, presently housed in temporary quarters. Average Annual Attendance: 12,000 (to Feb 1978). Mem: 2624; dues $7.50.
Income: $680,000 (financed by state appropriation).
Collections: Paintings and lithographs; sculpture; archaeological and paleontological reference collections.
Publications: Utah Historical Quarterly; Utah State Historical Society Newsletter.
Activities: Lect open to the public; awards given (Distinguished Fellow, Honorary); individual paintings and original objects of art lent to State Division of Fine Arts and Art Museums.
Library: Holdings—Vols 18,900; AV —Microfilm 3000; Other—Pamphlets 16,700.

UTAH STATE DIVISION OF FINE ARTS,* Carriage House Gallery, 609 E South Temple St, 84102. Tel: 801-533-5895, 5896, 5303, 6050. *Chmn* Franz Johansen; *Exec Dir* Ruth R Draper.
Estab 1899 as the Utah Art Institute by Utah State Legislature to promote the fine arts in Utah; presently a division within the Department of Development Services, State of Utah.
Income: Financed by state appropriation ($325,000) and federal appropriation.
Collections: State-owned collection of paintings, watercolors and sculpture housed in state-owned buildings; strong emphasis on WPA period.
Exhibitions: Statewide Painting and Sculpture Competition and Exhibition annually; special exhibits at Carriage House Gallery.
Activities: Division sponsors traveling exhibitions, regional art shows and statewide competitions in painting and sculpture, literature, drama, and music in cooperation with arts organizations throughout the state; the Division helps to support over 60 arts organizations statewide.

UTAH TRAVEL COUNCIL,* Council Hall, Capitol Hill, 84114. Tel: 801-533-5681. *Dir* Michael D Gallivan; *Asst Dir* Milt Jolley; *Exec Secy* Billie Van Pelt; *Information Dir* Maury Christensen; *Publicity Dir* Anne Brillinger.
Open Memorial Day - Labor Day 8:30 AM - 6 PM; rest of year 8:30 AM - 5 PM. No admis. Constructed in 1864-1866, served for almost 30 years as the seat of government of Salt Lake City and the meeting place of the territorial legislature; reconstructed on Capitol Hill and formally presented to the State of Utah in July 1963, now an official state information center and home of Utah Travel Council; contains small museum of pioneer and historic significance with paintings and furniture.
Publications: In-house newsletter; travel newsletter, quarterly.
Activities: Lending collection contains motion pictures 63, photographs 2000, transparencies 5000 for organizational and general public use; traveling exhibitions organized and circulated.

SPRINGVILLE

SPRINGVILLE MUSEUM OF ART, 126 E 400 South, 84663. Tel: 801-489-9434. *Dir* Timothy G Rose; *Asst Cur* Dusty Esmaili.
Open Tues - Sat 10 AM - 5 PM; Sun 2 - 5 PM; cl Mon. No admis. Estab 1903 for the collection and exhibition of fine art (painting, sculpture, photography, fiber arts), and as an educational resource. One of the largest museums in the mountain west, it has nine galleries with 15,000 sq ft of exhibit space and a theatre. Average Annual Attendance: 30,000. Mem: 300; dues $10.
Income: $60,000 (financed by membership, city and state appropriations). Purchases: $5,000 - $10,000.
Collections: American art for the first half of the 20th century; 18th & 19th century European art; †Cyrus Dallin bronzes; †Utah artists (especially John Hafen).
Exhibitions: Annual National April Show (national painting and two-dimensional invitational); June Quilt and Fiber Show; High Schools of Utah Show; Utah Valley Sculptors.
Publications: Museum Newsletter, quarterly.
Activities: Classes for adults and children; docent training; lect open to public, 12 vis lectr per yr; concerts; tours; museum shop selling books, reproductions and jewelry.
Library: Open to public for reference. Holdings: Vols 100; Per subs 10; Other—Archival photographs.

VERNAL

LITTLE GALLERY OF ARTS,* 155 E Main St, 84078. Tel: 801-789-3123. *Pres* LeOra Jacobe.
Open 1 - 9 PM. No admis. Estab 1952. Mem: 60; dues regular $5, exhibiting $10; meetings in January, April, July and Oct.
Income: Financed by membership and city and state approrpriation.
Exhibitions: Dinosaur Land Art Festival each summer; Crafts and Arts Show each October; Utah Potters Guild Show; one-man shows.
Publications: Arty Facts, quarterly.
Activities: Competitions and special events.

VERMONT

BENNINGTON

BENNINGTON MUSEUM,* W Main St, 05201. Tel: 802-442-2180. *Chief Cur* Peter W Cook; *Admin* Stanley R Pike Jr; *Cur Military & Mechanical Arts* Eugene R Kosche.
Open May 1 - Nov 30 9 AM - 4:30 PM; summer 9 AM - 6 PM; cl Dec, Jan & Feb. Inc 1876, opened building 1928; local historical museum with gallery. Grandma Moses Schoolhouse Museum. Average Annual Attendance: 80,000. Mem: 650; dues $10 and up; annual meeting spring.
Income: Approximately $150,000.
Collections: Largest collection of Bennington Pottery on public display; rare collections of American blown and pressed glass; a gallery of Grandma Moses paintings; collections of furniture; dolls; rare documents; historical material; Early American household items, contemporary Vermont and other European paintings and sculptures, and the famous Bennington Flag.
Activities: Lectures; gallery tours for organized classes of school children; gallery of changing exhibitions; Gift shop.
Library: *Librn* Charles G Bennett. Genealogical reference file for Bennington and surrounding area.

BRATTLEBORO

BRATTLEBORO MUSEUM AND ART CENTER, Old Railroad Station (Mailing Add: Box 800, 05301). Tel: 802-257-0124. *Pres* Peter Benton; *VPres* Mary Blair; *Secy* Marjorie Runnion; *Treas* Marilyn Benton; *Admin Dir* Nancy Huelsberg; *Admin Asst* Ruth Adams.
Open mid-May - mid-Dec Tues - Sun 1 - 4 PM, cl Mon. No admis but donations encouraged. Estab 1972 to promote and make accessible to the community the field of art and cultural history of Brattleboro; the museum is located in a railroad station built in 1915, now a Registered Historic Site. Average Annual Attendance: 5000 - 6000. Mem: 250; dues $5 - $100; annual meeting Jan.
Income: $16,000 (financed by membership, city appropriation and other funding).
Collections: Permanent exhibition of Estey Organ Exhibit (manufactured in Brattleboro in 19th Century).
Exhibitions: (1976-77) Juried Art Show; Brattleboro 1876; 19th Century Paintings in Brattleboro; Folk Art in Vermont 1776-1976; Juried Photo Show; Sculpture of Francis Shanafian; World of Royal Tyler; Walter Blodgett (watercolors); Stamp Exhibit; Art Lending Exhibit; Myron Ward Retrospective.

Activities: Classes for adults and children; lect open to the public, 5-6 vis lectr per yr; concerts; gallery talks; competitions; individual paintings lent to members and businesses; lending collection contains paintings, photographs; sales shop selling books, magazines, original art.

BROOKFIELD

COLLEGE OF THE AMERICAS, Museum of the Americas, (formerly located in Pensacola, Florida), Rt 14, 05036. *Pres* Earle W Newton.
Open at a later date, under construction. Estab 1971 to gather materials in support of Anglo-American and Hispanic-American studies.
Income: Financed by endowment.
Collections: Anglo-American paintings 16th - 19th century; English mezzotints; Hogarth prints and paintings; colonial maps; Hispanic-American decorative arts; Pre-Columbian artifacts; Latin American folk art.
Exhibitions: Anglo-American paintings exhibited 1960-72 at various museums in New England and Florida.
—**Library.** For reference only. Books in temporary storage.
Special Collections: Anglo-American art; American history; British history, Spanish and Latin American history and art.

BURLINGTON

UNIVERSITY OF VERMONT, Robert Hull Fleming Museum, 05401. Tel: 802-656-2090. *Dir* William C Lipke; *Cur* Nina Parris; *Registrar* Colleen Montgomery; *Pub Relations* Louisa Judge; *Admin Asst* Constance Kurth.
Open Mon - Fri 9 AM - 5 PM; Sat & Sun 1 - 5 PM. No admis. Estab 1973 as a fine arts Museum for the area and a teaching facility for the University. Four permanent galleries, one gallery for student exhibitions and three galleries of changing exhibits. Mem: 180; dues student $5, individual $10, family $15.
Income: Financed by endowment, membership, state appropriation and grants.
Collections: Oriental, ancient, Medieval and American art; costumes, ethnographic collections, especially native American; prints and drawings of various periods.
Exhibitions: Vision and Fantasy in Planning for Burlington, Vermont; Canadian Landscapes; Spectrum Multiples; Peruvian Portfolio; Senior Show; Burlington: the Centennial Decades 1860-1900; Pre-Columbian Art; Walton Blodgett; Between Friends/Entre Amis; Pat Adams, Works on Paper.
Publications: The Muse, Museum Calendar; comprehensive calendar.
Activities: Classes for children; dramatic programs; docent training; lect open to public and members, 12 vis lectr per yr; gallery talks; tours; traveling exhibitions organized and circulated; sales shop selling books, cards, calendars and museum publications.
Library: Wilbur Room. *Librn* Louisa Judge. Open to students and others for reference.

FAIRLEE

WALKER MUSEUM, Route 5, 05045. Tel: 802-333-9572. *Pres* Herbert Brooks Walker; *Dirs* Brooks & Noel Walker
Open July - Sept daily 10 AM - 5 PM. No admis, donations accepted. Estab 1960. Average Annual Attendance: 1000.
Collections: †Japanese room; Iranian Bazaar; †Chinese porcelains; †American decorative arts; furniture; †Canadian displays; †American Indian art; †18th and 19th century American paintings; prints and sculpture; †Polynesia.
Activities: Materials and items lent to libraries and schools, ethnographic, illustrative, economic surveys; Wagon loans by appointment; temporary and traveling exhibitions.
Library: For reference. Holdings: Vols 1000; AV—Kodachromes; Other—Photographic 1000.

MANCHESTER

SOUTHERN VERMONT ART CENTER, 05254. Tel: 802-362-1405. *Pres* Dr Ilsley S Zecher; *Dir* Thomas Reilly Dibble; *Dir Public Relations* Mrs Arthur Pierce.
Open June - mid-Oct daily 10 AM - 5 PM, cl Mon. Estab 1929 to promote education in the arts and to hold exhibitions of art in its various forms. Average Annual Attendance: 20,000. Mem: 1100; dues artist $15, layman $20 and higher; annual meeting Sept.
Income: $100,000 (financed by membership and sales).
Collections: Contemporary American sculptors and painters; loan collection.
Exhibitions: Annual exhibition for members; Fall Show; one-man and special exhibitions.
Publications: Annual catalog and brochures.

Activities: Classes for adults in painting, drawing, graphic arts, photography, sculpture, voice, weaving and pottery.
Library. Holdings—Vols 500 of arts and history.

MIDDLEBURY

MIDDLEBURY COLLEGE, Johnson Gallery, 05753. Tel: 802-388-2762. *Dir* David A Bumbeck; *Asst Dir* Glenn Andres.
Open Mon - Fri Noon - 5 PM; Sat 9 AM - Noon. No admis. Estab 1968 as a teaching collection and also to sponsor exhibitions of selected artists.
Income: Financed through the College.
Collections: †Paintings; †prints; †drawings; †sculpture.
Exhibitions: Hannes Beckmann: Paintings at Dartmouth 1971-75; Currier & Ives Prints; Vermont Landscape Images 1776-1976; Graphic Works.
Publications: Annual report.

SHELDON ART MUSEUM,* One Park St, 05753. Tel: 802-388-2117. *Pres* Harold M Curtiss; *Cur* Mrs Nina R Mudge.
Open June 1 - Oct 15 Mon - Sat 10 AM - 5 PM; winter hours by appointment. Admis adults $1, children 50¢. Estab 1882 for the preservation of portraits, furniture and artifacts of Middlebury. Seventeen rooms arranged as a 19th century Vermont home. Average Annual Attendance: 2500. Mem: 400; dues $3 and up.
Collections: Portraits; china; glass; pewter; historical material.
Activities: Educ Dept; guided tours.
Library: Open to the public by request. Holdings: Vols 8000; Other—Documents 40,000, bound copies of newspapers, manuscripts.

VERMONT STATE CRAFT CENTER AT FROG HOLLOW, Frog Hollow Rd, 05753. Tel: 802-388-4871. *Chmn Bd* David Crawford; *VChmn Bd* Deborah Clifford; *Exec Dir* Patricia J Nolan; *Secy* Nancy Wright; *Treas* Robert Perry.
Open Mon - Sat 10 AM - 5 PM. No admis. Estab 1971 to provide craft educational, informational and marketing services to schoolchildren, adults and professionals. The building was once a working mill. Average Annual Attendance: 40,000. Mem: 350; dues $10 - $25; annual meeting Sept.
Income: $175,000 (financed by membership, Federal & State grants, consignment receipts and tuition). Purchases: $500-$1000.
Collections: †Vermont crafts.
Exhibitions: Reflections: stained glass, blown glass and other reflective things; Annual Festival of Crafts; Things Made by Hand for Christmas; Wood; In An April Garden; Fibers and Fabrics.
Publications: Vermont Crafts Journal, quarterly; Bulletin, bimonthly.
Activities: Classes for adults and children; dramatic programs; lect open to public, 3 vis lectr per yr; original objects of art lent to non-profit organizations; traveling exhibitions organized and circulated; sales shop selling tote bags, posters, calendars, buttons.

MONTPELIER

WOOD ART GALLERY, 135 Main St, 05602. Tel: 802-229-0036. *Cur* Ronald Slayton; *Asst Cur* Olivia Bravakis.
Open Tues - Sat Noon - 4 PM; Sat. No admis. Estab 1895; set up by the late Montpelier artist Thomas Waterman Wood as a place to house and exhibit a portion of his oils and watercolors of genre paintings. Also an exhibit place for local and regional artists. The gallery has two exhibit areas—a large room 50' square and a small room 20' square. The rooms are lighted with fluorescent lights. Average Annual Attendance: 4000. Mem: 300; dues $5 - $25; annual meeting Dec.
Income: Financed by endowment and partial funding from city.
Collections: Paintings by Thomas Waterman Wood; Paintings by contemporaries DeHass, Durand, Deschamps, Wyant; a collection of American artists of 1920's and 30's.
Exhibitions: Monthly exhibits by local and regional artists and group shows by artists and craftsmen.
Publications: Monograph on the Wood Collection.
Activities: Lect open to public, 1-2 vis lectr per yr; gallery talks; competitions; individual paintings lent to other galleries, museums and businesses in the area.

RUTLAND

RUTLAND AREA ART ASSOCIATION, INC,* Chaffee Art Gallery, 16 S Main St, 05701. Tel: 802-775-0356. *Pres* Edith Smith.
Open daily 11 AM - 5 PM; Sun 1 - 4 PM. No admis. Estab 1961, inc 1962 and sponsored by the Rutland Area Art Association, to promote and maintain an educational and cultural center in Rutland for the area artists, photographers, craftsmen and others in the art field. Average Annual Attendance: 6000. Mem dues: inactive artists and laymen $5 and up, exhibiting $10; annual meeting Oct.
Income: Financed by city appropriation.

Exhibitions: Annual Members Exhibit, juried; Autumn Members Exhibit, juried; one-man and invitational exhibits; Art-in-the-Park outdoor festival; Foliage Festival; displays of photography, flower arrangements, hobby collections, special shows.
Publications: Calendar of Events, annually.
Activities: Art classes in summer for adults, teens and children; special events in performing arts; art lectures, musicals, craft and art demonstrations, slide shows.

SAINT JOHNSBURY

ST JOHNSBURY ATHENAEUM, 30 Main St, 05819. Tel: 802-748-8291. *Librn* Jean F Marcy.
Open Mon - Sat 9:30 AM - 5 PM; Mon & Fri open to 8 PM. No admis. Estab 1873 and maintained as a 19th century gallery; given to the townspeople by Horace Fairbanks. It is the oldest art gallery still in its original form in the United States—a one-room addition to the public library building.
Income: Financed by endowment and city appropriation.
Collections: 19th century American landscape paintings of the Hudson River School (Bierstadt, Colman, Whittredge, Cropsey, Gifford, Hart brothers); copies of masterpieces; sculpture.
Library: The art gallery is in the public library.

SHELBURNE

SHELBURNE MUSEUM, Route 7, 05468. Tel: 802-985-3344. *Pres* Samuel B Webb; *Dir* Kenneth E Wheeling; *Asst to Dir* Joseph Mullen; *Registrar* Margaret Moody.
Open Mon - Sun 9 AM - 5 PM (May 15 - Oct 15). Admis adults $5.00, children $2.50. Estab 1947 as a Museum of the American Spirit and to collect and preserve art and artifacts of Americana. The Webb Gallery (American Art); Electra Havemeyer Webb Memorial Building (European art); Beach Gallery (outdoor and sporting art). Average Annual Attendance: 135,000. Annual meeting June.
Income: Financed by endowment.
Collections: Americana: art, furniture, textiles, tools, folk art, china, glass, dolls, toys, carriages; 35 buildings and houses, the houses furnished as 18th & 19th century homes; European art.
Activities: Lect open to public, 7 - 8 vis lectr per yr; individual paintings and original objects of art lent to other museums; museum shop selling books, prints and slides.
Library: *Librn* Carroll Guitar. Open to the public for reference. Holdings: Vols 6600; Per subs 85. Special Subjects: Art, furniture, textiles.

SPRINGFIELD

SPRINGFIELD ART & HISTORICAL SOCIETY, 9 Elm St, 05156. Tel: 802-885-2415. *Pres* Henry Swierczynski; *VPres* Mrs Lawrence B Woolson; *Dir* Mrs Fred R Herrick; *Treas* Harold Bush; *Clerk* Virgil Erickson.
Open Noon - 4:30 PM. No admis. Estab 1955 for the purpose of presenting history, art and classes in the arts to the community; gallery maintained for monthly exhibits. Average Annual Attendance: 3000; Mem: 150; dues $7.50, $15 and $25; annual meeting Sept.
Income: $3500 (financed by endowment and membership).
Collections: Primitive portraits by H Bundy, Aaron D Fletcher and Ashel Powers; Richard Lee—pewter; Bennington pottery; paintings by local artists.
Exhibitions: Theorem Painting; Students Show; Art Vermont; Drawings by Aidron Duckworth; Paintings by Frank Woychiken; Member Show; Marilyn Blinkhorn Watercolors; Christmas Show and Sale.
Publications: Annual schedule of events and monthly notices.
Activities: Classes for adults and children; musical programs during the summer; lect open to the public; gallery talks; individual paintings lent; lending collection contains original art work, paintings, photographs, sculpture, slides; sales shop selling books, original art, slides.
Library. Tel: 802-885-2415. *Librn* Mrs. Fred R Herrick. Open to the public. Holdings: Vols 300; Per subs 3.

WAITSFIELD

BUNDY ART GALLERY,* PO Box 19, 05673. Tel: 802-496-3713. *Dir* Harlow Carpenter; *Admin* Elizabeth Joslin.
Open July 1 - Aug 31 weekdays 10 AM - 5 PM; Sun 1 - 5 PM; cl Tues and July 4. Estab 1962, inc 1963 to make contemporary art and an art library accessible to the public and to enhance the cultural life of surrounding communities. Average Annual Attendance: 2000.
Collections: †Contemporary painting and sculpture.
Activities: Concerts; traveling exhibitions booked.
Library: Holdings—Vols 450.

WINDSOR

SAINT-GAUDENS NATIONAL HISTORIC SITE, United States Department of Interior, National Park Service, Saint Gaudens Rd, PO Box Windsor VT 05089. *Cur* John H Dryfhout.
For information see Cornish, New Hampshire.

VIRGINIA

ALEXANDRIA

NORTHERN VIRGINIA FINE ARTS ASSOCIATION, 201 Prince St, 22314. Tel: 703-548-0035. *Pres* R Sherrard Elliot; *VPres* Mrs Robert L Montague; *Secy* Mrs Gerald Korn; *Exec Dir* Nancy F Achenbach.
Open Sept - May Tues - Sat 10 AM - 4 PM; Sun 1 - 4 PM; cl Mon. Estab 1964 to promote education, appreciation, participation and pursuit of excellence in all forms of art and crafts; to enrich the cultural life of the metropolitan area and Northern Virginia; main gallery space on main floor, with additional area available. Average Annual Attendance: 15,000. Mem: 650; dues single $20, double $25.
Exhibitions: Winners of the 8th Annual Juried Athenaeum Show: Betty Kubalak (graphics), Claire Monderer (paintings), Bob Romanowski (sculpture); John Toole (1815-60) Virginia Primitive into Painter; Annual Athenaeum Christmas Exhibit; Prayer Rugs; Alexandria, VA-The First 100 Years; 9th Annual Juried Show; Allen Carter-Horace Day (two-man show).
Publications: Newsletter, monthly.
Activities: Gallery talks; tours; competitions with awards; sales shop selling slides.

BLACKSBURG

BLACKSBURG REGIONAL ART ASSOCIATION,* c/o Bernard J Sabaroff, Pres, 2501 Capistrano St, 24060. Tel: 703-552-0441. *Secy* Pat Furey.
Estab 1950, a chapter of the Virginia Museum of Fine Arts dedicated to the encouragement and the enjoyment of the arts. Meetings several times per year; dues single $5, family $7.50.
Collections: †Collection of paintings (12) by contemporary artists who have exhibited in Blacksburg.
Exhibitions: Nine in last three years.
Activities: Traveling exhibitions organized and circulated from Virginia Museum of Fine Arts; lect open to the public, 3-5 vis lectrs per yr; concerts; dramatic programs; competitions.

VIRGINIA POLYTECHNIC INSTITUTE AND STATE UNIVERSITY
—**University Art Gallery,** 20 Owens Hall, 24061. Tel: 703-951-5547. *Head Art Department* Prof Dean Carter; *Gallery Coordr* Claudia Beckwith.
Open Mon - Fri 8 AM - 5 PM; Tues & Thurs 7 - 9 PM; Sat & Sun 1 - 5 PM. No admis. Estab 1969; new location Sept 1975 to serve needs of Art Department as a teaching gallery as well as to meet community needs in an area where there are few large art centers and museums; gallery is located in same building as Art Dept; exhibition area is approx 30 x 30 ft. Average Annual Attendance: 800 plus student use.
Income: Financed through Department's Operational Budget.
Collections: Student print collection.
Exhibitions: (1976-78) Art Faculty Exhibition; Watercolors from the Virginia Museum; Art Alumni Exhibition; Paperworks Exhibition; Bridges: The Spans of North America; Art Student Christmas Show and Sale; Popular Art Culture, Christiana Prints; Collectors' Exhibition; Crafts Invitational; Fifth Annual Invitational; Graduate Student Invitational; Senior Art Majors Exhibition; Milton Avery Prints: 1933-1955; Works on Paper by Jerome Neuner; Freshworks; Photographic Concepts of Nova Scotia and New Brunswick by Bob Veltri; Prints by Bill Lidh.
Publications: Exhibition calendar; some gallery announcements.
Activities: Docent training to college students; lect open to the public; 3 vis lectr per yr; gallery talks; individual paintings and original objects of art lent to faculty and staff offices on campus, as well as library and continuing education center; traveling exhibitions organized and circulated.
—**Squires Art Gallery,*** Squires Student Center, 24061. Tel: 703-951-5535. *Dir of Squires* Thomas C Lile; *Dir Arts* Thomas F Butterfield.
Open Mon - Sat 8 AM - Noon; Sun 9 AM - Noon. Estab Sept, 1969 to provide interesting and informative exhibits on the local and national level for the students, faculty and the college community; weekly meetings of students and advisor to plan shows and events. Average Annual Attendance: 50,000.
Income: $3000 - $5000 (financed by student activity fee and building operation). Purchases: $300.
Activities: Lect open to the public, 3 vis lectr per yr; competitions.

—**College of Architecture Library:** Tel: 951-6182, exten 703. *Dean* Charles Burchard; *Arch Librn* Robert E Stephenson.
Open Mon - Thurs 8 AM - 11 PM; Fri & Sat 8 AM - 5 PM; Sun 2 - 11 PM. Estab 1928 to provide library service to the College of Architecture and the other divisions of the University; gallery not maintained. Circ: 23,126.
Income: $58,331 (financed by membership, city and state appropriation). Purchases: $58,331.
Holdings: Vols 32,000; Per subs 380; AV—Cassettes, microfiche, microfilm; Other—Clipping files, exhibition catalogs, pamphlets.
Special Subjects: Architecture, art, building construction, urban affairs and planning.
Special Collections: Planning file of 2000 pieces.

CHARLES CITY

WESTOVER,* Charles City County, 23030. *Owner* Mrs B C Fisher; *Mgr* Mrs B C Pearce.
Grounds and Garden open daily 9 AM - 6 PM; admis $1. (House not open).
Built about 1730 by William Byrd II, Founder of Richmond, the house is considered an outstanding example of Georgian architecture in America, with steeply sloping roof, tall chimneys in pairs at both ends, the elaborate Westover doorway; three story central structure with two end wings. The path from the Caretakers House near the gate to the house is lined with tulip poplars over 100 years old; former kitchen is a separate small brick building, believed to be older than the residence. East of the house is the foundation of an old icehouse, a dry well with passageways leading under the house to the river. The Westover gates of delicate ironwork incorporate initials, WEB; lead eagles on the gateposts, supporting fence columns topped with stone finials cut to resemble pineapples, beehives, and other symbolic designs. Long-established boxwood garden with tomb of William Byrd II. Members of his family, and Capt William Perry, who died Aug 6, 1637, are located in old church cemetery one-fourth mile west of house.

CHARLOTTESVILLE

MONTICELLO,* Thomas Jefferson Memorial Foundation, PO Box 316, 22902. Tel: 804-295-2657. *Pres* Walter M Whitehill; *Cur-Dir* James A Bear, Jr.
Open Mar 1 - Nov 1, 8 AM - 5 PM; Nov 1 - Feb 28, 9 AM - 4:30 PM; admis adults $2, children 6-11 years and school groups, 50¢.
Monticello is owned and maintained by the Thomas Jefferson Memorial Foundation, a nonprofit organization founded in 1923. The home of Thomas Jefferson, designed by him and built 1769-1809, contains many original furnishings and art objects.

UNIVERSITY OF VIRGINIA

—**Art Museum,** Thomas H Bayly Memorial Bldg, Rugby Rd, 22903. Tel: 804-924-3592. *Cur* David B Lawall.
Open Tues - Sun 1 - 5 PM, cl Mon. No admis. Estab 1935 to make original works of art available to students of the University and to the general public. Average Annual Attendance: 18,000. Mem: 450; dues $5 up.
Income: Financed by membership and state appropriation.
Collections: †American art; †contemporary art; †art from the age of Jefferson; †Asian art; †19th and 20th century prints and drawings; ethnic art; 17th and 18th century European painting; European and American sculpture.
Exhibitions: (1976-78) Balcomb Greene; C C Wang; Anton Refregier; Philippe Hosiasson; Contemporary Realism; Ann Truitt.
Publications: Calendar, monthly; exhibition catalogs.
Activities: Docent training; extensive program of tours for-school children led by docents; lect open to the public, 3 vis lectr per yr; gallery talks; tours; individual paintings lent to other museums; museum shop selling books, original art, reproductions, slides.
—**Fiske Kimball Fine Arts Library,** Bayly Dr, 22903. Tel: 804-924-7024. *Librarian* Mary C Dunnigan; *Slide Librn* Marika S Simms.
Open school year Mon - Fri 8 AM - 11 PM; Sat 8 AM - 6 PM; Sun 1 - 11 PM. Estab 1970 as an academic research library for School of Architecture, Art and Drama Depts. Fifty percent of collection is noncirculating.
Income: $50,000-70,000 (financed by state appropriation and gifts).
Holdings: Vols 54,000 (Art) 85,000 (architecture) AV—Microfiche, microfilm, slides; Other—Exhibition catalogs, pamphlets, photographs.
Special Subjects: Architectural history; Art history.
Special Collections: Rare books.
Publications: Accession list; Slide library three times per yr.
Activities: Lect; tours.

FARMVILLE

LONGWOOD COLLEGE, Bedford Gallery, Pine St, 23901. Tel: 804-392-9359. *Chmn of Art Dept & Dir* Barbara L Bishop.
Open Mon - Fri 9 AM - noon, 1 - 5 PM; Sat & Sun 2 - 6 PM, excepting college holidays. No admis. Estab 1970 to present educational exhibits of professional artists for students and community.
Income: Financed by state appropriation.
Collections: †Art Dept collection; †collection of works by contemporary Virginia artists; †Thomas Sully Gallery Collection of 19th century American art.
Exhibitions: (1976-78) Barbara Bishop (prints, drawings, photographs); Ron and Barbara Wyancko (jewelry and weaving); Works by Bernard Martin; Virginia Artists in the International Women's Arts Festival; The Weinstein Collection of Contemporary Art; Mark Baldridge (Jewelry and metalwork; Craft Collectables II; Nancy and Jack Witt (paintings and sculpture); Scott McKinnis (prints); Victor Huggins and Fred Nichols (paintings); Homage/Yeatts Gallery; David Alexick (works); Paul Kline (sculpture); Craft Collectables III; Thomas Sully and His Contemporaries; and Works by David Freed.
Publications: Catalog for exhibit/Thomas Sully and His Contemporaries.
Activities: Lect open to the public; individual paintings and original objects of art lent; lending collection contains original art works.

FREDERICKSBURG

JAMES MONROE LAW OFFICE MUSEUM AND MEMORIAL LIBRARY, 908 Charles St, 22401. Tel: 703-373-8426. *Dir* Paulette Skirbunt Watson.
Open daily 9 AM - 5 PM; cl Christmas. Admis Adults $1, children 50¢, group rates available. Open to the public 1928. Owned by the Commonwealth of Virginia and under control of the Board of Regents of Mary Washington College. A National Historic Landmark. Established to keep in memory the life and service of James Monroe and of his contribution to the principles of government, to preserve his treasured possessions for present and future generations.
Income: Financed by Foundation, gifts and grants.
Collections: Louis XVI furniture purchased by the Monroes in France in 1794 and later used by them in the White House; portraits; sculpture; silver; china; jewelry.
Publications: Library of James Monroe, catalog.
Activities: Tours; museum shop selling books, reproductions, prints, slides and history related objects; exclusive items from local crafts people.
Library: Chmn Libr Committee Ruby Weinbrecht. Open by appointment only. Holdings: Vols 20,000; Other—Manuscripts, letters, documents.

HAMPTON

HAMPTON ASSOCIATION FOR THE ARTS AND HUMANITIES,* 22 Wine St, 23669. Tel: 804-723-9940. *Dir Fine Arts* James Steele; *Dir Photography* Colis Davis, Jr.
Open winter Mon - Fri 1 - 6 PM; Sat 10 AM - Noon; summer Mon - Sat 10 AM - 9 PM; cl school holidays. No admis. Estab 1966 as a non-profit organization to collect and exhibit art.
Collections: Paintings; sculpture; photography; archaeology.
Exhibitions: Temporary exhibitions; guest artist shows; students work.
Activities: Lectures; gallery talks; films.

HAMPTON INSTITUTE, College Museum, 23668. Tel: 804-727-5308. *Dir* Julia R Vodicka.
Open Mon - Fri 8 AM - 5 PM; Sat & Sun by appointment. No admis.
Income: Financed by college funds.
Collection: Contemporary Afro-American art; traditional African; American Indian and Oceanic art.
Activities: Lect open to the public; film series; individual paintings and original objects of art lent.

HARRISONBURG

JAMES MADISON UNIVERSITY, Sawhill Gallery, Duke Fine Arts Center, 22801. Tel: 703-433-6216. *Head, Art Dept* Dr J David Diller.
Open Mon - Fri 8 AM - noon, 1 - 4:30 PM. No admis. Estab 1967 to schedule changing exhibitions for the benefit of students and citizens of this area; one-room gallery of 1040 sq ft with movable panels. Average Annual Attendance: 7000 - 10,000.
Income: Financed by state appropriation, and is part of operation in Art Dept budget.
Collections: Staples Collection of Indonesian art; Sawhill Collection—mainly artifacts from classical civilizations; †small group of modern works.
Exhibitions: (1977-78) Selections from Sawhill Collection; Homes for Better Living: Laserworks by Lawrence Goodridge; Jeff Bayer (sculpture); prints from Univ of Nebraska; weaving and ceramics; JMU Faculty Show; Shenandoah sculpture; Exposure Time (photography

show); JMU Graduate Students Show; New York on Paper; Hiroshige Woodcuts; JMU Undergraduate Show; Regional High School Art.
Activities: Competitions.

LEESBURG

OATLANDS,* Rte 2, Box 352, 22075. Tel: 703-777-3174. *Adminr & Property Council & Staff of National Trust Interpretors* Miriam G Rabb; *Coordr Interpretive Progs* Carole T Scanlon.
Open April 1 - Oct 31, Mon - Sat 10 AM - 5 PM; Sun & legal holidays 1 - 5 PM; cl end of Oct - Mar 31; admis adults $1.50, senior citizens 75¢, group rates by arrangements; free to National Trust members. Average Annual Attendance: (1975) 21,200.
Oatlands is a Classical Revival Mansion constructed by George Carter, son of Robert (Councillor) Carter (circa 1800-06). Oatlands is a property of National Trust for Historic Preservation operated as an historic house museum and a community preservation center. It was partially remodeled in 1827 when the front portico with hand carved Corinthian capitals was added. Confederate troops were billeted here during the Civil War. The home remained in possession of the Carters until 1897.
In 1903, Mr and Mrs Corcoran Eustis of Washington, DC, bought Oatlands. Their daughters gave the property to the National Trust for Historic Preservation.
Oatlands is essentially a Carter House with the Eustis Collection of furniture. Greek-Revival ornament adorns the interior. Terraced boxwood, magnolias, a bowling green and a gazebo grace the elaborate formal gardens.
Property serves as a focal point for advancing historic preservation and develops new relationships among cultural, community preservation groups and National Trust members in its area. Responds to community preservation needs by acting as a link between community and appropriate regional or headquarters offices of National Trust.
Located in the heart of northern Virginia hunt country, the property is protected by 261 preservation easements which help insure the estate's continuing role as a center for equestrian sports and events which are produced by various groups in Loudon County. Interpretive Programs provide focus on Oatlands particular case study in historic preservation. 'Christmas at Oatlands' and Members Day during National Historic Preservation Week in early May. The Carriage House conference room may be reserved for meetings. Preservation shop.

LEXINGTON

WASHINGTON AND LEE UNIVERSITY
—**DuPont Gallery,** 24450. Tel: 703-463-9111, exten 350. *Chmn Art Division* Dr Gerard Maurice Doyon; *Secy* Shirley Hughes; *Dir* Dr Albert C Gordon.
Open Mon - Fri 8 AM - 5 PM; cl June, July & Aug. No admis. Estab 1929 in separate gallery, in existence since 1742, as teaching resource of the Art Department of the College of Liberal Arts. One room, 30 x 60 ft for temporary exhibits; one storeroom, offices, and studios. Average Annual Attendance: 40,000.
Income: Financed through the university.
Collections: Reeves Collection of Chinese export porcelain; Collection in storage until the university obtains a museum. European paintings from 17th-mid 19th centuries; a few contemporary works (students, faculty, alumni).
Exhibitions: Monthly exhibitions; annual student show; annual faculty show; Chinese Art exhibit; American Art Exhibition; French Art Exhibition.
Activities: Lect open to public, 10-20 vis lect per yr; gallery talks; original objects of art lent.
—**McCormick Library** (part of the main University Library). *Librn* Maurice Leach.
Open for reference to students, scholars, public.
Holdings: Vols 200,000; Per subs 100; Other—Slides 50,000.
Special Subjects: American Art of 18th & 19th centuries.
Special Collections: Rare books, 17th - 19th centuries.
—**Lee Chapel and Museum.** Tel: 703-463-9111, exten 289. *Dir* Robert C Peniston.
Open mid-Apr to mid-Oct Mon - Sat 9 AM - 5 PM; Sun 2 - 5 PM, mid-Oct to mid-Apr, Mon - Sat 9 AM - 4 PM; Sun 2 - 5 PM. No admis. Estab 1868 as a part of the University. It is used for concerts, speeches and other events; also to display the paintings, collections, and personal items of the Washington and Lee families. The Lee Chapel is a National Historic Landmark. Average Annual Attendance: 38,000.
Income: Financed through the university.
Collections: Lee archives; Custis-Washington-Lee art collection; recumbent statute of General Lee by Valentine; Lee family crypt; Lee's office.
Publications: Brochure.
Activities: Sales shop selling books, prints, slides, souvenirs.

LORTON

GUNSTON HALL PLANTATION, Gunston Road, 22079. Tel: 703-550-9220. *First Regent* Mrs Cabell Mayo Tabb; *Dir* Captain Walter W Price; *Mgr* Louise L Stockdale; *Exec Secy* Margaret C Roudabush.
Open daily 9:30 AM - 5 PM, except Christmas. Admis adults $2, students (6 - 15 yrs) 50¢. Estab 1949 to acquaint the public with George Mason, Colonial patriot, and his 18th Century house and gardens, covering 555 acres; owned and operated by the Commonwealth of Virginia. Average Annual Attendance: 48,000.
Income: $235,000 (financed by city and state appropriation, and admission fees).
Collections: 18th century English and American decorative arts, furniture and paintings, and 18th and 19th century family pieces.
Exhibitions: (1977-78) Buckland, Master Builder of the 18th century.
Activities: Docent training; lect open to the public, 8 vis lectr per yr; gallery talks; tours; artmobile; individual paintings and original objects of art lent to other museums; lending collection contains cassettes, film strips, motion pictures, slides; sales shop selling books, reproductions; Children's Touch Museum located in basement.
—**Library.** Tel: 703-550-9220. *Librn-Archivist* Bennie Brown Jr.
Open Tues - Sat 9:30 AM - 5 PM by appointment. Estab 1974 to re-create an 18th Century Virginia gentleman's library as a research source plus acquire a working reference collection on George Mason, and the decorative arts.
Income: Financed by endowment, city appropriation.
Holdings: Reference only. Vols 500; Per subs 50; AV—Microfiche, microfilm, slides; Other—Original Documents, pamphlets, photographs.
Special Subjects: Early Virginiana, Mason family, genealogy, decorative arts, rare books and documents.
Special Collections: Pamel C Copeland Collection; Robert Cartier Collection; Mason-Mercer Collection.

LYNCHBURG

LYNCHBURG FINE ARTS CENTER, INC, 1815 Thomson Dr, 24501. Tel: 804-846-8451. *Pres* Orion A Templeton; *Adminr* Jane McKee Mundy; *Secy & Bookkeeper* Donna M Hudson; *Art Coordr* Ron Boehmer.
Open Mon - Fri 9 AM - 5 PM; other hours depending upon programs. No admis to building, $4 for theatre and concert productions, $5 for musical play. Estab 1958 to promote interest in and appreciation and talent for art, music, dramatic literature and other fine arts. Mem dues student $15, single $30, double $50; annual meeting in June.
Exhibitions: Ten exhibitions each year, plus Virginia Museum exhibits.
Income: Financed by membership.
Publications: FACets, (newspaper), monthly except July.
Activities: Classes for adults and children; dramatic programs; docent training; lect open to the public, 2-3 vis lectr per yr; concerts; gallery talks; tours; competitions; exten dept serving youth—Concerts for youth, and theatre classes in public schools; Artmobile; sales shop selling original art.
Library: Open to staff and volunteers at the Center for reference.

RANDOLPH-MACON WOMAN'S COLLEGE ART GALLERY,* 2500 Rivermont Ave, 24504. Tel: 804-846-7392. *Chmn Art Dept* Elliott R Twery; *Cur* Kent Ahrens.
Open 9 AM - 9 PM. No admis. Estab a collection of American painting for general and specific educational use; endowment. Art gallery was built in 1952 in cooperation with the National Gallery of Art, it houses part of the permanent collection and is used for special exhibitions; open by appointment.
Collections: Extensive collection of American paintings; European and American graphics.
Activities: Objects lent; lectures; concerts; dramatic programs.
Library: Photography collection.

McLEAN

INDUSTRIAL DESIGNERS SOCIETY OF AMERICA, 1750 Old Meadow Rd, 22101. Tel: 703-893-5575. *Pres* Richard Hollerith; *VPres* Robert Smith; *Secy* Allace H Appel; *Exec Dir* Brian J Wynne; *Mem Secy* Celia Shifflett.
For further information see National and Regional Organizations.

MIDDLETOWN

BELLEGROVE, PO Box 137, 22645. Tel: 703-869-2028. *Pres* Mrs C Ridgley White; *Exec Dir Bd of Trustees* Wynn Lee.
Open April - Oct Mon - Sat 10 AM - 4 PM; Sun 1 - 5 PM; Nov - March by appointment. Admis varies. Open to the public in 1967, it is preserved as an historic house, and is the property of the National Trust for Historic Preservation and managed by Belle Grove, Inc, an independent, local nonprofit organization. It serves as a local preservation center and

resource for the interpretation of regional culture in the Shenandoah Valley. Built in 1794 for Major Isaac Hite, Jr, a Revolutionary War officer and brother-in-law of James Madison, Belle Grove was designed with the help of Thomas Jefferson. During the Battle of Cedar Creek in 1864, the house served as headquarters to General Phillip Sheridan. The property is a working farm, and Belle Grove maintains an active program of events for the visiting public.

Seasonal programs include summer archaeological program for students, Farm Craft Days co-produced with surrounding community groups as well as a railsplitting contest. Members Day during National Historic Preservation Week is in early May. A set of 10 x 8 inch drawings of Belle Grove, taken by Historic American Buildings Survey, are available from the Preservation Shop.

MOUNT VERNON

MOUNT VERNON,* 22121. Tel: 703-780-2000. *Regent Mt Vernon Ladies' Association* Mrs Thomas Turner Cooke; *Resident Dir* Charles C Wall.

Open to the public every day in the year from 9 AM; ent gate closes Mar 1 - Oct 1 at 5 PM; Oct 1 - Mar 1 at 4 PM; admis $1. Average Annual Attendance: Approx 1,250,000.

The home of George Washington, purchased 1858 from his great-grand-nephew by the Mt Vernon Ladies' Association of the Union, which maintains it. Annual meeting Oct.

The Mansion is fully furnished with original and period furniture, silver, portraits and prints. Large collection of relics. Library theme, George Washington. Personal papers; biographical; life of the period and locale. The estate includes spinning house, coach house, various quarters, restored flower and kitchen gardens. Also the tomb of George and Martha Washington.

POPE-LEIGHEY HOUSE,* 22121. Tel: 703-780-3118. *Adminr* George Smith; *Asst Adminr, Property Council & Staff of National Trust Interpretors* Susan Smith; *Coordr Interpretive Progs* Carole T Scanlon.

Open early Apr - end of Nov, Sat & Sun 9:30 AM - 4:30 PM; cl end of Nov - end of Mar; admis adults $1.25, senior citizens 60¢; combination ticket with Woodlawn Mansion, adults $2, senior citizens $1, group tours by special arrangement with administrator; appointments available for study groups and architects. Average Annual Attendance: 7500.

Pope-Leighey is a house museum of the National Trust for Historic Preservation, located on the grounds of Woodlawn. This residence was designed in 1940 by Frank Lloyd Wright for his client, the Loren Pope Family. Built of cypress, brick and glass, the Usonian structure contains such features as a flat roof, radiant heat, indirect lighting and built-in furniture, all designed by Frank Lloyd Wright, and all considered unusual for their time. Threatened by proposed construction of an interstate highway in 1964, Mrs Majorie Folsom Leighey, second owner, presented the property to the National Trust for Historic Preservation. It was then moved to the Woodlawn grounds.

Publications: Brochure and paperback history of house.

WOODLAWN,* 22121. Tel: 703-780-3118. *Adminr* George Smith; *Asst Adminr, Property Council & Staff of National Trust Interpretors* Susan Smith; *Coordr Interpretive Programs* Carole T Scanlon.

Open daily 9:30 AM - 4:30 PM, including legal holidays; cl Christmas. Admis adults $1.25, senior citizens 60¢, group rates by arrangement. Combination ticket (in season) with Pope-Leighey House (on grounds) adults $1.25, senior citizens 60¢, group rates for both houses. Average Annual Attendance: (1975) 53,000; Originally part of Mount Vernon. Built 1800-1805 for George Washington's daughter upon her marriage to Lawrence Lewis. It was designed with central pavilion and flanking wings by Dr William Thornton, winner of the architectural competition for the design of the United States Capitol. A group of Quakers, a pioneer anthropologist, a playwright and Senator Oscar W Underwood of Alabama were among Woodlawn's residents after the Lewises. In 1951 the foundation's trustees decided that the visiting public would be better served if Woodlawn was administered by the National Trust; The mansion furnishings are largely from the Federal and early Empire periods, and include Lewis family memorabilia and gifts from the Robert Woods Bliss and Colonel Garbish Collection.

Activities: Property serves as a focal point for advancement of historic preservation in northern Virginia. Through it are developed new relationships among cultural, community, preservation groups and National Trust members in its area. Responds to community preservation needs by acting as a link between community and appropriate regional or headquarters offices of National Trust. Operates as a small conference center for preservation-education programs produced by the National Trust such as the annual Woodlawn Conference for Historic Site Administration; participates in the National Trust Summer Intern Program.

Interpretive programs emphasize Woodlawn's particular case history in historic preservation. Needlework exhibit each March with accompanying needlepoint classes. Carols by candlelight in December.

NEWPORT NEWS

MARINERS MUSEUM, One Museum Dr, 23606. Tel: 804-595-0368. *Pres* Dr William J Hargis Jr; *Dir* William D Wilkinson; *Asst Dir for Admin* Alene Cofer; *Asst Dir for Coll* John O Sands; *Educ Officer* C Steven Laise.

Open Mon - Sat 9 AM - 5 PM; Sun Noon - 5 PM; cl Christmas Day. Admis adults $1.50, children 6-16 years 75¢, children under 6 free. Estab 1930, the museum is devoted to the culture of the sea and its tributaries, its conquest by man and its influence on civilization; thirteen galleries. Average Annual Attendance: 150,000. Mem: 500; dues student $7.50, individual $10, family $15.

Collections: †Crabtree Collection of miniature ships; †over 10,000 paintings; †over 1000 ship models; †thousands of marine artifacts.

Publications: The Journal, quarterly.

Activities: Classes for adults and children; dramatic programs, lect open to the public, 10 vis lectr per yr; gallery talks; tours; competitions; individual paintings and original objects of art lent; lending collection contains motion pictures 120, original art works 2000, original prints 8000, paintings 1000; museum shop selling books, reproductions, prints, slides, decorative items (maritime related).

—**Library.** Tel: 804-595-0368. *Librn* Ardie L Kelly; *Asst to Librn* Kathryn B Braig; *Photo Cataloger* Carolyn Ritger.

Open Mon - Sat 9 AM - 5 PM. Estab 1930. For reference only.

Income: Financed by endowment.

Holdings: Vols 55,000; Per subs 188; AV—Film strips, motion pictures, phonorecords; Other—Clipping files, manuscripts, memorabilia, original documents, pamphlets, photographs.

PENINSULA ARTS ASSOCIATION, Two Museum Dr (Mailing Add: Box 6438, 23606). Tel: 703-245-0367, 703-596-8175. *Pres* Conway Sheild III; *VPres* Mrs Ward Scull III; *Secy* Mrs Rodney Ricketts; *Dir* Mrs Garland F Robeson.

Open Mon - Fri 10 AM - 4 PM; Sat 10 AM - 2 PM. No admis. Estab 1962 to bring the best art possible, to educate the people of the Virginia Peninsula, and to encourage local artists; three galleries are maintained with changing exhibitions. Average Annual Attendance: 4000. Mem: 550; dues individual $18, family (includes Va. Museum membership) $21; annual meeting 4th Mon March.

Income: Financed by membership.

Exhibitions: Juried Art Shows; print shows; student show; watercolors; sculptures; crafts; National Watercolor Show; custom furniture; macrame wallhangings.

Publications: Newsletter to members, monthly.

Activities: Classes for adults and children; lect open to the public, 8 vis lectr per yr; gallery talks; competitions with cash awards and certificates of distinction; sales shop selling books, original art and crafts.

NORFOLK

CHRYSLER MUSEUM AT NORFOLK, Olney Road and Mowbray Arch, 23510. Tel: 804-622-1211. *Dir* Mario Amaya; *Adminr* Kenneth M Beam; *Chief Cur* Eric M Zafran; *Cur American Art* Thomas W Styron; *Cur Decorative Arts* Mark A Clark; *Cur Glass* Nancy O Merrill; *Registrar* Judith C Riley; *Dir Educ* Ann Dearsley-Vernon; *Pres Bd Trustees* Walter P Chrysler, Jr; *VPres Bd Trustees* Mrs Reid Spencer; *Chmn Bd Trustees* Henry Clay Hofheimer II.

Open Tues - Sat 10 AM - 4 PM; Sun 1 - 5 PM; cl Mon. No admis (donation $1). Estab 1905 as a memorial association housing a collection of tapestries and paintings donated in name of Irene Leache; Norfolk Soc of Arts founded in 1917 to house collection. Funds raised in 1920's for a building which became the Norfolk Museum of Arts and Sciences. WPA money and labor completed the present Florentine Renaissance style building in 1933. New additions were added in 1960's and 1970's. Named Chrysler Museum in 1971 when deeded collections of the Chrysler Museum of Provincetown, Mass. 85,000 sq ft houses 39 galleries. Average Annual Attendance: 140,000. Mem: 3335; dues friend $100, sustaining $50, family $25, individual $15, student & sr citizen $10.

Income: Financed by state appropriation.

Collections: †Italian Renaissance & Baroque; †18th century English; †17th century English; †French Empire; †16th, 17th & 18th century French; †French Impressionist; †Post Impressionists; †17th century Dutch; †Flemish; †Spanish; †Medieval; †Egyptian; †American art; †20th century art; †Greco-Roman; †Institute of Glass; †Early Renaissance; †Indian, Persian, Japanese and Chinese; †17th & 18th century French; †Institute of Textile Research & Design.

Exhibitions: Pre-Columbian Art; Oriental Arts; Prints of Jean Emile Laboureur; Glassworks (John Nygren and Flora Mace); Edwardo Paolozzi (sculptor); Faye Zetlin; Robert Indiana; David Hockney (prints); Robert Mapplethorpe (photographs); Virginia Artists' Invitational.
Publications: Bulletin, monthly; exhibition catalogs.
Activities: Classes for adults and children; docent training; lect open to public, 20 vis lectr per yr; gallery talks; tours; competitions with cash prizes; exten dept operates three historic homes; individual paintings and original objects of art lent to museums; traveling exhibitions organized and circulated; museum shop selling books, original art, reproductions, prints, slides, postcards, jewelry and toys.
—Jean Outland Chrysler Library. *Librn* Jean Chrysler.
Open to scholars on a selective basis.
Holdings: Vols 200,000; Other—Microfiche 12,000.
Special Collections: Frank Vanderlip Jr architecture library with extensive collection of books on glass and decorative arts; M Knoedler & Co Ltd of London art reference library containing all major are reference books, extremely rare annotated sales catalogs dating back to 18th century and rare monographs on all major artists.

HERMITAGE FOUNDATION MUSEUM, 7637 North Shore Rd, 23505. Tel: 804-423-2052. *Pres of Bd* Adm W P Chilton USN (Ret); *Dir* Philip R. Morrison; *Cur/Registrar* Lela M Hine; *Asst to Dir* Mary Jean Redon Levin.
Open daily 10 AM - 5 PM, except Christmas Day. Admis adults $1, children (6-18 yrs) 25¢, children under 6 and service persons free, groups (10 or more) half price, schools, scouts free. Estab 1937 to disseminate information concerning arts, and maintain a collection of fine art materials; mansion on 16-acre site houses major collections as well as two small changing exhibition galleries. Average Annual Attendance: 20,000. Mem: 375; dues $25; meeting four times per yr.
Income: $110,000 (financed by endowment and membership).
Collections: Major collection of decorative arts from various periods and countries; Oriental collection of Chinese bronzes and ceramic tomb figures, lacquer ware, jades and Persian rugs; Spanish and English furniture; 20th century paintings; English oak and teakwood woodcarvings.
Exhibitions: Art on Paper; Export Porcelain from a Private Collection; Henry Pitz (one-man show); American Illustrator; Student exhibitions from summer workshops; Currier and Ives; Isabel Bishop; Freshwork (Va. photographers); Contemporary American Graphics; The Photographs of Wright Morris; Bernard Chaet (paintings); Alexandre Georges (photographs).
Activities: Classes for adults and children; dramatic programs; docent training; lect open to the public and auxiliary lect for members only, 10-12 vis lectr per yr; concerts; gallery talks; tours; slides for sale.
Library: Cur Lela M. Hine. Open to students for reference only. Holdings: Vols 800, Per subs 6.

IRENE LEACHE MEMORIAL,* c/o Mrs Charles R Dalton, Jr, Pres, 556 Mowbray Arch, 23507. Tel: 804-623-8189. *VPres* Mrs Louis Jaffee; *Secy* Mrs Frank Nash Bilisoly; *Art Chmn* Julia Bristow; *Literary Chmn* Mrs Fred Martin; *Lecture Chmn* Mrs Arthur Porter.
Estab 1905 as a private foundation created to promote culture in Norfolk; owns object of art and helps to maintain room of early Renaissance art in the Chrysler Museum at Norfolk. Mem: 25, selected by election; annual meeting May.
Income: $13,000 (financed by endowment).
Activities: Lect open to the public; competitions with cash awards; original objects of art lent; lending collection contains paintings, sculpture, tapestries and furniture.

MacARTHUR MEMORIAL, One MacArthur Square, 23510. Tel: 804-441-2256. *Admin Asst* Edward J Boone Jr; *Supt* Jack W Wallin; *Secy* Janice Stafford Dudley; *Research Asst* Roger T Crew Jr.
Open Mon - Sat 10 AM - 5 PM; Sun 11 AM - 5 PM. No admis. Estab 1964 to memorialize General Douglas MacArthur and located in the Old Court House which was rebuilt in 1962; nine galleries contain memorabilia. Average Annual Attendance: 90,000 - 100,000.
Income: $189,595 (financed by city appropriation and Federal revenue sharing funds).
Collections: Objets d'art, gifts, murals, portraits, photographs, awards and personal property of General Douglas McArthur.
Exhibitions: (1976) Norfolk Photo Club exhibit.
Activities: Individual paintings and original objects of art lent to schools, museums, and municipal agencies; sales shop operated by MacArthur Memorial Foundation selling books, reproductions; prints, slides.
—MacArthur Memorial Library and Archives. Tel: 804-441-2256. *Admin Asst* Edward J Boone Jr; *Research Asst* Roger T Crew Jr.
Holdings: Vols 4000 reference; AV reference—Audio tapes, cassettes, microfiche, microfilm, motion pictures, phono-records, slides; Other—Clipping files, framed reproductions, memorabilia, original art works, original documents, photographs, prints, reproductions, sculpture.

Special Collections: Papers of Brigadier General H E Eastwood; Papers of Major General Charles A Willoughby; Papers of Major General Courtney Whitney.
Activities: Lect open to the public, 2 - 3 vis lectr per yr; tours; schol; traveling exhibitions organized and circulated.

NAVAL AMPHIBIOUS MUSEUM, Naval Amphibious Base, Little Creek, 23251. Tel: 804-464-7923, 464-8130. *Dir* F R Vila-Lobos; *Cur* W Lukonis.
Open Sat & Sun 1 - 5 PM; during week by appointment only. No admis. Estab 1970 to preserve the history of the Amphibious Force of the United States Navy. Average Annual Attendance: 25,000 - 30,000.
Income: Financed by federal appropriation.
Collections: Paintings; sculpture; ship models; silver; naval historical memorabilia.
Activities: Lectures; guided tours.

OLD DOMINION UNIVERSITY GALLERY, Hampton Blvd, 23508. Tel: 804-489-6213.
Open Mon - Sun 1 - 5 PM. No admis. Estab 1972 for the exhibition of contemporary work; the establishment of a public forum for contemporary artists; student exposure. Average Annual Attendance: 3000.
Income: Financed by endowment and city appropriation.
Exhibitions: Will Reiman; Charles Sibley; Jerry Noe; Josef Albers; Mo Leibowitz; Atomic Art.
Activities: Lect open to public, 10 vis lectr per yr; gallery talks; tours; competitions; exten dept.
Library: Open to students and faculty; to the public for reference.

RESTON

NATIONAL ART EDUCATION ASSOCIATION, 1916 Association Dr, 22091. Tel: 703-860-8000. *Exec Dir* John J Mahlmann; *Pres* Dr Elliott W Eisner, Dept of Art, Stanford University, Stanford, CA 94305; *Pres-Elect* Dr Kent Anderson, Milwaukee Public Schools, PO Drawer 10K, Milwaukee, WI 53201.
For further information see National and Regional Organizations.

NATIONAL ASSOCIATION OF SCHOOLS OF ART, 11250 Roger Bacon Dr, 5, 22090. Tel: 703-437-0700. *Pres* Paul B Arnold, Chmn Dept Art, Oberlin College, Oberlin, OH 44074; *Exec Secy* Samuel Hope.
For further information see National and Regional Organizations.

RICHMOND

AGECROFT ASSOCIATION, Agecroft Hall, 4305 Sulgrave Rd, 23221. Tel: 804-353-4241. *Pres & Dir* John C Williams; *Asst Secy Treas & Cur* William McKemie.
Open Tues - Fri 10 AM - 4 PM; Sat - Sun 2 - 5 PM. Admis adults $1, students and children 50¢, group rates by prior arrangements. Estab 1968 to exhibit 15th century Tudor Manor House brought over from England in 1925-26 and rebuilt in Richmond, together with furnishings and period object of art; it is said to be the oldest house in America though originally constructed in Lancaster, England. Average Annual Attendance: Approx 12,000.
Income: $250,000 (financed by endowment and admis).
Collections: 15th and 16th century furniture and objects of art depicting the Elizabethan life of the time, when Agecroft Hall was at its maximum enjoyment in England.
Activities: Guided tours for classes of school children and schools and college classes; audio visual introduction.
Library: Small library containing books, film strips, lantern slides, original art works and slides; lend to universities only.

ASSOCIATION FOR THE PRESERVATION OF VIRGINIA ANTIQUITIES,* 2705 Park Ave, 23220. Tel: 804-359-0239. *Pres* Mrs Kenneth R Higgins; *Exec Dir* Robert A Murdock; *Cur Coll* Conover Hunt.
Estab 1889 to acquire and preserve historic buildings, grounds, and monuments in Virginia. Mem: 6000; dues $1 - $300; annual meeting May.
Twenty-six branches administering forty properties in Virginia. Among the properties: Jamestown Island; Walter Reed Birthplace, Gloucester; Rolfe-Warren House, Surry County; John Marshall House, Richmond; Scotchtown, Hanover County; Mary Washington House and Rising Sun Tavern, Fredericksburg; Prestwould, Clarksville; Smithfield Plantation, Blacksburg; Farmers Bank, Petersburg; Cape Henry Lighthouse, Virginia Beach. Hours and admissions vary according to location.
Collections: Decorative arts—17th-19th century furniture, glass, ceramics, metalwork and textiles.
Publications: Discovery (newsletter), quarterly.
Library: Holdings—Vols 5000 on art and history available for use on premises.

FEDERATED ARTS COUNCIL OF RICHMOND, INC, 205 E Franklin St, 23219. Tel: 804-643-4993. *Pres* Adrienne G Hines; *VPres* Bradley Gunter; *Exec Secy* Mrs William Mitchell.
Open daily 9 AM - 1 PM. Estab to promote cultural interest in community and to act as a unified voice for member agencies. Mem: 350; dues Associate $10, participating $25; meetings May and Sept.
Income: $45,000 (financed by endowment, membership and city appropriation).
Publications: Newsletter, quarterly; Cultural Calendar.
Activities: Seminars open to public; competitions with awards.

HAND WORK SHOP, INC, 316 N 24th St, 23223. Tel: 804-649-0674. *Exec Dir* Ruth T Summers; *Educ Coordinator* Sally Garret; *Staff* Mary Lou Deal.
Open Tues - Sat 10 AM - 4:30, cl Mon. No admis. Estab 1963 as a nonprofit tax exempt organization dedicated to excellence in designer crafts, and as a retail outlet; the gallery consists of three rooms selling designer crafts made in the United States only. Average Annual Attendance: 20,000. Mem: 300; dues $10 - $100.
Income: $100,000 (financed by membership, state appropriation and grants).
Exhibitions: Monthly exhibitions.
Publications: Newsletters, monthly.
Activities: Classes for adults and children; docent training; workshops; lect open to the public; competitions; sales shop selling original art, slides and crafts.

VALENTINE MUSEUM, 1015 E Clay St, 23219. Tel: 804-649-0711. *Dir Coll* Jean DuVal Kane; *Asst Dir* Dr Bruce King; *Admin Asst* Donna Deekens; *Cur of General Coll* Elizabeth Childs.
Open Tues - Sat 1:30 - 5 PM; Sun 10 AM - 5 PM. Admis adults $1, children & students 50¢. Estab 1894 as a museum of the life and history of Richmond. Average Annual Attendance: 28,000. Mem: 1100; dues individual $15.
Income: $203,000 (financed by endowment, membership, city and state appropriation and gifts). Purchases: $500.
Collections: Costumes, †paintings, †photographs, sculpture, prints, jewelry, silver, glass, ceramics, †candlesticks and lace; Edward Virginus Valentine (a southern sculptor); William Ludlow Sheppard (drawings and watercolors); Conrad Wise Chapman (oils, almost entire life works); best collection of Southern photographs known.
Exhibitions: Closed for major renovation; to reopen in November 1978.
Publications: Silhouette, bimonthly; Profile, three times per yr; Visitor, monthly.
Activities: Classes for adults and children; dramatic programs; docent training; lect open to the public, 2 vis lectr per yr; competitions; exten dept serving city and area counties; individual paintings lent to member corporations and other museums; lending collection contains color reproductions 1500, paintings 200, photographs, decorative art objects; traveling exhibitions organized and circulated; museum shop selling books, original art, reproductions, prints, slides and silver; Junior Center.
—**Library.** Tel: 804-649-0711. *Cur of Library Materials* E Michale Schanches Saavedra.
Open to the public for reference only.
Holdings: Vols 1000; Per subs 20; Other—Photographs 20,000 (southern) c. 1849 - 1920.
Special Collections: Papers of Richmond authors.

VIRGINIA COMMONWEALTH UNIVERSITY
—**Anderson Gallery,** 907½ W Franklin St, 23284. Tel: 804-257-6910. *Dir* Harriet Dubowski.
Open Mon - Fri 10 AM - 4 PM; Sat & Sun 2 - 5 PM. Estab 1930, reopened 1970 as the showcase for the contemporary arts in Richmond; to expose the university and community to a wide variety of current artistic ideas and expressions; the gallery is situated on campus in a four-story converted mansion stable. There are six galleries with a variety of exhibition spaces. Average Annual Attendance: 20,000.
Collections: †Contemporary prints and paintings; cross section of prints from the 15th to 20th century covering most periods.
Exhibitions: Contemporary British Prints; Sam Gilliam: Extensions Part I; annual student shows; metals invitational; tactile exhibition; Abraham Rattner/Henry Miller: Our America; Charles Schmidt: The Mechanical Landscape; Manipulative Photography.
Publications: Catalogs and brochures, periodically.
Activities: Lectr open to the public, 6 vis lectr per yr; concerts; gallery talks; tours; competitions; individual paintings and original objects of art lent to various museums and universities; lending collection contains 100 original art works, 100 original paintings and photographs; traveling exhibitions organized and circulated.
—**School of the Arts Library,** 901 W Franklin St, 23284. Tel: 804-257-1683. *Dir* Joan L Muller; *Asst* Nancy S Brantley.
Open Mon - Fri 9 AM - 5 PM. Estab 1926 to support the teaching program of the eleven departments of the School of the Arts.

Income: Financed by state appropriation.
Holdings: AV—Slides 225,000 loaned to Faculty and students; Other—Exhibition catalogs 13,000 loaned to Faculty and graduate students.
Special Collections: Transparencies (2 x 2 inch) of works of art; Exhibit catalogs, worldwide in scope, from museums and galleries.

VIRGINIA HISTORICAL SOCIETY, 428 North Blvd (Mailing Add: PO Box 7311, 23221). Tel: 804-358-4901. *Dir* John M Jennings.
Open Mon - Fri 9 AM - 5 PM; Sat & Sun 2 - 5 PM. Admis $1. Estab 1831 for collecting, preserving, and making available to students and scholars research material relating to the history of Virginia; gallery maintained housing historical portraiture and paintings. Average Annual Attendance: 18,000. Dues $15 and up.
Income: Financed by endowment and membership.
—**Library.** Tel: 804-358-4901. *Librn* Howson W Cole.
Open Mon - Fri 9 AM - 5 PM, for reference only.
Holdings: Vols 200,000; Per subs 800; Other—Manuscripts, memorabilia, original art works, original documents, pamphlets, photographs, prints.

VIRGINIA MUSEUM OF FINE ARTS,* Boulevard & Grove, 23221. Tel: 804-770-6344. *Pres* Dr William H Higgins, Jr; *Dir* Dr R Peter Mooz; *Asst to Dir & Head Pub Information Dept* Fred Haseltine; *Head Publications Dept* George Cruger; *Head Design Dept* William Ryan; *Secy of Mus Coll Div* Helen Dohn; *Head* Pinkney Near; *Registr & Asst Cur* Elizabeth Culler; *Progs Dir* William Gaines; *Artmobile Coordr* David Pittman; *Supvr Loan-Own Art Serv* Julia Williams.
Open Tues - Sat 11 AM - 5 PM; Sun 1 - 5 PM; cl Mon. Admis 50¢, free Sat & Sun. Estab 1934; building opened 1936; theatre opened 1955; South Wing added 1970. Average Annual Attendance: 1,250,000 statewide. Mem: 13,700; dues $25 and higher; annual meeting May.
Collections: Representative examples of the arts from early Egypt to the present time, including paintings, sculpture, furniture and objects d'art. Comprehensive collections of early Greek vases (8th century to 4th century BC); archaic Chinese bronzes; archaic Chinese jades. Special Collections: The John Barton Payne Collection of paintings, prints and Portuguese furniture; T Catesby Jones Collection of 20th century European paintings and drawings; Lillian Thomas Pratt Collection of Czarist Jewels by Peter Carl Faberge; †Arthur and Margaret Glasgow Collection of Flemish and Italian Renaissance paintings, sculpture and decorative arts; Mrs Arthur Kelly Evans Collection of pottery and porcelain; Lady Nancy Astor Collection of English china; †Adolph D and Wilkins C Williams Collection of paintings, tapestries, china and silver; Branch Collection of Italian Renaissance paintings, sculpture and furniture. Nasli and Alice Heeramaneck Collection of art of India, Nepal, Kashmir and Tibet; Ailsa Mellon Bruce Collection of 18th century furniture and decorative arts; Dr. and Mrs. Arthur Mourot Collection of Meissen porcelain.
Exhibitions: (Biennials) Virginia Artists; Virginia Designers; Virginia Interior Designers; Virginia Architects/Planners; Virginia Photographers; Virginia Craftsmen. American Painting quadrennial; 25 special exhibitions annually.
Publications: Nine bulletins annually; catalogs for special exhibitions and collections; Arts in Virginia, 3 times annually; brochures, programs and invitations.
Activities: Gallery activities—Lectures in relation to current loan exhibitions; morning and evening classes for children and adults in painting, drawing, graphics, ceramics, weaving and dramatics; awards 10-15 fellowships annually to Virginia artists; 3 artmobiles travel to large and small communities throughout the state with exhibitions; one additional artmobile travels exclusively to college campuses; circulates more than 100 traveling exhibitions throughout the state. Statewide activities include 30 confederated organizations. Theatre activities—Seven drama productions each year; professional dance events; music concerts; and ten films yearly; Repertory Equity Theatre Company; lectures, workshops and demonstrations.
Participating in the museum's programs are The Fellows of the Virginia Museum, who meet yearly to counsel the museum on its future plans; The Women's Council, which sponsors and originates special programs; the Collectors' Circle, a group of Virginia art lovers who meet four times a year to discuss various aspects of collecting; the Corporate Patrons, state and local business firms who lend financial support to museum programs; and Virginia Museum Youth Guild.
—**Library:** *Librn* Betty Stacy.
Holdings: Vols 30,000 on art techniques and history of art.

ROANOKE

ROANOKE FINE ARTS CENTER, 302 23rd St, SW, 24014. Tel: 703-342-8945. *Exec Dir* Roy T Woodall; *Prog Coordinator* Ann D Masters; *Bus Mgr* Virginia B Porten; *Mem & Educ Coordinator* Dori B Fitzgerald; *Gallery Hostess* Carol D Bivens.

Open Tues - Sat 10 AM - 5 PM; Sun 1 - 5 PM. No admis. Estab 1951 to encourage and develop interest in the study of the arts; to provide ways and means for the purchase of works in the arts, and to exhibit fine arts and other works of art; old home with extremely fine architectural detail, whose main rooms have been turned into galleries; a gallery is also maintained in the downtown library. Average Annual Attendance: 10,000. Mem: 1300; dues $15 and up; annual meeting Sept.
Income: $110,650 (financed by endowment, membership).
Collections: Mediterranean artifacts; limited porcelain collection, and predominately local artists works.
Exhibitions: (1977) Twenty-five exhibitions.
Publications: Calendar of events, monthly.
Activities: Classes for adults and children; docent training; lect open to the public, 15 vis lectr per yr; concerts; gallery talks; tours; competitions; museum shop selling books, original art, reproductions, prints, handmade crafts including jewelry, children's items.
Library. Open to the public for reference. Holdings: Per subs 25.

STAUNTON

WOODROW WILSON BIRTHPLACE FOUNDATION,* 20 N Coalter St (Mailing Add: PO Box 24, 24401). Tel: 703-885-0897. *Dir* Raymond F Pisney.
Open daily 9 AM - 5 PM; cl Sun & holidays. Admis adults $1.50, children 6-16 75¢, children under 6 free; special rates for groups. Estab 1938 in the 1846 Presbyterian Manse which was the birthplace of Woodrow Wilson. Mem: Dues student $7.50, other $10-1000.
Collections: Paintings; sculpture; prints and drawings; photographs; decorative arts; furniture; musical instruments; rare books; manuscripts; textiles; historical material pertinent to the Wilson family.
Publications: Newsletter, bi-monthly; brochures, pamphlets and guides.
Activities: Educ dept; lectures; gallery talks; tours; films; loan programs; sales shop.
Library: *Librn* Margaret P Rolston. Holdings: Vols 2000.

STRASBURG

STRASBURG MUSEUM, E King St, 22657. Tel: 703-465-3175. *Pres* J J Crawford; *VPres* Mrs John F Cadden; *Secy* Mrs W B Bailes; *Treas* Mrs Paul Hatmaker; *Resident Potter* Mrs A L Dryer.
Open May to Oct 10 AM - 4 PM. Admis adults 50¢, children 25¢. Estab 1970 to present the past of a Shenandoah Valley community and to preserve the pottery-making tradition of Strasburg; the museum is housed in the former Southern Railway Depot, which was originally built as a steam pottery. Average Annual Attendance: 3600. Mem: 125; dues $2.50; annual meeting March.
Income: Financed by membership, admissions and gifts.
Collections: (Art) Indian artifacts, pottery.
Exhibitions: Models of pre-Civil War era shops and rooms.
Activities: Classes for adults and children in pottery making; museum shop selling books, original art, pottery and other local craft.

SWEET BRIAR

SWEET BRIAR COLLEGE, Babcock Art Library, 24595. Tel: 804-381-5451. *Librn* Henry James; *Cataloger* Patricia Wright; *Asst Librn* Mrs Jan Johnson; *Service Librn* Mary Hartman.
Estab 1961, when it was separated from Main library, and Babcock Art Building was opened; it is a private library, for reference only; small gallery in lobby and Reading Room of Babcock Fine Arts Building.
Income: Financed by college funds.
Holdings: Vols 5500; Per subs 22; AV—Cassettes, kodachromes, lantern slides; Other—Original art works, prints.
Exhibitions: (1976-77) Radical Realism; Virginia Printmakers; Recent Acquisitions of the Virginia Museum from Frances and Sydney Lewis Contemporary Art Fund; Whistler Etchings; 20th Century Photographs; Baskin Bronzes and Prints; William Blake; Illustrations of the Book of Job, on loan from Virginia Museum; The World of Willa Cather: Photographs by Lucia Woods; Drawings by Women (Exhibiting Artists Federation); A Survey of Intaglio Printmaking (Pratt Graphics Center); Senior Exhibition; Underclassmen Exhibition.

VIRGINIA BEACH

VIRGINIA BEACH ARTS CENTER, 18th and Arctic Ave (Mailing Add: PO Box 884, 23452). Tel: 804-428-9294. *Admin-Dir* Anthony J Radich; *Arts Consultant* F D Cossitt; *Office Mgr* Jean E Hipp; *Secy* Harriet Ross Smith.
Open Tues - Fri 9 AM - 5 PM; Sat 9 AM - 4 PM; Sun 1 - 4 PM. No admis. Estab 1952 to enable local artists to gather, sell their work and socialize; gallery is maintained in building loaned by the city; exhibition

space is 20 x 30 ft; classrooms occupy 8 medium sized rooms. Average Annual Attendance: 50,000. Mem: 12,000; dues individual $8 - $10, Family $15 - $18.50.
Income: Financed by membership, donations and classes.
Exhibitions: (1976-78) Boardwalk Art Show; Neptune Festival Art Show; Undiscovered Artists Show; Artmobile from Virginia Museum in Richmond; monthly exhibitions in main gallery.
Publications: Monthly newsletter.
Activities: Classes for adults and children; docent training; workshop by artists in residence; lectr open to the public, 4 - 6 vis lectr per yr; artmobile; individual paintings and original objects of art lent to members and donors as well as local business offices; lending collection contains original art works, original prints and paintings; sales shop selling, original art, prints, sculpture, ceramics, crafts, fibers, wood carvings, wall handings and weaving.

WILLIAMSBURG

COLLEGE OF WILLIAM AND MARY, Dept of Fine Arts, 23185. Tel: 804-253-4385. *Chmn* Dr Miles Chappell; *Registrar* Louise Kale.
Open Mon - Fri 9 AM - 4 PM. No Admis. Art Collection was started for teaching purposes and for the commemoration of the college's history, alumni and friends. Average Annual Attendance: 5000.
Income: Financed by endowment, city and state appropriations and donation.
Collections: Colonial and contemporary American painting; contemporary sculpture by Joseph Lonas; Oriental Art.
Exhibitions: (1977) Rubens in Prints. (1978) Arthur Strauss and the German Expressionists; Jules Kirschenbaum (paintings).
Publications: Catalogs and brochures, sporadically.
Activities: Lect open to the public.

COLONIAL WILLIAMSBURG FOUNDATION,* PO Drawer C, 23185. Tel: 804-229-1000. *Pres* Carlisle H Humelsine; *VPres & Dir Pub Relations* Donald J Gonzales; *Dir Press Bureau* Hugh De Samper; *Dir & Cur Coll* Graham S Hood.
Open 9 AM - 5 PM. Folk Art Collection free daily 12 AM - 6 PM. Average Annual attendance: 1,000,000.
The colonial area of this 18th century capital of Virginia, encompassing 173 acres with nearly 500 homes, shops, taverns, public buildings, and dependencies, has been carefully restored to its original appearance. Included are 90 acres of gardens and greens. The work was initiated by the late John D Rockefeller, Jr, in 1926.
There are more than 30 exhibition homes, public buildings and craft shops where guides and craftsmen in colonial costume show visitors the arts and decorations as well as the way of life of pre-Revolutionary Virginia. In addition, there are historic Bruton Parish Church, the Abby Aldrich Rockefeller Folk Art Collection and The Courthouse of 1770. The exhibition properties include 211 furnished gallery rooms.
The principal exhibitions are:
†The Capitol—one of colonial America's most important buildings—scene of Patrick Henry's oration against the Stamp Act.
†The Gaol—where debtors, criminals and Blackbeard's pirates were imprisoned.
†Raleigh Tavern—one of the most famous taverns of colonial times, where Virginia patriots plotted Revolutionary action, and social center of the capital.
†Brush-Everard House—small well-appointed home, typical of a comfortable but not wealthy colonial.
†Governor's Palace and Gardens—residence of royal governors. Outstanding English and American 18th century furnishings and extensive formal colonial gardens.
†Wythe House—home of George Wythe, signer of Declaration of Independence and teacher of Jefferson and John Marshall.
†Public Magazine—arsenal of the Virginia colony, now exhibiting colonial arms.
†Petyon Randolph House—original residence of the first president of the Continental Congress.
†Wetherburn's Tavern—among the most famous of 18th century Virginia's hostelries, over 200 years old.
†James Geddy House—original dwelling and workshop of a well-known colonial silversmith and businessman.
†Wren Building of the College of William and Mary—the oldest academic building in British America, with six rooms open to the public and the remainder still in use for college classes and faculty offices.
†Craft Shops—the trades and crafts of 200 years ago are carried on in 20 authentically furnished craft shops where artisans use the tools and methods of the 18th century.
Collections: Colonial Williamsburg, presents a cross-section of colonial Virginia life in the furnishings of the public buildings, taverns, shops and homes. The collections of American and English furnishings, with fre-

quent additions, include representative pieces, rare English pieces in the palace, 18th century American paintings, English pottery and porcelains, English silver, exceptionally fine textiles and rugs.

Information Center: Outside the historic area this modern center houses graphic exhibits of the restoration and colonial life. Continuous showings of a full-color, vista vision film, Williamsburg: The Story of a Patriot.

Publications: Books and brochures on Williamsburg and colonial life; gallery book of the Folk Art Collection; documentary motion pictures; audiovisual material.

Activities: Williamsburg Forum Series, annual events including Antiques Forum; Garden Symposium; regular performance of 18th-century dramas, organ recitals and concert music; slide lectures. Limited grant-in-aid program for researchers.

Library: Holdings—Vols 25,000 on American history.

ABBY ALDRICH ROCKEFELLER FOLK ART CENTER, 307 S England St (Mailing Add: PO Drawer C, 23185). Tel: 804-229-1000, exten 2424. *Dir* Beatrix T Rumford.

Open Mon - Fri Noon - 6 PM (winter); Mon - Fri Noon - 9 PM (summer). No admis. Estab 1939 for research, education and the exhibiting of one of the country's leading collections of American folk art of the 18th & 19th centuries. Nine galleries of American folk art, including a craft gallery. Average Annual Attendance: 150,000.

Collections: Painting: sculpture; decorative usefulwares; painted furniture; decoys; shop signs; needlework.

Exhibitions: Decorated Firearms from the Collection of Clay P Bedford; Making Faces: Aspects of American Portraiture; Portraits by Zedekia Belknap; Fraktur Writings attributed to Henry Young; American Coverlet Weavers.

Publications: Exhibition catalogs.

Activities: Traveling exhibitions organized and circulated; sales shop selling books, reproductions, prints and slides.

Library: Open to serious scholars of folk art for reference. Holdings: Vols 1500.

WASHINGTON

BELLEVUE

PACIFIC NORTHWEST ARTS AND CRAFTS ASSOCIATION,* 10310 NE Fourth St, 98004. Tel: 206-454-4900.

Estab 1947 to exhibit the work of artists and craftsmen of the Pacific Northwest presently housed at the Bellevue Public Library. Mem: Approx 40; monthly Board meeting.

Exhibitions: Special exhibitions; annual Outdoor Fair in July; annual awards approx $8500 all media; all work is for sale.

BELLINGHAM

WHATCOM MUSEUM OF HISTORY AND ART, 121 Prospect St, 98225. Tel: 206-676-6981. *Dir* George Thomas; *Cur* Rod Slemmons; *Registrar* Jan Olsen; *Educ Coordinator* Richard Vanderway; *Preparator* Bill McColl; *Admin Coordinator* Emil Miersen.

Open Tues - Sun noon - 5 PM; cl Mon, Fourth of July, Thanksgiving, Christmas and New Year's. No admis. Estab 1940 to collect, preserve, and use, through exhibits, interpretation and research, objects of historic or artistic value, and to act as a multi-purpose cultural center for the North West Washington area providing presentations in all aspects of the arts; seven galleries cover 3750 sq ft floor space and 625 linear ft wall space, plus a permanent history exhibit space. Average Annual Attendance: 80,000. Mem: 700; dues individual $15, family $25; annual meeting March.

Income: $160,000 (financed by city appropriation). Purchases: $15,000.

Collections: Virginia Wright Collection of North West art; Artists of Woodstock; New York Collection; †Contemporary North West art collection; †North West Coast Indian art collection; Darius Kinsey (photography); local historic photo archives.

Exhibitions: (1976-78) 5000 Years of Art; Selections from the Permanent Collection of Virginia and Bagley Wright; Richard Gilkey (paintings); Recent Works of Rob Gisher; Boyer Gonzales 24 Years; Cape Dorset Eskimo Prints and Sculpture; Kathy Roe (ceramic murals); Rod Burton (photographs).

Publications: Art and Events Calendar, monthly; Exhibit catalogs.

Activities: Classes for adults and programs for children; docent training; lect open to the public; concerts; gallery talks; tours; individual paintings and original objects of art lent mainly to other museums and galleries; traveling exhibitions organized and circulated; museum shop selling books, original art, prints and craftwork from around the world.

Library. For reference only, open to staff, and by appointment for general public. Holdings: Vols 500; Per subs 10 - 15. Special Subjects: North West Contemporary Art.

CLARKSTON

VALLEY ART CENTER INC, 842 Sixth St (Mailing Add: PO Box 65, 99403). Tel: 509-758-8331. *Exec Dir* Pat Rosenberger; *Co-Chmn* Veda Taylor; *Secy* Erma Holcroft; *Treas* Richard Schutte; *Admin Asst* Janice Trusty.

Open Mon - Fri 9 AM - 4 PM; Sun 2 - 5 PM, cl Sat. Estab 1968 to encourage and instruct in all forms of the visual arts and to promote the cause of art in the community; a portion of the Center serves as the gallery. Average Annual Attendance: 7000. Mem: 150; dues $10, $25, $50.

Income: Financed by membership and class fees.

Exhibitions: Annual Snake River Days Celebration Open Show and Exhibit; Lewis-Clark Art Association Show; Pen and Ink Show.

Publications: Newsletter, semi-annually.

Activities: Classes for adults and children; lect open to the public, 5 vis lectr per yr; gallery talks; tours; competitions; individual paintings lent to banks, business offices and professional people; traveling exhibitions organized and circulated; sales shop selling books, original art, reproductions, and fine handcrafts.

ELLENSBURG

CENTRAL WASHINGTON UNIVERSITY, Sara Spurgeon Gallery, 98926. Tel: 509-963-2665. *Chmn Art Dept* George Stillman; *Dir Art Gallery* James Sahlstrand.

Open Mon - Fri 8 AM - 5 PM. No admis. Estab 1970 to serve as university gallery as well as community function; the gallery is a large, single unit. Average Annual Attendance: 20,000.

Income: Financed by state appropriation.

Exhibitions: Virginia Myers (prints); Ron Adams; Faculty Show; Graduate Thesis Show; Student Shows; New Photographics.

Publications: Catalogs for all National shows.

Activities: Lect open to the public; competitions.

GOLDENDALE

MARYHILL MUSEUM OF ART, Star Route 677, Box 23, 98620. Tel: 509-773-4792. *Adminr* Dorothy Brokaw; *Dir Coll* Harvey Freer; *Pres Bd Dir* Capt A Leppaluoto.

Open daily 9 AM - 5 PM (Mar 15 - Nov 15). Admis adults $1.50; sr citizens $1.00; students (6-18) 50¢; under six free. Estab 1923 as a museum of art. Average Annual Attendance: 65,000. Mem: 100; dues $15.

Collections: Rodin sculpture and drawings; 19th century American and French sculpture; royal furniture designed by Marie, Queen of Roumania, and memorabilia; European and American paintings; American Indian baskets; Columbia River Basin prehistoric arts; antique and modern chessmen; World War II costumed French fashion mannequins.

Publications: Brochure and souvenir booklet.

OLYMPIA

STATE CAPITOL MUSEUM, 211 W 21st Ave, 98501. Tel: 206-753-2580.

Open Tues - Fri 10 AM - 4 PM; Sat & Sun noon - 4 PM; cl Mon. No admis. Estab 1941 to interpret history of the State of Washington and of the capital city; the one-room gallery presents changing monthly shows. Average Annual Attendance: 40,000. Mem: 300; dues individual $6, family $12; annual meeting June.

Income: $100,000 (financed by city and state appropriation, and local funds).

Collections: (Art) Winslow Homer woodcuts; Northwest Indian serigraphs; small collection of paintings by Washington artists; etchings by Thomas Handforth.

Publications: Museum newsletter, monthly.

Activities: Classes for adults and children; dramatic programs; docent training; lect open to the public; concerts; gallery talks; tours; individual paintings and original objects of art lent to State offices; lending collection contains original prints, paintings; traveling exhibitions organized and circulated; sales shop selling books, slides.

PULLMAN

WASHINGTON STATE UNIVERSITY, Museum of Art, 99164. Tel: 509-335-1910, 509-335-1603. *Dir* Harvey West; *Cur* Bruce Guenther; *Cur* Patricia Watkinson; *Registrar* Julianne Thompson; *Exec Secy* June Harbour.

Open Mon - Fri 10 AM - 4 PM; Mon & Fri 7 - 10 PM; Sat & Sun 1 - 5 PM. No admis. Estab 1974 to contribute the humanities educational purpose and goal of the university for the direct benefit of the undergraduate and graduate students; gallery covers 5000 sq ft and is centrally located on campus. Average Annual Attendance: 38,000.
Income: Financed by endowment, membership, state appropriation.
Collections: Late 19th century to present-day American art, with particular strength in the areas of the Ash Can School and North West regional art scene.
Exhibitions: (1976-78) The Human Image in the 20th Century (photography); Six from California; Wendell Brazeau Retrospective; Amistad II; Works on Paper, American Art; Goya; Smithson; People of the Cedar; Bi-Centennial Portfolio; Burns Photographs; Meyer Shapiro Portfolio; Two Decades, 1957-77: American Sculpture from NW Collections; Margaret Tomkins Retrospective; Ritual and Change, Art of the Sepik River, New Guinea; John Yeon: Buildings and Landscapes; Artist and Place: American Landscape Painting, 1860-1914.
Publications: Special Exhibition catalogs, two each yr.
Activities: Classes for adults; lect open to the public; gallery talks; tours; exten dept serving State of Washington; individual paintings and original objects of art lent to the art community of the State of Washington; lending collection contains cassettes, color reproductions, original art works; traveling exhibitions organized and circulated; museum shop selling books, magazines.

RICHLAND

ARTS COUNCIL OF THE MID-COLUMBIA REGION,* PO Box 735, 99352 Tel: 509-943-0524. *Pres* Helen B Maurer, *Secy* Marjorie Peterson; *Arts Coordr* Steven R Markstrom.
Open Mon - Fri 9 AM - 5 PM. No admis. Estab April 2, 1968 to encourage, promote and coordinate the arts. Mem: 140, dues $5, $10, $25; Board meeting third Thurs monthly.
Income: $10,000 (financed by membership).
Exhibitions: Several invitational and juried shows each year.
Publications: Calendar/Newsletter, monthly.
Activities: Classes for adults and children; artist-in-residence program covering two counties; dramatic programs; concerts; competitions; scholarships.
Library maintained.

SEATTLE

ALLIED ARTS OF SEATTLE, INC,* 107 S Main St, 98104. Tel: 206-624-0432. *Pres* Paul E S Schell; *First VPres* William E Talley; *Second VPres* Mrs Jonathan Whetzel; *Secy* Mrs D F Ellsworth; *Treas* Nancy Erickson; *Exec Dir* Alice Rooney.
Open 9 AM - 5 PM. No admis. Estab 1954 to promote and support the arts and artists of the Northwest and to help create the kind of city that will attract the kind of people who support the arts. Mem: 750; dues $2.50 - $25 depending on category; annual meeting Jan.
Income: $21,000 (financed by membership).
Publications: Allied Arts Newsletter, eleven times per year; calendar of cultural events, quarterly; directory of arts organizations in Puget Sound area, biannual.
Activities: Co-sponsorship with Seattle Public Schools of visits by school children to artists studios; schol; occasionally co-sponsors an exhibition in a Seattle gallery or museum.

AND/OR, Resources in Contemporary Arts, 1525 10th Avenue, 98122. Tel: 206-324-5880. *Librn* Ann Obery.
Open daily 11 AM - 6 PM. Estab 1975 to provide a focused and accessible resource of information about recent activities in the contemporary arts. For reference only. And/Or is an arts organization, with exhibition space, of which the library is a part.
Income: Financed by National Endowment for the Arts and locally matched funds.
Library: Holdings—Vols 800; Per subs 125; AV-Video tapes; Other—Clipping files, exhibition catalogs, original art works, original documents, pamphlets.
Special Subjects: Contemporary arts.
Activities: Tours available upon request.

CORNISH INSTITUTE OF ALLIED ARTS, Cornish Gallery, 710 E Roy, 98102. Tel: 206-323-1400. *Pres* Melvin Strauss; *VPres* David Shaw; *Registrar* Doris Tuck; *Chmn Fine Arts Dept* Craig Langager; *Chmn Design Dept* Victor Baumgartner.
Open Mon - Fri 10 AM - 5 PM; Sat 1 - 4 PM. No admis. Estab 1975 to support and enhance the visual arts curricula and reflect current trends in art. Gallery is 36 x 22 ft, lite-trak system, double door entry, 120 ft of free wall space, ten-foot ceilings, and tile floor.
Income: Financed through Institute.

Exhibitions: Robert Maki (sculpture); Robert Rauschenberg (prints, drawings); Tom Holland (paintings and sculpture); Chris Watts (drawings); Ralph Baker (paintings); Frank Okada (paintings); Walter Cotton (prints); Kathleen Rabel (prints); Faculty selected works; Albert Fisher (paintings); BFA Thesis Shows; Student Awards Show.
Publications: Gallery mailers.
Activities: Classes for adults; dramatic programs; lect open to public; gallery talks; competitions; exten dept serving adults interested in part-time study; traveling exhibitions organized and circulated.
—Poncho Library. *Librn* Ron McComb.
Open to students and faculty.
Holdings: Vols 3000; Per subs 65; Other—Slides 2000.

CORPORATE COUNCIL FOR THE ARTS, 421 Skinner Bldg, 98101. Tel: 206-447-4726. *Pres* Roland M Trafton; *VPres* David E Skinner; *Secy* Douglass A Raff; *Exec Dir* Robert E Gustavson.
Open 9 AM - 5 PM. Estab 1968 as a clearinghouse for corporate contributions to the arts, to monitor budgeting of art agencies, and assess ability of business to provide funding assistance; gallery not maintained. Mem: 300; qualif for mem: contribution of $100 or more; annual meeting first Wed August.
Income: $600,000 (financed by membership).
Publications: Periodic membership reports.

CHARLES AND EMMA FRYE ART MUSEUM, 704 Terry Ave (Mailing Add: PO Box 3005, 98114). Tel: 206-622-9250. *Pres & Dir* Mrs W S Greathouse.
Open weekdays 10 AM - 5 PM; Sun noon - 6 PM. No admis. Estab 1952 to display and preserve the Frye Art Collection; three galleries cover 30 x 60 ft, and four galleries cover 30 x 30 ft, plus foyer. Average Annual Attendance: 60,000.
Income: Financed by endowment.
Collections: Charles and Emma Frye Collection represents 13 nationalities and includes Boudin, Jongkind, Liebermann, Slevogt, Zugel, Stuck, Uhde, Zumbusch, Diaz, Llermitte, Leibl, Grubner, Manet, Monticelli, Soren Carlsen, Koester, Gabriel Max, Lenbach, Winterhalter, Kaulbach, Thoma, Degregger, Dahl, Baer, Lier, Hoch, Corrodi, Ziem, Willroider.
Exhibitions: Changing exhibitions in four galleries every two to four weeks.
Publications: Frye Vues, monthly.
Activities: Lect open to the public; gallery talks; tours.
Library. For reference only.

KING COUNTY ARTS COMMISSION, 300 King County Admin Bldg, 98104. Tel: 206-344-7580. *Chmn* Margaret Ellsworth; *Vice Chmn* Ina Bray; *Treas* Don Vogt; *Exec Secy* Robert L Johnson; *Prog Coordinator* Barbara McDonald; *Visual Arts Coordinator* Jerry Allen.
Open Mon - Fri 8:30 AM - 4:30 PM. No admis. Estab 1968 to provide cultural arts opportunities to the citizens of King County; the Arts Commission purchases and commissions many works of art for public buildings. Mem: 18; membership by appointment of County Executive; monthly meetings third Tues.
Income: $700,000 (financed by state appropriation and county government).
Publications: Arts newsletter, monthly.
Activities: Concerts; competitions with awards given; traveling exhibitions organized and circulated.

MUSIC AND ART FOUNDATION,* 710 E Roy St, 98102. Tel: 206-324-2660. *Pres* Mrs Walter Ricker.
Estab 1923 to stimulate and encourage young people to develop their talents in creative arts, literature and music. Mem: 2000; dues $2 and up; annual meeting May. Articles of Incorporation specifically state that assistance limited to legal residents of the state of Washington. Since 1954 has operated the Cornish School of Allied Arts in Seattle which was founded in 1914 by Miss Nellie Cornish.
Activities: Contributes to purchase funds of local groups; maintains Free Creative Art School for Children; sponsors dramatic programs and concerts.

SEATTLE ART MUSEUM,* Volunteer Park, 98112. Tel: 206-447-4710. *Pres of Board* John H Hauberg; *Pres & Dir Emeritus* Richard E Fuller; *Dir* Willis F Woods; *Cur Dept of Asian Art* Henry Trubner; *Dir Public Relations* Jeri McDonald.
Volunteer Park open weekdays 10 AM - 5 PM; Thurs 7 - 10 PM; Sun & holidays Noon - 5 PM; cl New Year's, Memorial Day, Thanksgiving & Christmas. Estab 1906, inc 1917; building opened 1933, gift to the city from Mrs Eugene Fuller and Richard Eugene Fuller, for the recreation, education and inspiration of its citizens. Average Annual Attendance: 226,000. Mem: Approx 4200; dues $10 and up; annual meeting Oct.
Collections: Eugene Fuller Memorial Collection with special emphasis on Japan, China, India, also Egypt, Ancient Greece and Rome, European, Near Eastern, Primitive and contemporary Northwest art; major holdings in Northwest art, including Tobey, Callhan, Graves, as well as contemporary art, especially American—Gorky, Pollock, Warhol and Lichtenstein;

Thomas D. Stimson Memorial Collection with special emphasis on Far Eastern art; selected highlights on Asian collection on permanent display with special emphasis of Japanese art—screens, paintings, sculptures and lacquers; also extensive Chinese and Indian collections; Norman Davis Collection with emphasis on Classical art; Manson F Backus Collection of prints; LeRoy M Backus Collection of drawings and paintings; Samuel H Kress Collection of 14th-18th century European paintings; Nasli and Alice Heeramaneck Collection of primitive art; Henry and Martha Isaacson Collection of 18th century European porcelain; Eugene Fuller Memorial Collection of Chinese jades from archaic through 18th century; indefinite loan of 18th century drawing room furnished by the National Society of Colonial Dames of American in the State of Washington.
Publications: Exhibits and activities calendar, bimonthly; Annual Report; Greek Coins and Cities, 1967; Tobey's 80, a Birthday Retrospective, 1969; Chinese Snuff Bottles; 1969; Chinese Jades, 1971; American Art: Third Quarter Century, 1973; Asiatic Art in the Seattle Art Museum, 1973; Four Decades of Collecting, 1973; Skagit Valley Artists.
Activities: Docent service; film programs, TV and radio programs; double lecture course under the Museum Guild; monthly programs for Senior Citizens (except July, Aug, Sept); adult art history classes; around 300 Treasure Box visits yearly to King County Public Schools' 5th - 6th grade classrooms and special groups; lect open to the public, 12 vis lectr per yr; tours; Bookshop.
Library: Librn Elizabeth de Fato; *Photography & Slide Librn* Jo H Nilsson. Reference. Holdings: Vols 9000; AV—Slides 44,000.
—**Modern Art Pavilion,*** Seattle Center 2nd N & Thomas St, 98109. Tel: 206-447-4795. *Cur* Charles Cowles; *Asst Cur* Sarah Clark; *Mgr* Tore Hoven.
Open Tues - Sun 11 AM - 6 PM; Thurs 11 AM - 8 PM; cl Mon, New Year's Day, Thanksgiving, Christmas. A branch of the Seattle Art Museum in the former British Pavilion at Seattle World's Fair, remodeled through a gift from Poncho (Asn) and a bequest from the late Richard Dwight Merrill into a year 'round exhibition facility, officially opened June 4, 1965; permanent collection and temporary exhibits of 20th century art. Average Annual Attendance: 108,000.
Activities: Docent service; Rental/Sales Gallery; Book shop.

SEATTLE PUBLIC LIBRARY,* Art & Music Dept, 1000 Fourth Ave, 98104. Tel: 206-624-2655. *Librn* Ronald A Dubberly; *Art & Music Librn* Carolyn Holmquist.
Open Mon - Thurs 9 AM - 9 PM; Fri & Sat 9 AM - 6 PM; cl Sun. No admis. Art Dept estab 1907.
Income: (Art) $30,000.
Holdings: (Art) Vols 68,146; Other—Bound periodicals 8469, framed color reproductions 24,283, photographs of Northwest architecture and views 26,771, large color reproductions 1536, original prints, drawings, paintings and sculpture 902.

SEATTLE WEAVER'S GUILD,* c/o Museum of History and Industry, 2161 E Hamlin St, 98112. Tel: 206-324-1125. *Pres* Carlene Striker, (15540 168th Ave NE, Woodinville, WA 98072); *Recording Secy* Anita Peckham; *Corresp Secy* Eleanor Helliwell.
Estab 1937 to further interest in hand weaving. Mem: 242; dues $10; monthly meetings except Dec, June, July and Aug.
Exhibitions: Northwest Craftsmen's Exhibition at the Henry Gallery; Northwest Association of Handweavers biannual conference.
Activities: Four regular monthly meetings are study sessions and four are program meetings, open to members and guests only; workshops throughout the year.
Library: For members only.

UNIVERSITY OF WASHINGTON
—**Henry Art Gallery,** 98195. Tel: 206-543-2280. *Dir* Richard Grove.
Open Mon - Fri 10 AM - 5 PM; Thurs 7 - 9 PM; Sat & Sun 1 - 5 PM. No admis. Estab 1927 by gift of Horace C Henry; Seven galleries cover 5000 sq ft of exhibition space. Average Annual Attendance: 62,000. Mem: 800; dues $5 up; annual meeting May.
Income: $125,000 (financed by membership, state appropriation, grants and gifts).
Collections: 19th Century American and European paintings; †contemporary paintings, sculpture, prints, drawings and ceramics; Stimson Collection of Master prints; †contemporary Japanese prints, folk pottery.
Exhibitions: (1976-78) Drawings by Bruce Conner; Japan Art Festival Exhibition 1976; School of Art student and faculty art exhibitions; Henry Gallery/Five Decades; The Metalsmith; Guy Anderson; Biennial Northwest Crafts Exhibition; The Warp and Weft of Islam; Eight Artists/Eight Rooms.
Publications: Index of Art in the Pacific Northwest, currently comprising ten volumes, distributed by University of Washington Press; Quarto (series of art history monographs), irregularly issued; catalogs.

Activities: Demonstrations, seminars, films; lect open to the public, 8 vis lectr per yr; gallery talks; tours; competitions; individual paintings and original objects of art lent to accredited museums; lending collection contains original art works 2000; traveling exhibitions organized and circulated.
—**Art Library,** 101 Art Bldg, DM 10, 98195. Tel: 206-543-0648. *Librn* Marietta M Ward.
Open Mon - Thurs 8 AM - 9 PM; Fri 8 AM - 5 PM; Sun 1 - 5 PM. Estab 1940 primarily to provide resources for the courses, degree and research programs of the School of Art, and serves as the Art Library for university community as a whole. Circ: 63,189.
Income: Financed by city appropriation.
Holdings: Vols 24,000; Per subs 406 reference; Other—Clipping files, exhibition catalogs, photographs, reproductions.
Special Subjects: Emphasis on art history, art education, painting, graphic design, sculpture, interior design, ceramic art, industrial design, printmaking, photography and metal design.
Activities: Library tours.
—**Costume and Textile Study Center, School of Nutrition, Sciences and Textiles,** 98195. Tel: 206-543-1739. *Cur* Virginia I Harvey; *Preparator* Krista Turnbull; *Conservator* Martha Fletcher; *Asst to Cur* Cathy Cerny; *Secy* Judy Jensen.
Open Daily 1 - 5 PM; No admis. Estab 1958 as a center for the maintenance and as a study collection of historic and ethnic costumes and textiles for use by the student, designer craftsman and scholar. A gallery is not maintained, items are displayed for study on tables. Average Annual Attendance: 3500.
Collections: Elizabeth Palmer Bayler Collection of textiles from India; Choate Collection of lace; Eugene Garbaty Collection; Harriet Tidball Collection.
Activities: Lectr open to the public, 2 - 3 vis lectr per yr; tours.
Library: Librn Andrea K Bebee. Open to the public for reference only. Holdings: Vols 2000; Per subs 20. Special Subjects: Weaving, embroidery, looms, textiles, costume.
—**Thomas Burke Memorial Washington State Museum.** Tel: 206-543-5590. *Dir* George I Quimby; *Cur Ethnology & Anthropology* Dr James Nason; *Cur Northwest Coast Indian Art* Bill Holm.
Open Tues - Sat 10 AM - 4:30 PM; Sun 1 - 4:30 PM. No admis. Estab 1889 for research and exhibitions.
Collections: Anthropology and natural history of the Northwest and the Pacific, specializing in primitive art of these regions.
Activities: Museum classes; circulates study collection.

SPOKANE

EASTERN WASHINGTON STATE HISTORICAL SOCIETY,* Cheney Cowles Memorial Museum, 2316 W First Ave, 99204. Tel: 509-456-3931. *Dir* Albert H Culverwell; *Cur Art* Fred Ploeger.
Open Tues - Sat 10 AM - 5 PM; Sun 2 - 5 PM; cl Mon. Estab 1916, Museum of history and art; fine arts gallery with regular monthly art exhibitions of Pacific Northwest artists. Average Annual Attendance: 83,000. Mem: 1100; dues $5 per person; annual meeting usually in May.
Income: Financed by membership, county, city and state appropriations.
Collections: Regional history including collection of Indian arts and handicrafts; historic house of 1898 by architect Kirtland K Cutter, interior restored and decorated with period furnishings; fine arts gallery.
Exhibitions: Approx 105 since 1967.
Publications: Museum Notes to all members, 10 issues per year.
Activities: Lect open to the public; concerts; lending collection contains Kodachromes 500; traveling exhibitions organized and circulated; museum shop.
Library: Librn Elinor Kelly. For reference. Holdings: Vols 4000; AV—Prints and negatives 15,000; Other—Newspaper clipping file, manuscripts; library use only, copies available on request.

FORT WRIGHT COLLEGE ART GALLERY, W 4000 Randolph Road, 99204. Tel: 519-328-2970, exten 45. *Chmn* Sister Paula M Turnbull.
Open daily 9 AM - 5 PM. No admis. The main purpose of this gallery is for presentation of student BFA exhibitions. It is adjacent to the main art building and is of substantial size.
Income: Financed through the College.
Collections: Student works retained from exhibitions.
Exhibitions: Student BFA shows; faculty shows; student art shows and sales.
Activities: Classes for adults; dramatic programs; lect open to public, 4 - 5 vis lectr per yr; competitions; exten dept serving Yakima, and Omak; museum shop.

SPOKANE FALLS COMMUNITY COLLEGE FINE ART GALLERY, W 3410 Fort George Wright Drive, 99204. Tel: 509-456-6100. *Div Chmn Creative Arts* Donald Nepean; *Chmn Fine Arts Dept* Jo Fyfe.

Open Mon - Fri 8:30 AM - 4 PM. No admis. Estab 1968 to bring in fine artists and craftsmen outside the Spokane area for the benefit of students and community. Gallery is 20 x 40 ft, carpeted, airy, with windows to front and back; in center of art building. Average Annual Attendance: 2000.
Collections: Glass vase, handblown; paintings.
Exhibitions: Dong Kingman; AGA Annual; Traveling Show, Smithsonian; National Print Show: painters, advertising artists, craftsmen.

SPOKANE PUBLIC LIBRARY, W 906 Main Ave, 99201. Tel: 509-838-3361. *Chairperson Bd of Trustees,* Mrs H L Grande; *Library Dir* Betty W Bender; *Asst Dir* Florence M Fray.
Open Mon - Thurs 9 AM - 9 PM; Fri & Sat 9 AM - 6 PM. Estab 1884 basically to meet citizens' education, information, recreation, and cultural lifelong learning needs through a variety of programs and facilities; gallery maintained to exhibit mainly local artists' work and changed monthly. Circ: 1,241,212 (1977).
Income: $1760,240 (financed by city appropriation). Purchases: $1,-522,425 (1977).
Holdings: Vols 462,924; Per subs 1394; AV—Audio tapes, cassettes, film strips, lantern slides, microfiche, microfilm, motion pictures, phonorecords, reels, slides, video tapes; Other—Clipping files, exhibition catalogs, framed reproductions, manuscripts, memorabilia, original art works, original documents, pamphlets, photographs, prints, reproductions, sculpture.
Special Subjects: Northwest History; genealogy.
Special Collections: Rare books.
Exhibitions: One each month in picture gallery.
Activities: Classes for adults and children; dramatic programs; lect open to the public, 9 vis lectr per yr; concerts; gallery talks; tours.

TACOMA

TACOMA ART MUSEUM, 12th and Pacific Ave, 98402. Tel: 206-272-4258. *Dir* Jon W Kowalek; *Educ Head* Gale Janes; *Design Center Aide* Lee Skinner.
Open Mon - Sat 10 AM - 4 PM; Sun noon - 5 PM. No admis. Estab 1895 to perpetuate the finest in the visual Fine Arts; Museum features galleries for permanent collection, traveling shows, and a specialized Children's Gallery. Average Annual Attendance: 150,000. Mem: 1300; annual meeting varies.
Income: $200,000 (financed by endowment, membership).
Collections: †American paintings and †sculpture; †American crafts (glass, ceramics, weaving, etc); †European and Asian works of art.
Exhibitions: Historic American Stained Glass; Jerry Uelsmann (photography); American Bicentennial Exhibition; Sculpture of Sir Jacob Epstein; Imperial Robes of China; Rembrandt etchings; Morris Graves; Mark Tobey; Japanese screens; contemporary American Art of the 70s.
Publications: Bulletin, monthly.
Activities: Docent training; lect open to the public, 24 vis lectr per yr; gallery talks; tours; competitions; individual paintings and original objects of art lent to other professional museums; lending collection contains paintings, sculpture; museum shop selling books, original art, reproductions, prints; Children's Gallery.
Library. Librn Sally Norris. Open to the public for reference only. Holdings: Vols 1000; Per subs 25. Special Collections: Unique collection of research material on Japanese woodcut.

TACOMA PUBLIC LIBRARY, Handforth Gallery, 1102 Tacoma Ave S, 98402. Tel: 206-572-2000. *Dir* Kevin Hegarty; *Asst Dir* Marile Creager; *Chief Librn* Gary Reese; *Dir Handforth Gallery* Clayton Kirking.
Open Mon - Thurs 9 AM - 9 PM; Fri & Sat 9 AM - 6 PM. Estab 1952 to extend library services to include exhibits in all media in the Thomas S Handforth Gallery. Circ: 1,237,000.
Income: Financed by city appropriation.
Holdings: Vols 594,700; Per subs 1759; AV—Audio tapes, cassettes, film strips, microfilm, motion pictures, phonorecords, reels, slides; Other—Clipping files, exhibition catalogs, framed reproductions, memorabilia; original art works, pamphlets, photographs, prints.
Special Subjects: Northwest Collection; genealogy; photographs of local and regional subjects; manuscripts.
Special Collections: City county and state documents; Federal document depository; Lincoln Collection; Kaiser Collection.
Exhibitions: Monthly change of exhibits.
Publications: Administrative Bulletin, weekly.
Activities: Classes for children; dramatic programs; lect open to the public, 3 - 4 vis lectr per yr; traveling exhibitions organized and circulated.

UNIVERSITY OF PUGET SOUND,* Kittredge Art Gallery, 1500 N Warner St, 98416. Tel: 206-759-3521, exten 326. *Gallery Dir* Marcia Jartun.

Open Mon - Fri 9 AM - 4 PM; Sun 1 - 4 PM. No admis. Estab for showing of student and professional works; university operated. Average Annual Attendance: 1000.
Collections: Abby Williams Hill, who painted Northwest scenes from the 1880s, to the 1930s.
Exhibitions: Local, community and regional art shows; faculty and student shows.
Publications: Monthly show bulletins.

WASHINGTON STATE HISTORICAL SOCIETY,* 315 N Stadium Way, 98403. Tel: 206-593-2830. *Dir* Bruce LeRoy.
Open Tues - Sat 9 AM - 4:30 PM; Sun 2 - 5 PM; cl Mon & holidays. Estab 1891; owns three buildings: Art gallery under direction of Society. Average Annual Attendance: 225,000. Mem: 964; dues $7 and up; annual meeting May.
Income: Financed by membership and other funding.
Collections: Pre-historic relics; †Indian and Eskimo artifacts, baskets, clothing, utensils; Oriental items; †Washington-Northwest pioneer relics.
Exhibitions: Changed monthly.
Publications: News Notes and sponsors Pacific Northwest Quarterly with the State University; books and pamphlets on Pacific-Northwest history.
Activities: Special school tours.
—**Hewitt Memorial Library:** *Librn* Frank L Green; *Asst Librn* Jeanne Engerman. Tel: 206-593-2830.
Open Tues - Sat 9 AM - 4:30 PM. Estab 1941 for research in Pacific Northwest history, for reference only.
Income: Financed by membership, state appropriation, and gifts.
Holdings: Vols 15,000; AV—Microfilm; Other—Clipping files, manuscripts, memorabilia, pamphlets, photographs.
Special Subjects: Railroads, lumber, fishing, Indians, missions, labor.
Special Collections: Asahel Curtis Photograph Collection of early Seattle.
Publications: Circuit Rider, quarterly.

WALLA WALLA

CARNEGIE CENTER OF THE ARTS,* Elliott Square, 109 S Palouse, 99362. Tel: 509-525-4270. 30-mem Bd of Trustees.
Open nine months Tues - Sat 11 AM - 4:30 PM; June & July Noon - 4 PM; cl Aug. No admis. Estab 1970 in 1905 Carnegie Library, built of Kansas brick and paneled with oak; inc 1971 as a non-profit educational organization. Mem: 750; dues from student $1 to life $1500 or more.
Income: Financed by endowments, dues, contributions, art sales and rentals, and gift shop.
Exhibitions: Professional exhibits, changing monthly, of the work of National Northwest artists; area artists' exhibit in August; youth gallery for display of art and craft work of school children.
Activities: Art and craft classes and workshops; lectures; recitals; rental-sales gallery; sales shop.
Library: Art books and fine antiques.

YAKIMA

ALLIED ARTS COUNCIL OF THE YAKIMA VALLEY, 5000 W Lincoln Ave, 98908. Tel: 509-966-0930. *Pres* Peggy Lewis; *First VPres* Bob Rash; *Second VPres* Anita Monoian, *Secy* Marie Halverson; *Exec Dir* Tom Tomlinson.
Open 9 AM - 5 PM. No admis. Estab 1962 to encourage, promote and coordinate the practice and appreciation of the arts among the people of Yakima Valley; general gallery shows changing monthly exhibits; Attic gallery rents art in addition to selling it. Mem: 600; dues $5 - $150.
Income: Financed by membership.
Exhibitions: Monthly exhibits by local and area artists.
Publications: Artscope (arts calendar), monthly.
Activities: Lect open to the public.
Library: Warehouse Library. Tel: 509-966-0930. *Librn* Fran Marble.

WEST VIRGINIA

CHARLESTON

CHARLESTON ART GALLERY OF SUNRISE, 755 Myrtle Rd, 25314. Tel: 304-344-8035. *Acting Exec Dir* Ellie Schaul; *Cur of Fine Arts* J Frederick Cain; *Acting Cur of Educ* Joan Lewis.
Open Mon - Sat 10 AM - 5 PM; Sun 2 - 5 PM. No admis. Sunrise is located on a 16 acre estate containing two restored mansions housing a children's museum, planetarium, art gallery, live animal fair and botanical center. The Art Gallery is situated in a Georgian style mansion known as Torquilstone. Mem: 16,000. Annual meeting Mid April.
Income: $300,000 (financed by endowment, membership, city and state appropriations).

Collections: †19th and 20th century paintings, prints, drawings and sculptures; decorative arts from the same periods. A major development program has been inaugurated with emphasis upon documenting the history of American art.
Exhibitions: Numerous exhibitions held throughout the year.
Activities: Classes for adults and children; dramatic programs; docent training; lect open to the public, 12 vis lectr per yr; concerts; gallery talks; tours; competitions; traveling exhibitions organized and circulated; museum shop selling books, original art, reproductions and prints.
Library: For reference only.

HUNTINGTON

HUNTINGTON GALLERIES, Park Hills, 25701. Tel: 304-529-2701. *Dir* Roberta Shinn Emerson; *Adminr* James C Lawhorn; *Cur Coll G* Eason Eige; *Cur Educ* Fredrick D Gros; *Development Officer* James F Weidman; *Registrar* David McGee; *Prog Coordinator* Janet Dooley; *Comptroller* Cynthia Riggs.
Open Tues - Sat 10 AM - 4 PM, Sun 1 - 5 PM; cl Mon. No admis. Estab 1952 to own, operate and maintain an art gallery for the collection of paintings, etchings, bronzes, porcelains, and all kinds of art and utility objects; to permit the study of arts and crafts, and to foster an interest in the arts. Three-building complex on 52 acres includes ten galleries, two sculpture courts, six studio workshops, a 10,000 volume capacity library, and auditorium. Average Annual Attendance: 70,000. Mem: 2000; dues, various; annual meeting June.
Income: Financed by endowment, membership, city and state appropriations and county funds.
Collections: American paintings; 18th century decorative arts; Georgian silver; Oriental prayer rugs; prints; sculpture; glass; American decorative arts.
Exhibitions: Paintings by Fairfield Porter; American Art: From the Limners to the Eight Henry Moore Lithographs: American Watercolor Society Exhibition; New American Glass: Focus West Virginia; Major Graphics of Edvard Munch; Currier and Ives Lithographs.
Publications: Bulletin, bimonthly; catalogs for exhibitions.
Activities: Classes for adults and children; docent training; lect open to public, 4 vis lectr per yr; concerts; gallery talks; tours; competitions; individual paintings and original objects of art lent to museums; traveling exhibitions organized and circulated; museum shop selling books, original art, reproductions, prints and crafts; junior museum.
Library: *Librn* Elizabeth Bostwick. Open to public for reference. Holdings: Vols 3000; Per subs 82.

MORGANTOWN

WEST VIRGINIA UNIVERSITY
—**Galleries A & B,** Evansdale Campus, 26506. Tel: 293-3140-2140. *Dean* Gilvert Trythall; *Chmn of Dept of Art* Urban Couch; *Cur CAC Galleries* John D Clarkson.
Open 10 AM - 5 PM. Estab 1968 primarily as teaching galleries for students, and for the pleasure of students, public and campus community; two galleries, 22 x 42 ft, flexible arrangements, approximately 600 running ft. Average Annual Attendance: 6000.
Income: Financed by state appropriation.
Collections: Paintings; prints; drawings.
Exhibitions: (1976-78) Peter Charles (sculpture); John Bond (sculpture); Anthony Hyde (paintings); Ben Freedman (drawings & prints); David Hanna (paintings); Grace Martin Taylor; Katherine Burnside; Marietta Crafts National Touring Exhibit; Jan L Cook (photography); Carol Martin (batiks); MFA Thesis Exhibits: Luther Nestor (watercolors).
Activities: Classes for children; dramatic programs; lect open to the public, 4 vis lectr per yr; concerts; gallery talks; individual paintings and original objects of art lent; lending collection contains film strips 80, Kodachromes 6000, lantern slides 500, motion pictures 6, original art works 500, original prints 300, paintings 150, slides 7000; traveling exhibitions organized and circulated.
Library: Holdings—Vols 5000; Per subs 36.
—**Creative Arts Center and Gallery,** 26506. Tel: 304-293-0111. *Cur Art & Dir Acq* John D Clarkson.
Open Mon - Fri 1 - 4 PM; cl National holidays. No admis. Estab 1867.
Collections: Paintings; music; costumes; theater.
Activities: Lectures; gallery talks; tours; concerts; drama; competitions; temporary traveling exhibitions.
Library: *Librn* Mrs Thomas Canning. Holdings: Vols 10,000; Other—music scores; records.

PARKERSBURG

PARKERSBURG ART CENTER, 220 Eighth St (Mailing Add: PO Box 131, 26101). Tel: 304-485-3859. *Dir* P Joseph Mullins; *Educ Coordinator* Jane Ellen Osborn.

Open Tues - Fri 10 AM - 4 PM; Sat - Sun 1 - 4 PM. No admis. Estab 1938 for the operation and maintenance of an art center and museum facility for the appreciation and enjoyment of art, both visual and decorative, as well as art history, crafts and other related educational or cultural activities, main gallery, 43 x 27 ft, and upper gallery, 38 x 27 ft, completely carpeted, air-conditioned and climate controlled. Average Annual Attendance: 10,000. Mem: 600; dues individual $15, family $25, sustaining $75, corporate or patron $125; annual meeting June.
Income: $79,000 (financed by endowment, membership and state appropriation).
Collections: Parmenides (sculpture by Beverly Pepper); The Hinge (watercolor by Rudolph Ohrning); Advice of Dreams (oil by Beveridge Moore); Patrick Henry Land Grant Document.
Exhibitions: Lilliputian Christmas; Private Collection of Frank J Kelly; Private Collection of African Art; Alfred Eisenstaedt Exhibit; two-person and group shows; Photography Competition; West Virginia State Invitational Competition.
Publications: Calendar of events, bimonthly; annual report.
Activities: Classes for adults and children; docent training; workshops; lect open to public, 4 vis lectr per yr; concerts; gallery talks; competitions;
Library: Open to public. Holdings: Vols 500; Per subs 5.

ROMNEY

HAMPSHIRE COUNTY PUBLIC LIBRARY,* Main St, 26757. Tel: 304-822-3185. *Pres* Carol Winland; *Secy* Mary Pugh; *Librn* Brenda Riffle.
Open Mon - Fri 10 AM - 5 PM; Sat 10 AM - 3 PM. No admis. Display cases, changed every month. Average Annual Attendance: 16,470.
Income and Purchases: $14,534.
Holdings: Vols 18,000.
Exhibitions: Various local artists' collection; private collections of rocks, antiques, displays of items of other countries; weaving; children's art.
Activities: Classes for adults and children; dramatic programs; concerts.

WHEELING

OGLEBAY INSTITUTE MANSION MUSEUM,* Oglebay Park, 26003. Tel: 304-242-7272. *Cur* Samuel J Wegner; *Exec Dir* S H Coulling; *Museum Dir* John A Artmberger.
Museum open 9:30 AM - 5 PM; Sun & holidays 1:30 - 5 PM; cl Thanksgiving, Dec 24, 25, 30 and Jan 1. Admis $1.50, children 12 and under free. Estab and inc 1930 to promote educational, cultural and recreational activities in Wheeling Tri-State area; building and grounds property of City. Average Annual Attendance: 30,000. Mem: Approx 1000; dues $10 and up.
Collections: Period rooms; †early glass made in Wheeling and the Midwest; †early china; †pewter.
Exhibitions: Current exhibits of art and other allied subjects change monthly in an exhibition wing adjoining the main house.
Activities: Day-long Antique Seminars twice a year; antique classes in furniture, glass and china; gallery talks.
Library: Highly specialized library on the early history of the area; many source books, prints, documents and maps.
—**Oglebay Institute Mansion Museum Committee.** *Chmn* Mrs R C Miller; *VChmn* R C Haylett Jr; *Secy* Mrs R E Di Bartolomeo.

WISCONSIN

BELOIT

BELOIT COLLEGE, Theodore Lyman Wright Art Center, 53511. Tel: 608-365-3391. *Dir & Cur* Marylou S Williams; *Acting Registrar* Jean Nykamp; *Museum Ast* Thomas Montvel-Cohen.
Open Mon - Fri 9 AM - 5 PM; Sat 11 AM - 5 PM; Sun 1 - 5 PM. No admis. Estab 1893; Wright Art Center built 1930 to house the collection for the enrichment of the college and community through exhibition of permanent collection and traveling and temporary regional art exhibitions of cultural and aesthetic value. A Georgian building architecturally styled after The Fogg Museum, Cambridge, Mass. Three galleries on main floor, on a large center court; Art Dept shares other floors in which two student galleries are included. Average Annual Attendance: 10,000-20,000. Dues $15.
Collections: Oriental; European and American paintings, sculpture and decorative arts; graphics—emphasis on German Expressionist and contemporary works; Pitkin Collection of Oriental art; Gurley Collection of Korean pottery, Japanese sword guard, Chinese snuff bottles and jades; Morse Collection of paintings and other art objects; †Neese Fund Collection of contemporary art; Fisher Memorial of Greek casts; furniture and sculpture of various periods; prints by Rembrandt, Durer, Whistler and others; †Ross Collection of graphics.

Exhibitions: Annual Beloit and vicinity exhibition; Clay and Fibers; Bicentennial Exhibition from Smithsonian Institution; Graphics Festival; Visions of the Orient; Arts of Oceania; Yeats Festival; Romantic Era Paintings; Quilts and Coverlets; Photographic Image.
Publications: Exhibition catalogs.
Activities: Classes for children; dramatic programs; docent training; lect open to public, 12 vis lectr per yr; gallery talks; tours; competitions; individual paintings lent to faculty offices and students; lending collection contains framed reproductions, and original prints; traveling exhibitions organized and circulated.
Library: Morse Library. *Librn* Vail Deale. Open to public, students and faculty. Special Subjects: Art library. Special Collections: Rare books.
—**Friends of the Wright Art Center.** Mem: 200; dues $5 and up; holds annual meeting.

EAU CLAIRE

UNIVERSITY OF WISCONSIN-EAU CLAIRE,* Foster Art Gallery, Fine Arts Center, 100 Water St, 54701. Tel: 715-836-3278. *Art Chmn* Charles Campbell; *Dir, Foster Art Gallery* Anders C Shafer.
Open Mon - Fri 11 AM - 5 PM; Sun 1 - 4 PM. Average Annual Attendance: 10,000.
Income: Financed by city and state appropriations.
Collections: Includes works by Knaths, Stamos, Dine, Falstrom and many others.
Exhibitions: BFA exhibits and shows, annual faculty shows and annual student art show and festival.
Activities: Teaching children with special problems; lect open to public, 1 - 6 vis lectr per yr; gallery talks; tours.

GREEN BAY

NEVILLE PUBLIC MUSEUM, 129 S Jefferson St, 54301. Tel: 414-497-3767. *Pres* Helen Fersley; *Dir* James L Quinn; *Chief Cur* Donn Quigley; *Cur Educ* Jeanne Schuldes; *Cur Art* James Kreiter; *Assoc Cur* Mary Schauer; *Museum Registrar* Bonita Cagle.
Open Mon - Sat 9 AM - 5 PM; Sun 2 - 5 PM. No admis. Estab 1915 as Green Bay Public Museum, names changed 1926. Average Annual Attendance: 100,000. Mem: 350; dues individual $5, family $10; annual meeting in the spring.
Income: Financed by city and county appropriation.
Collections: †Contemporary and historical paintings; †drawings; †prints and sculpture; Neville family portraits; David Belasco Collection of Victoriana antique furniture, †china, †glass, †silver, fans, lace, costumes and †accessories.
Exhibitions: Local art clubs exhibit annually; Northeastern Wisconsin Art Show annually with cash awards; rotating monthly exhibits.
Publications: Annual Report.
Activities: Classes for adults and children; lect open to the public, 4 vis lectr per yr; gallery talks; competitions; individual paintings and original objects of art lent to municipal offices; traveling exhibitions organized and circulated; sales shop selling reproductions and educational items.
Library: Open to the public for reference.

KENOSHA

KENOSHA PUBLIC MUSEUM, 5608 10th Ave, 53140. Tel: 414-656-6026. *Dir* Stephen H Schwartz; *Cur Educ* Paula Touhey; *Cur Exhib* Daniel Fredricksen.
Open Mon - Fri 9 AM - Noon and 1 - 5 PM; Sat 9 AM - Noon; Sun 1 - 4 PM. No admis. Estab 1936 to promote interest in general natural history and regional art. The gallery has 8000 sq ft of permanent exhibition space and 1000 sq ft for temporary exhibits. Average Annual Attendance: 40,000. Mem: 250; dues $10; annual meeting Apr.
Income: $127,000 (financed by city appropriation). Purchases: $1200.
Collections: Worldwide ethnology; regional artists; historic Wisconsin pottery; Oriental decorative arts; regional natural history.
Exhibitions: Yousouf Karsh: People who make our World; Roses.
Publications: Newsletter, monthly.
Activities: Classes for adults and children; lect open to public, 10 vis lectr per yr; gallery talks; tours; competitions; lending collection contains cassettes, color reproductions, film strips, framed reproductions, motion pictures, nature artifacts and slides; museum shop selling original art.
Library: Open to public for reference. Holdings: Vols 2000; per subs 20. Special Subjects: Natural history.

LA CROSSE

VITERBO COLLEGE ART GALLERY, 815 S Ninth St, 54601. *Dir* Sister Carlene Unset.

Open Mon - Fri 8 AM - 5 PM. Estab 1964 to exhibit arts and crafts which will be a valuable supplement to courses offered. The gallery is located in the center of the art department; 100 running feet; soft walls; good light.
Income: $2000 (financed by school appropriation). Purchases: $500.
Collections: Mrs Lynn Miller Collection of contemporary United States primitives; Peter Whitebird Collection of WPA project painting.
Activities: Classes for adults; dramatic programs; lect open to the public; gallery talks.

MADISON

MADISON ART CENTER, INC, 720 E Gorham St, 53703. Tel: 608-257-0158. *Dir* Joseph E Wilfer; *Asst to Dir* Jane Liska; *Pres Bd Dir* Phillip Levy.
Open Tues & Thurs 9 AM - 9 PM; Wed, Fri & Sat 9 AM - 5 PM; Sun 1 - 5 PM; cl Mon, holidays & Aug. No admis. Estab 1901, present building 1964, inc 1970. Seven galleries: Sales & rental gallery; gallery shop; special photo gallery, Rudolph E Langer Print Study Room; studio class rooms, auditorium-theatre, dark room, film editing; print shop; large park-like grounds on lake. Average Annual Attendance: 90,000. Mem: 1500; dues $10 and up.
Income: $100,000+. Purchases: $10,000.
Collections: Large print and drawing collection (Japanese, European, Mexican, American); paintings, sculpture, 16th and 17th century tapestries; current emphasis on contemporary Americans.
Exhibitions: Over 40 shows annually; 8-10 major shows usually organized by the staff; occasional loan or rented exhibitions; smaller shows include one-person shows, print exhibitions, photographic exhibitions, group shows and theme exhibitions.
Publications: Posters and announcements usually accompany each exhibition; catalogs for 6 - 10 shows per year.
Activities: Weekly film series; docent program; lect and demonstrations, 8 - 10 per yr; bus tours; print club; loan program to public schools; sidewalk art fair; gallery talks; classes for adults and children.
Library: For study and research. Small selection of books, catalogs and slides in addition to Print Study Room.

STATE HISTORICAL SOCIETY OF WISCONSIN,* 816 State St, 53706. Tel: 608-262-3266. *Dir* James Morton Smith; *Assoc Dir* Richard A Erney; *Asst Dir* William H Applegate; *Dir Museum* Thurman O Fox; *Cur Decorative Arts* Joan Severa; *Librn Dir Research* William F Thompson.
Open Mon - Fri 8 AM - 10 PM; Sat 8 AM - 4 PM; Sun Noon - 4 PM; cl holidays. No admis. Estab 1846, museum added 1854; organized to promote a wider appreciation of the American heritage, with particular emphasis on the collection, advancement, and dissemination of knowledge of the history of Wisconsin and of the Middle West. Average Annual Attendance: 487,000. Mem: 7000; dues $7.50 and up.
Income: Financed by state appropriation.
Collections: (Art) Furniture, dolls, china, glass, coins, historical material, iconographic collection, paintings and prints of over 355,000 photographs and slides.
Exhibitions: Frequent special exhibitions; 4 annual gallery changes.
Activities: Elementary school prog; Founders Day; regional meetings of local historians; historymobile; TV and radio programs; films; material lent to other museums; traveling exhibitions organized and circulated.
—**Library;** *Librn* Charles Shetler; *State Archivist* F Gerald Ham.
Holdings: Vols 388,000; AV—Microfilm 95,494 reels; Other—Pamphlets 400,000, manuscripts 25,175 cu ft.
Special Collections: State archives of over 26,000 cu ft Americana library including public documents collection; Newspaper collection of more than 35,000 vols.

UNIVERSITY OF WISCONSIN-MADISON
—**Memorial Union,** 800 Langdon St, 53706. Tel: 608-262-2263. Union South, 227 N Randall Ave, 53706. Tel: 608-263-2543. *Dir & Secy* Ted Crabb; *Art Coordr* Jan Marshall Fox.
Open 10 AM - 8 PM. No admis. Organization estab 1907 to provide a cultural program for the members of the university community; owns two fireproof buildings with three galleries. Average Annual Attendance: 193,000. Mem: 46,500 faculty, alumni and townspeople, plus 38,000 students; dues $30; annual meeting May.
Purchases: $1500.
Collections: Oil and watercolor paintings, prints, and sculptures, mostly by contemporary American artists.
Activities: Informal classes in arts and crafts; films; sidewalk art sales; periodic gallery talks; loan collection available on rental to students and members.
—**Elvehjem Art Center,** 800 University Ave, 53706. Tel: 608-263-2246. *Dir* Eric S McCready; *Asst Dir* David S Berreth; *Cur Coll* Carlton E Overland; *Registrar* Lisa C Calden; *Cur Educ* Anne Lambert; *Coordr* Doreen Holmgren.

Open Mon - Sat 9 AM - 4:45 PM; Sun 11 AM - 4:45 PM; cl holidays. No admis. Estab 1962, building opened 1970 to display, preserve, and build a general art collection of high quality for the study and enjoyment of students, community and state; three levels, 12 galleries covering 25,000 sq ft of exhibition space. Average Annual Attendance: 100,000. Mem: 2500; dues $7.50 - $250.
Income: Financed by endowment, membership, state appropriation and private sources. Purchases: Vary according to income.
Collections: Ancient Egyptian and Greek pottery, sculpture, glass and coins; Medieval painting and sculpture; Renaissance painting and sculpture, 17th, 18th, 19th and 20th century European painting, sculpture, and furniture and decorative arts; 18th, 19th and 20th century American painting, sculpture and furniture; 18th, 19th, and 20th century Russian paintings and icons; Indian sculpture and miniatures; 16th - 20th century prints/†general collection.
Exhibitions: Twelve to fourteen temporary exhibitions per year in all media, from varied period of art history.
Publications: Annual Bulletin; Calendar, quarterly, special exhibitions catalogs.
Activities: Education Department; classes for children; docent training; lect open to the public, 10-15 vis lectr per yr; concerts; gallery talks; tours; individual paintings lent to qualified art museums and galleries, for special exhibitions; traveling exhibitions organized and circulated; museum shop selling reproductions, gift items, catalogs, posters, exhibition related articles.
—**Kohler Art Library,** 800 University Ave, 53706. Tel: 608-263-2256. *Dir* William C Bunce; *Reference Librn* K Louise Henning.
Open Mon - Fri 8 AM - 5 PM; & 7 - 10 PM; Sat & Sun 1 - 5 PM. Estab 1970 to support the teaching and research needs of the Art History Dept and the Elvehjem Art Center. C 43,000.
Income: $107,753 (financed by endowment and state appropriation). Purchases: $42,484.
Library: Holdings—Vols 75,344; Per subs 280; AV—Microfiche, microfilm, slides; Other—Exhibition catalogs, pamphlets.
Special Subjects: Art, architecture, decorative arts.
Activities: Tours.

MANITOWOC

RAHR-WEST MUSEUM AND CIVIC CENTER. Park St at N Eighth, 54220. Tel: 414-684-4181. *Dir* Gary Whitbeck; *Museum Asst* Richard Quick; *Board Chmn* Mrs John D West.
Open Tues - Fri 9 AM - 4 PM; Sat & Sun 1 - 4 PM; cl Mon. No admis. Estab 1950 as an art center to serve the city of Manitowoc. Transitional gallery in new wing built 1975; period rooms in Victorian Rahr Mansion built c 1891; a historic register home. Average Annual Attendance: 5000. Mem: 237; dues $3 - $500; annual meeting held in Feb.
Income: $58,000 (financed by membership and city appropriation).
Collections: Schwartz Collection of Chinese ivories; Schuette Woodland Indian artifacts; 19th and 20th century American paintings and prints; contemporary art glass.
Exhibitions: Monthly changing exhibitions.
Publications: Quarterly Newsletter; exhibition catalogs.
Activities: Classes for adults and children; docent training; lect open to the public, 4 - 5 vis lectr per yr; gallery talks; tours; traveling exhibitions organized and circulated.
Library: Open to the public for reference only. Holdings: Vols 1500; Per subs 6. Special Subjects: Art reference.

MENOMONIE

UNIVERSITY OF WISCONSIN-STOUT, Gallery 209, Art Dept, 54751. Tel: 715-232-1428. *Dir* Orazio Fumagalli; *Cur* Eddie Wong.
Open Mon - Fri 9 AM - 5 PM. No admis. Estab 1966 to serve university and local community with exhibits of art. A single room gallery; cloth walls and track lighting. Average Annual Attendance: 9500.
Income: Financed by state appropriation.
Collections: Prints; drawing; sculpture; African art; paintings including works by Warrington Colescott; Georges Rovalt; Walter Quirt; Roy Deforest and Raphael Soyer.
Exhibitions: Changing exhibits.
Activities: Classes for children; lect, 2 - 3 vis lectr per yr; gallery talks.

MILWAUKEE

ALVERNO COLLEGE,* 3401 S 39th St, 53215. Tel: 414-671-5400. *Gallery Dir* Lucinda Hubing.
Open Mon - Fri 9 AM - 5 PM; Sun 2 - 5 PM; cl non-school days. Estab for the aesthetic enrichment of community and the aesthetic education of students. Gallery maintained.

CARDINAL STRITCH COLLEGE,* Studio San Damiano, 6801 N Yates Rd, 53217. Tel: 414-352-5400. *Head Dept* Sister Mary Tomasita.

Open daily 9 AM - 5 PM. No admis. Estab 1947 to encourage creative art in each individual.
Income: Financed by endowment, city and state appropriations, and tuition.
Collections: Folk crafts; paintings.
Exhibitions: Professor's works; senior graduating exhibitions; well-known area artists; acquisitions from distant lands; children's art; approx 5 exhibitions of student's work.
Publications: CSC News, monthly.
Activities: Classes for adults and children; dramatic programs; competitions; scholarships; lect open to public, 20 vis lectr per yr; competitions; scholarships; individual paintings and original objects of art lent; traveling exhibitions organized and circulated; concerts; book shop.
Library: Holdings—(Art) Vols 200; Other—Photographs.

MARQUETTE UNIVERSITY, Marquette Art Gallery, Memorial Library, Wisconsin Ave (Mailing Add: 134 Coughlin Hall, 53233). Tel: 414-224-7263. *Dir* Curtis L Carter; *Cur Asst* Wendy Rosefelt.
Open daily 8 AM - 10 PM. No admis. Estab 1950 to house the Universities permanent collection of art, to sponsor art shows and to exhibit traveling art exhibits.
Income: Financed through University.
Collections: 17th century Old Masters; Oriental art; Wisconsin painters; 20th century art.
Exhibitions: Karl Priebe Retrospective; Barbara Morgan (photographs); Romanian Contemporary Paintings; The Art of Design in Milwaukee Industry.
Publications: Catalogs of exhibits.
Activities: Lect open to public, 4 - 5 vis lectr per yr; tours; individual paintings and original objects of art lent.

MILWAUKEE AREA TECHNICAL COLLEGE, Kronquist Craft Gallery, 1015 N 6th St, 53203. Tel: 414-278-6600. *Gallery Dir* John Strachota.
Open daily. No admis. Estab 1961 to stimulate appreciation for fine metalwork; gallery is 30 x 40 ft, located on Sixth Floor of central building; glass display cases house permanent collection, spotlit walls for artwork, carpeted lounge area. Average Annual Attendance: 2500.
Collections: Sterling hollowware, flatware, jewelry and bronze castings by Emil F. Kronquist.
Exhibitions: Continuous graphic and applied art Student and Faculty Showings.

MILWAUKEE ART CENTER, 750 N Lincoln Memorial Dr, 53202. Tel: 414-271-9508. *Pres Bd Trustees* Sheldon B Lubar; *Dir* Gerald Nordland; *Assoc Dir* I Michael Danoff; *Controller* Hugh Morgan; *Cur Educ & Acting Cur Decorative Arts* Barbara M Brown; *Asst Cur* Verna Curtis; *Registrar* Thomas Beckman; *Public Relations* Jane A Glasberg.
Open Tues - Sun 10 AM - 5 PM. Admis adults $1; students & sr citizens 50¢; children under 12 with adult free. Estab 1888 to create an environment for the arts that will serve the people of the greater Milwaukee community. Large, airy, flexible galleries, including a sculpture court and outdoor display areas. Fine arts and decorative arts are mixed to create an overview of a period, especially in the fine American Wing. Small galleries provide for specific or unique collections. Average Annual Attendance: 150,000. Mem: 3800; dues family $25; individual $20; annual meeting May.
Income: Financed by endowment, membership, county and state appropriations, and fund drive.
Collections: All media from ancient Egypt to modern America; 19th & 20th century European and American art, including the Layton and Bradley Collections; the American Ash Can School and German Expressionism are emphasized; the Flagg Tanning Corporation Collection of Haitian art; the Von Schleinitz Collection of 19th century German painting, Mettlach steins, and Meissen porcelain; a study collection of Midwest architecture—the Prairie Archives.
Exhibitions: Six Decades: The News in Pictures; Cork Marcheschi and Eric Schwartz; The Bible Through Dutch Eyes; The Art of Ludwig Meidner; 19th Century Art by the American People; The American Indian and the American Flag; Naive Art in Yugoslavia; Jerome Krause and Thomas Uttech: Visions from the North Woods; American 1976, Collecting the Masters; Max Ernst Tapestries; Masters Prints from the Permanent Collection; the Afro-American Tradition in Decorative Arts.
Publications: MACPAK, bi-monthly; Gallery Guides; Catalogs.
Activities: Classes for adults and children; docent training; lect open to public, 5 vis lectr per yr; concerts; gallery talks; tours; competitions; traveling exhibitions organized and circulated; museum shop selling books, magazines, original art, reproductions, slides, cards.
—**Library.** *Librn* Betty Karow.
Open to the public for reference Tues & Thurs 10 AM - 4 PM.
Holdings: Vols 15,000; Per subs 31; Other—Vertical files, 27 drawers.
Special Subjects: 19th century German painting.

Special Collections: Prairie Archives material (architecture and decorative arts of the Frank Lloyd Wright period) gift of Jacobson; von Schleinitz bequest of material on Meissen porcelain and 19th century German painting.

MILWAUKEE PUBLIC LIBRARY
—Art and Music Department, 814 W Wisconsin Ave, 53233. Tel: 414-278-3000. *City Librn* Henry E Bates, Jr; *Supv Central Services* Kirk L Pressing; *Coordinator Fine Arts* June M Edlhauser.
Open Mon - Thurs 8:30 AM - 9 PM; Fri - Sat 8:30 AM - 5:30 PM; Sun 1 - 5 PM. No admis. Estab 1897. Circ: 430,445 (central library), 58,000 (art & music dept).
Income: $19,000 from budgeted funds, additional income from endowments. Purchases: $19,000.
Holdings: Vols 129,297; AV—Cassettes, film strips, microfiche, microfilm, motion pictures, phonorecords, slides and video tapes; Other—Clipping files, exhibition catalogs, framed reproductions, manuscripts, memorabilia, original art works, original documents, pamphlets, photographs, prints, reproductions and sculpture.
Special Subjects: Fine and applied arts, history of art, architecture, city planning, landscape architecture, numismatics, philately, crafts, decorative arts, costumes, photography, auction and exhibition catalogs and bound periodicals.
Publications: Milwaukee Reader, weekly.
—Charles Allis Art Library, 1630 E Royall Place, 53202. Tel: 414-278-3010. *Cur* Margaret Fish Rahill.
Open Tues - Sun 1 - 5 PM; Wed 6:30 - 9 PM. No admis. Average Annual Attendance: 30,000. The Allis home and art collection were presented to the city in 1945, including a $200,000 endowment fund to help maintain the building and collection.
Special Collections: The personal library of Mr Allis; Chinese, Japanese, Persian and Korean pottery and porcelain; Chinese jade; ancient glass; French silver and Limoges enamel; Japanese netsuke; Barye bronzes; 16th & 17th century Italian bronzes; Oriental rugs; paintings by French, American, Dutch, German, Italian and Norwegian artists; etchings and engravings by Durer, Rembrandt, Whistler, Meryon, Haden and Zorn; French furniture and art objects of the 14th, 15th & 16th centuries.
Exhibitions: Changing exhibitions including paintings, prints, sculpture and crafts of local artists.
Activities: Cultural groups, concerts, tours and film programs.

MILWAUKEE PUBLIC MUSEUM, 800 Wells St, 53233. Tel: 414-278-2700. *Dir* Dr Kenneth Starr; *Cur of History* Dr Rudolph Fornemann; *Cur Oriental, Classical and Decorative Art* John Luedtke; *Cur Anthropology* Dr Nancy Lurie; *Art Dir* Edward Green; *Asst Art Dir* Robert Frankowiak.
Open Daily 9 AM - 5 PM; cl holidays. Admis Milwaukee County residents adults $1, children 25¢, Mon no admis; non-Milwaukee County Residents adults $2, children 75¢. Estab 1882 to assemble, preserve, meaningfully organize, carry on research and promote interest in materials relevant to the fields of natural science, anthropology and human history; to use materials in exhibits and in organized education programs to educate, enlighten and provide pleasurable experiences for the public. Four floors of exhibits includes a decorative art gallery. Average Annual Attendance: 500,000. Mem: 2700; dues student $5, individual $12.50, family $20, Enrichment Club $50; annual meeting Nov.
Income: $2,929,911 (financed by county apropriations).
Collections: American Indian artifacts enlarge by donations; Western African art enlarged by donations; I A Dinerstein Art Collection; Carl Netzow Collection of antique jewelry; Pre-Columbian art enlarged by donations.
Publications: Lore, quarterly.
Activities: Classes for adults and children; dramatic programs; docent training; films, demonstrations; lectr open to the public, 10 - 12 vis lectr per yr; guided orientation; museum shop selling books, reproductions, prints, slides, jewery, ethnic arts and crafts; junior museum.
—Library. *Librn* Judith Turner. Open to public through regular admis fee. For reference only.
Holdings: Vols & Per bd 80,765; Per subs 850; AV—Microfilm; Other—Maps.
Special Subjects: Decorative arts; archaeology; anthropology.

MOUNT MARY COLLEGE,* Tower Gallery, 2900 Menomonee River Parkway, 53222. Tel: 414-258-4810. *Chmn* Sister M Regina Collins.
Open Mon - Fri 8 AM - 4:30 PM; Sat & Sun 1 - 4 PM. No admis. Estab 1940 to provide both students and local community with exposure to art experiences and to provide artists, both estab professionals and aspirants with a showplace for their work.
Income: Financed by private funds.
Collections: Antique furniture, 16th century and Victorian period; contemporary print collection; watercolors by Wisconsin artists.
Exhibitions: 6 Exhibitions a year.

UNIVERSITY OF WISCONSIN-MILWAUKEE
—Fine Arts Galleries, School of Fine Arts,* 3200 Downer Ave, 53201. Tel: 414-963-4946. *Dir* Fred R Parker.
Open daily 10:30 AM - 4 PM; Sat 10 AM - 3 PM; cl Sun. No admis. Estab 1967 to function as university museum/galleries in conjunction with the art department and/or other colleges on campus; also serves outside urban community.
Income: Financed by city and state appropriation.
Collections: †Large graphic collection, primarily current art; Oriental woodcuts; contemporary weaving; photography; drawings.
Exhibitions: Local, national and international artists; crafts and design shows; photography; MFA graduates; varied museum calibre exhibitions.
Activities: Lect open to public, 2 - 3 vis lectrs per yr; gallery talks; competitions; small photograph collection.
—Art History Galleries.* Tel: 414-963-4330, 963-4060. *Dir* John Lloyd Taylor.
Open Tues 5 - 9 PM; Wed - Fri 12 - 4 PM; cl Sun & Mon. No admis. Founded 1964. Exhibit space facilities.
Collections: Greek and Russian icons and liturgical objects; paintings; graphics.
Exhibitions: Permanent, temporary and traveling exhibitions.
Publications: Catalogs; bulletin.
Activities: Lectures; gallery talks; guided tours; inter-museum loan.
—Union Art Gallery, 2200 E Kenwood Blvd, 53201. Tel: 414-963-6310. *Gallery Mgr* Mary Zane Allen.
Open Mon - Fri 10 AM - 2 PM; Tues & Wed 6 - 8 PM. No admis. Estab 1971 to provide space for student art, primarily undergraduate, to be shown in group exhibits established by peer selection and apart from faculty selection. The gallery has approx 2500 sq ft, parquet floor, 275 running ft carpeted walls and bushhammered walls; ceiling height varies from 10 ft 9 in to 22 ft 6 in; natural light and overhead spot tracks. Average Annual Attendance: 45,000.
Income: Supported through student segregated fees.
Exhibitions: Undergraduate and graduate student exhibits; annual exhibit of alumni work.
Activities: Lectures, 3 vis lectrs per yr; gallery talks; competitions.

WISCONSIN PAINTERS AND SCULPTORS, INC,* c/o Tom Uttech, Pres, 2582 N Cramer, 53211. Tel: 414-964-3349. *VPres* Quido Brink; *Secy* Claudia Gorecki; *Treas* Muriel Mennen.
Estab 1900 to promote the welfare of Wisconsin painters and sculptors and to promote and develop Wisconsin art. Mem: 150; dues $8 and up; annual meeting Nov.
Exhibitions: Bi-annual exhibitions in Apr.
Activities: Active program of exhibitions and lectures in cooperation with the Art Center and allied groups in the State.

NEENAH

BERGSTROM ART CENTER AND MUSEUM, 165 N Park Ave, 54956. Tel: 414-722-4808. *Dir* Anne D Neer; *Cur Paperweights* Geraldin J Casper.
Open Wed, Thurs, Sat & Sun 1 - 5 PM; June - Aug Tues 1 - 5 PM. No admis. Estab 1959 to provide cultural and educational benefits to the public. Average Annual Attendance: 29,000. Mem: 40; annual meeting Dec.
Income: $70,000 (financed by endowment, state and county appropriations and gifts).
Collections: Evangeline Bergstrom Collection of antique and modern glass paperweights; †Ernst Mahler Collection of Germanic glass; †Wisconsin and Midwestern paintings; sculpture.
Exhibitions: Monthly exhibitions in varied media.
Publications: Museum Quarterly, quarterly.
Activities: Classes for adults and children; docent training; lect open to public, 6 vis lectr per yr; concerts; gallery talks; tours; exten dept serving an area of 50 miles radius; individual paintings and original objects of art lent to responsible museums; museum shop selling books, original art, prints, ceramics, paperweights and needlework.
Library: *Librn* Anne Neer. Open to the public for reference. Holdings: Vols 2000; Per subs 10. Special Subjects: Glass and art history.

OSHKOSH

OSHKOSH PUBLIC MUSEUM,* 1331 Algoma Blvd, 54901. Tel: 414-424-0452. *Pres Bd* Roy Martin; *Dir & Cur Art* John H Kuony; *Asst Dir & Cur Anthropology* Robert J Hruska.
Open Tues - Sat 9 AM - 5 PM; Sun 1 - 5 PM; cl Mon. No admis. Estab 1924 to collect and exhibit historical, Indian and natural history material relating to the area, and fine and decorative arts. City owned mansion near University of Wisconsin-Oshkosh campus. Average Annual Attendance: 85,000.
Income: Financed by city appropriation.
Collections: †American artists and 18th century English portraits; †pressed glass; †Indian artifacts.

Exhibitions: Monthly changing exhibits.
Activities: Classes for adults and children; art school; lect; annual Art Fair in July with awards; sales shop.
Library: Open for reference. Holdings: Vols 5000; Per subs; Other—Manuscripts, photographs.

PAINE ART CENTER AND ARBORETUM, 1410 Algoma St, 54901 (Mailing Add: PO Box 1097, 54901). Tel: 414-235-4530. *Dir* Ralph A Bufano; *Cur Horticulture* John Green; *Admin Asst* Jean Peters; *Cur Coll* Janet Rothe; *Cur Educ* Margot Castle.
Open Tues, Thurs, Sat & Sun 1 - 4:30 PM; from Memorial Day to Labor Day open Tues - Sun 1 - 4:30 PM; cl Mon and national holidays. Admis $1.00. Estab 1948 as a non-profit corporation to serve the needs of the upper midwest by showing fine and decorative arts and horticulture. Average Annual Attendance: 90,000. Mem: 500; dues $20.
Income: $10,000 (financed by endowment, membership).
Collections: Barbizon paintings; Icon collection; †Chinese collection; †English Portraits collection; †English Period Room setting (1500-1800); American cup plates; Persian rugs; ornamental horticulture.
Exhibitions: Antique Toys 1875-1950; Icons from Orthodox Church Museum of Finland; American Antique Furniture; Paine Permanent Collection; Retrospective: John McCrady; English Brass Rubbings; Contemporary Polish Posters; European Masters in Portraiture.
Publications: Newsletter, quarterly.
Activities: Classes for adults; dramatic programs; docent training; lect open to public, 2 vis lectr per yr; concerts; gallery talks; tours; competitions; individual paintings and original objects of art are lent to other museums and institutions; lending collection contains cassettes, original art works, original prints, paintings, photographs, sculptures and slides; traveling exhibitions organized and circulated; sales shop selling books, magazines, original art, reproductions and jewelry.
Library: Librn Jean Schaefer. Open to staff members and to the public upon request. Holdings: Vols 850; Per subs 30. Special Subjects: English furniture; decorative arts and architecture.

UNIVERSITY OF WISCONSIN, OSHKOSH, Allen Priebe Gallery, Corners of Elmwood and Woodland Ave, 54901. Tel: 414-424-0147 *Dir* Samuel A Yates; *Asst* Lynn Clogh.
Open Mon - Fri 10 AM - 3 PM; Mon - Thurs 7 - 9 PM; Sat & Sun 1 - 4 PM. No admis. Estab 1972 as a memorial to Allen Priebe, former professor in the University art department. The gallery is 60 x 40 ft, with inlaid floors, sunlights, carpeted walls, and numerous partitions. Average Annual Attendance: 16,000.
Income: Financed by state appropriation and student allocations.
Exhibitions: Edward S Curtis, The North American Indian; The Rosenberg Collection of 19th and 20th Century Masters; Alice Neel, Paintings from 1935-1976; Henri Matisse, the Weatherspoon Cone Collection of Sculpture and Lithographs; Beyond Illustration: The Art of *Playboy;* Four Black Artists: Benny Andrews, Al Loving, Reginald Gammon, Alfred Smith; Fiber Structures with Ruth Kao, Jean Stamsta, and Jim Peters.
Publications: Posters of upcoming shows.
Activities: Classes for adults and children: docent training; workshops; lect open to public, 6 vis lectr per yr; gallery talks; junior museum, Priebe Annex, Arts & Communications Center, VW-O campus.

RACINE

RACINE ART ASSOCIATION, 2519 Northwestern Ave, 53404. Tel: 414-636-9177. *Pres* Richard J Jensen; *VPres* Norma Pearson; *Secy* Lorna Hennig; *Project Dir* Bruce Pepich; *Secy* Mildred Shields; *Educ* Sylvester Jerry.
Open Mon - Thur 11 AM - 9 PM; Fri - Sun 1 - 5 PM. No admis. Estab 1941 to foster and aid the establishment and development of public art galleries and museums, programs of education and training in the fine arts, and to develop public appreciation and enjoyment of the fine arts. Maintains an art gallery with six galleries. Average Annual Attendance: 50,000. Mem: 400; dues $10 and up; annual meeting May.
Income: $70,000-$75,000 (financed by membership and fund raising).
Publications: Newsletter, quarterly.
Activities: Classes for adults and children; lect open to public, 2 vis lectr per yr; competitions; scholarships; traveling exhibitions organized and circulated.
Library: Volunteer staff. Open to the public. Holdings: Vols 700; Per subs 12. Special Collections: Warrington Colescott and Francis Myers Graphics.

CHARLES A WUSTUM MUSEUM OF FINE ARTS, 2519 N Western Ave, 53404. Tel: 414-636-9177. *Dir* George M Richard; *Cur Exhib* William Blaesing.

Open Mon - Thurs 11 AM - 9 PM; Fri - Sun 1 - 5 PM. No admis. Estab 1940 to serve as cultural center for greater Racine community. There are five galleries in old (1856) residence converted for exhibition purposes. Average Annual Attendance: 40,000.
Income: $150,000 (financed by endowment, city and county appropriations, private gifts and programs). Purchases: $500-$1000.
Collections: WPA Project paintings and prints; contemporary Wisconsin watercolors.
Exhibitions: Watercolor Wisconsin; local group and school shows; A Century Plus of Wisconsin Watercolors; What Artists Collect; Clay and Fiber; Architecture as Art.
Activities: Classes for adults and children; lect open to public, 3 - 6 vis lectr per yr; concerts; gallery talks; tours; competitions; exten dept serving Racine County; individual paintings and original objects of art lent to other institutions; lending collection contains original art works, original prints; traveling exhibitions organized and circulated; museum shop selling original art.
Library: Wustum Art Library. Open to public for reference. Holdings: Vols 600; Per subs 10 - 12.

RIPON

RIPON COLLEGE ART GALLERY,* Harwood Union Bldg, 54971. Tel: 414-748-8110. *Dir* E M Breithaupt.
Open Mon - Fri 9 AM - 4 PM. No admis. Estab 1965 to provide student body with changing exhibits. Average Annual Attendance: 4000.
Collections: Paintings, sculpture, print, multi-media.
Activities: Individual paintings lent to schools; lantern slides 20,000.

RIVER FALLS

UNIVERSITY OF WISCONSIN, RIVER FALLS, Gallery 101, Cascade St, 54022. Tel: 715-425-7803. *Gallery Dir* Thomas F Hunt.
Open Mon - Fri 9 AM - 5 PM & 7 - 9 PM; Sat & Sun 1 - 5 PM. No admis. Estab 1973 to exhibit artists of regional and national prominence; and for educational purposes; one gallery. Average Annual Attendance: 80,000.
Income: $5000 (financed by state appropriation, and student activities funds).
Collections: †Regional Artists; †National and International Artists; WPA Artists.
Exhibitions: Stu Luckman; Phoebe Helman; Rose Mary Mack; Art Faculty Exhibit; Invitation Print Exhibit; The American Progression: 1830's to 1950's; Morton Subotnick; Area High School Exhibit; Invitational Glass Exhibit; Fine Arts Festival: Jewelry; Senior Exhibit; Student Juried Exhibit.
Activities: Lect open to public; gallery talks.

SHEBOYGAN

JOHN MICHAEL KOHLER ARTS CENTER,* 608 New York Ave, 53081. Tel: 414-458-6144. *Dir* Ruth Kohler.
Open Tues - Sun 1 - 5 PM; Mon 7 - 9 PM; cl national holidays. No admis. Estab 1967 to provide aesthetic and educational opportunities in the creative visual and performing arts. Five exhibitions, theater, four studio-class rooms, library, sales gallery. Average Annual Attendance: 100,000. Mem: 650; dues student $7.50, active $15, contributing $25-$50, sustaining $50-$100 and up.
Income: Financed by membership. Purchases: $89,000.
Collections: Kuehne Collection of 6000 prehistoric Wisconsin Indian artifacts; contemporary prints including Warhol, Hunt, Piene, Wunderlich, and others; furniture; glass; ceramics.
Publications: Newsletter, quarterly; exhibition catalogs; annual report.
Activities: Classes for adults and children in all phases of the visual arts as well as dance, theatre and music; lectures; demonstrations; summer theater; film series; concerts; tours; sales gallery.
Library: Art books and periodicals.

WEST BEND

WEST BEND GALLERY OF FINE ARTS, 300 S Sixth Ave (Mailing Add: PO Box 426, 53095). Tel: 414-334-9638. *Pres* Joan Pick; *Exec Dir* E G Kocher; *Exec Secy* F J Derer.
Open Wed - Sun 1 - 4:30 PM; cl Mon & Tues. No admis. Estab 1961 to encourage the varied art interests of the community. A large colonial style building with eight gallery exhibit rooms and three basement art classrooms. Average Annual Attendance: 3500. Mem: 450; annual meeting Feb.
Income: Financed by endowment, membership and donations. Purchases: $2000.
Collections: Carl von Marr Collection; †current Wisconsin art.
Exhibitions: Monthly exhibitions; annual show.
Publications: Bulletin, monthly.

Activities: Classes for adults and children; lect open to public, 8 vis lectr per yr; gallery talks; tours; competitions with cash awards; individual paintings lent to business organizations; lending collection contains books and paintings.
Library: Open to members. Holdings: Vols 300; Per subs 4.

WYOMING

BIG HORN

BRADFORD BRINTON MEMORIAL RANCH MUSEUM, State Road 335 (Mailing Add: PO Box 23, 82833). Tel: 307-672-3173. *Dir* James Taylor Forrest; *Asst Dir* Ed Smyth.
Open May 15 - Labor Day daily 9 AM - 5 PM. No admis. Estab 1961 to show a typical well-to-do ranch of the area of northern Wyoming as established in the late 19th Century; two galleries and house museum. Average Annual Attendance: 13,000.
Income: $100,000 (financed by endowment).
Collections: American art and few pieces of European art, largely of the 19th and 20th Century; collections include Western American art by Frederic Remington, Charles M Russell; Plains Indians artifacts; furniture; china; silver.
Exhibitions: (1976-77) Special showing from the permanent collection of the work of three American artists: Will James, Hans Kleiber, and Ed Borein.
Publications: Monographs on artists in the collection from time to time.
Activities: Sales shop selling books, original art, reproductions, prints, slides.
Library: Open to staff, and to the public by appointment. Holdings: Vols 1200.

CASPER

CENTRAL WYOMING MUSEUM OF ART, 104 Rancho Rd, 82601. Tel: 307-235-5247. *Dir* Kathryn Round; *Pres Board of Dir* Perry Kay Lathrop; *Secy* Jackie Ellis.
Open daily 11:30 AM - 4:30 PM. No admis. Estab 1967 to display traveling exhibits and workshop presentations. Average Annual Attendance: 30,000.
Income: Financed by membership.
Exhibitions: Traveling shows.
Publications: Newsletters, monthly.
Activities: Classes for children, lect open to the public, 12 vis lectr per yr.

CHEYENNE

WYOMING COUNCIL ON THE ARTS, 200 W 25th St (Mailing Add: State of Wyoming Offices, 82002). Tel: 307-777-7742. *Chmn* James M Boyle; *Vice Chmn* Peter Hassrick; *Secy* Donna Dickson; *Exec Dir* John Buhler; *Prog Coordinator* Marian Kline; *Coordinator Artists in Schools/Dir Poetry Prog* David J Fraher.
Open Mon - Fri 8 AM - 5 PM. Estab 1967 to encourage the study and presentation of all the arts, develop interest and participation in the arts, and to raise standards of local art groups. The Council grants funds to local groups for various activities. Mem: 10; membership appointed by the Governor; meeting quarterly.
Income: $346,000 (financed by state appropriation and Federal grants).
Publications: WCA News, bimonthly.
Activities: Artists-in-Schools provides artists in residence, poets in residence, and filmmakers in residence.

WYOMING STATE ART GALLERY, Barrett Building, 82002. Tel: 307-777-7519. *Dir Wyoming State Archives and Historical Dept* William H Williams; *Cur Wyoming State Art Gallery* Laura H Hayes.
Open Mon - Fri 8 AM - 5 PM; Sat 9 AM - 5 PM. No admis. Estab 1969 to collect, preserve and to exhibit the work of Wyoming and Western artists. Average Annual Attendance: 50,000.
Income: Financed by state appropriation.
Collections: Work by Wyoming and Western artists.
Activities: Classes for adults; docent training; lect open to public, 3 vis lectr per yr; gallery talks; original objects of art lent to State agencies; lending collection contains film strips, original art works, paintings; traveling exhibitions organized and circulated; museum shop selling books, original art, reproductions, slides and souvenir items.
Library: Open to the public for reference. Holdings: Vols 350.

CODY

BUFFALO BILL MEMORIAL ASSOCIATION,* PO Box 1020, 82414. Tel: 307-587-2268. *Chmn* Mrs Henry H R Coe; *Secy* Melvin C McGee; *Dir* Don Hedgpeth; *Exec Secy* Joyce Mayer; *Cur Plains, Indian Museum* Leo A Platteter; *Cur Buffalo Bill Museum* Richard I Frost.
Open daily Sept - May 8 AM - 5 PM; June - Aug 7 AM - 10 PM. Admis varies; group rates. Estab 1917 to preserve and exhibit art, artifacts and memorabilia of the Old West; to operate Buffalo Bill Museum, Plains Indian Museum, Whitney Gallery of Western Art, and Winchester Firearms Museum.
Income: $150,000 (financed by admissions and private funds).
—Whitney Gallery of Western Art
Collections: Catlin, Russell, Remington, Sharp, Bierstadt, Miller and all documentary artists of the Old West.
Exhibitions: Annual exhibition of prominent contemporary Western Atists; loan exhibitions.
Activities: Gallery talks; sales shop selling books, prints, Indian artifacts and postcards.
Library: Open to the public for reference. Holdings: Vols 2000; Other—Photograph collection.

CODY COUNTRY ART LEAGUE,* 836 Sheridan Ave, 82414. Tel: 307-587-3597. *Pres* Mrs George W Tresler; *VPres* Richard B Frazier; *Secy* Mrs Jesse Frost; *Dir* Mrs Gordon Way; *Exhibit Chmn* Mrs L A Johnson; *Pub Chmn* Mrs S J Duggleby; *Educ & Prog Chmn* Mrs James Gilbert; *Representative of Past Pres* Mrs William Mack.
Open Noon - 8 PM. No admis. Estab 1964 for promotion of artistic endeavor among local and area artists; exhibits, displays, and sales. Average Annual Attendance; 15,000. Mem 115, dues $10; annual meeting Dec.
Income: $18,365 (financed by endowment, membership, grants from Wyoming Council on the Arts, yearly auction, and sponsors). Purchases: $18,064.
Collections: One work each by Nicholas Eggenhoffer and Robert Myers.
Exhibitions: Western States Art Exhibit ($500 purchase award and over $1000 in other prizes); one-man shows.
Activities: Classes for adults and children; dramatic programs; films; workshops; lect open to public, 2-3 vis lectr per yr; competitions.

DUBOIS

WIND RIVER VALLEY ARTISTS' GUILD, Box 26 82513. *Pres* Gardell Dano Christensen; *VPres* Eva Ribble; *Secy* Margaret Mabbott.
Estab 1948 to promote art and interest in art, and to hold an annual exhibit of Art Works. Mem: 125; dues $5.
Income: Financed by membership and patrons.
Collections: †Fremont County Library Collection.
Exhibitions: Annual National Art Exhibit.
Publications: Newsletter, 6 times a year.
Activities: Workshops; competitions with cash award.

LARAMIE

UNIVERSITY OF WYOMING ART MUSEUM, Fine Arts Bldg, N 19th St, 82071. Tel: 307-766-2374. *Dir* James T Forrest; *Cur Coll* Jerry A Berger; *Cur Exhib* William A Litt, Jr.
Open Sun - Fri 1:30 - 5 PM during spring and fall semester; Sun - Fri 1 - 4:30 PM during summer sessions, cl holidays. Estab 1968 to serve as an art resource center for faculty, students and the general public; the museum serves as a training ground for students interested in museums as a profession. Exhibition space consists of two galleries totaling 5625 sq ft; work room, receiving room, storage vault, offices and outdoor sculpture court. Average Annual Attendance: 12,000. Mem: 300; dues $10 and up.
Income: $75,000 (financed by state appropriation and friends organization). Purchases: $2500.
Collections: 19th and 20th century European paintings, graphics and sculpture; 19th century American paintings, graphics and sculpture; 20th century American †paintings, †graphics and †sculpture.
Exhibitions: Eskimo Prints and Sculpture; Indian Miniature and Asian Art; Thomas and Mary Nimmo Moran Etchings; 100 Years of Artist Activity in Wyoming 1837-1937; Jack Beal Drawings and Lithographs; Printmaking West; Institute of American Indian Arts Students' Works; Robert I Russin Sculpture; Works by Ernest Trova; National Association of Women Artists Graphics; Patterns and Sources of Navajo Weaving; plus others.
Publications: Annual Report; exhibition catalogs with most exhibits.
Activities: Lectr open to the public, 6 vis lectr per yr; gallery talks; tours; individual paintings and original objects of art lent to other museums; lending collection contains original art works 1000, original prints 600 and paintings 400; traveling exhibitions organized and circulated.

ROCK SPRINGS

SWEETWATER COMMUNITY FINE ARTS CENTER, 400 C St, 82901. Tel: 307-382-4599. *Dir* Allen L Keeney; *Secy* Mary V Paterson; *Finance Officer* Mary Kornitnik.
Open Mon - Fri 1 - 5 PM & 6:30 - 8:30 PM; Sat 2 - 5 PM, cl Sun. No admis. Estab 1966 to house permanent art collection and hold various exhibits during the year; Halseth Gallery houses permanent art collection. Average Annual Attendance: Approx 5000.
Income: Financed by endowment, city appropriation, and county funds.
Collections: †Rock Springs High School permanent collection.
Exhibitions: Several during the year.
Publications: Calendar of events, two or three a year.
Activities: Classes for adults; dramatic programs; musical programs; competitions.

AMERICAN SAMOA

PAGO PAGO

JEAN P HAYDON MUSEUM,* PO Box 1540, 96799. Tel: 633-4347. *Chmn Bd Trustees* Palauni Tuiasosopo; *Cur* Fa'ailoilo Lauvao; *Asst Cur* Diana P Saulo.
Open Mon - Fri 10 AM - 4 PM; Sat 10 AM - Noon. No admis. Estab 1971 for preservation of Samoan culture, history and custom.
Income: Financed by city or state appropriations and grants from NEA.
Collections: Samoan village life; US Navy history; natural sciences; Polynesian artifacts.
Library: Reference library; Holdings: Other—Photograph collection, 16 mm films, and slides.

PUERTO RICO

PONCE

MUSEO DE ARTE DE PONCE (Ponce Art Museum), The Ltuis A Ferre Foundation, Avenida de las Americas, (Mailing Add: PO Box 1492, 00731). *Dir* Dr Rene Taylor; *Asst Dir* Mari Carmed Ramirez; *Conservator* Anton Konrad.
Open Mon & Wed - Fri 10 AM - Noon & 1 - 4 PM; Sat 10 AM - 4 PM; Sun 10 AM - 5PM; cl Tues. Admis adults $1, children 50¢. Estab to exhibit a representative collection of European paintings and sculpture; also Puerto Rican art. Seven hexagonal galleries on upper floor; three rectangular galleries on lower floor. Mem: 600; dues $15.
Income: Financed by endowment and membership.
Collections: 14th - 18th century paintings and sculpture; 19th century art; Latin American and contemporary art.
Exhibitions: (1976) Contemporary Latin American art; (1977) Collective of 40 New York Artists; (1978) Retrospective of Puerto Rican Artist Lorenzo Homar.
Activities: Lect open to the public, 2 - 3 vis lectr per yr; concerts; tours; individual paintings and original objects of art lent to other museum; museum shop selling books, original art, reproductions, prints, slides and plaster copies of pre-Columbian artifacts.
Library: *Librn* Mrs Ana Zayas. Open to public for reference. Holdings: Vols 4000; Per subs 4.

RIO PIEDRAS

UNIVERSITY OF PUERTO RICO,* Museum of Archaeology, History and Art, 00931. Tel: 809-764-0000. *Dir* Dr Osiris Delgado; *Cur Archaeology* Luis A Chanlatte; *Cur Art* Pedro J Gispert.
Open Mon - Fri 9 AM - 9 PM; Sat 8 AM - Noon & 1:30 - 5 PM; cl Sun & National holidays: No admis. Estab 1940.
Collections: Puerto Rican paintings of the past and present; sculpture; archaeology.
Exhibitions: Temporary exhibitions from the collection and from museum loans.
Activities: Lectures; guided tours; concerts.

SAN JUAN

ATENEO PUERTORRIQUENO,* Ponce de Leon, Stop One, 00902. Tel: 809-725-1265. *Exec Dir* Clara S Lergier.
Open Mon - Fri 9 AM - 9 PM; Sat 9 AM - 5 PM; cl Sun & holidays. No admis. Estab 1876. Mem: Dues $12.

Collection: Puerto Rican paintings; sculpture; prints and drawings; decorative arts, historical material.
Publications: Annual catalogs, reports.
Activities: Lectures; gallery talks; guided tours; films; concerts; dance recitals; competitions; dramas; temporary exhibitions; book shop.
Library: *Librn* Ada Nivea Rodriguez. Holdings: Vols. 12,000.

INSTITUTE OF PUERTO RICAN CULTURE, Museo de Bellas Artes (Museum of Fine Arts), Calle del Santo Cristo de la Salud 253, 00915. Tel: 809-723-2320. *Exec Dir* Luis M Rodriquez Morales; *Dir Prog Fine Arts* Maria E Somoza; *Adminr* Raul Joglar.
Open 9 AM - 5 PM. No admis. Estab 1977 for the exhibition of paintings and sculptures of Puerto Rican artists in a chronological way from 18th - 20th centuries.
Income: Financed by state appropriation.
Collections: Campeche-Oller Hall—religious and profane paintings of these two painters; 1900 Hall—exhibition of paintings of the period by Ramon Frade, Miguel Pou and Oscar Colon Delgado; Primitive Paintings Hall—works of Manuel Hernandez; documental and folklorical painting of the history of Puerto Rico; contemporary artists.
Exhibitions: Changing exhibitions of contemporary artists—Jaime Mejias; Julio Suarez; Carmen Alvarez Feldman; Julio Micheli and Andres Rodriguez Santos; Raul Acero; Wilfredo Labiosa; Angel Pepin; Grupo VI.
Activities: Lect open to public; gallery talks, tours; exten dept; individual paintings and original objects of art lent to educational and cultural organizations, government offices; lending collection contains original art works; original prints, paintings; traveling exhibitions organized and circulated.

INSTITUTO DE CULTURA PUERTORRIQUENA (Institute of Puerto Rican Culture), Apartado 4184, 00905. Tel: 809-724-0700. *Exec Dir* Luis M Rodriquez Morales.
Open Mon - Sun 8 AM - Noon & 1 - 5 PM. No admis. Estab 1955 to stimulate, promote, divulge and enrich Puerto Rico's cultural and historical heritage.
Income: Financed by endowment, and state appropriation.
Collections: Puerto Rican art, archaeology and historical collections.
Publications: Revista del Instituto de Cultura Puertorriquena, quarterly.
Activities: Educ dept; lect open to public; gallery talks; concerts; tours; competitions; exten dept serving cultural centers around the Island; artmobile; individual paintings and original objects of art lent to Govt agencies, universities and cultural centers; lending collection contains motion pictures, original art works, original prints, paintings, photographs; traveling exhibitions organized and circulated; sales shop selling books, records, and craft items; junior museum; the Institute has created 16 museums around the island and has five more in preparation, including museums of historical collections; art museums, and archaeological museums.
Library: General Library of Puerto Rico, Avenida Ponce de Leon 500. *Librn* Miguel A Nieves. Open for reference to public, investigators and students. Special Collections: Pre-Columbian archaeological collections.

LA CASA DEL LIBRO,* (The House of Books), Calle del Cristo 255, 00901. Tel: 809-723-0354. *Dir* David Jackson McWilliams; *Pres* Rafael Fabregas; *VPres* Max Goldman; *Treas* Miguel A Ferrer.
Open Mon - Fri 11 AM - 5 PM; Sat 2 - 5 PM. No admis. Estab 1955 as a museum-library devoted to the history and arts of the book and related graphic arts. Average Annual Attendance: 14,000. Mem: Approx 350; dues $10 and up.
Income: $26,000 (financed by membership and state appropriation).
Collections: Bibliography of graphic arts; early printing, especially 15th and 16th century Spanish; modern fine printing; calligraphy; binding; book illustration; papermaking.
Exhibitions: Gallery has displays on the first floor relating to printing and other arts of the book, such as: Spanish Incunables; Printing of Music in Books; The Boundaries of the World; Concrete Poetry; Editions of the Quixote; Por los Caminos del Dia; Original Art Work for the Emperor's New Clothes; The Illustrated Book in Puerto Rico; Book Plates; Objetivos de Julio Plaza; Fifteen Years of Posters at La Casa del Libro.
Activities: Some classes for adults; visits·from school groups, students of library science and workers in graphic arts; material available, no fees; occasional lect open to the public; gallery talks; original objects of printing arts lent; material must be used on the premises; traveling exhibitions organized and circulated to schools and colleges in Puerto Rico; book shop.
Library: 5000 items.

Corporate Art Holdings in the United States

CALIFORNIA

GLENDALE

GLENDALE FEDERAL SAVINGS AND LOAN ASSOCIATION, 401 N Brand Blvd, 91209. Tel: 213-956-3800. *Architectural Designer* Pam Coak.
Hours for viewing collections at the various branches: Mon - Thurs 9 AM - 4 PM; Fri 9 AM - 6 PM. Estab so that the association can have its own art collection; the pieces of art are hung in various offices and branches throughout California.
Collections: A relatively small collection consisting of California scenes.

LOS ANGELES

GOLDEN STATE MUTUAL LIFE INSURANCE CO, 1999 W Adams Blvd, 90018. Tel: 213-731-1131, exten 267. *Dir Public Relations & Advertising* William E Pajand.
Open during normal office hours. Estab 1965 to create a showplace for the viewing of Afro-American art; employees and policy owners can view art in all of the offices as part of the total business environment. Average Annual Attendance: 2000-2500.
Activities: Tours; purchase prizes; individual objects of art lent on a very limited basis.

SAN FRANCISCO

BANK OF AMERICA CORP AND BANK OF AMERICA FOUNDATION, 555 California St (Mailing Add: PO Box 37000, 94137). Tel: 415-622-8674. *Art Cur* Jean Higuera.
Open Mon - Fri 8 AM - 5 PM. Estab 1968 to educate employees on current and past trends in the art field, to provide an aesthetic atmosphere, and to offer exposure to the works of artists who are trying to establish their careers. The Plaza Gallery has lobby area for large scale pieces of art, two smaller galleries for photographs and prints. Average Annual Attendance: Approx 500,000.
Purchases: $15,000 by the bank.
Collections: A variety of collections ranging from well known local contemporary pieces, such as Diebenkorn, to internationally known pieces, such as Vasarely; large number of prints and graphics by local artists.
Exhibitions: Monthly exhibitions.
Activities: Lectures; individual objects of art are occasionally lent to museums who may need a particular piece from the collection to complete an exhibit being given at the museum.

DELAWARE

WILMINGTON

WILMINGTON TRUST COMPANY, Tenth & Market, 19899. Tel: 302-655-4011, exten 236. *VPres* C R McPherson.
In public areas of banking offices art may be viewed from 9 AM - 3 PM; in nonpublic areas viewing by request and appointment only. Estab 1950 to support the local art community. Art is displayed in the banking offices.
Purchases: $5000.
Collections: A collection of watercolors by Delaware artists of Delaware scenes expanded to include nearby Brandywine Valley.

FLORIDA

MIAMI

SOUTHEAST BANKING CORPORATION, First National Bank of Miami, 100 S Biscayne Blvd, 33131. Tel: 305-577-3000. *Mgr Fine Arts Dept* Jean H Johnson.
Estab 1973 to maintain a quality corporate art collection; for the support of local, state and national artists; and for donations and support of local visual nonprofit art organizations, such as museums.
Collections: Over a thousand pieces of art including graphics, sculpture, oils, and tapestries.
Activities: Artmobile traveling to 47 specified Southeast Banks throughout the State of Florida.

ILLINOIS

CHICAGO

THE FIRST NATIONAL BANK OF CHICAGO, One First National Plaza, 60670. Tel: 312-732-4000. *Consult* Katharine Kuh; *Cur* Robert Middaugh.
Open 10 AM - 3 PM. Estab 1968 to provide a pleasant atmosphere for employees via works of art of the highest quality. The collection serves as an educational process for employees who may not come into contact with art otherwise. The collection is housed throughout the bank offices.
Collections: Works of art ranging from the sixth century BC until today; including works of art from Asia, the Near East, Africa, Latin America, the South Seas, Australia, the Caribbean basin, Europe and America.
Activities: Gallery talks; tours.

THE NORTHERN TRUST COMPANY, 50 S La Salle St, 60675. Tel: 312-630-6000, exten 3288. *Staff Designer* Edward R Schauble.
Open by appointment only. Estab 1889; the corporate art collection strives to provide a special quality to the customer and staff environments in the bank. The art collection is displayed in the lobbies and throughout the bank buildings.

PLAYBOY ENTERPRISES, INC, 919 N Michigan Ave, 60611. Tel: 312-751-8000. *VPres Corp Art & Graphics, Dir PEI & Art Dir Playboy Magazine* Arthur Paul; *Art Librn* John Zywicki.
Prearranged tours only. Estab 1954 for a comprehensive collection of illustrations from the past 24 years by fine artists, as well as commercial artists whose works have been commissioned for use in the magazine.
Purchases: Only occasional purchases to expand already large collection.
Collection: Collection of fine illustrated art done in all media which includes work by many famous artists and illustrators.
Activities: Tours; Annual Playboy Illustration Awards, winning art receives $1000, runner-up $500, in two categories, fiction and nonfiction; individual objects of art lent for shows and exhibitions; traveling exhibitions organized and circulated for museums, schools and galleries throughout the world.

EVANSTON

WASHINGTON NATIONAL INSURANCE COMPANY, 1630 Chicago Ave, 60201. Tel: 312-866-3084. *Second VPres* Ferrell E White.
The collection is not ordinarily available for public viewing; it is put on display two days annually, coinciding with George Washington's birthday. Commissioned by the company to artist Walter Haskell Hinton, the series was begun in early 1930s to portray the person of George Washington in a less militaristic and more humanistic fashion, holding to

historic authenticity. Most pictures are displayed in executive corridor of company's home office.

Collection: Original oil paintings of George Washington. The paintings provide perspective and insight into the various stages of Washington's life from vigorous youth to surveyor and soldier; from member of Virginia's House of Burgesses to Commander-in-Chief during the Revolutionary War; and finally, from President to his later years at Mount Vernon.

Activities: Lectures are given on George Washington's birthday.

LONG GROVE

KEMPER INSURANCE COMPANIES, Rte 22 & Kemper Dr, 60049. Tel: 312-540-2000. *Art Cur* Joan E Robertson. Tel: 312-540-2502.
Open by appointment only, Mon - Fri 8:15 AM - 4:30 PM. Estab 1973 as an essential part of the company's well-being, to enhance the working environment, and to reflect the diverse backgrounds of the employees through a variety of subject matter, styles, and media. Monthly exhibitions are held along a 90 ft wall in the staff lounge, there is no tract lighting. The collection is throughout a 500,000 sq ft building, mostly in four 500 ft long corridors. Average Annual Attendance: 2000 employees; 1500 visitors.

Purchases: $30,000-$50,000.

Collections: †One permanent collection is housed at the international headquarters, which emphasizes contemporary Chicago and midwest connected artists, and realistic art in half of the collection.

Activities: Lectures; commitment of funds to purchase art works from local art fairs, art shows, and Illinois State Fair Professional Art Show; a local art history major is allowed to intern with the art curator; individual objects of art lent to retrospectives and one-person shows, or traveling group-shows if borrower pays transportation and insurance costs; donations are made to the Annual Chicago Art Awards; the art curator's time is available for judging shows and for lectures.

MASSACHUSETTS

BOSTON

FEDERAL RESERVE BANK OF BOSTON, 600 Atlantic Ave, 02106. Tel: 617-973-3000. *Cultural Affairs Coordr* Sally Fitzgerald.
Open Mon - Fri 9 AM - 5 PM. Estab 1978 to provide stimulating work environment for employees, and to contribute to the cultural growth of New England. The gallery is 27 x 178 ft, with adjoining 420-seat auditorium—the art collection is dispersed throughout the 32-floor building.

Collections: Paintings by Richard Anuszkiewicz, Thelma Appell, Ellen Banks, Gene Davis, Helen Frankenthaler, Maud Gatewood, Robert Goodnough, Morris Louis, William Monaghan, Lowell Nesbitt, George Nick, Kenneth Noland, Katherine Porter, Richard Pousette-Dart, Michael Russo, Susan Shatter, Frank Stella, Estaban Vicente, Neil Welliver, Stephen Woodburn, and Jack Youngerman; tapestry by Helena Hernmarck; over 200 prints and posters.

Exhibitions: The Iceberg and Its Shadow is on exhibit. This 80 ft plate glas sculpture is on loan to the bank by the Albert and Vera List Collection and the Massachusetts Institute of Technology during most of 1978.

Activities: lectures; in 1979 expect to have continuing cultural exhibitions, each with a duration of approx two months. Presently Larry Bell's The Iceberg and Its Shadow is on exhibit. This 80 ft plate glas sculpture is on loan to the bank by the Albert and Vera List Collection and the Massachusetts Institute of Technology during most of 1978.

WESTWOOD

WILLIAM UNDERWOOD COMPANY, One Red Devil Lane, 02090. Tel: 617-329-5300. *Projects Specialist* Joan Thacher Tiffany; *Gallery Cur* William A Bagnall.
Open Mon - Fri 9 AM - 4 PM. Estab 1976 to provide an opportunity for employees and the community to view a wide range of art work, and to provide support for artists by sponsoring exhibition program. Space is specifically designed and used for gallery at the company's executive offices in corporate headquarters, with special lighting and accessible location. Average Annual Attendance: 1500.

Purchases: Amount varies; recent emphasis has been on support of exhibition program rather than purchases.

Collections: Contemporary sculpture; 19th century engravings.

Activities: Lectures; gallery talks; William Lyman Underwood (1864-1929) photograph show organized and circulated to museums; preservation and conservation of collection of photographs by William Lyman Underwood, totaling over 2000 lantern slides, glass plate negatives and original prints. The President of the company, George C Seybolt's leader-

ship in the arts is supported by the company in his activities as a member of the National Council on the Arts and Chairman of the National Museum Services Board.

MICHIGAN

DETROIT

COOPERS & LYBRAND, 400 Renaissance Center, 48243. Tel: 313-962-7000. *Personnel in Charge of Coll* Jerome Y Halperin, Lloyd A Schwartz and Edward J Premo.
Open by appointment only 9 PM - 5 PM. Estab 1978 to help support local Michigan artists, and to create a pleasant working environment for the employees.

Activities: Individual objects of art lent for a specific showing.

MINNESOTA

MINNEAPOLIS

FEDERAL RESERVE BANK OF MINNEAPOLIS, 250 Marquette Ave, 55414. Tel: 612-340-2446. *Sr VPres* John MacDonald; *Art Adminr* Ann Haugland.
Open by reservation only. Estab 1972 to enrich the bank's environment, and to provide a gesture of support for the region's art community. Art is placed throughout the bank.

Purchases: Vary annually.

Collections: Permanent Regional Collection—Minnesota, North and South Dakota, Montana, northwestern Wisconsin, upper peninsula of Michigan.

Activities: Individual objects of art lent for exhibit purposes only, usually to the artist who has done the work being loaned.

GENERAL MILLS, INC, 9200 Wayzata Blvd, 55426 (Mailing Add: PO Box 1113, Minneapolis, MN 55440). Tel: 612-540-7269. *Art Cur* Donald McNeil.
Open by appointment only. Estab 1958 to add beauty and cultural stimulation to the working environment of the employees; to benefit the visual arts through patronage; and to provide an additional arts resource for the local community. The collection is dispersed throughout the entire Main General Office bldg.

Purchases: (1976-77) $60,000.

Collections: 20th-century †painting, †sculpture, †graphics, and †tapestries; 19th century oriental painting and woodblocks; exterior †sculpture.

Activities: Lectures; tours; individual objects of art lent to special exhibition and one-man shows upon request; a future goal is to organize and circulate traveling exhibitions.

LUTHERAN BROTHERHOOD, a Fraternal Benefit Society, 701 Second Ave S, 55402. Tel: 612-340-7261. *Fine Arts Coordr* Ms Joan Sheldon.
Estab 1958; the Lutheran Brotherhood's Fine Arts Program is dedicated to promoting the fine arts, both sacred and secular, among Lutherans and their communities, throughout the United States. The Lutheran Center Gallery is located on the court level of the society headquarters, the gallery features exhibits by amateur and professional artists. Due to its ideal location and lovely setting, the center is becoming one of the Twin City area's most popular galleries. The Traveling Art Galleries are made up of art works chosen during the Annual National Lutheran Student Art Award Program—senior category, held each spring. The art works were submitted by Lutheran students, nationwide, and are now a part of the LB Permanent Art Collection. Average Annual Attendance: 1977 Over 100,000 people viewed the Traveling Galleries.

Purchases: $2000 - $3500.

Collection: Includes works that were commissioned and executed by leading Midwest artists.

Activities: Tours of facilities, including explanations of collection pieces; competitions; awards; individual objects of art occasionally lent, by special arrangement between Lutheran Brotherhood and group requesting work; traveling exhibitions organized and circulated to churches, colleges, art festivals, county fairs, homes for the aged, hospitals, and student centers

NEW JERSEY

PRINCETON

E R SQUIBB & SONS, INC, Rte 206 (Mailing Add: PO Box 4000, 08540). Tel: 609-921-4000. *Mgr Community Relations* Lora W Jones.
Open Mon - Fri 9 AM - 4:30 PM; Thurs until 9 PM; Sun 1 - 5 PM; cl Sat. Estab 1972 as a community service. The collection is placed in various private offices and corridors and not available for public viewing. Exhibitions are held in the Squibb Gallery measuring 63 x 87 ft, with glass-walled with removable interlocking panels, which suspend from chrome fixtures in the ceiling and are arranged differently for each exhibition. The gallery overlooks a 12-acre lake. Average Annual Attendance: 60,000.
Collections: Contains some 325 dye transfer photographs by Viennese photographer Ernst Haas.
Exhibitions: Eight public month-long exhibitions are held each season from Sept to June, varying in style and technique to serve the wide-ranging, sophisticated art tasks of well-educated area residents. Some exhibitions are mounted to benefit charities.
Activities: Gallery talks; tours; awards given to local art associations; three color photography exhibitions have been initiated and given to organized groups for traveling schedules.

NEW YORK

ARDSLEY

CIBA-GEIGY CORPORATION, 444 Saw Mill River Rd, 10502. Tel: 914-478-3131, exten 2606. *Mgr Corporate Art Services* Markus J Low.
Hours for viewing collection by appointment. Estab 1959 as a means to enrich the working environment, and to give support to young or lesser known artists. The collection is displayed in offices, corridors, conference rooms and reception areas at various company locations.
Collections: Over 450 †oils, †watercolors, †gouache, †collages, †drawings, †multiples, and some †sculptures from the New York School, in particular abstract expressionist, as well as geometric and figurative art; also works by Swiss, and to a lesser extent works by French, Spanish, South American and Japanese artists.
Activities: Individual objects of art lent upon request for a limited duration; traveling exhibitions organized and circulated upon request to museums and educational institutions, generally once per year with limited duration; an award winning film, From the Man (1970) dealing with the effect of art on business, is available upon request.

NEW YORK

CHASE MANHATTAN BANK, Art Program, 410 Park Ave, 10022. Tel: 212-223-6131. *Dir Art Program* Vacant; *Assoc Dir Art Program* Merrie Good.
Estab 1959 to enrich the bank environment for customers and employees.
Purchases: Vary according to current needs.
Collections: 4700 works including †paintings, †graphics, †sculpture, †photographs, †original works on paper, largely contemorary American; the overall collection is dispersed in over 200 locations in the city and state of New York, as well as overseas.
Activities: Occasional tours; individual objects of art lent to museums, artists, and galleries whenever feasible and when requested; traveling exhibitions are organized and circulated on rare occasions.

M GRUMBACHER, INC, 460 W 34th St, 10001. Tel: 212-279-6400. *Dir Public Relations* Dan Daniels.
Fine Arts Painting Collection is not presently ready for public viewing; Palette Collection Traveling Show is in preparation. Estab c 1957 to give purchase prize money to artists for fine arts work. Palette paintings are a different way of presenting artists work to the public.
Collections: Palette Paintings by Artists, traveling exhibit, being revised and updated; Fine Arts Traveling Exhibit in planning stages.
Publications: Palette Talk, quarterly.
Activities: Technical talks and painting demonstrations by artists; tours; awards given to art societies and associations in United States; traveling exhibitions organized and circulated; motion picture film library—fine arts painting, films by Rex Brandt, Lajos Markos, Valdi S Maris, available to colleges, universities, and art societies.

THE PORT AUTHORITY OF NEW YORK AND NEW JERSEY, One World Trade Center, 10048. Tel: 212-466-4211. (John F Kennedy International Airport Collection, Bldg 50, Jamaica, NY 11430. Tel: 212-656-5555). *Adminr Architectural Services* Saul S Wenegrat.
Open 24 hours a day, 7 days a week. Estab for public viewing of art. Average Annual Attendance: 2,000,000.
Collections: World Trade Center Collection—includes 6 major pieces of sculpture including works by Calder, Nagare, and Miro. Kennedy International Airport Collection—includes over 200 works by major artists from around the world including Calder, Picasso, and Dali.
Activities: Individual objects of art lent to museums for major shows.

WARNER COMMUNICATIONS INC, 75 Rockefeller Plaza, 10019. Tel: 212-484-8000. *Office of Corporate Contributions* Mary E McCarthy.
In 1976 the Robert O Dougan Collection of Victorian Photographs owned by the company, was placed on a long term loan as a promised gift to The Metropolitan Museum of Art, The Museum of Modern Art, and The Art Museum, Princeton University. In addition, the company has established a substantial purchase fund at the Metropolitan intended primarily for the acquisition of 20th century photographs.
Collection: Consists of approximately 1000 original photographs dating from 1842 to 1870 by major masters of Victorian photography, including D O Hill and Robert Adamson, W H Fox Talbot, Francis Frith, John Thomson, Maxime DuCamp, Julia Margaret Cameron, Thomas Annan, C E Watkins, and many others. The collection is preserved as single prints, in albums and in books illustrated with original photographs. The collection also includes illustrated handbooks, manuals and treatises describing technical aspects of the medium, materials that are now in the custody of Princeton University.

PURCHASE

PEPSICO, INC, Anderson Hill Rd, 10577. Tel: 914-253-2900. *Dir Community Programs* Katherine F Niles.
Open 9 AM - 5 PM. Estab 1970 to display 20th century sculpture in the gardens of the World Headquarters. The public is invited to visit the gardens to enjoy the sculpture. It is through sharing this experience of fine art that the company speaks a universal language. Average Annual Attendance: Thousands stroll the gardens in a year's time.
Collection: Sculpture Collection which includes works by sculptors from America, England, France, Italy and Switzerland among others. Each piece has been selected on its artistic merit and placed in a natural setting in the gardens of the World Headquarters. The artists and their pieces are as follows: Alberto Giacometti, Standing Woman II and III (black bronze); Alexander Calder, Hats Off (steel plate, painted Calder Red); Arnaldo Pomodoro, Grande Disco (polished bronze); Jacques Lipchitz, Towards a New World (bronze); Henry Moore, Locking Piece (bronze), Reclining Figure (black bronze) and Double Oval (bronze); David Wynne, Girl with a Dolphin (bronze), The Dancers (bronze), Dancer with a Bird (bronze), Girl on a Horse (bronze) and Grizzly Bear (fossil marble); Auguste Rodin, Eve (bronze); Henri Laurens, Le Matin and Les Ondines (both bronze); Seymour Lipton, The Wheel (bronze on monel metal) and The Codex (nickel silver on monel metal); Peter Throssell, Standing Figures (slate); David Smith, Cube Totem Seven & Six (polished stainless steel); Louise Nevelson, Celebration II (Corten steel painted black); Isamu Noguchi, Energy Void (black granite).
Activities: Upon request and by arrangement an audiovisual presentation of the Sculpture Collection is shown, along with a lecture by Thomas Folds, the former Dean of Education at Metropolitan Museum. Presentation and lecture are given for groups of 15 or more.

OKLAHOMA

TULSA

BANK OF OKLAHOMA (Formerly National Bank of Tulsa), Bank of Oklahoma Tower, One Williams Center, 74103 (Mailing Add: PO Box 2300, 74192). Tel: 918-588-6000. *Chmn Board & Chief Exec Officer* Eugene Swearingen; *Special Projects Coordr* Marsha McKinney.
Open by special appointment, Mon - Fri 8 AM - 5 PM. Estab 1969 to enhance the city of Tulsa's collections of contemporary art, and to allow more people to be introduced to and enjoy contemporary art; art is displayed throughout the bank.
Purchases: $10,000-$20,000.
Collections: Representative sample of numerous contemporary artists, including Joseph Albers, Calder, Gabor Peterdi, Ilya Bolotowsky, Julian Stanczak, Wolf Kahn.
Activities: Contributions are made to the University of Tulsa Art Program.

OREGON

PORTLAND

FIRST NATIONAL BANK OF OREGON, 1300 SW Fifth Ave, 97201 (Mailing Add: PO Box 3131, 97208). Tel: 503-225-2202 Public Relations. *Sr VPres* John Van Bodegom.
Open Mon - Fri 8:30 AM - 5 PM. Estab 1972 in conjunction with opening of new headquarters bldgs, to encourage and give recognition to the talents of Pacific Northwest artists, while enriching the environment of the persons who work in and visit bank headquarters. The collection is displayed in office areas throughout the headquarters complex.
Purchases: Vary.
Collections: Over 400 works by Pacific Northwest artists, includes—paintings, prints, sculpture, collages, and textiles.
Activities: Tours; individual objects of art are occasionally loaned to art organizations to be included in exhibitions; works by Oregon artists are also displayed in First National's 147 branch offices.

PENNSYLVANIA

PHILADELPHIA

THE INSURANCE COMPANY OF NORTH AMERICA, 1600 Arch St (Mailing Add: PO Box 7728, 19101). Tel: 215-241-4894. *Cur* Debra J Force.
Hours for viewing the collections have not been established as yet; at present tours are made by appointment. Estab 1966 to exhibit the company's holdings which are especially strong in fire and marine-related objects. One large gallery with two lobby exhibits; the first lobby exhibit combines fire, marine, and Americana; the second lobby exhibits are devoted to fire and marine.
Purchases: No formal program for acquisitions at this time.
Collections: Marine—mostly †19th century British oils, 17-19th century maps, and ship models; fire—full-size apparatus, †models, fire marks, Currier and Ives prints, engine panels, equipment, and firemen's dress; Americana—Birch prints, especially of Philadelphia, and †watercolors.
Activities: Tours; lectures provided if the need arises; individual objects of art lent for short-term exhibits.

PITTSBURGH

AVM CORPORATION, Suite 3729, Mellon Bank Bldg, 525 William Penn Place, 15219. Tel: 412-355-0400. *Chmn & Pres* Harold J Ruttenberg.
Open 9 AM - 5 PM. Estab 1974 to provide individuals working in the offices, and visitors an aesthetic experience. The collection is the personal property of the chairman and his wife, consisting principally of works of art of artists identified with Israel, with some American artists included.
Collection: Approximately 75 works of art consisting of oils, watercolors, drawings, etchings, lithographs and silk screens distributed among five offices and a large Board Room.

TEXAS

AUSTIN

BANK OF AUSTIN GALLERY, 2501 S Congress (Mailing Add: PO Box 3488, 78764). Tel: 512-447-4411, Exten 230. *VPres Public Relations* Mary Faulk Koock.

Open Mon - Fri 9 AM - 2 PM; other times by appointment. Estab 1975 for the purpose of making art and artists accessible to the community. The gallery is located on mezzanine level of the bank on the north side, with an all glass wall having a broad skylight in the center. Average Annual Attendance: Approx 4000-5000.
Purchases: $6000-$7000.
Exhibitions: Rotating exhibits, continuously changing every two weeks; sculpture, ceramics and quilts are sometimes displayed in addition to the paintings.
Activities: Lectures; tours.

VIRGINIA

RICHMOND

FEDERAL RESERVE BANK OF RICHMOND, 701 E Byrd St, 23219 (Mailing Add: PO Box 27622, 23261). Tel: 804-643-1250. *Mgr Records Mgt Dept & Bank Archivist* Sue I Johnson; *Asst VPres & Secy* Bradley H Gunter.
Open 8:45 AM - 4:45 PM. Estab 1978 to enhance the working environment of the bank, and to provide intellectual and aesthetic stimulation and enjoyment for the staff and visitors. Works of art are displayed in public areas throughout the bank.
Collection: 20th century art, without regard to any particular medium of expression or artistic discipline. The collection emphasizes works of art created by artists in the geographical area served by the bank.
Activities: Lectures; tours; individual objects of art lent to museums and other institutions.

UNITED VIRGINIA BANKSHARES, INC, 900 E Main St, 23219. Tel: 804-782-5000. (Norfolk Gallery: 5 Main Plaza E, Norfolk, VA 23510. Tel: 804-446-3000). *Asst VPres & Staff Interior Designer* Lucy B Turlington.
Open 9 AM - 5 PM. Estab 1969 for the enjoyment of the public and the employees. Gallery area is designated in main lobby. Average Annual Attendance: Approx 9000.
Activities: Lectures; gallery talks; various types of competitions are held statewide for purposes of collecting art; awards; schol in art offered in cooperation with Virginia Humanities of Art & Science; traveling exhibitions organized and circulated for affiliate banks; the Norfolk Gallery shows not only state art, but also national shows as well.

WASHINGTON

SEATTLE

WASHINGTON MUTUAL SAVINGS BANK, 1101 Second Ave, 98101. Tel: 206-464-4634. *Sr VPres* Carsten Lien.
Open during bank business hours. Estab to support art in the Pacific Northwest by enhancing the environment of the bank.
Purchases: $25,000.
Collection: Generally consists of paintings and sculpture.
Activities: Tours given in special circumstances; awards are given to several community art endeavors; individual objects of art lent to museums on request; generally support art and art activities in the Pacific Northwest through grants and contributions.

National Organizations in Canada

CANADIAN ARTISTS' REPRESENTATION (CAR),* c/o Giuseppe Albi, Exec Secy, 309-12708 90th St, Edmonton, AB T5E 3L5. Tel: 403-475-1598. *Nat Representative* Sylvain Voyer.
Estab Sept 1967 as an association of professional artists, national in membership, with provincial and city chapters; deal with artists' rights in government dealings, payment of artists' fees by public galleries, and in general any matters that deal with the welfare of artists in society. Local members meet on local schedule, National Provincial Representatives meet twice a year; mem 1500 nationally; dues $5 - $10. Small collection of art periodicals.
Income: Financed by membership and Canada Council grant.
Publications: National CAR News, Ontario (CAROT), and Maritimes (CARGO), quarterly.

CANADIAN CONFERENCE OF THE ARTS, 3 Church St, Suite 47, Toronto, ON M5E 1M2. Tel: 416-364-6351. *Nat Dir* John Hobday; *Treas* Russell Disney; *Secy* John A Paterson.
Estab 1945 to encourage and to advance the role of the arts and culture in Canada's national life, and to serve the interests of Canadian artists and the Canadian public. Mem: 1150; dues individuals $20, organizations based on budget; annual meeting May.
Income: Financed by membership and grants.
Publications: Arts Bulletin, bimothly; Handbook Series—Who We Are, Who's Who, Who Does What, Who's Got the Money, updated annually.
Activities: Awards given Diplôme d'Honneur, to persons who have contributed outstanding service to the arts in Canada.

CANADIAN CRAFTS COUNCIL (CONSEIL CANADIEN DE L'ARTISANAT), 16-46 Elgin St, Ottawa, ON K1P 5K6. Tel: 613-235-8200. *Pres* Orland Larson; *VPres* Mary E Hogg; *Secy* Ann Mortimer; *Exec Dir* Peter H Weinrich.
Open Mon - Fri 9 AM - 5 PM. Estab 1974 to encourage the highest quality Canadian crafts and improve standards of craftsmen through education and information. Mem: 25,000; dues individuals $20; annual meeting Oct.
Income: $100,000 - $250,000 (financed by membership and federal appropriation).
Collections: †Massey Foundation collection of contemporary Canadian crafts.
Exhibitions: (1976-78) Canadian Cultural Centre, Paris and Other European Centres; Artisan '78; traveling exhibition.
Publications: Artisan, bimonthly.
Activities: Traveling exhibitions organized and circulated.
Library: Open to public for reference only. Holdings: Vols 500; Per subs 25. Special Subjects: Crafts.

CANADIAN GUILD OF POTTERS, c/o Gordon Barnes, Pres, 11 Catherine Ave, Aurora, ON L4G 1K4. *First VPres* David Green and Allen Crimmons; *Secy* Marlene Smith.
Estab 1936 to act as a voice for the potters in Canada, currently being restructured. Mem: 10; dues $1; annual meeting May.
Income: Financed by membership.

CANADIAN MUSEUMS ASSOCIATION (ASSOCIATION DES MUSEES CANADIENS), 331 Cooper St, Suite 400, Ottawa, ON K2P 0G5. Tel: 613-233-5653. *Pres* J C Finlay; *VPres* Dr George MacBeath; *Secy* Dr George Lammers; *Exec Dir* R R Inglis; *Head Training Resources Div* Theodore T Poulos; *Head Publ Div* Gary J Sirois.
Estab 1947 to advance public museum services in Canada, to promote the welfare and better administration of museums, and to foster a continuing improvement in the qualifications and practices of museum professions. Mem: 1325; dues $25 - $500; annual meeting first week of June.
Income: Financed by membership, and government grants.

Publications: Museogramme, monthly; Gazette, quarterly.
Activities: Correspondence course in basic museology; book sales; bursary program; travel grants.
Library: Open for reference only. Holdings: Vols 600; Per subs 75. Special Subjects: Museology.

CANADIAN SOCIETY FOR EDUCATION THROUGH ART, Faculty of Education, University of Regina, Regina, SK S4S 0A2. *Pres* John M Emerson; *Secy Gen* Dr Les Groome.
Estab 1954 to promote art education in Canada. Average Annual Attendance: 300. Mem: Approx 1000; dues affiliate $2, professional $20; annual meeting Oct.
Income: Financed by membership.
Publications: Newsletter, quarterly; Journal; Research Bulletin.
Activities: Schol; workshops; research; annual conference.

CANADIAN SOCIETY OF PAINTERS IN WATERCOLOUR,* c/o Julius Griffith, Secy, 102 Hillsdale Ave W, Toronto, ON M5P 1G3. Tel: 416-366-1607. *Pres* Viktoras Brickus.
Estab 1925, inc 1936. Mem: 38; dues $20; annual meeting May.
Exhibitions: Annual exhibition opening in a different Canadian city each November, with a second showing in Jan or Feb in another large center.
Activities: Organizes traveling exhibitions in Canada and other countries through National Gallery, and Art Gallery of Ontario Extension Services; holds a seminar about every two years on watercolour and related media; awards annual Canadian Society of Painters in Watercolour Prize.

MARITIME ART ASSOCIATION,* c/o Frank Gillard, Treas, 40 West Lane, Moncton, NB E1C 6T7. *Pres* Mrs Mischa German-van Eck, Box 37 Site 17 RR 5, Armdale, Halifax, NS B3L 4J5; *Exhib Dir* Elizabeth Taylor.
Estab 1934 to coordinate work of art societies in New Brunswick, Newfoundland, Nova Scotia and Prince Edward Island. Mem: 27 societies paying corporate dues of $5 and higher; annual meeting May.
Member Organizations: Clare Arts Council, College Ste-Anne, Church-Point, NS; Dartmouth Heritage Museum, Dartmouth, NS; Fredericton Society of Artists, Fredericton, NB; Moncton Art Society Inc, Moncton, NB; St Andrews Music, Art and Drama Club, St Andrews, NB; Town of Amherst, Amherst, NS; Western Counties Regional Library, Yarmouth, NS; Woodstock Art Club, Woodstock, NB; and individual members.
Activities: Lecture tours; lending collection contains lantern slides; regional and traveling exhibitions organized of Maritime Artists.

PRINTING AND DRAWING COUNCIL OF CANADA,* c/o University of Calgary Art Gallery, 2920 24th Ave NW, Calgary, AB T2N 1N4. Tel: 403-288-5172. *Chmn* J K Esler.
Estab 1977 following merger of the Society of Canadian Painter-Etchers and Engravers and the Canadian Society of Graphic Arts.
Activities: Annual exhibition in Mar, organizes traveling exhibitions; maintains three print cabinets in Royal Ontario Museum, Toronto, Public Library and Museum, London, Ont and University of Toronto. Administers G A Reid Silver Memorial Award for best print in annual exhibition; Nicholas Hornyansky Memorial Award; Edits print of the year, selected by vote, to subscribers. Maximum edition 75 prints. Maintains Archives & Prints of 3-4 purchase awards, annually.

PROFESSIONAL ART DEALERS ASSOCIATION OF CANADA INC, 65 Queen St W, Suite 1800, Toronto, ON M5H 2M5. Tel: 416-868-1540. *Pres* John K Robertson; *Admin VPres* Aaron M Milrad; *VPres* Sam Markle; *Secy* Barbara Ensor.

Estab 1966 to further art in Canada. Mem: 48, members must have five years in operation plus approved reputation, general exhibitions, financial integrity; dues $200; annual meeting May.
Income: Financed by membership and appraisal fees.
Publications: General information brochure.
Activities: Schol.

ROYAL ARCHITECTURAL INSTITUTE OF CANADA, 151 Slater St, Suite 1104, Ottawa, ON K1P 5H3. Tel: 613-232-7165. *Pres* W Donald Baldwin; *VPres* Irving Boigon; *Exec VPres* Robbins Elliott; *Exec Secy-Treas* Robert Christie.
Open 9 AM - 5 PM. Estab 1908 to promote a knowledge and appreciation of architecture and of the architectural profession in Canada and to represent the interests of Canadian architects.
Publications: Architecture Canada Directory, annually.
Library: Vols on architecture, building and construction.

ROYAL CANADIAN ACADEMY OF ARTS, 601 - 11 Yorkville Ave, Toronto, ON M4W 1L3. Tel: 416-922-5535. *Pres* John C Parkin; *VPres* C Blakeway Millar; *Exec Dir* Rebecca Sisler.
Estab 1880 to better the visual arts field in Canada through exhibitions. Mem: 447, membership open to visual artists concerned with excellence in their own medium: dues $35; annual meeting late Nov.
Income: Nonprofit association financed by membership.
Exhibitions: (1976) Spectrum Canada, Complexe Desjasrdins, Montreal; (1978) Designers/RCA, Macdonald Gallery, Toronto.
Publications: Newsletter, infrequent publ.
Activties: Traveling exhibitions organized and circulated.

SCULPTOR'S SOCIETY OF CANADA, 21 Dunblaine Ave, Toronto, ON M5M 2R6. Tel: 416-366-1607. *Pres* Irene Blogg; *Secy* Betty Moss.
Estab 1928 to promote the art of sculpture, to present exhibitions (some to travel internationally), and to educate the public about sculpture. Mem: 107, qualifications: professional sculptor; dues $25; meetings once a month.
Income: $10,000 (financed by membership, provincial appropriation and sales commissions).
Exhibitions: (1977) Dimension-Four.
Activities: Workshops; lect open to the public.

SOCIETY OF CANADIAN ARTISTS,* 45 Brixham Terrace, Downsview Ont M3M 2R9. *Pres* Anne Meredith Barry; *Secy* Jeanette Nestel; *VPres & Treas* Kazuo Hamasaki.
Estab in 1957 as the Society of Cooperative Artists and operated the first cooperative gallery in Toronto. In 1967 the name was changed to the Society of Canadian Artists and the gallery moved to larger premises. In 1968 the members decided to give up the gallery and concentrate on organizing group art shows for its members in galleries in and around Toronto. Mem: 94 membership by jury; dues $25.
Income: Financed by membership.
Exhibitions: Juried All Members Show, 3 - 4 times per yr; cultural exchanges with artists of other areas.
Publications: Art Magazine, 6 times year.
Activities: Original objects of art lent with fee; lending collection contains color reproductions, photographs; traveling exhibitions organized and circulated.

Canadian Art Organizations

ALBERTA

BANFF

BANFF CENTRE, Walter Phillips Gallery, PO Box 1020, T0L 0C0. Tel: 403-762-3391. *Cur* Barry Morrison; *Asst Cur* Lorne Falk; *Asst to Cur* Yvonne Jackson.
Open daily 1 - 5 PM. No admis. Estab 1977 to serve the community and students of the visual arts department at the Banff Centre, School of Fine Arts. Gallery is 15.24 x 21.34 m, with 60.96 m of running space. Average Annual Attendance: 15,000.
Income: Financed by provincial and public funding.
Collections: Walter J Phillips Collection; Group of Seven; Contemporary works.
Exhibitions: Dennis Burton; Tatsuzo Shimaoka; Banff Centre Faculty Exhibition; Lee Freelander; Southwest Indian Art.
Activities: Lect open to public; individual paintings and original objects of art lent.
Library: *Librn* Betty Macaulay.

CALGARY

ALBERTA COLLEGE OF ART GALLERY, 1301 16th Ave NW, T2M 0L4. Tel: 403-284-8655. *Head of College* Kenneth Sturdy; *Secy* Darleen Jones; *Sr Cur* Ronald Moppett.
Open Tues - Fri Noon - 8 PM; Sat & Sun 2 - 5 PM. No admis. Estab 1958 to offer temporary exhibitions and related programs in all aspects of visual arts as didactic campus function and as public gallery. Two adjoining exhibition galleries affording 450 square meters of floor space with carpeted walls totalling 131 meters in length. Average Annual Attendance: 22,000.
Income: Financed by city appropriation and Department of Advanced Education & Manpower. Purchases: $2400.
Collections: Works by staff and students; contemporary Canadian graphics; ceramics.
Exhibitions: Canadian Canvas; Fibre, Clay & Metal; Fringe Research; Roger Shimomura (paintings and prints); Katie Ohe (sculpture); Graduating Students Exhibition; Changes: 11 Artists Working on the Prairies; Doug Haynes (painting); Dennis Burton (painting); Minnesota Massacre (panorama paintings); Contemporary Crafts of the Americas (mixed media); Allan Fleming (graphic design).
Activities: Classes for adults and children; lect open to public, 18 vis lectr per yr; gallery talks; individual paintings and original objects of art lent to other galleries; lending collection contains books, cassettes, film strips, motion pictures, original art works, and slides; traveling exhibitions organized and circulated.
—*Library.* *Librn* Michael William Parkinson. Open to students, staff, and public.
Holdings: Vols 5000; Per subs 50; Other—Prints, slides.
Special Subjects: Studio courses: ceramics, fabrics, painting, printmaking, metals, visual communications, photography.

ALBERTA SOCIETY OF ARTISTS,* Alberta College of Art, 1301 17th Ave, Room S545, T2M 0L4. Tel: 403-289-6641. *Pres* Barbara Roe Hicklin; *Dir Information & Research Centre* Dr Archie F Key.
Estab 1931 as an association of professional artists designed to foster and promote the development of visual and plastic fine arts primarily within the province. Mem: Approximately 100; dues $15; annual meeting May.
Publications: Highlights, (newsletter), bi-monthly.

CALGARY ARTISTS SOCIETY,* c/o Zaidee Finch, Secy, 3728 35th Ave SW, T3E 1A5. Tel: 403-249-1385. *Pres* Pat Gordon; *Treas* Ted Ranshaw.
Estab 1965 to foster and improve standard of art of members and community. Mem: 40; dues $15; monthly meeting first Thurs.
Income: $1000 (financed by membership and government grants).
Exhibitions: Allied Arts Building; Public Library; Kensington Arts Gallery, Calgary.
Activities: Classes for adults and children; lect for members only, 3 vis lectr per yr; gallery talks; competitions; original objects of art lent; lending collection contains photograph collection available to certain members only.

GLENBOW-ALBERTA INSTITUTE, Ninth Ave and First St SE, T2G 0P3. Tel: 403-264-8300. *Dir* Duncan Cameron; *Chief Cur* Hugh Dempsey; *Acting Cur-in-Charge Art Dept* Monique Westra; *Supervisor of Exhib Production* David Cunningham; *Art Registrar* Pam Wilkinson.
Open Daily 9 AM - 5 PM. Admis adults $1, senior citizens, students and children 50¢, children under 12 free. Estab 1966 to preserve the history and heritage of Western Canada and its people; to make a collection readily available to students, researchers and general public in the Western Provinces; three floors totaling 86,000 sq ft provide permanent and temporary exhibition space. Average Annual Attendance: 68,000. Mem: 2500, dues $5 - $100; annual meeting August.
Income: $2,500,000 (financed by city and state appropriation and federal funds).
Collections: Western Canadiana; contemporary Canadiana; Eskimo.
Exhibitions: (1976) Through Canadian Eyes; Western Untitled; Rothman's International Realist Show; National Ceramics Exhibition, Calgary; (1977) Exposure: Canadian Contemporary Photographers; Birds of Prey; Janet Mitchell; American Masters in the West; James Marshall; Jim Nicoll; The Atlantic Coast: An Illustrated Journal; Recent Drawings—Bill Laing/Dennis Evans; Young Contemporaries 76; L L Fitzgerald and Bertram Brooker-Their Drawings; C W Jefferys; Carl Rungius; Norman Yates; Tapestry Exhibition; Winold Reiss; Alberta Art Foundation; Selections from the Permanent Collection; Harry S Thomson Photographs; Munakata Shiko/Naoko Matsubara; Canadian Society of Painters in Watercolor Exchange Exhibition; Alberta Society of Artists; The Bison in Art; (1978) Frederic Marlett Bell-Smith; William Perehudoff; 20th Century Nova Scotia Folk Art; Artists' Stamps and Stamp Images; Enns, Evans and Ulrich Exhibition; Terry Shortt; Adolph Gottlieb: Pictographs; Jack Wise.
Publications: Monthly bulletin; books and catalogs intermittently.
Activities: Educ dept; docent training; lectr open to the public, 8 vis lectr per yr; tours; exten department serving Southern Alberta; traveling exhibitions organized and circulated; museum shop selling books, magazines, prints and slides.
Library: *Librn* Len Gottselig. Open to the public for reference. Holdings: Vols 30,000; Per subs 300.

PRINTING AND DRAWING COUNCIL OF CANADA,* c/o University of Calgary Art Gallery, 2920 24th Ave NW, T2N 1N4. Tel: 403-288-5172. *Chmn* J K Esler.
For further information see National Organizations in Canada.

UNIVERSITY OF CALGARY, ART GALLERY, 2920 - 24th Ave, NW, T2N 1N4. Tel: 403-284-5987. *Cur* J Brooks Joyner; *Secy* Ruby Fong; *Gallery Technician* Catharine Macavity; *Gallery Technician* Mrs J Cardinal Schubert.
Open Mon - Fri 10 AM - 4 PM; Sat 1 - 5 PM. No admis. Estab 1976 to create an artistic atmosphere for the exhibiting of fine art both for the academic community and the general public. Exhibitions are often used

by instructors for teaching examples; gallery is approximately 2000 sq ft in area with about 200 running feet of wallspace, and equipped with track lighting. Average Annual Attendance: 3000.
Income: Financed by state appropriation. Purchases: $12,000.
Collections: Roloff Beny - A Visual Odyssey; Western Canadian art consisting of sculpture, oils, watercolors, prints, and photography.
Activities: Docent training; lect open to the public; gallery talks; individual paintings and original objects of art lent to offices on campus; traveling exhibitions organized and circulated.

EDMONTON

ALBERTA ART FOUNDATION, 11th Floor, CN Tower, 10004 - 104th Ave. Tel: 403-432-3261 or 427-2031. *Chmn* Norman Yates; *Secy* WH Kaasa; *Coordinator* W Tin Ng.
Estab 1972 to collect and to exhibit art works pertinent to the Province of Alberta.
Income: Financed by city and state appropriation.
Collections: Alberta Art Foundation Collection.
Publications: Newsletter, quarterly; Annual Report.
Activities: Exten dept serves provincial, national and international public galleries, museums and educational institutes; traveling exhibitions organized and circulated; individual paintings and original objects of art lent.

CANADIAN ARTISTS' REPRESENTATION (CAR), * c/o Giuseppe Albi, Exec Secy, 309-12708 90th St, T5E 3L5. Tel: 403-475-1598. *Nat Representative* Sylvain Voyer.
For further information see National Organizations in Canada.

DEPARTMENT OF CULTURE, GOVERNMENT OF THE PROVINCE OF ALBERTA.
—Cultural Development Division, * CN Tower 10004 104th Ave, T5J 0K5. Tel: 403-427-2565. *Dir Visual Arts* Leslie F Graff.
Open Mon - Fri 8:15 AM - 4:30 PM. No admis. Estab to provide assistance to the Province of Alberta in the development of the visual arts and crafts; a small, informal gallery approx. 400 sq ft created for the purpose of training community personnel in the handling of exhibitions. Average Annual Attendance: 150,000 - 200,000.
Income: Financed by city and state appropriations.
Exhibitions: Local sculpture and paintings.
Publications: Various technical journals, articles of history and others, 10-15 per year.
Activities: Leadership training for instructors who work with adults and/or children; serves entire province; material available to residents of Alberta; course fees only; lect open to the public; competitions; schol; individual paintings and original objects of art lent; lending collection contains Kodachrome slides 150, photographs.
Library: For reference. Holdings: Vols 500.
—Provincial Museum of Alberta, 12845 102nd Ave, T5N 0M6. Tel: 403-452-2150. *Dir* Bruce A McCorquodale; *Head Cur Human History* Eric C Waterton; *Exten Supervisor* Jose Villa-Arce; *Display Supervisor* Gordon E Johnston.
Open winter Mon - Sat 9 AM - 5 PM; Sun 11 AM - 9 PM; summer 9 AM - 9 PM daily. No admis. Estab 1967 to preserve and interpret the human and natural histories of the province of Alberta; four major areas divided equally into human and natural history under broad themes of settlement history, anthropology, natural history habitat groups, and natural history interpretive displays.
Average Annual Attendance: 430,000.
Income: $1,600,000 (financed by state appropriation).
Purchases: Average $20,000.
Collections: †Historical: †ethnographical; †folk life; archaeological; fine and decorative arts; †geology; †palaeontology.
Exhibitions: Approx. 20 feature exhibits.
Publications: Occasional series; Museum Notes; Publication Series; occasional papers.
Activities: Classes for adults and children; lect open to the public; competitions; extension dept serving province of Alberta; Museumobiles; individual artifacts lent; traveling exhibitions organized and circulated; sales shop selling books.
Historical Resources Library: *Librn* Jocelyn Toon. For reference to staff and public. Holdings: Vols 14,000; Per subs 150.

EDMONTON ART GALLERY, 2 Sir Winston Churchill Square, T5J 2C1. *Dir* T Fenton; *Business Mgr* A Sidlo; *Head of Extension* Ms L Muehlenbachs; *Cur* R Ouellet; *Cur* D Clark.
Open Mon, Tues, Wed, Sat 10:15 AM - 5 PM; Thurs & Fri 10:15 AM - 10 PM; Sun 12:15 - 5 PM. No admis. Estab Nov 8, 1923 to collect and exhibit paintings, sculptures, photographs and other works of visual art and to teach art appreciation; gallery covers 63,000 sq ft; exhibition area 20,000 sq ft. Average Annual Attendance: 200,000. Mem: 1300; dues $20.
Income: $800,000 (financed by membership, city appropriation, state appropriation and federal grants). Purchases $119,000.

Collections: †Historical Canadian art; †Contemporary Canadian art; †Contemporary International art; Historical European and American Art; †Contemporary & Historical photography.
Exhibitions: 35 in-house exhibitions and 26 extension shows.
Publications: Edmonton Art Gallery Bulletin, 6 copies per year.
Activities: Classes for adults and children; docent training; workshops; lect open to the public, 6 vis lectr per yr; concert; gallery talks; tours; extension dept serving Alberta and British Columbia interior; individual paintings and original objects of art lent to smaller galleries in area, and other large galleries; traveling exhibitions organized and circulated; sales shop selling books, magazines, original art, reproductions, craft items; junior museum maintained.
Library: *Librn* Ms C Dakus. Open to the public. Holdings: Vols 1500; Per subs 15.

EDMONTON WEAVERS' GUILD, * 13816 110th A Ave, T5M 2M9. Tel: 403-455-5602. *Pres* Margaret Berg; *Secy* Monica Hughes.
Estab to foster arts of weaving, spinning and dyeing in Edmonton district and to encourage beginners and aim for high standard of workmanship. Mem: 130; dues $3; meetings third Wed of Sept, Nov, Jan, March and May.
Income: Financed by membership.
Publications: Newsletter, two per month.
Activities: Five members' workshops meeting every two weeks; occasional workshops given by craftspeople from other regions or countries, usually 3-day; lect open to the public with slides often given along with workshops.
Library. Holdings—Vols 187; periodicals dealing with weaving, spinning, dyeing; yarn sample cards.

PROVINCIAL ARCHIVES OF ALBERTA, Alberta Culture, Historical Resources Division, 12845 - 102 Ave, T5N0M6. Tel: 403-452-2150. *Provincial Archivist* A D Ridge; *Asst Provincial Archivist* W B Speirs; *Senior Archivist* J E Dryden.
Open Mon - Fri 9 AM - 4:30 PM. Estab 1967 to identify, evaluate, acquire, preserve, arrange, and describe and subsequently make available for public research, reference and display those diversified primary and secondary sources that document and relate to the overall history and development of Alberta. Maintains an art gallery for major exhibitions of archival sources and historical themes.
Income: Financed by provincial appropriation. Purchases: $36,000.
Holdings: Vols 14,000; Per subs 150; AV—Audio tapes, cassettes, microfiche, microfilm, motion pictures, phonorecords, reels, slides; Other—Clipping files, manuscripts, original art works, original documents, pamphlets, photographs, and prints.
Special Subjects: Ethno-cultural groups and activities, immigration and land settlement, genealogy, local histories, religious archives.
Special Collections: Government and public records.
Exhibitions: Documentary Heritage; several small displays each year highlighting recent accessions.

UKRAINIAN ARTS AND CRAFTS MUSEUM, * 10611 110 Ave, T5H 1H7. Tel: 403-426-0074. *Pres* Mrs N Bodnar; *Chmn* Mrs J Verchomin.
Open Mon - Sat by appointment; Sun 2 - 5 PM. No admis. Estab 1941.
Collections: Paintings and sculpture; drawings and prints; textiles; national costumes and historical material.
Activities: Lectures; guided tours; films; study clubs, loan service; TV and radio programs.
Library: *Librn* Mrs P Slepchuk. Holdings: vols 2500; Other—Manuscripts. Special Subjects: Ukrainian arts and crafts; general culture.

UNIVERSITY OF ALBERTA, University Art Gallery and Museum, Ring House One, T6G, 2E2. Tel: 403-432-5834, 403-432-5818. *Cur* Helen Collinson; *Registrar* Sylvia Mentz; *Departmental Secy* Susan Heth; *Exhib Designer* Virginia Penny.
Open Mon, Tues, Wed, Fri 11 AM - 4 PM; Thurs 11 AM - 9 PM; Sun 2 - 5 PM. No admis. Estab 1964 to display items from the University's permanent collection and from traveling exhibitions from outside sources; Gallery is located in former residence of the University President, which has now been converted to an art gallery; three exhibition areas on first floor, and two on second; space totals 350 running ft. Average Annual Attendance: 4000.
Income: Financed by state appropriation and University funds.
Collections: Paintings, sculpture, graphics, ethnographic material, textile collections, furniture and antiquities.
Exhibitions: (1976-77) Printmaking exhibition: Dwight Pogue and Five Calgary Printmakers; Bonnie Sheckter MVA Presentation; Photographic Exhibition; Honore Daumier: Lithographs; Classical Narratives in Master Drawings; Staff Show from University of Alberta Dept of Art and Design; Alberta Art Foundation Print Show; Joe Plaskett (pastels); Rex Calhoun (batiks); Creative Clothing Winning Entries; Hooked Rugs: A

Canadian Tradition; C I L Painting Collection; Alex Bruning; Hannah Aaron MVA Show; A Closer Look; Indian Art Exhibition.
Activities: Competitions; traveling exhibitions organized and circulated.
Library: For reference to staff. Holdings: Vols 500. Special Subjects: Mainly contemporary Canadian art, museum management and conservation techniques

LETHBRIDGE

ALLIED ARTS COUNCIL OF LETHBRIDGE, The Bowman Arts Centre, 811 Fifth Ave S T1J 0V2. Tel: 403-327-2813. *Pres* Terry Morris; *VPres* F Michael Wright; *Secy* Karen J Kay.
Open Mon - Fri 10 AM - 11 PM. No admis. Estab 1958 to encourage and foster cultural activities in Lethbridge, to provide facilities for such cultural activities, and to promote the work of Alberta and Western Canadian artists. Average Annual Attendance: 1500. Mem: 300; dues $15; annual meeting Feb.
Income: $39,000 (financed by membership and city appropriation).
Exhibitions: Local exhibitions: painters, potters, fabric makers, and children's art; provincial government travelling exhibits; one-man shows: sculpture, silversmithing, photography, paintings, and prints.
Publications: Calendar of arts, weekly.
Activities: Classes for adults and children; dramatic programs; concerts; competitions; scholarships; traveling exhibitions organized and circulated; sales shop selling original art.

UNIVERSITY OF LETHBRIDGE ART GALLERY,* 4401 University Dr, T1K 3M4. Tel: 403-329-2111. *Chmn Art Dept* L E Weaver; *Gallery Dir* B J McCarroll.
Open Mon - Fri 8:30 AM - 4:30 PM; Sun 1 - 4 PM. No admis. Estab 1968 for public service and the teaching mechanism.
Income: Financed by city and state appropriations.
Collections: Some professional prints and drawings; student work.
Exhibitions: Local and regional shows in addition to those traveling exhibitions by the National Gallery, The Winnipeg Gallery and The Western Association of Art Museums, approx ten shows per year.
Activities: Lect open to the public; gallery talks; tours; individual paintings and original objects of art lent; lending collection contains Kodachromes 10,000; motion pictures 20-25.
Library maintained.

MEDICINE HAT

ALLIED ARTS COUNCIL,* 8, 503A Third Ave SE, T1A 2M2. *Pres* G P J Parish; *Secy* Kay Cooney.
Estab approx 10 years ago to encourage and promote activities of a cultural nature in our community; organization has not been active for the past two years; many of the functions formerly carried out by the Council have been undertaken by the local community college.
Income: Financed by membership.

MEDICINE HAT PUBLIC LIBRARY, 414 First St SE, T1A 0A8. Tel: 403-527-5551. *Pres* Alan Sheldon.
Open Mon - Fri 9 AM - 9 PM. No admis. Estab 1914 to provide display area for traveling and local art shows.
Activities: Dramatic programs; lect open to the public; 10 vis lectr per yr; concerts.
Holdings: (Art) Vols 2000.

MUNDARE

BASILIAN FATHERS,* Box 379, T0B 3H0. Tel: 403-764-3860. *Dir* Rev Justin Ewaschyshyn.
Open May - Oct Mon - Sat 10 AM - 6 PM. Donations accepted. Estab 1951.
Collections: Ukrainian folk art, arts and crafts; historical church books.
Library: Holdings—Vols 650.

SPIRIT RIVER

PEACE REGION ARTS SOCIETY,* PO Box 297, T0H 3G0. Tel: 403-864-3035. *Chmn* E C Stacey; *Exec Secy* Mrs M Moulds; *Mem Officer* D Gibson; *Finance Officer* Mrs F Calk; *Recording Secy* Miss K Hoskin.
Estab Nov 2, 1974; a unified body of people concerned about the betterment of the arts atmosphere in the Peace Region of Alberta; Society is a source of contact with and information about the artists and performers in the area; exposure through selling and performing exhibitions. Mem: 320; dues $2; annual meeting April; Board meetings open to guests.
Income: Financed by membership, provincial and government grants.

Exhibitions: Peace Region Arts Festival held in conjunction with annual meeting, location varies.
Publications: Newsletter, bi-monthly.

BRITISH COLUMBIA

BURNABY

BURNABY ART GALLERY, 6344 Gilpin St, V5G 2J3. Tel: 604-291-9441. *Dir* Jack N Hardman; *Asst to Dir* Elisa Anstis; *Educ and Special Events Coordinator* Georgian Hansen; *Pres Bd Trustees* June Binkert.
Open Mon - Fri 10 AM - 5 PM; Wed 10 AM - 9 PM; Sat & Sun Noon - 5 PM. No admis. Estab 1967 to exhibit work, paintings, sculpture, prints, drawings, and crafts of Canadian and other artists and to hold Education and Special Event programs. Situated in old house built in 1909, in 25 acres of Century Gardens. Average Annual Attendance: 45,000. Mem: 500; dues $5 - $15; annual meeting May.
Income: Financed by membership, city and provincial appropriation.
Collections: Canadian prints, contemporary and historical.
Exhibitions: Changing monthly exhibitions; about 25 individual exhibitions per year.
Publications: Paper BAG, quarterly.
Activities: Classes for adults and children; lect open to public; concerts; gallery talks; tours; individual paintings and original objets of art lent to galleries; traveling exhibitions organized and circulated; museum shop selling books, magazines, original art, reproductions, prints and local crafts; junior museum (Turret Room).

SIMON FRASER UNIVERSITY,* Simon Fraser Gallery, Centre for the Arts, Academic Quadrangle 3004, V5A 1S6. Tel: 604-291-4266. *Cur & Dir Exhibitions* James Warren Felter.
Open Mon 1:30 - 4 PM, & 5 - 8 PM; Tues - Fri 10 AM - 1 PM, & 2 - 4 PM; cl Sat & Sun. No admis. Estab 1971. Average Annual Attendance: 25,000.
Income: Financed by public university appropriations.
Collections: The Simon Fraser Collection, including contemporary and Eskimo art; international graphics.
Exhibitions: Major traveling exhibitions of traditional and contemporary art along with selections from the Collection.
Publications: Exhibition catalogs, occasionally.
Activities: Extension program; individual paintings and original objects of art lent; traveling exhibitions organized and circulated.
Library: For reference. Holdings: AV—Slides; Other—Artists file, art gallery file.

WESTERN CANADA ART ASSOCIATION INC,* c/o Centre for the Arts, Simon Fraser University, V5A 1S6. Tel: 604-291-4266. *Chmn* James Warren Felter; *Secy/Treas* Betty Anne Yuill.
Estab 1970 to promote high standard of excellence and uniform methods in the care and presentation of works of art; to assist developing visual art centres in Western Canada; to encourage cooperation among members, and between members and other gallery and museum associations. Mem: 47 organizations; dues individual subscribing $5, associate $10, active $20.
Income: Financed by membership.
Publications: WCAA Newsletter, 6-8 per year.
Activities: Training committee, organization and presentation of gallery training workshops.
Library: For members only.

CHILLIWACK

COMMUNITY ARTS COUNCIL OF CHILLIWACK,* Box 53, V2P 6H7. Tel: 604-792-2069. *Pres* Murray Mackie; *Secy & Coordr* Susan Hohby; *VPres* Clint Hames.
Open 9 AM - 4 PM. Estab 1960 as Arts Council, Arts Centre estab 1972, to encourage all forms of art in the community. Mem: 200; dues single $3, organizational $5; annual meeting June.
Income: Financed by endowment and membership.
Collections: 26 Salish weavings.
Exhibitions: Local artists' exhibitions, including oils, watercolor, prints, pottery, wood carving, weavings and other fabric arts.
Publications: Arts Council Newsletter, 8 per year.
Activities: Classes for adults and children; dramatic programs; concerts; schol.

COQUITLAM

PLACE DES ARTS,* 166 King Edward St, V3K 4T2. Tel: 604-526-2891. *Dir* Lenore Peyton.

Open Mon - Thurs 9 AM - 10 PM; Fri & Sat 9 AM - 4 PM. No admis. Estab Sept 1, 1972 as a cultural, community crafts and resource center, an art school and gallery. Average Annual Attendance: 3000.
Income: Financed by municipal and fine arts council program funds.
Exhibitions: Bi-weekly shows of artists and craftsmen throughout the year.
Publications: Newsletter and program, every two months.
Activities: Special Education Department serving retarded young adults, school children, senior citizens and women's groups; satellite courses within the school of the district on request; classes for adults and children; dramatic programs; lect open to the public; concerts; gallery talks; schol.
Library: Holdings—Vols 20.

DAWSON CREEK

SOUTH PEACE ART SOCIETY, 10100 13th St, V1G 3W7. Tel: 604-782-2601. *Pres* Phyllis Mackay; *VPres* Gary Humphrey; *Secy* Shirley Ravelli.
Open Oct - May 1 - 5 PM; June - Sept 9 AM - 9 PM. Admis 35¢, or family $1. Estab 1963 to encourage artists to develop and give exposure to local work; also in circulating shows provincial and national; gallery maintained in combined Art Gallery/Museum which share city building with Tourist Center; museum displays mostly natural history. Average Annual Attendance: 10,000. Mem: 30; Qualif for mem: Interest in the Arts, and a willingness to work; dues $3; meeting third Thurs each month.
Income: Financed by membership, admissions, donations and commissions.
Activities: 150 paintings supplied by members of the Society available for rental service.

KELOWNA

KELOWNA CENTENNIAL MUSEUM & NATIONAL EXHIBIT CENTRE, 470 Queensway Ave, V1Y 6S7. Tel: 604-763-2451. *Pres* C W Knowles; *Secy* Sadie Conrad; *Cur/Dir* Ursula Surtees; *Museum Educator* Leslie Hopton.
Open summer Mon - Sat 10 AM - 5 PM, 6 - 8 PM; Sun 2 - 5 PM; winter Tues - Sat 10 AM - 5 PM. No admis. Estab 1935 as a community museum, a national exhibit center where traveling exhibits are received and circulated; gallery maintained for local art exhibits and small traveling exhibits. Annual meeting March.
Income: Financed by membership, city and state appropriation.
Exhibitions: National and provincial exhibitions on festive beads, lighting, multi-culture items, archaeological items, stern wheeler travel and conservation; many private exhibitions, including silver, pottery, weapons and coins.
Publications: Two volumes of interior Salish Indians 'Lak-La-Hai Ee' on food and dwellings; one pictorial book of Kelowna.
Activities: Classes for adults and children; lect open to the public; individual items lent to schools; lending collection contains lantern slides 2000; traveling exhibitions organized and circulated.
Library: Holdings—Photograph collection.

NELSON

KOOTENAY SCHOOL OF ART GALLERY, Silver King Road, V1L 1C8. Tel: 604-352-6601. *Dir* D O MacGregor; *Chief Instructor & Cur* Ernest H Underhill.
Open daily 9 AM - 4 PM. No admis. Estab 1962. A 40 x 60 ft gallery with optional partitions; fluorescent lighting and adjustable floodlamps; two storage rooms off gallery. Average Annual Attendance: 5000.
Income: Financed by provincial appropriation.
Exhibitions: Changing exhibitions every two weeks during school year with shows from organized traveling exhibitions; student shows in May and June.
Publications: Calendar, yearly.
Activities: Classes for adults; docent training; lect open to public, 12 vis lectr per yr; gallery talks; tours; exten dept; individual paintings and original objects of art lent to educational institutions; lending collection contains cassettes, film strips, motion pictures, original art works, original prints, paintings, phonorecords and slides 25,000; traveling exhibitions organized and circulated.
Library: *Librn* D O MacGregor. Open to students. Holdings: Vols 1300; Per subs 12.

PRINCE GEORGE

PRINCE GEORGE ART GALLERY, 2820 15th Ave, V2L 3P1. Tel: 604-563-6447 or 563-9484. *Pres* Janet Perry; *Treas* June Parker; *Coordinator* Denise McCallum.

Open Tues - Sat 10 AM - 5 PM; Wed 7 - 9 PM. No admis. Estab 1970 to foster development of arts and crafts in the community; to foster and promote artists. A wood frame building, 5,849 sq ft including two 1200 sq ft galleries, with track-lighting, and carpeted. Average Annual Attendance: 14,000. Mem: 323; dues $10; annual meeting June.
Income: $8000 (financed by membership, city and provincial appropriations, and grants).
Publications: Newsletter, monthly.
Activities: Classes for children; docent training; lect open to public, 8 vis lectr per yr; gallery talks; tours for schoolchildren; competitions; exten dept serving northern British Columbia; individual paintings and original objects of art lent to members; lending collection contains books, original art works, paintings; traveling exhibitions organized and circulated; sales shop selling books, original art, reproductions, prints.
Library: *Librn* Fran Evans. Open to members. Holdings: Vols 20; Per subs 7; Other—Funding and information brochures.

PRINCE RUPERT

MUSEUM OF NORTHERN BRITISH COLUMBIA, Prince Rupert Museum Art Gallery, McBride St & First Ave, (Mailing Add: PO Box 669, V8J 3S1). Tel: 604-624-3207. *Cur* M J Patterson; *Pres Bd Dir* Dr R G Large; *VPres Bd Dir* J H Jeffries.
Open Mon - Sat 9 AM - 4 PM (Oct-Apr); 9 AM - 9 PM (May-Sept). No admis. Estab 1924, new building opened 1958, to collect, maintain, and display the history of the north coast, particularly of the Prince Rupert area. One main hall has two small side galleries, and a third gallery is the Museum Art Gallery, which is shaped to resemble a native long house. Average Annual Attendance: 75,000. Mem: 45; dues $1; annual meeting May.
Income: $25,000 (financed by provincial appropriation, and donations). Purchases: $3200.
Collections: †Historical collections; †native Indian collections; †contemporary north coast Indian art; natural history; coin collection; †photographs.
Exhibitions: A continually changing display program: fine arts exhibitions from large Galleries, and local artists shows.
Activities: Classes for adults and children; lect open to public, 5 vis lectr per yr; concerts; gallery talks; tours; competitions.
Library: A small reference library for staff use. Holdings: 100; Per subs 3; Other—some archival materials.

PRINCE RUPERT ART CLUB,* c/o Ms Johan C Woodland, *Corresp Secy* 658 Seventh Ave E, V8J 2J6. Tel: 604-624-9045. *Pres* Anna Thornton; *Treas* Isobel Moore.
Estab 1949. Mem: 50; affiliated Picture Loan Society 200; dues $3, includes membership in the Prince Rupert Community Arts Council; annual meeting June.
Activities: Exhibit local and outside art in hotel lobbies, air terminals, restaurants; organize art classes during winter; arrange workshops throughout the year in a wide variety of arts and crafts, some of them taught by professionals; finance opening nights for exhibits given by Prince Rupert artists; encourage participation in the arts by sponsoring a social evening each week in the Art Room, at which each person attending may work on whatever project he chooses, in whatever medium he chooses; informal help is available when necessary from other members of the Art Club; frame, display, rent and sell through the Picture Loan Society paintings and prints of young artists in Canada and the US, watercolors, silk screen, collage, woodcuts.

RICHMOND

RICHMOND ARTS CENTRE,* 767 Minoru Gate, V6Y 1R8. Tel: 604-278-1755. *Dir* William Anderson.
Open daily 2 - 5 PM; Mon - Fri 7 - 9 PM. No admis. Estab 1967; gallery maintained. Average Annual Attendance: 36,000.
Income: Financed by city appropriation.
Collections: Oil paintings, ink and wash, and pencil and ink sketches of local or related importance.
Exhibitions: Change every three weeks.
Publications: Newsletter, bimonthly.
Activities: Classes for adults and children; dramatic programs; photograph collection prints 200 for reference; junior museum.
Library: For reference. Holdings: Vols 60; AV—Taped interviews on local history, summarized and indexed 400 hours.

VANCOUVER

ARTISTS GALLERY, 555 Hamilton St, V6B 2R1. Tel: 604-687-1345. *Dir* Naomi Yoshizawa; *Asst* Julie Abbott; *Asst* Olga Froehlich.

Open Tues - Fri 10 AM - 5 PM; Sat 1 - 5 PM; cl Mon. No admis. Estab 1971 as an exhibition space for BC artists; as a non-profit gallery for the City of Vancouver Art Collection and Loan Program; the gallery has a medium sized exhibition area with space at back for storage of collection, and framing area. Average Annual Attendance: 8000.
Income: Financed by city and state appropriation. Purchases: $300,000.
Collections: †City of Vancouver Art Collection.
Exhibitions: Exhibitions by local BC artists; special exhibitions of recent acquisitions of artists on grant.
Activities: Gallery talks; tours; competitions; individual paintings and original objects of art lent.

COMMUNITY ARTS COUNCIL OF VANCOUVER, 315 W Cordova St, V6B 1E5. Tel: 604-683-4358. *Pres* James Craig; *Secy* W M Nowell; *Hon Secy* J Springer; *Hon Treas* R O Sanderson; *VPres Policy & Planning* Mrs J G Fleming; *VPres Performing Arts* Mrs S Neville; *VPres Admin* Mrs H C Millham; *VPres Visual Arts* Mrs H B Norris; *VPres Civic Arts* D Fairbrother; *Recording Secy* Miss J Jardine.
Open 10 AM - 4 PM. No admis. Estab 1946 as a society dedicated to the support of arts, with a wide range of interest in the arts; to promote standards in all art fields including civic arts; serves as liaison centre; small gallery/office shows works of emerging artists who have not exhibited before. Mem: 700; dues individual $5, groups or family $10; annual meeting Sept.
Income: Financed by membership, donations and British Columbia Cultural Fund.
Exhibitions: Approximately 12 shows a year.
Publications: Newsletter, ten issues per year.

CRAFTSMEN'S ASSOCIATION OF BRITISH COLUMBIA, 801 - 207 W Hastings St, V6B 1H7. Tel: 604-681-9613. *Pres* Roger Stribley; *VPres* Carol Drechsler; *Secy* Linda Gammon; *Exec Dir* Gail Rogers.
Open Mon - Fri 10 AM - 4 PM. No admis. Estab 1975 to promote and encourage the finest quality of craft work in the province. Maintains an art gallery to exhibit the craft work being done in British Columbia. Mem: 550; dues $10; annual meeting April.
Income: Financed by endowment, and membership.
Exhibitions: Musical instruments; fibres; jewellery; ceramics.
Publications: Craft Contacts, monthly.
Activities: Specific workshops; competitions with prizes.
Library: Librn Jean Plummer. Holdings: Vols 55; Per subs 4.

UNIVERSITY OF BRITISH COLUMBIA
—**Fine Arts Gallery,** Main Library Bldg. V6T 1W5. Tel: 604-228-2759 or 228-4381. *Dir & Head of Fine Arts Dept* Dr George Knox; *Cur of Exhib* Glenn Allison.
Open winter Tues - Sat 10:30 AM - 5 PM; summer Mon - Fri 10 AM - 4:30 PM. No admis. Estab 1958, the exhibitions are organized from numerous sources and thus the gallery is able to bring to the university the widest variety of material representative of the principal trends in art, past and present; the gallery covers 27,000 sq ft. Average Annual Attendance: 15,000.
Income: $15,000 (financed by departmental funds).
Exhibitions: (1976) L'Art Francais; Faculty Exhibition; Graduating Class Exhibition; Jack Darcus Mokuhan (woodcuts of Munakata and Matsubara); Paolozzi. (1977) Surfacing Systems; Transition; Frederick A Verner; Graduating Class; For the Birds; Ngwalndu, and exhibition of objects from sacred spaces of New Guinea; Jim Hansen; Jennifer Dickson; Dennis Burton Retrospective.
Publications: Catalog, annually.
Activities: Lect open to the public, 2 vis lectr per yr; gallery talks; traveling exhibitions organized and circulated; original art pieces by exhibiting artist available for sale.
Library: Librn Melva Dwyer. Open to students and general public.
—**Museum of Anthropology,** 6393 NW Marine Dr, V6T 1W5. Tel: 604-228-6774. *Dir* M M Ames; *Cur of Ethnology* Marjorie Halpin; *Exten Cur* Hindy Ratner; *Archivist* Audrey Shane; *Curatorial Asst* Inge Ruus; *Admin Officer* Ria Rowe; *Cur of Ethnology/Public Programming* Madeline Bronsdon Rowan; *Designer* Bill McLennan; *Technician* Len McFarlane; *Vis Designer* Herb Watson.

VANCOUVER ART GALLERY, 1145 W Georgia St, V6E 3H2. Tel: 604-682-5621. *Pres* Ken Bagshaw; *Dir* Luke Rombout; *Chief Cur* Alvin Balkind; *Cur* Jo-Anne Birnie-Danzker & Peter Malkin; *Assoc Cur* Ted Lindberg.
Open Tues - Sat 10 AM - 5 PM; Fri 10 AM - 10 PM; Sun 1 - 5 PM; cl Mon. No admis. Estab 1931 to inform, to collect, to preserve. Site provided by the city; building enlarged in 1951. Mem: 1553; dues individual $15; family $20; sr citizens $5; annual meeting March.
Income: Financed by local, provincial and federal government grants.
Collections: 17th-20th century European painting; Canadian painting, sculpture, graphics; Emily Carr Collection; contemporary American painting and graphics.

Exhibitions: Changing Visions: The Canadian Landscape; Four Places; European Drawings in Canadian Collections; Clark MacDougall; James Wilson Morrice; Canadian Tapestries, 1977; From This Point of View: 60 Painters, Sculptors, Photographers, Graphic, and Video Artists; Giorgio Morandi; Transparent Things; David Craven: Recent Paintings; Another Dimension II.
Publications: Vanguard, ten times a year.
Activities: Docent training; lect for members; gallery talks; tours; exten dept serving all regions of British Columbia; individual paintings and original objects of art lent to Exhibition Centres in the Province; lending collection contains original art works, original prints, paintings, photographs, sculpture; traveling exhibitions organized and circulated; sales shop selling books, magazines, reproductions, prints, Eskimo prints and sculpture, native Indian graphics.
—**Library.** Librn Jean Martin.
Open to the public for reference.
Holdings: Vols 7492; Per subs 115; Other—Exhibition catalogs 10,000, Canadian artist biography files, auction records, Gallery archives, clippings.
Special Subjects: Fine arts specializing in Canadian and contemporary art.

VANCOUVER CITY ARCHIVES,* 1150 Chestnut St, V6J 3J9. Tel: 604-736-8561. *Dir* Sue M Baptie; *Deputy Dir* John R Chang; *Chief Cur* Mrs Sheelagh Draper; *Cur Coll* William McKee.
Open Mon - Fri 10 AM - 6 PM; other times by appointment; cl weekends and legal holidays. No admis. Estab 1933.
Income: Financed by city appropriation.
Collections: Paintings; drawings; prints; photographs; maps and charts; civic records; manuscripts.
Activities: Classes for adults and children; lectures; docent training; tours; temporary exhibitions.
Library: Available for researchers upon request. Holdings: Vols 3500.

VICTORIA

ART GALLERY OF GREATER VICTORIA, 1040 Moss St, V8V 4P1. Tel: 604-384-4101. *Dir* Roger Boulet; *Cur Asian Art* Joan Stanley-Baker; *Dir Emeritus* Colin Graham; *Asst to Dir* Robert Amos.
Open Tues - Sat 10 AM - 5 PM; Sun Noon - 5 PM. Admis 50¢; Thurs 7:30 - 9 PM free. Estab 1949 as an art museum with equal attention to contemporary art, history of art, especially Canadian; Asian art. Old mansion with new wing; 6 modern galleries. Average Annual Attendance: 50,000. Mem: 2000; dues $12.
Income: Financed by membership, city and provincial appropriations, national funds.
Collections: Contemporary Canadian, American and European; European painting and decorative arts from 16th to 19th centuries; Primitive arts; Japanese art from Kamakura to contemporary; Chinese art; Tibetan art; Indian art; Persian art.
Exhibitions: Rotating exhibitions.
Publications: Arts Victoria, 6 times per year.
Activities: Educ dept; docent training; lect open to public; exten dept serving the area and nation; traveling exhibitions organized and circulated; sales shop selling books, reproductions, local and Canadian crafts.
Library: Librn Robert Amos. Open to members for reference. Holdings: Vols 7000; Per subs 25.

OPEN SPACE GALLERY, Secession Gallery of Photography, 510 Fort St (Mailing Add: PO Box 5207, Station B, V8R 6N4). Tel: 604-383-8833.
Open Tues - Fri 10 AM - 5 PM; Sat Noon - 5 PM. No admis. Estab 1975 for the encouragement and promotion of photography as a fine art and of those photographers, particularly in Western Canada, who are engaged in making photographs as art. The gallery has 3000 sq ft, 220 running feet with full light grid controlled to level for works of art on paper. Average Annual Attendance: 10,000. Mem: 220; dues $10.
Income: $110,000 (financed by federal and provincial appropriations).
Exhibitions: Art Grice; Tom Knott; Vahe Guseleimain; Mattie Gunterman; Tim Porter; Robert Doisneau; Richard Holden; Ken Straiton; Contemporary Young British Photographers; Tom Gore; Marian Bancroft.
Publications: Secession Excerpts from the Literature of Photography, periodic.
Activities: Classes for adults; lect open to public, 5 vis lectr per yr; gallery talks; competitions.
Library: Open to all for reference. Holdings: Vols 200; Per subs 10. Special Subjects: Literature relating to photography, especially Canadian.

PROVINCIAL ARCHIVES OF BRITISH COLUMBIA, 655 Belleville St, V8V 1X4. Tel: 604-387-3621. *Provincial Archivist* A R Turner; *Asst Provincial Archivist* D B Mason.

Open Mon - Fri 9 AM - 5 PM. Estab 1910 to collect and preserve all records relating to the historical development of British Columbia. Maintains an art gallery for exhibiting archival materials, and a small gallery for exhibiting paintings by Emily Carr.
Income: Financed by provincial appropriation.
Holdings: Vols 51,000; Per subs 300; AV—Audio tapes, microfilm; Other—Clipping files, exhibition catalogs, manuscripts, original art works, original documents, pamphlets, photographs.
Special Subjects: British Columbia history.
Publications: Sound Heritage, quarterly.

UNIVERSITY OF VICTORIA, Maltwood Art Museum and Gallery, Finnerty Road (Mailing Add: PO Box 1700, V8W 2Y2). Tel: 604-477-6911, exten 6169. *Dir & Cur* Martin Segger.
Open Mon - Fri 10 Am - 4 PM. No admis. Estab 1968 to collect, preserve, and exhibit the decorative arts. Three thousand square feet of environmentally controlled exhibition space. Average Annual Attendance: 150,000.
Income: Financed by provincial appropriation and endowment.
Collections: †Maltwood Collection of Decorative Art; †Contemporary Art.
Exhibitions: Permanent collections, continuing and rotating.
Activities: Individual paintings and original objects of art lent to galleries and museums; lending collection contains books 700, nature artifacts 1000, original art works 400, sculpture 50; traveling exhibitions organized and circulated.

WEST VANCOUVER

WEST VANCOUVER VISUAL ARTS SOCIETY,* c/o Norma Sorensen, *Pres,* 993 Sinclair, V7V 3W1. Tel: 604-922-1450. *Secy* Myrtle Mayall; *VPres* Mrs F Lightheart; *Treas* Mrs W D M Patterson.
Estab 1968, inc as a nonprofit society 1970, to provide a greater opportunity for people in the community to participate in the enjoyment of the visual arts; special emphasis has been directed toward exhibitions of high quality; part-time gallery maintained until the heritage building which housed it was moved; efforts are being made to have this building restored as an arts center to be part of beautiful waterfront historic square. Mem: 35; dues $2; annual meeting Sept.
Income: Financed by membership, provincial and municipal government grants and private foundations.

WHITE ROCK

WHITE ROCK PAINTING AND SKETCH CLUB, Art Centre, Marine Dr. (Mailing Add: Box 85) Tel: 604-536-2432. *Pres* Sheila Symington; *VPres* Myrle Phillips; *Secy* Louise Kilby.
Not open until fall 1978. Estab 1970 for the betterment of art; gallery not maintained. Mem: 130; dues $3; meeting fourth Wed of each month, annual meeting fourth Wed June.
Income: $1000, plus $250 Grant (financed by membership, commission on sales, provincial grant).
Exhibitions: (1976-77) Variety of exhibitions in various locations.
Activities: Classes for adults; lect open to members only, 6 vis lectr per yr; gallery talks; tours; schol; extension dept serving south of Fraser River, Surrey BC, and White Rock BC; individual paintings lent to community-Art Council Picture Loan to rent to public; lending collection contains original art works, paintings; traveling exhibitions organized and circulated.
Library: Librn Iris McCredy. Open to members. Holdings: Vols 30; per subs 2.

MANITOBA

BRANDON

BRANDON ALLIED ARTS COUNCIL, 1036 Louise Ave, R7A 0Y1. Tel: 204-727-1036. *Pres* L D Whitehead; *First VPres* Dr Lorne Watson; *Second VPres* H Carroll; *Treas* D K Shuttleworth; *Secy* Aneta Kenny; *Dir* K Marlow; *Asst* Gail Roberts.
Open Mon - Sat 9 AM - 5 PM; Sun 2 - 5 PM. No admis. Estab 1960 to promote and foster cultural activities in Western Manitoba. Average Annual Attendance: 2400. Mem: 700; dues $6 - $20; annual meeting May.
Income: $45,000 (financed by membership, city and provincial appropriations, federal grants).
Exhibitions: Changing monthly exhibitions of Western Manitoba and nationally known artists.
Publications: Bulletin, every 2 months.

Activities: Classes for adults and children; lect open to public, 2 vis lectr per yr; gallery talks; tours; competitions; individual paintings and original objects of art lent to members; lending collection contains original art works, original prints, paintings, weavings.
Library: Brandon Allied Arts Centre Library. *Librn* Joyce Holland. Open to members. Holdings: Vols 2000.

DAUPHIN

DAUPHIN ALLIED ARTS CENTRE, 104 First Ave NW. *Admin* Ms Emily Kutcher.
Open 1 - 5 PM. No admis. Estab Jan 1973 as an amalgamation of the arts in Dauphin for a united voice; small gallery exhibiting works of local artists; changing monthly. Average Annual Attendance: 20,000. Mem: 50; dues $5; annual meeting Jan.
Income: $30,000 (financed by rental fees).
Exhibitions: Art Show; Pottery Show.
Publications: Newsletter, monthly.
Activities: Classes for adults and children; dramatic programs; instruction in all crafts; lect open to the public, 5 vis lectr per yr; gallery talks; competitions with awards given; schol; lending collection contains film strips 100; traveling exhibitions organized and circulated; original art for sale.
Library: Open to the public. Holdings: Vols 200.

PORTAGE LA PRAIRIE

PORTAGE AND DISTRICT ARTS COUNCIL, PO Box 215, R1N 3B5. *Pres* Mrs Nell Owens; *Secy* Debra Maxwell.
Estab 1976 as a coordinating body of local arts groups.

WINNIPEG

LE FRONT DES ARTISTES CANADIENS (Canadian Artists' Representation), 44-221 McDermott Ave, R3B 0S2. Tel: 204-943-5948. *National Representative* Bill Lobchuk; *Vice-Representatives* Gary Greenwood & Dale Amundson; *Secy* L F Shiels.
Estab 1971 as an association of professional artists practicing in the visual arts. It acts on behalf of these artists to deal with all aspects and issues in the profession, to solve problems by a collective and democratic mode of action. Mem: 1000 (open to practicing professional artists); dues $12 - $25; annual meeting May.
Income: Financed by endowment and membership.
Publications: CARFAC News, quarterly.
Activities: Lect open to public.

MANISPHERE GROUP OF ARTISTS,* c/o Ellen B Cringan, 82 Cordova St, R3N 0Z8. Tel: 204-489-4417. *Pres* Hans Osted; *Secy* Ethel Percy; *Gen Mgr* Mo Renaud; *Pres Board of Dir* George Prost.
Estab 1970 to further the work of the artist at the local and community levels. Mem: 60; dues $8; annual meeting Oct 1.
Income: Financed by membership.
Collections: Organization purchases one of the works from the annual juried show.
Exhibition: Juried shows of one American segment and one Canadian segment; four exhibitions of members works yearly.
Activities: Educational department activities, teaching in rural areas, regular classes plus workshops in oils, printmaking, watercolors, pottery, acrylics and pastels; lect open to the public; gallery talks; tours; competitions; schol; individual paintings and original objects of art lent; traveling exhibitions organized and circulated.

MANITOBA ASSOCIATION OF ARCHITECTS,* 710-177 Lombard Ave, R3B 0W9. Tel: 204-942-7767. *Pres* L Plotkin; *Exec Secy* Mrs M Tobin.
Estab 1906, inc 1910: Provincial Architectural Registration Board and professional governing body. Mem: 200; dues $110; annual meeting Jan.
Activities: the Manitoba Association of Architects has established a joint lectureship fund with the School of Architecture at the University of Manitoba, and has established a practice of bringing three or more outstanding lecturers to Winnipeg each year for university and public lectures. The Association has established a yearly donation of $300 in prizes awarded to students pursuing the course at the School of Architecture, University of Manitoba.

PROVINCIAL ARCHIVES OF MANITOBA,* 200 Vaughan St, R3C 1T5. Tel: *Archivist* John A Bovey.
Open Mon - Fri 10 AM - 5 PM; cl holidays. No admis. Estab 1952.
Income: Financed by provincial appropriation through the Minister of Tourism, Recreation and Cultural Affairs.

UNIVERSITY OF MANITOBA GALLERY 1 1 1, School of Art, R3T 2N2. Tel: 204-474-8318. *Dir Exhibs* Daniel Mato.

Open Mon - Fri 9 AM - 9 PM. No admis. Estab 1946, Gallery 1 1 1 estab 1965 to provide exhibitions for students and faculty on the university campus; exhibitions also open to the public. Average Annual Attendance: 20,000.
Collections: †Contemporary Canadian and American painting, sculpture and prints.
Exhibitions: Exhibitions from Museum of Modern Art, American Federation of Arts, Smithsonian Institution, National Gallery of Canada and others; annual exhibitions by the students of the School of Art.
Activities: Discussion groups, workshops; lect; gallery talks.
—**Faculty of Architecture Exhibition Centre,** Architecture Building *Dir of Exhib* Donald Ellis.
Open Mon - Fri 9 AM - 10:30 PM; Sat 9 AM - 5 PM. Estab 1959 with the opening of the new Faculty of Architecture Building to provide architectural and related exhibitions for students and faculty on the University campus and particularly for architecture students; exhibitions also open to the public. Average Annual Attendance: 15,000.
Exhibitions: Exhibitions from National Gallery of Canada, Smithsonian Institution, American Federation of Arts, Museum of Modern Art and from other private and public sources; annual exhibitions by the students in the Faculty of Architecture.
Activities: Lect; gallery talks; symposia.
Art Libraries: At School of Art, Faculty of Architecture and the University Library.

WINNIPEG ART GALLERY, 300 Memorial Blvd, R3C 1V1. Tel: 204-786-6641. *Dir* Roger L Selby; *Admin Officer* James Bristow; *Head Pub Prog* Emmett Hannibal; *Admin Cur* Ann David; *Head Design* Dept Glenn Tinley.
Open Tues - Sat 11 AM - 5 PM; Sun Noon - 5 PM; cl Mon. No admis. Estab 1912, inc 1963. Rebuild and relocated 1968, opened 1971, to present a diversified, quality level program of Art in all media, representing various cultures, past and present. Educational function to surrounding community; to act as a major art resource for Canadian prairies. Average Annual Attendance: 250,000. Mem: 3000; dues $7.50 and up; annual meeting June.
Income: $1,700,000 (financed by endowment, membership, city and provincial appropriations). Purchases: $100,000.
Collections: Paintings, sculpture, graphics and other media; †Canadian Art; †Eskimo Art.
Exhibitions: Master Paintings from the Hermitage, and the State Russian Museum, Leningrad; Gold for the Gods, Lima, Peru.
Publications: Calendar of Events, monthly; exhibition catalogues.
Activities: Classes for adults and children; docent training; lect open to public, 20-30 vis lectr per yr; concerts; gallery talks; tours; exten dept serving the Canadian prairies; traveling exhibitions organized and circulated; sales shop selling books, reproductions, prints, slides and gift items.
—**Library.** *Chief Librn* David William Rozniatowski; *Library Asst* Sheila Anderson.
Open Tues - Fri 11 AM - 5 PM; Sat Noon - 4 PM. Estab 1954 to serve as a source of informational and general interest materials for members and staff of the Winnipeg Art Gallery, and to art history students. Circ: 1500.
Income: Financed by membership, city and provincial appropriations. Purchases: $100,000.
Holdings: Vols 8600; Per subs 43; Other—Clipping files, exhibition catalogs, manuscripts, memorabilia, original documents, pamphlets, photographs, prints, reproductions.
Special Subjects: Canadian art, Eskimo art.
Special Collections: Rare books on Canadian and European art, archival material pertaining to Winnipeg Art Gallery.

WINNIPEG SKETCH CLUB, 434 Assiniboine Ave, R3C 0Y1. Tel: 204-943-4772. *Pres* Frances Crane; *VPres* Alice Anderson; *Secy* Marjorie Hughes.
Open to members only. Estab 1914 to provide a ground where members may meet for the purpose of advancing their studies by means of sketch meetings and for the encouragement of work done independently. Mem: 90; Qualif for mem: Approval of work submitted to the executive committee, and an interest in club activities; dues $10; annual meeting first week in Feb.
Income: Financed by membership.
Collections: There is an archives collection of work by past and present members.
Exhibitions: There is an annual juried exhibition in the Manitoba Archive Bldg; members also take part in exhibits at the Assiniboine Park Conservatory and office buildings which wish to exhibit work; many local shows are open to submitted work.
Publications: Only to club members.
Library: Librn Muriel King. Tel: 204-943-4772. Open to members only.

NEW BRUNSWICK

CAMPBELLTON

GALERIE RESTIGOUCHE, 39 Andrew St (Mailing Add: PO Box 674, E3N 3H1). Tel: 506-753-5750. *Dir & Cur* Rene Jean.
No admis. Estab 1975 for exhibitions and activities. Building has 4800 sq ft; the Exhibition Hall is 1500 sq ft, small gallery 400 sq ft; 230 running feet. Average Annual Attendance: 10 - 15 thousand. Mem: 185; dues $10.
Income: $46,500 (financed by federal, provincial, and city appropriations and by Art Society).
Activities: Classes for children; dramatic programs; lect open to public; concerts; gallery talks; tours; traveling exhibitions organized and circulated.

FREDERICTON

BEAVERBROOK ART GALLERY, 703 Queen St (Mailing Add: PO Box 605, E3B 5A6). Tel: 506-455-6551. *Cur* Ian G Lumsden; *Asst Cur* Paul A Hachey.
Open winter Sept 4 - May 31 Tues - Sat 10 AM - 5 PM; Sun Noon - 5 PM; cl Mon; summer June 1 - Sept 3 Tues - Sat 10 AM - 9 PM; Sun Noon - 9 PM; cl Mon. Admis adults 50¢, students & members free; also booked tours. Estab 1959 to foster and promote the study and the public enjoyment and appreciation of the arts; three major galleries upstairs: British, Canadian, and High galleries; Exhibition, Pillow Porcelain Room, and Foyer galleries downstairs. Average Annual Attendance: 40,000. Mem: 556; dues single $5, couple $7.50.
Income: $210,000 (financed by endowment, and private foundation). Purchases: $25,000.
Collections: Canadian paintings, drawings and prints, early 19th century to contemporary; British paintings, drawings, prints and sculpture, 16th century to contemporary; 18th and 19th century British porcelain.
Exhibitions: Bloomsbury Painters and their Circle; The Queen comes to New Brunswick: Paintings and Drawings by Molly Lamb Bobak; Drawings by Jack Weldon Humphrey: 1923 - 1966.
Publications: Quarterly announcing gallery's program; exhibition catalogs.
Activities: Lent open to the public, 3-4 vis lectr per yr; concerts; gallery talks; tours; extension dept serving New Brunswick as well as the rest of Canada; individual paintings lent to recognized art galleries and museums which operate as educational institutions; lending collection contains original art works 1246; sculpture; traveling exhibitions organized and circulated; sales shop selling books, magazines, reproductions, exhibition catalogs, Christmas cards, postcards, and hasty-notes.
Library: Open to gallery personnel only, for reference.

NEW BRUNSWICK CRAFT SCHOOL, Hut #3, Woodstock Road, E3B 5H1. Tel: 506-453-2305. *Dir Craft* George Fry.
Open Mon - Fri 8:30 AM - 4:30 PM. Estab 1947 as a training school for professional craftspeople. Small gallery; craft related shows monthly. Average Annual Attendance: 1800.
Income: Financed by provincial government.
Collections: New Brunswick Permanent Craft Collection.
Exhibitions: Glass from private collections; Elizabeth Gurrier: Stitchery and Soft Sculpture; Freeman Patterson: Photography; student and staff projects.
Publications: Provincial Craft Directory.
Activities: Classes for adults; lect open to public, 12 vis lectr per yr; original objects of art lent; traveling exhibitions organized and circulated.
Library: A very small but growing library which is primarily for students.

MONCTON

MARITIME ART ASSOCIATION,* c/o Frank Gillard, Treas, 40 West Lane, M1C 6T7. *Pres* Mrs Mischa German-van Eck, Box 37 Site 17 RR 5, Armdale Halifax, NS B3L 4J5; *Exhib Dir* Elizabeth Taylor.
For further information see National Organizations in Canada.

UNIVERSITÉ DE MONCTON GALLERIE D'ART. Tel: 506-858-4081. *Dir* Eulalie Boudreau; *Secy* Alfreda Haché; *Asst* Georges Bergeron; *Pres* Raoul Dionne.
Open daily 2 - 4 PM; Wed 7 - 9 PM. No admis. Estab 1865 to offer outstanding shows to the University students, and also to the public. A gallery of modest size, with suitable lighting, situated near the library and museum. Average Annual Attendance: 8000.
Income: $15,000 (financed through the University). Purchases: $750.
Collections: Following artists are represented in permanent collection: Rita Letendre; Bruno Bobak; Gordon Smith; Toni Onley; Hilda Lavrie; Alex Colville; Claude Roussel; Hurtubise; Romeo Savoie; Tom Forrestall; Georges Goguin; Fernand Leduc.

Exhibitions: Erns Roch; Arthur Gladu; Sylvia Heyden; Francophones of NB; Pavel Skalnik; Karl Spital & Rene Herbert; Beverly Pugh.
Activities: Lect open to public, 5 vis lectr per yr; gallery talks; tours; individual paintings and original objects of art lent to University staff; lending collection contains original art works, original prints, paintings, photographs, sculpture; traveling exhibitions organized and circulated.
Library: Champlain. *Librn* A Levesque. Open to students and the public. Holdings: Vols 4000.

SACKVILLE

MOUNT ALLISON UNIVERSITY,* Owens Art Gallery, York St, E0A 3C0. Tel: 506-536-2040. *Dir* Christopher Youngs.
Open Mon - Fri 10 AM - 5 PM; Sat & Sun 2 - 5 PM; also Wed 6:30 - 9 PM; cl school holidays. No admis. Estab 1893, rebuilt 1972, the building includes five gallery areas, a lecture hall and reading room.
Collections: Paintings; sculpture and broad collection of graphics; parts of collection on display throughout the campus.
Activities: Classes for children and adults; lectures; gallery talks; guided tours; films; concerts; dance recitals; competitions; temporary and traveling exhibitions; art rental service.

SAINT ANDREWS

SUNBURY SHORES ARTS AND NATURE CENTRE, INC, 139 Water St (Mailing Add: PO Box 100, E0G 2X0). Tel: 506-529-3386. *Pres* David Walker; *Dir* Henrik Kreiberg; *Exec Secy* Nan Belding.
Open weekdays 9 AM - Noon, 1:30 - 5 PM. No admis. Estab 1964 to act as link for, and harmonize views of scientist, artist, and industrialist; gallery maintained, 200 running ft, fire and burglar protection, security during hours, controllable lighting, street frontage. Average Annual Attendance: 750. Mem: 350; dues individual $5, family $10; annual meeting Sept.
Income: Financed by endowment, membership, and grants.
Publications: Brochure, summer annually; Sunbury Notes, quarterly.
Activities: Lect open to the public, 10-15 vis lectr per yr; gallery talks; schol.
Library: Open to the public. Holdings: Vols 250; Per subs 10.

SAINT JOHN

ARCHITECTS ASSOCIATION OF NEW BRUNSWICK,* c/o Freda M Large, Exec Secy, PO Box 910, Rothesay E0G 2W0.
Inc. 1933; Mem: 41; dues $100 and up; annual meeting Jan.

NEW BRUNSWICK MUSEUM, 277 Douglas Ave, E2K 1E5. Tel: 506-693-1196. *Dir* David Ross; *Cur Art* Robert Percival; *Cur Canadian History* Gregg Finley; *Archivist:* Monica Robertson.
Open winter 2 - 5 PM; summer 10 AM - 9 PM. Admis adults $1; children 50¢; sr citizens & students with card free. Estab 1842 to collect, conserve, exhibit and interpret the Human & Natural history of New Brunswick in relation to itself and to the outside world. Six major galleries for permanent exhibits, three galleries for changing temporary exhibits. Average Annual Attendance: 60,000. Mem: 600; dues $15; annual meeting June.
Income: $900,000 (financed by membership, federal and provincial appropriations). Purchases: $5000.
Collections: (Art) New Brunswick & Maritime artists.
Publications: The Beacon, 6 per year; Journal of the New Brunswick Museum, yearly.
Activities: Classes for children; docent training; lect open to public, 12 vis lectr per yr; gallery talks; exten dept serving New Brunswick; individual paintings and original objects of art lent to museums and galleries; traveling exhibitions organized and circulated; sales shop selling books, and gifts.
Library: *Librn* M Robertson. Open to public for reference. Holdings: Vols 30,000; Per subs 60.

NEWFOUNDLAND

SAINT JOHN'S

MEMORIAL UNIVERSITY NEWFOUNDLAND, Art Gallery, Arts and Culture Centre. Tel: 709-753-1200, exten 2211. *Cur* Edythe Goodridge; *Coordinator of Operations* Edward Cadigan; *Coordinator of Exhibitions* Patricia Grattan.
Open Tues - Sun Noon - 10 PM; cl Mon. No admis. Estab 1963 to display contemporary Canadian art, to promote contemporary Newfoundland work, and to reflect the cultural history of the province. Three galleries with 130 running feet each. Average Annual Attendance: 60,000.

Income: Financed through the University, and federal funding.
Collections: Canadian art of the 1960s and 1970s.
Exhibitions: Newfoundland Folk Painting; Boatman Series by Gerald Squires.
Activities: Dramatic programs; concerts; gallery talks; tours; workshops; exten dept serving the province; artmobile; individual paintings and original objects of art lent to other institutions; traveling exhibitions organized and circulated.
Library: Open to artists, docents, and members.

NEWFOUNDLAND MUSEUM, Duckworth St. Tel: 709-737-2460. *Dir* Martin Bowe; *Asst Dir* David Mills; *Cur Coll* Victoria Dickenson; *Chief Pub Prog* Oonagh O'Dea; *Information Officer* Elizabeth Callaghan.
Closed for renovations. No admis. Estab 1878 as the Athenaeum, for the preservation of Provincial Heritage. Galleries undergoing complete reorganization.
Income: Financed by federal and provincial appropriations.
Collections: Beothuk, Thule, and Maritime archaic artifacts; maps; prints; fisheries development; military history material.
Library: Open to researchers for reference. Special Subjects: Military history. Special Collections: Mercury Series of National Museums in Archaeology, Ethnology, Restoration.

NOVA SCOTIA

DARTMOUTH

DARTMOUTH HERITAGE MUSEUM, Wyse Road. *Dir* G S Gosley; *Secy* Mrs R Gargan; *Asst Art* Mrs E Richter.
Open (summer) 9 AM - 9 PM; (winter) 1 - 5 PM. No admis. Estab 1968 to collect and preserve the story of the City of Dartmouth. Average Annual Attendance: 44,000. Mem: 50; dues $2; annual meeting June.
Income: Financed by City appropriation.
Collections: †Nova Scotia glass; dolls; †artifacts (local history); aircraft models; †works of art.
Activities: Tours of school classes; classes for adults and children.

HALIFAX

ART GALLERY OF NOVA SCOTIA, 6152 Coburg Rd (Mailing Add: PO Box 2262, B3J 3C8). *Cur* Bernard Riordon.
Open summers Mon - Sat 10 AM - 7:30 PM, Sun Noon - 7:30 PM; winters Mon - Sat 10 AM - 5 PM; Sun Noon - 5 PM. Estab 1975 to replace the Museum of Fine Art; Centennial Art Gallery estab 1967 situated in the Powder Magazine of the Halifax Citadel. Average Annual Attendance: 50,000. Mem: 360; dues student $1, individual $5, family $10.
Income: Financed by membership and Provincial Government Grant.
Collections: 190 works of art; paintings, prints and sculpture.
Publications: Bulletin, twice a year.
Activities: Classes for adults and children; lect open to the public, 2 vis lectr per yr; gallery talks; tours; traveling exhibitions organized and circulated; art sales and rental service.

DALHOUSIE UNIVERSITY ART GALLERY, University Dr, B34 3J5. Tel: 902-424-2403. *Dir* Ernest W Smith; *Cur Paintings* Evelyn Holmes; *Asst Cur* Mark Holton.
Open Tues - Sat 1 - 5 & 7 - 9 PM; Sun 2 - 5 PM; cl Mon and holidays. No admis. Estab 1818.
Collections: Canadian and American paintings, sculpture, prints and graphics; archaeology.
Exhibitions: Temporary and traveling exhibitions; organized exhibitions for schools.
Publications: Exhibition catalogs.
Activities: Lectures; gallery talks; guided tours; films; concerts; competitions; TV and radio programs; docent training.

EYE LEVEL GALLERY,* Marble Building, 1672 Barrington St, Tel: 902-425-6412. *Pres* Roger Savage; *Secy* Hattie Prentice; *Coordr* Susan Beaver.
Open Mon - Sat Noon - 5 PM. No admis. Estab 1973 as an artist cooperative gallery to provide exhibition opportunities for contemporary regional artists; gallery consists of three rooms, located on second floor. Mem: 57; dues $5; monthly meetings last Thurs.
Income: Financed by endowment and membership.
Publications: Eye Level Newsletter, monthly.
Activities: Classes for adults; demonstrations; dramatic programs; lect open to the public; gallery talks; tours; competitions; original objects of art lent; traveling exhibitions organized and circulated; slide collection of Nova Scotia artists.

MOUNT SAINT VINCENT UNIVERSITY ART GALLERY, Seton Academic Centre, Bedford Highway, B3M 2J6. Tel: 902-443-4450, exten 160. *Dir Art Gallery* Mary Sparling; *Exhib Officer* Mern O'Brien; *Accessionist/Secy* Lawna Stewart.
Open Mon - Fri 9 AM - 5 PM; Sat, Sun & holidays Noon - 5 PM. No admis. Estab 1970 and operating throughout the year with continuously-changing exhibitions of local, regional, national and international origin in the area of fine arts and crafts; situated on the main floor and mezzanine. Average Annual Attendance: 16,000.
Income: Financed by university funds.
Collections: The Art Gallery is custodian of a collection of pictures, ceramics and pottery of the late Alice Egan Hagen of Mahone Bay, noted Nova Scotia potter and ceramist, which is on permanent display in Rosaria Hall. It also has a growing permanent collection.
Exhibitions: (1976) Images of Lunenburg County by Peter Barss (photographs); Atlantic Ephemera from the collection of Lou Collins; Pots des Fleurs by Walter Ostrom (ceramics); Leather in Three Dimensions by Rex Lingwood; Jewish Experience in the Art of the Twentieth Century, the works of contemporary Canadian Jewish artists included. (1977) Third Annual University Community Show; Charlotte Hammond (paintings); Modern European Graphics; Works by Jim Shirley; Images of Imprisonment: Springhill 1974-1975, by Ray Wolf (photographs); Selected Works, 1975-1977, by Ron Shuebrook (paintings, drawings, constructions); Henri Gaudier-Brzeska, 1891-1915 (sculpture and drawings); Henry M Rosenberg, 1858-1947 (landscapes and portraits); Naillies by David Partridge (nail sculptures); Swedish Textile Art-Five Temperaments; Metamorphosis Housewife by Sue Boone (prints and drawings); Inuit Women in Transition; From Craft into Art, contemporary Nova Scotia sculpture (fibre, metal, wood and clay); African Masks; Homage to Sarain Stump (Cree and Shoshone Indian artist); Hines on Hines; Older Ways: Traditional Nova Scotian Craftsman (photographs); Figures and Stitchery; Silkscreens by Henri Bettinville; Dickens Illustrations; Fourth Annual University Community Show. (1978) The Expressionist Image (prints and drawings).
Publications: Gallery News; catalogs.
Activities: Classes for adults and children; lect open to the public, 12 vis lectr per yr; concerts, gallery talks; tours; competitions; individual paintings and original objects of art lent to other galleries; lending collection contains cassettes; traveling exhibitions organized and circulated.

NOVA SCOTIA ASSOCIATION OF ARCHITECTS, Suite 630, 5991 Spring Garden Rd, B3H 1Y6. Tel: 902-423-7607. *Exec Secy* Kae Worsley.
Estab 1932. Mem: 116; annual meeting Feb.

NOVA SCOTIA COLLEGE OF ART AND DESIGN,* Anna Leonowens Gallery, 153 Granville St, B3J 3J6. Tel: 902-422-7381, exten 184. *Pres* Garry Neill Kennedy; *Dean* James Davies; *Dir* Robert MacKeeman.
Open daily. Estab for educational purposes. One small and one large gallery.
Income: Financed by city and state appropriations and tuition.
Exhibitions: 30-40 exhibitions per year.
Publications: Ten books, one periodical.
Activities: Extension dept has courses throughout the province.
—Library, 5163 Duke St, B3J 1N6. Tel: 902-422-7381, exten 181. *Dir* John Murchie; *Asst Dir* Mary Snyder.
Open Mon - Fri 9 AM - 12 midnight; Sat & Sun 1 PM - 12 midnight. Circ: 18,000.
Income: $150,000 (financed by city and state appropriation and tuition). Purchases: $45,000.
Holdings: Vols 15,000; Per subs 300; AV—Audiotapes, cassettes, microfiche, microfilm, phonorecords, slides 55,000, videotapes; Other—Exhibition catalogs, pamphlets.
Special Subjects: Contemporary art; 19th-20th century art history; Canadian art history.
Special Collections: Artists' books.

PUBLIC ARCHIVES OF NOVA SCOTIA, Cobury Rd, B3K 5K5. Tel: 902-423-7040. *Provincial Archivist* Hugh A Taylor; *Assoc Archivist* Dr Phyllis R Blakely.
Open Mon - Fri 8:30 AM - 10 PM; Sat 9 AM - 6 PM; Sun 1 - 10 PM. Estab 1931 to preserve Nova Scotian heritage; maintains art gallery of portraits and historical paintings.
Income: Financed by provincial appropriations.
Holdings: Vols 40,000; AV—Microfiche, microfilm, slides; Other—Clipping files; manuscripts, memorabilia, original art works, original documents, pamphlets, photographs.
Publications: Numerous special publications.

ONTARIO

ALMONTE

R TAIT MCKENZIE MEMORIAL MUSEUM, Mill of Kintail, RR#1, K0A 1A0. Tel: 613-256-3610. *Cur & Admin* vacant.
Open (May - Oct) Wed - Sat & Mon 10 AM - 6 PM; Sun 2 - 6 PM; cl Tues. Admis 50¢. Estab 1952 as a private museum, publicly owned since 1973, as a memorial to Dr R Tait McKenzie, Canadian sculptor, physical educator, surgeon, and humanitarian. Average Annual Attendance: 9000.
Income: Financed by provincial government grant.
Collections: Seventy original athletic, memorial and monumental sculptures, nearly all in plaster; six hundred pioneer artifacts, mostly collected by Dr McKenzie.
Exhibitions: Athletic sculpture plaque exhibited in connection with Olympiad in Montreal 1976.
Activities: Classes for adults and children; film shows; lect open to public; nature walks; competitions; sales shop selling medal reproductions, slides.
Library: Now being developed.

AURORA

CANADIAN GUILD OF POTTERS, c/o Gordon Barnes, *Pres*, 11 Catherine Ave, L4G 1K4. *First VPres* David Green; *Second VPres* Allen Grimmons; *Secy* Marlene Smith.
For further information see National Organizations in Canada.

BRAMPTON

PEEL MUSEUM AND ART GALLERY,* 7 Wellington St E L6W 1Y1. Tel: 416-451-9051. *Pres* Grant Clarkson; *Secy* R E Jones; *VPres & Museum Comt Pres* Mrs R H Bull; *Treas* John Jacobs; *Art Gallery Comt Pres* Lenore Kummell; *Dir* Lydia A Ross.
Open daily 1:30 - 4:30 PM. Admis adults 35¢, students and children 15¢, mem free. Estab 1968. Average Annual Attendance: 5000. Mem: Over 200; dues $2; annual meeting May 15.
Income: Approx $7000 (financed by membership and appropriations). Purchases art gallery $1000, museum $1000.
Collections: †Pioneer artifacts—19th century Ontario; †Indian artifacts—Iroquois.
Exhibitions: Changing art shows promoting local artists.
Activities: Classes for adults and children; pioneer craft classes; archives; lect open to the public, 3 vis lectr per yr; free school tours through both museum and art gallery.
Library: Reference. Holdings: Vols 200.

BRANTFORD

ART GALLERY OF BRANT, INC, 76 Dalhousie St (Mailing Add: PO Box 1747, N3T 5V7). Tel: 519-753-7581. *Dir* Val Greenfield; *Chmn* John Sterne; *Secy* Edie Mountjoy.
Open Tues - Fri 9 AM - 5 PM; Sat 10 AM - 5 PM; cl Sun & Mon. No admis. Estab 1971 as a non-profit public art gallery serving the citizens of Brantford and Brant County. Store-front gallery; one main gallery room. Average Annual Attendance: 20,000. Mem: 375; dues student & senior citizens $2, individual $7, family $10, sustaining $25; annual meeting Sept.
Income: Financed by membership, city and provincial appropriations, local foundations.
Collections: †Original prints and drawings by contemporary Canadian artists; works of historical nature by local area artist Robert Whale; Original prints by European and American artists.
Publications: Calendar of Events, quarterly; annual report; catalogues for exhibitions throughout the year.
Activities: Classes for adults and children; docent training; film series; lect open to public; 8 vis lectr per yr; galley talks; competitions; individual paintings and original objects of art lent to galleries and businesses; traveling exhibitions organized and circulated.
Library: Open to anyone for reference. Holdings: Vols 35.

BRANT COUNTY MUSEUM, 57 Charlotte St, N3T 2W6. Tel: 519-752-2483. *Pres* Sam Wyatt; *Cur Dr* Irmgard Jamnik.
Open Tues - Sat 10 AM - 5 PM; July & Aug 10 AM - 9 PM; cl Mon & major holidays. No admis. Estab 1908.
Income: Financed by county appropriation.
Collection: Portraits and paintings; early Indian history; historical figures.
Publications: Annual brochure.
Library: Holdings—Vols 500. Special Collections: Rare books; first editions of history and archaeology; old bibles available for research on premises under supervision of curator.

GLENHYRST ARTS COUNCIL OF BRANTFORD INC,* 20 Ava Rd, N3T 5G9. Tel: 519-756-5932. *Pres* John S Canning; *Exec Dir* William S Bragg.
Open Tues - Fri 2 - 8 PM; Sat & Sun 2 - 6 PM; cl Mon. No admis. estab 1957; Arts centre occupies 11-room house left to the city by the late E L Cockshutt, maintained by the city. Average Annual Attendance: 20,000.
Income: Financed by membership and fund-raising events.
Collections: †Small permanent collection.
Exhibitions: Held on regular basis.
Publications: Newsletter, monthly.
Activities: Classes for adults and children; lect open to the public, vis lectr; competitions.
Library: Very small reference library.

CHATHAM

THAMES ARTS CENTRE, 75 William St N, N7M 4L4. Tel: 519-354-8338. *Dir* David K McNeil; *Gallery/Educ Coordinator* Tim Child.
Open Tues - Sun 1 - 5 PM. No admis. estab 1963 to operate as a regional arts centre, to advance knowledge and appreciation of, and to encourage, stimulate and promote interest in the study of culture and the visual and performing arts; art gallery maintained; designated national Arts Centre for the presentation of visual art works and museum related works, to the public of this county. Average Annual Attendance: 12,000 (gallery). Mem: 600; dues single $10, family $17; annual meeting June.
Income: Financed by membership, city and state appropriation, and National Museum Grants.
Exhibitions: (1977-78) On View visual arts Ontario and ritual sculpture of Black Africa; local artists invitational; Oh! Fun and Games, and invitational games; Chatham-Kent Heritage II; Museums in Education, the British Council; The CIL Collection; Walter Bachinski Retrospective; Michel Binette: Glimpses of my World; Federick Hagen: The Mind and the Hand; Japanese Ukiyo-e Prints; Collins, Pachter and Tinkl.
Publications: Thames Arts Centre bulletin, quarterly.
Activities: Classes for adults and children; dramatic programs; docent training; workshops; demonstrations; film series; theatre series; lect open to the public; concerts; gallery talks; tours; lending collection contains slides 1500.
Special Subjects: Thames Art Centre has a 700-seat theatre for the Performing Arts, and mini-theatre.

HAMILTON

ART GALLERY OF HAMILTON, 123 King St W, L8P 4S8. Tel: 416-527-6610. *Dir* Glen E Cumming; *Cur* Andrew J Oko; *Asst to Dir* Ted Pietrzak; *Educ & Exten Officer* Sheila Greenspan; *Community Relations* Keith Courtney; *Preparator* Dan Thorburn; *Registrar* Margaret Haupt.
Open Tues - Sat 10 AM - 5 PM; Thurs Eve 7 - 9 PM; Sun 1 - 5 PM; No admis. Estab Jan 31, 1914 to develop and maintain a centre for the study and enjoyment of the visual arts; 76,000 sq ft building, 24,000 sq ft of exhibition space, brand new gallery opened Oct 1, 1977. Average Annual Attendance: 150,000. Mem: 3280; dues single $15, family $25; annual meeting last Thurs May.
Income: $809,400 (1978 budget) (financed by endowment, membership, city and state appropriation and federal grants). Purchases: $100,000 (1978 budget).
Collections: Principally †Canadian fine arts, but also †American, †British and other European.
Exhibitions: (1976) Best of L'il Abner; Irene Hepburn Recent Work; Picasso and The Vollard Suite; The Electric Show; Western Image (photos); Ontario Community Collections; Nicholas Poussin; James Spencer, Waves and Mountains; Martha Haslanger; Richard Owen; Steve Pilcher; Grant MacDonald; John Newman; Ontario Now Part I; William Kurelek; Prairie Boys Summer; Camera and Dr Barnardo; Walter Bachinski; CKOC Juried Show. (1977) Ontario Now Part II; 100 Years Evolution of the Ontario College of Art; Saskatchewan Photography; Karel Appel Graphics; Aspects of Realism.
Publications: Art Gallery of Hamilton (calendar), monthly.
Activities: Classes for adults and children; docent training; lect open to the public, 18 vis lectr per yr; concerts; gallery talks; tours; extension dept; individual paintings and original objects of art lent to other galleries and museums; lending collection contains original prints 1542, paintings 1280, sculpture 124, drawings 448; traveling exhibitions organized and circulated; museum shop selling books, magazines, reproductions.
—Muriel Isabel Bostwick Library. *Registrar* Margaret Haupt.
Open to gallery members and researchers for reference.
Holdings: Vols 3000; per subs 14.
Special Subjects: Good references on Canadian art history and large holding of exhibition catalogs relating to this field.

DUNDURN CASTLE,* Dundurn Park, York Blvd, L8R 3H1. Tel: 416-552-5313. *Dir* Brig Gen Willis Moogk; *Asst Dir* Mary Alix Groneau.

Open mid-June to Labor Day daily 10 AM - 5 PM; evening appointments for groups of 25 or more; Labor Day to mid-June, booked tours mornings and evenings, open to public 1 - 4 PM, except school holidays 10 AM - 4 PM; cl Christmas and New Year's Day; children must be accompanied by adults. Dundurn, the home of Sir Allan Napier MacNab; Hamilton's Centennial Project was the restoration of this historic house; built in 1832-35, it was tenured by MacNab until his death in 1862. The terminal date of the furnishings is 1855. Approximately 37 rooms are shown; three-room on-site museum; demonstrations; seminars. Average Annual Attendance: 90,000.
Income: Financed by City of Hamilton, owner and operator.

JORDAN

JORDAN HISTORICAL MUSEUM OF THE TWENTY,* Vintage House, Main St, L0R 1S0. Tel: 416-562-5242. *Secy* Barbara Coffman; *Dir* H L Crowfoot.
Open May - Oct daily Noon - 6 PM. No admis. Estab 1953 to preserve the material and folklore of the area known as The Twenty, Mile Creek vicinity. Average Annual Attendance: 20,000. Mem: 820; annual meeting Dec.
Income: $14,500.
Collections: Archives, textiles, glass, china, furniture, historical material.
Activities: Special displays as requested by the community; Pioneer Day first Sat after Canadian Thanksgiving holiday.

KINGSTON

QUEEN'S UNIVERSITY, Agnes Etherington Art Centre, K7L 3N6. Tel: 613-547-6170 or 6171. *Acting Dir & Cur* Frances K Smith; *Assoc Cur* William Muysson; *Registrar* vacant; *Curatorial Asst* Linda Milrod.
Open Tues - Fri 10 AM - 5 PM; Tues & Thurs 7 - 9 PM; Sat & Sun 1 - 5 PM. No admis. Estab 1957 to provide the services of a public art gallery and museum for the community and region; about 7000 sq ft of gallery space, in four separate areas, showing a balanced program of exhibitions of the contemporary and historical, of national, international and regional art. Average Annual Attendance: 30,000. Mem: 850 (in the Gallery Association, a community oriented body which supports and extends the program); dues $6 - $25; annual meeting May.
Income: $320,000 (financed by endowment, city and state appropriation and University and Canada Council funds).
Purchases: $20,000.
Collections: †Canadian paintings, sculpture, prints, historical and contemporary; †European graphics; ethnological collection; Old Master paintings.
Exhibitions: (1976-77) About 30 exhibitions mounted each year, notably French lithography: The Restoration Salons; Horatio Walker Retrospective; Henry Moore; C W Jefferys.
Publications: Bulletin, bimonthly; exhibition publications; catalogs; studies.
Activities: Classes for adults and children; docent training for school groups; studio classes; lect open to the public, 10 vis lectr per yr; concerts; gallery talks; tours; individual paintings lent by Gallery Association Art Rental to private individuals and businesses; lending collection contains original prints, paintings; traveling exhibitions organized and circulated.
Library: Tel: 613-547-6170/6171. Open to students, researchers and the public for reference only. Holdings: Per subs 4; Other—Exhibition catalogs, reference books, Canadian art, overall total 1000. Special Collections: Archival records on a few Canadian artists where special study has been undertaken; George Harlow White, Goodridge Roberts, Daniel Fowler, Andre Bieler.

KITCHENER

KITCHENER-WATERLOO ART GALLERY, 43 Benton St, N2G 3H1. Tel: 519-745-6671. *Dir* Robert Ihrig; *Cur* Bradley Blain; *Registrar* Paul Blain; *Secy* Dolores Fromm; *Pres Bd of Dir* Judge D A Bean; *First VPres* Raymond Stanton; *Second VPres* Ann Gawman; *Treas* J M Carty; *Secy* G Eastman.
Open Tues - Sat 10 AM - 5 PM; Tues - Thurs Eve 7 - 9 PM; Sun 1 - 5 PM. No admis. Estab 1956 for the promotion of the visual arts; gallery is located in a renovated church. Average Annual Attendance: 26,000. Mem: 600; dues single $10, family $15, business $25; annual meeting June.
Income: Financed by membership, city and state appropriation; and Federal funds.
Collections: Contemporary Canadian with emphasis on regional work.
Publications: Calendar of events, quarterly; exhibition catalogs.
Activities: Classes for adults and children; docent training; lect open to the public, 4 vis lectr per yr; gallery talks; tours; competitions; extension dept serving Waterloo region; individual paintings and original objects of

art lent to members only; lending collection contains original art works 300, original prints 250, paintings 100; traveling exhibitions organized and circulated.

Eleanor Calvert Memorial Library: Librn Nancy Francis (vol). Open to members only. Holdings: Vols 1000; Per subs 12; Other—Slides.

KLEINBURG

MCMICHAEL CANADIAN COLLECTION, L0J 1C0. Tel: 416-893-1121. *Dir* Dr Robert McMichael; *Chmn Bd Trustees* J Allyn Taylor; *VChmn Bd Trustees* Warren E Jones.

Open Tues - Sun Noon - 5:30 PM, school tours in the morning, by appointment. No admis. Estab 1965 to give a better understanding of Canadian art to people of all ages. Average Annual Attendance: 280,000.

Income: Financed by the Province of Ontario.

Collections: Canadian Group of Seven and their contemporaries (Tom Thomson, Emily Carr, David Milne, etc); Candian Eskimo and Indian art.

Publications: The McMichael Canadian Collection (book).

Activities: Classes for children; concerts; gallery talks; tours; exten dept serving Ontario; individual paintings and original objects of art lent; museum shop selling books, reproductions, and prints.

Library: Librn Donna Cooper. Holdings: Mainly archival material.

LONDON

LONDON ART GALLERY ASSOCIATION, 305 Queens Ave, N6B 3L7. Tel: 519-672-4580. *Pres* George L Bowie; *VPres* Mrs David Conklin; *Secy* Nancy Postian; *Exec* Janet B Delancy.

Open Mon - Fri 9 AM - 9 PM; Sat 9 AM - 5 PM; Sun 2 - 5 PM. Estab 1964 to foster and interest in Art the City of London and area, and to build a separate Art Gallery in the City; gallery not maintained. Mem: 700; dues individual $7, family $10; annual meeting May.

Income: $10,000 (financed by membership).

Activities: Classes for children; film and lecture series; members tours of other cities' galleries; lect open to the public, 8 vis lectr per yr; tours.

LONDON PUBLIC LIBRARY AND ART MUSEUM,* 305 Queens Ave, N6B 1X2. Tel: 519-432-7166. *Dir* E Stanley Beacock; *Cur Art Museum* Mrs Paddy O'Brien; *Asst Cur Registration* Miss J Kelly; *Asst Cur Educ & Extension* Donald DeGrow; *Asst Cur Installations* Anne Garwood Roney; *Docent Supvr* Kate McCabe; *Extension Officer* Daniela Presetnik; *Communications Officer* Valerie Greenfield.

Open Mon - Fri 9 AM - 9 PM; Sat 9 AM - 5 PM; Sun, public & civic holidays, gallery only 2 - 5 PM. No admis. Present building opened in 1940, additions 1951, 1967. Average Annual Attendance: 80,000. London Art Gallery Association and Women's Committee mem: 1000; dues (LAGA) $2 - $10.

Income: Library and art gallery approx $2,160,000 (financed by municipal appropriation). Purchases: Approx $8000.

Collections: Canadian †painting, †sculpture and †graphics; some British paintings.

Exhibitions: Average of 35 per year; two branch galleries, 12 each per year; one annual open juried exhibition, Annual Western Ontario Exhibition; purchase awards approx $3000 annually.

Activities: Children's classes; high school art classes; films; demonstrations; special events; two picture rental services; docent training; lect, and lect series; tours; extension services.

Library: Special reference. Holdings: Vols 200.

UNIVERSITY OF WESTERN ONTARIO, McIntosh Art Gallery, 1151 Richmond St, N6A 3K7. Tel: 519-679-3181 or 679-6027. *University Art Cur* Maurice Stubbs; *Asst Cur* Daniel M Miller; *Secy* Margaret Allen.

Open (Sept-Apr) Mon - Fri Noon - 5 PM; Sat & Sun 2 - 5 PM; Wed & Thurs 7 - 9 PM; (May-Aug) Mon - Fri Noon - 4 PM; Sun 2 - 5 PM; cl Sat. No admis. Estab 1942; three galleries with a total square footage of 2960. Average Annual Attendance: 12,000. Mem: 91.

Income: Financed by endowment, membership, provincial appropriation, special grants; University funds. Purchases: $2000.

Collections: Canadian art.

Exhibitions: John de Visser: Newfoundland (photographs); Imprint '76; Landscape and Megalith: Walter Redinger (sculpture); Contemporary Canadian Crafts; Electric Art; Richard Tuttle; Four Artist Printmakers; Visual Arts Department Faculty; Romanesque Sculpture; Medieval Manuscripts; Viewpoint: 3-man show; John O'Henly photographs; Ultrastructure: An Aesthetic experience (electron micrographs by University scientists).

Publications: Bulletin, bimonthly; Catalogues for exhibitions.

Activities: Lect open to public, 4 - 6 vis lectr per yr; concerts; gallery talks; tours; individual paintings and original objects lent to galleries; traveling exhibitions organized and circulated.

Library: Open to gallery staff and museology students. Holdings: Vols 250; Per subs 3.

NIAGARA FALLS

OAK HALL,* Portage Rd, S (Mailing Add: c/o The Niagara Parks Commission, Box 150, L2E 6T2). Tel: 416-356-2241. *Cur* L Burns.

Open daily mid-June - Labor Day 11 AM - 7 PM. Admis adults 50¢, children 12 and under free. Estab 1959, the restored home of the late Sir Harry Oakes.

Income: Financed by Niagara Parks Commission, a self-sustaining provincial agency.

Collections: Early Niagara prints and oils on display in gallery.

Publications: Historical Niagara Frontier Revisited, annual promotional brochure.

OAKVILLE

OAKVILLE PUBLIC LIBRARY AND CENTENNIAL GALLERY,* 120 Navy St, L6J 2Z4. Tel: 416-845-3405. *Chief Librn* R B Moses; *Gallery Cur* Esther Demeny.

Open Mon - Fri 10 AM - 9 PM; Sat 10 AM - 5 PM; Sun 2 - 5 PM. No admis. Estab 1967 for a greater awareness of the diversified role of the gallery in the total visual arts scene; Fine Arts Gallery has 2000 sq ft area, with 150 running ft of wallspace, and 20 x 18 ft sculpture court. Average Annual Attendance: 25,000.

Income: $40,000 - $50,000 plus residence within library complex (financed by city and provincial appropriations).

Collections: †Original paintings, drawings, prints and sculpture; †native Canadian arts; also 41 pieces of sculpture replicas.

Exhibitions: 74 exhibitions since 1970, including 3 - 4 major ones yearly.

Publications: Happenings, monthly; 2 - 3 exhibition catalogs yearly.

Activities: Lect open to the public; vis lectr; gallery talks; tours; extension dept serving Oakville and area; material available to general public; fees are 1% of works value; material lent; individual paintings and original objects of art lent; lending collection contains original art works 63, sculpture replicas 41, photographs 34; traveling exhibitions organized and circulated.

TARAS H SHEVCHENKO MUSEUM AND MEMORIAL PARK FOUNDATION, 1363 Dundas St, W L6J 4Z2. Tel: 416-827-2651. Toronto Office: 42 Roncesvalles Ave, Toronto M6R 2K3. Tel: 416-535-1063. *Pres & Cur* Peter Prokop; *Secy* Stanley Dobrowolsky.

Open Sun, July & Aug Noon - 5 PM; others by appointment. Admis by voluntary donation. Estab 1952, a 16.5 acre park, complete with monument and museum opened to the public as a symbol of the unity and brother of Ukrainian Canadians with Canadians of all national origins.

Income: Financed by donations.

Collections: Reproductions and copies in oil and watercolor of Taras H Shevchenko's own paintings and sketches and also paintings done by other artists and authors representing some aspects of T H Shevchenko's life. Display and handicrafts—ceramics from Ukraine, handicrafts made by Ukrainian Canadians and exhibits of Ukrainian pioneer life in Western Canada.

OSHAWA

ROBERT McLAUGHLIN GALLERY, Civic Centre, L1J 3Z3. Tel: 416-576-3000. *Dir* Joan Murray; *Asst to Dir* Jane MacDonald; *Asst Cur/Registrar* Jennifer Watson; *Curatorial Asst* Allan Walkinshaw; *Educ & Exten* Michael Burtch; *Publicity & Pub Relations* Bernice Bradt.

Open Mon - Fri Noon - 5 PM, Eve 7 - 9 PM; Sat Noon - 5 PM; Sun 2 - 5 PM. No admis. Estab Feb 1967 as The Art Gallery of Oshawa, in May 1969 as the Robert McLaughlin Gallery; Main Gallery 28 x 46 x 15 ft, North Gallery 24 x 31 x 10 ft, South Gallery 18 x 27 x 10 ft, with foyer and Director's office. Average Annual Attendance; 27,000. Mem: 375; dues student $2.50, single $10, family $15; annual meeting Feb.

Income: Financed by endowment, membership, and city appropriation.

Collections: Canadian 19th and 20th Century paintings, drawings, sculpture and prints; major collection of works by Painters Eleven; Japanese wood block prints.

Exhibitions: (1976) Christmas Celebration; Photographers of Durham Region; Spring in February: Robert Holmes (1861-1930) and J Fenwick Landsdowne (1937-   ); Graham Coughtry Retrospective; Roy Kiyooka: 25 Years; Of Human Bondage; Louis Stokes (sculptor); Carl Schaefer Retrospective; Canadian Landscapes; Painters Eleven (1953-1960); The Objective Object: Peter Brown; The Ontario Community Collects; Art Mart, annual gallery crafts event; Robin MacKenzie: New York. (1977) Christmas Festival; Me, Myself and I Juried exhibition of photographs by school children of Durham Region; Edmund Alleyn: une belle je journee; Charles William Jeffeys, 1869-1951; Arthur Handy Retrospective; Dennis Burton Retrospective; Durham Region Prints; Quebec TV & Co by Ernest Gendron; Rose Festival Children's art; Alexandra

Luke: A Tribute; Photographers of Durham Region; Terence Shortt: A Retrospective; Art Mart, annual gallery crafts event; Show and Tell. (1978) a Terrible Beauty: The Art of Canada at War.
Publications: Bulletin, monthly; Annual Report; Calendar of Events, annually; Exhibition catalogs.
Activities: Classes for adults and children; docent training; lect open to the public, 10 vis lectr per yr; concerts; gallery talks; tours; competitions; extension dept; individual paintings and original objects of art lent to school, institutions, and industry; lending collection contains cassettes 100, color reproductions 300, framed reproductions, original art works 90, original prints 20, paintings 50, photographs, slides 4500; traveling exhibitions organized and circulated; sales shop selling books, original art and local crafts.
Library: Tel: 416-576-3000. *Librn* Mark Warren.
Open to gallery members.
Holdings: Vols 3500.
Special Subjects: Research of Painters Eleven and 19th and 20th Century works.

OTTAWA

ASSOCIATION DES MUSEES CANADIENS (Canadian Museums Association), 331 Cooper St Suite 400, K2P 0G5. Tel: 613-233-5653. *Pres* J C Finlay; *VPres* Dr George MacBeath; *Secy* Dr George Lammers; *Exec Dir* R R Inglis; *Head Training Resources Div* Theodore T Poulos; *Head Publ Div* Gary J Sirois.
For further information see National Organizations in Canada.

CONSEIL CANADIEN DE L'ARTISANAT (CANADIAN CRAFTS COUNCIL), 16-46 Elgin St K1P 5K6. Tel: 613-235-8200. *Pres* Orland Larson; *VPres* Mary E Hogg; *Secy* Ann Mortimer; *Exec Dir* Peter H Weinrich.
For further information see National Organizations in Canada.

NATIONAL FILM BOARD PHOTO GALLERY, Still Photography Division, Tunney's Pasture, 150 Kent St, K1A 0M9. Tel 613-992-5258. *Dir* Lorraine Monk.
Open daily Noon - 6 PM; cl major holidays. No admis. Estab 1939, affiliated with National Film Board of Canada, Montreal.
Collections: Creative photography by Canadian photographers.
Publications: Exhibition catalogs; quarterly brochure.
Activities: Gallery talks; guided tours; temporary and traveling exhibitions.

NATIONAL GALLERY OF CANADA,* Lorne Bldg, Elgin & Slater Sts, K1A 0M8. Tel: 613-992-4636. *Dir* Dr Hsio-Yen Shih; *Deputy Dir* J Martin; *Asst Dir* Gyde V Shepherd; *Asst Dir Admin* R Jelking; *Chief Cur* Dr Robert H Hubbard; *Cur Adminstr* P Théberge; *Research Cur & Lectr Canadian Art* J R Ostiguy; *Cur Post Confederation Canadian Art* D Reid; *Cur Early Canadian Art* J Trudel; *Cur Drawings* Mrs M C Taylor; *Cur Prints* D Druick; *Cur Photography* J Borcoman; *Cur Contemporary Art* Brydon E Smith; *Research Cur European Art* Dr Myron Laskin, Jr; *Asst Cur European Art* Louise d'Argencourt; *Head Restoration & Conservation Lab* Mervyn Ruggles; *Head National Prog* R Graburn; *Head Publ* P Smith; *Head Educ* M Pantazzi; *Registrar* A Fronton; *Coordr Ottawa Exhib* N Clark; *Chief Information & Public Relations* Janine Smiter.
Open 10 AM - 6 PM; Tues & Thurs 10 AM - 10 PM; Sun & holidays 2 - 6 PM; cl Christmas Day; cl Mon Oct - Apr. No admis. Founded 1880 under the patronage of the Governor-General, the Marquess of Lorne, and his wife the Princess Louise; first inc 1913 and charged with the development and care of the National Collections and the promotion of art in Canada. Since 1968 the gallery has been a part of the National Museums of Canada, reporting to a Board of Trustees estab for the Corporation. The Gallery is housed (since 1960) in the Lorne Bldg, with 8 floors devoted to exhibition space, auditorium, workshops, offices, laboratories and cafeteria. Average Annual Attendance: 450,000.
Collections: Canadian painting, sculpture and decorative arts from 17th to 20th century; European painting and sculpture from 14th to 20th century; contemporary American art; prints and drawings of principal schools; photography; diploma works of the Royal Canadian Academy of the Arts. Among the principal acquisitions 1970-1972 were European painting, sculpture including Klimt (Hope I), Mondrian (Composition 1936-42) Bartolomeo Veneto (Portrait of a Young Woman), Il Morazzone (The Raising of Lazarus), Benson (Portait of a Man), de Hondecoeter (Landscape with a Musical Gathering), Carpeau (Bacchante), Dalou (Seated Woman Reading) and a group of medieval works. Poussin (Martyrdom of St Erasmus); Puget (Bust of a King); Patel (Landscape with Rest of the Flight to Egypt); Poelanburgh (Clorinda Savug Alinda & Safronia from the Stake); Bernini (Bust Urban VIII); American painting and sculpture including Noland (Untitled), Serra (Davidson Gate), Gorky (Charred Beloved II), Marden (3 Deliverate Greys for Jasper Johns), Graves (Variability and Repetition of Variable Forms). Prints and drawings by Lewis Sutherland, Bartlett, Oldenburg,

Picasso, Rouault, Rauschengerg, Lichtenstein, Warnol, Joh, Gainsborough, Cezanne, Bandinelli, Hamilton, Hayter. Canadian works by Patterson, Snow, Wieland, Pilot, Borduas, Fitzgerald, Milne, Tousignant, Walker, Breeze, Peel, Levine, Vaillancourt, Urquhart, Zelenak, Lafrance, and Sasseville.
Exhibitions: Exhibition of art collections from abroad, from its own holdings and from private and public sources are organized and circulated in Canada and abroad.
Publications: Annual reviews; Bulletin, semiannual; exhibition catalogs; Canadian Artists Monographs; National Programme Journals.
Activities: Lectures, films, gallery talks and guided tours at the gallery and lecture tours throughout Canada; broadcasts and telecasts; loan collection of films on art; slides for sale; conservation; sales desk for publications, reproductions and postcards.
—**Library,** 75 Albert St K1A 0M8. *Chief Librn* Mrs M N Balke; *Depty Librn Coll* Miss J Hunter; *Librn Technical Services* Murray Waddington; *Reference Librn* Miss M Vilcins; *Serials Librn* Mrs I Van Lierde; *Art Documentalist* Miss S Hasbury.
Open Mon - Fri 10 AM - 6 PM. Estab 1918 to support the research and information requirements of gallery personnel; to make its collections of resource materials in the fine arts available to Canadian libraries and scholars; and to serve as a source of information about Canadian art and art activities in Canada. Circ: To gallery personnel only and on interlibrary loan.
Income: $330,400 (financed by state appropriation and federal government). Purchases: $482,000.
Holdings: Vols 55,000; Pers subs 1165; AV—Microfiche, microfilm, phonorecords; Other—Clipping files, exhibition catalogs, manuscripts, pamphlets.
Special Subjects: Canadian art, post-medieval Western art with special emphasis on painting and sculpture, prints and drawings, photography.
Special Collections: Canadiana; Art Documentation; Prints and Drawings; Photography; Conservation of Art.
Exhibitions: (1977) Original Christmas Cards by Canadian Artists.
Publications: Artists in Canada, files in National Gallery Library, annual; Serials Currently Received, annual.
Activities: Libr tours.

NATIONAL MUSEUM OF MAN, Metcalfe and McLeod Sts, K1A 0M8. *Dir* Dr W E Taylor Jr; *Asst Dir Operations* Dr J F Pendergast; *Asst Dir Pub Prog* B A Tyler; *Asst Dir Admin* W J Kozar; *Chief Archaeological Survey of Canada* Dr R Marois; *Chief Canadian Ethnology Service* A McFadyen Clark; *Acting Chief Canadian Centre for Folk Culture Studies* P Tilney; *Chief Educ & Cultural Affairs Div* F Corcoran; *Chief Nat Prog Div* J Lochhead; *Chief History Div* Dr F Thorpe; *Chief Cur Canadian War Museum* L Murray.
Open Tues - Sun 10 AM - 6 PM; summer Tues & Wed 10 AM - 10 PM; Thurs - Sun 10 AM - 6 PM. No admis. Estab 1968 as one of four component Museums of the National Museum Corporation; to trace the development of Man from prehistoric times to the present, particularly Canadian development, museum houses on the first floor the development of early man, and the technology of Canada's indigenous peoples and archaeological method of recovering such past; on the second floor, overview of the Plains Indians and Iroquois; on the third floor, overview of the West Coast Indians, and traveling exhibits; on the fourth floor, Canadian history to present and tracing the contribution made by ethnic peoples in Canada. Average Annual Attendance: 410,000 (average of 1975-77).
Income: $8,000,000 (financed by Federal government funding). Purchases:-$325,000.
Collections: †Archaeological Collection; †Ethnological Collection; †Folk Culture Collections; †Historical Collection; †War Collection.
Exhibitions: Asia Calling; Bo'jou Neejee: Profiles of Canadian Indian Art; The Camera and Dr Barnardo; Contemporary Canadian Indian Art; Gift of the Raven: Canadian Northwest Coast Indian Art; Land of the Maple Leaf-Home of the Beaver; The Inuit Print; The Last Best West; Memories: Photographs of the Northwest Coast Indians; Ontario Prehistory; Shamans and Spirits: Myths and Medical Symbolism in Eskimo Art.
Publications: Several series of publications and periodicals, 200 titles published in last five years.
Activities: Classes for adults and children; dramatic programs; docent training; lect open to the public, several vis lectr per yr; competitions; exten dept serving nationally and internationally circulating NMM temporary exhibits; individual artifacts and original artifacts lent to museums and other institutions meeting NMM borrowing specifications regarding security, environment, etc; traveling exhibitions organized and circulated; museum shop selling books, magazines, reproductions, prints.

NATIONAL MUSEUMS OF CANADA, Esplanade Laurier, 300 Laurier W, K1A 0M8. Tel: 613-995-9832. *Acting Secy-Gen* Jennifer R McQueen.
The individual museums under the National Museums of Canada are as follows:

National Gallery of Canada, Lorne Bldg, Elgin & Slater Sts. Tel: 613-992-4636. *Dir* Dr Hsio-Yen Shih.

National Museum of Man, Metcalfe & McLeod Sts. Tel: 613-992-3497. *Dir* Dr W E Taylor, Jr. Canadian War Museum, 330 Sussex Dr. Tel: 613-992-2774. *Cur* L F Murray.

National Museum of Natural Sciences, Metcalfe & McLeod Sts. Tel: 613-996-3102. *Dir* Dr Louis Lemieux.

National Museum of Science and Technology, 1867 St Laurent Blvd. Tel: 613-998-4566. *Dir* Dr D M Baird.

National Aeronautical Collection, Rockcliffe Air Force Base. Tel: 613-993-2010.

The beginning of the National Gallery of Canada are associated with the founding of the Royal Canadian Academy of Arts in 1880. Until 1907 the National Gallery was under the direct control of a minister of the Crown but in that year an Advisory Arts Council consisting of three persons outside government was appointed to administer grants to the National Gallery. In 1913 the National Gallery was incorporated by Act of Parliament and placed under the administration of a board of trustees appointed by the Governor General in Council. Since 1960 the National Gallery has occupied the Lorne Building in Ottawa.

The National Museum of Man and the National Museum of Natural Sciences evolved from the collections of the Geological Survey of Canada in the nineteenth century. The collections were transferred to the newly built Victoria Memorial Museum Building in 1911. The National Museum of Canada was formally established in 1927. In 1957 this Museum was divided into two branches - Human History and Natural History - with an additional branch, Science and Technology, being established in 1966.

In April 1968 a new act amalgamated these three branches, together with the National Gallery of Canada, under the aegis of one corporation known as the National Museums of Canada. The purposes of the Corporation are to demonstrate the products of nature and the works of man, with special but not exclusive reference to Canada, so as to promote interest therein throughout Canada and to disseminate knowledge thereof. (National Museums Act, RSC 1970 C.N-12). Average Annual Attendance: Exceeds 2½ million at all museums.

Activities: Conducted tours; talks and lectures; film and theatre presentations; traveling exhibitions. Each museum maintains a boutique that sells prints, books, bulletins, recordings, models, artifacts, postcards, and slides.

—**Library,** 2086 Walkley Rd, K1A 0M8. *Chief Libr Div* Valerie Monkhouse.

Open Mon - Fri 9 AM - 4:30 PM. Estab 1845 to serve the staff of the Corporation of the National Museums of Canada and other workers in subject areas related to the disciplines of the Museums. Circ: To staff of the Corporation; other users may use collection for reference purposes or borrow through interlibrary loan.

Income: Financed by the government. Purchases: (1976-77) $2,641,572.

Holdings: Vols 120,000; Per subs 1322; AV—Microfiche, microfilm; Other—Exhibition catalogs, manuscripts, pamphlets.

Special Subjects: Museology; anthropology, including archaeology; folk culture studies; biology; conservation of art objects and restoration; historical studies of Canadian aviation, Canadian social and military history, and of science and technology; mineral sciences.

Special Collections: Anderson Collection (mammalogy); C M Sternberg Reprint Collection (palaeontology); Human Relations Area Files (anthropology).

Publications: Monthly list of accessions to the library.

OTTAWA PUBLIC LIBRARY, 120 Metcalfe St, K1P 5M2. Tel: 613-236-0301. *Dir* Claude Aubry; *Asst Dir* Jean de Temple; *Admin Officer* Wilfred Blain.

Open Mon - Thurs 10 AM - 9 PM; Fri 10 AM - 6 PM; Sat 9:30 AM - 5 PM. Estab 1906 to serve the community as a centre for general and reliable information; to select, preserve and administer books and related materials in organized collections; to provide opportunity for citizens of all ages to educate themselves continuously. Circ: 2,168,049.

Income: $4,559,000 (financed by city and provincial appropriations, fees and fines). Purchases: $578,226.

Holdings: Vols 593,639; Per subs 777; AV—Cassettes, film strips, microfiche, microfilm, motion pictures, phonorecords, reels; Other—Clipping files, pamphlets.

Special Collections: Local history collection (Ottawa Room)—maps, books, pamphlets about Ottawa and region plus books by local authors, city directories); Foreign Languages Collection (over 35 different languages); Women's Collection instituted during International Women's Year (bilingual).

Exhibitions: Monthly exhibits highlighting local artists, craftsmen, photographers, collectors.

Publications: Bulletin, monthly; booklists; film catalogs, brochures.

Activities: Lect open to public; library tours.

PUBLIC ARCHIVES OF CANADA
—**Public Archives Library,** 395 Wellington St, K1A 0N3. Tel: 613-992-2669. *Dominion Archivist* Dr W I Smith.

Open daily 9 AM - 9 PM. Estab 1872 to acquire and preserve significant Canadian archival material in all media relating to all aspects of Canadian life and to the development of the country, and to provide suitable research services and facilities to make this documentation available to the public.

Income: Financed by federal appropriation.

Holdings: (Art) Vols 1000.

Exhibitions: Toronto photographer: F W Micklethwaite; French-Canadian historian: Francois Xavier Garneau; Illustrated children's books.

Publications: Catalogue of publications available on request.

—**Laurier House,** 335 Laurier Ave E, K1N 6R4. Tel: 613-992-8142. *Cur* Valerie Proctor.

Open Tues - Sat 10 AM - 5 PM; Sun 2 - 5 PM; cl Mon. No admis. Estab 1951. An historic house; former residence of two Prime Ministers, Sir Wilfrid Laurier and the Rt Hon William Lyon Mackenzie King, and containing furniture and memorabilia belonging to a third Prime Minister, Lester Pearson. The house is primarily furnished in the style of its last occupant, the Rt Hon William Lyon Mackenzie King, with space given to the Laurier Collection. In 1974 the Lester Pearson study was installed. Average Annual Attendance: 25,000.

Income: Financed by endowment, and federal government.

Exhibitions: A Child's Best Friend (a doll display); Our Shared Responsibility (a photographic exhibit on the care and handling of artifacts).

OWEN SOUND

TOM THOMSON MEMORIAL GALLERY AND MUSEUM OF FINE ART, 840 First Ave W (Mailing Add: Box 312, N4K 3P5). Tel: 519-376-1932.

Open Tues - Sun; cl Mon; Wed & Fri 7 - 9 PM. Admis 50¢. Estab 1967 to collect and display paintings by Tom Thomson, and to educate the public by different exhibitions, tours, films, classes, and artists. Two galleries with paintings by Tom Thomson on permanent display; changing exhibitions in both galleries. Average Annual Attendance: 10,000. Mem: 350; dues single $6; family $10.

Income: Financed by city appropriation.

Collections: Tom Thomson; Group of Seven; †contemporary Canadian artists; 19th century artists.

Publications: Bulletin, ten a year.

Activities: Classes for children; docent training; lect open to public; gallery talks; tours; competitions; museum shop selling books, reproductions, prints, and postcards.

Library: Open for reference. Holdings: Vols 9; Per subs 7; Other—Catalogs of exhibitions. Special Subjects: Books and files on Tom Thomson.

PARRY SOUND

PARRY SOUND PUBLIC LIBRARY, 29 Mary St, P2A 1E3. Tel: 705-746-9601. *Librn* Laurine Tremaine; *Asst* Leslie Piekarz.

Open Mon - Fri 10 AM - 9 PM; Sat 10 AM - 6 PM. Estab 1889 to promote education, leisure interests and cultural enrichment for the community. Circ: 50,000.

Income: $62,000 (financed by endowment, membership, city and provincial grants, miscellaneous sources). Purchases: $20,000.

Holdings: Vols 25,300; Per subs 146; AV—Cassettes, phonorecords; Other—Clipping files, pamphlets.

SAINT CATHARINES

RODMAN HALL ARTS CENTRE,* (formerly St Catharines and District Arts Council), 109 St Paul Crescent, L2S 1M7. Tel: 416-684-2925. *Pres* Dr D Steele, *Secy* Arnel Pattemore; *Dir* A Peter Harris; *Secy to Dir* Joanne Rolfe.

Open Tues - Sun 1 - 5 PM. Estab 1956; Art Centre activities, to stimulate greater public interest in all phases of cultural activity, provide increased opportunity for public enjoyment of drama, music, painting and the allied arts, and to support, encourage and endeavour to effect the establishment of a civic centre to provide auditorium facilities, space for suitable display and housing of fine art, and headquarters for all affiliated organizations interested in arts and letters; four galleries display monthly exhibitions of all types as well as concerts and recitals. Average Annual Attendance: 35,000. Mem: 900; dues single $7, family $10, sustaining $40, life $300, patron $500, founder $1000.

Income: $42,000 (financed by city and provincial grants). Purchases: $3000.

Collections: Collections of contemporary Canadian art.

Publications: Bulletin and advance invitations, monthly.

Activities: Classes for adults and children; drama programs; lect open to the public, 6 vis lectr per yr; concerts; gallery talks; tours; competitions; individual paintings lent to schools; original objects of art lent; lending collection contains lantern slides 1000; Book shop.
Library: Reference only. Holdings: Vols 100. Art Rental Gallery, manned by Women's Committee of St Catharines and District Arts Council; rent only to individual members and member organizations.

SARNIA

SARNIA PUBLIC LIBRARY AND ART GALLERY,* 124 Christina St S, N7T 2M6. Tel: 519-337-3291. *Dir* R T Bradley.
Open Mon - Fri 9 AM - 9 PM; Sat 9 AM - 5:30 PM; Sun Oct - May 2 - 5 PM. No admis. A collection of Canadian paintings instituted in 1919 and administered by the Women's Conservation Art Association of Sarnia. The collection was turned over to the Sarnia Library Board in 1956 and additions are being made from time to time. Average Annual Attendance: 33,300.
Collections: Canadian paintings; sculpture; Eskimo carvings; a collection of old photographs of Sarnia and Lambton County are stored in the gallery.
Exhibitions: Twelve to fifteen shows a year, either traveling from other galleries or initiated by the Sarnia Art Gallery.
Activities: Children's art classes in July and August.

SIMCOE

EVA BROOK DONLY MUSEUM, 109 Norfolk St S, N3Y 2W3. Tel: 519-426-1583. *Cur* William Yeager; *Managing Dir* Kenneth S McArthur.
Open Wed - Sun 1:30 - 5 PM; other times by appointment. Admis adult 50¢, student 25¢, children under 12 free; $3 per year mem, children free if with adult, tours $5 per 35, 10¢ each additional person. Estab 1946 to display and aid research in the history of Norfolk County. Average Annual Attendance: 2800. Mem dues: individual, family $5.
Income: Financed by endowment, membership, city and provincial appropriation.
Collections: Large collection of important early documents and newspapers; paintings 370 of historic Norfolk by W E Cantelon; display of artifacts of the 19th century Norfolk County; historical material.
Exhibitions: Concerned mainly with focusing new light on some aspects of the permanent collection.
Library: Reference. Photograph collection for reference and display.

STRATFORD

GALLERY/STRATFORD, 54 Romeo St N, N5A 4S9. *Dir* Robert F Swain; *Pres Bd Trustees* Mrs W P Gregory.
Open (June - Sept) Mon - Sat 10 AM - 8 PM; Sun 11 AM - 5 PM; (Oct - May) Tues - Fri & Sun 1 - 5 PM; Sat 10 AM - 5 PM; cl Mon. Admis $1.00, children under 12 free. Estab 1967 as a non-profit permanent establishment open to the public and administered in the public interest, for the purpose of studying, interpreting, assembling and exhibiting to the public. Average Annual Attendance: 64,000. Mem: 600; annual meeting March.
Income: $180,000 (financed by membership, city appropriation, and federal grant).
Collections: Works of art on paper.
Exhibitions: Changing exhibits, monthly, geared to create interest for visitors to Stratford Shakespearean Festival.
Publications: Calendar of Events, quarterly.
Activities: Classes for adults and children; docent training; lect open to public, 4 vis lectr per year; concerts; gallery talks; tours; competitions; exten dept serving art in the schools; traveling exhibitions organized and circulated; sales shop selling books, prints, slides, and crafts.
Library: Open for reference. Holdings: Vols 500; Per subs 12.

SUDBURY

LAURENTIAN UNIVERSITY MUSEUM AND ARTS CENTRE, John St at Nelson, (Mailing Add: Dept Cultural Affairs, Laurentian University, P3E 2C6). Tel: 705-675-1151, exten 400. *Dir* Pamela Krueger; *Educ & Exten Officer* Lise Melhorn.
Open Tues & Fri Noon - 9 PM; other days Noon - 5 PM; cl Mon; mornings by appointment. No admis. Estab 1968 to present a continuous program of exhibitions, concerts and events for the people of the Sudbury and District area; to encourage the use of and support of the Museum and Arts Centre; Gallery I (main floor) covers 1326 sq ft, Gallery II (second floor) covers 1326 sq ft. Average Annual Attendance: 20,000. Mem: 200; dues single $3; family $6; annual meeting June.
Income: Financed by endowment, membership, city appropriation.
Collections: Over 400 works by Canadian artists, both contemporary and historical including a collection of Eskimo prints and sculpture.

Exhibitions: (1976) Secondary School Art; Elementary School Art; Reach Adults through Kids; Canada-Photographs; Canada's Multicultural Heritage: Exposure: Canadian Contemporary Photographers; Eskimo Carvings; Woodland Indian Collection; Demonstrations and Sale of Indian Works; David Kaye; Ontario Community Collects; Jill Maycock; Oryst Sawchuk: The Nickel Rim; David Blake; Ivan Wheale Solo Exhibition; Exhibition and Sale; NOAA 20th Annual Exhibition. (1977) Bryan Maycock; Joy Walker; Maria Merrifield and Jim McDonald; NOAA 10th Annual Graphics Exhibition; Exhibition of watercolors and fine pencil drawings; Susan Watson; Secondary School Art; David Blackwood; Elementary School Art; The Last Best West Exhibition; Down to Earth; On View; Montosh Chowdhury; Quilt Draw; Canadian Art in Sudbury; Mary Conroy's Quilts and Collectables; Painters in a Landscape—The Laurentians; Sudbury Art Club Juried Show; Kosso Eloul. (1978) Victoria's Reign Selections; NOAA 21st Annual Exhibition; Henri Cartier-Bresson; Contemporary Eskimo and Indian Art; NOAA 11th Annual Graphics Exhibition: Rita Letendre.
Publications: Communique, every six weeks.
Activities: Lect open to the public, 15 vis lectr per yr; concerts; tours; individual paintings and original objects of art lent to other galleries; lending collection contains original art works 361; traveling exhibitions organized and circulated; sales shop selling books, hasty-notes, postcards.
Library: Open to public for reference only. Holdings: Vols 150; Per subs 7.

SUTTON WEST

SIBBALD POINT PROVINCIAL PARK, Eildon Hall, RR2, L0E 1R0. Tel: 416-722-3268. *Park Supt* M E Charbonneau; *Museum Cur* Mrs M Brown.
Open Tues - Sun (June - Sept) 10 AM - 5 PM. No admis (park entrance fee). Estab 1960 to preserve and exhibit, for entertainment and educational purposes an intact 1830's manor house and grounds, complete with interior accoutrements. Large frame house with display rooms. Average Annual Attendance: 2057.
Income: Financed by provincial appropriation.
Collections: Artwork, furnishings, and personal belongings of the Sibbald family.
Library: Open to the public for reference upon written request. Holdings: Vols 100. Special Collections: Family diaries, family portraits.

THUNDER BAY

LAKEHEAD VISUAL ARTS,* c/o Robert Boorman, Pres, 301 S Vickers St, P7E 1J6. Tel: 807-662-4090. *Secy* Lorraine Campbell.
Summer Gallery open June - Sept 2 - 10 PM. Admis. Estab 1952 for the promotion of the visual arts. Mem: 89; dues individual $7.50, family $10; monthly meetings first Mon.
Income: $1500 (financed by membership, city and state appropriations). Purchases: $1000.
Collections: Silver Collection.
Exhibitions: Spring Show every year in May.
Publications: Newsletter, bi-monthly.
Activities: Classes for adults; lect open to the public, 6 vis lectr; gallery talks; competitions; schol.

TORONTO

ART GALLERY OF ONTARIO, 317 Dundas St W, M5T 1G4. Tel: 416-361-0414. *Dir* William J Withrow; *Chief Cur* Richard J Wattenmaker; *Secy-Treas* Michael E George; *Manager Pub Affairs* Alex MacDonald; *Head Educ Services* James Williamson.
Open Tues, Fri - Sun 11 AM - 5:30 PM; Wed & Thurs 11 AM - 9 PM. Admis adults $1, students & children 50¢, under 12 free. Estab 1900 to cultivate and advance the cause of the visual arts in Ontario; to conduct programs of education in the origin, development, appreciation and techniques of the visual arts; to collect and exhibit works of art and displays and to maintain and operate a gallery and related facilities as required for this purpose, and to stimulate the interest of the public in matters undertaken by the Gallery. Average Annual Attendance: 342,278. Mem: 16,000; dues individual $15, family $25, supporting $50, catalogue subscriber $25; annual meeting June.
Income: Financed by membership, city and provincial appropriations, and earned income. Purchases: $475,955.
Collections: †Canadian historical and contemporary art; †American and European art (16th century to present); †Henry Moore sculpture.
Exhibitions: Form and Freedom; Molinari; Van Wittel; Wildflowers: Robert Holmes; Art from Zaire; Recent Acquisitions of Contemporary Prints and Drawings; Robert Sinclair: Pertaining to Space; Charles William Jefferys; Henry Moore Drawings; Painters in a Landscape: The Laurentians; Watercolors from the Victoria and Albert Museum; The Inuit Print; Contemporary Sculpture; Esmark Collection of Currier and Ives; Gottlieb Pictographs; Kathe Kollwitz.

Publications: Events, 6 times per year.
Activities: Classes for adults and children; dramatic programs; docent training; lect open to public; concerts; gallery talks; tours; exten dept serving the province; individual paintings and original objects of art lent to members and corporations; traveling exhibitions organized and circulated; sales shop selling books, magazines, reproductions, prints, slides and jewelry.
—**Edward P Taylor Reference Library.** Tel: 416-361-0414, exten 339, 340, 341, and 389. *Librn* Sybille Pantazzi; *Library Coordinator* Mrs Lee Greenough; *Library Research Asst* Larry Pfaff.
Open Tues, Wed & Fri 10 AM - 5 PM; Thurs 10 AM - 9 PM. Estab 1933 to collect printed material for the documentation and interpretation of the works of art in the Gallery's collection and to provide the staff with the necessary source material for the compilation of exhibition catalogues and other publications, and for the preparation of lectures. Circ: Non-circulating.
Holdings: Vols 25,000; Per subs 50; Other—Clipping files, exhibition catalogs, manuscripts, original documents, pamphlets, photographs, reproductions.
Special Subjects: Canadian, American & European art from the Renaissance to the present, concentrating mainly on painting, sculpture, drawing and engraving.
Special Collections: Canadian Illustrated Books; Alan Garrow Collection of British illustrated books and wood engravings of the 1860's; Canadian book-plates; international guide books; Robert D McIntosh Collection of books on sepulchral monuments.
Publications: Annual report; Events, bimonthly.

ART METROPOLE, 241 Yonge St, M5B 1N8. Tel: 416-368-7787. *Pres* Jorge Saia; *VPres* Ronald Gabe; *Secy* Michael W Tims; *Dir Film & Video* Margaret Gale; *Publications Dir* David Buchan.
Open Mon - Sat Noon - 6 PM. No admis. Estab 1974 as a nonprofit agency formed to collect, promote, publish and distribute work by international artists in non-traditional formats; basically books, periodicals, recordings, film and videotapes.
Holdings: Vols 15,000; Per subs 120.
Special Subjects: Video, books by artists, performance by artists.
Collections: Ongoing collection of books by artists.
Publications: Catalog of available stock, semi-annually.
Activities: Lectures; traveling exhibitions organized and circulated. Sales shop selling books, magazine, and original art.

ARTS AND LETTERS CLUB OF TORONTO, 14 Elm St, M5G 1G7. *Pres* John A Morrow; *Secy* William Osler.
Estab 1908. Mem: 450; annual meeting May.
Collections: Heritage Collection (art by members now deceased); Club Collection (art by members, and others).
Exhibitions: Frequent.
Library: Open to club members and researchers for reference. Holdings: Vols 2000. Special Subjects: Literature, architecture, music, paintings, sculpture, and stage.

ASSOCIATION OF CANADIAN INDUSTRIAL DESIGNERS (ONTARIO),* 55 University, M5J 2H7. Tel: 705-862-1799. *Pres* William Sloan; *Secy* Frank Young, 55 York St, Suite 512. M5J 1R7. Tel: 705-363-8374.
Estab 1948 to promote and foster a high standard of design in industrial products as a service to the public, the manufacturing industries, and the national culture and economy. Mem: 20; dues $75; annual meeting Nov.

CANADIAN CONFERENCE OF THE ARTS, 3 Church St, Suite 47, M5E 1M2. Tel: 416-364-6351. *Nat Dir* John Hobday; *Treas* Russell Disney; *Secy* John A Paterson.
For further information see National Organizations in Canada.

CANADIAN SOCIETY OF PAINTERS IN WATERCOLOUR,* c/o Julius Griffith, Secy, 102 Hillsdale Ave W, M5P 2G3. Tel: 416-366-1607. *Pres* Viktoras Brickus.
For further information see National Organizations in Canada.

CENTRE FOR EXPERIMENTAL ART AND COMMUNICATION, 15 Duncan St, M5H 3H1. Tel: 416-593-4111. *Pres* Amerigo Marras; *VPres* Suber Corley; *Secy* John Faichney; *Video Officer* Saul Goldman; *Film Officer* Ross McLaren; *Publ* Bruce Eves; *Admin* Lily Chiro; *Art Dir* Amerigo Marras.
Open Mon - Sat 11 AM - 5 PM & 8 - 10 PM. No admis. Estab 1973 to provide the production, presentation and dissemination of radical and marginal art. Average Annual Attendance: 15,000.
Income: $160,000 (financed by endowment, city and provincial appropriation).
Exhibitions: Contextual Art seminars; Behaviour workshops; Participation at Documenta 6; Polemics.
Publications: Strike, bimonthly.

Activities: Classes for adults and children; theoretical and technical classes; lect open to public, 12 vis lectr per yr; concerts; grants to individual artists resident in Ontario; exten dept serving foreign countries chiefly; traveling exhibitions organized and circulated.
—**Library.** *Art Librn* John Faichney.
Open to scholars and students for reference.
Holdings: Vols 4000; Per subs 200; Other—Videotapes, audiotapes, disc, films.
Special Subjects: Performance arts, sociological art, language art. Special Collections: European videotapes.

LYCEUM CLUB AND WOMEN'S ART ASSOCIATION OF CANADA,* 23 Prince Arthur Ave, 5. Tel: 416-922-2060. *Recording Secy* Miss J Colgrove.
Open 9:30 AM - 4:30 PM; Sat 10 AM - 1 PM. Estab 1885. Branches in Ontario in Hamilton, Owen Sound, St Thomas, Peterborough and Oshawa. Mem: Approx 250; annual meeting April.
Activities: Special exhibitions; drawing, painting; study groups; awards Founder's memorial schol to art students annually; schols given to Ontario College of Art, Royal Conservatory of Music, National Ballet.
Library: Holdings—Vols 500 including extensive Canadiana.

METROPOLITAN TORONTO LIBRARY BOARD
—**Fine Art Department,** 789 Yonge St, M4W 2G8. Tel: 416-928-5214. *Head Fine Art Dept* Alan Suddon.
Open Mon - Fri 9 AM - 9 PM; Sat 9 AM - 5 PM; Sun (Oct 15-Apr 30) 1:30 - 5 PM. Estab 1959 for public reference.
Income: Financed by city appropriation.
Holdings: Vols 36,066; Per subs 390; AV—Audio tapes, cassettes, microfiche, microfilm, phonorecords, slides; Other—Clipping files, exhibition catalogs; memorabilia.
Special Subjects: Fine and decorative arts; printing and printing design; costume.
Special Collections: Private presses with emphasis on Canadian; printed ephemera; postcards, scenic and greeting.
—**Baldwin Room (Canadian History Department).** Tel: 416-928-5275. *Head Canaidan History Dept* Edith G Firth.
Open Mon - Fri 9 AM - 9 PM; Sat 9 AM - 5 PM; Sun (Oct 15-Apr 30) 1:30 - 5 PM.
Estab 1960 to house rare Canadiana, including paintings, prints, and photographs; to support Canadian historical research.
Holdings: Other—Original art works, photograph, and prints.
Special Collections: J Ross Robertson Collection—4400 paintings, prints, and photographs; Toronto and Early Canada Collection—paintings 60,000, prints and photographs.

NIGHTINGALE ARTS ASSOCIATION, A SPACE, 85 St Nicholas St, M4Y 1W8. Tel: 416-964-3627. *Dir* Victor Coleman, Marien Lewis & John Mays.
Open Noon - 6 PM. Estab 1971 to provide a community artspace which maintains a policy of supporting regional culture, giving lesser-known artists the essential opportunity to make their work known to the public. Maintains an art gallery. A space used for performance: visual art displays, dance, readings, video, etc.
Income: $80,000 (financed by endowment, membership).
Publications: Only Paper Today, monthly.
Library: Holdings—Per subs 60; AV—Video tapes; Other—Clipping files, exhibition catalogs; memorabilia, original documents, pamphlets, photographs.

ONTARIO ASSOCIATION OF ARCHITECTS,* 50 Park Rd, M4W 2N5. Tel: 416-929-0623. *Exec Dir* Brian Parks.
Estab 1890. Mem: 140.
Activities: Sponsors exhibition of new building materials and techniques; awards annual cash prizes through School of Architecture, University of Toronto, and Ryerson Institute of Technology, Ontario College of Art, University of Waterloo, and Carleton University.

ONTARIO ASSOCIATION OF ART GALLERIES, 38 Charles St E, M4Y 1T3. Tel: 416-920-8378. *Pres* Judith Nasby; *VPres* Robert Swain; *Secy* Rory O'Donal; *Coordr* Pamela Gibb; *Special Projects Officer* Diane Sage; *Admin Asst* Janice Bishop.
Open 9 AM - 5 PM. Estab 1968 to encourage cooperation among member galleries and museums; to encourage cooperation between OAAG and the Arts Council and all similar agencies, whether government or not, involved in the cause of the visual arts; to assist the development of visual arts centres in the Province of Ontario; to promote high standards of excellence and uniform methods in the care and presentation of art; to serve as an advisory body in matters of professional interest in the Province of Ontario; gallery not maintained. Mem: 77; dues full member, museum .1% of total budget, affiliate $25, business $250; annual meeting June.
Income: Financed by membership, Ontario Arts Council, Ministry of Culture and Recreation, and National Museums.

Publications: Magazine, twice per year; Newsart, 3 times per year.
Activities: Training seminars under gallery development and professional development committees.
Library: Resource Centre. Open to members. Holdings: Vols 300; Per subs 10.

ONTARIO COLLEGE OF ART, Gallery Seventy Six,* 100 McCaul St, M5T 1W1. Tel: 416-366-4977, exten 62. *Pres* Dr Paul D Fleck. *Cur* Brian Kipping.
Open Mon - Fri 10 AM - 5 PM; Sat & Sun Noon - 5 PM. Art College estab 1876, gallery estab 1970 for faculty and student exhibitions and to exhibit outside work to benefit the college. Average Annual Attendance: 15,000.
Income: Financed by College.
Collections: Small print collection.
Publications: Invitations; small scale catalogs.
Activities: Concerts; dramatic programs; competitions; individual paintings and original objects of art lent; traveling exhibitions organized and circulated.
Library: Holdings—Other—Slide collection of past exhibitions.
—**Library, Audio/Visual Centre.** Tel: 416-362-5311, exten 54/55. *Dir* Ian Carr-Harris; *Head Technical Services* Diana Myers; *Head Public Services* Richard Milburn; *Head AV Services* Michael Levin.
Open Mon - Fri 9 AM - 10 PM. Estab to support the curriculum.
Income: Financed through the College. Purchases: $50,000.
Holdings: Vols 14,000; Per subs 350; AV—Audio tapes, cassettes, microfiche, microfilm, slides, video tapes; Other—Clipping files, exhibition catalogs, pamphlets.

ONTARIO CRAFTS COUNCIL, 346 Dundas St W, M5T 1G5. Tel: 416-366-3551. *Pres* Douglas Mantegna; *VPres* Ann Tomlinson & Jean Burke; *Secy* Eileen Best; *Exec Dir* Paul Bennett; *Managing Dir* Eileen Best; *Regional Development Dir* Beth Dingman; *Coordinator Craft Resource Centre* Irene Bollinger.
Open Tues - Sat 10 AM - 5:30 PM. No admis. Estab 1976 to foster crafts and craftsmen in Ontario. Maintains an art gallery. Average Annual Attendance: 12,000. Mem: 3200; dues $15; annual meeting May.
Income: Financed by membership and provincial appropriation, and guild shop.
Collections: †Canadian Contemporary Crafts.
Exhibitions: Ontario Crafts Regional Juried Exhibition; various changing exhibits.
Publications: Craftsman (magazine); Craftnews (newsletter).
Activities: Docent training; tours; competitions; traveling exhibitions organized and circulated; sales shop selling original art, prints, reproductions, and handcrafted Canadian items.
Library: Craft Resource Centre Library. *Librn* Irene Bollinger. Open to the public for reference. Holdings: Vols 400; Per subs 80; Other—Portfolios of craftsmen, archives of craft groups and individuals. Special Subjects: All aspects of fibre, clay, metal, glass, enamel, leather, wood.

ONTARIO SOCIETY OF ARTISTS,* 8 York St, M5J 1R2. Tel: 416-366-1607. *Pres* Ian Trowell; *Secy* Nomi Cameron.
Estab 1872 for the encouragement of original art in Ontario. Mem: 110; annual meeting March.
Activities: Holds annual exhibition in spring, open to all Canadian artists; jury; makes awards; annual small picture exhibition; organizes traveling exhibitions in Ontario; exhibitions circulated.

PROFESSIONAL ART DEALERS ASSOCIATION OF CANADA, INC, 65 Queen St W, Suite 1800, M5H 2M5. Tel: 416-868-1540. *Pres* John K Robertson; *Admin VPres* Aaron M Milrad; *VPres* Sam Markle; *Secy* Barbara Ensor.
For further information see National Organizations in Canada.

ROYAL CANADIAN ACADEMY OF ARTS, 601 - 11 Yorkville Ave, M4W IL3. Tel: 416-922-5535. *Pres* John C Parkin; *VPres* C Blakeway Millar; *Exec Dir* Rebecca Sisler.
For further information see National Organizations in Canada.

ROYAL ONTARIO MUSEUM,* 100 Queen's Park, M5S 2C6. *Chmn Bd* G D Wotherspoon; *Dir* Dr James E Cruise; *Assoc Dir Curatorial* Barbara Stephen; *Cur European Dept* H Hickl-Szabo; *Cur Ethnology Dept* H Fuchs; *Chief Archaeologist* A D Tushingham; *Cur Far Eastern Dept* D Dohrenwend; *Cur Egyptian Dept* N B Millet; *Cur Greek & Roman Dept* Neda Leipen; *Cur Canadiana Dept* D B Webster; *Cur Textiles Dept* Dorothy K Burnham; *Cur West Asian Dept* T C Young Jr; *Registrar* Dorothea Hecken; *Assoc Cur-in-Charge Conservation Dept* B Leech; *Chief Photographer* L Warren; *Information Asst* Jane Court.
Open Mon - Sat 10 AM - 5 PM; Sun 1 - 9 PM (Canadiana Bldg 1 - 5 PM). Admis adults 50¢; Sigmund Samuel Canadiana Bldg, 14 Queen's Park Crescent W, 5, free. Estab 1912 as the Provincial Museum. Average Annual Attendance: 1,200,000. Mem: 4500; dues $25 - $5000.

Collections: The outstanding features are the world-famous Chinese collections and the Lord Lee of Fareham Collection of medieval and Renaissance objects d'art; also extensive collections of American Indian and world ethnological material; pre-historic Greek and Roman art and archaeology; European Medieval, Renaissance and post-Renaissance art; Egyptian and Western Asian art and archaeology; Harry Wearne Collection of printed and painted textiles; early Ontario weaving; Japanese and Indian art; French-Canadian Collection; Sigmund Samuel Canadiana Collection; paintings; books; maps, housed in separate building.
Publications: Rotunda, quarterly.
Activities: Adult courses; special exhibitions; research facilities; archaeological and ethnological field work in Canada and overseas; courses for Ontario schools and universities; concerts; lectures and film showings.
Library: Head Librn Judith Morgan. Reference, also Far East Library.

SCULPTOR'S SOCIETY OF CANADA, 21 Dunblaine Ave, M5M 2R6. Tel: 416-366-1607. *Pres* Irene Blogg; *Secy* Betty Moss.
For further information see National Organizations in Canada.

UNIVERSITY OF TORONTO
—**Hart House,** 7 Hart House Circle, M5S 1A1. Tel: 416-978-2436. *Programme Advisor* Judith Schwartz.
Open Mon 11 AM - 9 PM; Tues - Sat 11 AM - 5 PM; Sun 2 - 5 PM. No admis. Estab 1919 to support art in Canada and to also (when possible) help artists who have not as yet had the opportunity to show their work in a professional capacity; a modern setting with a total wall space of 147 running ft, track lighting, temperature and humidity control; outdoor quadrangle for summer sculpture shows.
Income: Financed by membership. Purchases: $2000.
Collections: Canadian art from 1890 to the present, with purchases made each year from 1923 to the present.
Exhibitions: (1976) David Wright; Clyde McConnell and Dirk Van Wyk; Hart House Crafts Club Show; Camera Club Show; George Ebelt; University Students and Staff Open Exhibition; Michael Durham; Betty Moss and Hannah Sandberg; Hart House Permanent Collection Show, Saul Jaskus, Jiri Ladocha; Christie Kingsland; Diane Pugen. (1977) Powan Ng; Vaclav Vaca; Hart House Crafts Club Exhibition; Hart House Camera Club Annual Exhibition; Barbara Zittrer; University Students and Staff Open Exhibition; Jean-Philippe Vogel; Adele Duck and Brian Brown; Native Canadian Art-Tradition and Aspiration; Stan Hughes; Larry Middlestadt; Robert (RFM) McInnis; Janet Willson and Brenda Mitchell. (1978) Graphex 6; Nancy Hazelgrove; Kristina Redziejowski; Lanny Shereck and Zofia Dlugopolska; Gary Greenwood: Crafts Exhibition; Ron Baker; Anna Myers; Dieter Hastenteufel; Luigi Bellini; Baltic Art Juried Exhibition.
Activities: Docent training; lect for members only, 12 vis lectr per yr; gallery talks; tours; individual paintings and original objects of art lent to art galleries.
—**Fine Arts Library,** 100 St George St Room 6032B, M5S 1A1. Tel: 416-978-3290. *Dir* W McAllister Johnson; *Research Librn* Andrea Retfalvi.
Open Mon - Fri 10 AM - 5 PM. Estab 1936. For reference only.
Income: Financed by state appropriation and Department of Fine Arts.
Holdings: Books; Other—Exhibition catalogs, framed reproductions, photographs, reproductions.
Special Subjects: History of art and archaeology.
Special Collections: Catalog materials including temporary, permanent, dealer and auction catalogs; photographic archives in various field of Western art.
Publications: Canadian Illustrated News (Montreal): Index to Illustrations, quarterly.

VISUAL ARTS ONTARIO, 8 York St, M5J 1R2. Tel: 416-366-1607. *Chmn Bd* Anne Meredith Barry; *VChmn Bd* Alan Bakes; *Secy-Treas* Irene Hepburn; *Exec Dir* William J S Boyle; *Exec Asst* Janni de Savoye; *Communications Officer* Gail J Habs; *Regional Coordr* Bruce Richards; *Secy* Laura Lerand.
Open 9 AM - 5 PM. Estab 1974 to further the awareness and appreciation of the visual arts. Mem: 4500; dues individual $10, affiliates $50, Mem organizations $250.
Income: $100,000 (financed by membership, provincial appropriation, and private donations).
Collections: Archival material from several major professional art societies.
Exhibitions: On View (a two-year touring exhibition of Ontario art).
Publications: Artviews, bimonthly; The Index of Ontario Artists, biannually; The Visual Arts Handbook, biannually.
Activities: Docent training; workshops for professional artists; traveling exhibitions organized and circulated; an art rental program designed for government offices and corporations called The Bare Facts.
Library: A resource library open to the public for reference. Holdings: Archival material and current art periodicals. Special Subjects: Archives for Society of Canadian Painters-Etchers and Engravers; Canadian So-

ciety of Painters in Watercolour; Sculptors Society of Canada; Society of Canadian Artists; Ontario Society for Education Through Art; Ontario Society of Artists; Canadian Society of Graphic Art.

YORK UNIVERSITY, Art Gallery, Ross Bldg N145, 4700 Keele St, Downsview, M3J 1P3. Tel: 416-667-3427. *Cur Coll York University & Gallery Dir* Michael Greenwood.
Open Mon - Fri 10 AM - 4:30 PM; Sun 2 - 5 PM; cl Sat. No admis. Estab 1970 to provide for a large university community and for the general public a program of changing art exhibitions covering a wide spectrum of historical periods and cultures. The Gallery is 12.20m x 9.16m, the ceiling height is 2.55m, with bays and movable screens. Average Annual Attendance: 10,000.
Income: $40,000 (financed by province of Ontario).
Exhibitions: Another World: Salon and Academy Painting, 1805-1925; Human Images through the Ages: The Finlayson Collection; John Howlin: Recent Paintings; Douglas Bentham: New Sculpture; Three Centuries of French Posters; Romanesque Architectural Fragments; Art Deco Tendencies in Canadian Art; The Camera and Dr Barnardo; Ernest Lindner: Drawings; Bloomsbury Painters and their circle; Esther Warkov Drawings; The Automatic Drawings of Alma Rumball; Ethiopian Art from the Rayfield Collection; The Howarth Collection of Art and Artifacts from New Guinea.
Publications: Exhibition catalogs, occasionally.
Activities: Gallery talks; original objects of art lent to art institutions; traveling exhibitions·organized and circulated; sales counter selling catalogs.
Library: Scott Library. Open to members of the University. Special Collections: Germain Bazin Art Library.

WATERLOO

UNIVERSITY OF WATERLOO, Arts Centre Gallery, N2L 3G1. Tel: 519-884-4281. *Adminr* Marlene Bryan; *Installations Officer & Designer* Peter McLay.
Open Mon - Fri 9 AM - 4 PM; Sun 2 - 5 PM; (June - Aug) cl Sun. No admis. Estab 1962.
Collections: Contemporary Canadian Art.

WINDSOR

ART GALLERY OF WINDSOR, 445 Riverside Dr W, N9A 6T8, Tel: 519-258-7111. *Dir* Dr Kenneth Saltmarche; *Cur* E D Fraser; *Educ Cur* Megan Bice; *Business Mgr* Ken Furguson; *Pres Bd of Dir* Sylvia Curry; *Publ* Pat Morris.
Open Tues, Thurs, Fri, Sat 10 AM - 5 PM; Wed 10 AM - 10 PM; Sun 1 - 5 PM; cl Mon. No admis. Estab 1936 and from 1943 to 1975 occupied space in Willistead, the former Edward C Walker mansion in Walkerville. In 1970 the former Carling Brewery and Warehouse complex was converted toward a permanent home for the Gallery, and on Sept 17, 1975 the new Gallery building was opened; the Gallery contains 56,000 sq ft of space on three flors; it is environmentally-controlled and highly fire resistant; outdoor sculpture terrace. Average Annual Attendance: 125,000. Mem: 1700; dues student $5, out-of-town $10, single $15, family $25, patron $50; annual meeting date varies.
Income: $475,000 (financed by membership, provincial appropriation, and federal funds). Purchases: $100,000 (1977).
Collections: †Mostly Canadian paintings, prints and drawings and sculpture ranging from 18th Century to the present; some antique furniture and European works (mostly paintings); †Eskimo prints and sculpture.
Exhibitions: (1976-78) Over 100 exhibitions; major exhibitions include: Changing Visions: The Canadian Landscape; Ontario Community Collects; William Ronald: 25 years; Polish Tapestries; Canadian/American Contemporaries; Oriental Rugs; Claude Tousignant: 25 Years; Homer Watson of Doon; Sculpture from Art Bank; C W Jeffreys; Graham Coughtry Retrospective; Ronald Bloore; Silver from Birks Collection; Peter Kilisnyk; Aspects of Realism; Kenneth Lochhead Retrospective; Adolph Gottlieb Pictographs; Paterson Ewen; A J Casson; Louis de Niverville; Young British and Canadian Contemporaries; Photographs by Henri Cartier-Bresson; Annual Regional Juried Exhibitions; Annual Exhibition and Sale of Canadian art.
Publications: Projections (bulletin), bimonthly; catalogs for exhibitions.
Activities: Classes for children; dramatic programs, docent training; films; lect open to the public, 2-10 vis lectr per yr; concerts; tours; individual paintings and original objects of art lent to other galleries; traveling exhibitions organized and circulated; museum shop selling books, magazines, original art, reproductions, prints and crafts; Children's Gallery, a Junior Museum.
Library: Tel: 519-258-7111. Open to staff and members. Holdings: Vols 200, Per subs 6; Other—Catalogs and museum bulletins.

WOODSTOCK

WOODSTOCK PUBLIC LIBRARY AND ART GALLERY,* 445 Hunter St, N4S 4G7. Tel: 519-539-6761. *Chmn of Library Bd* Alexandra Prytulak; *Cur Art Gallery* Lillie Telfer.
Open Mon, Wed, Thurs & Fri Noon - 8 PM; Tues Noon - 9 PM; Sat 10 AM - 6 PM. Estab 1966 to bring art to the people; two galleries; picture loan collection. Average Annual Attendance: Gallery 23,000. Mem: 300.
Income: Financed by city and provincial appropriations.
Collections: Small Canadian collection.
Exhibitions: Changes every three weeks.
Activities: Classes for adults and children; films lect open to the public; concerts; tours of exhibitions; competitions.
Library: Record lending; audiovisual department.

PRINCE EDWARD ISLAND

CHARLOTTETOWN

CONFEDERATION CENTRE ART GALLERY AND MUSEUM, PO Box 848, C1A 7L9. Tel: 902-892-2464. *Chmn* Robert MacLeod; *Secy* Frank J Storey; *Dir* Dr Moncrieff Williamson; *Personal Asst & Secy* Janet MacGregor; *Cur* Mark Holton; *Registrar* Judy MacDonald.
Open Tues - Sat 10 AM - 5 PM; Sun 2 - 5 PM; cl Mon. No admis. Estab 1964 as a national collection devoted to Canadian art and fine crafts. Average Annual Attendance: 100,000. Mem: 600; dues individual $5; family $10.
Income: Financed by federal, provincial, city and the private sector.
Collections: Robert Harris paintings and drawings; †Canadian art early and contemporary; †Canadian fine crafts.
Exhibitions: An average of thirty exhibitions a year from our own and circulating collections; special exhibitions each July and August to coincide with summer festival.
Activities: Classes for adults and children; dramatic programs; contemporary dance; exten dept serving province; lect open to public; tours; concerts; lending collection contains paintings, Kodachromes 7000, motion pictures 12, film strips 50, slides; traveling exhibitions organized and circulated; junior museum.
Library: Open for reference. Holdings: Vols 1547; Other—Photographs 200.

QUEBEC

ARVIDA

LE COMITE DES ARTS D'ARVIDA,* CP 53, G7S 4K6. *Pres* Mrs E L Lavoie; *Secy* Mrs Claire Freve.
Open weekdays 9 AM - 5 PM & 7 - 10 PM; weekends 2 - 5 PM & 7 - 10 PM. Estab 1942 to provide exhibitions in the entry of the City Hall, Arvida. Mem: 200; dues $1; annual meeting Sept.

BASILIQUE SAINT ANNE

PERES REDEMPTORISTES,* Basilique Sainte Anne, G0A 1C0. Tel: 418-827-3781. *Dir* Rev S Baillargeon.
Open June - Oct daily 10 AM - 5 PM. Admis adults $1, children 50¢. Estab 1960, governed by the church.
Collections: Paintings; sculpture; history; historic buildings.

CAUGHNAWAGA

MUSEE KATERI TEKAKWITHA,* Mission Saint Francois Xavier, CP 70, J0L 1B0. Tel: 514-632-6030. *Dir* Paul-Emile Beaudoin.
Open daily 9 AM - Noon & 1 - 5 PM. No admis. Estab as a mission in 1667.
Collections: Old paintings; Canadian church silver; historic chapel; archives.
Publications: Kateri.

CHICOUTIMI

LA SOCIETE DES ARTS DE CHICOUTIMI,* 534 Jacques-Cartier Ru E, G7H 1Z5. Tel: 418-549-3618. *Dir* Jacques Laforge; *Deputy Dir* Jerome Lagare; *Asst Dir* Paquerette Hudon.
Open Mon - Wed 9 AM - Noon & 1:30 - 5 PM. No admis. Estab 1963. Mem: Dues $4.
Income: Financed by city appropriation and membership.
Collections: Paintings; sculpture; graphics; ceramics.
Publications: Monthly journal.
Activities: Gallery talks; films; traveling exhibitions.

DORVAL

DORVAL CULTURAL CENTRE, 1401 Lakeshore Drive, H9S 2E5. Tel: 514-636-6000. *Coordinator* Louise Rivet; *Animator* Linda Burdayron & Danyelle Brodeur.
Open 2 - 9 PM. No admis. Estab 1967 to promote culture and art. Maintains an art gallery.
Income: Financed by city appropriation.
Exhibitions: Iranian Art and Handicrafts; Copper Enameling Paintings; Sculptures; Paintings; Quilts from Historic Quebec; Photography; Tapestries.
Publications: Leisuregram, quarterly.
Activities: Classes for adults and children; dramatic programs; lect open to public; concerts; gallery talks, tours.

JOLIETTE

MUSEE D'ART DE JOLIETTE, 145 Wilfrid Corbeil, J6E 4T4. Tel: 514-756-0311. *Pres* Father Wilfrid Corbeil; *VPres* Judge Jacques Dugas; *VPres* Serge Joyal; *Secy* Raymond Lapierre; *Treas* Charles Robillard.
Open Tues - Thurs 2 - 5 PM & 7 - 9:30 PM; Sat & Sun 2 - 5 PM. Admis adults $1, children 25¢. Estab 1961, moved to new building 1976, for educational purposes and to house the collections which were increasing. Gallery 6 and Contemporary Gallery, temporary exhibitions; Sacred Art Gallery and European gallery; permanent collection. Average Annual Attendance: 15,000; annual meeting March.
Income: $66,000 (financed by provincial appropriation and private donations). Purchases: $5000.
Collections: †European Art; †Canadian Art; †Contemporary art; †Amerindian Art; †Pre-Columbian Art; †Sacred Art of Quebec.
Exhibitions: Contemporary painting, sculpture, print and photo.
Activities: Classes for children; lect open to public, concerts; gallery talks; tours; traveling exhibitions organized and circulated; sales shop selling books, reproductions, prints.
Library: Open to University students, historians and the public for reference. Holdings: Vols 1000.

MONTREAL

ASSOCIATION DES GRAVEURS DU QUEBEC,* (Association of Engravers of Quebec), 5131 Ave Durocher, H2V 3X7. Tel: 514-279-1175. *Pres* Guy Girard; *Secy* Marc Beaulé.
Estab 1970 to promote etching and engraving and diffuse it. Mem: 100; dues $100; annual meeting Nov 30.
Income: Financed by provincial subvention.
Activities: Competitions; lending collection of photographs; traveling exhibitions organized and circulated.

SAIDYE BRONFMAN CENTRE* (YM-YWHA & NHS), 5170 Cote Ste Catherine Rd, H3W 1M7. Tel: 514-739-2301. *Exec Dir* Nahum Ravel; *Dir Visual & Fine Arts Dept* George M Dyens; *Dir Dept Performing Arts* Muriel Gold; *Dir Harvey Golden Inst* Cindy Chazan.
Open Mon - Thurs 9 AM - 9 PM; Fri 9 AM - 3:30 PM; Sun 10 AM - 4 PM; cl Sat. No admis. Estab 1967 as a non-profit cultural centre for the promotion and dissemination of the arts; located in building given by Phyllis Lambert and her mother, Saidye Bronfman. 3000 sq. ft. gallery. Average Annual Attendance: 90,000.
Income: Financed by membership.
Exhibitions: Three major exhibitions per year from traveling exhibitions; student exhibitions.
Publications: Exhibition catalogs.
Activities: Educ dept—Courses in visual and fine arts, performing arts, general studies and Jewish studies; lect open to the public, 3 visiting lectr per year; concerts; 10 gallery talks; scholarships.

CHATEAU DE RAMEZAY,* Antiquarian and Numismatic Society of Montreal, 290 Notre Dame St E, H2Y 1C5. Tel: 514-861-3708. *Cur* Joseph Kamen; *Asst Cur* Robert Prud'homme.
Open Tues - Sat 10 AM - 5 PM; Sun 2 - 5 PM; cl Mon & holidays. Admis adults $1, children under 14, 25¢. Estab 1895 in residence (1705) of Claude de Ramezay, governor of Montreal. Average Annual Attendance: 40,000. Mem: Dues individual $5, life $100.
Collections: Early Canadian portraits; woodcarving; handicrafts; furniture; numismatic collection.
Library: Holdings—Vols 2200 Canadian history.

CONCORDIA UNIVERSITY, Sir George Williams Art Galleries, 1455 deMaisonneuve Blvd, H3G 1M8. Tel: 514-879-5917. *Dir* Edwy F Cooke; *Cur* Donald F Andrus; *Registrar* Patrick Landsley.

Open Mon - Fri 11 AM - 9 PM; Sat 11 AM - 5 PM. No admis. Estab 1962 to display in a scholarly fashion the University collection, provide a venue for a variety of significant touring exhibitions chosen from within the region and across Canada, all with the idea of providing an interesting cultural milieu both for the university and public alike; three galleries, 4000 sq ft with 521 running feet, located in mezzanine area. Average Annual Attendance: 66,000.
Income: Financed by university funds.
Collections: Modern and contemporary Canadian art; small collection of indigenous arts of Africa, Meso-America, New Guinea.
Exhibitions: (1976-78) Henry Sandham (1842-1912); Ruth Beer: Sculptures; Undergraduate Introductory Printmaking; Master of Arts in Art Education Annual Exhibition; Les Tait: Watercolors; Works on Paper; Mervyn Dewes: Paintings; Atlantic Coast: An Illustrated Journal; The Benner Boys, work by Tom and Ron Benner; Faculty of Fine Arts Exhibition; Paul Lussier: Prints; Contemporary Canadian Prints; Primitive Sculpture; Graham Coughtry Retrospective; Eduardo Paolozzi; Faculty of Fine Arts Annual Undergraduate Exhibition; Soundscape; Student Work in graphic design; Fire and Ice by Cyril Ryan (photographs); Exhibition of Works from the Permanent Collection; Ann Kipling: Drawings; Norman Yates: Drawings and Paintings; Graduate Students in Fine Arts, Fall Exhibition; Pnina Gagnon: On the Human Body; Roger Fry Artist and Critic; Ron Webber: Photography; Edwy Cooke: Recent Watercolors; Edwy Cooke: A Retrospective Exhibition; Advanced Drawing by Fine Arts Students; Peter Kolisnyck: Recent Work; Ukiyo-E; Glimpses into the Floating World; Paterson Ewen: Recent Paintings; Ann McCall: Prints; Members of the Faculty of the Fine Arts Collect . . .: Michael Thompson: Paintings; Annual Fine Arts Student Exhibition; Sue Real: Drawings; Eva Brandl: Sculptures; Graham Cantieni: Drawings; Graduate Students in Fine Arts, Spring Exhibition; Selections from the Concordia University Collection of Art.
Activities: Lect open to the public, 3 vis lectr per yr; traveling exhibitions organized and circulated; book store.

FEDERATION DES CENTRES CULTURELS DE LA PROVINCE DE QUEBEC,* 1415 Jarry E, H2E 2Z7. Tel: 514-374-4700. *Pres* Phillippe Sauvageau; *Admin Secy* Eva Tetreault.
Open daily. No admis. Estab 1967. Mem: Dues individual $25, institutional $50.
Income: Financed by state appropriation.
Collections: Paintings; sculpture; graphics; theatre.
Exhibitions: Temporary and traveling exhibitions in addition to selected exhibitions from the collection.
Publications: Nouvelles FCCQ, revue.
Activities: Lectures; gallery talks; concerts; films; dance recitals; dramas; hobby workshops; competitions; lending program to other museums.
Library Holdings—Vols 5000 of general books; manuscripts.

GUILDE CANADIANNE DES METIERS D'ART, QUEBEC,* (Canadian Guild of Crafts, Quebec), 2025 Peel St, H3A 1T6. Tel: 514-849-6091. *Managing Dir* Virginia J Watt.
Mem Dues: $14 and up; annual meeting April.
Collections: Permanent collection of Eskimo and Indian arts and crafts.
Exhibitions: Works by professional craftsmen and artists from Canada; group and one-man shows.
Activities: Instruction in weaving, on-loom and off-loom; macrame, decoupage, design for wall hangings and silversmithing.
Library: Reference.

LA SOCIETE DES DECORATEURS-ENSEMBLIERS DU QUEBEC,* (Interior Decorators' Society of Quebec), Studio G, 451 St Sulpice St. Tel: 514-878-1113. *Pres* Anselme Lapointe; *VPres* Ginette Levesque; *Second VPres* Rene Studler; *Secy* Marie Jose Ratelle; *Treas* Real Chevalier.
Open 9 AM - 5 PM. Estab 1935 as a nonprofit professional association. Mem: 285; dues $125.
Income: $30,000 (financed by membership).
Exhibitions: Traveling exhibit in the Province of Quebec.
Publications: News Bulletin. 10 issues per year.
Activities: Education Comt to improve the level of teaching in interior design; lect for members only.

MONTREAL MUSEUM OF FINE ARTS, 3400 Ave du Musee, H3G 1K3. Tel: 514-285-1600. *Pres* David M Stewart; *Dir* Jean Trudel; *Chief Exten Services* Daniel Amadei; *Chief Conservator* Robin Ashton; *Conservator* Rodrique Bedard; *Cur Decorative Arts* Ruth Jackson; *Assoc Cur Dept Prints and Drawings* Dr Micheline Moisan; *Research Cur* Dr Myra Nan Rosemfeld; *Cur Contemporary Canadian Art* Normand Theriault; *Registrar* Elaine Tolmatch.
Open Tues - Sun 11 AM - 5 PM; cl Mon. Admis $1. Estab 1860 as an Art Association for the exhibition of paintings; museum estab 1916. Average Annual Attendance: 275,000. Mem: 11,000; dues $20 and up; annual meeting Sept.

Income: Financed by endowment, membership and provincial appropriation.
Collections: Saidye and Samuel Bronfman Collection of Contemporary Canadian art; Lucile Pillow Collection of porcelain; Harry T Norton Collection of ancient glass; The Parker Lace Collection; Japanese incense boxes; collection of African Art by Fr Gagnon; Chinese, Near Eastern, Peruvian, Inuit primitive art; painting, sculpture and decorative arts from 3000 BC to the present; French, Spanish, Dutch, British, Canadian and other schools; European decorative arts.
Exhibitions: Master paintings from The Hermitage and the State Russian Museum; Leningrad; Guido Molinari Retrospective; Gold of the Gods; Japanese Incense Boxes rediscovered; Art in Quebec in the Wake of the Conquest; Alfred Stevens; Hundertwasser; many others.
Publications: Collage (a calendar of events).
Activities: Educ dept; docent training; lect open to public; concerts; gallery talks; tours; exten dept serving Quebec and other provinces; individual paintings and original objects of art lent to art galleries and cultural centers; museum shop selling books, original art, reproductions, prints, slides.
—Library. *Librn* Juanita Toupin.
Open for reference to students, scholars, teachers, researchers.
Holdings: Vols 30,000; Per subs 500; Other—Exhibition catalogs 13,000, art sales catalogues 19,000, vertical file material.
Special Collections: Costumes; Canadiana.

MUSEE D'ART CONTEMPORAIN, Cite du Havre, H3C 3R4. Tel: 514-873-2878. *Dir* Louis Letocha; *Admin Asst* Hector Thisdale; *Dir Exhib* vacant; *Dir Travelling Exhib* Anne-Marie Sioui.
Open Tues - Sat 10 AM - 6 PM; Thurs 10 AM - 10 PM; Cl Mon. No admis. Estab 1964. Conservation and information about contemporary art are the most important aspects of the museum; also to present contemporary artists to the general public. The building is a medium-sized two-story art museum and with an exhibition area of 2,200 sq meters divided in four galleries and a foyer. Average Annual Attendance: 80,000.
Income: $1,200,000 (financed by Provincial grant). Purchases: $200,000.
Collections: Contemporary art (international, †Canadian and †Quebecois): paintings, sculptures, drawings, engravings, photographs.
Exhibitions: Quebec Designs; Serge Lemoyne (painting); Luce Deupuis (sculpture); Mario Merola (sculptures, bas relief); Louis Cane (painting); Marilyn Milburn (design); Three generations of Quebec art 1940-1950-1960; Emme Lake Workshops (paintings); Bruce Parsons (painting); Avant-garde European Art; Retrospective Paul Klee (painting); Dennis Oppenheim (retrospective).
Publications: Atelier, quarterly; Catalogs of exhibitions.
Activities: Lect open to public, 15 vis lectr per yr; concerts; gallery talks; tours; competitions; exten dept serving Quebec province; traveling exhibitions organized and circulated; sales shop selling books, magazines, reproductions, prints, slides.
—Library. *Librn* Isabelle Montplaisir.
Open Tues - Fri 10 AM - 5 PM. Estab 1967.
Income: Financed by Provincial grant. Purchases: $12,000.
Holdings: Vols 4050; Per subs 125; AV—Microfiche, microfilm, slides, video tapes, photographs; Other—Clipping files, exhibition catalogs, manuscripts, original documents, pamphlets, photographs.
Special Subjects: Contemporary art.
Special Collections: Archives of Paul Emile Borduas (Painter, 1905-1960); about 12,500 items including writings, correspondence, exhibition catalogs.

MUSEE DE L'EGLISE NOTRE-DAME, 430 St Sulpice St, H2Y 2V5. Tel: 514-842-2925. *Pastor & Dir* Father Fernand Lecavalier.
Open Mon - Sat 9 AM - 4:30 PM; Sun Noon - 4:30 PM. Admis adults 50¢, children 25¢. Estab June 7, 1937 as an historical and religious museum. Average Annual Attendance: 28,000.
Income: $13,326 (financed by admission fee and Church of Notre Dame).
Collections: Silverware, medals, paintings, Old Greek and Roman coins; religious ornaments, furniture, statues, volumes, manuscripts, documents, pertaining to the history of Canada.

ORDER OF ARCHITECTS OF QUEBEC,* 1825 Dorchester Blvd W, H3H 1R4. Tel: 514-937-6168. *Pres* Paul-Andre Tetreault; *Secy* Antoine Ghattas.
Open 9 AM - 5 PM. Estab 1890. Mem: 1303; dues $275; annual meeting May.
Publications: Register.
Library: Reference library of documentary and architectural books.

PAVILION OF HUMOUR, Man and His World, H3C 1A0. Tel: 514-872-6079. *Cur* Robert La Palme; *Deputy Cur* Andre Carpentier; *Asst* Paula Kirouac; *Secy* Josee Vanier.
Open June 21 - Labor Day 10 AM - 8:30 PM. Estab 1968 to show graphic humor from 60 countries, plus humorous sculptures borrowed from anywhere; Pavilion of Humour is part of Man and His World. Average Annual Attendance: 300,000.
Income: $250,000 (financed by endowment and city and state appropriations).
Collections: Strip cartoons; drawings from Pulitzer Prize winners; drawings from Reuben Award winners; drawings on International Salon of Cartoons winners; collection of American editorial cartoons from 1867 to now; collection of panel cartoons from 1860s to present.
Publications: Catalogs for Cartoonist of the Year exhibition and International Salon of Cartoons.
Activities: Material available to universities and museums; competitions; objects of art lent; traveling exhibitions organized and circulated; original books and money are also distributed to winners in a junior cartoon exhibition.
Library: Reference. Holdings: Vols 2744.

SAINT JOSEPH'S ORATORY,* 3800 Queen Mary Ch, H3V 1H6. Tel: 514-733-8211. *Dir* Marcel Lalonde; *Artistic Cur* Paul LeDuc.
Open daily 10 AM - 5 PM. Admis adults 50¢, children 25¢; special group rates. Estab 1953 as art museum and shrine.
Collections: Ancient and contemporary art.
Activities: Concerts; films.
Library: Open to the public for use on the premises, and for inter-library loan. Holdings: Vols 80,000; AV—Microfilm; Other—Photographs.

SOCIETE DES ARTISTES PROFESSIONNELS DU QUEBEC,* (Society of Professional Artists of Quebec), 4545 St Denis. Tel: 514-845-4171. *Pres* Reynald Piché; *Secy* Julien Patenaude.
Open 9:30 AM - 5:30 PM. No admis. estab 1966 in defense of the artists in visual arts; promotion of members; consultants in the establishment of new policies in arts; experimental gallery. Mem: 200; dues $15; annual meeting Jan 1.
Income: Financed by membership, city and state appropriations.
Activities: Documentation Center, possibility of lectures and films in the gallery; dramatic programs; lect open to the public; concerts; lending collection contains slides 2000.

SOCIETY OF THE MONTREAL MILITARY & MARITIME MUSEUM, St Helen's Island Museum, The Old Fort, St Helen's Island (Mailing Add: PO Box 1024 Station A, H3C 2W9). Tel: 514-861-6738. *Mgrs* Bruce D Bolton and Guy P E Duchesneau; *Cur* Guy Vandeboncoeur.
Open summer daily 10 AM - 5 PM; cl Mon, Sept - April. Admis mid-June to Labour Day adults 50¢, children and groups 25¢. Estab 1955 to exhibit artifacts relating to Canada's colonial history, with emphasis on military and maritime themes; located in an old British Arsenal, built between 1820-24; galleries cover theme chronologically and by collection. Average Annual Attendance: 100,000. Mem: 100; dues $2; annal meeting May.
Income: $650,000 (financed by endowment, membership, city and state appropriation, federal funds and donations).
Collections: (Art) Prints from 1500 to the present.
Exhibitions: (1976-78) The American Nightmare - Canada 1776; Photographs by Gilles Rivest - Click; The End of an Era - Scarlet to Khaki.
Publications: The 4-M's Society Newsletter, irregularly.
Activities: Lect open to the public and some to members only, 10 vis lectr per year; concerts; museum shop selling books, reproductions, prints, slides.
—Macdonald-Stewart Library. *Librn* Elizabeth F Hale.
Open to researchers and members for reference.
Holdings: Vols 6000; Per subs 50.

PERCE

LE CENTRE D'ART DE PERCE,* G0C 2L0. *Dir* Thomas Tommi.
Open July - Aug 10 AM - 10 PM. No admis. Estab 1955 to promote art in all its forms; gallery of contemporary arts and crafts. Average Annual Attendance: 15,000.
Income: $10,000 (financed by endowment).
Collections: Permanent collections of Alberto Tommi's late paintings.
Publications: Le Centre D'Art de Perce, annually.
Activities: Classes for children; dramatic programs; concerts; photograph collection.

QUEBEC

L'UNIVERSITE LAVAL,* Ecole des Arts Visuels, Pavillon de la Faculte des Arts, Cite Universitaire, 61K 7P4. Tel: 418-656-7631. *Dir* Pierre Larochelle.
Open Mon - Fri 10 AM - 10 PM; cl holidays. No admis. Estab 1921.

Collections: Paintings; sculpture; graphics; decorative arts; art color slides.
Exhibitions: Temporary and traveling exhibitions, changing monthly.
Library: Open to the public for use on the premises. Holdings: Vols: 25,000 art books and color slides; original prints and works of art available for study.

MARIE DE L'INCARNATION CENTER AND MUSEUM,* 12 rue Donnacona (Mailing Add: CP 760, H3C 2V2. Tel: 418-692-2523. *Dir* S Noella Rivard; *Archivist-Conservator* S Marcelle Boucher.
Open Mon - Sat 10 AM - Noon & 2 - 5 PM; Sun 2 - 5 PM. No admis. Estab 1946, affiliated with the Ursuline Monastery; located in 1644 house of Madame de la Peltrie.
Collections: Paintings; sculpture; furniture and decorative arts used in Monastery and school; textiles; music; Indian artifacts.
Activities: Guided tours; manuscript collection; sales shop selling books and religious articles.

MUSEE DES AUGUSTINES DE L'HOTEL DIEU OF QUEBEC,* 32 rue Charlevoix, G1R 3R9. Tel: 418-692-2892. *Supvr* Sr Jeanne Roy; *Conservator* Sr Claire Gagnon.
Open daily 9 - 11 AM & 2 - 5 PM; Sun 2 - 5 PM; other times by appointment; cl Carnival Time. No admis. Estab 1939 in the Monastere des Augustines (1695).
Collections: Paintings; sculpture; archives; medical history.
Library: Holdings—Vols 2000 Library of religious and medical books available for research upon special request.

MUSÈE DU QUÈBEC, Parc des Champs de Bataille, G1S 1C8. Tel: 418-643-2150. *Dir* Andre Juneau; *Conservator Ancient Art* Claude Thibault; *Conservator Contemporary Art* Ginette Masse; *Conservator & Ethnographer* Therese La Tour.
Open daily 9 AM - 5 PM; Sun & holidays 1 - 5 PM. Estab 1933 under Government of Province of Quebec. Branch Museums, Hotel Chevalier, 5 Champlain St; Old French Canadian Homestead.
Collections: †Paintings; sculpture; †furniture by Quebec artists and carvers from the 17th century to the present.
Exhibitions: Rotating exhibitions.
—**Bibliotheque des Art (Art Library).** *Chief Librn* F Lafortune; *Asst* Diane Aubry, Luce Gariepy & Philippe Trefry.
Open 9 AM - 5 PM. Estab 1933.
Income: $150,000 (financed by city appropriation). Purchases: $35,000.
Holdings: Vols 15,000; Per subs 325; AV—Audio tapes, cassettes, lantern slides, microfiche, microfilm, motion pictures, phonorecords, slides, video tapes; Other—Clipping files, exhibition catalogs, pamphlets, photographs. Special Subjects: Art, and ethnography.

MUSÉE DU SÈMINAIRE DE QUÈBEC, 6, Rue de l'Université (Mailing Add: CP 460). Tel: 418-692-3981. *Conservateur* Jean-Marie Thivierge; *Conservateur/Adjoint* Jean-Pierre Paré.
Open 10 AM - 4 PM. Admis 50¢. Estab 1874. Average Annual Attendance: 10,000.
Income: Financed by state appropriation and university funding.
Collections: Paintings, furniture, gold, coins, stamps, Chinese artwork.

RIMOUSKI

LE MUSÈE REGIONAL DE RIMOUSKI, 35 W St Germain, G5L 4B4. Tel: 418-724-2272. *Dir Museum* Jean-Louis le Breux; *Pres Bd Dir* Gaetan Garon; *Pres Exec Comt* Romain Rousseau.
Open (summer) Mon - Fri 10 AM - 10 PM; Sat & Sun 2 - 10 PM; (winter) Thurs - Sun 2 - 5 PM & 7 - 9 PM. No admis. Estab 1972 for the diffusion of fine arts, painting, sculpture, and tapestry; to present local, national and international exhibitions and organize itinerant exhibitions. An old church, built in 1823, now historical monument, completely restored inside, beautiful frame of wood, three floors of exhibitions. Average Annual Attendance: 60,000. Mem: 400; annual meeting May.
Income: $135,000 (financed by membership, city and provincial appropriations, annual subscription campaign).
Collections: Canadian art, paintings, sculpture, and silversmithing; European paintings.
Exhibitions: Festival d'automne de Rimouski; Collection d'oeuvres d'art de la Compagnie mutuelle d'assurance La Laurentienne; Cent-onze dessins du Quebec; Vibrations colorées de Rita Letendre; L'Ame des Grands Voiliers; Art et Culture de l'Est du Quebec; L'Oeuvre de Suzanne Guite.
Activities: Lect open to public; concerts; traveling exhibitions organized and circulated; sales shop selling reproductions, prints, and slides.
Library: Open to the public for reference. Holdings: Vols 1500; Per subs 40; Other—Documents 600, slides 8000.

SHAWINIGAN

CENTRE CULTURAL DE SHAWINIGAN, 2100 Dessaules (Mailing Add: CP 400, G9N 6V3). Tel: 819-539-4822 and 5333. *Dir* Henry J Blanchard; *Asst Dir* Jean-Luc Houde; *Secy* Nicole Collins.
Open 1 - 10 PM; Admis $1 - $10. Estab Oct 14, 1967, gallery maintained. Average Annual attendance: 100,000.
Income: Financed by city appropriation.
Activities: Classes for adults and children; dramatic programs; concerts; lending collection contains original art works, original prints, paintings, sculpture, slides; original art for sale.

SHERBROOKE

UNIVERSITY OF SHERBROOKE CULTURAL CENTER, Art Gallery, J1K 2R1. Tel: 819-565-5446. *Art Dir* Graham Cantieni; *Promotions* Johanne Brouillet.
Open Mon - Thurs 12:30 - 5 PM & 7:30 - 9:30 PM; Fri 2 - 5 PM; Sun 2 - 5 PM; Sat & Sun Eve 7:30 - 9:30 PM, when there is a show. No admis. Estab 1964 to introduce public to the best art work being done in Canada and to place this work in an historical (ie European) and geographical (ie American) context; gallery conforms to museum standards supplemented by extensive exhibition areas open to the public. Average Annual Attendance: 18,000.
Income: $80,000 (financed by city and state appropriation and university funds).
Collections: Contemporary Quebec graphics and paintings.
Exhibitions: (1976-78) Approx 40 exhibitions including "Métiers d'art des Cantons de l'est" (crafts); "Concours d'art graphique québécois-Sherbrooke 1977 (prints and drawings); in preparation: "Arts visuels des Cantons de l'est".
Publications: Bulletin, monthly.
Activities: Lect open to the public, 20 vis lectr per yr; concerts; gallery talks; tours; competitions; lending collection contains original prints 200, paintings 60, phonorecords 500; traveling exhibitions organized and circulated.

TROIS RIVIÈRES

CENTRE CULTUREL DE TROIS RIVIÈRES, 1425 Place de l'Hôtel de Ville. Tel: 418-374-3521, exten 216. *Dir* Francois Lahaye.
Open 9 AM - Noon, 1:30 - 5 PM & 7 - 10 PM. Estab 1967.
Income: Financed by city appropriation.
Activities: Classes for adults and children; dramatic programs.

VAUDREUIL

MUSEE HISTORIQUE DE VAUDREUIL,* (Vaudreuil Historial Museum) 431 Blvd Roche (Mailing Add: CP 121, Darion, J7V 2N3). Tel: 514-455-2092. *Pres* Lucien Theriault; *Secy* Pierre Emond; *VPres* Fernande Letourneau; *Dir* David Aird; *Mgr* Andree Boileau.
Open Tues Sat 9 AM - Noon & 1 - 5 PM; Sun Noon - 5 PM. Admis adults 75¢, children 25¢. Estab 1953. Average Annual Attendance: 10,000. Mem: 100; dues $5; annual meeting May 26.
Income: Financed by endowment.
Collections: Paintings, portraits and sculpture; historic documents; woodworking and farming; antique pottery, furniture; historic material; Edison Gramophone, c 1915.
Exhibitions: Ten local artists' exhibits; les instruments d'eclairage; les moules and le moulage domestique.
Publications: Vaudreuil Soulanges, Western Gateway of Quebec; Musee de Vaudreuil Catalog (selectif).
Activities: Classes for children; concerts; original objects of art lent; book shop.
Library: Volumes for reference only. Holdings: AV—Cylinders 600; Other—Photographs.

VICTORIAVILLE

CENTRE D'ART DE VICTORIAVILLE,* 752 Notre Dame West, G6P 1T8. Tel: 819-758-1674. *Pres* Suzanne Bastien.
Open Sept - June daily 1 - 9 PM; cl July & Aug. No admis. Estab 1960. Mem: Dues children $1, teenagers $1.50, adults $3.
Collections: Paintings; sculpture; prints and drawings.
Exhibitions: Temporary and traveling exhibitions from inter-museum loan.
Activities: Educ dept—Classes for adults, children, undergraduate and graduate college students; lectures; films; dance recitals; concerts; competitions.
Library: Vols 800 of art books available for use by special request.

VILLE SAINT-LAURENT

MUSÈE D'ART DE SAINT-LAURENT, 615 Blvd Sainte-Croix, H4L 3X7. Tel: 514-747-6521, exten 314. *Dir and Conservator* Gérard Lavallée; *Pres* Louise Èthier.
Open Thurs - Fri 11 AM - 5 PM; Sun 11 AM - 5 PM. No admis. Estab 1962.
Collections: Traditional arts of French Canada from 17th-19th century—furniture, sculpture, wood carving, silver, textiles, ceramics, metalwork, and artifacts; Indian Artifacts—costumes, ceramics, tools, stones.
Exhibitions: Modern Art; Photography; Handicraft.
Publications: Album: Images Taillées du Québec.
Activities: Lect open to public.

SASKATCHEWAN

LLOYDMINSTER

LLOYDMINSTER BARR COLONY MUSEUM COMMITTEE, c/o City Hall, 5011 49 Ave, S9V 0T8. Tel: 403-825-5655 or 825-3726. *Chmn* Richard Larsen; *Secy* Blaire L Bowsfield; *Cur* Mrs D Barradell.
Open 9 AM - 9 PM. Admis adults 60¢, students 35¢, children 15¢. Estab 1965 to promote an interest in the history of our city. Mem 5; dues donations.
Income: Financed by donations.
Collections: Imhoff paintings and Fuch's Wildlife and Antique Museum.

MOOSE JAW

MOOSE JAW ART MUSEUM,* Crescent Park, S64 4N6. Tel: 306-692-4471. *Dir* Austin T Ellis; *Asst Dir* Joan Goodnough.
Open June 1 - Sept 30 Tues - Sun 2 - 5 PM & 7 - 9 PM; Oct 1 - May 30 Tues - Sun 2 - 5 PM, Thurs & Fri 7 - 9 PM; cl Mon & holidays. Donations welcome. Estab 1931. Mem: Dues student $1, single $5, family $10, donor $20, patron $35.
Income: Financed by city appropriation.
Collections: Paintings; Sioux and Cree Indian art; archaeology; ethnology; history.
Publications: Newsletter, semi-annually.
Activities: Lectures; gallery talks; guided tours; concerts; films; temporary and traveling exhibitions.

PRINCE ALBERT

JOHN M CUELENAERE LIBRARY, Grace Campbell Gallery, 125 12th St E, S6V 1B7. Tel: 306-763-8496. *Head Librn* Eleanor Acorn.
Open weekdays Noon - 8:30 PM; Sat 9 AM - 5 PM. No admis. Estab 1973 as a public library with an art gallery of 100 linear ft.
Income: Financed by city appropriation.
Library: Open to the public. Holdings: Vols 65,000; Per subs 210; Other—Records and cassettes.

REGINA

REGINA PUBLIC LIBRARY
—**Dunlop Art Gallery,** 2311 12th Ave, S4P 0N3. Tel: 306-569-7576. *Dir & Cur* WP Morgan; *Asst Cur* Pamela Perry.
Open Mon - Fri 9:30 AM - 9 PM; Sat 9:30 AM - 6 PM; Sun 1:30 - 5 PM; cl holidays. No admis. Estab 1947. Average Annual Attendance: 80,000.
Income: Financed by city appropriation.
Collections: Small permanent collection of paintings and drawings.
Exhibitions: About 18 per year. These include local, provincial, national, international professional artists; loan exhibitions; amateur, children's and grassroots art.
Publications: At The Library, monthly; Exhibition catalogues.
Activities: Lect open to public; gallery talks; competitions; individual paintings lent to individuals; traveling exhibitions organized and circulated.
—**Prairie History Room.** Tel: 306-569-7591. *Chmn Bd* Morris Anderson; *Chief Librn* Ronald Yeo; *Librn in Charge* Dorothy Hayden.
Open Mon - Fri 1 - 5:15 PM; Mon & Tues 6 - 9 PM; Sat 9:30 - 5:15 PM. No admis. Estab 1973 as a resource centre for Regina and Saskatchewan history, and for the collection and preservation of Canadiana. Limited access room on mezzanine floor of Regina Public Library with access to book and AV facilities of a large modern public library. Average Annual Attendance: 5000.
Income: Financed through the Library.
Collections: 1800 volumes of Canadiana; 1200 pictures, maps, photographs, pamphlets, tapes, clippings of Regina and area.
Exhibitions: Three major displays.

CANADIAN SOCIETY FOR EDUCATION THROUGH ART, Faculty of Education, University of Regina, S4S 042. *Pres* John M Emerson; *Secy* Gen Dr Les Groome.
For further information see National Organizations in Canada.

SASKATCHEWAN ARTS BOARD,* 200 Lakeshore Dr, S4S 0A4. Tel: 206-584-1122. *Chmn* Paul Rezansoff; *Exec Dir* Vern Bell; *Visual Arts Officer* Lea Collins; *Literary & Theatre Officer* Jean Freemen; *Arts Exten Officer/Dir Saskatchewan School of the Arts* James Ellemers.
Open 8:30 AM - 5 PM; summer hours 8:30 AM - 4:30 PM. Estab 1948 as an autonomous agency for promotion and development of the arts in Saskatchewan; Board is composed of 7-15 appointed, unpaid members, whose major concern at the present time is the support and development of professionals and professional standards within the province.
Income: Financed by annual provncial government grant.
Collections: †Permanent collection containing over 600 works by Saskatchewan artists and artisans only, dating from 1950 to present; purchased mainly from current exhibitions around the province; part of the permanent collection hangs in the Saskatchewan Centre of the Arts, Regina.
Publications: Annual Report; services and programs brochure; brochures for Saskatchewan School of the Arts classes.
Activities: Programs include individual and group assistance grants, workshop assistance, aid for exhibitions, community assistance for the performing arts, script reading service, play-script duplication subsidy, community artists program, and consultative services; operates Saskatchewan School of the Arts at Echo Valley Centre, summer classes for young people and fall and spring classes for adults are offered in a wide variety of crafts, visual and performing arts.

UNIVERSITY OF REGINA, Norman Mackenzie Art Gallery, College and Scarth Sts, S4S 0A2. Tel: 306-523-5801. *Dir* Nancy Dillow; *Cur of Exhib* Carol Phillips; *Admin Officer* Joy Paull.
Open Mon - Fri Noon - 5 PM; Sat & Sun 1 - 5 PM; Wed & Thurs 7 - 10 PM. No admis. Estab 1953. House and display legacy of Norman Mackenzie with intention of adding to the collection and providing loan exhibitions from Saskatchewan. A small university gallery which also serves as a community gallery for a city of 160,000 people and the surrounding area. Five individual galleries with running space of approx 600 feet. Average Annual Attendance: 34,000.
Collections: 15th-19th century European paintings; works of old Masters; Canadian and American contemporaries.
Exhibitions: Esther Warkov Drawings; Saskatchewan Artists Series; Tim Scott: British sculptor; Young Contemporaries; Contemporary Yugoslav Graphics; Eleven Early British Columbia Photographers; Making Marks: Current Canadian Drawings; Bloomsbury Painters and Their Circle; Inside Nova Scotia: Architectural Textiles for Interiors; Regina 25 Years: 1952-1977; Realism in Canada.
Publications: Tabloid, six times a year.
Activities: Classes for children; dramatic programs; docent training; lect open to public, 10 vis lectr per yr; concerts; gallery talks; tours; exten dept serving Rural Saskatchewan; individual paintings and original objects of art lent to galleries; traveling exhibitions organized and circulated.
Library: NMAG Resource Centre. *Librn* Pat Roulston. Open to the public for reference. Holdings: Vols 1000; Per subs 32; Other—Exhibition catalogues 1200, vertical files 800. Special Subjects: Canadian art. Special Collections: Regional press clippings from 1925.

SASKATOON

NUTANA COLLEGIATE INSTITUTE, Memorial Library and Art Gallery, 411 11th St E, S7N 0E9. Tel: 304-653-1677. *Principal* Ron Perkins; *Asst Principal* Mona Finlayson; *Librn* Philip Listoe.
Open 8 AM - 4 PM. No admis. Estab 1919 to instill in students an appreciation for art and to provide a lasting memorial to the students who lost their lives in the two world wars. Average Annual Attendance: 700.
Collections: A unique collection of over 50 paintings by Canadian artists.
Exhibitions: Autumn Garland (C F Jeffreys); In Northern Waters (F M Bell-Smith).
Publications: Booklets on paintings in the gallery and the artists, occasionally.

SASKATCHEWAN ASSOCIATION OF ARCHITECTS, LM1 Phoenix House, 226 20th St E, S7K 0A6. *Pres* Roger James Walls; *Secy-Treas* Ian Innes.
Estab 1911. Mem: 95; dues $275; annual meeting Feb.
Activities: Schol; book prize given to architectural technology student at Saskatchewan Technical Institute, Moose Jaw (4 twice a year).

Collections: Regional, national and international art.
Exhibitions: About 25 per year: Works from Falconforme Press; Rolph Pryne Paintings; Scandinavian Heritage; Antique Canadian Glass: McGowan Collection; Eight Calgary artists; Thirty-six Canadian artists; Paintings by Tim Deverall; Ernest Lindner retrospective; Antoni Tapies; Permanent Collection; Saskatoon Juried show; Selective Saskatchewan drawings; Commemorative China; Selections from the Winnipeg Art Gallery; James Francis, sculpture.
Publications: Folio, monthly.
Activities: Classes for adults and children; lect open to the public; concerts; gallery talks; tours; exten dept serving western Canadian provinces; original objects of art lent to galleries, offices and homes; traveling exhibitions organized and circulated; sales shop selling books, magazines, original art, prints, reproductions, and gift items.
Library: Librn Joan Steel. Open to the public for reference. Holdings: Vols 4000; Per subs 40; Other—Slides, photographs, phonorecords, pamphlet files. Special Subjects: Canadian art; Saskatchewan art.

SASKATOON GALLERY AND CONSERVATORY CORPORATION, 950 Spadina Crescent E, (Mailing Add: PO Box 569, S7K 3L6). Tel: 306-652-8355. *Dir & Cur* JE Climer; *Asst Cur* G Moppett; *Exten Officer* M Gibson; *Business Mgr* R Moldenhauer; *Pres* RF Dilts; *VPres* F Alexson; *Secy* L Whelan.
Open daily 10 AM - 10 PM. No admis. Estab 1964 to exhibit, preserve, collect, works of art and to encourage the development of the visual arts in Saskatoon, and to provide the opportunity for citizens to enjoy, understand and to gain a greater appreciation of the fine arts. Maintains an art gallery. Average Annual Attendance: 225,000.
Income: $486,000 (financed by city and federal appropriations). Purchases: $25,000.
Collections: Regional, national and international art.

Exhibitions: About 25 per year: Works from Falconforme Press; Rolph Pryne Paintings; Scandinavian Heritage; Antique Canadian Glass: McGowan Collection; Eight Calgary artists; Thirty-six Canadian artists; Paintings by Tim Deverall; Ernest Lindner retrospective; Antoni Tapies; Permanent Collection; Saskatoon Juried show; Selective Saskatchewan drawings; Commemorative China; Selections from the Winnipeg Art Gallery; James Francis, sculpture.
Publications: Folio, monthly.
Activities: Classes for adults and children; lect open to the public; concerts; gallery talks; tours; exten dept serving western Canadian provinces; original objects of art lent to galleries, offices and homes; traveling exhibitions organized and circulated; sales shop selling books, magazines, original art, prints, reproductions, and gift items.
Library: Librn Joan Steel. Open to the public for reference. Holdings: Vols 4000; Per subs 40; Other—slides, photographs, phonorecords, pamphlet files. Special Subjects: Canadian art; Saskatchewan art.

UNIVERSITY OF SASKATCHEWAN, SASKATOON, Art Department Gallery, S7N 0W0. Tel: 306-343-4528. *Gallery Supervisor* Robert Christie.
Open Mon, Wed & Fri 10 AM - 4 PM; Sun, Tues & Thurs 2 - 5 PM & 6 - 9 PM. No admis. Estab approximately 1960 for the education of students and local public; gallery covers approximately 3000 sq ft of floor space, 300 running feet of wall space. Average Annual Attendance: 5000.
Income: $11,000 (financed by provincial and federal government appropriations and university funds).
Exhibitions: Constantly changing exhibitions of art works; internationally organized and traveling shows.
Publications: Show announcements, every three weeks.
Activities: Traveling exhibitions organized and circulated, on a limited basis.

ARGENTINA

BUENOS AIRES

CENTRO DE ARTE Y COMMUNICACION (Center of Art and Communication), Elpidio González 4070, 1407. Tel: 566-8046/8066. *Pres* Jorge Glusberg; *VPres* Leonardo Glusberg; *Secy* Amelia Montes; *Dir Architectural Dept* Carlos A Sallaberry; *Cur* Eduardo Ring; *Video Coordr* Renato Santucci; *Sound Coordr* Rafael H Antonacci; *Music Dept* Rodolfo Arizaga, Mariano Etkin and Eduardo Kusnir; *Courses & Conferences* Enrique Dimant and Juan Carlos Albertoni; *Architecture Coordr* Diego Forero, Jorge Aslan, Alfredo Gentile and Gerardo Schon; *Industrial Design* Hector Compaired, Reinaldo Leiro, Leonardo Perel and Jorge Pechersky.

Open 11 AM - 9 PM; cl Sun. Estab 1969 to introduce in Argentina, on a pedagogycal level, the most important events of experimental and avant-garde art from international art centers and also present the Latin American circuit from the artistical activities. Gallery consists of three floors, each 16m x 20m; documentation center consists of two floors each 18m x 30m. The Center holds exhibitions of objects, paintings, engravings; also courses and conferences on art, architecture, music. Average Annual Attendance: 20,000. Mem: 150, qualifications: to be interested in avant-garde art and other activities held at the Center.
Income: Financed by membership.
Collections: 150 motion pictures on art, architecture, †music; 400 video-tapes; photograph collection of 7000 †prints; collection of 5000 slides; catalogs and bulletins on every art exhibition and seminary held by the Center in Argentina and abroad.
Exhibitions: (1976-78) Italian Contemporary Architecture; Architects Martorell-Bohigas-Mackay (Spain); Architect Luis Barragan (Mexico); Franz Erhard Walther (Germany); Yutaka Matsuzawa (Japan); Christo (USA); Barry Flanagab (England); French Contemporary Engravings; American Contemporary Posters; Aaron Marcus (USA); Donald Burgy (USA); Art Systems in Israel; XIV Sao Paulo Biennial; David Lamelas (Argentina); Image and Words (traveling exhibition); Architect Felix Candela (Spain); Fifty Years with Photography (international exhibition); Ricardo Cristobal (Spain); Gerald Minkoff, Muriel Olesen (Switzerland); 30 Years in North American Art; Regina Vater (Brazil); 50 Works of Artists from Paris; Architect Pablo Cárlodalatri (Italy); Fred Forest (France); Andrzej Partum (Poland); John Baldessair, Douglas Davis (USA); Drawings from Peru.
Publications: Catalogs for shows and activities in the country and abroad, 30 a yr; Yellow paper information on activities, 300 a yr.
Activities: Educ dept; lect open to the public, 550 vis lectrs per yr; gallery talks; competitions with cash, medals and steel cubes awards; artmobile; individual paintings and original objects of art lent to other local and abroad museums and art centers; lending collection contains books 6895, cassettes 450, color reproductions 350, lantern slides 5000, motion pictures 150, original art works 200, original prints 300, paintings 150, photographs 7000, sculpture 75, catalogs; traveling exhibitions organized and circulated.
—**Library,** Viamonte 452. *Librn* Lidia Rabinovich.
Holdings: Vols 4500; Other—Bulletins.
Special Subjects: Books, catalogs and bulletins on art, sociology of art, communication, epistemology, research in architecture, industrial design, video, conferences, and exhibitions.

ESCUELA SUPERIOR DE BELLAS ARTES ERNESTO DE LA CARCOVA (National Superior School of Fine Arts Ernesto de la Carcova), Sculpture Museum, Tristán Achával Rodríguez 1701, 1107. *Rector & Prof* Germen Gelpi; *Regent & Prof* Jorge Guillermo Luna Ercilla; *Secy* Nelida María Luisa Guido.

Open Mon - Fri 9 AM - 3 PM. No admis. Estab for the exhibition of didactical elements of the school. The gallery consists of two large rooms. Average Annual Attendance: 21,900.
Income: Included in the school budget, financed by state appropriation.
Collections: Reproductions of first quality of important pieces of the world sculpture through the ages—Egyptian, Sumerian, Greek, Roman, Romanic, Gothic and the Renaissance, including Michelangelo's David and Moses.
—**Enrique Prince Library.** *Librn* Elsa Rosenthal de Sosa.
Open to all fine arts students for reference only.
Holdings: Vols 2600; Other—Magazines, plates, slides.
Special Subjects: Painting, engraving, sculpture, drawing, set-designing.

MUSEO NACIONAL DE ARTE DECORATIVO* (National Museum of Decorative Art), Av del Libertador 1902. Tel: 83-8814. *Dir* Dr Federico Aldao.
Estab 1937.
Collections: Furniture; sculptures; tapestries; European and Souh American works.
Publications: Exhibition catalogs; guides.
Activities: Lect; concerts.

MUSEO NACIONAL DE BELLAS ARTES* (National Museum of Fine Arts), Avda Libertador Gen San Martin 1473. Tel: 83-8814. *Dir* Samuel F Oliver; *Conservator* Samuel Paz.
Open Wed - Mon 3 - 7 PM. Estab 1895.
Collections: European paintings (16th-20th centuries); sculpture; Argentine and American paintings.
Activities: Auditorium for audiovisual programs, films, concerts and lectures; modern pavilion for special exhibitions.
Library: (Art) Holdings—Vols 35,000.

ROSARIO

MUSEO MUNICIPAL DE BELLAS ARTES JUAN B CASTAGNINO* (Municipal Museum of Fine Arts), Avda Pellegrini, 2202 Parque Independencia. Tel: 27310. *Dir* Horacio E Correas.
Open Wed - Sat 4 - 7 PM; Sun & holidays 10 AM - Noon & 4 - 7 PM. No admis. Estab 1920; the present building inaugurated 1937. Average Annual Attendance: 100,000.
Income: Financed by appropriation.
Collections: European and American paintings and sculpture from 16th century to contemporary; includes works by El Greco, Goya, Titian, Jose de Ribera, and Valdes Leal; complete collection of Argentine art from 19th century to present.
Publications: Exhibition catalogs.
Activities: Concerts, dramatic programs, competitions.

AUSTRALIA

ADELAIDE

ART GALLERY OF SOUTH AUSTRALIA, North Terrace, 5000. Tel: 08-223-8911. *Dir* David Thomas; *Deputy Dir* Ronald Appleyard; *Cur Decorative Arts* Dick Richards; *Cur Paintings* Ian North; *Cur Prints & Drawings* Alison Carroll; *Cur Historical Coll* John Tregenza; *Cur Presentations* Ian Maidment; *Cur Art Educ* Don Hein.
Open Mon - Sat 10 AM - 5 PM; Wed 10 AM - 9 PM; Sun 1:30 - 5 PM. No admis. Estab 1881 for the public display of works of art including paintings, sculpture, prints, etc, and items of historical interest relating to the exploration and colonization of the State of South Australia. Gallery is a stone, brick, concrete and steel structure; Elder Wing 19th century

neo-classical style, opened 1900; Melrose wing 20th century Art Deco style, opened 1936; three-story north wing opened 1962. Average Annual Attendance: 366,563.
Income: $680,000 (financed by state appropriation and bequests and gifts). Purchases; $160,000.
Collections: Representative selection of Australian and European paintings and sculpture; large collection of prints, drawings, silver, glass and ceramics; collection of South East Asian ceramics; collections of furniture, coins and medals; extensive South Australian Historical Collection.
Exhibitions: American Figure Drawing; Form and Freedom; British Artist's Prints; The Artist's Medium; Engravings and Etchings by Durer and Rembrandt; William Delafield Cook; Australian Realist Painters; South Australia Illustrated; Rundle Mall Sculpture Maquettes; Diane Arbus; Art Treasures from Adelaide; Jean Arp; David Hockney Prints; Master Drawings from the Albertina, Vienna; The Chinese Exhibition.
Publications: Annual Bulletin; Annual Report; catalogues to major exhibitions.
Activities: Classes for children; docent training; lect open to public; exten dept; artmobile; individual paintings and original objects of art lent to schools and organizations; traveling exhibitions organized and circulated; sales shop selling books, magazines, original art, reproductions, slides.
Library: Part-time Librarian. Open for reference to staff and serious students. Holdings: Vols 6000; Per subs 120; Other—Catalogues 20,000. Special Subjects: Visual arts.

BRISBANE

QUEENSLAND ART GALLERY,* Fifth Floor (6th Floor Administration), MIM Bldg, 160 Ann St, 4000 (temporary premises). Tel: 292138. *Dir* Raoul Mellish; *Asst Dir* Robert Cunningham.
Open Mon - Sat 10 AM - 5 PM; Sun 2 - 5 PM; cl Christmas, Good Friday & Anzac Day. Estab 1895.
Collections: Predominantly Australian art, paintings and drawings; European paintings and sculpture, including works by leading Impressionists.
Exhibitions: Continuous exhibition program from the permanent collection; loan exhibitions from overseas; Annual Trustees' Prize $2500; biennial LJ Harvey Memorial Prize for Drawing $500.
Activities: Educ prog for school, tertiary and adult audiences; classes for children; lect; exhibition openings.
Library: Holdings—Slides, tapes, film. Special Subjects: Australian art.

HOBART

TASMANIAN MUSEUM AND ART GALLERY, 5 Argyle St (Mailing Add: GPO Box 1164M, 7001). Tel: 002-232696. *Dir* D R Gregg; *Cur Art* Carl Andrew; *Art Conservator* Romek Pachucki; *Art Educ Officer* Stephen Rainbird.
Open 10 AM - 5 PM. No admis. Estab 1829 as a state museum and art gallery with emphasis on Tasmanian material and relevant material from other places. Gallery has a display area of 2755 sq meters. Average Annual attendance: 115,000.
Income: Financed by state appropriation. Purchases: $13,300A.
Collections: †Tasmanian 19th century paintings; †Australian contemporary art; †British 18th & 19th century watercolours; †photography.
Exhibitions: British Artists Prints 1961-79; Contemporary Japanese Prints; The Tasmanian Aboriginal in Art; Barlach/Kollwitz Sculptures; The sculpture of Thailand; Diane Arbus Photographs; David Hockney Graphics, Illusion and Reality; Paul Nash.
Publications: Annual Report; catalogues and handbooks, irregularly.
Activities: Classes for adults and children; lect open to public, concerts; gallery talks; exten dept serving Tasmania; artmobile; individual paintings and original objects of art lent to other galleries; traveling exhibitions organized and circulated; sales shop selling books, reproductions, slides.
Library: Librn Janet Middleton. Open for reference to the public upon application. Holdings: Vols 5000; Per subs 50. Special Subjects: Tasmania and Australia.

LAUNCESTON

QUEEN VICTORIA MUSEUM,* Wellington St, 7250. Tel: 003-316777. *Dir* W F Ellis; *Gallery Officer* J A McPhee; *Display Officer* J W Swift.
Open Mon - Fri 10 AM - 5 PM; Sun 2 - 4 PM. No admis. Estab 1891 as headquarters of a professionally conducted complex of art galleries, theatres, museums and educational services conducted mainly as a city authority but extending over half the state. Average Annual Attendance: 90,000.
Income: $210,000 (financed by city and state appropriations). Purchases: $3000.
Collections: Visual art collections, relating to Australia; colonial period (1803-1900); †contemporary work.
Exhibitions: Approx 15 annually.

Publications: Records of the Queen Victoria Museum, approx 4 per year.
Activities: Lect open to public, 10 vis lectr; gallery talks; tours; concerts; dramatic programs; competitions; exten dept serving 13,000 sq miles; traveling exhibitions organized and circulated; individual paintings and original objects of art lent; trailside museums.
Library: Reference Library. Holdings: Vols 8000; Other—Photograph collection of prints 750.

MELBOURNE

NATIONAL GALLERY OF VICTORIA, 180 St Kilda Road, 3004. Tel: 03-62-7411. *Dir* Eric Rowlison; *Deputy Dir* Kenneth Hood; *Secy* R P Nolan.
Open Tues - Sun 10 AM - 5 PM; Wed 10 AM - 9 PM; cl Mon. Admis 50¢ (with concessions to pensioners and families). Estab 1861 as a public art gallery. The present gallery was opened in 1968, it is a large bluestone building built around three rectangular courtyards with galleries on three floors and service areas below. Average Annual Attendance: 750,000. Mem: 8000; dues ordinary $12, family $18.
Income: Financed by state appropriation. Purchases: $200,000.
Collections: †Old master and modern paintings and sculpture; †old master and modern prints and drawings; †Asian art; †Australian art; †ceramics; †glass; †woodwork; †metalwork; †costumes; †textiles; †antiquities; †trival art; †photography.
Exhibitions: A continuous program of temporary exhibitions is arranged.
Publications: Art Bulletin of Victoria, annually; catalogues and handbooks to the collections.
Activities: Classes for children; docent training; lect open to public, 3 vis lectr per yr; original objects of art lent to state and local government department and offices; traveling exhibitions organized and circulated; museum shop selling books, reproductions, slides.
Library: Librn Patricia Forster. Open for reference to staff and voluntary guides. Holdings: Vols 7000; Per subs 40; Other—Catalogues, slides.

PERTH

WESTERN AUSTRALIAN ART GALLERY,* Beaufort St, 6000. Tel: 28-7233. *Dir* Frank Norton; *Deputy Dir* Bertram Whittle; *Sr Cur* Lou Klepac.
Open Mon - Fri 10:30 AM - 5 PM; Sat 9:30 AM - 5 PM; Sun 2 - 5 PM; during special exhibitions Wed 7:30 - 10 PM. Estab 1895 as part of the Western Australian Museum; it became an autonomous body by Act of Parliament in 1960. Average Annual Attendance: 112,000.
Income: $400,000 (financed by state appropriation). Purchases: $80,000.
Collections: Oils; watercolours; prints and drawings, sculptures; Australian Aboriginal artifacts and primitive art; antique and modern furniture; antique and modern silver and gold ware; ceramics, glass and pottery.
Exhibitions: Biennially, Perth Prize for Drawing International, alternating with Western Australian Artists Exhibition.
Activities: Tours; educational and holiday activities; traveling exhibitions organized and circulated.
Library: Holdings—Vols 1200.

SYDNEY

ART GALLERY OF NEW SOUTH WALES, Art Gallery Road, Domain, 2000. Tel: 02-211-2100. *Dir* vacant; *Acting Dir* Gil Docking; *Asst Dir* David P Millar; *Acting Sr Cur & Cur European & American Art* Renee Free; *Cur Prints & Drawings* Nicholas Draffin; *Conservation* Alan Lloyd.
Open Mon - Sat 10 AM - 5 PM; Sun Noon - 5 PM; cl Christmas Day and Good Friday. Estab 1874, the state art museum. In 1972 the Art Gallery reopened after being closed for remodeling. Average Annual Attendance: 300,000.
Collections: Australian art; primitive art; Australian aboriginal including notable burial posts and bark paintings; Melanesian; European painting and sculpture—Hogarth, R E Pine, Reynolds, Wilson, Turner, Constable, Etty, Danby, John Gibson, Madox Brown, Burne-Jones, Leighton, Poynter, Fildes, Sickert, Gore, Nash, Ben Nicholson, Sutherland, Moore, Hepworth, Pasmore, Davie, Strozzi, Stomer, Van Bijlert, Van Bloemen, Tiepolo, Corot, Boudin, Fantin-Latour, Pissarro, Bonnard, Monet, Hayden, Leger, Zadkine, Albers, Morris Louis; prints and drawings—a good systematic collection including Mantegna, Durer, Callot, Rembrandt, Piranesi, Canaletto, Goya, Turner, Constable, Meryon, Whistler, Munch, Matisse, Picasso; Oriental art—Chinese ceramics, Chinese bronzes; Tibetan, Japanese and Chinese paintings; Japanese ceramics; Japanese woodcuts; Thai sculpture; Persian ceramics; Persian and Indian miniatures; decorative arts—British pewter, 17th-18th century; English porcelain, 18th century and Victorian; contemporary tapestries, Lurcat and Matisse.
Exhibitions: Recent Australian art; John Constable; 17th Century Pastoral Holland; Paul Klee; Two Masters of the Weimar Bauhaus; Hirshfield-Mack and Lyonel Feiniger; Ladies in Landscapes; Modern Masters: Manet to Matisse; Victorian Olympians; Australian art in the

1870's; Victorian Social Conscience; The Chinese Exhibition; Prints from the Albertina; The Heritage of American art; British Painting 1600-1800.
Publications: Art Gallery Annual; special exhibition catalogs.
Activities: Lect open to public; films; docent training; gallery talks; tours; traveling exhibitions organized and circulated; bookshop.
Library: Open to staff for reference.

MUSEUM OF APPLIED ARTS AND SCIENCES,* 659-795 Harris St, Broadway, 2007. Tel: 02-211-3911. *Pres* Sir John Hurley; *Dir* J L Willis; *Deputy Dir* H H G McKern; *Cur Arts* J P Wade.
Open daily 10 AM - 5 PM; Sun 2 - 5 PM; cl Good Friday and Christmas Day. No admis. estab 1880 to display and offer scholarships in the applied arts and sciences; administered by Bd of Seven Trustees. Average Annual Attendance: 230,000.
Income: Financed by endowment and state appropriation.
Collections: (art) †Ceramics; glass; metalwork; ivory; textiles; costume; musical instruments; numismatics; Asian arts; ship models.
Publications: Annual report; bulletins; guides; leaflets.
Activities: Educ dept conducts teaching sessions; exten dept serving area schools; photograph collection lent on approval of director; book shop.
Library: For reference only. Holdings: Vols 10,000.

AUSTRIA

GRAZ

NEUE GALERIE AM LANDESMUSEUM JOANNEUM,* (New Gallery at Provincial Museum), Sackstrasse 16, 8010. *Dir* Dr Wilfried Skreiner; *Cur* Dr Alexander Wied; *Cur* Werner Fenz.
Open 9 AM - 6 PM. Admis 5 Sh. Average Annual Attendance: 10,000. Dues approx 50,000 Sh.
Income: $50,000 (financed by province and state appropriations). Purchases: $10,000.
Collections: Painting of the 19th & 20th centuries, especially Austrian, Biedermeier; Styrian painters of the 19th century, two pictures of Egon Schiele; drawings and watercolors (20,000) of Austrian and German artists; international graphic art of the 20th century.
Exhibitions: Approx 50 Austrian, Italian and Yugoslavian painters exhibitions since 1970.
Activities: Exten dept serving Styria, Italy and Yugoslavia; lect open to public, 30 vis lectr per yr; gallery talks, concerts, competitions; scholarships; individual paintings and original objects of art lent; lending collection contains photographs; traveling exhibitions organized and circulated.
Library: For reference only. Holdings: Vols 5000.

LINZ

WOLFGANG-GURLITT-MUSEUM, Neue Galerie der Stadt Linz (New City Gallery), Hauptplatz 8, A-4020. Tel: 072 22/241 04. *Dir* Peter Baum.
Open Mon - Fri 10 AM - 6 PM; Sat 10 AM - 1 PM; cl Sun. No admis. Estab 1947. Average Annual Attendance: 25,000.
Collections: 19th and 20th century paintings, drawings, sculptures and prints; about 480 paintings and small sculptures; 2600 graphics.
Exhibitions: About 12 changing exhibitions in one year are shown.
Publications: Catalogs, 6 a year.
Activities: Classes for children; 12 vis lectrs per yr; tours; museum shop selling prints and catalogs.
Library: Holdings—Vols 7000. Special Collections: Kubin Collection.

SALZBURG

SALTZBURGER MUSEUM CAROLINO AUGUSTEUM,* (Salzburg Museum), Museumsplatz 6, Postfach 525, A-5010. Tel: 43 1 45, 41 1 37 (06222). *Dir Ethnology, History of Civilization, Arts and Crafts* Dr Freidrike Prodinger; *Cur Art History* Dr Albin Rohrmoser; *Cur Ethnology* Dr Kurt Conrad; *Cur Prehistory* Fritz Moosleitner; *Cur Theatrical Sciences & Pub Relations* Dr Volker Kutschera; *Cur Restoration* Annemarie Fiebich-Ripke; *Admin* Otto Rainer.
Open daily 9 AM - 5 PM; cl Nov 1. Estab 1834. Average Annual Attendance: 400,000.
Income: 1,600,000 Austrian schillings (financed by city appropriation). Purchases: 500,000 Austrian schillings.
Collections: Prehistoric and Roman archaeology; medieval art; baroque, 19th century, modern art; prints and drawings; coins; musical instruments; furniture; historical chambers.
Exhibitions: Frequent special changing exhibitions at the Salzburg Museum and at the Museum Pavilion.
Publications: Jahresschrift, annually; Schriftenreihe, occasionally; catalogs on major exhibitions; postcards, slides, posters.

Activities: Symposia on important changing exhibitions; gallery talks; demonstrations; concerts; tours; lending services to other exhibitors; sales shop selling books; production of silent and sound pictures on Austrian national customs, local theatre history and on research work on toys.
Library: Open Mon - Fri 9 AM - Noon. Holdings: Vols 55,000; Other—Technical literature, local archives.
—**Volkskundemuseum** (Folklife Museum), Monatsschlosschen near Castle of Hellbrunn.
Open Apr - Oct, daily 10 AM - 6 PM. Estab 1924.
Collections: Folklife—furniture, costumes, faience, miniature farmhouses, perchten-masks, imigration.
—**Burgmuseum** (Castle of Hohensalzburg)
Open daily 9 AM - 5 PM; cl Nov 1. Estab 1959.
Collections: Local history of defense; arms and armor; guilds furniture; flags; wrought iron; history of law.
—**Museum Pavilion,** Mirabellgarten.

VIENNA

GEMALDEGALERIE DER AKADEMIE DER BILDENDEN KUNSTE IN WIEN (Art Gallery of the Academy of Fine Arts), Schillerplatz 3, A-1010. Tel: 0222 57 95 16. *Dir* Dr Heribert R Hutter; *Asst* Dr Renate Trnek; *Head Conservator* Peter Halbgebauer.
Open Tues 10 AM - 2 PM; Wed 10 AM - 1 PM & 3 - 6 PM; Thurs & Fri 10 AM - 2 PM; Sat & Sun 9 AM - 1 PM; cl Mon. Admis öS 10.-, 5.-, 1.-, students free. Estab 1822 to house the collections of Count Anton Lamberg-Sprinzenstein who, at his death in 1822, willed his collections to serve as teaching materials and examples for the students of the Academy of Art. Other collections followed: Prince Liechtenstein, W von Wurzbach and others. Average Annual Attendance: 14,000.
Income: Financed by state appropriation.
Collections: Paintings of the 12th-18th centuries—Hieronymus Bosch, Hans Baldung Grien, 17th century Dutch (Rembrandt, Ruisdael, van Goyen, Jan Both and others), Flemish (Rubens, Jordaens, van Dyck), Tiepolo, Magnasco, Guardi.
Exhibitions: Annual exhibition from the permanent collection.
Publications: Bildhefte der Akademie, annually.
—**Kupferstichkabinett der Akademie der bildenden Kunste†** (Print and Drawing Collection of the Academy of Fine Arts). *Dir* Dr Albert Massiczek.
Open Mon - Fri 10 AM - Noon & 2 - 4 PM after notification; time-to-time expositions Mon - Sat 9 AM - Noon. Estab 1773. Average Annual Attendance: 14,000.
Collections: Drawings and prints of the 15th-20th centuries, expecially Italian, Netherland, German; Gothic architectural drawings, Durer, Rembrandt, Nazarenes, Daffinger (watercolors of flowers), Thomas Ender, Rudolf von Alt. More than 28,000 drawings, 29,000 prints, and 21,000 photographs.

GRAPHISCHE SAMMLUNG ALBERTINA,* (Albertina Graphic Art Collection), Augustinerstrasse 1, 1010. Tel: 52-4232, 5769. *Dir* Dr Walter Koschatzky.
Study Room open Mon - Thurs 1 - 4 PM; cl during July & Aug; Exhibition Mon, Tues, Thurs, Fri 10 AM - 4 PM; Wed 10 AM - 6 PM; Sat & Sun 10 AM - 1 PM. Estab 1769. Average Annual Attendance: 80,000.
Collections: Drawings (44,000), watercolors, and prints of all schools 14th - 20th centuries; sketchbooks, miniatures and posters. This is one of the largest (1,800,000) and best print collections in Europe.
Activities: Vienna Graphic Biennial Exhibition.
Library: Holdings—Vols 45,000.

KUNSTHISTORISCHES MUSEUM (Museum of Fine Arts) 1 Burgring 5, A-1010. *Dir* Dr Friderike Klauner.
Open Tues - Fri 9 AM - 1 PM & 7 - 9 PM; Sat - Sun 9 AM - 1 PM; cl Mon. Estab 1891.
Collections: Egyptian and Oriental collections; antiques; ceramics; jewelry and tapestries; paintings; weapons; old music instruments; historical carriages and costumes; the collection of Schloss Ambras.
Exhibitions: Gotter, Heroen, Menschen; Portraitgalerie zur Geschichte Osterreichs 1400-1800; Peter Paul Rubens; Giovanni da Bologna; Ephesos Museum.
Library: Holdings—Vols 70,000; Other—Photograph collection, prints 50,000.

MUSEUM DES 20 JAHRHUNDERTS,* (Museum of the 20th Century). Schweizergarten, 1010. Tel: 65-5121 & 65-0642. *Dir* Dr Alfred Schmeller; *Asst* Wilhelm Gaube.
Open Mon, Tues, Fri, Sat 10 AM - 4 PM; Sun 10 AM - 1 PM; Wed 2 - 9 PM; cl Thurs. Admis OS 5; special exhibitions OS 10, students and children free. Estab 1962 for the collecting and conservation of modern art.
Income: Financed by city and state appropriations.

Collections: Works of the 20th century—Munch, Bonnard, Nolde, Kandisnky, Klee, Beckmann, Ernst, Kokoschka, Leger, Matisse, Moore, Laurens, Marc, Wotruba, Arp, Archipenko, Barlach, Boekl, Delaunay, Gleizes, Hofer, Hoflehner, Jawlensky, Kirchner, Miro, Picasso, Rodin, Rosso, and others.
Publications: Catalogs.
Activities: Classes for adults; dramatic programs; weekly seminars; exten dept; lect open to public; concerts; traveling exhibitions organized and circulated.
Library: Holdings— Other—Photograph collection.

OSTERREICHISCHE GALERIE (Austrian Gallery), Prinz Eugen-Str 27, Oberes Belvedere, A 1030 (Mailing Add: Postfach 12, A 1037). Tel: 72 64 21 or 72 43 58. *Dir* Dr Hans Aurenhammer; *Cur* Dr Hubert Adolph; *Cur* Dr Elfriede Baum; *Cur* Dr Gerbert Frodl; *Cur* Dr Michael Krapf.
Open Tues - Thurs & Sat 10 AM - 4 PM; Fri 10 AM - 1 PM; Sun 9 AM - Noon; cl Mon. Estab 1903 for the collection, exhibition and publication of Austrian art (excepting drawings, watercolors, prints and arts and craft) from the Middle Ages until the present day. Average Annual Attendance: 160,000.
Income: Financed by state appropriation.
Collections: Austrian Gallery of 19th & 20th century art; Museum of Austrian Baroque Art; Museum of Austrian Medieval Art.
Exhibitions: Curt Stenvert; Andre Verlon; Alfred Wickenburg; Leopold Hauer; Peredwischniki; Jon Ev Scheffer v Leonhardshoff; Osterreichische Barockmaler aus der Nationalgalerie Prag; Philipp Otto Runge und Caspar David Friedrich.
Publications: Mitteilungen, annually.
Library: For reference, not open to public. Holdings: Vols 4000; Other—Photographs.

BELGIUM

ANTWERP

INTERNATIONAAL CULTUREEL CENTRUM, (International Cultural Centre,) Meir 50, 2000. Tel: 031-31-91-81 or 31 91 82. *Dir* Florent Bex; *Asst* Glenn Van Looy.
Open daily 10 AM - 5 PM. No admis. Estab 1970 to organize exhibitions of contemporary art. Average Annual Attendance: 150,000.
Income: Financed by state appropriation.
Exhibitions: Hergé; Joseph Kosuth; Flaus Ritterbusch; Fifth International Encounter on Video; Luca Patella; Nicola; Benelux Wereldstad; J M Bertholin; Pierre Daquin; Carmengloria Morales; Claude Rutault; Noma Dome; S Arakawa; James Lee Byars; Bill Vazan; C Vandemortel; L Halflants; C Uytterhaegen;.
Publications: Catalogues of exhibitions.
Activities: Lect open to public, 19 per yr; concerts; traveling exhibitions organized and circulated; sales shop selling books, prints.
Library: *Librn* Dany Smet. Open to public for reference. Holdings: Contemporary art, music, theatre, film, video.

KONINKLIJK MUSEUM VOOR SCHONE KUNSTEN,* (Royal Museum of Fine Arts), Leopold de Waelplein, 2000. Tel: 38 58 75. *Cur-in-Chief* Dr G Gepts; *Asst Cur* Dr A Monballieu; *Asst Cur* J Buyck; *Educ Service* M De Vos-De Jong.
Open daily; cl Mon. Admis 5 Belgian francs; free Sun, Wed & Sat afternoon. Estab 1843. Average Annual Attendance: 60,000.
Collections: Masterpieces (4000); five centuries of Flemish painting; important works of Leys, De Braekeleer, Ensor, Wouters, Smits, and Permeke; a survey of Western painting.
Exhibitions: Special shows according to the year's program.
Publications: Jaarboek van het Koninklijk Museum voor Schone Kunsten Antwerpen, annually; catalogs.
Activities: Vis lect; gallery talks; junior museum.
Library: Holdings—Vols 35,000.

MUSEUM MAYER VAN DEN BERGH, Lange Gasthuisstraat 19, B-2000. Tel: 031/324237. *Dir* F Baudouin; *Cur* Hans M J Nieuwdorp.
Open 10 AM - 5 PM; cl Mon. No admis. Estab 1904 for the preservation of the former private collection of Sir Fritz Mayer van den Bergh. House built in Flemish 16th-century style: nine rooms; modern extension (1974), three rooms. Average Annual Attendance: 40,000.
Income: Financed by city appropriation.
Collections: European painting 13th-18th century, especially Flemish 15th-16th century; Flemish sculpture 14th-16th century; decorative arts, ivories and illuminated manuscripts of the Middle Ages; ceramics and porcelain; textiles; furniture; applied arts; numismatics; prints; antique pottery and sculpture; painted windows.
Publications: Catalog.
Activities: Sales shop selling reproductions, slides and illustrated catalogs.

Library: Open to scholars for reference only. Holdings: Vols 2000. Special Collections: Sale catalogs 1875-1901.

MUSEUM PLANTIN-MORETUS (Plantin-Moretus Museum), Vrijdagmarkt 22. Tel: 03/33 06 88. *Dir* Dr L Voet; *Asst Dir* F de Nave.
Open daily 10 AM - 1 PM. No admis. Estab 1976: 16th - 17th century printing plant and patrician's house.
Income: Financed by city appropriation.
Collections: 16th-18th century manuscripts, designs, punches and matrices, moulds, wood blocks and copper plates.
Activities: Advanced Institute for printing art.
Library: Holdings—Vols 30,000. Special Collections: Incunabula (including Gutenberg Bible), old Antwerp impressions; photograph collection.

MUSEUM SMIDT VAN GELDER (Smidt van Gelder Museum), Belgielei 91,2000. Tel: 03-39 06 52 & 39 10 90. *Chief Asst* Maria Snoeckx.
Open Tues - Sun 10 AM - 5 PM; cl Mon. Estab 1949 as a private collection given to the City. Average Annual Attendance: 13,000.
Income: Financed by city appropriation.
Collections: Museum arranged as an 18th century aristocratic living house with 18th century French furniture and paintings and Dutch paintings from the 17th & 19th centuries; tapestries; 18th century Chinese and European porcelains.
Library: Reference library. Holdings: Vol 600; Other—Prints 1000, in photograph collection.

OPENLUCHTMUSEUM VOOR BEELDHOUWKUNST, MIDDEL-HEIM (Open air Museum for Sculpture Middelheim), Middelheimlaan 61, 2020. Tel: 031-27 15 34. *Cur* F Baudouin; *Asst Cur* M R Bentein.
Open daily 10 AM - Sunset. No admis, except during biennials. Estab 1950 to exhibit contemporary sculpture, starting with Rodin, and up to the present day, as well as to make a collection for the biennials; a beautiful park; small sculpture in a pavilion. Average Annual Attendance: 125,000.
Income: Financed by city appropriation.
Collections: Contemporary sculpture, medals, drawings and graphics by sculptors.
Exhibitions: 14th Biennial for sculpture.
Publications: Catalogues of the collection; exhibition catalogues.
Activities: Educ dept; lect; gallery talks; tours; sales desk selling reproductions, catalogues.
—**Lode Craeybeck Documentation Center,** Middelheimlaan 61.
Open daily 10 AM - 4 PM. Estab 1950 as a library of the museum. Since 1976 was renamed to collect all possible information on contemporary sculpture and environmental art.
Income: Financed by city appropriation.
Holdings: Vols 28,500; Per subs 40; AV—Slides; Other—Exhibition catalogs, photographs.
Publications: Catalogue of the Library; Monographies 1975, Part I.

RUBENIANUM, Belgiëlei 91, B 2000. Tel: 031/39 10 90. *Keeper Art Historical Mus City of Antwerp* Frans Baudouin; *Asst Keeper* Nora de Poorter.
Open Mon - Fri 8:30 AM - 4:30 PM. Estab 1950 as the art-historical department and documentation center of the City of Antwerp concerning Rubens, and Flemish art of the 16th & 17th centuries. Its first aim is the publication of the Corpus Rubenianum Ludwig Burchard.
Income: Financed by city appropriation.
Collections: Library and documentation of the Nationaal Centrum voor de Plastische Kunsten van de 16de en de 17de Eeuw are incorporated.
Publications: Corpus Rubenianum Ludwig Burchard (an illustrated Catalogue Raisonne of the work of P P Rubens in 26 parts, based on material of Dr Ludwig Burchard).

STEDELIJK PRENTENKABINET (Municipal Gallery of Graphic Arts), Vrijdagmarkt 23. Tel: 031/322455. *Dir* Dr L Voet; *Asst Dir* F de Nave.
Open Mon - Fri 10 AM - 4 PM. No admis. Estab 1936 for research work on Flemish graphic art.
Income: Financed by city appropriation.
Collections: Old drawings—Rubens, Van Dyck, Jordaens, E and A Quellin, Schut, etc. Modern Drawings—J Ensor; Rik Wouters; W Vaes; Fl Jesspers; H Leys, etc. Old engravings—Galle, Wiericx, Jegher, Goltzius, W Hollar, Hogenbergh, etc. Modern engraings—Ensor, W Vaes, Masereel, Cantre, J Minne; Antwerp iconographic collection.
Library: Holdings—Vols 9000; Other—Photograph collection of approx 15,000 prints.

BRUGES

STEDELYKE MUSEA (City Museums), Dyver, 12, 8000. Tel: 399-11. *Dir* Dr A Janssens de Bisthoven; *Cur* Dr V Vermeersch; *Cur* Drs D De Vos; *Cur* Drs W Dezutter; *Educ Dept* Mrs Plavwers.
Open Daily Mar - Sept 9·30 AM - Noon & 2 - 6 PM; Oct - Feb 10 AM - Noon & 2 - 5 PM. Admis 20 francs, groups 10 francs, students 5 francs. Estab in 18th century; consists of four museums Groeningemuseum, Gruuthusemuseum, Arentshuis and Museum Voor Volkskunde, Mailing Add: Balstraat, 27. Average Annual Attendance: 300,000.
Income: Financed by city appropriation.
Collections: Groeningemuseum—Flemish paintings and modern art: Gruuthusemuseum—Furniture, numismatics, sculpture, tapestries, textile art; Arentshuis—Paintings, porcelain, furniture of the 18th and 19th century; Museum voor Volkskunde—Folklore.
Activities: Classes for adults and children: lect open to the public, 4 vis lectr per yr; individual paintings and original objects of art lent to other museums; sales shop selling books, reproductions, prints and slides.
Library: Holdings—Vols 8000; Per subs 450.

BRUSSELS

MUSEES ROYAUX D'ART ET D'HISTOIRE,* (Royal Museums of Art and History), 10 Parc du Cinquantenaire, 1040. Tel: 733 96 10. *Cur* Rene de Roo.
Open 9:30 AM - 12:30 PM & 1:30 - 5 PM; cl Mon. Estab 1835.
Collections: *Egyptian, Greek, Oriental and classical art; *Roman, Belgium; *Medieval, Renaissance and modern art—furniture, tapestries, textiles, lace, glass, ceramics, silver; *Far Eastern art; †American archaeology; †ethnography; †folklore.
Publications: Bulletin, annually.
Activities: Lect organized by Educ Service on subjects relating to the collections, principally ancient art and archaeology, Medieval & Renaissance manufacturing arts, folklore, ethnography; 50 vis Dutch and French vis lectr per yr; gallery talks; tours.
Library: Holdings—Vols 150,000.

MUSEES ROYAUX DES BEAUX-ARTS DE BELGIQUE,* (Royal Museums of Fine Arts of Belgium), rue du Musée 9. Tel: 02-513 96 30. *Dir* Philippe Roberts-Jones; *Cur Ancient Art* Henri Pauwels; *Cur Modern Art* Francine-Claire Legrand.
Estab 1830.
Collections: Medieval, Renaissance and modern paintings, drawings and sculpture.
Publications: Bulletin, regularly.
—**Musée d'Art Ancien,** rue de la Regence 3. *Dir* F C Legrand.
Collections: Paintings, drawings and sculpture of the 19th-20th century.
Exhibitions: Temporary exhibitions.
—**Musée Constantin Meunier,** rue de l'Abbaye 59.
Collections: Paintings, drawings and sculptures by Constantin Meunier; the artist's house and studio.
—**Musée Wiertz,** rue Vautier 62.
Collections: Paintings of Antoine Wiertz.

LIEGE

MUSEES D'ARCHEOLOGIE ET D'ARTS DECORATIFS (Liege Museums of Archeology and Decorative Arts), 13, Quai de Maastricht, 4000. *Dir* Dr Joseph Philippe; *Asst Cur* M Jean Beguin; *Asst Cur* Marie-Claire Gueury.
Open 10 AM - 12:30 PM & 2 - 5 PM; Sun & holidays 10 AM - 4 PM. Curtius Museum estab 1909, Ansembourg Musuem in 1905, and the Glass Museum 1959. Mem: 400.
Income: Financed by city and state appropriations.
Collections: Musee Curtius—archeology; decorative arts from prehistory to 18th century; Musee du Verre—history and art of glass; Musee d" Ansembourg—18th century decorative arts of Liege, housed in a mansion of the same period.
Exhibitions: Nouvelle Presentation des Collections Internationales du verre. Collection of International Glass.
Publications: Bulletin de l'Association Internationale pour l"Histoire du Verre, annually; plus Annales of the Association.
Activities: Lect open to public, 45 vis lectr per yr; gallery talks; museum shop selling books, slides.
Library: Open for reference. Holdings: Per subs 550.

VERVIERS

MUSEES COMMUNAUX BEAUX-ARTS ET ARCHEOLOGIE (Community Museum of Fine Arts and Archaeology), Beaux Arts-rue Renier, 17 (Archeologie-rue des Raines, 42). Tel: 087/331695. *Cur* V Bronowski.

Open Mon - Thurs & Sat 9 AM - Noon & 2 - 5 PM; Sun 10 AM - 1 PM & 3 - 6 PM. No admis. Estab 1884.
Income: Financed by appropriation.
Collections: Ancient and modern painting and sculpture; graphic arts; ceramics; furniture; Roman antiquities; regional archaeology; folk arts.
Exhibitions: Eight exhibitions of fine arts and archaeology a year.
Publications: Guide books.
Activities: Classes for children; lect open to public.

BOLIVIA

LA PAZ

MUSEO NACIONAL DE ARQUEOLOGIA,* (National Museum), Calle Tihuanacu 93, Casilla oficial 64. Tel: 29624. *Dir* Gregorio Cordero Miranda; *Ast Dir* Olga Joffre Chavez; *Secy* Victor Vera; *Cur Archaeology* Federico Diez de Medina.
Estab 1846, reinaugurated 1960. Average Annual Attendance: 9,500.
Collections: Anthropology; ethnology; archaeology; zoology; numismatics; folklore; traditional native arts and crafts; colonial art; Lake Titicaca district exhibitions.
Publications: Anales de Museo, Centenario del Museo 1940.
Activities: Study of Archaeology, cultural exchange with the exterior, services to tourists, college & institutions.
Library: Holdings—Vols 3000.

BRAZIL

OURO PRETO

MUSEU DA INCONFIDENCIA,* (History of Democratic Ideals and Culture in Minas Gerais), Praca Tiracentes, 139, 35,400. Tel: 332. *Dir* Orlandino Seitas Fernandes.
Open Noon - 5:30 PM. Estab 1938. Inaugurated 1944 to honor the first movement towards Brazil's independence, the Inconfidencia Mineira, which took place in Ouro Preto, then the capitol of Minas Gerais; to explain how this movement and its ideals first appeared; to show a general view of the cultural development of Minas Gerais to the public through the collections. Average Annual Attendance: 150,000.
Income: The Museum belongs to the Federal Government and is an organ of the Ministry for Education's Department for the Preservation of the National Historic and Artistic Property. It has no Board of Trustees and no membership. All expenditures are paid directly by the Federal Treasury.
Collections: Objects related to the 1789 revolutionaries of Minas Gerais (the Inconfidentes); †wood carvings; †furniture; painting; sacred arts; silver.
Special collections: Tombs containing the remains of the Inconfidentes who died exiled in different regions of Africa; original drawings, documents, and wood carvings by Antonio Francisco Lisboa, the Little Cripple, who is Brazil's most important artist and who was also a sculptor and architect.
Library: Holdings—Vols 2200; Per subs and works 1600. Special Subjects: Brazil's history and history of art, with emphasis on Minas Gerais problems. Special Collections: Portuguese, Spanish, and Latin American arts and history; documents that belonged to Barao de Camargos, an ancient Senator who lived in Ouro Preto, and documents from all the Ouro Preto's offices of notary public during the colonial period.

RIO DE JANEIRO

MUSEU DE ARTE MODERNA (Museum of Modern Art), Beira-Mar Ave (Mailing Add: Box 44, ZC-39, 20,000). Tel: 231-1871. *Pres* Dr Ivo Pitangui; *VPres* Dr Gilberto Marinho; *Exec Secy* Dr Alvaro Americano; *Treas* Dr Leonidas Lopes Borio; *Exec Dir* Heloisa Aleixo Lustosa; *Asst Exec Dir* Dr Septimus Mendonca Clark.
Open Noon - 7 PM. Admis 80¢. Estab 1948 to document the evolution of the Contemporary Fine Arts. The Museum of Modern Art is an outstanding architectural project by Alfonso Eduardo Reidy. It consists of a connected three-story building of two blocks—one for temporary exhibitions and collections, and the other for the administration, courses, library, experimental displays and film collection. Average Annual Attendance: 33,000. Mem: 2000.
Income: Financed by endowment, state appropriation.
Collections: Foreign painters—Picasso, Marino Marini, Calder, Kothko, Motherwell, Albers, Lassaw; Modern Art—Di Cavalcanti, Brecheret, Portinari, Guignard, Djanira, Cildo Meirelles, Valtercio Caldas (painting, sculpture and graphics). Special emphasis on Brazilian artists connected with experimental avant-garde.

Exhibitions: Sergio Camargo, Yung (Unconscious Image); Color's Language; Brazilian Popular Art, Retrospective Abelardo Zaluar, João Camara Filho, Carl Bucher, Rolf I Iseli and Urs L'uthi; Brazilian Constructive Projects of Arts; Hundertwasser, Ouro do Peru.
Publications: Bulletin, monthly.
Activities: Classes for adults and children; lect open to public, 20 vis lectr per yr; concerts; gallery talks; sales shop selling books, magazines, original art, reproductions, prints.
—**Library.** *Head Librn* Dr Alicia Dantas Leite; *Librn* Germana Maria Camarao Costa.
Open daily 2 - 7 PM for reference. Estab 1968 to enable the public to consult documentaries related to the Arts in general.
Holdings: Vols 9000; Per subs 300; AV—Reels, slides; Other—Exhibition catalogs, original art works, original documents, pamphlets, photographs, prints, reproductions, sculpture.
Special Subjects: Modern and contemporary arts.
Exhibitions: Cartography in Switzerland; Stamps.
Publications: Library Bulletin, annually.

MUSEU NACIONAL DE BELAS ARTES (National Museum of Fine Arts), Ave Rio Branco 199. *Dir & Prof* Edson Motta; *Chief Technical Dept* Margarida Maria Barbosa da Silva Guimarães.
Open Tues - Fri 12:30 - 6:30 PM. No admis. Estab 1937 to collect, guard and exhibit the works of art belonging to the federal patrimony, propagate and expand the knowledge of fine arts by promoting the utilization of the educative resources existing in the museum. First floor of gallery has temporary exhibition room; second floor has Brazilian art of the 19th and 20th century; on the third floor is the foreign gallery. Average Annual Attendance: 30,000.
Income: Financed by state appropriation.
Collections: 19th century Brazilian art, works by outstanding painters; †20th century Brazilian art; †foreign collections—works by French, Italian, English, Dutch, Portuguese, Spanish and German masters.
Exhibitions: (1976-78) 66 exhibitions.
Publications: Boletim, every 3 months; gallery guides and catalogs.
Activities: Classes for adults; docent training; lect open to public; concerts; gallery talks.
—**Library.** *Chief Librn* Vera Monteiro Pereira.
Open 1:30 - 6:30 PM. Estab 1937 as a reference library.
Income: Financed by state appropriation.
Holdings: Vols 6000; Other—Exhibition catalogs, pamphlets.

SAO PAULO

MUSEU DE ARTE DE SAO PAULO* (Sao Paulo Art Museum), Av Paulista 1578. *Dir* R M Bardi.
Open 2 - 6 PM. Founded 1947.
Collections: †Ancient and modern paintings and sculptures; Italian, 13th-20th centuries; French, 16th-20th centuries; Spanish and Portuguese, 16th-19th centuries; Flemish, Dutch, and German, 15th-20th centuries; British, 18th-20th centuries; American, 19th-20th centuries; Brazilian, 17th-20th centuries; representative works by Portinari and Lasar Segall.
Exhibitions: Printing and photography exhibitions.
Activities: Art history school; exhibitions, printing and photography.

CEYLON

COLOMBO

COLOMBO NATIONAL MUSEUM, Albert Crescent (Mailing Add: PO Box 854, 7). Tel: 94767. *Dir* Dr P de Silva; *Asst Dir* vacant; *Cur Entomology* Dr Gunawardena; *Cur Ethnology* S Lakdusinghe; *Cur Anthropology* P Endegama; *Cur Educ & Publication* Mrs W M Fernando.
Open Mon - Thurs & Sun 9 AM - 5 PM. Admis adults 25¢; children 10¢; students in groups and clergy free. Estab 1877 for cultural, scientific and educational purposes. Average Annual Attendance: 208,307.
Income: $3,820 (financed by state appropriation).
Collections: Antiquities of Sri Lanka; rare books and palm leaf manuscripts of Sri Lanka.
Exhibitions: Photographic exhibition of Monuments and Antiquities of several non-aligned countries; several temporary exhibitions by Embassies of the Peoples Republic of China, USSR and France.
Publications: Spolia Zeylanica.
Activities: Classes for children; lect open to public, 15 vis lectr per yr; sales shop selling books and prints.
Library: *Librn* C I Karunanayake.
Open for research and reference.
Holdings: Vols 500,000; Per subs 4,133; Other—Manuscripts 3,570.

Special Subjects: Ceyloniana Natural History, archaeology, art and architecture.

CHILE

SANTIAGO

MUSEO DE ARTE POPULAR AMERICANO* (Art of the American Peoples Museum), University of Chile, Faculty of Fine Arts, Cerro Santa Lucia. Tel: 3 01 38. *Dir* Patricio Court del Pedregal.
Open Tues - Sat 10 AM - 5:30 PM; Sun 3 - 6 PM. No admis. Estab 1944 for the study and exposure to popular American art. Three rooms with showcases and panels for exhibition.
Collections: Popular art of the American peoples; collection of araucarian silver.
Exhibitions: Pesebres, retablos e imagineria religiosa; Tejidos indigenas y populares de America; Artesania Popular Mexicana; Arte Popular Chileno; Arte Popular Rumano; Arte y Artesanias de China Popular.
Publications: Exhibition catalogs, annually.
Activities: Exten dept serving the faculty of fine arts; traveling exhibitions organized and circulated; lectures.
Library: Reference library. Holdings: Vols 3500; Other—Photograph collection.

MUSEO NACIONAL DE BELLAS ARTES (National Museum of Fine Arts), Parque Forestal s/n, (Mailing Add: Casilla 3209). *Cur* Nena Ossa.
Open Tues - Sat 10 AM - 6 PM; Sun 10 AM - 2 PM. Admis $6, students $3. Estab 1880 to show the Chilean collection of fine arts (painting and sculpture). Permanent collection—15 galleries; temporary exhibitions—8 galleries. Average Annual Attendance: 280,000. Mem: 11.
Income: $1,800,000.
Collections: Chilean painting; Spanish painting; Baroque painting; Sculpture in general.
Exhibitions: Ten contemporary exhibitions from abroad; 16 national exhibitions, contemporary and retrospective.
Publications: Exhibition catalogs; a general catalog.
Activities: Classes for children; docent training; lect open to public; competitions; individual paintings and original objects of art lent to government institutions.
Library: *Librn* Doralisa Duarte P. Open for reference to students and the public. Holdings: Vols 1380.

CHINA, REPUBLIC OF

TAIPEI

NATIONAL PALACE MUSEUM, Shih-Lin, Wai Shuang Hsi, 111. Tel: 881 20 2014. *Dir* Dr Chiang Fu-tsung; *Deputy Dir* Li Lin-ts'an; *Acting Deputy Dir & Cur Dept Calligraphy & Painting* Chiang Chaoshen; *Cur Dept Rare Books & Documents* Peter Chang.
Open daily 9 AM - 5 PM. Admis 40¢; Estab 1925 in Peiping, re-opened in the present building 1965, to serve as a center of Chinese Art, to conserve, research and exhibit the former Imperial collections of the Ch'ing Dynasty. Average Annual Attendance: 1,500,000.
Income: Financed by state appropriation.
Collections: Jades, bronzes, pottery, porcelain, oracle bones, enamelware, carved lacquer, painting, calligraphy, tapestry, embroidery, writing implements, miniature crafts, rare and old books, Ch'ing dynasty court and governmental documents.
Publications: Bulletin, bimonthly; National Palace Museum Quarterly; Newsletter, monthly.
Activities: Programs for school children; lect open to public; traveling exhibitions organized and circulated; sales shop selling books, reproductions, prints and slides.
—**Library.**
Open for reference to researchers and students.
Holdings: Vols 180,000; Per subs 60.
Special Subjects: Chinese art, art history, sinology.
Special Collections: Rare books collection, 153,222 volumes, includes more than 70 wood-block editions printed during the Sun dynasty. Palace Memorials of the Ch'ing dynasty and other Ch'ing dynasty archival materials.

COLOMBIA

BOGOTA

COLOMBIAN INSTITUTE OF CULTURE, Museum of Colonial Art, Carrera 6 No 9-77. Tel: 241 6017. *Dir* Francisco Gil Tovar.
Open Tues - Sat 9 AM - 7 PM; Sun and holidays 10 AM - 5 PM. Admis adults 5 pesos, children 2 pesos. Estab 1942 to promote culture. The Museum is a dependency of the national cultural directorate and reflects, through the 17th century mansion that it occupies and the works of art that it conserves, that period in which the nation formed part of the Spanish Empire. Average Annual Attendance: 32,000.
Income: Financed by state appropriation.
Collections: Painting, drawings, decorative carving, furniture and silver relating to aesthetics and life in New Granada between 1550 and 1820; large collection of paintings and drawings of Gregorio Vasquez Ceballos (1638-1711); native master Figueroa and Joaquin Gutierrez; gilded trunks of the 17th century.
Exhibitions: Artistic Fusion; Angels and Devils in the Colony; Little pictures in big frames; Religious Colonial Art; Images of Colombia; Birth and Infancy of Jesus in Colonial Art; Drawings of Gregorio Vasquez Ceballos; Didactic Synthesis of Art of New Granada; one-person exhibitions dedicated to authors, schools, themes.
Publications: Bulletin, monthly.
Activities: Classes for adults and children; docent training; artmobile.

CYPRUS

NICOSIA

CYPRUS MUSEUM, Museum St. Tel: 402190. *Cur* Kyriakos Nicolaou; *Asst Cur* vacant.
Open daily 8 AM - 5:30 PM, Sun 10 AM - 1 PM. Admis 100 mils. Estab 1909 to collect, preserve and exhibit antiquities dating from the Neolithic period (sixth millenium BC) to Graeco-Roman times (4th century AD). Average Annual Attendance: 34,493.
Income: $5000 (financed by state appropriation). Purchases $5000.
Collections: Neolithic stone tools and vessels; early bronze-age pottery; sanctuary and ploughing models; Mycenaean vases; middle and late bronze-age geometric, archaic, classical, Hellenistic and Graeco-Roman pottery; terra cotta figurines from Ayia Irini; sculpture including the fine Tarsos head, the Aphrodite of Soli, and the bronze statue of Septimus Sevarus; bronzes, coins, jewelry, lamps, glass, other minor works of art; bronze cauldron from Salamis; terracotta figurines; the silver trays from Lambousa; others.
Library: Librn Lygia Ierodiakonou. Open to the public for reference. Holdings: Vols 10,500; Per subs -10. Special Subjects; Cypriot, Greek and Roman, and near East archaeology.

CZECHOSLOVAKIA

BRATISLAVA

SLOVENSKA NARODNA GALERIA* (Slovak National Gallery), Razusovo nabrezie 2, 89013. Tel: 383 04 & 321 66. *Dir* Dr Stefan Mruskovic; *Chief Dept Slovak & European Art to 19th century* Dr Karol Vaculik; *Chief Dept Contemporary Art* Dr Silvia Ileckova; *Chief Dept Graphic Art* Dr Eva Trojanova; *Chief Dept Nonprofessional Art* Dr Katarina Schreiberova.
Estab 1948 as the leading national art institution. The main exhibition halls in Bratislava under reconstruction since 1972; at present all the collections concentrated in the castle of the central Slovakian city of Zvolen and in the castle of the locality of Červený Kameň. Open 10 AM - 6 PM. The permanent installation of paintings and graphics by one of the leading artists of the Slovak modern art, Ludovit Fulla, in the city of Ruzomberok.
Collections: Slovak and European painting (4500), mostly Italian, Flemish and Dutch; sculpture (1700); graphics and drawings (17,000); insitic art (700); applied arts (1400).
Exhibitions: Permanent collection; specialized exhibitions; international exhibitions organized by Slovak National Gallery; Biennale of Illustrations Bratislava, an exhibition of children's books illustrations; Triennale of Insitic (Naive) Art Exhibition, extended to include all forms of nonprofessional art.
Publications: Selected material from each symposium—The Problems of Contemporary Children's Books Illustrations, The Gothic Art in Slovakia, On the Nonprofessional Art, On the Contemporary Slovak Art, and others; Bulletin Ars Populi, 2-3 times a year.
Activities: National and international symposiums and seminars; traveling exhibitions organized and circulated; competitions with awards.
Library: Holdings—Vols 40,000.

BRNO

MORAVSKA GALERIE V BRNE* (Moravian Gallery at Brno), Husova ulice 14, 66 226. Tel: 20 151/24 809. *Art Historian & Dir* Jiri Hlusicka.
Open daily 10 AM - 6 PM; cl Mon. Admis 1, 2, 4, Czech crowns. Estab 1817 as a regional gallery of fine arts; collects all-world art; specialised in Moravian Art.
Income: Financed by state appropriation.
Collections: †Fine art collection—painting, sculpture, graphic art since 14th century to present; †Applied art collection—glass, furniture, textiles, jewelry, ceramics, graphic design, photography; Oriental art collection. Over 100,000 pieces in both collections.
Exhibitions: Biennale of Graphic design; Cut glass triennale; Biennale of Czechoslovak contemporary photography; and other exhibitions from own collections or lent exhibitions from other Czech and foreign institutions.
Publications: Bulletin of Moravian Gallery, 3 per year; catalogs; Museology Papers, 4 per year.
Activities: Classes for adults; lect open to public; gallery talks; tours; concerts; exten dept serving south Moravia; original objects of art lent for exhibitions only; traveling exhibitions organized and circulated.
—**Library.** *Librn* Karel Holesovsky; *Asst Librn* Marie Dohnalova.
Open daily 9 AM - 6 PM; cl sun. Estab 1873. The only public library in Moravia specializing in art literature. Open to students, scholars, collectors and art lovers.
Income: Financed by state appropriation.
Holdings: Vols 64,000; Per subs 150.
Special Collections: Old prints; rare Moravian books and fine prints, bookbindings (20th century).
Exhibitions: Bookbindings by Jindrich Svoboda; Art literature from the Soviet Union.

LITOMERICE

SEVEROCESKA GALERIE VYTVARNEHO UMENI* (North Bohemian Gallery of Fine Arts), Michalska 7, 2338. Tel: 23 38. *Dir* Otakar Votocek.
Open Mon - Fri 10 Am - Noon & 2 - 5 PM; Sat & Sun 10 AM - 5 PM. Admis adults 2 Kcs, students 1 Kcs. Estab 1958 as a collection of 13th-20th century North Bohemian paintings and sculptures.
Income: Financed by city and state appropriations.
Collections: Gothic art of the 13th-16th centuries; Renaissance paintings and sculptures of the 15th-16th centuries; Barok art of the 17th-18th centuresi; †art of the 19th century; collection of contemporary art; special collections of naive paintings and sculpture.
Exhibitions: Approx 10 mutual exhibitions yearly; Dutch paintings of the 17th century; North-Bohemian county in the works of the painters and graphic artists; Art Protis, tapestry; Russian Ikons; Naive Art.
Activities: Classes for children; lect open to public, 8 vis lectr per yr; gallery talks; tours; concerts; exten dept serving North Bohemian county; traveling exhibitions organized and circulated; individual paintings and original objects of art lent; lending collection contains books, color reproductions, lantern slides, slides, original prints, photographs, sculpture.
Library: Holdings—Vols 5,000.

PRAGUE

NARODNI GALERIE V PRAZE (National Gallery of Prague), Hradcanske Namesti, 15, 1 Hradcany. Tel: 35 24 41-3 & 53 68 67. *Pres* Dr Jiri Kotalik; *Deputy Dir & Chief Graphic Art Coll* Dr Libuse Jandova; *Chief Ancient Art Coll* Dr Jiri Masin; *Chief Modern Art Coll* Dr Vaclav Prochazka; *Chief Oriental Art Coll* Dr Lubor Hajek; *Deputy Dir* Vladimir Benes.
Open daily 10 AM - 6 PM; cl Mon. Admis 2 crowns. Estab 1796 as picture gallery of the Society of Patriotic Friends of Art; 1901 estab Gallery of Modern Art; 1945 both collections united in the National Gallery; to collect and expertly safeguard the collections of Czech and world paintings, sculpture and graphic art works. Average Annual Attendance: 800,000.
Income: Financed by state appropriation.
Collections: Old European art; French and European art of the 19th and 20th century; Old Czech art; modern art; graphic art; Czech sculpture of the 19th and 20th century; Oriental art.
Exhibitions: (1976) Alfred Kubin; Masterpieces of Czech Painting in Prague Castle Collection; 100 Old Czech Drawings; Josef Kubicek Sculpture; Slovak Gothic Art; Drawings and watercolors in Museum and Galleries of the German Democratic Republics; Scythian Art in Soviet Museums; Contemporary Medals in Poland; From Monet to Leger—Masterpieces of Puskin's Museum in Moscow and Hermitage in Leningrad; Vlastimil Rada; Emilio Greco—Graphic Art 1964-1975; Bulgarian Painting of the 20th Century; Homage to Tizian; (1977) Jaroslav Grus Paintings; European Graphic Art in the Collections of the University in

Lutych; Czech Painting of the First Half of the 20th Century in the Gallery of Art in Ostrava; Guido Maines, Sobeslav Pinkas Paintings; Bretislav Benda; Ludovit Fulla; Three Masterpieces: Tintoretto, El Greco, Frans Hals; Vaclav Hollar Drawings 1607-1677; Collection of the Oriental Art; Impressionism—French and German Painting in the State Museum in Dresden; Czech Sculptores Drawings, Belgian Drawing and Graphic Art of the 16th and 17th centuries;/ Russian and Soviet Art in Czechoslovak Museum and Galleries; Homage to P P Rubens; Josef Lada Paintings; Kojosi Saito—100 graphics (1948-1976).

Publications: Bulletin of the National gallery; exhibition catalogs; guides to collections.

Activities: Classes for adults and children; lect open to the public, 20 vis lectr per yr; individual paintings and original objects of art lent to galleries and museums in Czech and abroad; traveling exhibitions organized and circulated; sales shop selling reproductions and slides.

—Library. *Head of the Service* Dr Helena Obrova.
Estab 1945 to serve exclusively the Gallery and experts; character of the library corresponds to the Gallery Collections.
Income: Financed by state appropriation.
Holdings: Vols 39,000; Per subs 5000; AV—Microfilm; slides.

STATNI ZIDOVSKE MUZEUM (State Jewish Museum), Jachymova 3, 110 01. Tel: 633-74. *Dir* Dr Miroslav Jaros; *Deputy Dir* Dr V Sadek; *Chief of Dept Expositions* Dr A Frankova.
Open Sun - Fri 9 AM - 5 PM; cl Sat. Admis adults 5 Kcs, students 3Kcs. Estab 1950 to inform the public about the history of Jews in Bohemia and Moravia; Jewish Cemetery of the 15th-18th centuries and the old-new synagogue of the 13th century. Average Annual Attendance: 700,000.
Collections: Silver liturgical objects; textiles from synagogues of historic interest; children's drawings and works of painters from the concentration camp Terezin; library of ancient books with a collection of Hebrew manuscripts; historical archival materials of Bohemian and Moravian Jewish religious communities.
Publications: Judaica Bohemiae, biannually.
Activities: Exhibitions, scientific research on the field of the history of Jews in Bohemia and Moravia.
Library: Holdings—Vols 80,000.

DENMARK

AALBORG

NORDJYLLANDS KUNSTMUSEUM (Art Museum of Northern Jutland), Kong Christians Alle 50, 9000. *Dir* L Rostrup Boyesen; *Cur* H P Jensen; *Cur* Jorn Otto Hansen.
Open Tues - Sun 10 AM - 5 PM; cl Mon. Admis 5DKr. Estab 1972 as an art gallery. Average Annual Attendance: 100,000.
Income: Financed by city and state appropriation. Purchases: 150,000 DKr.
Collections: Collection of painting, sculpture and graphics from this century, Danish and international. Main museum for the Cobra movement.
Exhibitions: Approx 75 exhibitions per year, mostly on international level, painting, sculpture, graphic, textile, and ceramic.
Publications: Bulletin, monthly.
Activities: Classes for adults and children; lect open to public, 5 vis lectr per yr; concerts; galley talks; traveling exhibitions organized and circulated; museum shop selling magazines, original art, reproductions, prints.
Library: Open for reference to the public. Holdings: Vols 40,000; Per subs 50.

AARHUS

AARHUS KUNSTMUSEUM* (Aarhus Art Museum), Vennelystparken, 8000. Tel: 13 52 55. *Dir* Kristian Jakobsen.
Open Tues - Fri 10 AM - 4 PM; Sat - Sun 10 AM - 5 PM; cl Mon. No admis. Estab 1958. Average Annual Attendance: 70,000.
Income: Financed by endowment and city appropriation. Purchases: $30,000.
Collections: Danish art—painting, sculpture, graphic arts, 1750 to present time; European art, mostly recent graphics; a few outstanding works 17th century and later.
Exhibitions: Several every year.
Activities: Lect open to public; concerts; junior museum.
Library: Holdings— Other—Photograph collection.

CHARLOTTENLUND

ORDRUPGAARD COLLECTION, Vilvordevej 110, 2920. Tel: 01 OR 11 83. *Dir* Vacant.
Open May - Sept daily except Mon 2 - 5 PM; Oct - Apr, Sat & Sun 2 - 4 PM. Admis 2 Danish crowns.

Collections: Wilhelm Hansen Collection, paintings by Delacroix, Corot, Courbet, Manet, Degas, Renoir, Pissarro, Sisley, Gauguin, Cezanne and other French and Danish artists from the 19th century.

COPENHAGEN

NY CARLSBERG GLYPTOTHEK (Carlsberg Gallery), Dantes Plads, 1556. *Dir* F Johonsen; *Cur French & Danish Art* H E Nørregaard Nielsen; *Cur Greek & Roman Art* J Christiansen.
Open Summer daily 10 AM - 4 PM; Winter weekdays 12 AM - 3 PM; Sun 10 AM - 4 PM; cl Mon all year. Admis 3 kroner; Wed & Sun free. Estab 1897. Average Annual Attendance: 155,000.
Collections: †Egyptian, †Greek, †Etruscan, and †Roman sculpture; †Danish and †French paintings and sculptures from 19th century.
Library: Reference library. Holdings: Vols 35,000.

DET DANSKE KUNSTINDUSTRIMUSEUM* (Museum of Decorative Art), Bredgade 68, 1260. Tel: 14 94 52. *Pres* Jørgen Trolle; *Dir* Erik Lassen; *Keepers* Vibeke Woldbye & Jorg Jørgen Schou-Christensen.
Open daily 1 - 4 PM; Sept 1 - May 31, Tues 1 - 9 PM; cl Mon. Estab 1894.
Collections: European decorative art from the middle ages to the present—furniture, carpets and tapestries, porcelain and pottery, silverware, jewelery, textiles and bookbindings; Chinese and Japanese art and handicrafts.
Exhibitions: Approx 20 exhibitions per year.
Publications: Kunstindustrimuseets Virksomhed.
Activities: Lect, 2-3 vis lectr per yr.
—Library. *Librn* Svend Eriksen.
Open weekdays 10 AM - 4 PM; Sept 1 - May 31, Tues 10 AM - 9 PM; cl Mon.
Holdings: Vols 50,000; Other—Photograph collection.

KOBENHAVNS BYMUSEUM (Copenhagen City Museum), Vesterbrogade 59, 1620. Tel: 01 210772. *Cur* Steffen Linvald; *Asst Cur* John Erichsen.
Open Tues - Sun 10 AM - 4 PM; Tues 7 - 9 PM; cl Mon. Admis adults 1 kr, children 50 ore. Estab 1901 to record the history and development of Copenhagen from 1167 up till now.
Income: Financed by city appropriation.
Collections: Topographical paintings, drawings and prints; photographs 1850 to the present.
Exhibitions: John Christensen, paintings and drawings from Norrebro; Prince and horse—J F J Saly's equestrian monument of Frederik V 1753-74; Copenhagen slum.
Publications: Kobenhavns Bymuseum, yearly.
Activities: Concerts.

NATIONALMUSEET* (National Museum), Prinsens Palae, Frederiksholms Kanal 12. Tel: 13 44 11. *Dir* Dr PV Glob; *Keeper Danish Prehistoric Coll* Mogens Orsnes; *Keeper Danish Historical Coll* Harald Langberg; *Keeper Danish Folk Museum* H Rasmussen; *Keeper Ethnographic Coll* Dr Torben Monberg; *Keeper Coll Classical Antiquities* Dr ML Buhl; *Keeper Royal Coll of Coins and Medals* Otto Morkholm; *Keeper Open-air Museum at Sorgenfri* P Michelsen.
Estab 1807; consists of ten divisions.

STATENS MUSEUM FOR KUNST (Royal Museum of Fine Arts), Sølvgade, 1307.
—Department of Painting and Sculpture, Sølvgade, 1307. Tel: 01 11 21 26. *Dir* Jørn Rubow; *Chief Cur* Bente Skovgaard; *Cur* Hanne Westergaard and Olaf Koester; *Asst* Else Lofthus; *Restorer* Acting for Chief Restorer Steen Bjarnhof, Henrik Bjerre; *Restorers* Lone Bøgh, Elena Berlowicz, Mette Bjarnhof and Anne-Dorte Rogild.
Open 10 AM - 5 PM; Wed 10 AM - 8 PM; cl Mon. No admis. Estab 1896 to collect, conserve, examine and publish Danish painting and sculpture and foreign (mostly west-European) painting and sculpture. Average Annual Attendance: 200,000.
Income: Financed by endowment and state appropriation. Purchases: 750,000 Danish crowns.
Collections: †Old, modern and contemporary Danish art; †Old and modern French art; †Old Italian, Dutch, Flemish art (mostly painting); †Scandinavian art.
Exhibitions: (1976-78) Carl Larsson; Hundertwasser: Austria presents Hundertwasser to the Continents; Tapestries from The Royal Collection, Stockholm Castle; Danish Artists in Rome in the 19th Century; Hans Christian Andersen's Flowers; paintings and flower-arrangements from the 19th century.
Publications: (Kunstmuseets Arsskrift) The Royal Museum of Fine Arts Yearbook.

Activities: Lect open to public; concerts; gallery talks; tours; individual paintings and original objects of art lent to other museums and collections; lending collection contains phonorecords 200; sales shop selling prints, slides, catalogs and posters.
Library: *Cur* Dr Harald P Olsen. Reference library open to the public. Holdings: Vols 50,000; Per subs 150; Other—Exhibition and auction catalogs, documentary newspaper clippings.
—Den kongelige Kobberstiksamling (Department of Prints and Drawings), Sølvgade, DK-1307. Tel: 01 11 21 26. *Keeper* Erik Fischer; *Asst Keepers* Jan Garff and Jan Würtz Frandsen; *Asst* Inger Hjorth Nielsen.
Open 10 AM - 5 PM; Wed 10 AM - 8 PM; cl Mon. No admis. Estab 1835 to collect, conserve, examine and publish prints and drawings. Average Annual Attendance: 200,000.
Purchases: Approx $1800 per yr.
Collections: Mostly European prints and drawings from about 1400 to the present, including a large collection of Danish items.
Exhibitions: (1975-78) Jens Juel, Drawings; Goya's La Tauromaquia; J M W Turner, 90 watercolours and drawings from the British Museum, London; 50 watercolours and drawings by J T Lundbye 1845-1846; Dutch drawings and prints; Three Young Danish Draughtsmen: Lene Adler Petersen, Sys Hindsbo, and Pia Schutzmann; Omaggio a Michelangelo, 13 prints from the portfolio Omaggio a Michelangelo, published by the Bruckmann-Stiftung, Munich; Asger Jorn's Graphic Work, 1933-1972; Hogarth in focus, 117 etchings and engravings; Three Young Danish Draughtsmen: Mogens Hoff, Per Kirkeby, and Peter Lautrop; A Collector's Donation, the Herbert Melbye Bequest; Watercolours and Drawings by William Scharff; Ole Kielberg, One-man show; Dan Sterup-Hansen, One-man show; Piranesi, Prints and Drawings; Three Young Danish Draughtsmen: Henrik Have, Mogens Kølkjaer, and Hanne Sejrbo Nielsen.
Publications: Exhibition catalogs.
Activities: Sales shop selling prints, slides, catalogs and posters.
Library: *Librn* Marianne Rørup. Reference library open to the public. Holdings: Vols 37,829; Per subs 49; Other—W Gernsheim's Corpus Photographicum of Drawings; catalogs of auctions and small exhibition catalogs. Special Subjects: Books and other documentation on art on paper. Special Collections: 20th century illustrated books, mainly French with original prints.

THORVALDSEN MUSEUM, Porthusgade 2, 1213 K. Tel: 01 121532. *Mayor* Bent Nebelong; *Dir* Dr Dyveke Helsted; *Cur* Dr Bjarne Jornaes; *Cur Educ* Dr Eva Henschen; *Cur Archaeology* Dr Torben Melander.
Open daily (May-Sept) 10 AM - 4 PM; (Oct-Apr) 10 AM - 3 PM; cl Tues during winter months. Admis Sun, Wed & Fri free, other days 2 Kr. Opened to public 1848 as a museum for the works of the sculptor Bertel Thorvaldsen (1770-1844) and for his collections. It was built from 1839 to 1848 by the young architect, M G Bindesboll, whom Thorvaldsen had chosen and who created a very untraditional building. He used strong colours, both in the ochre yellow facades, decorated by the painter Jorgen Sonne with a frieze depicting Thorvaldsen's return to Copenhagen in 1838, and in the interior where changing wall colors, ceilings with polychrome Pompeian motifs, and tesselated terracotta floors form the background to Thorvaldsen's white marble sculptures. Average Annual Attendance: 70,000.
Income: 3,500,000 DKr (financed by city appropriation).
Collections: Sculpture and drawings by Thorvaldsen; 19th century European paintings and drawings; Greek, Etruscan and Roman marbles, bronzes, gems and vases.
Exhibitions: Johan Tobias Sergel, 1740-1814, (drawings); Rome in Early Photographs, The Age of Pius IX.
Publications: Bulletin, irregularly.
Activities: Educ dept; didactic activities for children; lect open to public, 5-10 vis lectr per yr; concerts; tours in English, German and Danish; individual paintings and original objects of art lent to other museums; museum shop selling books, reproductions, prints, slides, catalogues, posters and copies in Parian ware.
Library: Open for reference to scholars. Holdings Vols 5000. Special Subjects: Neoclassical and Romantic art; the artistic connections between Italy, especially Rome, and Denmark in the 18th & 19th centuries. Special Collections: Thorvaldsen's own library.

HUMLEBAEK

LOUISIANA MUSEUM OF MODERN ART, Gammel Strandvej 13, 3050. Tel: 03-190719. *Dir* Knud W Jensen; *Treas* Børge Hansen; *Cur* Hugo Arne Buch; *Ed* Hans Erik Wallin.
Open 10 AM - 5 PM. Admis 10 Danish kroner. Estab 1958 to introduce new trends in modern art from all over the world to a Danish public. Average Annual Attendance: 250,000 - 300,000. Mem: 20,000; dues single 77 Danish kroner; couples 97 Danish kroner; firms 275 Danish kroner.
Income: Financed by endowment, membership, city and state appropriation.

Collections: Modern Art from 1950; Sculpture—Arp, Henry Moore, Giacometti, Calder, Max Ernst, Tinguely, Laurens, Richier, Gabo, Max Bill, Sekine, Cesar Mancoga, Kienholz, Ipousteguy, Kivijärvi, Mike, Minguzzi; Painting—Albers, Alechinsky, Corneille, Fontana, Sam Francis, Herbin, Hundertwasser, Klein, Warhol, Dine, Louis.
Exhibitions: (1976 to present) CAYC; Hockney; Nouvelle Peinture Francaise; Louis Cane; Let's Mix all Feelings Together; Henry Moore; Giacometti; Achnaton and Nefertiti; Soho; Downtown Manhattan Prints by Alechinsky; Ten Israeli Artists; Bob Morris Environment; Claes Oldenburg drawings; Artists for Amnesty; German Art Today; Art from Bali; Chinese Peasant Paintings; Alternative Architecture; Pompeji AD 79; Sam Francis; McCrory Collection (Constructivists); Christo Running Fence; Babylon; Art From Mesopotamia, Soto and Hantai.
Publications: Louisiana Revy, 3 times per yr; Louisiana Klubben, 6 times per yr.
Activities: Concerts; sales shop selling books, magazines, reproductions, prints, slides; collection of art books for internal use, especially on modern art.

ECUADOR

QUITO

NATIONAL MUSEUM OF COLONIAL ART OF THE CASA DE LA CULTURA ECUATORIANA, Calles Cuenca y Mejía 915, 2550. Tel: 212-297. *Dir* Carlos Rodríguez.
Open Tues - Sun 10 AM - 1 PM & 3 - 6 PM; cl Mon. Admis 5 sucres. Founded 1914 the museum is of authentic colonial style, dating from the 17th century. Its first owner was Marquis of Villacís; its last owner was Dr Angel Sáenz, who sold the building to the government of Dr Carlos Arroyo del Rie. The building was restored by the Ministry of Public Works, under the direction of the painter Nicolás Delgade, who was its director in 1944. The museum has two floors, the first floor contains works from the 19th century; the second floor, the halls and the galleries contain works from the 17th and 18th centuries. Average Annual Attendance: 2400. Mem: 10; dues 454.800 sucres.
Income: 33.000 sucres (financed by state appropriation).
Collections: Collections that date from the 18th century.
Exhibitions: (1976-78) One exposition of many artists from Ecuador; Guillermo Carpie Rejas; Florencie Sánchez Rivera; Jesé Enrique Guerrero; exposition from Mexico done by children; an exposition presented by Luis Chacón, Venezuela; Ugarte from Quito.
Publications: Museum guide.
Activities: Individual paintings and original objects of art lent to the Ministries and other important institutions; museum shop selling slides.

EGYPT

ALEXANDRIA

GRECO-ROMAN MUSEUM,* Museum St. *Dir* Youssef Hanna Shehata; *Librn* Lila Halim Nesim.
Estab 1892. Average Annual Attendance: 88,000.
Income: 18,000 Egyptian pounds.
Collections: Exhibits from the Coptic, Roman and Greek eras.
Publications: Annual Report.
Library: Open 9 AM - 4 PM. Holdings: Vols 12,000.

CAIRO

COPTIC MUSEUM,* Masr Ateeka. *Dir* Dr Bahur Labib.
Open 8 AM - 1 PM (summer); 9 AM - 4 PM (winter). Estab 1910.
Collections: Sculpture; frescos; woodcarvings; metalwork; architecture; ivory; pottery; glass; manuscripts; textiles; icons; bone.
Publications: Guides; catalogs; 2-vol work covering the principal churches of Cairo and Alexandria, and the monasteries of Egypt.
Library: Holdings—Vols 7,000.

EGYPTIAN MUSEUM, Sh Selim Hassan. *Dir* Dr Dia Abou-Ghazi; *First Sub-Dir* Ibrahim Abd el-Salam el-Nawawy; *Sub-Dir* Mohammed Ahmed Mohsen; *First Cur* Mrs Saniyeh Abd el Aal; *Cur* Mrs Mahasen Nasar.
Open daily 9 AM - 4 PM; Fri 9 - 11:30 AM & 1:30 - 4 PM. Admis 75¢, mummies room 25¢. Estab 1858, present building 1902. The ground floor contains objects arranged chronologically according to ancient Egyptian history; the first floor is arranged according to categories. Average Annual Attendance: 50,000.
Income: Approx $1,000,000 (financed by state appropriation).

Collections: Ancient Egyptian art—Pharaonic Period, Hellenistic and Roman Periods; Complete sets of jewelry, papyrus and coins from tombs—Hemaka tomb, Yuya and Thuya, and Tutankhamen.
Exhibitions: The Egyptian Museum in 1955-75.
Publications: Catalogue General du Musée; sets on excavations.
Activities: Classes for children; dramatic programs; docent training; lect open to public; traveling exhibitions organized and circulated; museum shop selling books, magazines, original art, reproductions, prints and slides.
—**Library,** Sh Mariette Pacha. *Dir* Dr Dia Abou-Ghazi; *Archaeologist* Nabil Mahfouz.
Open daily 9:30 AM - 1:30 PM; Fri 9 - 11 AM; cl Mon. Estab 1858 to serve the staff of the antiquities service and those studying ancient civilizations. A reference library.
Income: Approx $12,500 (financed by state appropriation).
Holdings: Vols 35,025; Per subs 100.
Special Subjects: Ancient civilizations up to the Middle Ages.
Publications: Annales du Service des Antiquites, annually, supplements, irregularly; Catalogue de la Bibliotheque irregularly.

ENGLAND

BATH

AMERICAN MUSEUM IN BRITAIN, Claverton Manor, BA2 7BD. *Dir & Cur* Ian McCallum; *Deputy Dir* G M Candler.
Open Tues - Sun 2 - 5 PM; cl Mon (Apr-Oct). Admis £1, sr citizens & children 80p, grounds only 30p. Estab 1961 to fulfill a desire to increase Anglo-American understanding and to interpret the history and arts of the United States. The museum has 18 period furnished rooms from 17th to 19th centuries, and a folk art gallery. Average Annual Attendance: 112,000.
Publications: America in Britain, 3 times a year.
Activities: Classes for children; lect open to public, 20 vis lectr per yr; concerts; gallery talks; tours; individual paintings and original objects of art lent to The John Judkyn Memorial; traveling exhibitions organized and circulated; museum shop selling books, and slides.
Library: *Librn* Margaret Irwin. Open for reference to students.

BRIGHTON

ROYAL PAVILION, ART GALLERY AND MUSEUMS, Church St, BN1 1UE. Tel: 273-603005. *Dir* John Morley.
Open daily (Oct-June) 10 AM - 5 PM; (July-Oct) 10 AM - 8 PM. Admis 50 pence. Built in its present form in 1822 as the seaside palace of the Prince Regent. Average Annual Attendance: 350,000.
Income: Financed by city appropriation.
Collections: Magnificent interiors in the Chinese taste, with regency furniture and works of art of the period.
Publications: Report, every 2-3 years.
—**Art Gallery and Museum.**
Open Tues - Sat 10 AM - 5:45 PM; Sun 2 - 5 PM; cl Mon. No admis. The museum was built in 1808 and opened as a museum in 1873. The Gallery was estab 1851. Average Annual Attendance: 200,000.
Collections: Old master paintings; English watercolours; the Willett Collection of ceramics; archaeology, ethnology, ethnography, and important collection of art nouveau and art deco.
Activities: Classes for adults; lect open to public; gallery talks; tours; museum shop selling books, magazines, reproductions, prints and slides.
—**Grange Art Gallery and Museum,** The Green, Rottingdean, BN2 7HA. Tel: 273-31004. *Keeper* M Waller.
Open Thurs - Sat & Mon - Tues 10 AM - 5 PM; Sun 2 - 5 PM; cl Good Friday, Christmas and Boxing Day. No admis. Estab 1954 as a branch museum and art gallery administered by Brighton Borough Council.
Income: Financed by Brighton Borough Council.
Collections: Books, illustrations and letters of Rudyard Kipling; †selection of toys from National Toy Museum Collection; Sussex Room—local history.
Publications: Guide to Kipling Room.
—**Preston Manor (Thomas-Stanford Museum),** Preston Park, BN1 6SD. Tel: 273-552101.
Open Wed - Sat 10 AM - 5 PM; Sun 2 - 5 PM; cl Good Friday, Christmas & Boxing Day. Admis adults 30 pence, students and sr citizens 20 pence, children 15 pence. Estab 1933. The Georgian and Edwardian house, the home of the Stanford family, was given to Brighton Corporation on the understanding that the fine furniture, paintings, etc would be displayed in their period settings as they were in the donor's lifetime. A furnished country house with small collections of fine silver, paintings, books, glass & Chinese porcelain "Dogs of Fo". Average Annual Attendance: 13,000.
Income: Financed by Brighton Borough Council.

Collections: Silver, furniture (16th-19th centuries), paintings, glass, ceramics, books relating to Sussex and archival material; original 16th century Spanish leather wall hangings; the MacQuoid Bequest of fine furniture, silver and paintings.
Exhibitions: Children and Food; Toys of War—A Pacifist's Approach.
Publications: Preston Manor Guide, occasionally.
Library: Open for reference to students upon application to Keeper. Holdings: Vols 500. Special Subjects: Books about Sussex or written by men born in Sussex; books by John Selden; archives relating to Sussex. Special Collections: John Selden Collection.

BRISTOL

CITY ART GALLERY,* Queen's Rd, BS8 1RL. Tel: 272 299971. *Dir* A D P Wilson; *Cur Applied Art* E C Witt; *Asst Cur Applied Art* K Walton; *Cur Fine Art* F W Greenacre; *Cur Oriental Art* P Hardie; *Conservator Prints & Watercolors* R W Harper.
Open Mon - Sat 10 AM - 5:30 PM. Estab 1905.
Income: Financed by city appropriation.
Collections: †Paintings, drawings, sculpture, British and Continental, 13th-20th century; †English pottery, porcelain, silver, glass, furniture; †Bristol porcelain and glass; †Schiller collection of Oriental ceramics, glass and metalwork.
Exhibitions: Circulating exhibitions from Arts Council and others.
Publications: Abstracts, quarterly; exhibition catalogs and guides.
Activities: Lect open to public; concerts.
Library: Open for reference. Holdings: Vols 600.
—**Red Lodge,** Park Row. Tel: 2 1903.
A 16th century mansion, panelled interiors, period furnishings.
—**Georgian House,** Queens Road, Clifton. Tel: 272 299971.
Open 10 AM -5 PM; cl Sun. No admis. Estab 1937, a period house (18th century) exhibiting paintings and decorative arts from the collections of the City Art Gallery, based on the date 1790, but including some earlier examples. Average Annual Attendance: 31,000.
Income: Financed by city appropriation.
Collections: 18th century furniture and paintings; works of art made in Bristol; pastels by James Sharples; Bristol-made furniture and porcelain.
Activities: Sales shop selling books and postcards.

CAMBRIDGE

UNIVERSITY OF CAMBRIDGE, Fitzwilliam Museum, Trumpington St, CB2 1RB. *Dir* A M Jaffe; *Keeper Coins and Medals* G Pollard; *Keeper Antiquities* R Nicholls; *Keeper Applied Arts* R Crighton; *Keeper Paintings & Drawings* D Robinson; *Keeper Prints* E Chamberlain; *Keeper Admin* J Huskilson.
Open Tues - Sat 10 AM - 5 PM; Sun 2:15 - 5 PM. Estab 1816 to collect, do research on, exhibit, works of art. Average Annual Attendance: 175,000.
Income: Financed through the University.
Collections: Antiquities; coins; European ceramics; Oriental works of art; textiles; arms and armour; furniture and sculpture; prints; paintings and drawings.
Exhibitions: Many changing exhibitions during the year.
Publications: Annual Report.
Activities: Lect open to public; concerts; gallery talks; tours; original objects of art lent to museums; museum shop selling books, reproductions, prints, and slides.
—**Library,** Department of Manuscripts and Printed Books. *Librn* P Woudhuysen.
Open for reference by written application only. Estab 1816 to collect illuminated manuscripts, music, literary, scientific, historical manuscripts, rare books, autograph letters; and as a reference library for the Museum.
Income: Financed through University.
Holdings: Vols 80,000; Per subs 250; AV—Microfilm; Other—Exhibition catalogs, manuscripts, memorabilia, original document, pamphlets.
Special Collections: Illuminated manuscripts; manuscript music; literary manuscripts; letters; private press books, incunabula; rare books of all periods.
Exhibitions: The Art of the Book: Morris and after.

LINCOLN

LINCOLNSHIRE MUSEUMS, USHER GALLERY, Lindum Road, LN2 1NN. Tel: 522 27980. *Dir* Antony J H Gunstone; *Keeper of Art* Richard H Wood; *Asst Keeper of Art* Diana J O'Connell.
Open Mon - Sat 10 AM - 5:30 PM; Sun 2:30 - 5 PM. No admis. Estab 1927 to house the collection of decorative art material formed by a local jeweller James Ward Usher. Average Annual Attendance: 70,000.
Collections: Watercolours by Peter de Wint; topographical paintings of Lincolnshire; silver; glass; ceramics; James Ward Usher Collection; coins.

Exhibitions: Paintings and Drawings (Richard Whittern); Sculptures and Etchings (Enzo Plazzotta); Sculptures and Drawings (Martin Wolverson); Glass Constructions (David Reekie); 18th Century English wine glasses, decanters, silver bottle-labels; Drawings and Crafts; Paintings (Liz Underhill); Dutch Genre Paintings; Paintings and Ceramics (Judith Oyler, Audsley Power, Avril and David Morris; Historic Wallpapers).
Activities: Individual paintings and original objects of art lent to subscribers; Friends of Lincoln.

LIVERPOOL

WALKER ART GALLERY, Merseyside County Council, William Brown St, L3 8 EL. Tel: 051-227-5234. *Dir* Timothy J Stevens; *Keeper Foreign Art* Edward S Morris; *Keeper British Art* Mary G Bennett; *Educ Officer* A M Lewis; *Admin Officer* M J Lindop.
Open weekdays 10 AM - 5 PM; Sun 2 - 5 PM. Estab 1871 for the conservation and display of the permanent collection; and for organization of loan exhibitions. Art gallery is comprised of some 17 display galleries, restoration studio, office accomodation, education room and workshop. Average Annual Attendance: 220,000.
Annual Expenditure: 419,480 (financed by state appropriation). Purchase Fund: Approx 10,000.
Collections: European painting, sculpture, watercolors, drawings, prints 1300 - present day, including notable collections of Italian and Netherlandish painting 1300-1600 and 19th century British painting.
Exhibitions: (1976-77) John Moores and Peter Moores Exhibitions and American Artists in Europe Exhibition.
Publications: Annual Report and Bulletin.
Activities: Classes for children; lect open to public, approx 2 vis lectrs per yr; gallery talks; tours; traveling exhibitions organized and circulated; museum shop selling books, magazines, reproductions, prints and slides.
Library: Reference library open to the public by appointment. Holdings: Vols 10,000. Special Subjects: Catalogs, museum and art gallery annual reports and bulletins.

LONDON

AIR GALLERY, 125-129 Shaftesbury Ave, WC2H 8AD. *Dir* Moira Kelly; *Admin Asst* Nicky Bennett.
Open Tues - Sat 10 AM - 6 PM; cl Sun & Mon. No admis. Estab 1975 to show the work of young artists who have not had major exhibitions elsewhere. Four galleries in all; main galleries of about 3000 sq ft plus one smaller gallery for showing works on paper, c 500 sq ft. Average Annual Attendance: 5000.
Income: Financed by state appropriation and grant aided from Arts Council of Great Britain.
Exhibitions: Major exhibitions of young artists.
Activities: Lect open to public, 12 vis lectrs per yr; gallery talks; sales shop selling books, magazines, original art and prints.

BRITISH LIBRARY,* Reference Division, Great Russell St, WC1B 3DG. Tel: 01-636 1544. *Chmn British Library Bd* Viscount Eccles; *Chief Exec* Dr H T Hookway; *Dir Gen Reference Div* D T Richnell.
Galleries open Mon - Sat 10 AM - 5 PM; Sun 2:30 - 6 PM; Reading Room open Mon, Fri & Sat 9 AM - 5 PM; Tues, Wed & Thurs 9 AM - 9 PM. Admission for research to the Public Reading Rooms at Great Russell Street is by ticket. Estab 1795 as the British Museum Library; name changed 1973; the organization's purpose is to make its 10 million books and manuscripts available to readers in the reading rooms, to give photographic and other services and to run exhibitions. The Library maintains four galleries of printed books and manuscripts. Average Annual Attendance: 600,000.
Income: $24,000,000 (financed by city and state appropriations).
Holdings: Vols 9½ millions; Other—Western manuscripts 75,000, Oriental manuscripts 30,000, charters and rolls 100,000, detached seals and casts of seals 18,000, Greek and Latin papyri 3,000, Egyptian papryi.
Publications: The British Library Journal, six monthly.
Activities: Lect open to public; tours; photograph collection; book shop.

BRITISH MUSEUM, Great Russell St, WC1B 3DG. *Dir* D M Wilson.
Open Mon - Sat 10 AM - 5 PM; 2:20 - 6 PM. No admis. Estab 1753. It is the national museum of archeology and antiquity, showing the works of man from all over the world from pre-historic to comparatively modern times. Average Annual Attendance: 4,000,000.
Collections: Coins and medals; Egyptian, Western Asiatic, Greek and Roman art; Roman Britain; Medieval and later; prints and drawings; Oriental art; ethnography.
Exhibitions: Chinese Paintings of the Ch'ing dynasty (1644-1912); Animals in Art; 19th century French Landscape; Drawings and Sketches; The Tribal Eye; American Indian Art—The Inverarity Collection; Bulgarian Village Arts; The Otavalo; Turquoise Mosaics from Mexico.
Activities: Lect open to public; films; gallery talks.

COURTAULD INSTITUTE OF ART GALLERIES, Woburn Square. Tel: 580 1015. *Dir* Peter Lasko; *Cur Coll* Philip Troutman; *Asst to Cur* Suzanne Alexander; *Academic Asst* William Bradford.
Open Mon - Sat 10 AM - 5 PM; Sun 2 - 5 PM. No admis. Estab 1958. The Galleries are a department of the Courtauld Institute of Art, London University. They have on permanent exhibition the collections of the Courtauld Institute and provide temporary exhibitions of works of art. One floor with natural overhead lighting, paintings not glazed; the collections arranged chronologically. Galleries for temporary exhibitions. Average Annual Attendance: 110,000.
Income: Financed through London University.
Collections: Samuel Courtauld Collection of French Impressionist and Post Impressionist paintings (Monet, Sisley, Pissarro, Renoir, Degas, Manet, Cezanne, Gauguin, Van Gogh, Serrat, Toulouse-Lautrec. . .); The Lord Lee of Fareham Collection of European Old Master paintings (Simone Martni, Botticelli, Veronese, Rubens, Cranach. . . to Gainsborough and Goya); The Gambier-Parry Collection of Old Master paintings and other works of art (mainly Italian primitives, 14th & 15th century; Bernardo Daddi, Lorenzo Monaco, Fra Angelico, Verrocchio. . .); The Roger Fry Collection of French and English, early 20th century.
Exhibitions: Samuel Courtauld Centenary Exhibition; Roger Fry Portraits; Dutch Drawings from the Witt Collection, II—other than landscape; Enlgish Landscape Watercolours, 1750-1850; The Graphic Work of Felix Vallotton; Drawings by Guercino and the Baroque Masters; Watercolours, the Witt Collection; Spanish Drawings from the Witt Collection; Bulgarian Icons.
Activities: Lect open to public; gallery talks; tours; individual paintings and original objects of art lent to other museums; museum shop selling books, magazines, reproductions, prints, slides and catalogues of exhibitions.

DULWICH COLLEGE PICTURE GALLERY, College Rd.
Admis 25p. Estab to display the Dulwich College Art Collection for public benefit; representative of many of the most famous schools and painters of 17th century Europe with additional works from 18th century English, French and Venetian masters. Average Annual Attendance: 17,000 - 18,000.
Collections: Collection from 1626 onwards; gallery 1815; Alleyn, Cartwright, Bourgeois, Linley, Fairfax Murray.
Activities: Sales shop selling books, reproductions, prints, slides.

NATIONAL GALLERY, Trafalgar Square, WC2N 5DN. Tel: 01-839-3321. *Dir* Michael Levey; *Keeper* Allan Braham; *Scientific Adviser* Garry Thomson; *Chief Restorer* Arthur Lucas; *Publ Manager* Gordon Booth.
Open Mon - Sat 10 AM - 6 PM; Sun 2 - 6 PM. No admis. Estab 1824 to house the national permanent collection of Western European painting (c 1300 to c 1900). Main Floor Galleries have 46 exhibition rooms and the Lower Floor Galleries, 10 exhibition rooms. Average Annual Attendance: 2,500,000.
Income: Financed by state appropriation and trust funds. Purchases: £ 1,730,000.
Collections: Western European painting, c 1300 to c 1900, principal schools, Italian, French, German, Spanish, Early Netherlandish, Dutch, British.
Exhibitions: Art in 17th Century Holland; Late Gothic Art from Cologne; Painting in Focus series; many smaller exhibitions.
Publications: National Gallery News, monthly.
Activities: Classes for adults and children; lect open to public; gallery talks; museum shop selling books, magazines, reproductions, prints, slides, photographs, postcards.

QUEEN'S GALLERY,* Buckingham Palace, Lord Chamberlain's Office, St James's Palace, SW1 (Entrance on Buckingham Palace Road). Tel: 930 3007. *Registrar* J L Titman.
Open Tues - Sat and bank holidays 11 AM - 5 PM; Sun 2 - 5 PM; cl Mon except bank holidays. Admis adults 30p, children, students with vaid card, and old age pensioners 10p. A small art gallery where items in the Royal Collection are put on view to the general public.

ROYAL COLLEGE OF ART, Kensington Gore, SW7 2EU. Tel: 01-584-5020. *Rector & VProvost* Richard Guyath; *Pro-Provost* Sir Anthony Lousada; *Treas* John Grittall; *Registrar* Brian Cooper; *Bursar* Russell Brown.
Open 10 AM - 6 PM. No admis. Estab 1837, received Royal Charter 1967, for higher education in Art and Design. Various exhibition areas used mainly for exhibitions of students' work.
Income: Financed through College.
Exhibitions: Students' work from various departments including painting, graphic arts, textiles, industrial design, ceramics, sculpture, photography; annual Degree Shows.
Activities: Lect open to public, 1 vis lectr per yr.

SOUTH LONDON ART GALLERY, Peckham Road, SE5 8UH. *Cur* K A Doughty; *Deputy Cur* P W Taylor; *Keeper* K Sharpe.
Open daily 10 AM - 6 PM; Sun 3 - 6 PM. No admis. Estab 1891 as a public art gallery for the benefit of the inhabitants of the London Borough of Southwark and the public at large. Sustained war damage 1941, re-opened 1949 partially restored. A large Victorian exhibition gallery with a glass roof and which is completely lit by daylight. There is approx 221 feet of single line hanging space. A second gallery was bombed during the war and longterm plans exist for its reconstruction. Average Annual Attendance: 20,000.
Income: $50,000 (financed by city appropriation). Purchases: $5,000.
Collections: Contemporary British art; †20th century original prints; †topographical paintings and drawings of local subjects; paintings of the Victorian period.
Exhibitions: Stuart Sutcliffe (1940-1951) Drawings and Paintings; Constant Lambert Retrospective Exhibition (1905-1951); 1b Langellot—Ceramics, Objects and Graphics; Val Princep RA (1838-1904)—A Jubilee Painter.
Activities: Classes for children; lect open to public, 6 vis lectr per yr; gallery talks; competitions; junior museum.

TATE GALLERY,* Millbank, SW1P 4RG. Tel: 828 1212. *Dir* Sir Norman Reid.
Open Mon - Sat 10 AM - 6 PM; Sun 2 - 6 PM; cl Good Friday, Christmas Eve, Christmas Day, Boxing Day and New Year's Day. Estab 1897 by Sir Henry Tate. Average Annual Attendance: 900,000.
Collections: British painting from the 16th century to the present; modern foreign painting from Impressionism onwards, and modern sculpture. Especially fine examples of the works of Hogarth, Blake, Turner and the Pre-Raphaelites. The total number of works in the collections 5500, approx 4,000 prints.
Exhibitions: Special exhibitions held regularly throughout the year.
Publications: Photography and publication of coloured prints and transparencies, photographs, postcards, books and catalogs.
Activities: Lect open to public are given on Tues at 1 PM; on Thurs at 1 PM & 3 PM; Sat & Sun at 3 PM.

VICTORIA AND ALBERT MUSEUM, Cromwell Rd, SW7 2RL. Tel: 589 6371. *Dir* Dr Roy Stong; *Keeper Architecture & Sculpture* J G Beckwith; *Keeper Ceramics* J V G Mallet; *Keeper Paintings, Prints, Drawings & Photographs* C Kauffman; *Keeper Metalwork* C Blair; *Keeper Textiles* D King; *Keeper Furniture* P K Thornton; *Keeper Oriental Dept* J C Irwin; *Keeper Far Eastern Section* J G Ayers; *Keeper Conservation* Dr J Ashley-Smith; *Keeper Educ* Mrs M Mainstone; *Keeper Indian Art* R Skelton; *Keeper Museum Services* J Physick.
Open Mon - Thurs 10 AM - 5:30 PM; Sun 2:30 - 6 PM; cl Good Friday, Christmas Day, Christmas Eve, Boxing Day, New Year's Day. Estab 1852. Average Annual Attendance: 2,000,000.
Income: £3,447,990 (financed by state appropriation). Purchases: £610,000.
Collections: †Collections of fine and applied arts of all Countries, periods and styles; including Oriental art. European collections are mostly post-Classical; architectural details; †art of the book; bronzes; calligraphs; †carpets; †ceramics; †clocks; costumes; †cutlery; †drawings, †embroideries; †enamels; engravings; †fabrics; †furniture; glass; gold and silversmiths' work; ironwork; ivories; †jewelry; lace; lithographs; manuscripts; †metalwork; miniatures; †musical instruments; oil paintings; †posters; †pottery and porcelain; †prints; †sculpture; †stained glass; tapestries; †theatre art; vestments, watches; †watercolors; †woodwork.
Exhibitions: Fashion 1900-1939; The Makers; American Art—Towards Independence; Ansel Adams; Minton; Tonic to the Nation; The Artist of Disney; Faberge; Eduard Paolozzi; Change and Decay—The Future of our Churches; The Wireless Show; Bible in British Art; Textiles for the Church; After Alice—A Hundred Year's of Children's Books.

WALLACE COLLECTION, Hertford House, Manchester Square, W1M 5RA. Tel: 01-935-0687/8. *Dir* T W I Hodgkinson; *Asst to Dir* R A Cecil; *Asst to Dir* J S Ingamells.
Open Mon - Sat 10 AM - 5 PM; Sun 2 - 5 PM. No admis. Estab 1897, opened as a national museum 1900, to display as appropriately as possible Lady Wallace's grand bequest to the nation in the London house of the founders of the collection, the large private mansion of the Marquesses of Hertford and Sir Richard Wallace.
Income: Financed by state appropriation, and through Trustees.
Collections: Paintings and works of art of all European schools, especially the French in the 18th century; sculpture; miniatures; French furniture; Sèvres porcelain; goldsmiths' work; European and Oriental arms and armour.
Publications: Catalogues, guides, booklets on the collection.
Activities: Lect open to public, 2 vis lectr per week; gallery talks, tours; sales shop selling catalogues, guides, booklets, prints, slides and postcards.
Library: Not open to public, and based on the collection.

WELLINGTON MUSEUM, Apsley House, 149 Piccadilly, W1V 9FA. *Officer in Charge* H V T Percival.
Open Tues - Thurs & Sat 10 AM - 6 PM; Sun 2:30 - 6 PM. No admis. Estab 1952 to display the art collection and personal relics of the first Duke of Wellington (1769-1852) in his town house. The house was built 1771-78 from designs by Robert Adam, extensively altered 1828-30 by Benjamin Dean Wyatt. Average Annual Attendance: 100,000.
Income: Financed by state appropriation.
Collections: Paintings, services of porcelain, silver plate, sculpture, furniture, military orders, swords, medals, snuff boxes, and other personal relics of the first Duke of Wellington.
Exhibitions: Permanent exhibition of political caricatures.
Activities: Lect open to public, 12 vis lectr per yr; gallery talks; tours; individual paintings and original objects of art lent to museums and art galleries; sales shop selling books, reproductions, slides.

WORSHIPFUL COMPANY OF GOLDSMITHS, Goldsmiths' Hall, Foster Lane, EC2. Tel: 01-606-8971. *Clerk* Peter Jenkins; *Art Dir* Graham Hughes; *Deputy Warden of Assay Office* Mr Forbes; *Dir Research* Mr Gainsbury; *Cur* Miss Ransome-Wallis.
Open 10 AM - 5 PM strictly by appointment and usually for people associated with the craft. No admis. In existence by 1100, royal charter in 1327, as a guild for craftsmen of gold and silver and as a centre of London hallmarking.
Income: Financed by self.
Collections: †Antique plate; †modern silver, jewelry and medals.
Exhibitions: Extensive exhibitions of the 4 collections both in the UK and abroad.
Publications: The Review, annually.
Activities: Hallmarking gold, silver and platinum wares; technical advisory service for the trade, artist-craftsmen and students; placing graduate apprentices; motion pictures; 35mm color slides and photographs in lending collection; photograph collection; lect open to public, once a month; concerts; competitions; scholarships.
Library: Librn Miss Hare. Holdings: Vols 6000; AV—35mm color slides; photographs.

MANCHESTER

MANCHESTER CITY ART GALLERIES, Mosley St. *Dir* T P C Clifford; *Keeper Fine Art* J B Treuherz; *Keeper Decorative Arts* M R Parkinson; *Keeper Costume* Mrs V Foster; *Keeper Military Coll* P R Russell-Jones; *Keeper Conservation* B Cardy.
Open Mon - Sat 10 AM - 6 PM; Sun 2:30 - 5 PM. No admis. Estab 1882 to educate and entertain the public. City Art Gallery in centre of city and 6 branch galleries in Greater Manchester. Average Annual Attendance: 350,000.
Income: Financed by city appropriation. Purchases: £52,000.
Collections: †British Art 17th century to present day; †Pre-Raphaelite painting; †Assheton-Bennett Collection of Dutch 17th century painting; †English silver; †Thomas Greg Collection of English Pottery; †Royal Lancastrian pottery; †English enamels; †Tylecote Collection of glass; †English costume.
Exhibitions: Adolphe Valette; A Pre-Raphaelite Passion (The private collection of L S Lowry); Randolph Caldecott.
Publications: Events card, quarterly.
Activities: Classes for children; lect open to public; concerts; gallery talks; tours; exten dept serving schools and colleges in Northwest England; artmobile; individual paintings and original objects of art lent to educational institutions; lending collection contains framed reproductions, original art works 860, original prints 500, paintings, sculpture.

UNIVERSITY OF MANCHESTER, Whitworth Art Gallery, Whitworth Park M15 6ER. *Dir* C R Dodwell; *Keeper* Francis W Hawcroft; *Keeper of Textiles* Joan Allgrove; *Asst Keeper Prints* Michael Clarke.
Open Mon - Sat 10 AM - 5 PM; Thurs 10 AM - 9 PM. No admis. Estab 1889 to collect, display and preserve works of art and to arrange special exhibitions. Built in 1890's and extension completed 1908; interior modernized 1960's. In addition to galleries for displaying permanent collections, there are two exhibition galleries, a lecture hall, print room, textile study room and library. Average Annual Attendance: 92,649. Mem: 1000; dues 3.
Income: Financed by city appropriation and through University. Purchases: 10,000.
Collections: †British drawings and watercolors; †textiles; †wallpapers; †Old Master and modern prints; †contemporary British paintings and sculpture.
Exhibitions: Medieval and Early Renaissance Treasures in the North West; Qashqa'i of Iran; Landscape in Flemish and Dutch Drawings of the 17th century; Rita Donagh; Hollywood Film Costume; Northern Young Contemporaries; Peter Lanyon: Paintings, drawings and constructions.
Publications: Annual Report, yearly.

Activities: Lect open to public, 6 vis lectr per yr; competitions; exten dept serving Greater Manchester County; individual paintings and original objects of art lent to art galleries and museums; lending collection contains framed reproductions, prints, slides, original prints, paintings, photographs; traveling exhibitions organized and circulated; sales shop selling books, reproductions, prints, slides.
Library: Open for reference to students and scholars, by appointment. Holdings: Other—Exhibition catalogues; monographs on art and artist in collection, on textiles, wallpapers and prints.

OXFORD

OXFORD UNIVERSITY, Ashmolean Museum of Art and Archaeology, Beaumont St, OX1 2PH. *Dir* D T Piper; *Secy* R B Winter; *Publ Officer* R I H Charlton; *Keeper Dept Antiquities* H J Case; *Keeper Dept Western Art* K J Garlick; *Keeper Heberden Coin Room* C M Kraay; *Keeper Dept Eastern Art* J C Harle; *Cur Cast Gallery* C M Robertson; *Secy Griffith Institute* H J Case.
Open Mon - Sat 10 AM - 4 PM; Sun 2 - 4 PM. No admis. Estab 1683. Average Annual Attendance: 180,000.
Income: Financed through University.
Collections: British, European, Mediterranean, Egyptian and Near Eastern archaeology; Italian, Dutch, Flemish, French and English oil paintings: Old Master and modern drawings, watercolors and prints; miniatures; European ceramics; sculpture and bronzes; English silver; objects of applied art; Hope Collection of engraved portraits; coins and medals of all countries and periods; casts from the antique; Chinese and Japanese porcelain, painting and lacquer; Chinese bronzes; Tibetan art; Indian sculpture and painting; Islamic pottery and metalwork.
Publications: Annual Report.
Activities: Lect open to public; museum shop selling books, reproductions, prints, slides and replicas.
Library: Open for reference to University staff and students.

PLYMOUTH

PLYMOUTH CITY MUSEUM AND ART GALLERY, Drake Circus, PL4 8AJ. Tel: 752-68000, exten 2087. *Dir* James Barber; *Sr Keeper & Keeper of Art* Robin M Thomas; *Asst Keeper of Art* C Jeremy Pearson; *Keeper of Conservation* James Manning; *Keeper of Archaeology* Mrs C Gaskell Brown.
Open Mon - Thurs & Sat 10 AM - 6 PM; Fri 10 AM - 8 PM; Sun 3 - 5 PM. No admis. Estab 1899 to provide for the instruction and enjoyment of the citizens of Plymouth and of visitors; comprehensive collections of high quality in the fine and decorative arts, archaeology and natural history, with specialization in regional aspects in all subjects. The main museum and art gallery building was erected in 1910 and contained 2 large exhibition galleries; 2 smaller galleries were added in 1938; 1 large and 1 small gallery were added in 1976. Mem: 220; dues 1.50 and up.
Income: 185,770 (financed by city appropriation). Purchases 3000.
Collections: General collections of paintings and drawings with West Country specialization, works by Sir Joshua Reynolds, James Northcote, William Payne, Samuel Prout, Stanhope Forbes and contemporary artists; Collection of Cookworthy's Plymouth & Bristol porcelain; English, Continental and Oriental ceramics; Dorothy Doughty Royal Worcester porcelain figures; silver with special reference to Plymouth hallmarked pieces; the Eddystone Lighthouse salt being outstanding; the Clarendon Loan Collection of portraits of 16th and 17th century English worthies; the Cottonian Collection of old master drawings, pictures, and engravings, medieval books of hours (2) and early printed books.
Exhibitions: A regular succession of temporary exhibitions is arranged, some drawn from the Gallery's reserve collections; others mounted by outside bodies.
Activities: Classes for adults and children; dramatic programs; docent training; lect open to public, 6 vis lectr per yr; gallery talks; concerts; tours.

SHEFFIELD

SHEFFIELD CITY ART GALLERIES, Surrey St, S1 1XZ. Tel: 742-734781/2. *Dir* H F Constantine; *Deputy Dir* J Spalding; *Keeper Mappin Art Gallery* James Hamilton.
Sheffield City Art Galleries maintains two galleries to present a broad spectrum of art of the highest quality to the public of Sheffield and its environs.
—Graves Art Gallery.
Open Mon - Sat 10 AM - 8 PM; Sun 2 - 5 PM. No admis. Estab 1934 and situated in the centre of the city. Average Annual Attendance: 250,000.
—Mappin Art Gallery, Weston Park, S10 2TP.
Open Mon - Sat 10 AM - 5 PM; Sun 2 - 5 PM. No admis. Estab 1887; a neo-classical building with three 19th century galleries, and five 20th century galleries. Average Annual Attendance: 180,000.

Income: Financed by city appropriation.
Collections: Modern British Art; English portraits; English watercolours; Old Masters (Italian, Dutch and Spanish); French painting; Victorian Art (including Pre-Raphaelites); 18th and 19th century oil landscapes; contemporary painting, sculpture and graphics; Oriental art including the Grice Collection of Chinese ivories.
Exhibitions: French Paintings from the Courtauld Collection; Bernard Leach, pottery; Arshile Gorky, paintings and drawings; 500 Years of English Printmaking, William Caxton; Bill Brandt; Howard Hodgkin; Constable, Drawings and Watercolours; Carpets of Central Persia; Robert Rauschenberg; Peruvian Ground Drawings; Roger Fry Portraits; Live-In Architecture; Edward Burra; Malevitch and the Russian Suprematists; Norman Shaw, architectural drawings; John Swanson, graphics; German Naive Paintings; The Burrell Collection; David Hockney, photographs; Victor Burgin; Art into Landscape; Christopher Wood; Drawings from the Courtauld Collection; Erte, fashion and theatre design; Jack Smith; Micael Ayrton; Photography in Switzerland 1840 to present; Beyond Light: Liliane Lijn and Bill Culbert; New York in the Thirties, Berenice Abbott; The Quashqa'i of Iran; William Tucker; H Gaudier Brzeska; W Heath Robinson, drawings.
Publications: Look What's On, quarterly.
Activities: Classes for adults and children; lect open to public; concerts; gallery talks; tours; competitions; exten dept serving the City; individual paintings and original objects of art lent to schools, colleges, community centres, private individuals; lending collection contains color reproductions; framed reproductions; original art works; original prints; paintings; photographs; sculpture; slides; traveling exhibitions organized and circulated; sales shop selling books, magazines, reproductions, prints, slides.

WOLVERHAMPTON

CENTRAL ART GALLERY, Lichfield St, WV1 1DU. Tel: 0902 24549. *Cur* David Rodgers; *Keeper Art* Brandan Flynn; *Keeper Applied Art* YvonneSongs; *Keeper Local History* Peter Neero.
Open Mon - Sat 10 AM - 6 PM. No admis. Estab 1884 as an art gallery and museum. Victorian classical—three galleries on ground floor; four galleries on first floor. Average Annual Attendance: 100,000. Mem: 300; dues 2.
Income: £139,000 (financed by city appropriation). Purchases: £4000.
Collections: Oriental applied art and weapons; †18th century British paintings; 19th and 20th century British paintings and watercolors; †Contemporary British and American art.
Exhibitions: A Social History of Tea Drinking; The Cranbrook Colony; British Glass 1650-1900; David Hockney Graphics.
Publications: Quarterly.
Activities: Lect open to public; concerts; gallery talks; tours; individual paintings and original objects of art lent to corporation departments; lending collection contains original art works 60; traveling exhibitions organized and circulated; sales shop selling original art, prints and catalogs.
Library: Reference library open to staff and others by appointment. Holdings: Vols approx 600; Per subs 4; Other—Sales catalogs.

YORK

YORK CITY ART GALLERY, Exhibition Square, YO1 2EW. Tel: 904 23839. *Cur* Richard Green; *Art Asst* Janet Hughes.
Open Mon - Sat 10 AM - 5 PM; Sun 2:30 - 5 PM. No admis. Estab 1879 to provide a permanent collection of works of art and local topography, together with exhibitions, lectures, an art library and other supporting activities and services for the citizens of, and visitors to, York. Built to the designs of Edward Taylor for the Yorkshire Fine Art and Industrial Exhibition of 1879, the gallery has a facade in Italian Renaissance style; entrance hall; two galleries on ground floor; staircase leading to upstairs gallery, and exhibition room and projected print room. Average Annual Attendance: 60,000. Mem: 220; dues £2; annual meeting Feb.
Income: Financed by city appropriation. Purchases: £2,000. Collections: †British and European paintings from 1350 to the present, including the Lycett Green Collection of Old Masters; †paintings and drawings by York artists, notably William Etty; †watercolors, drawings and prints, mostly local topography; modern stoneware pottery.
Exhibitions: Just What Is It?; The Dutch Mezzotint and England; Paintings from the Bunell Collection; Ken Gray: Electrosculpturer; Drawings from Dijon.
Publications: Preview (bulletin), 3 times per year.
Activities: Classes for adults and children; lect open to public, 6 vis lectr per yr; concerts; gallery talks; tours; competitions; museum shop selling reproductions, slides, catalogs of collections, exhibition catalogs, and postcards.

Library: Open to all for reference. Holdings: Vols 7000; Per subs 10. Special Subjects: European post-mediaeval art—paintings, drawings and watercolors, prints, sculpture, particularly of the British school.

ETHIOPIA

ADDIS ABABA

ADDIS ABABA UNIVERSITY, Museum of the Institute of Ethiopian Studies, Entoto St (Mailing Add: PO Box 1176). Tel: 110844, exten 352. *Mus Cur & Dir* Dr Girma Kidane; *Head Mus Technician* Kessela Markos; *Head Photographic Coll* Abeke Kefleyesus.
Open weekdays 8:30 AM - 12:30 PM & 2:30 - 5:30 PM; Sat & Sun 8:30 AM - 12:30 PM. Admis 50¢, students free. Estab 1963 to develop and operate an ethnographic museum, including household artifacts, clothes, musical instruments, traditional paintings, and church paraphernalia. Average Annual Attendance: 25,000.
Purchases: $10,000.
Collections: 6000 pieces in ethnological collections; 395 pieces in collection of paintings, the oldest c 15th century; 1350 pieces in collection of crosses, the oldest c 11th - 12th centuries.
Exhibitions: France, Nigeria, USSR.
Publications: Catalogs and albums, irregularly.
Activities: Classes for children; dramatic programs, docent training; lect open to public; individual paintings and original objects of art lent to other museums or galleries of other countries; sales shop selling books, magazines, reproductions, prints and slides.
Library: Cur Dr Girma Kidane. Small reference library. Holdings: Negatives in photograph collection 7000; color slides 1200.

FINLAND

HELSINKI

SUOMEN KANSALLISMUSEO* (National Museum of Finland), Mannerheiminte (Mailing Add: PO Box 913, 10). Tel: 40251. *Dir* Toini-Inkeri Kaukonen.
Open Sept-Apr, weekdays 11 AM - 3 PM; Tues 6 - 9 PM; Sun 11 AM - 4 PM. The National Board of Antiquities and Historical Monuments, previously the Archaeological Commission, of which the National Museum is a branch, estab 1884 as a research institute and museum. In 1893 the Historical-Ethnographical Museum of the Helsinki University, the collections of the Finnish Archeological Society and the Ethnographical Museum of the Finnish Undergraduates Corporation were united under the name of the State Historical Museum and later as the National Museum. In 1916 the first departments were opened to the public.
Collections: Prehistoric Dept with Finnish and Comparative Collections; Finnish Historical Dept with a Collection of Coins and Medals; Ethnographical Dept with Finnish, Finno-Ugrian and Comparative Ethnographical Collections. The Open-Air Museum at Seurasaari (Folison) and the museums at Suomenlinna (Sveaborg) are branches of the National Museum.
Library: Holdings—Vols 73,000, includes the Finnish Archaeological Society.

TURKU

TURUN TAIDEMUSEO* (Turku Art Museum), Puolalanpuisto, 10. Tel: 11 810. *Pres* Leif B Sourander; *Dir* Erik Bergh; *VPres* Osmo Laine.
Open weekdays 10 AM - 4 PM; Thurs also 6 - 8 PM; Sun 10 AM - 6 PM; cl Mon Sept 11 - May 31: Admis adults 1 mk, students and children 0.50 mk. Estab Turku Art Association 1891, Turku Art Museum 1904. Average Annual Attendance: 50,000. Mem: 1324; dues 7 mk; permanent mem 140 mk.
Income: Financed by city and state appropriations.
Collections: Collection of 19th & 20th century Finnish art, paintings, drawings, prints and sculpture; international print collection, 19th & 20th centuries.
Exhibitions: Continuing program of changing exhibitions.
Activities: Lect open to public; gallery talks; tours; original objects of art lent; Turku Art School, the oldest in Finland, estab 1830.
Library: Reference Library. Holdings: Other—Photograph collection of prints 500; posters.

FRANCE

ANGERS

MUSEE DES BEAUX-ARTS (Museum of Fine Arts), 10 rue du Musée, 49000. *Conservator* Viviane Huchard; *Asst Conservator* Catherine Lagrue.
Open (winter) 10 AM - Noon & 2 - 4 PM; (summer) 9 AM - Noon & 2 - 6 PM. Admis 1F; students free. Museum was built 1493-95 by Olivier Barrault. It houses the collection of the marquis de Livois and other statesmen; also the works of sculptor David d'Angers (1788-1839).
Income: Financed by city appropriation.
Collections: Paintings—Primitive art of various schools; French painters of the 17th & 18th centuries—Boucher, Pater, Lancret, Chardin, Greuze, de Troy, Fragonard; French painters of the 19th century—Gerard, Ingres, Delacroix, Gericault; contemporary French artists; sculptors of the 18th century; works of David d'Angers—statues, busts, bas-relief, statuettes, medallions; Italian, Dutch, Belgian and Spanish painters of the 17th and 18th centuries.

AVIGNON

MUSEE DU PETIT PALAISE,* Place du Palais des Papes, 84000. *Chief Cur* George de Loye; *Conservator* Sylvain Gagniere.
Open daily. No admis. Estab 1976 in the old 14th-15th century Archbishop's Palace.
Collections: Italian paintings covering the period from 14th century Florence to 16th century Venice; Medieval paintings of the Avignon and Italian Schools; Medieval sculpture from Avignon.

DIJON

MUSÉE DES BEAUX-ARTS DE DIJON (Museum of Fine Arts), Place de la Sainte-Chapelle, 21000. *Staff* M Quarre; Mlle Geiger, Mme Guillaume, Mlle Mornat.
Open 9 AM - Noon & 2 - 6 PM.
Collections: Paintings, sculpture, objects of art, furniture.
Publications: Bulletin de la Societe des Amis des Musee de Dijon.

FONTAINEBLEAU

MUSÉE NATIONAL DU CHATEAU DE FONTAINEBLEAU* (National Museum of Fontainebleau), Fontainebleau 77300. Tel: 422 27 40. *Cur* Jean-Pierre Samoyault; *Cur* Mme Samoyault-Verlet; *Cur* B Chevallier.
Open 10 AM - Noon & 2 - 6 PM; Oct 1 - Apr 1, 2 - 5 PM. Estab in the 12th century.
Income: Financed by state appropriation.
Collections: 16th - 19th century paintings, furniture and interiors.
Activities: Book shop.
Library: Holdings—Photograph collection.

LILLE

MUSEE DES BEAUX-ARTS DE LILLE (Museum of Fine Arts), Place de la Republique, 59000. *Conservator* Herve Oursel; *Asst* Annie Scottez.
Open daily 10 AM - 12:30 PM & 2 - 5 PM; cl Tues and holidays. Admis 2,70 F.
Income: Financed by city appropriation.
Collections: Western European art from 15th - 20th centuries—paintings, sculptures, ceramics, objects of art, coins and medals.
Exhibitions: Peinture flamande au temps de Rubens dans les Musées du Nord de la France; Dessins parisiens des 19e et 20e siecles; Vic Gentils.
Activities: Classes for adults and children; traveling exhibitions organized and circulated; museum shop selling books, reproductions, slides.

LYON

MUSEE DES BEAUX ARTS, PALAIS ST PIERRE* (Museum of Fine Arts), 20 place des Terreaux, 69001. Tel: 28-07-66. *Cur* Madeleine Rocher-Jauneau.
Open daily 10 AM - Noon & 2 - 6 PM. No admis. Estab in the 17th century in the Monastery of the Nuns of St Pierre as a museum of painting, sculpture and objects of art. Mem: 1100; dues 10 F.
Collections: Gothic and Renaissance art; paintings of the French, Flemish, Dutch, Italian and Spanish Schools; local painters; modern art and murals by Punes de Chavannes; ancient, medieval and modern sculpture; French, Italian, Oriental and Hispano-Moorish ceramics; drawings; prints; furniture; coins; painting of the Lyonnaise school since the 17th century; Egyptian, Greek and Roman antiquities; Islamic art; French art since the Middle Ages.

Publications: Bulletin des Musees et Monuments Lyonnais, quarterly; illustrated guides.
Activities: Lect for high school and college students; photographs; book shop.

ORLEANS

MUSÉE DES BEAUX-ARTS (Museum of Fine Arts), 1 place de la République, 45000. Tel: 38 87 39 22. *Cur* David Ojalvo; *Asst* Mme Moindreau; *Secy* Mlle Furet.
Open Apr - Sept, 10 AM - Noon & 2 - 6 PM; Oct - Mar, 10 AM - Noon & 2 - 5 PM. Admis 2 F. Estab 1825 to exhibit French paintings of the 16th-20th centuries; foreign schools of the 16th-18th centuries; sculpture of the 16th-20th centuries. The print room open by appointment.
Collections: Deruet (les quatre elements); Vouet; Le Nain; La Hyre; Baugin; Watteau; Boucher; Fragonard; Hubert Robert; Gauguin; pastels of the 18th century; group of portraits by Perronneau.
Exhibitions: Dessins Francais du 16e au 18e S; Gaudier-BRZESKA; Les Ponts d'Orléans; Vingt-cinq ans d'acquisitions; Raoul Dufy.

PARIS

INSTITUT DE FRANCE, Musée Condé, Chantilly, 60500. Tel: 15 4 457 0362. *Conservator of Coll* Raymond Cazelles; *Asst to Museum* Amelie Lefebure.
Open 10:30 AM - 5 PM. Admis 7 F. Estab 1897.
Collections: Paintings, ceramics, manuscripts, mobiles.
Publications: Bulletin du Musée Condé.
Library: *Librn* Francoise Chapard. Open for reference. Holdings: Vols 150,000. Special Subjects: Art and history; French literature of the 19th century.

MUSEE COGNACQ-JAY (Cognacq-Jay Museum), 25 Boulevard des Capucines, 75002. Tel: 0735566. *Dir* Mlle Thérèse Burollet.
Open 10 AM - 5:30 PM; cl Mon & Tues. Estab 1928.
Income: Financed by city appropriation.
Collections: 18th century works of art; paintings of Boucher, Fragonard, Tiepolo; Quentin de la Tour pastels; drawings by Fragonard, Watteau; sculpture by Lemoyne, Clodion, Falconet, Houdon; art of silversmiths; miniatures.

MUSEE D'ART MODERNE (BEAUBOURG), Centre National d'Art et de Culture Georges Pompidou, Rue des Archives.
Open daily until 10 PM. No admis. Estab 1976, opened January 1977; the building has transparent walls, wide open doors, outdoor escalators. The center houses the museum, an industrial design center, a public library for contemporary writing, and institute of music research, a theatre for showing old films, and a tree-covered mall for modern music, drama, poetry readings, ballets and other entertainment.
Collections: The previous Musee d'Art Moderne on the Avenue du President Wilson closed on September 14, 1976, and its collection of contemporary paintings and sculpture are installed in the new museum. Collection is presently being increased.
Exhibitions: The inaugural exhibitions were Works by Marcel Duchamp and Paris-New York-Paris. There have been constantly changing exhibitions since, with large crowds attending each new exhibition.
Activities: Classes for children; lectures; gallery talks; tours; concerts of 20th century music.
Library: Free access library of contemporary literature, art and music.

MUSEE DE CLUNY* (Cluny Museum), 6 Place Paul Painleve (V) 75005. Tel: 325-6200. *Dir* Francis Salet.
Open daily 10 AM - 12:45 PM & 2 - 5 PM; cl Tues.
Collections: †Tapestries, enamels, sculptures, ivories and furniture of the Middle Ages.

MUSEE DU JEU DE PAUME (Gallery of Impressionists), Place de la Concorde, 75001. Tel: 260 12 07. *Chief Conservator* Helene Adhemar.
Open Wed - Mon 9:45 AM - 5:15 PM; cl Tues. Admis 5 F; Sun 2.50 F. The Gallery, the original orangerie of the Palais de Tuileries, was estab 1862; it was remodeled in 1954 and again in 1969.)
Collections: Collection of Impressionists.
Publications: Catalog of the Musee du Jeu de Paume.
Activities: Museum shop selling books, reproductions, slides.

MUSÉE DU LOUVRE* (Louvre Museum), Palais du Louvre, Place du Carrousel, 75041. Tel: 260 39 26. *Dir* Pierre Quoniam; *Cur Oriental Antiquities* Pierre Amiet; *Cur Egyptian Antiquities* Christian Desroches Noblecourt; *Cur Greek & Roman Antiquities* Francois Villard; *Cur Sculpture* Victor Beyer; *Cur Paintings* Michel Laclotte; *Cur Drawings* Maurice Sérullaz; *Cur Orangerie & Jeu de Paume Galleries* Helene Adhemar.

Open daily 9:45 AM - 5:15 PM; cl Tues & holidays. Estab 1793. The collections are divided into six departments and offer a panorama of the arts of all periods. Average Annual Attendance: 3,000,000.
Collections: Drawings, sculpture, paintings, and decorative arts; Islamic art; Coptes antiquities; the Edmond de Rothschild Collection.
Library: Holdings—Vols 100,000.

MUSEE DU PETIT PALAIS* (Municipal Museum), Av W Churchill. Tel: 265 99-21. *Chief Cur* Adeline Cacan.
Open daily Wed - Sun 10 AM - 6 PM; cl Mon & Tues. Estab 1902.
Collections: Egyptian, Greek, Etruscan antiquities; Roman bronzes, ceramics, coins; objets d'art of the Middle Ages and the Renaissance; paintings and drawings of the 17th and 18th centuries; tapestries, furniture, porcelains of Sevres and Saxe; Chinese collections; drawings and paintings of the 19th century.
Exhibitions: Changing temporary exhibitions.
Library: Holdings—Vols 10,000; Other—Prints 7000.

MUSEE NATIONAL DES MONUMENTS FRANCAIS* (National Museum of French Sculpture and Murals), Palais de Chaillot, Place du Tracadero, 75116. Tel: 727 97 27 & 727 35 74. *Cur* Philippe Chapu; *Keepers* Francois Hiliare & Christian de Merindol.
Open Wed - Mon 9:45 AM - 12:30 PM & 2 - 5 PM; cl Tues. Estab 1880.
Collections: Full scale casts of the principal French monuments and sculpture from the beginning of Christianity to the 19th century; full scale reproductions of medieval murals.
Publications: Guides.
Library: Open to students of the Louvre and archeologists, Mon - Fri 10 AM - Noon & 2 - 5 PM; cl Sat & Sun. Holdings: Vols 10,000 (history of art); Other—Photographs 200,000, copies of medieval murals 2,000. Special Subjects: Archeology, history of art; Special Collections: Photograph collection of prints 20,000.

UNION CENTRALE DES ARTS DECORATIFS (Central Union of Decorative Arts)
—Musee des Arts Decoratifs (Museum of Decorative Arts), 107 rue de Rivoli, 75001. Tel 260 32.14. *Pres* Robert Bordaz; *Secy* Pierre Meilhac; *Chief Cur* Francois Mathey; *Cur* Yvonne Brunhammer; *Cur* Gerard Mabille; *Cur* Marie-Noele de Gary; *Cur* Nadine Gasc; *Cur* Odile Nouvel.
Open Wed - Sat 10 AM - Noon & 2 - 5 PM; Sun 10 AM - 5 PM. Admis 5 F. Estab 1863 to adapt beauty to industry. Gallery maintained for exhibition of decorative art, architecture and art. Average Annual Attendance: 80,000. Mem: 3200; dues 50 F; annual meeting June.
Income: Financed by city and state appropriations and membership.
Collections: Home decor of the French Middle Ages; Oriental art; tapestry collection; Dubuffet bequest; department of design; †textiles; †paper paints.
Activities: Lectures with guided tours; films; original objects of art lent; traveling exhibitions organized and circulated.
—Bibliotheque des Arts Decoratifs (Library of Decorative Arts). *Chief Conservator* Genevieve Picon; *Conservator* Genevieve Bonte; *Conservator* Josiane Sartre.
Open Tues - Sat 10 AM - 5:30 PM; Mon 1:45 - 5:30 PM. Estab 1864 to adapt beauty to industry. Open to the public for reference.
Holdings: Vols 100,000; Per subs 300; Other—Collection Iconographique Maciet.

REIMS

MUSÉES SAINT-DENIS,* 8 Rue Chanzy, 51100. Tel: 47 28 44. *Conservator* F Pomarede; *Asst Conservator* J P Bonna; *Asst* M Guillemain.
Open 10 AM - Noon & 2 - 6 PM. No admis. Estab 1795 as a museum of art, archeology and local history.
Income: Financed by city appropriation.
Collections: †10 designs by Cranach; †paintings on canvas of the 15th-16th centuries; 16th century tapestries of de Saint Revii; 17th-18th century paintings; †25 paintings by Corot; †French paintings of the 19th century; ceramics; art and archeological antiques.
Activities: Expositions, classes and service for scholars.
Library: Holdings—Vols 2000; prints in photograph collection 1000.

STRASBOURG

MUSÉE DE L'OEUVRE NOTRE DAME* (Cathedral Museum), 3 Place du Chateau, 67000. Tel: 32 59 00. *Conservation* Hans Zumstein & Marie-Josée Forte.
Open Apr - May daily 10 AM - Noon & 2 - 5 PM; cl Good Friday, Easter and May 1; June - Sept daily 10 AM - Noon & 2 - 6 PM; cl July 14; Oct - Mar daily 10 AM - Noon & 2 - 4 PM; cl Nov 1, Christmas and New Year's.

Collections: Houses dating from 14th, 16th & 17th centuries, grouped around the House of Charity. Romanesque rooms—sculptures of the 11th and 12th centuries; stained glass windows from Strasbourg's former Romanesque Cathedral. Gothic rooms—originals of the finest 13th century sculptures from the Cathedral; drawings of the Cathedral's Houses of Charity of the 13th-15th centuries; meeting room of the Lodge of Stonemasons and Stonecutters (1580). 15th century rooms—sculptures, stained glass, Alsatian paintings. Renaissance rooms—graphic arts and illustration of books produced at Strasbourg from 1500 to 1600; paintings, drawings and stained glass by Grien; archives; rooms devoted to Renaissance furniture and sculpture; still-life room; development of gold and silverware in Strasbourg from 15th to 19th century. Collection of glass.
Publications: Catalogs of collections.

MUSÉE DES BEAUX-ARTS* (Museum of Fine Arts), Chateau des Rohan, 2 Place du Chateau, 67000. Tel: 35 29 06. *Dir* Jean-Daniel Ludmann.
Open Apr - May daily 10 AM - Noon & 2 - 5 PM; cl Good Friday, Easter & May 1; June - Sept daily 10 AM - Noon & 2 - 6 PM; cl July 14; Oct 1 - Mar 31 10 AM - Noon & 2 - 4 PM; cl Tues, Nov 1, Dec 25, Jan 1. Admis 1 F, half fee for groups of ten, students, children, and the military. Occupies two floors of the Rohan Castle, which also contains the Archaeological Museum, the Museum of Decorative Arts, the Print Department, and the Library.
Collections: Paintings of the chief European schools, 14th-19th century, from Giotto to modern times; works by Filippino Lippi, Corregio, Veronese, Tintoretto, Tiepolo, Guardi, El Greco, Zurbaran, Goya, Memling, Lucas of Leyden, van Heemskerk, Rubens, Van Dyck, De Hoogh, Marmion, Valentin, Vouet, Tassel, Watteau, Boucher, Chardin, Fragonard; also Corot, Rousseau, Pissaro, Sisley, Degas, Monet, Renoir and others; Gauguin, Signac, Vuillard, Dufy, Braque and others of the modern school.

TOULOUSE

MUSEE DES AUGUSTINS* (Museum of Augustins), 2 ter rue Alsace-Lorraine, 31000. Tel: 21 68 00. *Cur* Denis Milhau; *Secy* Alfred Deflandre.
Open daily 10 AM - Noon & 2 - 6 PM; cl Tues. Admis 1 F. Estab 1795 and housed in the former Augustine convent of which parts date from the 14th and 15th centuries. Maintains gallery.
Income: Financed by city and state appropriations.
Collections: Romanesque, Gothic and modern sculpture of Languedoc; paintings of the 16th-20th centuries, French, Italian, Flemish, Spanish.
Activities: Classes for children; lect open to public, 200 vis lectr per yr; exten dept serving schools; traveling exhibitions organized and circulated.
Library: Reference library. Holdings: Vols 4,000; Other—Prints in photograph collection 1,000.

TOURS

MUSEE DES BEAUX-ARTS* (Museum of Fine Arts), 18 Place Francais Sicard, 37000. Tel: 05 68 73. *Chief Conservator* Mrs M N Pinot de Villechenon; *Asst Conservator* S Guillot de Suduiraut.
Open Nov - Feb 9 AM - Noon & 2 - 5 PM; cl Tues; Mar - Oct 9 AM - Noon & 2 - 6 PM; June - Sept 9 AM - 11 PM; cl Jan 1, May 1, July 14, Nov 1, Dec 25. Admis 2 F 50. Estab 1793 as a museum of the French Revolution; installed into the Palais of the Archbishop in 1910.
Income: Financed by municipal appropriation.
Collections: Italian paintings of the 13th-16th centuries; primitives; Mantegna; French paintings and furniture of the 18th century; work of Largillieu, Lancret, Boucher, Lerroneau, Terborch, Vigon, Degas, Challot, Demoulin, Rembrandt, Rubens, Delacroix, Boulanger, Chasseriau, Monet, Bourdale, Calder; sculpture by La Moyne, Houdon, Bourdelle; tapestries.
Exhibitions: Peintures francais de XVII's du musee du Louvre; Images d'unes France; La ceramique touraugelle au XIX's; Gravures de Picasso.
Activities: Overhead photographs for viewing; lect open to public.
Library: For reference.

VERSAILLES

MUSEE NATIONAL DU CHATEAU DE VERSAILLES* (National Museum of the Chateau of Versailles), Palais de Versailles, 78000. Tel: 950 58 32. *Cur* Gerald van der Kemp; *Cur* Pierre Lemoine.
Open 10 AM - 5 PM. Admis 5 F. Estab 1837 for the conservation and display of the Royal Apartments and the collections they contain.
Collections: Furniture, paintings and objects of art contained in the Royal Apartments; paintings of the 16th-19th centuries contained in the History Museum of France.

Activities: Bureau of Cultural Affairs organizes visiting conferences for the purpose of educating scholars; original objects of art lent; lect open to the public.
Library: For reference only.

GERMANY, FEDERAL REPUBLIC OF

AACHEN

SUERMONDT-LUDWIG-MUSEUM DER STADT AACHEN, Wilhelmstrasse 18, 5100. Tel: 0241-472580. *Dir* Dr Ernst-Gunther Grimme; *Cur* Martin Mayer; *Cur* Hella Lorenz.
Open Tues - Fri 10 AM - 5 PM; Sat & Sun 10 AM - 1 PM. No admis. Estab 1880 to present a general view of European art from the Classical Period to the present. Average Annual Attendance: 70,000. Mem: 1600; dues DM 10.
Income: Financed by city appropriation.
Collections: Sculpture from the Roman to Baroque; graphic art (ceramics, textiles); portraits from Middle Ages to the present; paintings from the Middle Ages to the Baroque.
Exhibitions: Eight rotating exhibitions; sculpture exhibition.
Publications: Aachener Kunstblatter.
Activities: Classes for adults and children; lect open to public; gallery talks; tours; original objects of art lent; museum shop selling books, magazines, reproductions.
Library: *Librn* Renate Puvogel. Open to the public. Holdings: Vols 15,000; Per subs 8.

BERLIN

STAATLICHE MUSEEN PREUSSISCHER KULTURBESITZ* (State Museums, Foundation for Prussian Cultural Treasures), Stauffenbergstrasse 41, 30. Tel: 2609. *Dir* Dr Stephan Waetzoldt.
(Estab 1830.) Museums in Dahlem open Tues - Fri 9 AM - 5 PM; Sat - Sun 9 AM - 5 PM; cl Mon. Museums in Charlottenburg open Sat - Thurs 9 AM - 5 PM; cl Fri. Nationalgalerie open Mon Noon - 8 PM; Tues - Sun 9 AM - 5 PM; cl Fri. Antiquities Collection open Mon, Thurs & Fri 9 AM - 5 PM; Sat - Sun 10 AM - 5 PM; Wed 2 - 9 PM; cl Tues. Average Annual Attendance: 1,500,000.
Collections in Dahlem, Arnimallee 23/27, 33.
  Picture Gallery. *Dir* Dr Henning Bock. Paintings from 13th - 18th centuries, Old Dutch, Old German, Italian, Netherlands and French works, including Durer and 26 paintings by Rembrandt.
  Dept of Sculpture. *Dir* Dr Peter Bloch. †Late antiquity to classicism, among others Riemenschneider, Donatello.
  Dept of Prints and Drawings. *Dir* Dr Matthias Winner. †300,000 drawings, prints and illustrated books of all epochs of European art; greatest collection of Durer drawings, Bruegel and Rembrandt.
  Museum of Ethnology, Lansstrasse 8 33. *Dir* Dr Kurt Kreiger. †300,000 items of different cultures. Dept of Oceania, ships, houses, masks; Ancient America, ceramics, gold; South Asia, masks, string puppets; Africa, North America, East Asia (China, Tibet) and Europe; Junior Museum; Museum for the Blind.
  Museum of Indian Art. *Dir* Dr H Hartel. †Central Asiatic Frescoes of the early middle ages from Turfan and Indian Sculpture.
  Museum of Far Eastern Art. *Dir* Dr B von Ragué. Paintings, ceramics of China and Japan.
  Museum of Islamic Art and Antiquities. *Dir* Dr Klaus Brisch. †Glass, ceramics, tapestry, stucco, metal, ebony and book design from Near East, North Africa and Spain.
  Museum of German Folklore. *Dir* Dr Theodor Kahlmann. On exhibit from 1976.
  Museums in Charlottenburg
  Egyptian Antiquities. *Dir* Dr J Settgast. †All periods, bust of queen Nofretete and sculptures from Tel el Amarna.
  Greek and Roman Antiquities. *Dir* Dr K Vierneisel. †Bronzes, vases, marble sculptures, gold jewelry up to the Byzantine period, Hildesheimer Silberfund (silvertrove).
  Museum of Pre- and Protohistory. *Dir* Dr A von Mueller. †Objects found by excavation and in settlements in Europe and Asia from Old Stone Age to the height of the Middle Ages.
  Museum of Arts and Crafts. *Dir* Dr Franz-Adrian Dreier. †Objects from the middle ages to the 20th century, Welfenschatz.
  Plaster cast House: 7000 different forms.
In the Center of Berlin
  Art Library and Lipperheide Costume Library, Jobens-Strasse 2, 12. Estab 1867. *Dir* Dr Ekhart Berckenhagen. 11,000 drawings of architecture and design, prints and rare books; 125,000 volumes of history of art and costume.

Nationalgalerie, Potsdamerstrasse 50, 30. *Dir* Dr Dieter Honisch.
†Paintings, sculptures and drawings 19th and 20th centuries, C D Frederich, Mensel, French and German impressionists; modern exhibitions.

BONN

RHEINISCHES LANDESMUSEUM BONN (RHINELAND MUSEUM), Colmantstrasse 14-16, D 5300. Tel: 02221/63 21 58. *Dir* Dr Christoph B Rüger; *Dept Dir* Dr Walter Janssen.
Open Tues - Fri 9 AM - 5 PM; Wed 9 AM - 9 PM; Sat & Sun 10 AM - 6 PM. Admis DM 1, children to 18 0,50; groups 0,50. Estab 1820, and in 1873 as Rhineland Regional Museum for the purpose of collecting and showing Rhineland history and art from prehistoric times to the present. Average Annual Attendance: 140,000.
Income: Financed by state appropriation and Landschaftsverband Rheinland.
Collections: Prehistoric times, Roman period, Frankish period, and medieval archaeology, art from the Middle Ages until today, and coins.
Exhibitions: Rheinische Aufgrabungen '75; Archäologie in einer Grobstadt (Berlin); Groteskèr Jugendstil: Carl Strathmann; Die Maler - Jochem und Rudi; Karl Blossfeld, Fotografien 1900-1932; Modellbilder: Chr Boltanski/Annette Messager; 200 Jahre amerikanische Malerie; Die zwanziger Jahre im Porträt; Holzschnitt im neuen China.
Publications: Bonner Jahrbucher, annual; Das Rhein. Landesmuseum Bonn, research series.
Activities: Classes for children; lect open to the public; concerts; gallery talks; tours; museum shop selling books, reproductions, slides.
—**Library:***Librn* Johannes Seifert. Open to the public for reference only.
Open Mon - Fri 8 AM - 12:30 & 1 - 4 PM; Tues & Thurs Eve until 5:30 PM. Estab 1841 originally as Library of the Verein von Altertumsfreunden still a part of the museum's library.
Income: Approximately DM 45.000 (financed by membership and Landschaftsverband Rheinland).
Holdings: Vols 70,000; Per subs 500.

STADTISCHES KUNSTMUSEUM BONN (Art Museum of the City of Bonn), Rathausgasse 7, 5300. Tel: 773686. *Dir* Dr Dierk Stemmler; *Asst* Dr Udo Liebelt.
Open daily 10 AM - 5 PM, Thurs 10 AM - 9 PM; Cl Mon. Average Annual Attendance: 90,000.
Income: Financed by membership, city appropriation.
Collections: Art of the 20th century, especially August Macke and the Rhenish expressionists; German art since 1945; graphic arts.
Exhibitions: August Macke, Aquarele un Zeichnungen; Franz Erhard Walther, Diagramme zum 1 Werksatz; Kunst der 60er und 70er Jahre aus Bonner Privatbesitz; Ulrich Ruckriem.
Publications: Bestandskataloge: August Macke und die Rheinischen Expressionisten; 1949-1974 25 Jahre Kunst in der Bundesrepublik.
Activities: Concerts; traveling exhibitions organized and circulated; sales shop selling reproductions, prints, slides, and catalogs.
Library: Holdings—Vols 4000; Per subs 20. Special Subjects: Contemporary art.

BREMEN

KUNSTHALLE BREMEN* (Bremen Art Gallery), Am Wall 207, 28. Tel: 32 47 85. *Dir* Dr Gunter Busch; *Cur* Dr Jurgen Schultze; *Asst Cur* Dr Annemarie Winther; *Asst Cur* Dr Bernhard Schnackenburg; *Asst Cur* Dr Gerhard Gerkens.
Open Tues 10 AM - 4 PM & 7 - 9 PM; Wed & Thurs 10 AM - 4 PM; Fri 10 AM - 4 PM & 7 - 9 PM; Sat & Sun 10 AM ، 2 PM; cl Mon. Admis DM .50, for special exhibitions DM 1 to DM 2. Estab 1823. Gallery houses European art since the Middle Ages. Mem: 2730; dues DM 15 and up; annual meeting.
Collections: European paintings, Middle Ages to modern, especially French and German art of the 19th century, drawings, sculpture and prints; 17th - 20th century plastic collections; coins and medals up to the end of the 19th century; 18th and 19th century Japanese drawings and prints.
Publications: Schriften zu Kunstwerken der Kunsthalle Bremen; exhibition catalogs; Meisterwerke der Kunsthalle Bremen; Katalog der Lemalde des 19 und 20 Jahrhunderts in der Kunsthalle Bremen.
Activities: Classes for adults; scholarships; lect open to the public, 15-18 vis lectr per yr; gallery talks; traveling exhibitions organized and circulated; objects of art lent.
Library: Reference library. Holdings: Vols 40,000; Other—Prints 400, photographs 4600.

BRUNSWICK

HERZOG ANTON ULRICH-MUSEUM* (Duke Anton Ulrich Museum), Museumstrasse 1; Medieval section: Burg Dankwarderode, Burgplatz, D-33 Braunschweig. Tel: 0531 49589 & 0531 49378. *Dir*

Rudiger Klessman; *Chief Cur* Dr Bodo Hedergott; *Cur* Dr Christian von Heusinger; *Asst* Dr Sabine Jacob.
Open Tues - Sun 11 AM - 4 PM; Wed 11 AM - 8 PM; Medieval Section open Tues - Sun 10 AM - 4 PM; cl Mon. Estab 1754. Average Annual Attendance: 58,000.
Income: Financed by state appropriations.
Collections: Egyptian, Greek and Roman Antiquities; Medieval Art; †European paintings of the 15th-18th centuries; †prints and drawings from the 15th century tq the present time; illustrated books; †European Renaissance and Baroque decorative art, including bronzes, wood and ivory carvings, Italian majolica, French 16th century enamels, porcelain, glass, clocks, furniture, laces, waxes; Chinese lacquers.
Publications: Catalogs and guides.
Activities: Lectures; concerts.
Library: For reference only. Holdings: Vols 30,000.

COLOGNE

MUSEEN DER STADT KOLN* (Cologne City Museums), An der Rechtschule. Tel: 221-2373. *Gen Dir* Dr Gerhard Bott.
—**Wallraf-Richartz-Museum, Museum Ludwig.** *Dir* Karl Ruhrberg; *Cur Modern Art* Dr Kurt Locher; *Cur Modern Art* Dr Evelyn Weiss & Dr Rainer Budde; *Cur Engravings* Dr Hella Robels & Dr Dieter Ronte.
Open daily 10 AM - 5 PM; Thurs & Tues 10 AM - 8 PM. Admis 1 DM; groups, students and children .50 DM. Estab 1824. Mem: 1,750.
Collections: Wallraf-Richartz-Museum: Painting from 13th century to 1900, especially old Cologne painting and Netherlandish painting; 19th century sculpture. Museum Ludwig: Painting and sculpture from 1900 to the present, especially Expressionism and contemporary art.
Exhibitions: Lovis Corinth; Bertel Thorvaldsen; Peter Paul Rubens.
Publications: Yearbook; bulletin.
Activities: Classes for adults and children; docent training; traveling exhibitions organized and circulated; museum shop selling books and prints.
Library: *Librn* Dr Albert Schug. Open to the public for reference. Holdings: Vols 130,000; Per subs 730.
—**Romisch-Germanisches Museum,*** Roncalliplatz. Tel: 221-2304. *Dir* Dr Hugo Borger; *Cur Prehistory, Provincial Roman Archaeology* Dr Peter La Baume; *Cur Classical Archaeology* Dr Jörgen Bracker; *Cur Early Christian Archaeology* Dr Gunther Ristow; *Cur Prehistory* Dr Walter Meier-Arendt.
Open Schatzkammer in der Alten Wache (Treasures in the Old Guardhouse), daily 10 AM - 5 PM; Thurs 10 AM - 10 PM; Dionysos-Mosaik, daily 10 AM - 8 PM, Tues & Fri 7 - 10 PM; Prätorium, daily 10 AM - 5 PM. Estab 1946.
Collections: †Pre- and early historic discoveries; †Roman escavations; †Roman glass and industrial arts; †gold ornaments of the era of migrating tribes.
Activities: Lect open to public; gallery; tours; discussions; seminars.
Library: Holdings—Vols 18,000.
—**Rautenstrauch-Joest Museum fur Volkerkunde (Ethnography),*** Ubierring 45. Tel: 311065/66. *Dir* Dr Axel von Gagern; *Cur American Indian Art* Dr Ingeborg Bolz; *Cur Art of Indonesia and the South Seas* Dr Waldemar Stohr; *Cur African Art* Dr Klaus Volprecht.
Open Sun - Wed 10 AM - 5 PM; Thurs - Sat 10 AM - 8 PM. Estab 1906.
Collections: †Culture and art of the non-European peoples.
Activities: Lect open to public; gallery talks; tours; films; seminars.
Library: Holdings—Vols 38,000.
—**Kolnisches Stadtmuseum im Zeughaus*** (Cologne City Museum), Zeughaustrasse 1. Tel: 221-2352. *Dir* Dr Hugo Borger; *Cur Art History* Dr Werner Juttner; *Cur Cologne Folklore* Dr Max-Leo Schwering; *Cur Folk Art* Dr Maria Schmidt.
Open daily 10 AM - 5 PM; Thurs until 10 PM. Estab 1888.
Collections: †National history; †national development; †religious and rural art and culture; †trade and industrial arts of Cologne; †graphic arts of Cologne and the Rhineland; †photograph collection of the Rhineland (145,000 prints).
Activities: Lect open to public; gallery talks; tours; seminars.
Library: Holdings—Vols 12,000.
—**Kunstgewerbemuseum (Arts and Crafts Museum),** Overstolzenhaus, Rheingasse 8-12, 5. Tel: 221-9521. *Dir* Dr Brigitte Klesse; *Chief Cur* Dr Gisela Reineking von Bock; *Cur* Dr Carl-Wolfgang Schumann; *Asst Cur* Dr Rudiger Joppien.
Open daily 10 AM - 5 PM. Admis adults DM 1; students DM 0.50. Estab 1889 to propagate interest in the applied and decorative arts. Approx 600 square meters in the permanent exhibition rooms at the Overstolzenhaus, a medieval house of the 13th century. Since the old museum was bombed during the war, no adequate gallery has been established—a permanent home is planned for 1985. Average Annual Attendance: 35,000. Mem: 200.
Income: Financed by city appropriation.
Collections: European applied arts from the Middle Ages to the present time; some holdings in Islamic arts; approx 25,000 objects.

Exhibitions: Textile Objects; Weisses Gold und Bunte Seide; Bader, Duft und Seife; Sammlung Giorgio Silzer, Berlin; Walter Gropius, Bauten und Projekte; Emil Lettre—Andreas Mortiz; Stiftung Elisabeth Treskow, Schmuck aus 3000 Jahren; Piet Zwart—ein niederlandischer Designer; Kommunaler Wohnbau, Wien 1923-1934.
Publications: Bulletin.
Activities: Preparation of scholarly catalogs of holdings; sales shop selling books, reproductions, slides.
Library: Open to the public for reference. Special Subjects: Glass, furniture, ceramics, metalwork.
—**Museum für Ostasiatische Kunst** (Museum of East Asian Art), Universitatstrasse 100, 5000. *Dir* Dr Roger Goepper; *Chief Cur* Dr Edith Dittrich; *Cur* Dr Ulrich Wiesner; *Cur* Dr Masako Shono; *Cur* Dr Ji-hyun Whang.
Open Mon - Thurs & Sat - Sun 10 AM - 5 PM; Fri 10 AM - 8 PM. Admis DM 1. Estab 1913. Average Annual Attendance: 15,000.
Collections: Art of China, Korea and Japan, especially Buddhist art from Japan, Korean ceramics, Chinese bronzes, and Japanese lacquers.
Exhibitions: Masterworks from China, Japan, Korea; Chinese Art from the Collection of Gustav VI, King of Sweden.
Publications: Catalog.
Activities: Classes for adults and children; museum shop selling books, reproductions, prints, slides.
Library: Librn Dr Ji Hyun Whang. Open Mon - Thurs 10 AM - 5 PM; Fri 10 AM - 12:30 PM. Holdings: Vols 10,000; Per subs 35. Special Subjects: The arts of Korea, China, Japan and matters related to them.
—**Schnutgen Museum,*** Cacilienstrasse 29 (Caciliendirche). Tel: 221-2310. *Dir* Dr Anton Legner; *Cur Art of the Middle Ages* Dr Anton von Euw.
Open daily 10 AM - 5 PM; Wed 7 - 10 PM. Estab 1906.
Collections: †Religious art, early Middle Ages to Baroque.
—**Kunsthalle Holn*** (Cologne Art Gallery), Josef-Haubrich-Hof 1. Tel: 221-2335. *Dir* Dr Helmut R Leppien.
Open daily 10 AM - 8 PM; Mon and Fri until 10 PM. Estab 1967 for showing special exhibitions. Average Annual Attendance: 170,000.

DUSSELDORF

KUNSTSAMMLUNG NORDRHEIN-WESTFALEN (Nordrhein-Westfalen Art Collection), Jacobistr 2, Schloss Jagerhof, 4. Tel: 0211/357525. *Dir* Dr Werner Schmalenbach; *Cur* Dr Volkmar Essers.
Open Tues - Sun 10 AM - 5 PM; Wed 10 AM - 8 PM; cl Mon. Admis DM 1. Estab 1961 as a 20th century art collection. Gallery is an 18th century castle. Average Annual Attendance: 50,000.
Income: Financed by state apropriation.
Collections: Paintings of the 20th century starting from Fauvism, Expressionism and Cubism, it represents the main streams of contemporary art.
Exhibitions: Paul Klee; Picasso; American Painting since 1950.
Activities: Classes for adults and children; lect open to public, 96 vis lectr per yr; tours.
—**Library.** *Librn* Gudrun Harms; *Asst to Librn* Helga Obschruff.
Not open to the public. Estab 1962 for the needs of the scientific staff members, will be opened to the public in 1982. Maintains an art gallery.
Income: Financed by city appropriation.
Holdings: Vols 39,500; Per subs 32; Other—Exhibition catalogs, original art works.
Special Subjects: Art of the 20th century.

STADTISCHE KUNSTHALLE* (City Art Gallery), Grabbeplatz 4, 4 (Postfach 1120). Tel: 36 57 83. *Dir* Jurgen Harten; *Exec Secy* Renata Sharp; *Delegate Dir* Dr Katharina Schmidt; *Asst* John Matheson; *Asst* Dr Jaroslav Borovicka.
Open 10 AM - 8 PM; cl Mon. Admis 2 DM, students 0.050 DM. Estab 1967.
Income: Financed by city and state appropriations.
Publications: Exhibition catalogs.
Activities: Concerts; dramatic programs.

FRANKFURT

LIEBIEGHAUS, MUSEUM ALTER PLASTIK (Museum of Sculpture), Schaumainkai 71. Tel: 611/63 89 07. *Dir* Dr Herbert Beck; *Staff* Dr Peter C Bol.
Open Tues - Sun 10 AM - 5 PM; Wed 10 AM - 8 PM; cl Mon. Estab 1906-1907, to exhibit sculpture. Average Annual Attendance: 60,000. Mem: 1,300.
Income: Financed by city appropriation.
Collections: Sculpture from Ancient Times to the Middle Ages.
Exhibitions: Kunst um 1400 am Mittelrehein—Ein Teil der Wirklichkeit; Elfenbenarbeiten aus der Sammlung Hupsh; Olympia—eine archaische Grabung; Die Nabataer—Eine arabische Kultur der Antike; Altarkunst des Barock.

Activities: Classes for adults and children; docent training; lect open to the public, 3000 vis lectr per yr; original objects of art lent to different institutions; museum shop selling books, prints, slides.
Library: Open to the public. Holdings: Vols 10,000; Per subs 50.

MUSEUM FUR KUNSTANDWERK* (Museum of Arts and Crafts), Schaumainkai 15,6. Tel: 212 4037. *Dir* Peter Wilhelm Meister; *Cur* Dr Analiese Ohm.
Open daily 1 - 5 PM; Wed 1 - 8 PM; cl Mon. No admis. Estab 1877 for decorative arts from the Middle Ages to the 20th century, and Asiatic art. Average Annual Attendance: 25,000.
Income: Financed by city appropriations. Purchases $20,000.
Collections: Ceramics; furniture; glass; bronzes; silverwork; pewter; iron work; textiles; manuscripts.
Activities: Photograph collection of 2000 prints for reference.
Library: Reference library. Holdings: Vols 5,000.

STADELSCHES KUNSTINSTITUT (Staedel Art Institute), Durerstrasse 2, D-6000. Tel: 0611 617092. *Dir* Dr Klaus Gallwitz; *Cur* Dr Paul Eich; *Cur* Dr Christian Lenz; *Cur* Dr Lutz S Malke; *Cur* Dr Margret Stuffman; *Cur* Dr Hans-Joachim Ziemke.
Open Thurs - Sun 10 AM - 5 PM; Wed 10 AM - 8 PM. Admis DM 2; Sun free. Estab 1816 to gather and to exhibit works of art for the public. A large building with 20 bigger rooms and 40 smaller rooms for paintings, an auditorium, a department of prints and drawings, a library, workshops and store-rooms. Average Annual Attendance: 150,000.
Income: Financed by endowment, city and state appropriations. Purchases: DM 500,000.
Collections: European schools from the 14th to 20th centuries; Old Masters; Italian—Fra Angelico, Bellini, Botticelli, Pontormo, Tiepolo; early Netherland—Master of Flémalle, van Eyck, van der Weyden, van der Gos, Bouts, Bosch; Dutch and Flemish—Rubens, Jordaens, Rembrandt, Hals, Vermeer; Spanish and French—Velasquez, Poussin, Claude; German—Durer, Holbein, Altdorfer; 19th & 20th centuries romantics, French Impressionists and modern paintings; drawings; prints.
Exhibitions: Russian Painting from 1890 to 1917; French Drawings from the Art Institute of Chicago; The Nazarenes; George Rickey; Dada in Europe.
Publications: Stadel-Jahrbuch, bi-annually.
Activities: Lect for members; concerts; gallery talks; tours; museum shop selling books, reproductions, slides.
Library: Librn Dr Marlinde Reinold, Dr Sofie Bauer. Open to public for reference. Holdings: Vols 37,406.

HAMBURG

HAMBURGER KUNSTHALLE* (Hamburg Art Hall), Glockengiesserwall, 2. Tel: 24 82 51. *Dir* Dr Werner Hofmann.
Open Tues, Thurs - Sun 10 AM - 5 PM; Wed 10 AM - 7 PM; cl Mon. Admis DM 1. Estab 1869. Average Annual Attendance: 350,000.
Collections: Recent schools of Western Art for paintings and sculptures; masterworks of painting from 14th century to present, including Bertram, Francke, Cranach, Rembrandt, Tiepolo, Runge, Menzel, Manet, Liebermann, Kokoschka, Kandinsky, Picasso, Claude Lorrain, Boucher, Friedrich, Munch, Nolde, Arp, Beckmann, Klee, Leger, Jones Hockney; sculpture of 19th and 20th centuries, including Schadow, Hildebrand, Rodin, Maillol, Kolbe, Barlach, Lehmbruck, Marini, Moore, Giacometti, Rickey, Calder, Arp, Uhlmann, Segal, Nachi, Man Ray, Luginbuhl, Grasel; medals from 15th-20th centuries; ancient coins; prints and drawings from 14th-20th centuries.
Publications: Catalogs of permanent collection and exhibitions; series, irregularly; Zur Sache; special issues.
Activities: Lect open to public, 10 vis lectr per yr.
Library: Holdings—Vols 70,000.

HANNOVER

KESTNER-MUSEUM,* Trammplatz 3, 3000. Tel: 1 68 21 20/27 30. *Dir* Dr Peter Munro; *Cur* Dr Christel Mosel; *Asst Cur* Dr Margildis Schulter.
Open Tues, Wed, Fri 10 AM - 4 PM; Sat 10 AM - 6 PM; Sun 10 AM - 1 PM; cl Mon. No admis. Estab 1889.
Income: Financed by city appropriation.
Collections: Egyptian, Greek, Etruscan and Roman art objects, and Medieval art; illuminated manuscripts, incunabula, handicrafts of 15th-20th centuries; prints and drawings of 15th-20th centuries; ancient, Medieval and modern coins and medals.
Publications: Catalogs of exhibitions, irregularly.
Activities: Lect open to public; concerts; photograph collection of approx 10,000 prints.
Library: Holdings—Vols 17,000.

KARLSRUHE

STAATLICHE KUNSTHALLE (State Art Gallery), Hans Thoma Str 2-4, D 7500. Tel: 071-135355. *Dir* Dr Horst Vey; *Deputy Dr* Dr Werner Zimmerman; *Dir Engraving* Dr Johann Eckart von Borries; *Dir Educ* Dr Anneliese Reuter.
Open Tues - Sun 10 AM - 1 PM & 2 - 5 PM; No adm, cl Mon. Estab 1803 for collecting and exhibiting.
Income: Financed by state appropriation.
Collections: 15th-20th century German painting and graphics; 17th-20th century Dutch and Flemish paintings and graphics.
Exhibitions: Changing exhibitions.
Publications: Yearbook.
Activities: Classes for adults and children; docent training; lect open to public, 500 vis lectr per yr; gallery talks; competitions; junior museum.
—**Library.** Tel: 0721 1353358. *Librn* Sabine Schwermer.
Open for reference Tues, Wed & Thurs 10 AM - Noon & 2 - 4 PM.
Income: Financed by state appropriation. Purchases: $40,000.
Holdings: Vols 110,000; Per subs 405; Other—Clipping files, exhibition catalogs, memorabilia, original art works, pamphlets, photographs, prints.
Special Collections: Exhibition catalogues; art sales catalogues, art periodicals.

MUNICH

BAYERISCHEN STAATSGEMALDESAMMLUNGEN (Bavarian State Galleries of Art), 2 Meiserstr 10, 8000. Tel: 089 55911. *General Dir* Dr E Steingraber; *Cur 20th Century Art* Dr Wolf-Dieter Dube; *Cur 19th Century Art* Dr Eberhard Ruhmer; *Cur 20th Century Art* Dr Carla Schult-Hoffmann; *Cur Netherlandish Paintings* Dr Peter Eikemeier; *Cur Old German Paintings* Dr Gisela Goldberg; *Dir German Baroque Paintings* Dr Rudiger an der Heiden; *Cur French Paintings* Dr JG Prinz von Hohenzollern; *Cur Flemish Paintings* Dr Ulla Krempel; *Cur Italian Paintings* Dr Rolf Kultzen; *Restoration Dept* Richard Lohe & Rainer Schomann; *Pub Relations* Dr Liselotte Camp; *Dir Restoration Dept* Dr Hubert Falkner von Sonnenburg; *Restoration Dept* Dr Frank Preusser; *Restoration Dept* Bruno Heimberg; *Restoration Dept* Johann Koller.
This organization administers art galleries of the Bavarian State. It has a laboratory for conservation and scientific research of paintings. Average Annual Attendance: 450,000.
Income: Financed by state appropriation.
Publications: Annual report.
Library: For use of staff members only.
—**Alte Pinakothek (Old Picture Gallery),** Barerstr 27. Tel: 089 286105.
Open Tues - Sun 9 AM - 4:30 PM; Tues 7 Thurs 7 - 9 PM; cl Mon. Estab 1836; founded upon the collections of the Bavarian Princes (since 1520).
Collections: European Old masters.
—**Neue Pinakothek and Staatsgalerie Moderne-Kunst (New Picture Gallery and State Gallery of Modern Art),** Prinzregentenstr 1. Tel: 089 292710.
Open daily 9 AM - 4:30 PM; Thurs 7 - 9 PM; cl Mon.
Collections: 19th and 20th century art—European paintings and sculpture.
—**Schackgalerie,** Prinzregentenstr 9.
Open daily 9 AM - 4:30 PM; cl Tues.
Collections: Late Romantic German art.

BAYERISCHES NATIONALMUSEUM* (Bavarian National Museum), Prinzregentenstrasse 3, 22. Tel: 22 25 91. *Gen Dir* Dr L Kriss-Rettenbeck; *Cur Folk Art* Dr J Bauer; *Cur Furniture* Dr G Himmelheber; *Cur Theater* Dr H Huesmann; *Cur Clocks* Dr K Maurice; *Cur Ceramics* Dr R Ruckert; *Cur Sculpture* Dr A Schadler; *Cur Textiles* Dr A Voelker; *Cur Sculpture* Dr P Volk; *Cur Conservation* Dr R Wackernagel.
Open Apr - Sept Tues - Fri 9:30 AM - 4:30 PM; Oct - May 9 AM - 4 PM; Sat & Sun 10 AM - 4 PM. Estab 1855. Branch museums: Theatermuseum, Galeriestrasse 4a, 22. Tel: 22 24 49. Meissener Porzellan-Sammlung, Stiftung Ernst Schneider, Schloss Lustheim bei Schleissheim. Freundeskreis der Bayerischen Nationalmuseums.
Collections: European art from 900-1850, paintings, sculpture, decorative arts; bronze, ceramics, clocks, furniture, glass, ivory, metalwork, stained glass, tapestries; folk art; Meissen porcelain.
Publications: Munchner Jahrbuch der bildenden Kunst, annually; Bildfuehrer; Forschungshefte.
Activities: Lect open to public, 50 vis lectr per yr; book shop.
Library: Holdings—(Art) Vols 45,000.

MUISKA—MUSEUM, Metzstrasse 31, 80, D-8000. Tel: 089-453280. *Pres* Gisela van Frankenberg; *Chmn* Angelika Hoerl-Binegger; *Art-Cur in Charge of Serigraphed Reproductions* Uli Binegger.

Open Fri 4 - 8 PM. No admis. Estab 1977 for the translation of art from all times and races with the help of the Afro-American artist Lawrence Compton Kolawole's Motion-Art and its 24 ground-motives into informations, concerning all scientific faculties. The museum is divided into 12 sections, each showing examples of antique (back to rock-carving) plus modern art which represents 2 of the 24 ground-motives in a discovered order of mankinds history. Mem: 15; dues $50; annual meeting Aug.
Income: Financed by membership and private donations.
Collections: Gisela von Frankenberg's Collection of †Kolawole's Motion-Art, consisting of paintings, sculptures, drawings and big-size photographs of antique art; plus a self-developed Sun-Computer of universal signs as key.
Exhibitions: Permanent exhibition called 25,000 Years Knowledge as Art.
Publications: Quarterly bulletin.
Activities: Lect open to public; lending collection contains color reproductions and slides; museum shop selling original art, prints and catalogs.
Library: Librn Gisela von Frankenberg. Reference library and information-system open to everyone. Holdings: Vols 120. Special Subjects: Ancient Egypt, Africa, esoterics and the manuscripts of the 3 vols Nommo-Logie (in prep for publ) written by Gisela von Frankenberg, as fundament for a new science and research-center in 1980.

STAATLICHE GRAPHISCHE SAMMLUNG (National Graphic Collection), Meiserstr 10, D-8000 2. Tel: 089 5591/341. *Dir* Dr Dieter Kuhrmann; *Nat Cur* Dr Annegrit Schmitt; *Cur* Dr Gisela Scheffler; *Cur* Dr Richard Harprath; *Cur* Dr Konrad Renger.
Open Mon - Fri 9 AM - 1 PM & 2 - 4:30 PM. Estab 1758 for the collection of prints and drawings of Western European and American masters. Average Annual Attendance: 13,000.
Income: Financed by state appropriation.
Collections: German, Netherlandish, Italian, French, English and American prints and drawings.
Exhibitions: Die Berge; Wolfgang Gafgen; Ommagio a Michelangelo; American Historical Images; Willi Baumeister: Gilgamesch; David Hockney; Italienische Zeichnungen aus eigenem Besitz; Ernest Wilhelm Nay; Italienische Zeichnungen der Stiftung Ratjen; Walter Pichler.
Publications: Exhbition catalogs, irregularly.
Activities: Lect open to public; original objects of art lent to other print rooms; traveling exhibitions organized and circulated.
—**Library.** Librn Liselotte Becher.
Holdings: Vols 25,000; Per subs 20; Other—Exhibition catalogues of graphics.
Special Subjects: Illustrated books.

STAATLICHE SAMMLUNG AGYPTISCHER KUNST (State Collection of Egyptian Art), Residenz, Hofgartenstr (Mailing Add: Meiserstr 10, D-8,2). Tel: 089 55 91 350. *Dir* Dr Dietrich Wildung.
Open 9:30 AM - 4 PM; Tues 7 - 9 PM; cl Mon. Admis DM 1.50. Estab 1970 to collect and preserve Egyptian art from prehistory to Coptic period. Average Annual Attendance: 40,000. Mem: 400; dues 75 DM; annual meeting June.
Income: Financed by state appropriation. Purchases: DM 40,000.
Exhibitions: Vou Troja bis Amarna; Götter—Pharaoheh Egyptian Art from Caros and Alexandria; Blumen der Wuste.
Publications: Studien zur altagyptischen Kultur, 2 vols per yr.
Activities: Lect open to public, 2-3 vis lectr per yr; original objects of art lent to museums; lending collection contains original prints, photographs, sculpture, slides.

STADTISCHE GALERIE IM LENBACHHAUS* (Lenbach House City Gallery), Luisenstrasse 33, 2. Tel: 52 14 31. *Dir* Dr Michael Petzet; *Cur* Dr Erika Hanfstaengl; *Cur* Dr Rosel Gollek.
Open daily 9 AM - 4:30 PM; cl Mon. Admis adults 1.50 DM; students .50 DM. Estab 1925 to collect objects of art produced in Munich and Bavaria, mainly paintings and sculptures. Average Annual Attendance: 100,000.
Income: $80,000 (financed by city and state appropriations). Purchases $30,000.
Collections: †Paintings of the 19th century (Munich school); Franz von Lenbach, his paintings and private collection of art objects; †The Blue Rider and Kandinsky and Klee; Art Nouveau; Neue Sachlichkeit; †contemporary art, prints and drawings, 19th and 20th centuries.
Activities: Collaboration with schools, guided tours, courses in painting; lect open to the public, 10 vis lectr per yr; concerts.
Library: Holdings—Vols 3,000; Other—Photograph collection.

NUREMBERG

GERMANISCHES NATIONALMUSEUM* (Germanic National Museum), Kornmarkt 1, 85. Tel: 20 39 71. *Chief Dir* Dr Arno Schonberger.

Open Oct - Mar, Tues - Sat 10 AM - 4 PM; Sun 10 AM - 1 PM; Apr - Sept, Mon - Sat 10 AM - 5 PM; Sun 10 AM - 4 PM. Admis DM 0.50. Estab 1852. Average Annual Attendance: 190,000. Mem: 8000; dues DM 10.
Collections: Paintings; graphics; sculpture; weapons; instruments; coins; musical instruments; archives; textiles; furniture; toys; ancient historical objects.
Activities: Lectures; gallery talks; tours; concerts.
Library: Holdings—Vols 300,000; Photograph collection with 50,000 negatives.

GHANA

ACCRA

GHANA NATIONAL MUSEUM,* Barnes Rd, (Mailing Add: PO Box 3343). Tel: 2 16 33. *Chmn Bd* Dr Oku-Ampofo; *Dir* Richard B Nunoo.
Open Tues - Sun 8 AM - 6 PM. No admis. Estab 1957 to display archaeological, ethnographic, historic and artistic materials from Ghana and neighboring countries. One section of the museum is devoted to works by modern Ghanaian artists and sculptors working mostly with traditional themes. Average Annual Attendance: 70,000.
Income: Financed by government subvention.
Collections: Ghanaian and African archaeology, history, ethnography, modern art and sculpture.
Publications: Museum Handbook, occasional papers, irregularly.
Activities: Lect open to the public, 6 vis lectr per yr; exten dept serving schools in the area; tours.
Library: Open to the museum staff. Holdings: Vols 1100; Other—Photograph collection of prints 1000.

GREECE

ATHENS

BENAKI MUSEUM, 1, odos Koumbari, 138. Tel: 3612694, 3611617. *Chmn* Lambros Eftaxias; *Dir* Dr Angelos Delivorrias; *Cur Greek-Roman Antiquities Dept & Prof* Lila Marangou; *Cur Photographic Archives Dept* Emilia Yeroulanou.
Open Nov 1 - May 31, 8:30 AM - 2 PM; June 1 - Oct 31, 8:30 AM - 2 PM & 4:30 - 7:30 PM. Admis 40 drachmas, students 20 drachmas, entrance free on Sun. Estab 1931, the house of Emmanuel Benakis was donated to the State by his children and was transformed into a museum by Anthony Benakis in order to house his private collections. Gallery consists of—Greek-Roman Antiquities Dept; Byzantine and Post-Byzantine Dept; Greek Popular Dept; Greek Historical Relics Dept; Historical Archives Dept; Photographic Archives Dept; Eastern Art Dept. Average Annual Attendance: 90,000. Mem: 600 (The Friends of the Benaki Mus); dues 400 drachmas.
Income: 2.500.000 drachmas (financed by admission fees, endowment and state appropriation).
Collections: Ancient Greek art, chiefly jewelry; Byzantine and post-Byzantine art, icons and minor crafts; Greek popular art and historical relics; Greek Historical Archives: collections of Islamic art and Chinese porcelain.
Exhibitions: (1976-77) Byzantine Icons of Cyprus; Athens During the Turkish Occupation; Ten Centuries of Greek Script; Traditional Cotton Clothes; Selection of Historical Documents; Traditional Agricultural Cultivations.
Publications: Catalogs and guides.
Activities: Lectures for members only; original objects of art lent to other museums participating in international exhibitions; traveling exhibitions organized and circulated; museum shop selling books, reproductions, prints, slides, jewelry, postcards.
—Library. *Librn* Mrs Pitsa Tsakona.
Open to the public for reference only.
Holdings: Vols 18,000; Per subs 50; Other—manuscripts 500.
Special Collections: 2,000 watercolors, engravings and sketches; rare books, incunabula.

NATIONAL PINAKOTHIKI AND ALEXANDER SOUTZOS MUSEUM, 50, Vass Constantinou Ave, 516. Tel: 711-010. *Dir* Dr Dimitrios Papastamos; *Restorer* Mrs Evdoxia Carayanni.
Open winter, Oct 15 - May 15, daily 9 AM - 4 PM; summer, daily 9 AM - 8 PM; Sun 10 AM - 2 PM; cl Mon. Admis 20 drachmas. Estab 1900 as a picture gallery for Greek painting, sculpture and prints from the 17th to the 20th century; European painting and prints from the 14th to the 20th century. The museum consists of two main parts, the first of which houses temporary exhibitions while the permanent collections are displayed in the second. Average Annual Attendance: 120,000. Mem: 115; dues 200 drachmas; annual meeting Aug.
Income: Financed by endowment and state appropriation.

Collections: 14th-20th century European painting, including El Greco, Caravaggio, Jordaens, Poussin, Tiepolo, Mondrian and Picasso; engravings, including Dürer, Rembrandt, Goya; impressionist, post-impressionist and contemporary drawings; 17th-20th century Greek paintings, sculptures and engravings.
Exhibitions: Panorama of French Art 1960-1975; Graphics by Oskar Kokoschka; Contemporary Bulgarian Paintings; Recent British Art; Contemporary Yugoslavian Art; French Medieval Sculpture; Fifteen Finnish Artists; 19th and 20th century Hungarian Prints; Restrospective Exhibitions of S Papaloukas, A Kontopoulos, A Asteriadis, A Diamantis, V Semertzidis, G Busianis, D Yoldassis, D Diamantopoulos.
Publications: Catalogs of all exhibitions and studies on aspects of contemporary art.
Activities: Classes for children; lect open to the public, 4 vis lectrs per yr; 4 concerts; gallery talks; tours; extension dept; individual paintings lent; sales shop selling books, magazines, prints.
Library: Open to students and scholars for reference only.

HONG KONG

HONG KONG MUSEUM OF ART,* City Hall, Edinburgh Place. Tel: 5-224-217. *Cur* L C S Tam; *Asst Cur* Irene Kho.
Open Sun & public holidays 1 - 6 PM; weekdays 10 AM - 6 PM; cl Thurs. No admis. Estab 1962 to provide, through the museum's collections, displays and specialized staff, an education centre for all residents of Hong Kong. Average Annual Attendance: 300,000.
Income: HK$ 50,000 (financed by Hong Kong taxpayers). Purchases: HK $300,000.
Collections: Chinese antiquities including the Henry Yeung Collection; historical paintings, prints and drawings of Hong Kong, Macao and China, including Chater, Sayer, Law and Ho Tung Collections; contemporary works by local artists.
Exhibitions: Permanent display of Chinese art plus regular special exhibitions such as Contemporary Hong Kong Art, Contemporary Prints by Chinese artists, Exhibition of Chinese Blue and White Porcelain, Chinese Puppets and Crafts of the Middle Kingdom.
Publications: Exhibition catalogs and books; reproductions and postcards; free newsletter, monthly.
Activities: Guided tours for schools; competitions on museum's exhibits; children's art competitions.

HUNGARY

BUDAPEST

MAGYAR NEMZETI GALERIA (Hungarian National Gallery), Budavári Palota, 1250 Budapest, PO Box 31. Tel: 160-100. *Dir Gen* Dr G E Pogány; *Deputy Dir Gen* Dr Bálint Szege and Mrs Gyöngyi Éri; *Scientific Secy* Éva Pénzes.
Open Tues - Sun 10 AM - 6 PM; cl Mon. Admis 3 forints, children free, free entry on Sat. Estab 1957 for the collection, conservation, and exhibition of works of Hungarian plastic arts. Average Annual Attendance: 710,000.
Income: Financed by state appropriation. Purchases: 1,790,000 forints.
Collections: †Ancient Hungarian art; †modern Hungarian paintings; †modern Hungarian sculpture; †Hungarian graphic art; †medal cabinet; †Contemporary Hungarian Collection; †naive art.
Exhibitions: (1976-77) 114 exhibitions.
Publications: Catalogs; bullctin Annales; exhibition catalogs.
Activities: Classes for children; dramatic programs; docent training; lect open to public; concerts; gallery talks; tours; competitions; individual paintings and original objects of art lent to museums, exhibition halls; traveling exhibitions organized and circulated; sales shop selling reproductions.
—Library. *Head* Eva Rózsa.
Open 10 AM - 5 PM. Estab 1957 for the research work of the museum staff. Circ: 5000.
Holdings: Vols 40,000; Per subs 103; AV—Slides; Other—Exhibition catalogs.
Special Subjects: History of art; history of Hungarian art—11th-20th centuries.
Special Collections: Books on history of art and exhibition catalogs of the Hungarian National Gallery and of the museums abroad.

SZEPMUVESZET MUSEUM,* (Museum of Fine Arts) Dizsa Gyorgy ut 41, 1062. Tel: 429-759. *Dir-Gen* Dr Klara Garas; *Head Prints & Drawings* Dr A Czobor; *Head Old Sculpture* Dr E Eszlary; *Head Modern Art* Dr D Pataky; *Deputy Dir* Dr T Szentleleky; *Head Greek & Roman Antiquities* Dr J Gy Szilagyi; *Head Old Pictures* Dr M H Takacs; *Head Egyptian Antiquities* Dr V Wessetzky.

Open weekdays 10 AM - 6 PM; Sun 10 AM - 6 PM; cl Mon. Admis 3 florins per person, free for students and schools. Estb 1906 to collect works of art within the spheres of classic archaeology and European art history, 13th - 20th century. Average Annual Attendance: 400,000. Mem: 500; annual meetings four times per year.

Income: Financed by city and state appropriations.

Collections: †Old pictures, 13th-18th century; †prints and drawings, 14th-20th century; †modern paintings and sculpture, 19th-20th century; †Egyptian, Greek and Roman antiquities.

Publications: Bulletin, semi-annually; catalogs.

Activities: Educational department, guided tours for schools and groups, and educational program for adults; free university; classes for adults and children; lect open to the public; gallery talks; original objects of art lent; traveling exhibitions organized and circulated.

Library: Holdings—Vols 50,000; Per subs 1200; Other—Photographs.

ICELAND

REYKJAVIK

LISTASAFN EINARS JONSSONAR (Einar Jonsson Museum), Eiriksgata. *Dir* Olafur Kvaran; *Chmn* Jon Auduns.
Open May - Aug, Tues - Sun 1:30 - 4 PM; winter, Sun & Wed 1:30 - 4 PM. Admis 75 Icel krones. A museum containing almost all works of the sculptor Einar Jonsson (1874-1954) donated by him to the Icelandic State.

Income: Financed by state appropriation.

THJODMINJASAFN,* (National Museum of Iceland), Sudurgata, PO Box 1439. Tel: 1-67-79, 1-32-64. *Dir* Fil kand Thor Magnusson; *Cur* Gisli Gestsson; *Cur Textiles* Elsa E Gudjonsson; *Cur* Halldor J Jonsson; *Cur* Arni Bjornsson; *Cur* Thorkell Grimsson.
Open Sept 1 - May 31, Sun, Tues, Thurs, Sat 1:30 - 4 PM; June - Aug daily 1:30 - 4 PM. No admis. Estab 1863; archaeology, ethnology, folklore. Average Annual Attendance: Approx 40,000.

Income: Approx $4000 (financed by state appropriation).

Collections: Archaeological and ethnological artifacts, Icelandic antiquities, portraits, numismatics.

Publications: Árbók (yearbook), published by the Archaeological Society.

Library: Unknown number of volumes; photograph collection for lending and reference.

INDIA

BARODA

MUSEUM AND PICTURE GALLERY,* Sayaji Park, 5, 390005. Tel: 64 605, 63 609. *Dir* S K Bhowmik; *Keeper Art & Archaeology Sections* Shri M N Gandhi.
Open weekdays 9:30 AM - 5 PM; Thurs 10 AM - 5 PM. Museum estab 1894; Picture Gallery estab 1920. Average Annual Attendance: 600,000.

Collections: Indian archaeology, prehistoric and historic; Indian art, Ancient, Medieval and Modern; coins; Modern Italian paintings; Asiatic and Egyptian collections; Greek, Roman and European civilizations and art; European paintings.

Exhibitions: Four exhibitions are arranged every year.

Publications: Bulletin, annually.

Activities: Film shows and lecture series are a regular feature of the museum; 5 vis lectr per yr.

CALCUTTA

INDIAN MUSEUM,* 27 Jawaharlal Nehru Rd, 700013. Tel: 23-98-55. *Dir* Dr S Roy.
Open winter 10 AM - 4:30 PM; summer 10 AM - 5 PM. Estab in 1814 through the efforts and collections of the Asiatic Society of Bengal which had been founded in 1784. Average Annual Attendance: 4,500,000. Being under a Board of Trustees and subsidized by the Union Government of India, the Board meets 4 times a year; annual general meeting third week of March.

Income: Apprx Rs 1,000,000 (financed by Grant-in-aid from Union Government). Purchases: Approx Rs 80,000.

Collections: (Art) Textiles, miniature paintings, ivory, metalware, ceramics, woodcarvings, bronzes, papiermache, jade, crystal, gold and silver ornaments: (Archaeology) Copper and stone implements of prehistoric and proto-historic origin; stone sculptures; terracotta objects; bronze figures; steatite objects; stucco figures; coins, etc; (Anthropology) Tribal and regional objects including sets of cultural objects represented by garments, headdress, ornaments, weapons, utensils, etc.

Activities: University classes in archaeology, art, the sciences and museology; discussion seminars; special programs of Students' Day held on every Sat with documentary films and special guided tours of the museum; lect.

Library: Holdings—Vols 4000; Per subs 1500; Other—Journals, memoirs, pamphlets, reports.

NEW DELHI

LALIT KALA AKADEMI (National Academy of Art), Rabindra Bhavan, Ferozeshan Rd, 110001. Tel: 387241. *Chmn* Karl J Khandalavala; *Ed* S A Krishnan.
Open 10 AM - 5 PM on all working days. Estab 1954 by the Government of India as an autonomous body of artists, critics, art historians and state representatives, variously elected and partly nominated. The Academy is a Central State Organization to evolve a program to further the cause of art and artists through publications, exhibitions, artists' camps, surveys, seminars, and a major triennial of world art held in New Delhi.

Income: Financed by state appropriation.

Collections: Permanent collection of paintings, sculptures and graphics.

Exhibitions: Both at home and abroad.

Publications: Monographs; large multicolor reproductions; portfolios; scholarly publications; treatises; and two journals—Lalit Kala (ancient) and Lalit Kala Contemporary, biannually.

Activities: Artists workshop with well-equipped studios for painters, sculptors, ceramists and printmakers.

Library: Open 10 AM - 5 PM on all working days for scholars, students and artists. Holdings: Archival material of slides, photographs, catalogs.

NATIONAL GALLERY OF MODERN ART,* Jaipur House, Dr Zakir Husain Rd, 110003; Tel 38-2835, 38-4560, 38-4640. *Dir* Dr L P Sihare; *Restorer* Sukanta Basus; *Deputy Keeper Educ* Dr Anis Farooqi; *Deputy Keeper Art Collection* K S Mathur; *Deputy Keeper Publ* Y C Gajwe; *Sr Guide Lectr* S K Sahni; *Sr Technical Asst* Chintamani Vyas; *Guide Lectr* Shri R N Batham; *Technical Asst* B K Pant; *Photographer* P K Ray.
Open weekdays 10 AM - 5 PM; cl Mon. No admis. Inaug March 29, 1954 to develop a representative collection of Indian and international modern art, essentially painting, sculpture and graphic covering a span of more than a hundred years and put them on view to the public; the Museum has a very intensive special exhibition, educational and publication program.

Income: Financed by the Government of India, Union Ministry of Education and Social Welfare, under whom it is functioning as a subordinate office.

Collections: Indian contemporary paintings, sculptures and graphics. These are displayed in a chronological order as far as possible so as to give a bird's eye view of the evolution of modern Indian art since 1857; the collection of art objects is made through purchase and gifts. There is an art purchase committee comprised of Indian experts and on their recommendations art objects are acquired for the permanent collection.

Publications: Postcards; color reproductions; monographs; Hand Book of Paintings and Graphics; Hand Book of Sculptures; Hand Book of Bengal School; exhibition catalogs.

Activities: Short term art appreciation seminars for students and teachers organized; gallery talks at 11 AM & 3 PM daily by guide lectrs; conducted tours on prior appointment; Mobile Exhibition Bus; art objects lent only under special circumstances; lending collection contains Kodachrome slides 3000; traveling exhibitions organized and circulated.

Library: Reference. Holdings: Vols 4900; Other—Prints 300.

NATIONAL MUSEUM OF INDIA,* Janpath, 11. Tel: 38-5441/44. *Dir* N R Bannerjee.
Open 10 AM - 5 PM; cl Mon. Estab 1949. Average Annual Attendance 200,000.

Collections: Large in scope; all collections active. Prehistory; Indus Valley culture; †sculptures (stone and terra cottas) from 3rd century BC to 18th century; bronzes; †miniatures and drawings c 14,000; mural paintings; †Sanskrit, Persian, Arabic, Indian language manuscripts C 10,000; †coins, c 40,000; †arms; †decorative arts; †ethnology; Central Asian antiquities and murals; Museum Conservation Laboratory.

Exhibitions: Four - five per year.

Publications: Annual Bulletin; special publications on art and archaeology.

Activities: Cultural programs; educational movies related to archaeology, monuments, art; lect open to the public, 10-20 vis lectr per yr; guided tours.

Library: Holdings—Vols 15,000; Per subs 100; on archaeology, art, Indology.

IRELAND

DUBLIN

HUGH LANE MUNICIPAL GALLERY OF MODERN ART, Charlemont House, Parnell Square, 1. Tel: 01-741903. *Cur* Ethna Waldron; *Clerical Officer* Patricia Flavin.
Open Tues - Sat 10 AM - 6 PM; Sun 11 AM - 2 PM; cl Mon. Estab 1908; in present premises since 1933. The house is an 18th century town house, once the home of Lord Charlemont. The collection of paintings owes its inception largely to the generosity and public spirit of Sir Hugh Lane. Average Annual Attendance: 45,000.
Income: Financed by city appropriation. Purchases: £20,000.
Collections: The Lane Collection is made up largely of 19th century French works. There are approx 20 pictures from the Lane Collection on view in the Lane Room. The works of Irish artist Jack B Yeats, brother of the poet, are on view in the Yeats room; works by contemporary painters.
Exhibitions: Temporary exhibitions are held monthly; modern art exhibition ROSC.
Activities: Lect open to public; concerts; gallery talks; tours; individual paintings and original objects of art lent to government offices, libraries; lending collection contains original art works, original prints, paintings.

NATIONAL GALLERY OF IRELAND, Merrion Square W, 2. Tel: 01 767571. *Dir* James White; *Asst Dir* Michael Wynne; *Restorer Paper* Maighread McParland; Restorer Painting; Andrew O'Connor; *Educ Officer* N O'Sullivan; *Registr* Eibhlin McCarthy.
Open Mon - Sat 10 AM - 6 PM; Sun 2 - 5 PM; Thurs 10 AM - 9 PM. No admis. Estab 1854 to show all aspects of Western painting. Gallery consists of 42 rooms containing 2000 works of art. Average Annual Attendance: 557,345.
Income: Financed by govenment endowment. Purchases: From grants and bequests.
Collections: †American, British, Dutch, Flemish, French, German, Greek, Italian, Irish, Russian, and Spanish art.
Exhibitions: Frequent temporary exhibitions.
Publications: Catalogs.
Activities: Classes for adults and children; treasure hunts for children, to identify and explain pictures; lect open to public; concerts; gallery talks; tours; individual paintings and original objects of art lent to museums and art galleries; sales shop selling books, reproductions, prints and slides.
—Art Reference Library. *Librn* Ann Stewart.
Holdings: Vols 20,000; Per subs 160; Other—Exhibition and sales catalogs.
Special Subjects: Irish art of all periods.
Special Collections: Photographs, slides, posters, collections of Irish artists.

NATIONAL MUSEUM OF IRELAND,* Kildare St, 2. Tel: 76-55-21. *Dir & Keeper Antiquities* Dr J Raferty; *Keeper Art* John Teahan; *Keeper Folklife* A B O'Riordain.
Open Tues - Sat 10 AM - 5 PM; Sun 2 - 5 PM; cl Mon. Estab 1731 by Royal Dublin Society. Average Annual Attendance: 173,000.
Comprises †Irish Antiquities Division, †Art and Industrial Division, †Natural History Division, Irish Folklife Division.
Publications: Occasional guides to collections and specialist catalogs of particular collections. ·
Library: Holdings—Vols 10,000.

ISRAEL

HAIFA

MUSEUM OF ANCIENT ART,* 4 Bialik St (Mailing Add: PO Box 4811). Tel: 04-64-07-75. *Dir* Dr Joseph Elgavish.
Municipal museum estab 1948.
Collections: *Greek and Roman sculpture and terra cottas; †Canaanite and Biblical terracottas; finds from excavations at Shikmona (ancient Haifa) from the Bronze Age to the Byzantine Period; Coptic textiles and portrait painting from Egypt; †provincial Roman coins; Greek coins from Palestine.
Publications: Album Shikmona, The City Museum of Ancient Art, Haifa; The excavations of Shikmona, A Seleucian Garrison Camp from Hasmonean Times.
Activities: Children's courses on Ancient Art; teenagers' circles in Israeli archaeology; lect to school classes.

MUSEUM OF MODERN ART,* 26 Shabtai Levi St. Tel: 04-64-07-75. *Dir/Cur* Gabriel Tadmor; *Cur* Judith Shen-Dar; *Pub Relations* N Vodnizky.
Open Mon - Thurs 10 AM - 1 PM & 4 - 7 PM; Fri 10 AM - 1 PM; Sat 10 AM - 2 PM; cl Sun. Estab 1951. Average Annual Attendance: 10,500.
Income: $13,000.
Collections: †Israel paintings, sculpture, drawings and prints; †Modern French, English, American and German paintings; 19th and 20th century prints; †archives of reproductions; †posters. Special collection—of paintings by the late artist M Shemi Hall.
Exhibitions: Special biannual shows, Young Israeli Artists' Show, in honor of the late Dr. Schiff, with prize awards.
Activities: Weekdays, films, lect and student lect; gallery talks; Sat lect for tourists in English; lending collection contains reproductions and slides for schools.
Library: 8000 items with emphasis on modern art.

JERUSALEM

ISRAEL MUSEUM, POB 1299, Hakirya, 91000. Tel: 02-36341, exten 227. *Dir General* Yoram Ravin; *Chief Cur Bronfman Archaeological Museum* Dr Yaakov Meshorer; *Chief Cur Arts* Dr Martin Weyl; *Cur Youth Wing* Ayala Gordon; *Dir Public Affairs* Meir Meyer.
Open Sun, Mon, Wed, Thurs 10 AM - 5 PM; Fri & Sat 10 AM - 2 PM; cl Tues. Admis adults IL 15; students IL 5; under 18, IL 3; school classes IL 2. Estab 1965 as a comprehensive museum. Average Annual Attendance: 800,000. Mem: 5,800; dues IL 180; annual meeting Apr or May.
Income: Financed by endowment, membership, city and state appropriation.
Collections: Archaeological wing; Judaica; ethnography; art; 18th century English dining room; 18th century French period room; 18th century Venetian room; Billy Rose art garden; Shrine of the Book (housing the Dead Sea Scrolls); Youth Wing.
Exhibitions: Danese, Profile of a Producer—A Tribute to Sam Zacks; Anuszkiewicz, acrylic paintings 1966-76; Contemporary American Prints; 2nd Triennale of Photography; The Jewish Quarter, Jerusalem; The Artist and the Photograph; Cristo-Wrapped Coast, De Stijl; Old Master Drawings from the collection of the Duke of Devonshire at Chatsworth; Ancient Art—The Norbert-Schimmel Collection; Anna Ticho—50 years of Drawings.
Publications: Israel Museum News, annually; program, monthly.
Activities: Classes for adults and children; dramatic programs; docent training; lect open to public; concerts; gallery talks; tours; competitions; traveling exhibitions organized and circulated; museum shop selling books, reproductions, prints, slides, and postcards; junior museum.
—Library for Art and Archaeology. *Chief Librn* Yaffa Szereszewski; *Librn* Naama Marom; *Librn* Elisheva Rechtman; *Librn* Carmela Teichman.
Open Sun, Mon, Wed, Thurs 10 AM - 2 PM; Tues 4 - 8 PM. Estab 1965 for use of staff, students and teacher, and the general public.
Income: Financed by endowment.
Holdings: Vols 55,000; Per subs 200; Other—Clipping files, exhibition catalogs.

TEL-AVIV

HAARETZ MUSEUM, University St, Ramat Aviv (Mailing Add: PO Box 17068, 61170). Tel: 03-415244-248. *Dir Gen Haaretz Mus* J Caleff; *Secy Haaretz Mus* Miss S Hassou; *Dir Inst for Promotion Art & Science* Dr E Landau; *Pub Relations Officer in Charge Activities & Members Orgn* Miss P Unger; *Dir Theater Mus* Y Gabay.
Open 9 AM - 4 PM; Fri 9 AM - 1 PM; Sat 10 AM - 2 PM. Admis $1 on weekdays; Sat free. Founded in 1952, opened to public 1959; originally founded as a pavilion-style museum of the east Mediterranean, aiming to familiarize the public, especially the youth, with the rich cultural heritage of this cradle region of humanity. Museums that were added are the Theater Museum with a collection of historical data concerning the Jewish theater in the last hundred years, and the Independence Hall with an adjacent museum. Average Annual Attendance: 600,000. Dues 120 lira.
Income: Financed by city and state appropriation and contributions. Purchases: $10,000.
Collections: †Ancient glass; †ceramics; †coins; prehistoric finds; †Jewish ritual and secular art objects; †Jewish costumes; †scientific and technical apparatus; historical documents of Tel Aviv-Yafo; traditional work tools and methods.
Exhibitions: (1976-78) Numismatic Museum - 4 exhibitions; Tel-Aviv-Yafo Historical Museum - 2 exhibitions; Theater Museum - 1 exhibition; Ceramics Museum - 6 exhibitions; Ethnography and Folklore Museum - 11 exhibitions; Glass Museum - 2 exhibitions; Yajo Antiquities Museum - 2 exhibitions.
Publications: Yearbook, biannually.

Activities: Classes for children; dramatic programs; docent training; lect open to public, 25 vis lectrs per yr; gallery talks; tours; museum shop selling books, reproductions and slides.

—Central Library. *Librn* Ernest Heinemann; *Asst Librn* Miriam Kumpan.

Open Sun - Thurs 8:30 AM - 2:30 PM; Fri 8:30 AM - 12:30 PM. Estab 1958, the library is mainly intended as a reference library for the museum staff, but also serves the general public and students.

Income: Financed by city appropriation. Purchases: $2800.

Holdings: Vols 6500; Per subs 35.

Special Subjects: Ancient glass; near East archaeology, history, ceramics, Bible, Greco-Roman archaeology, history, numismatics, alphabet.

TEL AVIV MUSEUM,* Helena Rubinstein Pavilion, 6 Tarsat St. Tel: 24-71-96; New Building, 27-29 Shaul Hamelekh Blvd. Tel: 25-73-61. *Dir & Chief Cur* Dr Marc Scheps; *Cur* Mira Friedman.

Open 10 AM - 1 PM & 4 - 7 PM. Helena Rubinstein Pavilion estab 1959; New Building estab 1971.

Collections: Old Masters: Fine examples of the English, Italian, French, Dutch Schools fo the 16th to 18th century. French School: 19th century—Delacroix, the Barbizon School, Corot (oils and drawings), major works by Impressionists including Renoir, Degas, Pissarro, Monet, Whistler and Post Impressionists (Signac, etc). 20th Century: Fauves and their generation; Van Dongen, Vlaminck, Marquet, Marie Laurencin, Suzanne Valadon, Utrillo. Cubism: Juan Gris, Leger, Jacques Villon, Picasso. Dada Surrealism: About 50 significant works by Arp, Taeuber-Arp, Janco, Herold Lam, Matta, Ernst, Picabia, deChirico, Tanguy, Masson, Charles Seliger, etc. Jewish Parisian School: a large number of Chagall, Kisling, Pascin, Modigliani, Lipchitz, Soutine and others. National Schools: 19th and 20th century—Russian: among others, a collection of 28 works by Archipenko. Belgian: 17 major works by Ensor and works by others. German Expressionists: oils, drawings by Schmidt-Rottluff; Nolde, Pechstein, Heckel, Kokoschka. American: paintings from the Ash Can School to Baziotes, Jackson Pollock, Noland and Morris Louis. English: Pre-Raphaelites, significant series of 18th and 19th century watercolors. Italian: Morandi, Boccioni, Prampolini, Marino Marini, Rotella, and others. South American: Portinari, Rivera, Tamayo, Siqueiros, Morado, Lazar Segal, and others. Polish: Lebenstein. A comprehensive collection of Jewish and Israeli painters of the 19th and 20th century. Good examples of sculpture, 19th and 20th century by Rodin, Degas, Epstein, Barlach, Lehmbruck, Lipchitz, Henry Moore.

Exhibitions: The Museum organizes about 20 exhibitions annually on one-man, group exhibitions, Israeli and Foreign. The Graphic Department (12,000 items) includes Rembrandt, Goya, Daumier and a large survey of modern and contemporary graphics.

Activities: Classes for children and adults; films; youth centers; lectures; Chamber music concerts; traveling art exhibitions.

Library: Helena Rubinstein Art Library at the New Building has a collection of volumes 18,000 (books and periodicals) covering most fields of art.

ITALY

FLORENCE

GALLERIA DEGLI UFFIZI,* (Uffizi Gallery), Piazzale degli Iffizi, 50125. Tel: 21-83-41/45. *Dir* Dr Luciano Beti.

Estab 16th century.

Collections: The finest collection of Florentine Renaissance painting in the world. In addition to other very important collections in the Uffizi-Gallery, one of the best in Italy for antique statues, tapestries, miniatures, not to mention the famous drawing collection, there is a unique and complete collection of artists' self portraits, ranging from the 16th - 20th century; this was begun in the 17th century by Cardinale Leopoldo de' Medici, and continued by his successors.

GALLERIA PALATINA (Palatine Gallery), Palazzo Pitti, Piazza Pitti, 1, 50125. Tel: 26 06 95, 27 03 23. *Dir* Dr Marco Chiarini.

Open Mon - Sat 8:30 AM - 2 PM; Sun & holidays 9 AM - 1 PM; cl Tues. Admis 200 Lire, 100 holidays, No admis Sun. Estab 17th century.

Income: Supported by Government appropriations.

Collections: Paintings from 15th - 18th centuries, Raffaello, Tiziano, Andrea del Sarto.

—Museo degli Argenti. *Dir* Dr Kirsten Aschengreen Piacenti.

Collections: Silver, gold, enamels, ivories, tapestries, amber jewels from the 15th - 18th centuries.

—Appartamenti Monumentali.

Collections: Tapestries and furniture of the 18th and 19th centuries.

—Galleria d'Arte Moderna (Gallery of Modern Art). Tel: 28 70 96. *Dir* Dr Sandra Pinto; *Secy* Gualberto Carrai.

Open daily 10 AM - 4 PM; Sun 9 AM - 1 PM; cl Tues. Admis. 1.50 lire. Estab 1924 as a show of the permanent collections of Italian art of the 19th and early 20th century existing in Florence.

Income: Financed by state and city appropriations.

Collections: Italian mainly Tuscan art of the 19th and 20th century.

Publications: Catalog of exhibitions.

Activities: Lectures; photography collection; library.

GENOA

GALLERIA DI PALAZZO BIANCO,* White Palace Gallery), via Garibaldi 11, 16100. *Dir* Dr Arch Vincenzo Oddi.

Open Tues - Sat 9:30 - 11:45 AM & 2:30 - 5:45 PM; Sun 9:30 - 11:45 AM; cl Mon, legal and religious holidays. Estab 1892.

Collections: Paintings by Genoese and Flemish Masters and other schools, sculpture and tapestries; treasures include Paganini's violin and the letters of Columbus, preserved in Palazzo Tursi.

LUCCA

MUSEO NAZIONALE DI VILLA GUINIGI,* (National Museum of Villa Guinigi), via della Quarquonia, 55100. Tel: 460-33. *Dir* Dr Clara Barrachini.

Open summer 9:30 AM - 1 PM, 3 - 6 PM; winter 9:30 - 2 PM; cl Mon. Estab July 20, 1968; documentation of arts and crafts in Lucca through the centuries (from prehistory to approx 1850).

Collections: Roman and late Roman sculptures and Mosaics; Romanesque, Gothic, Renaissance and Neoclassical sculpture; Old Master paintings, 12th - 18th century; wooden inlays and sculpture; ancient textiles; Medieval goldsmiths' art; photograph collection approx prints 1000.

PINACOTECA NAZIONALE,* (National Picture Gallery), Palazzo del Governo, piazza Napoleone, 55100. Tel: 45 915. *Dir* Dr Antonino Caleca.

Open 8 AM - 2 PM; Sun 9 AM - 1 PM; cl Mon. Admis 1 L. Estab 1875 for exhibition of Lucchese works of art. Average Annual Attendance: 30,000.

Income: Financed by appropriations.

Collections: Paintings from churches and palaces of the city and territory, also from the Medici family and the Tuscan, Venetian, French and Flemish Schools; photograph collecton.

MANTUA

GALLERIA E MUSEO DEL PALAZZO DUCALE,* (Gallery and Museum of the Palazzo Ducale), Piazza Sordello, 46100. Tel: 2-02-83. *Dir* Dr Ilaria Toesca Bertelli.

Open Tues - Sat 9 AM - 2 PM; Sun 9 AM - 1 PM. Admis L150. Estab as a monument to the Gonsaga family who lived here for centuries; contains capital works of art, including Mantegna frescoes, Castello and Pisanello murals. Average Annual Attendance: 70,000.

Collections: Classical antiquities; Renaissance and later paintings; classical sculpture, prehistorical relics from Mantuan territory; Egyptian antiquities; Medieval sculpture, Renaissance and Baroque sculpture; 13th - 19th century paintings; numismatic collection.

Publications: Catalog, fully illustrated.

Library: For reference only, closed to public. Holdings: Vols 2000; Other—Photographs 17,000.

MILAN

MUSEO D'ARTE ANTICA* (Museum of Ancient Art). Castello Sforzesco. *Dir* Dr Mercedes Garberi.

Open 9:30 AM - 12:30 PM & 2:30 - 5:30 PM. cl Mon. Estab 1879.

Collections: Sculpture from Middle Ages to 16th century; paintings including works by Mantegna, Lippi, Bellini, Lottl, Tintoretto, Tiepolo, Guardi, Foppa and others; ancient and contemporary drawings.

Library: Holdings—Vols 41,000.

—Civiche Raccolte de Arte Applicata (Collection of Minor Arts, Piazza Castello, 20122. Tel: 02 803071. *Dir* Dr Clelia Alberici.

Open 9:30 AM - 12:30 PM & 2:30 - 5:30; cl Monday. No admis. Estab to serve the public. Galleries are in the castle. Average Annual Attendance: 500,000.

Income: Financed by city appropriation.

Collections: Mobiles; armor; sculpture; ceramics; ivories; bronzes; textiles; costumes; ironworks; coins; porcelains. Musical intruments.

Exhibitions: Costumes.

Publications: Rassegna di studi e di notizie, annually.

Activities: Exten dept serving the Modern Art Gallery; original objects of art lent to other museums; museum shop selling books.

—Racolta delle stampe Achille Bertarelli (Bertarelli Collection of Engravings). *Dir* Dr Clelia Alberici.

Open 9 AM - Noon & 2:30 - 5 PM; cl Sat & Sun.

Holdings: Vols 30,000; Other—Engravings 600,000, exhibition catalogs.
Special Subjects: Engravings.
Exhibitions: Incisioni di Pietro Testa; Stampe Popolari Lombarde dell'800.
—**Raccolte Archaeologiche e Numismatiche** (Collection of Archeology and Coins), Castello Sforzesco & Corse Magenta 15. *Dr Ermanno Arslan.*
Open 9:30 AM - 12:30 PM & 2:30 - 5:30 PM.
Collections: Castello Sforzesco—Prehistoric and later; ancient Egyptian, antique and modern coins; Corso Magenta—Greek, Etruscan and Roman collections.
Activities: Lect for open to public; sales shop selling catalogs and postcards.
Library: Holdings—Vols 4,423. Special Subjects: Coins, Antique coins.
—**Museo di Milano*** (Museum of Milan), Vedi Sant'Andrea 6. *Dir* Dr Ermanno Arslan.
Open 9:30 AM - 12:30 PM & 2:30 - 5:30 PM; cl Mon.
Collections: Paintings of Milan subjects of the 19th century.

MUSEO POLDI PEZZOLI,* (Poldi Pezzoli Museum), via Manzoni 12, 20121. Tel: 79-48-89. *Dir* Dr Alessandra Mottola Molfino.
Open daily 9:30 AM - 12:30 PM, 2:30 - 5:30 PM; holidays 9:30 AM - 12:30 PM, 2:30 - 5:30 PM; Thurs also 9 - 11 PM; cl Mon, New Year's, Easter, May 1, Aug 15, Nov 1, Christmas. Admis L 500. Estab 1881. Mem: 600; Assembly of members of Associazione Amici del Poldi Pezzoli.
Collections: Paintings, Italian and foreign from 14th - 18th centuries; archaeology, carpets, antique weapons and armor; pottery, glasses, glass windows, gold, jewels, furniture, bronzes, Islamic objects, clocks and watches.
Publications: Catalogs of exhibitions indicated above and of the museum collections; brief guide to the museum.
Activities: Classes for adults; educational section for children; restoration of ancient arms and armors; lect open to the public, 130 vis lectr per yr; schol; photograph collection for reference, prints 2047.
Library: Reference. Holdings: Vols 3000.

PINACOTECA AMBROSIANA (Ambrosian Picture Gallery), Piazza Pio XI, 2, 20123. Tel: 02-800146. *Dir* Dr Angelo Paredi.
Open daily 9:30 AM - 5 PM; cl Sat. Admis (weekdays) Lire 300; Sun free. Estab 1618. Average Annual Attendance: 35,000.
Collections: Leonardo; Raphael; Botticelli; Titian; Caravaggio.
Library: Biblioteca Ambrosiana.

PINACOTECA DI BRERA (Brera Picture Gallery), via Brera 28, 20121. Tel: 02/800985 - 808387 - 862634. *Dir* Dr Carlo Bertelli.
Open daily 9 AM - 2 PM; Sun & holidays 9 AM - 1 PM; cl Mon. Admis Lit 200. The proceeds derived from admission fees go to the State Treasury for the support of the Museums of the State. Average Annual Attendance: Approx 100,000.
Collections: Paintings and drawings of the 14th to 20th centuries.
Activities: The Pinacoteca, in collaboration with the Friends of Brera and Museums of Milan, sponsors special courses which are open to the public. In these courses the more important works in the Pinacoteca collection are explained in eight lessons.

MODENA

GALLERIA E MUSEO ESTENSE (Este Gallery and Museum), Piazza S Agostino. Tel: 059-222145 or 235004. *Dir* Dr Giorgio Bonsanti.
Open Tues - Sat 9 AM - 2 PM; Sun 9 AM - 1 PM; cl Mon. Admis L 150.
One vestibule, two corridors, four large rooms. Average Annual Attendance: 4,000.
Income: Financed by state appropriation.
Collections: Paintings, sculptures, bronzes, minor arts, coins, medals, drawings, and prints—most of them from the Este family.
—**Biblioteca della Soprintendenza** (Superintendent's Library). *Librn* Dr Mazzino Fossi.
Open to the public.
Library: Holdings—Vols 7000; Per subs 26.

NAPLES

MUSEO DE CAPODIMONTE (Mt Capodi Museum), Reggia di Capodimonte. Tel: 081-7410881. *Dir* Raffaello Causa; *Asst Supt* Nicola Spinosa; *Supervisor & Dir Drawings & Prints* Alba Costamagna; *Dir Museo Villa Pignatelli* Salvatore Abita; *Supervisor & Dir Museo S Martino* Teodore Fittipaldi; *Supervisor & Dir Museo Villa Floridiana* Vega de Martini.
Open Mon - Sat 9 AM - 2 PM; Sun & holidays 9 AM - 1 PM; cl Mon. Admis 150 lira. Estab 1956. Average Annual Attendance: 220,000.
Income: Financed by state appropriation.

Collections: Italian and foreign paintings from 13th-19th centuries; small bronzes and medals from the Renaissance; tapestries from 16th-18th centuries; ivory and objects of minor art; Italian Majolica; Italian and foreign porcelains; Murano glass; armour from 15th-19th centuries; furniture, 18th & 19th centuries; drawing and prints collections of 15th-19th century.
Activities: Lect open to public, 36 vis lectr per yr; concerts; gallery talks; tours; exten dept serving the area; artmobile; traveling exhibitions organized and circulated; museum shop.
Library: *Librn* Vega de Martini. Open for reference. Holdings: Vols 8,600.

MUSEO NAZIONALE DI SAN MARTINO,* (National Museum), Piazzele San Martino, 80100. Tel: 37-70-05. *Dir* Dr T Fittipoldi.
Estab 18th century.
Collections: Works of art from Farnese, Borgia, and Noia Collections, and works recovered from excavations in Southern Italy, particularly in Pompeii and Herculaneum. A foremost collection of ancient bronzes, wall paintings and mosaics; 17th century pictures and paintings, 13th-17th century sculpture, majolicas and porcelains; section of modern prints, paintings and engravings.

PADUA

MUSEO CIVICO DI PADUA,* (Municipal Museum), Piazza del Santo, 10, Tel: 2-31-06, 2-37-13. *Dir* Dr Alessandro Prosdocimi.
Open 9:30 AM - 1:30 PM.
Income: Financed by city appropriations.
Collections: Lapidary Collection; Archaeological Museum; Gallery of Pictures; Bottacin Museum—Greco-Roman, Paduan, Venetian, Italian, Napoleonic coins and medals. Art Gallery—Painting, sculpture, bronzes, ceramics, industrial arts.
Publications: Bollettino del Museo Civico di Padua, semi-annual.
Library: Holdings—Vols 350,000; Other—Photographs.

PERUGIA

GALLERIA NAZIONALE DELL'UMBRIA,* (Umbrian National Gallery), Palazzo dei Priori, Corso Vannucci, 06100. Tel: 12e 233-85. *Dir* Dr Francesco Santi.
Open 9 AM - 2 PM. Admis L 150. Estab 1863; documentation of the arts (painting, sculpture, jewels) in Umbria from the 13th century - 18th century. Average Annual Attendance: 45,000.
Income: Financed by state appropriation.
Collections: Paintings from the Umbrian School from the 13th - 18th century; 13th, 14th, 15th century sculpture; Medieval ivory; jewels (Umbria-Siena) 13th and 14th centuries; furniture of the Renaissance.
Exhibitions: Annual shows (lasting a week at the museum) on the restoration of art works in cooperation with two churches and museums in the region of Umbria.
Publications: F Santi, Itinerary of the Gallerie Nazionale dell' Umbria (brief guide); catalog of Romanesque and Gothic works.
Library: For specialized study only. Holdings: Vols 3995; Other—Photographs, negatives (inactive) 25,000, positives (active) 25,000.

PISA

MUSEO NAZIONALE DI SAN MATTEO,* (St Matteo National Museum), Convento di San Matteo, Lungarno Mediceo, 56100. Tel: 237-50. *Dir* Dr Antonino Caleca.
Open summer 9:30 AM - 4 PM; winter 9:30 AM - 2 PM; cl Mon. Admis L 100. Estab 1846; documentation of art in Pisa throughout the centuries.
Income: Financed by appropriation.
Collections: Old Master paintings, 11th - 18th century; marble and wooden sculpture 10th - 18th century; medieval illuminated manuscripts; Renaissance tapestries; Roman and Italian coins and medals.
Activities: Concerts; photographs; prints 1000.

ROME

GALLERIA BORGHESE,* (Borghese Gallery), Piazzale Scipione Borghese 5, 00197. Tel: 85-85-77. *Dir* Dr Sara Staccioli.
Open 9 AM - 2 PM; holidays 9 AM - 1 PM; cl Mon. Estab 1616.
Collections: Classical and Baroque sculptures—G Bernini, Canova; paintings by Lorenzo di Credi, Andrea del Sarto, Dosso Dossi, Domenichino, Raffaello, Veronese, Antonello da Messina, Tiziano, Caravaggio.

GALLERIA DORIA PAMPHILJ,* (Dorian Gallery), Piazza del Collegio Romano 1/a, 00186. *Dir* Dr Eduard A Safarik.

Collections: Paintings by Correggio, Titian, del Piombo, Lorrain, Filippo Lippi, Velazques, Carracci, Caravaggio.

GALLERIA NAZIONALE D'ARTE ANTICA - PALAZZO BARBERINI (National Gallery in Barberini Palace), Via Quattre Fontane 13, 00 Tel: 06/4750184. *Dir* Dr ssa Giuseppina Magnanimi.
Open Tues - Sat 9 AM - 2 PM; Sun 12:30 - 1:30 PM; cl Mon. This National Gallery of Rome will include in the next time all pictures of the public collections—Barberini, Corsini, Torlonia, Chigi, Dusmet for a complete exhibition from 12th-18th century. The gallery contains Italian and Flemish paintings from 12th-17th century. The gallery is in Palazzo Barberini, built of Roman baroque art (Maderno, Bernini, Borromini, Pietro da Cortona). Average Annual Attendance: Approx 25,000.
Income: Financed by state appropriation.
Collections: Corsini 1883; Torlonia 1892; Monte de Pieta 1895; Hertz 1915; Chigi 1918; Dusmet 1943; Barberini 1952.
Activities: Educ dept; gallery talks; tours.
Library: Only for interior use.
—**Galleria Nazionale D'Arte Antica - Palazzo Corsini (National Gallery in Corsini Palace),** Via della Lungara 10, 00. Tel/ 06/6542323. *Dir* Dr ssa Giuseppina Magnanimi.
Open Tues by appointment from 10 AM - 1 PM. Estab for Italian and Flemish pictures of 17th-18th centuries. Average Annual Attendance: 5000.
Collections: Corsini.

MUSEI CAPITOLINI,* (Museum of Sculpture), Piazza del Campidoglio 1471, 00100. Tel 6-61-3071. *Dir* C Pietrangeli.
Open daily 9 AM - 2 PM; Tues - Thurs, also 5 - 8 PM; Sat, also 9 - 11:30 PM; cl Mon. Average Annual Attendance: 250,000.
Collections: †Ancient sculptures 3500, †paintings, pottery, †bronzes; †tapestry and other works of art.

MUSEO NAZIONALE ROMANI,* (National Museum of Rome), Viale Delle Terme di Diocleziano, 00185. Tel: 06 46-05-30, 46-08-56. *Supt of Roman Antiquities* Prof Gianfilippo Carettoni; *Dir* A La Regina; *Asst to Supt* Dr Piera Ferioli.
Open weekdays 9 AM - 2 PM; holidays 9 AM - 1 PM. Estab 1889.
Income: Financed by city or state appropriation.
Collections: Greek Hellenistic and Roman sculpture and bronzes; glass; pictures and mosaics; numismatics; archaelogical collection.
Activities: Education Department.

SASSARI

MUSEO NAZIONALE G A SANNA,* (G A Sanna National Museum), via Roma 64, 07100. Tel: 27-22-03. *Dir* F Nicosia.
Open 9 AM - 2 PM. Admis L 100. No admis Settimana dei Musei exhibition. Estab 1930; enlargement and reorganization in line with didactic standards and modern esthetics.
Income: Financed by state appropriation.
Collections: Archeological collections, picture gallery with Medieval and Modern Art; sculptures; collection of Sardinian ethnography.
Exhibitions: Museum weeks.
Activities: Visiting students; lect open to the public with special permission; 30 vis lectr per yr.
Library: Holdings—Vols 2000; Other—Photographs.

TORINO

MUSEO CIVICO,* (Municipal Museum) via Magenta, 31 10128. Tel: 54-18-22. *Dir* Dr Rosanna Maggio Serra; *Cur Numismatics* Dr Anna Serena Fava; *Cur Antique Art Collection* Dr Silvana Pettenati.
Open 9 AM - 8 PM; cl Mon. Admis L100; free on holidays.
Income: Financed by city and state appropriations.
Collections: Antique and modern art from 4th - 20th century; coins; sculpture; paintings.
Publications: Catalogs for temporary shows and for each section of the museum.
Activities: Lect open to the public; original objects of art lent; lending collection contains photographs 27,200; traveling exhibitions organized and circulated.
Library: Holdings—Vols 32,894.

TRIESTE

CIVICO MUSEO REVOLTELLA-GALLERIA D'ARTE MODERNA (Revoltella Civic Museum-Gallery of Modern Art); Via Armando Diaz 27. Tel: 040 750436 & 68562. *Dir* Dr Giulio Montenero.

Open daily 9 AM - 1 PM; cl Mon. Average Annual Attendance: 18,400. Mem: 7; dues 3. Estab 1872 to maintain the buildings inherited by the foundation in their original decor; increasing the number of pictures, sculptures, and graphic arts. The temporary exhibits are prepared in the communal hall of art at the Constanzi Palace in Trieste.
Collections: Pictures, sculptures and graphic arts by artists from the region of Friuli-Venezia Giulia, Italian artists and some European artists.
Exhibitions: Cento Pittori della Regione; La Carnia—Biennale d'art Contemporanea; Mostra postuma di Sabino Coloni; Federico Righi; Edoardi Devetta; Augusto Cernigoj; Mostra postuma di Ruggero Rovan.
Activities: Lect open to public.
Library: Holdings—Vols 4,000; Other—Photograph collection, prints 5,000.

VATICAN CITY

MONUMENTI MUSEI E GALLERIE PONTIFICIE (Vatican Museums and Galleries), Tel: 06 698 3332. *Dir Gen* Deoclecio Redig De Campos; *Secy-Treas* Walter Persegati; *Cur for Classical Art (Greek & Roman Sculpture)* Georg Daltrop; *Cur Etruscan Antiquities (Etruscan Mus)* Francesco Roncalli; *Cur for Oriental Antiquities (Egyptian Mus)* Gianfranco Nolli; *Cur for Mediaeval & Modern Art* Fabrizio Mancinelli; *Cur for Ethnographical Coll* Giuseppe Penkowski; *Asst Cur for Modern Religious Art Coll* Mario Ferrazza.
Open 9 AM - 2 PM; July - Sept, 9 AM - 5 PM. Admis 1500 lire, 500 lire for holders of International Student Card. Estab c 1510; organized as a museum in the years 1770-75. Average Annual Attendance: 1,500,000.
Income: Financed by state appropriation.
Exhibitions: (1976) Graphics by American Artists; (1977) Mostra su San Paolo, 254 works of art donated to Pope Paul VI on his 80th birthday.
Publications: Bollettino Dei Musei Vaticani, yearly.
Activities: Educ dept; lect and occasional tours; sales shop selling books, reproductions, prints, slides, cassettes.
Library: Not open to the public - for curators only.
—**Museo Pio Clementino,** founded by Clemens XIV and Pius VI in 1784.
—**Museo Chiaramonti and Braccio Nuovo,** founded by Pius VII in 1810 and 1822.
—**Museo Gregoriano-Profano,** founded by Gregory XVI in 1844, formerly located at Lateran Palace. Greek and Roman sculpture and antiquities.
—**Museo Gregoriano Etrusco,** founded by Gregory XVI in 1837. Greek, Roman and Etruscan antiquities.
—**Museo Gregoriano Egizio,** founded by Gregory XVI in 1839. Egyptian antiquities, mummies.
—**Museo Pio-Cristiano,** founded by Pius IX in 1854, formerly at the Lateran Palace. Early Christian Art.
—**Medieval and Modern Art.**
Chapel of Nicholas V, painted by Beato Angelico 1448-1450; Sistine Chapel, built by Sistus IV 1475-1483, and frescoed by several masters of 15th century and by Michelangelo 1508-1512 and 1535-1541; Borgia Apartment with frescoes by Pinturicchio 1492-1495, and others; Loggia and Stanze painted by Raphael 1508-1520; Gallery of the Tapestries with works of 16th and 17th centuries; Pinacoteca Vaticana, founded by Pius XI in 1932, with painting, frescoes, tapestries of Byzantine, Medieval and Modern periods.
—**Museo Missionario Etnologico,** founded by Pius XI in 1926-27, formerly at the Lateran Palace. Ethnological Collection.
—**Collection of Modern Religious Art,** inaugurated by Paul VI in 1973.
—**Museo Sacro, Museo Profano, Salone Sistino (Vatican Library).** Old fabrics, ceramics, ivories, frescoes, tapestries, illuminated books.

JAPAN

KURASHIKI

OHARA BIJITSUKAN,* Ohara Art Gallery, 1-1-15 Chuo. Tel: 0864-22-0005. *Cur* Shin-ichiro Foujita.
Open April - Oct 9 AM - 5 PM; Nov - Mar 9 AM - 4 PM. Admis 100 yen, student 50 yen. Estab 1930 to exhibit and collect the fine arts.
Collections: Modern European and American paintings and sculpture; modern Japanese oil paintings and sculpture; Ancient Egyptian, Turkish and Persian ceramics and sculpture; modern Japanese pottery and textiles.
Activities: Lect open to the public; gallery talks; Book shop.
Library maintained.

KYOTO

KYOTO KOKURITSU KINDAI BIJUTSUKAN (National Museum of Modern Art, Kyoto), Enshoji-cho, Okazaki, Sakyo-ku. *Dir* Michiaki Kawakita; *Chief Cur* Tadao Ogura; *Cur* Takeo Uchiyama; *Cur* Shigeki Fukunaga.

Open 10 AM - 5 PM. Admis adults 200 Yen; students 60 Yen; children 40 Yen. Estab 1963 for exhibitions and research of modern art, in particular, trends in contemporary art, modern handi-crafts and artists who have been active in Kyoto. The total area of the buildings is 2,050 sq meters and the building has two stories and a basement. Exhibition halls on the first and second floors have each 684 sq meters. The building is reinforced concrete. Average Annual Attendance: 204,012. Mem: 600; dues 1000 Yen.

Income: Financed by state appropriation.

Collections: Kawakatsu Collection which consists of 418 pieces of pottery by Kanjiro Kawai; ceramic works by artists abroad; †handicrafts works by contemporary artists; †paintings by the artists who have been active in Kyoto mainly; †contemporary print works in Japan and Japanese artists who are active abroad; †contemporary sculptures.

Exhibitions: Old Italian Prints; Artists of Kinreisha Group; Masterpieces of Russian Paintings; Bird's Eye View of Contemporary Art; Fiber Works—The Americas and Japan; Fontanesi, Ragusa and the art of Japan in early Neiji period; Picasso Exhibition; The Art of Noriyuki Ushijima.

Publications: Miru, monthly.

Activities: Lect open to public, 10-12 vis lectr per yr; gallery talks, tours; traveling exhibitions organized and circulated.

NARA

NARA KOKURITSU HAKUBUTSUKAN,* (Nara National Museum) 50 Noboriojicho, Nara Park. Tel: 22-2771. *Dir* Dr Bunsaku Kurata; *V Dir* H Naito; *Chief Cur* H Nishimura.

Open 9 AM - 4:30 PM; cl Mon. Admis adults 80 yen, children 30 yen. Estab 1895; reorganized Aug 1952 and attached to the Committee of the Protection of the Cultural Properties; originally established to display relics of the large Buddhist temples of the area.

Collections: Classification of Buddhist arts—iconographies in sculptures, pictures, and ritual tools; styles of Buddhist statues, 6th - 14th century; Forms of Temple—formal development of the temples and detailed techniques of architecture; other statues, relics, scrolls; Tea House, originally installed in the garden of the Imperial Monastery and later moved to the garden of the Museum.

Exhibitions: Special annual exhibitions—Shosoin Treasure, last of Oct to early Nov (2 wk); Buddhist Art on some special theme, April - May.

TOKYO

BRIDGESTONE BIJUTSUKAN,* (Bridgestone Museum of Art), 1-1 Kyobashi, Chuo-ku. Tel: 563-0241. *Pres* Shojiro Ishibashi; *Exec Dir* Yasuo Kamon; *Chief Cur* Takatsugu Rokujo.

Open 10 AM - 5:30 PM; cl Mon. Admis 100 yen. Estab 1952; permanent display of Ishibashi Collection; five exhibit rooms, and lobby. Average Annual Attendance: 100,000.

Income: Financed by endowment.

Collections: Foreign paintings, mainly Impressionism and after; Japanese Western style paintings, late 19th century to present age; foreign sculptures, from ancient times to present age; foreign original prints, from 17th century to present age; foreign glass wares, bronze wares and pottery, from ancient times to early modern times.

Publications: Catalogs in Japanese, English and French; illustrated catalogs in Japanese and English; Annual Report.

Activities: Educational Department; lect open to public, 44 vis lectr per yr.

Library: For reference. Holdings: Vols 2200; Other—Photographs.

KOKURITSU SEIYO BIJUTSUKAN (National Museum of Western Art), Ueno Park, Taito-ku, 110. Tel: 03-828-5131. *Dir* Dr Chisaburo F Yamada; *Chief Cur* Hideo Tomiyama; *Cur* Nobuyuki Senzoku; *Cur* Haruki Yaegashi; *Cur* Koichi Koshi; *Cur* Sabroh Hasegawa; *Cur* Madoka Ikuta; *Cur* Koji Yukiyama.

Open 9:30 AM - 5 PM; cl Mon; Admis 200 Yen. Estab 1959 to display French paintings and sculptures of the Matsukata Collection (Expressionists and Rodin) and to build up a collection of European art for display in order to show to Japanese public the tradition of European art and its historical development, and at the same time to give Japanese the opportunity to appreciate the aesthetic achievement of Europeans in visual arts. Gallery designed by Le Corbusier. Average Annual Attendance: 550,000.

Income: Financed by state appropriations. Purchases: 650,000 - 700,000.

Collections: Matsukata Collection consists of paintings 300 and sculptures 63 including Monet 12 and Renoir 3; Rodin 55 including The Gate of Hell, Les Bourgeois de Calais and Le Pensur; paintings by Old Masters.

Exhibitions: Masterpieces of World Art from American Museums; Vincent van Gogh Exhibition; Renaissance Decorative Arts from The Robert Lehman Collection of The Metropolitan Museum of Art; Master Paintings from The Heritage Museum, Leningrad.

Publications: Bulletin Annuel du Musée National d'Art Occidental; catalogues of our collection and catalogues of special exhibitions.

Activities: Traveling exhibitions organized and circulated; lectures open to the public.

Library: For reference only.

NIPPON MINGEI-KAN,* (Japanese Folk Art Museum), 861 Komabamachi, Meguro-ku. Tel: 461-8742. *Cur* S Hamada.

Collections: 20,000 objects of folk-craft art from all parts of the world.

TOKYO KOKURITSU HAKUBUTSUKAN,* (Tokyo National Museum), 13-9 Ueno Park, Daito-ku. *Dir* Sei Saito.

Open 9 AM - 4 PM; cl Mon. Founded 1871; the largest art museum in Japan, containing 86,000 pieces of art.

Collections: Japanese and Far Eastern paintings, calligraphy, sculpture, metalwork, ceramic arts, textiles, lacquerware and archaeological exhibits.

Publications: Museum, monthly.

TOKYO KOKURITSU KINDAI BIJUTSUKAN (National Museum of Modern Art, Tokyo), 3 Kitanomaru Koen, Chiyoda-ku, 102. Tel: 03 214-2561 or 214 2565. *Dir* Kenji Adachi; *Deputy Dir* Kazuo Anazawa; *Chief Cur Fine Art* Tamon Miki; *Cur Painting* Yoshikazu Ewasaki; *Cur Prints* Hisae Jufii; *Cur Sculpture* Toru Asano; *Cur Exhib & International Exchange* Yasushi Takizawa; *Cur Educ & Pub Relations* Masahiro Koike; *Admin Chief* Kensuke Koiwa.

Open Tues - Sun 10 AM - 5 PM; cl Mon and year end and New Year Holidays. Admis adult 200 yen. Estab 1952, new building completed 1969, as a place to show permanent and special exhibitions mainly modern and contemporary Japanese art and to introduce world art trends. First floor houses temporary exhibitions; second to fourth floors galleries, permanent collections. Average Annual Attendance: 299,408. Mem: 1000, dues 2,300 yen.

Income: Financed by state appropriation.

Collections: Japanese-style paintings 576, oil paintings 716, prints 1113, sculpture 205, drawings 115, watercolours, calligraphies.

Exhibitions: Realistische Tendenzen deutscher Kunst 1919-1933; Rufino Tamayo; The Retrospective Exhibition of Yukihiko Yasuda; Koshiro Onchi and Tsukuhae; Exposition Marc Chagall; Cubism; Fiber Works—Europe and Japan; Retrospective Exhibition of Shoji Hamada; Peintre Naifs; Fontanesi, Ragusa e l'arte giapponese nel primo periodo Meiji; Fiber Works—Americas and Japan; Commemorative Exhibition for Opening of the Crafts Gallery; Masterpieces of Contemporary Japanese Crafts; Caspar David Friedrich und sein Kreis; Marino Marini.

Publications: Bulletin, monthly; exhibition catalogues; annual report.

—**National Film Center,** 7-6, 3-chrome, Kyobashi, Chuo-ku, 104. Tel: 03 561-0823. *Cur Film* Sadamu Maru.

Open 12:30 - 8 PM; film shows at 1 and 6:15 PM. Admis adult 200 yen. Estab 1952, now uses old museum building. Average Annual Attendance: 78,290.

Collections: Feature films 1140; documentary and news reels 2542; animation films 150.

—**Crafts Gallery,** Kitanomaru Koen. Tel: 03 211-7781. *Chief Crafts Gallery* Nobuhiko Sugihara; *Cur Ceramics* Mitsuhiko Hasebe; *Cur Lacquer* Tadaomi Goke.

Open Tues - Sun 10 AM - 5 PM; cl Mon, year end and New Year Holidays. Admis 200 yen. Estab 1977. Average Annual Attendance: 33,365.

Collections: Ceramics 282; dyeing and weaving 320; lacquer ware 157; metal works, and others.

TOKYO-TO BIJUTSUKAN,* (Tokyo Metropolitan Fine Art Gallery), Ueno-Park, Daito-ku, 110. Tel: 03-823-6921. *Dir* Haruo Imai; *Cur in Chief* Akira Asahi.

Open Tues - Sun 9 AM - 4:30 PM; cl Mon & Dec 29 - Jan 3. Estab 1925; new building opened Sept 1, 1976; contains gallery; auditorium, library and studios and provides rental galleries. Average Annual Attendance: 1,320,000.

Collections: †Contemporary paintings, sculptures and crafts.

Exhibitions: The museum originates three or four major exhibitions each year; 160 art groups exhibitions a year at the rental galleries.

Publications: News of Museum, monthly; catalog of special exhibition.

Activities: Painting class; films: vis lectrs.

Library: Open to the public. Holdings: Vols 7000, mainly on Japanese art; Per sub 70.

WAKAYAMA

KOYASAN REIHOKAN,* (Museum of Buddhist Art), Koyasan, Koya-cho, Ito-gun. *Dir* Chikyo Yamamoko.

Open 8 AM - 5 PM, or 9 AM - 4 PM. Admis 200 yen. Estab 1921 to keep the treasures handed down in Koyasan, one of the centers of Japanese Buddhism.

Collections: More than 25,000 pieces of paintings, sculptures, calligraphy, manuscripts, images and sutras, some of them registered National Treasures and important cultural properties.

KOREA

SEOUL

NATIONAL MUSEUM OF KOREA, Kyong Bok Palace, 1 Sejongro, Chongro-ku. Tel: 72-9295. *Dir-Gen* Sunu Choi; *Dir Kyongju Mus* Han Byongsam; *Dir Puyo Mus* Kunkil Gee; *Chief Cur* Yagmo Chong; *Cur in Charge of Registr* Nanyong Lee; *Cur in Charge of Archaeology* Ingu Kang.
Open 9 AM - 6 PM. Admis adults 150 won, children 70 won. Estab 1915. Average Annual Attendance: 538,000. Mem: 800.
Income: Financed by governmental appropriation.
Collections: Pottery, ceramics, bronze wares, Buddhist sculptures, paintings and calligraphy (historical and artistic materials).
Exhibitions: 5,000 Years of Korean Arts; Special Exhibition of Paintings Selected from National Museum Collections; Special Exhibition of Cultural Relics Found off Sinan Coast.
Publications: Misul Charyo, biannually; Museum News, monthly.
Activities: Classes for adults; lect for members only; traveling exhibitions organized and circulated; museum shop selling books, reproductions.
—**Library,** Kyong Bok Palace, Sejongro-1, Jongro-ku. *Librn* Eun-hee Kim.
Open to museum staff and members.
Holdings: Vols 10,000.
Special Subjects: Art history, archaeology.

LEBANON

BEIRUT

AMERICAN UNIVERSITY OF BEIRUT, Archaeological Museum, Tel: 340740, exten 2523. *Acting Cur* Helga Seeden; *Secy* Lamia Awad; *Grad Asst* Helene Sadir.
Open Mon - Fri 8 AM - 4 PM. No admis. Estab 1868 to house a teaching and study collection. Two galleries containing 51 show cases; the exhibits are arranged in chronological sequence, dating from the Palaeolithic to the Islamic periods. Average Annual Attendance: 3000.
Income: $1000 (financed by endowment). Purchases: $1000.
Collections: Palaeolithic-Neolithic flint collection; †Bronze and Iron Age Near Eastern pottery collections; †Bronze figurines, weapons and implements of the Bronze Age Near East; Graeco-Roman imports of pottery from Near East sites; Phoenician glass collection; substantial coin collection; Palmyrene funerary sculpture; pottery collection for Islamic periods.
Publications: Berytus Archaeological Studies, annually.
Activities: Classes for adults; extension courses in Archaeology; gallery talks; tours; museum shop selling books, photographs.
Library: Jafet. *Librn* J Khoury. Open to the community. Holdings: Vols & Per subs 45,000. Special Subjects Near Eastern Archaeology.

MUSEE NATIONAL,* (National Museum of Lebanon), rue de Damas. Tel: 401-00/440. *Dir & Chief Cur* Emir Maurice Chehab.
Open winter 9 - Noon, 2 - 5 PM; summer 9 - Noon, 3 - 6 PM. Estab 1920.
Collections: Objects and statues of the prehistoric period; collections of jewelry and statues of the Phoenician period; sarcophagus of Ahiram (13th century BC), depicting the prototype of the whole modern alphabet; anthropological sarcophagi of the Greco-Persian period; Dr C Ford Collection of 25 sarcophagi of the Green and Helenistic epoch; collections of jewelry in gold of the Roman, Byzantine and Arabic periods; sarcophagi and reliefs, mosaics and goblets of the Greco-Roman period; Byzantine mosaics; collections of monies in gold, in silver, and in bronze, of the Phoenician, Helenmistic, Roman, Byzantine and Arabic periods; ceramics and wainscoting of the Arabic period.
Publications: Bulletin du Musee de Beyrouth, annually; Etudes et Documents d'Archeologie (Publications des fouilles enterprises au Liban); texts and historical documents.

MALTA

VALLETTA

NATIONAL MUSEUM,* Auberge de Provence, Kingsway. Tel: 2-52-93. *Dir* Francis S Mallia; *Dir Fine Arts* John Cauchi; *Asst Cur Archaeology* Tangred Goudeer.

Open winter 8:30 AM - 1:30 PM, 2 - 4:30 PM; summer 8:30 AM - 1:30 PM. Admis 10¢. Estab 1905. Average Annual Attendance: 500,000.
Income: Financed by government.
Collections: Prehistoric archeological remains; 17th and 18th century works of art; collection of works by Martha Prati; †contemporary art.
Exhibitions: Council of Europe Exhibition; regular exhibitions of contemporary art.
Publications: Annual Report.
Activities: Lect; tours; schol.
Library Holdings—Vols 2000.

MEXICO

CHOLULA

UNIVERSIDAD DE LAS AMERICAS, Galeria de Arte (University of the Americas, Gallery of Art) Department of Graphic Arts and Design, Ex-Hacienda de Santa Catarina Martir (Mailing Add: PO Box 100, Santa Catarina Martir). Tel: 47-06-55, exten 127-128. *Chairperson* Pamela M de Artasanchez; *Instr* Ignacio Cabral Perez; *Instr* Fernando Rodriguez Lago; *Instr* Sandra Beliza de Vazquez.
Open 8 AM - 5 PM. No admis. Estab 1969 to promote cultural and artistic events for the benefit of the university community. One-man gallery located in the Library Building of the campus at the university. Average Annual Attendance: 3000.
Exhibitions: (1976-78) Ricardo Arredondo; Julieta Sarmiento; Roberto Castro Silva; Guillermina Rugerio.
Activities: Classes for adults; lect open to public; tours; extension dept; artmobile; lending collection contains color reproductions, framed reproductions, motion pictures, slides 15,000.
Library: *Librn* Amador Zapata. Holdings: Vols 130,000; Per subs 1750 for reference only. Special Collections: Porfirio Diaz Collection; Eddy Collection; and Herrera Carrillo Collection.

GUADALAJARA

MUSEO DEL ESTADO,* (National Museum).
Founded 1700 as a seminary.
Collections: Early Mexican objects; folk art and costumes; archaeological discoveries.

MEXICO CITY

MUSEO DE ARTE MODERNO,* (Museum of Modern Art), Bosque de Chapultepec, 5. Tel: 553 63 13. *Dir* Fernando Gamboa; *Coordr* Juan Acha; *Coordr* Mariana Frenk-Westheim; *Coordr* Maria Elena C de Christensen; *Cur* Jorge Guadarrama; *Admin* Alfredo Ramirez Herrara; *Secy* Eva Ramirez Pena.
Open Tues - Sun 11 AM - 7 PM. Estab 1964. Average Annual Attendance: 600,000.
Income: Financed by state appropriation from the National Institute of Fine Arts.
Collections: Jose Maria Velasco, academic bridge to 20th century Mexican painting, 51 works; first six decades of 20th century Mexican painting, 124 works; contemporary art (1950-1973), Mexican and foreign, 70 works; international works, a donation which is on temporary exhibition in the Museo de Arte Moderno.
Exhibitions: Mexican and International exhibitions of Modern Art.
Publications: One catalog published in conjunction with each exhibition; Artes Visuales, tri-annual magazine.
Activities: Films; lect and round table discussions; guided tours.

MUSEO DE SAN CARLOS (Museum of San Carlos), Puente de Alvarado 50, 1. Tel: 535-1256. *Dir* Graciela Reyes Retana; *Cur* Aurea Ruiz de Gurzo; *Cur Museography* Pilar de la Fuente de Trezabal; *Educ Services* Elena Watsztein.
Open Tues - Sun 11 AM - 5 PM; cl Mon. No admis. Estab 1968 to act as a cultural organism in the community; to allow the public to see and understand European painting from 14th-19th centuries; and to establish a bond between the styles produced in Europe and our national art. Average Annual Attendance: 150,000.
Income: Financed by state appropriation.
Collections: Spanish, French, Flemish, Netherlandish, Italian, English paintings from 14th-19th centuries; 19th century Mexican sculpture.
Exhibitions: Permanent European collection; several temporary exhibitions of Gothic, Renaissance, Baroque and 19th century art.
Publications: Catalogs of exhibitions, bimonthly.
Activities: Classes for adults and children; lect open to public, 10 vis lectr per yr; concerts; gallery talks; individual paintings and original works of art lent to other museums; traveling exhibitions organized and circulated; museum shop selling books.
Library: Art Library. *Librn* Aurea Luiz de Gurza. Open to the public for reference. Holdings: Vols 3000.

MUSEO NACIONAL DE ANTROPOLOGIA (National Museum of Anthropology), Ave Paseo de la Reforma Y Gandhi S/N, 10. Tel: 553-62-66. *Dir* Alberto Ruz Lhuillier; *Head Anthropological Dept* Arqla Noemi Castillo; *Head Ethnographical Dept* Teresa Sepulveda; *Head Museographical Dept* Prof Mario Vasquez; *Head Promotion Dept* Gabriela Guzman; *Head Pub Relations* Margarita A de Laris; *Head Educ Dept* Maria Eugenia Sanchez Bueno.
Open Tues - Sat 9 AM - 7 PM; Sun 10 AM - 6 PM. Admis 15 pesos; Sun 10 pesos, children under 13 free. Estab 1964 for educational purposes. 12 Archaeological Halls, dealing with Prehispanic cultures; 11 Halls dealing with actual Indian groups; Orientation Room—Audiovisual light and sound. Average Annual Attendance: 1,200,000.
Income: Financed by state appropriation.
Collections: Archaeological and ethnographical.
Exhibitions: Artesanias chinas; Musica en el Antiguo Israel.
Activities: Classes for adults and children; docent training; lect open to public; tours; original objects of art lent; traveling exhibitions organized and circulated; museum shop selling books, magazines, reproductions, prints, slides and popular art.
Library: Librn Yolanda Mercader. Open to the public for reference. Holdings: Vols 250,000; Other—Maps, film strips. Special Collections: Codeces.

MUSEO NACIONAL DE ARTES Y INDUSTRIAS POPULARES,* (National Museum of Industrial Arts), Av Juarez 44, 1. Tel: 510 34 04 & 521 66 79. *Dir* Dr Carlos Espejel.
Open daily 10 AM - 7 PM & 10 AM - 8 PM. Estab May 1951 for exhibit and sale of traditional Mexican crafts; the Museum supports three regional museums of crafts—Museo Regional de la Ceramica at Tlaquepaque, Jalisco; Museo Regional de Arte Popular de la Huatapera at Uruapan, Mich; and Museo de la Laca, Chiapa de Corzo, Chis.
Collections: Major †permanent collections of Mexican popular arts and crafts with emphasis on native pottery, textiles and lacquer.
Exhibitions: Exhibits of Mexican pottery.
Publications: Books and booklets on crafts; Ceramica Popular Mexicana.
Activities: Operates workshops for the training of craftsmen; operates provincial museums of arts and crafts; contests; schol to craftsmen.
Library: Arts and crafts with emphasis on Mexico and Latin America.

MUSEO NACIONAL DE HISTORIA,* (National Historical Museum), Castillo de Chapultepec. *Dir* Dr Felipe Lacouture.
Estab 1822; moved to Chapultepec Castle 1941, opened 1944, attached to the National Institute of Anthropology and History.
Collections: History of Mexico since the Spanish Conquest; Mexican and European porcelain, ceramics, mosaics, jewelry, textiles; 19th century paintings; ornamental wooden statues, religious art and cultural history.
Publications: Sere Cientifica.

MONTERREY

MUSEO REGIONAL DE NUEVO LEON (Regional Museum of Nuevo Leon), Obispo Verger, Cerro del Obispado, (Mailing Add: Apdo Postal 566 Suc C). *Dir* Felipe J Garcia Campuzano; *Cur* Israel Cavazos Gza.
Open Tues - Sat 10 AM - 1 PM & 3 - 6 PM; Sunday 10 AM - 5 PM; cl Mon. No admis. Estab 1956 to extend cultural interests. Average Annual Attendance: 40,000. Mem: 13.
Income: Financed by state appropriation.
Collections: Permanent collection.
Library: Holdings—Vols 70. Special Collections: Guias de Zonas Arqueologicas y Monumentos Prehispanicos.

PUEBLA

MUSEO DE ARTE "JOSE LUIS BELLO Y GONZALEZ" (Museum of Art), Ave 3 Poniente 302. Tel: 41-94-75. *Dir* Alicia Torres de Araujo; *Secy* Silvia Martínez Machorro; *Leaders* Isabel Navarro Lima, Rosario Pastrana Jiménez, Guadalupe Galindo García and Consuelo Perez Lara; *Warders* Guadalupe Sánchez Garcia, Enrique Morales Méndez, Caridad Saldaña-Guerrero and Ma de Lourdes Arista Cerezo.
Open 10 AM - 5 PM. Admis $5. Estab 1944 to diffuse art. The museum was the house of Mariano Bello y Acedo. The rooms are decorated with floor carpets, stuccos and richly provided with French style curtains; there are 14 rooms. Average Annual Attendance: 25,000.
Income: $125,000 (financed by state appropriation and admission fee).
Collections: Agustin Arrieta, coppers, calamine, Puebla's ceramic (Talavera) lace, ivories, forged irons, Chinese porcelain; religious ornaments; European and Mexican furniture with marquetry; engravings; bronzes; pictures; sculptures; watches; enamels; miniatures; crystal; European porcelain.

Exhibitions: (1976) Casa de la Cultura of this city, a painting by Agustin Arrieta; (1977) Exhibition Mexico, in Spain inauguration of his art in the Spanish Museum of Contemporary Art of Madrid.
Publications: Pamphlets.
Activities: Classes for adults and children; lect for members only, 50 vis lectrs per yr; concerts; gallery talks; tours; lending collection contains color reproductions, photographs, motion pictures, film strips, catalogs 5000, postcards; museum shop.
Library: Open to members only. Holdings: Vols 1028; Per subs 3. Special Subjects: Books of Art. Special Collections: Mexican History.

NETHERLANDS

ALKMAAR

STEDELIJK MUSEUM ALKMAAR (Alkmaar Municipal Museum), Doelenstraat 3. *Dir* K J Kreik.
Open 10 AM - Noon & 2 - 5 PM; cl Sat. Admis. Estab 1861 to encourage interest in the history of Alkmaar and art.
Income: Financed by city appropriation.
Collections: Archaeological items; tiles; dolls and other toys.
Exhibitions: Cor en Kees Hak; Theo Ros; Jan Deckwitz en Otto Heuvelink; Gerrit Brinkman; Piet Lont; Doorwerken; Potjeslatijn; Tour-in; Dirk Bakker; Geologische Vereniging; Arthoteek; Overtoom; Gouden Naald; Simon Erb; Bob van der Born; AKV Grafici.
Activities: Individual paintings and original objects of art lent to public offices and other museums.

AMSTERDAM

MUSEUM "HET REMBRANDTHUIS" (Rembrandthouse Museum), Jodenbreestraat 4-6, 1011 NK. Tel: 020-24 94 86. *Cur* Eva Ornstein-van Slooten; *Asst Cur* Cecile van Oosterwijk.
Open Mon - Sat 10 AM - 5 PM; Sun & holidays 1 - 5 PM. Admis adults fl.50, children f0.50, groups (min 15) fl.00. Estab 1906 to maintain the house Rembrandt lived in from 1639-1660 and show his works—in this instance prints and drawings; 17th century interior furnished with contemporary furniture. Average Annual Attendance: 100,000. Mem: 1000; due fl0.00.
Income: Financed by endowment and earned income.
Collections: Almost complete collection of Rembrandt's etchings; 8 drawings by Rembrandt; †drawings by Rembrandt's pupils; paintings by Rembrandt's pupils and teachers.
Exhibitions: Rembrandt and Rubens, prints.
Publications: Kroniek van het Rembrandthuis, twice yearly.
Activities: Sales shop selling books, reproductions, prints, slides.
Library: Open to public for reference, by request. Special Subjects: Rembrandt's work, especially the etchings, and other Dutch artists of his period.

RIJKSMUSEUM (State Museum), Stadhouderskade 42. Tel: 020 73 21 21. (Mailing Add: Hobbemastraat 21, 1071 XZ). *Dir General* Dr S H Levie; *Intendant* R van Eijle; *Dir Dept Paintings* Dr P J J van Thiel; *Dir Dept Decorative Art* Dr A L den Blaauwen; *Head Dept Dutch History* Dr W H Vroom; *Dir Printroom* Dr J W Niemeijer; *Head Dept Asiatic Art* Dr K W Lim.
Open daily 10 AM - 5 PM; Sun 1 - 5 PM. Admis Dfl 3, Wed free. Estab 1808 as a National Gallery of Art; the actual building was completed in 1883 and contains 250 rooms open to the public. Average Annual Attendance: 1,300,000.
Income: Financed by state appropriation.
Collections: †Dutch paintings 15th-19th centuries; †prints and drawings from all parts of the world; †sculpture and applied art; †Dutch history; †Asiatic art.
Exhibitions: Lering en Vermaak (Dutch 17th century genre paintings); Borobudur (Art and Religion on Java); Oriental rugs and carpets; The Age of Harunobu (Japanese woodcuts).
Publications: Bulletin, quarterly.
Activities: Classes for adults and children; individual paintings and original objects of art lent to other galleries and museums; museum shop selling books, reproductions, prints, slides.
—**Library,** Jan Luykenstr la (Mailing Add: PO Box 50673, 1007 DD). Tel: 020-732121. *Librn* Mrs E van der Vossen-Delbruck; *Asst Librn* Y Grose.
Open Mon - Wed & Fri - Sat 10 AM - 5 PM; cl Thurs & Sun. Estab 1885 as a reference library for the Rijksmuseum.
Income: Financed by state appropriation.
Holdings: Vols 50,000; Per subs 400; Other—Exhibition catalogs.
Special Subjects: History of art.
Special Collections: Museum and exhibition catalogs; auction catalogs.

RIJKSMUSEUM VINCENT VAN GOGH (Vincent Van Gogh State Museum), Paulus Potterstraat 7 1071 CX. Tel: 020-764881. *Dir General* Dr S H Levie; *Cur* Dr H van Crimpen; *Cur* Mrs L Couvée-Jampoller.
Open Mon - Sat 10 AM - 5 PM; Sun & holidays 1 - 5 PM. Admis Hfl 3. Estab 1973 to house the family collection of Vincent van Gogh. Average Annual Attendance: 500,000.
Income: Financed by city and state appropriation.
Collections: Paintings by Vincent van Gogh and contemporaries; drawings by Vincent van Gogh and contemporaries; prints, letters by Vincent van Gogh.
Exhibitions: World Press Photo; Japanese Prints; Theo van Gogh collection.
Activities: Workshop; sales shop selling books, reproductions, prints, slides.
—Library. *Staff* Mrs L Couvée-Jampoller & Miss S J Pabst.
Open 10 AM - 5 PM. Estab 1973 to inform museum visitors, scientists, students, journalists, etc, about the life and work of Vincent van Gogh and his contemporaries.
Income: Financed by state appropriation.
Holdings: Vols 9000; Per subs 30; AV—Film strips; microfiche; motion pictures; phonorecords; slides; Other—Clipping files, exhibition catalogs, reproductions, manuscripts, original art works, original documents, photographs; prints; reproductions.
Special Subjects: The life and work of Vincent van Gogh and his time.
Special Collections: Theo van Gogh collection.

STEDELIJK MUSEUM-AMSTERDAM (Municipal Museum), Paulus Potterstraat 13. (Mailing Add: PO Box 5082, 1007 AB). Tel: 020-73.21.66. *Dir* E L L de Wilde; *Deputy Dir* J van Loenen Martinet; *Deputy Managing Dir* W H Brabander; *Head Dept Painting & Sculpture* R M Dippel; *Head Dept Prints & Drawings* A J Petersen; *Head Dept Applied Art* W Bertheux; *Cur Communication Dept* Mrs J F W van Droffelaar & T van Grootheest; *Research Cur* J M Joosten.
Open Mon - Sat 9:30 AM - 5 PM; Sun 1 - 5 PM. Admis Adult 2DFL, children under 16 1DL; group rates. Estab 1895, new wing opened 1954. Average Annual Attendance: 319,000.
Collections: International paintings and sculptures dating from 1850 to the present day; Cezanne, Monet, Van Gogh, European expressionism, Chagall; paintings by Malevich, Mondrian, Matisse, Dubuffet, Cobra-group; European and American tendencies after 1960 (Pop Art, Zero, Nouveau Realisme, Colorfield Painting, Conceptual Art); Dutch Art 1850 to the present; Printroom—drawings, graphic art, especially Werkman, Cobra; applied art and design—especially ceramics, glass, textiles, furniture (Rietveld), posters, typography, photography, bibliophile editions.
Exhibitions: Approx 30 group exhibitions and one-person shows dedicated to art tendencies since 1960.
Activities: Guided tours for school children (10-13); concerts of contemporary music; films; information desk; reproduction dept—posters, reproductions, postcards, books, catalogs for sale; subscriptions and season-tickets; restaurant with terrace.
—Library.
Temporary change in hours. May & June Open Thurs & Fri, first Sat of month; July & Aug cl; Sept & Oct Open Thurs & Fri, first Sat of month. From Nov 1, 1978 normal opening hours: Mon - Sat 9:30 AM - 5 PM.
Holdings: Vols 18,000; Per subs 150; Other—Exhibition catalogues 70,000.
Special Subjects: Modern Art 1850 to the present.

ARNHEM

GEMEENTEMUSEUM ARNHEM (Municipal Museum of Arnhem), Utrechtseweg 87, 6812 AA. Tel: 085-431841. *Dir* P L A Janssen; *Cur* H Driessen; *Cur* J R de Groot; *Cur* C van Kooten; *Cur* R Neerincx; *Cur* R Borman.
Open Mon - Sat 10 AM - 5 PM; Sun & holidays 11 AM - 5 PM. No admis. Estab 1852. The building was built in 1873-75; remodeled in 1912 and used as a museum; a new wing was added in 1956, it has a panoramic view of the river Rhine. Average Annual Attendance: 100,000.
Income: Financed by city appropriation.
Collections: Dutch painting 17th-20th century (new realism); drawings and prints of the 18th-20th centuries; topographical and historical maps of the province of Gelderland; silverware of the 18th-19th centuries; copper; bronze; tin Dutch 15th-19th centuries; Delftware; provincial archaeology and history; Chinese porcelain 15th-18th centuries.
Publications: Information leaflets.
Activities: Educ dept; docent training; lect open to public; gallery talks; museum shop selling books, original art, reproductions, prints, slides.
Library: Open for reference to interested person on request. Holdings: Vol 2500; Per subs 10; Other—Catalogs 5,000.

DELFT

STEDELIJK MUSEUM HET PRINSENHOF, (Het Prinsenhof State Museum), St Agathaplein I. Tel: 015-13111, exten 335 and 339. *Dir* Dr R A Leeuw; *Cur* Dr I Spaander; *Public Relations* G Singeling.
Open daily 10 AM - 5 PM; Sun & holidays 1 - 5 PM; begun as the Museum Historische Zaal in 1833, became City Museum and Archives, 1906; estab 1947 as a museum for fine arts of Delft and Holland and for the history of William the Silent and the 80-year war; Gallery, DeVolle Maan, for contemporary art, mainly Delft artists.
Income: Financed by city and state appropriation.
Collections: Dutch Art of the 15th, 16th, 17th and 18th centuries; Delftica; Delft silver; †Delft ware; Delft tapestries; collection of paintings of Orange-Nassau family, expecially William the Silent and the 80-year war.
Exhibitions: DPG Humbert de Superville; Incons; Bijbels and Burges; Water Als Vijan; Water Als Uriend; Zwitserland Project; Antoni Van Leeuwenhoek; Contour.
Publications: Museum Information, quarterly.
Activities: Classes for children; concerts; original objects of art lent; museum shop selling books, prints and slides.
Library: For reference only. Holdings: Vols 3800; Other—Photographs.

EINDHOVEN

MUNICIPAL VAN ABBEMUSEUM, (Eindhoven Municipal Museum), Bilderdijklaan 10, (Mailing Add: PO Box 235, 5600 AE). Tel: 040-448555, exten 2199. *Dir* R H Fuchs; *Cur* J Bremer; Cur J Debbaut; *Cur* Ms M Suren.
Open Mon - Sat 10 AM - 5 PM; Sun & holidays 1 - 5 PM. Admis adults Dfl 1, children Dfl 0.50. Estab 1936 as a museum of the art of the 20th century; city property.
Income: Financed by membership and city appropriation.
Collections: Collection ranges from Cubism to the latest trends in art (conceptual art, etc); specialities, neoconstructivism, Zero, Postpainterly Abstraction, Lissitzky-collection, concept art.
Exhibitions: Approx 25 changing exhibitions per year. (1976) Alan Charlton, Edgar Fernhout, Peter Struycken, David v/d Kop, Lawrence Weiner, Reinier Lucassen, Daniel Buren, Wessel Couzijn, Sigmar Polke, Laura Grisi, Mari Boeyen, Stanley Brouwn, Eugène Atget, Marie McClelland. (1977) Ulrich Rückriem, Peter Roehr, Victor Burgin, Peter Downsbrough, Niele Toroni, Dan Graham, Barry Flanagan, Michael Asher, Hamish Fultin, Robert Barry, Markus Lüpertz.
Publications: Exhibition catalogs; artistbooks, occasionally; information bulletins, occasionally.
Activities: Lect open to the public; tours; traveling exhibitions organized and circulated; sales shop selling books, magazines, reproductions.
Library: Librn Aloys van den Berk. Open to the public for reference. Holdings: Vols 10,000; Other—Exhibition catalogs 21,500, magazines 6000.

GRONINGEN

GRONINGEN MUSEUM VOOR STAD EN LAND,* (Groningen Museum), Praediniussingel 59. Tel: 17 29 29. *Dir* Dr A Westers; *Adjunct/Dir & Cur Paintings & Drawings* P I M Vries; *Scientific Asst* P ter Hofstede; *Cur Oriental Ceramics* Miss J M Cochius; *Scientific Asst Silver* J H Leopold; *Cur Mediaeval & Later History* Dr E A J Boiten; *Cur Archaeology* Dr J W Boersma.
Open 10 AM - 5 PM; cl Mon. Admis fl 0.50. Estab 1894. Average Annual Attendance: 36,500.
Income: Financed by state appropriation.
Collections: Oriental ceramics, European ceramics, silver, local archaeology, local history; paintings and drawings from the 16th to the 20th century, mainly Dutch, including Hofstede de Groot Collection. 17th century and Veendorp Collection, second half 19th century.
Exhibitions: Principally modern art.
Publications: Annual Report.
Activities: Concerts; original objects of art lent; prints 1500 for reference.
Library: For reference. Holdings: Vols 1000.

HAARLEM

FRANS HALSMUSEUM (Frans Hals Museum), Groot Heiligland 62. *Dir* D H Couvée, *Cur Ancient Art* Dr P Biesboer; *Asst Ancient Art* W Zetteler; *Cur Modern Art* Dr M Hoogendonk; *Educ Dept* Dr G F Walberg; *Asst Educ Dept* C Brinkgreve.
Open daily 10 AM - 5 PM; Sun & holidays 1 - 5 PM. Admis Dfl 1.75, children Dfl 0.75, groups Dfl 1.75, from Nov-Feb free. Estab 1862 to show permanent collection of ancient and modern art, and temporary exhibitions; to attract visitors by showing socio-cultural exhibitions. Average Annual Attendance: 160,000.
Income: Financed by city appropriation.

Collections: Group portraits by Frans Hals; portraits, still lifes and landscapes of the Haarlem School from 16th-19th century; period rooms; silver; old pharmacy; doll's house; Dutch art of the 20th century.
Exhibitions: Socio-cultural exhibitions.
Activities: Educ dept; traveling exhibitions organized and circulated; sales shop selling books, reproductions, slides.

TEYLERS MUSEUM, Spaarne 16, (Mailing Add: Damstraat 21, 2011 HA.) Tel: 023-32 01 97. *Board of Trustees* H E Stenfert Kroese, C W D Vrijland, L van Nouhuys, G Beets, L H Graaf Schimmelpenninck; *Cur Physics* Dr J Kistemaker; Dr J H C Walenkamp; *Deputy Cur Art Coll* J H van Borssum Buisman; *Cur Coins & Medals* Dr H E van Gelder.
Open March-Sept, Tues - Sat 10 AM - 5 PM; first Sun of month 1 - 5 PM; Oct-Feb, Tues - Sat 10 AM - 4 PM; first Sun of month 1 - 4 PM. Admis adults Dfl 2; children Dfl 0.75. Estab 1778 to promote art and science. The oldest part of the museum dates from 1780; a new wing was added in 1880, 7 rooms. Attendance: 22,000. Mem: 200.
Income: Financed by Foundation.
Collections: Drawings 16th-19th century Dutch, Italian, and French School; 19th century Dutch paintings; cabinet of coins and medals.
Activities: Classes for adults and children; lect open to public, 5 vis lectr per yr; concerts; tours; original objects of art; sales shop selling books, reproductions, slides.
Library Librn J G de Bruijn. Estab 1778 for the promotion of science. Holdings: Vols 120,000; Per subs 1200.

THE HAGUE

HAAGS GEMEENTEMUSEUM,* (Municipal Museum of The Hague), Stadhouderslaan 41, PO Box 72, 2076. Tel 51 41 81. *Dir* Dr T van Velzen; *Deputy Dir & Head Ancient Art Dept* Dr Beatrice Jansen; *Head Modern Art Dept* Dr J L Locher; *Head Music Dept* Dr C C J von Gleich; *Head History Dept* Dr W M van der Mast; *Head Prints Dept* Dr C H A Broos.
Open weekdays 10 AM - 5 PM; Sun & holidays 1 - 5 PM; Wed 8 - 10 PM. No admis excepting special fees for temporary exhibitions, and special reduced fees for groups. Estab 1883; the present museum was built by the well-known architect Dr H P Berlage in 1935; extension for temporary exhibitions since 1962. Average Annual Attendance: 219,000.
Mem: Approx 1700 (Society of Friends of the Municipal Museum of The Hague); dues f15.
Collections: Ancient decorative arts collection includes Delft pottery, Italian and Spanish majolica, Chinese pottery and porcelain, Islamic pottery; Hague silver 17th-19th century; Hague porcelain 1776-1784; Egyptian, Roman, Islamic, Venetian and Dutch glass; objects in bronze and Dutch pewter; Dutch Period Rooms 1680-1780; art of the Ancient World: Greek pottery, terracottas, Coptic textiles; ancient Indonesian art, Dutch colonial furniture; Modern Art Collection includes paintings, sculpture and decorative arts of the 19th and 20th century; Dutch artists: Jongkind, Weissenbruch, van Gogh; largest collection of works (257) by Piet Mondrian, van Doesburg and other members of the Stijl group; recent trends: Karel Appel, Constant, Westerik and Visser. Foreign artists, notably: Bonington, Monet, Redon; Expressionists: Kirchner, Kokoschka; Picasso, Lissitzky; sculptures by Arp, Moore, Lipchitz, Bacon, Vasarely, Kitaj. Printroom: Large collection of prints and drawings of Dutch and foreign masters of the 19th and 20th century, notably: Redon, Bresdin; Toulouse Lautrec, German Expressionists; Mondrian, Werkman; Escher, Heyboer and living Dutch artists. Music Department: Unique survey of musical instruments·from four centuries and five continents. Among the about 2600 instruments (of which one half is on permanent exhibition) are famous Italian and Flemish harpsichords (Celestini, Ruckers), Dutch stringed instruments (Jacobs, Rombouts), German and French wind instruments (Grenser, Gautrot). From Indonesia a complete gamelan-orchestra. Frequent museum concerts, guided tours (cassette records).
Publications: General and specific publications related to each department. Modern Art: Catalog of paintings (1962) and sculptures (1972); Mondrian (1974). Ancient Decorative Arts: Catalogs of Dutch glass (1962) and Hague silver (1962); guides to the collections of European and Islamic Decorative Arts; many picture books concerning the various collections (also in English). Music Department: Catalog of wind instruments, volume I (1970); selection of old European instruments; catalogs of the music library I and II (1969, 1973).
Activities: Courses for adults and children in basic principles of modern art; history of art; applied arts; Winter Programs (Sept-May) film programs; explicatory slide-shows relating to exhibitions; museum lessons for schools (10,000 children); visual quizzes for children during holidays; children's workshop (only children of visitors); exchange market held regularly for collectors of art reproductions; lectures; concerts; gallery talks; guided bus tours viewing, i.e. important monuments in The Hague, art nouveau architecture in The Hague and Brussels.
 —**Museum Bredius,*** Prinsegracht 6 (PO Box 72, 2076). Tel: 63 16 03. Dr T van Velzen.

Open weekdays 10 AM - 5 PM; Sun & holidays 1 - 5 PM; Wed 8 - 10 PM. Admis f 0.25. The well-known art-historian, Dr A Bredius, donated his collection and private 17th century house in 1946, to the municipality of The Hague, on loan since 1923.
Collections: Paintings by Rembrandt, Steen, Seghers, Terborch, Ruisdael and others; drawings by Breughel, van Goyen; furniture, silver, glass, porcelain.

KONINKLIJK KABINET VAN SCHILDERIJEN (Mauritshuis), (Royal Picture Gallery), Korte Vijverberg 8. Tel: 46 92 44. *Dir* H R Hoetink; *Asst* F J Duparc.
Open weekdays 10 AM - 5 PM; Fri 8 - 10 PM; Sun 11 AM - 5 PM. Building erected 1633; museum estab 1816.
Collections: Paintings of the Dutch and Flemish Masters of the 15th, 16th and 17th centuries.
Publications: Catalogs; illustrated guidebooks; Annual Report.

HERTOGENBOSCH

NOORDBRABANTS MUSEUM, Bethaniestraat 4, 5211 LJ. Tel: 073-13.87.12. *Dir* Dr M M A van Boven; *Cur* J C T M van Laarhoven; *Cur* Dr M Trappeniers.
Open Mon - Fri 10 AM - 5 PM; Sat & Sun 1 - 5 PM. No admis. Estab 1925 to study and display art and history of the province of Noord-Brabant. The building is a late-gothic church of 1470 c; the ground floor houses the permanent exhibition of local history and paintings; the upper floor has changing exhibitions. Average Annual Attendance: 38,000.
Income: $230,000 (financed by membership, city appropriation, and sales).
Collections: Local archaeology; coins and medals; arts and crafts 1500-1800; painting and sculpture 1500-1900; religious art. All collections have an emphasis on local history.
Exhibitions: De achtergrond belicht; Op de penning; In 't bonte uithangteken; Retrospective Paul van Hoeydonck; Drie schilders uit Oostende—Ensor-Spilliaert-Permerke; Acter slot en grendel (sleutels en sloten); Het magisch realisme in Italie, Mario en Edita Broglio; Kloosters in Brabant; Romeins glas en aardewerk.
Activities: Exten dept serving Noord-Brabant; individual paintings and original objects of art lent; traveling exhibitions organized and circulated; sales shop selling books and reproductions.

HOORN

WESTFRIES MUSEUM,* (Westfrisian Museum), Rode Steen 1 (Mailing Add: Kerkstraat 10, 1900). Tel: 02290-57 83. *Dir* W A Braasem; *Archaeology Dept* Mrs T Y v/d Walle; *Sr Research Asst* H W Saaltink; *Admin* Mrs W N Mallekote.
Open April - Oct daily 10 AM - 5 PM; Sun Noon - 5 PM; Oct - April daily 10 - Noon, 2 - 5 PM; Sun in Oct & March 2 - 5 PM. Admis f.1, children f0.50; families consisting of more than three persons f2.50. Estab 1880, building dates from 1632. Average Annual Attendance: 40,000.
Income: f.350,000 (financed by appropriations). Purchases: f.20,000.
Collections: 17th and 18th interiors with fine fittings; †16th-19th century paintings; †china; †glass; †silverware; †objects of trade; †navigation; and †business; costumes; †objects of folk art; collections from the Westfrisian area and the town culture of the old trading-town Hoorn; 20th century painting.
Exhibitions: Several expositions each year.
Publications: Annual Report.
Activities: Concerts; original objects of art lent; photograph collection for reference.
Library: Reference. Holdings: Vols 200.

LEIDEN

STEDELIJK MUSEUM DE LAKENHAL (Leyden Municipal Museum), Oude Singel 28-32, 2312 RA. Tel: 071 144044. *Cur History* I W L Moerman; *Cur Modern Art* J P Sizoo; *Head Educ Dept* S M Blokhuis; *Adminr* J M van Leeuwen; *Dir* M L Wurfbain.
Open Mon - Sat 10 AM - 5 PM; Sun & holidays 1 - 5 PM. Admis adults 1.50 guilders; children .75 guilders. Estab 1874 to preserve paintings, sculpture, arts and crafts from Leyden and surroundings, and to present these to the public in their historical context. The building dates back to 1640 with extensions in 1890 and 1920 for paintings, and in 1918 for arts and crafts, and exhibitions. Average Annual Attendance: 35,000-40,000. Mem: 550, dues 12.50 guilders.
Income: $900,000 (financed by city appropriation). Purchases: $24,000.
Collections: †Paintings (Lucas van Leyden, Rembrandt, Steen, van Goyen and others—2000 items); †sculpture (mediaeval, 17th-20th century); †silver; glass; tapestries; furniture; pewter; tiles; ceramics; arms; period rooms.
Exhibitions: Eight per year. Geschildert tot Leyden anno 1626 et al; Leids Zilver et al; Lucas van Leyden et al.

Publications: Bulletins, quarterly; catalogs, 6-8 times per year.
Activities: Classes for children; docent training; lect open to public; concerts; tours; individual paintings and original objects of art lent to institutions; museum shop selling books, magazines, reproductions, slides, and catalogs.
—**Library.** *Librn* P M Couwenbergh; *Dir* M L Wurfbain.
Open Mon - Sat 10 AM - 12:30 PM; Mon & Wed 2 - 5 PM. Estab 1978 to offer staff and visitors information on Leyden, the Lakenhal Museum and western European art.
Income: Financed through Museum. Purchases $2,000.
Holdings: Vols 7000; Per subs 70; AV—Slides; Other—Clipping files, exhibition catalogs, photographs, reproductions.
Special Subjects: Art and culture of the Netherlands.

OTTERLO

RYKSMUSEUM KROLLER-MULLER (Kroller-Muller State Museum), National Park De Hoge Veluwe, 6730 AA. Tel: 08382-241. *Dir* Dr R W D Oxenaar; *Secy* M A Geerlings; *Deputy Dir* Dr E Joosten; *Cur* Dr P H Hefting; *Cur* Dr A V D Woud.
Open Wed - Sat 10 AM - 5 PM; Sun 11 AM - 5 PM. No admis. (Admis to National Park). Estab 1938. Average Annual Attendance: 400,000.
Income: Financed by state appropriation.
Collections: 19th & 20th century art—paintings, drawings, sculptures, sculpture garden, sculptor drawings; van Gogh collection (278 works).
Publications: Museum Journal, 6 times a year.
Activities: Individual paintings and original objects of art lent to museums and galleries; traveling exhibitions organized and circulated; museum shop selling books, reproductions, prints, slides and catalogs.
Library: Open for reference to students.

ROTTERDAM

MUSEUM BOYMANS-VAN BEUNINGEN, Mathenesserlaan 18 (Mailing Add: PO Box 2277, 3015). Tel: 36.05.00. *Dir* Dr W A L Beeren.
Open Mon - Sat 10 AM - 5 PM; Sun 11 AM - 5 PM. Estab 1847.
Collections: Paintings of the Netherlands from the brothers Van Eyck to Vincent Van Gogh; Italian and French paintings from the 15th-19th centuries and contemporary paintings; old and modern drawings and graphic art; ceramics; glass; pewter; silver; lace; furniture; works by Kandinsky, Franz Marc, Oscar Kokoschka, Salvador Dali, and others; 21 paintings by Rubens; some of the outstanding works include Hubert and Jan Van Eyck's The Three Marys at the Open Sepulchre; Heronimus Bosch's The Prodigal Son; Pieter Breughel's The Tower of Babel; Rembrandt's Portrait of Rembrandt's Son Titus.
Library: Holdings—Vols 90,000.

NEW ZEALAND

AUCKLAND

AUCKLAND CITY ART GALLERY,* Kitchener St, 1. Tel: 74 650, exten 663. *Pres* Councillor Dr R H L Ferguson; *Secy* Dorothy J Wheery; *Dir* Ernest W Smith; *Registrar & Cur Paintings & Sculpture* Eric Young; *Exhibitions Officer* John Maynard; *Cur Prints & Drawings* Anne Kirker; *Conservator* Eileen Maitland; *Designer* Ross Ritchie; *Outreach Mgr* Don Soloman.
Open Mon - Thurs 10 AM - 4:30 PM; Fri 10 AM - 8:30 PM; Sat & Sun 1 - 5:30 PM. Estab 1887 as a general purpose gallery of the fine arts with collections for exhibition and study and facilities for the organization and receipt of touring exhibitions; provides art services to general public, schools and university and support to New Zealand artists; seven exhibition areas with full facilities devoted to permanent and special exhibitions. Average Annual Attendance: 135,00. Mem: 650; dues student $3, individual $8, family $12; annual meeting Aug. or Sept.
Income: $400,000 (financed by endowment, membership, city and state appropriation). Purchases: $35,000.
Collections: General collection of European paintings and sculpture from 12th century on; American and Australian paintings; European and American prints and drawings; New Zealand painting, sculpture and prints (except Maori). All collections being added to with special emphasis on contemporary international prints, British painting and New Zealand art of all media and dates.
Publications: Auckland City Art Gallery Quarterly; catalogs.
Activities: Outreach Program serving particularly Polynesian communities in Auckland; dramatic programs; concerts; book shop.
Library: *Librn* Tim Garrity. For reference. Holdings: Vols 8000; AV—Color slides; Other—Photographs.

DUNEDIN

DUNEDIN PUBLIC ART GALLERY, Logan Park (Mailing Add: PO Box 566). *Dir* Leslie Charles Lloyd; *Asst Dir* Frank Holdsworth Dickinson; *Secy* Harold Joffre Tyrie.
Open Mon - Fri 10 AM - 4:30 PM; Sat, Sun & holidays 2 - 5 PM. No admis. Estab 1925 for the exhibition of picture collection, furniture, porcelain. The gallery was built in 1925 and consists of twelve exhibition rooms, plus a conservation laboratory and a training centre. Average Annual Attendance: 27,000. Mem: 711; dues $3.88; annual meeting May.
Income: Financed by endowment, membership, city appropriation. Purchases: $6,000-10,000.
Collections: †Major collection in Australian, English, and New Zealand paintings; Italian paintings.
Exhibitions: Approx 32 changing exhibitions per year.
Publications: Art Gallery News and Views, infrequently.
Activities: Lect open to public; concerts; gallery talks; tours; career training for conservation; exten dept serving provinces in South Island; traveling exhibitions organized and circulated; sales shop selling reproductions, prints.
Library: Staff reference library.

INVERCARGILL

ANDERSON PARK ART GALLERY, Myross Bush Rd, Waikiwi (Mailing Add: PO Box 755). *Pres* K A Ballinger; *Dir* J Husband; *Secy* Mrs J Taylor; *Treas* Mrs P Green.
Open daily 2 - 4:30 PM; cl Mon, Fri & Christmas Day. No admis, except for special exhibitions 30¢. Estab 1951 for the collection of contemporary works of art. The gallery is the former home of the late Sir Robert Anderson. It was offered to Invercargill City Council for use as a public park and gallery. It is set in ten acres of garden and fifty acres of native bush on the outskirts of the city. Mem: 120; dues single $3, double $5; committee meets monthly.
Income: Approx $6000 (financed by endowment, membership and city appropriation). Purchases: $550.
Collections: Contemporary New Zealand art.
Exhibitions: (1976-78) QE II Spinners and Weavers Exhibition; spring exhibitions held each October; City Winter Arts Festival, society Floral Art Club and Spinners and Weavers Guild share this at Anderson Park.
Activities: Occasional lect open to public.

NAPIER

HAWKES BAY ART GALLERY AND MUSEUM, Herschel St (Mailing Add: PO Box 429). Tel: 57781. *Dir* J S B Munro; *Asst Dir* H M Hull; *Secy* Mrs T Pattenden.
Open Mon - Fri 10:30 AM - 4:30 PM; Sat, Sun & holidays 2 - 4:30 PM. Admis adult 50¢, children 20¢, family $1. Estab 1856 as a regional museum. Holt Gallery contains Maori artifacts; Bestall Gallery, fine arts; Malden Gallery, itinerant exhibitions; also an Historical Research Library. Average Annual Attendance: 45,000. Mem: 1700; dues $4; annual meeting May.
Income: $42,000 (financed by endowment, membership, city appropriation). Purchases: $5,000.
Collections: †New Zealand painting and sculpture; Maori artifacts; †antiques.
Exhibitions: New Zealand Painting 1920-1940; Photographs by James White; Victorian Painting and Antiques; The Active Eye—contemporary New Zealand photography; Annual Exhibition of Members Painting; Benson & Hedges Art Award; Painting and Sculpture by George Edwards; Women's Suffrage in New Zealand; Gwen Malden Retrospective Exhibition.
Publications: Newsletter, quarterly.
Activities: Classes for children; concerts; objects of art lent to other museums; lending collection contains film strips, cassettes, lantern slides, motion pictures, original art works, original prints, paintings 250, photographs 5,500, sculpture, maps and plans 1,000.
Library: *Librn* Mrs J McLeod. Open to the public for reference. Holdings: Vols 8,000; Other—Photographs and maps. Special Subjects: Hawkes Bay History.

WANGANUI

SARJEANT GALLERY, Queens Park (Mailing Add: Box 637). Tel: 57052. *Dir* W H Milbank; *Registrar* Kate Martin; *Technician* J Shearman.
Open Mon Noon - 4:30 PM; Tues - Fri 10 AM - 4:30 PM; Sat, Sun & holidays 1 - 4:30 PM. No admis. Estab 1917 to collect and exhibit works of art for the information and interest of the general public. The gallery is built on the Greek cross principle with a sculpture court in the centre. The Front Gallery exhibits 18th, 19th & 20th century international

works; the West Wing, New Zealand paintings; the East Wing and Back Gallery are devoted to touring and local exhibitions. Average Annual Attendance: 30,000.
Income: Financed by endowment, and city appropriation. Purchases: $2,000 plus donated amounts.
Collections: †New Zealand collection of paintings; †local works; European works; Photographic works (based around Denton Collection); †sculpture and applied arts.
Exhibitions: Kites; Denis Mitchell sculpture; Art in the Mail; New Zealand Drawing Exhibition; LP Cover Art; Doris Lusk Watercolors; Spinning and Weaving from New Zealand; Queen Elizabeth II Arts Council Collection; The Work of Vivian Smith; Paintings by P Clairmont; Wooden Toys; Colin McCahon; David Moore.
Activities: Traveling exhibitions organized and circulated.
Library: Open for reference to interested persons and staff. Holdings: Not catalogued. Special Subjects: New Zealand art and British Victoriana.

WELLINGTON

NATIONAL ART GALLERY OF NEW ZEALAND,* Buckle St. Tel: 859 703. *Dir* Melvin N Day; *Educ Officer* I A Hunter; *Cur* George Packwood; *Asst Cur* Carol Quirk.
Open daily 10 AM - 4:45 PM. Estab 1936 to house National Collection of art works, archival preservation, acquisition of good representative works of art to augment collection, educative centre in art for New Zealand. Average Annual Attendance: 85,000.
Income: NZ$14,000 (financed by government appropriation). Purchases: NZ$35,000.
Collections: Archdeacon Smythe Collection; British, European, Australian and New Zealand painting and sculpture; Sir Harold Beauchamp Collection of early English watercolors, drawings and illustrations; Nan Kivell Collection of contemporary British original prints: Sir John Ilott Collection of graphics; Harold Wright Collection of graphics; Monrad Collection of early European graphics; National Collection of New Zealand drawings; a small collection of Old Master drawings; †John Weeks Collection.
Publications: Catalogs in conjunction with exhibitions.
Activities: Direction of art education programs in schools and universities of New Zealand; original objects of art lent; lending collection contains photographs; traveling exhibitions organized and circulated; Publications Desk.
Library: Reference. Holdings: Vols 2000.

NORWAY

BERGEN

VESTLANDSKE KUNSTINDUSTRIMUSEUM,* (Western Norway Museum of Applied Art), Nordal Brunsgate, 9, 5000. Tel: 21 51 087. *Hon Consul Pres* Frithjof Meidell Andersen; *Museum Dir* Peter M Anker; *Cur* Mrs Thale Riisöen.
Open May 15 - Aug 31 weekdays 10 AM - 3 PM; Sun Noon - 3 PM; off season every day except Mon Noon - 3 PM; No admis. Estab 1887 to encourage Norwegian industry and crafts as regards tastefulness and appropriate work, and to try to develop the taste of the general public in a similar way. Average Annual Attendance: 25,000. Mem: Approx. 400; approx four meetings a year in connection with lectures, opening of temporary exhibitions.
Income: (120,000) (financed by endowment, membership, and government appropriation). Purchases: $2460.
Collections: The General Munthe Collection of Chinese art; the Anna B & William H Singer Collection of art and antiquities; †collections of old European arts and crafts, antique Bergen silver, contemporary Norwegian and European ceramics, glass, furniture, textiles, metalwork and Chinese arts from the Renaissance to modern times.
Publications: Vestlandske Kunstindustrimuseums Årbók (Yearbook every 3-5 years); exhibition catalogs.
Activities: Receives classes from the primary school level upwards, also students from art colleges and from the University Department of Art History, for teaching and lectures given by the staff; certain courses are also arranged in cooperation with various popular educational organizations; lect open to the public and a few for members only, 2-3 vis lectr per yr; concerts; gallery talks; tours; schol; collection contains photographs 15,000; Kodachromes (5x5 cm) 3800 slides (8x8 cm) 800.
Library: Holdings—Vols 15,000; Other—Booklets 3800.

LILLEHAMMER

LILLEHAMMER BYS MALERISAMLING (Lillehammer Art Museum), Kirkegaten 69, 2600. Tel: 062 51944. *Chief Exec* Ole Rønning Johannesen.

Open Mon - Sat 10 AM - 3 PM; Sun Noon - 4 PM. Admis NKr 2. Estab 1927 to give exhibitions of art (painting, sculpture, graphic art). Average Annual Attendance: 15,000.
Income: Financed by city appropriation.
Collections: Norwegian paintings, sculpture and graphic art from 19th and 20th centuries.
Exhibitions: Ten exhibitions of contemporary Norwegian art.
Publications: A year book.
Activities: Lect open to public, 16 vis lectr per yr; concerts; gallery talks; tours.
Library: Reference library for use of staff. Holdings: Vols 1,000.

OSLO

CITY OF OSLO ART COLLECTION, Munch Museum, Toyengaten 53 (Mailing Add: PO Box 2812 Kampen, 5). *Dir* Alf Boe; *Chief Cur* Arne Eggum; *Cur* Gerd Woll; *Museum Lectr* Marit Lande Pedersen.
Open Tues - Sat 10 AM - 8 PM; Sun Noon - 8 PM; cl Mon. Admis adults NKr 5, children NKr 2. Estab 1963 to take care of the bequest of Edvard Munch to the City of Oslo, and to show selected items of the collections. The museum covers 1150 sq meters of exhibitions area, including a concert hall which is also used for changing exhibitions. The museum contains a library, offices, storerooms, and a technical department. Average Annual Attendance: 217,355.
Income: Financed by city appropriation.
Collections: Paintings, prints and drawings of Edvard Munch; works by the sculptor Gustav Vigeland (Nobelsgt 32); contemporary paintings (donated by Rolf E Stenersen); decorations, monuments and sculptures belonging to the city of Oslo.
Exhibitions: Strindberg maler; Arstidende-polsk landskapskunst.
Activities: Classes for adults and children; lect open to public; concerts; gallery talks.
—*Library. Librn* Frida Tank.
Open to museum staff and researchers for reference.
Holdings: Vols 11,470; Per subs 24; Other—Clipping file concerning Edvard Munch 1895 to present.
Special Subjects: Books and articles concerning Munch.
Special Collections: Munch's own library.

KUNSTINDUSTRIMUSEET I OSLO (The Oslo Museum of Applied Art), St Olavs Gate 1. Tel: 02-203578. *Pres* Hans Höegh; *Dir* Lauritz Opstad; *Cur* Inger Marie Kvaal Lie; *Cur* Aase Bay Sjövold; *Cur* Albert Steen; *Conservator Textiles* Kari Fostervoll.
Open daily 11 AM - 3 PM; cl Mon; Jan 15 - May 1 & Sept 15 - Dec 1, 7 - 9 PM. No admis. Estab 1876 to further the aesthetic value of the products of artisans and promote the understanding for these values among the public. The gallery has six stories, exhibitions are in four of them; ground floor: changing exhibitions, mainly modern; first floor: Old Norwegian collections from the Middle Ages until 1850; second floor: collections from abroad 1600-1850; third floor: modern applied art, textiles, costumes. Average Annual Attendance: 60,000.
Income: $400,000 (financed by city and state appropriation). Purchases: $35,000.
Collections: †Furniture, †silver, †ceramics, †glass, †textiles, old and modern.
Exhibitions: Approx 10 every year, plus traveling exhibition.
Publications: Yearbook, triannually; catalogs.
Activities: Classes for adults; lect open to public, 4 vis lectrs per yr; concerts; gallery talks; tours; lending collection contains books 30,000, slides 2500; traveling exhibitions organized and circulated; sales shop selling books, prints and slides.
—*Library.* Tel: 02-20 14 07. *Head Librn* Ase Markussen; *Librn* Lise Arheim and Turid Aakhus.
Open Mon - Sat 11 AM - 3 PM. Estab 1876 to supply the museum in its research into the fields of applied art, arts and crafts. The largest Norwegian library in these fields, lends books to the public and is also an institutional research library.
Income: $5000 (financed by city appropriation).
Holdings: Vols 31,000; Per subs 150; Other—Exhibition catalogs.
Publications: Bibliographies covering the publications of the museum; a rev ed covering 1876-1976 will be published soon.

NASJONALGALLERIET,† (National Gallery), Universitetsgaten 13, 1. Tel: 20 04 04. *Dir* Knut Berg; *Keeper Sculpture* Oscar Thue; *Keeper Paintings* Magne Malmanger; *Keeper Prints & Drawings* Sidsel Helliesen; *Chief Restorer* Leif Plahter.
Open Mon - Fri 10 AM - 4 PM; Sat 10 AM - 3 PM; Sun Noon - 3 PM; Wed & Thurs also 6 PM - 8 PM. Estab 1837, the principal art gallery in Norway.
Collections: †Norwegian painting and sculpture; European paintings with examples of modern French, Danish and Swedish art; icons; prints and drawings; small collection of Greek and Roman sculpture; a collection of casts.

Library: Librn Vivi Greftegreff. Holdings: Vols 25,000; collection of exhibition catalogs and slides.

NORSK FOLKEMUSEUM,* (Norwegian Folk Museum), Bygdöy, 2. Tel: 55 80 90. *Dir* Halvard Björkvik.

Open summer 10 AM - 6 PM; winter 10 AM - 4 PM. Admis 5 Kr. Estab 1894.

Collections: †The Open Air Museum totals about 150 old buildings, all original. Among them are the Stave Church from Hallingdal; farmsteads from different districts of the country; single buildings of particular interest; The Old Town—18th century town houses. †Urban Collections—Norwegian town interiors from the Renaissance to the present; Henrik Ibsen's study; the first Parliament Hall of Norway (1814); post-Renaissance costumes; †other collections include peasant art and furniture; post-medieval church art; woven tapestries; tools and techniques of old Norwegian farming; toys and dolls, modern and primitive musical instruments. Average Annual Attendance: 300,000.

Income: $650,000.

Publications: Annual yearbook.

—Norsk Folkemuseums bibliotek (library): Museumsveien 10. *Librn* Randi Foss.

Open 9 AM - 3 PM. Estab 1894 to serve staff of the museum, although library is open to the public, for reference only.

Income: Financed by state appropriation. Purchases: $7000.

Holdings: Vols 35,000; Per subs 450; AV—Slides; Other—Manuscripts, photographs.

Special Subjects: European cultural anthropology, history, history of art, costume and textile history.

Publications: Yearbook (By og Bygd.)

NORSK SJÖFARTSMUSEUM,* (Norwegian Maritime Museum), Bygdöynes, 2. Tel: 55 63 95. *Dir* Sven Molaug; *Cur* Bard Kolltveit.

Boat Hall oepn April 15 - Sept 30, 10 AM - 8 PM; Oct 1 - April 14, 10:30 AM - 4 PM; Tues & Thurs 10:30 AM - 9 PM; Library open Oct - April 8:30 AM - 4 PM; May - Sept 8:30 AM - 3 PM; Sat 8:30 AM - 2 PM; Tues 8:30 AM - 9 PM. Estab 1914, museum opened 1974, to collect and exhibit items illustrating Norwegian maritime civilization. Average Annual Attendance: 105,000. Mem: 500; annual meeting May.

Collections: Ship models, paintings, photographs of ships, tools, instruments and other items pertaining to maritime collections; the Polarship Gjoa; special exhibitions of small crafts; archives pertaining to maritime history.

Publications: Norsk Sjofartsmuseum; Arsberetning, annually.

Activities: Instruction of school classes; underwater excavations; semi-weekly meetings during the winter for divers; courses in rope-work, seamanship, etc; training ship, Svanen, (one-week expeditions during the summer); lectures; Souvenir shop.

Library: Librn Else Marie Thorstvedt. Holdings: Vols 16,000; Per subs 200; Other—Manuscripts, maps.

UNIVERSITETETS SAMLING AV NORDISKE OLDSAKER,* (University Museum of National Antiquities), Frederiksgate 2, 1. Tel: 33 00 70. *Dir* Dr Sverre Marstrander; *Head Stone & Bronze Age Dept* Irmelin Martens; *Head Early Iron Age Dept* Wencke Slomann; *Head Viking Age Dept* Charlotte Blindheim; *Head Medieval Age Dept* Martin Blindheim.

Open summer 11 AM - 3 PM, winter Noon - 3 PM. Estab 1828 for the exhibition of finds from the prehistoric periods, medieval church art and objects from medieval towns; the Viking ship finds with magnificent grave goods in the Viking Ship Museum at Bygdöy (branch museum); responsibility for archaeological finds and for the preservation of prehistoric monuments in the southeastern and southern part of Norway; educational and research institution (Scandinavian archaeology) of the University of Oslo.

Income: Financed by state appropriation. Purchases: $100,000.

Collections: Material from the Norwegian Stone, Bronze and Iron age; church art and profane objects from the Medieval Age.

Publications: Universitetets Oldsaksamlings Árbók, yearbook; Skrifter, proceedings; guides.

Activities: Lecture in Scandinavian archaeology; special lect open to the public.

Library: Holdings—Vols 30,000; Other—Photograph prints 30,000.

PAKISTAN

KARACHI

NATIONAL MUSEUM OF PAKISTAN, Burns Garden. Tel: 211341, exten 42. *Supt of Mus* Taswir Husain Hamidi; *Asst Supt Archaeology* Dr Muhammad Sharif; *Asst Supt Archaeology (Manuscripts)* Hidayatul-

lah Siddiqui; *Asst Supt Archaeology (Ethnography)* Inayat-ur-Rahman; *Asst Supt Numismatics* Mrs Pervin Tufail Nasir; *Tech Officer* Mr Qamaruddin.

Open 10 AM - 5 PM; cl Fri. Admis adults 50 paisa, children 25 paisa, students free. Estab 1950 to collect, preserve, study and exhibit the records of the cultural history of the country and to promote a learned insight into the personality of its people. To promote research work, to create understanding among the masses for the appreciation of their cultural heritage and sense of preservation for the relics of their rich past. Average Annual Attendance: Aprox 100,000.

Income: Approx 30,000 rupees.

Collections: Prehistoric and protohistoric period material from the Indus Valley sites; Gandhara sculptures in stone, stucco and terra-cotta; gold jewelry from Taxila; Hindu sculptures in stone; Islamic period glass, pottery, scientific instruments and carpets; ethnological material from the various regions of Pakistan; manuscripts, largely of Muslim period; miniature paintings, specimen of calligraphy and a large collection of coins spreading from 6th century BC to 19th century AD.

Exhibitions: (1976-) Thirty exhibitions.

Publications: Catalogs, guide books, and brochures.

Activities: Classes for children; lect open to public; gallery talks, traveling exhibitions organized and circulated; sales shop selling books, reproductions.

Library: Primarily meant for museum staff and research scholars. Special Subjects: Archaeology, history, museology, art and architecture.

LAHORE

LAHORE MUSEUM, Shahrah-E-Quaid-E-Azam. Tel: 53641 and 56472. *Chmn* B A Kureshi; *Dir* Dr Saifur Rahman Dar; *Keeper Muslim Period Coll* F M Anjum Rehmani; *Keeper Coins & Medals* Mrs Tahira A Beg; *Display Officer* Mrs Nusrat Ali; *Public Relations Officer* Mrs Zarina Khurshid; *Modeler* Mr Salahuddin; *Chemist* Waseem Ahmad; *Tourist Guide* Miss Salma Jaffery and Mr Abudul Hafeez.

Open 9 AM - 4 PM. Admis adults 50 paisas, children 25 paisas, conducted students tours free. Estab 1890 for education in the different fields of coins, paintings, Gandhara, Indus, Hindu and Islamic civilizations. Galleries are devoted to various subjects of archaeology, history, fine arts, crafts and ethnology. Average Annual Attendance: 228,976.

Income: Financed by state appropriation.

Collections: †Miniature paintings; †Gandhara, †Hindu, †Indus, †Islamic and general paintings; †contemporary paintings; †Sadequain's paintings; †ethnological art; †Pakistan movement; †stamps and †coins collection; †Jaina Mandar Collection.

Exhibitions: (1976-77) Modern Calligraphies; Iqbal in Paintings.

Publications: Catalogs of manuscripts and rare publications; exhibition catalogs; catalogs of antiquities and rare articles; list of newspapers and journals; catalogs of paintings and coins in the museum.

Activities: Lect open to public, 12 vis lectrs per yr; museum shop selling books, magazines, original art, reproductions, slides, postcards, plaster casts.

PESHAWAR

PESHAWAR MUSEUM,* Grand Trunk Rd. *Cur* S M Jaffar.
Estab 1907.

Collections: Mainly sculptures of the Gandhara School containing images of Buddha, Bodhisattvas, Buddhist deities, reliefs illustrating the life of the Buddha and Jataka stories; architectural pieces and minor antiquities; also an art gallery.

Publications: Guides and handbooks.

RAWALPINDI

ART GALLERY SOCIETY OF CONTEMPORARY ART,* Rawalpindi Gallery of Modern Art, 25 Civil Lines. Tel: 6 27 27. *Pres* Abdul Hafeez Pirzada; *Secy* Mrs Nafisa Ahmad; *Exec Dir* Miss Zubeida Agha; *Treas* S M Saeed; *Asst in Charge* Mohd Iqbal.

Open 9:30 AM - 1 PM & 3 - 5:30 PM. No admis. Estab Oct 31, 1961; main objective was to provide a show window to the artists; to help sell their work, and to introduce the young and upcoming artists, and also maintain a high standard for the exhibitions. Average Annual Attendance: 3000 - 4000. Mem: restricted; dues $2.50; meeting first week of June and second week of Oct.

Income: Financed by membership and grant-in-aid.

Collections: Thirty-three paintings by top Pakistani and foreign arts; permanent collection is not on view due to lack of space

Exhibitions: 45 Art Exhibitions including three Anniversary Shows; Turkish artists; Persian Miniatures; British Graphics; French Graphics; German Paintings; American Prints; A R Chughtai; Zebeida Agha; Shakir Ali; Ahmed Parvez; Colin David; Children's Paintings; 25th Anniversary of Pakistan Day and RCD paintings.

Activities: Lect open to the public; tours; art film shows; original objects of art lent; 200 prints provided to AICA; traveling exhibitions organized and circulated.

TAXILA

ARCHAEOLOGICAL MUSEUM,* Rawalpindi, Taxila District. *Custodian* M A Halim.
Open winter 9 AM - 4 PM; summer 9 - Noon, 2 - 6 PM. Estab 1928, member of Museums Association of Pakistan. Average Annual Attendance: 40,000.
Collections: Sculptures of stone and stucco of Ganhara and Indo-Afghan School; gold and silver ornaments; pottery; other antiquities from Taxila Sites ranging from 7th century BC to 5th century AD.
Exhibitions: Temporary exhibitions are held on special occasions.
Activities: Lectures on the archaeology of Pakistan with special reference to Taxila are arranged for the college and University students.
Library: Holdings—Vols 40,000.

PERU

LIMA

MUSEO DE ARTE,* (Museum of Art) Paseo Colon 125. Tel: 32 62 42. *Dir* Dr Alberto Santibanez Salcedo.
Open Thurs - Sun 10 - Noon, 3 - 7 PM. Admis 30¢, students free; Sun morning free. Estab 1960; permanent exhibits of Peruvian art from the different historical periods; six galleries. Average Annual Attendance: 200,000.
Income: $4600 (financed by membership and government appropriation).
Collections: Pre-Inca and Inca collections; ceramics; textiles; carvings; Colonial painting, metals, sculptures, furniture, religious art; Republic paintings; modern paintings, sculpture and furniture.
Exhibitions: Temporary exhibitions usually changed monthly.
Publications: Guides and catalogs.
Activities: Classes for children; guidance of groups of students, teaching; public cinema, fees; educational programs for students; lect open to the public, 12 vis lectr per yr; gallery talks; tours, in English and Spanish weekly; competitions; lending collection contains Kodachromes, reproductions, photographs, slides; traveling exhibitions organized and circulated; Book shop.
Library: Holdings:—Vols 1000 for reference.

MUSEO NACIONAL DE LA CULTURA PERUANA,* (National Museum of Peruvian Culture), Avenida Alfonso Ugarte 650, Apdo 3048. Tel: 23 58 92. *Pres* Dr Luis E Valcarcel; *Dir* Dr Rosalia Avalos de Matos.
Estab 1946.
Collections: Popular art; ethnography of Amazonic tribes; folklore; ethnology; linguistics.

PHILIPPINES

MANILA

UNIVERSITY OF SANTO TOMAS, Museum of Arts and Sciences, Calle Espana. Tel: 21-00-81, exten 269. *Dir* Fr Jesus M Merino-Antolinez; *Asst Dir* Maria Teresa Delmar.
Open 9 AM - Noon & 2 - 5 PM. No admis. Estab 1848 as a museum to house collections started in 1682; started as an aid to medicine and pharmacy classes, developed into a repository of natural history specimens, and Philippine culture items; completed by art gallery. The Main Hall is divided into sections—natural history, ethnology, archeology, and art. Average Annual Attendance: 40,000.
Income: Financed through the university. Purchases: $6,000.
Collections: †Philippine art; †coins; †stamps; †ethnology of the Philippines; †Chinese trade pottery; †shells; †medals; †cultural, historical and archeology items.
Exhibitions: No exhibitions—remodelling has been going on since 1976.
Activities: Individual paintings and original objects of art lent to museums and exhibitions.
Library: Open to the public by arrangement. *Librn* Fr Javier Arrazola. Holdings: Vols 200,000; Per subs 3,000. Special Collections: Large collection of rare books.

POLAND

CRACOW

MUZEUM NARODOWE W KRAKOWIE,* (National Museum in Cracow), ul Manifestu Lipcowego 12. Tel: 281-40, 273-03. *Dir* Tadeusz Chruscici; *Far Eastern Art* Dr Zofia Alber; *Polish Iconography* Dr Jerzy Banach; *Arms & Armour* Dr Irena Grabowski; *Manuscripts* Dr Adam Homecki; *Icons* Janina Klosinska; *Polish Painting & Sculpture of the 14th-18th Centuries* Dr Maria Kopff; *Polish Illuminated Manuscripts* Dr Barbara Miodonska; *Greek & Roman Art* Dr Janusz Ostrowski; *Polish Modern Art* Prof Dr Mieczyslaw Porebski; *Polish Coins* Dr Janusz Reyman; *European Painting of the 15th-17th Centuries* Dr Marek Rostworowski; *Italian Painting* Dr Anna Rozycka Bryzek; *Ancient Coins* Dr Stefan Skowronek; *Deputy Dir Polish Art of 16th-18th Centuries;* Dr Franciszek Stlot; *Textiles, Polish Costumes* Dr Maria Taszycka; *Arms & Armour, Near Eastern Minor Arts* Dr Zdzislaw Zygulski.
Estab 1879 for historic and artistic collections of Polish and foreign art and objects of culture. Average Annual Attendance: 350,000. Association of Museum Friends.
Collections: National Museum in Cracow consists of several departments with various collections. The Director and Administration seat is in the Palace of E Hutten Czapski. The Emeryk Hutten Czapski Department, ul Manifestu Lipcowego 12—graphics 120,000, numismatic collections 250,000, old books 45,000. Department of Textiles, ul Smolensk 9. Dzolayski House, pl Szczepanski 9—departments of arms and armour, Far Eastern art, icons. Gallery of Polish painting and sculpture of the 16th-18th centuries, Gallery of Polish painting and sculpture of the 19th-20th centuries. Czartoryski Collection.
Publications: Rozprawy i Sprawozdania Muzeum Narodowego w Krakoie, annually; various catalogs, guides and monographs.
Activities: Classes for children; 1-2 temporary exhibitions per month; films on art; lect for schools; concerts; guided tours; traveling exhibitions.
—Czartoryski Library and Archives, ul Sw Marka 17: For reference.
Library: Holdings:—Vols 208,000 on history, art and culture. Other —Documents 13,300, illuminated codices, incunabula.
—Galeria Polskiego Malarstwa i Rzezby od 14 do 18 wieku (Gallery of Polish Painting and Sculpture of the 14th-18th Centuries), pl Szczepanski 9, Kamienica Szolayskich. Tel: 570-21.
Open daily 10 AM - 4 PM; Mon Noon - 6 PM; Sun 10 AM - 4 PM; cl Tues and days after holidays. Admis zl 4.
Collections: Very valuable and exquisite collection of Polish painting and sculpture, mostly of Cracow school, from the 14th through 18th century, among them the famous sculpture Madonna of Kruzlowa (c 1400).
—Galeria Malarstwa Polskiego w XIX (Gallery of Polish Painting of the 19th Century), Rynek Glowny, Sukiennice. Tel: 571-46.
Open daily 10 AM - 4 PM; Thurs Noon - 6 PM; Sun 10 AM - 4 PM; cl Tues and days after holidays. Admis zl 4.
Collections: Famous collection of Polish paintings, which formed a foundation of the National Museum in Cracow; the Nero's Torches by Siemiradski, the historical compositions by Matejko; The Prussian Homage, among others.
—Galeria Sztuki Polskiej W XX (Gallery of Polish Painting and Sculpture of the 20th Century) Al Trzeciego Maja 1. Tel: 333-77.
Open daily 10 AM - 4 PM; Wed Noon - 6 PM; Sun 10 AM - 4 PM; cl Mon and days after holidays. Admis zl 4.
Collections: Very outstanding collection of Polish painting and sculpture from the Modern Art Movement (Mloda Polska) until the present time with a large representation of the artists of Cracow.
—Zbiory Czartoryskich (Czartoryski Collection) ul Pijarska 15. Tel: 535-16.
Open daily 10 AM - 4 PM; Thurs Noon - 6 PM; Sun 9 AM - 3 PM; cl Wed and days after holidays. Admis zl 4.
Polish national relics, decorative and Oriental art, arms and armour, Egyptian, Greek and Roman art, painting gallery (Leonardo daVinci, Lady with an Ermine; Rembrandt Landscape).
—Dom Jana Matejki, ul Florianska 41. Tel: 575-62.
Open daily 10 AM - 4 PM; Fri Noon - 6 PM; Sun 9 AM - 3 PM; cl Mon and days after holidays. Admis zl 4.
Biographic museum of Jan Matejko, the outstanding Polish painter of the second half of the 19th century who with his great historical compositions largely contributed to the national culture and consciousness.

PANSTWOWE ZBIORY SZTUKI NA WAWELU (Wawel State Collections of Art), Wawel 5. *Pres* Dr Jerzy Szablowski; *Mgr* Stanislaw Ciéckiewicz.
Open 9 AM - 5 PM. Admis zl. 10. Estab 1925; research works of archaeology, history of art and history connected with the monuments situated on the Wawel Hill and in the Wawel Museum; restoration of the works of art; educational works; organization of permanent and temporary exhibitions.
Income: Financed by government appropriation.

Collections: King Sigismond August's 16th Century Collection of Flemish Tapestries, †Western European painting, Italian Renaissance furniture, †Western-European and Oriental pottery, †Polish, Western-European and Oriental weapons, Oriental carpets and tents; Royal Treasury: crown jewels, historical relics, banners, gold objects.
Exhibitions: Thousand years of Polish-Hungarian relations (together with the National Museum of Budapest); Thousand years of art in Poland (two exhibitions in Paris and in London organized together with the National Museum of Cracow); Court Art of Vasa Dynasty in Poland (together with the Staatens Historiska Museum in Stockholm).
Publications: Studia do Dziejow Wawelu, Zrodla do Dziejow Wawelu, Biblioteka Wawelska, irregularly.
Activities: Special courses for staff members; lect open to public; concerts; classes for adults and children; competitions.
Library: Holdings—Vols 8572; Per subs 1749 for reference; no permanent lending collection but any print supplied on request.

LODZ

MUZEUM SZTUKI, Wieckowskiego 36. Tel: 382-73. *Dir* Ryszard Stanislawski; *Cur* Dr Teresa Kmiecinska-Kaczmarek; *Cur* Janina Ladnowska; *Cur* Dr Maria Potemska; Mieczyslaw Potemski.
Open Tues Noon - 7 PM; Wed 10 AM - 5 PM; Thurs 11 AM - 7 PM; Fri, Sat 10 AM - 5 PM; Sun and holidays 10 AM - 4 PM. Admis 6 zloty. Estab 1930.
Collections: Paintings of Wladyslaw Strzeminski; Karol Hiller; Sculptures of Katarzyna Kobro; Collection of Mateusz B Grabowski; collection of group "a.r."
Exhibitions: Albrecht Durer—Woodcuts and Etchings; Contemporary Art from Mateusz B Grabowski's Collection; Elementary Forms of Contemporary Painting and Drawing in the Netherlands; Pottery Forms—7 Contemporary British Artists; Constantin Brancusi; World of the Real Imagination—contemporary prints; Hannah Hoch; Selfportraits of Polish Artists; Richard Anuszkiewicz. Arata Isozaki; Rubens' Graphic School; Marcel Maeyer; Vladimir Majakovski.
Activities: Classes for adults and children; lect open to public; traveling exhibitions organized and circulated.
Library. Librn Dr Jacek Ojrzynski. Open to the public for reference. Holdings: Vols 16,500; Per subs 111. Special Subjects: History of Art; Contemporary Art.

WARSAW

MUZEUM NARODOWE,* (National Museum), Al Jerozolimskie 3, 00-495.Tel: 21 10 31. *Dir* Dr Stankslaw Lorentz; *VDir* Dr Kazimierz Michalowski; *Keeper of Educ Dept* M Plominska.
Open Tues 10 AM - 8 PM; Thurs Noon - 6 PM; Sun & holidays 10 AM - 5 PM; other days 10 AM - 4 PM; cl Mon. Admis adults zl 7, children zl 5, Thurs free. Estab 1862. Branch museums: Palaces in Warzaw-Wilanow, Lazienki, Krolikarnia and outside Warsaw - Nieborow and the museum in Lowicz. Average Annual Attendance: 300,000.
Income: Financed by state appropriations.
Collections: †Antiquities; Medieval art; †Polish and European art from the 15th century to the present; numismatics; graphic art; paintings; sculpture; drawings and prints; †decorative art.
Publications: Rocznik Muzeum Narodowego w Warszawie (Annual of the National Museum in Warsaw); Bulletin du Musee National de Varsovie, quarterly; exhibition catalogs and others.
Activities: Classes for adults; Educational department service to the visitors at the national museums, action of the popularization of art, cycles of popular talks and discussions, art film shows; lect open to the public; concerts; competitions; original objects of art lent; lending collection contains photograph negatives 106,000, slides 8000; traveling exhibitions organized and circulated; Club of Young Friends of the Museum; Book shop.
Library: Holdings—Vols 90,000.

WROCLAW

MUZEUM NARODOWE WE WROCLAWIU,* (National Museum), Plac Powstańców Warszawy 5, 50-153. Tel: 3 88 39. *Dir* Dr Leszek Itman; A Chrzanowska; J Gebczak; W Gluziński; M Hermansdorfer; P Lukaszewicz; T Orszulok; D Ostowska; J Piatek; T Pieniazek; J Pietraszko, I Rylska; W Siedlecka; J Smaka; M Starzewsk; B Steinborn; W Świderska, A Zawisza; A Ziomecka.
Open summer May 1 - Sept 30, Tues & Wed 10 AM - 4 PM; Thurs Noon - 7 PM; Fri 10 AM - 2 PM; Sat 11 AM - 5 PM; Sun 11 AM - 6 PM; cl Mon. Winter Oct 1 - April 30, Tues, Wed, & Thurs 10 AM - 4 PM; Fri 10 AM - 2 PM; Sat 11 AM - 5 PM; Sun 11 AM - 6 PM; cl Mon. No admis. Estab 1948 for collecting, conservation, scientific research, education and the organization of cultural activities; 1970 it

became National Museum; departments are Etnographical Museum, the Bolków Castle and the Cistercian Abbey - Lubiaz. Average Annual Attendance: 70,000.
Income: Financed by appropriations.
Collections: †Collection of Silesian stone carvings 12th - 16th centuries; †collection of Medieval Art 14th - 16th centuries; †Polish painting 18th - 20th century; †collection of Silesian art 16th - 18th century; †collection of decorative hunters arms 16th - 18th century; †collection of contemporary art, painting, sculpture, glass and ceramics.
Publications: Roczniki Sztuki Śaskiej, annually; catalogs, guides and others.
Activities: Classes for children and adults; Educational-extension department; shows, cinema programs; dramatic programs; lect open to the public; competitions; Book shop.
Library: For reference. Holdings: Vols 70,000; Other—Photographs.

PORTUGAL

LISBON

MUSEU NACIONAL DE ARTE ANTIGA (National Museum of Ancient Art), Largo 9 de Abril. Tel: 664151 & 672725. *Dir & Cur Painting* Maria Alice Beaumont; *Cur Sculptures* Sergio de Andrade; *Cur Ceramics* Rafael Calado; *Cur Jewelry* Fernanda Passos Leite; *Asst Cur Furniture* Maria Helena Mendes Pinto; *Cur Pub Relations* Jose Luis Porfirio; *Educ Service* Madalena Cabral.
Open Tues - Sun 10 AM - 5 PM; Thurs & Sat 10 AM - 7 PM; cl Mon & holidays. Admis $500; free Sat & Sun. Estab 1884. Alvor Palace houses European art and Oriental carpets; the New Building (1939) houses Portuguese and Oriental art. Average Annual Attendance: 50,000. Mem: 500; dues 50$00 (ESC).
Income: Financed by state appropriation.
Collections: Portuguese art—paintings from the 15th-19th centuries; sculpture (13th-18th centuries); ornamental art (goldsmith art, ceramics; furniture, textiles); foreign art—painting, sculpture, goldsmith art, ceramic; Persian carpets; Oriental art of Portuguese influence.
Exhibitions: Illuminated Manuscript (16th century); Oriental Art Namban; French Portraits (1610-1789); English Medieval Alabasters, drawings from the collection of Albertina's gallery (facsimile).; The Nativity (Portuguese paintings, engravings and sculptures).
Publications: Bulletin.
Activities: Classes for adults and children; docent training; lect open to public; concerts; gallery talks; museum shop selling books, slides, and postcards.
—**Library.** Rua das Janelas Verdes, 2.
Open to the public.
Holdings: Vols 18,000; Per subs 30.
Special Collections: Patino Room (late 18th century French designed Boiseries, furniture, savonierie carpet); Gulbenkian donation; capela das Albertas (16th-17th centuries); colored glazed tiles, 14th-20th centuries; Convento da Madre de Deus.

MUSEU NATIONAL DE ARTE CONTEMPORANEA,* (National Museum of Contemporary Art), Rua Serpa Pinto 6. Tel: 36 80 28. *Dir* Maria de Lourdes Barthold.
Founded 1911.
Collections: Contemporary painting and sculpture.

PORTO

MUSEU NACIONAL DE SOARES DOS REIS (National Museum of Soares Dos Reis), Rua de D Manuel II. Tel: 27110. *Dir* Maria Emília Amaral Teixeira; *Cur* Maria Clementina Quaresma; *Cur* Maria Teresa Viana; *Cur* Catarina Maia e Castro.
Open 10 - 12 AM & 2 - 5 PM; cl Mon. Admis 5$00 Tues & Wed; Sat & Sun free. Estab 1833 for maintaining the collections of the museum. The ground floor of the gallery has religious art and pottery; first floor has modern painting and temporary exhibition; second floor has decorative arts. Average Annual Attendance: 50,000.
Income: Financed by state appropriation.
Collections: Old and †modern paintings; sculpture; goldsmith; glass; jewelry; pottery; porcelain; furniture.
Exhibitions: (1976-78) North American Contemporary Posters; The Poster in Poland; Eduardo Nery; Portuguese Contemporary Engravement; Alberto Carneiro e Angelo de Sousa; Liberation: 14 American artists; Leal da Câmara; R B Kitaj; Contemporary Polish Painting; Hans Hofmann; Maiakovsky; A Future for Our Past; Picture in the Portuguese Modern Art; Erotism in the Modern Portuguese Art; Emília Nadal; Cruz Filipe; German Engravement from 1960 to 1970; Rubens Works in Antwerp (colored pictures); From Bonnard to Miró - Homage to Tériade;

African Sculpture; Jiří Kolár; Works and Projects of the 70's - New York; Augusto Gomes; Marcel Mayer; French Art 1960 to 1975; Rubens and José de Guimarães.
Publications: Museu, biannually.
Activities: Classes for children; dramatic programs; lect open to public; concerts; gallery talks; tours for schools; sales shop selling catalogs and slides.
—**Library.**
Open to the public for reference only.
Holdings: Vols 8800.
Special Subjects: Art history.

RHODESIA

SALISBURY

NATIONAL GALLERY OF RHODESIA,* PO Box 8155, Causeway. Tel: 2 05 41. *Dir* Brian Bradshaw; *Keeper* C M Till.
Open Tues - Sun 9 AM - 5 PM; cl Mon. Estab 1957.
Collections: Ancient and modern European paintings and sculpture; tapestries; African traditional and local contemporary sculpture and paintings; large loan collections exhibited.
Activities: Friends of the Gallery organization, lectures and films. African sculpture workshop functioning since 1961. Annual exhibition of Rhodesian artists.
Library: Holdings—Vols 1600; Periodicals and newspaper section.

ROMANIA

CLUJ-NAPOCA

MUZEUL DE ARTA CLUJ-NAPOCA,* (Museum of Art); Piata Libertatii 30. Tel: 26952. *Pres Scientific Council* Dr Virgil Vatasiano; *Dir* Alexandra Rus..
Open Mon & Thurs 11 AM - 7 PM. Estab 1951.
Income: Financed by state appropriation.
Collections: Romanian and European art including paintings, graphics and sculpture of the 15th - 20th centuries; decorative arts.
Publications: Exhibition catalogs, semi-annually.
Activities: Classes for adults and children; dramatic programs; concerts; individual paintings and original objects of art lent; schol; traveling exhibitions organized and circulated; junior museum; Book shop.
Library: Holdings—Vols 3000; Other—Photographs 2000; Romanian books of art and catalogs of art.

SCOTLAND

DUNDEE

DUNDEE MUSEUMS AND ART GALLERY, Albert Square, DD1 1DA. Tel: 0382-25492. *Dir* James D Boyd; *Deputy Dir* Vacant; *Keeper Natural History* A B Ritchie; *Keeper Antiquities* C A Zealand; *Keeper Art* G Deslandes.
Open Mon - Sat 10 AM - 5:30 PM. No admis. Estab 1873 to provide the town of Dundee and surrounding area with a public service, by conserving, storing, displaying and publicizing the museums collection of art, natural history and antiquity. Four large Victorian galleries and one gallery specially designed to hang watercolors, prints and drawings. Mem: Approx 100; annual meeting May.
Income: Financed by city appropriation.
Collections: 17th century Venetian and Flemish works; 18th, 19th and 20th century Scottish and English paintings; a varied selection of watercolors and prints from the 18th to 20th century.
Publications: Showcase, quarterly.
Activities: Classes for adults and children; lect open to public, 3 vis lectrs per yr; concerts; gallery talks 10; tours 10-15; exten dept; individual paintings and original objects of art lent to public institutions in Dundee; traveling exhibitions organized and circulated; museum shop selling books, magazines, original art, reproductions, prints, slides and postcards.

EDINBURGH

NATIONAL GALLERIES OF SCOTLAND
—**National Gallery of Scotland,** The Mound EH2 2EL. *Dir* Colin Thompson; *Keeper National Gallery of Scotland* Hugh Macandrew; *Keeper of Prints & Drawings* Keith Andrews.

Open Mon - Sat 10 AM - 5 PM; Sun 2 - 5 PM. No admis. Estab 1850 to house the national collections of paintings, sculpture and the graphic arts from the 14th century to the present day. Neo-classical building by William Playfair with modern extension opened 1978. Average Annual Attendance: 338,000.
Income: Financed by national government.
Collections: Painting, drawings and prints, some sculpture 14th - 19th centuries.
Exhibitions: The Department of Prints and Drawings has regular exhibitions from its own holdings.
Publications: Bulletin, quarterly; Annual Report.
Activities: Educ dept; lect open to public, 4 vis lectr per yr; gallery talks; competitions; sales shop selling books, magazines, prints, slides.
—**Scottish National Gallery of Modern Art,** The Royal Botanic Garden, EH3 5LR. *Keeper* Douglas Hall.
Open Mon - Sat 10 AM - 6 PM; Sun 2 - 6 PM. No admis. Temporarily (since 1960) in large 18th century mansion in Royal Botanic Garden; will move into a converted early 19th century school building before 1982.
Collections: 20th century painting, sculpture and graphic art.
Exhibitions: The Edward James Collection; America, America.
—**Scottish National Portrait Gallery,** 1 Queen St, EH2 1JD. *Keeper* Robin Hutchison.
Open Mon - Sat 10 Am - 5 PM; Sun 2 - 5 PM. No admis. Estab 1889 to collect and exhibit portraits of the principal figures in Scottish history. A neo-Gothic building, shared with National Museum of Antiquities.
Collections: Portraits of Scottish men and women prominent in all fields of human endeavor.
Exhibitions: Childhood in 17th century Scotland.

ROYAL SCOTTISH MUSEUM,* Chambers St, EH1 1JF. Tel: 225 7534. *Dir Dept Art & Archaeology* Dr Norman Tebble. D Waterston.
Open weekdays incl Sat 10 AM - 5 PM; Sun 2 - 5 PM; cl Dec 25, Jan 1 & 2. Estab 1854; a national museum administered by the Scottish Education Dept. Friends of the Royal Scottish Museum, a society, is connected with the Museum. Average Annual Attendance: 550,000.
Collections: The decorative arts of the world and the natural and applied sciences.
Exhibitions: Special temporary exhibitions are held from time to time.
Activities: Public lectures and film programs are held in the Museum's Lecture Theatre, Gallery Talks in the halls and galleries; Book shop and public tea room.
Library: *Librn* Miss D C P Smith.

GLASGOW

GLASGOW MUSEUMS AND ART GALLERIES,* Kelvingrove, G3 8AG. Tel: 334-1134. *Dir* T A Walden; *Deputy Dir* George Buchanan; *Keeper of Archaeology* Jack Scott; *Keeper of Burrell Collection* William Wells; *Keeper of Fine Art* Alasdair Auld; *Keeper of Decorative Art* Brian Blench.
Open weekdays 10 AM - 5 PM; Sun 2 - 5 PM. Estab 1856 as a scientific institution responsible for the recording of local history, archaeological excavations and biological and geological field work throughout the West of Scotland, always willing to deal with enquiries from the public; concerned with the quality of life, the organization offers, in addition to permanent collections, a continuous program of special loan exhibitions. Average Annual Attendance: 950,000.
Income: $65,000 (financed by city appropriation). Purchases: $90,000 (with central government grant-in-aid).
Collections: Pictures, regarded as the finest municipal art collection in Great Britain, representative of Italian, Dutch, Flemish and French Schools; British and Scottish art; silver; stained glass; furniture; tapestries; sculpture; ceramics; arms and armour; ship models; archaeology and ethnography collections; all are being enlarged by purchase or gift.
Exhibitions: Fifteen per year, 25% organized by Glasgow museums.
Publications: Scottish Art Review, biannually; Calendar of Events, quarterly; Programs of exhibitions, monthly; What's Happening, quarterly.
Activities: Classes for adults and children; intra-mural teaching; classes are brought from schools and other establishments to the museums; film program; Saturday art club; courses for teachers; visits to schools; lect open to the public, 28 vis lectr per yr; concerts; gallery talks; tours; competitions; lending collection contains photographs 5000; book shop.
Library: For reference. Holdings: Vols 12,500.

SOUTH AFRICA, REPUBLIC OF

CAPE TOWN

MICHAELIS COLLECTION, Old Town House, Greemarket Square. Tel: 43 40 15. *Chmn Board of Trustees* Mayor of Capetown. *Dir* W H Gravett.

Open 10 AM - 5:30 PM. Admis 10¢. Estab 1917 to house collection of 16th and 17th century Dutch and Flemish masters donated to the nation by Sir Max Michaelis. Average Annual Attendance: 30,000.

Income: $30,000. Purchases: $3000.

Collections: †Dutch and Flemish paintings and graphic art of the 16th - 18th centuries.

Publications: General catalog; special catalog; Annual Reports.

Activities: Classes for adults and children; dramatic programs; lectures; concerts.

Library: For reference. Holdings: Vols 500.

SOUTH AFRICAN NATIONAL GALLERY, Government Ave, 8001 (Mailing Add: PO Box 2420, 8000). *Dir* Dr Raymund H van Niekerk; *Asst Dir* Hans Fransen; *Paintings & Sculpture* Valerie Leigh; *Conservator* Edgar C L Bosman; *Educ Dept* Miss Pat Kaplan.

Open Tues - Sat 10 AM - 5:30 PM; Sun 10 AM - 5 PM; Mon 1 - 5 PM. Admis 20¢, Wed & Sat free. Estab 1871, inc 1895, present bldg 1931. Gallery is a single-story bldg of 15 galleries. Average Annual Attendance: 90,000. Mem: 700; dues single R5, family R7; Society of Friends of the Gallery meetings arranged monthly.

Income: R250.000 (financed by state appropriation). Purchases: R40.000.

Collections: South African art 19th and 20th century; European art 15th-20th century; 400 South African and 500 foreign paintings; 620 South African and 440 foreign drawings and watercolors; 500 South African and 1300 foreign prints; 100 South African, 40 traditional African and 100 foreign sculptures.

Exhibitions: (1976-78) Hundertwasser; Wolf Kibel; Agam; Rodim and his Contemporaries; English and South African Watercolours; The Japanese Colour Print; The Art of the Printmaker; German Expressionist Prints; Six South African Photographs; Early 20th Century English Paintings; Landscapes from the Permanent Collection of J S Morland.

Publications: Agenda, monthly bulletin; exhibition catalogs.

Activities: Educ dept; lect open to public, 6-8 vis lectrs per yr; concerts; gallery talks; tours; individual paintings and original objects of art lent to other institutions; lending collection contains slides 3000; traveling exhibitions organized and circulated; sales shop selling reproductions, slides, catalogs, postcards.

—*Library.* *Librn* Josephine Minicki.

Open Mon - Fri 7:45 AM - 3:45 PM. Reference and research library for staff and public.

Income: R5000 (financed by city appropriation).

Holdings: Vols 6000; Per subs 63; Other—Clipping files, exhibition catalogs, pamphlets.

Special Subjects: Books and periodicals on restoration; books on photography; books and clippings on South African art and architecture.

Publications: Information sheets.

DURBAN

DURBAN ART GALLERY, City Hall, Smith St (Mailing Add: PO Box 4085, 4000). *Cur* Miss E S J Addleson; *Art Technician* D Smith; *Educ Officer* Miss M Shaw.

Open Mon, Tues, Thurs - Sat 9:30 AM - 5 PM; Wed 9:30 AM - 2 PM; Sun 2:30 - 5 PM. No admis. Estab 1892 to provide exhibitions of contemporary art for the benefit of the public and the city's cultural program. It is housed in the City Hall, which is a fine Victorian building in the neo-Baroque style. Average Annual Attendance: 200,000.

Income: Financed by city appropriation. Purchases: $10,000.

Collections: †Dutch and Flemish 17th century; †French 19th century; †Victorian; †South African; †contemporary art; †Chinese ceramics; †Sevres ceramics.

Exhibitions: Joseph Herman; Rodin; David Goldblatt; Agam; Traditional Indian costume of Guatemala; The Animal in Art; German Expressionist Graphics; Facsimiles of William Blake.

Activities: Classes for children; lect open to public, 2 vis lectr per yr; concerts; gallery talks; tours.

JOHANNESBURG

JOHANNESBURG ART GALLERY, Joubert Park. Tel: 725-3130. *Dir* Mrs P A Senior; *Asst Dir* vacant.

Open Tues - Sun 10 AM - 5 PM; Sun & Wed 7 - 9 PM during summer; cl Mon. No admis. Estab 1915 as a modern art museum reflecting international and local movements and trends. Gallery designed and built by the English architect Edwin Lutyens (pseudo neo-classic). Average Annual Attendance: 90,000.

Income: Financed by city appropriation.

Collections: 17th century Dutch collection; 19th century French collection; 19th century English collection; South African collection; international modern art; approx 2500 prints from Durer to the present.

Exhibitions: Emile Antoine Bourdelle; 500 years of the woodcut; The Rise of Lithography; Wolf Kibel retrospective; 20th Century Lithographs; Rubens and the Reproductive Engraving; Graphic Art in Germany Today; Guest Artist: Jo Smail; Berenice Michelow; Museums in Education; The Camden Town Group.

Publications: Catalog list; history of gallery.

Activities: Classes for adults and children; docent training; working with art teachers; lect open to public, 8 vis lectr per yr; concerts; gallery talks; tours; competitions; museum shop selling books, reproductions, slides, postcards, photographs and greeting cards.

Library: Open to staff and docents, or by appointment, for reference. Holdings: Vols 5,000; Per subs 22. Special Subjects: Reference works to the collection.

KIMBERLEY

WILLIAM HUMPHREYS ART GALLERY, Civic Centre (Mailing Add: PO Box 885). Tel: 0531-28031. *Cur* Mrs R J Holloway.

Open Mon - Sat 10 AM - 1 PM & 2:30 - 5:30 PM; Sun 2:30 - 5:30 PM. Admis adults 10¢, children 5¢, only on weekends and public holidays. Estab 1952. Average Annual Attendance: 25,000. Mem: 175; dues 200 rands.

Income: 55,000 rands (financed by city appropriation).

Collections: Representative collection of Flemish, Dutch, English, and French old masters; †collection of South African works of art.

Exhibitions: Approx 10 temporary exhibitions held per annum.

Activities: Lect open to public, 2 vis lectrs per yr; concerts; individual paintings and original objects of art lent to other museums in the Republic of South Africa.

Library: *Dir* Mrs R J Holloway. Open to the public for reference only. Holdings: Vols 362; Per subs 3.

PIETERMARITZBURG

TATHAM ART GALLERY, 2nd Floor, City Hall, Commercial Road (Mailing Add: PO Box 321, 3200). Tel: 27031, exten 127. *Cur* Lorna Ferguson.

Open Mon - Fri 10 AM - 5 PM. No admis. Estab 1903. The top floor of City Hall was made available to house the municipal art collection. It is divided into two main galleries—painting and sculpture, and graphics. Average Annual Attendance: 5,000. Mem: 100; dues R1,000; annual meeting June.

Income: Financed by city appropriation. Purchases: $20,000.

Collections: †19th & 20th century English and French paintings and sculpture; †19th and 20th century English graphics; †modern European graphics; †South African painting and sculpture 1920-1940; the Whitwell bequest.

Publications: Newsletter, quarterly; exhibition catalogs.

Activities: Lect open to public, 2 vis lectr per yr; concerts; gallery talks; tours; competitions; individual paintings and original objects of art lent to accredited art institutions; traveling exhibitions organized and circulated.

PORT ELIZABETH

KING GEORGE VI ART GALLERY, One Park Dr, 6001. Tel: 041-28589. *Dir* Clayton S Holliday; *Tech Asst* Julian Gous; *Secy* Betty Ann Young.

Open Mon 2 - 6 PM; Tues - Sat 10 AM - 12:45 PM & 2 - 6 PM; Sun 2:30 - 5:30 PM; public holidays 10:30 AM - 12:30 PM & 2:30 - 5:30 PM. Estab 1957 for the development of permanent collections; to provide a centre for art for Port Elizabeth and hinterland; two buildings flanking entrance to St George's Park with the Main Hall consisting of three galleries; Arts Hall consists of a major hall and sunken gallery. Average Annual Attendance: 25,000.

Income: Financed by city appropriation.

Collections: †English painting; †South African art; †international graphics; Oriental miniatures; Oriental ceramics.

Exhibitions: AGAM; British and South African watercolors; Wolf Kibel; Rodin; Oskar Forel; Josef Herman.

Publications: Occasional newsletter.

Activities: Lect open to the public, 2 vis lectr per yr; concerts; gallery talks; individual paintings and original objects of art lent to registered borrowers, including schools, firms and private citizens; lending collection contains framed reproductions 350; original prints; sales shop selling reproductions, prints, postcards.

Library: Open to students for reference. Holdings: Vols 1500; Per subs 5. Special Subjects: English painting.

PRETORIA

PRETORIA ART MUSEUM, Arcadia Park, Schoeman St, 0083. Tel: 444271. *Dir* Dr A J Werth; *Asst Dir* Katinka Kempff; *Professional Asst* D Craffert.

Open Tues - Sat 10 AM - 5 PM; Wed 7:30 - 10 PM; Sun 1 - 6 PM. No admis. Estab 1963 to collect and exhibit South African art and European art (mainly graphics). The museum is a modern building in park-like surroundings; there are four main galleries and one small gallery, plus a sculpture entrance hall. Average Annual Attendance: 60,000. Mem: 600; dues R5.
Income: Financed by city appropriation. Purchases: R20,000.
Collections: 17th century Dutch art; 19th and 20th century South African, †European and American graphics mostly 20th century.
Exhibitions: Average of eight exhibitions annually usually work by South African artists, retrospective or group exhibition; usually one important overseas exhibition such as Hundertwasser, Rodin and Bourdelle. (1978) Turner Watercolor Exhibition.
Publications: Bulletin, quarterly.
Activities: Lect open to public, 3 vis lectr per yr; concerts; gallery talks; tours; competitions; individual paintings lent to accredited museums; traveling exhibitions organized and circulated; museum shop.
Library: Open to the public for reference. Holdings: Vols 950; Per subs 20; Other—Newspaper clippings; slides; photographs.

SPAIN

BARCELONA

MUSEO DE ARTE CATALUNA,* (Museum of Ancient Art), Palacio Nacional, Parque de Montjuich. *Dir* Juan Ainaud de Lasarte.
Estab 1934.
Collections: Romanesque and Catalan Gothic paintings and sculpture; Renaissance and Baroque paintings.
Activities: Scholarships given.

MUSEO DE ARTE MODERNO,* (Museum of Modern Art), Palacio de la Ciudadela. Tel: 319 57 30, *Dir* Juan Barbeta Antones.
Open 9:30 AM - 1:45 PM; cl Mon. Estab 1946. Schol given.
Collections: Modern art.
Exhibitions: Commemorative expositions.
Publications: Exhibition catalogs.
Library: Holdings—Vols 50,657 in art and history.

BILBAO

MUSEO DE BELLAS ARTES,* (Museum of Fine Arts), Parque de Doña Casilda de Iturriza. *Pres* Lorenzo Hurtado de Saracho; *Secy* Tomas Zorrila Lequerica; *Dir* Crisanto de Lasterra.
Open varies in season 10 AM - 1:30 PM, & 4 - 6:30 PM. No admis. Estab Oct 5, 1908; modern section Oct 25, 1924, to exhibit artworks; gallery exhibits different shows periodically.
Income: 14 - 25 million/pts. (financed by city appropriation).
Collections: Classical art; Romanesque art; Gothic art; Renaissance art; Traditional Spanish 12th century art; 12th century Romantic art; †Basque modern and contemporary art; †general contemporary art.
Exhibitions: Anthological, non-commercial ones.
Activities: Lect open to the public, 5 vis lectr per yr; gallery talks; tours; photograph collection for reference.
Library: For reference. Holdings: Vols 1000.

MADRID

MUSEO CERRALBO, Ventura Rodriguez 17, 8. Tel: 2-47-36-46. *Dir of Found of the Mus* Dr Consuelo Sanz-Pastor y Fernandez de Pierola.
Open 9 AM - 2 PM; cl Thurs. Admis 50 pesetas, except students. Estab 1924. The Foundation was bequeathed to Spain by its founder Enrique de Aguilera y Gamboa, 17th Marquis of Cerralbo. His palace, which is now the museum, was built in 1886.
Collections: Paintings, 15th to 19th centuries; drawings and prints; coins and medals; furniture; arts and crafts.
Publications: Guide of the Cerralbo Museum; Cerralbo Museum; Cataloguqe of Drawings; Museums and Collections of Spain.
Activities: Lect open to public; concerts; gallery talks; tours; sales shop selling books, slides.
Library: Holdings—Vols 11,549; Per subs 7. Special Subjects: Art, history, archaeology, numismatics.

MUSEO DEL PRADO,* (National Museum of Paintings and Sculpture), Calle de Felipe Iv. Tel: 468 09 50. *Dir* Xavier de Salas Y Bosch.
Open 10 AM - 5 PM, or 6 PM according to the season of the year. Estab 1819.
Collections: Paintings from 14th - 19th century; sections of 19th and 20th century in the Cason of Buen Retiro; Ancient and Renaissance sculptures; drawing, jewels and medals.
Publications: Catalogs.
Activities: Weekly public lectures.
Library: Holdings—Vols 10,000.

MUSEO ROMANTICO (Museum of the Romantic Epoch), San Mateo 13, 4. Tel: 448-10-45 & 448-10-71. *Dir* Maria Elena Gomez-Moreno; *Cur* Manuel Casamar; *Secy* Paul Diez; *Restorer* Manuel Perez Tormo.
Open 10 AM - 6 PM; Sun 10 AM - 2 PM; cl Mon. Estab 1924. Average Annual Attendance: 10,000.
Collections: †Paintings, †furniture, †books and †decorations of the Spanish Romantic period.
Activities: Lectures, exhibitions and concerts.
Library: *Librn* Manuel Llanes. Books and reviews on history, literature, art of the romantic period. Holdings: Collection of engravings 5000, lithographs.

TOLEDO

CASA Y MUSEO DEL GRECO,* (El Greco's House & Museum), Calle de Samuel Levi. Tel: 22 40 46. *Dir* Maria Elena Gomez-Moreno.
Open 10 AM - 2 PM, 3 - 6 PM; summer until 7 PM. Admis 15 pesetas. The Casa y Museo del Greco is supported by the Fundaciones Vega-Inclán. Estab 1910. Average Annual Attendance: 250,000.
Collections: Furniture, objects of the period; paintings of El Greco, including the series of Christ and the Apostles; other paintings of various periods, 15th to 18th century.
Publications: Catálogo de las Picturas de la Casa y Museo del Greco, 1968.
Library: By permission only. Works referring to Toledo and El Greco.

VALENCIA

MUSEU DE BELLAS ARTES DE VALENCIA,* (Valencia Fine Arts Museum), Calle de San Pio V, 9. Tel: 65 07 93. *Dir & Conservator* Felipe-Vincente Garin Llombart.
Open 10 AM - 2 PM. Estab 1839; housed in an old palace.
Income: Financed by city and state appropriations.
Collections: Paintings and sculpture of the 15th - 20th centuries; archeological section; photograph collection.

SWEDEN

GOTHENBURG

GÖTEBORGS KONSTMUSEUM (Gothenburg Art Gallery), Götaplatsen 412 56. *Dir* Karl-Gustaf Hedén; *Cur Modern Dept* Nils Ryndel; *Cur Old Masters Dept* Björn Fredlund; *Asst Cur Graphics & Drawings* Ingrid Mesterton and Küllike Montgomery; *Cur Exhib Dept* Häkan Wettre; *Asst Cur Deposit Dept* Lena Boethius.
Open Tues-Fri 12 AM - 3 PM; Sat & Sun 10 AM - 5 PM; Wed 5 - 9 PM. Admis adults Sw Cr 1; children Sw Cr 50. Estab 1861. Main bldg was inaugurated in 1925; new wing in 1968. Average Annual Attendance: 150,000.
Income: Financed by city appropriation. Purchases: $30,000.
Collections: †Scandinavian art, 17th century to the present; †old masters, especially Dutch and Flemish 17th century; French art, 1800-1945; †contemporary art (international collection; †prints and drawings.
Activities: Classes for children; lect open to public, 10 vis lectrs per yr; concerts; gallery talks; tours; extension dept; individual paintings and original objects of art lent to museums, galleries and libraries; lending collection contains books 180, Kodachromes approx 50, original prints 131, paintings 78, photographs approx 100, sculpture, slides 6211; sales shop selling books, reproductions, prints, slides and postcards.
—**Library.** Tel: 031-189537.
Open winter weekdays 12 AM - 3 PM; Sat & Sun 10 AM - 5 PM; Wed 5 - 9 PM; cl Mon; summer every day 11 AM - 4 PM
Income: Financed by city and state appropriation.
Holdings: Vols 7500; Per subs 15; AV—Audiotapes, lantern slides, motion pictures, slides, videotapes; Other—Clipping files, exhibition catalogs, original art works, photographs, prints, reproductions, sculpture.
Exhibitions: About 25 exhibitions a year.
Publications: Exhibition catalogs.

ROHSSKA KONSTSLOJDMUSEET (Rohss Museum of Arts and Crafts), 37-39 Vasagatan. Tel: 031-188930. *Dir* Jan Brunius; *Cur Coll* Thomas Baagoe; *Cur Exhib* Karin Aasma; *Asst Cur Textiles* Marianne Erikson; *Asst Cur* Gunnel Kernell.
Open Mon - Fri Noon - 3 PM; Sat & Sun 10 AM - 5 PM. No admis. Estab 1916 to collect and exhibit all kinds of craftsmanship and industrial design—old and new. Average Annual Attendance: 75,000.
Income: Financed by city appropriation.
Collections: †Textile; †furniture; the Falk Simon Bequest of old silver; †ceramics; †bookbindings; †glass; metalworks.

Exhibitions: 48-exhibitions during the year, mostly concerning modern domestic culture.
Publications: Yearbook, every 3 years.
Activities: Educ dept; classes for children; lect open to public; concerts; gallery talks; tours; traveling exhibitions organized and circulated; sales shop selling books, magazines, and postcards.
—**Library.** *Librn* Thomas Baagoe.
(Open to specialists and researchers.)
Holdings: Vols 28,000; Per subs 18.

MARIEFRED

SVENSKA STATENS PORTRAHSAMLING,* (Swedish State Portrait Gallery), Gripsholm Castle, S-150-30. Tel: 01 59/10194. *Cur* Ulf G Johnsson. *Asst Keeper* Lars Sjoeberg.
Open May 15 - Aug 31 daily 10 AM - 5 PM; opening hours reduced during the winter months. Admis Swedish crowns 4:50. Estab c 1550; administrated by Nationalmuseum, Stockholm.
Collections: Portraits, mainly Swedish, from 15th century to modern times, approx 3500 items.
Activities: Authorized guides May - Aug for school and visiting.

STOCKHOLM

KUNGLE MYNTKABINETTET STATENS MUSEUM FOR MYNT MEDALS OCH PENNINGHISTORIA (Royal Coin Cabinet National Museum of Monetary History), Storgatan 41 (Mailing Add: PO Box 5405, S-114 84). Tel: 08/63 07 70. *Keeper* Brita Malmer; *Deputy Keeper* Ulla Westermark; *Asst Keeper* Iamas Sarkany; *Asst Keeper* Ernst Nathorst-Boos.
Open Mon - Fri 11 AM - 4 PM; Sat & Sun Noon - 5 PM. Admis adults 5 sw cr, students 3 sw cr. Estab 1975, formerly a department of the Museum of National Antiquities, it is a museum for monetary history and medals. There are four exhibition rooms. Average Annual Attendance: 21,000.
Income: Financed by state appropriation.
Collections: Coins (400,000); medals (35,000); bank notes (40,000). The collections range over the entire world and all periods.
Exhibitions: Fran wampum till varldsvaluta (From Wampum to hard currency); Mynt i Mittens rike (Coins from The Middle Kingdom); Pengar i Frankrike (Coins in France); Fran aes rude till lira i Italien (From aes rude to lira in Italy); With Swedish Crown—The monetary history of the Swedish colony St Barthelemy 1784-1878.
Publications: Numismatica stockholmiensis; annual report.
—**Library, Numismatic Section.** *Librn* Dr Anders Hedvall.
Open to the public.
Holdings: Vols 35,000.
Special Subjects: Numismatics.

NATIONALMUSEUM,* Box 16 176, S-103-24. Tel: 24 42 00. *Dir* Dr Bengt Dahlback; *Head Painting & Sculpture Dept* P Grate; *Head Prints & Drawings Dept* P Bjurstrom; *Head Applied Arts* D Widman; *Head Royal Castles Collection* Ulf G Johnsson.
Open daily 11 AM - 5 PM; Tues 11 AM - 9 PM. Estab 1792.
Collections: †Paintings, miniatures, icons, sculpture, prints, and drawings, arts and crafts. Administers the State collections of paintings and sculptures in the royal castles and Gustaf III's antikmuseum (The Collection of Antiquities of Gustaf III) in the Royal Palace of Stockholm; collections of 20th century paintings and sculptures, housed in Moderna museet (The Museum of Modern Art). Collections of ancient Far Eastern Art in Ostasiatiska museet (Museum of Far Eastern Art).
Publications: Bulletin; Annual Report; Yearbook; catalogs.
Library: Holdings—Vols 165,000; Other—Clippings 620,000.

NORDISKA MUSEET* (Swedish Museum), 14/18 Djurgarden. Tel: 63 05 00. *Dir* Dr Sune Zachrisson; *Keeper Buildings, Household & Furnishings* Kersti Holmquist; *Keeper Textiles & Dress* Dr Elisabet Hidemark; *Keeper Cultural Field Research* Dr Goran Rosander; *Head Educ & Pub Relations* Skans Torsten Nilsson; *Head Adminr* Greger Oxhammar; *Chmn Institute Folk Life Research* Mats Rehnberg.
Open Tues - Fri 10 AM - 4 PM; Sat & Sun Noon - 5 PM; cl Mon. Estab 1873 to further the knowledge of the culture and history of the Swedish people through scientific research on one hand and popular teaching and intructing on the other. Average Annual Attendance: 200,000.
Collections: †Folk art; †handcrafts; †period furnishings; †costumes; approx one million exhibits.
Exhibitions: Permanent exhibitions giving a survey representative of the field of action of the museum, with about eight temporary exhibitions a year.
Publications: Yearbook; catalogs of collections; books on folklore.
Activities: Guided visits and prize competitions for school children and a lively collaboration with educational organizations. Two or three lecture series per year.

—**Library,** 6 - 16 Djurgardsvagen, S-115, 21. *Librn-in-chief* Dr Jan-Ojvind Swahn.
Open 10 AM - Noon & 1 - 3 PM. Estab 1884 to collect literature on ethnology, folk art.
Income: Financed by city appropriation. Purchases: $71,000.
Holdings: Vols 120,000; Per subs 300.
Special Subjects: Swedish (Scandinavian) ethnology and culture history.
Special Collections: The John Bottiger collection of literature on arts and crafts; The August Strindberg Library; The Viktor Rydberg Library.
Publications: Bibliografiska meddelanden fran Nordiska Museets bibliotek, quarterly.

OSTASIATISKA MUSEET (Museum of Far Eastern Antiquities), Skeppsholmen (Mailing Add: Box 163 81, 103 27). Tel: 08 244200. *Dir* Bo Gyllensvard; *Cur* Jan Wirgin; *Cur* Per-Olow Leijon.
Open Wed - Sun Noon - 4 PM; Tues Noon - 9 PM; cl Mon. Admis 5 Sw Crowns. Estab 1963 to display in permanent and temporary exhibitions Art and Handicraft from the Far East, primarily from China, India, Korea and Japan from ancient times to the present. Six galleries solely devoted to Chinese art; one gallery for Indian art, and one for the arts of Korea and Japan. Average Annual Attendance: 50,000. Mem: 600; dues 75 Sw Crowns.
Income: Financed by city appropriation. Purchases: $8,000 plus gifts.
Collections: Approx 110,000 objects in the permanent collection including Chinese art from neolithic times to the present, stone-age pottery, bronzes, Buddhist sculpture, painting and porcelain; Indian art; Korean art; Japanese art.
Exhibitions: The Arts of Thailand; Woman in China; Peasant paintings from Huhsien county; Shooting Orioles—a painting by Ma Yuan; Paintings by Asian children; Paintings and handicraft from Korea.
Publications: Bulletin, annually.
Activities: Classes for adults and children; docent training; lect open to public, 600 vis lect per yr; gallery talks; tours; traveling exhibitions organized and circulated; museum shop selling books, magazines, reproductions, prints.
Library: *Librn* Margareta Martens. Open for reference to scholars. Holdings: Vols 300 meters; Per subs 300 meters.

STATENS HISTORISKA MUSEUM (Museum of National Antiquities), Storgatan 41 (Mailing Add: PO Box 5405 S 114 84). *Dir* Olov Isaksson; *Keeper of Museum Dept* Bjorn Ambrosiani; *Head Exhib Dept* Eric Sorling; *Cur Educ Dept* Maj Odelberg.
Open Mon - Fri 11 AM - 4 PM; Sat & Sun Noon - 5 PM; Thurs 7 - 9 PM. Admis 5 sw cr (includes Historical News). Estab 1855 to protect and illustrate old culture. Average Annual Attendance: 120,000-200,000.
Income: Financed by state appropriation.
Collections: Prehistory, medieval art, wooden sculpture, gold and silver treasures from Viking period up to 17th century.
Exhibitions: Women of ancient time; cribs; Valamo monastery; The truth about Sigismund Vasa and his sons; Faroe pictures; After the Flood (an exhibition from Iraq); From pot to shard.
Publications: Annual report; Historical News, quarterly.
Activities: Classes for adults and children; lect open to public, 25 vis lectr per yr; concerts; tours; traveling exhibitions organized and circulated; museum shop selling books, reproductions, prints, slides; junior museum.
—**Library of the Royal Academy of Letters, History and Antiquities.** *Librn* Anders Hedvall.
Open to the public.
Holdings: Vols 150,000; Per subs 2100; Other—Prints and drawings 1000.
Special Subjects: Archaeology, medieval history of art, numismatics, preservation of cultural monuments.

SWITZERLAND

BASEL

MUSEUM FÜR VÖLKERKUNDE AUND SCHWEIZERISCHES MUSEUM FÜR VOLKSKUNDE BASEL (Museum of Ethnological Collections and Folklore), Augustinergasse 2/Münsterplatz 20 (Mailing Add: PO Box 1048, 4001). Tel: 061 25 82 82. *Dir* Dr Gerhard Baer; *Cur Oceania* Dr Christian Kaufmann; *Cur Indonesia* Dr Urs Ramseyer; *Cur America* Dr Annemarie Seiler; *Cur Africa, Textiles* Dr Renée Boser; *Cur Prehistory, India* Dr Susanne Haas; *Cur Textiles* Dr Marie-Louise Nabholz *Cur Educ Dept* Dr Brigitta Hauser; *Cur Europe* Dr Theo Gantner.
Museum fur Volkerkunde is closed until 1981 for alterations. Schweizerisches Museum fur Volkskunde open Tues - Sun 10 AM - Noon & 2 - 5 PM. Admis free Wed afternoon and weekends. Estab 1893. Average Annual Attendance: 80,000.
Collections: Melanesia, Polynesia, Asia, East Indonesia, Africa, America, Switzerland; collection of textiles.

Exhibitions: Permanent and special exhibitions.
—*Library. Librn* Elisabeth Idris.
Open Mon - Fri 8:45 - 11:45 AM & 2 - 5 PM.
Holdings: Vols 30,000.

OFFENTLICHE KUNSTSAMMLUNG-KUNSTMUSEUM BASEL,*
(Museum of Fine Arts), St Albangraben 16, CH-4010. Tel: 22 08 28, *Dir*
Dr Franz Meyer; *Secy* Verena Trueb; *Cur Paintings* Dr Paul-Henry
Boerlin; *Cur Prints & Drawings* Dr Dieter Koepplin.
Open June - Sept, 10 AM - 5 PM; Oct - May, 10 AM - Noon, 2 - 5 PM;
cl Mon. Estab as private collection about 1550; founded as public collec-
tion 1662; new building 1936. Average Annual Attendance: 220,000.
Collections: †15th and 16th century paintings, including Konrad Witz,
Grünewald, Holbein and others; †16th & 17th century Dutch paintings;
†19th and 20th century paintings from Corot to the present; sculptures
by Rodin and 20th century artists; American painting since 1945; prints
and drawings from Upper Rhine, German and Swiss Masters.
Exhibitions: Regular exhibitions from the collections of prints and drawings.
Library: Librn Nikolaus Meier. Holdings: Vols 100,000 art.

BERNE

KUNSTMUSEUM BERN,* (Museum of Fine Arts Bernc), Hodler-
strasse 12, CH, 3011. Tel: 22-09-44. *Dir* Dr Hugo Wagner; *Cur* Dr
Sandor Kuthy.
Open 10 AM - Noon, 2 - 5 PM; Tues 8 - 10 PM; cl Mon morning. Estab
1879; enlarged 1936. Average Annual Attendance: 45,000.
Collections: †Italian Masters; †Niklaus Manuel; Dutch and contempo-
rary artists; †Swiss Baroque Masters; †Swiss 19th and 20th century
Masters; †French and other European Masters of the 19th and 20th cen-
turies. A great collection of †Paul Klee works of 2600 items; †Foundation
Hermann and Margrit Rupf, important Cubist collection; 20,000 draw-
ings and engravings; illustrations.
Publications: Berner Kunstmitteilungen, issued 8 times a year; catalogs
of collections and temporary exhibitions.
Library: Holdings—Vols 30,000.

CHUR

BÜNDNER KUNSTHAUS CHUR,* (Bündner Art Museum), Post-
platz, 7000. Tel: 22 17 63. *Dir* Hans Hartmann; *Secy* Trudy Caflisch.
Open daily except Mon 10 AM - Noon, 2 - 5 PM; first and third Fri
each month open also 7:30 - 10 PM. Admis to permanent exhibit SFr 1,
special show, 3 - 4. Estab 1900 for support of local art, Swiss art and
modern art.
Income: Financed by endowment, membership, city and state appropriation.
Collections: Angelika Kauffmann; Giovanni Segantini; Ferdinand Hodler; Giovanni, Augusto, Alberto Giacometti; E L Kirchner; Swiss
painting; plastic art, 19th and 20th centuries.
Publications: Exhibition catalogs.
Activities: Dramatic programs; concerts; competitions; photograph collection for reference only; traveling exhibitions organized and circulated;
Book shop.
Library: For internal use only.

GENEVA

MUSEE D'ART ET D'HISTOIRE Museum of Art and History), Cabi-
net des estampes, 5 Promenade du Pin, 1204. Tel: 022/29 60 33. *Cur*
Charles Goerg.
Open during meetings and temporary exhibitions. No admis. Estab 18th
century; for collection, research, and information. Three exhibition
rooms. Average Annual Attendance: 20,000.
Income: Financed by city appropriation. Purchases: $40,000.
Collections: Prints (German, Italian, French, Dutch, Spanish, and Swiss
of the 15th-19th centuries); Prints of the 20th century from all countries;
Japanese prints of the 18th & 19th centuries.
Exhibitions: Martin Schongauer; Denise Mennet; Timbres et tampons
d'artistes; Jean Tinguely (dessins et gravures pour les sculptures); Diables
et Diableries (gravures du 15th century).
Publications: Exhibition catalogs.
Activities: Classes for adults and children; lect open to public; prints and
original objects of art lent to museums; lending collection contains origi-
nal prints 200,000, photographs 2,000; traveling exhibitions organized
and circulated; museum shop.
—**Library of Art and Archaeology.**
Open Mon - Fri 9 AM - 7 PM; Sat 9 AM - Noon & 2 - 5 PM; cl Sun.
Estab 1952 for scientific research.
Income: Financed by city appropriation. Purchases: $100,000.

Holdings: Vols 100,000; Per subs 1,200; AV—Microfiche, slides;
Other—Catalogs of exhibitions, reproductions.

MUSEE D'ART MODERNE (Modern Art Museum), Petit Palais, 2
Terrasse Saint-Victor, 1206. *Pres & Founder* M Oscar Ghez.
Open daily 10 AM - Noon & 2 - 6 PM; cl Mon morning. Estab 1968 for
cultural purposes. The Petit Palais is an elegant Second Empire home
converted into a unique museum. There are six floors of paintings, sculptures, and drawings which comprise part of the collection of Oscar Ghez
and form an exhibit entitled From Renoir to Kisling and Picasso. Average Annual Attendance: 30,000. Mem: 1,500; dues Fr 50.
Income: Financed by endowment.
Collections: Covers the period 1880-1930, includes Impressionists, Poin-
tillists, Post-Impressionists, Nabis, Fauves, Expressionists, and Naifs or
Primitives of the 20th century.
Exhibitions: Carzou; 200 Japanese Artists; Fanfani Amintore; The Symbolism.

LA CHAUX DE FONDS

MUSÉE DES BEAUX-ARTS ET SOCIÉTÉ DES AMIS DES ARTS
(Museum of Fine Arts) 33 Rue des Musées, 2300. Tel: 039˙22 13 50.
Pres M Andre Sandoz; *Dir & Cur* Paul Seylaz.
Open daily 10 AM - Noon & 2 - 5 PM; cl Mon. No admis, except for
special exhibits. Estab 1864 for the enrichment of the permanent collec-
tion and the organization of exhibitions; chiefly modern art. The gallery
has 10 rooms on 2 floors and a hall for exhibition space, constructed in
1926. Mem: 500; dues S Fr 25.
Income: Financed by membership and city appropriation.
Collections: Works of local artists as Leopold Robert à le Corbusier and
contemporaries; Swiss works of the 19th and 20th centuries; contemporary art including French, English, Spanish, Italian, German, Polish and
Japanese.
Exhibitions: Jean Cornu; Kolol-Vary; Mario Radice; Scialoja; De Ro-
mans; Cruz-Diez; B Schweizer (optical art) sculptors including Poncet,
Vignando, Ramseyer, Conde, Wiggli; 54th Exposition Biennale Canton-
ale.
Publications: Exhibition catalogs.
Activities: Classes for adults and children; dramatic programs; docent
training.

SAINT GALLEN

HISTORISCHES MUSEUM (Historical Museum), Museumstrasse 50,
9000. *Dir* Dr Ricco Labhardt; *Conservator* Rudolf Hanhart; *Technical
Asst* Max Winiger.
Open June - Sept, Tues - Sun 10 AM - Noon & 2 - 4 PM; cl Mon; Oct -
May, Tues - Sat 2 - 4 PM; Sun 10 AM - Noon & 2 - 4 PM. Admis 2 Fr;
free Wed, Sat & Sun. Estab 1921. Average Annual Attendance: 16,000.
Income: Financed by city appropriation.
Collections: Weapons; porcelain; pewter; glass and glasspainting; period
rooms; Burgundian standards of 1476; graphics; costumes; furniture; eth-
nology; textiles.
Exhibitions: Romischer Gutshof.
Publications: Museumsbrief.

SCHAFFHAUSEN

MUSEUM ZU ALLERHEILIGEN (All Saints' Museum), Klosterplatz,
CH-8200. *Dir* Dr Max Freivogel.
Open Apr - Oct 9 AM - Noon & 1:30 - 5 PM; Nov - Mar 10 AM -
Noon & 1:30 - 4:30 PM. No admis. Estab 1938 to encourage interest and
skill in art. Average Annual Attendance: 50,000-90,000.
Collections: Prehistoric; Roman; 19th century art; industrial art.
Exhibitions: Zwischen Improvisation und Fuge; Die Staufer.
Activities: Traveling exhibitions organized and circulated.

SOLOTHURN

KUNSTMUSEUM SOLOTHURN (Solothurn Art Museum), Werkhof-
strasse 30. *Conservator* Andre Kamber.
Open Tues - Sat 10 AM - Noon & 2 - 5 PM; Sun 10 AM - Noon & 2 - 4
PM; cl Mon. Estab to house a collection of Swiss art. Average Annual
Attendance: 24,000. Annual meeting Aug.
Income: Financed by city appropriation. Purchases: SFr 30,000.
Collections: Large collection of Frank Buchser and O Frohlicher; Cuno
Amiet; Max Gubler; Ferdinand Hodler; watercolors of Otto Morach; B
Luginbuhl; J Tinguacly; Hans Stocker; Karl Walser; Oscar Wiggli;
Schang Hutter; Rolf Iseli; Franz Eggenschwiler; Andre Thomkins; Heinz
Schwarz; Robert Muller; Rolf Spinnler; Hermann A Sigg; Mauboules;
Dieter Roth; Bernhard Luthi; Meret Oppenheim; Alois Carigiet.

Exhibitions: 9 Oltener-Kinstler; Martin Disler; Cuno Amiet; Johann Christian Flury; The Museum of Drawers (H Distel); Gian und Erica Pedretti; Dieter Roth—eine Buchverzwei.
Publications: Kataloge zu den Ausstellungen.

WINTERTHUR

KUNSTMUSEUM WINTERTHUR,* (Art Museum), Museumstrasse 52, CH-8400. Tel: 84 51 62. *Cur* Dr Rudolf Koella.
Open 10 - Noon, 2 - 5 PM; cl Mon morning. Estab 1866. Administered by Museum Association. Average Annual Attendance: 12,000. Mem: 960.
Collections: Swiss painting and sculpture since 1700; portraits by Anton Graff; French, Italian and German painting and sculpture of the 19th and 20th centuries; drawings; 16th century stained glass.
Exhibitions: Annual show of local artists; Tri-annual show of artists from Canton of Zurich; two to three exhibitions a year of contemporary Swiss and International art; retrospective exhibits.
Publications: Collection and exhibition catalogs.
Activities: Two lect per year, generally on contemporary art.
Library: Holdings—Vols 3200.

ZURICH

KUNSTHAUS ZURICH (Museum of Fine Arts), Heimplatz 1, (Mailing Add: Box 8024) 8001. *Dir* Dr F Baumann; *Vice-Dir* Dr E Billeter; *Adminr* E Graf; *Cur Graphic Coll* Dr U Perucchi.
Open Tues - Fri 10 AM - 9 PM; Sat & Sun 10 AM - 5 PM; Mon 2 - 5 PM. Admis Sfr 2 and Sfr 5. Estab 1910 as an official Zurich Museum of Fine Arts. The gallery includes space for the permanent collection and changing exhibitions, a graphic arts room, a photo gallery and a foyer for exhibiting. Average Annual Attendance: 300,000. Mem: 6,000; dues adults Sfr 50; juniors Sfr 10.
Income: Financed by membership, and city and state appropriations.
Collections: Paintings 15th-20th centuries, mainly 19th and 20th; medieval and modern sculptures; Alberto Giacometti-Foundation.
Activities: Classes for children; concerts; original objects of art lent; traveling exhibitions organized and circulated; museum shop selling books, original art, reproductions, prints, slides.
—**Library.** *Librn* Dr U Perucchi.
Open to members of Zurcher Kunstgesellschaft, students and professors.
Holdings: Vols 40,000; Per subs 90; Other—Exhibition catalogs, museum bulletins; annual reports; auction catalogs; manuscripts.
Special Subjects: Fine arts—paintings, sculpture, prints, especially 19th and 20th century.

MUSEUM RIETBERG ZÜRICH, Gablerstrasse 14 & 15, CH 8002. Tel: 25 45 28. *Dir* Dr Eberhard Fischer; *Cur East Asia* Prof Dr Helmut Brinker.
Open main building (Villa Wesendonck) Tues - Sun 10 AM - 5 PM, also Wed Eve 8 - 10 PM; cl Mon. No admis. Estab 1952 as a museum of non-western art; entrance room houses ancient Oriental art, one room Pre-Columbian art, four rooms Indian and Southeast Asian art, six rooms East Asian art, three rooms African art, and one of Oceanic art. Average Annual Attendance: 40,000. Mem: 550; dues SFr 50.-; annual meeting dates vary.
Income: Financed by city appropriation. Purchases: $50,000.
Collections: Baron von der Heydt Collection; †Japanese sculpture; †Chinese painting; †Indian painting; †African art.
Exhibitions: (1976-78) The Art of the Dan (West Africa); The Lion as a Symbol of Power; Poetic painting-painted poetry (Japanese literati-paintings); Indian playing cards; Gold in the Art of West Africa.
Publications: Catalogs to exhibitions.
Activities: Lect open to the public, members are spec. invited, 10 vis lectr per yr; concerts; traveling exhibitions organized and circulated; sales shop selling books, reproductions, prints, slides, postcards.
Library: Open by appointment for reference. Holdings: Vols 6000. Special Collections: Library of late Prof Osvald Sirén; late Baron von der Heydt and others.
—**Museum Rietberg** Zurich am Hirschengraben 20, 8001. Tel: 47 96 52. Open Tues - Fri 2 - 7 PM; Sat & Sun 2 - 5 PM; Thurs Eve 8 - 10 PM; cl Mon. Estab 1974.
Exhibitions: Special temporary exhibitions on non-European art.

SCHWEIZERISCHES LANDESMUSEUM (Swiss National Museum), Museumstrasse 2 (Mailing Add: PO Box 2760, CH-8023). Tel: 01-221 10 10. *Dir* Dr Hugo Schneider; *VDir* Dr Jenny Schneider.
Open Mon 2 - 5 PM; Tues - Sun 10 AM - Noon & 2 - 5 PM; cl holidays. No admis. Estab 1898. The museum houses the largest collections relating to the cultural history of Switzerland. Its study collections serve as a basis for scientific research. The permanent and changing exhibitions on display give a comprehensive survey of Swiss culture from prehistoric times to the present. Average Annual Attendance: 280,000.

Income: Financed by state appropriation. Purchases: Sw fr 400,000.
Collections: Prehistory and ancient history; excavations; weapons; banners; uniforms; military items; goldsmith's art; nonferrous metals; pewter; ceramics; glassware; textiles; costumes; jewelry; coins; medals; stained glass; paintings, prints and drawings; statuary; furniture; interiors; clocks and watches; musical instruments; farming implements; ancient crafts and trades.
Publications: Annual report; Zeitschrift fur schweizerische Archaeologie und Kunstgeschichte, quarterly.
Activities: Educ dept; docent training; lect open to public, 1200 vis lectr per yr; gallery talks; tours; sales shop selling books, slides.
—**Library.** *Librn* Martin R Scharer.
Open Mon - Fri 8 AM - Noon & 2 - 5 PM. Estab 1898.
Holdings: Vols 70,000; Per subs 900; Other—Exhibition catalogs.
Special Subjects: Prehistory, art, handicraft, numismatics, military, folklore.

SYRIA

DAMASCUS

NATIONAL MUSEUM OF DAMASCUS, Reda Saeed St. *Gen Dir* Dr Afif Bahnassi.
Open winter 8 AM - 1 PM & 2 - 4 PM; summer 9 AM - 1 PM & 4 - 9 PM. Estab 1919.
Collections: Ancient Oriental, Greek, Roman, Byzantine, Islamic and modern art.
Publications: Annales Archeologiques Arabes Syrienne, yearly.
Activities: The Directorate-General of Antiquities is located here to preserve and conserve Syrian antiquities and to supervise the archaeological museums and the excavations.
Library: *Librn* Rihab Daoud. Holdings: Vols 15,000.

TUNISIA

LE BARDO

MUSEE NATIONAL DU BARDO,* (Bardo National Museum), Le Bardo. Tel: 261-002. *Dir* Ennaifer Mongi.
Open 8 AM - Noon, 2:30 - 6 PM. Estab 1888.
Income: Financed by Government appropriation.
Collections: Greek and Roman antiquities; modern Islamic art; largest collection in the world of Roman mosaics.
Publications: Antiquités Africaines, also notes and articles; National Institute of Archaeology is the publisher.
Activities: Guides for student and adult tours; traveling exhibitions; photograph collection.
Library: Books and photograph collection.

TURKEY

ISTANBUL

ISTANBUL ARKEOLOJI MUZELERI (Archaeological Museums of Istanbul), Sultanahmet. Tel: 279069 & 279070. *Dir* Necati Dolunay; *Asst Dir* Ismail H Kose; *Cur Museum of Ancient Orient* Edibe Uzunoglu; *Cur Cuneiform Tablet Coll* Fatma Yildiz & Veysel Donbaz; *Cur Non-Islamic Coins* Nekriman Olcay; *Cur Islamic Coins* Teoman Caniklioglu; *Cur Laboratory Preservation* Fehamet Camcioglu; *Cur Laboratory Restoration* Nejat Ozatay. *Cur Photography* Turhan Birgili.
Open Tues - Sun 9:30 AM - 5:30 PM; cl Mon. Admis 50¢; $1 for each camera. Estab 1846 to show to the public the richness of antiquities of the country. Average Annual Attendance: 160,000. Mem: 120; dues $6; annual meeting Apr.
Income: $50,000 (financed by state appropriation).
Collections: Sarcophagi, statues, portraits, architectural pieces, inscriptions, pottery, glass, metal, coins and cuneiform tablets from 6000 BC-1500 AD.
Exhibitions: Changing exhibitions from permanent collection.
Publications: Annual of the Archaeological Museums of Istanbul.
Activities: Lect for members, 4 vis lectr per yr; concerts; sales shop selling reproductions, prints, slides.
—**Library.** *Librn* Havva Kivircik; *Asst Librn* Filiz Aytan.
Open 9:30 AM - 5:30 PM. Estab 1846 as a resource to members of museums and universities.
Income: Financed by state appropriation. Purchases: $2,000.
Holdings: Vols 45,000; Other—Manuscripts.

TOPKAPI SARAY MUSEUM, Sultanahmed. Tel: 28 3546-47. *Dir* Dr Kemal Cig; *Asst Dir* M Pazi.

Open daily 9:30 AM - 5 PM; cl Tues. Admis adult 15 TL; children half-price. Estab 1924 to offer exhibitions of art.

Income: Financed by state appropriation.

Collections: (Art) Chinese and Japanese porcelains; Sultan's costumes; miniatures and portraits of Sultans; clocks and watches; holy relics; Turkish embroideries; throne room; Sami Ozgiritli's collection of furniture; tiled kiosk; collection of rugs and embroideries; Alay Kiosk exhibit of Kenan Ozbel; calligraphy.

—Library of Manuscripts. *Librn* Dr F Gagman, Dr. Z Akalay.

Open to researchers for reference.

Holdings: Vols 20,000; Other—Turkish and Persian manuscripts.

TURK VE ISLAM ESERLERI MUZESI,* (Museum of Turkish and Islamic Art), Süleymaniye, 6 Sifahane St. Tel: 22 1888. *Dir* Can Kerametli.

Open daily 10 AM - 5 PM; cl Mon. Estab 1914.

Collections: Collection of the oldest Turkish carpets; old Korans; books with miniatures and illumination; metalwork and ceramics; sculpture in stone and stucco, wood carvings; fermans and monograms of the sultans, and other monuments of Islamic art.

USSR

MOSCOW

STATE MUSEUM OF ORIENTAL ART,* 16 Obukha St. Tel: 227-34-29. *Dir* Dr V S Manin; *Exec Secy* Dr Natalie S Sitcheva; *Art Secy* Vladimir I Bissoodnov.

Open 11 AM - 7 PM; cl Mon. Admis adults 30 copeck, children and students 10 copeck. Estab 1918 to collect and study Eastern peoples' arts; gallery maintained.

Income: Financed by Government of USSR.

Collections: Collections of Chinese, Indian, Japanese art, Mongolian, African, Soviet Eastern Republics, Indonesian, Korean, Persian art; carpets; textiles; ceramics.

Exhibitions: Soviet Eastern Republics; Soviet painters; Mongolian art; Iranian carpets; Antiquities of Tunis, Contemporary Japanese prints and others.

Publications: Scientific works; exhibition catalogs.

Activities: Classes for children; reading lectures; researching scientific work; lect open to the public; photograph collection; traveling exhibitions organized and circulated.

Library maintained.

URUGUAY

MONTEVIDEO

MUSEO NACIONAL DE ARTES PLASTICAS* (National Museum of Fine Arts), Tomas Giribaldi 2283 esq Julio Herrera y Reissig, Parque Rodo. Tel: 43 800. *Dir* Angel Kalenberg.

Open winter 2 - 6 PM; summer 6 - 10 PM; cl Mon. No admis. Estab 1911. Average Annual Attendance: 300,000.

Income: Financed by government appropriation.

Collections: Juan Manuel Blanes, Carlos Federico Saez, Rafael Barradas, Pedro Figari, Joaquin Torres Garcia, Alfredo de Simone, Jose Cuneo, Carlos Gonzalez. 4,217 paintings, engravings, sculptures, drawings, and ceramics.

Publications: Exhibition catalogs, quarterly.

Activities: Exten dept serving museums; lect open to public, 6 vis lectr per yr; gallery talks; tours; concerts; competitions; traveling exhibitions organized and circulated; original objects of art lent.

Library: Open for reference. Holdings: Vols 4,500.

VENEZUELA

CARACAS

MUSEO DE BELLAS ARTES* (Museum of Fine Arts), Parque Sucre, Los Caobos, 105. Tel: 54 37 92. *Dir* Miquel G Arroyo; *Secy* Prisca Dale de Moleiro; *Conservation Dept* Carlos Duarte; *Cur Prints & Drawings* Gerd Leufert; *Asst to Cur* Alvaro Sotillo.

Open daily 9 AM - Noon & 3 - 5:30 PM; cl Mon. Estab 1938; enlarged 1953, 1957, 1963 and 1974. Average Annual Attendance: 200,000.

Collections: Venezuelan Painting from the end of the 19th century to the present; contemporary sculpture; Pre-Columbian art; Egyptian art; Chinese porcelain; European porcelain; Latin American paintings and sculpture, including primitives; European painting; collection of prints and drawings.

Exhibitions: Approx 24 per year.

Activities: 12 lect per yr; gallery talks; classes for children.

Library: Holdings—Vols 3,100; Other—Catalogs, magazines.

WALES

CARDIFF

NATIONAL MUSEUM OF WALES, Cathays Park. Tel: 39 7951-9. *Pres* Colonel Sir William Crawshay; *VPres* W A Twiston Davies; *Treas* Colonel H Morrey Salmon; *Secy* D W Dykes; *Dir* Dr D A Bassett; *Keeper of Archeology* G C Boon; *Keeper of Art* Dr P Cannon-Brookes.

Open Oct - Mar 10 AM - 5 PM; Apr - Sept 10 AM - 6 PM. No admis. Estab 1907 to teach the world about Wales and the Welsh about their fatherland. It includes a remarkable collection of modern European painting and sculpture which has helped to earn the Museum its international standing. Average Annual Attendance: 300,000.

Income: Financed by city and state appropriation.

Collections: (Art) Pyke Thompson Collection includes ceramics, enamels, prints and watercolors; great artists of the early 19th century—Girtin, Turner, Cotman, Cox and de Wint; later artists as Rossetti, Holman Hunt, Henry Moore and Goodwin. Jackson Collection consists mainly of English silver including a unique Anglo-Saxon spoon; a spoon which bears, perhaps, the earliest extant example of the London hall-mark; a complete set of 13 Apostle spoons. Nance Collection specializes in the pottery and porcelain of Swansea and Nantgarw. Davies Collection includes pictures of the Barbizon School by Corot and Diaz and others; Old Masters; British paintings and drawings; prints; French art of the late 19th century; French Impressionists including Daumier and Monet.

Exhibitions: Paintings from the Reserve; Watercolor Society of Wales; Western Mail Children's Art Exhibition; Sun Pictures (Kodak); Greek and Roman Terracottas; Fragile Stones make Art; National Art-Collections Fund Week.

Publications: Monthly program.

Activities: Classes for children; lect open to public; concerts; gallery talks; individual paintings and original objects of art lent to bona fide art galleries and museums; traveling exhibitions organized and circulated; museum shop selling books, magazines, reproductions, prints, slides.

—Library. *Librn* W J Jones.

Open for reference by arrangement with library staff. Estab 1912 to support research in the departments.

Holdings: Vols and bound periodicals 100,000; Per subs 500.

Special Collections: Private libraries of the Cardiff Naturalists' Society and the Cambrian Archaeological Association.

Activities: Cooperation with other libraries through inter-lending schemes such as those of the British Lending Library and the Wales Regional Library Bureau.

SAINT FAGANS

WELSH FOLK MUSEUM,* near Cardiff. Tel: Cardiff 56 1357-8. *Cur* T M Owen; *Keeper Material Culture* J G Jenkins; *Keeper Oral Traditions & Dialects* Vincent H Phillips.

Open Apr - Sept Mon - Sat 10 AM - 7 PM; Sun 2:30 - 7 PM; Oct - Mar Mon - Sat 10 AM - 5 PM; Sun 2:30 - 5 PM. Open all Bank Holidays incl Good Friday, Easter Monday, Whit-Monday; cl Christmas Day and Boxing Day. Admis adults 10p, children 5p. Estab 1947. Average Annual Attendance: 170,000.

In the village of St Fagans, four miles west of Cardiff, is the Welsh Folk Museum. It comprises an open air museum, including the Elizabethan mansion of St Fagan's Castle, the rooms of which are furnished in period style, its gardens and grounds, and an adjoining area of eighty acres of woodland. Buildings from all parts of Wales are re-erected there, craftsmen may be seen practicing their crafts, and a selection of the diverse material which is the study of folk-life is exhibited in a new museum block. With these collections and activities the Welsh Folk Museum illustrates the old way of life in Wales.

YUGOSLAVIA

BELGRADE

MUSEUM OF MODERN ART, USCE SAVE BB, 11071. Tel: 011-326-544. *Dir* Miodrag B Protic; *Chief Cur* Draga Panic; *Head of Documentation* Marija Pusic.

Open Fri - Wed 10 AM - 7 PM; cl Thurs. Admis 10,000 dinars. Estab 1959 to collect and exhibit works of Yogoslav art since 1900. The gallery houses the permanent display and has room for temporary exhibitions. Average Annual Attendance: 100,000.
Income: Financed by city appropriation, and the Republic of Serbia.
Collections: †Painting; †sculpture; †drawings; †prints; †tapestry; †new media; †foreign collection of prints.
Exhibitions: Der Blaue Reiter; German Expressionism (Die Brucke)—prints; American Painting 1846-1976; International Exhibition of Plastic Arts; Yanis Gaitis; Danish Design; Art in Belgium from the end of the 18th century.
Publications: Exhibition catalogs.
Activities: Classes for adults and children; lect open to public, 7 vis lectr per yr; gallery talks; tours; exten dept serving the area; traveling exhibitions organized and circulated; museum shop selling reproductions, slides and catalogs.
Library: Librn Olga Caric. Open to the public. Holdings: Vols 2444; Per subs 36; Other—Catalogs 10,350.

LJUBLJANA

MODERNA GALERIJA (Modern Art Gallery), Tomsiceva 14, 6100. Tel: 061 21-709. *Dir* Zoran Krzisnik; *Cur Museum Coll* Melita Stele-Mozina; *Cur Documentation* Ljerka Menase; *Cur Exhib* Majda Jerman.
Open Tues - Sun 10 AM - 6 PM; cl Mon. Admis adults 5 Din, students 3 Din, groups 2 Din. Estab 1948 to collect contemporary works of art in Slovenia; permanent collections of Slovene art; and to mount exhibitions. Average Annual Attendance: 10,000.
Income: Financed by city and state appropriations.
Collections: *Slovene painting; *sculpture and graphic art from 1900 to present.
Exhibitions: Retrospective exhibitions of Slovene artists—Miha Máles, France Mihelic, Matej Sternen; Oskar Kokoschka; Dusan Dzamonja; New British art; Fantasy in graphic art from 16th century to present; International Exhibition of Graphic Art in Ljubljana.
Publications: Exhibition catalogs.
Activities: Classes for adults and children; lect open to public, 12 vis lectr per yr; concerts; gallery talks; tours; traveling exhibitions organized and circulated.
Library: Holdings—Vols 17,206; Per subs 93.

NARODNA GALERIJA (National Art Gallery), Prezihova ulica 1/pp 432, Yu-61001. Tel: 21-765 & 21-249. *Dir* Dr Anica Cevc; *Asst* Dr Ksenija Rozman; *Asst* Polonca Vrhunc.
Open Tues - Sat 10 AM - 6 PM; Sun 10 AM - 1 PM; cl Mon. Admis adults N din 8, students and groups N din 3. Estab 1918 for the presentation of Slovenian art from the 13th century to the beginning of the 20th century. Average Annual Attendance: 40,000.
Income: Financed by city and state appropriations.
Collections: Slovenian sculptures and paintings from the 13th to the beginning of the 20th century; copies of mediaeval frescoes; foreign masters from the 14th century to the beginning of the 20th century.
Exhibitions: New Acquisitions of the Narodna galerija 1965-1975; Slovenian towns and settlements in the past; Francesco Caucig/Kavcic (1755-1828).
Publications: Exhibition catalogs.
Activities: Lect open to public; concerts; tours; original objects of art lent to museums; traveling exhibitions organized and circulated; museum shop selling reproductions, catalogs.
Library: Open for reference to collaborators of the Gallery; students, scholars and other interested persons. Holdings: Vols 9,436; Other—Photonegatives, slides, bibliographic files concerning Slovenian art.

ZAGREB

GALERIJE GRADA ZAGREBA,* (City Art Galleries), Offices; Rokov perivoj 4, 41000. Tel: 041 424 490. *Dir* Radoslav Putar. Open 11 AM - 1 PM; 5 - 8 PM. Admis 3 dinars. Estab 1961. Average Annual Attendance: 20,000.
Income: Financed by endowment.
Publications: Bit International, Spot (photography journal) and regular catalogs.

Activities: Orginal objects of art lent; photograph collection; traveling exhibitions organized and circulated; book shop.
Library maintained.
—**Galerija Suvremene Umjetnosti,** (Gallery of Contemporary Art), Katarinin trg 2, (Mailing Add: PO Box 233, 41000). Tel: 041-443-227. *Chief Cur* Bozo Bek; *Cur* Marijan Susovski; *Cur* Davor Maticevic.
Open 11 AM - 1 PM, & 5 - 8 PM. Admis 5 dinar. Estab 1955; gallery collects and exhibits contemporary art; organizes exhibitions of avant-garde Yugoslavian artists and artists from abroad; promotes experimental and new trends as well as new media in art. Average Annual Attendance: 20,000.
Income: Financed by city appropriation.
Collections: †Graphics, †paintings, †sculpture, †objects of art, †conceptual works, †video, †film.
Exhibitions: Polish photography; Photography from San Francisco; Ulay; Graphics from Portugal: Photography as Art; Gorgona, Martinis; Iveković; Dobrovi; German Expressionism; Video meeting; Gudac, Bucan; Confrontations; Young Yogoslav Cineasts; De Lale; III World Exhibition of Photography.
Publications: Documenti, irregularly ; SPOT, four times a year.
Activities: Lect open to the public, 10 vis lectr per yr; concerts; gallery talks; tours; individual paintings and original objects of art lent to organizations and institutions; traveling exhibitions organized and circulated; museum shop selling books, magazines, original art, prints, slides.
Library: Librn Marijan Susovski. Open to professionals. Holdings: Vols 5000, Per subs 20.
—**Galerija Primitivne Umjetnosti,** (Gallery of Primitive Art), Cirilometodska 3, (Mailing Add: Katarinin trg 2, 41000). Tel: 041-443-294. *Chief Cur* Dr Boris Kelemen; *Cur* Tomislav Sola.
Open 11 AM - 1 PM & 5 - 8 PM. Admis 5 dinars & 3 dinars for groups. Estab Nov 1, 1952 to gather, keep and exhibit naive art of Yugoslavia and foreign countries; gallery consists of six exhibit rooms, 197 sq meters, 119,5 running meters.
Income: Financed by city and state appropriation.
Collections: About 700 works of Yugoslav and foreign naive artists.
Exhibitions: (1976) In the gallery: Nikola Kovacević; Ivan Generalić; Sava Sekulić; three exhibitions from the collection; Outside the gallery: Paris; Grand Palais; Belfast; Dublin; Glasgow; London; museum tour in USA. (1977) In the gallery: Matija Skurjeni; Naivi 77/International.
Exhibition: Ivan Lacković; Outside the gallery: Recklinghausen; Tokyo; Osaka; museum tour in USA.
Activities: Lect open to the public; traveling exhibitions organized and circulated; sales shop selling original art, reproductions, prints.
Library maintained.
—**Atelier Ivan Mestrović,*** (Studio Mestrović), Mletacka 8, 41000. Tel: 041-445-075. *Chief Cur* Vesna Barbic.
Estab 1959; private studio of Ivan Mestrovie and works (sculptures).
Income: Financed by endowment.
—**Galerija Benko Horvat,*** (Collection Benko Horvat), Rokov perivoj 4, 41000. Tel: 041-424-490. *Chief Cur* Dimitrije Basicevic.
Estab 1948; collections of prints, drawings and paintings of the 15th - 19th centuries.
Income: Financed by endowment.

STROSSMAYEROVA GALERIJA STARIK MAJSTORA* (Strossmyer's Gallery of Old Masters), Zrinjski trg 11, 41000. Tel: 441 849. *Pres* Dr Grga Novak; *Dir* Prof Vinko Zlamalik; *Cur* Prof Ljerka Gasparovic.
Open Tues 5 - 7 PM; Wed & Fri 10 AM - Noon; Thurs & Sun 10 AM - 1 PM. Admis 5 and 10 dinar. Estab 1884 for the preservation, exhibition and explanation of Old Masters; under the control of the Yugoslav Academy of Sciences and Fine Arts.
Income: Financed by city and state appropriation.
Collections: Paintings and sculpture with emphasis on the Italian school from Renaissance to 18th century, 15th-16th century Austrian painting, 16th century German art, 16th-18th century Flemish and Dutch School and 18th-20th century French School.
Library: Open for reference. Holdings: Vols 13,000; Other—Photograph collection.

ART SCHOOLS

ARRANGEMENT AND ABBREVIATONS
KEY TO ART SCHOOLS

ARRANGEMENT OF DATA

Name of institution and address; zip code and telephone number where possible.

Name of Director (Dir), Chairman (Chmn) or head (Head) of school or department; Primary Art Faculty.

Number of full time (FT) and part time (PT) instructors.

Year school and Art Department was established (Estab).

Control of institution, whether public (Pub), private (Pvt), or denominational (Den).

Student body is co-educational unless noted as men (M), or women (W).

Classes are held during the day (D), evening (E) or day and evening (D&E).

Entrance requirements including entrance examinations.

Degrees conferred and number of years required for graduation.

Scholarships (Schol) and fellowships (Fels) granted.

Number of studio courses (SC), lecture courses (LC), graduate courses (GC).

Enrollment (Enrl), day (D), evening (E), nonmajor (Nonmaj), major (Maj) and other.

Tuition by the academic year (Yr), semester (Sem), credit hour (Cr Hr); campus residence availability.

Summer School: Name of Head of Art Department or Director of Summer Session; enrollment; tuition; duration; courses.

ABBREVIATIONS AND SYMBOLS

Acad — Academic
Admis — Admission
AM — Morning
Approx — Approximate, Approximately
Assoc — Associate
Asst — Assistant
c — circa
C — Course
Cert — Certificate
Chmn — Chairman
Cl — Closed
Col — College
Coordr — Coordinator
Cr — Credit
D — Day
Den — Denominational Control
Dept — Department
Dipl — Diploma
Dir — Director
Div — Division
Dorm — Dormitory
E — Evening
Educ — Education

Enrl — Enrollment
Ent — Entrance
Ent Req — Entrance Requirements
Estab — Established
Exam — Examination
Fel(s) — Fellowship(s)
FT — Full Time Instructor
GC — Graduate Course
Gen — General
Grad — Graduate
HS — High School
Hr — Hour
Incl — Including
Instr — Instructor
Jr — Junior
Lab C — Laboratory Course
LC — Lecture Course
Lect — Lecture(s)
Lectr — Lecturer(s)
Maj — Major in Arts
Nonres — Nonresident
PM — Afternoon
Pres — President

Prin — Principal
Prof — Professor
Prog — Program
PT — Part Time Instructor
Pts — Points
Pub — Public
Pvt — Private
Reg — Registration
Req — Requirements
Res — Residence, Resident
SC — Studio Course
Schol — Scholarship
Sem — Semester
Sr — Senior
Tui — Tuition
TV — Television
Undergrad — Undergraduate
Univ — University
W — Women
Wk — Week
Yr — Year(s)

* No response to questionnaire
‡ Denotes course is offered as major

United States Art Schools

ALABAMA

ATHENS

ATHENS COLLEGE,* Art Department, Beaty St. 35611. Tel: 205-232-1802, exten 203. Instrs FT 1.
Estab 1832; state upper div; D&E; ent req HS dipl; degrees BA and BS 2 yr; schol; SC 26, LC 6, enrl D 951, E 590, maj 15.
Courses: Art Education; Ceramics; Commercial Art; Costume Design & Construction; Drawing; Graphic Arts; Handicrafts, History of Art & Archaeology; Painting; Photography; Sculpture; Stage Design; Teacher Training; Theatre Arts.
Summer School: Term of 15 wks beginning June 4.

AUBURN

AUBURN UNIVERSITY,* School of Architecture and Fine Arts, Department of Art, 36830. Tel: 205-826-4373. Dean E K McPheeters; Head C Hiers; Instrs FT 18, PT 3.
Estab 1928; pub; D; ent req HS dipl, ACT/SAT; degrees BFA 4 yr and MFA 2 yr; SC 48, LC 9, GC 19; enrl 300.
Courses: Design; Drawing; Illustration; Painting; Printmaking; Sculpture.
Adult Hobby Classes: Courses—Drawing; Painting.

BIRMINGHAM

BIRMINGHAM-SOUTHERN COLLEGE,* Art Department, 800 Eighth Ave. W, 35204. Tel: 320-328-5250. Chmn Raymond John Mac-Mahan; Instrs FT 4.
Estab 1946; den; D; ent req HS dipl, ACT/SAT scores C average; degrees AB, BS, BFA, BM and BME 4 yr; financial aid awarded, some leadership schol available on variable basis; SC 22, LC 8, interim term courses of 4 or 8 wk, 4 req of each student in 4 yr period; approx enrl 500, maj 50.
Tuition: $2,000 per yr.
Courses: Art Education; Drawing; Graphic Arts; Graphic Design; History of Art & Archaeology; Painting; Sculpture.
Children's Classes: Enrl approx 20. Laboratory for training teachers.
Summer School: 8 wk beginning June 11 and Aug 10. Courses—Advanced Painting; Graphics; Sculpture; Art and Music; Painting & Drawing; Problems in Composition.

SAMFORD UNIVERSITY,* Art Department, 800 Lakeshore Dr, 35209. Tel: 205-870-2840, 870-2849. Chmn Dr Lowell C Vann; Instrs FT 3, PT 1.
Estab 1841; pvt; D; ent req HS dipl, ent exam, ACT/SAT; degrees BA and BSEduc 4 yr; SC 24, LC 4, GC 1.
Tuition: $53 per sem hr plus fees.
Courses: Advertising Design; Art Education; Ceramics; Commercial Art; Costume Design & Construction; Drawing; Graphic Arts; Graphic Design; Handicrafts; History of Art & Archaeology; Painting; Photography; Sculpture; Stage Design; Teacher Training; Theatre Arts.
Adult Hobby Classes: Enrl 40. Courses—Ceramics; Drawing; Painting.
Summer School: Tui $53 per sem hr for term of 5 wk beginning June 7. Courses—Regular semester courses on rotating basis.

UNIVERSITY OF ALABAMA IN BIRMINGHAM, Department of Art, University College, Building 3, 35294. Tel: 205-934-4941. Chmn Dept & Prof John M. Schnorrenberg, PhD; Assoc Prof John Dillon, MFA; Assoc Prof Edith Frohock, MFA; Asst Prof Fred Ream, PhD; Asst Prof Richard Urban, MFA; Asst Prof Howard Risatti, PhD; Instrs FT 8, PT 4.

Estab 1966, dept estab 1974; pub; D&E; ent req HS dipl, ACT/SAT; degrees BA; SC 38, LC 27, GC 12; enrl D 741, E 210, maj 159, grad 2.
Tuition: Res—Undergrad $630 yr, $210 per sem, $28 per hr, grad $675 yr, $225 per sem, $34 per hr; Nonres—Undergrad $1260 yr, $420 per sem, $56 per hr; grad $1350 yr, $450 per sem, $68 per hr.
Courses: Aesthetics; ‡Art History; Drawing; ‡Graphic Design; ‡Painting; ‡Printmaking; ‡Sculpture; Teacher Training; Theatre Arts.
Adult Hobby Classes: Enrl 150; tui $35-$50. Courses—Basic Art; Calligraphy; Portraiture; Stained Glass.
Children's Classes: Enrl 40; tui $15. Courses—Art for mothers and children; Basic drawing; Sculpting with wire and papier mache.
Summer School: Enrl 173; tui as above for term of 11 wks beginning June 9. Courses—Range over all fields and are about one half regular offerings.

BREWTON

JEFFERSON DAVIS STATE JUNIOR COLLEGE,* Art Department, Alco Dr, 36426. Tel: 205-867-4832. Instr John B. Spicer; Instr Kathy A Smith.
Estab 1965; pub; D&E; ent req HS dipl or equiv cert; degrees AA and AS 2 yr; SC 10, LC 1; enrl D 700, E 332, maj 25.
Tuition: $67.50 per quarter; no campus res.
Courses: Introduction to Art; Basic Design; Beginning Painting; Ceramics; Crafts; Drawing; Fundamentals of Photography.
Summer School: Enrl 200. Courses—Ceramics; Drawing; Introduction to Art.

FLORENCE

UNIVERSITY OF NORTH ALABAMA (formerly Florence State University), Department of Art, 35630. Tel: 205-766-4100, exten 334. Head Dept & Prof Mort E Smith, MFA; Asst Prof Albert Charles Hausmann, MFA; Asst Prof Fred Owen Hensley, MFA; Asst Prof Myrt W Hubbuch, MA; Asst Prof Thomas E Mims, MFA; Asst Prof Lawman F Palmer, MEd; Instr Jacqueline Simone Innes, MA; Instr Duane L Phillips, MFA; Instr Elizabeth Walter, MA.
Estab 1872; dept estab approx 1930s; pub; D; ent req HS dipl, or GED, ACT; degrees BS and BA 4 yr; MA 30 sem hr; SC 46, LC 6, enrl D 675, nonmaj 475, maj 200, GS 20.
Tuition: Res—Undergrad $275 per sem, $30 per hr; campus res room & board $1040.
Courses: Art Education; Art History; Calligraphy; Ceramics; Collage; ‡Commercial Art; Drafting; Drawing; Handicrafts (general crafts), Illustration in Commercial Art; Lettering; Painting, ‡Photography; Printmaking; Sculpture; Teacher Training.
Summer School: Tui $140 for term of 8 wks beginning June 4. Courses—most studio/lecture areas.

HUNTSVILLE

ALABAMA A&M UNIVERSITY, Art Education Department, 35762. Tel: 205-859-7354. Head Dept Clifton Pearson, EdD; Asst Prof Robert Adams, MA; Asst Prof Lakin Boyd, MA; Asst Prof William Nance, MFA: Instr Jimmie Dawkins, MFA; Instr Oscar Logan, MFA.
Estab 1875, dept estab 1966; pub; D&E; ent req HS dipl; degrees BS (Art Educ); SC 18, LC3; enrl nonmaj 430, maj 35, GS 10.
Tuition: Res—Undergrad $205 per sem; Nonres—Undergrad $345 per semi; campus res $496.
Courses: ‡Art Education; Art History; Ceramics; Drawing; Handicrafts (fibers); Painting; Printmaking; Sculpture; Teacher Training.

Summer School: Courses—Various specialized workshops and art education offerings.

UNIVERSITY OF ALABAMA IN HUNTSVILLE, Department of
Art, 4701 University Dr, 35807 (Mailing Add: PO Box 1247, 35807). Tel: 205-895-6114. *Chmn Dept & Prof* Jeffrey J Bayer, MFA; *Assoc Prof* Richard C Pope, MFA; *Assoc Prof* John P Dempsey, MA; *Asst Prof* John A Sarn, PhD; *Instr* Rosemarie T Bernardi, MFA.
Estab 1969 (as independent, autonomous campus), dept estab 1965; pub; D&E ent req HS dipl, ACT; degrees BA; schol; SC 46, LC 14, enrl D 150.
Tuition: Res—Undergrad $215 (8-13 hrs.), $28 per hr; campus res pvt rm $68 mo.
Courses: Advertising Design; ‡Art Education; ‡Art History; Calligraphy; Collage, ‡Commercial Art; Drafting; Drawing; Film; Graphic Arts; Illustration; Industrial Design; Interior Design; Lettering; Mixed Media; Painting; Photography; ‡Printmaking; ‡Sculpture.
Adult Hobby Classes: Courses—Calligraphy; Watercolor; other misc. workshops offered through Division of Continuous Education.
Summer School: Dir Jeffrey J Bayer. Tui $215 for 8-13 hrs for term of 10 wk beginning mid-June. Courses—Varies from summer to summer, part of the 46 studio classes and some art history will be offered.

JACKSONVILLE

JACKSONVILLE STATE UNIVERSITY, Art Department, Pelham, 36265. Tel: 205-435-9820, exten 293. *Head* Dr Emilie E Burn, EdD; *Instr* Gail Z McCain, MA; *Assoc Prof* L R Manners, MA; *Asst Prof* Marvin Shaw, MFA; *Asst Prof* Phil Carpenter; MFA; *Asst Prof* Bill Page, MFA.
Estab 1883; pub; D&E; ent req HS dipl; ACT; degrees BS and BA 4 yr; SC 22, LC 8, GC 4; enrl D 7000, E 24, nonmaj 55, maj 75, GS 11; others office campus 15.
Tuition: Res—Undergrad $250 per sem, $22 per cr hr; grad $257 per sem, $28 per cr hr; campus res room and board $900 per yr.
Courses—‡Art Education; Art History; Ceramics; Commercial Art; Drawing; Graphic Arts; Jewelry; ‡Painting; Printmaking; Sculpture; Teacher Training.

LIVINGSTON

LIVINGSTON UNIVERSITY,* Division of Fine Arts, 35470. Tel: 205-652-5241. *Chmn* Dennis P. Kudlawiec; Instrs FT 3.
Estab 1835; state; degrees BA BS BMus MEd MSc; schol; enrl 1800.
Tuition: $165 per quarter, room and board $299 to $331.
Courses: Art Appreciation; Art Education; Art for the Teacher; Ceramics; Crafts; Design; Freehand Drawing; Graphics; History of Art; Industrial Design; Painting; Mechanical Drawing; Metal Work; Woodworking.

MARION

JUDSON COLLEGE,* Art Department, 36756. Tel: 205-683-2011. *Coordr* Sara Lucille Parker; Instrs FT 1, PT 1.
Estab 1838; den; D (a few evening classes); W; ent req HS grad, adequate HS grades and ACT scores; degree BA 3-4 yr; schol, workshops, loans, grants; SC 12, LC 6; enrl 450.
Tuition: Campus res available.
Courses: Crafts; Commercial Art; Design; Drawing; Painting; Watercolor; Special projects courses according to students' needs.
Adult Hobby Classes: Enrl 5. Courses—Studio drawing; Painting.
Children's Classes: Enrl 15. Courses—Studio Drawing.

MOBILE

SPRING HILL COLLEGE, Fine Arts Department, 36609. Tel: 205-460-2371. *Chmn & Assoc Prof* Daniel A Creagan, MA; *Instr* Barbara Patten, MFA; *Instr* Thomas Loehr, MFA.
Estab 1830, dept estab 1965; den; D&E; ent req HS dipl, ACT, CEEB, SAT; degrees BA Art and BA Art Therapy 4 yr; SC 6, LC 1, enrl D 40, nonmaj 35; maj 5;
Tuition: Undergrad $1260 per sem, $80 per hr; campus res room & board $770 per sem.
Courses: Art Education; Art History; ‡Art Therapy; ‡Ceramics; Drawing; Film; Graphic Design; ‡Painting; Photography; ‡Textile Design; Video.

UNIVERSITY OF SOUTH ALABAMA, Department of Art, 307 University Blvd, 36688. Tel: 205-460-6335. *Chmn & Assoc Prof* James E Kennedy, MAT; *Prof* John H Cleverdon, MA; *Asst Prof* Robert J Bantens, PhD; *Prof* James E Conlon, MA; *Prof* Lee M Hoffman, MFA; *Instr* Philippe Oszuscik; *Asst Prof* Lloyd L Patten, MS; *Assoc Prof* Linda Schele, MFA.

Estab 1963, dept estab 1964; pub; D&E; ent req HS dipl, ACT; degrees BA, BFA and BA Art Hist 4 yr; SC 32; LC 25; enr maj & 150.
Tuition: Res—Undergrad $14 per cr hr; campus residence room and board.
Courses: Advertising Design; Aesthetics; Architecture; Art Education; Art History; Ceramics; Commercial Art; Drawing; Graphic Arts; Painting; Photography; Printmaking; Sculpture.
Summer School: Chmn James E Kennedy. Tui $14 per cr hr. Courses—Drawing; Painting; Three-Dimensional Design.

MONTEVALLO

UNIVERSITY OF MONTEVALLO,* College of Fine Arts, Art Department, 35115. Tel: 205-665-2521, exten 224. *Dean* John Stewart; *Chmn* L Frank McCoy; Instrs FT 4.
Estab 1896; pub; D&E; ent req ACT; degrees BA, BS and BFA 4 yr; schol, work study; SC 35, LC 10, GC 7; enrl maj 80, others 2800.
Tuition: Res—Undergrad & grad $1345-$1605 per session (includes room and board); Nonres—Additional $210 per session.
Courses: Advertising Design; Art Education; Art History; Ceramics; Crafts; Design; Painting; Photography; Printmaking; Sculpture.
Summer School: Enrl 1000; two 5 wk sessions beginning June 5 and July 5.

MONTGOMERY

AUBURN UNIVERSITY AT MONTGOMERY, Art Department, 36109. Tel: 205-279-9110, exten 292. *Head Dept & Prof* Joseph Schwarz, PhD; *Prof* Charles Shannon, Dipl; *Asst Prof* Philip Coley, MFA; Instrs FT 4, PT 3.
Estab 1972; pub; D&E; ent req HS dipl; degrees BA; SC 18, LC 5, GC 4, enrl D 400, nonmaj 150, maj 50.
Tuition: Res—Undergrad $175 yr; no campus residence.
Courses: Art Education; Art History; Drawing; Graphic Arts; Painting; Photography; Sculpture.
Adult Hobby Classes: Courses—Painting.
Summer School: Head Joseph Schwarz. Tui $175. Courses—Same as above.

HUNTINGDON COLLEGE,* Department of Art, 1500 E Fairview Ave, 36106. Tel: 205-263-1611, exten 55. *Dir* Mae Belle Gay; Instrs PT 8.
Estab 1973; non-credit continuous educ prog; E; enrl 119.
Courses: Architectural Drafting; Architectural Rendering; Creative Thinking; Graphics; Lectures; Open Studio; Painting; Photography; Sculpture.

TROY

TROY STATE UNIVERSITY,* Department of Art, 36081. Tel: 205-566-3000, exten 278. *Dean School of Fine Arts* Dr John M Long; *Head Dept* Dr R C Paxson; Instrs FT 7.
Estab 1957; pub; ent req HS grad, ent exam; degrees BA and BS (Arts and Sciences) BA, BS and MS (Art Education); schol and fel; SC 23, enrl 100; LC 11, enrl 175.
Courses: ‡Aesthetics; ‡Art History; Commercial Art; Crafts; Design; Drawing; Graphic Arts; Jewelry; Lettering; Museology; Painting; Photography; Pottery; Sculpture; Teacher Training.
Summer School.

TUSKEGEE INSTITUTE

TUSKEGEE INSTITUTE,* Division of Humanities, College of Arts and Sciences, Art and Architecture Dept, 36088. Instrs FT 3.
Estab 1881; pvt; degree 4 yr.
Courses: Applied Art; Art Appreciation; Basic Design; Color; Crafts; Interior Design; Teacher Training; Textile Design; Weaving.

UNIVERSITY

UNIVERSITY OF ALABAMA, Art Department, Box F, 35486. Tel: 205-348-5967. *Chmn Dept & Prof* Angelo Granata, MFA.
Estab 1831, dept estab 1919; pub; D&E; ent req HS dipl, ACT; degrees BA and BFA 4 yr; MFA 2 yr; MA 1 yr; schol; SC 43, LC 12, GC 18, enrl D 950; maj 240; GS 17.
Tuition: Res—Undergrad & grad $333.75; nonres—Undergrad & grad $706.25; campus res room & board.
Courses: Art Education; Art History; Ceramics/Glass; Drawing and Design; Graphic Design; Painting; Photography; Printmaking; Sculpture.

Summer School: Dir Angelo Granata. Enrl 300; two 5 wk terms beginning June. Courses—Same as above.

ALASKA

ANCHORAGE

UNIVERSITY OF ALASKA AT ANCHORAGE,* College of Arts and Science, Department of Art, 2533 Providence Ave, 99504. Tel: 907-279-6622. Instrs FT 4, PT 5.
Pub; D&E; open enrl; degrees AA in art, BA in art 4 yr; schol; SC 22, LC 3-5; enrl 800.
Tuition: No campus res.
Courses: Art Education; Ceramics; Drawing; Graphic Arts; History of Art and Archaeology; Jewelry; Metalcraft; Painting; Photography; Sculpture; Stage Design; Teacher Training; Theatre Arts; Weaving.
Adult Hobby Classes: Same as in regular prog.
Summer School: Term of 13 wk beginning May. Courses—Ceramics; Drawing; Painting.

FAIRBANKS

UNIVERSITY OF ALASKA,* Department of Art, Fine Arts Complex, 99701. Tel: 907-479-7530. *Acting Head* Charles W Davis; Instrs FT 4, PT 1.
Estab 1963; pub; D&E; ent req HS diploma; degree BA 4 yr; schol; SC 28, LC 4, enrl D293, E 50, maj 45.
Tuition: Res—$160 per sem; Nonres—Undergrad $300 per sem, grad—$240 per sem, under 8 cr hr $20 per cr hr.
Courses: Ceramics; Drawing; Graphic Arts; History of Art & Archaeology; Jewelry; Lettering; Painting; Sculpture; Textile Design.
Adult Hobby Classes: Enrl 30 per class; tui $90 per 3 cr hr. Courses—Crafts; Drawing; Painting; under the direction of the community college.
Children's Classes: Enrl 40; tui $45 per 8 wk on Sat. Courses—Ceramics; Drawing & Painting; Sculpture; under the direction of the community college.
Summer School: Dir Dr William Pennebaker. Tui $63 per studio course plus lab fee $20 for term of 3 or 6 wk. Courses—Drawing; Painting; Printmaking; Sculpture; Watercolor.

ARIZONA

FLAGSTAFF

NORTHERN ARIZONA UNIVERSITY, Art Department, 86001. Tel: 602-523-4612. *Head* Dr R Piotrowski, EdD; *Primary Art Faculty;* Dr Donald Bendel, EdD; Dr Ruth Wingfield, PhD; Ellery Gibson, MS; Bruce Horn, MFA; Richard Beasley, MFA; M Webster, MFA; W Williams, MFA; vis prof—Kent Ibsen, Glass, spring workshop.
Estab 1899; pub; D&E; ent req HS dipl, ACT; degrees BFA and BS 4 yr, MA 1-2 yr; schol; SC 56, LC 19, GC 8-10; enrl D 400, E 100, nonmaj 250, maj 350, grad 20.
Tuition: Res—Undergrad & grad $400 yr, $200 per sem; Nonres—Undergrad & grad $1400 yr, $700 per sem; campus res available.
Courses: Advertising Design; Art Education; Art History; Calligraphy; Ceramics; Commercial Art; Conceptual Art; Constructions; Goldsmithing; Graphic Arts; Graphic Design; History of Art & Archaeology; Illustration; Jewelry; Lettering; Mixed Media; Museum Staff Training; Painting; Photography; Printmaking; Sculpture; Silversmithing; Teacher Training; Textile Design.
Adult Hobby Classes: Courses—Most of the above studio areas.
Children' Classes: Sat Morning art classes 6-15 yr.
Summer School: Dir R Piotrowski. Courses—Art History; Ceramics; Glass; Graphics; Paintings; Sculpture; Weaving.

MESA

MESA COMMUNITY COLLEGE, Department of Art, 1833 W Southern Ave, 85201. Tel: 602-833-1261, exten 270. *Chmn Dept Art* Jim Garrison, MA; *Primary Art Faculty:* Gene Corno, MA; Bill Voss, MA; Woodward Payne, MA; Marlan Miller, MA; Karen Stone, MFA; Ned Tuhey, MA.
Estab 1965; pub; D&E; ent req HS dipl or GED; degree AA 2 yrs; schol; SC 8, LC 5; enrl D 646, E 394.
Tuition: Res—$45 (10 hrs or more), $25 (9 hrs or more); Nonres—$715 (12 hrs or more), $60 (1-11 hrs); no campus res.

Courses: Advertising Design; Art History; Commercial Art; Drawing; Graphic Design; Handicrafts; History of Art & Archaeology; Jewelry; Lettering; Painting; Sculpture.

PHOENIX

GRAND CANYON COLLEGE, Art Department, 3300 W. Camelback Rd, 85061. Tel: 602-249-3300, exten 227. *Chmn* Dr. Crawford L. Russell, EdD; *Instr* Cary Adkins, MFA; *Instr* E. Lewis Lankford, BFA; *Instr* Anita H. Chestney, MFA.
Estab 1951; den; D&E; ent req HS dipl; degrees BA and BS; schol; SC 23, LC 10; enrl D 175, E 75, nonmaj 75, maj 40.
Tuition: Res—Undergrad $1329 yr; $610 per sem, or $45 hr; Nonres—Undergrad $1451 yr; $72.50 per sem, $45 per hr; campus res board and room.
Courses: Aesthetics; ‡Art History; Ceramics; Drawing; Jewelry; Mixed Media, Painting, Printmaking; Sculpture; Teacher Training.

KACHINA SCHOOL OF ART, 3801 N 30th St, 85016. Tel: 602-955-5930. *Dir* Jay Datus; Instrs FT 4, E 2.
Estab 1947; pvt; dipl, cert 36 mo; SC 5, LC 1; home study courses year round.
Courses: Advertising Design; Display; Drawing; Fashion Illustration; Graphic Arts; Illustration; Industrial Design; Interior Design; Lettering; Oil Landscape; Painting; Textile Design; Watercolor.

PHOENIX COLLEGE,* Department of Art & Photography, 1202 W Thomas Rd, 85013. Tel: 602-264-2492, exten 256. *Chmn* Doug Brooks, Instrs FT 7, PT 22.
Estab 1948; pub; ent req HS dipl; degree AA 2 yr; schol; enrl E 100, maj 125, others 500.
Tuition: Res—$45 per sem.
Courses: Art Appreciation; Basic Design; Ceramics; Commercial Art; Crafts; Drawing and Composition; Drawing & Perspective; Interior Design; Life Drawing; Mexican Arts & Crafts; Oil Painting; Painting; Photography (basic & color); Sculpture; Watercolor, Weaving.

PRESCOTT

YAVAPAI COLLEGE, Art Department, 86301. Tel: 602-445-7300. *Chmn* Glen L Peterson, MFA; *Instr* Edward V Branson, MA; *Instr* Elaine W Farrar, MA; *Instr* Vincent N Kelly, MA; *Instr* Richard B Marcusen, MFA.
Estab 1966, dept estab 1969; pub; D&E; ent req HS dipl; degrees AA 2yr; schol; SC 50, LC5; enrl D 1650 (total), E 1563 (total).
Tuition: Res—Undergrad $75 per sem, 1-6 cr hrs $36, $6 per cr hr; Nonres—Undergrad $650 per 12 hours; campus res $230, board $395 per sem.
Courses: Advertising Design; Art History; Ceramics; Commercial Art; Drafting; Drawing; Glass; Handicrafts (batik, crafts, dyeing, macrame, spinning; stitchery, weaving, wood); Indian art survey; Sculpture; Stained Glass; Watercolor; Welded metal.
Adult Hobby Classes: Enrl open; tui per course. Courses—Retirement college.
Children's Classes: Enrl open; Tui $15 per course. Courses—Ceramics; Drawing; Painting.
Summer School: Dir Donald D Hiserodt. Enrl open; tui $12 per sem hr for term of 6 wks beginning June 4. Courses—Ceramics; Drawing; Jewelry; Painting; Photography; Printmaking.

TEMPE

ARIZONA STATE UNIVERSITY, Department of Art, 85281. Tel: 602-965-3469. *Dean College of Fine Arts* Jules Heller, PhD; *Chmn* Leonard Lehrer, MFA.
Estab 1885; pub; D&E; ent req HS dipl, ACT; degrees BA and BFA 4 yr; MFA 3 yr; MA 2 yr; EdD 3 yr; SC 80, LC 74, GC 84; enrl D 33,000; maj 1600, grad 145.
Tuition: Res—Undergrad & grad $225 per sem; Nonres—Undergrad and grad $820; campus res room and bd $1200.
Courses: Aesthetics; ‡Art Education; ‡Art History; ‡Ceramics; ‡Drawing; ‡Graphic Design; Illustration; Intermedia; Jewelry; Lettering; Mixed Media; ‡Painting; ‡Photography; ‡Printmaking; ‡Sculpture; Textile Design; Wood Art; Watercolor; Papermaking; Furniture Construction.
Summer School: Chmn Leonard Lehrer. Tui $26 sem hr for term of 5 wks beginning June - July and July - August. Courses—Same as academic year.

THATCHER

EASTERN ARIZONA COLLEGE, 85552. Tel: 602-428-1133, exten 47. *Head* Justin Fairbanks, MFA; *Instr* David Meyer, BFA; Instrs PT 9.

Estab 1888, dept estab 1946; pub; D&E; ent req HS dipl or GED; degrees AA 2 yr; schol; SC 25, LC 3; enrl D 105, E 202, maj 12.
Tuition: Res—Undergrad $170 yr, $85 per sem, $28.50 PT, $18.50 per hr; Nonres—Undergrad $1200 yr, $600 per sem; $120 per month, $50 PT; campus res room and board $460 per yr, $230 per sem.
Courses: Advertising Design; Art History; Ceramics; Commercial Art; Drafting; Drawing; Handicrafts (weaving, lapidary); Illustration; Jewelry, Lettering; Painting; Photography; Sculpture; Silversmithing.

TUCSON

TUCSON MUSEUM OF ART SCHOOL,* 179 N Main Ave, 85705. Tel: 602-622-1327. *Dir of Educ* Thomas William Wiper; Instrs PT 21.
Estab 1924; pvt; D&E; no ent req; schol; SC 42, LC 2; enrl D&E 1139.
Tuition: Varies per course; no campus res.
Courses: Assemblage; Basket Weaving; Ceramics; Drawing; Fencing; Graphic Arts; Handicrafts; History of Art & Archaeology; Jewelry; Modern Dance; Painting; Photography; Sculpture; Textile Design; Three Dimensional Design; Weaving; Woodwork.
Adult Hobby & Children's Classes: Courses—Art; Crafts; Ceramics; Drawing; Dance; Painting; Sculpture; Theatre Workshop.
Summer School: Enrl 300.

UNIVERSITY OF ARIZONA, College of Fine Arts, Department of Art, 85721. Tel: 602-884-1251. *Dept Head* Howard Conant, EdD; *Coordr Painting/Drawing* Robert W McMillan, PhD; *Coordr Crafts,* Maurice Grossman; MA; *Coordr Photography* Harold Jones, MFA; *Coordr Art History* Robert M Quinn, PhD; *Coordr Art Education* Warren H Anderson, PhD; *Coordr Graphic Design* Carl Heldt, BFA; *Coordr Printmaking* Lynn Schroeder, MFA; vis prof—different visiting artist/scholar each semester, fall and spring.
Estab 1891, dept estab 1927; pub; D; ent req HS dipl, ACT; degrees BFA (Studio), BFA(Art Education) and BA(Art History) 4 yr, MFA(Studio) and MA(Art History or Art Education) 2—3 yrs; schol; SC 30, LC 21, GC 32; enrl D 3094, maj 570; grad 75.
Tuition: Res—Undergrad & grad $225 per sem; Nonres—Undergrad & grad 7-11 units $45 per unit, 12 or more units $545 per sem plus registration fee $275 per sem; campus res room & board res $1,905, nonres $3,095.
Courses: Advertising Design; Art Education; Art History; Ceramics; Commercial Art; Drawing; Graphic Arts; Graphic Design; Handicrafts (fibers); Illustration; Jewelry; Painting; Photography; Printmaking; Sculpture; Silversmithing.
Summer School: The University of Arizona offers two summer sessions each summer. Catalog (available in April) request by writing to: Summer Session Office, University of Arizona, Tucson, AZ 85721.

ARKANSAS

ARKADELPHIA

OUACHITA BAPTIST UNIVERSITY, School of Arts and Sciences, Department of Art, 400 Ouachita St (Mailing Add: Box 755, 71923). Tel: 501-246-4531, exten 196. *Chmn* Phares Raybon, MA; *Primary Faculty* Betty Berry, MSE.
Estab 1886, dept estab 1934; den; D; ent req HS dipl, ACT; degrees BA, BSE, BS and BME 4 yr, MSE and MME 1 yr; schol; SC 11, LC 2.
Tuition: Res & Nonres—Undergrad $715 per sem, $40 cr hr, grad $35 cr hr.
Courses: ‡Advertising Design; Aesthetics; ‡Art Education; Art History; Ceramics; Commercial Art; Costume Design and Construction; Graphic Arts; Handicrafts (Weaving, Macrame, Tole); History of Art and Archaeology; Illustration; Interior Design; Lettering; Painting; Photography; Sculpture; Teacher Training; ‡Theatre Arts.
Summer School: Dir Mike Arrington. Enrl 550; tui $35 cr hr; two terms of 5 wks beginning June 5.

CLARKSVILLE

COLLEGE OF THE OZARKS, Department of Art, Ward and College St, 72830. Tel: 501-754-3431. *Head Dept & Assoc Prof* Lyle Ward, MFA.
Estab 1836, dept estab 1952; den; D; ent req HS dipl, ACT; degrees BA and BS 4 yr; schol; SC 9; LC 2; enrl D 83, nonmaj 8, maj 17.
Tuition: Res & Nonres—Undergrad $810 yr; campus res room & board $900-$950.
Courses: Art Education; Art History; Art Appreciation; Ceramics; Drawing; Painting.
Summer School: Dir Lyle Ward. Workshop in Art Education and/or Painting.

COLLEGE CITY

SOUTHERN BAPTIST COLLEGE, 72476. *Chmn* Jerry Gibbons, MS; *Prof* Gerry McGough.
Den; D&E; schol.
Tuition: Campus res room and board.
Courses: Art Education; Ceramics; Conceptual Art; Drawing; Graphic Design; Painting; Theatre Arts.
Summer School: Dir Dr Jerrol Swain. Tui $560 for 12-16 hrs, $37.50 for less than 12 hrs, $32.50 for each additional hr over 16 hrs.

CONWAY

UNIVERSITY OF CENTRAL ARKANSAS, Art Department, 72032. Tel: 501-329-2931, exten 224. *Head Dept* Dr Jerry D Poole; Instrs FT 6.
Estab 1908; pub; ent req HS dipl; degrees 4 yr; SC 14, LC 4.
Tuition: Campus res.
Courses: Advanced Design; Art Appreciation; Art History; Ceramics; Color & Design; Commercial Art; Crafts; Drawing & Painting; Illustration; Lettering; Printmaking; Sculpture; Teacher Training.
Summer School.

FAYETTEVILLE

UNIVERSITY OF ARKANSAS, Art Department, 72701 (Mailing Add: FA 116, 72701). Tel: 501-575-5202. *Chmn Dept & Prof* Neppie Conner; MA; *Assoc Prof* Thomas D Turpin, MFA; *Assoc Prof* Robert P Sweeney, MFA; *Asst Prof* John W Smith, EdD; *Asst Prof* Robert F Ross, MFA; *Assoc Prof* Leo R Davis, MFA; *Asst Prof* Walter D Curtis; MFA; *Asst Prof* Edward C Bernstein, MFA.
Estab 1871; pub; D&E; ent req HS dipl, ent exam,GED; degrees MFA 2½ yr and BA 4 yr; schol; SC 34, LC 16, GC 20; enrl D 13,500, nonmaj 650, maj 260 GS 30.
Tuition: Res—Undergrad & grad $460 yr, $230 per sem, $23 per cr hr; Nonres—Undergrad & grad $630 yr, $315 per sem, $54.50 per cr hr; Registration and tui fees waived for students 60 yrs or older; campus res room & board $1105.
Courses: Advertising Design; Art Education; Art History; Calligraphy; Ceramics; Commercial Art; Constructions; Drawing; Graphic Arts; Graphic Design; Jewelry; Lettering; Painting; Photography; Printmaking; Sculpture; Teacher Training.
Adult Hobby Classes: Courses—Painting; Sculpture; Ceramics.
Summer School: Assoc Provost Dr Kenneth R Cook.

HELENA

PHILLIPS COUNTY COMMUNITY COLLEGE,* Department of English and Fine Arts, Box 785, 72342. Tel: 501-338-6496, exten 61. *Chmn* Larry Spakes; Instrs FT 1, PT 1.
Estab 1966; pub; D&E; ent req HS dipl, ent exam, GED; degrees AA and AAS 2 yr; schol; SC 8, LC 1; enrl D&E 55.
Tuition: Res—$10 per cr hr; Nonres—$15 per cr hr.
Courses: Ceramics; Drafting; Drawing; History of Art & Archaeology; Painting.
Summer School: Tui same. 5 wk term beginning May 28.

LITTLE ROCK

ARKANSAS ARTS CENTER, Mac Arthur Park, 72203 (Mailing Add: PO Box 2137, 72203). Tel: 501-372-4000. *Exec Dir* Townsend Wolfe, BFA; *Dir of Educ* Rebecca Rogers Witsell, BFA; *Primary Faculty* Rosemary Fisher, Dipl; Don Hayes, MFA; Randall Timmone, MFA; Fred Wilson, MA; Cathryn Rounsavall, MFA; Linda Ettinger, MS; Instrs FT 5, PT 20; visiting artist workshop prog- special prog- week-long-sessions various nationally known prof artists.
Estab 1960, dept estab 1965; pub; D&E; open to anyone-age 3 through adult; schol; SC 56, LC 1; enrl D 300, E 324 children and adults.
Tuition: 12-week course for adults-$58 12 wk course for children-$32 dance classes-$25 per mo.
Courses: Art History; Ceramics; Design; Drawing; Glass; Goldsmithing; Graphic Arts; Graphic Design; Handicrafts; Jewelry; Painting; Photography; Pottery; Printmaking; Sculpture; Silversmithing; Stage Design; Theatre Arts; Woodworking.
Summer School: Dir of Educ Rebecca Rogers Witsell. Term of 8 wk Courses—same as regular session.

PHILANDER SMITH COLLEGE,* Department of Art, 812 W 13th St, 72203. *Chmn* Ralph L Odom; Instrs FT 1, PT 3.
Estab 1952; pvt; degrees BA 4 yr (in cooperation with the Arkansas Arts Center); schol; SC 12, LC 4; enrl 600; maj 5, others 35.
Tuition: $475 for 36 weeks.
Courses: Afro-American Art History; Art Appreciation; Arts & Crafts; Art History; Basic Design; Drawing; Painting; Printmaking; Sculpture.
Summer School: Dir Dr Crawford Mims.

UNIVERSITY OF ARKANSAS AT LITTLE ROCK,* Department of Art, 32nd & University Sts, 72204. Tel: 501-565-7531, exten 323. Instrs FT 6, PT 4.
Estab 1928; pub; D&E; ent req HS grad; degree BA 4 yr; schol; SC, LC; enrl 5000.
Courses: Art Education; Art History; Commercial Art; Crafts; Design; Drawing; Painting; Pottery; Printmaking; Sculpture.

MAGNOLIA

SOUTHERN ARKANSAS UNIVERSITY, Magnolia Branch, Jackson & Southern University, 71753. Tel: 501-234-5120, exten 224. *Chmn* Willard C Carpenter, MA; *Asst Prof* Fred Henry, MFA; *Asst Prof* Dianne O'Hern, MA.
Estab 1909; pub; D&E; ent req HS dipl; degrees BA and BSE 4 yr; schol; SC 18, LC 4; enrl D 240, nonmaj 190, maj 50.
Tuition: Res—Undergrad $100 per sem, grad $23 per sem hr; Nonres—Undergrad $230 per sem, $33 per sem hr.
Courses: Art Education; Art History; Ceramics; Drawing; Graphic Arts; Painting; Printmaking; Sculpture; Teacher Training; Theatre Arts.
Summer School: VPres Acad Affairs Dr L H Logan.

PINE BLUFF

SOUTHEAST ARKANSAS ARTS AND SCIENCE CENTER, Little Firehouse Studio (Mailing Add: 200 E Eighth, 71601). Tel: 501-536-3375. *Prog Supervisor* Alan Lisembly, BSE; Instrs FT 1, PT 4-5; vis prof varies according to curriculum.
Estab 1966; pvt; D&E; community oriented curriculum; classes are noncredit; no degrees granted; SC 14, LC 1; enrl D 200, E 250, non-credit students.
Tuition: $15-$75 per course; No campus res.
Courses: Art Education; Art History; Ceramics; Drawing; Graphic Arts; Jewelry; Painting; Photography; Printmaking; Raku Pottery; Theatre Arts.
Children's Classes: Enrl 15, tui $15 per course. Courses—Crafts; Drawing; Mixed Media; Painting; Pottery; Weaving. Special workshops with guest artists.
Summer School: Dir Alan Lisembly, BSE.

RUSSELLVILLE

ARKANSAS TECH UNIVERSITY, Department of Art, 72801. Tel: 501-968-0244. *Head Dept* Ed Wilwers, MFA; *Asst Prof* Ron Reynolds, MS; *Asst Prof* Gary Barnes, MA.
Estab 1909; pub; D&E; ent req HS dipl; degrees BA and BFA 4 yr; schol; SC 28, LC 5, GC 1; enrl D 200, nonmaj 130, maj 75.
Tuition: Res—Undergrad $245 per sem, $21 per cr hr, grad $25 per cr hr; Nonres—Undergrad $420 per sem, $36 per cr hr, grad $42.50 per cr hr; No campus res.
Courses: Advertising Design; Aesthetics; Architecture; Art Education; Art History; Ceramics; Commercial Art; Conceptual Art; Display; Drafting; Drawing; Exhibit and Display; Graphic Arts; Graphic Design; Illustration; Industrial Design; Lettering; Painting; Printmaking; Teacher Training.
Summer School: Head Dept Ed Wilwers. Enrl 30-50; tui res—$90, nonres—$155 for term of 6 wk beginning June 5 and July 10. Courses—Drawing; Design; Painting; Art Education; Art History.

SEARCY

HARDING COLLEGE, Department of Art, Box 938, 72143. Tel: 501-268-6161, exten 426. *Prof Art & Head Dept* Elizabeth Mason, MA; *Assoc Prof* Don Robinson, MA; *Asst Prof* Faye Doran, DEd; *Asst Prof* Paul Pitt, MA; *Instr* Lowell Carr, MFA; *Instr* Stanley Greene, BSE.
Estab 1932; pvt; D; ent req HS dipl, ACT; degrees BA and BS 4 yrs; schol; SC 21, LC 12, GC 6; enrl 600, nonmaj 350, maj 90, grad 5.
Tuition: Campus res room and board.
Courses: Advertising Design; Aesthetics; ‡Art Education; ‡Art History; Ceramics; Commercial Art; Drawing; Graphic Arts; Jewelry; Painting; Sculpture; Teacher Training.
Summer School: Asst to the Pres James F Carr, EdD.

SILOAM SPRINGS

JOHN BROWN UNIVERSITY, Art Department, 72761. Tel: 501-524-3131. *Head Dept & Asst Prof* Doris I Brookhart, MFA, *Instr* Phyllis B. Pope, MFA.
Estab 1919; pvt; D; ent req HS grad; SC 9, LC 3, no maj.

Tuition: $1600 yr, $800 per sem, $67.50 per sem hr; campus res room & board $1150.
Courses: Art Education; Art History; Commercial Art; Design and Color; General Art; Handicrafts (copper tooling, enameling, jewelry, macrame, mosaic, pottery, weaving); Illustration; Painting; Teacher Training.

STATE UNIVERSITY

ARKANSAS STATE UNIVERSITY, Department of Art, Drawer AAAA, 72467. Tel: 501-972-3050. *Prof Art & Chmn Dept* Karl Richards, PhD; *Prof* Evan Lindquist, MFA; *Assoc Prof* T R Baker, DEd; *Assoc Prof* James Johnson, MFA; *Assoc Prof* R E Mitchell, MFA; *Asst Prof* Tom Chaffee, MFA; *Asst Prof* John Keech, MFA; Instrs FT 14.
Estab 1909, dept estab 1938; pub; D&E; ent req HS dipl; degrees BFA, BSE and BS 4 yrs; schol; SC 33, LC 10, GC 4; enrl D 800, E 100, nonmaj 800, maj 180, grad 3.
Tuition: Res—$230 per sem, $20 per sem hr; Nonres—$380 per sem, $30 per sem hr; campus res room and board $820 per yr.
Courses: ‡Advertising Design; Aesthetics; ‡Art Education; Art History; Calligraphy; ‡Ceramics; ‡Commercial Art; Constructions; Drawing; ‡Graphic Arts; ‡Graphic Design; History of Art & Archaeology; ‡Illustration; ‡Jewelry; Lettering; ‡Painting; ‡Printmaking; ‡Sculpture; ‡Silversmithing; Stage Design; ‡Teacher Training; Theatre Arts.
Adult Hobby Classes: Enrl 100; tui $20 per sem hr. Courses—Painting; Ceramics; Jewelry; Printmaking.
Summer School: Tui res—$105, nonres—$165 for term of 5 wks beginning June 5 and July 10. Courses—Art Education; Art Appreciation; Drawing; Painting; Art History; Commercial Art; Watercolor; Selected Studio Courses.

CALIFORNIA

APTOS

CABRILLO COLLEGE,* Visual Arts Division, 6500 Soquel Dr, 95003. Tel: 408-425-6464. *Chmn* Holt E Murray; Instrs FT 9, PT 10.
Estab 1959; pub; D&E; ent req HS dipl; degrees AA 2 yr; SC 46, enrl 24, LC 7, enrl 45.
Courses: Ceramics; Drawing; Graphic Arts; Graphic Design; Handicrafts; History of Art & Archaeology; Jewelry; Painting; Photography; Sculpture; Textile Design.
Summer School.

ARCATA

HUMBOLDT STATE UNIVERSITY,* Art Department, 95521. Tel: 707-826-3625. Instrs FT 20.
Estab 1913 pub; D&E; degrees BA 4 yr, BA with credential, 5 yr; schol; SC 35, LC 11, GC 11.
Tuition: Campus res.
Courses: Ceramics; Graphic Design; Design; Jewelry & Metalsmithing; Painting; Photography; Printmaking; Sculpture; Teacher Training.
Children's Classes: Enrl 10; art 12.
Summer School: Enrl 800; for 6 wk from June 22.

BAKERSFIELD

BAKERSFIELD COLLEGE,* Art Department, 1801 Panorama Dr, 93305. Tel: 805-871-7120. *Head Dept* Victor Bracke; Instrs FT 10, PT 2.
Estab 1913; pub; D&E; ent req ent exam, open door policy; degree AA 2 yr; SC 16, LC 4; enrl D 6000, maj 150-200.
Tuition: None.
Courses: Architecture; Ceramics; Commercial Art; Drafting; Drawing; Glassblowing; Graphic Arts; History of Art & Archaeology; Illustration; Jewelry; Lettering; Painting; Photography; Sculpture; Stage Design; Theatre Arts.
Adult Hobby Classes: Enrl 100-150. Courses—Ceramics; Painting.
Summer School: Dir Dr Richard Harkins. For term of 6 wk beginning June. Courses—Ceramics; Design; Drawing; Figure Drawing; Photography.

BELMONT

COLLEGE OF NOTRE DAME,* Department of Art, 1400 Ralston Ave, 94002. Tel: 415-593-1601. *Chmn* Robert David Ramsey; Instrs FT 2, PT 6.

Estab 1951; den; D&E; ent req HS grad, ent exam; degrees BA 3½-4 yr, MAT; schol; SC 18, LC 12; enrl D 200, E 70, maj 50.
Courses: Aesthetics; Art Education; Ceramics; Costume Design; Drawing; Environmental Design; Etching; History of Art & Archaeology; Interior Design; Painting; Photography; Sculpture; Silk Screen; Weaving.
Summer School: Dir Mary Emmanuel Donnelly. Upper division courses as in regular program plus special art education workshops; 6 wk term.

BERKELEY

UNIVERSITY OF CALIFORNIA AT BERKELEY, College of Letters and Science, Department of Art and History of Art, 94720. *Prof & Co-Chmn Dept* James Cahill, PhD; *Assoc Prof & Co-Chmn Dept* Jerrold Ballaine, MFA; History of Art Faculty FT 13, vis instr 4; Art Faculty FT 15, vis instr 4-6.
Estab 1868; pub; D; ent req undergrad ent req same as for ent to Univ; degrees in art: BA, MA, MFA; in history of art: BA, MA, PhD; schol; SC approx 20, LC approx 60.
Tuition: Res—Undergrad $237 per quarter, grad $257 per quarter; Nonres—Undergrad $872 per quarter, grad $892 per quarter; campus res.
Courses: Art History; Ceramics; Drawing; Painting; Printmaking; Sculpture.

CARMEL

CARMEL ART INSTITUTE,* PO Box 9, 93921. Tel: 408-624-9951. *Pres & Dir* John Cunningham; Instrs FT 3.
Estab 1938, inc 1955; pvt; D (Mon through Fri); 4 yr course for Fine Arts, objective painter; Certificate of Completion. Approved for veterans.
Courses: Aesthetics; Anatomy; Design; Etching; Lithography; Painting.
Summer School: Two 6 wk sessions.

CHICO

CALIFORNIA STATE UNIVERSITY, CHICO, Art Department, 95929. Tel: 916-895-5331 or 895-5218. *Chmn* Richard Hornaday.
Estab 1887; pvt; D&E; ent req ent exam & test scores; degrees BA 4 yr, MS 1½ yr minimum; SC 39, LC 29, GC 29; enrl nonmaj & maj 1704, grad 59.
Tuition: Res—$85.50 per sem for less than 6 cr hrs, $100.50 per sem for over 6 cr hrs. Nonres—Same as resident plus $52.50 additional fee for each sem unit up to 15 units. $787.50 for 15 units or more.
Courses: Aesthetics; Art History; ‡Ceramics; ‡Collage; ‡Drawing; ‡Painting; ‡Printmaking; ‡Sculpture; ‡Teacher Training.
Summer School: Chmn Richard Hornaday. Courses—Same as above.

CLAREMONT

PITZER COLLEGE,* Department of Art, 1050 N Mills Ave, 91711. Tel: 714-626-8511. *Prof Art* C H Hertel; Instrs FT 3, PT 1.
Estab 1964; pvt; D; ent req HS dipl, various criteria, apply Dir of Admis; degree BA 4 yr; schol; SC 8, LC 6; enrl Sept-June maj 19, grad 10 (Claremont Grad School).
Tuition: $4070, campus res $5990.
Courses: Aesthetics; Ceramics; Drawing; Environments; Graphic Arts; History of Art & Archaeology; Painting; Photography; Sculpture; Weaving. As one of the Claremont Colleges, cross-registration in Ceramics, Environments, Film Arts, Graphic Arts and Weaving.

POMONA COLLEGE, Art Department, College & E Bonita Aves, 91711. Tel: 714-626-8511, exten 2221. *Prof & Chmn Dept* Gerald M Ackerman, PhD; *Asst Prof* Judson J Emerick, PhD; *Instrs* David Rubin, MA; *Vis Asst Prof* Gail L Geiger, PhD; *Assoc Prof* David W Steadman, PhD; *Asst Prof* Charles Daugherty, MFA; *Asst Prof* Timothy App, MFA; *Asst Prof* Norman P Hines, MFA; *Lectr* Leland Rice, MFA; *Prof* Samella Lewis, PhD; *Assoc Prof* Arthur D Stevens, PhD.
Estab 1887; pvt; D; ent req HS dipl; degree BA 4 yr; schol; SC 20, LC 22; enrl D 150, nonmaj 130, maj 20.
Tuition: Res—Undergrad $2925 per sem, $5850 yr; Nonres—$2000 per sem, $4000 yr; campus res, room & board.
Courses: Art History; Ceramics; Collage; Conceptual Art; Constructions; Drawing; Graphic Arts; History of Art & Archaeology; Painting; Photography; Sculpture.

SCRIPPS COLLEGE, Art Department, Lang Art Bldg, Ninth at Columbia, 91711. Tel: 714-624-2616. *Assoc Prof & Chmn Dept* Arthur D Stevens, PhD; *Assoc Prof* Neda Al-Hilali, MFA; *Prof* Alan Blizzard, PhD; *Prof* Aldo Casanova, PhD; *Prof* Paul Darrow, MFA; *Prof* James Fuller, MA; *Prof* Paul Soldner, MFA.
Estab 1928, dept estab 1933; pub; D; ent req HS dipl; degrees BA; schol; enrl D 580, nonmaj 480, maj 100.
Tuition: Res—$6200 yr.
Courses: Architecture; Art History; Ceramics; Drawing; Film; History of Art & Archaeology; Painting; Photography; Printmaking; Sculpture; Fabrics; Watercolor.

COLUMBIA

COLUMBIA COLLEGE, Department of Physical, Creative & Performing Arts, PO Box 1849, 95310. Tel: 209-586-3141, exten 214, 248. *Chmn Dept* David Purdy, MA; *Instr* Joel Bauber, MA; *Instr* Dale Bunse, MFA.
Estab 1968; pub; D&E; ent req HS dipl or over 18 yrs old; degree AA 2 yrs; SC 50, LC 4; enrl D 100, E 75, nonmaj 90, maj 10.
Tuition: None; no campus res.
Courses: Art History; Calligraphy; Ceramics; Costume Design & Construction; Drawing; Jewelry; Lettering; Painting; Photography; Printmaking; Sculpture; Silversmithing; Stage Design; Textile Design; Theatre Arts.
Summer School: Dir C H Palmer. Courses—Ceramics; Watercolor.

COMPTON

COMPTON COMMUNITY COLLEGE,* Art Department, 1111 E Artesia Blvd, 90221. Tel: 213-635-8081, exten 283. Instrs FT 1, PT 5.
Estab 1929; pub; D&E; ent req HS dipl, 21 yrs of age; degree AA 2 yr; schol; SC 16, LC 6; enrl D 3500, E 2000, maj 18.
Courses: Advertising Design; Afro-American Art; Art Education; Design; Drafting; Drawing; General Crafts; History of Art & Archaeology; Lettering; Painting; Photography; Showcard Writing; Theatre Arts (separate dept).
Summer School: Courses—Art Appreciation; History.

CORONA DEL MAR

BRANDT PAINTING WORKSHOPS, 405 Goldenrod Ave, 92625. Tel: 714-675-0093. *Co-Dir* Rex Brandt, BA; *Co-Dir* Joan Irving; vis prof—George Post, watercolor, 4 wks.
Estab 1946; pvt; D; ent req grad degree in art or equivalent; schol; SC 3; enrl D 145.
Tuition: 11 day session $175; no campus res. Summer School only.
Courses: Painting.

CORONADO

CORONADO SCHOOL OF FINE ARTS, 176 C Ave (Mailing Add: PO Box 156, 92118). *Dir* Monty Lewis; Instrs FT D 2, E 1, PT 6.
Estab 1944; pvt; dipl 3-4 yr; SC, LC; enrl D 50, E 25, children 15.
Tuition: $120 per 4 wk, PT $78 per 4 wk, children 4 Sat AM $20. Approved for Veterans and Foreign Students.
Courses: Advertising Design; Art History; Commercial Art; Fine Arts; Graphic Arts; Illustration; Mural Decoration; Painting; Sculpture.
Summer School: Dir Monty Lewis. Enrl 75; tui $120 per 4 wk; Watercolor Seminar $76 per 4 wk, $120 per 8 wk.

COSTA MESA

ORANGE COAST COLLEGE,* Division of Fine Arts, 2701 Fairview, 92626. Tel: 714-556-5514. *Chmn* Paul Cox; Instrs FT 38, PT 55.
Estab 1946; pub; D&E; ent req ent exam; degree AA 2 yr; schol; SC 288, LC 52; enrl D 1500, E 1400, Maj 2397.
Tuition: No tuition; no campus res.
Courses: Advertising Design; Architecture; Art Education; Basic Crafts; Ceramics; Commercial Art; Display; Drafting; Drawing; Exhibition Design; Fashion Arts; Graphic Arts; Graphic Design; History of Art & Archaeology; Illustration; Industrial Design; Interior Design; Jewelry; Landscape Architecture; Lettering; Museum Staff Training; Occupational Therapy; Painting; Photography; Sculpture; Stage Design; Teacher Training; Textile Design; Theatre Arts; Weaving Fibers.
Adult Hobby Classes: Courses—Furniture Refinishing.
Summer School: Courses offered same as above.

CYPRESS

CYPRESS COLLEGE, Fine Arts Dvision, 9200 Valley View St, 90630. Tel: 714-826-2220, exten 292. *Chairperson* Lester Johnson, MA.

Estab 1966; pub; D&E; ent req HS dipl; degree AA 2 yrs; enrl D 12,100.
Tuition: $47.50 per unit; no campus res.
Courses: Advertising Design; Art History; Ceramics; Costume Design & Construction; Drawing; Film; History of Art & Archaeology; Jewelry; Painting; Printmaking; Sculpture; Stage Design; Textile Design; Theatre Arts.
Adult Hobby Classes: Adults may take any classes offered both day and extended; also offer adult education classes.
Summer School: Extended Day Coordr Dr Bonnie Fouste.

DAVIS

UNIVERSITY OF CALIFORNIA, DAVIS,* College of Letters and Science, Art Department, 95616. Tel: 916-752-0105. *Prof & Head Dept* Richard D Cramer; Instrs FT 17.
Estab 1952; pub; D; degrees BA 4 yr, MA, MFA; schol; SC 28, LC 35; enrl Maj 130, others 1000.
Tuition: Res—$228.50; Nonres—$635 per quarter.
Courses: Architectural Design; Art History; Ceramics; Drawing; Film Making; Graphic Arts; Painting; Photography; Sculpture.
—Laboratory for Research in the Fine Arts and Museology. Tel: 916-752-0106. *Acting Dir* R D Cramer.
Along with the basic study of conservation and museum techniques and the training of museum workers, the Laboratory is building archives which will list the contents and appropriate date of collections in California from major museums which share the cooperative effort with the Laboratory.

DOMINGUEZ HILLS

CALIFORNIA STATE UNIVERSITY, DOMINGUEZ HILLS,* Department of Fine Arts, 1000 E Victoria, 90747. Tel: 213-532-4300. *Prof & Chmn* Marshall Bialosky; Instrs FT 9, PT 3.
Estab 1965; pub; D&E; ent req upper one-third of HS class; degree BA 4 yr; SC 35, LC 25; enrl maj 130.
Tuition: None; no campus res.
Courses: Aesthetics; Design; Drawing; Graphics; History of Art & Archaeology; Painting; Sculpture; Teacher Training.

EL CAJON

GROSSMONT COLLEGE,* Art Department, 8800 Grossmont College Dr, 92020. Tel: 714-465-1700. Instrs FT 11.
Estab 1961; pub; D&E; no ent req; unit and curriculum req for grad; degree AA; schol; SC 22, LC 1; total enrl 1000.
Tuition: None; no campus res.
Courses: Ceramics; Composition; Drawing; History of Art; Painting; Photography; Primitive Art; Sculpture.
Summer School: Courses—Ceramics; Drawing; Photography.

EUREKA

COLLEGE OF THE REDWOODS,* Art Department, 95501. Tel: 707-443-8411. Instrs FT 5 PT 8.
Estab 1964; pub; D&E; ent req HS grad; degree AA 2 yr; schol; SC 15, LC 3 per quarter; enrl 4000, art maj 75.
Courses: Art Fundamentals; Ceramics; Commercial Art; Drafting; Drawing; Fabrics; Graphic Arts; History of Art & Archaeology; Jewelry; Lettering; Painting; Photography; Sculpture.
Summer School: Courses to be announced; tui free.

FRESNO

CALIFORNIA STATE UNIVERSITY, FRESNO, Art Department, Maple & Shaw Aves, 93740. Tel: 209-487-2516. *Chmn Dept* Roger Bolomey, MA; *Prof* Joyce Aiken, MA; *Assoc Prof* Terry Allen, BFA; *Assoc Prof* Charles Gaines, MFA; *Prof* Heinz Kusel, MA; *Prof* Ed Lund, MFA; *Prof* Ara Dolarian, MA; *Asst Prof* Raphael Reichert, PhD.
Estab 1911, dept estab 1915; pub; D&E; ent req HS dipl, SAT, ACT, CEEB; degrees BA, MA; schol; enrl D 1200, nonmaj 980, maj 220, grad 50.
Tuition: Res—Undergrad $104 per sem, $87 part-time, grad dependent upon number of units; Nonres—$891.50 per sem, $874.50 part-time, grad dependent upon number of units; campus res room & board.
Courses: Aesthetics; Art Education; Art History; Calligraphy; Ceramics; Collage; Conceptual Art; Drawing; Goldsmithing; Graphic Design; Jewelry; Lettering; Mixed Media; Gallery Staff Training; Painting; Photography; Printmaking; Sculpture; Silversmithing; Teacher Training; Textile Design.
Adult Hobby Classes: Tui $35 unit. Courses—Various.

Summer School: Tui $35 unit for term of 6 wks beginning June 15. Courses—Various, mainly Ceramics.

FULLERTON

CALIFORNIA STATE UNIVERSITY, FULLERTON, Art Department, 92634. Tel: 714-870-3471. *Dean Sch Arts* Jerry Samuelson, MA; *Chmn Dept* Don Lagerberg, MA.
Estab 1957, dept estab 1959; pub; D&E; ent req HS dipl, SAT or ACT; degrees BA 4 yrs, MA 1 yr; SC 62; LC 27, GC 12; enrl grad 117, undergrad 806.
Tuition: Res—Undergrad & grad $80 per 6 units, $95 for 6.1 or more units; Nonres—Undergrad & grad $52.50 per units plus $95; no campus res.
Courses: Architecture; Art Education; Art History; Calligraphy; Ceramics; Display; Drawing; Film; Goldsmithing (metal); Graphic Arts; Graphic Design; Weaving, Woodworking; History of Art & Archaeology; Illustration; Jewelry; Lettering; Museum Staff Training; Painting; Photography; Printmaking; Sculpture; Silversmithing (metal); Teacher Training; Textile Design.

FULLERTON COLLEGE,* Fine Arts/Art Department, 321 E Chapman Ave, 92634. Tel: 714-871-8000. *Chmn* Kenneth W Helvey; Instrs FT 20, PT 8.
Estab 1913; pub; D&E; ent req HS dipl, ent exam; degree AA 2 yr; schol.
Tuition: No campus res.
Courses: Advertising Design; Aesthetics; Architecture; Art Education; Ceramics; Commercial Art; Costume Design & Construction; Drafting; Drawing; Fashion Arts; Graphic Arts; Graphic Design; Handicrafts; History of Art & Archaeology; Illustration; Industrial Design; Jewelry; Landscape Architecture; Lettering; Painting; Photography; Sculpture; Stage Design; Teacher Training; Textile Design; Theatre Arts.

GILROY

GAVILAN COLLEGE,* Art Department, 5055 Santa Terese Blvd, 95020. *Chmn Humanities Div* Kent Child; Instrs FT 2, PT 6.
Estab 1919; pub; D&E; ent req HS dipl or 18 yr of age; degree AA 2 yrs; SC 15, LC 2; enrl D 150, E 75, maj 30.
Tuition: None to res; no campus res.
Courses: Ceramics; Drafting; Drawing; Graphic Arts; History of Art & Archaeology; Jewelry; Painting; Photography; Sculpture; Teacher Training; Theatre Arts.
Adult Hobby Classes: Enrl 25. Courses—Ceramics.
Summer School: Courses—Ceramics; Drawing; Painting.

GLENDALE

GLENDALE COLLEGE, Department of Fine Arts, 1500 N Verdugo Rd, 91208. Tel: 213-240-1000. *Chmn Dept* Robert Belknap, MA; *Prof* Leonard de Grassi, MA; *Assoc Prof* Clyde Johnson, BA; *Prof* Robert E Thomsen, MA; *Prof* Robert W Brown, MA; *Prof* Louis Gross, MA; *Prof* Martin Mondrus, MA; *Asst Prof* Andrew Georgias, MA; *Prof* Emil Miller, MA.
Estab 1927; pub; D&E; ent req HS dipl, ent exam; degree AA 2 yrs; SC 25, LC 7; enrl D 4100, E 3900, nonmaj 800, maj 200.
Tuition: None.
Courses: Advertising Design; Architecture; Art History; Ceramics; Commercial Art; Drafting; Drawing; Film; Graphic Arts; Graphic Design; History of Art & Archaeology; Jewelry; Lettering; Painting; Photography; Printmaking; Sculpture; Stage Design; Theatre Arts.
Summer School: Dir Dr Charles Wheelock. Term of 8 wk beginning end of June. Courses—Art History; Photography.

HAYWARD

CALIFORNIA STATE UNIVERSITY, HAYWARD, Art Department, 94542. Tel: 415-881-3111. Instrs FT 18, PT 1-3.
Estab 1960; pub; D&E; ent req HS dipl, ent exam, ACT; degree BA 4 yr; schol; SC 30, LC 12; enrl 9000.
Tuition: Varies per unit and type of program.
Courses: Aesthetics; Architecture (lecture); Ceramics; Drawing; History of Art; Lettering; Museum Staff Training; Painting; Photography; Printmaking; Sculpture.
Summer School.

CHABOT COLLEGE,* Humanities Division, 25555 Hesperian Blvd, 94545. Tel: 415-782-3000, exten 287. *Chmn* R Glenn Leuning; Instrs FT 240, PT 400.
Estab 1961; pub; D&E; ent req HS dipl; degree AA 2 yr; schol; SC 27, LC 5.

Tuition: None to res; Nonres—$24.49 per quarter unit, 15 units or more, $367.35 per yr; no campus res.
Courses: Advertising Design; Art Education; Ceramics; Commercial Art; Costume Design & Construction; Drafting; Drawing; History of Art & Archaeology; Illustration; Lettering; Painting; Sculpture; Stage Design; Theatre Arts.
Summer School: Term of 6 wk. Courses—Art History; Drawing; Introduction to Art; Sculpture.

HOLLYWOOD

HOLLYWOOD ART CENTER SCHOOL,* 2025-2027 N Highland Ave, 90028. Tel: 213-851-1103. Instrs FT 1, PT 7.
Estab 1912; pvt; D&E; ent req HS dipl, submission of art work; cert 3 yrs; SC 6; enrl D 40, E 12.
Courses: Advertising Design; Ceramics; Commercial Art; Costume Design & Construction; Display; Drafting; Drawing; Fabric Design; Furniture; Graphic Arts; Graphic Design; History of Art; Illustration; Industrial Design; Interior Design; Lettering; Painting; Sculpture; Textile Design.

HUNTINGTON BEACH

GOLDEN WEST COLLEGE, Fine and Applied Arts Division, 15744 Golden West St, 92647. Tel: 714-892-7711, exten 553. *Chmn* John Wordes, MA; *Primary Art Faculty* R Alderette, MA; P Sopocko, MA; R Camp, MFA; H Warner, MA; J Heard, MA; D Ebert, MA; N Tornheim, MA; B Conley, MA; R Schiffner, MA; J Wordes, MA; K Mortenson, MFA; P Donaldson, MA; H Clemans, MA; Instrs PT 22.
Estab 1966; pub; D&E; ent req HS dipl; degree AA 2 yrs; SC 12, LC 6; enrl D 10,000, E 11,000.
Tuition: Nonres—Undergrad $48 per unit.
Courses: ‡Advertising Design; Art History; Calligraphy; Ceramics; Costume Design & Construction; Display; Drafting; Drawing; Film; Graphic Arts; Graphic Design; Illustration; Interior Design; Jewelry; Lettering; Mixed Media; Painting; Photography; Printmaking; Sculpture; Silversmithing; Stage Design; Textile Design; Theatre Arts; Video.
Summer School: Dir Dr Loren Moll.

IDYLLWILD

UNIVERSITY OF SOUTHERN CALIFORNIA, IDYLLWILD CAMPUS, Idyllwild School of Music and the Arts, PO Box 38, 92349. Tel: 714-659-2171. *Chmn Painting & Drawing Workshops* Francoise Gilot; *Primary Art Faculty* Joseph Mugnaini, Fritz Scholder, Sueo Serisawa, Susan Peterson, Charlene Weisberg and Maria Martinez.
Estab 1880, sch estab 1950; pvt; D; ent req interest; degrees are not granted by the Idyllwild Campus, credits (university) can be earned through USC - LA Campus; documentation is provided to high school so that credits can be given; schol; SC 2. The Idyllwild School of Music and the Arts is a summer program only with courses in the arts for all ages. Term of 10 wks, beginning June 18th, enrl open.
Tuition: Ranges from $128 to $165 wk; campus res room & board.
Courses: Ceramics; Drawing; Graphic Arts; Graphic Design; Handicrafts (weaving, sandpainting, basketweaving); Jewelry; Painting; Photography; Sculpture; Silversmithing; Theatre Arts (dance & drama).
Adult Hobby Classes: Enrl open; tui $165 wk. Courses—Tewa Pottery; Hopi Silversmithing; Navajo Two Grey Hills Weaving; Sandpainting.
Children's Classes: Enrl open; tui $70 - $75 per wk, $35 for ½ day program. Day and residential Children's Arts Program; also Youth Ceramics.

IRVINE

UNIVERSITY OF CALIFORNIA, IRVINE,* School of Fine Arts, Studio Art Department, 92717. Tel: 714-833-6648. *Dean* Clayton Garrison; *Chmn* Melinda Wortz; Instrs FT 8, PT 4.
Estab 1965; pub; D; ent req HS dipl; degrees BA(Studio Art) 4 yr, MFA(Art); schol; SC 24, LC 2, GC 4.
Tuition: Nonres—$635 per quarter, $952.50 per sem.
Courses: Ceramics; Costume Design & Construction; Drawing; History of Art & Archaeology; Motion Pictures; Painting; Sculpture; Stage Design; Theatre Arts.

KENTFIELD

COLLEGE OF MARIN, Department of Art, 94904. Tel: 415-485-9480. *Chmn Dept* Martin C Stoelzel, MFA, *Primary Art Faculty* Rick Hall, MFA; Deborah Loft, MA; Glen Miller, MA; Timo Pajunen, MFA; Alton Raible, MFA; Nancy Soper, MA; Gilbert Wheat, MA; Thano Johnson, MA; Allan Widenhofer, MA; Betty Wilson, MA; Tom Johnson, MA.

Estab 1926; pub; D&E; ent req HS dipl, ent exam; degree AA, AS 2 yrs; SC 48, LC 8; enrl D 5000.
Tuition: Res—Only tui is for lab fees for some classes; Nonres—$840 per sem, $56 per unit; no campus res.
Courses: Advertising Design; Architecture; Art History; Calligraphy; Ceramics; Drawing; History of Art & Archaeology; Illustration; Interior Design; Jewelry; Museum Staff Training; Painting; Photography; Printmaking; Sculpture; Textile Design.
Adult Hobby Classes: Courses—Drawing; Calligraphy; Printing; Illustration.
Children's Classes: College for Kids (varied).
Summer School: Dir Cal Darrow. Courses—Drawing; Painting; Ceramics; Color; Textile Arts.

LAGUNA BEACH

LAGUNA BEACH SCHOOL OF ART, 2222 Laguna Canyon Rd, 92651. Tel: 714-494-1520. *Admin Dir* Ruth Osgood Salyer; *Primary Art Faculty* Ray Jacob, Lewis Cohen, Sueo Serisawa, Armen Gasparian, Maria Klein, Jerry Podany, Roger Armstrong, David Bowen and Charla Ilgner.
Estab 1962; pvt; D&E; ent req HS dipl or desire to learn at any age beyond high school; degrees BFA 4 yrs, cert of completion 3 yrs; schol; SC 20, LC 1.
Tuition: Res—$70 each 6 hr class per quarter.
Courses: Art History; Ceramics; Collage; Drawing; Graphic Arts; Graphic Design; Interior Design; Jewelry; Mixed Media; Painting; Photography; Printmaking; Sculpture; Silversmithing.
Children's Classes: Enrl 15; tui $20 per quarter. A 2 hr class on Sat.

LA JOLLA

UNIVERSITY OF CALIFORNIA, SAN DIEGO, Visual Arts Department, B-027, 92093. Tel: 714-452-2860. *Assoc Prof & Chmn Dept* Standish D Lawder, PhD; *Prof* David Antin; *Assoc Prof* Eleanor Antin; *Prof* Harold Cohen; *Prof* Manny Farber; *Prof* Newton Harrison; *Acting Prof* Madlyn Kahr; *Prof* Allan Kaprow; *Assoc Prof* Sheldon Nodelman; vis prof—Jerome Rothenberg, poetry/performance, 1978-79.
Estab 1967; pub; D&E; ent req HS dipl; degrees BA(Studio Art, Art History/Criticism, & Communications/Visual Arts) 4 yrs; MFA(Studio or Art Criticism) 2-3 yrs; schol; SC 55, LC 30, GC 15; enrl D 3600, maj 245, grad 35.
Tuition: Res—Undergrad & grad $232 per quarter; Nonres—Undergrad & grad $635 per quarter; campus res $684 per quarter (3 quarters/yr).
Courses: Art History; Collage; Conceptual Art; Drawing; Film; Intermedia; Mixed Media; Painting; Photography; Sculpture; Video; Art Criticism/Film Criticism.

LANCASTER

ANTELOPE VALLEY COLLEGE, 3041 W Ave K, 93534. Tel: 805-943-3241. *Dean* Jeannine Andrews, MS; *Primary Art Faculty* Pat Hinds and Richard Sim.
Estab 1929; pub; D&E; degree AA 2 yrs.
Tuition: Nonres—Undergrad $1170 yr; no campus res.

LAVERNE

LA VERNE COLLEGE,* Division of Humanities, 1950 Third St, 91750. Tel: 714-593-3511, exten 269. *Assoc Prof Art* Joella Mahoney; Instrs FT 2, PT 3.
Estab 1899; pvt; D&E; ent req HS dipl; degree BA(Art) 4 yr; schol; SC 12, LC 4; enrl D 125, E 60, Maj 6.
Courses: Batik; Ceramics; Drawing; History of Art & Archaeology; Painting; Photography; Quilt & Patch Work; Sculpture; Stained Glass; Theatre Arts.

LONG BEACH

CALIFORNIA STATE UNIVERSITY AT LONG BEACH,* Art Department, 6101 E Seventh St, 90840. Tel: 213-498-4376. *Chmn* Howard G Hitchcock; Instrs FT 50, PT 25.
Estab 1949; pub; ent req HS grad, ent exam; degrees BA, BFA 4 yr, MA, MFA; SC 164, LC 26, GC 23; enrl 2000.
Tuition: Res—$196 per yr; Nonres—$787.50 per yr; campus res $1450-$1700 per yr.
Courses: Art Education; Art History; Ceramics; Display & Exhibition; Drawing; General Art; General Crafts; Graphic Design; Illustration; Industrial Design; Interior Design; Metalsmithing & Jewelry; Painting; Printmaking; Sculpture; Textile Design.

Summer School: Dean Dr Roderick Peck. Tui $35 per unit for one 6 wk session from June 22.

LONG BEACH CITY COLLEGE, Department of Art, 4901 E Carson St, 90808. Tel: 213-420-4319. Head Dept Art Ted Baird, MA; Primary Art Faculty Joseph Donat, MA; James Simpson, MA; Richard Keyes, MA; Joseph Hooten, MA; Robert McMenomy, MA.
Pub; D&E; ent req HS dipl, ent exam; degrees AA and Cert 2 yrs; SC 13, LC 2; enrl in dept D 400, E 200, nonmaj 450, maj 150.
Tuition: None.
Courses: Advertising Design; Art History; Ceramics; Collage; Commercial Art; Drawing; Fashion Arts; Film; Handicrafts (stained glass, weaving); History of Art & Archaeology; Illustration; Jewelry; Lettering; Mixed Media; Painting; Photography; Printmaking; Sculpture; Stage Design; Theatre Arts; Video.
Adult Hobby Classes: Enrl 800; tui none. Courses—Drawing; Painting; Crafts.
Summer School: Tui none. Courses—Same as above.

LOS ANGELES

ART IN ARCHITECTURE/JOSEPH YOUNG, 1434 S Spaulding Ave, 90019. Tel: 213-933-1194 or 656-2286. Dir Joseph L Young, AB & Hon Doctorate; vis faculty of architects, art historians, city planners, landscape architects and arts administrators.
Estab 1955; pvt; D; ent req HS dipl, cert or dipl from professional art school; schol; SC 4, LC 4; enrl varies throughout yr as study programs are structured to fit needs of individual artist.
Tuition: $900 for annual nine month program.
Courses: Aesthetics; Architecture; Art History; Collage; Conceptual Art; Constructions; Drafting; Drawing; Graphic Design; Intermedia; Mixed Media; Mosaics; Painting; Photography; Sculpture; Stained Glass.
Professional art in architecture studio that has an apprentice program in the design, execution and installation of commissions.

CALIFORNIA STATE UNIVERSITY, LOS ANGELES, Art Department, 5151 State University Drive, 90032. Tel: 213-224-3521. Chmn T W Little, MA; Assoc Chmn Charles Borman, MA.
Estab 1947; pub; D&E; ent req HS dipl, ent exam; degrees BA(Art) 4 yr, MA(Art) 1 yr; SC 85, LC 12, GC 9; enrl D 2500 (Art), nonmaj 45%, maj 55% GS 180 (per quarter).
Tuition: Res—Undergrad and grad $62 per quarter; Nonres—Undergrad and grad $35 per hr; no campus res.
Courses: Advertising Design; Aesthetics; Art Education; Art History; Calligraphy; Ceramics; Commercial Art; Costume Design and Construction; Drawing; Enameling; Fashion Arts; Graphic Arts; Graphic Design; Handicrafts (textiles, weaving); History of Art and Archaeology; Illustration; Interior Design; Jewelry; Lettering; Painting; Photography; Printmaking; Sculpture; Silversmithing; Teacher Training; Textile Design.
Children's Classes: Courses—Art 450; Art Education Workshop (Saturday classes).
Summer School: Summer Quarter same as any academic quarter.

EL CAMINO COLLEGE, Division of Fine Arts, 16007 Crenshaw Blvd, 90506. Tel: 213-532-3670 Exten 526. Dean Div Lewis E Giigel, EdD; Instrs FT 19, PT 21.
Estab 1947; pub; D&E; ent req HS dipl; degree AA 2 yrs; schol; SC 46, LC 6; enrl D 2650, E 1380, nonmaj 3319, maj 711.
Tuition: None; no campus res.
Courses: ‡Advertising Design; Architecture; Art History; Calligraphy; Ceramics; Costume Design & Construction; Display; Drafting; Drawing; Goldsmithing; Handicrafts (enameling); History of Art & Archaeology, ‡Industrial Design; Interior Design; Jewelry; Lettering; Museum Staff Training; Painting; Photography; Printmaking; Sculpture; Silversmithing; Stage Design; Textile Design; Theatre Arts.
Children's Classes: Subjects—Exploration of Children's Art.
Summer School: Enrl Limited; tui none for term of 6 wks, beginning June 19. Courses—Art Appreciation; Freehand Drawing; Ceramics.

LOS ANGELES CITY COLLEGE, Department of Art, 855 N Vermont Ave, 90029. Tel: 213-663-9141, exten 240. Chmn & Prof Kazuo Higa, MA; Prof Russell Cangialosi, PhD; Prof Clyde Kelly, MA; Prof Paul Pascoe, MA; Assoc Prof Olga Kooyman, MA; Assoc Prof Raoul De Sota, MA; Asst Prof Phyllis Muldavin, MA; Asst Prof Gloria Bohanon, MA; Asst Prof Lee Whitten, MA; Instrs PT 11.
Estab 1929; pub; D&E; ent req HS dipl and over 18 yrs of age; degrees AA 2 yr; schol; SC 48, LC 8; enrl D 450, E 150; nonmaj approx ⅔, maj approx ⅓.
Tuition: No tuition $6.50 student fee but not required.

Courses: ‡Advertising Design; Aesthetics; Architecture; ‡Art History; Ceramics; ‡Commercial Art; Display; Drawing; ‡Graphic Design; Handicrafts; ‡History of Art and Archaeology; Lettering; ‡Painting; Printmaking; Sculpture.
Adult Hobby Classes: Enrl 2090; tui approx $20 per class of 8 wk.
Children's Classes: Tui approx $20 per class for 8 wk.
Summer School: Chmn Kazuo Higa. Enrl 250. Tui none term of 6 wk, beginning June 19. Courses—Basic courses only.

LOYOLA MARYMOUNT UNIVERSITY, College of Fine and Communication Arts, Department of Art, 80th St & Loyola Blvd, 90045. Tel: 213-642-3099 or 642-3059. Dean Col Fine & Communication Arts Carl Melvin Davidson, PhD; Assoc Prof Art & Chmn Dept Genevieve Underwood, MFA; Prof Pauline Khuri-Majoli, MA; Assoc Prof Regina Buchholz, PhD; Asst Prof Teresa Munoz, MA; Asst Prof Rudolf Fleck, MA; Asst Prof Katherine Harper Lorenzana, PhD; Asst Prof Susan Barnes Robinson, Ph.D.
Estab as Marymount Col in 1940, merged with Loyola Univ 1968; pvt; D; ent req HS dipl; degree BA 4 yrs; schol; SC 37, LC 21.
Tuition: Campus res room & board.
Courses: Advertising Design; ‡Art Education; ‡Art History; Ceramics; Display; Drawing; Film; Jewelry; Lettering; Mixed Media; Painting; Photography; Printmaking; Sculpture; Silversmithing; Stage Design; ‡Studio Arts; Theatre Arts.
Summer School: Dean Continuing Educ & Summer Session Dr Leon Levitt.

OCCIDENTAL COLLEGE,* Art Department, 1600 Campus Rd, 90041. Tel: 213-259-2749. Chmn George R Goldner; Instrs FT 5, PT 3.
Estab 1887; pvt; D; ent req HS dipl, col transcript, SAT, recommendations; degree BA 4 yr; col schol & grants according to need; SC 19, LC 25, GC 5; enrl maj 50, others 300.
Tuition: $1317, Campus res $540-$605 per term (3 terms, plus summer session).
Courses: Art Education; Art History; Drawing; Graphics; Painting; Sculpture; Theory & Criticism.
Summer School: Enrl art dept 25. Courses—Art Education; Art History; Ceramics (SC); Glass Blowing (SC).

OTIS ART INSTITUTE, 2401 Wilshire Blvd, 90057. Tel: 213-387-5288. Acting Dir/Dean Peter D Clothier, PhD; Chmn Intermedia Miles Forst; Chmn Printmaking Shiro Ikegawa; Chmn Ceramics Helen Watson; Chmn Gen Studies Wanda Westcoast; Chmn Drawing Charles White; Chmn Painting Emerson Woelffer.
Estab 1918; pub; D&E; ent req 30 sem hr; degrees BFA 2 yrs, MFA 2 yrs; schol; SC 52, LC 16, GC 24; enrl D 330, E 78, maj 102, grad 98, others 208.
Tuition: $1600 per yr, $830 per sem, $65 per unit; special classes $75 per unit; no campus res.
Courses: Aesthetics; Art History; Ceramics; Collage; Conceptual Art; Constructions; Drawing; Graphic Arts; History of Art & Archaeology; Intermedia; Mixed Media; Painting; Printmaking; Sculpture; Video.
Adult Hobby Classes: Enrl 208; tui $140 per unit. Courses—Painting; Drawing; Ceramics; Printmaking; Sculpture.
Summer School: Tui $65 for term of 6 wks beginning mid-June. Courses—Painting; Drawing; Ceramics; Printmaking; Sculpture; Intermedia.

UNIVERSITY OF CALIFORNIA, LOS ANGELES,* College of Fine Arts, Department of Art, 405 Hilgard Ave, 90024. Tel: 213-825-1770. Instrs 53.
Estab 1919; degrees AB 4 yr, MA, MFA, PhD; teaching assistantships; enrol maj 700. General Catalog may be obtained from Office of Admis for information on admis req, fees, schol.
Courses: Ceramics Design; Costume Design; Drawing; Glass Design; Graphic Design; History of Art; Industrial Design; New Forms & Concepts; Painting; Photography; Prints; Sculpture, Textiles Design; Video Design.

UNIVERSITY OF SOUTHERN CALIFORNIA,* School of Architecture and Fine Arts, Department of Fine Arts, 90007. Tel: 213-746-2788. Instrs FT 16, PT 6.
Dept Fine Arts estab 1887; pvt; D&E; degrees AB, BFA 4 yr, AM, MFA, PhD; enrl maj in Fine Arts 187.
Tuition: $128 per unit.
Courses: Art Education; Art History; Three-Dimensional Arts; Two-Dimensional Arts.
Junior Art Program: Enrl 55; tui $30 per sem. Courses—Two-Dimensional & Three-Dimensional Art.
Summer School: Tui $128 per unit; 7 wk session from June 18-August 4.

WOODBURY COLLEGE,* Division of Professional Arts, 1027 Wilshire Blvd, 90017. Tel: 213-482-8491. Chmn Rosalie F Utterbach.

Estab 1884; pvt; D&E; degree BS (Professional Arts) 5 yr; enrl maj 525, others 1600; accelerated study.
Courses: Art Education; Commercial Art; Fashion Design; Interior Design.

MALIBU

PEPPERDINE UNIVERSITY,* Fine Arts Division, 24255 Pacific Coast Hwy, 90265. *Chmn* L E McCommas; *Instrs* FT 4, PT 1.
Estab 1937; pvt; D; grad 8 trimesters, with credential 10 trimesters; degrees BA, MA; schol; LC 5, workshop 23; enrl maj 35, others 135.
Tuition: $119 per unit; room and board per trimester $880; campus res semiprofessional.
Courses: Crafts; Fine Arts; Teacher Training (Professional, 5 yr).
Summer School: Tui $82 sem unit.

MARYSVILLE

YUBA COLLEGE,* Fine Arts Division, N Beale Rd, 95901. Tel: 916-742-7351. *Chmn* Carol McGee; *Instrs* FT 14, PT varies.
Estab 1927; pub; D&E; ent req HS grad or 18 yr of age; degree AA 2 yr; schol; SC 23, LC 2; enrl total 1437, maj 493.
Tuition: None to res; Nonres—$420 per yr, foreign (Visa) $200 per yr; campus res $1200 per yr.
Courses: Advertising Design; Aesthetics; Art Education; Ceramics; Drafting; Drawing; Graphic Arts; Lettering; Painting; Photography; Sculpture; Stage Design; Theatre Arts.
Summer School: Dean & Assoc Dean Community Educ Rex McDougal. Term of 6 wk beginning mid-June. Courses—Full curriculum, plus Home Decorative Arts; Lapidary; Navajo Silversmithing; Non-Loom Weaving.

MENDOCINO

MENDOCINO ART CENTER, INC, 45200 Little Lake St (Mailing Add: PO Box 36, 95460). Tel: 707-937-5818. *Exec Dir* Robert N Avery, Jr, BFA; *Chairperson Textile Arts* Lolli Jacobsen, MFA; *Chairperson Fine Arts* Charles Stevenson, BA.
Estab 1959, inc 1974; pvt; D&E; ent req interview and portfolio; cert of completion in painting/drawing and textile arts, 3 yrs each; SC 24, LC 6; enrl D 18, maj 18.
Tuition: $1500 yr, $45 wk; campus res $800 yr.
Courses: Art Education; Art History; Calligraphy; Ceramics; Collage; Conceptual Art; Constructions; Costume Design & Construction; Display; Drawing; Graphic Arts; Illustration; Mixed Media; Painting; Photography; Printmaking; Sculpture; Textile Design.
Adult Hobby Classes: Enrl 10-25 maximum; tui $45 per wk. Courses—Wood Carving; Dollhouse Building; Watercolor; Stained Glass; Sculpture.
Children's Classes: Enrl 35 maximum; tui $25 per wk. Courses—Multimedia.
Summer School: Exec Dir Robert Avery, Jr. Enrl approx 90-100 wk; tui $45 for 1 wk, $365 for 9 wks beginning June 26. Courses—Over 40 classes in almost all media.

MODESTO

MODESTO JUNIOR COLLEGE, Arts, Humanities and Speech Division, College Ave, 95366. Tel: 209-526-2000, exten 270. *Chairperson Div* Lloyd E Faulkner, MA; *Instr* Raymond E Bates, MA; *Instr* Paul J Corrigan, MA; *Instr* Terry L Hartman, MA; *Instr* Walter F Lab, MAA; *Instr* Daniel W Petersen, MA; *Instr* Jerry M Reilly, MFA; *Instrs* Joseph G Remsing, MA; faculty FT 259, PT 385.
Estab 1921, div estab 1964; pub; D&E; ent req grad of accredited high school, minor with California High School Proficiency Cert and parental permission, 11th and 12th graders with principal's permission, persons 18 or older who are able to profit from the instruction; degrees AA and AS 2 yrs; schol; enrl 16,024 total.
Tuition: Res—$4 health fee; Nonres—$42 per sem unit to maximum of $631 per sem plus health fee; no campus res.
Courses: Advertising Design; Architecture; Art History; Ceramics; Display; Drafting; Drawing; Enameling; Film; Jewelry; Lapidary; Lettering; Painting; Photography; Printmaking; Sculpture; Silversmithing; Theatre Arts.
Adult Hobby Classes: Subjects—Arts & Crafts; Lapidary.
Summer School: Dir Dr Julius C Manrique. Courses—a wide variety offered. Tui $2 health fee.

MONTEREY

MONTEREY PENINSULA COLLEGE, Division of Creative Arts, Art Department, 980 Fremont St, 93940. Tel: 408-649-1150. *Chairperson Div Creative Arts* Joe L Hysong, MA; *Chairperson Dept Art* Richard N Janick, MA; *Instr* Peter Pilat, MA; *Instrs* Pat Boles, BA; *Instr* Richard

Bibler, MA; *Instr* Alex Gonzales, MFA; *Instr* Pam Durr, MA; *Instr* Joe Tanous, MA; *Instr* Skip Kadish, MA.
Estab 1947; pub; D&E; ent req HS dipl, 18 yrs old or older; degree AA and AS 2 yrs; schol; SC 17, LC 8; enrl D 1343, E 623, maj 160.
Tuition: None to res; Nonres—$28 per unit; no campus res.
Courses: Architecture; Art History; Ceramics; Drawing; Jewelry; Lettering; Mixed Media; Painting; Photography; Sculpture; Silversmithing; Textile Design.
Summer School: Dir Joe L Hysong. Term of 6 wks beginning June. Courses—Same as above.

MONTEREY PARK

EAST LOS ANGELES COLLEGE,* Art Department, 1301 E Brooklyn Ave, 91754. Tel: 213-263-7261. *Instrs* FT 7, PT, 21.
Estab 1949; pub; D&E; ent req ent exam; degree AA 2 yr; SC 35, LC 10; enrl D 700, E 620, maj 1320.
Courses: Advertising Design; Aesthetics; Ceramics; Commercial Art; Costume Design & Construction; Display; Drawing; Fashion Arts; Graphic Arts; Graphic Design; History of Art & Archaeology; Illustration; Jewelry; Lettering; Painting; Sculpture; Textile Design; Weaving.
Children's Classes: Enrl 120. Courses—Ceramics; Drawing; Painting; Sculpture.

NORTHRIDGE

CALIFORNIA STATE UNIVERSITY, NORTHRIDGE, Department of Art-Two Dimensional Media, 18111 Nordhoff St, 91330. Tel: 213-885-2348. *Dept Chmn* Art Weiss, MFA.
Estab 1956; pub; D&E; ent req HS dipl, GRE, SAT; degrees BA 4-5 yrs, MA; SC 13, GC 5; enrl in dept D&E 2231, grad 101.
Courses: ‡Advertising Design; Airbrush; Animation; Calligraphy; ‡Drawing; ‡Graphic Arts; ‡Graphic Design; Illustration; Lettering & Typography; Packaging Graphics; ‡Painting; ‡Photography; ‡Printmaking; Reproduction Graphics.
Summer School: Dir Art Weiss. Tui $39 per unit for 8 wks beginning June 26. Courses—Drawing; Painting; Photography; Airbrush; Advertising Graphics; Beginning Design; Packaging; Reprographics; Illustration.

NORWALK

CERRITOS COMMUNITY COLLEGE,* Art Department, 11110 Alondra Blvd, 90650. *Chmn* Wilburt Fenner; *Instrs* FT 9, PT 20.
Estab 1956; pub; D&E; ent req HS dipl or 18 yrs of age; degree AA 2 yrs; schol; SC 36, LC 6.
Tuition: None for res; Nonres $32 per unit.
Courses: Aesthetics; Architecture; Ceramics; Commercial Art; Display; Drawing; General Crafts; Graphic Arts; Graphic Design; History of Art & Archaeology; Jewelry; Lettering; Museum Staff Training; Painting; Photography; Sculpture; Theatre Arts.

OAKLAND

CALIFORNIA COLLEGE OF ARTS AND CRAFTS, 5212 Broadway, 94618. Tel: 415-653-8118. *Pres* Harry X Ford, MA; *Primary Art Faculty* Viola Frey, Dr Ruth Boyer, Marvin Lipofsky, Florence Resnikoff, Steve Reott, Andry Addkison, Dean Snyder, Dr Piroja Shroff, Dr Michael Wright, Mary Snowden, Vincent Perez, Dennis Leon, Hugh Wiley, Harry Critchfield, Charles Gill, Bella Feldman, John Dunbar, Dr Trude Piatkowski, and Robert Harper.
Estab 1907; pvt; D&E; ent req HS dipl, Sat or ACT requested not required, C grade-point average, 1 sem of lab science; degrees BFA 4 yrs, MFA 1½ yrs, MAEd 2 yrs, 3-yr cert; schol; SC 24, LC 58, GC 5; enrl D 1081, nonmaj 128, maj 953, grad 126, exten school 152.
Tuition: Per trimester $1425; campus res.
Courses: Advertising Design; Aesthetics; Architecture; Art Education; Art History; Calligraphy; ‡Ceramics; ‡Crafts; Conceptual Art; Drafting; ‡Drawing; ‡Environmental Design; ‡Ethnic Studies; Film; ‡Fine Arts; ‡General Design; ‡Glass; Goldsmithing; Graphic Arts; ‡Graphic Design; History of Art & Archaeology; ‡Illustration; ‡Interior Design; ‡Jewelry; Lettering; Mixed Media; ‡Painting; ‡Photography; Printmaking; ‡Sculpture; Silversmithing; Teacher Training; Textile Design; ‡Textiles; ‡Video/TV; Wood.
Adult Hobby Classes: Enrl 152; tui $50-$70. Courses—Design; Drawing; Painting; Photography; Film & TV; Printmaking; Papermaking.
Children's Classes: Enrl 75; tui $35 per cl. Courses—Crafts; Drawing; Printmaking; Ceramics.
Summer School: Dir Ken Davids. Enrl 230 per session; tui $135 for term of 5 wks beginning mid May, June, July. Courses—Full range.

HOLY NAMES COLLEGE,* Art Department, 3500 Mountain Blvd, 94619. Tel: 415-436-0111. *Instrs* FT 2, PT 7.

Estab 1917; pvt; D&E; ent req HS dipl; degree BA 4 yrs; schol; SC 30, LC 3.
Courses: Art Education; Bookbinding; Calligraphy; Ceramics; Drawing; History of Art & Archaeology; Jewelry; Lettering; Painting; Photography; Printmaking; Textile Design; Weaving.

LANEY COLLEGE,* Art Department, 900 Fallon St, 94607. *Chmn* Carol Joy & Ted Odza; Instrs FT 10, PT 9.
Estab 1962; pub; D&E; ent req HS dipl; degree AA 2 yrs; SC 52, LC 8; enrl art dept D 1600, E 600.
Courses: Advertising Design; Architecture; Cartooning; Ceramics; Commercial Art; Costume Design & Construction; Display; Drafting; Drawing; Fashion Arts; Graphic Arts; Graphic Design; History of Art & Archaeology; Illustration; Industrial Design; Interior Design; Jewelry; Kinetic Art; Landscape Architecture; Lettering; Macrame; Painting; Photography; Sculpture; Stage Design; Textile Design; Theatre Arts.

MILLS COLLEGE, Art Department, 5000 MacArthur Blvd (Mailing Add: PO Box 9975, 94613). Tel: 415-632-2700, exten 263. *Prof Art & Chmn Dept* Ralph S DuCasse, MFA; *Prof* Robert A Dhaemers, MFA; *Vis Lucie Stern Prof* Ron Nagle, MFA; *Lectr* Carol Molly Prier, MFA; *Lectr* Joanne Leonard, BA; *Lectr* Ralph Reed, MFA; *Lectr* William Wu, MA; *Assoc Prof* Wanda Corn, PhD; *Asst Prof* Joanne Bernstein, PhD.
Estab 1852; pvt; D; ent req HS dipl, SAT, Advanced Placement Exam; degrees BA 4 yrs, MFA 2 yrs; schol; SC 23, LC 22, GC 20; enrl grad 16-20.
Tuition: Res—Undergrad $5550 yr, grad $1500 yr, $750 per sem, $250 per course, $125 per ½ course; Nonres—Undergrad $3512 yr; Other $170 course to adult; campus res room & board $1990 yr.
Courses: Aesthetics; ‡Art History; Ceramics; Collage; Constructions; Costume Design & Construction; Drawing; Film; Illustration; Intermedia; Mixed Media; Museum Staff Training; Painting; Photography; Practice of Art; Printmaking; Sculpture; Stage Design; Theatre Arts; Video.
Children's Classes: Subjects—Ceramics.

OCEANSIDE

MIRACOSTA COLLEGE, Creative Arts Department, 92054. Tel: 714-757-2121, exten 270. *Chmn* Howard Ganz, MA; *Instrs* Kristina Rice, MFA; *Instrs* Daniel Camp, MFA; *Instrs* Erik Gronberg, MA.
Estab 1934; pub; D&E; ent req HS dipl, GED test, probationary student; degrees AA and AS normally 2 yrs; schol; SC 12, LC 4, enrl maj 200.
Tuition: Res—no fee; nonres—$42 per sem unit of college credit with max of $630 per sem; no campus res.
Courses: Aesthetics; Art History; Ceramics; Drafting; Drawing; Film; Graphic Arts; Handicrafts (design workshop in crafts, design workshop in fibers); Interior Design; Jewelry; Painting; Photography; Printmaking; Sculpture; Stage Design; Theatre Arts.
Summer School: Courses—Ceramics; Free -Hand Drawing; Life Drawing; Painting; Watercolor Painting.

OROVILLE

BUTTE COMMUNITY COLLEGE, Humanities Division (III), Rte 1, Box 183 A, 95965. Tel: 916-895-2544. *Div Chairperson* Joseph Rich, MA; *Coordr* Albert J Walsch, Jr, MA; *Prof* John R Wilson, MA; *Prof* Jeffrey Nelson, MA; *Ceramic Coordr* Dr Ronald Benson, PhD; vis prof—Sal Casa and Ruben Heredia, commercial art.
Estab 1968; pub; D&E; ent req HS dipl or 18 yrs or older; degree AA 2 yrs; schol; SC 21, LC 4; enrl D 3100, E 4000.
Tuition: $5-$9 per cr hr; no campus res.
Courses: Ceramics; Commercial Art; Costume Design & Construction; Drafting; Fashion Arts; Photography; Video.
Adult Hobby Classes: Subjects—Stained Glass; Macrame.
Summer School: Dir Ken Lucas. Tui $5-$9 per cr hr.

PALM DESERT

COLLEGE OF THE DESERT,* Art Department, 43-500 Monterey Ave, 92260. Tel: 714-346-8041. Instrs FT 3, PT 4.
Estab 1962; pub; D&E; ent req HS dipl, ent exam; degree AA 2 yrs; schol; SC 10, LC 3; enrl D 150, E 150, maj 15.
Tuition: None; no campus res.
Courses: Ceramics; Crafts; Drawing; History of Art; Introduction to Art; Painting; Photography; Printmaking; Sculpture.

PASADENA

ART CENTER COLLEGE OF DESIGN, 1700 Lida St, 91103. Tel: 213-577-1700, exten 264. *Pres & Dir* Don Kubly, BA; *Acad Dean* Dr Harvey, PhD; *Communication Design Chmn* Chuck Davidson, BFA; *Fine*

Arts Dept Chmn Laurence Drieband, MFA; *Film Dept Chmn* Jim Jordan, BA; *Photography Dept Chmn* Charles Potts, BPA; *Industrial Design Chmn* Keith Teter, BS.
Estab 1930; pvt; D&E; ent req HS dipl, ACT, SAT if no col background, portfolio required, at least 12 samples of work in proposed maj; degrees BFA 4 yrs, MFA additional 48 units plus master's proj & thesis; schol; SC 168, LC 82, GC 22; enrl D 1000, E 200, nonmaj 200, maj 1000, grad 20.
Tuition: Res—$1400 for 15 wk sem (trimester); no campus res.
Courses: ‡Advertising Design; ‡Advertising Illustration; Art Education; Art History; ‡Commercial Art; Display; Drawing; ‡Environmental Design; ‡Fashion Arts; ‡Fashion Illustration; ‡Film; Graphic Arts; ‡Graphic Design; ‡Graphic Packaging; History of Art & Archaeology; ‡Illustration; ‡Industrial Design; Landscape Architecture; Lettering; Painting; ‡Photography; ‡Product Design; ‡Transportation Design; Video.

PASADENA CITY COLLEGE, Art Department, 1570 E Colorado St, 91106. Tel: 213-578-7238. *Chmn Dept* Walter W Girdner, MA; *Area Chmn Design* John Caldwell, MA; *Area Chmn Studio Art* Ben Sakaguchi, MA; *Area Chmn Photography* Norm Abbey, MA; *Area Chmn Art Hist* Vern Wells, MA & Dick Cassady, MA; *Area Chairperson Apparel Arts* Lily Heftman, MA; *Area Chmn Crafts* John Dickenhof, MA; *Area Chmn Ceramics* Phil Cornelius, MA.
Estab 1902, dept estab 1916; pub; D&E; ent req HS dipl; degrees AA 2 yrs; SC 50; enrl D 2000, E 1200, nonmaj 3200, maj 400.
Courses: Advertising Design; Architecture; Art History; Ceramics; Commercial Art; Costume Design & Construction; Display; Drafting; Drawing; Fashion Arts; Film; Graphic Arts; Graphic Design; Handicrafts; History of Art & Archaeology; Illustration; Interior Design; Jewelry; Lettering; Museum Staff Training; Painting; Photography; Printmaking; Sculpture; Silversmithing; Stage Design; Textile Design; Video.
Summer School: Dir John Dickenhof. Courses—Complete program.

POMONA

CALIFORNIA STATE POLYTECHNIC UNIVERSITY, POMONA, School of Arts, Art Department, 3801 Temple Blvd, 91768. Tel: 714-598-4567. *Chairperson & Prof* Diane Divelbess, MFA; *Prof* Walter Glaser, MFA; *Prof* Yoram Makow, MA; *Prof* Karl Winchell, MA; *Assoc Prof* Stanley Wilson, MFA; *Assoc Prof* Charles Frederick, MFA; *Assoc Prof* Maren Henderson, MFA; *Lectr* James Dobbs, MA.
Estab 1966; pub; D&E; ent req HS dipl, plus testing; degrees BA 4 yrs; SC 66, LC 15; enrl D approx 300, E approx 50, nonmaj 150, maj 140, others 20.
Tuition: Res—Undergrad (commuting) $153 quarterly, (living in dorms) $603 quarterly; campus res $1809 yr.
Courses: Advertising Design; Aesthetics; Art Education; Art History; Calligraphy; Ceramics; Collage; Commercial Art; Constructions; Display; Drafting; Drawing; Graphic Arts; Graphic Design; Handicrafts (batik, woodworking, enameling); History of Art & Archeology; Illustration; Jewelry; Lettering; Mixed Media; Museum Staff Training; Painting; Printmaking; Sculpture; Silversmithing; Teacher Training; Textile Design.
Summer School: Regular summer quarter of 10 wks.

PORTERVILLE

PORTERVILLE COMMUNITY COLLEGE, Department of Fine Arts, 900 S Main St, 93257. Tel: 209-781-3130, exten 66. *Chmn Dept & Prof* Florence S Offutt, MA; *Prof* Tom Howell, MA; *Assoc Prof* Phil Simons, MA; vis prof—Peter Flint, jewelry, Fall & Spring; Instrs FT 50, PT 80.
Estab 1927; pub; D&E; ent req HS dipl or over 18 yrs of age; degrees AA and AS 2 yrs; SC 18, LC 3; enrl in dept D 300, E 78, nonmaj 320, maj 58.
Tuition: Res—None; Nonres—$43 per unit; no campus res.
Courses: Art History; Ceramics; Drawing; Goldsmithing; Handicrafts (weaving); Jewelry; Painting; Photography; Sculpture; Silversmithing; Textile Design; Theatre Arts.
Adult Hobby Classes: Subjects—Jewelry; Weaving.
Summer School: Dir Nero Pruitt. Enrl 700; tui $43 per unit for term of 6 wks beginning June 13. Courses—Jewelry; Weaving; Ceramics.

REDDING

SHASTA COLLEGE, Art Department, Fine Arts Division, 1605 Old Oregon Trail 96001. Tel: 916-241-3523, exten 361. *Dir Div Fine Arts* Judith Knowles, MA.
Estab 1950; pub; D&E; ent req HS dipl; degrees AA 2 yr.
Courses: Art History; Ceramics; Commercial Art; Drawing; Film; Jewelry; Painting; Photography; Printmaking; Sculpture.

REDLANDS

UNIVERSITY OF REDLANDS,* Division of Fine and Performing Arts, Department of Art, 1200 W Colton Ave, 92373. *Dean Div* Wayne R Bohrnstedt; *Chmn Dept* John P Brownfield; Instrs FT 5.
Estab 1909; pvt; D&E; ent req HS grad, ent exam; degrees BA and BS 4 yr, MA, ME, MAT; schol and fel; SC 18; LC 12; enrl 1500.
Tuition: $1862.50 for 18 units, $3725 for 35 units; campus res.
Courses: Art History; Ceramics; Drawing & Painting; Ethnic Art; Graphic Arts; Jewelry; Painting; Sculpture; Teacher Training.
Summer School: Tui $42.50 per unit, three terms (two for 5 wk and one for 3 wk), June 1-19, June 22-July 24 and July 23-Aug 28.

RIVERSIDE

LOMA LINDA UNIVERSITY, LA SIERRA CAMPUS, Art Department, 92515. Tel: 714-785-2170. *Chmn* Roger Churches; *Asst Prof* Bob Seyle; *Asst Prof* Clarence Grey; *Asst Prof* Sunny Inez; *Asst Prof* Agnes Eroh.
Estab 1950; den; D&E; ent req HS dipl; degrees BA, BS, 4 yrs.
Tuition: Campus res room & board.
Courses: Aesthetics; Art Education; Ceramics; Drafting; Drawing; History of Art & Archaeology; Occupational Therapy; Painting; Photography; Sculpture; Stained Glass; Teacher Training.

RIVERSIDE CITY COLLEGE, Fine Arts Division, Department of Art, 4800 Magnolia Ave, 92506. Tel: 714-684-3240, exten 267. *Head Dept* O K Harry; Instrs FT 6, PT 6.
Estab 1917; pub; D&E; ent req HS dipl or over 18 yrs age; degree AA 2 yrs; SC 20, LC 3; enrl D 910, E 175.
Tuition: Res—free; Nonres—$39 per unit, maximum $465 per sem; no campus res.
Courses: Advertising Design; Art Education; Ceramics; Commercial Art; Drawing; Graphic Arts; Graphic Design; History of Art & Archaeology; Illustration; Jewelry; Lettering; Painting; Sculpture; Teacher Training.
Summer School: Dir James Duncan. Enrl 225; term of 6 wk beginning June 21. Courses—Art for Elementary Teachers; Art History; Ceramics; Drawing; Painting; Sculpture.

UNIVERSITY OF CALIFORNIA, RIVERSIDE, Art History Department, 92521. Tel: 714-787-4627. *Chmn* Richard G Carrott, PhD; *Prof* Dericksen M Brinkerhoff, PhD; *Assoc Prof* Thomas O Pelzel, PhD; *Asst Prof* Francoise Forster-Hahn, PhD.
Estab 1954; pub; D; ent req HS dipl, res grade-point average 3.1, nonres grade-point average 3.4; degrees BA 4 yrs, MA 2 yrs; LC 18; GC 5; enrl maj 20, grad 10.
Tuition: Res—Undergrad $234 per quarter, grad $243 per quarter; Nonres—Undergrad $874 per quarter, grad $878 per quarter; campus res room & board $490 per quarter.
Courses: Art History.

ROCKLIN

SIERRA COLLEGE, Humanities Division, Art Department, 5000 Rocklin Rd, 95677. Tel: 916-624-3333, exten 284. *Chmn Div* Loren Orr, MA; *Instr* Jim Adamson, MA; *Instr* Fritz Blodgett, MA; *Instr* John Hamilton, MA; *Instr* Bob Ridley, MA.
Estab 1914; pub; D&E; ent req English Placement Test; degrees AA and AS; SC 18, LC 4; enrl approx 9000 D&E.
Tuition: Health fee $2; campus res.
Courses: Art Education; Art History; Ceramics; Collage; Conceptual Art; Costume Design & Construction; Drafting; Drawing; Film; Goldsmithing; History of Art & Archaeology; Jewelry; Painting; Photography; Printmaking; Sculpture; Silversmithing; Stage Design; Theatre Arts; Video.
Adult Hobby Classes: Subjects—Woodcarving; Weaving.

ROHNERT PARK

CALIFORNIA STATE COLLEGE, SONOMA, Department of Art, 1801 E Cotati Ave, 94928. Tel: 707-664-2151. *Chairperson* Dr Susan Moulton, PhD; *Prof* William Morehouse, MA; *Asst Prof* Dr Susan McKillop, PhD; *Assoc Prof* Shane Weare, MFA equivalent; *Asst Prof* Don Potts, MA; *Asst Prof* J DeFeo, MFA; *Asst Prof* Donna-Lee Phillips, MA; *Gallery Dir* Inez Storer, MFA; *Prof* Dr Leland Gralapp, PhD; vis profs on short-term lect-demonstration basis.
Estab 1965; pub; D&E; ent req HS dipl, SAT; degree BA(Art) 4 yrs; SC 42, LC 15, GC 1; enrl D 1300, E 40, nonmaj 200, maj 350, grad 20.
Tuition: Res—Undergrad $85 per sem, $65 part-time; Nonres-Undergrad $787.50 per yr, $52 per unit; campus res room & board $1800 yr.
Courses: Aesthetics; Architecture; Art Education; Art History; Ceramics; Collage; Conceptual Art; Constructions; Costume Design & Construction; Drawing; Film; Graphic Arts; History of Art & Archaeology; Intermedia; Mixed Media; Museum Staff Training; Occupational Ther-

apy; Painting; Papermaking; Photography; Printmaking; Sculpture; Stage Design; Teacher Training; Theatre Arts; Video; Women in Art.
Summer School: Dir Dr Stuart Cooney. Tui $35 per unit for a variety of terms beginning early June. Courses—All types.

SACRAMENTO

AMERICAN RIVER COLLEGE, Department of Art, 4700 College Oak Dr, 95841. *Chmn* James S Kaneko, MA; *Primary Art Faculty* Phyllis Y Robbins, MA; Joe Patitucci, BA; Jean A Pratt, MA; Gary L Pruner, MA; John H Kaneko, MA; Tom J Brozovich, MA.
Estab 1954; pub; D&E; ent req HS dipl; degree AA 2 yrs or more; schol; SC 50, LC 12; enrl D 10,000, E 10,000, nonmaj 5000, maj 5000.
Tuition: None.
Courses: Advertising Design; Art Education; Art History; Calligraphy; Ceramics; Commercial Art; Conceptual Art; Constructions; Costume Design & Construction; Display; Drawing; Fashion Arts; Film; Graphic Arts; Graphic Design; Handicrafts; History of Art & Archaeology; Interior Design; Jewelry; Lettering; Mixed Media; Painting; Photography; Printmaking; Sculpture; Silversmithing; Teacher Training; Textile Design; Theatre Arts.
Summer School: Dean Anne Stewart. Tui none; Courses—Classes listed above.

CALIFORNIA STATE UNIVERSITY, SACRAMENTO,* Department of Art, 6000 J St, 95819. Tel: 916-454-6166. *Chmn* P Hitchcock; Instrs FT 30.
Estab 1950; pub; D; ent req HS dipl, ent exam; degrees BA 4 yrs, MA; schol; SC 40, LC 18, GC 12; enrl maj 606.
Courses: Art Education; Art History; Ceramics; Cinematography; Crafts; Drawing; Jewelry; Painting; Printmaking; Sculpture.
Summer School: Enrl 225; 1 wk pre-session, 6 wks.

SACRAMENTO CITY COLLEGE, Art Department, 3835 Freeport Blvd, 95822. Tel: 916-449-7551. *Subject Area Rep* Darrell E Forney, MFA; *Instr* Gregory Kondos, MA; *Instr* Larry Welden, MAEd; *Instr* Willard Melton, MFA; *Instr* Patricia Tool McHugh, MA; *Instrs* Laureen Landau, MFA; *Instr* Al Byrd, MFA; *Instr* David Curry, MA; *Instr* George Esquibel, MA.
Estab 1927, dept estab 1929; pub; D&E; ent req HS dipl; degrees AA 2 yrs; SC 17, LC 9; enrl D 880, E 389.
Tuition: None; no campus res.
Courses: Art Education; Art History; Ceramics; Commercial Art; Costume Design & Construction; Drafting; Drawing; Film; Painting; Photography; Printmaking; Sculpture; Stage Design; Theatre Arts; Video.
Summer School: Dir Darrell E Forney. Courses—Watercolor; Drawing; Oil/Acrylic; Design; Art History.

SALINAS

HARTNELL COLLEGE,* Art and Photography Departments, 156 Homestead Ave, 93901. Tel: 408-758-8211. *Chmn Fine Arts* Robert Lee; Instrs FT 3, PT 3.
Estab 1922; pub; D&E; ent req HS dipl; degree AA 2 yrs; SC 14, LC 3; enrl D 350, E 160, maj 30.
Tuition: None; no campus res.
Courses: Architecture; Ceramics; Commercial Art; Drafting; Drawing; Graphic Arts; History of Art & Archaeology; Jewelry; Metalsmithing; Painting; Photography; Sculpture; Stage Design; Theatre Arts.
Summer School: Enrl 150; tui free; begins approx June 15. Courses—Art Appreciation; Ceramics; Drawing; Film Making; Photography.

SAN BERNARDINO

CALIFORNIA STATE COLLEGE AT SAN BERNARDINO, Fine Arts Department, 5500 State College Pkwy, 92407. Tel: 714-887-7459. *Chmn Dept* Leo Doyle, MFA; *Primary Art Faculty* Julius Kaplan, PhD; Poppy Soloman, MA; Don Woodford, MFA; Bill Warehall, MFA; Jan Morzinski, MFA; Roger Lintault, MFA; Jose Moran, MFA.
Estab 1965; pub; D&E; ent req HS dipl, SAT; degree BA 4 yrs; schol; enrl D 4000, maj 125.
Tuition: Res—Undergrad $48 per 15 units; Nonres—Undergrad $29 per unit; campus res room & board $1450 yr.
Courses: Advertising Design; Art History; Ceramics; Glassblowing; Jewelry; Painting; Printmaking; Sculpture; Textile Design; Woodworking & Furniture Design.

SAN BERNARDINO VALLEY COLLEGE,* Art Department, 701 S Mt Vernon Ave, 92403. Tel: 714-885-9231. *Head Dept* David Lawrence; Instrs FT 224, PT 510.
Estab 1926; pub; D&E; ent req HS dipl or 18 yrs of age; degrees AA and AS 2 yrs; schol; enrl D 750, E 400, maj 230.

Tuition: Res—none; Nonres—$1110 per yr; no campus res.
Courses: Advertising Design; Architecture; Art Education; Artistic Weaving; Ceramics; Costume Design & Construction; Drafting; Drawing; History of Art & Archaeology; Landscape Architecture; Lettering; Photography; Sculpture; Theatre Arts.
Summer School: No tui.

SAN DIEGO

SAN DIEGO MESA COLLEGE, Art Department, 7250 Mesa College Dr, 92111. Tel: 714-279-2300, exten 239. *Chairperson Art Dept* Barbara Winston Blackmun, MA; *Instr* John Conrad, EdD; *Instrs* Albert J Lewis, MA; *Instr* Elinor Meadows, MA; *Instr* Hiroshi Miyazaki, MA; *Instr* Malcolm Nichols, MA; *Instr* James Clark, MA; *Instr* Walter Chapman, MA; *Instr* Anita Waehrer, MA; *Instr* Ross Stockwell, MA.
Estab 1964; pub; D&E; ent req HS dipl, or age 18; degree AA 2 yrs; schol; SC 29, LC 7; enrl in col D 10,000, E 10,000, maj 350.
Tuition: Res—none; Nonres—$38 per unit; no campus res.
Courses: ‡Architecture (Separate Department); ‡Art History; ‡Ceramics; Drafting; ‡Drawing; Handicrafts (fibers); History of Art & Archaeology; ‡Interior Design; Jewelry; Lettering; ‡Painting; Photography; Sculpture; ‡Theatre Arts.
Summer School: Tui $38 per unit; all basic courses, advanced courses vary.

SAN DIEGO STATE UNIVERSITY, Department of Art, 92182. Tel: 714-286-6800, 286-5124. *Chmn* Fredrick Orth, MFA; *Grad Coordr* Robert Berg, MFA.
Estab 1897; pub; D&E; ent req HS dipl; degrees BA 4 yrs, MA; schol; SC 140, LC 35, GC 30; enrl maj 1021.
Tuition: Campus res room & board.
Courses: Advertising Design; Aesthetics; Architecture; Art Education; ‡Art History; ‡Ceramics; Commercial Art; Conceptual Art; Costume Design & Construction; Drawing; Environmental Design; Fashion Arts; Gallery Design; Goldsmithing; Graphic Arts; ‡Graphic Design; Handicrafts (weaving); History of Art & Archaeology; Intermedia; ‡Interior Design; ‡Jewelry; Lettering; Mixed Media; ‡Painting; ‡Printmaking; ‡Sculpture; Silversmithing; Teacher Training; Textile Design.
Adult Hobby Classes: Six majors are offered in the department: Painting; Printmaking; Crafts (ceramics, textiles, jewelry, enameling, furniture design); Graphic Communications; Sculpture; Art History; Environmental Design.

UNITED STATES INTERNATIONAL UNIVERSITY,* School of Performing and Visual Arts, 10455 Pomerado Rd, 92131. Tel: 714-271-4300. *Dean Sch* Netter Worthington; Instrs FT 4, PT 2.
Estab 1966; pvt; D; ent req HS dipl, interview, portfolio, letters of recommendation; degrees BA(Advertising, Costume, Set Design, Painting & Drawing or Teaching), BFA 4 yrs; schol; SC 27, LC 4; enrl D 300.
Tuition: $850 per quarter, $60 per unit.
Courses: Advertising Design; Art Education; Ceramics; Commercial Art; Costume Design & Construction; Drafting; Drawing; Fashion Arts; Graphic Arts; Graphic Design; History of Art & Archaeology; Illustration; Painting; Sculpture; Stage Design; Teacher Training; Theatre Arts.
Summer School: Dir Netter Worthington. Tui $60 per unit for term of 8 wk beginning June 14. Courses—Drawing; Introduction to Visual Thinking; Painting.

UNIVERSITY OF SAN DIEGO,* Art Department, Alcala Park, 92110. Tel: 714-291-6480. *Chmn* Therese Truitt Whitcomb; Instrs FT 2, PT 3.
Estab 1952; pvt; D&E; ent req HS dipl, SAT; degree BA 4 yrs; schol; SC 19, LC 7; enrl univ 2300, maj 50.
Tuition: $105 per unit; campus res $700-$1000 per sem.
Courses: Art in Elementary Education; Ceramics; Design; Drawing; Enameling; Exhibition Design; History of American Art; History of Art Seminars; History of Contemporary Art; History of Modern Art; History of Oriental Art; Painting; Photography; Printmaking; Sculpture; Survey of Art History; Weaving.
Summer School: Tui $105 per unit for terms of 3 wk, 6 wk, 3 wk beginning June 1; 4 courses offered.

SAN FRANCISCO

ACADEMY OF ART COLLEGE, 625 Sutter St, 94102. Tel: 415-673-4200. *Pres* Richard A Stephens, MFA; *Dir Advertising/Graphic Design* Michael Dattel, BFA; *Dir Illustration* Barbara Bradley, BFA; *Dir Fine Art* Michael Woods, MFA; *Dir Photography* John Yates, MFA; Instrs FT 20, PT 40.
Estab 1929; pvt; D&E; ent req HS dipl; degrees BFA 4 yrs, MFA 2 yrs past BFA; schol; SC 100, LC 50; enrl D 1050, E 150, grad 20.

Tuition: Res—Undergrad $1900 yr, $950 per sem, $78 per unit, grad $2000 yr, $1000 per sem, $90 per unit; campus res room & board $2000 yr.
Courses: Advertising Design; Aesthetics; Art Education; Art History; Calligraphy; Ceramics; Collage; Commercial Art; Conceptual Art; Display; ‡Drawing; ‡Fashion Arts; Film; Goldsmithing; ‡Graphic Arts; ‡Graphic Design; Handicrafts; History of Art & Archaeology; ‡Illustration; Jewelry; Lettering; ‡Painting; ‡Photography; ‡Printmaking; ‡Sculpture; Textile Design; Video.
Adult Hobby Classes: Enrl 75; tui $78 per unit. Courses—Portrait Painting; Basic Painting; Pottery; Ceramics.
Summer School: VPres Donald A Haight. Tui $500 for term of 6 wks beginning June 26. Courses—Fine & Commercial Art.

CITY COLLEGE OF SAN FRANCISCO, Art Department, 50 Phelan Ave, 94112. Tel: 415-239-3156. *Chairperson* John Whitney, MA; *Coordr Fine Art* Alan Brooks, MA; *Coordr Professional Art* Arthur Irwin, MA.
Estab 1935; pub; D&E; degree AA 2 yrs; SC 45, LC 10; enrl col D 15,000, E, 11,000
Tuition: None.
Courses: Basic Design; Ceramics; Drawing; Graphic Arts; Graphic Design; History of Art; Illustration; Industrial Design; Jewelry; Lettering; Metal Arts; Painting; Sculpture.
Summer School: Courses offered same as regular yr.

DE YOUNG MUSEUM ART SCHOOL, Golden Gate Park, 94118. Tel: 415-558-3109. *Curator-in-Charge* Elsa Cameron; *Chmn Drawing & Painting* Jerry Concha; *Chmn Photography* John Friedman; *Chmn Textiles* Patricia Hickman; *Chmn Metal Arts* Janet Tyne; *Chmn Ceramics* Tad Sekino; *Chmn Art History* Tom Gates; *Chmn Children's Classes* Eileen Lew.
Estab 1966; pub; D&E; schol; SC 96, LC 7; enrl D 750, E 1750.
Courses: Art History; Calligraphy; Ceramics; Costume Design and Construction; Drawing; Goldsmithing; Graphic Arts; Jewelry; Mixed Media; Museum Staff Training; Painting; Photography; Printmaking; Sculpture; Silversmithing; Teacher Training; Textile Design; Video.
Adult Hobby Classes—As above.
Children's Classes: Courses—Mixed Media.

LONE MOUNTAIN COLLEGE,* Art Department, 2800 Turk Blvd, 94118. Tel: 415-752-7000, exten 240 or 241. *Chmn* Robert J Brawley; Instrs FT 3, PT 9.
Estab 1930 as San Francisco Col for Women, became Lone Mountain Col 1970; pvt; D&E; ent req HS dipl, ent exam; degrees BA, BFA 4 yrs, MA, MFA; schol; SC 32, LC 14, GC 25; enrl maj 75, grad 61.
Courses: Advertising Design; Aesthetics; Art Education; Ceramics; Commercial Art; Costume Design & Construction; Drawing; Fashion Arts; Graphic Arts; Graphic Design; Handicrafts; History of Art; Jewelry; Lettering; Museum Staff Training; Occupational Therapy; Painting; Photography; Sculpture; Stage Design; Stained Glass; Teacher Training; Textile Design; Theatre Arts; Weaving.
Summer School: Dir Robert J Brawley. Enrl 25; term of 6 wks; Studio Art Program.

ARTHUR W PALMER ART SCHOOL,* Studio 303, 545 Sutter St, 94102. Tel: 415-982-0152. *Head* Arthur W Palmer.
Estab 1945; pvt; D&E; ent req ent exam; noncredit; SC 4.
Tuition: Four 3 hr lessons $30.
Courses: Drawing; Painting; Portrait Drawing & Painting.
Adult Hobby Classes: Continuous enrl; tui 4 lessons for $30. Courses—Portrait, Figure, Still Life.

SAN FRANCISCO ART INSTITUTE, Admissions Office, 800 Chestnut St, 94133. Tel: 415-771-7020. *Dean Col* Roy Ascott; *Chmn Filmmaking Dept* Gunvor Nelson; *Chmn Painting Dept* Sam Tchakalian; *Chmn Printmaking Dept* Gordon Kluge; *Chmn Photography Dept* Harry Bowers; *Chmn Sculpture Dept* Jim Pomeroy.
Estab 1871; pvt; D&E; ent req HS dipl or GED; degrees BFA 4 yrs, MFA 2 yrs; schol; SC 80, LC 22, GC 11; enrl nonmaj 89, maj 660, grad 95.
Tuition: $2460 yr, $1230 per sem, $355 per course; no campus res.
Courses: Art History; Ceramics; Drawing; ‡Film; ‡Painting; ‡Photography; ‡Printmaking; ‡Sculpture; Video.
Summer School: Dean Col Roy Ascott. Tui $355 for term of 6 wks beginning June 19. Courses—Above areas.

SAN FRANCISCO STATE UNIVERSITY,* School of Creative Arts, Department of Visual Arts, 1600 Holloway Ave, 94132. Tel: 415-469-2176. Instrs FT 29, PT 8.
Estab 1899; pub; degrees BA 4 yrs, MA; LabC and SC 70, LC 10; enrl maj 500, master candidates 80.
Courses: Art Education; Art History; Ceramics; Design; Metal Arts-Jewelry; Painting; Photography; Printmaking; Sculpture; Textiles.

RUDOLPH SCHAEFFER SCHOOL OF DESIGN, 2255 Mariposa St, 94110. Tel: 415-863-0715. *Dir* Rudolph Schaeffer; *Primary Art Faculty* John Cardess Campbell, John Neil Parker, John White, Wayne Davis, William Lathrop and Jyk-San; vis prof—Evans Ecke, art history, sch yr.
Estab 1926; pvt; D&E; dipl 3 yr prog; schol; SC all, LC 3; enrl D 100, E 40, grad 22.
Tuition: Res—Undergrad $2400 yr; no campus res.
Courses: Drafting; Drawing; Interior Design.
Summer School: Enrl 25; tui $425 for term of 6 wks beginning June 12. Courses—Color & Architectural Graphics.

SAN JOSE

SAN JOSE CITY COLLEGE, School of Fine Arts, 2100 Moorpark Ave, 95128. Tel: 408-298-2181, exten 327. *Dir Instr* Edwin L Stover, PhD; *Instr* Luis Gutierrez, MFA; *Instr* Ramon E Oeschger, MA; *Instr* Steve Salisian, MA; *Instr* Luraine Tansey, MA; *Instr* James M Wayne, MA; *Instr* Joseph Zirker, MFA.
Estab 1921; pub; D&E; ent req HS dipl or 18 yrs of age or older; degree AA 2 yrs; SC 7, LC 2; enrl D 320, E 65.
Tuition: No campus res.
Courses: Art History; Ceramics; Commercial Art; Drawing; Jewelry; Painting; Printmaking; Theatre Arts.

SAN JOSE STATE UNIVERSITY, Art Department, 125 S Seventh St, 95192. Tel: 408-277-2541. *Chmn Dept* Kathleen Cohen, PhD; *Art Educ Coordr* Rosalie Asch, EdD; *Art Hist Coordr* Bruce Radde, PhD; *Ceramics Coordr* James Lovera; *Crafts Coordr* David Castleberry, MFA; *Design Coordr* Stewart Baron, MA; *Painting/Drawing Coordr* Randall Sadler, MFA; *Printmaking/Photog Coordr* Geoffrey Bowman, MA; *Sculpture Coordr* John Battenberg, MA.
Estab 1857, dept estab 1911; pub; D&E; ent req HS dipl, GPA, ACT or SAT; degrees BA(Art), BA(Art Hist) and BS(Graphic Design) 4 yrs; BS(Interior Design) and BFA 4½ yrs; MA 1 yr, MFA 2 yrs; SC 89, LC 28, GC 25; enrl D 4968, grad 210.
Tuition: Res—Undergrad & grad $82 general fees; Nonres—Undergrad & grad $1300 yr, $650 per sem, $43 per unit; campus res $1300 yr.
Courses: Architecture: ‡Art Education; ‡Art History; ‡Ceramics; Collage; Drawing; Graphic Arts; ‡Graphic Design; Illustration; ‡Industrial Design; Intermedia; ‡Interior Design; Jewelry; Lettering; Museum Staff Training; ‡Painting; ‡Printmaking; ‡Sculpture; Silversmithing; Teacher Training; Textile Design.
Summer School: Assoc Dean Continuing Educ Paul M Bradley. Tui $38.15 for unit, 3 sessions, 3, 6 and 6 wks beginning June 5th Courses—Vary.

SAN LUIS OBISPO

CALIFORNIA POLYTECHNIC STATE UNIVERSITY AT SAN LUIS OBISPO, Art Department, 93407. Tel: 805-546-2324, 546-2325, 546-2350. *Prof & Head Dept* Thomas V Johnston, DA; *Prof* Roger Bailey, MFA; *Assoc Prof* Pierre Rademaker, MFA; *Prof* Bernard Duseck, MA; *Prof* Robert Reynolds, MA; *Prof* Helen Kelley, MS; *Asst Prof* Clarissa Hewitt, MFA; *Assoc Prof* Donald Bjorkman, MFA.
Estab 1901, dept estab 1969; pub; D&E; ent req HS dipl, portfolio review; degree BS(Applied Art & Design) 4 yrs; SC 40, LC 12; Enrl D 1000, E 100, nonmaj 1100, maj 80.
Tuition: Res—Undergrad $3000 yr; Nonres—Undergrad $1380; campus res room & board $560 yr.
Courses: Advertising Design; Art History; Ceramics; Drawing; Graphic Arts; Graphic Design; Jewelry; Lettering; Painting; Photography; Printmaking; Sculpture; Silversmithing.
Summer School: The dept offers a summer quarter prog, limited in course offerings.

CUESTA COLLEGE, Art Department, PO Box J, 93406. Tel: 805-544-2943, exten 267. *Chmn Fine Arts Div* Chester Amyx, MA; *Primary Art Faculty:* Robert Pelfrey, MA; Barry Frantz, MA; Rupert Deese, MFA.
Estab 1964; pub; D&E; ent req HS dipl or Calif HS Proficiency Exam; degrees AA and AS; schol; enrl in col D 3200, E 3082.
Tuition: No campus res.
Courses: Art History; Ceramics; Display; Drawing; Graphic Design; Jewelry; Mixed Media; Painting; Printmaking; Sculpture; Stage Design; Theatre Arts; Video.
Summer School: Chmn Div Fine Arts Chester Amyx.

SAN MARCOS

PALOMAR COLLEGE, Art Department, 1140 W Mission Rd, 92069. Tel: 714-744-1150, exten 345. *Chmn* Rita A White; *Assoc Prof* Harry E Bliss, MFA; *Assoc Prof* George D Durrant, MA; *Assoc Prof* James C Hulbert, BPA; *Assoc Prof* Frank Jones, MFA; *Assoc Prof* Anthony J

Lugo, MA; *Assoc Prof* Val G Sanders, MA; *Assoc Prof* James T Saw, MA; *Assoc Prof* Donna Tryon Sakakeeny, MA; vis prof—drawing fall 78 and ceramics and glass, spring 79.
Estab 1950; pub; D&E; ent req ent exam; degree AA 2 yr; schol; SC 31, LC 4; enrl D 775, E 200.
Tuition: None; no campus res.
Courses: Art History; ‡Ceramics; Collage; ‡Commercial Art; ‡Drawing; Glassblowing; Graphic Arts; Graphic Design; Handicrafts (crafts design); Illustration; ‡Jewelry; Lettering; Life Drawing; ‡Painting; ‡Printmaking; Sculpture; ‡Silversmithing; Stained Glass; 2-D and 3-D Design.
Summer School: Courses—Basic courses except commercial art and graphic design.

SAN MATEO

COLLEGE OF SAN MATEO, Fine Arts Division, 1700 W Hillsdale Blvd, 94402. Tel: 415-574-6288. *Div Dir* Leo N Bardes.
Pub; D&E; ent req HS dipl.
Tuition: None; no campus res.
Courses: Architecture; Art History; Ceramics; Commercial Art; Drafting; Drawing; Film; History of Art & Archaeology; Interior Design; Jewelry; Lettering; Painting; Photography; Printmaking; Sculpture; Theatre Arts.

SAN PABLO

CONTRA COSTA COLLEGE, Department of Art, 2600 Mission Bell Dr, 94806. Tel: 415-235-7800. *Dept Head* James Eakle, MA; *Instr* Robert McLean, MA; *Instr* Paul Pernish, MFA; *Instr* Patrick Tidd, MA.
Estab 1950; pub; D&E; ent req HS dipl or 18 yrs old; degrees Cert of Achievement 1 yr, AA and AS 2 yrs; SC 10, LC 16; enrl D 468, E 200.
Tuition: Res—Undergrad none; Nonres—Undergrad $41 per sem unit, maximum $1230 per acad sem; no campus res.
Courses: Art History; Ceramics; Graphic Arts; Painting; Photography; Sculpture.
Summer School: Assoc Dean Continuing Educ William Vega. Enrl 50; tui free for term of 8 wks beginning June 26. Courses—Art; Art Appreciation.

SANTA ANA

SANTA ANA COLLEGE, Art Department, 17th & Bristol, 92706. Tel: 714-835-3000. *Dean Acad Affairs* Richard Sneed, PhD; *Instr* Gene L Isaacson, MFA; *Instr* George E Geyer, MA; *Instr* Frank Molner, MA; *Instr* Sharon E Ford, MA; *Instr* Estelle Friedman, MFA; *Instr* Patrick Crabb, MA; *Instr* Michael Johnson, MA; *Instr* Mayde Herberg, MA.
Estab 1915, dept estab 1960; pub; D&E; ent req HS dipl; degree AA 2 yrs; schol; SC 21, LC 5; enrl D 280, E 160, maj 57.
Tuition: Charged for out of state students only; no campus res.
Courses: Advertising Design; Architecture; Art History; Ceramics; Commercial Art; Display (Gallery only); Drawing; Film; Graphic Arts; Graphic Design; Handicrafts (beginning crafts); Interior Design; Jewelry; Museum Staff Training; Painting; Photography; Printmaking; Sculpture.
Adult Hobby Classes: Courses—Stained Glass; Batik and Dyeing Process.
Summer School: Dir Dean Lee Ford. Enrl 3000; tui free for term of 8 wks beginning late June. Courses—Ceramics; Design; Drawing; Painting.

SANTA BARBARA

UNIVERSITY OF CALIFORNIA, SANTA BARBARA, Art Department, 93106. Tel: 805-961-3138. *Assoc Prof Art & Chmn Dept* Larry M Ayres, PhD.
Estab 1868, dept estab 1950; pub; D; ent req HS dipl; degrees BA 4 yrs, MFA 2 yrs, MA 2 yrs, PhD 7 yrs, schol; SC 32, LC 17, GC 7; enrl in dept D 539, grad 58.
Courses: Art Education; Ceramics; Collage; Drawing; Painting; Printmaking; Sculpture.

SANTA CRUZ

UNIVERSITY OF CALIFORNIA AT SANTA CRUZ, Art Board of Studies, Performing Arts Bldg, 95064. Rotating Chmn; Instrs FT 14, PT 5.
Pub; D; ent req HS dipl; degree BA 4 yrs; SC per quarter 11, LC per quarter 3; enrl D approx 7000, maj 80.
Courses: Aesthetics; Ceramics; Drawing; Graphic Arts; History of Art & Archaeology; Painting; Photography; Sculpture; Stage Design; Theatre Arts.
Summer School: Dir Theodore Campbell.

SANTA MARIA

ALLAN HANCOCK COLLEGE,* Fine Arts Department, 800 S College Dr, 93454. Tel: 805-922-7711. *Head* George Muro; Instrs FT 11, PT 7.
Estab 1920; pub; D&E; ent req HS dipl, over 18 and educable; degree AA 2 yrs; SC 24, LC 4; enrl D 800, E 220, maj 115.
Courses: Advertising Design; Art Education; Ceramics; Costume Design & Construction; Display; Drawing; Graphic Arts; History of Art & Archaeology; Jewelry; Lettering; Painting; Photography; Serigraphy; Stage Design; Theatre Arts; Weaving.
Adult Hobby Classes: Enrl 35; tui $3. Courses—Painting and Life Drawing.
Summer School: Enrl 230; term of 6 wks beginning June 18. Courses—Ceramics; Crafts; Drawing; Opera Workshop; Repertory Theatre; Watercolor.

SANTA MONICA

RUSTIC CANYON ARTS AND CRAFTS CENTER,* Los Angeles City Department of Recreation and Parks, 601 Latimer Rd, 90402. Tel: 213-454-9872. *Dir* Carlyn Medaglia; Instrs PT 14.
Estab 1963; pub; D&E; no degrees; classes for adults and children; 10 wk sessions; SC 38.
Courses: Ceramics; Copper Enameling; Drawing; Jewelry; Painting; Sculpture.

SANTA ROSA

SANTA ROSA JUNIOR COLLEGE, Art Department, 1501 Mendocino Ave, 95401. Tel: 707-527-4298. *Prof Art & Chmn Dept* James M Rosen, MFA; *Prof* Maurice Lapp, MA; *Prof* Jean Yates, MA; *Prof* Elizabeth Quandt, MFA; *Prof* Max Hein, MFA; *Prof* Sarah Gill, PhD; *Prof* John Watrous, MFA; *Prof* Will Colier, MFA; vis profs—Wayne Thiebaud, Nathan Olivera and Alan Gussow, 1 wk to 3 months.
Estab 1918, dept estab 1935; pub; D&E; ent req HS dipl; degree AA 2 yrs; schol; SC 40, LC 8; enrl D approx 200, E approx 400, nonmaj 100, maj 100.
Tuition: Res—Undergrad none; Nonres—Undergrad $510 per sem, $34 per unit; campus res.
Courses: Advertising Design; Art History; Calligraphy; Ceramics; Commercial Art; Conceptual Art; Display; Drawing; Graphic Design; Handicrafts (ceramic sculpture, fiber arts); Intermedia; Interior Design; Jewelry; Lettering; Mixed Media; Museum Staff Training; Painting; Photography; Printmaking; Sculpture; Textile Design.
Summer School: *Chmn Dept* James Rosen. Term of 6 wks beginning June 20. Courses—Painting; Drawing; Sculpture; Jewelry; Ceramics; Printmaking; Design; Art History.

SARATOGA

VILLA MONTALVO, Center for the Arts, PO Box 158, 95070. Tel: 408-867-3421. *Chmn* Mrs Jean Ryan; Instrs FT 8.
Estab 1953; pvt; SC 8, LC 1; enrl 120.
Tuition: $25 for eight 3 hr lessons. Children's classes $25 for 6 Sat AM; enrl 14.
Courses: Ceramics; Drawing; Painting.
Summer School: *Chmn* Mrs Joseph Ryan. Enrl 90; tui $25 for 8 wk term beginning mid-June.

WEST VALLEY COLLEGE,* Art Department, 14000 Fruitvale Ave, 95050. Tel: 408-867-2200. *Chmn* Charles Escott; Instrs FT 11, PT 37.
Estab 1964; pub; D&E; ent req HS dipl or 18 yrs of age; 8 degrees 2 yrs; SC 51, LC 12; enrl D 1260, E 801.
Tuition: Reg fee under $10; no campus res.
Courses: Aesthetics; Architecture; Ceramics; Commercial Art; Costume Design & Construction; Drafting; Drawing; Furniture Design; Graphic Arts; History of Art & Archaeology; Jewelry; Landscape Architecture; Lettering; Man & Materials; Museum Staff Training; Occupational Work Experience; Painting; Photography; Sculpture & Metal Casting; Stage Design; Stained Glass; Theatre Arts; Weaving.
Adult Hobby Classes: Many classes offered by Community Services Dept; tui varies.
Summer School: Tui under $10 for term of 6 wks beginning mid-June. Courses—Ceramics; Drawing; Jewelry; Sculpture.

SIMI VALLEY

GISELA DAWLEY ART STUDIO, 4848 Seminole Circle, 93063. Tel: 805-526-7125. *Owner-Instr* Gisela Dawley, MF.
Estab 1964; pvt; D&E; children and adults; SC 3, LC 1; enrl D 60, E 20.
Tuition: $3 an hr; no campus res.
Courses: Art History; Drawing; Painting; Teacher Training.

Adult Hobby Classes: Enrl 30; tui $3 per hr. Courses—Painting; Watercolor; Drawing.
Children's Classes: Enrl 60; tui $3 per hr. Courses—Painting; Watercolor; Drawing.
Summer School: Enrl 30; tui $3 per hr for term of 6 wks beginning June 15.

SOUTH LAKE TAHOE

LAKE TAHOE COMMUNITY COLLEGE, Art Department, PO Box 14445, 95702. Tel: 916-541-4660, exten 45. *Chmn Art Dept* David Foster, MA.
Estab 1975; pub; D&E; ent req HS dipl; degree AA 2 yrs; schol; SC 22, LC 6; enrl D 375, E 150, nonmaj 300, maj 75.
Tuition: $2 per quarter.
Courses: Art History; Ceramics; Color; Design; Drawing; Graphic Arts; Painting; Printmaking; Sculpture.
Summer School: Courses—Primitive Pottery; Landscape Drawing; Art Media Workshop.

STANFORD

STANFORD UNIVERSITY, Department of Art, Cummings Art Bldg, 94305. Tel: 415-497-3404. *Chmn Dept Art* Lorenz Eitner, PhD; Instrs FT 18, PT 1.
Estab 1891; pvt; D; ent req HS dipl; degrees BA 4 yrs, MA 1 yr, MFA 2 yrs, PhD 5 yrs; schol; SC 38, LC 55; GC 19 (seminars); enrl 836, maj 120, grad 30.
Tuition: $5130 per yr; campus res room and board $1970 per yr.
Courses: Art Education (with School of Education); ‡Art History; ‡Drawing; Graphic Design; ‡Painting; ‡Photography; ‡Printmaking; ‡Sculpture; Textile Design.
Summer School: *Dir* Lorenz Eitner. Enrl 300; term of 8 wks beginning mid-June.

STOCKTON

SAN JOAQUIN DELTA COLLEGE,* Art Department, 5151 Pacific Ave, 95207. Tel: 209-466-2631, exten 307. Instrs FT 7.
Estab 1935; pub; D&E; ent req HS dipl; degree AA 2 yrs; schol; SC 12, LC 2; enrl D 7000, E 6000, maj 100.
Tuition: None; no campus res.
Courses: Ceramics; Drafting; Drawing; Graphic Arts; History of Art & Archaeology; Jewelry; Lettering; Painting; Photography; Sculpture; Stage Design; Theatre Arts.
Adult Hobby Classes: Enrl 25 per class; tui $6 per class; Courses—Ceramics; Drawing; Jewelry; Painting.

UNIVERSITY OF THE PACIFIC,* Department of Art, 3600 Pacific Ave, 95211. Tel: 209-946-2242. *Chmn* Larry Walker; Instrs FT 7, PT 1.
Estab 1851; pvt; ent req HS grad with 20 sem grades of recommending quality earned in the 10th, 11th and 12th years in traditional subjects, twelve of these grades must be in acad subj; 4 yr & grad school available (4-1-4 calendar prog); 15 (4 unit) full courses, 16 (2 unit) SC, 5 LC, Independent Study; enrl maj 60-75, 800 per yr.
Tuition: $4216 per yr, $184 per unit (6½ to 11½ units), $144 per unit (½ to 6 units), campus res $1956.
Courses: Applied Arts; Art Education; Consumer Design; Crafts; Drawing & Painting; Fine Arts; Museology & Art History; Sculpture & Ceramics.
Summer School: Two 5 wk sessions.

SUISUN CITY

SOLANO COMMUNITY COLLEGE,* Suisun Valley Rd, PO Box 246, 94585. Tel: 707-643-2761. *Instr* Dorothy Herger; Instrs FT 3, PT 4.
Estab 1945; pub; D&E; ent req HS dipl; degree AA 2 yrs; SC 16, LC 5; enrl D 215, E 60.
Tuition: None; no campus res.
Courses: Ceramics; Commercial Art; Drawing; Form & Composition; Fundamentals of Art; History of Art; Jewelry Design; Lettering; Painting; Printmaking; Sculpture; Stained Glass Window Making; Survey of Modern Art.
Summer School: *Dean Summer Session* William Cochran. Courses—Art Appreciation; Art Workshop.

THOUSAND OAKS

CALIFORNIA LUTHERAN COLLEGE, Art Department, 60 Olson Rd, 91360. Tel: 805-492-2411, exten 367. *Chmn Art Dept* B M A Weber, MFA; *Assoc Prof* John Solem, MA; *Asst Prof* Jerry Slattum, BA; *Instrs* Jim Hugunin, MA; *Lectr* Mrs K Neprud, BA.
Estab 1961; pvt; D&E; ent req HS dipl, SAT or ACT, portfolio suggested; degrees BA 4 yrs; MA(Educ) 1 - 2 yrs; schol; SC 12, LC 7; enrl in dept D 110, nonmaj 46, maj 64.
Tuition: Res—Undergrad $4200 per yr, $2600 per sem, $87 PT; campus res room & board $1500 yr.
Courses: Advertising Design; Art Education; Art History; Calligraphy; Ceramics; Collage; Commercial Art; Costume Design & Construction; Drawing; Fashion Arts; Graphic Arts; Graphic Design; History of Art & Archaeology; Illustration; Mixed Media; Painting; Photography; Printmaking; Sculpture; Stage Design; Teacher Training; Theatre Arts.
Summer School: Dir Dr John Cooper. Tui $75 per unit for term June-July, July-Aug. Courses—Drawing; Design; Pottery; Sculpture.

TUJUNGA

McGROARTY CULTURAL ART CENTER, 7570 McGroarty Terrace, 91040. Tel: 213-352-5285. *Dir* Evaline V Carrie, MA; Instrs FT 4.
Estab 1953; pub; D&E; no ent req; schol; SC 20, LC 1; enrl D 250; E 100.
Tuition: Fees for adults $10-$23 per 10 wks session; fees for children and teens $8-$10 per 10 wks session.
Courses: Aesthetics; Art Education; Art History; Calligraphy; Ceramics; Collage; Costume Design & Construction; Drawing; Goldsmithing; Graphic Arts; Handicrafts (creative stitchery & loom weaving); Jewelry; Mixed Media; Painting; Textile Design.

TURLOCK

CALIFORNIA STATE COLLEGE, STANISLAUS, Art Department, 800 Monte Vista Ave, 95380. Tel: 209-633-2431. *Prof Art & Chmn Dept* Winston McGee, MA; *Prof* Martin Camarata, MA; *Prof* Ralf Parton, MA; *Assoc Prof* James Piskoti, MFA; *Vis Lectr* Hope B Werness, PhD; *Vis Lectr* Albert Stewart, MFA; *Vis Lectr* Celeste Rehm, MFA.
Estab 1963; dept estab 1967; pub; D&E; ent req HS dipl; degree BA 4 yrs; Printmaking Cert Prog, Special Masters Degree Prog; schol; SC 27, LC 6, GC 4; enrl D 400, E 50, nonmaj 350, maj 100, grad 12.
Tuition: Res—Undergrad & grad $190 yr, $83.50 per sem, $59.50 PT, $23 winter term; Nonres—Undergrad & grad are same as res plus $52.50 per unit, $766 for 13 units; no additional fees for students taking more than 13 units; campus res.
Courses: Art History; Ceramics; Drawing; Film; Gallery Management; Graphic Arts; History of Art & Archaeology; Painting; Photography; Printmaking; Sculpture; Teacher Training; Theatre Arts.
Children's Classes: Enrl 40; tui $25 per 10 wks. Courses—Painting/Drawing.
Summer School: Chmn Winston McGee. Enrl 50. Courses—Ceramics.

VALENCIA

CALIFORNIA INSTITUTE OF THE ARTS,* School of Art, 24700 McBean Pkwy, 91355. Tel: 805-255-1050. *Pres* Robert Fitzpatrick; *Acting Dean* Stephan Von Huene; Instrs FT 10.
Estab 1970; pvt; ent req portfolio, health cert; degrees BFA, 4 yrs, MFA; schol; SC, Projects; enrl D 130 first yr; 150 in 1973.
Tuition: Campus res.
Courses: Drawing; Graphics; Painting; Photography; Post Studio; Sculpture; Video; Visual Information.

VENICE

VENICE PAINTING, DRAWING AND SCULPTURE STUDIO, INC, 346 Sunset Ave, 90291. Tel: 213-399-5435. *Chmn Painting Dept* Jan Saether; *Chmn Sculpture Dept* Martine Olga Vaugel; *Teacher* Robert G Cunningham, MFA; *Teacher* Corinne West Hartley; *Teacher* Bonnie Helmer, BA; *Teacher* Jill Gibson; *Teacher* Antonio Borrani.
Estab 1976; pvt; D&E; ent req submittance of a portfolio; no degrees granted; SC 22; enrl D 50, E 50.
Tuition: $40-$65 monthly; no campus res.
Courses: Drawing; Graphic Design; Painting; Sculpture.
Children's Classes: Tui $40 per month. Courses—Painting.
Summer School: Dir Martine Olga Vaugel. Courses—Same as above.

VENTURA

VENTURA COLLEGE,* Fine Arts Division, 4667 Telegraph Rd, 93003. Tel: 805-642-3211, exten 229. Instrs FT 13, PT 15.
Estab 1925; pub; D&E; ent req HS dipl or 18 yrs of age; degrees AA and AS; schol; SC 50, LC 15; enrl D 500, E 500, maj 300; extensive noncredit evening prog.
Tuition: None to res; no campus res.
Courses: Advertising; Art Education; Ceramics; Commercial Art; Costume Design & Construction; Display; Drafting; Drawing; Fashion Arts; General Crafts; Graphic Arts; Graphic Design; History of Art & Archaeology; Illustration; Industrial Design; Jewelry; Painting; Photography; Sculpture; Stage Design; Textile Design; Theatre Arts.
Summer School: Assoc Dean Eric Nicolet. Many of the regular session courses are offered.

VISALIA

COLLEGE OF THE SEQUOIAS, Fine Arts Division, Art Department, Mooney Blvd, 93277. Tel: 209-733-2050. *Chmn* George C Pappas, MA; *Instr* Ralph Homan, MA; *Instr* Gene Maddox, MA; *Instr* Robert Marcellus, MA; *Instr* Alfred Pietroforte, MA; *Instr* Barbara Strong, MA.
Estab 1925, dept estab 1940; pub; D&E; ent req HS dipl, must be 18 yrs of age; degree AA 2 yrs; schol; SC 12, LC 4; enrl D 60, E 37, maj 10.
Tuition: None; no campus res.
Courses: Aesthetics; Art Education; Art History; Ceramics; Commercial Art; Drawing; Film; Graphic Arts; History of Art & Archaeology; Lettering; Museum Staff Training; Painting; Printmaking; Sculpture; Stage Design; Theatre Arts.
Adult Hobby Classes: Courses—Ceramics; Jewelry; Stained Glass; China Painting.
Summer School: Dir George C Pappas. Courses—Drawing; Painting; Stained Glass.

WALNUT

MOUNT SAN ANTONIO COLLEGE,* Art Department, 1100 N Grand Ave, 91789. Tel: 714-598-2811, exten 259. *Chmn* Ronald B Ownbey; Instrs FT 14, PT 3.
Estab 1945; pub; D&E; ent req over 18 yrs of age; degrees AA and AS 2 yrs; SC 24, LC 5; enrl D 2254, E 852, maj 500.
Tuition: None to res; no campus res.
Courses: Advertising Design; Ceramics; Commercial Art; Drafting; Drawing; Fibers; Graphic Arts; History of Art; Illustration; Lettering; Metals & Enamels; Painting; Photography; Sculpture; Theatre Arts.
Summer School: Enrl art 150; term of 6 wks beginning June 21. Courses: Ceramics; Drawing; History of Art; Life Drawing; Printmaking.

WEED

COLLEGE OF THE SISKIYOUS, Art Department, 800 College Ave, 96094. Tel: 916-938-4463, exten 239. *Head Dept* Barry R Barnes, MA.
Estab 1957; pub; D&E; ent req HS dipl; degree AA 2 yrs; schol; SC 15, LC 2; enrl D 1200, maj 20.
Tuition: None to res; campus res.
Courses: Art History; Ceramics; Collage; Constructions; Drafting; Drawing; Graphic Arts; History of Art & Archaeology; Painting; Photography; Printmaking; Sculpture.

WHITTIER

RIO HONDO COLLEGE, Fine Arts Department, 3600 Workman Mill Rd, 90608. Tel: 213-692-0921, exten 361. *Chmn Dept* John R Jacobs, MA; Instrs FT 21, PT 16.
Estab 1962; pub; D&E; ent req HS dipl; degree AA 2 yrs; Sc 18, LC 3; enrl D&E 2546, nonmaj 50, art maj 150.
Tuition: None; no campus res.
Courses: Advertising Design; Art History; Ceramics; Commercial Art; Costume Design & Construction; Display; Drawing; Film; Graphic Arts; History of Art & Archaeology; Illustration; Jewelry; Lettering; Painting; Photography; Printmaking; Sculpture; Stage Design; Theatre Arts; Video.
Summer School: Enrl approx 200; tui free for term of 6 wks beginning June 20.

WHITTIER COLLEGE,* Department of Art, Stauffer Art Center, 90608. Tel: 213-693-5032, exten 299. *Chmn* Robert W Speier; Instrs FT 2, PT 2.
Estab 1901; pvt; D&E; ent req HS dipl, credit by exam, CLEP, CEEBA; degree BA 4 yrs; schol & fel; SC 12, LC 12; enrl approx 552-560 per sem.
Tuition: $3250 per yr, FT $115 per unit, PT $115 per unit, audit $60 per unit, grad $115 per unit; campus res $1524.
Courses: Art Education; Ceramics; Drawing; Graphic Arts; History of Art & Archaeology; Painting; Photography; Sculpture.
Adult and children's classes for special students; tui $4.

Summer School: Enrl approx 25; July 7 - July 31, Aug 4 - Aug 29. Courses—California Landscape Painting; Color; Elementary Art Education Workshops.

WILMINGTON

LOS ANGELES HARBOR COLLEGE, Art Department, 1111 Figueroa Place, 90744. Tel: 213-518-1000. *Art Dept Chmn* John Cassone, MA; *Asst Prof* Nancy E Webber, MFA; *Prof* Jarmila Havlena, MFA; *Asst Prof* Jon L Grider, MA; *Assoc Prof* Frank P Matranga, MA; Instrs FT 5, PT 15.
Estab 1949; pub; D&E; ent req HS dipl; degree AA 2 yrs; SC 48, LC 11; enrl D 6500, E 2500.
Tuition: Res—none; Nonres—$44 per unit.
Courses: ‡Advertising Design; Architecture; Art History; Ceramics; Commercial Art; Costume Design & Construction; Drawing; Fashion Arts; Graphic Design; Handicrafts; History of Art & Archaeology; Jewelry; Lettering; Painting; Photography; Printmaking; History of Art & Archaeology; Jewelry; Lettering; Painting; Photography; Printmaking; Sculpture; Silversmithing; Stage Design; Theatre Arts; Video.
Summer School: Art Dept Chmn John Cassone. Courses—Art History; Art Fundamentals.

WOODLAND HILLS

PIERCE COLLEGE, Art Department, 91371. Tel: 213-347-0551. *Head Dept Assoc Prof* John Kuczynski, MA; *Assoc Prof* Howell Pinkston, MA; *Prof* Alfred Van Auker, MFA; *Assoc Prof* Roberta Barrager, MFA; *Asst Prof* Alfred Carrillo, MFA; *Assoc Prof* John W Corbeil, MA; *Asst Prof* James Crandall, MA; *Assoc Prof* John deKramer, BE; *Prof* Garo Gazurian, MA; *Prof* Milton Hirschl, MFA; *Prof* Eli Karpel, MA; *Prof* Walter Smith, MFA; *Asst A* Nancy Snooks, MFA; *Instrs* Paul C Nordberg, AA.
Estab 1947, dept estab 1956; pub; D&E; ent req HS dipl 18 yrs and over; degrees AA 60 units; schol; SC 35, LC 3; enrl D&E 23,000.
Tuition: $44 per unit; no campus res.
Courses: ‡Advertising Design; ‡Architecture; Art Education; ‡Art History; Ceramics; Commercial Art; ‡Constructions; Display; ‡Drafting; Drawing; Film; Graphic Arts; Graphic Design; History of Art and Archaeology; ‡Illustration; ‡Industrial Design; Interior Design; Jewelry; ‡Landscape Architecture; Lettering; Painting; ‡Photography; Printmaking; ‡Restoration and Conservation; Sculpture; Stage Design; ‡Theatre Arts; Video.
Summer School: Dir Asst Dean Barry S Haskell.

COLORADO

BLACK HAWK

BLACKHAWK MOUNTAIN SCHOOL OF ART, 251 Main Street, 80422. (Mailing Add: 453 Roslyn Place Chicago, IL 60614). Tel: 303-582-5235. *Dir* Michael S Parfenoff, MFA; *Instrs* Ken Bowman, BFA; Michael J Reardon, MAE; Thomas Macauly, MFA; Michael S Parfenoff, MFA.
Estab 1963; pub; D&E summers only; ent req letter of recommendation and a personal contract; degrees none; SC 6, LC 3; enrl D 25-35.
Tuition: $950 term beginning June 21 through Aug 2; campus res room & board included in total cost.
Courses: Ceramics; Constructions; Drawing; Film; Graphic Arts; Mixed Media; Painting; Photography; Printmaking; Sculpture.

BOULDER

UNIVERSITY OF COLORADO AT BOULDER, Department of Fine Arts, Fine Arts Bldg, Room 104, 80309. Tel: 303-492-6504. *Chmn* George E Woodman, MFA; *Instrs* FT 44.
Estab 1861; pub; D&E; ent req HS dipl; degrees BA or BFA(Art, Art History and Studio Arts) 4 yr; MA(Art Educ and Art Hist) 3-5 yr; MFA(Studio Arts) 2-3 yr; schol; SC 51, LC 48, GC 66, nonmaj 400, maj 455, GS 100, others 100.
Tuition: Res—Undergrad and grad $614 per yr, $307 per sem; Nonres—Undergrad and grad $2456 per yr, $1228 per sem; campus res room & board $1390-$1672.
Courses: Art Education; Art History; Ceramics; Drawing; Jewelry; Painting; Phography; Printmaking; Sculpture; Studio Arts.
Children Classes: Enrl 20-35; tui $20 per sem, Sat mornings.
Summer School: Enrl varies; tui $310 for term of 5 wks beginning first wk in June/July. Courses—Art Education; Art Education & Art History; Basic Drawing; Basic Painting; Basic Sculpture; Ceramics; Intermediate Photo; Jewelry; Photography I & II; Painting; Watermedia.

COLORADO SPRINGS

COLORADO COLLEGE, Department of Art, 80903. Tel: 303-473-2233, exten 510. *Chmn* Mary Chenoweth, MFA; *Prof* Bernard Arnest; *Prof* James Trissel, MFA; *Assoc Prof* Mary Chenoweth, MFA; *Asst Prof* Carl Reed MFA; *Instr* Roger Aikin, PhD; *Instr* Gale Murray, PhD; *Instr* Ruth Kolarik, PhD.
Estab 1874; pvt; D; ent req HS dipl or equivalent and selection by admissions committee; degrees BA and MAT 4 yr; schol; SC 20, LC 20; enrl D 1800, maj 40.
Tuition: Res—Undergrad $3600 per yr; campus res room and board $1400.
Courses: Art Education; Art History; Collage; Drawing; Graphic Design; Painting; Photography; Printmaking; Sculpture.
Summer School: Dean Gilbert R Johns. Tui $65 per cr hr for term of 8 wks beginning June 19. Courses—Art Education; Photography.

DENVER

COLORADO INSTITUTE OF ART, 200 E Ninth Ave, 80203. Tel: 303-837-0825. *Pres* John T Barclay; *Dir of Educ* James Graft.
Estab 1952; pvt; D&E; ent req HS dipl; degrees dipl 2 yr; schol; SC all; Enrl D 600, E 100, nonmaj 100 maj 600.
Tuition: Res—Undergrad $525 per quarter; Nonres—Undergrad $525 per quarter; Photography $600; campus res $1800.
Courses: ‡Advertising Design; Commercial Art; Drawing; ‡Fashion Arts; Graphic Design; Illustration; ‡Interior Design; Lettering; Mixed Media; Painting; ‡Photography.
Adult Hobby Classes: Tui $100 per 36 hrs. Courses—Drawing and Painting; Interior Decorating; Photography.
Children's Classes: Tui $15 per 16 hrs; advanced placement is available.

COLORADO WOMEN'S COLLEGE, Department of Art, Montview Blvd & Quebec, 80220. Tel: 303-394-6938, 394-6921. *Chmn* Maynard Whitney; *Assoc Prof* Elizabeth Schoeberlein; *Asst Prof* Suzanne Martin; *Instrs* Bernie Marek; vis prof—artist-in-residence Joyce Eakins, Painting, 1977-78.
Estab 1898; pvt; D; ent req HS dipl; degrees BA 4 yr, BFA 5 yr, schol; SC 30, LC 15; enrl D 158, maj 45.
Tuition: Res & Nonres—Undergrad $100 per cr hr. Campus res board and room $2000.
Courses: ‡Art Education; ‡Art History; Ceramics; Conceptual Art; Drawing; Jewelry; ‡Mixed Media; Painting; Photography; Printmaking; Sculpture; Stage Design; Teacher Training; Textile Design; Theatre Arts.
Summer School: Dir James Polt. Enrl 15 per class; tui $100 per cr hr for term of 3 wks beginning May—July. Courses—Jewelry; Painting; Photography; Primitive Pottery; Printmaking.

LORETTO HEIGHTS COLLEGE,* Department of Art, 3001 S Federal Blvd, 80236. Tel: 303-922-4011. *Prog Dir* Max Di Julio; *Instrs* FT 2, PT 3.
Estab 1880; pvt; D&E; ent req HS dipl, ent exam; degrees BA, BS and BFA 4 yr; SC 8, LC 4.
Tuition: $3150 per yr; campus res $4900.
Courses: Art Education; Ceramics; Drawing; Graphic Arts; History of Art and Archaeology; Jewelry; Lettering; Painting; Sculpture; Weaving.
Summer School: Courses—Ceramics; Glass; Jewelry; Printmaking; Weaving.

ROCKY MOUNTAIN SCHOOL OF ART,* 1441 Ogden St, 80218. Tel: 303-832-1557. Instrs FT 10.
Estab 1963; pvt; D&E; ent req portfolio of work; cert 2 yr; schol; enrl D 100, E 25.
Tuition: No campus res.
Courses: Advertising Design; Commercial Art; Drawing; Fashion Arts; Fine Art; Graphic Design; History of Art & Archaeology; Illustration; Lettering; Painting.
Summer School: June-August.

UNIVERSITY OF COLORADO AT DENVER, Department of Fine Arts, 1100 14th St, Box 103, 80202. Tel: 303-629-2626. *Chmn* Ludwik Turzanski, MFA; *Asst Prof* John R Fudge, MFA; *Assoc Prof* Gerald C Johnson, MFA; *Assoc Prof* Charles L Moone, MFA; *Assoc Prof* Ernest O Porps, MFA; vis prof Joyce Strauss, art history, spring 78.
Estab 1876, dept estab 1955. Pub; D&E; ent req HS dipl, ACT or SAT, previous academic ability and accomplishment; degrees BA and BFA 4 yr schol; SC 21, LC 13, GC 11; enrl maj 114.
Tuition: Res—Undergrad & grad $364 yr, $182 per sem; Nonres—Undergrad & grad $1454 yr, $727 per sem; no campus res available.
Courses: Art History; ‡Drawing; Film; ‡Painting; ‡Photography; ‡Printmaking; ‡Sculpture; Performance Art Seminar.
Adult Hobby Classes: Tui $2—$40 per class. Courses—Drawing; Painting; Sketching; Glass Etching; Stained Glass; Needlework; Spinning; Wood Inlay; Rug Braiding.

Summer School: Dir Ludwik Turzanski. Tui Same and regular sem, term of 10 wk beginning June 12. Courses—Studio workshops; Art History.

UNIVERSITY OF DENVER, School of Art, Iliff & South Gaylord, 80210. Tel: 303-753-2846. *Dir* Mel Strawn, MFA.
Estab 1880; pvt; D; ent req HS dipl; degrees BA and BFA 4 yr, MFA 2 yr MA 4 quarters; honors program; schol; SC 44, LC 33, GC 50; enrl D 450, nonmaj 170-200, maj 176, GS 40.
Tuition: $4170 per yr, $1390 per sem, $99 per quarter hr; campus res room and board.
Courses: Advertising Design; ‡Art Education; ‡Art History; ‡Ceramics; Commercial Art; ‡Drawing; Film; Graphic Arts; Graphic Design; Handicrafts (off-loom weaving; fabric dyeing); ‡Graphic Communications Design; Interior Design; Jewelry; Lettering; ‡Museum Staff Training (graduate level only) ‡Painting; ‡Photography; ‡Printmaking; ‡Sculpture.
Adult Hobby Classes: Enrl 25; tui $35-$60 per course. Courses—Ceramics, Drawing, Jewelry, Painting, Photography, Printmaking.
Summer School: Dir Mel Strawn. Enrl 100; tui $1390 per sem of 8 wks beginning 6/19-8/18. Courses—Several Art History courses; Special workshops in Ceramics; Photography and Design; Workshop-Seminar in conjunction with Aspen Design Conference.

FORT COLLINS

COLORADO STATE UNIVERSITY, Department of Art, 80523. Tel: 303-491-6774. *Chmn* Peter A Jacobs, EdD; *Asst Chmn* William Imel, MA; *Coordr* Carolyn Anderson, MFA; *Coordr* Ken Hendry, MFA; *Coordr* Dave Dietemann, MFA; *Coordr* Jack Orman, MFA; *Coordr* John Berland, MFA; *Coordr* Mary Jean Nelson, PhD; *Coordr* Perry Ragouzis, EdD; Instrs FT 30, PT 5.
Estab 1870, dept estab 1950; pub; D&E; ent req HS dipl; degrees BA and BFA 4 yr, MFA 70 hrs; schol; SC 95, LC 10, GC 20 nonmaj 2200, maj 550, GC 15.
Tuition: Res—Undergrad & grad $274.50 per sem; Nonres—Undergrad & grad $1098.50; plus $89 fee per sem; campus res $2926 res, $4574 nonres.
Courses: ‡Advertising Design; ‡Art Education; ‡Art History; ‡Ceramics; ‡Commercial Art; Conceptual Art; ‡Drawing; Goldsmithing; ‡Graphic Design; Illustration; ‡Interior Design; ‡Jewelry; ‡Painting; Photography; ‡Printmaking; ‡Sculpture; Silversmithing; ‡Teacher Training; ‡Textile Design.
Summer School: 4 wk and 8 wk sessions beginning May 20 and June 19.

GOLDEN

FOOTHILLS ART CENTER, INC, 809 15th St, 80401. Tel: 303-279-3922. *Exec Dir* Marian J Metsopoulos, MA; Instrs PT 10.
Estab 1968; pvt; D&E (Winter & Spring Classes); no ent req.
Tuition: $20-$54 for 6-10 wks class.
Courses: Calligraphy; Drawing; Jewelry; Painting; Pottery; Printmaking; Watercolor.
Children's Classes: Enrl limited; tui $15-$20 for 8-10 wks class. Courses—Pottery; Printmaking.
Summer School: Exec Dir Marian J Metsopoulos. Workshops for adults and classes for children beginning in June.

GRAND JUNCTION

MESA COLLEGE,* Department of Art, 81501. Tel: 303-248-1323. *Chmn* Donald E Meyers; Instrs FT 3, PT 1.
Estab 1925; pub; D&E; ent req HS dipl, GED; degrees AA, BA(Visual & Performing Arts) 4 yr; schol; SC 12, LC 4; enrl D, maj 100.
Tuition: Res—$369 per yr; Non res—$1470; all students pay $10 application and evaluation fee.
Courses: Advanced Studio; Art in the Home; Ceramics; Civilization and the Arts; Color; Craft Survey; Critical Analysis; Drawing; Early Childhood Art; Figure Drawing; History of Art; Jewelry; Man Creates; Painting; Printmaking; Sculpture.
Adult Hobby Classes: Painting.
Summer School: Enrl 40. Tui res $15 per cr hr, nonres $34 per cr hr. Courses—Ceramics; Drawing; Jewelry.

GREELEY

UNIVERSITY OF NORTHERN COLORADO, Department of Fine Arts, 80639. Tel: 303-351-2143. *Chmn* Dr Robert B Turner, PhD; *Assoc Prof* Herb Schumacher, EdD; *Asst Prof* Hyun Shin, EdD; *Asst Prof* Frederick Myers, MFA; *Instrs* Susan Hoover, MFA; *Asst Prof* Betty Johnson, EdD; *Asst Prof* David Haas, MA; *Assoc Prof* William Cordiner, MA; vis prof 2 per yr.
Estab 1889; pub; D&E; ent req HS dipl; degrees BA.

Tuition: Res—Undergrad and grad $20 per cr hr 6 or less hr, $140 per sem 7 to 18 hrs; Nonres—Undergrad and grad $80 per cr hr 6 or less hrs, $560 per sem 7 to 18 hrs; campus res.
Courses: Art Education; Art History; Ceramics; Drawing; Graphic Arts; Intermedia; Jewelry; Painting; Printmaking; Sculpture; Teacher Training; Video.
Summer School: Chmn Dr Robert B Turner. Courses—Comparative Arts Program in Florence, Italy Workshops in Weaving & Ceramics in Steamboat Springs Colorado, Study of the Indian Arts of Mesa Verde, Mesa Verde workshop & on campus courses.

GUNNISON

WESTERN STATE COLLEGE OF COLORADO, Department of Art, 81230. Tel: 303-943-3083. Instrs FT 7.
Estab 1911; pub; D&E; ent req HS dipl, special exam; degree 4 yr; SC 29, LC 7, GC 8; enrl 850.
Courses: Art Education; Calligraphy; Ceramics; Design; Drawing; Introduction to Art; Jewelry; Painting; Printmaking; Sculpture; Studio Art; Weaving.
Summer School: Dir Dr Edwin H Randall. 2, 5, 8 and 10 wk courses.

LA JUNTA

OTERO JUNIOR COLLEGE, Art Department 81050. Tel: 303-384-4446. *Head Dept* Kenneth Brandon; Instrs FT 1.
Estab 1941; pub; D&E; ent req HS grad; degrees AA and AAS 2 yr; schol; SC 12, LC 3; enrl 776.
Tuition: Res—$339 12 - 18 hrs; Nonres—$389; campus res $1209 - $1284.
Courses: Ceramics (E only); Creative Design; Drawing (D&E); History of Art; Metal Sculpture; Oil Painting (D&E); Watercolor.

PUEBLO

UNIVERSITY OF SOUTHERN COLORADO, BELMONT CAMPUS, Department of Art, 2200 Bonforte Blvd, 81005. Tel: 303-549-2552. *Prof* Edward R Sajbel, MA; *Prof* Lewis Tilley, MFA; *Assoc Prof* Dr Mildred Montverde, PhD; *Assoc Prof* Robert Hench, MA; *Asst Prof* Robert Wands, MA; *Asst Prof* Carl Jensen, MFA; *Assoc Prof* Orlin Helgoe, MFA; *Assoc Prof* Jo Ann Brassill, MFA; vis prof—Hap Tivey, Light Sculpture, Fall 77.
Estab 1933; pub; D&E; ent req HS dipl, GED, Open Door Policy; degrees BA and BS 4 yr; schol; SC 66, LC 19, GC 2; enrl D 700, E 50, nonmaj 150, maj 600.
Tuition: Res—Undergrad $309 18 hr sem; Nonres—Undergrad $965 18 hr sem; campus res.
Courses: Advertising Design; Art Education; Art History; Ceramics; Collage; Commercial Art; Drawing; Film; Graphic Design; Illustration; Jewelry; Museum Staff Training; Painting; Photography; Printmaking; Sculpture; Silversmithing; Teacher Training.
Summer School: Dir Dr Don Janes. Courses—Art Education in the Elementary School; Art History; Ceramics; Introduction to Art; Painting.

STERLING

NORTHEASTERN JUNIOR COLLEGE, Department of Art, 80751. Tel: 303-522-6600, exten 671. *Head Dept* Peter L Youngers, MFA; *Instrs* Larry Presteich, MA.
Estab 1941; pub; D&E; ent req HS dipl, GED; degrees AA 2 yr; schol; SC 16; LC 2; enrl D 103, E 23, nonmaj 73, maj 30, others 23.
Tuition: Res—in county $7 cr hr, out county $70 quarter, $15 cr hr; Nonres—$280 quarter, $25 cr hr; all students $56 college fee; campus res $1150.
Courses: Art Education; Art History; Ceramics; Display; Drawings; Handicrafts (basic crafts); Lettering; Mixed Media; Painting; Printmaking; Sculpture; Teacher Training.
Adult Hobby Classes: Enrl 100; tui $7 per cr hr. Courses—Basic Crafts; Ceramics; Drawing; Macrame; Painting; Stained Glass.
Summer School: Dir Dick Gritz. Courses—vary each year.

VAIL

COLORADO MOUNTAIN COLLEGE, Workshop for Art & Critical Studies, 81657. Tel: 303-476-4040. *Dir* Randy Milhoan, BFA; *Asst Dir* Jane Gregorius, MFA; *Dir Dance Dept* Denise Brimer, BA; vis prof—the workshop hires a wide variety of teachers from all over the country each summer.
Estab 1971; pub; D&E (summers only); schol; SC approx 64 ea summer, LC varies, GS 2-4; enrl D approx 1000, nonmaj 100, maj 900.
Tuition: Res—$6 per unit per quarter plus reg fee; Nonres—$45 per unit per quarter plus reg fee; no campus res.

Courses: Art Education; Art History; Calligraphy; Ceramics; Collage; Conceptual Art; Constructions; Drawing; Film; Film History; Goldsmithing; Handicrafts (crochet, felting; leather crafts, macrame; paper making; sculpture, soft sculpture, weaving); Illustration; Interior Design; Jewelry; Lettering; Mixed Media; Painting; Photography; Printmaking; Sculpture; Silversmithing; Stained Glass.
Adult Hobby Classes: Courses—Crochet; Weaving.
Children's Classes: Enrl 30 per wk; tui $23 per wk. Courses—Batik; Ceramics; Painting; Printmaking; Puppet Making; Sculpture.
Summer School: Enrl 1000; tui $6 per in district unit, $13 per res (instate) unit, $45 per nonres unit for term of 3, 6 or 8 wks beginning July 3. Courses—same as above.

CONNECTICUT

BRIDGEPORT

HOUSATONIC COMMUNITY COLLEGE, Art Department 06680. Tel: 203-579-6400. *Chmn & Prof* Burt Chernow, MA; *Primary Faculty* David Kintzler, MFA; Ronald Abbe, MFA; Michael Stein, MFA; Barbara Rothenberg, MFA; Mary Fish, MFA; occasional vis prof.
Estab 1967, dept estab 1968, pub; D&E; ent req HS dipl; degrees AA 2 yr; SC 15, LC 5, enrl maj 100.
Tuition: $200 per sem, $100 per sem.
Courses: Art Education; Art History; Ceramics; Collage; Constructions; Drafting; Drawing; Film; History of Art and Archaeology; Mixed Media; Painting; Photography; Sculpture; Teacher Training.
Adult Hobby Classes: Varied.
Summer School: Dir Dr Joseph Shive. Courses—Same as above.

SACRED HEART UNIVERSITY, Department of Fine Arts, PO Box 6460, 00606. Tel: 203-374-9441, exten 210. *Chmn* Virginia F Zic, MA; *Instr* William McCarthy, MFA; *Adjunct-Instr* William Decker, MFA; *Assoc Prof* Victor Caglioti, MA.
Estab 1963, dept estab 1977; pvt; D&E; ent req HS dipl; degrees BA 4 yr; SC 10, LC 3; enrl D 185, E 26, nonmaj 160, maj 21.
Tuition: $1225 per sem: no campus res.
Courses: Art History; ‡Drawing; Graphic Design; ‡Illustration; Lettering; ‡Painting; Sculpture.
Summer School: Term of 5 wks beginning June and July.

UNIVERSITY OF BRIDGEPORT, College of Fine Arts, Art Department, University and Iranistan Ave, 06602. (Mailing Add: University Ave, 06602). Tel: 203-576-4436. *Acting Chmn* Peter E Schier, MS; *Prof* Eileen Lord, PhD; *Assoc Prof* Robert Morris, MA; *Assoc Prof* August Madrigal, MA; *Assoc Prof* Paul Vazquez, MFA; *Asst Prof* Arthur Nager, MFA; *vis prof*—Jonathan Goddard, graphic design, 78.
Estab 1927, dept estab 1947; pvt; D&E; ent req portfolio for BFA candidates only, college boards; degrees BA, BS and BFA 4 yr, AA 2 yr, MS 1 yr, certificate 1 yr; schol; SC 38, LC 24, GC 15; enrl D 1150, E 200, nonmaj 1070, maj 260, GS 22.
Tuition: Res—Undergrad $1680 per sem, grad $90 per cr hr; Nonres—Undergrad $85 per cr hr, grad $90 per cr hr; campus res room & board.
Courses: ‡Advertising Design; ‡Art Education; ‡Art History; ‡Art Therapy; Calligraphy; ‡Ceramics; Commercial Art; Crafts; Drafting; Drawing; ‡Film; Graphic Arts; ‡Graphic Design; Handicrafts (weaving); Illustration; ‡Industrial Design; Jewelry; Lettering; ‡Painting; ‡Photography; ‡Pre-Architecture; ‡Printmaking; ‡Sculpture; Silversmithing; Stage Design; Teacher Training; Textile Design; ‡Theatre Arts; Video.
Adult Hobby Classes: Enrl open; tui $50 per course. Courses—most crafts.
Summer School: Acting Chmn Peter E. Schier. Tui $85 for hr for term of 5 wks beginning May or June. Courses—Color; Crafts; Design; Drawing; Painting.

DANBURY

WESTERN CONNECTICUT STATE COLLEGE, 180 White Street, 06810. Tel: 203-797-4000. *Chmn* Robert Alberetti, MFA; *Primary Faculty* Rosalie Appel, MFA; Walter Boelke, MFA; David Holzman, BA.
Estab 1800's; pub; D&E; ent req HS dipl; degrees BA (graphic communications) 4 yr; schol; SC 30, LC 3-6, GC 5; enrl D 25.
Tuition: Res—Undergrad $540 yr, $32 per cr hr, grad $40 per cr hr; Nonres—Undergrad $1530 yr; campus res room & board res and nonres $1250.
Courses: Advertising Design; Aesthetics; Architecture; Art Education; Art History; Ceramics; Commercial Art; Drawing; Film; Graphic Arts; Graphic Design; Handicrafts (cloth as an art form); History of Art and

Archaeology; Illustration; Jewelry; Lettering; Mixed Media; Painting; Photography; Printmaking; Sculpture; Silversmithing; Teacher Training; Theatre Arts; Video.
Summer School: Dir Dr Jack Rudner. Courses—same as above.

GREENWICH

PROPERSI GALLERIES AND SCHOOL OF ART INC, 44 W Putnam Ave, 06830. Tel: 203-869-4430. *Dir & Instr.* August Propersi; *Instr* William Fraccio; *Instr* Jacques Maloubier; *Instr* Joseph Krasnansky.
Estab 1958; pvt; D&E; ent req HS dipl, portfolio; dipl, 3 yrs; schol; SC 7, LC 2; enrl D 45, E 45, nonmaj 27, maj 63.
Tuition: $1900 per yr; no campus res.
Courses: Advertising Design; Commercial Art; Communications; Conceptual Art; Drawing; Fashion Arts; Fashion Illustration; Graphic Design; Illustration; Lettering; Mixed Media; Painting; Studio Skills.
Adult Hobby Classes: Enrl 10; tui $209 per sem. Courses—Painting; Oils; Watercolor.
Children's Classes: Enrl 15; tui $157 per sem. Courses—Drawing; Art History; Painting.
Summer School: Dir August Propersi. Tui $370 for term of 7 wks beginning July 5. Courses—Same as above.

GUILFORD

GUILFORD ART AND MUSIC SCHOOL, Art Branch, 87 Whitfield St, 06405. Tel: 203-453-6180. *Dir* Lydia Noble Booth; *Instr* Alex Domonkos, BFA; *Instr* Raymond J Baldelli, MA; *Instr* David Cain, BA; *Instr* Charles Gruppe, MFA.
Etab 1976; pub; D&E; no ent req; cert of course of study; SC 15; enrl D 45, E 25.
Tuition: $250 to $500; no campus res.
Courses: Advertising Design; Calligraphy; Commercial Art; Drawing; Fashion Arts; Fashion Illustration; Graphic Arts; Graphic Design; Illustration; Interior Design; Mixed Media; Painting; Photography.
Children's Classes: Courses—Drawing; Painting.

HAMDEN

PAIER SCHOOL OF ART, INC,* 6 Prospect Court, 06511. Tel: 203-777-7319. *Pres* Edward T Paier; Instrs FT 18, PT 17.
Estab 1946; pvt; D&E; ent req HS grad, presentation of portfolio, transcript of records, recommendation; degrees no credit; SC 10; LC 6; GC 1; enrl D 385, E 150.
Tuition: $2050 per yr.
Courses: Advertising Design; Commercial Art; Drawing; Fashion Arts; Graphic Arts; Graphic Design; History of Art & Archaeology; Illustration; Interior Design; Lettering; Painting; Photography; Technical Illustration.
Summer School: Dir E T Paier. Enrl 150; term of 6 wk beginning July. Courses—part-time and unit subjects available.

HARTFORD

TRINITY COLLEGE, Department of Fine Arts, 300 Summit Street, 06106. Tel: 203-527-3151. *Chmn* Michael Mahoney, PhD; *Dir* George Chaplin, MFA; *Prof* Thomas Baird, MA; *Artist-in-Residence* Stephen Wood, MFA.
Estab 1823, dept estab 1941; pvt; D; ent req HS dipl; degrees BA 4 yr; schol; SC 25, LC 24; enrl D 750, nonmaj 600, maj 100.
Tuition: $3950 yr, campus res room & board $1670.
Courses: Aesthetics; ‡Art History; Drawing; Graphic Arts; Painting; Printmaking; Sculpture; Stage Design; ‡Studio Arts; Theatre Arts.

MIDDLETOWN

WESLEYAN UNIVERSITY, Art Department, 06457. Tel: 203-347-9411. *Chmn* John Martin, B Arch; *Prof* John Frazer, MFA; *Prof* John Risley, MFA; *Assoc Prof* John T Paoletti, PhD; *Adj Assoc Prof* Richard S Field.
Estab 1831, dept estab 1928; pvt; D; ent req HS dipl; degrees BA and MALS (summer school); schol; SC 29; LC 37; enrl D 750.
Tuition: $4300 yr; campus res room & board.
Courses: Aesthetics; Architecture; Art Education; Art History; Calligraphy; Ceramics; Drafting; Drawing; Film; Graphic Arts; Graphic Design; History of Art and Archaeology; Industrial Design; Intermedia; Jewelry; Mixed Media; Painting; ‡Photography; Printmaking; Sculpture; Silversmithing; Teacher Training; Theatre Arts; Typography; Urban Studies.
Summer School: Dir James L Steffensen, Jr.

NEW BRITAIN

CENTRAL CONNECTICUT STATE COLLEGE, Department of Art, 1615 Stanley St, 06050. Tel: 203-827-7326. *Prof Art & Chmn Dept* Walter J LaVoy, DEd; Instrs FT 16, PT 21.
Estab 1849; pub; D&E; ent req HS dipl, screening required for admission to dept; degrees BA and BS(Art Educ) 4 yrs; SC 36, LC 8, GC 20; enrl D 200, E 150, nonmaj 1000, maj 200, grad 500.
Courses: Advertising Design; Art Education; Art History; Ceramics; Costume Design & Construction; Display; Drafting; Drawing; Graphic Arts; Handicrafts (Weaving, Stained Glass); Jewelry; Lettering; Painting; Photography; Printmaking; Sculpture; Silversmithing; Stage Design; Teacher Training; Theatre Arts; Video.
Children's Classes: Enrl 6-17 yr olds; tui $6. Courses—Vary.
Summer School: Dean Exten Col R Tupper. Tui $35 per cr hr for term of 5 wks beginning July 5. Courses—varied and comprehensive.

NEW CANAAN

SILVERMINE GUILD SCHOOL OF THE ARTS, 1037 Silvermine Rd, 06850. Tel 203-866-0411. *Dir* Robert Franco.
Estab 1939; pvt; D&E; ent req none; degrees none, advanced classes in painting-seminars; SC 60, LC 1; enrl 560.
Tuition: No campus res.
Courses: Advertising Design; Air Brush Painting; Calligraphy; Cartooning; Ceramics; Chinese Landscape Painting; Collage; Commercial Art; Conceptual Art; Design; Drawing; Graphic Arts; Graphic Design; Handicrafts (weaving, framemaking); Illustration; Jewelry; Mixed Media Painting; Photography; Printmaking; Sculpture; Silversmithing.
Children's Classes: Courses—Art Workshops; Dance Classes.
Summer School: Dir Robert Franco. 8 wk prog. Courses—same as above.

NEW HAVEN

ALBERTUS MAGNUS COLLEGE, Art Department, 700 Prospect St, 06511. Tel: 203-777-6631. *Chmn* Sister Thoma Swanson, MFA; *Prof* Denise Buckley, MFA; *Prof* Mark Wallack, MS; *Prof* Juliana D'Amato, PhD; *Prof* Marta Staiti, MA; Instrs FT 2, PT 3.
Estab 1925, dept estab 1970; pvt; D&E; ent req HS dipl, SAT, CEEB; degrees BA 8 sem; schol; SC 20, LC 9, Enrl D 160.
Tuition: $2950 two sem, $93 per cr hr; campus res room & board $1850.
Courses: Aesthetics; Art Education; Art History; Art Therapy; Ceramics; Collage; Drawing; Handicrafts (weaving); History of Art and Archaeology; Lettering; Mixed Media; Painting; Photography; Printmaking; Sculpture; State Design.
Summer School: Dir Sister Jane McDermott. Courses—Crafts Workshop.

SOUTHERN CONNECTICUT STATE COLLEGE, Department of Art, 501 Crescent St, 06515. Tel: 203-397-4279. *Dept Head & Assoc Prof* Elizabeth Turner Hall, MFA. Instrs FT 21, PT 8.
Estab 1893; pub; D&E; ent req HS dipl, SAT; degrees BS, MS Art Educ) BA (Art History) and BA (Studio Art) 4 yr; SC 40, LC 18, GC 20; enrl D 400, GS 400.
Tuition: Res—$500 yr, $32 per cr hr; Nonres—$1400 yr, $40 per cr hr; campus res room & board.
Courses: Advertising Design; Aesthetics; Art Education; Art History; Ceramics; Commercial Art; Drawing; Goldsmithing; Graphic Arts; Graphic Design; Handicrafts; History of Art and Archaeology; Illustration; Jewelry; Lettering; Mixed Media; Painting; Photography; Printmaking; Sculpture; Silversmithing; Teacher Training.
Summer School: Dir George Cole. Two terms of 5 wks beginning May 30 and July 5.

YALE UNIVERSITY

—School of Art, 180 York St, 06520. Tel: 203-436-0308. *Dean* Andrew Forge; *Prof* William Bailey, MFA; *Assoc Prof* David vonSchlegell; *Prof* Alvin Eisenman, MA; *Dir* Howard S Weaver, BA; *Prof* Gabor Peterdi, MA; *Assoc Prof* John Hill, MFA; vis prof—Larry Fink, Photography 77-78.
Estab 1868; pvt; D; ent req HS dipl, must have BA or BFA, portfolio and application; degrees MFA 2 yr; schol; GC 95.
Tuition: $4000 yr; campus res room.
Courses: Drawing; Film; Graphic Design; Painting; Photography; Printmaking; Sculpture.
—Department of the History of Art* (Yale College and Graduate School). Box 2009, 56 High St, 06520. Tel: 203-436-8853. *Dir* Undergrad Studies Anne Coffin Hanson; *Dir* Grad Studies George L. Hersey; *Admin Asst* Nancy A Walchli; Instrs FT 27, PT 2.
Estab 1940; pvt; D; undergrad maj leading to BA, grad prog; ent req BA and foreign language, offering PhD degree; training for small groups in all principal fields of History of Art, museum training; schol; fel and assistantships.

Courses: Change each yr.
**—School of Architecture, ***Tel: 203-436-0550, *Dean* Cesar Pelli.
Estab 1869; pvt; ent req Bachelor's degree, grad record exam; degrees MArch, 3 yr MEnviron Design 2 yr; enrl 150 maximum.

NEW LONDON

CONNECTICUT COLLEGE
—Department of Art, Mohegan Avenue, 06320. Tel: 203-442-5391. *Chmn* David Smalley; *Asst Prof* Barkley L Hendricks; *Assoc Prof* Peter Leibert; *Prof* Richard Lukosius; *Asst Prof* Maureen McCabe; *Prof* William McCabe; *Prof* William McCloy; *Asst Prof* Robert Straight.
Estab 1911; pvt; D; ent req HS dipl, ent exam; degrees BA 4 yr; schol; SC 20, LC 34 (art history).
Tuition: $4330 yr; campus res room & board $1620.
Courses: Many offered in a variety of areas.
Summer School: Dir David Smalley. Courses—Ceramics; Drawing; Painting; Photography; Printmaking; Sculpture.
—Department of Art History, 06320. Tel: 203-442-5391. *Chmn* Charles Price; *Instrs* Richard Arms; *Assoc Prof* Nancy Fabbri; *Prof* John Knowlton; *Prof* Edgar Mayhew; *Instrs* Barbara Zabel.

NORWICH

NORWICH ART SCHOOL, The Norwich Free Academy, Art Department, 108 Crescent Street, 06360. Tel: 203-887-2505. *Dir & Head Art Dept* Frank T Novack, MFA; *Primary Faculty* John R Fix, MA; Caroline A Battisto, AFA; Theodora C Goberis; Joseph P Gualtiere; Janet M Mol, BFA; Mary-Anne Stumpo, MA; Dennis H. Driscoll, BFA, Johanna D Vacca, MA; Melody Leary, BFA; Daniel C Charron, BS.
Estab 1890; pvt; D&E; ent req HS dipl & submission of portfolio for one year basic art post high school programs; degrees one yr Basic Art Program post high school plus special Fine Arts Program for high school students beginning 10th grade; SC 18, LC 2; enrl D 685, E 100, fine arts maj 850.
Tuition: Res—$1492 yr, $585 per sem plus supplies; no campus res.
Courses: Art History; Ceramics; Design; Drawing & Composition; Fashion Arts; Goldsmithing; Handicrafts (weaving & macrame); History of Art & Archeology; Painting; Photography; Poster & Layout; Printmaking; Sculpture; Silversmith; Textile Design.
Adult Hobby Classes: Enrl 75; tui $25 for 15 wk session. Courses—Ceramics; Drawing; Jewelry & Metalsmithing; Painting.
Children's Classes: Enrl 121; tui $35 for 30 wk session. Courses—Collage; Design; Drawing; Murals; Painting; Pottery; special program for advanced students in all studio or art history courses to prepare portfolio for further art college education.
Summer School: Dir Carolyn Andrews or Judith Pflum. Enrl 15-18 each class; tui $50 for term of 6 wk beginning 1st wk of July. Courses—General Art; Ceramics.

STORRS

UNIVERSITY OF CONNECTICUT, Art Department, 06268. Tel: 203-429-3930. *Head Dept* Richard Thornton, MFA; *Prof* Harold Spencer, PhD; *Prof* John Gregoropoulos, BA; *Prof* Robert Crossgrove, MFA; *Prof* Anthony Terenzio, MFA; *Prof* Minnie Negoro, MFA; *Prof* Gerard Doudera, MFA; *Assoc Prof* Joyce Brodsky, MA.
Estab 1882, dept estab 1950; pub; D; ent req HS dipl; degrees BA (Art History, BFA (Studio) 4 yr; SC 32, LC 20; enrl D 1300.
Tuition: Res—Undergrad & grad $270, Nonres—Under grad & grad $615; campus res room & board.
Courses: Advertising Design; Architecture; Art History; Ceramics; Commercial Art; Drawing; Graphic Design; History of Art and Archaeology; Painting; Photography; Printmaking; Sculpture.
Summer School: Tui $45 per cr hr; two terms beginning 5/22 and 8/15. Courses—Ceramics; Drawing; History of Photography; Lithography; Painting; Sculpture; Watercolor.

VOLUNTOWN

FOSTER CADDELL'S ART SCHOOL, Rt 49, RFD 1, 06384. Tel: 201-376-9583. *Head Dept* Foster Caddell.
Estab 1958; D&E; enrl D 75, E 50.
Tuition: $275 yr; no campus res.
Courses: Drawing; Painting; Pastel.
Summer School: Tui $100 per wk. Courses—Summer workshops and Seminars; Painting Demonstrations and Lecture.

WEST HARTFORD

HARTFORD ART SCHOOL OF THE UNIVERSITY OF HARTFORD, 200 Bloomfield Ave, 06117. Tel: 203-243-4391, 243-4398. *Dean* Bernard Hanson, MA; *Asst to the Dean* Steven Keller; MA; *Prof*

Wolfgang Behl; *Asst Prof* Nancy Geismann, MFA; *Assoc Prof* Lloyd Glasson, MFA; *Instr* Walter Hall, MFA; *Assoc Prof* Gary Hogan, MS; *Assoc Prof* Christopher Horton, MAT; *Asst Prof* Leland Johnston, MFA; *Instr* Heidi Katz, MFA; *Asst Prof* Doris Kinsella, BA; *Instr* Maria Kurcbart, MFA and MAT; *Assoc Prof* G W Martin, MFA; *Assoc Prof* Peter McLean, MFA; *Asst Prof* Mitchell Peerless, MFA; *Instr* David Salle, MFA; *Asst Prof* Alan Sondheim, MA; *Instrs* Frederick Wessel, MFA; *Asst Prof* Stephan Zaima, MFA; *Prof* Rudolph Zallinger, MFA; *Prof* Paul Zimmerman, MFA.
Estab 1877; pvt; D&E; ent req HS dipl, SAT, solution of Hartford Art School's Premlinary Art Problems; degrees BFA and BFA (Art Ed major) 4 yr, MFA and MA Ed 2 yr; schol; SC 70, LC 5, GC 32; enrl D 300, E 200, nonmaj 125, maj 300, GS 75.
Tuition: Res—Undergrad $2950 yr, $1475 per sem, $80 per cr hr (evening), grad $75 per cr hr; Nonres—Undergrad $2950 yr, $1475 per sem, $75 per cr hr; campus res board and room $1569.
Courses: Advertising Design; Art Education; Ceramics; Conceptual Art; Drawing; Film; Illustration; Intermedia; Painting; Performance; Photography; Printmaking; Sculpture; Video.
Summer School: Dean Bernard Hanson; Tui—same for term of 4 - 6 wks beginning July.

SAINT JOSEPH COLLEGE,* Department of Fine Arts, 1678 Asylum Ave, 06117. Tel: 203-232-4571. Instrs FT 2, PT 1.
Estab 1932; pvt; D&E; W; ent req HS dipl, CEEB; degrees BA, BS and MA 4 yr; schol; SC 5, LC 7, enrl D 104.
Tuition: $260 yr; campus res $1650.
Courses: Art Education; Batik; Drawing; Enameling; Fundamentals of Design; History of Art; Mosaic; Painting; Weaving.

WEST HAVEN

UNIVERSITY OF NEW HAVEN, School of Arts and Sciences, Department of Fine Arts, 300 Orange Ave, 06516. Tel: 203-934-6321, exten 258. *Chmn & Prof* Elizabeth Moffitt; MA; *Asst Prof* Edward Maffeo, MA; *Asst Prof* Joan Gardner, MFA; Instrs FT 3, PT 12.
Estab 1927, dept estab 1972; pvt; D&E; ent req HS dipl; degrees BA and BS 4 yr, AS 2 yr; SC 30, LC 5; enrl D 350, E 110.
Tuition: Res—Undergrad $4277 yr, $2139 per sem; Nonres—Undergrad $2642 yr, $1321 per sem, $60 per cr hr; campus res $1580.
Courses: ‡Advertising Design; Art History; Calligraphy; Ceramics; Collage; Commercial Art; Constructions; Dimensional Design; Drawing; Fashion Arts; Film Animation; Graphic Arts; Graphic Design; Handicrafts (weaving); History of Art and Archaeology; Illustration; Independent Study; Interaction of Color; Interior Design; Lettering; Mixed Media; Painting; Photography; Printmaking; Sculpture; Textile Design.
Summer School: Dir Richard Lipp. Tui $60 per cr hr for two terms of 5 wks beginning June 12th and July 20th. Courses—Ceramics; Drawing; History of Art; Painting; Photography; Sculpture.

WESTPORT

FAMOUS ARTISTS SCHOOL, 17 Riverside Ave, 06880. Tel: 203-227-8471. *Pres & Dir* Fritz Henning; *Chmn Advisory Board* Steven Dohanos; *Advisory Board members* Robert Peak; Bernard Fuchs; George Giusti; Joseph Hirsch; Dong Kingman; Robert Heindel; Franklin McMahon; Will Barnet; Mark English.
Estab 1947; pvt; all teaching through home study; degree cert 3 yr; enrl D 3000.
Courses: Advertising Design; Collage; Commercial Art; Drawing; Fashion Arts; Graphic Arts; Graphic Design; Illustration; Lettering; Mixed Media; Painting; Photography.
Children's Classes: Tui $498 yr. Courses—for talented young people (13-18).

WILLIMANTIC

EASTERN CONNECTICUT STATE COLLEGE, Art Department, Windham St, 06226. Tel: 203-456-2331, exten 507. *Chmn* Julian Akus; Instrs FT 3, PT 4.
Estab 1881; pub; D&E; ent req HS dipl; degrees BA (Fine Arts) and BS (Art) 4 yr; schol; enrl D 300, E 75, maj 40.
Tuition: $450 per yr plus $250 fee; campus res $870.
Courses: Ceramics; Crafts (enameling); Drawing; Graphic Arts; History of Art; Painting; Sculpture.
Summer School: Dir Kenneth H Lungy. Courses—Art & Craft Workshop.

WOODSTOCK

ANNHURST COLLEGE, Fine Arts Department, 06281. Tel: 203-928-7773, exten 65. *Chmn* Suzanne Marie Roy, MEd; *Prof* Russell Wootton, MFA; *Instrs* Kenneth Gielle.
Estab 1941, dept estab 1970; pvt; D&E; ent req HS dipl; degrees BA 4 yrs; schol; SC 19, LC 4; enrl D 46, E 52, nonmaj 11, maj 35, others 52.
Tuition: $2526 per yr, $1263 per sem, $80 per cr hr; campus res room and board $1936 per yr.
Courses: Art Education; Art History; Calligraphy; Ceramics; Drawing; Graphic Design; Handicrafts (weaving); Lettering; Painting; Photography; Printmaking; Sculpture; Stage Design; Teacher Training; Theatre Arts.
Summer School: Tui $80 per cr hr for term of 6 wk, beginning June 26. Courses—Ceramics; Drawing; Painting; Photography.

DELAWARE

DOVER

DELAWARE STATE COLLEGE,* Art Education Department, 19901. Instrs FT 3, PT 1.
Estab 1960, pub; D&E; ent req HS dipl, SAT; degree BA(Art Educ) 4 yr; schol; SC 13, LC 9, enrl over 60 (maj and nonmaj).
Courses: Advertising Design; Aesthetics; Art Education; Ceramics; Commercial Art; Drawing; Graphic Arts; Handicrafts; History of Art and Archaeology; Illustration; Jewelry; Lettering; Painting; Photography; Sculpture; Stage Design; Teacher Training; Theatre Arts.

NEWARK

UNIVERSITY OF DELAWARE, Department of Art, 19711. *Chmn* Daniel K Teis, PhD; *Coordr* Norman Sasowaky, EdD; *Coordr* Charles Rowe, MFA; *Coordr* Joe Moss, MA; *Coordr* John Weiss, MFA; *Coordr* Harwood Ritter, MA; *Coordr* Victor Spinski, MFA; *Coordr* Rosemary Hooper, MFA; *Coordr* Anne Graham, MFA.
Estab 1833; pub; D&E ent req Portfolio, BFA program (Sophomore Year); degrees BA, BS and BFA 4 yr; MFA 2 yr; MA 1 yr; SC 62, LC 2, GC 12, nonmaj 600, maj 400, GS 30.
Tuition: Res—Undergrad $1000 yr, grad $45 per cr hr; Nonres—Undergrad $2113, grad $108 per cr hr; campus res room & board $1100.
Courses: ‡Art Education; ‡Ceramics; ‡Drawing; ‡Graphic Design; ‡Handicrafts (fibers); ‡Jewelry; ‡Painting; ‡Photography; ‡Printmaking; ‡Sculpture.

REHOBOTH BEACH

REHOBOTH ART LEAGUE, INC, PO Box 84, 19971. Tel: 302-227-8408. *Head Dept* Mary L Pearce; *Primary Faculty* John I Lewis, MA; James Drake Iams, BA; Debra Jahnigan, MA; Betty Hessemer, MA; Marion Farquharson; Richard Harrison; Howard S Schroeder, BA; Dorothy H Lewis; Nanette Cunliffe; *vis prof*—Arthur Barbour, watercolor, 2 day workshop; Instrs FT 9, PT 9.
Estab 1938; pvt; D; ent req interest in art; SC 7, enrl D 400, others 400.
Tuition: $45-$55 depending on class; no campus res.
Courses: Ceramics; Drawing; Graphic Arts; Painting; Printmaking; Music.
Adult Hobby Classes: Tui $45. Courses—Ceramics; Drawing; Music; Painting; Printmaking; Weaving.
Children's Classes: Tui $20-$70. Courses—Art forms.
Summer School: Dir Mary L Pearce. Courses—as above.

DISTRICT OF COLUMBIA

WASHINGTON

AMERICAN UNIVERSITY, Department of Art, Massachusetts & Nebraska Aves NW, 20016. Tel: 202-686-2114. *Prof Art & Chmn Dept* Ben L Summerford; *Prof* Robert A D'Arista; *Prof* Helene M Herzbrun; *Assoc Prof* Lucinao J Penay, MA; *Assoc Prof* Stephen Pace; *Prof* Mary D Garrard, PhD; *Assoc Prof* Norma Broude, PhD; *Asst Prof* Michael Graham, MFA; vis profs—Philip Guston, Jack Tworkov, Charles Cajori and Esteban Vicente, 3 times a yr.
Estab 1893, dept estab 1945; pvt; D&E; ent req HS dipl; degrees BA, BFA(Studio Art), BA(Design), BA(Art Hist) and BS(Art Educ) 4 yrs, MA(Art Hist) 18 months, MFA(Painting, Sculpture, Printmaking) 2 yrs; schol; SC 19, LC 14, GC 26; enrl D&E 1520, maj 191, grad 65.
Tuition: $1845 per sem, $123-$129 per cr hr; campus res.

Courses: Advertising Design; Art Education; Art History; Ceramics; Drawing; Graphic Arts; Graphic Design; History of Art & Archaeology; Illustration; Lettering; Painting; Printmaking; Sculpture.
Summer School: Dir Ben L Summerford. Tui $123-$129 per cr hr. Courses—Studio & Art History; Design.

CATHOLIC UNIVERSITY OF AMERICA
—Department of Architecture & Planning, 20064. Tel: 202-635-5000. *Chmn* Dr Forrest Wilson, PhD; *Lectr* Thomas Walton, MArch; *Lectr* Walter Roth, MArch; *Assoc Prof* Ted Naos, MArch; *Assoc Prof* John Tanik, MArch; *Assoc Prof* Dr Peter Lizon, PhD; vis critics in architectural design courses.
Estab 1887, dept estab 1930; den; D&E; ent req HS dipl, SAT; degrees BSArch 4 yr, MArch 2 yr, MPlanning 6 yr, MUrban Design & PhD Arch; SC 6, LC 12 per sem, GC 39 per sem; enrl D 260, maj 260, grad 80.
Tuition: Undergrad $3350 yr, $1675 per sem, $120 per cr hr; Grad $3450 yr, $1775 per sem, $130 per cr hr; campus res room and board $850 per yr.
Courses: ‡Architecture; Drafting; History of Art & Archaeology; History and Theory of Modern Architecture; Photography.
Adult Hobby Classes: Tui $30 per 8 wk session. Courses—Photography.
Children's Classes: Tui $200 per 2 wk session. Courses—Experiences in architecture.
Summer School: Dir John McDermott. Enrl 150; tui $90 per cr hr for term of 5-7 wk beginning mid May. Courses—Design Studio; History of Architecture; Mechanical Equipment Planning; Structures; Theory of Architecture.
—Graduate School of Arts & Sciences,* Division of Art. *Head* Thomas P Rooney; Instrs FT 6, PT 2.
Estab 1937; degrees granted.
Courses: Ceramics; Design; Drawing; Graphic Arts; History of Art; Metalsmithing; Painting; Sculpture.
Summer School: Chmn Thomas P Rooney. Term of 6 wk.

CORCORAN SCHOOL OF ART, 17th St & New York Ave, NW
20006. Tel: 202-638-3211. *Dean* Peter G Thomas, MA; *Chmn Foundation & Second Year* Rona Slade, ADT; *Chmn Third Year* Robert Stackhouse, MA; *Chmn Visual Communications* K K Ramkissoon, MA; *Chmn Complementary Studies* Andrew Judson, BA; *Chmn Drawing & Design* A Brockie Stevenson; *Chmn Ceramics* William Lombardo, MFA; *Chmn Printmaking Dept* Jack Perlmutter; *Chmn Sculpture* Berthold Schmutzhart; *Chmn Photography* Paul Kennedy; Dipl; various vis profs.
Estab 1890; pvt; D&E; ent req HS dipl, portfolio and interview for degree/diploma candidates; degrees BFA 4 yr; schol; SC 20, LC 7; enrl D 650, E 250, nonmaj 725, maj 175, others 650.
Tuition: $2550 yr, $1275 per sem, $265 per 3 cr hr course; no campus res.
Courses: ‡Aesthetics; Art History; ‡Ceramics; ‡Commercial Art; ‡Drawing; ‡Film; ‡Graphic Arts; ‡Graphic Design; History of Photography; ‡Illustration; ‡Painting; ‡Photography; ‡Printmaking; ‡Sculpture; Watercolor; Typography.
Children's Classes: Tui $135 per sem. Saturday Ages 11 - 14. Courses—Drawing; Painting; Sculpture; Ceramics; Printmaking; Watercolor—Ages 15-18 College Prep Workshop.
Summer School: Dean Peter G Thomas. Adult— Tui $250 for 5-6 wk, beginning June 21 - August 25. Courses—Drawing, Painting, Sculpture; Visual Communications, Photography; Printmaking; Watercolor. High School—(15-18) Tui $125 for term of 4 wks beginning June 26. Pre-College Workshop, Portfolio Prep. Courses—Drawing, Painting; Ceramics; Printmaking. Junior High—(11-14) Tui $125 for 4 wk, beginning June 26 - August 17. Summer Session in Maine in Photography, Fine Arts —(Adult) Tui $590 (included room and board).

GEORGE WASHINGTON UNIVERSITY, Department of Art, 20052.
Tel: 202-676-6086. *Chmn* Lilien F Robinson, PhD; *Asst Prof* Jeffrey C Anderson, PhD; *Asst Prof* Constance C Costigan, MFA; *Asst Prof* H I Gates, MFA; *Asst Prof* Fuller O Griffith, MFA; *Prof* Francis S Gruber, PhD; *Asst Prof* D Michael Hitchcock, PhD; *Asst Prof* Jerry L Lake, MFA; *Prof* William A MacDonald, PhD.
Estab 1821, dept estab 1893; pvt; D&E; ent req HS dipl, ent exam; degrees BA 4 yr; MA 2-2½ yr, MFA 2 yr; schol; SC 103, LC 74, GC 68; enrl D 1500, maj 190, GS 196.
Tuition: $2800 per yr; $1400 per sem, $105 per cr hr; campus res room and board $1690-$2020.
Courses: Advertising Design; Architecture; ‡Art History; ‡Ceramics; Display; ‡Drawing (Undergrad only); Film; ‡Graphic Arts; ‡Graphic Design; History of Art and Archaeology; Illustration; Interior Design; Jewelry; Lettering; Mixed Media; ‡Museum Staff Training; ‡Painting; ‡Photography; ‡Printmaking; ‡Sculpture; Typography; Visual Communication.
Summer School: Dean William F Long. Tui $105 per hr for term of 3 separate terms beginning May 15th.

GEORGETOWN UNIVERSITY, Department of Fine Arts, 20057. Tel:
202-625-4085. *Head Dept* Clifford T Chieffo, MA; *Assoc Prof* Daniel Brush, MFA; *Asst Prof* Dr Carra Ferguson, PhD; *Asst Prof* Eugene M Geinzer, MFA; *Prof* Dr Donn Murphy PhD; *Asst Prof* Dr Ken Haley, PhD; *vis prof*—Toby Benjamin, art history, spring 78.
Estab 1789, dept estab 1960; pvt; D; ent req HS dipl; degrees BA 4 yr; SC 8, LC 6; enrl D 600 (includes nonmaj), maj 12 per yr.
Tuition: $3240 yr, $108 per cr hr; campus res room & board.
Courses: Aesthetics; ‡Art History; ‡Drawing; Graphic Arts; ‡Painting; ‡Printmaking; ‡Sculpture; Stage Design; Theatre Arts.
Children's Classes: Courses—Directed studies with individual attention.
Summer School: Enrl 20-30; tui $255 for term of 5 wks beginning June 12. Courses—Introduction to History of Art, Television Production.

HOWARD UNIVERSITY,* Department of Art, College of Fine Arts,
Sixth St & Fairmount St NW, 20001. Tel 202-636-7047. *Dean* Thomas J Flagg; *Chmn* Starmanda Bullock; Instrs FT 16.
Estab 1921; pvt; D&E; degrees BFA, MA (History of Art and Art Educ) and MFA 2 yr; schol and fel; enrl 200, others 450.
Tuition: $782.50 per sem; campus res.
Courses: Art Education; Art History; Ceramics; Design; Painting; Photography; Printmaking; Sculpture.

IMMACULATA COLLEGE OF WASHINGTON, Department of Fine
Arts, 20016. Tel: 202-966-0040. *Chmn* Yolanda R Frederikse, MA; *Asst Prof* Emily Hammood, PhD; *Asst Prof* Sister Annette Cecile Hoerner, MA.
Estab 1902; dept estab 1956; den; D&E; ent req HS dipl; degrees AA 2 yr; enrl D 150, E 350.
Tuition: Campus res.
Courses: Art History; Calligraphy; Commercial Art; Drawing; Graphic Design; Lettering; Mixed Media; Painting; Theatre Arts.

TRINITY COLLEGE, Department of Fine Arts, 20015. Tel: 202-244-
3715. *Head Dept* Dr Liliana Gramberg, Doctorate; *Prof* Dr Ilona Ellinger, PhD.
Estab 1897; den; D&E; ent req HS dipl SAT or ACT, recommendation; degrees BA and BS 4 yr; MAT and MBA 2 yr; schol; SC 8, LC 2-3; enrl D 120, maj 25, grad 20.
Tuition: $3100 per yr, $1550 per sem, $85 per cr hr; campus res room & board $1800.
Courses: Aesthetics; Art History; Calligraphy; Drawing; Graphic Arts; Graphic Design; Handicrafts (metal art); History of Art and Archaeology; Lettering; ‡Painting; Photography; Printmaking; Sculpture; Teacher Training; Techniques of Etching; Textile Design.
Summer School: Dir Dr J Van Dien. Courses—Various courses offered.

FLORIDA

BOCA RATON

COLLEGE OF BOCA RATON,* Department of Art, Military Trail,
33431. Tel: 305-395-4301. *Head Dept* E J Ranspach; Instrs FT 1, PT 3.
Estab 1963; pub; D&E; ent req open door; degrees AA and BA 2-4 yr; schol; SC 6, LC 2; enrl D 50, E 20, maj 6.
Courses: Advertising Design; Commercial Art; Drawing; Fashion Arts; Graphic Arts; History of Art & Archaeology; Industrial Design; Painting; Photography; Sculpture; Stage Design; Textile Design.

FLORIDA ATLANTIC UNIVERSITY,* Art Department, 33431. Tel:
305-395-5100, exten 2573. *Chmn* Claire V Dorst; Instrs FT 7, PT 1.
Estab 1964; pub; D&E; ent req AA; degrees BFA and BA 2 yr; SC 37, LC 14, GC 1; enrl D 1600, maj 150, grad 8, special students 7.
Tuition: Res—$16.50 per cr hr; Nonres—$51.50 per cr hr; campus res $190 per quarter.
Courses: Aesthetics; Applied Art; Art Education; Ceramics; Commercial Art; Costume Design & Construction; Drawing; Graphic Arts; Handicrafts; History of Art; History of Architecture; Jewelry; Lettering; Museum Staff Training; Painting; Photography; Sculpture; Stage Design; Teacher Training; Theatre Arts; Weaving.
Summer School.

BRADENTON

ART LEAGUE SCHOOL OF THE ART LEAGUE OF MANATEE
COUNTY,* 209 9th St W, 33505. Tel: 813-746-2862. Instrs D PT 7, E PT 3.
Estab 1952; pvt; D&E; SC 17.
Courses: Ceramic Sculpture & Design; Drawing; Landscape; Oil Landscape; Painting; Portrait; Pottery; Sketching; Watercolor, (experimental).
Children's Classes: Sat morning.

MANATEE JUNIOR COLLEGE, Department of Art, 33507. (Mailing Add: PO Box 1849). Tel: 813-755-1511, exten 254. *Prof* Edward Camp, MFA; *Prof* Cortez Francis, MF; *Prof* James McMahon, MFA; *Prof* Priscilla Stewart, MA; Instrs FT 4, PT 1.
Estab 1958; Pub; D&E; ent exam HS dipl, SAT; degrees AA and AS 2 yrs; schol; SC 16, LC 3, GC 8 (for AA); enrl D approx 704, E approx 440, maj 75.
Tuition: Res—Undergrad $14 per chr hr; Nonres—Undergrad $26 per cr hr.
Courses: Art Education; Art History; Ceramics; Collage; Drafting; Drawing; Graphic Arts; Handicrafts (crafts, macrame, mosaic, paper design, weaving); History of Art and Archaeology; Interior Design; Lettering; Painting; Printmaking; Sculpture; Textile Design.
Adult Hobby Classes: Enrl approx 100; tui $15 per sem. Courses—Drawing Techniques; Painting (Sumie); Religion and Art.
Summer School; Dir Stephen Dorcheck. Tui $13 per cr hr for term of 6 wks. Courses—Art History; Art Appreciation; Ceramics; Craft Design; Drawing.

CLEARWATER

FLORIDA GULF COAST ART CENTER, INC, 222 Ponce de Leon Blvd, 33516. Tel: 813-584-8634. *Mgr* Charles H B Latshaw.
Estab 1949; pvt; D&E; no ent req; no degrees; enrl D 315.
Tuition: No res facilities.
Courses: Ceramics; Creative Writing; Crewel; Drafting; Drawing; Handicrafts; History of Art & Archaeology; Jewelry; Painting; Photography; Sculpture; Weaving; Wood Carving.
Children's Classes: Tui $30 per 10 wks. Courses—Art Sampler grades 1-3; Art Youth grades 4-6; Young Adult General Drawing & Painting grades 6,7,8.

CORAL GABLES

UNIVERSITY OF MIAMI, Department of Art, PO Box 3248106, 33124. Tel: 305-284-2542. *Chmn* Gerald G Winter, MFA; *Primary Faculty:* Eugene Massin, MFA; Ken Uyemura, MFA; R W Downs, MFA; Edward Ghannam, MFA; Peter Zorn, MFA; Dr William E Betsch, PhD; Christine Federighi, MFA.
Estab 1925; dept estab 1960; pvt; D&E; ent req HS dipl, SAT; degrees BA and BFA 4 yr; schol; SC 81, LC 15, GC 25; enrl D 1300, nonmaj 1000, maj 300, GS 25.
Tuition: Res & Nonres—Undergrad $3400 yr, $1700 per sem, $130 per cr hr; Res & Nonres—Grad $3500 yr, $1750 per sem, $134 per cr hr; campus res $630.
Courses: ‡Advertising Design; ‡Art Education; Art History; ‡Ceramics; Commercial Art; ‡Drawing; ‡Graphic Arts; ‡Graphic Design; Handicrafts (weaving); ‡History of Art & Archaeology; Illustration; Lettering; Painting; Photography; Printmaking; Sculpture; Teacher Training.

DE LAND

STETSON UNIVERSITY,* Art Department, 32720. Tel: 904-734-4121, exten 248. *Head Dept* Fred Messersmith; Instrs FT 2, PT 1.
Estab 1880, den; ent req col boards; degrees 4 yr; schol; SC 5, LC 5, LabC 5; enrl 200.
Tuition: $2725 yr.
Courses: Art Education; Art History; Commercial Art; Ceramics; Design; Drawing & Painting; Graphics; Introduction to Art; Photography; Sculpture.

DUNEDIN

DUNEDIN FINE ARTS AND CULTURAL CENTER, 1143 Michigan Blvd, 33528. Tel: 813-734-5371. *Dir* Deborah K Eckstein, BA; *Instr* Frank Federico; *Instr* Frank Hawkins; *Instr* Canning Young; *Instr* Charles Hines; *Instr* Charles Holder; *Instr* Mickey Rains; *Instr* Leslie MacGregor.
Estab 1975; pub; D&E and weekends; no ent req; schol; SC 20-25, LC 5-10; enrl approx 900.
Tuition: Members $25-$45; nonmembers $28-$48; no campus res.
Courses: Aesthetics; Art for Handicapped; Art History; Ceramics; Collage; Drawing; Handicrafts (weaving); Landscape Design; Painting; Photography; Printmaking; Sculpture; Textile Design; Theatre Arts.
Children's Classes: Tui $15-$25 per quarter. Courses—Fine Arts.
Summer School: Dir Deborah K Eckstein. Enrl approx 250; tui $15-$45 for two 5 wk sessions, beginning June. Courses—Visual Arts.

FORT LAUDERDALE

ART INSTITUTE OF FORT LAUDERDALE, 3000 E Las Olas Blvd, 33316. Tel: 305-463-3000. *Pres* Mark Wheeler, BA; *Dir Admissions* Robert S Peterson, BBA; *VPres & Dir Education* Frank Raia, MA; *Dir*

Advertising Design, Chuck Ax; *Dir Photography* Dennis Harkins, MA; *Dir Fashion,* Barry Holcomn, LLD; *Dir Interior Design* Frank Nedabylek; *Curriculum Chmn Fashion Merchandising* Jack Rose, BA; *Curriculum Chmn Fashion Illustration* John Miele; *Asst Chmn Advertising Design* Nevin Meinhardt, BS.
Estab 1968; pvt; D&E; ent req HS dipl; degrees AS (technology); schol; enrl D 800, E 130, nonmaj 130, maj 800, others 50.
Tuition: Varies with major; campus res available, rates vary with dorm.
Courses: ‡Advertising Design; Art History; ‡Commercial Art; Conceptual Art; Display; Drafting; Drawing; ‡Fashion Arts; ‡Fashion Illustration; ‡Fashion Merchandising; Graphic Arts; Graphic Design; Illustration; ‡Interior Design; Lettering; Mixed Media; Painting; ‡Photography; Video.
Adult Hobby Classes: Tui $75 for 10 wks. Courses—Airbrush; Basic Photography; Color Photography; Creative Photography; Drawing; Graphics; Human Figure; Interior Decorating; Painting; Photography; Photo Retouching.
Children's Classes: Tui $175 for 4 wks during the summer.
Summer School: Same as regular semester.

FORT LAUDERDALE MUSEUM OF THE ARTS,* Art School, 426 E Las Olas Blvd, 33301. Tel: 305-463-5184. *Dir* George S Bolge; Instrs PT 3-4.
Estab 1959; pvt; 2 - 3 hr wk no credit; grad courses in Art Appreciation, Internship in Museum work; enrl 20, 3 terms per yr.
Summer Classes: Two Children's. Courses—Art Appreciation; Painting; Photography; Sculpture; Slab Pottery; Watercolor; Weaving.

FORT MYERS

EDISON COMMUNITY COLLEGE,* Department of Art, College Pkwy, 33901. Instrs FT 1, PT 1.
Estab 1962; pub; D&E ent req HS dipl; degrees AA and AS 2 yr; schol.
Tuition: Res—No tuition.
Courses: Art Education; Commercial Art; Dimensional Design; Drawing; History of Art & Archaeology; Interior Design; Jewelry; Lettering; Painting; Sculpture;
Adult Classes: Enrl 20. Courses—any non-cr activity of interest for which a teacher is available.

GAINESVILLE

UNIVERSITY OF FLORIDA, Department of Art, 302C, APA Complex, 32611. Tel: 904-392-0211. *Chmn* Eugene E Grissom, MFA; *Prof* Kenneth A Kerslake, MFA; *Prof* Phillip A Ward, MFA; *Graduate Research Prof* Jerry N Uelsmann, MFA; *Prof* Hiram D Williams, MEd; *Prof* Geoffrey J Naylor, MFA; *Assoc Prof* Jack C Nichelson, MFA; *Assoc Prof* John L Ward, MFA; Instrs FT 21.
Estab 1925; pub; D&E; ent req HS dipl, SAT, ACT, TOEFL, SCAT or AA degree (transfers must have 2.0 average) GRE; degrees BAA and BFA 4 yrs; MFA 2 yrs; schol; SC 40, LC 26, GC 11; enrl Maj 200 upper div, GS 16.
Tuition: Res—Undergrad $15-$22 per cr hr, grad $16.50-$24 per cr hr; Nonres—Undergrad $38-$62 per cr hr, gråd $51.50-$64 per cr hr; campus res $570 per yr without air conditioning, $735 per yr with air conditioning.
Courses: ‡Art Education; ‡Art History; ‡Ceramics; ‡Drawing; ‡Graphic Design; Jewelry; Lettering; ‡Painting; ‡Photography; ‡Printmaking; ‡Sculpture.

HOLLYWOOD

SOUTH FLORIDA ART INSTITUTE OF HOLLYWOOD, 1301 S Ocean Dr, 33019. Tel: 305-923-6490. *Dir* Elwin Porter.
Estab 1958; pvt; D&E; ent req portfolio; cert fine arts and cert graphic art 2 and 4 yrs; schol; SC 30, LC 2, GC 2; enrl D 230, E 20.
Tuition: $900 per yr, $500 per sem, $125 per month; no campus res.
Courses: Advertising Design; Ceramics; Commercial Art; Drawing; Graphic Design; Jewelry; Painting; Photography; Printmaking; Sculpture.
Children's Classes: Enrl 30; tui $20 per 10 wks. Courses—Mixed Media.
Summer School: Dir Elwin Porter. Tui $450 for term of 15 wks beginning May 15. Courses—Drawing; Painting; Sculpture; Ceramics; Printmaking; Design; Photography.

INDIALANTIC

ELIOT McMURROUGH SCHOOL OF ART,* 306 Fifth Ave, 32903. Tel: 305-723-8876. *Faculty Dir* Eliot S McMurrough; Instrs FT 1, PT 4.
Estab 1954; pvt; D&E: ent req genuine desire for study; dipl 4 yr; schol; enrl D 24, E 10, maj 24.
Tuition: No campus res.

Courses: Anatomy; Art Education; Basic Forms; Color; Commercial Art; Composition; Design; Drawing; Painting; Perspective; Sculpture; Tools & Uses.

JACKSONVILLE

FLORIDA JUNIOR COLLEGE AT JACKSONVILLE, SOUTH CAMPUS,* Art Department, 11901 Beach Blvd, 32216. Tel: 904-646-2111. *Chmn Div Fine Arts & Humanities* Jim Schupp; Instrs FT 6.
Estab 1966; pub; D&E; ent req HS dipl; degrees AA and AS 2 yr; schol; SC 14, LC 6; enrl D 150, E 75.
Tuition: Res—$12 per cr hr; Nonres—$24 per cr hr; no campus res.
Courses: Batik; Blockprinting; Ceramics; Drawing; Glaze Techniques; Graphic Design; Handicrafts; History of Art & Archaeology; Leathercraft; Macrame; Painting; Weaving.
Adult Hobby Classes: Enrl 75-80; for term of 6 wk beginning June. Courses—Art Appreciation; Crafts; Drawing; Painting.

JACKSONVILLE UNIVERSITY,* College of Fine Arts, Department of Art, University Blvd N, 32211. Tel: 904-744-3950. *Dean* Frances Bartlett Kinnie; Instrs FT 4, PT 8.
Estab 1932; pvt; D&E; ent req HS dipl, ent exam; degrees BFA (studio art, art history) and BA Ed 4 yr; SC 29, LC 16; enrl D 403, maj 80.
Tuition: $1125 yr.

LAKE CITY

LAKE CITY COMMUNITY COLLEGE,* Art Department, 32055. Tel: 904-752-1822, exten 274. Instrs FT 1, PT 2.
Estab 1962; pub; D&E; ent req HS dipl; degree AA 2 yr; SC 9, LC 2; enrl D 160, 80, maj 10.
Courses: Ceramics; Composition; Drawing; Handicrafts; Jewelry; Painting; Sculpture; Weaving.

LAKE WORTH

PALM BEACH JUNIOR COLLEGE,* Department of Art, 4200 Congress Ave, 33460. Tel: 305-965-8000, exten 257. Instrs FT 8, PT 5.
Estab 1935; pub; D&E; ent req HS dipl or over 25; degrees AA and AS 2 yr; SC 20, LC 5; enrl D 3400, E 3200, maj 200.
Courses: Advertising Design; Architectural Drawing; Basic Design; Ceramics; Commercial Art; Drawing; Enameling; Graphic Arts; Graphic Design; Handicrafts; History of Art & Archaeology; Interior Design; Jewelry; Lettering; Painting; Photography; Sculpture; Typography.
Adult Hobby Classes: Courses—Floral Design; Jewelry; Picture Frame Making; Weaving.
Summer School: Courses—Art Appreciation; Design; Drawing; History of Art; Photography.

LAKELAND

FLORIDA SOUTHERN COLLEGE, Art Department, 33802. Tel: 813-683-5521. *Coordr Dept* Ms Donna M Stoddard, M Ed; *Assoc Prof* Banton S Doak, EdS; *Instr* Gale L Doak, MA; *Assoc Prof* Downing Barnitz, MFA; *Asst Prof* Beth M Ford, MA.
Estab 1885; den; D; ent req HS dipl; Degrees AB and BS 128 hr; schol; SC 20, LC 6, maj 34.
Tuition: Res—Undergrad $3800 yr, $1900 per sem, $55 per cr hr; Nonres—Undergrad $2240 yr, $1120 per sem; campus res room and board $1560.
Courses: Ancient & Medieval Art; Architecture; Art Education; Art History; Art in Contemporary Living; Ceramics; Design (19th & 20th century art); Drawing; Graphic Arts; Handicrafts (weaving, crafts); Instrsumental Drawing; Jewelry; Lettering; Painting; Photography; Renaissance & Baroque Art; Sculpture; Silversmithing (creative metal); Teacher Training; Theatre Arts.
Adult Hobby Classes: Tui $25 per 6 wk. Courses—Graphics; Interior Design; Oil Painting.
Summer School: *Dean* David Mobberley. Tui $60 per cr hr for 2 terms of 4 wks beginning June and July.

MARIANNA

CHIPOLA JUNIOR COLLEGE,* Art Department, 32446. Tel: 904-482-4935. *Chmn* Richard H Vait; Instrs FT 1, PT 1.
Estab 1954; pub; D&E; ent req HS dipl; degree AA 2 yr; schol; SC 14, LC 2; enrl D 60.
Courses: Ceramics; Drafting; Drawing; History of Art & Archaeology; Industrial Design; Jewelry; Painting; Sculpture; Stage Design; Theatre Arts.

MIAMI

MIAMI-DADE COMMUNITY COLLEGE, Art Department, South & North Campus and New World Center, 11011 SW 104 Street, 33176. Tel: 305-596-1281. *Chmn Art Department* Margaret M Pelton, MS.
Estab 1960; dept estab 1967; pub; D&E; ent req open door; degrees AA and AS 2 yr; schol; SC 14, LC 4; enrl E 300, nonmaj 150, maj 150.
Courses: Architecture; Art Education; Art History; Ceramics; Commercial Art; Costume Design and Construction; Drafting; Drawing; Fashion Arts; Graphic Arts; Graphic Design; Illustration; Interior; Design; Jewelry; Landscape Architecture; Museum Staff Training; Painting; Photography; Printmaking; Sculpture; Stage Design; Theatre Arts.
Adult Hobby Classes: Tui $10-$15. Courses—Whatever people are interested in.
Summer School: Tui $15 per cr hr for term of 6 wks beginning June.

MIAMI SHORES

BARRY COLLEGE,* Department of Art, 11300 NE Second Ave, 33161. Tel: 305-758-3392. Instrs FT 4, PT 3.
Estab 1940; pvt; D&E; ent req HS dipl, portfolio for BFA; degrees BA, BFA, BA (Educ) 4 yr; schol SC 8, LC 2; enrl D 300, E 60, maj 40.
Tuition: $1200 per sem; campus res $600 per sem.
Courses: Advertising Design; Art Education; Ceramics; Commercial Art; Costume Design & Construction; Drawing; Fashion Arts; Graphic Arts; Graphic Design; History of Art & Archaeology; Illustration; Jewelry; Painting; Photography; Sculpture; State Design; Teacher Training; Textile Design; Theatre Arts.

OCALA

CENTRAL FLORIDA COMMUNITY COLLEGE, Humanities Department, State Rd 200, 32670. Tel: 904-237-2111. *Chmn Dept of Humanities* Charles Adams, MA; *Assoc Prof* Cramer Swords, MA; *Instr* Ed Franklin, BA.
Estab 1957; pub; D&E; ent req HS dipl; degrees AA and AS 2 yr; SC 5, LC 1; enrl 2015, nonmaj 85, maj 15.
Tuition: $10 per sem cr.
Courses: Art History; Ceramics; Drawing; Painting; Printmaking.

PANAMA CITY

GULF COAST COMMUNITY COLLEGE, Department of Fine Arts, 5230 W Highway 98, 32401. Tel: 904-769-1551, exten 272. *Chmn* Norman J Hair, MM; *Asst Prof* Sharron Barnes, MA; *Assoc Prof* Roland L Hockett, MS; *Assoc Prof* Louise L Lewis, MA.
Estab 1957; pub; D&E; ent req HS dipl; degrees AA 2 yr; SC 5, LC 2, enrl D 300, E 70, nonmaj 330, maj 40.
Tuition: Res—Undergrad $12 per cr hr; Nonres—Undergrad $15 per cr hr.
Courses: Advertising Design; Art History; Ceramics; Commercial Art; Drawing; Graphic Arts; Graphic Design; Illustration; Lettering; Photography; Printmaking.
Adult Hobby Classes: Courses—Painting; Macrame.

PENSACOLA

PENSACOLA JUNIOR COLLEGE,* Department of Visual Arts, 1000 College Blvd, 32504. Tel: 904-476-5410, exten 268. *Head Dept of Art* Carl F Duke; Instrs FT 11, PT 1.
Estab 1948; pub; D&E; ent req HS dipl; degrees AS and AA 2 yr; schol; enrl maj 100.
Tuition: Res—$12 per cr hr; Nonres—$24 per cr hr; no campus res.
Courses: Advertising Design; Ceramics; Drawing; Graphic Arts; History of Art & Archaeology; Illustration; Jewelry; Lettering; Macrame; Painting; Photography; Sculpture; Weaving.
Summer School.

UNIVERSITY OF WEST FLORIDA, Department of Art, Alpha College, 32504. *Chmn* Robert L Armstrong, PhD; *Prof* John T Carey, PhD; *Asst Prof* Shirley L Bolton, EdD; *Asst Prof* Stephen K Haworth, MFA; *Assoc Prof* Henry J Heuler, MFA; *Asst Prof* William A Silhan, EdD; *Asst Prof* Duncan E Stewart, MFA; *Assoc Prof* Robert B Marshman, MFA.
Estab 1967; pub; D&E; ent req students usually have the AA degree when they enter; degrees BA 2 yr; SC 20, LC 10, enrl D 80, E 10, nonmaj 40, maj 80.
Tuition: Res—Undergrad $16.50 per quarter hr, grad $22 per quarter hr; Nonres—Undergrad $51.50 per quarter hr, grad $62 per quarter hr; campus res room and board $375.
Courses: ‡Art Education; ‡Art History; Ceramics; Commercial Art; Drawing; Graphic Arts; Jewelry; Lettering; Painting; Photography; Printmaking; Sculpture; Silversmithing; ‡Studio Art; Teacher Training.

Adult Hobby Classes: Tui $15 per course; Courses—Leisure Class Series.
Summer School: Same as above.

SAINT AUGUSTINE

FLAGLER COLLEGE, Visual Arts Department, King St, 32084. Tel: 904-829-6481. *Chmn* Robert M Hall, MED; *Asst Prof* Enzo Torcoletti, MFA; *Instr* Don Martin, MFA.
Estab 1968; pvt; D&E; ent req HS dipl; degrees BA 4 yr; schol; SC 29, LC 7; enrl D 50, maj 45.
Tuition: $1800 yr; campus res room and board $1200.
Courses: Art Education; Art History; Drawing; Graphic Design; Jewelry; Mixed Media; Painting; Photography; Printmaking; Sculpture; Silversmithing; ‡Teacher Training; ‡Theatre Arts.
Summer School: Dir Dr Drew Dillon. Tui $60 per hr for term of 4 or 6 wk beginning May. Courses—Ceramics; Creative Photography; Landscape Drawing.

SAINT PETERSBURG

ST PETERSBURG JUNIOR COLLEGE,* Department of Humanities, 6605 Fifth Ave N, 33733. Tel: 813-546-0011. Instrs FT 7.
Estab 1927; pub; D&E; ent req HS dipl; degrees AA and AS 2 yr; schol; SC 13, LC 3; enrl D 7031, E 2478.
Tuition: Full-time students pay matriculation and tuition fee $13 per cr hr; Nonres—$28 per cr hr; no campus res
Courses: Advertising Design; Aesthetics; Ceramics; Design I & II; Drafting; Drawing; Graphic Arts; History of Art & Archaeology; Painting; Photography; Sculpture; Stage Design; Survey in Crafts; Theatre Arts.
Summer Classes; Majority of above classes.
—**Clearwater Campus,** 2465 Drew St, 33515.
Estab 1865. Same information as above.

SARASOTA

FRIENDS OF THE ARTS AND SCIENCES, HILTON LEECH STUDIO, 33581. Tel: 813-924-5770. *Consultant Special Projects* Mrs Katherine L Rowland; *Instr* Emily Holmes; *Instr* Elden Rowland; *Instr* James H Pete Carmichael; *Vis Profs*—Marc Moon; Nicholas Reale; Valfred Theline.
Estab 1946; dept estab 1963; pvt; SC 16; enrl D 200, E 10.
Tuition: varies from $40 to $75 per workshop; no campus res.
Courses: Drawing; Painting; Photography.

NEW COLLEGE OF THE UNIVERSITY OF SOUTH FLORIDA,* Humanities Division, Fine Arts Department, 5700 N Tamiami Trail, 33580. Tel: 813-355-1151. Instrs FT 4.
Estab 1963; pvt; D; ent req ent exam, SAT; degree BA (Fine Arts) 3 yr; SC 6, LC 5; enrl D 150-200, maj 15.
Courses: Aesthetics; Ceramics; Drawing; Graphic Arts; History of Art & Archaeology; Painting; Sculpture; Stained Glass.

RINGLING SCHOOL OF ART, 33580. Tel: 813-958-9486. *Pres* Robert E Perkins, MA-LHD; *Dean of Faculty* Robert Osborne, MA; *Dean of Students* George Kaiser, BA; *Chmn Painting* Morris Mitchell, MA; *Chmn Graphic Design* Len Jossel; *Chmn Interior Design* Cheryl Stanzione, AA.
Estab 1931; pvt; D; ent req HS dipl; degrees BFA 4 yr, cert 3 yr. SC 44, LC 2; enrl D 455.
Tuition: Res & Nonres—Undergrad $1160 yr, $580 per sem; campus res room and board $1420.
Courses: Advertising Design; Art History; Commercial Art; Graphic Arts; Graphic Design; History of Art; Illustration; Interior Design; Lettering; Painting; Photography; Printmaking; Sculpture.

TALLAHASSEE

FLORIDA A&M UNIVERSITY, Department of Visual Arts & Humanities, 32307. Tel: 904-599-3161. *Chmn* H L Williams, EdD; *Assoc Prof* G F Hooper, EdD; *Asst Prof* R F Yrabedra, PhD; *Asst Prof* K A Falana, MFA; *Assoc Prof* L Y Tucker, MFA; *Assoc Prof* C L Williams, MFA; *Assoc Prof* J E Compton, PhD; *Instrs* E Ashdown, PhD; Instrs FT 7, PT 1.
Estab 1887; pub; D&E; ent req HS dipl, ent exam; degrees BS and BA 4 yr; enrl D 5887, nonmaj 5800, maj 87.
Tuition: Srs & Jrs $16.50 per cr hr; Soph & Freshman $15 per cr hr.
Courses: Art Education; Art History; Ceramics; Drawing; Handicrafts (basketry, papier mache, weaving); History of Art & Archaeology; Lettering; Painting; Printmaking; Sculpture; Teacher Training; Textile Design.

Summer School: Enrl 125; tui same as above for term of 9 and 7 wks beginning June. Courses—Ceramics; Design; Drawing; Humanities; Lettering; Public School Arts; Textile Design; Wood, Metal & Plastics.

FLORIDA STATE UNIVERSITY, School of Visual Arts, 32306. *Acting Dean* J L Draper. Pub; D&E; schol.
—**Art Department,** 236 Fine Arts Bldg, 32306. 904-644-6474. *Chmn & Acting Dean* Jerry L Draper, PhD; *Prof* Francois Bucher, PhD; *Prof* Trevor Bell, MFA; *Prof* Arthur Deshaies, MFA; *Prof* James Roche, MFA; *Prof* William Walmsley, MFA; *Assoc Prof* Robert Fichter, MFA; *Assoc Prof* Patricia Rose, PhD; *Vis Prof*—John Moffitt, art hist, 77-78.
Estab 1857, dept estab 1911; pub; D&E; ent req HS dipl, C average and upper 40% of graduating class, SAT; degrees BA, BFA, MFA, MA, PhD; schol; SC 36, LC 46, GS 34; enrl maj 329, grad 40.
Tuition: Res—Undergrad $700 yr, $15 per hr lower level, $16.50 upper level, grad $1035 yr, $22 per hr non thesis, $24 per hr grad thesis & dissertation; Nonres—Undergrad $23 per hr lower level, $35 per hr upper level, grad $40 per hr; campus res room and board $1720 yr.
Courses: Advertising Design; Art Education; ‡Art History; Commercial Art; Conceptual Art; Constructions; Drawing; Fashion Arts; Film; Graphic Arts; Graphic Design; History of Art & Archaeology; Illustration; Interior Design; Lettering; Museum Staff Training; Painting; Photography; Printmaking; Sculpture; ‡Studio Art.
Summer School: Tui In state $9 per hr lower level, $10.50 per hr upper level; Out of state $32 per hr lower level, $45.50 per hr upper level for term of 8 wk beginning June 19.
—**Art Education/Craft Design,** 123 Education Bldg, 32306. Tel: 904-644-5473, 644-5474. *Chmn* Dr Virginia M Brouch, EdD; *Prof* George R Bocz, MA; *Prof* William Harper, MA; *Prof* Ralph Hurst, MFA; *Prof* Ivan E Johnson, EdD; *Prof* Marylou Kuhn, PhD; *Prof* Judith Kula, PhD.
Estab 1857, dept estab 1948; pub; D&E; ent req HS dipl, also slide review for crafts design; degrees BA 4, MA 1, EdD/PhD 3, Advan MAE 2; schol; SC 27, LC 34, GS 29; enrl D 250, E 60, nonmaj 40, maj 190, grad 25, other 10.
Tuition: Res—Undergrad $51 per hr lower level, $16.50 per hr upper level, grad $22 per hr non thesis, $24 per hr theses or dissertation; Nonres—Undergrad $38 per hr lower level, $51.50 per hr upper level, grad $62 per hr no thesis $64 per hr thesis or dissertation; campus res $3275-$3452 depending on class and residence.
Courses: ‡Art Education; Ceramics; Jewelry; Textile Design; Woods/Synthetics; ‡Craft Design.
Summer School: Regular quarter. Courses—Regular program.

LEMOYNE ART CENTER, 32301. Tel: 904-222-8800. *Dir* Nancy J McIntyre. Teaching staff varies from term to term consisting of prof artists in the community.
Estab 1964; pvt; D&E; schol;
Tuition: $400 per yr, 4 quarters.
Courses: Ceramics; Drawing; Mixed Media; Painting; Photography; Printmaking.
Adult Hobby Classes: Enrl 10-14; tui $35 per 8 wk course; Courses—Ceramics; Drawing; Painting; Photography; Printmaking.
Children's Classes: Tui $25 per 8 wk course. Courses—Cartooning; Ceramics; Drawing; Painting; Puppetry.

TALLAHASSEE COMMUNITY COLLEGE, Art Department, 32304. Tel: 904-576-5181. *Chmn Art Program* Ruth Dryden Deshaies, MA.
Estab 1966; pub; D&E; ent req HS dipl; degrees AA 2 yr; SC 8, LC 2; enrl D 130, E 40.
Tuition: $11 per sem hr.
Courses: Art History; Drawing; Painting; Photography.

TAMPA

UNIVERSITY OF SOUTH FLORIDA,* College of Fine Arts, Art Department, 4202 Fowler Ave, 33620. Tel: 813-974-2360. *Chmn* George Pappas; Instrs FT D 20.
Estab 1956; pub; ent req HS grad, 14 units cert by HS, ent exam; degrees BA(Art) min 180 quarter hrs and MFA 72 quarter hrs.
Tuition: Res—Undergrad $15 per cr hr, grad $22 per cr hr; Nonres—Undergrad $38 per cr hr, grad $62 per cr hr.
Courses: Art History; Ceramics; Cinematography; Drawing; Graphics; Painting; Photography; Sculpture.
Summer School: One to four equal yearly quarters.

UNIVERSITY OF TAMPA,* Fine Arts Division, Department of Art, Plant Park, 33606. Tel: 813-253-8861. Dept Art Instrs FT 5.
Estab 1930; pvt; D&E; degrees 4 yr; SC 17, LC 8.
Courses: Art Education; Ceramics; Design; Drawing; History of Art; Painting; Printmaking; Sculpture.

WEST PALM BEACH

NORTON SCHOOL OF ART,* 1451 S Olive Ave, 33401. Tel: 305-832-5194. *Dir* E K Hunter; Instrs FT 4-5, E 3.
Estab 1941; pvt; ent req none; degree none; enrl 250 (adults) 150 (children and teenagers).
Tuition: Adult courses various rates.
Courses: Art History; Ceramics; Drawing; Painting; Sculpture.

WINTER HAVEN

POLK COMMUNITY COLLEGE, Division of Communications and Fine Arts, 33880. *Division Dir* Dion K Brown, EdS; *Prof* Bob Morrisey, MFA; *Prof* Gary Baker, MFA; *Prof* Jane Jaskevich, MEd.
Estab 1964; pub; D&E; ent req HS dipl; degrees AA and AS 2 yr; schol; SC 10, LC 1: enrl D 175, E 50.
Tuition: Res—Undergrad $13 per cr hr; Nonres—Undergrad $27 per cr hr; no campus res.
Courses: Advertising Design; Art History; Ceramics; Drafting; Drawing; Film; Graphic Arts; Interior Design; Painting; Photography; Sculpture; Video.
Adult Hobby Classes: Enrl 60; tui $1 per class hr. Courses—Calligraphy; Ceramics; Christmas Crafts; Interior Design; Jewelry.

WINTER PARK

ROLLINS COLLEGE,* Department of Art, Main Campus, 32789. Tel: 305-646-2000. *Chmn* Hallie Lu Hallman; Instrs FT 4.
Estab 1885; pvt; D&E; degrees 4 yr; schol; SC 11, LC 10, enrl D&E 250.
Courses: Aesthetics; Art History; Art History Survey; Design; Drawing & Painting; Humanities Foundation; Principles of Art; Sculpture.

GEORGIA

ATHENS

UNIVERSITY OF GEORGIA,* Franklin College of Arts & Sciences, Division of Fine Arts, 30602. Tel: 404-542-2121. *Dean* John C Stephens; *Head Dept* Prof Ruzicka.
Opened 1801, chartered 1875; degrees 4 yr; schol & fel ($2725 — 9 mo masters level, $2925 — 9 mo doctorate level, grad assistantships available through grad school of Univ of Georgia and others).
Tuition: Campus res.
—**Department of Art.** Instrs FT 54, PT 1.
Estab 1932; degrees; SC 75, LC 29, GC 69; enrl undergrad maj 800, grad 100, others 1500.
Courses: Art Education; Art History; Art—Home Economics; Ceramics; Fabric Design; Graphic Design; Interior Design; Jewelry & Metal Work; Painting & Drawing; Photographic Design; Printmaking; Sculpture.
Summer School: Dir Edmund B Feldman. Tui $169 for 11 wks.

ATLANTA

ATLANTA AREA TECHNICAL SCHOOL, Department of Commercial Art, 1560 Stewart Ave SW, 30310. Tel: 404-758-9451. *Head Dept* Don M Ballentine.
Estab 1967; pub; D&E; ent req HS dipl, ent exam; degrees AA in conjunction with The Atlanta Jr Col; SC 13; enrl D 25, E 25.
Tuition: $27 per quarter plus testing fees.
Courses: Advertising Design; Advertising Print Production Art; Commercial Art; Graphic Arts; Photography; Video.

ATLANTA COLLEGE OF ART, 1280 Peachtree St NE, 30309. Tel: 404-892-3600. *Pres* William J Voos, MFA; *Academic Dean* Anthony J Greco, MFA; *Instr* Santo Bruno, MFA; *Instr* Neill Clark, PhD; *Instr* Scott Gilliam, MFA; *Instr* Norman Wagner, MS; *Instr* Fred Gregory, MFA; *Instr* William Nolan, MFA.
Estab 1928; pvt; D&E; ent req HS dipl, ent exam, SAT, portfolio of Art Work; degrees BFA 4 yr; schol; SC 96, LC 48; enrl D 238, E 129, nonmaj 129, maj 238.
Tuition: $2300 yr; no campus res.
Courses: Advertising Design; Art History; Conceptual Art; Constructions; Drawing; Film; Graphic Arts; Graphic Design; Illustration; Intermedia; Lettering; Mixed Media; Painting; Photography; Printmaking; Sculpture; Video.
Children's Classes: Enrl 80; tui $80 for 8 wks. Courses—Crafts; Drawing; Painting; Printmaking; Sculpture.
Summer School: Dir John Dougherty. Enrl 400; tui $65 for term of 8 wks. Courses—Studio Arts.

CLARK COLLEGE, Department of Art, 240 Chestnut St SW, 30314. Tel: 404-681-3080, exten 346. *Chmn Art Dept* Dr Emmanuel V Asihene, PhD.
Estab 1869; dept estab 1964; pvt; D; ent req HS dipl; degrees BA and BA(Art Education) 4 yr Honors Program; SC 8, LC 8; enrl D 300, nonmaj 242, maj 58.
Tuition: Res—Undergrad $3435.30 yr; Nonres—Undergrad $2150.30 yr; campus res $1285.
Courses: Art Education; Drawing; Photography; Printmaking.

EMORY UNIVERSITY, Department of Art History, 30322. Tel: 404-377-2411, exten 7511. *Head Dept Prof* Thomas W Lyman; *Prof* William R Crelly, PhD; *Assoc Prof* John Howett, PhD; *Asst Prof* Clark Poling, PhD; *Asst Prof* Linda Hyman, PhD; Mollie Michala, MFA; *Affiliate* William Archie Brown, MFA; *Affiliate* Eyck Strickland; *vis prof* William Scranton, archaeology, annual seminar.
Estab 1847; pvt; D; ent req HS dipl, ent exam, SAT; degrees MA(Art History) and PhD through Institute of Liberal Arts; schol; SC 4, LC 29, GC 18; enrl nonmaj 600, maj 20, GS 27.
Tuition: $3750 yr; campus res.
Courses: Art History; Ceramics; Drawing; Film; Handicrafts (weaving); History of Art and Archaeology; Photography; Video.
Summer School: Dir Dean Thigpen. Enrl 15; tui $1600-1800 for term of 6 wks beginning June 15. Courses: Seminars in Europe (variable) 10 hours credit.

GEORGIA INSTITUTE OF TECHNOLOGY, College of Architecture, 225 North Avenue NW, 30332. Tel: 404-894-3880. *Dean* William L Fash, M Arch; *Assoc Prof* Neill W Connah, MFA; *Asst Prof* Albert H Smith, MFA; *Instr* Jessica P McLean, MFA; *Lecturer* Joe de Cassares Reshower, Cert.
Estab 1885; dept estab 1908; pub; D; ent req HS dipl, CEEB; degrees BS, BS(Industrial Design) and BS(Building Construction) 4 yr; M Arch and MCP 2 yr; schol; SC 41; enrl D 904, maj 904, GS 165.
Tuition: Res—Undergrad and grad $676.50 yr, $225.50 per quarter; Nonres—Undergrad and grad $1843.50 yr, $614.50 per quarter; campus res room and board $1225.
Courses: Architecture; Building Construction; City Planning; Industrial Design.
Summer School: Tui—same. Courses—varies.

GEORGIA STATE UNIVERSITY,* 33 Gilmer St SE, 30303. Tel: 404-577-2400, exten 332, 577-2400, exten 333. *Head Dept Prof* Joseph S Perrin; Instrs FT 38, PT 4.
Estab 1914; pub; ent req HS dipl, ent exam, college board, interview; degrees BVA and AB(Art) 4 yr; schol; SC 80, LC 17; enrl maj 300, others 20.
Courses: Advertising Design; Art History; Ceramics; Drawing; Graphic Arts; Handicrafts (weaving, jewelry, metalwork); Illustration; Interior Design; Lettering; Painting; Sculpture; Teacher Training; Textile Design.
Summer School: Enrl 450; term of 9 wk beginning June.

AUGUSTA

AUGUSTA COLLEGE, Department of Fine Arts, Walton Way, 30904. Tel: 404-828-3211. *Head Dept & Prof* Eloy Fominaya, PhD; *Assoc Prof* Nathan Bindler, MA; *Asst Prof* Jack King, MFA; *Asst Prof* Eugenia Comer, MFA; *Asst Prof* Richard Frank, MFA; *Asst Prof* Cecilia Voelker, PhD.
Estab 1925, dept estab 1965; pub; D&E; ent req HS dipl, SAT; degrees MA 5 yr, BA and BFA 4 yrs and AA 2 yr; schol; SC 46, LC 4, GC 1; enrl D 150, E 30, nonmaj 10, maj 140, GS 5.
Tuition: Res—Undergrad $145 per quarter, $12 per quarter hr; Nonres—Undergrad $238 per quarter, $32 per quarter hr; no campus res.
Courses: Advertising Design; Art Education; Art History; Ceramics; Commercial Art; Constructions; Drafting; Drawing; Fashion Arts; Glassblowing; Graphic Arts; Graphic Design; Handicrafts; Illustration; Lettering; Mixed Media; Painting; Printmaking; Sculpture; Teacher Training.
Adult Hobby Classes: Enrl 25; tui $30 per 10 sessions. Courses—Painting.

CARROLLTON

WEST GEORGIA COLLEGE,* Art Department, 30017. Tel: 404-834-1235. *Chmn* Derrill M Maxwell.
Estab 1975; pub; D; ent req HS dipl, ent exam; degrees AB(Studio, Art Educ) 4 yr; schol; SC 24, LC 10, GC 1; enrl maj 124.
Tuition: $536 per yr, PT $12 per quarter hr; Nonres—$238 per quarter, PT $20 per quarter hr; campus res $140 to $165 per quarter.

Courses: Aesthetics; Art Education; Ceramics; Graphic Arts; Graphic Design; History of Art & Archaeology; Painting; Photography; Sculpture; Teacher Training; Textile Design; Weaving.
Adult Hobby Classes: Courses—Ceramics; Drawing; Painting.
Summer School: Courses—Art Education; Drawing; Graphics; Painting.

CLEVELAND

TRUETT-McCONNELL COLLEGE, 30528. *Head* Maurice Blaine Caldwell, MFA.
Estab 1946; den; D&E; ent req HS dipl, SAT; degrees AA and AS 2 yr; SC 10, LC 2; enrl D 700, nonmaj 98, maj 15.
Tuition: $2300.
Courses: Aesthetics; Art History; Ceramics; Drawing; Graphic Design; Handicrafts; Painting; Sculpture; 3-Design.
Children's Classes: Enrl 21; tui $20. Courses—Children's Art.

COCHRAN

MIDDLE GEORGIA COLLEGE (Junior College Unit of the University of Georgia),* Department of Art, 31014. Tel: 912-934-6221, exten 288. Instrs FT 2
Pub: D&E; ent req HS dipl, GED; degree AA 2 yr; SC 6; enrl D 270, E 45.
Tuition: $343 payable one third in advance each quarter; campus res $355 to $370.
Courses: Art Education; Ceramics; Commercial Art; Drawing; Lettering; Painting.
Summer School: Dir Robert R Nason. Enrl 30; term of 10 wk beginning approx June. Courses—as above.

COLUMBUS

COLUMBUS COLLEGE,* Division Fine Arts, Department of Art, Algonquin Dr, 31907. Tel: 404-568-2047. *Chmn* John H Anderson; Instrs FT 7, PT 1.
Estab 1949; pub; D&E; ent req HS dipl, ent exam; degrees BS(Art Educ), BA(Art) and MEd(Art Educ) 4 yr; schol; SC 29, LC 7, GC 14; enrl D 300, E 50, maj 130, grad 20.
Tuition: $145 for 12 or more quarter hr; Nonres—$483; no campus res.
Courses: Art Education; Ceramics; Costume Design & Construction; Drawing; Graphic Arts; History of Art & Archaeology; Illustration; Jewelry; Macrame; Painting; Photography; Sculpture; Stage Design; Teacher Training; Textile Design; Theatre Arts; Weaving.
Adult Hobby Classes: Enrl 60. Courses—various subjects.
Children's Classes: Enrl 60. Courses—various subjects.
Summer School: Enrl 200; term of one quarter. Courses—Art History; Studio.

DALTON

DALTON JUNIOR COLLEGE, Division of Humanities, PO Box 2168, 30720. *Chmn Div of Humanities* Dr Thomas A Wilkerson, EdD; *Instr* Ronald O McBride, MS; *Instr* Elizabeth G Williams, MA.
Estab 1967, dept estab 1974; pub; D&E; ent req HS dipl and SAT; degrees AA 2 yr; SC 3, LC 3; enrl D 300, E 60, nonmaj 200, maj 30.
Tuition: Res—Undergrad $116 per quarter; Nonres—Undergrad $158 per quarter.
Courses: Art History; Design; Drawing; History of Art & Archaeology; Introduction to the Visual Arts; Painting.

DECATUR

AGNES SCOTT COLLEGE, Department of Art, 30030. Tel: 404-373-2571. *Chmn* Marie Huper Pepe, PhD; *Assoc Prof* Robert F Westervelt, PhD; *Assoc Prof* Leland Steven, MFA; *Instr* Terry McGehee, MFA.
Estab 1889; pvt; D; degrees BA 4 yr; schol; SC 13, LC 15; enrl nonmaj 200, maj 23.
Tuition: Res—Undergrad $1950 yr; Nonres—Undergrad $4450 yr.
Courses: Aesthetics; Architecture; Art Education; Art History; Ceramics; Drawing; Graphic Arts; History of Art and Archaeology; Painting; Printmaking.

FORSYTH

TIFT COLLEGE, Department of Fine Arts, 31029. Tel: 912-994-6689. *Assoc Prof* Charles Ensign, MA.
Estab 1849, dept estab 1976; den; D; ent req HS dipl, SAT; degrees BA and BS 4 yr; SC 6, LC 3; enrl D 5, nonmaj 40-50, maj 5, others 1.
Tuition: Res—Undergrad $1335 yr; Nonres—Undergrad $2610 yr; campus res room and board $1200.

Courses: Art Education; Art History; Commercial Art; Drawing; Painting; Photography; Teacher Training.

GAINESVILLE

BRENAU COLLEGE, Art Department, 30501. Tel: 904-532-4341, exten 254. *Dir* Bill Gingles, MVA; *Assoc Prof* Nancy Heitz, MA; *Instr* Martha Burpitt, MFA; *Instr* Susan Gingles, MFA.
Estab 1878; pvt; D&E; ent req HS dipl; degrees BA and BS 4 yr; schol; SC 28, LC 8; enrl D 60, E 10, nonmaj 25, maj 45.
Tuition: $3500 yr (includes room and board), $38 per cr hr; campus res.
Courses: Advertising Design; ‡Art Education; Art History; Calligraphy; Ceramics; ‡Commercial Art; Drawing; Graphic Design; ‡Handicrafts; History of Art and Archaeology; ‡Interior Design; Jewelry; Lettering; Painting; Photography; Printmaking (silkscreen); Sculpture; Textile Design.

LA GRANGE

LAGRANGE COLLEGE,* Art Department, 30240. Tel: 404-882-2911, exten 491. *Head Dept* Maxie Chambliss Estes; Instrs FT 2.
Estab 1831; pvt; D&E; ent req HS dipl, ent exam; degree BA 4 yr; schol; SC 11, L C 2; enrl maj 40.
Tuition: $2562 per yr, incl room and board.
Courses: Art Education; Commercial Art (textile); History of Art; Painting; Photography; Printmaking; Sculpture.

MACON

MERCER UNIVERSITY,* Art Department, 1400 Coleman Ave, 31207. Tel: 912-743-1511, exten 235. *Chmn* Marshall Daugherty; *Instrs* FT 4.
Estab 1945; den; D; ent req HS dipl; degree BA 4 yr; SC 9, LC 7, GC 2; enrl maj 15.
Tuition: $2664 per yr; campus res room and board $1341.
Courses: Art Education; Ceramics; Drawing; Graphic Arts; History of Art; Sculpture;
Summer School: Dir Dr Paul Cable. Term of 9 wk beginning June. Courses—Drawing; Painting; Sculpture.

WESLEYAN COLLEGE,* School of Fine Arts, 31201. Tel: 912-477-1110. *Chmn* Thomas A Prochaska; *Instrs* FT 3.
Estab 1836; pvt; W; ent req schol & others; degree BFA 4 yr; SC 39, LC 9; enrl 600.
Tuition: Res—$3950.
Courses: Art Education; Ceramics; Commercial Art; Graphic Arts; Painting; Sculpture.

MOUNT BERRY

BERRY COLLEGE, Art Department, 30149. *Chmn* T J Mew, PhD; *Asst Prof* Jere Lykins, MEd; *Instr* Tom Pitts, MA.
Estab 1902, dept estab 1942; pvt; D&E; ent req HS dipl, SAT, CEEB, ACT; degrees; BA, BS & BME 4 yr; schol; SC 24, LC 9; enrl D 122, nonmaj 38, maj 84, others 7.
Tuition: Res—Undergrad $3150 yr; Nonres—Undergrad $3630 yr; campus res room and board available.
Courses: Aesthetics; Art Education; Art History; Calligraphy; ‡Ceramics; Collage; Conceptual Art; Constructions; Drawing; Ecological Art; Film; Graphic Design; Handicrafts (weaving); ‡History of Art & Archeology; Intermedia; Mixed Media; ‡Painting; Photography; Printmaking; Sculpture; Teacher Training; Video.
Summer School: Dir Dr T J Mew. Courses—Varies.

ROME

SHORTER COLLEGE, Art Department, Shorter Ave, 30161. Tel: 404-232-2463. *Head Dept Asst Prof* Jane M McCord, MFA; *Instr* Richard Pumphrey, MFA.
Estab 1873, dept estab 1900; den; D; ent req HS dipl; degrees AB (Art) and BS (Art Ed) 4 yr; schol; SC 5; enrl D 140, nonmaj 115, maj 25.
Tuition: Res—Undergrad $1775 per yr; Nonres—Undergrad $2925 per yr; campus res.
Courses: ‡Art Education, Art History; Ceramics; Commercial Art; Drawing; Handicrafts (textiles, enameling); History of Art and Archeology; Painting; Photography; Sculpture; Teacher Training; Textile Design.

STATESBORO

GEORGIA SOUTHERN COLLEGE, Department of Art, 30458. *Head Dept* Stephen Bayless, EdD; *Assoc Prof* Bronislaw Bak, MFA: *Asst Prof*

Kenneth Guill, MA; *Assoc Prof* Henry Iler, MFA; *Assoc Prof* Joseph Olson Jr, EdD; *Instr* David Posner, MFA; *Instr* Tom Raab, MFA; *Asst Prof* Bernard Solomon, MFA; *Asst Prof* Thomas Steadman, MFA.
Pub; D&E; ent req HS dipl; degrees AB and BSEd 4 yr.
Tuition: Res—Undergrad $145 per quarter sem; Nonres—Undergrad $383 per quarter sem; campus res room and board $885.
Courses: Art Education; Art History; Ceramics; Commercial Art; Constructions; Drawing; Graphic Arts; Graphic Design; Lettering; Mixed Media; Painting; Photography; Printmaking; Sculpture; Teacher Training; Textile Design.
Adult Hobby Classes: Enrl 40; tui $35 per 10 wks. Courses—Painting; Photography.
Children's Classes: Offered in Laboratory School.

VALDOSTA

VALDOSTA STATE COLLEGE,* Department of Art, Patterson St, 31601. Tel: 912-247-3319, 247-3330. *Head Dept* Irene Dodd; *Instrs* FT 9.
Estab 1911; pub; D; ent req SAT; degrees AB, BFA and BFA (Art Ed) 4 yr; SC 25, LC 10, GC 9; enrl 400, maj 120, total 4500.
Tuition: Res—$182 12 or more quarter hr, $12.08 per hr; Nonres—$420 less than 12 quarter hr, $31.91 per hr; plus other fees.
Courses: Advertising Design; Art Education; Ceramics; Commercial Art; Drawing; Graphic Arts; Graphic Design; History of Art; Illustration; Museum Tour; Painting; Photography; Sculpture; Teacher Training; Weaving.
Children's Classes: Crafts; Drawing; Sculpture; Watercolor.
Summer School.

YOUNG HARRIS

YOUNG HARRIS COLLEGE,* Department of Art, 30582. Tel: 404-379-2161. *Chmn* Richard Aunspaugh; *Instr* Vee Brown; Instrs FT 2.
Estab 1886; den; D; ent req HS dipl; degree AFA 2 yr; schol; SC 6, LC 4; enrl D 540, maj 48.
Tuition: $900 per yr; PT $407; campus res $1245.
Courses: Design; Drawing; History of Art & Archaeology; Painting; Sculpture.
Adult Classes: Enrl 18; tui none. Courses—Painting.
Children's Classes: Enrl 20; tui none 4 wk in summer.

HAWAII

HONOLULU

FOUNDRY ART CENTER,* 899 Waimanu St, 96813. Tel: 808-533-2609. Instrs FT 5, PT 10-20.
Estab 1969; pvt; D&E; ent req prerequisites according to course; degrees cert of completion; SC 10, LC 2.
Courses: Aesthetics; Ceramics; Copper Enameling; Drawing; Graphic Arts; Handicrafts; Language of Art; Language of Drawing; Macrame; Painting; Sculpture; Textile Design; Weaving; Woodcarving.
Children's Classes: Tui $25; Courses—Arts and crafts.
Summer School: Term of 8 wk.

HONOLULU ACADEMY OF ARTS,* Studio Program, 900 Beretania St, 96814. Tel: 808-538-3693. *Cur* Joseph Feher; Instrs FT 3, PT 1.
Estab 1946; pvt; ent req 16 yr of age with talent; degree 3 yr; schol.
Tuition: $220 half day; $440 full day per sem.
Courses: Drawing; Painting; Printmaking (etching & lithography).
Summer School: Tui $85 for 6 wk half days. Courses—Drawing; Painting; Printmaking.

HONOLULU COMMUNITY COLLEGE, Department of Art, Department of Commercial Art, Department of Graphic Art, 96817. Tel: 808-845-9211. *Chmn* Kit Kowalke, MFA; PT professionals working in the field of Design, Illustration, Advertising and related disciplines.
Pub; D&E; ent req 18 yrs of age, eng & math requirements, motivation, interest in learning, willingness to work; degrees AS 2 yr; SC 20, LC 2; enrl D 150, maj all.
Tuition: Res—Undergrad $40 per sem, $3.50 per sem, $3.50 per cr hr; Nonres—Undergrad $450 per sem, $35 per cr hr.
Courses: ‡Advertising Design; Commercial Art; Drafting; Drawing; Film; ‡Graphic Arts; ‡Graphic Design; ‡Illustration; Lettering; Painting; ‡Photography; Textile Design; Video.

KAPIOLANI COMMUNITY COLLEGE,* Pensacola Campus, 620 Pensacola St, 96814. Tel: 808-531-4654, exten 142.
—**Diamond Head Campus,** 4303 Diamond Head Rd, 96816. Tel: 808-735-3127. Instrs FT 1, PT 3.

Estab 1965; pub; D&E; ent req ent exam; degrees AA and AS 1-2 yr; schol; SC 6, LC 7; enrl D 3800, E 500.
Tuition: No campus res.
Courses: Art Appreciation; Art History (Asian & Western); Ceramics & Macrame; Drawing & Painting; Introduction to Visual Arts; Jewelry; Light & Color; Perception; Textile Design.
Adult Classes: Enrl 25 per class; tui depends on amount of units. Courses—Ceramics & Macrame; Drawing & Painting; Jewelry; Textile Design.
Summer School: Enrl 700; tui depends on amount of units taken for term of 6 wk; Courses—Change each summer.

UNIVERSITY OF HAWAII AT MANOA, Department of Art, 2535 The Mall, 96822. Tel: 808-948-8251. *Chmn* John Wisnosky, MFA; Instrs FT 30, PT 30.
Estab 1907; pub; D&E; ent req HS dipl, GED, SAT or ACT; degrees BA (Art History), (BA Studio) and BFA 4 yr; schol; SC 64, LC 34; enrl maj 600, GS 60.
Tuition: Res—Undergrad $225 per sem, $19 per cr hr, grad $275 per sem, $24 per cr hr; Nonres—Undergrad $562.50 per sem, $48 per cr hr, grad $687.50 per sem, $58 per cr hr; plus campus res.
Courses: ‡Art History; ‡Ceramics; Drawing; Graphic Arts; Graphic Design; ‡Painting; Photography, ‡Printmaking; ‡Sculpture; ‡Textile Design.
Adult Hobby Classes: Evenings only. Courses—Chinese Brush Painting; Drawing; Painting.
Summer School: Dean Robert Sakai. Tui $30 per cr hr for nonres plus fees, beginning May and July. Courses—Art History (Western and Pacific); Ceramics; Drawing; Design; Painting; Printmaking; Sculpture.

KAHULUI

MAUI COMMUNITY COLLEGE,* Art Program, 310 Kaahumanu Ave, 96732. Instrs FT 1, PT 3.
Estab 1967; pub; D&E; ent req ent exam; degree AS 2 yr; schol; SC 8, LC 2; enrl D 300, E 100.
Courses: Advertising Design; Architecture; Batik; Ceramics; Copper Enameling; Display; Drafting; Drawing; Graphic Arts; Graphic Design; History of Architecture; History of Art & Archaeology; Jewelry; Painting; Photography; Sculpture (Welding); Textile Design; Weaving.
Adult Hobby Classes: Enrl 60; tui $10-$30. Courses—Batik; Silk Screen; Jewelry.
Summer School; Enrl 40; term of 6 wk beginning June. Courses—Introduction to the Visual Arts.

LIHUE

KAUAI COMMUNITY COLLEGE,* Department of Art, RR1, Box 216, 96766. Tel: 808-245-6741. Instrs FT 2, PT 1.
Estab 1965; pub; D&E; ent req HS dipl; degrees AA and AS 2 yr; schol; SC 6, LC 2; enrl D 965, E 468.
Courses: Ceramics; Drafting; Drawing; Graphic Arts; History of Art & Archaeology; Painting; Photography; Watercolor.
Summer School: Term of 6 wk beginning June and July. Courses—Ceramics; Photography; Watercolor.

PEARL CITY

LEEWARD COMMUNITY COLLEGE, Arts and Humanities Division, 96-045 Ala Ike, 96782. Tel: 808-455-0350. *Head Div* Douglas Kaya; *Instr* Richard Hayashida, MFA; *Instr* Barbara Saromines, MA; *Instr* Kay M Davidson, MFA; *Instr* Allyn Bromley, MFA; Lectr Vickie Chock, MFA; Lectr Ellen Schroeder, MFA.
Estab 1968; pub; D&E; ent req over 18 yrs of age; degrees AA and AS 2 yr; schol; SC 11, LC 3; enrl D 400, E 100.
Tuition: Res—Undergrad $45 per sem, $3.50 per cr hr; Nonres—Undergrad $455 per sem, $38 per cr hr; no campus res.
Courses: Art History; Ceramics; Costume Design and Construction; Drafting; Drawing; Graphic Arts; History of Art; Painting; Photography; Printmaking; Sculpture; Theatre Arts.
Summer School: Dir Div Chmn, Enrl 100; tui $60 per term of 7 wks beginning June 13th. Courses—Ceramics; Introduction to Visual Art.

IDAHO

BOISE

BOISE STATE UNIVERSITY,* Art Department, 1910 University Blvd, 83725. Tel: 208-385-1247. *Chmn* Louis A Peck; Instrs FT 21, PT 11.
Estab 1932; pub; D&E; ent req HS dipl; degrees BA, BFA, BA (Educ), BFA (Educ), BA (Advertising Design) and BFA (Advertising Design) 4 yr; schol; SC 51, LC 8, GC 4; enrl D 2539, maj 441, GS 14.

Tuition: $366 per yr, PT $20 per sem hr; Nonres—$520 per sem.
Courses: Advertising Design; Art Education; Ceramics; Commercial Art; Drawing; Graphic Arts; Graphic Design; History of Art & Archaeology; Illustration; Jewelry; Lettering; Metal; Painting; Photography; Sculpture; Teacher Training; Textile Design.
Summer School: Tui $21 per sem hr; Courses—Art Education; Art History; Design; Drawing; Introduction to Art; Painting.

LEWISTON

LEWIS-CLARK STATE COLLEGE, Art Department, 83501. Tel: 208-746-2341. Instrs FT 2. *Discipline Coordr* Robert Almquist, MFA; *Instr* Brian L Sprague, MFA.
Estab 1893; pub; D&E; ent req HS dipl, GED cert, ACT; degrees BA and BS 4 yr; schol; SC 15, LC 2; enrl D 236, E 23, maj 23.
Tuition: Res—Undergrad $328 per yr; Nonres—Undergrad $1028 per yr; other PT (up to 7 cr) $12 per cr; campus res room and board $1199.36.
Courses: Art Education; Art History; Ceramics; Composition; Drawing; Graphic Arts; History of Art and Archaeology; Independent Study; Painting; Printmaking; Sculpture; Stage Design; Teacher Training; Theatre Arts; Video; Watercolor.

MOSCOW

UNIVERSITY OF IDAHO, Department of Art and Architecture, 83843. Tel: 208-885-6272. *Head Dept* Paul Blanton; *Chmn & Assoc Prof* George T Wray; MFA; *Prof* Geo Roberts, MS; *Assoc Prof* David Moreland, MFA; *Assoc Prof* Frank Cronk, MFA; *Prof* Nelson Curtis, MFA; *Asst Prof* David Giese, MFA; *Asst Prof* Lynn Haagensen, MFA; *Asst Prof* Jim Engelhardt, BA.
Estab 1923; pub; D&E; ent req HS dipl; degrees BA and BFA 4 yr, MFA 2 yr minimum, MA 1 yr; schol; SC 30, LC 6, GC 8; enrl D 450 (Art and Architecture), nonmaj 345 (Architecture), maj 105 (Art), GS 18 (Art).
Tuition: Res—Undergrad $20 per cr hr, grad $100 per yr, $50 per sem, $25 per cr hr; Nonres—Undergrad $1200 per yr, $600 per sem, $30 per cr hr, grad $1300 per yr, $650 per sem, $30 per cr hr; campus res room and board $480.
Courses: Advertising Design; ‡Architecture; ‡Art Education; ‡Ceramics; ‡Commercial Art; Drafting; Drawing; Graphic Arts; Graphic Design; Illustration; ‡Interior Design; ‡Jewelry; Landscape Architecture; ‡Painting; Photography; ‡Printmaking; ‡Sculpture.

NAMPA

NORTHWEST NAZARENE COLLEGE,* Art Department, Holly at Dewey, 83651. Tel: 208-467-8412. Instrs FT 3.
Den D&E; ent req HS dipl; Degrees AA and AB 4 yr; schol; SC 12, LC 5; enrl D 200, E 40, maj 24.
Courses: Advertising Design; Art Education; Ceramics; Commercial Art; Crafts for Teachers; Drafting; Drawing; Graphic Arts; History of Art & Archaeology; Illustration; Lettering; Painting; Sculpture; Teacher Training.
Adult Hobby Classes: Courses—Crafts.
Summer School: Courses—Art Education.

POCATELLO

IDAHO STATE UNIVERSITY,* Department of Art, PO Box 8004, 83209. Tel: 208-236-2361. *Chmn* Dennis Snyder; Instrs FT 7, PT 4.
Estab 1901; pub; D&E; ent req HS dipl, GED, ACT; degrees BA, BFA and MFA 4 yr; SC 32, LC 6, GS 22; enrl maj 75, GS 15, total 500.
Tuition: Res—$205 per sem; Nonres—$630 per sem; campus res $1260 per yr.
Courses: Art Education; Art History; Ceramics; Design; Drawing; Metals; Painting; Printmaking; Sculpture; Weaving.

REXBURG

RICKS COLLEGE, Department of Art, 83440. Tel: 208-356-2339. *Head Dept* Richard Bird, MA; *Primary Faculty:* Arlo Coles, MA; Robert Powell, MA; Brent Gehring, MA; Oliver Parson, MA; Robert Worrell, MA.
Estab 1888; pvt; D&E; ent req HS dipl; degrees AAS, AAdv Design and AFA 2 yr; schol; SC 23, LC 1; enrl D 123, maj 123.
Tuition: $355 per sem LDS mem; $460 non LDS mem; campus res.
Courses: ‡Advertising Design; Art Education; Art History; Ceramics; ‡Commercial Art; Drawing; Graphic Design; History of Art and Archaeology; Illustration; Interior Design; Lettering; Painting; Sculpture; Teacher Training.
Summer School: Tui $355.

TWIN FALLS

COLLEGE OF SOUTHERN IDAHO, Art Department, PO Box 1238, 83301. Tel: 208-733-9554 exten 260. *Chmn Prof* Lavar Steel, MS; *Assoc Prof* Michael Green, MFA; *Assoc Prof* M Kent Jeppesen, MFA.
Estab 1965; pub; D&E; ent req HS dipl, ACT; degrees dipl or AA; schol; SC 26, LC 2; enrl D 3000, E 2000, nonmaj 50 maj 45.
Tuition: Res—Undergrad $175 per yr, $87.50 per sem, $8.75 per sem hr; Nonres—Undergrad $600 per yr, $300 per sem, $30 per cr hr; campus res room and board.
Courses: Art History; Ceramics; Drawing; Handicrafts (weaving); Jewelry; Lettering; Mixed Media; Painting; Photography; Sculpture; Silversmithing; Theatre Arts.
Adult Hobby Classes: Enrl 15 per class; tui $30 per sem. Courses—Jewelry; Photography; Pottery; Weaving.
Children's Classes: Enrl 15 per class; tui $20 per 10 wks. Courses—Drawing; Painting; Puppets.
Summer School: Tui $44 per class beginning June 5th. Courses—Ceramics; Drawing; Painting; Photography.

ILLINOIS

BELLEVILLE

BELLEVILLE AREA COLLEGE, Art Department, 2500 Carlyle Rd, 62221. *Chmn Art Dept* Wayne L Shaw, EdS, MFA; Instrs FT 3, PT 15.
Estab 1948; pub; D&E; ent req HS dipl; degrees AA and AS 2 yrs; schol; SC 36, LC 9; enrl D 4000, E 3500, Maj 200.
Tuition: Res—Undergrad $400 acad yr; Nonres—Undergrad $600 per yr; no campus res.
Courses: Advertising Design; Art Education; Art History; Ceramics; Commercial Art; Drawing; History of Art & Archaeology; Jewelry; Painting; Photography; Sculpture; Theatre Arts.
Adult Hobby Classes: Enrl 175; tui $9 per hr. Courses—Ceramics; Design; Drawing; Jewelry; Photography.
Summer School: Dir Wayne Shaw. Enrl 175; tui $9 per sem hr for term of 8 wks beginning June 5. Courses—Art History; Ceramics; Drawing; Jewelry; Photography.

BLOOMINGTON

ILLINOIS WESLEYAN UNIVERSITY, School of Art, 61701. Tel: 309-556-3077. *Dir Sch Art* John Mulvany, MFA; *Primary Art Faculty* Fred Brian, MFA; Ed McCollough, MA; Sandra Martin, MFA; Barton McNeil, MFA; Donna Page, MFA.
Estab 1855, sch estab 1946; pvt; D; ent req HS dipl, SAT; degrees BA, BFA and BFA with Teaching Cert 4 yrs; enrl nonmaj 150, maj 75.
Courses: Art Education; Art History; Ceramics; Conceptual Art; Drawing; Film; Graphic Arts; History of Art & Archaeology; Painting; Photography; Printmaking; Sculpture; Teacher Training.
Summer School: Enrl 15; tui $400 for term of 3 wks. Courses—Photography; Printmaking; Papermaking.

CARBONDALE

SOUTHERN ILLINOIS UNIVERSITY, School of Art, 62902. Tel 453-2571. *Dir* Milton F Sullivan, MA; *Asst to the Dir* Patricia C Beene, MA; *Chmn of Metals,* Brent Kington, MFA; *Chmn Sculpture* Thomas Walsh, MFA; *Chmn 2-D* Robert Paulson, MFA; *Chmn Art Educ* Roy Abrahamson, PhD; *Chmn Art History* George Mavigliano, MA; *Printmaker/Drawer* Hergert Fink, MFA.
Estab 1874; pub; D&E; ent req HS dipl, ACT (score of 19), upper 50% of class; degrees BA & BS 4 yr, MFA 2 yr; schol; SC 100, LC 24, GS 28; enrl D 1304, E 338, nonmaj 672, maj 500, grad 70, others 400.
Tuition: Res—Undergrad & grad $371.35 per sem, $22 per cr hr; Nonres—Undergrad & grad $895.25 per sem, $66 per cr hr; campus res room and board.
Courses: ‡Advertising Design; Aesthetics; ‡Architecture; ‡Art Education; Art for Elementary Education; ‡Art History; ‡Ceramics; Collage; ‡Commercial Art; Conceptual Art; Constructions; ‡Costume Design & Construction; ‡Drafting; ‡Drawing; Fashion Arts; ‡Film; ‡Goldsmithing; ‡Graphic Arts; ‡Graphic Design; ‡History of Art & Archaeology; Illustration; Industrial Design; ‡Jewelry; Lettering; Mixed Media; Museum Staff Training; ‡Painting; Photography; ‡Printmaking; ‡Sculpture; ‡Silversmithing; Stage Design; ‡Teacher Training; Textile Design/Fibers; ‡Foundry; ‡Weaving; ‡Blacksmithing; ‡Glassblowing; Some classes listed are offered through School of Technical Careers.
Adult Hobby Classes: Enrl 40 per sem; tui $10-$15 per sem. Courses—Drawing; Ceramics; Fibers; Jewelry.

Children's Classes: Enrl 40; tui $10 per class. Courses—Differ with each semester.
Summer School: Enrl 500; tui $22 per hr for term of 8 wk beginning June 12. Courses—Selection from above list plus workshops in Art Therapy; Foundry; Blacksmithing and high school art workshop.
—**Department of Design.*** *Chmn* Wayne L St John; Faculty 10.
Estab 1956; pub; degrees BA 4 yr. MS 2 yr. ent req students transferring from another university cannot receive credit for design courses but will be evaluated on the basis of his or her work; degrees BA 4 yr, MS 2 yr; enrl maj 120.
Courses: Basic Design; Product-Shelter Design; Visual Design.

CARLINVILLE

BLACKBURN COLLEGE,* Department of Art, 62626. Tel: 217-854-3231. *Chmn* James M Clark; Instrs FT 2, PT 2.
Estab 1949; pvt; D&E; ent req HS grad; degree BA 4 yrs; schol; SC 14, LC 7; enrl maj 40.
Tuition: $2040 per yr; campus res $380.
Courses: Art History; Ceramics; Drawing & Painting; Painting; Printmaking; Teacher Training; Theatre Arts.

CHAMPAIGN

UNIVERSITY OF ILLINOIS, URBANA-CHAMPAIGN, College of Fine and Applied Arts,* 61820. Tel: 217-333-1661. *Dean* Jack H McKenzie; Instrs FT 260, PT 150.
Estab 1931; pub; D; ent req HS grad, ent exam; degrees Bachelors 4 yrs, Masters, Doctors; schol, fel, assistantships; enrl undergrad 2600, grad 585.
Adult Hobby Classes: Scheduled through University Extension.
Children's Classes: Sat; Summer Youth Classes; Summer Schol.
—**Department of Art and Design,** Fourth & Peabody Dr (Mailing Add: 143 Fine Arts Bldg). Tel: 217-333-0855. *Prof Art & Design & Acting Head Dept* Eugene C Wicks, MFA; *In Charge Art Educ* George W Hardiman, EdD; *In Charge Art Hist* Jerrold Ziff, PhD; *In Charge Graphic Design* Raymond Perlman, MFA; *In Charge Indust Design* Edward J Zagorski, MFA; *In Charge Undergrad Painting* Glenn R Bradshaw, MFA; *In Charge Grad Painting* M Douglas Hilson, MFA; *In Charge Photography* Arthur Sinsabaugh, BA; *In Charge Sculpture* Frank Gallo, MFA.
Estab 1867, dept estab 1877; pub; D&E; ent req HS dipl, ACT, SAT, CLEP; degrees BFA 4 yrs, MA 1 yr, MFA 2 yrs, EdD/PhD 5 yrs; schol; SC 119, LC 72, GC 77; enrl maj 563, grad 106, others 15 nondegree grad.
Tuition: Res—Undergrad $814 per yr, $407 per sem, PT $292 per sem, grad $844 per yr, $422 per sem, PT $302 per sem; Nonres—Undergrad $1986 per yr, $993 per sem, PT $692 per sem, grad $2076 per yr, $1038 per sem, PT $722 per sem; campus res room and board $1628 per sem.
Courses: ‡Art Education; ‡Art History; ‡Ceramics; ‡Cinematography; Drawing; Film; ‡Graphic Design; ‡History of Art & Archaeology; ‡Industrial Design; Jewelry; Museum Staff Training; ‡Painting; ‡Photography; ‡Printmaking; ‡Sculpture; Silversmithing; Teacher Training.
Children's Classes: Enrl 220; tui $16 per sem. Courses—Creative Arts for Children.
Summer School: *Dir* Eugene C Wicks. Courses—Foundation and lower division courses with some limited offerings and independent study at upper division and graduate levels.

CHARLESTON

EASTERN ILLINOIS UNIVERSITY, Art Department, FAA 216, 61920. Tel: 217-581-3410. *Acting Chmn Dept* Ben P Watkins, PhD; *Prof* Lynn Trank, PhD; *Prof* June Krutza, PhD; *Prof* Ray Stapp, DEd; *Prof* Carl Shull, DEd; *Prof* Carl Emmerich, DEd; *Assoc Prof* Bill Heyduck, DEd; *Assoc Prof* Gary Knoop, MFA; vis prof—Arnold Levine, painting, spring 78; Instrs FT 23, PT 6.
Estab 1895, dept estab 1930; pub; D&E; ent req HS dipl, Grad—MAT or GRE; degrees BA 4 yrs, MA 1 yr, Specialist Ed 2 yrs; Grad MA Prog; schol; enrl D 1700, E 76, nonmaj 1400, maj 260, grad 20, others workshops.
Tuition: Res—Undergrad $702 per yr, $351 per sem, $27.25 per hr, grad $732 per yr, $366 per sem, $29 per hr; Nonres—Undergrad $1722 per yr, $861 per sem, $70.25 per hr, grad $1812 per yr, $906 per sem, $74 per hr; campus res.
Courses: Advertising Design; Art Education; Art History; Ceramics; Commercial Art; Drawing; Goldsmithing; Graphic Arts; Handicrafts (weaving); History of Art & Archaeology; Jewelry; Lettering; Painting; Printmaking; Sculpture; Silversmithing; Teacher Training; Textile Design.
Adult Hobby Classes: Enrl 25-30. Courses—Crafts.
Children's Classes: Elementary Art Activities.

CHICAGO

AMERICAN ACADEMY OF ART, 220 S State St, 60604. Tel: 312-939-3883. *Dir* Irving Shapiro; Instrs FT 18, PT 8.
Estab 1923; pvt; D&E; ent req HS dipl, portfolio; degree AA 2-3 yrs; schol; SC 10; enrl D 350, E 600.
Tuition: $2125 per yr, $1150 per sem; no campus res.
Courses: Advertising Design; Cartooning; Commercial Art; Drawing; Graphic Arts; Graphic Design; Illustration; Interior Design; Lettering; Painting; Photography.
Summer School: *Dir* Irving Shapiro. Enrl 300 FT, 500 PT; tui $370 for term of 8 wks beginning June 26. Courses—General.

CHICAGO ACADEMY OF FINE ARTS, 65 E Southwater St, 60601. Tel: 312-782-1140. *Dir* Mary M Hamper, MA; *Dept Fine Arts* Fred Berger, BA; *Dept Interior Design* Antony Patano, MFA; *Dept Communicating Arts* Patricia S Olson, BFA; *Dept Photography* Herbert J Kahn, BA; *Dept Animation/Cartooning* Barry F Young, MFA.
Estab 1902; pvt; D; ent req HS dipl or GED; degree BFA 4 yrs; enrl D 225.
Tuition: $2250 per yr. $1125 per sem; ½ tuition for sr citizens; no campus res.
Courses: Advertising Design; Animation/Cartooning; Commercial Art; Drawing; Fashion Arts; Film; Graphic Arts; Graphic Design; Illustration; Interior Design; Painting; Photography; Printmaking.
Summer School: *Dir* Mary M Hamper. Tui $75 per sem cr, same as for regular school yr. Courses—multilevel courses from the 4 major depts.

CITY COLLEGES OF CHICAGO,* Central Administration Offices, 180 N Michigan Ave, 60601. Tel: 312-269-8000.
Pub; D&E; ent req HS dipl, ACT; degrees AA, dipl, AAS and dipl applied science 2 yrs.
Tuition: $11 per cr hr per sem, $3.75 per sem cr hr per term (more than 6 hrs), PT $1.50 per sem cr hr per term (less than 6 hrs), out-of-city $24.73 per sem cr hr, out-of-state $44 per sem cr hr; lab fees vary; no campus res; adult educ courses.
—**Daley College,** Art and Architecture Department, 7400 S Pulaski Rd, 60652. Tel: 312-735-3000.
Estab 1960; enrl 4700.
Courses: Art Education; Ceramics; Drafting; Drawing; Graphic Arts; Graphic Design; History of Art & Archaeology; Illustration; Painting; Photography; Sculpture; Weaving.
—**Kennedy-King College,** Art and Humanities Department, 6800 S Wentworth Ave, 60621. Tel: 312-962-3200.
Estab 1935; enrl 9010.
Courses: Art Education; Drafting; Drawing; History of Art & Archaeology; Industrial Design; Painting; Photography; Radio-TV; Theater Arts.
—**Loop College,** Art and Humanities Department, 64 E Lake St, 60601. Tel: 312-269-8000.
Estab 1962; enrl 10,600.
Courses: Art Education; Drafting; Drawing; History of Art & Archaeology; Industrial Design; Painting; Theater Arts.
—**Malcolm X College,** Art and Humanities Department, 1900 W Van Buren St, 60612. Tel: 312-942-3000.
Estab 1911; enrl 5000.
Courses: Art Education; Ceramics; Drafting; Drawing; History of Art; Industrial Design; Painting; Radio-TV; Sculpture; Theater Arts.
—**Olive-Harvey College,** Art and Humanities Department, 10001 S Woodlawn Ave, 60628. Tel: 312-568-3700.
Estab 1957; enrl 4700.
Courses: Art Education; Drafting; Drawing; History of Art & Archaeology; Industrial Design; Painting; Theater Arts.
—**Truman College,** Art and Humanities Department, 1145 W Wilson Ave, 60640. Tel: 312-878-1700.
Estab 1956; enrl 3800.
Courses: Art Education; Ceramics; Drafting; Drawing; History of Art & Archaeology; Industrial Design; Painting; Photography; Theater Arts.
—**Wright College,** Art and Humanities Department, 3400 N Austin Ave, 60634. Tel: 312-777-7900. Instrs FT 5.
Estab 1934; pub; D&E; ent req HS dipl; degree AA 2 yrs; SC 15, LC 5; enrl D 3000, E 2500.
Courses: Advertising Design; Architecture; Ceramics; Commercial Art; Drafting; Drawing; Graphic Design; History of Art & Archaeology; Lettering; Painting; Sculpture; Textile Design.
Adult Hobby Classes: Enrl 30 per class; tui $3 for 8 sessions. Courses—Watercolor; Oil Painting; Interior Design.
Summer School: Term of 8 wks beginning July 2. Courses—Painting; Figure Drawing.

CONTEMPORARY ART WORKSHOP, 542 W Grant Place, 60614. Tel: 312-525-9624. *Dir* John W Kearney, BA; *Sculpture* Paul Zakoian, MA.
Estab 1950; pvt; D&E; ent req for studios artists must submit slides; no degrees granted; apprentice prog.
Tuition: $70 for 10 wks.
Courses: Painting; Sculpture.
Adult Hobby Classes: Tui $70 for 10 wks. Courses—Sculpture.
Children's Classes: Summer courses—Painting; Sculpture; Theatre.

DePAUL UNIVERSITY, School of Liberal Arts and Sciences, Department of Art, 2323 N Seminary, 60614. Tel: 312-321-8194. *Assoc Prof & Chmn Dept* Sally Kitt Chappell, PhD; *Assoc Prof* William Conger, MFA; *Assoc Prof* Robert Donley, MFA; *Asst Prof* Stephen Luecking, MFA.
Estab 1897, dept estab 1965; pvt; D; ent req HS dipl, SAT or ACT; degree BA (Art) 4 yrs; SC 20, LC 12; enrl D 30 art maj.
Tuition: All tuition fees are subject to change, contact admissions office for current fees; campus res.
Courses: Aesthetics; Architecture; Art Education; Art History; Ceramics; Commercial Art; Conceptual Art; Drawing; Film; Graphic Arts and Design; History of Art & Archaeology; Museum Staff Training; Painting; Photography; Printmaking; Sculpture; Teacher Training.
Summer School: Dir Sally Kitt Chappell.

FELICIAN COLLEGE, Art Department, 3800 W Peterson Ave, 60659. Tel: 312-539-1919. *Art Dir* Mary Lauriane, MFA; *Instrs* Tobi Abrams, BS; *Lectr* John Kalk, MA.
Estab 1953; pvt; D&E; ent req HS dipl; degree AA 2 yrs; enrl D 15, E 25.
Tuition: $1020 per yr, $510 per sem.
Courses: Art Education; Art History; Drawing; Mixed Media; Painting.
Summer School: Dir Mary Lauriane. Tui $90 for term of 15 wks beginning June 17. Courses—Methods in Teaching Art; Creative Art.

HARRINGTON INSTITUTE OF INTERIOR DESIGN, 410 S Michigan e, 60605. Tel: 312-939-4975. *Dean* Robert C Marks.
Estab 1931; pvt; D&E; ent req HS dipl, interview; professional dipl 3 yr prog; enrl D 193, E 198.
Tuition: $2250 per yr, $1125 per sem; campus res room & board $1900 per yr (Roosevelt University's Dormitory nearby is used).
Courses: Interior Design.

ILLINOIS INSTITUTE OF TECHNOLOGY*
—College of Architecture, Planning and Design, Department of Architecture, 3300 S Federal St, 60616. Tel: 312-567-3262. *Dean* James Ingo Freed; *Acting Chmn* David C Sharpe; *Instrs* FT 9.
Estab 1895 as Armour Institute, consolidated with Lewis Institute of Arts and Sciences, 1940; pvt; degrees BArch, MSArch, MSCity and Regional Planning 5 yrs; normal enrl 200.
Courses: Architecture.
—Institute of Design, 3360 S State St, 60616. Tel: 312-567-3250. *Chmn* Dietmar R Winker; *Instrs* FT 17, PT 2.
Estab 1937; pvt; D&E; ent req CEEB exam, schol standing; degrees BS(Design) 4 yrs, MS(Visual Educ, Visual Design, Product Design, Photography); schol; enrl D 275; E 115.
Tuition: $1500 per sem.
Summer School: Dir Jack Weiss; Grad Art Educ Prog.

INSTITUTE OF LETTERING AND DESIGN, 202 S State St, Box A-3380, 60604. Tel: 312-341-1300. *Dir* Sidney Borden.
Estab 1948; pvt; D&E; ent req HS dipl, waived if student is interviewed; enrl D 49, E 30.
Tuition: $1500 per sem, $200 monthly, $75 for 12 sessions.
Courses: Advertising Design; Calligraphy; Commercial Art; Graphic Arts; Graphic Design; Lettering; Photography.

LOYOLA UNIVERSITY OF CHICAGO, Fine Arts Department, 820 N Michigan Ave, 60611. *Asst Prof Art & Acting Chmn Fine Arts Dept* Mary S Lawton, PhD; *Assoc Prof* Ralph Arnold, MFA; *Prof* Margaret Dagenais, MAE; *Asst Prof* Kent Follette, MFA; *Assoc Prof* Juliet Rago, MFA; *Asst Prof* Justine Wantz, MFA; *Prof* Jean Unsworth, MFA.
Estab 1870, dept estab 1970; den; D & E; no ent req; degrees BA and BS 4 yrs; SC 25, LC 17.
Tuition: $2500 per yr, $1275 per sem; $70 per hr; campus res room & board $705.
Courses: Art Education; Art History; Calligraphy; Ceramics; Commercial Art; Drawing; Goldsmithing; Graphic Arts; Jewelry; Lettering; Painting; Photography; Printmaking; Sculpture; Stage Design.
Summer School: Dir Phyllis Gallagher. Courses—Commercial Art; Art History; Art Appreciation; Painting; Drawing; Photography.

NORTH PARK COLLEGE, Art Department, 5125 N Spaulding, 60625. Tel: 312-583-2700, exten 391. *Chmn Dept* Neale Murray, MA; *Prof* Gail Bradley, MA; *Prof* Lenore Pressman, MA; *Prof* Ralph Varde; *Prof* Lars Sponberg.
Estab 1957; den; D&E ent req HS dipl; degree BA 4 yrs; schol; SC 18, LC 5; enrl D 40.
Tuition: Res—Undergrad $4770 per yr; Nonres—Undergrad $3250; campus res room & board.
Courses: Advertising Design; Aesthetics; Art Education; Art History; Calligraphy; Ceramics; Commercial Art; Drawing; Illustration; Photography; Printmaking; Sculpture; Teacher Training.
Adult Hobby Classes: Tui $35 per term. Courses—Painting; Calligraphy.
Summer School: Enrl 25; tui $190 course for term of 8 wks beginning June 12. Courses—Drawing; Painting; Ceramics; Sculpture.

NORTHEASTERN ILLINOIS UNIVERSITY,* Art Department, St Louis at Bryn Mawr Ave, 60625. Tel: 312-583-4050, exten 580, 581. *Instrs* FT 12, PT 2.
Estab 1869; pub; D&E; ent req HS dipl, GED test, upper half high school class or higher ACT score; degree BA 4 yrs; schol; SC 44 LC 22; total enrl 10,200, art maj 175, grad 1583, others 798.
Courses: Art Education; Ceramics; Crafts; Drawing; Graphic Design; History of Art & Archaeology; Industrial Design; Jewelry; Lettering; Metal Enameling; Painting; Photography; Printmaking; Sculpture; Teacher Training.

RAY-VOGUE SCHOOLS, 750 N Michigan Ave, 60611. Tel: 312-787-5117. *Dir* Wade Ray; *Dept Heads* Norman Mier, Sandra Souyoul, Robert Miller, Karen Amirsoltani, John Goehlich and Jeanne Radysh.
Estab 1916; pvt; D&E; ent req HS dipl, portfolio review; dipl 1 or 2 yr courses; SC 7; enrl D 350, E 125.
Tuition: $1960 per yr, $980 per sem; no campus res.
Courses: Advertising Design; Commercial Art; Display; Fashion Arts; Fashion Merchandising; Graphic Design; Illustration; Interior Design; Photography.
Adult Hobby Classes: Enrl 85; tui $110 for 20 eve. Courses—Dress Design; Photography.
Summer School: Dir Wade Ray. Enrl 190; tui $490 for 10 wks beginning June 23. Courses—Dress Design; Interior Design; Commercial Art; Photography; Fashion Illustration.

SCHOOLS OF THE ART INSTITUTE OF CHICAGO,* Jackson Blvd at Columbus Dr, 60603. Tel: 312-443-3700. *Dir* Donald J Irving; *Chmn Grad Div* Tom Steger; *Chmn Undergrad Div* Iola Rigacci; *Instrs* FT 75, PT 20.
Estab 1866; pvt; ent req portfolio; degrees BFA 4 yrs, MFA; SC 103, LC 22; enrl FT 750, PT 400.
Tuition: $78 per cr hr; undergrad $2808 per sem, grad $2340 per sem.
Courses: Art History & Aesthetics; Design & Communication; Education; Fashion Design; Fiber/Clay/Fabric; Filmmaking; Generative Systems; Painting & Drawing; Photography; Printmaking; Sculpture; Sound/Music; Video.
Summer School: Dir Donald J Irving. Enrl 500; term of 4 full days for 8 wks.

UNIVERSITY OF CHICAGO, Department of Art, 5540 S Greenwood, 60637. Tel: 312-753-3879. *Chmn & Assoc Prof* Charles E Cohen, PhD; *Prof* Pramod Chandra, PhD; *Prof* Francis H Dowley, PhD; *Prof* Edward Maser, PhD; *Prof* Earl Rosenthal, PhD; *Prof* Harrie Vanderstrappen, PhD; *Assoc Prof* Charles E Cohen, PhD; *Assoc Prof* Linda Seidel, PhD; vis prof—Margaret Root, Ancient art, 77-78; Ernst Gombrich, Art History/Cultural History, spring 78.
Estab 1892; pvt; D; ent req contact college of admissions; degrees BA 4 yr, MA 1 yr, PhD 4 - 6 yr; schol; SC, LC and GC varies; enrl maj 11, grad 104, others 3.
Tuition: Undergrad $1365 per quarter (4 courses); grad $1435 per quarter (3 courses); campus residence $1300 per yr.
Courses: Aesthetics; Architecture; ‡Art History; Ceramics; Collage; Conceptual Art; Drawing; Film; Graphic Arts; Graphic Design; ‡History of Art & Archaeology, Mixed Media; Museum Staff Training; Painting; Photography; Printmaking; Sculpture; Video.
Summer School: Enrl varies; tui $300 for term of 10 wk beginning June. Courses—Varies.

UNIVERSITY OF ILLINOIS AT CHICAGO CIRCLE, College of Architecture, Art and Urban Sciences, PO Box 4348, 60680. Tel: 312-996-3351, Art and Design 996-3337. *Dean* Alan M Voorhees; *Dir* Richard R Whitaker, Jr; *Dir School of Art & Design* Edward Colker; *Chmn Dept Hist Architecture & Art* Donald Ehresmann; Vis prof—Carol Ballard, Communications Design, 77-78, Mary K Stoppert, sculpture, 77-78 Instr FT 80, PT 28.
Estab 1946; pub; D; ent req 3 units of English plus 13 additional units; rank in top one-half of high school class for beginning freshman; transfer

students 3.25 grad point average; degrees BA(Design), BA(Studio Arts), BA(Art Educ), 4 yr; MFA(Studio Art or Design), 2 yr; BArch, 4 yr, MArch 5 yr; schol; SC 79, LC 10, GC 3; enrl D 579, nonmaj 325, maj 579, GS 17.
Tuition: Res—Undergrad $789 yr, grad $819 yr; Nonres—Undergrad $1959, grad $2049; no campus res.
Courses: ‡Art Education; Ceramics; Drawing; Film; ‡Industrial Design; ‡Painting; ‡Photography; ‡Printmaking; ‡Sculpture; Video; ‡Communications Design; ‡Comprehensive Design; ‡Studio Arts.
Children's Classes: Enrl 50; tui $5. Courses—Saturday school in connection with art education classes.
Summer School: Dir Edward Colker, Enrl 30% of regular term; tui $204 for Res—Undergrad $204, Nonres—Undergrad $498 for term of 8 wk beginning June.

UNIVERSITY OF ILLINOIS AT THE MEDICAL CENTER, CHICAGO, Department of Biocommunication Arts/Medical Art, 833 South Wood St, Room 245-S, Pharmacy Bldg 60612. Tel: 312-996-7337. *Dir & Prof* Emil W Hospodar, BA; *Assoc Prof* William Schwarz, BS; *Assoc Prof* Alfred Teoli, MFA; *Asst Prof* Robert Parshall, BS; *Asst Prof* Alice Katz, MEd.
Estab 1963, dept estab 1967; pub; D; ent req HS dipl, also same as college of Fine and Applied Arts, Champaign; degrees BS, 4 yr.

CHICAGO HEIGHTS

PRAIRIE STATE COLLEGE,* Art Department, 197th & Halsted, 60411. Tel: 312-756-3110. *Chmn* Dr Albert Piarowski; Instrs FT 3, PT 14.
Estab 1958; pub; D&E; ent req HS dipl, ACT; degree AA 2 yrs; SC 24, LC 6; enrl dept 300, maj 200.
Tuition: $17.50 per cr hr; out of district $35 per cr hr; out of state $55 per cr hr.
Courses: Advertising Design; Design; Drawing (multimedia); History of Art; Illustration; Interior Design; Life Drawing; Materials Workshop; Painting; Photography; Production Processes; Sculpture.
Summer School: Dir Dr Albert Piarowski. Tui $14 per cr hr for term of 8 wks. Courses—Art History Tour; Design; Drawing; Materials Workshop; Painting; Photography.

DECATUR

MILLIKIN UNIVERSITY, Art Department, 1184 W Main St. 62522. Tel: 217-424-6227. *Chmn Art Dept* Marvin L Klaven, MA; Instrs FT 3, PT 1.
Estab 1901, dept estab 1904; pvt; D&E; ent req HS dipl, ACT; degrees BA and BFA 4 yrs; schol; SC 47, LC 3; enrl D 1500, nonmaj 25, maj 40.
Tuition: $3300 per yr; campus res room & board $1425 yr.
Courses: Art Education; Art History; Ceramics; Commercial Art; Drawing; Graphic Arts; History of Art & Archaeology; Jewelry; Mixed Media; Painting; Printmaking; Sculpture; Theatre Arts.
Summer School: Dir Special Programs William Lewis. Enrl 25; tui $87.50 cr hr for term of 7 wks beginning June 13. Courses—Studio (Painting, Drawing, Printmaking).

DE KALB

NORTHERN ILLINOIS UNIVERSITY, College of Visual and Performing Arts, Department of Art, 60115. Tel: 815-753-1473. *Chmn Dept* Art Robert L Even, PhD; *Asst Chairperson Dept* Helen Merritt, MFA; *Grad Coordr* Carl Hayano, MAE; *Area Coordr* Elisabeth Bond, MSEd; *Area Coordr* J Dimitri Liakos; *Area Coordr* Eleanor Caldwell, EdD; *Area Coordr* William Brown, EdD; *Area Coordr* Gordon Dorn, MFA.
Estab 1895; pub; D&E; ent req HS dipl; degrees BS, BA, BFA 4 yrs, MA, MSEd 2 yrs, MFA 3 yrs, EdD 3 yrs; schol; SC approx 140, LC approx 606, GC approx 70; enrl D 5000, maj 1200, grad 215.
Tuition: Res—$2940 per yr; Nonres—$3940 per yr; campus res room & board.
Courses: ‡Advertising Design; Aesthetics; Architecture; ‡Art Education; ‡Art History; ‡Ceramics; Commercial Art; Costume Design & Construction; Display; Drafting; Drawing; Film; Graphic Arts; Graphic Design; Handicrafts; History of Art & Archaeology; Illustration; Industrial Design; Intermedia; ‡Interior Design; ‡Jewelry; Lettering; Mixed Media; Museum Staff Training; Occupational Therapy; Painting; Photography; ‡Printmaking; ‡Sculpture; Silversmithing; Stage Design; Teacher Training; Textile Design; Theatre Arts; Video.
Summer School: Dir Robert L Even. Tui res $125, nonres $375. Courses—vary.

EDWARDSVILLE

SOUTHERN ILLINOIS UNIVERSITY AT EDWARDSVILLE, Department of Art and Design, 62026. Tel: 618-692-3071. *Chmn Dept*

David C Huntley, MFA; *Asst Chmn Dept* Joseph A Weber, MA; *Head Art History* Floyd Coleman, PhD; *Head Printmaking* Robert R Malone, MFA; *Head Drawing & Grad Adv* Dennis Ringring, MFA; *Head Painting* Michael J Smith, MFA; *Head Sculpture* Kenneth G Ryden, MFA; *Head Fiber & Fabrics* Judith A Millis, MFA; several vis artists in each area each quarter.
Estab 1869, dept estab 1959; pub; D&E; ent req HS dipl, ACT; portfolio req for BFA and MFA; degrees BA, BS and BFA 4 yrs, MFA 3 yrs, MS 2 yrs; schol; SC 65, LC 26, GC 45; enrl D 450, E 125, maj 250, grad 62.
Tuition: Res—Undergrad & grad $690 per yr, $230 per quarter, $86.80 for 5 hrs, $158.40 for 5-12 hrs; Nonres—Undergrad & grad $1788 per yr, $596 per quarter, $208.80 for 5 hrs, $402.40 for 5-12 hrs; campus res room & board.
Courses: Aesthetics; Art Education; Art History; Ceramics; Collage; Commercial Art; Drawing; Film; History of Art & Archaeology; Jewelry; Mixed Media; Painting; Photography; Printmaking; Sculpture; Silversmithing; Stage Design; Teacher Training; Textile Design; Theatre Arts; Video.
Summer School: Chmn David C Huntley: term of 12 wks beginning June 19. Courses—Full Curriculum.

ELMHURST

ELMHURST COLLEGE, Art Department, 190 Prospect, 60126. Tel: 312-279-4100, exten 300. *Chairperson Art Dept* Sandra Jorgensen, MFA; *Assoc Prof* John Weber, MFA; *Asst Prof* Carole R Brown, MFA; *Instrs* Richard Paulsen, MFA; Instrs FT 4, PT 2.
Estab 1871; den; D&E; ent req HS dipl, ACT or SAT; degrees BS, BA and BM 4 yrs; schol; SC 13, LC 8; enrl D 1550, E 1100, maj 32.
Tuition: $3070 per yr, $1365 per sem, $340 course, $85 per hr; campus room & board $1610 yr.
Courses: Architecture; Art Education; Art History; Collage; Conceptual Art; Constructions; Drawing; History of Art & Archaeology; Painting; Photography; Printmaking; Sculpture.
Summer School: Enrl 1000; tui $272 course for term of 8 wks beginning June 14. Courses—Regular Curriculum.

EVANSTON

NORTHWESTERN UNIVERSITY, EVANSTON, College of Arts and Sciences
—**Department of Art,*** 60201. Tel: 312-492-7346. *Chmn Dept* J Wesley Burnham; Instrs FT 7, PT 5.
Estab 1924; pvt; degrees AB 4 yrs, MA, MFA; schol and fel; SC 15, LC 8, GC 5; normal enrl 300-500
Tuition: $1540 each quarter.
Courses: Interior Architecture and Design; Practice of Art; Teaching of Art.
—**Department of Art History,** 1859 Sheridan Rd, 60201. Tel: 312-492-3230. *Prof Art Hist & Chmn Dept* Carl W Condit, PhD; *Prof* James Breckenridge; PhD; *Asst Prof* Frederick Levine, PhD; *Assoc Prof* Betty Iverson Monroe, PhD; *Asst Prof* Olan A Rand, Jr, PhD; *Asst Prof* Leland M Roth, PhD; *Asst Prof* Thomas L Sloan, PhD.
Estab 1851; pvt; D; ent req HS dipl, SAT or ACT; degrees BA 4 yrs; MA 1 yr, PhD 3 yrs; schol; LC 36, GC 15; enrl maj 29, grad 15.
Tuition: Undergrad $4620 per yr, $1540 per quarter; Grad $4290 per yr, $1430 per quarter; PT $550 per course; campus res room and board.
Courses: Architecture; ‡Art History.

FREEPORT

HIGHLAND COMMUNITY COLLEGE,* RFD 2, Pearl City Rd, 61032. Tel: 815-235-6121. *Instr* Jody Schultz; Instrs FT 1, PT 4.
Estab 1962; pub; D&E; ent req HS dipl, ent exam; degrees AS, AA, ABA, AAS 2 yrs; schol; SC 6, LC 1; enrl 126.
Courses: Art History; Art Materials & Processes; Design; Drawing; Introduction to Art; Painting; Pottery; Printmaking.
Continuing Education Classes: Enrl 278. Courses—Basic Drawing; Oil; Charcoal; Printmaking; Sculpture; Pottery; Handweaving & Related Crafts; Rosemaling; Macrame; Needlepoint. Occasional summer workshops for High School and Elementary School students.
Summer School: One course offered each year.

GLEN ELLYN

COLLEGE OF DuPAGE, Art Department, Lambert Rd at 22nd St, 60137. Tel: 312-858-2800. *Primary Art Faculty* Pamela B Lowrie, MS, MA; Patricia Kurriger, PhD; Adnon Ertas, MFA; John C Lemon, MFA; John A Wantz, MA; Karl Owen, MAT and Willard Smith, MS.
Estab 1966; pub; D&E; ent req completion of application; degrees AA(Art) and AAS(Interior Design, Fashion Design, Commercial Art) 2 yrs; SC 24, LC 5.
Tuition: $11.50 per cr hr; no campus res.
Courses: Aesthetics; Architecture; Art History; Ceramics; Commercial Art; Costume Design & Construction; Drafting; Drawing; Fashion Arts;

Graphic Arts; Illustration; Interior Design; Jewelry; Landscape Architecture; Painting; Photography; Printmaking; Sculpture; Textile Design; Theatre Arts.
Children's Classes: Subjects—Ceramics.
Summer School: Tui $11.50 per hr for term of 3, 5 or 10 wks. Courses—Vary.

NAGUIB SCHOOL OF SCULPTURE, INC, 1 S 101 Rt 53, 60137. Tel: 312-858-7797. *Dir & Prof* Mustafa Naguib.
Estab 1973; pvt nonprofit corp; D&E; ent req HS dipl or over 18 yrs; cert for 3 yr cert prog; enrl D 10, E 15, maj 10, others 15.
Tuition: $1200 per sem of 12 wks, PT $15 per 3 hr session; campus res room & board approx $640.
Courses: Drawing; Sculpture.
Adult Hobby Classes: Tui $15 per 3 hr class. Courses—Sculpture; Life Drawing.
Children's Classes: Tui $15 per 3 hr class. Courses—Sculpture.
Summer School: *Dir* Mustafa Naguib. Tui $600 for term of 6 wks. 30 Day Technology of Sculpture Workshop $500. Bronze Casting Workshop $700 for 5 wks.

GODFREY

LEWIS & CLARK COMMUNITY COLLEGE,* Art Department, 5800 Godfrey Rd, 62035. Tel; 618-466-3411, exten 275. *Chmn Div Communications & Humanities* William Gardner; Instrs FT 2, PT 3.
Estab 1970, formerly Monticello College; pub; D&E; ent req HS dipl, ent exam, open door policy; degree AA 2 yrs; schol; SC 13, LC 2; enrl D 1800, E 600, maj 40.
Tuition: $10 per sem hr; commuting col.
Courses: Advertising Design; Basic Design; Ceramics; Drafting; Drawing; Handicrafts; History of Art; Painting; Sculpture; Weaving.
Adult Hobby Classes: Enrl 30; tui $10 per sem hr. Courses—Interior Design; Introduction to Drawing & Painting; Antiques.
Summer School: Enrl 15; pre-summer 4 wk session painting on-location, 4 hrs daily; $30 for 3 sem cr hr; summer courses, painting, advanced and beginning; term of 8 wks beginning June 18.

GREENVILLE

GREENVILLE COLLEGE, Department of Art, 62246. Tel: 618-664-1840. *Chmn Art Dept* Donald P Hallmark, MA; *Instr* C Lane Raiser, MFA; *Instr* Steven Heilmer, MFA; *Instr* Anna Raiser, BS.
Estab 1892; pvt; D&E; ent req HS dipl, ACT; degrees BA, BS 4 yrs; SC 8, LC 4; enrl nonmaj 120, maj 35.
Tuition: $2752 per yr, $1376 per sem; campus res room & board $1450 yr.
Courses: ‡Advertising Design; ‡Art Education; Art History; ‡Ceramics; ‡Drawing; ‡Graphic Design; ‡Painting; Printmaking; ‡Sculpture; Teacher Training.
Summer School: *Dir* Frank Thompson. Enrl 250; tui $344 or $688 for term of 8 wks beginning June. Courses—Introduction to the Fine Arts.

JACKSONVILLE

MacMURRAY COLLEGE,* Art Department, 62650. Tel: 217-245-6151. *Chmn Dept* John B Northcutt; Instrs FT 2.
Estab 1846; den; 4 yr degrees; SC 29, LC 6.
Courses: Advertising Design; Ceramics; Costume Design; Drawing & Painting; Industrial Design; Interior Design; Teacher Training; Textile Design.

JOLIET

COLLEGE OF ST FRANCIS,* Division of Humanities and Fine Arts, Art Department, 500 Wilcox, 60435. Tel: 815-726-7311, exten 270. *Chmn Div* Marjorie Marion; Instrs PT 4.
Estab 1950; pvt; D&E; ent req HS grad, ent exam; degrees BS, BA(Art or Art Educ) 4 yrs; SC 19, LC 6; enrl D 150, E 20, maj 70.
Tuition: $1080 per yr; campus res $695 per yr.
Courses: Aesthetics; Architecture; Art Education; Ceramics; Drawing; Enameling; Graphic Arts; History of Art & Archaeology; Jewelry; Lettering; Painting; Sculpture; Teacher Training; Textile Design.
Children's Classes: Enrl 20 (limit); tui $80 for 16 wk lessons, 2 hrs Sat AM. Courses—Art in variety of media.
Summer School: Tui $105 for term of 6 wks beginning June. Courses—Art Courses; Ceramics; Calligraphy.

JOLIET JUNIOR COLLEGE, Art Department, 1216 Houbolt Ave, 60436. Tel: 815-729-9020, exten 423. *Chmn Dept* William Fabrycki, MA; *Primary Art Faculty* Sharlene Kassiday, MFA; James Dugdale, MA; Sue Latocha, MA; and Earl Kurtz, MA; short-term vis profs.
Estab 1901, dept estab 1920; pub; D&E; ent req HS dipl, ent exam; degree AA 2 yrs; schol; SC 15, LC 4; enrl D 10,000, maj 120.

Tuition: $13 per sem cr for res of Ill Dist 525; from $33.10 to $54.62 per sem cr for res outside Ill Dist 525; no campus res.
Courses: Art Education; Art History; Ceramics; Drawing; History of Art & Archaeology; Interior Design (in different dept); Jewelry; Painting; Silversmithing; Two-Dimensional & Three-Dimensional Design.
Summer School: *Dir* William Fabrycki. Courses—Same as Winter School.

KANKAKEE

OLIVET NAZARENE COLLEGE, Department of Art, 60901. Tel: 815-939-5229. *Assoc Prof Art & Chmn Dept* Harvey A Collins, MFA; *Asst Prof* Dottie Bishop, MA.
Estab 1907, dept estab 1953; den; D&E; ent req HS dipl; degrees BS and BA 4 yrs, MEd and MTheol 2 yrs; schol; SC 14, LC 4; enrl D 100, nonmaj 80, maj 21.
Tuition: $1940 per yr, $970 per sem, $81 per sem hr; campus res room & board.
Courses: ‡Art Education; Art History; ‡Ceramics; Drawing; Film; Graphic Arts; Graphic Design; History of Art & Archaeology; Lettering; ‡Painting; Photography; Printmaking; Sculpture; Teacher Training; Textile Design.
Summer School: *Dir* Harvey A Collins. Tui $58 per hr for term of 5 wks beginning June 26. Courses—Ceramics; Painting; Introduction to Fine Arts.

LAKE FOREST

BARAT COLLEGE,* Department of Art, 700 E Westleigh Rd, 60045. Tel: 312-234-3000, exten 328. Instrs FT 4, PT 4.
Estab 1858; den; D; W only; ent req HS dipl, ent exam; degree BA 4 yrs; schol; SC 32, LC 16; enrl maj 58.
Courses: Architecture; Ceramics; Drawing; Graphic Arts; Graphic Design; History of Art & Archaeology; Illustration; Painting; Photography; Theatre Arts.
Summer School: Courses—Ceramics; Drawing; Painting.

LAKE FOREST COLLEGE, Department of Art, Sheridan Rd, 60045. Tel: 312-234-3100, exten 324. *Chmn Dept* Alex F Mitchell, MA; *Prof* Franz Schulze, MFA; *Prof* Michael Croydon, ARCA; *Instr* Laura McKeon, MA; *Lectr* Ramona Mitchell, Staatsexamen; *Lectr* Robert Orr, BA.
Estab 1857; pvt; D&E; ent req HS dipl, SAT, CEEB or ACT; degree BA 4 yrs; schol; SC 8, LC 21; enrl in sch D 1050, maj 38.
Tuition: Res—Undergrad $5635 per yr, $3484/$2165 per sem; Nonres—Undergrad $4035 per yr, $2522/$1515 per sem; $492 per course; campus res room & board $1520 per yr, $1715 with fees.
Courses: Aesthetics; Architecture; Art Education; Art History; Drawing; Film; Graphic Arts; History of Art & Archaeology; Painting; Photography; Sculpture; Teacher Training.
Summer School: *Chmn* Alex F Mitchell. Courses—Photography.

MACOMB

WESTERN ILLINOIS UNIVERSITY, Department of Art, 61455. Tel: 309-298-1549. *Chmn Dept* Neil A Chassman, MFA; vis artists in various media.
Estab 1900, dept estab 1968; pub; D&E; ent req HS dipl; degrees BA 4 yrs, MA 2 yrs; schol SC 40, LC 30, GC 50; enrl maj 250.
Tuition: Res—Undergrad $227.25 per quarter term, grad $237.25 per quarter term; Nonres—Undergrad $567.25 per quarter term, grad $597.25 per quarter term; $8 per quarter hr over 18 res; $24 per quarter hr over 18 nonres; campus res room & board.
Courses: Advertising Design; ‡Art Education; Art History; ‡Ceramics; ‡Commercial Art; Conceptual Art; Costume Design & Construction; Drafting; ‡Drawing; Fashion Arts; Goldsmithing; ‡Graphic Design; ‡Handicrafts (weaving, metalworking); Illustration; Interior Design; ‡Jewelry; ‡Painting; ‡Printmaking; ‡Sculpture; Stage Design; Teacher Training; Theatre Arts.
Summer School: *Dir* R Law, EdD. High School Summer Arts Program.

MOLINE

BLACK HAWK COLLEGE, Art Department, 6600 34th Ave, 61265. Tel: 309-796-1311, exten 232. *Chmn Dept* Joseph F Ramsauer, MFA; *Asst Prof* Philip Johnson, MS; *Asst Prof* William Hannah; *Assoc Prof* Jan Rorem, MFA.
Estab 1962; pub; D&E; ent req HS dipl; degree AA 2 yrs; SC 15, LC 3; enrl D 500, E 150, nonmaj 450, maj 200.
Tuition: Res—Undergrad $16 hourly; Nonres—Undergrad $60 hourly; outside dist res undergrad $38 hourly; no campus res.
Courses: Advertising Design; Art History; Calligraphy; Ceramics; Drawing; Film; Graphic Design; Handicrafts; Jewelry; Lettering; Painting; Photography; Printmaking; Sculpture.

Summer School: Chmn Joseph E Ramsauer. Enrl 20; tui $48 for term of 6 wks beginning June 5. Courses—Ceramics, beginning and advanced.

MONMOUTH

MONMOUTH COLLEGE,* Department of Art, Art Center, N Ninth St, 61462. Tel: 309-457-2341. *Head Dept* Harlow B Blum; Instrs FT 2, PT 2.
Estab 1930; pvt; D; ent req 15 units incl English, history, social science, foreign language, mathematics & science, SAT or ACT tests; degree BA; schol, grants; SC 16, LC 4.
Courses: Advanced Special Topics; Contemporary Art; Drawing; Filmmaking; Independent Study; Introduction to History of Art Sequence; Introductory Art Workshop; Painting; Photography; Printmaking; Sculpture; Secondary Art Methods; Seminar in Oriental Art; Senior Art Seminar; Studio A, B & C.
Summer School: Registr Dr Milton Bowman. Courses—Beginning Drawing; Beginning Printmaking.

NORMAL

ILLINOIS STATE UNIVERSITY, Center for the Visual Arts, Art Department, 61761. Tel: 309-438-5621. *Chmn Art Dept* Fred V Mills, EdD; Instrs FT 50; vis profs—6 different ones each yr, painting, fall & spring.
Estab 1857; pub; D&E; ent req HS dipl; degrees BA and BS 4 yrs, BFA 5 yrs, MA, MS, MFA, EdD; schol; SC 50, LC 35, GC 40; enrl D 5000, E 300, nonmaj 1972, maj 3076, grad 452.
Tuition: Res—undergrad & grad $602 per yr, $301 per sem, $18 per hr; Nonres—undergrad $1264 per yr, $632 per sem, $45 per hr, grad $1064 per yr, $532 per sem.
Courses: ‡Advertising Design; ‡Art Education; ‡Art History; ‡Ceramics; Commercial Art; Conceptual Art; Constructions; Display; ‡Drawing; Film; ‡Goldsmithing; ‡Graphic Arts; ‡Graphic Design; ‡History of Art & Archaeology; Illustration; ‡Jewelry; Lettering; Mixed Media; Museum Staff Training; Occupational Therapy; ‡Painting; ‡Photography; ‡Printmaking; ‡Sculpture; ‡Silversmithing; ‡Teacher Training; ‡Textile Design.
Summer School: Tui res $149.75, nonres $266.25 for term of 8 wks beginning June 20.

PEORIA

BRADLEY UNIVERSITY,* Layton School of Art, 61606. Tel: 309-676-7611, exten 258, 385, 285. *Acting Dir* James A Hansen; Instrs FT 10.
Pvt; ent req HS grad; degrees AB, BS, BFA 4 yrs; MA, MFA; schol; enrl maj 116, others 400.
Tuition: $1375 per sem.
Courses: Art History; Art Metal; Ceramics; Drawing; Film; Graphic Design; Jewelry; Painting; Photography; Printmaking; Sculpture.

QUINCY

QUINCY COLLEGE, Department of Art, 62301. Tel: 217-222-8020. *Chmn* Rev Thomas Brown; Instrs FT 3.
Estab 1860, dept estab 1953; ent req HS grad ACT or SAT ent exam; degrees BA, BS, BFA 4 yrs; SC 21, LC 13; enrl maj 35, total enrl D 775, E 150.
Tuition: $1300 per sem; campus res $265-$330 per sem.
Courses: Aesthetics; Ancient & Mediaeval Art; Art Seminar; Ceramics; Commercial Art; Contemporary Art Seminar; Drawing; Film Making; Fundamentals (Two-Dimensional & Three-Dimensional); Modern Art; Non-Western Art; Painting (Oil & Mixed Media); Photography; Printmaking; Renaissance & Baroque Art; Sculpture; Special Problems; Watercolors; Weaving.
Seminar in Europe (Summer): Optional Junior Year Abroad.
Summer School: Dir in Art Rev Thomas Brown. Tui $60 per sem hr for 8 wks beginning June 5 or 4 wks beginning June 5 or July 3.

RIVER GROVE

TRITON COLLEGE,* School of University Transfer Studies, 2000 Fifth Ave, 60171. Tel: 312-456-0300, exten 467. Instrs FT 5, PT 6
Estab 1965; pub; D&E; ent req HS dipl, some adult students are admitted without HS dipl but with test scores indicating promise; degree AA 2 yrs; SC 17, LC 3; enrl D 650, E 150, Maj 138, adults and non-cr courses.
Tuition: No campus res.
Courses: Advertising Design; Art Education; Ceramics; Commercial Art; Drawing; Experimental Design; Graphic Arts; Graphic Design; History of Art & Archaeology; Illustration; Lettering; Painting; Printmaking; Recreational Arts & Crafts; Sculpture; Theatre Arts.

Adult Hobby Classes: Enrl 550; tui $11 per hr. Courses—Continuing Education Classes; Drawing; Painting; Ceramics; Theatre Arts; Jewelry; Crafts; Sculpture; Candle Making; Stained Glass; Quilting; Plastics.
Summer School: Term of 8 wks beginning June. Courses—Most of above courses are offered.

ROCK ISLAND

AUGUSTANA COLLEGE,* Art Department, 61201. Tel: 309-794-7000. *Chmn Dept* Alvin Ben Jasper; Instrs FT 3, PT 5.
Estab 1860; den; D&E; ent req HS grad plus exam; 4 yr degree; schol, fel; SC 8, LC 9, LabC 3; enrl 2000.
Tuition: $870 per quarter.
Courses: Art History; Ceramics; Crafts; Design; Drawing; Elementary School Art Methods; Fabric Introduction to Visual Arts; Jewelry; Life Drawing; Painting; Photography; Printmaking; Sculpture; Secondary School Art Methods.
Children's Classes: Sat.

ROCKFORD

ROCK VALLEY COLLEGE, Department of Art, 3301 N Mulford Rd, 61101. Tel: 815-226-3721. *Chmn* R David Gustafson, MS; *Teacher* Suzanne Kaufman, MA; *Teacher* Lester Salberg, MFA; Faculty FT 2, PT 1.
Estab 1964, dept estab 1965; pub; D&E; open enrollment; degrees AA, AS and AAS 2 yrs; SC 10, LC 4; enrl D 158, nonmaj 70, maj 27.
Tuition: $15 per cr hr; no campus res.
Courses: Aesthetics; Art Education; Art History; Drawing; Painting; Printmaking.
Adult Hobby Classes: Enrl 40; tui $16-$19 per course. Courses—Painting; Drawing; Ceramics; Weaving.
Summer School: Enrl 27; tui $15 per cr hr for term of 8 wks beginning June 6. Courses—Drawing; Design; Painting.

ROCKFORD COLLEGE, Department of Fine Arts, Clark Arts Center, 5050 E State St, 61101. Tel: 815-226-4000. *Prof Art & Chmn Dept Fine Arts* Philip Dedrick, MA; *Prof & Dir Gallery* Hon Ching Lee, MFA; *Prof* Robert McCauley, MFA; *Prof* Andrew Langoussis, MFA; *Prof* Judith Moonelio, MFA.
Estab 1847, dept estab 1848; pvt; D&E; ent req HS dipl, SAT or ACT; degrees BA, BFA and BS 4 yrs, MAT and MLS 2 yrs; schol; SC 20, LC 3-4; enrl D 600, E 600, nonmaj 24, maj 16.
Tuition: $1500 per sem; campus res room & board $1310 yr.
Courses: Aesthetics; ‡Art History; ‡Ceramics; Costume Design & Construction; ‡Drawing; Graphic Arts; Handicrafts (weaving); ‡History of Art & Archaeology; Painting; Papermaking; Printmaking; ‡Sculpture; Stage Design; Teacher Training; Textile Design.
Summer School: Dir Dr Curtis Moore. Tui $42 per cr hr. Courses—Fine Arts (Studio); Art History; Stage Design.

SPRINGFIELD

SPRINGFIELD COLLEGE IN ILLINOIS, Department of Art, 1500 N Fifth, 62702. Tel: 217-525-1420. *Head Dept* Regina Marie-Fronmüller, MA; *Primary Art Faculty* Marian Buck Hoopes, BA and John Seiz, MA.
Estab 1929, dept estab 1968; pvt; D&E; ent req HS dipl, ACT; degree AA 2 yrs; SC 12, LC 4; enrl D 27, E 6, nonmaj 11, maj 16.
Tuition: Res—Undergrad $1600 per yr, $800 per sem; Nonres—Undergrad $1950 per yr, $1150 per sem; private room $500 per sem.
Courses: Art History; Ceramics; Drawing; Life Drawing; Mixed Media; Painting; Photography; Printmaking; Sculpture; Two and Three-Dimensional Design; Weaving.
Adult Hobby Classes: Subjects—Pottery and Weaving.
Children's Classes: Enrl 20; tui $30 for 2 wks in summer. Courses—Art for Children 6-9 yrs; 10-14 yrs.
Summer School: Dir Regina Marie Fronmüller. Term of 6 wks beginning May 30 & July 5. Courses—Photography; Photographic Serigraphy.

SUGAR GROVE

WAUBONSEE COMMUNITY COLLEGE, Creative Arts Division, 60554. Tel: 312-466-4811, exten 324. *Chairperson* Carol J Viola, Cert of Advanced Standing; *Primary Art Faculty* Stuart Sewell, Cert of Advanced Standing, Joseph Hernandez, MFA and Charles Juister, MA.
Estab 1967; pub; D&E; ent req HS dipl, open door policy for adults without HS dipl; degrees AA, AS and AAS 2 yrs; schol; SC 8, LC 3; enrl D approx 275, E approx 200, maj 25.
Tuition: $13 per sem hr; no campus res.
Courses: Art Education; Art History; Ceramics; Drawing; Jewelry; Painting; Teacher Training ; Theatre Arts; Video.
Adult Hobby Classes: Enrl 175; tui $13 per sem hr. Courses—Drawing; Painting; Jewelry; Ceramics; Stained Glass.

Summer School: Asst Dean Instrs Carol J Viola. Tui $13 for term of 8 wks beginning June 6. Courses—Many of above.

WHEATON

WHEATON COLLEGE,* Department of Art, 501 E Seminary, 60187. Tel: 312-682-5050. *Chmn Dept* Miriam Hunter; Instrs FT 4, PT 2.
Estab 1861; pvt; D&E; ent req HS dipl; degree BA 4 yrs; schol; SC 20, LC 5; total enrl 2378, maj 50.
Tuition: $922 per quarter; campus res $262 per quarter.
Courses: Advertising Design; Aesthetics; Art Education; Ceramics; Drawing; Graphic Arts; Graphic Design; History of Art & Archaeology; Painting; Photography; Sculpture; Teacher Training.

WINNETKA

NORTH SHORE ART LEAGUE,* 620 Lincoln, 60093. Tel: 312-446-2870. *Pres* Abby Block; Instrs PT 25.
Estab 1924; pvt; D&E; no ent req; no degrees; schol to Chicago Art Inst grad; SC 28; enrl D 280, E 75.
Tuition: 16 wks, 3 hr a session; no campus res.
Courses: Critique; Drawing; Graphic Arts; Graphic Design; Handicrafts; Jewelry; Painting; Photography; Pottery; Sculpture; Stitchery; Woodcut.

INDIANA

ANDERSON

ANDERSON COLLEGE, Art Department, 1100 E Fifth & College, 46011. Tel: 317-644-0951, exten 458. *Chmn* Raymond A Freer, MFA; *Prof* Donald Weisflog, MFA; *Prof* Paul Palnik, MFA; Faculty PT 5.
Estab 1928; pvt; D&E; ent req HS dipl, ent exam plus recommendation; degrees BA 4 yr; schol; SC 30; LC 3; enrl nonmaj 15, maj 60.
Tuition: $3720 yr, $1860 per sem; campus res room $500 yr.
Courses: Advertising Design; Art Education; Art History; Ceramics; Commercial Art; Drawing; Graphic Arts; Graphic Design; History of Art & Archaeology; Illustration; Jewelry; Lettering; Museum Staff Training; Painting; Photography; Printmaking; Sculpture; Stage Design; Teacher Training.
Summer School: Dir Robert Smith, Tui $87 per cr hr.

BLOOMINGTON

INDIANA UNIVERSITY, BLOOMINGTON,* Department of Fine Arts, 47401. Tel: 812-337-7766. *Chmn* Thomas F Coleman; Instrs FT 35, PT 58.
Estab 1911; pub; D ent req admis to the Univ; degrees AB; BFA, BS 4 yrs, MA, MFA, MAT, PhD; schol; SC 55, LC 100, GC 110; enrl maj undergrad 430, grad 135 (65 Art History, 70 Studio), others 5600.
Tuition: Res—$27 per cr hr; Nonres—$66 per cr hr; campus res.
Courses: Ceramics; Drawing; Graphic Design; History of Art; Jewelry & Silversmithing; Painting; Photography; Printmaking; Printed Textiles; Sculpture; Woven Textiles; Teacher Training (with Sch of Educ).
Summer School: Tui res $27 per cr hr; Nonres $66 per cr hr.

EVANSVILLE

INDIANA STATE UNIVERSITY, EVANSVILLE,* Art Department, 8600 University Blvd, 47712. Tel: 812-426-1251. *Head Dept* Dr Blevins; Instrs FT 5, PT 1.
Estab 1969; pub; D&E; ent req HS dipl; degrees BS (Art Educ), BA (Art) 4 yrs; schol; SC 27, LC 4; enrl D 150, E 30, maj 90.
Courses: Aesthetics; Art Education; Ceramics; Commercial Art; Drafting; Drawing; Furniture Design; History of Art & Archaeology; Jewelry; Painting; Photography; Sculpture; Stained Glass; Teacher Training.
Adult Hobby Classes: Enrl 25. Courses—Silkscreen.

UNIVERSITY OF EVANSVILLE, Art Department, PO Box 329, 47702. Tel: 812-479-2043. *Prof Art & Chmn Dept* Leslie Miley, Jr, MFA; *Assoc Prof* Nanene Engle, MAT; *Assoc Prof* Howard Oagley, MA; *Asst Prof* William Richmond, MFA; *Asst Prof* Carolyn Roth, MFA; *Asst Prof* Paul McDowell, MFA.
Estab 1854; pvt; D&E; ent req HS dipl; degrees BA (Educ), BS (Art), BFA 4 yrs, MA 1 yr; school; SC 22, LC 11, GC 11, enrl D 800, E 400, maj 72, grad 21.
Tuition: Campus res.
Courses: Aesthetics; Art Education; Art History; Ceramics; Drawing; History of Art & Archaeology; Jewelry; Lettering; Painting; Printmaking; Sculpture; Teacher Training.

FORT WAYNE

INDIANA UNIVERSITY-PURDUE UNIVERSITY, Department of Fine Arts, 1026 W Berry St, 46804. Tel: 219-482-5201. *Prof Art & Chmn Dept Fine Arts* Russell L Oettel, MFA; *Prof* Stanley Lee, PhD; *Prof* Noel Dusendschon, MFA; *Assoc Prof* Clyde Burt; *Assoc Prof* Hector Garcia, MFA; *Assoc Prof* Donald Kruse, BS; *Assoc Prof* Leslie Motz, MFA.
Estab 1920, dept estab 1976; pub; D&E; degrees AB and BFA 4 yrs; schol; SC 96, LC 5; enrl nonmaj 85, maj 167, others 10.
Tuition: Res—$32 per cr hr; Nonres—$63 per cr hr; no campus res.
Courses: ‡Advertising Design; Art History; ‡Ceramics; ‡Commercial Art; ‡Drawing; Film; ‡Graphic Arts; Graphic Design; ‡History of Art & Archaeology; Illustration; ‡Jewelry; ‡Painting; Photography; ‡Printmaking; ‡Sculpture; Silversmithing; ‡Textile Design.
Children's Classes: Enrl 150; tui $30 for 10 wks. Courses—Ceramics; Painting; Sculpture.
Summer School: Chmn Russell L Oettel. Tui $32 per cr hr beginning May 22. Courses—Ceramics & Paintings.

SAINT FRANCIS COLLEGE, Art Department, 2701 Spring St, 46808. Tel: 219-432-3551, exten 236. *Head Art Dept* Maurice A Papier, MS, MA; *Asst Prof* Rick Cartwright, MFA; *Assoc Prof* Sufi Ahmad, MFA.
Estab 1890; den; D&E; ent req HS dipl, Class Rank in HS, SAT; degrees AA (Commercial Art) 2 yrs, BA and BS (Art or Art Educ) 4 yrs, MA (Art Educ) 1 yr; schol; SC 22, LC 6, GC 14; enrl D 90, maj 90.
Tuition: Undergrad $45 per sem hr, grad $52 per sem hr; campus res room & board $1500 yr.
Courses: Advertising Design; ‡Art Education; Art History; Calligraphy; Ceramics; ‡Commercial Art; Display; Drawing; Fashion Arts; Graphic Arts; Graphic Design; Illustration; Interior Design; Jewelry; Lettering; Painting; Photography; Printmaking; Sculpture; ‡Teacher Training.
Children's Classes: Enrl 80; tui $30 per sem. Courses—Art.
Summer School: Term of 5 wks beginning June. Courses—Drawing; Painting; Ceramics; Sculpture; Art History; Weaving; Photography; Commercial Art.

FRANKLIN

FRANKLIN COLLEGE,* Art Department, 46131. Tel: 317-736-8441. *Chmn Dept* Luigi Crispino; Instrs FT 1, PT 1.
Estab 1834; den; D; ent req HS grad; degree BA 4 yrs; SC 9, LC 4; enrl 700.
Tuition: Incl room and board $3960 per yr.
Courses: Art Education; Basic Design; Ceramics; Drawing; Painting; Print Shop; Sculpture.

GOSHEN

GOSHEN COLLEGE, Art Department, 1600 S Main St, 46526. Tel: 219-533-3161, exten 354. *Prof Art & Chmn Dept* Marvin Bartel, EdD; *Prof* Abner Hershberger, MFA; *Asst Prof* Judy Wenig-Horswell, MFA.
Estab 1950; den; D&E; ent req HS dipl, top 50% of class; degrees AB with Art Major and AB with Art Major and Indiana Teaching Cert; schol; enrl D 145, E 25, nonmaj 60, maj 40.
Tuition: $2735 per yr, $1235 per trimester, $110 per hr; campus res room & board $1260 yr.
Courses: Aesthetics; Art Education; Art History; Ceramics; Drawing; Handicrafts (weaving); Jewelry; Painting; Photography; Printmaking; Sculpture; Teacher Training; Textile Design.
Children's Classes: Enrl 20; tui $28 per 10 sessions. Courses—Art; Drawing; Printmaking; and others.
Summer School: Acad Dean John Lapp. Tui $265 for term of 3½ weeks beginning end of Apr, ending in late July. New York Art Study; Florence, Italy Tour.

GREENCASTLE

DePAUW UNIVERSITY, Art Department, 46135. Tel: 317-653-9721, exten 451. *Chmn Art Dept* William Meehan, MA; *Prof* Ray H French, MFA; *Asst Prof* Robert D Kingsley, MFA; *Instr* David W Herrold, MFA.
Estab 1837; pvt; D&E; ent req HS dipl, schol standing upper half, SAT exam; degrees BA and BM 4 yrs, MA, MAT; schol; SC 18, LC 8, GC 9; enrl D 300, E 20, maj 50, grad 20.
Tuition: $3542 per yr, $1771 per sem; campus res room & board $795 per sem.
Courses: Advertising Design; Art Education; Art History; Ceramics; Commercial Art; Drawing; Illustration; Jewelry; Painting; Printmaking; Sculpture; Teacher Training.

HAMMOND

PURDUE UNIVERSITY, CALUMET CAMPUS, Department of Art, 46323. Tel: 219-844-0520, exten 422. *Head Dept Art* Edwin Cohen, PhD; *Primary Art Faculty* John Mohamed, MA; Andrew Smock, MA; Mary Geimen, MA and Barbara Meeker, MA.
Estab 1946; pub; D&E; ent req HS dipl; schol; SC 1-4, LC 1-2, GC 1.
Tuition: Res—Undergrad $23 per sem, grad $28 per sem; Nonres—Undergrad $43 per sem, grad $53 per sem; no campus res.
Courses: Art Education; Art History; Ceramics; Commercial Art; Drawing; Film; Industrial Design; Jewelry; Painting; Teacher Training; Theatre Arts; Video.

HANOVER

HANOVER COLLEGE, Department of Art, 47243. Tel: 812-866-2151.
Assoc Prof Art & Chmn Dept James W Shaffstall, MFA; *Asst Prof* John Z Thomas, MFA; *Assoc Prof* Robert Rosenthal, PhD; *Assoc Prof* Lee Schroeder, MS.
Estab 1827, dept estab 1967; pvt; D; ent req HS dipl; degrees BS and BA 4 yrs; schol; SC 16, LC 4; enrl D 960.
Tuition: $2315 per yr; campus res room & board $1220 per yr.
Courses: Advertising Design; Aesthetics; Art Education; Art History; Ceramics; Collage; Commercial Art; Constructions; Drawing; Film; Graphic Arts; Graphic Design; Jewelry; Painting; Photography; Printmaking; Sculpture; Stage Design; Teacher Training; Textile Design; Theatre Arts; Video.

INDIANAPOLIS

HERRON SCHOOL OF ART, INDIANA UNIVERSITY-PURDUE UNIVERSITY, INDIANAPOLIS, 1701 N Pennsylvania St, 46202. Tel: 317-923-3651. *Dean* Arthur Weber; *Chmn Design Prog* Henry Aguet, MFA; *Chmn Art Educ Prog* William Detmers, MAE; *Chmn Printmaking Prog* Robert Eagerton, BA; *Chmn Sculpture Prog* Gary Freeman, MFA; *Chmn Found Prog* Aaron Law, MFA; *Chmn Painting Prog* Richard Nickolson, MFA; *Chmn Art Hist Prog* Samuel Roberson, PhD.
Estab 1902; pub; ent req portfolio; degrees BFA and BAE 4 yrs, MAE 5 yrs; schol; SC 112, LC 16, GC 20; enrl D 314, nonmaj 300, 310, grad 16.
Tuition: Res—Undergrad $24 per cr hr, grad $55 per cr hr; Nonres—Undergrad $36 per cr hr, grad $82 per cr hr; no campus res.
Courses: Advertising Design; Art Education; Art History; Ceramics; Commercial Art; Constructions; Drawing; Graphic Arts; Graphic Design; Handicrafts (Furniture Design); History of Art & Archaeology; Illustration; Mixed Media; Painting; Photography; Printmaking; Sculpture; Teacher Training; Video.
Summer School: Enrl 151; tui $24 per cr hr for term of two 6 wks sessions. Courses—Drawing; Painting; Three-Dimensional Design; Art Education; Ceramics; Art History; Photography; Sculpture.

INDIANA CENTRAL UNIVERSITY, Fine Arts Department, 1400 E Hanna Ave, 46227. Tel: 317-788-3253. *Prof Art & Chmn Dept Fine Arts* Gerald G Boyce, MFA; *Asst Prof* Dee Schaad, MFA; *Asst Prof* Earl Snellenberger, MFA.
Estab 1902; den; D&E; ent req HS dipl, SAT, upper half of HS class; degrees BA and BS 4 yrs; schol; SC 24, LC 7, GC 7; enrl D 360, E 150, maj 36, grad 60.
Tuition: Commuter $2230 per yr; campus res room & board $3500 per yr.
Courses: Aesthetics; Architecture; ‡Art Education; Art History; Ceramics; Commercial Art; Drawing; Graphic Arts; History of Art & Archaeology; Jewelry; Lettering; Painting; Photography; Printmaking; Sculpture; Silversmithing; Textile Design.

MARIAN COLLEGE, Art Department, 3200 Cold Springs Rd, 46222. Tel: 317-924-3291, exten 244. *Instr Art & Coordr* Mary de Paul Schweitzer, MEd; *Lectr* Peggy Lovett, MA; *Lectr* Karen Wolf, MA; *Lectr* Ania Beczkeiwicz, MA; *Lectr* Patric O'Keeffe; *Lectr* Dolorita Carper, MEd.
Estab 1936; den; D&E; ent req HS dipl, SAT or ACTP; degrees AA 2 yrs; BA and BS 4 yrs; schol; SC 22, LC 4; enrl dept D 30, E 6, nonmaj 11, maj 30.
Tuition: $965 per sem, $80 per sem hr; campus res room & board $1140 yr.
Courses: Aesthetics; Art Education; Art History; Art Therapy; Audiovisual; Ceramics; Drawing; Handicrafts (Arts & Crafts); Interior Design; Museum Staff Training; Painting; Printmaking; Sculpture; Stage Design; Teacher Training; Theatre Arts.
Adult Hobby Classes: Enrl 15; tui $38 per sem hr. Courses—Arts & Crafts.

MUNCIE

BALL STATE UNIVERSITY, Art Department, 2000 University Ave, 47306. Tel: 317-285-5638. *Head Art Dept* Ned H Griner, DEd; Faculty FT 26.
Estab 1918; pub; D&E; ent req HS dipl; degrees BS 4 yrs, MA 1 yr, DEd 4 yrs grad work minimum; schol; SC 28, LC 21, GC 40; enrl nonmaj 633, maj 600, grad 25.
Tuition: Res—Undergrad & grad $240 per quarter; Nonres—Undergrad & grad $480 per quarter; campus res room & board.
Courses: Advertising Design; Aesthetics; ‡Art Education; Art History; ‡Ceramics; Drawing; Film; Graphic Arts; ‡Graphic Design; History of Art & Archaeology; ‡Interior Design; ‡Jewelry; Lettering; ‡Painting; ‡Photography; ‡Printmaking; ‡Sculpture; ‡Silversmithing; ‡Teacher Training.
Adult Hobby Classes: Enrl 20; tui $35 per person. Courses—Painting.
Children's Classes: Enrl 75; tui $5 per child. Courses—General Art Activities.
Summer School: Enrl 7000; tui $140 for term of 5 wks beginning June. Courses—Art Education; Art History; Studio.

NEW ALBANY

INDIANA UNIVERSITY SOUTHEAST, Fine Arts Department, Grantline Rd, 47150. Tel: 812-945-2731, exten 343. *Prof Art & Chmn Dept Fine Arts* Jonas A Howard, MA; *Asst Prof* John R Guenthler, MFA; *Asst Prof* Susan M Matthias, MFA.
Estab 1945, dept estab 1966; pub; D&E; ent req HS dipl; degree BA 4 yrs; SC 25, LC 2; enrl D 130, E 35, nonmaj 85, maj 45.
Tuition: Res—Undergrad $21 per hr, grad $26 per hr; Nonres—Undergrad $42 per hr, grad $52 per hr; no campus res.
Courses: Art Education; Art History; Ceramics; Drawing; Painting; Printmaking; Teacher Training; Textile Design; Theatre Arts.
Adult Hobby Classes: Enrl 35; tui $25 per sem. Courses—Watercolor; Crafts.
Summer School: Enrl 50; Term of 2 sessions of 6 wks beginning May 15, July 5. Courses—Same as above.

NORTH MANCHESTER

MANCHESTER COLLEGE, Art Department, College Ave, 46962. Tel: 219-982-2141, exten 276. *Prof & Head Dept* James R C Adams, MFA; *Prof* Max I Allen, MFA; *Asst Prof* Stephen Batzka, BA.
Estab 1889; den; D&E; ent req HS dipl; degrees AA 2 yrs, BA and BS 4 yrs; schol; SC 15, LC 3; enrl D 45, maj 15.
Tuition: $2370 per yr; campus res room & board $1220 per yr.
Courses: Advertising Design; Art Education; Art History; Ceramics; Drawing; Film; Graphic Arts; Handicrafts (weaving); History of Art & Archaeology; Lettering; Mixed Media; Museum Staff Training; Painting; Photography; Printmaking; Sculpture; Teacher Training; Textile Design.

NOTRE DAME

ST MARY'S COLLEGE,* Department of Art, 46556. Tel: 219-284-4074. Instrs FT 8, PT 1.
Estab 1855; pvt; D&E; W; ent req CEEB, standing, recommendations, others; degrees BA and BFA 3½-5 yrs; schol, fel; SC 21, LC 10; enrl maj 117, others 418.
Tuition: $2850 per yr.
Courses: Art Education; Ceramics; Design; Drawing; Jewelry; Painting; Photo Silkscreen; Photography; Printmaking; Sculpture; Weaving.
Rome Program: Both Studio and Lecture: Courses—Art History; Design; Drawing.

UNIVERSITY OF NOTRE DAME,* Department of Art, 46556. Tel: 219-283-7602. *Chmn* Rev James F Flanigan; Instrs FT 9, PT 2.
Estab 1855; pvt; D; ent req upper third HS class, ent exam; degrees AB, BFA 4 yrs, MA, MFA; fel; SC 38, LC 8, GC 20; enrl maj 100.
Tuition: $3300 per yr; campus res.
Courses: Advertising Design; Art History; Ceramic Sculpture; Drawing; Fibre; Industrial Design; Painting; Photography; Pottery; Printmaking; Sculpture; Welding Sculpture.
Summer School: Chmn Rev James F Flanigan. Enrl 50; 15 courses in Studio and Art History, chiefly for high school art teachers working on advanced degrees.

OAKLAND CITY

OAKLAND CITY COLLEGE,* Division of Fine Arts, 47660. Tel: 812-749-4781, exten 53. *Chmn* Dr Marie M McCord; Instrs FT 4, PT 1.
Estab 1961; den; D&E; ent req HS dipl, SAT; degrees AA 2 yrs, BA and BS 4 yrs; schol; SC 10, LC 5; enrl maj 35.
Courses: Advertising Design; Art Education; Ceramics; Drawing; History of Art & Archaeology; Lettering; Macrame; Painting; Pottery; Sculpture; Teacher Training; Weaving.

Summer School: Two 5 wk terms; 14 art maj. Courses—Painting; Pottery; plus others.

RICHMOND

EARLHAM COLLEGE, Art Department, National Rd W, 47374. Tel: 317-962-6561, exten 410. *Chmn Art Dept* Bernard L Derr, PhD; *Asst Prof* Peter Barnett, PhD; *Prof* Garrett Boone, MFA; *Artist in-Residence* Mitsuo Kakutani.
Estab 1847; den; D; ent req HS dipl; degree BA 4 yrs; schol; SC 10, LC 7; enrl maj 10.
Tuition: $3350 per yr, $395 per course; campus res room & board $1162.
Courses: Aesthetics; Art History; Ceramics; Drawing; Film; Graphic Arts; Graphic Design; Lettering; Mixed Media; Museum Staff Training; Painting; Photography; Printmaking; Sculpture; Stage Design; Theatre Arts; Video.

SAINT MARY-OF-THE-WOODS

SAINT MARY-OF-THE-WOODS COLLEGE, Art Department, 47876. Tel: 812-535-4141.
Estab 1840; den; D; ent req HS dipl, SAT or ACT; degrees AS 2 yrs, BA and BS 4 yrs; schol; SC 15, LC4; enrl maj 15.
Tuition: $2450 per yr, $1225 per sem, $100 per hr; campus res room & board $1370.
Courses: ‡Art Education; Art History; Ceramics; Drawing; Intermedia; Painting; Photography; Printmaking; Teacher Training.

SAINT MEINRAD

SAINT MEINRAD COLLEGE,* Department of Art, 47577. Tel: 812-357-6575. *Head Dept* Donald Walpole; Instrs PT 4.
Estab 1854; pvt; D&E; admission and registration in the sch; SC 3, LC 3; enrl D 36, E 30.
Courses: Advertising Design; Aesthetics; Ceramics; Drawing; Graphic Design; History of Art & Archaeology; Painting; Theatre Arts.
Adult Hobby Classes: Enrl 30. Courses—Painting; Ceramics.

SOUTH BEND

INDIANA UNIVERSITY AT SOUTH BEND, Fine Arts Department, Northside at Greenlawn Blvd, 46615. Tel: 219-237-4278. *Assoc Prof Art & Acting Chmn Fine Arts Dept* Harold Zisla, AM; *Assoc Prof* Anthony Droege, MFA; *Assoc Prof* Harold Langland, MFA; *Assoc Prof* Jack Brewer, PhD; *Asst Prof* Alan Larkin, MFA.
Estab 1964; pub; D; ent req HS dipl; degree BA(Fine Arts) 4 yrs; SC 16, LC 4; enrl D 450, nonmaj 300, maj 150.
Tuition: No campus res.
Courses: Art History; Drawing; Graphic Arts; Graphic Design; Painting; Printmaking; Sculpture; Teacher Training.
Summer School: Two sessions of 6 wks duration. Courses—Painting; Drawing; Sculpture.

TERRE HAUTE

INDIANA STATE UNIVERSITY, TERRE HAUTE, Art Department, 47809. Tel: 812-232-6311, exten 2222. *Acting Chairperson Dept* James E Garthwaite, EdD; Instrs FT 19, PT 1.
Estab 1870; pub; D&E; ent req HS dipl; degrees BS and BFA 4 yrs; MS, MA and MFA 2 yrs; SC 67, LC 47, GC 65; enrl D 2350, E 250, maj 275, grad 30.
Tuition: Res—Undergrad & grad $26.50 per cr hr; Nonres—Undergrad & grad $54.50 per cr hr; campus res room & board $680.
Courses: Art Education; Art History; Ceramics; Commercial Art; Drawing; Goldsmithing; Graphic Design; Jewelry; Mixed Media; Painting; Photography; Printmaking; Sculpture; Silversmithing; Woodworking & Furniture Design.
Summer School: Dir Dr Harriett Darrow. Tui res $27.50, nonres $55.50 for term of two 5 wks beginning June. Courses—Same as above.

UPLAND

TAYLOR UNIVERSITY, Art Department, 46989. Tel: 317-998-2751, exten 322. *Chmn Art Dept* Ray E Bullock, EdD; *Prof* Jack D Patton, MA; *Prof* Craig Moore, MFA.
Estab 1846, dept estab 1968; pvt; D&E; ent req HS dipl, SAT, Recommendations; degrees BA and BS 4 yrs; SC 12, LC 7; enrl D 175, E 16, nonmaj 125, maj 50.
Tuition: Res—$2700 per yr; Nonres—$4000 per yr; campus res room & board $1300 per yr.
Courses: Advertising Design; Aesthetics; ‡Art Education; Art History; Calligraphy; Ceramics; Collage; Drawing; Graphic Arts; Jewelry; Lettering; Mixed Media; Painting; Photography; Printmaking; Puppetry; Sculpture; Silversmithing; Stage Design; ‡Teacher Training.

Children's Classes: Enrl 40; tui free. Courses—Drawing; Painting; Pottery; Design; Jewelry.
Summer School: Dir Dr Ray E Bullock. Courses—Art for Elementary Teachers; Photography; Survey of Fine Arts.

VINCENNES

VINCENNES UNIVERSITY, Art Department, 1002 N First St, 47591. Tel: 812-882-3350. *Asst Prof Art & Art Coordr* James G Gorman, MFA; *Asst Prof* Amy Delap Jendrzejewski, MFA; *Asst Prof* Bernard Vinzani, MFA.
Estab 1801; pub; D&E; ent req HS dipl or GED; degrees AA and AS 2 yrs; schol; SC 17, LC 4; enrl maj 32.
Tuition: Res—Undergrad $650 per yr, $325 per sem, $21 per hr; Nonres—Undergrad $1150 per yr, $575 per sem, $37 per hr; campus res room & board $1180 per yr.
Courses: Advertising Design; Art History; Ceramics; Commercial Art; Drawing; Graphic Arts; Handicrafts (general exposure crafts class); Lettering; Painting; Photography; Printmaking; Sculpture; Textile Design.
Summer School: Dir James G Gorman. Enrl 15-20; tui $21 per hr for term of 5 wks beginning May 30 and July 5. Courses—Drawing; Painting; Photography; Ceramics; Printmaking.

WEST LAFAYETTE

PURDUE UNIVERSITY, LAFAYETTE,* School of Humanities, Social Science and Education, Department of Creative Arts, Art & Design Section, 47907. Tel: 317-494-8702. *Head Dept* R G Beelke; *Chmn Dept* W A McGill; Instrs FT 33.
Estab 1925; pub; degrees BA 4 yrs, MA; schol; SC 50, LC 22, GC 22, some E classes; enrl maj 394, others 1746.
Tuition: Nonres—$950; campus res $1520.
Courses: Art History; Ceramics; Film & Video; Graphics; Industrial Design; Interior Design; Jewelry; Painting; Photography; Sculpture; Teacher Education; Visual Design; Weaving.

WINONA LAKE

GRACE COLLEGE, Department of Art, 46590. Tel: 219-267-8191, exten 156. *Assoc Prof Art & Head Dept* Jean L Coverstone, MA; *Asst Prof* Art Davis, MA.
Estab 1952, dept estab 1971; pvt; D&E; ent req HS dipl, SAT; degrees 4 yr Art Major and 4 yr Art Education Major, and 2 yr cert; SC 12, LC 3; enrl maj 30, nonmaj 80.
Tuition: $65 per hr; campus res room & board.
Courses: Art Education; Art History; Ceramics; Drawing; Film; Graphic Design; Handicrafts (survey); Painting; Photography; Printmaking; Sculpture; Teacher Training.
Adult Hobby Classes: Enrl 12; tui $65 per hr. Courses—Survey of Crafts.
Summer School: Dir Jean L Coverstone. Tui $65 per hr for term of 4 wks. Courses—Drawing II; Photography.

IOWA

AMES

IOWA STATE UNIVERSITY
—College of Home Economics
Department of Applied Art, 215 Mackay Hall, 50011. Tel: 515-294-6724. *Chmn Dept* Jon Sontag, PhD; *Coordr Drawing-Painting* Elizabeth Miller, MFA; *Coordr Interior Design* Janet Navin, MA; *Coordr Crafts* Terry Tow, MA; *Coordr Advertising Design* Ronald Fenimore, MA; *Coordr Art Educ* Dennis Dake, MA; *Coordr Design* Nancy Polster, MA.
Estab 1858, dept estab 1920; pub; D&E; ent req HS dipl; degree BA(Advert Design, Art Educ, Craft Design & Interior Design); SC 45, LC 15, GC 6; enrl nonmaj 1500, majr 815, grad 20.
Tuition: Res—Undergrad $735 per yr, $245 per quarter, grad $858 per yr, $286 per quarter; Nonres—Undergrad $1701 per yr, $567 per quarter, grad $1818 per yr, $606 per quarter; campus res room and board.
Courses: ‡Advertising Desing; ‡Art Education; Art History; Calligraphy; Ceramics; Drawing; Fashion Arts; Goldsmithing; Graphic Design; Handicrafts (wood design, weaving); Illustration; ‡Interior Design; Jewelry; Painting; Printmaking; Sculpture; Silversmithing; Teacher Training; Textile Design.
Summer School: Dir Dr Jon Sontag. Tui $123 for term of 5 wks beginning June 7. Courses—Drawing; Painting; Ceramics; Interior Design; Calligraphy; Advertising Design; Art Education.
—College of Engineering
Department of Architecture.* Tel: *Head Dept* Sanford R Greenfield.
Department of Landscape Architecture.* Tel: 515-294-5676. *Head Dept* Thomas A Barton; Instrs FT 10.

Estab 1929; pub; D; ent req HS dipl, upper half of class; degrees BS(Landscape Archit) 4 yrs, MLandscape Archit; assistantships; SC 13, LC 5, GC 10, SLC 6; enrl maj 122, grad 10, urban planning undergrad 65, grad 8.
Tuition: Res—$245 per quarter; Nonres—$567 per quarter; room and board $1185 per yr.
Courses: Landscape Architecture; Urban Planning.

BOONE

DES MOINES AREA COMMUNITY COLLEGE, Art Department, 1125 Hancock Dr, 50036. Tel: 515-432-7203. *Head Dept & Instr* Jo Myers, MA.
Estab 1927, dept estab 1970; pub; D&E; ent req HS dipl; degree AA 2 yrs; SC 3, LC 2; enrl D 100, E 60.
Tuition: Res—Undergrad $600 per yr, $150 per quarter, $15 per cr hr; Nonres—Undergrad $1200 per yr, $300 per quarter, $30 per cr hr; campus res room & Board.
Courses: Art History; Life Drawing; Painting; Stage Design; Teacher Training (Art in the Elem Schs); Theatre Arts.

CEDAR FALLS

UNIVERSITY OF NORTHERN IOWA, College of Humanities and Fine Arts, Department of Art, 50613. Tel; 319-273-2077. *Head Dept* Joseph M Ruffo, MFA; *Asst Prof* Diana Barrie, MFA; *Asst Prof* Allan Brookes, PhD; *Assoc Prof* Marjorie Campbell, MA; *Prof* David Delafield, EdD; *Asst Prof* Felipe Echeverria, MFA; *Asst Prof* Reed Estabrook, MFA; *Prof* Don Finegan, MFA; *Prof* Ken Gogel, MA; *Prof* Harry Guillaume, EdD; *Assoc Prof* Edwin Harris, MA; *Assoc Prof* Shirley Haupt, MFA; *Prof* Clifford Herrold, EdD; *Prof* Ken Lash, MA; *Prof* John Page, MFA.
Estab 1876, dept estab 1945; pub; D&E; ent req HS dipl, ACT; degrees BA and BFA 4 yrs, MA 1 yr; schol; SC 30, LC 10, GC 10; enrl D 350, E 30, nonmaj 150, maj 350, grad 15.
Tuition: Res—Undergrad $694 per yr, $347 per sem, grad $726 per yr, $363 per sem; Nonres—Undergrad $1320 per yr, $660 per sem, grad $1518 per yr, $740 per sem; campus res room & board $1020 per yr.
Courses: Art Education; Art History; Ceramics; Commercial Art; Drawing; Film; Graphic Arts; Graphic Design; History of Art & Archaeology; Illustration; Jewelry; Painting; Photography; Printmaking; Sculpture; Silversmithing; Teacher Training.
Summer School: *Head Dept* Joseph M Ruffo. Enrl 3538; tui $195 for term of 8 wks beginning June 5. Courses—same curriculum as acad yr but limited.

CEDAR RAPIDS

COE COLLEGE, Department of Art, 52402. Tel: 319-398-1669. *Chmn Dept* Charles Stroh, MFA; *Prof* Robert L Kocher, MA; *Asst Prof* Art Morrison, MFA; *Instr* John Beckelman, MFA; *Instr* David Goodwin, MFA; *Gallery Dir* Shirley Donaldson, BA.
Estab 1851; pvt; D&E; ent req HS dipl, SAT, ACT or Portfolio; degree BA 4 yrs; schol; SC 15, LC 8; enrl D 1200.
Tuition: Campus res room & board $4600 per yr.
Courses: Art Education; Art History; Ceramics; Drawing; Illustration; Painting; Photography; Printmaking; Sculpture; Teacher Training; Textile Design; Theatre Arts.
Summer School: *Chmn Dept* Charles Stroh. Enrl average 80; tui $220 per course for term of 5 wks beginning in June and mid-July. Courses—Ceramics; Photography; American Art History; Painting; Drawing.

KIRKWOOD COMMUNITY COLLEGE, Department of Fine Arts, 6301 Kirkwood Blvd SW, 52406. Tel: 319-398-5534. *Dept Head* Charles Traylor, MFA; *Primary Art Faculty* Ray Mullen, MFA, Doug Hall, MFA and John Puffer, MFA.
Estab 1966; pub; D&E; ent req HS dipl; degree AA 2 yrs; SC 18, LC 6; enrl D 150, E 50.
Tuition: $14 per cr hr; no campus res.
Courses: Art History; Ceramics; Drafting; Drawing; Fashion Arts; Graphic Arts; Lettering; Occupational Therapy; Painting; Photography; Printmaking; Sculpture.
Summer School: *Dir* Charles Traylor. Tui $14 per cr hr. Courses—Ceramics; Drawing; Painting; Art Appreciation.

MOUNT MERCY COLLEGE, Art Department, 1330 Elmhurst Dr NE, 52402. Tel: 319-363-8213, exten 256. *Assoc Prof Art & Chmn Dept* Charles Barth, MS; *Asst Prof* Jane Gilmor, MFA; *Asst Prof* Thomas Jackson, MFA.
Estab 1928, dept estab 1960; pvt; D&E; ent req HS dipl, ACT; degree BA 4 yrs; SC 20, LC 6; enrl D 150, E 35, nonmaj 150, maj 35.

Tuition: $2385 per yr, $1060 per sem, $195 per course; campus res room & board $810.
Courses: ‡Art Education; Art History; Drawing; Painting; Photography; Printmaking; Sculpture; Textile Design.
Summer School: *Dir* Robert Lesniak. Courses—Watercolor; Collage.

CENTERVILLE

INDIAN HILLS COMMUNITY COLLEGE, Department of Art, N First St, 52544. Tel: 515-856-2143, exten 27. *Head Dept Art* Richard H Dutton, MA.
Estab 1932, dept estab 1967; pub; D&E; ent req HS dipl or equal open door; degree AA 2 yrs; schol; SC 10; enrl D 70, E 30, nonmaj 50, maj 16.
Tuition: Res—$348 per yr; Nonres—$762 per yr; no campus res.
Courses: Art History; Commercial Art; Drawing; Graphic Design; Painting; Photography.
Adult Hobby Classes: Enrl 22; tui $38 for 12 wks. Courses—Painting.
Summer School: *Dir* Dick Sharp. Courses—Art Appreciation; Painting; Design; European Art Tours.

CLINTON

MOUNT SAINT CLARE COLLEGE, Art Department, 400 N Bluff, 52732. Tel: 319-242-4023. *Head Dept* Veronica Langner, MFA; *Primary Art Faculty* Joan Richeson, MA.
Estab 1928; den; D&E; ent req HS dipl; degree AA 2 yrs; schol; SC 5, LC 1; enrl nonmaj 65; maj 14.
Tuition: $600 per sem; campus res room & board $1300 per yr.
Courses: Art Appreciation; Basic Design; Calligraphy; Ceramics; Drawing; Painting.
Summer School: Courses—Painting; Calligraphy; Art Appreciation.

CRESTON

SOUTHWESTERN COMMUNITY COLLEGE, Art Department, 1501 W Townline Rd, 50801. Tel: 515-782-7081. *Dir Arts & Sci* Richard Engleson, MA; *Instr Art* P Terry Gieber, MA; *Instr Art* Mary Ellen Kimball, BA.
Estab 1966; pub; D&E; ent req HS dipl; degree AA 2 yrs; SC 6, LC 3; enrl in sch D 550, E 200, nonmaj 40, maj 15, others 15.
Tuition: Res—$220 per sem, $18.50 per cr hr; Nonres—$330 per sem, $27.50 per cr hr; no campus res.
Courses: Art Education; Art History; Ceramics; Design; Drawing; Painting; Teacher Training.
Adult Hobby Classes: Enrl 10-30; tui $30 per sem. Courses—All areas with sufficient interest.

DAVENPORT

MARYCREST COLLEGE,* Art Department, 1607 W 12th St, 52804. Tel: 319-326-9512. *Chmn* Clarice Eberdt; *Instrs* FT 3, PT 6.
Estab 1939; den; D&E; ent req HS dipl; degrees BA 3-4 yrs, MA; schol; SC 35, LC 15, GC 13; enrl D 446, E 129, maj 68, grad 56.
Courses: Advertising Design; Aesthetics; Art Education; Ceramics; Commercial Art; Costume Design & Construction; Drafting; Drawing; Fashion Arts; Graphic Arts; Graphic Design; History of Art & Archaeology; Illustration; Jewelry; Lettering; Museum Staff Training; Painting; Photography; Sculpture; Stage Design; Teacher Training; Theatre Arts.
Summer School: *Dir* Dr R Schwieso. Courses—Independent Study; Painting; Readings.

SAINT AMBROSE COLLEGE,* Art Department, 518 W Locust St, 52803. Tel: 319-324-1681, exten 344, 242, 243. *Chmn Dept* John Schmits; *Instrs* FT 4, PT 1.
Estab 1892; den; D&E; ent req HS dipl; degree BA 4 yrs; schol; SC 17, LC 12; enrl D 450, E 40, maj 55.
Tuition: $76 per sem hr; campus room $220 to $350 per sem, board $345 to $391 per sem.
Courses: Advertising Design; Art Education; Calligraphic Study; Ceramics; Commercial Art; Drafting; Drawing; Graphic Arts; Graphic Design; History of Art & Archaeology; Illustration; Lettering; Painting; Photography; Sculpture; Teacher Training.

DECORAH

LUTHER COLLEGE,* Art Department, 52101. Tel: 319-387-1110. *Acting Head Dept* Douglas Eckheart; *Instrs* FT 4, PT 3.
Estab 1861; den; D; ent req HS dipl or ent exam; degree BA 4 yrs; schol; SC 13, LC 5, enrl D 160.
Tuition: $3985 per yr.

Courses: Aesthetics; Art Education; Ceramics; Drawing; Graphic Arts; History of Art & Archaeology; Lettering; Painting; Stage Design; Teacher Training; Theatre Arts.
Summer School: Courses—Drawing; Painting.

DES MOINES

DRAKE UNIVERSITY, Art Department, 25th & University Ave, 50311. Tel: 515-271-2863. *Chairperson Dept* Condon Kuhl, MFA; *Prof* Jules Kirschenbaum; *Prof* Stanley Hess, MFA; *Prof* Lee Ferber, MFA; *Prof* Jotin Hicks, EdD; *Prof* Richard Black, MSAE; *Prof* William Darr, MFA; *Prof* Florence Kawa, MA; Instrs FT 19, PT 4.
Estab 1881; pvt; D&E; ent req 2 pt average in HS or previous col; degrees BFA 4 yrs, MFA; schol; SC 55, LC 15, GC 33; enrl D 275, maj 275, grad 15.
Tuition: $1715 per sem, $114 per cr hr; campus res room & board $1680 per yr.
Courses: ‡Advertising Design; Aesthetics; ‡Art Education; ‡Ceramics; ‡Commercial Art; Constructions; Costume Design & Construction; Creative Arts Therapy; ‡Drawing; Film; ‡Goldsmithing; ‡Graphic Arts; ‡Graphic Design; Handicrafts; History of Art & Archaeology; Illustration; ‡Interior Design; ‡Jewelry; Lettering; Mixed Media; ‡Painting; Photography; ‡Printmaking; Restoration & Conservation; ‡Sculpture; ‡Silversmithing; Stage Design; Teacher Training; Textile Design; ‡Theatre Arts; Video.
Summer School: Dir Donald Wallace. Courses—Painting; Drawing; Art History; Ceramics; Sculpture; Jewelry; Art Education.

DUBUQUE

CLARKE COLLEGE,* Department of Art, 1550 Clarke Dr, 52001. Tel: 319-588-6300. *Chmn* Joan Lingen; Instrs FT 4, PT.
Estab 1843; den (Catholic but all den accepted); D&E; W (men in art dept); ent req HS grad, 16 units and Col Ent Bd; degree BA(Art) 4 yrs; SC 15, LC 4; enrl maj 50, others 200.
Courses: Art History; Ceramics; Drawing & Painting; Jewelry; Lettering; Printmaking; Sculpture; Teacher Training.
Adult Continuing Education Program: D & E.
Summer School: Enrl art 50; three 3 wks sessions; address all inquiries to Registrar, Summer Session.

FOREST CITY

WALDORF COLLEGE,* Art Department, 50436. *Chmn Dept* John Nellermoe; Instrs FT 1, PT 1.
Estab 1903; den D; ent req HS dipl, ACT or SAT; degrees AA, AC and AAS 2 yrs; schol; SC 4; enrl D 80, maj 15.
Tuition: $1030 per yr; campus res $634.
Courses: Ceramics; Drafting; Drawing; History of Art; Painting; Woodcrafts.

FORT DODGE

IOWA CENTRAL COMMUNITY COLLEGE, Department of Art, 330 Ave M, 50501. *Assoc Prof Art* Robert J Halm, MFA; *Instr* Raymond R Atwood, MA.
Pub; D&E; ent req HS dipl; degree AA 2 yrs; SC 4, LC 2; enrl D 120, E 15, nonmaj 117, maj 18.
Tuition: Res—$220 per sem, $18.50 per hr; Nonres—$330 per sem, $27.75 per hr; campus res room & board $1210 per yr.
Courses: Art History; Collage; Drawing; Mixed Media; Painting; Sculpture.

GRINNELL

GRINNELL COLLEGE, Department of Art, 50112. Tel: 515-236-6181, exten 521. *Prof Art & Chmn Dept* William W Wolf III, PhD; *Prof* Richard Cervene, MFA; *Prof* A Richard Turner, PhD; *Prof* Louis G Zirkle, MFA; *Asst Prof* Merle Waller Zirkle, MFA; *Asst Prof* Robert H McKibbin, MFA.
Estab 1846, dept estab 1930; pvt; D; ent req HS dipl, SAT or ACT; degree BA 4 yrs; schol; SC 9, LC 9; enrl D 150, nonmaj 125, maj 25.
Tuition: $5670; campus res room & board.
Courses: Aesthetics; Art Criticism; Art Education; Art History; Ceramics; Conceptual Art; Constructions; Drawing; Graphic Arts; Handicrafts (loom & off-loom weaving); History of Art & Archaeology; Jewelry; Painting; Printmaking; Sculpture; Silversmithing.

INDIANOLA

SIMPSON COLLEGE, Art Department, 50125. Tel: 515-961-6251, exten 665. *Chairperson Dept* Gaile Gallatin, MA.

Estab 1860, dept estab 1965; pvt; D&E; ent req HS dipl, ACT or SAT; degrees BA and BM 4 yrs; schol SC 3, LC 3; enrl D 67, maj 6.
Tuition: $3180 per yr, $1570 per sem, $105 per sem hr; campus res room & board $1190 per yr.
Courses: Art Education; Art History; Ceramics; Drawing; Fibers; History of Art & Archaeology; Jewelry; Macrame; Mixed Media; Painting; Photography; Printmaking; Silversmithing; Stage Design; Teacher Training; Textile Design; Theatre Arts; Video; Weaving.

IOWA CITY

UNIVERSITY OF IOWA, School of Art and Art History, 52242. Tel: 319-353-4550. *Dir Sch* Wallace J Tomasini, PhD; Faculty Members FT 38.
Estab 1847, sch estab 1911; pub; D&E; ent req HS dipl, ACT or SAT plus upper ½ rank in high school; degrees BA and BFA 4 yrs, MA 1½ yrs, MFA 2 yrs, PhD 5 yrs; schol; SC 60, LC 18, GC 55, enrl D 620, maj 430, grad 190.
Tuition: Res—Undergrad $375 per sem, grad $429 per sem; Nonres—Undergrad $855 per sem, grad $909 per sem, campus res room & board $1270 per yr.
Courses: ‡Art Education; ‡Art History; ‡Ceramics; ‡Conceptual Art; ‡Drawing; ‡Goldsmithing; ‡Graphic Arts; ‡Graphic Design; ‡History of Art & Archaeology; Intermedia; ‡Jewelry; Lettering; Mixed Media; ‡Painting; ‡Photography; ‡Printmaking; ‡Sculpture; ‡Silversmithing; Stage Design; Teacher Training; Video.
Summer School: Dir Wallace J Tomasini. Enrl undergrad 160, grad 135; tui res undergrad $341, grad $390; Nonres undergrad $775, grad $825 for term of 8 wks beginning June 5. Courses—Full range of studio, art history, and art education courses.

LeMARS

WESTMAR COLLEGE,* Art Department, 51031. Tel: 712-546-7081, exten 231. *Head Dept* Gary R Bowling; Instrs FT 1, Artist-in-Residence PT 1.
Estab 1890; pvt; D; ent req ACT, SAT or PSAT; degrees BA, BMEd and BAS 4 yrs; enrl 700, maj 22.
Courses: Art Education; Art History; Art Philosophy & Criticism; Business World of Art; Ceramics; Commercial Art Principles; Crafts; Design; Drawing Techniques; Foundations of Art; Graphic Communication; Life Drawing; Oil Painting Techniques; Sculpture Techniques; Synthetic Media & Color; Watercolor.
Adult Hobby Classes: JANUS Continuing Education for Retired Persons.

MASON CITY

NORTH IOWA AREA COMMUNITY COLLEGE,* Department of Art, 500 College Dr, 50401. Tel: 515-423-1264, exten 204. Instrs FT 1.
Estab 1964; pub; D&E; ent req HS dipl; degree AA 2 yrs; schol; SC 4, LC 2; enrl D 198, E 25, maj 30.
Courses: Art Education; Basic Design; History of Art & Archaeology; Painting.
Adult Hobby Classes: Enrl 30. Courses—Painting; Crafts.
Summer School: Term of 5 wks beginning early June. Courses—Art Essentials.

MOUNT PLEASANT

IOWA WESLEYAN COLLEGE,* Art Department, 52641. Tel: 319-385-2211. *Head Dept* Theodore Rasmussen; Instrs FT 2.
Estab 1842; den; 4 yr degrees; schol; SC 10, LC 4; enrl maj 32.
Courses: Art Education; Art History; Ceramics; Drawing; Graphic Arts; Introduction to Art; Painting; Sculpture; Secondary Art; Special Problems; Twentieth Century Art History.

MOUNT VERNON

CORNELL COLLEGE, Art Department, Armstrong Hall, Fine Arts, 52314. Tel: 319-895-8811, exten 128. *Head Dept* Hank Lifson; Instrs FT 3.
Estab 1853; den; D; ent req HS dipl; degrees BA, BSS and BPhil 4 yrs; schol; SC 30, LC 3; normal enrl 900.
Tuition: $2600 per yr.
Courses: Art History; Batik; Ceramics; Conceptual Art; Design; Drawing; Jewelry; Metal & Fiber Design; Painting; Sculpture; Weaving.

ORANGE CITY

NORTHWESTERN COLLEGE, Art Department, 51041. Tel: 712-737-4904. *Assoc Prof Art & Chmn Dept* John Kaericher, MFA; *Instr* Rein Van Derhill, MFA.
Estab 1882, dept estab 1965; den; D&E; ent req HS dipl; degree BA 4 yrs; schol; SC 25, LC 3-4; enrl D 200, nonmaj 175, maj 23-25.
Tuition: Campus res room & board.
Courses: Advertising Design; Aesthetics; Art Education; Art History; Ceramics; Drawing; Graphic Arts; Graphic Design; History of Art & Archaeology; Mixed Media; Painting; Photography; Printmaking; Sculpture; Stage Design; Teacher Training; Theatre Arts.

OTTUMWA

OTTUMWA HEIGHTS COLLEGE, Division of Fine Arts, Grandview at Elm, 52501. Tel: 515-682-4551. *Primary Art Faculty* Richard D Coram, BA and Mary K Modeen, MA.
Estab 1925; pvt; D&E; ent req HS dipl, GED, ACT or SAT; degrees AA, AAS and AAA 2 yrs; schol; SC 3, LC 2; enrl D 73, E 5.
Tuition: $48 per sem; campus res room & board $1340 per yr.
Courses: Ceramics; Drawing; History of Art & Archaeology; Painting.

PELLA

CENTRAL COLLEGE, Art Department, 50219. Tel: 515-628-4151. *Prof Art & Head Dept* Lawrence Mills, PhD; *Assoc Prof* John Vruwink, MFA; *Assoc Prof* Joline De Jong, MA.
Estab 1853; pvt; D&E; ent req HS dipl, ACT; degree BA 4 yrs; schol; SC 20, LC 6; enrl D 180, nonmaj 140, maj 40.
Tuition: $2700 per yr; campus res room & board $1350 per yr.
Courses: Aesthetics; Art Education; Art History; Ceramics; Drawing; Film; History of Art & Archaeology; Interior Design; Jewelry; Lettering; Painting; Photography; Silversmithing; Teacher Training; Theatre Arts.
Children's Classes: Enrl 40; part of Elementary School Art Program.

SIOUX CITY

BRIAR CLIFF COLLEGE, Art Department, 3303 Rebecca St, 57038. Tel: 712-279-5321, exten 452. *Chairperson* William J Welu, MFA; *Instr* Mary Ann Lonergan, MA.
Estab 1930; den; D&E; ent req HS dipl, ACT; degrees BA and BS 4 yrs; schol; SC 7, LC 7; enrl D 250, nonmaj 150, maj 30.
Tuition: $680 per trimester, $68 per hr; campus res room & board $1054 per yr.
Courses: Art Education; Art History; Calligraphy; ‡Ceramics; ‡Collage; ‡Conceptual Art; ‡Drawing; Graphic Design; ‡Intermedia; Lettering; ‡Mixed Media; ‡Painting; Printmaking; ‡Sculpture; Teacher Training.
Summer School: Tui $55 per term of 6 wks beginning June 12, Courses—Elementary Art Education; Ceramics; Drawing; Independent Studio Courses.

MORNINGSIDE COLLEGE,* Art Department, 1501 Morningside Ave, 51106. Tel: 712-277-5212. *Chmn Dept* Frank Breneisen; Instrs FT 2.
Pvt; D&E; ent req HS dipl; degrees BA and BS (Art Educ) 4 yrs; SC 17, LC 4; enrl D 161, maj 35.
Tuition: $2654 per yr; campus res $990 per yr.
Courses: Art Education; Ceramics; Drawing; Painting; Photography; Sculpture; Teacher Training; Textile Design.
Summer School: Dir Glen R Rasmussen. Tui $30 per hr for two 5½ wk terms, beginning June 8 and July 15: Courses: Art History; Art Education; Ceramics.

SIOUX CITY ART CENTER, 513 Nebraska St, 51101. *Asst Dir Bruce* A Bionomann, MFA; *Primary Art Faculty:* Marvel Cox, BA; Diane Mumm, BA; John Gordon, MFA; David Wost, BFA; Peggy Parris, BA; Ernest Ricehill, BA; Gary Bowling, MA.
Estab 1938; pvt; D&E; SC 14-20, LC 1-2; enrl D 100, E 400.
Tuition: None.
Courses: Art Education; Art History; Ceramics; Drawing; Interior Design; Jewelry; Mixed Media; Painting; Photography; Printmaking; Sculpture; Silversmithing; Teacher Training.

KANSAS

ATCHISON

BENEDICTINE COLLEGE, Art Department, 66002. Tel: 913-367-6110. *Chmn* Sister Helen Buening, MFA; *Prof* Dennis McCarthy, MFA.
Estab 1971; den; D; ent req HS dipl, ent exam; SC 15, LC 3; enrl D 145, nonmaj 123, maj 22.

Tuition: Campus res room and board $3800.
Courses: Art Education; Art History; Calligraphy; Ceramics; Drawing; Graphic Arts; Interior Design; Jewelry; Painting; Photography; Printmaking; Sculpture; Stage Design; Teacher Training; Textile Design; Theatre Arts.

BALDWIN

BAKER UNIVERSITY,* Department of Art, 66006. Tel: 913-594-3362, exten 538.
Chmn Walter J Bailey; Instrs FT 2, PT 1.
Estab 1858; pvt; D; ent req HS dipl, provision made for entrance without HS dipl by interview and committee action; degree AB (Art) 4 yr; schol; SC 11, LC 3; enrl D 105, maj 28.
Tuition: $2020; campus res $1190.
Courses: Art Education; Ceramics; Drawing; Graphic Arts; History of Art & Archaeology; Painting; Sculpture; Teacher Training; Textile Design.
Summer School: Seminar on the Creative Process.

COFFEYVILLE

COFFEYVILLE COMMUNITY JUNIOR COLLEGE, Art Department, 67337. Tel. 316-251-7700, exten 47. *Head Dept Instr* Douglas Keller, MA.
Estab 1923, dept estab 1969; pub; D&E; ent req HS dipl; degrees AA; schol; SC 8, LC 2; enrl D 75, E 60, nonmaj 25, maj 110.
Tuition: Res—Undergrad approx $375 per yr (includes $41.50 fees); Nonres—Undergrad $33.50 per cr hr (includes $41.50 fees); campus res $1100.
Courses: Art History; Ceramics; Drawing; Handicrafts; Painting; Photography; Printmaking; Sculpture.
Adult Hobby Classes: Courses—Crafts.

COLBY

COLBY COMMUNITY COLLEGE, Visual Arts Department, 1255 South Range, 67701. Tel: 913-462-3984. *Head Dept* Kenneth Eugene Mitchell, MA; *Primary Faculty* Ronnald I Bruner, MA; Vicki L Mitchell, BA.
Estab 1965, dept estab 1966; pub; D&E; ent req HS dipl; degrees AA 2 yr; schol; SC 18, LC 8; enrl D 141, E 210, maj 18.
Tuition: Res—Undergrad $430 per yr, $215 per sem hr, $15 per cr hr; Nonres—Undergrad $1500 per yr, $750 per sem; campus res room and board $1260 per yr.
Courses: Art Education; Art History; Calligraphy; Ceramics; Commercial Art; Color Structure and Design; Costume Design and Construction; Drafting; Drawing; Fashion Arts; Figure Drawing-Advanced; Graphic Arts; Graphic Design; Handicrafts (3D Design); History of Art and Archaeology; Interior Design; Jewelry; Lettering; Painting; Photography; Problems in Drawing; Problems in Painting; Sculpture; Stage Design; Teacher Training (Elementary Art Education); Theatre Arts; Watercolor I & II.
Adult Hobby Classes: Enrl 10-20; tui $15 per hr.
Summer School: Enrl 5-20; tui $15 per cr hr for term of 4 wks beginning June 1. Courses—Drawing; Jewelry; Watercolor.

EL DORADO

BUTLER COUNTY COMMUNITY COLLEGE, Art Department, PO Box 888, Towanda & Haverhill, 67042. Tel: 316-321-4457. *Chmn* Robert H Chism, MA; *Instr* Lynn B Havel, MFA; *Instr* Peter Johnson, MFA.
Estab 1927, dept estab 1964; pub; D&E; ent req HS dipl, ACT, EED, other various ways to enter; degrees AA 2 yr; schol; SC 13, LC 1; enrl D 168, E 57.
Courses: Art History; Ceramics; Design; Drawing; Interior Design; Painting; Printmaking; Silversmithing.

EMPORIA

EMPORIA STATE UNIVERSITY, Department of Art, 66801. Tel: 316-343-1200, exten 246. *Chmn* Donald Perry, MFA.
Estab 1863, dept estab early 1900's; pub; D&E; ent req HS dipl, HS Srs may enroll in regular classes; degrees BFA and BSEd 4 yr; schol; SC 42, LC 15, GC 30; enrl D 700, E 250, maj 200, GS 45.
Tuition: Res—Undergrad and grad $264 per sem; Nonres—Undergrad and grad $564 per sem; campus res room & board $1250.
Courses: Art Education; Art History; Art Therapy; Ceramics; Commercial Art; Costume Design and Construction; Display; Drafting; Drawing; Fashion Arts; Goldsmithing; Graphic Arts; Handicrafts (weaving);

History of Art and Archaeology; Illustration; Interior Design; Jewelry; Mixed Media; Painting; Photography; Printmaking; Sculpture; Silversmithing; Stage Design; Teacher Training; Textile Design; Theatre Arts.
Summer School: Tui—Res $13.25 per sem hr; Nonres—$30.25 per sem hr for term beginning June 5th. Courses—Most of the regular classes.

HAYS

FORT HAYS STATE UNIVERSITY, Department of Art, 67601. Tel: 913-628-4287. *Chmn* John C Thorns Jr, MFA; *Assoc Prof* Eugene Harwick, MFA; *Prof* Darrell McGinnis, MA; *Assoc Prof* Kathleen Kucher, MFA; *Instr* Ellen Schiferl, ABD.
Estab 1902, dept estab 1930; pub; D&E; ent req HS dipl; degrees BA and BFA 4 yr, MFA (applied for & needing approval) 2-3 yr, AA and MA 2 yr; schol; SC 59, LC 19, GC 29; enrl D 889, E 22, nonmaj 668, maj 196, GS 40, others 7.
Tuition: Res—Undergrad and grad $20.75 per cr hr; Nonres—Undergrad and grad $40.75 per cr hr; other—various incidental fees; campus res room and board $578 and up.
Courses: ‡Advertising Design; ‡Art Education; ‡Art History; ‡Art Therapy; Calligraphy; ‡Ceramics; ‡Collage; ‡Commercial Art; ‡Conceptual Art; ‡Constructions; ‡Drawing; Goldsmithing; ‡Graphic Arts; ‡Graphic Design; ‡Handicrafts; ‡History of Art and Archaeology; ‡Illustration; Intermedia; ‡Interior Design; ‡Jewelry; Lettering; ‡Mixed Media; ‡Painting; ‡Photography; ‡Printmaking; ‡Sculpture; ‡Silversmithing; Stage Design; ‡Teacher Training; ‡Textile Design; Theatre Arts; Video.
Summer School: Enrl 300; tui $20.75 per cr hr for term of 8 wks beginning June 4th. Courses—Studio Courses & Workshops.

HESSTON

HESSTON COLLEGE, 67062. Tel: 316-327-4221, exten 240. *Head Dept Instrs* John Blosser, MFA.
Estab 1915; den; D&E; ent req HS dipl; degrees AA 2 yr; SC 9; LC 1; enrl nonmaj 50, maj 5.
Tuition: Campus res room and board.
Courses: Art History; Ceramics; Drafting; Drawing; Painting; Photography.

HUTCHINSON

HUTCHINSON COMMUNITY JUNIOR COLLEGE, Art Department, 1300 N Plum, 67501. Tel: 316-663-5781, exten 113. *Chmn* Dave Blackim, MA; *Prof* Dennis Chegwidden, MFA; *Prof* Roy Swanson, BFA; *Prof* Jane Dronberger, MA.
Estab 1928; pub; D&E; ent req HS dipl; degrees AA 2 yr; schol; SC 17, LC 4; enrl D 215, E 41, nonmaj 180, maj 29.
Tuition: 1-7 hrs $12 per cr hr plus $25.50 fees, 7 or more hrs $9 per hr plus $51 fees; campus res room and board $1060 per yr.
Courses: ‡Art Education; ‡Art History; ‡Ceramics; ‡Drawing; ‡Graphic Design; ‡History of Art and Archaeology; ‡Jewelry; ‡Painting; ‡Printmaking; ‡Sculpture; ‡Silversmithing; ‡Theatre Arts.

INDEPENDENCE

INDEPENDENCE COMMUNITY JUNIOR COLLEGE, Fine Arts Department, College Avenue & Brookside Drive, 67301. Tel: 316-331-4100. *Dept Head Pres* Neil Edds, MA; *Instrs* Leonard E Wood, MA.
Pub; D&E; ent req HS dipl; degrees AA; schol; SC 8; enrl D 60, E 10, nonmaj 64, maj 6.
Tuition: No campus res.
Courses: Ceramics; Drawing; Painting; Sculpture; Silversmithing; Stage Design.

IOLA

ALLEN COUNTY COMMUNITY COLLEGE, Art Department, 66749. Tel: 316-365-5116. *Dept Head & Instr* Omer Knoll, MS.
Estab 1965; pub; D&E; ent req HS Dipl or GED; degrees AA 2 yr; schol; SC 5, LC 2; enrl D 400, E 300, nonmaj 20, maj 6.
Tuition: Res—Undergrad $335 per yr; Nonres—Undergrad $1095 per yr; campus res room and board.
Courses: Art Fundamentals; Art History; Ceramics; Commercial Art; Design (2nd and 3rd dimensional); Drawing; Handicrafts (leather, Macrame, copper enameling); Painting; Photography; Printmaking; Sculpture; Student Published Yearbook.
Summer School: Tui $8 per cr hr. Courses—all courses.

LAWRENCE

UNIVERSITY OF KANSAS, School of Fine Arts,* 66044. Tel: 913-864-4401. *Dean Sch* J Moeser.

Pub; degrees BFA, BAE, BS, MFA 4-5 yrs; schol and fel. Freshman Common Curriculum (required for all new freshmen), Roger Shimomura, Advisor, enrl 250.
—**Department of Design.*** *Chmn* Richard Branham; *Instrs* FT 24, PT 12.
Estab 1921; SC 83, LC 32, GC 26; enrl maj 250, grad 40.
Courses: Advertising Art; Ceramics; Design; Editorial Art; Graphic Design; Industrial Design (5 yr); Interior Design (5 yr); Jewelry; Silversmithing; Textile Design in Weaving.
—**Department of Painting and Sculpture.*** *Chmn* Michael Ott; *Instrs* FT 18, PT 5.
Estab 1885; SC 50, GC 25; enrl maj 150.
Courses: Art History; Painting; Printmaking; Sculpture; Theatre Design.
—**Department of Occupational Therapy.*** *Chmn* Joan Wyrick; *Instrs* FT 8, PT 4.
Estab 1965; LC 25, LabC 10, hospital field work; enrl 200.
Courses: Occupational Therapy.
—**Department of History of Art (College of Liberal Arts and Sciences),*** Spooner Hall, 66044. Tel: 913-864-3616. *Chmn* Chu-Tsing Li; *Instrs* FT 7, PT 8.
Estab 1951; pub; D; degrees BA and BFA 4 yrs, MA, PhD; LC 23, GC; enrl maj 75, grad 30, others 900.
Courses: Chinese & Japanese Art; History of Art; North American Art; Western European Art.
—**Department of Visual Arts Education,** 109 Bailey Hall, 66044. Tel: 913-864-3167. *Prof Visual Arts Educ & Chmn Dept* Philip H Rueschhoff, EdD; *Assoc Prof* Marguerite Baumgartel, EdD; *Instr* Dixie Glenn, MA.
Estab 1865, dept estab 1969; pub; D&E; ent req HS dipl, ent exam; degrees BAE 4 yrs, MA 1-6 yrs, EdD and PhD 3-6 yrs; schol; GC 12; enrl D 535, maj 123, grad 123, others 289.
Tuition: Res—$344.40 per sem, $28.85 per cr hr; Nonres—$839.40 per sem, $66.85 per cr hr; campus res room and board variable.
Courses: Visual Arts Education.
Summer School: Term of 16 wks beginning June.

LEAVENWORTH

SAINT MARY COLLEGE, Art Department, 66048. Tel: 913-682-5151. *Head Dept* Sister M Rebecca Conner, MA; *Primary Faculty* Sister Carmen Echevarria, MA; Sister Frances Marie Grady, MA.
Estab 1923; pvt; D&E; ent req HS dipl; degrees BA, BS, BSW, BM and BME 4 yr; schol; SC 25, LC 5; enrl nonmaj 80, maj 10.
Tuition: $1750 per yr; PT $70 per cr hr; campus res room and board $1225.
Courses: Art Education; Art History; Calligraphy; Ceramics; Commercial Art; Drawing; Graphic Arts; Handicrafts (weaving, stitchery); History of Art and Archaeology; Interior Design; Jewelry; Lettering; Mixed Media; Painting; Photography; Printmaking; Sculpture; Teacher Training; Textile Design.
Children's Classs: Enrl 30; tui $200 per 2 wks. Courses—Crafts Camp; Painting (Saturday).
Summer School: Tui $210 for term of 3 wk. Courses—variables 3 wk workshop.

LIBERAL

SEWARD COUNTY COMMUNITY COLLEGE, Art Department, North Hwy 83 (Mailing Add: Box 1137, 67901). Tel: 316-624-1951, exten 74. *Head Art Dept* Steve Heckman, MFA; *Instr* Robert Carder, MA.
Estab 1969; pub; D&E; ent req HS dipl; degree AA 2 yrs; schol; SC 13, LC 6; enrl D 650 (school), E 350 (school).
Tuition: Res—$12 per cr hr; Nonres—$37.50 per cr hr; campus res room & board $1210 per yr.
Courses: Art Appreciation; Art Education; Art History; Ceramics; Costume Design & Construction; Drawing; History of Art & Archaeology; Painting; Photography; Sculpture; Stage Design.
Summer School: Dir Steve Heckman. Tui $12 per cr hr for term of 6 wks beginning June 4. Courses—Varied and subject to change.

LINDSBORG

BETHANY COLLEGE, Box 111, 67456. Tel: 913-227-3311, exten 146. *Asst Prof* Daniel Mason, MFA; *Assoc Prof* Ray Kahmeyer, MA; *Asst Prof* Don Osborne, MFA; *Instr* Bruce Woods, MFA.
Den; D; ent req HS dipl; degrees BA 3-4 yr; schol; SC 19; LC 3; enrl D 195, nonmaj 135, maj 60.
Tuition: $3150 yr, $190 per course; campus res room and board.

Courses: ‡Art Education; Art History; Ceramics; Drawing; History of Art & Archaeology; Painting; Photography; Printmaking; Sculpture; Studio Concentration.
Summer School; Acad Dean Dr L Loyd Foester.

MANHATTAN

KANSAS STATE UNIVERSITY, 66506. Tel: 913-532-5950.
—**Art Department, Art Bldg,** 66506. Tel: 913-532-6605. *Prof Art & Head Dept* Jerrold Maddox, MFA; *Prof* Angelo Garzio, MFA; *Prof* Oscar V Larmer, MFA; *Assoc Prof* Elliott Pujol, MFA; *Assoc Prof* John Vogt, MFA; *Assoc Prof* Rex Replogle, MFA; *Assoc Prof* Gary Woodward, MFA.
Estab 1863, dept estab 1965; pub; D&E; ent req HS dipl; degrees BS (Art Educ) jointly with Col Educ 4 yrs, BA and BFA 4 yrs, MA (Art) 2 yrs; schol; SC 45, LC 19, GC 7; enrl D 1940, E 60, nonmaj 1800, maj 200, grad 15.
Tuition: Res—$345 per sem; Nonres—$840 per sem; campus res.
Courses: Art Education; Art History; Ceramics; Drawing; Graphic Design; Jewelry; Lettering; Painting; Printmaking; Sculpture; Textile Design.
Summer School: Dir Jerrold Maddox. Enrl 150; tui res $24 per cr hr, nonres $57 per cr hr for term of 4 to 8 wks beginning June 5. Courses—Most of above, varies from summer to summer.
—**College of Architecture and Design.*** Dean Bernd Foerster; Instrs FT 53.
Estab 1904; degrees BArch, BInterior Arch and BLandscape Arch 5 yrs, MAarch, MLandscape Arch, MRegional & Community Planning; enrl approx 1150.
Courses: ‡Architecture; ‡Interior Architecture; ‡Landscape Architecture; ‡Regional & Community Planning.
Summer School: Dean Bernd Foerster. 8 wks from June 4.
—**College of Home Economics,*** Department of Clothing, Textiles and Interior Design. *Dean* Ruth M Hoeflin.
Estab 1914; enrl 420, Fashion Marketing maj 221, Textile Science maj 10, Fashion Design maj 43, Interior Design maj 146.
Summer School: 8 wks from June 7.

MCPHERSON

MCPHERSON COLLEGE, Art Department, 1600 E Euclid, 67460. Tel: 316-241-0731, exten 18. *Chmn* Mary Ann Robinson, MA.
Estab 1887; den; D&E; ent req HS dipl, ACT; degrees AB 4 yr; schol; SC 14, LC 5; enrl D 150, maj 10, others 140.
Tuition: Res—Undergrad $3360-$3500 per yr, $1680 per sem, $67 per cr hr; campus res room and board $500.
Courses: ‡Art Education; Art History; Ceramics; Drawing; Graphic Arts; ‡Interior Design; Lettering; Museum Staff Training; Painting; Printmaking; Teacher Training; Textile Design.
Summer School: Dir Dr Dayton Rothrock. Term of 10 wks beginning end of May. Courses—Varied Liberal Arts.

OTTAWA

OTTAWA UNIVERSITY,* Department of Art, Tenth & Cedar Sts, 66067. Tel: 912-242-5200. *Dir* Pal T Wright; *Instrs* FT 2, PT 1.
Estab 1865; pvt; D; ent req HS grad, SAT, ACT; degree BA 4 yr; schol; SC 16, LC 5; enrl D 35, maj 5.
Courses: Art Education; Ceramics; Drawing; Fashion Arts; Graphic Arts; Graphic Design; History of Art & Archaeology; Painting; Photography; Sculpture.

OVERLAND PARK

JOHNSON COUNTY COMMUNITY COLLEGE, Communications/Arts Division, College Blvd at Quivira Rd, 66210. Tel: 913-888-8500, exten 550. *Dir* James M Williams, MA; *Coordr Commercial Art Prog* Dorothy Wadsworth, MFA; *Instr* Judy Brazil, BA; *Instr* Karen Schory, MFA; *Instr* Jean Howard, MFA; *Instr* Ron Hicks, MS.
Estab 1969; pub; D&E; ent req HS dipl or equivalent; degree AA 2 yrs; SC 30, LC 4; enrl D 200, E 100.
Tuition: Res—$14.50 per cr hr; Nonres—$36.50 per cr hr; no campus res.
Courses: Art Education; Art History; Calligraphy; Ceramics; Commercial Art; Graphic Arts; Graphic Design; Handicrafts (weaving); Jewelry; Lettering; Painting; Photography; Printmaking; Sculpture; Silversmithing.
Summer School: Enrl 100; tui $14.50 per cr hr for term of 8 wks beginning June 5.

PITTSBURG

PITTSBURG STATE UNIVERSITY, Art Department, 1701 S Broadway St, 66762. *Chmn* Reed Schmickle, MA; *Assoc Prof* Robert Blunk Jr, MS; *Assoc Prof* Harry E Krug, MS; *Assoc Prof* Robert Russell, MFA; *Assoc Prof* Marjorie Schick, MFA; *Assoc Prof* Laurence A Wooster, MA; *Asst Prof* Alex Barde, MS.
Estab 1903, dept estab 1921; pub; D&E; ent req HS dipl; degrees BFA and BSEd 4 yr, MS 36 hr; SC 48, LC 12, GC 14; enrl D 600, E 50, nonmaj 400, maj 200, GS 30.
Tuition: Res—Undergrad and grad $225.25 per sem, $13.50 per sem hr; Nonres—Undergrad & grad $555.25 per sem, $33.50 per sem hr; campus res room and board $1148 per yr.
Courses: ‡Art Education; Art History; ‡Ceramics; ‡Drawing; Film; ‡Jewelry; ‡Occupational Therapy; ‡Painting; Photography; ‡Printmaking; ‡Sculpture; ‡Silversmithing; ‡Teacher Training.
Summer School: Enrl 200; tui Res—$16.50 per cr hr; Nonres—$36.50 per cr hr for term of 8 wks beginning June 5th. Courses—as above.

PRATT

PRATT COMMUNITY COLLEGE, Art Department, 67124. Tel: 316-672-5641. *Chmn* Gene Wineland, MA.
D&E; ent req HS dipl; degrees AA and AS; schol; SC 12, LC 1.
Tuition: $215 per sem, $10 per sem hr.
Courses: Art History; Commercial Art; Display; Drawing; Graphic Design; Interior Design; Jewelry; Lettering; Painting; Photography; Printmaking; Silversmithing.

SALINA

KANSAS WESLEYAN UNIVERSITY,* Art Department, Santa Fe & Clafin St, 67401. Tel: 913-827-5541. *Head Dept & Assoc Prof* George F Chlebak; Instrs FT 1.
Estab 1886; den; degree AB 4 yr; schol; SC 8, LC 3; enrl maj 15, others 500 for two sem.
Tuition: $1810 per yr; campus res.
Courses: Design; Drawing & Painting; History of Art.
Summer School: Enrl 125; for term of 8 wk beginning June.

STERLING

STERLING COLLEGE, Art Department, 540 E Main, 67579. Tel: 316-278-3609, exten 245. *Head Dept & Prof* Gordon Zahradnik, MFA; *vis prof*—Ceramics, Painting.
Estab 1876; den; D&E; ent req HS dipl; degrees AB and BS; schol; SC 16, LC 2; enrl D 556.
Tuition: Campus res room and board.
Courses: Advertising Design; Art Education; Art History; Calligraphy; Ceramics; Collage; Commercial Art; Copper Enameling; Costume Design and Construction; Drawing; Fibers; Graphic Arts; Graphic Design; Handicrafts; History of Art and Archaeology; Interior Design; Jewelry; Lettering; Painting; Photography; Printmaking; Textile Design; Theatre Arts.
Adult Hobby Classes: Enrl 25; tui $20. Courses—all area.
Children's Classes: Courses—Art Education.

TOPEKA

WASHBURN UNIVERSITY OF TOPEKA,* Department of Art, Mulvane Art Center, 17th and Jewell Sts, 66621. Tel: 913-235-5341. *Head Dept* R J Hunt; Instrs FT 4, PT.
Estab 1900; pub; ent req HS dipl; degrees AB and BFA 4 yr; SC 11, LC 5; enrl maj 60, others 280.
Courses: Art History & Appreciation; Ceramics; Design; Drawing; Metalcraft & Jewelry; Painting.
Children's Classes: Tui $18 for twelve 1½ sessions.
Adult Classes: Tui $22 for twelve 3 hr sessions.

WICHITA

FRIENDS UNIVERSITY, Art Department, 2100 University Ave, 67213. Tel: 316-363-9131, exten 315. *Head Dept* Dee M Connett, MA; *Asst Prof* Clinton Thornton, MFA; *Instr* Judy Dove, MFA; *Instr* Mary Thornton, Artist-In-Residence, BA.
Estab 1898; den; D&E; ent req HS dipl; degrees BA and BS 4 yr; schol; SC 18, LC 4; enrl D 329, E 37.
Tuition: Res—Undergrad $3500 yr or $1750 per sem (includes room, board & student fees), 1-6 hrs $60 per cr hr, 7-11 hrs $75 per cr hr; Nonres—Undergrad $2295 per yr, $1147.50 per sem; campus res.

Courses: Art Education; Art History; Calligraphy; Ceramics; Commercial Art; Drawing; Graphic Arts; Graphic Design; History of Art and Archaeology; Jewelry; Painting; Photography; Printmaking; Sculpture; Silversmithing; Teacher Training.
Adult Hobby Classes: Courses—Drawing; Jewelry; Painting.
Summer School: Tui $60 per cr hr for term of 6 wks beginning June 5th.

SCHOOL OF THE WICHITA ART ASSOCIATION,* 9112 E Central, 67206. Tel: 316-686-6687. *Dir* John R Rouse; Instrs 20.
Estab 1923; pvt; D&E; schol; enrl 300.
Courses: Art History; Ceramics; Commercial Art; Drawing; Enameling; Fashion Design; Painting; Photography; Pottery; Printmaking; Silversmithing; Weaving.
Summer School: 6 wk June-July.

WICHITA STATE UNIVERSITY, College of Fine Arts, Division of Art, 67208. Tel: 316-689-3555. *Head Dept & Asst Dean* Robert M Kiskadden, MFA; *Chmn Art Educ* James R Bartz, MA; *Chmn Art History* Mira P Merriman, PhD; *Chmn Graphic Design* Clark Britton, MAA; *Chmn Studio Arts* John D Boyd, MFA; vis prof—4 or 5 yr, painting, printmaking, ceramics, sculpture, 3 to 4 days.
Estab 1895, dept estab 1901; pub; D&E; ent req HS dipl; degrees BAE and BFA 4 yr, MFA 2 yr, MA 1 yr; schol; enrl D 1149, E 194, nonmaj 78, maj 285, GS 51, others 2.
Tuition: Res—Undergrad and grad $19.85 per cr hr per 15 hrs or more; Nonres—Undergrad and grad $45.85 per cr hr per 15 hrs or more; no campus res.
Courses: ‡Art Education; ‡Art History; ‡Ceramics; Drawing; ‡Graphic Design; Illustration; Lettering; ‡Painting; Photography; ‡Printmaking; ‡Sculpture; Teacher Training.
Summer School: Tui as above for term of 8 wks beginning June 5th.

WINFIELD

SOUTHWESTERN COLLEGE, 67156. *Prof* Warren D Brown, MA; *Adj Prof* William Boulware, MA.
Estab 1885; pvt & den; D&E; ent req HS dipl; degrees BA 4 yr; schol; SC 12, LC 4.

KENTUCKY

ANCHORAGE

LOUISVILLE SCHOOL OF ART, 100 Park Rd, 40223. Tel: 502-245-8836. *Dir* Bruce Yenawine, MA; *Assoc Dir* Diana Arcadipone, MFA; *Primary Faculty* Lida Gordon, MFA; Peter David Bodnar III, MFA; Garry Kaulitz, MFA; Skip Koebbeman, MFA; David Schneider, MFA; Nadene Wegner, MFA; Mary Ann Currier, MA; Alma Lesch, MA; Margaret Meloy, MA; Les Nash, PhD; Phil Wakeman, MA.
Estab 1909; pvt; D&E; ent req HS dipl HS transcripts, transfer transcripts, application form & fee, portfolio, interview; degrees BFA 4 yr; schol; SC 25, LC 4; enrl D 82 FT, E 74 PT, nonmaj 74, Maj 82.
Tuition: $750 per yr, $250 per sem, $70 per cr hr; no campus res.
Courses: Aesthetics; Art History; ‡Ceramics; Collage; Conceptual Art; Constructions; Drawing; Goldsmithing; Graphic Design; Handicrafts (textiles); Illustration; ‡Jewelry; Mixed Media; ‡Painting, Photography, ‡Printmaking; ‡Sculpture; ‡Silversmithing; ‡Textile Design.
Adult Hobby Classes: Enrl 74 PT; tui $70 per one credit. Courses—Ceramics; Drawing; Life Drawing; Metal; Painting; Prints; Sculpture; Textiles.
Summer School: Tui $80 for term of 4 wks beginning June. Courses—Metal; Painting; Photography; Prints; Textiles.

BARBOURVILLE

UNION COLLEGE, Art Department,* College St, 40906. Tel: 606-546-4151. *Head Dept* Elizabeth Burke; Instrs FT 1, PT 1.
Den: D&E; ent req HS dipl; degrees BA, BS and MA (Educ) 4 yr.
Courses: Art Appreciation; Art Education; Art Fundamentals; Drawing; History of Art; Painting; Recreational Arts and Crafts; Teacher Training; Theatre Arts.

BEREA

BEREA COLLEGE, Art Department, 40404. Tel: 606-986-9341, exten 292, 986-9341, exten 293, 986-9341, exten 294. *Chmn* Lester F Pross, MA; *Prof* Dorothy Tredennick, MA; *Assoc Prof* Sally Wilkerson, MFA; *Assoc Prof* Neil DiTeresa, AM; *Assoc Prof* Walter Hyleck, MFA; *Instr* William Morningstar, MFA; *Instr* Gregory Preston Spaid, MFA; *Instr* Christopher Pierce, MFA.

Estab 1855, dept estab 1936; pvt; D; ent req HS dipl (preference given to students from Southern appalachian region); degrees BA 4 yr; schol; SC 14, LC 8; enrl D 325, maj 54.
Tuition: None; campus res room and board $1236.
Courses: Art Education; Art History; Ceramics; Drawing; Painting; Photography; Printmaking; Sculpture; Teacher Training; Textile Design; Theatre Arts.

BOWLING GREEN

WESTERN KENTUCKY UNIVERSITY,* Art Department, Ivan Wilson Ctr for Fine Arts, Room 441, 42101. Tel: 502-745-3940. *Head Dept* Walter Stomps; Instrs FT 14, PT 1.
Pub; D; ent req HS dipl; degrees BA and BFA 4 yr; SC 7 LC 2; enrl maj 220.
Tuition: $240 per sem; Nonres—$600; campus res $193 to $205 per sem.
Courses: Aesthetics; Art Education; Ceramics; Drawing; Graphic Arts; History of Art & Archaeology; Painting; Sculpture; Teacher Training; Weaving.
Summer School: Tui $120; Nonres $300 for term of 8 wk beginning June.
Courses: Art Education; Art History; Design; Drawing; Painting.

CAMPBELLSVILLE

CAMPBELLSVILLE COLLEGE, Fine Arts Division, 42718. Tel: 502-465-6516. *Head Dept* Lawrence Reed; *Assoc Prof* Robert Stapp, MFA; *Instr* Tommy Clark, MFA; *Instr* Jerry Bennett, MEd; *Instr* Joseph DeSpain, MA; *Assoc Prof* L M Hamilton, MA.
Estab 1906, dept estab 1967; den; D&E; ent req HS dipl, ACT; degrees BA, BS, BS (Med Tech), BM and BChM 4 yr, AA, AS, ASLS and ASSW 2 yr; schol; SC 28, LC 5; enrl D 35, E 10, nonmaj 12, maj 22, others 8 minors.
Courses: Advertising Design; Architecture; Art Education; Art History; Ceramics; Commercial Art; Conceptual Art; Display; Drafting; Drawing; Graphic Arts; Graphic Design; Handicrafts; History of Art and Archaeology; Jewelry; Painting; Photography; Printmaking; Sculpture; Silversmithing; Stage Design; Teacher Training; Textile Design; Theatre Arts.
Summer School: Tui $785 for term of 8 wks beginning June 5th. Courses—Art Education; Art Appreciation; Drawing; Painting.

DANVILLE

CENTRE COLLEGE OF KENTUCKY,* Art Department, 40422. Tel: 606-236-5211. *Chmn* Tom Gaines; Instrs FT 4.
Estab 1819; pvt; degree 4 yr; SC, LC; enrl D 750-800.
Courses: Ceramics; Commercial Art; Design; Drawing & Painting; History of Art; Printmaking; Sculpture.
Adult Hobby Classes: Courses—Ceramics; Drawing; Painting.

FORT MITCHELL

THOMAS MORE COLLEGE, Art Department, PO Box 85, 41017. Tel: 606-341-5800. *Chmn* Sister M de 'DEO, MFA; *Prof* Darrell Brothers, MFA.
Estab 1921; pvt; D&E; ent req HS dipl; degrees BA, BES, BS, AA and AES; SC 9, LC 4; enrl D 12, E 5, maj 17.
Tuition: $49.50 per sem hr; campus res room and board $1560.
Courses: Aesthetics; Art Education; Art History; Ceramics; Drawing; Painting; Photography; Sculpture; Teacher Training; Theatre Arts.

GEORGETOWN

GEORGETOWN COLLEGE, Fine Arts Division, Art Department, 40324. Tel: 502-863-8351. *Chmn* Charles James McCormick; Faculty FT 2.
Estab 1829; den; D; ent req HS transcript, ACT; degree BA 4 yr; schol and grants; SC 14, LC 6; enrl 1150.
Tuition: Res—$1045 per term; Nonres—$1095 per term; 4-1-4 curriculum; Jan interterm; Travel Classes.
Courses: Advanced Painting; Art Appreciation; Art History; Art Survey; Ceramics; Drawing; Graphics; Oil Painting; Photography; Public School Art; Secondary Art; Sculpture; Three-Dimensional Design; Two-Dimensional Design.
Summer School: Three 3 wk modules of one course each. Courses—Art Education; Art Humanities; Studio Classes.

HIGHLAND HEIGHTS

NORTHERN KENTUCKY UNIVERSITY,* Art Department, 526 Johns Hill Road, 41076. Tel: 606-292-5100. *Chmn* Dr Bill Parsons; *Instrs* FT 15, PT 2.
Estab 1968; pub; D&E; ent req HS grad, ACT scores; degrees BA (Art Educ), BFA, BMus, BMusEd; SC 31, LC 10.
Tuition: $210 per sem, PT $18 per cr hr; Nonres $475 per sem, PT $40 per cr hr.
Courses: Art Education; Ceramics; Drawing; History of Art & Archaeology; Journalism; Music; Painting; Photography; Printmaking; Radio & TV; Sculpture; Speech; Theatre Arts.
Summer School: As above.

LEXINGTON

TRANSYLVANIA UNIVERSITY, Studio Arts Dept, 300 N Broadway, 40508. Tel: 606-233-8246. *Chmn* Gary Anderson, DMus; *Instr* Dan Selter, MA; *Instr* Louise Calvin, MA.
Estab 1780; pvt; D&E; ent req HS dipl; degrees BA and BS; schol; SC 20, LC 3; enrl D 105, E 14, maj 18.
Courses: Art Education; Art History; Ceramics; Costume Design and Construction; Drafting; Drawing; History of Art and Archaeology; Mixed Media; Painting; Sculpture; Stage Design; Teacher Training; Theatre Arts.

UNIVERSITY OF KENTUCKY,* College of Fine Arts, Department of Art, 40506. Tel: 606-258-9000, exten 2452, 258-9000, exten 2453. *Dean* J Robert Wills Jr; *Chmn* Prof Joseph Fitzpatrick; *Instrs* FT 20, PT 1.
Estab 1918; pub; degrees BA, MA and MFA 4 yr; schol and grad assistantships; SC 23, LC 19, GC 6; enrl maj 200, others 800.
Tuition: Res $275, nonres $750; campus res.
Courses: Art Education; Ceramics; Drawing; History of Art; Painting; Printmaking; Sculpture; Textiles.
Summer School: Enrl 200; tui res $154, nonres $400 for 8 wk beginning June. Courses—Art Education; Drawing; History of Art; Painting.

LOUISVILLE

UNIVERSITY OF LOUISVILLE, Allen R Hite Art Institute, Department of Fine Arts, Belknap Campus, 40208. Tel: 502-588-6794. *Dir* Dario A Covi, PhD; *Prof* Henry J Chodkowski, MFA; *Prof* E Thomas Marsh, MAT; *Prof* Mary Spencer Nay, MA; *Instrs* FT 14, PT 6.
Estab 1846, dept estab 1935; pub; D&E; ent req HS Dipl, CEEB; degrees BA 4 yr, MA 1 to 2 yrs; schol; SC 42, LC 35 GC 40; enrl D 1000 (per sem), E 120, nonmaj 900, maj 130, GS 40.
Tuition: Res—Undergrad $550 per yr, $275 per sem, $23 per cr hr, grad $620 per yr, $310 per sem $26 per cr hr; Nonres—Undergrad & grad $1980 per yr, $990 per sem, $82 per cr hr; campus res room and board $1945.
Courses: Art Education; Art History; Ceramics; Drawing; Graphic Design; Handicrafts; History of Art and Archaeology; Jewelry; Painting; Photography; Printmaking; Sculpture; Teacher Training; Textile Design.
Summer School: Tui $340, nonres $990 for 2 terms of 5 wks beginning June 15th. Courses—three or four of above courses.

MIDWAY

MIDWAY COLLEGE,* Art Department, Stephens St, 40347. Tel: 606-846-4423, exten 27. *Chmn* Virginia Hutton; *Instrs* FT 1.
Den; D; W; ent req HS dipl, ACT; degree 2 yr; schol; SC 7, LC 3; enrl 55.
Courses: Art Education; Basic Design; Ceramics; Decorative Textiles; Drawing; Historical Furniture; Lettering; Painting.

MOREHEAD

MOREHEAD STATE UNIVERSITY, Art Department, Claypool-Young Art Building, 40351. (Mailing Add: UPO Box 714). Tel: 606-783-3232, 783-2193. *Head Dept* Dr Bill R Booth, PhD; *Assoc Prof* Douglas Adams, MA; *Asst Prof* Franz Altschuler, BFA; *Instr* Louise A T Booth, MA; *Assoc Prof* Ryan Howard, PhD; *Assoc Prof* Roder H Jones, EdD; *Prof* Jose A Maortua, MFA; *Asst Prof* Gene J Pyle, AB; *Asst Prof* Joe D Sartor, MA; *Assoc Prof* Maurice Strider, MA; *Asst Prof* Donald B Young, MA.
Estab 1922; pub; D&E; ent req HS dipl, ACT; degrees BA 4 yr, MA 1 yr; schol; SC 40, LC 16, GC 28; enrl D 900, E 20, nonmaj 800, maj 180, GS 55, others 145.
Tuition: Res—Undergrad $240 per sem, grad $275 per sem; Nonres—Undergrad $600 per sem, grad $700 per sem, other PT Res—Undergrad $20, grad $31; Nonres—$50, grad $78; campus res room and board $300.

Courses: Advertising Design; ‡Art Education; Art History; Calligraphy; Ceramics; ‡Commercial Art; ‡Drawing; Fashion Arts; ‡Graphic Arts; ‡Graphic Design; Handicrafts (weaving); History of Art and Archaeology; Illustration; Lettering; ‡Painting; Photography; Printmaking; Sculpture; ‡Teacher Training.
Adult Hobby Classes: Courses—Ceramics, Crafts, Oil Painting; Watercolor painting; Weaving.
Summer School: Courses—same as above on demand.

MURRAY

MURRAY STATE UNIVERSITY, College of Creative Expression, Art Department, 42071. Tel: 502-762-3784. *Chmn* Robert W Head, MFA; *Primary Faculty* Karen W Boyd, MFA; Michael Brun, MFA; Harry Furches, MFA; Michael Johnson, MFA; William Lew, PhD; Dale Leys, MFA; Luke Oas, MFA; William Ransom, MFA; Fred Shepard, MFA; Jerry Speight, MA; Jim Stickler, MFA; Mary Jane Timmerman, MFA; Vernon Town, MFA; Melody Weiler, MFA; Jim White, MFA; Robert Wozniak, MFA; Richard Jackson, MFA.
Estab 1925, dept estab 1931; pub; D&E; ent req HS dipl from accredited KY HS, out of state must rank in the upper half of their HS and/or ACT test score of 22 or above; degrees BA, BS and BFA 4 yr, MAEd, MACT and MA (Studio) approx 1 ½ yrs; schol; SC 104, LC 44, GS 29; enrl D 700, E 50, nonmaj 114, maj 290, GS 8.
Tuition: Res—Undergrad $480 per yr, $240 per sem, $20 per sem hr, grad $550 per yr, $275 per sem, $31 per sem hr; Nonres—Undergrad $1200 per yr, $600 per sem, $50 per sem hr, grad $1400 per yr, $700 per sem, $78 per sem hr; campus res room and board $940.
Courses: Advertising Design; ‡Art Education; Art History; ‡Ceramics; Commercial Art; ‡Design Materials; ‡Drawing; ‡Graphic Design; History of Art and Archaeology; ‡Jewelry; ‡Painting; ‡Photography; ‡Printmaking; ‡Sculpture; Silversmithing; Teacher Training, Textile Design.
Children's Classes: Enrl 25; tui 410 per 6 wks. Courses—Sat workshop for grades 1-9 various media used. Special program for advanced students summer workshop for HS students (they stay on campus); tui, room and board is $89 per wk.
Summer School: Enrl 100; tui Res—Undergrad $120, grad $138; Nonres—Undergrad $300, grad $350 for term of 8 wks beginning 2nd wk of June.

OWENSBORO

BRESCIA COLLEGE,* Art Department, 120 W Seventh St, 42301. Tel: 502-685-3131, exten 289. *Chmn* Fred Stephens; *Instrs* FT 6.
Estab 1950; den; D&E; ent req HS dipl, ent exam, ACT, GED; degrees AA, BA, BS and BM (Music & Music Educ) 4 yr; schol; SC 22, LC 10; enrl D 400, E 360, maj 50.
Courses: Advertising Design; Aesthetics; Architecture; Art Education; Ceramics; Drafting; Drawing; Graphic Arts; History of Art; Lettering; Painting; Photography; Teacher Training; Textile Design; Three-Dimensional Design.
Adult Hobby Classes: Same as above.
Summer School: Enrl 50; tui for term of 6 wk beginning June. Courses—Ceramics; Drawing; Photography.

KENTUCKY WESLEYAN COLLEGE,* Department of Fine Arts, 3000 Frederica St, 42301. *Chmn* Dr Emil G Ahnell; *Instrs* FT 1.
Dept estab 1950; den; degree BA 4 yr; schol; SC 11, LC 4; enrl maj 40.
Tuition: Campus res.
Courses: Advertising Design; Art Appreciation; Art History; Arts and Crafts; Ceramics and Sculpture; Commercial Art; Drawing, Painting & Design-4 yr; Graphic Arts; Illustration; Jewelry; Teacher Training; Watercolor.
Summer School: Enrl 60. Courses—Art Survey; Art for the Elementary Schools.

PIPPA PASSES

ALICE LLOYD COLLEGE,* Art Department, 41844. *Chmn* Golden Glen Hale; *Instrs* FT 1, PT 1.
Estab 1922; pvt; D&E; ent req HS dipl, ent exam; degrees AA and CA 2 yr; schol; SC 6, LC 1; enrl maj 5.
Courses: Drawing; Painting; Photography; Sculpture.
Adult Hobby Classes: Enrl 40; tui free. Courses—Ceramics.

RICHMOND

EASTERN KENTUCKY UNIVERSITY,* Art Department, 40475. Tel: 606-622-2046. *Chmn* Daniel N Shindelbower; *Instrs* FT 14, PT 2.
Estab 1910; pub; D; ent req HS grad; degrees BA, BFA and MA (Educ) 4 yr; SC 30, LC 6, GC 6 (5 of which may be repeated twice).

Courses: Drawing Media; Figure Drawing; Figure Painting; Graphics II; Greek & Roman Art; Metal Casting; Painting Media; Sculpture, Synthetic Media; Senior Exhibition; Twentieth Century Painting.
Summer School: Tui campus res available beginning June.

WILLIAMSBURG

CUMBERLAND COLLEGE,* Department of Art, Walnut St, College Sta Box 523, 40769. Tel: 606-549-0498. *Acting Head Dept* Russell A Parker; Instrs FT 4.
Estab 1959; den; D&E; ent req HS dipl, special approval may be granted for admission; degrees BA and BS 4 yr; schol; SC 26, LC 12; enrl D 720, E 90, maj 38.
Tuition: $1165 per yr; campus res $860.
Courses: Aesthetics; Art Education; Basketry; Batik; Ceramics; Drawing; Enameling; Graphic Arts; Handicrafts; History of Art & Archaeology; Jewelry; Lettering; Museum Staff Training; Painting; Sculpture; Teacher Training; Weaving.
Summer School: Enrl 110; term of 5 wk beginning June. Courses—Art Appreciation; Art History; Two and Three Dimensional Studio.

WILMORE

ASBURY COLLEGE, Art Department, 40390. Tel: 606-858-3511. *Head Dept Prof* Rudy Medlock, MFA; *Prof* Knippers, MFA; *Prof* Savage, MA; *Prof* Seifert, MA; *Prof* Webster, MFA.
Estab 1892; pvt; D&E; ent req HS dipl; degrees AB and BS 4 yr; schol; SC 30, LC 6; enrl D 1250, maj 65, others 250.
Tuition: $500 per quarter; campus res room and board $1000.
Courses: Aesthetics; Art Education; Art History; Ceramics; Drawing; Handicrafts (batik, weaving); Lettering; Mixed Media; Painting; Photography; Printmaking; Sculpture; Stage Design; Teacher Training; Theatre Arts.
Children's Classes: Enrl 13; tui $12 per 5 lessons. Courses—Drawing; Painting.
Summer School: Enrl 12 each; term of four to eight wks beginning June 7th. Courses—Crafts; Drawing; Painting.

LOUISIANA

BATON ROUGE

LOUISIANA STATE UNIVERSITY, Department of Fine Arts, 70803. Tel: 504-388-5403. *Head Dept* Dr Walter E Rutkowski, DEd; *Asst Prof* Gerald Bower, MFA; *Prof* Jim Burke, MFA; *Prof* Tom Cavanaugh, MFA; *Asst Prof* Marchita Mauck, PhD; *Prof* Sid Garrett, MFA; *Prof* Paul Dufour, MFA; *vis prof*—Edward Clark, painting, one semester.
Estab 1874, dept estab 1935; pub; D&E; ent req HS dipl, ACT scores; degrees BFA 4 yr, MFA 2 additional yr; schol; SC 90, LC 40 GC 40.
Tuition: Res—Undergrad and grad $410 per yr, $205 per sem, $65-$175 PT; Nonres—Undergrad $1240 per yr, $620 per sem, $200-$525 PT, grad $910 per yr, $405 per sem, $120-$310 PT; campus res room and board $1600.
Courses: Advertising Design; Aesthetics; Art Education; Art History; Ceramics; Commercial Art; Conceptual Art; Constructions; Drafting; Drawing; Film; Goldsmithing; Graphic Arts; Graphic Design; History of Art and Archaeology; Illustration; Interior Design; Jewelry; Landscape Architecture; Lettering; Mixed Media; Painting; Photography; Printmaking; Sculpture; Silversmithing; Teacher Training.
Summer School: Tui- $122 for term of 9 wks beginning June 5th. Courses—varies.

HAMMOND

SOUTHEASTERN LOUISIANA UNIVERSITY, Department of Art, 70402. *Head Dept & Prof* Ronald M Zaccari, EdD; *Instrs* C Roy Blackwood, MFA; *Prof* Hymel G Falgoust, MA; *Asst Prof* Ronald Kennedy MFA; *Asst Prof* Barbara Tardo, MA; *Assoc Prof* Barbara Walker, PhD.
Estab 1925; pub; D&E; ent req HS dipl, ACT; degrees BA (Educ) and BA (Humanities) 4 yr; SC 25, LC 4, GS 2; enrl D 109, E 75, maj 109;
Courses: Aesthetics; Art Education; Art History; Ceramics; Drawing; Goldsmithing; Graphic Arts; Jewelry; Painting; Photography; Printmaking; Sculpture; Teacher Training.

LAFAYETTE

UNIVERSITY OF SOUTHWESTERN LOUISIANA,* School of Art and Architecture, 70501. Tel: 318-233-3850, exten 521, 522, 523. *Dir* Michel Pillet; Instrs FT 31, PT 5.
Estab 1900; pub; degrees BArch and BFA 4-5 yr; enrl univ 13,500.

Courses: Advertising Design; Architecture; Art Education; Ceramics; Choreographic Design; Fine Arts; Interior Architecture; Photography.

LAKE CHARLES

McNEESE STATE UNIVERSITY, Department of Visual Arts, Ryan St, 70609. Tel: 318-477-2520. *Head Dept* Nowell A Daste, MA; *Assoc Prof* Grace Ramke, MFA; *Asst Prof* Constance Davis, MFA; *Asst Prof* William Iles, MFA; *Asst Prof* James A Hooper Jr, MA.
Estab 1950, dept estab 1953; pub; D&E; ent req HS dipl; degrees BA (Art Educ) and BA (Studio Arts) 4 yr; schol; C 24, LC 4, GC 1; enrl D 85, E 15, nonmaj 215, maj 85.
Tuition: Res—Undergrad and grad $900; Nonres—Undergrad and grad $350.
Courses: Advertising Design; Architecture; Art Education; Art History; Drafting; Drawing; Handicrafts (survey crafts course); Painting; Printmaking; Sculpture; Teacher Training.
Adult Hobby Classes: Enrl 15 ea; tui $75 per sem. Courses—Drawing and Composition; Painting.
Summer School: Courses—Varies, (course from the standard dept course offerings).

METAIRIE

DAVID SCHOOL OF BASIC ART INC,* 5050 W Esplanade, 70002. Tel: 504-888-3630. *Pres* David W Jenks; Instrs FT 4.
Estab 1969; pvt; D&E; ent req none in particular; degree none; SC 6; enrl 125 per wk.
Courses: Aesthetics; Drawing; Painting.
Children's Classes: Eight wk course, Sat and after school weekdays.

MONROE

NORTHEAST LOUISIANA UNIVERSITY, College of Liberal Arts, Department of Art, 71209. Tel: 318-342-3110. *Head Dept Prof* Edward E Schutz, EdD; *Prof* James B Edwards, PhD; *Assoc Prof* Robert G Ward, MFA; *Asst Prof* Brian R Fassett, MA; *Asst Prof* Richard E Hayes, MFA; *Asst Prof* Gary L Ratcliff, MFA; *Asst Prof* Jean F Taylor, MA; *Asst Prof* Jo Ella Williams, MA.
Estab 1931, dept estab 1956; pub; D&E; ent req HS dipl; degrees BA and BFA 4 yr, MEd; SC 28, LC 4, GC 9; enrl nonmaj 300, maj 150, GS 3.
Tuition: Res—$80-$206; Nonres—$80-$521 (depending on credit load); campus res room and board.
Courses: Advertising Design; Aesthetics; Art Education; Art History; Ceramics; Drawing; Fiber Art; Graphic Arts; Handicrafts; Jewelry; Lettering; Painting; Photography; Printmaking; Sculpture; Teacher Training; Weaving.
Summer School: Tui—res $41-$64; Nonres—$14-169 (depending on credit load). Courses—Too varied to list.

NATCHITOCHES

NORTHWESTERN STATE UNIVERSITY OF LOUISIANA, Department of Art, 71457. Tel: 318-357-4544. *Head Dept* Grady Harper, PhD; *Prof* Billy J Bryant, DEd; *Assoc Prof* Charles V Coke, MA; *Assoc Prof* Rivers C Murphy, MFA; *Asst Prof* Robert Recort, MFA; *Assoc Prof* Mary C Roberts, DEd; *Assoc Prof* James C Thorn, MFA.
Estab 1885; pub; D&E; degrees BA and BS 4 yr, MA 2 yr, special prog for advanced students MA in Art; SC 67, LC 17, GC 36, enrl maj 93, GS 9.
Courses: ‡Advertising Design; ‡Art Education; Art History; Ceramics; Collage; Commercial Art; Drawing; Fashion Arts; Graphic Arts; Graphic Design; Illustration; ‡Interior Design; Lettering; Mixed Media; Painting; Photography; Printmaking; Sculpture; Teacher Training; Textile Design.
Adult Hobby Classes: Courses—Drawing; Painting.

NEW ORLEANS

DELGADO JUNIOR COLLEGE,* Department of Fine Arts, 615 City Park Ave, 70119. Tel: 504-486-7373. Instrs FT 2, PT 2.
Dept estab 1967; pub; D&E; ent req HS dipl, 18 yr old; degrees AA and AS 2 yr; schol; SC 12-20, LC 12-20; enrl D 150, E 65, maj 60.
Tuition: No campus res.
Courses: Art Appreciation; Drawing; History of Art & Archaeology; Painting.

LOYOLA UNIVERSITY OF NEW ORLEANS,* Department of Visual Arts, 6363 St Charles Ave, 70118. Tel: 504-866-5471, exten 240. *Chmn* Brother Gebhard Frohlich; Instrs FT 3, PT 2.
Den; D&E; ent req HS dipl, ent exam; degrees BA Visual Arts 4 yr; schol; SC 9, LC 3; enrl D 150, E 45, maj 28.

Courses: Ceramics; Drawing; Painting; Sculpture; Teacher Training.
Summer School: Enrl 40; term of 6 wk beginning in June; Courses—Drawing; Painting; Sculpture.

JOHN McCRADY ART SCHOOL OF NEW ORLEANS,* 910 Bourbon St, 70016. Tel: 504-529-5268. Instrs PT 4.
Estab 1942; pvt; D&E; ent req HS dipl, ent exam, examples or color slides of work; degree none; schl; SC 4.
Courses: Advertising Design; Commercial Art; Drawing; Fashion Arts; Graphic Design; History of Art & Archaeology; Illustration; Lettering; Painting; Textile Design.
Adult Hobby Classes: Courses—Painting (various mediums and techniques).
Children's Classes: Courses—All subjects.
Summer School: Dir Mary B McCrady. Term June and July.

NEW ORLEANS ART INSTITUTE, 2926 Canal St, 70119. Tel: 504-822-1453. *Dir* Walter A Labiche.
Estab 1970; pvt; D&E; ent req HS equivalent; degrees dipl; enrl D 22, E 22.
Tuition: $93.50 full time, $70 ¾ time.
Courses: Advertising Design; Air Brush; Calligraphy; Commercial Art; Fashion Arts; Graphic Arts; Graphic Design; Illustration; Isometrics; Lettering; Mixed Media; Painting; Photography Retouching; Technical Illustration.

SOUTHERN UNIVERSITY IN NEW ORLEANS, Art Department, 6400 Press Dr, 70126. Tel: 504-282-7157, exten 257. *Head Dept & Prof* Jack Jordan, MFA; *Asst Prof* Roscoe Reddix, MA; *Asst Prof* Sara Dickenson, MA; *Asst Prof* Rodney Ferguson, MFA.
Estab 1951, dept estab 1960; pub; D&E; ent req HS dipl; degrees BA 4 yr; enrl D 21, E 26, nonmaj 700, maj 47.
Courses: Art Education; Art History; Ceramics; Commercial Art; Drawing; Fashion Arts; Graphic Arts; Handicrafts; Painting; Photography; Printmaking; Sculpture; Teacher Training.

TULANE UNIVERSITY
—School of Architecture,* 70018. Tel: 504-865-6472. *Dean* William K Turner; Instrs FT 18, PT 3.
Sch estab 1907; pvt; degrees BArch, 5 yrs, MArch; enrl 310.
Courses: ‡Architecture.
—Newcomb College, Art Department, 60 Newcomb Place, 70118. Tel: 504-865-4631. *Chmn* Pat Trivigno, MA; *Assoc Chmn Art Hist* Caecilia Davis, PhD; *Prof* Norman B Boothby, MFA; *Prof* Jessie J Poesch, PhD; *Prof* Donald Robertson, PhD; *Prof* James L Steg, MFA; *Prof* Jules Struppeck, MA; *Assoc Prof* Franklin Adams, MA; *Assoc Prof* Harold E Carney, MFA; *Assoc Prof* Arthur Kern, MFA; *Asst Prof* Gene Koss, MFA; *Instrs* Elizabeth Langhorne, PhD; *Asst Prof* Richard Tuttle, PhD.
Col estab 1886, dept estab 1894; pvt; D&E; ent req admis to one of Cols of Tulane Univ; degrees BA (Studio Art), BFA (Studio Art) and BA (Art Hist) 4 yrs, MA (Art Hist) and MFA (Studio Art) 2 yrs, MAT (Studio or Art Hist) 4 yrs; schl; SC 22, LC 8, GC 18; enrl D 944, E approx 120, nonmaj 700, maj 100, grad 25.
Tuition: $1770 per sem, $405 per unit, $147 per sem hr; campus res, room $820-$900 per yr, board $390-440 per sem.
Courses: Art Education; ‡Art History; ‡Ceramics; Drawing; ‡Painting; ‡Photography; ‡Printmaking; ‡Sculpture; Teacher Training.

UNIVERSITY OF NEW ORLEANS, Department of Fine Arts, 70122. Tel: 504-283-0493. *Chmn* Peggy McDowell, MA; *Prof* William Thomas Young, EdD; *Assoc Prof* Calvin Harlan, MFA; *Assoc Prof* Howard Jones, MFA; *Assoc Prof* Jim Richard, MFA; *Assoc Prof* George Rowan, MFA; *Asst Prof* Doyle Gertjejansen, MFA; *Asst Prof* Carolyn K Lewis, PhD; *Asst Prof* John P Smith, MA.
Estab 1958, dept estab 1968; pub; D&E; ent req HS dipl; degrees BA 4 yr, MFA 2 yr; SC 16, LC 11, GC 3; enrl D 14,000 (university), nonmaj 1000, maj 150, GS 14.
Tuition: Res—Undergrad $424 per yr, $212 per sem, $83-$180 PT, grad $424 per yr, $212 per sem, $98-$180 PT; Nonres—Undergrad $627 per sem, $241-$545 PT, grad $412 per sem, $178-$340 PT, campus res room and board $1332.
Courses: Art Education; ‡Art History; Drawing; ‡Graphic Arts; ‡Painting; Photography; ‡Printmaking; ‡Sculpture.
Summer School: Tui $139 for term of 6 wks beginning June. Courses—Art History; Art Structure; Drawing; Graphics, Painting.

XAVIER UNIVERSITY OF LOUISIANA, Department of Fine Arts, Palmetto and Pine St, 70125. Tel: 504-486-7411, exten 284, 351. *Chmn* John T Scott, MFA; *Asst Prof* Charles Graves, MFA; *Asst Prof* Lloyd Bennett, MFA; *Prof* Claudine McKay, MFA; *Prof Emeritus* Numa Rousseve, MA; *Instr* Martin Payton, MFA; *Instr* Diane Lehder, MA.
Estab 1926, dept estab 1935; den; D&E; ent req HS dipl, SAT or ACT, health cert, C average at least; degrees BA, BFA, BS and MA; schl; SC 48, LC 10; enrl D 50, E 12, nonmaj 10 maj 52.

Tuition: Res—Undergrad $1700 per yr, $50 per sem, $75 per cr hr, $60 overload; Nonres—Undergrad $76 per cr hr; campus res room and board $1260.
Courses: ‡Advertising Design; Aesthetics; ‡Art Education; Art History; Calligraphy; ‡Ceramics; Collage; Construction; ‡Drawing; Film; ‡Graphic Arts; ‡Graphic Design; Handicrafts (batik, leather, tie-dye); Jewelry; Lettering; Mixed Media; ‡Painting; Photography; ‡Printmaking; ‡Sculpture; Stage Design; Teacher Training; Textile Design; Theatre Arts; Video.
Adult Hobby Classes: Courses—Creative Crafts.

PINEVILLE

LOUISIANA COLLEGE,* Department of Art, 71360. Tel: 318-487-7262. *Chmn* John T Suddith; *Asst Prof* Charles Jeffress.
Den; ent req HS grad; degrees BA and BS 4 yr, 49 hr of art req plus 78 hr acad for degree; LC, Lab C; enrl maj 30.
Courses: Art Education; Studio Arts.

RUSTON

LOUISIANA TECH UNIVERSITY,* School of Art and Architecture, PO Box 6277, Tech Station, 71270. Tel: 318-257-3909. *Dir* Joseph W Strother; Instrs FT 19, PT 6.
Estab 1904; pub; D; ent req HS dipl; BA, BFA, MA and MFA 4 yr; SC 98, LC 8, GC 87; enrl maj 652, others 538.
Tuition: $116.50 per quarter.
Year round program on Rome, Italy Campus.
Courses: Architecture; Commercial Art; Crafts; Design; Fine Arts; General Art; Interior Design; Photography; Teacher Training; Textiles, Clothing & Related Art (in Home Ec).
Summer School.

SHREVEPORT

CENTENARY COLLEGE OF LOUISIANA, Department of Art, Centenary Blvd, 71104. Tel: 318-869-5261. *Prof Art & Chmn Dept* Willard Cooper, MFA; *Adj Prof* Elizabeth Friedenberg, MA; *Lectr* David Horner, MFA; *Lectr* B Lee Sutton, BID.
Estab 1825; den; D&E; ent req HS dipl, SAT or ACT; degree BA 4 yrs; schl; SC 22, LC 8; enrl D 125 sem.
Tuition: $1920 per yr, $75 per hr; campus res room and board $800 per yr.
Courses: Aesthetics; Art Education; Art History; Ceramics; Commercial Art; Drafting; Drawing; Graphic Arts; Handicrafts (weaving); ‡Painting; Printmaking; Teacher Training.
Ault Hobby Classes: Enrl 550 (for people over 60); no tui. Courses—Studio Art & Appreciation.
Summer School: Dir Willard Cooper. Tui $37.50 per hr for term of 8 wks beginning June 5. Courses—Drawing; Painting; Art History.

THIBODAUX

NICHOLLS STATE UNIVERSITY, Department of Art, 70301 (Mailing Add: PO Box 2025, 70301). *Head Dept & Assoc Prof* Dr Armando Garzon-Blanco, PhD; *Asst Prof* Lula Ameen, MED; *Asst Prof* John Mayne, MFA; *Instr* Leonard Dowhie, MFA; *Instr* Michael Howes, MFA; Instrs FT 5, PT 2.
Estab 1948; pub; D&E; ent req HS dipl, ACT exam; degrees BA 4 yr; SC 73, LC 6; enrl D 100; nonmaj 20, maj 80, others 20. Res—Undergrad $210 per sem, Nonres—Undergrad $525 per sem; campus res room and board $480.
Courses: ‡Advertising Design; Art Education; Art History; ‡Ceramics; Commercial Art; Conceptual Art; ‡Drawing; Graphic Arts; Graphic Design; Illustration; Industrial Design; Mixed Media; ‡Painting; Photography; ‡Printmaking; ‡Sculpture; Teacher Training.
Summer School: Dean Dan S Montz; Enrl 3000; tui $110, Nonres—$270 for term of 9 wks beginning June 6th. Courses—Advertising Design; Art Education; Art History; Ceramics; Painting; Photography; Printmaking; Sculpture.

MAINE

BRUNSWICK

BOWDOIN COLLEGE, Art Department, Visual Art Center, 04011. Tel: 207-725-8731, exten 697, 695. *Chmn* Thomas Cornell, BA; *Dir* Larry Lutchmansingh, PhD; *Primary Faculty* Jeffrey Muller, PhD; Philip C Beam, PhD; Joseph Nicoletti, MFA; John McKee, MA; James Harley, MA.

Estab 1794; pvt; D&E; ent req HS dipl; degrees BA 4 yr; schol; SC 15, LC 18; enrl D 655, maj 47.
Tuition: $4100 per yr, campus res room and board $1680.
Courses: ‡Art History, ‡Painting.

DEER ISLE

HAYSTACK MOUNTAIN SCHOOL OF CRAFTS, 04627. Tel: 207-348-2816, 348-6946. *Dir* Howard M Evans; Instrs FT 28.
Estab 1951; pvt; summer school; D; ent req HS dipl; enrl D 75.
Tuition: $60 per wk, plus shop fees.
Courses: Ceramics; Fabric Structure & Embellishment; Glassblowing; Graphics; Handicrafts (stained glass, weaving); Jewelry; Metalsmithing; Photography; Woodworking.

GORHAM

UNIVERSITY OF MAINE AT PORTLAND-GORHAM, Art Department, College Ave, 04038. Tel: 207-780-5460. *Chmn* Juris K Ubans, MFA; *Assoc Prof* Michael G Moore, MFA; *Assoc Prof* Patt Franklin, MFA; *Asst Prof* Duncan Hewitt, MFA; *Asst Prof* Jean Henry, MA; *Assoc Prof* Lawrence Rakovan, MAE; *Assoc Prof* Jeana Bearce, MA; Faculty PT 7.
Estab 1956; pub; D&E; ent req HS dipl plus portfolio sophomore year; degrees BA, BFA, BS 4 yr; SC 9, LC 2; enrl maj 120.
Tuition: Res—Undergrad $600 yr, $30 per cr hr; Nonres—Undergrad $1800 yr, $90 per cr hr; campus res room and board res—$1395; nonres—$1515.
Courses: Aesthetics; Art Education; Art History; Ceramics; Drawing; Painting; Photography; Printmaking; Sculpture; Textile Design.
Summer School: Dir Continuing Educ Dept William Mortensen. Tui $30 per cr hr for term of 3-6 wk, beginning May 20. Courses—Art History; Studio.

HINCKLEY

HINCKLEY SCHOOL OF CRAFTS, 04944. Tel: 207-453-9991. *Dir* Susan L. Steele, BA; *Instrs* Gayle Fraas, BS; *Instr* Joy Warren; *Instr* Lou Leal, *Instr* Sandy Wiley, BFA; *Instr* Gayle Jann, BA; Duncan Slade, Artist-in-Residence, BS.
Estab 1977, pvt; D&E; schol; SC 7, enrl D 60, E 40.
Tuition: Campus res room and board.
Courses: Ceramics; Jewelry; Natural Dyeing; Photography; Spinning; Textile Design; Weaving.
Adult Hobby Classes: Enrl 60, tui $50 plus materials per 10 wks. Courses—all classes are adult education.
Children's Classes: Enrl varies; tui $6 per day. Courses—One day workshops once a month.
Summer School.

KENNEBUNKPORT

ROGER DEERING SCHOOL OF OUTDOOR PAINTING,* Ocean Ave & Elm St, 04046. Tel: 207-294-8632. *Dir* Roger Deering; *Registrar and Secy* Winifred Deering.
Estab 1940; pvt; D; enrl 15 ea course.
Summer School: Term of 5 wks beginning June through July.
Courses—Demonstrations; Lectures; Marine and Landscape oil and watercolor; Outdoor Painting classes.

LEWISTON

BATES COLLEGE, Liberal Arts College,* Art Department, 04240. Tel: 207-783-3941. *Chmn* Donald Lent; Instrs FT 3, PT 1.
Estab 1864, dept estab 1964; pvt; D; degree BA 4 yr; SC 9, LC 13; enrl 1200 total.
Courses: Ceramics; Drawing; Painting; Printmaking.

ORONO

UNIVERSITY OF MAINE, Art Department, 04473. Tel: 207-581-7691. *Chmn Prof* Michael H Lewis, MFA; *Prof* Vincent A Hartgen, MFA; *Assoc Prof* David O Decker, MA; *Assoc Prof* Ronald Ghiz, MFA; *Asst Prof* Barbara Cushing, MFA; *Asst Prof* William Eickhorst, EdD; *Asst Prof* C Regina Kelley, MFA.
Estab 1862, dept estab 1946; pub; D&E; ent req HS dipl, 3 CEEB achievement tests; degrees BA and BS 4 yr; SC 24, LC 24; enrl D 178, maj 178.
Tuition: Res—Undergrad $795 per yr, $397.50 per sem; Nonres—Undergrad $2263 per yr, $1131.50 per sem; campus res room and board $1605.

Courses: Aesthetics; ‡Art Education; Art History; Commercial Art; ‡Drawing; Film; ‡Painting; Printmaking; ‡Sculpture; Teacher Training.
Summer School: Dir Edward W Hackett. Tui $30 per cr hr. Courses—Art Education Workshop and Laboratory; Basic Drawing; Basic Painting; Fundamentals of Painting; Principles of Art; Problems in Art; Teaching of Art.

PORTLAND

PORTLAND SCHOOL OF ART, 04101. Tel: 207-775-3052. *Dir* William C Collins, MFA; *Instr* Richard A Butz, MFA; *Instr* Edwin P Douglas, MFA; *Instr* John Eide, MFA; *Instr* Allan R Gardner, Dipl; *Instr* Joseph Guertin, BFA; *Instr* Ernest T Thompson, Dipl; *Instr* John T Ventimiglia, MFA; *vis prof*—Harold Schremmer, silver & light metals, Spring 1978.
Estab 1882; pvt; D&E; ent req HS dipl, portfolio; degrees BFA 4 yr. Under Maine law, an academically advanced high school senior may take the freshman yr at Portland School of Art for both HS and Portland School of Art credit. SC 37, LC 9; enrl D 193 E 160, maj 193, others 3 PT.
Tuition: $1162.50 per yr; plus student activity fee $10, lab fees (other than major), $15-$20 sem; lab fees (majors) $15-$50 per sem; no campus res.
Courses: Art History; ‡Ceramics; Drawing; ‡Graphic Design; History of Art and Archaeology; ‡Jewelry; ‡Painting; ‡Photography; ‡Printmaking; ‡Sculpture; ‡Silversmithing.
Adult Hobby Classes: Enrl 160; tui $75 per cr. Courses—Ceramics; Design; Drawing; Photography; Printmaking.
Children's Classes: Enrl 140; tui $75 per class. Courses—Ceramics; Drawing; Photography; Sculpture; Silversmithing.
Summer School: Enrl 81; tui $75 per cr for term of 6 wk beginning June 19. Courses—Art History; Ceramics; Two Dimensional Design; Three Dimensional Design; Drawing; English; Graphic Design; Jewelry & Silversmithing; Painting; Photography; Printmaking; Sculpture; Watercolor.

SKOWHEGAN

SKOWHEGAN SCHOOL OF PAINTING AND SCULPTURE, Box 449, 04976. (Mailing Add: Winter Office 329 East 68th St, New York, NY, 10021). Tel: 207-474-9345. *Dir* Joan C Franzen; vis prof—six each yr, painting, sculpture.
Estab 1946; pvt; summer school for independent work; ent req presentation of slide portfolio; degrees credits recognized for transfer, no degrees; enrl 65.
Tuition: Summer only $1950 includes room and board (residency required).
Courses: Drawing; Fresco Technique; Painting; Sculpture.

SPRINGVALE

NASSON COLLEGE,* Art Department, 04083. Tel: 207-324-5340. *Dir* George Burk; Instrs, FT 2.
Estab 1935; pvt; D&E; ent req ent exam; degrees 4 yr; SC, LC.

WATERVILLE

COLBY COLLEGE, Art Department, 04901. Tel: 207-873-1131, exten 215. *Chmn Art Dept* James M Carpenter, PhD; *Prof* William B Miller, PhD; *Assoc Prof* Harriett Matthews, MFA; *Asst Prof* Barbara Kassel, MFA; *Asst Prof* Germaine Fuller, MA; *Asst Prof* Margaret Miller, BA; different vis artists each Jan.
Estab 1813, dept estab 1944; pvt; D&E; ent req HS dipl; degree BA 4 yrs; schol; SC 12, LC 17; enrl D 350, nonmaj 305, maj 45.
Tuition: $4300 per yr; campus res.
Courses: Art History; History of Art & Archaeology; Painting; Sculpture.

MARYLAND

BALTIMORE

COLLEGE OF NOTRE DAME OF MARYLAND, Art Department, 4701 N Charles St, 21210. Tel: 301-435-0100. *Chmn & Prof* Ruth Nagle Watkins, MEd; *Prof* Mary John Bersch, MFA; *Assoc Prof* Virginia Adams, MFA; Gladys Goldstein, BA; pvt; den; D&E; ent req HS dipl, ent exam; degrees BA 4 yrs; schol; SC 16, LC 8; enrl D 285, nonmaj 250, maj 35.
Tuition: Res—Undergrad $4100 yr, $2050 per sem; Nonres—Undergrad $2500 per yr, $1250 per sem; campus res room and board $1600.

Courses: Advertising Design; Aesthetics; Art History; Ceramics; Collage; Commercial Art; Drawing; Film; Graphic Arts; Graphic Design; Handicrafts (batik, weaving, macrame, rug hooking, basketry); History of Art & Archaeology; Painting; Photography; Printmaking; Sculpture; Stage Design; Teacher Training.
Adult Hobby Classes: Enrl 200; tui $60 per cr. Courses—Same as regular classes.
Summer School: Dir Mary Ly McNeal. Tui $60 per cr. Courses—Advanced painting; watercolor.

COMMUNITY COLLEGE OF BALTIMORE, Department of Art, 2901 Liberty Heights Avenue, 21215. Tel: 301-396-7980. *Chmn Prof* Bennard B Perlman, MA; *Prof* Nelson Adlin, MA; *Prof* Allyn O Harris, MFA; *Assoc Prof* Frieda Sohn, BA; *Assoc Prof* David Bahr, MFA; *Assoc Prof* Carlton Leverette, MFA; *Asst Prof* Mary Ann E Mears, MA; Instrs FT 7, PT 4.
Estab 1947; pub; D&E; ent req HS dipl, ent exam, also adm with HS equivality; degrees AA 2 yr; schol; SC 17, LC 2; enrl D&E 9400, nonmaj 250, maj 85.
Tuition: City res—$360 per yr, $180 per sem, $18 per cr hr; State res—$720 per yr, $360 per sem, $36 per cr hr; Nonres—$1080 per yr, $540 per sem; $54 per cr hr; no campus res.
Courses: Advertising Design; ‡Art Education; Art History; Ceramics; ‡Commercial Art; Drawing; Fashion Arts; Graphic Arts; Graphic Design; History of Art and Archaeology; Interior Design; Jewelry; Lettering; ‡Painting; ‡Photography; Printmaking; Sculpture; Textile Design.
Summer School: Tui same as above per cr hr for term of 5 wks beginning June.

COPPIN STATE COLLEGE, Art Department, 2500 West North Avenue, 21218. Tel: 301-448-5925, 448-5929. *Head Dept Coordr* Luke A Shaw, Instrs FT 1, PT 2.
Degrees: BA, BS and MA; schol; SC 6, LC 7; enrl D 350, E 45, others Minor.
Tuition: No campus res.
Courses: Advertising Design; Art Education; Art History; Calligraphy; Ceramics; Collage; Drawing Film; Graphic Design; History of Art and Archaeology; Lettering; Painting; Photography; Printmaking; Sculpture; Teacher Training; Theatre Arts.

JOHNS HOPKINS UNIVERSITY, Charles & 34th Sts, 21218. Tel: 301-366-3300, exten 381, 1234.
—**Department of the History of Art.*** *Chmn* Herbert L Lessler; Instrs FT 7, PT 2.
Estab 1947; pvt; D&E; degrees 4 yrs; schol; LC; enrl 10-30 in advanced courses, c 200 in introductory courses.
Tuition: $3750 per yr; campus res.
Courses: History of Art.
—**School of Medicine, Department of Art as Applied to Medicine,** 725 N Wolfe St, 21205. Tel: 301-955-3213. *Assoc Prof Art as Applied to Med & Dir Dept* Ranice W Crosby, MLA; *Asst Prof* Gary P Lees, MS; *Asst Prof* Leon Schlossberg; *Instr* Marjorie Gregerman, BA; *Instr* Howard C Bartner, MA; *Instr* Elizabeth Blumenthal; *Instr* J Lindsey Burch; *Instrs* Timothy Hengst, MA.
Univ estab 1876, Sch Med estab 1893, dept estab 1911; pvt; D; ent req Baccalaureate degree; degree MA 2 yr; schol; SC , LC 5, GC 14; enrl 14, grad 13, special 1.
Tuition: $4050 per yr; campus res room and board $1164 per yr.
Courses: Display; Drawing; Graphic Design; Illustration; Intermedia; Mixed Media; Painting; Photography; Sculpture; Video.

MARYLAND INSTITUTE,* College of Art, 1300 W Mt Royal Ave, 21217. Tel: 301-669-9200. *Acting Pres* Theodore E Klitzke; Instrs FT 49, PT 46.
Estab 1826; pvt; D&E; ent req HS grad, exam; degrees BFA and MFA 4 yr, dipl, cert; schol; enrl D 1107, E 554, Sat 280.
Tuition: $2850 per yr; campus res $2200.
Courses: Art Teacher Education; Ceramics; Crafts; Designer-Craftsman; Drawing; Foundation; Graphic Design & Illustration; Interior Design; Painting; Photography; Printmaking; Sculpture.
Summer School: Dean Tom Scott. Enrl 654; tui $50 per cr hr.
—**Hoffberger School of Painting,** *Artist-in-Residence* Grace Hartigan.
Enrl: limited to 20; fel awarded annually for study at the graduate level.
Tuition: Limited.
—**Rinehart School of Sculpture.** *Sculptor-in-Residence* Norman Carlberg.
Free fel awarded annually for study at the the graduate level.
Tuition: Limited.
—**Mount Royal School of Painting.** *Artist-in-Residence* Seymour Shapiro.
Fel awarded annually for study at the graduate level.
Tuition: Limited.

MORGAN STATE UNIVERSITY, College of Arts & Sciences, Department of Art, Hillen Road at Coldspring Lane, 21239. Tel: 301-444-3020. *Chmn* Oliver Patrick Scott, MA; *Asst Prof* Suzanne Daniel, MA; *Asst Prof* Samuel L Green, MA; *Instrs* Thelma Hill, BS; *Assoc Prof* James E Jones, MFA; *Prof* James S Lewis; MFA; *Assoc Prof* Patrick F McQuire, MFA; *Asst Prof* Kenneth L Royster, MFAE.
Estab 1867, dept estab 1950; pub; D&E; ent req HS dipl; degrees BA (Art) and BS (Art Educ) 4 yr, MA (Art History/Museology) and MA (Art Studio) 2 yr; schol; SC 28, LC 11, GC 17; enrl D 340, E 50, nonmaj 250, maj 140, GS 11.
Tuition: Res—Undergrad $830 per yr, $415 per sem, grad $38 per cr hr; Nonres—Undergrad $1750 per yr, $865 per sem; campus res $1721.
Courses: Aesthetics; ‡Architecture; Art Appreciation; ‡Art Education; ‡Art History; Ceramics; Costume Design and Construction; Drafting; Drawing; Film; ‡Graphic Design; Handicrafts (weaving); Interior Design; Jewelry; ‡Landscape Architecture; Lettering; Mixed Media; Museum Staff Training; ‡Painting, ‡Photography; Printmaking; ‡Sculpture; ‡Stage Design; Teacher Training; Textile Design; Theatre Arts; Video.
Children's Classes: Enrl 20; tui $10 per sem. Courses—Painting, Printmaking; Sculpture.
Summer School: Dir Dr Beryl W Williams. Tui $35 per cr for term of 6 wks beginning June and July. Courses—Art Education; Art Appreciation; Basic Design; Photography.

SCHULER SCHOOL OF FINE ARTS, 5 E Lafayette Ave, 21202. Tel: 301-685-3568. *Dir* Hans C Schuler; Instrs PT 3.
Estab 1959; pvt; D&E; degrees 4 yr; SC 9, GC 3, enrl D 50, E 30, grad 2.
Tuition; $1200 per yr, part time students pay by schedule for sem.
Courses: Drawing; Graphic Arts; Painting; Sculpture.
Children's Classes: Tui $165-$225 (Summer Ages 14 and over).
Summer School: Dir Hans C Schuler. Enrl 30; tui $180 for term of 6 wk beginning June; $270 for 6 hr Courses—Drawing; Oil Painting; Sculpture; Watercolor.

TOWSON STATE COLLEGE,* Department of Art, 21204. Tel: 301-823-7500, exten 297. *Chmn* James W Flood; Instrs FT 24, PT 8.
Estab 1866, pub; D&E; ent req HS grad; degrees BA, BS and MEd (Art Educ) 4 yr;
Courses: Art Education; Art History; Ceramics; Drawing; Enameling; Graphic Arts; Jewelry; Painting; Sculpture; Textile Design; Weaving & Textiles; Wood & Metal.
Summer School: Enrl 450; two 5 wk sessions.

BEL AIR

HARFORD COMMUNITY COLLEGE,* Humanities Division, 401 Thomas Run Rd, 21014. Tel: 301-879-8920. *Chmn* Dr Claire Eckels; Instrs FT 4 PT 5.
Estab 1957; pub; D&E; ent req HS dipl: degree AA 2 yrs; schol; SC 17, LC 4; enrl FT 1000, PT 1000.
Tuition: No campus res.
Courses: Architectural Drawing; Ceramics; Design; Drawing; Graphic Arts; History of Art & Archaeology; Interior Design; Painting; Photography; Sculpture.

BOWIE

BOWIE STATE COLLEGE, Department of Fine and Performing Arts, Jericho Park Road, 20715. Tel: 262-3350, exten 441, 442. *Head Dept* Dr Charles W Stallings, EdD; *Asst Prof* Clark Mester Jr, MA; *Asst Prof* Robert Ward; *Assoc Prof* Amos White IV, MFA.
Estab 1865, dept estab 1968; pub; D; ent req HS dipl; degrees BA (Art) and BS (Art Educ); SC 7, LC 3; enrl D 1600, E 350, nonmaj 180, maj 45.
Tuition: Res—Undergrad and grad $750 per yr; Nonres—Undergrad and grad $1650 per yr; campus res.
Courses: Art Education; Art History; Ceramics; Collage; Drawing; Graphic Arts; Mixed Media; Painting; Photography; Printmaking; Sculpture; Teacher Training.
Summer School; Dir Dr Ida Brandon. Courses—Ceramics; Media Workshop.

CATONSVILLE

CATONSVILLE COMMUNITY COLLEGE, Art and Applied Art Department, 21228. Chmn Dr James J Linbsz.
Estab 1957; pub; D&E; ent req HS dipl; degrees AA 2 yr, special prog in Applied Art & Design, Art History, Art Education, Fine Arts; schol; SC 26, LC 6; enrl D 600, E 400, nonmaj 200, maj 300.
Tuition: $15 per sem hr; no campus res.

Courses: Advertising Design; Aesthetics; Architecture; Art Education; Art History; Ceramics; Commercial Art; Drafting; Drawing; Film; Graphic Arts; Graphic Design; History of Art and Archaeology; Illustration; Lettering; Painting; Photography; Sculpture; Theatre Arts; Video.
Summer School: Same as above.

COLLEGE PARK

UNIVERSITY OF MARYLAND,* Art Department, J Millard Tawes Fine Arts Center, 20742. Tel: 301-454-2717. *Chmn* Dr George Levitine; Instrs FT 35, PT 3.
Estab 1944; pub; D; ent req HS dipl, upper half of class; degrees BA, MA, MFA and PhD 4 yr; SC 37, LC 26, GC 17; enrl 3500, maj 700, GS 100.
Tuition: $784 per yr, Nonres—$2174, $44 per cr hr; campus res $878.
Courses: Art Education; Drawing; Graphic Arts; History of Art & Archaeology; Museum Training; Painting; Sculpture; Studio Art.
Summer School: Tui $31 per cr hr for term of 6 wk beginning May through July, second session July through Aug. Courses—as above.

CUMBERLAND

ALLEGANY COMMUNITY COLLEGE,* Art Department, Willow Brook Rd, 21502. Tel: 301-724-7700. *Head Dept* Jerry L Post; Instrs FT 1.
Estab 1966; pub; D&E; ent req HS dipl; degree AA 2 yr; schol; SC 6, LC 1; enrl D 30, E 9.
Tuition: No campus res.
Courses: Ceramics; Drawing; Painting; Survey of Art History; Theatre Arts; Two & Three Dimensional Design.
Summer School: Term of 6 wk beginning July. Courses—Painting; Two-Dimensional Design.

EMMITSBURG

MOUNT SAINT MARY'S COLLEGE, Fine Arts Department, 21727. Tel: 301-447-6122. *Chmn* Lewis McAllister, MA; *Prof* Dorothea Barrick O'Toole, MFA; *Prof* John Lyle, MA; *vis prof*—Betty Pronzas, pastel artist; Arthur Weihrer, wood-carving.
Estab 1808; pvt; D&E; ent req HS dipl, Sat; degrees BA and BS 4 yr, MFA 2 yrs; schol; SC 9, LC 10; enrl D 1200, maj 12.
Tuition: $2500 per yr, $1250 per sem; campus res room and board $1425.
Courses: Art History; Drawing; Painting; Sculpture; Theatre Arts.

FREDERICK

HOOD COLLEGE,* Fine Arts Department, 21701. Tel: 301-663-3131. *Chmn* A Russo; Instrs FT 3.
Estab 1893; pvt; W; degrees 4 yr; SC 10, LC 7; enrl 750.
Tuition: $4750 per yr.
Courses: Art Appreciation; Design & Applied Arts; History of Art; Painting; Sculpture.

FROSTBURG

FROSTBURG STATE COLLEGE,* Department of Art & Art Education, 21532. Tel: 301-689-4351. *Head Dept* George Kramers; Instrs FT 8.
Estab 1898; pub; D; ent req HS dipl; degree BA (Art, Art Educ), BS and MEd (Art Educ) 4 yr; SC 25, LC 5; enrl D 230, maj 150, GS 13.
Tuition: $310 per sem; Nonres—$735 per sem; campus res room $1256 to $1424 per yr, meals $616 to $674.
Courses: Advertising Graphics; Art Education; Art History; Ceramics; Drawing; Graphic Design; Jewelry; Painting; Photography; Printmaking; Sculpture; Teacher Training; Textile Design; Two & Three Dimensional Design.
Children's Classes: Tui $5. Sat school prog.
Summer School: Tui $25 per cr hr for term of 4½ wk beginning May.

LARGO

PRINCE GEORGE'S COMMUNITY COLLEGE, Art Department/Humanities Division, 301 Largo Rd, 20870. Tel: 301-336-6000, exten 324. *Chmn* Jerry Parsons, MFA; *Assoc Prof* Doyle Eskew, MFA; *Assoc Prof* Cecile C Huff, MFA; *Assoc Prof* Gerald King, MFA; *Assoc Prof* John Krumrein, MFA; *Assoc Prof* Joseph Mayer, MFA.
Estab 1958, dept estab 1967; pub; D&E; ent req HS dipl & CGP test; degree AA; school; SC 18, LC 2; enrl D 220, E 140 maj 3%.
Tuition: In County $15.50 per cr hr; In State $36 per cr hr; Out of State $63 per cr hr; no campus res.

Courses: Advertising Design; Art History; Ceramics; Drawing; Illustration; Jewelry; Lettering; Painting; Printmaking; Sculpture.

SAINT MARYS CITY

SAINT MARY'S COLLEGE OF MARYLAND, Humanities Division, 20686. Tel: 301-994-1600, exten 286. *Chmn* Edward E Foster, PhD; *Artist-in-Residence* Earl F Hoffman; *Asst Prof* Joseph B Ross, MA; *Assoc Prof* William Thomas Rowe, MFA; *Asst Prof* Norma Strickland, MFA; *Instrs* Sandra L Underwood, MA; *Assoc Prof* Jonathan Ingersoll, MS.
Estab 1964; pub; D&E; ent req HS dipl, SAT scores; degrees BA and BS 4 yr; schol; SC 14, LC 16; enrl D 155, E 43, nonmaj 128, maj 70.
Tuition: Res—Undergrad $600 per yr; Nonres—Undergrad $1500 per yr; campus res room and board $1135.
Courses: Art Education; Art History; Ceramics; Drawing; Graphic Arts; Handicrafts (loom weaving); History of Art and Archaeology; Jewelry; Museum Staff Training; Painting; Photography; Printmaking; Sculpture; Stage Design; Theatre Arts.
Adult Hobby Classes: Enrl 10 min; tui $30 per student. Courses—Bread Dough, Ceramics; Eggury; Photography.
Children's Classes: Enrl 10 min; tui $30 per student; Courses—Arts; Crafts; Drawing.
Summer School: Dir Dr John Rushbrook. Enrl 7-15 students; tui $30 per cr for term of 6 wks. Courses—Ceramics; Film Study Course; Glass Blowing; Jewelry; Sculpture; Watercolor.

SALISBURY

SALISBURY STATE COLLEGE, Art Department, College and Camden Ave, 21801. Tel: 301-546-3261, exten 417. *Chmn* Kent N Kimmel, MA; *Asst Prof* James L Burgess, MA; *Instr* John R Cleary, MFA; *Instr* Ursula M Ehrhardt, MA; *Asst Prof* Nancy L Lytwyn, MS; *Asst Prof* Marie A Tator, MA.
Estab 1925, dept estab 1970; pub; D&E; ent req HS dipl; SAT verbal and math; degrees BA, BS and BSW 4 yr; MA and MEd 1 yr; SC 26, LC 7, GC 1; enrl nonmaj 400, maj 70, GS 2.
Tuition: Res—Undergrad $705 per yr, $352.50 per sem, $25 per cr hr, other $20 reg/coll ctr; Nonres—Undergrad $1605 per yr, $802.50 per sem, $35 per cr hr, other $20 reg/coll ctr, grad $48 per cr hr, $20 reg/coll ctr; campus res room and board $1300.
Courses: Aesthetics; ‡Art Education; ‡Art History; ‡Ceramics; ‡Commercial Art; Costume Design and Construction; Drawing; ‡European Field Study; Film; ‡Graphic Design; ‡Handicrafts (design in fiber crafts); History of Art and Archaeology; ‡Independent Study; Museum Staff Training; ‡Painting; ‡Photography; ‡Principles of Color; ‡Printmaking; ‡Sculpture; Stage Design; ‡Teacher Training.
Summer School: Dir Dr Harold Schaeffer; Courses—Various Art Education and Studio Courses.

SILVER SPRING

MARYLAND COLLEGE OF ART AND DESIGN, 10500 Georgia Ave, 20902. Tel: 301-649-4454. *Pres* Terrence J Coffman; *Primary Art Faculty:* Oscar Chelimsky, BA; Debra Schaeffer, MFA; Ellen Vincent, MFA; Maurice Clerman; Jack Hammond, MEd; Christopher Bartlett, BEd.
Estab 1955; pvt; D&E; ent req HS dipl, portfolio interview; degree AA 2 yrs; schol; SC 30, LC 12; enrl D 125, E 50, nonmaj 135, maj 40.
Tuition: $2340 per yr, $780 per quarter, $60 per cr hr; no campus res.
Courses: Advertising Design; Art History; Ceramics; ‡Commercial Art; ‡Drawing; Graphic Arts; Graphic Design; Illustration; ‡Painting; Photography; Printmaking; Sculpture.
Children's Classes: Enrl 12, tui $50 per course. Courses—Drawing & Painting.
Summer School: Dir Terrence J Coffman. Tui same as above. Courses—Same as regular quarters.

TOWSON

GOUCHER COLLEGE, Dept of Visual Arts, 21204. Tel: 301-825-3300. *Chmn Prof* Hilton Brown, MFA.
Estab 1885; pvt; D; ent req HS dipl, SAT achievements tests (CEEB); American College Testing Prog; degrees MA 4 yr, MA (Dance-Movement Therapy) 2 yr (beg Sept 1978); schol; SC 38; LC 18; enrl D 970, nonmaj 558, maj (art) 29, maj (other fields) 383.
Tuition: $3700 per yr, $1850 per sem, $462 per 4 sem hr course, MA in Dance-Movement Therapy $104 per sem hr; campus res room and board $2000 plus $75 health fee req.

Courses: Aesthetics; Art History; Art Therapy; Ceramics; Constructions; Costume Design and Construction; Drawing; Film; Graphic Design; Handicrafts (weaving); History of Art and Archaeology; Museum Staff Training; Painting; Photography; Printmaking; Restoration and Conservation; Sculpture; Stage Design; Teacher Training; Theatre Arts.
Summer School: Dir Asst Prof Fontaine M Belford. Enrl 160; tui $50 per cr for term of 4 wks beginning June 12 and July 10th. Courses—(Art) Dance; Fibers Workshop; Nature Drawing Workshop; Photography; Pottery Workshop; Theatre.

WESTMINSTER

WESTERN MARYLAND COLLEGE,* Art Department, 21157. Tel: 301-848-7000, exten 241. *Head Dept* Wasyl Palijczuk; Instrs FT 3, PT 1.
Estab 1867; independent; D&E; ent req HS dipl, ent exam, SAT; degrees BA, BS and MEd 4 yr; SC 15½, LC 12½, GC 6; enrl D 1113, maj 35-50, GS 13.
Tuition: $3175 per yr; campus res $1450.
Courses: Aesthetics; Art Education; Ceramics; Design I & II; Drawing I & II; History of Art & Archaeology; Illustration & Lettering; Introduction to Art; Jewelry; Lettering; Painting I & II; Photography (Jan term & summer); Printmaking; Sculpture I & II; Teacher Training; Watercolor.
Children's Classes: Enrl over 12; Sat AM conducted by coll students.
Summer School: Two 5 wk terms beginning June 21. Courses—Ceramics; Painting; Printmaking; Sculpting; Weaving.

MASSACHUSETTS

AUBURNDALE

LASELL JUNIOR COLLEGE,* Art Department, 1844 Commonwealth Ave, 02166. *Head* Leonie S Bennett; Instrs FT 5, PT 1.
Estab 1851; pvt; D&E; W; ent req HS dipl, ent exam in some depts, portfolio in art dept; degrees AA and AS 2 yrs; schol.
Courses: Advertising Design; Aesthetics; Art for Child Study; Ceramics; Design & Color; Drawing; History of Art & Archaeology; Jewelry; Painting; Photography; Three-Dimensional Design.

AMHERST

AMHERST COLLEGE, Department of Fine Arts, Mead Art Bldg, 01002. Tel: 413-542-2335. *Chmn Dept* Frank Trapp; Instrs FT 7.
Estab 1822; pvt; D; ent req HS dipl; degree BA 4 yrs; schol; SC 15, LC 15.
Tuition: Approx $4550 per yr; campus res approx $1854.
Courses: Aesthetics; History of Art; Painting; Sculpture; Serigraphy.

UNIVERSITY OF MASSACHUSETTS, AMHERST
—College of Arts and Sciences, Department of Art,* 01002. Tel: 413-545-1902. *Prof Art & Chmn Dept* George Wardlaw; Instrs FT 41.
Art Dept estab 1958; pub; ent req HS grad, portfolio required, 15 units HS, ent exam; degrees BA (Studio, Art Hist) and BFA (Studio, Interior Design, Art Educ) 4 yrs, MA (Art Hist), MFA (Ceramics, Painting, Printmaking, Sculpture), MS (Interior Design), MAT; SC 40, LC 19, GC 20; enrl maj undergrad 600, grad 65.
Courses: Art Education; Ceramics; Computer Graphics; Design Graphics; Drawing; Glassblowing; History of Art; Interior Design; Light Workshop; Painting; Photography; Printmaking; Sculpture; Teacher Training; Three-Dimensional Design; Two-Dimensional Design.
—College of Food and Natural Resources, Department of Landscape Architecture and Regional Planning (Landscape Architecture Program), 01003. Tel: 413-545-2255. *Prof & Head* E Bruce MacDougall, PhD; *Dir MLA Prog* Nicholas Dines, MLA.
Estab 1903; pub; D; ent req Bachelor's degree, grad rec, exams, portfolio; degrees MLA 3 yrs; SC 6, LC 5; enrl 35.
Tuition: Res—$335 per sem, $33.50 per cr hr; Nonres—$775 per sem, $77.50 per cr hr; campus res room and board $4000 per yr.
Courses: Drafting; Drawing; Landscape Architecture.

BEVERLY

ENDICOTT COLLEGE, Art Department, 376 Hale St, 01915. Tel: 617-927-0585. *Head Art Dept* J David Broudo, EdM.
Estab 1939; pvt; D; W; ent req HS dipl; degrees AA and AS 2 yrs; schol; enrl D 205, nonmaj 13, maj 192.
Tuition: Res—$4350 per yr (comprehensive fee: tuition, room & board); Nonres—$2600 per yr.

Courses: Advertising Design; Art History; Ceramics; ‡Commercial Art; ‡Costume Design & Construction; Drafting; Drawing; Fashion Arts; Fiber (Weaving); Graphic Arts; Illustration; ‡Interior Design, Jewelry; Painting; ‡Photography; Printmaking; Sculpture; Silversmithing.

MONTSERRAT SCHOOL OF VISUAL ART, Dunham Rd (Mailing Add: Box 62, 01915). Tel: 617-922-8222. *Dir* Joseph Jeswald; *Primary Art Faculty* Oliver Balf, Ethan Berry, Roger Martin, Barbara Moody, Thorpe Feidt, George Gabin, Paul Scott, Dennis Sweeney, Vincent Varvaro and Vincent Ricci.
Estab 1970; pvt; D&E; ent req personal interview and portfolio review; dipl granted 4 yrs; schol; SC 43, LC 3; enrl D 100, E 200.
Tuition: $1400 per yr, $700 per sem, $230 per yr per course; no campus res.
Courses: Advertising Design; Art History; Ceramics; Collage; Commercial Art; Drawing; Graphic Arts; Graphic Design; Illustration; Jewelry; Mixed Media; Painting; Photography; Printmaking; Sculpture; Silversmithing.
Adult Hobby Classes: Enrl 120; tui $60 per 10 wks. Courses—Same as above.
Children's Classes: Enrl 40; tui $35 per 8 wks. Courses—Drawing; Painting.
Summer School: Dir Joseph Jeswald. Enrl 220; tui $40-$70 for term of 8 wks beginning June 26. Courses—Same as above.

BOSTON

ART INSTITUTE OF BOSTON, 700 Beacon St, 02215. Tel: 617-262-1223. *Pres* William H Willis, Jr, MFA; *Chmn Design Dept* Karyl Spiller, MFA; *Chmn Fine Arts Dept* Doninec Cretara, MFA; *Chmn Photography Dept* Bruce Kinch, MFA; *Chmn Found Dept* Nathan Goldstein, MFA; *Chmn Acad Studies* Robert Simon, MFA.
Estab 1912; pvt; D&E; ent req HS dipl, portfolio and interview; degrees (with Northeastern University) BS (Art) and BFA yrs vary; schol; SC 80, LC 20; enrl D 400, E 150.
Tuition: Res—$3400 per yr, $1700 per sem; Nonres—$1750 per yr, $875 per sem; campus res room & board $1650 per yr.
Courses: ‡Advertising Design; Art History; Calligraphy; ‡Ceramics; Collage; ‡Commercial Art; Drawing; Film; Graphic Arts; ‡Graphic Design; History of Art & Archaeology; ‡Illustration; Interior Design; Lettering; Mixed Media; ‡Painting; ‡Photography; ‡Printmaking; ‡Sculpture.
Adult Hobby Classes: Enrl 200; tui $50 per cr. Courses—Continuing education offers most of the above typically 2-3 cr each.
Summer School: Dir Barbara J Apel. Enrl 150; tui $50 per cr for term of 8 wks beginning July 15. Courses—Most of above.

BOSTON CENTER FOR ADULT EDUCATION, 5 Commonwealth Ave, 02116. Tel: 617-267-4430. *Exec Dir* Harriet McLean; *Primary Art Faculty:* Tom Shooter, Dipl; Ellen Stutman, MFA; Alexander Farquharson, Dipl; Shirley Pransky, Dipl.
Estab 1933; pvt; D&E; ent req open to all over 18; no degrees; schol; SC 26, LC 2; enrl D 2300, E 11,218.
Tuition: $42 for art or craft studio course; $34 for lecture course; no campus res.
Courses: Advertising Design; Art History; Calligraphy; Ceramics; Display; Drawing; Graphic Design; Handicrafts; History of Art & Archaeology; Lettering; Painting; Photography; Printmaking; Sculpture; Theatre Arts.
Summer School: Same as winter program.

BOSTON STATE COLLEGE, Art Department, 625 Huntington Ave, 02115. Tel: 617-731-3300, exten 262, 263. *Chairperson Dept* Ronald Polito, EdD; *Prof* Constantine Arvanites, MFA; *Prof* Robert Bertolli, EdD; *Prof* John V Cody, EdM; *Prof* Robert DiGiovanni, MFA; *Prof* Truman Egleston, MFA; *Prof* Joseph Fiorello, AM; *Prof* Walter Fox Tree, MA; *Prof* Gretchen D Lipchitz, MA; *Prof* Christine Nelson, MA, JD; *Prof* Carolyn St Pierre, MA, JD; *Prof* Vincent J Tringale, MEd; *Prof* Clifford S Wrigley, MEd.
Estab 1852; pub; D&E; ent req HS dipl, SAT, Student Descriptive Questionnaire; degrees BA, BS and BSN 4 yrs, MA, MS; SC 20, LC 14, GC 17; enrl D 869, E 229.
Tuition: Res—Undergrad $250 per sem, $20 per cr; Nonres—Undergrad $625 per sem, $53 per cr; no campus res.
Courses: Advertising Design; Architecture; Art Education; Art History; Ceramics; Collage; Commercial Art; Conceptual Art; Drawing; Film; Graphic Arts; Handicrafts (jewelry fabrication); History of Art & Archaeology; Jewelry; Mixed Media; Painting; Photography; Sculpture; Teacher Training; Video.
Summer School: Dir William T Morrissey. Tui $75 res, $96 nonres for one 3 credit course beginning June to mid-Aug.

BOSTON UNIVERSITY, School of Visual Arts, 855 Commonwealth Ave, 02215. Tel: 617-353-3371. *Dir* Edward F Leary, EdM; *Prof* David Aronson; *Prof* Harold Tovish; *Assoc Prof* William Berry; *Assoc Prof* James Weeks; *Assoc Prof* Nancy Smith; *Prof* Philip Guston; sch has vis profs.
Estab 1869, sch estab 1954; pvt; D; ent req HS dipl, portfolio and SAT or ACT; degrees BFA 4 yrs, MFA 2 yrs; schol; SC 38, LC 12, GC 15; enrl 385, nonmaj 200, maj 100, grad 85.
Tuition: $4230 per yr, $132 per cr; campus res room & board $1900 per yr.
Courses: ‡Art Education; Drawing; ‡Graphic Design; Jewelry; ‡Painting; Photography; Printmaking; ‡Sculpture; ‡Studio Teaching (grad level); Teacher Training; Typographic Design.
Children's Classes: High School Drawing Class; enrl 25; tui free.
Summer School: Dir Edward F Leary. Tui $82.50 per cr for term of 6 wks beginning May 23 and July 5. Courses—Drawing; Painting; Sculpture; Printmaking; Art Education.

BUTERA SCHOOL OF ART, 111 Beacon St, 02116. Tel: 617-536-4623. *Dir* Joseph L Butera, MFA; *Head Commercial Art* Hal Trafford; *Head Sign Painting* Stan Morrisson.
Estab 1932; pvt; D&E; ent req HS dipl, portfolio; dipl 2 yr and 3 yr progs; enrl D 100, E 60.
Tuition: $1800-$1950 per yr; independent dormitories available.
Courses: Advertising Design; Art Education; Art History; Calligraphy; Commercial Art; Drawing; Fashion Arts; Graphic Arts; Graphic Design; Illustration; Lettering; Painting; Sign Painting.

CHAMBERLAYNE JUNIOR COLLEGE, Department of Graphic and Applied Arts, 128 Commonwealth Ave, 02116. Tel: 617-536-4500. *Chmn Dept* Herbert T Anderson; *Prof* Henry A Tate, PhD; *Instr.* Maria Vitagliano, MFA; *Instrs* Stephanie Highberg, MFA; *Instr.* Ingrida Kraulitis, MFA; *Area Head* Joanne M Vascovitch, BFA; *Instr* Dwight Carter, BFA; *Instr.* Gladys Maynard.
Estab 1892, dept estab 1952; pvt; D&E; ent req HS dipl; degree AAS 2 yrs; SC 23, LC 11; enrl D 253, E 38, maj 253.
Tuition: Res—$4195 per yr, $65 per cr hr; Nonres—$2020 per yr; campus res $4195 per yr.
Courses: Architecture; Art History; Ceramics; ‡Commercial Art; Conceptual Art; ‡Costume Design & Construction; Drafting; Drawing; Fashion Arts; ‡Graphic Arts; ‡Illustration; ‡Interior Design; Jewelry; ‡Landscape Architecture; Painting; Sculpture; Textile Design.
Summer School: Dir Francis X Cronin. Tui $65 per cr hr for term of 12 wks beginning June 1. Courses—Same as regular academic year.

EMMANUEL COLLEGE, Art Department, 400 The Fenway, 02115. Tel: 617-277-9340, exten 204. *Chairperson Dept* Theresa Monaco, MFA; *Asst Prof* Michael Jacques, MFA; *Instr* Patricia M Lyster, BA, Master Weaver; *Instr* C David Thomas, MFA; *Prof* Ellen Marie Glavin, PhD; *Instr* David Kowal, Cand PhD; *Instr* Jean Thomas, MA.
Estab 1919, dept estab 1960; pvt; D&E; ent req HS dipl, SAT, 3 Achievements, Portfolio; degrees BA 4 yrs, BFA 4-5 yrs; schol; SC 41, LC 14, GC 9; enrl D 300, E 50, nonmaj 200, maj 100, grad 15.
Tuition: $90 per cr hr; $70 per cr hr for students without BA; campus res room & board $1305 per yr.
Courses: Aesthetics; Art Education; Art History; ‡Ceramics; Commercial Art; Drawing; ‡Fiber Arts; Graphic Arts; Graphic Design; Handicrafts; History of Art & Archaeology; Illustration; Mixed Media; Occupational Therapy; ‡Painting; Photography; ‡Printmaking; Sculpture; Teacher Training; Textile Design.
Adult Hobby Classes: Tui $25-$35; Courses—Fibers; Drawing; Sculpture; Printmaking.
Summer School: Dean Catherine Theresa Rice. Enrl 100; tui $85 per cr hr for term of 1 wk beginning July for 2 wks. Courses—Fibers; Printmaking; Art Therapy; Sculpture.

MASSACHUSETTS COLLEGE OF ART, 364 Brookline Ave, 02215. Tel: 617-731-2340. *Pres* John F Nolan, MS; *Acad Dean* Donald R Lettis, MFA; *Chmn Fine Arts/2D* George B Nick, MFA; *Chmn Fine Arts/3D* Dan Dailey, MFA; *Chmn Design* William J Hannon, BFA; *Chmn Art Educ* Diana Korzenik, DEd; *Chmn Media* Johanna Gill, PhD; *Chmn Critical Studies* Athanasios Bouloukos, PhD.
Estab 1873; pub; D&E; ent req HS dipl, SAT and Portfolio; degrees BFA 4 yrs, MFA 2 yrs, MSAE 1 yr; SC 400, LC 250, GC 50; enrl D 1094, E 1900, maj 1058, grad 90, others 1800.
Tuition: Res—$500 per yr; Nonres—$1250 per yr; continuing educ $25 per cr hr; no campus res.
Courses: Advertising Design; Aesthetics; Architecture; Art Education; Art History; Calligraphy; Ceramics; Commercial Art; Conceptual Art; Constructions; Costume Design & Construction; Display; Drafting; Drawing; Fashion Arts; Film; Glassblowing; Goldsmithing; Graphic Arts; Graphic Design; History of Art & Archaeology; Illustration; Industrial Design; Intermedia; Interior Design; Jewelry; Landscape Architecture;

Lettering; Mixed Media; Painting; Photography; Printmaking; Sculpture; Silversmithing; Stage Design; Stained Glass; Teacher Training; Textile Design; Theatre Arts; Video.
Adult Hobby Classes: Tui $25 per cr hr. Courses—All areas.
Children's Classes: Enrl 750; tui $10. Courses—All Areas.
Summer School: Dir Continuing Educ Dr Dorothy Simpson. Enrl 900; tui $25 per cr hr. Courses—All areas.

NEW ENGLAND SCHOOL OF ART AND DESIGN, 28 Newbury St, 02116. Tel: 617-536-0383. *Pres* J W S Cox, BA; *Dean & Found Chmn* James F Smith, BA; *Chairwoman Graphic Design* Myra Lee Conway, MA; *Chmn Fine Arts* William Maynard, BA; *Chmn Fashion Illustration* Frank Raneo, BA; *Acting Chmn Interior Design* Angus Crowe, MArch.
Estab 1923; pvt; D&E; ent req HS dipl, portfolio; dipl 3 yrs; enrl D 200, E 160, maj 200.
Tuition: $1800 per yr, $900 per sem, $50 per class hr per sem; no campus res.
Courses: ‡Advertising Design; Art History; Calligraphy; Commercial Art; Drafting; Drawing; ‡Fashion Arts; ‡Fine Arts; Graphic Arts; ‡Graphic Design; Illustration; Industrial Design; ‡Interior Design; Landscape Architecture; Lettering; Painting; Photography; Printmaking; Sculpture.
Summer School: Dean Summer Div James F Smith. Enrl approx 200; tui $100 to $300 per course for term of 8-10 wks beginning early June. Courses—Those above.

SCHOOL OF FASHION DESIGN, 136 Newbury St, 02116. Tel: 617-536-9343. *Head Art Dept* Isabelle Torroella, Baccalaureat; *Art Instr* Maria Lesieur; *Art Instr* Rita Berkowitz, BA; *Art Instr* Kathy Fay, BS/Dipl.
Estab 1934; pvt; D&E; ent req HS dipl; no degrees, 2 yr cert or 3 yr dipl; schol; enrl D approx 90, E approx 150.
Tuition: $1500 per yr, $160 per course; no campus res.
Courses: Costume Design & Construction; Drawing; Fashion Arts; Illustration; Photography; Textile Design; Theatre Arts.
Summer School: Instrs Rita Berkowitz. Tui $160 for term of 5 wks beginning July 10. Courses—Fashion Sketching; Life Drawing.

SCHOOL OF THE MUSEUM OF FINE ARTS, 230 The Fenway, 02115. Tel: 617-267-9300. *Dean* Bruce K MacDonald, PhD.
Estab 1876; pvt; D&E; ent req HS dipl, HS and col transcripts, portfolio; degrees BFA 4 yrs, BSEd 5 yrs, MFA 2 yrs (all degrees in affiliation with Tufts University); schol; SC 129, LC 13; enrl D 609, E 310, grad 22, others 25.
Tuition: $3125 per yr; $4150 for 2 yr prog; Dipl $2650 per yr; E $175 per sem course; no campus res.
Courses: Art Education; Ceramics; Drawing; Film; Goldsmithing; Graphic Design; Intermedia; Jewelry; Painting; Photography; Printmaking; Sculpture; Silversmithing; Stained Glass; Video.
Summer School: Enrl 10 per class minimum; tui $260 for term of 6 wks beginning June 26.

VESPER GEORGE SCHOOL OF ART,* 44 St Botolph St, 02116. Tel: 617-267-2045. *Dir* Fletcher Adams; Instrs D FT 21, E FT 5.
Estab 1924; pvt; ent schol 3 yrs.
Courses: Advertising Art; Design; Fashion Illustration; Fine Arts; Illustration; Interior Decoration.
Children's Classes: Sat.

BROCKTON

BROCKTON ART CENTER, Art Workshops, Oak St, 02401. Tel: 617-588-6000. *Art Workshops Coordr* Beverly Edwards, BA; *Instrs* Stan Folsom, PhD; *Instr.* Patrick Bell, MFA; *Instr.* Jorgen Henriksen, MFA; *Instr* Polly Egelson, MFA; *Instr* Dorian Goldman, MFA; *Instrs* Judy Brown, MFA; *Instr.* JoAnn Rothschild, MFA; Instrs PT 23.
Estab 1970; pvt; D&E; ent req HS dipl; degrees through Massachusetts College of Art; schol; SC 30, LC 2, GS 10; enrl D 400, E 300, nonmaj 30, grad 20, other 650.
Tuition: $50-$60 per course for 10 wk term additional $10 per cr hr for credit; no campus res.
Courses: Art Education; Art History; Calligraphy; Cartooning; Ceramics; Collage; Drawing; Film; Graphic Arts; Graphic Design; Handicrafts (weaving); Illustration; Jewelry; Mixed Media; Museum Staff Training; Painting; Printmaking; Sculpture; Teacher Training; Textile Design; Theatre Arts.
Children's Classes: Term of 10 wk. Courses—Drawing; Painting; Printmaking; Sculpture.
Summer School: Dir Beverly Edwards. Enrl 150-200; tui $50-$55 for term of 5 wk beginning July 10. Courses—Same as regular session.

CAMBRIDGE

HARVARD UNIVERSITY, 02138. Tel: 617-495-1000.
—**Department of Fine Arts,*** Fogg Museum, 02138. Tel: 617-495-2377. *Chmn Dept* Oleg Grabar; Instrs FT 14.
Estab 1874; pvt; Men (Radcliffe Col for W); degrees 4 yrs; schol and fel; LC 26 incl GC 12; enrl undergrad Harvard, 53, Radcliffe, 49, grad Harvard (incl W) 80.
Courses: History of Art.
—**Department of Visual and Environmental Studies,** 19 Prescott St, 02138. Tel: 617-495-3251. *Chmn Dept* Louis Bakanowsky, MA; *Studio Prof* Dimitri Hadzi, MA; *Prof* Eduard F Sekler, PhD; *Prof* Albert Szabo, MArch; *Studio Prof* Alfred Guzzetti, PhD; *Sr Lectr* Paul Rotterdam, PhD; *Sr Lectr* Flora Natapoff, MA; *Sr Lectr* Robert Gardner, MA.
Estab 1972; pvt; D; ent req HS dipl, SAT, Achievements; degree BA 4 yrs; schol; SC approx 48, LC approx 20; enrl approx 1610, nonmaj approx 1300, maj 110, grad approx 200.
Courses: Architecture; Drawing; Environmental Design; Film; Film Theory; Graphic Design; Painting; Photography; Printmaking; Sculpture.
—**Graduate School of Design,*** Departments of Architecture, City and Regional Planning, Landscape Architecture, and Urban Design Program, Gund Hall, 02138. *Dean* Maurice Dorney Kilbridge; Instrs FT and PT 90.
Ent req; degrees AB, SB, BLA, BCP or BArch or equivalent; schol and fel; enrl 500.
Courses: Architecture; City & Regional Planning; Landscape Architecture; Urban Design.

MASSACHUSETTS INSTITUTE OF TECHNOLOGY,
—**School of Architecture and Planning,*** Departments of Architecture and Urban Studies and Planning, 77 Massachusetts Ave, 02139. Tel: 617-253-1000. *Dean* William L Porter; *Head Dept Architecture* N John Habraken; *Head Dept Urban Studies & Planning* Langley C Keyes; Instrs FT 72, PT 38.
Estab 1865; pvt; degrees SB(Art & Design), SB(Urban Studies), MArch, AS(Advanced Studies), MCP, PhD(City Planning), PhD(Arch, Art Environ Studies) 2, 4 and 6 yrs; SC, LC, GC; enrl 504.
—**Center for Advanced Visual Studies,** 40 Massachusetts Ave, W11, 02139. Tel: 617-253-4415. *Head Dept & Prof* Otto Piene.
Estab dept 1967; pvt; D&E; ent req none for MS degree; degrees MS 2 yr; SC 9, LC 1, GC 5; enrl D&E 250, nonmaj 240, grad 6, other 5.
Tuition: Same as Institute.
Courses: Architecture; Art Education; Art History; Film; Graphic Arts; Graphic Design; History of Art and Archaeology; Mixed Media; Photography; Printmaking; Video.

CHICOPEE

COLLEGE OF OUR LADY OF THE ELMS, Department of Art, 291 Springfield St, 01013. Tel: 413-598-8351, exten 22. *Chmn Dept* James McDowell; *Asst Prof* Theresa Amiot.
Estab 1928, dept estab 1950; pvt; D&E; ent req HS dipl, Col Ent Exam (Verbal and Math); degree BA 4 yrs; schol; SC 14, LC 6; enrl D 120, nonmaj 89, maj 31.
Tuition: Res—$4000 per yr; Nonres—$2700 per yr.
Courses: Art Education; Art History; Calligraphy; Ceramics; Drawing; History of Art & Archaeology; Jewelry; Lettering; Painting; Printmaking; Sculpture; Teacher Training; Theatre Arts.

DOVER

CHARLES RIVER CREATIVE ARTS PROGRAM, 56 Centre St, 02030. Tel: 617-785-0068 or 785-1260. *Dir* Priscilla B Dewey.
Estab 1969; pvt; summer school; D; ent req none.
Courses: Ceramics; Costume Design & Construction; Drawing; Film; Mixed Media; Painting; Photography; Printmaking; Silversmithing; Stage Design; Theatre Arts; Video.

FRAMINGHAM

FRAMINGHAM STATE COLLEGE, Art Department, May Hall, 100 State St, 01701. Tel: 617-620-1220, exten 333. *Prof Art & Chmn Dept* Stephen Durkee, MS; *Instr* James Eng, MFA; *Asst Prof* Frederick A Fiandaca, MA; *Asst Prof* Leah Lipton, MA; *Asst Prof* Arthur B Mazmanian, MFA; *Asst Prof* Eugene E Sullivan, MFA; *Asst Prof* Brucia Witthoft, MA.
Estab 1839; pub; D&E; ent req HS dipl; degree BA 4 yrs; schol; SC 20, LC 15, GC 20; enrl D 110 art maj, E 20.
Courses: Art Education; Art History; Ceramics; Commercial Art; Drawing; Film; Graphic Design; Handicrafts; Interior Design; Jewelry; Painting; Photography; Printmaking; Sculpture; Silversmithing; Teacher Training; Video.

Summer School: Dir Joseph Palladino. Enrl 25; tui $130 per course for term of 6 wks beginning end of June. Courses—Art; Drawing; Painting.

FRANKLIN

DEAN JUNIOR COLLEGE, Visual and Performing Arts Department, 99 Main St, 02038. Tel: 617-528-9100. *Chairperson Dept* Lawry Reid, MFA; *Dir Art Therapy* Suzanne Canner, MA; *Asst Prof* Richard Dean, MFA; *Assc Prof* John Fulgoni, MA; *Prof* John Locke, MA; *Asst Prof* Myron Schmidt, MA; *Assoc Prof* Stanley Sobocinski, EdM; *Instr* John Hagon, MM.
Estab 1865, dept estab 1960; pvt; D&E; ent req HS dipl; degrees AA and AS 2 yrs; schol; SC 10, LC 4; enrl D 220, E 30, nonmaj 170, maj 80.
Tuition: $3500 per yr; campus res room & board $1700 per yr; $5200 total cost.
Courses: Art Therapy; Fashion Merchandising; Theatre Arts; Visual Arts.

GREAT BARRINGTON

SIMON'S ROCK EARLY COLLEGE, Fine Arts Division, Studio Arts Department, Alford Rd, 01230. Tel: 413-528-0771. *Chairperson Studio Arts Dept* Eunice Agar, BA; *Instrs* William Jackson, MFA.
Estab 1966; pvt; D&E; ent req personal interview; degrees AA 2 and 3 yrs, BA 4 yrs; schol; SC 14, LC 4.
Tuition: $4100 per yr, room & board $1600.
Courses: Aesthetics; Art History; Ceramics; Collage; Drafting; Drawing; History of Art & Archaeology; Jewelry; Painting; Photography; Printmaking; Sculpture; Theatre Arts.
Adult Hobby Classes: Enrl 40; tui $30-$80 per course. Courses—Picture Framing; Drawing; Ceramics; Art History; Collecting.

GREENFIELD

GREENFIELD COMMUNITY COLLEGE, Art Department, 10 College Dr, 01301. Tel: 413-774-3131. *Head Art Dept* T Budgehyde, MFA; *Primary Art Faculty:* Peter Dudley, MFA; Christopher James, MAT; Margaret Stein, MFA; Pamela Sacher, MA; *Art Historian* Joan Rising, MFA.
Estab 1962; pub; D&E; ent req HS dipl; degrees AA and AS 2 yrs; schol; SC 16; enrl in sch D 1400, E 400, maj 110.
Tuition: Res—$300 per yr, $150 per sem; Nonres—$900 per yr, $441 per sem.
Courses: Advertising Design; Art History; Commercial Art; Constructions; Display; Drawing; Graphic Arts; Graphic Design; History of Art & Archaeology; Illustration; Painting; Photography; Printmaking.
Summer School: Dir T Budgehyde. Tui $20 per cr hr for term of 6 wks beginning June. Courses—Painting; Drawing; Art History; Photography.

HOLYOKE

HOLYOKE COMMUNITY COLLEGE,* 303 Homestead Ave, 01040. Tel: 413-538-7000, exten 270. *Head* Frank Cressotti; Instrs FT 3, PT 1.
Estab 1946; pub; D&E; ent req HS dipl, portfolio; degree AA 2 yrs; schol; SC 7, LC 4; enrl D 115, E 20, maj 50.
Tuition: Res—$150 per sem; Nonres—$441 per sem.
Courses: Art Education; Drawing; Graphic Arts; Graphic Design; History of Art & Archaeology; Painting; Photography.
Summer School: Dir William Murphy. Courses—Depends on demand.

LONGMEADOW

BAY PATH JUNIOR COLLEGE,* Department of Art, 588 Longmeadow St, 01106. Tel: 413-567-0621. Instrs FT 2, PT 10.
Estab 1947; pvt; D&E; W; ent req HS dipl; degree AFA 2 yrs; schol; SC 18, LC 2; enrl D 475, E 200, maj 40.
Courses: Ceramics; Drawing; Foundation Art; Graphic Arts; History of Art & Archaeology; Painting; Photography; Sculpture.
Adult Hobby Classes: Enrl approx 175; tui $36; courses—12 subjects.
Summer School: Chmn Charles B Hayward. Term of 6 wks beginning June. Courses—Vary annually.

LOWELL

UNIVERSITY OF LOWELL, Department of Art, One University Ave, 01854. Tel: 617-454-8011 or 454-7811, exten 455. *Assoc Prof Art & Chairperson Dept* Brenda Pinardi, MFA; *Instr* Michael Costello, MFA; *Asst Prof* Liana Cheney, PhD; *Assoc Prof* Carlton Plummer, MFA; *Assoc Prof* Leo Panas, EdM; *Asst Prof* Fred Faudie, MA; *Asst Prof* Robert Griffith, MFA.

Estab 1975 (merger of Lowell State College and Lowell Technological Institute); pub; D&E; ent req HS dipl, SAT, interview; degrees BA (Art) and BS (Art Educ) 4 yrs; SC 24, LC 11; enrl D 1200, E 25, nonmaj 450, maj 150.
Tuition: Res—Undergrad $525 per yr, $262.50 per sem; Nonres—Undergrad $1300 per yr, $650 per sem; campus res room & board $1500 per yr.
Courses: Art Education; Art History; Studio Art.
Adult Hobby Classes: Enrl 10-15 per course; tui approx $44 per course. Courses—Drawing; Painting; Jewelry; Watercolor; Ceramics; Wood Sculpture; Commercial Stained Glass; Quilt Making; Photography; Interior Design.
Summer School: Dir Ernest James. Courses—Photography; Survey of Art (Ceramics, Graphics, etc).

MEDFORD

TUFTS UNIVERSITY, Fine Arts Department, 11 Talbot Ave, 01880. Tel: 617-628-5000, exten 396. *Assoc Prof Art & Chmn Fine Arts Dept* Madeline H Caviness, PhD; *Asst Prof* Margaret Floyd, PhD; *Asst Prof* Ivan Galantic, PhD; *Asst Prof* Pamela Allara, PhD; *Asst Prof* Barbara White, PhD; vis prof—Robert Maeda, Chinese art historian, spring sem.
Pvt; D; ent req HS dipl; degrees BA, BS and BEd 4 yrs; schol.
Tuition: $4150 per yr; campus res room & board $1180 per yr.
Courses: Ceramics; Drawing; Graphic Arts; History of Art & Archaeology; Jewelry; Occupational Therapy; Painting; Photography; Sculpture.

NEW BEDFORD

SWAIN SCHOOL OF DESIGN, 19 Hawthorn St, 02740. Tel: 617-997-3159. *Pres* William E Britain, MA; *Chmn Fine Arts* Jean Lozinski, PhD; *Primary Art Faculty:* Thomas Corey, BA; John Osborne, MFA; Russell Daly, MFA; David L Smith, MFA; Leo Kelley, MA.
Estab 1881; pvt; D; ent req HS dipl, portfolio; degree BFA 4 yrs; schol; SC 16, LC 16; enrl D 210, maj 210.
Tuition: $2400 per yr, $1200 per sem, $80 per course; no campus res.
Courses: Art History; Drawing; Graphic Design; History of Art & Archaeology; Painting; Photography; Printmaking; Sculpture.

NEWTON

LASELL JUNIOR COLLEGE,* Department of Art, 1844 Commonwealth Ave, 02166. Tel: 617-243-2000. *Assoc Prof Art & Chmn Dept Art & Music* Leonie S Bennett, MFA; *Instrs* FT 5, PT 1.
Estab 1851; pvt; D&E; W; ent req HS dipl, ent exam in some depts, portfolio in art dept; degrees AA and AS 2 yrs; schol.
Tuition: $2900 per yr; room and board $2100 per yr.
Courses: Advertising Design; Aesthetics; Art for Child Study; Ceramics; Design & Color; Drawing; History of Art & Archaeology; Jewelry; Painting; Photography; Three-Diensional Design.

NORTH DARTMOUTH

SOUTHEASTERN MASSACHUSETTS UNIVERSITY, College of Visual and Performing Arts, Old Westport Rd, 02747. Tel: 617-997-9321, exten 301, 302. *Dean Col* Dietmar R Winkler; *Chairperson Music Dept* Eleanor Carlson, DMA; *Chairperson Art Educ* Peter London, EdD; *Chairperson Fine Arts* T Frank McCoy, MFA; *Chairperson Design* Margot Neugebauer, MFA; *Chairperson Art Hist* Thomas Puryear, PhD; *Coordr Gallery* Robert E Barry, MAT; col has vis profs; Faculty FT 28, PT 12.
Estab 1895, col estab 1948; pub; D&E; ent req HS dipl, SAT, portfolio; degrees BFA and BA 4 yrs, MFA and MAE 2-5 yrs; SC 75, LC 41, GC 7; enrl D 450.
Tuition: Res—Undergrad & grad $480 per yr, $240 per sem; Nonres—Undergrad $592 per yr, grad $1110 per yr, $555 per sem; campus res room & board $2024 per yr.
Courses: Advertising Design; Aesthetics; Art Education; Art History; Calligraphy; Ceramics; Collage; Commercial Art; Conceptual Art; Display; Drafting; Drawing; Film; Goldsmithing; Graphic Arts; Graphic Design; History of Art & Archaeology; Illustration; Intermedia; Jewelry; Lettering; Mixed Media; Occupational Therapy; Painting; Photography; Printmaking; Sculpture; Silversmithing; Stage Design; Teacher Training; Textile Design; Theatre Arts; Video; Other-Dance, Music, Voice, Opera Workshop, Animation, Instrsumental Music.
Summer School: Dean Dr Robert E Piper.

NORTHAMPTON

SMITH COLLEGE, Art Department, 01063. Tel: 413-584-2700. *Chairperson Art Dept* Helen Searing, PhD; *Prof* Elliot Melville Offner, MFA; *Assoc Prof* Peter Garland, MArch; *Asst Prof* Gary Niswonger,

MFA; *Asst Prof* Peter Johnson, MFA; *Instr* Susan Heideman, MFA; *Instr* A Lee Burns, MFA; *Instr* Pamela Endacott, MFA; Faculty FT 19, PT 6.
Estab 1875, dept estab 1877; pvt; D; W; ent req HS dipl, Col Bd Exam; degree BA 4 yrs; schol; SC 24, LC 34; enrl maj 170.
Tuition: $6600 per yr incl room & board; campus res.
Courses: Aesthetics; Architecture; Art Education; Art History; Calligraphy; Constructions; Costume Design & Construction; Drafting; Drawing; Graphic Arts; Graphic Design; History of Art & Archaeology; Intermedia; Landscape Architecture; Mixed Media; Museum Staff Training; Painting; Photography; Printmaking; Sculpture; Stage Design.

NORTON

WHEATON COLLEGE,* Art Department, 02766. Tel: 617-285-7722. *Chmn Dept* Thomas J McCormick; *Instrs* FT 7.
Estab 1834; pvt; W; degree AB 4 yrs; schol; SC 6, LC 18; enrl 1143.
Tuition: $6300 incl room and board.
Courses: Basic Design; Drawing & Painting; Graphic Arts; History of Art; Sculpture.

PAXTON

ANNA MARIA COLLEGE,* Department of Art, Sunset Lane, 01612. Tel: 617-757-4586. *Chmn Dept* David T Green; *Instrs* FT 3.
Estab 1948; pvt; D&E; ent req HS dipl, ent exam; 4 yrs; schol; SC 15, LC 12; enrl D 190, E 144, maj 56.
Courses: Advertising Design; Aesthetics; Art Education; Ceramics; Drawing; Enameling; Handicrafts; History of Art; Lettering; Macrame; Modeling; Occupational Therapy; Painting; Photography; Rug Design; Sculpture; Silk Screen; Stitchery; Teacher Training; Weaving.
Summer School: Dir Clarice Chauvin. Term of 6 wks beginning June. Courses—Crafts for the Retarded; Lettering; Oil Painting; Watercolor Techniques.

PITTSFIELD

BERKSHIRE COMMUNITY COLLEGE, Department of Fine Arts and Visual Communication, West St, 01201. Tel: 413-499-4660. *Assoc Prof Art & Prog Chmn Dept Fine Arts & Visual Commun* Nancy Delaiti, MA; *Asst Prof* Julio Granda, MFA; *Instrs* Benigna Chilla, MFA; *Prof* Robert M Boland, MFA; *Instrs* Philip Lief, MFA.
Estab 1960, dept estab 1961; pub; D&E; ent req HS dipl, studio art testing, portfolio; degree AA 2 yrs; schol; SC 16, LC 4; enrl D 72, E 75, nonmaj 12, maj 72.
Tuition: Res—$150 per sem; Nonres—$441 per sem; no campus res.
Courses: Advertising Design; Art History; Calligraphy; Commercial Art; Constructions; Costume Design & Construction; Drawing; Graphic Arts; Graphic Design; Mixed Media; Painting; Photography; Printmaking; Stage Design; Theatre Arts.
Summer School: Div of Continuing Educ. Enrl 75; tui $66 per course for term of 7 wks beginning June 15. Courses—Drawing; Painting; Design; Photography.

PROVINCETOWN

CAPE SCHOOL OF ART, Lowell St, 02657. Tel: 617-487-0703. *Dir* Henry Hensche.
Estab 1930; pvt summer school; D; ent req none.
Tuition: $150 for 2 months, July-August.
Courses: Art History; Drawing; Painting.

PROVINCETOWN WORKSHOP, A SCHOOL OF PAINTING AND DRAWING,* 492 Commercial St, 02657. Tel: 617-487-0973. *Dirs* Victor Candell and Leo Manso; *Instrs* FT 2.
Estab 1958; pvt; D&E; summers only; ent req ent exam; schol recommendation by dept heads or prof.
Courses: Art Education; Drawing; Graphic Arts; Painting.

SALEM

SALEM STATE COLLEGE, Art Department, Lafayette St, 01970. Tel: 617-745-0556, exten 265. *Chmn Dept* N E Wagman, Jr, ME(Art); *Prof* Elissa Ananian, MAT; *Prof* Thomas Leary, MFA; *Prof* Ingrida Mangulis; *Prof* Stephen Panosian, MEd; *Prof* Mark Roudzens, MFA; *Prof* Vito Sammarjano, MEd; *Prof* Arthur Smith, MEd.
Estab 1854; pub; D&E; ent req HS dipl; degree BA 4 yrs; internships; schol; SC 19, LC 8, GC 5; enrl maj 102.
Tuition: Res—$640 per yr; Nonres—$1340 per yr; campus res.

Courses: Art Education; Art History; Ceramics; Drawing; Film; Graphic Arts; History of Art & Archaeology; Jewelry; Painting; Photography; Printmaking; Sculpture; Silversmithing; Stage Design; Teacher Training.

SOUTH HADLEY

MOUNT HOLYOKE COLLEGE, Art Department, College St, 01075. Tel: 413-538-2245. *Assoc Prof Art & Chmn Dept* John L Varriano, PhD; *Prof* Leonard DeLonga, MFA; *Prof* Jean C Harris, PhD; *Assoc Prof* Martha Leeb Hadzi, PhD; *Asst Prof* Grant Holcomb, PhD; *Asst Prof* Joan L Esch, PhD; *Asst Prof* Barry Seace, MFA; *Asst Prof* Marion G Miller, MFA; *Asst Prof* Diane F Zervas, PhD; vis profs—Barbara Lekberg, sculture & design, 2 yrs; Ibram Lassaw, sculpture, 2 sem.
Estab 1837; pvt; W; D; ent req HS dipl; degree AB 4 yrs; schol; SC 14, LC 33; enrl 289, maj 30.
Tuition: $3900 per yr; campus res room & board $1900 per yr; $5800 total.
Courses: ‡Art History; Drawing; Graphic Arts; Graphic Design; ‡History of Art & Archaeology; ‡Painting; ‡Printmaking; ‡Sculpture.

SPRINGFIELD

SPRINGFIELD COLLEGE, Department of Visual and Performing Arts, 263 Alden St, 01109. Tel: 413-787-2332. *Chmn Dept* William Blizard, MA; *Asst Prof* Armand Balboni, MA; *Instr* Sam Annind, MA; *Adj Prof* Emil Schndrr, MA; *Instr* Paul Sena; vis prof—Howard Blehel, photography, 1 acad yr.
Estab 1885, dept estab 1971; pvt; D&E; ent req HS dipl, SAT, portfolio; degrees BA and BS 4 yrs; schol; SC 30, LC 6; enrl D 335, E 10, nonmaj 300, maj 35.
Tuition: $2607 per yr, room and board $1739 per yr, $4346 total, $79 per sem hr; campus res.
Courses: Advertising Design; Art History; ‡Art Therapy; Ceramics; Collage; Conceptual Art; Constructions; ‡Creative Arts Therapy; Drawing; ‡Environmental Design; Graphic Arts; Illustration; Intermedia; Mixed Media; ‡Museum Staff Training; Occupational Therapy; ‡Painting; Photography; ‡Printmaking; Restoration & Conservation; ‡Sculpture; Stage Design; Theatre Arts; Video.
Summer School: Dir David Wuerthele. Enrl 1000; tui $79 per sem hr for term of 3 or 6 wks beginning May 30. Courses—Painting; Photography; Drawing, Sculpture; Ceramics.

STOCKBRIDGE

BEAUPRE,* A Creative and Performing Arts Center, 01262. *Dir* Mrs Stanley North; Instrs FT 2.
Estab 1944; pvt; W; Summer Day School; ent req none; offers a Major in Art for girls 9-15; term of 6 wks beginning June 27.
Courses: Ceramics; Drawing; Lettering; Macrame; Mobiles; Painting; Stitchery; Tie Dyeing; Weaving.

TRURO

TRURO CENTER FOR THE ARTS AT CASTLE HILL, INC, Castle Rd (Mailing Add: Box 756, 02666). Tel: 617-349-3714. *Dir* Joyce Johnson; *Instr* Bruce Hoadley, PhD; *Instr* John Wallace, MFA; *Instr* Sidney Simon; *Instr* Xavier Gonzalez; *Instr* Alan Dugan; *Instr* Hal Riegger, MFA; *Instr* Elloyd Hanson.
Estab 1972; pvt summer school; D&E; ent req none; no degrees, credits granted through Lesley College and Massachusetts College of Art; SC 50, LC 3, GC 30; enrl 3-400.
Tuition: $45 for one wk; no campus res.
Courses: Art History; Cartooning; Ceramics; Collage; Constructions; Drawing; Dyeing from Nature; Film; Fresco Painting; Goldsmithing.

WALTHAM

BRANDEIS UNIVERSITY, Department of Fine Arts, 02154. Tel: (617) 647-2555. *Chairwoman* Elaine P Loeffler; Instrs FT 11, PT 1.
Estab 1948; pvt; D; ent req HS dipl, college board ent exam; degree BS 4 yrs; schol; SC 10, LC 28; enrl 2800.
Tuition: $4315; campus res available.
Courses: Design; Drawing; Graphic Arts; History of Art; Painting; Sculpture.

WELLESLEY

WELLESLEY COLLEGE, Art Department, 02181. Tel: 617-235-0320, exten 306. *Prof Art & Chmn Dept* Richard W Wallace, PhD; *Prof* Lilian Armstrong, PhD; *Asst Prof* Margaret D Carroll, PhD; *Assoc Prof* Anne de Clapp, PhD; *Assoc Prof* Eugenia P Janis, PhD; *Assoc Prof* Miranda C

Marvin, PhD; *Assoc Prof* Peter J Fergusson, PhD; *Prof* James Wilson Rayen, MFA; *Prof* Kenworth W Moffett, PhD; *Prof* James F O'Gorman, PhD; occasional vis profs.
Estab 1875; pvt; D; ent req HS dipl; degree BA 4 yrs or 3½ on accelerated prog; schol; SC 3, LC 41; enrl approx 2093.
Tuition: Res—$6106 per yr; Nonres—$3910 per yr; campus res room & board.
Courses: Art History; Drawing; Graphic Arts; Painting; Photography; Printmaking; Sculpture; Stage Design; Theatre Arts.

WESTFIELD

WESTFIELD STATE COLLEGE, Art Department, Western Ave, 01085. Tel: 413-568-3311, exten 256. *Prof Art & Chmn Dept* Arno Maris, MFA.
Estab 1972; pub; D&E; ent req HS dipl; degree BA(Fine Arts) 4 yrs.
Tuition: Res—$500 per yr; Nonres—$1200 per yr; Room rent $680-950 per yr; Meals $500 per yr; Student fees $115 per yr.
Courses: Advertising Design; Art Education; Art History; Ceramics; Commercial Art; Drawing; Graphic Arts; Illustration; Lettering; Mixed Media; ‡Painting; Printmaking; Sculpture; Teacher Training.

WESTON

REGIS COLLEGE, Department of Art, 235 Wellesley St, 02193. Tel: 617-893-1820. *Prof Art & Chmn Dept* Louisella Walters, MFA; *Assoc Prof* Marie DeSales Dinngen, PhD; *Assoc Prof* Alice Walsh, MA; *Ceramist* Mary Deweerd Edick, AB; *Lectr* William Gavin, MA; *Painter* Carol Barsha, MFA; *Lectr* Phyllis London, MA; *Art Therapist* Patricia Hanify Boardman, MA.
Estab 1927, dept estab 1944; den; D&E; ent req HS dipl, SAT, various tests; degree AB 4 yrs; schol; SC 12, LC 12; enrl D 250, nonmaj 200, maj 50.
Tuition: Res—$3750-$4100 per yr; Nonres—$2300 per yr; campus res room & board $1450 per yr.
Courses: Aesthetics; Art Education; Art History; Art Therapy; Ceramics; Drawing; Graphic Arts; Handicrafts (Enameling, Weaving, Stained Glass); History of Art & Archaeology; Painting; Printmaking; ‡Sculpture.

WILLIAMSTOWN

WILLIAMS COLLEGE, Department of Art, 01267. Tel: 413-597-2377. *Chmn Dept* Eugene J Johnson, PhD; Instrs FT 9, PT 13; vis prof—Robert Sterling Clark, history of art.
Estab 1793, dept estab 1903; pvt; D; ent req HS dipl; degrees BA 4 yrs; MA(Hist of Art) 2 yrs; schol; SC 14, LC 40, GC 10; enrl 1338, maj 62, grad 20.
Tuition: $4500 per yr; campus res room & board $2100 per yr.
Courses: Architecture; Art History; Drawing; History of Art & Archaeology; Painting; Photography; Printmaking; Sculpture.

WORCESTER

ASSUMPTION COLLEGE, Department of Fine Arts and Music, 500 Salisbury St, 01609. Tel: 617-752-5615, exten 259. *Chmn Dept* Richard E Lamoureux, PhD; *Prof* Richard Richards, MA; *Asst Prof* J Michael Russom, MFA; *Instr* Keith Daniel, PhD Cand.
Estab 1904, dept estab 1976; den; D&E; ent req HS dipl; degrees BA 4 yrs, MAT, MA, Cert Advan Grad Study; schol; enrl D 600, E 25, grad 25.
Tuition: $2550 per yr; campus res room & board $1475 per yr; total $4025 per yr; $85 per cr hr.
Courses: Aesthetics; Architecture; Art Education; Art History; Drawing; Graphic Arts; History of Art & Archaeology; Painting; Printmaking; Theatre Arts.
Summer School: Dir Dr Claire Quintal. Tui $65 per cr hr.

CLARK UNIVERSITY, Art Program, Department of Visual and Performing Arts, 950 Main St, 01610. Tel: 617-793-7561. *Assoc Prof Art & Chmn Art Prog & Dept Visual & Performing Arts* Donald W Krueger, MFA; *Assoc Prof* Samuel P Cowardin III, PhD; *Asst Prof* Bonnie Lee Grad, PhD.
Estab 1887; pvt; D&E; ent req HS dipl, portfolio; degrees BA 4 yrs, BFA 4½ yrs; schol; enrl D 100, maj 40.
Tuition: $3875 per yr; campus res room & board $1655 per yr.
Courses: Aesthetics; Art Education; Art History; Ceramics; Commercial Art; Drawing; Film; Graphic Arts; Graphic Design; Handicrafts (fiber, wood); History of Art & Archaeology; Illustration; Intermedia; Painting; Photography; Printmaking; Sculpture; Stage Design; Teacher Training; Theatre Arts; Video.

COLLEGE OF THE HOLY CROSS, Department of Fine Arts, College St, 01610. Tel: 617-793-2237. *Chmn Dept* Joan N Italiano, MFA; *Assoc Prof* John P Reardon, MFA; *Asst Prof* James P Monson, MFA; *Asst Prof* Virginia C Raquin, PhD; *Asst Prof* John P Reboli, PhD; *Asst Prof* Joseph Scannell, MA; dept has vis profs.
Estab 1843, dept estab 1954; den; D; ent req HS dipl, SAT and achievements; degree BA 4 yrs; schol; SC 12, LC 15; enrl 500, maj 37.
Tuition: $3775 per yr; campus res.
Courses: Aesthetics; ‡Art History; Ceramics; Drawing; Graphic Arts; History of Art & Archaeology; Museum Staff Training; Painting; Printmaking; Sculpture; Stage Design; Theatre Arts.

CRAFT CENTER, 25 Sagamore Rd, 01605. Tel: 617-753-8183. *Dir* Angelo Randazzo, MFA; *Asst Dir* John I Russell, MFA; *Instr* Tim McCreight, MFA; *Instr* Leon Nigrosh, MFA; *Instr* Anne Forbes, MFA; *Instr* Ron Rosenstock, MA; *Instr* Judy Daner, BFA; *Instr* Ronnie Wolfe, BFA; center has vis profs.
Estab 1952; pvt; D&E; ent req portfolio review; no degrees, 2 yr crafts cert; schol; SC 13; enrl D 250, E 350.
Tuition: $1350 per yr; $55 for 10 wks; no campus res.
Courses: Ceramics; Drawing; Enameling; Furniture Refinishing; Jewelry; Photography; Printmaking; Silversmithing; Stained Glass; Weaving; Woodworking.
Adult Hobby Classes: Enrl 320; tui $55 for 10 wks. Courses—Furniture Restoration; Enamelng; Stained Glass; Jewelry; Woodworking; Ceramics; Weaving; Printmaking; Photography.
Summer School: Dir Angelo Randazzo. Enrl 70; tui $180 for term of 3 wks beginning July 6. Courses—Jewelry; Woodworking; Photography; Basketry; Enameling; Weaving; Ceramics.

SCHOOL THE WORCESTER ART MUSEUM, 55 Salisbury St, 01608. Tel: 617-799-4406, exten 66. *Dean* Sante Graziani, MFA.
Estab 1896; pvt; D; ent req HS dipl, no degrees granted, cert awarded after completion of 3 yr prog; schol; SC 21, LC 2; enrl 125.
Tuition: $825 per sem; no campus res.
Courses: Advertising Design; Art History; Ceramics; Commercial Art; Drawing; Graphic Arts; Graphic Design; Handicrafts (clay, fiber, metal); Illustration; Jewelry; Painting; Photography; Printmaking; Sculpture; Video.

MICHIGAN

ADRIAN

ADRIAN COLLEGE, Art Department, 110 S Madison, 49221. Tel: 517-265-5161, exten 246. *Chmn Art Dept* Michael Cassino, MFA; *Asst Prof* Norman Knutson, MFA; *Instrs* Richlyn McArthur, MFA; vis prof—Doramae O'Kelley, art hist, 77-78.
Estab 1859, dept estab 1962; den; D&E; ent req HS dipl; degrees BA, BA with Teaching Cert and BFA 4 yrs; schol; SC 27, LC 6; enrl in dept D 250, E 50, nonmaj 200, maj 30.
Tuition: $1375 per sem, $70 per sem hr; $640 per yr for room, $866 per yr for board.
Courses: Art Education; Art History; ‡Ceramics; Drawing; ‡Painting; Photography; ‡Printmaking; Silversmithing; Two & Three-Dimensional Design.

SIENA HEIGHTS COLLEGE, Art Department, 1247 Siena Heights Dr, 49221. Tel: 517-263-0731, exten 272. *Prof Art & Chairperson Dept* Jeannine Klemm, EdD; *Primary Art Faculty:* Joseph Bergman, MFA; Sister Celeste Mary Bourke, MFA; Sister Barbara Cervenka, MFA; Sister Jean Agnes Klemm, PhD; David Mulligan, MFA; Rev David Van Horn, MFA.
Estab 1919; pvt; D&E; ent req HS dipl; degrees BFA and BA 4 yrs, AFA 2 yrs; SC 56; enrl in dept D 200, maj 96, grad 3.
Tuition: Undergrad $68 per cr hr, grad $73 per cr hr; campus res room & board $1150 per yr.
Courses: Advertising Design; Aesthetics; Art Education; Art History; Calligraphy; Ceramics; Costume Design & Construction; Drawing; Fashion Arts; Fibers; Goldsmithing; Graphic Arts; History of Art & Archaeology; Jewelry; Painting; Photography; Printmaking; Sculpture; Silversmithing; Stage Design; Teacher Training; Textile Design; Theatre Arts.
Summer School: Dir Jeannine Klemm. Tui $68 per cr hr, July 5-Aug 1. Courses—Fibers & Graphics.

ALBION

ALBION COLLEGE, Department of Visual Arts, 49224. Tel: 517-629-5511, exten 246. *Assoc Prof Art & Chmn Dept Visual Arts* Frank Machek, MFA; *Prof* Richard Leach, MFA; *Instrs* Richard Brunkus, MFA; *Instrs* Jeff Spaulding, MFA; *Instr* Elissa Olenych, MFA; vis profs in all media, one & two day visits.
Estab 1835; den; D&E; ent req HS dipl; degrees BA and BFA 4 yrs; SC 32, LC 8; enrl in col D 1672.
Tuition: $3175 per yr, $1587 per sem; campus res room & board $1540 per yr.
Courses: Art History; Ceramics; Drawing; Film; Liberal Arts; Painting; Photography; Printmaking; Sculpture; Stage Design; Teacher Training; Theatre Arts.
Summer School: Acad Dean Dr Neil Thorburn. Tui $70 per sem hr for term of 7 wks beginning May 15.

ALLENDALE

GRAND VALLEY STATE COLLEGES, Art Department, College Landing, 49401. Tel: 616-895-6611, exten 486. *Prof Art & Chairperson Dept* Beverly J Berger, MFA; *Prof* Donald A Kerr, MFA; *Asst Prof* Gray Sweeney, PhD; *Asst Prof* Whitney Sevin, MFA; *Assoc Prof* Chester Alkema, MFA; *Instr* Gregory Jaris, MFA; *Asst Prof* Takeshi Takahara, MFA; *Instr* Arthur Blom, MFA; vis prof—Jeffrey Weinstein, printmaking, winter term 78.
Estab 1960; pub; D&E; ent req HS dipl or equivalent; degrees BA, BS and BFA 4 yrs; SC 33, LC 6; enrl D 7469, nonmaj 328, maj 147, grad 10.
Tuition: Res—Undergrad $162 per yr, $18 per cr hr, grad $216 per yr, $24 per cr hr; Nonres—Undergrad $369 per yr, $41 per cr hr, grad $477 per yr, $53 per cr hr; campus res $1455 per yr.
Courses: Art Education; Art History; Ceramics; Drawing; Jewelry; Painting; Photography; Printmaking; Sculpture; Silversmithing.

ALMA

ALMA COLLEGE, Department of Art and Design, 614 W Superior, 48801. Tel: 517-463-2141, exten 323 & 405. *Chmn* Kent Kirby, MFA; *Assoc Prof* Edward Jacoma; *Asst Prof* Jeffrey Havilill.
Estab 1886; pvt; D&E; degrees BA, BFA; schol; SC 10, LC 3; enrl D 200, maj 15.
Tuition: Res—$3348; campus res room and board $1567.
Courses: Art Education; Art History; Ceramics; Drawing; Film; Graphic Design; History of Art & Archaeology; Jewelry; Museum Staff Training; Painting; Photography; Printmaking; Sculpture; Teacher Training; Textile Design.

ANN ARBOR

UNIVERSITY OF MICHIGAN, ANN ARBOR
—**School of Art,** 2000 Bonisteel Blvd, 48109. Tel: 313-764-0397. *Dean Sch* George V Bayliss, MFA; several vis profs.
Estab 1817, sch estab 1974; pub; D&E; ent req HS dipl, portfolio exam; degrees BFA 4 yrs, MA 1 yr, MFA 2 yrs, MS (Med Illustration) 2½ yrs; schol; SC 50, LC 6, GC 12; enrl D approx 430, E 25, nonmaj 100, maj 430, grad 35, special students 6.
Tuition: Res—Undergrad $554 per sem, grad $792 per sem; Nonres—Undergrad $1771 per sem, grad $1953 per sem; campus res room and board.
Courses: Advertising Design; Art Education; Calligraphy; Ceramics; Drawing; Film; Graphic Arts; Graphic Design; Illustration; Industrial Design; Interior Design; Jewelry; Lettering; Mixed Media; Painting; Photography; Printmaking; Sculpture; Silversmithing; Textile Design; Video.
Summer School: Dean George V Bayliss. Enrl varies; tui res $287, nonres $870 for term of spring or summer, spring May 1 to June 30, summer July 1 to Aug 30. Courses—Vary from yr to yr.
—**College of Literature,** Science and the Arts, Department of History of Art.* Tel: 313-764-5400. Instrs FT 11.
Dept estab 1910; pub; degrees BA, MA, PhD; schol and fel; enrl maj 100, grad 75.
Courses: History of Art; Museology.

BATTLE CREEK

KELLOGG COMMUNITY COLLEGE,* Arts Department, 49016. Instrs FT 3, PT 9.
Estab 1962; pub; D&E; no ent req; degree AA 2-4 yrs; schol; enrl D 2200, E 2000, maj 50.
Courses: Advertising Design; Architecture; Art Education; Ceramics; Commercial Art; Costume Design & Construction; Drafting; Drawing; Graphic Arts; Graphic Design; History of Art & Archaeology; Illustration; Industrial Design; Jewelry; Lettering; Painting; Photography; Sculpture; Stage Design; Teacher Training; Theatre Arts.
Adult Hobby Classes: Courses—In all areas.
Summer School: Courses—Basic Art.

BENTON HARBOR

LAKE MICHIGAN COLLEGE, Department of Art, 2755 E Napier Ave, 49022. Tel: 616-927-3571. *Asst Prof* Ken Schaber, MA.
Estab 1943; pub; D&E; ent req open door policy; degree AA 2 yrs; schol; SC 10, LC 5; enrl total 3377.
Tuition: Res—$420 per yr, $210 per sem; Nonres—$600 per yr, $300 per sem; no campus res.
Courses: Art Education; Art History; Ceramics; Drawing; Jewelry; Painting; Printmaking; Sculpture.

BERRIEN SPRINGS

ANDREWS UNIVERSITY,* 49104. Tel: 616-471-7771. *Chmn* Greg Constantine; Instrs FT 4.
Estab 1952; den; D&E; ent req HS grad; degrees BS (Art Educ), BA 4 yrs, MAT; SC 18, LC 5; enrl 130, maj 35.
Tuition: Room & board $1441 per quarter.
Courses: Advertising Design; Art Education; Ceramics; Design; Drawing; Painting; Photography; Printmaking; Sculpture; European Study.
Summer School: 8 wk session beginning June.

BIRMINGHAM

BIRMINGHAM-BLOOMFIELD ART ASSOCIATION, 1516 S Cranbrook Rd, 48009. Tel: 313-644-0866. *Exec Dir* Kenneth R Gross, MFA.
Estab 1956; pub; D&E; no ent req; no degrees; schol; SC 90-100, LC 4; enrl 3000 total.
Tuition: No campus res.
Courses: Aesthetics; Art History; Basic Design; Basic Drawing; Batik; Calligraphy; Ceramics; Collage; Commercial Art; Drawing; Goldsmithing; Graphic Arts; Graphic Design; Handicrafts (leaded glass, enamels, blown glass); Illustration; Intermedia; Jewelry; Mixed Media; Painting; Sculpture; Silversmithing; Surface Design; Textile Design.
Children's Classes: Courses—Drawing; Painting; Crafts; Pottery; Metals; Glass; Sketching.
Summer School: Same program on abbreviated basis.

BLOOMFIELD HILLS

CRANBROOK ACADEMY OF ART, 500 Lone Pine Rd, 48013. Tel: 313-645-3300. *Pres* Roy Slade; *Head Design Dept* Katherine & Michael McCoy, MA; *Head Fiber Dept* Gerhardt Knodel, MA; *Head Metalsmithing Dept* Richard C Thomas, MFA; *Head Painting Dept* George Ortman; *Head Photography Dept* Carl Toth, MFA; *Head Printmaking Dept* Connor Everts, BA; *Head Sculpture Dept* Michael D Hall, MFA.
Estab 1932; pvt; D; ent req portfolio; degrees 2 yrs for BFA with 2 yrs at accredited col, MFA and MArch 2 yrs; schol; enrl 155, grad 145.
Tuition: $2700 per yr; campus res room & board $1500 per yr.
Courses: Architecture; Ceramics; Design; Fiber; Metalsmithing; Painting; Photography; Printmaking; Sculpture.

DEARBORN

HENRY FORD COMMUNITY COLLEGE, Art .Department, 5101 Evergreen Rd, 48121. Tel: 313-271-2750, exten 295. *Chmn Dept* Robert J Ferguson; Instrs FT 6, PT 19.
Estab 1938; pub; D&E; ent req HS dipl; degree AA 2 yrs; schol; SC 25, LC 9; enrl D 3500, E 7500, maj 600.
Tuition: Res—$10 per cr hr; Nonres—$15 per cr hr, plus lab fees; drive in campus.
Courses: Advertising Design; Art Education; Ceramics; Commercial Art; Drafting; Drawing; Graphic Arts; History of Art & Archaeology; Jewelry; Materials; Painting; Photography; Sculpture; Teacher Training; Textile Design; Weaving.
Summer School: Dir Robert J Ferguson. Tui $10 per cr hr, nonres $15. Courses—Advanced Drawing; Art Appreciation; Art History; Basic Drawing; Basic Two-Dimensional Design; Black & White Photography; Ceramics; Directed Study; Life Drawing.

DETROIT

CENTER FOR CREATIVE STUDIES—COLLEGE OF ART AND DESIGN, 245 E Kirby, 48202. Tel: 313-872-3118. *Pres* Jerome Grove, BA; *Chmn Advertising Design* Powell Tripp, Dipl; *Chmn Photography* Bob Vigiletti, BA; *Chmn Fine Arts* Jay Holland, Cert; *Chmn Crafts* Michael Vizzini, Cert; *Chmn General Studies* Harry Smallenberg, PhD.

Estab 1929; pvt; D&E; ent req HS dipl and portfolio; degrees BFA 4 yr; schol; enrl D 650, E 200, Others 300.
Tuition: $2650 yr, $1325 per sem.
Courses: ‡Advertising Design; Aesthetics; Art History; Calligraphy; ‡Ceramics; Drawing; ‡Glass; ‡Graphic Arts; Illustration; ‡Industrial Design; ‡Jewelry; Lettering; ‡Painting; ‡Photography; ‡Printmaking; ‡Sculpture; ‡Textile Design.
Adult Hobby Classes: Tui varies with class. Courses—Most of the above.
Summer School: Dean Arthur Greenblatt. Enrl 250; tui $595 for term of 8 wk beginning June 12. Courses—Fine Arts; Crafts; Advertising Design; Photography.

MARYGROVE COLLEGE, Department of Art and Art History, 8425 W McNichols Rd, 48221. Tel: 313-862-8000. *Assoc Prof Art & Art Hist & Chmn Dept* Helen Sherman, PhD; *Asst Prof* Rose DeSloover, MFA; *Prof* Sister Edith Kenny, DEd; *Assoc Prof* Sister John Louise Leahy, DEd; *Asst Prof* James Lutomski, MFA; *Assoc Prof* David Vandegrift, MFA.
Estab 1910; pvt; D&E; ent req interview with portfolio; degrees BA and BFA 4 yrs; SC 37, LC 20, GC 5; enrl D 150, E 25, nonmaj 90, maj 60, grad 5.
Tuition: Undergrad $75 per cr hr; Grad $80 per cr hr; campus res room & board.
Courses: Advertising Design; Aesthetics; Art Education; Art History; ‡Ceramics; Collage; Commercial Art; Conceptual Art; Constructions; ‡Drawing; ‡Graphic Arts; Graphic Design; ‡History of Art & Archaeology; Mixed Media; ‡Painting; Photography; ‡Printmaking; ‡Teacher Training.
Adult Hobby Classes: Enrl 65; tui $35-$90 per course. Courses—Photography; Drawing; Painting.
Children's Classes: Enrl 100; tui $20-$50 per course. Courses—Painting; Ceramics; Photography.
Summer School: Dean Continuing Educ Thomas Plofchan. Enrl 40, tui $75 per cr hr for term of two 6 wk terms. Courses—Basic Courses, Graduate and Undergraduate.

WAYNE STATE UNIVERSITY, College of Liberal Arts, Department of Art and Art History, 450 W Kirby St, 48202. Tel: 313-577-2980. *Prof & Chmn Dept* G Alden Smith, MFA; Instrs FT 40, PT 35.
Estab 1868, dept estab 1936; pub; D&E; ent req HS dipl; degrees BA, BA(Art Hist) and BFA 4-5 yrs, MA, MA(Art Hist) and MFA(Studio Art) 2-3 yrs; SC 150, LC 75, GC 84 studio, 60 art hist; enrl D&E 2500, maj 650, grad 200.
Tuition: Res—Undergrad $310-$341 per sem, grad $404 per sem; Nonres—Undergrad $840-$917 per sem, grad $1098 per sem; campus res.
Courses: ‡Advertising Design; ‡Architecture (Interior only); ‡Art History; ‡Ceramics; Commercial Art; ‡Drawing; ‡Goldsmithing (Metals); ‡Graphic Arts; ‡Graphic Design; ‡Industrial Design; ‡Jewelry; Lettering; ‡Museum Staff Training (in coop with Detroit Inst of Arts); ‡Painting; ‡Photography; ‡Printmaking; ‡Sculpture; ‡Silversmithing; ‡Textile Design.
Summer School: Dir G Alden Smith; 4 quarters annually, same administration; for courses offered see catalog.

EAST LANSING

MICHIGAN STATE UNIVERSITY, College of Arts and Letters, Department of Art, 113 Kresge Art Center, 48828. Tel: 517-355-7610. *Chmn Dept* Roger L Funk; Instrs FT 38, PT 2.
Estab 1855; pub; D&E; ent req HS dipl; degrees BA and BFA 4 yrs, MA 1 yr, MFA 2 yrs; schol; SC 76, LC 49, GC 88; enrl D 2000, nonmaj 1000, maj 550, grad 100.
Tuition: Res—Undergrad $21.50-$23 per cr hr, grad $28 per cr hr; Nonres—Undergrad $46-$47.50 per cr hr, grad $52.50 per cr hr; campus res room & board $495.75.
Courses: ‡Advertising Design; ‡Art Education; ‡Art History; ‡Ceramics; ‡Commercial Art; ‡Drawing; ‡Film; ‡Goldsmithing; ‡Graphic Arts; ‡Graphic Design; ‡History of Art & Archaeology; ‡Industrial Design; ‡Jewelry; ‡Painting; ‡Photography; ‡Printmaking; ‡Sculpture; ‡Silversmithing; ‡Teacher Training.
Adult Hobby Classes: Tui $30-$40 per class, these meet once per wk. Courses—Painting; Drawing; Photography; Sculpture; Jewelry.
Children's Classes: Saturday Art Program $10 per quarter. Courses—Fabrics & Fibers; Painting; Drawing; Photography; Printmaking; Two & Three-Dimensional Media.
Summer School: See Leland, Michigan.

FLINT

CHARLES STEWART MOTT COMMUNITY COLLEGE, Fine Arts Division, 1401 E Court St, 48503. Tel: 313-762-0443. *Chmn Dept* Samuel E Morello, MFA; *Primary Art Faculty:* Dorothy Bates, MA; Thomas Bomnert, MFA; Robert Caskey, MFA; Thomas Nuzum, MFA;

William O'Malley, MAe; Douglas Warner, MSDes; Barbara White, MFA.
Estab 1923; pub; D&E; ent req HS dipl or 19 yrs old; degree AA 2 yrs; schol; enrl D&E 250, maj 250.
Tuition: Dist res—$16 per cr hr; state res—$27 per cr hr; Nonres—$39 per cr hr; no campus res.
Courses: Art Education; Art History; Ceramics; Drafting; Drawing; Film; Jewelry; Painting; Photography; Printmaking; Sculpture; Stage Design; Teacher Training; Theatre Arts; Video.
Summer School: Chmn Samuel E Morello. Tui same as above; 8 wk sessions, first May 15 - July 1, second July 1 - Aug 15. Courses—Vary.

GRAND RAPIDS

AQUINAS COLLEGE, Art Department, 1607 Robinson Rd SE, 49502. Tel: 614-459-8281. *Chmn Dept* Ronald Watson, MFA; *Assoc Prof* Larry Blovits, MFA; *Assoc Prof* James Karsina, MFA; *Asst Prof* Diane Shaffer, MFA.
Estab 1940, dept estab 1965; pvt; D&E; ent req HS dipl; degrees BA and BFA 4 yrs; schol; SC 28, LC 9; enrl D 250, nonmaj 210, maj 40.
Tuition: $2636 per yr, $1318 per sem; campus res room & board $1400 per yr.
Courses: Art Education; Art History; Basic Design; ‡Drawing; ‡Painting; ‡Printmaking; ‡Sculpture; Teacher Training.

CALVIN COLLEGE, Art Department, 1801 E Beltline, 49506. Tel: 616-949-4000, exten 326. *Assoc Prof Art & Chmn Dept* Edgar G Boeve, MSD; *Asst Prof* Helen Bonzelaar, MA; *Asst Prof* Carl J Huisman, MFA; *Assoc Prof* Robert A Jensen, MFA; *Assoc Prof* Chris Stoffel Overvoorde, MFA; *Instr* Brenda Van Halsema, MA; *Instr* Timothy Van Laar, MFA; vis prof—Ronald Pederson, sculpture, 77-79.
Estab 1876, dept estab 1965; den; D&E; ent req HS dipl, SAT or ACT; degrees BA(Art), BA(Art Educ) and BFA(Art) 4 yrs, MAT; schol; SC16, LC 4, GC 5; enrl maj 130, grad 4, others 4.
Tuition: $1115 per sem, $285 per class; campus res room & board $1080 per yr.
Courses: Aesthetics; Architecture; ‡Art Education; ‡Art History; Ceramics; Collage; Conceptual Art; Costume Design & Construction; Drawing; Film; Graphic Art; History of Art & Archaeology; Jewelry; ‡Occupational Therapy; Painting; Photography; Printmaking; Sculpture; Stage Design; ‡Teacher Training; Theatre Arts.
Summer School: Chmn Art Dept Edgar G Boeve. Enrl varies; tui $225 for term of 3 wks beginning May. Courses—Vary.

GRAND RAPIDS JUNIOR COLLEGE,* Art Department, 143 Bostwock NE, 49502. Tel: 616-456-4572. *Chmn* Glenn T Raymond; Instrs FT 4, PT 4.
Estab c 1920; pub; D&E; ent req HS dipl or ent exam; degree AA 2 yrs; schol; SC 17, LC 2; enrl D 250, E 75, maj 60.
Tuition: no campus res.
Courses: Art Education; Ceramics; Drafting; Drawing; Graphic Arts; History of Art & Archaeology; Jewelry; Painting; Sculpture; Teacher Training.
Sumer School: Term of 8 wks beginning June. Courses—Art History & Appreciation; Teacher Training.

KENDALL SCHOOL OF DESIGN, 1110 College Ave, 49503. Tel: 616-451-2886. *Dir* Phyllis I Danielson, PhD; *Chmn Found* Connie Phillips, BA; *Chmn Visual Commun* Ron Riksen, BA; *Chmn Interiors* Erli Gronberg, BA; Instrs FT 15, PT 8.
Estab 1928; pvt; D; ent req HS dipl, ACT, SAT, portfolio; degrees cert 3 yrs, BFA 4 yrs with Aquinas College; schol; SC 64, LC 9; enrl D 400, nonmaj 55, others 20.
Tuition: $1500 per yr, $50 per cr hr.
Courses: Advertising Design; Architecture; Art History; Commercial Art; Drawing; Furniture Design; Graphic Arts; Graphic Design; Illustration; Interior Design; Lettering; Painting; Textile Design.
Children's Classes: Courses—Drawing; Painting; Design.
Summer School: Full semester, May - July; same program as above.

HILLSDALE

HILLSDALE COLLEGE, Art Department, 49242. Tel: 517-437-7341, exten 288. *Acting Dir* Bert C Fink, MFA; *Assoc Prof* Rosamond Joy Stewart, MA; *Instr* Samuel Knecht, MFA.
Estab 1844; pvt; ent req HS dipl, SAT; degrees BA, BS and BLS 4 yrs; SC 12, LC 5; enrl D 1000, nonmaj 150, maj 8.
Tuition: $3090 per yr, $1545 per sem; campus res room & board.
Courses: Art Education; Art History; Ceramics; Drawing; Jewelry; Painting; Printmaking; Sculpture; Teacher Training.
Summer School: Dir Dr Jerome Fallon. Courses—Vary.

HOLLAND

ART SCHOOL OF THE CRAFTS GUILD, 0-380 S 168th Ave, Rte 7, 49423. Tel: 616-335-3402. *Dir* Alleene Lowery Fisher.
Estab Detroit 1927, Holland 1948; pvt; enrl limited to 10.
Tuition: $300 per month yr round.
Courses: Drawing; Design; Painting.
Home Study Courses: Oil Painting Fundamentals; Still Life; Portraiture; Landscape. $300 month.

HOPE COLLEGE, Art Department, 49423. Tel: 616-392-5111, exten 3170. *Chmn Art Dept* John M Wilson, PhD; *Asst Prof* Bruce McCombs, MFA; *Assoc Prof* Delbert Michel, MFA; *Prof* Robert Vickers, MA; vis profs change from year to year.
Estab 1866, dept estab 1962; den; D&E; ent req HS dipl, CEEB-SAT or ACT; degrees BA and BM 4 yrs; schol; SC 18, LC 12; enrl in dept D 185, E 61, nonmaj 228, maj 18.
Tuition: Res—$4195 per yr; Nonres—$2850 per yr; campus res room & board $1345 yr.
Courses: Architecture; Art Education; Art History; Ceramics; Drawing; History of Art & Archaeology; Painting; Photography; Printmaking; Silkscreen; Sculpture; Teacher Training; Two-Dimensional & Three-Dimensional Design.
Summer School: Dir Dr Donald Williams. Tui $55 per cr hr. Courses—Vary from yr to yr.

HOUGHTON

MICHIGAN TECHNOLOGICAL UNIVERSITY, Humanities Department, 49931. Tel: 906-487-2007. *Head Dept* Dr Arthur P Young; *Lectr* Lenore K Evans, AB.
Estab 1885, dept estab 1927; pub; D&E; ent req HS dipl; no degrees granted in art; SC 6, LC 3; enrl nonmaj approx 150.
Tuition: Res—Undergrad $861 per yr, grad $906 per yr; Nonres—Undergrad $2001 per yr, grad $2046 per yr; campus res room & board $1549.50 per yr.
Courses: Art Appreciation; Drawing; Painting; Theatre Arts; Three-Dimensional Design.
Children's Classes: Enrl 20; tui $140 live-in per wk. Summer Youth Program offers Sketching and Painting July 9, July 16 & July 23 starts.
Summer School: Instrs Lenore Evans. Tui $67 res, $155 nonres for term of 1 wk beginning July 10 & July 17. Courses—Drawing; Painting.

INTERLOCHEN

INTERLOCHEN ARTS ACADEMY, Department of Visual Art, 49643. Tel: 616-276-9221, exten 272. *Chairperson Dept* Lary Lien, MFA; *Instr* James Alley, MFA; *Instr* John Church, MFA; *Instrs* Lina Dean, BFA; *Instr* Jean Parsons, MFA; *Instr* Wayne Brill, BS.
Pvt; D; ent req portfolio; HS dipl; schol; enrl 70, nonmaj 40, maj 30.
Tuition: $4500 per yr, includes room and board.
Courses: Ceramics; Drawing; Foundation Design; Goldsmithing; Jewelry; Metalsmithing; Painting; Photography; Printmaking; Sculpture; Silversmithing; Textile Design; Weaving (Fiber).
Summer School: Dir George Wilson. Term of 8 wks beginning June 25.

JACKSON

ELLA SHARP MUSEUM,* 3225 Fourth St, 49203. Tel: 517-787-2320. *Cur of Art Educ for Young People* Millie Hadwin; Instrs FT 3, PT 20.
Estab 1965; pvt; D&E; ent req mus mem; schol; SC 10, LC 5; enrl adults and children approx 200.
Tuition: Varies with type of course being offered. Courses offered in conjunction with the Adult Enrichment Dept, Jackson Community College, Jackson.
Courses: Art Education; Ceramics; Drawing; Fabric & Fiber Arts; Graphic Arts; Graphic Design; Indian Crafts; Macrame; Museum Staff Training; Painting; Photography; Quilting; Sculpture; Stitchery; Textile Design; Theatre Arts; Weaving.

KALAMAZOO

KALAMAZOO COLLEGE, Art Department, 1200 Academy St, 49007. Tel: 616-383-8422. *Chmn Dept* Bernard S Palchick, MFA; *Primary Art Faculty:* Marcia J Wood, MFA; Billie Fischer, PhD; dept has vis profs.
Estab 1833, dept estab approx 1940; pvt; D; ent req HS dipl, SAT, ACT, class rank; degree BA 4 yrs; schol; SC 14, LC 10; enrl in sch 1500, nonmaj 350 (dept), maj 38, others 5.
Tuition: $5000 per yr; campus res.
Courses: Art Education; ‡Art History; ‡Ceramics; Drawing; ‡Painting; ‡Printmaking; ‡Sculpture.

KALAMAZOO INSTITUTE OF ARTS, Genevieve and Donald Gilmore Art Center, 314 S Park St, 49007. Tel: 616-349-7775. *Assoc Dir Educ* Kirk Newman, MFA; *Head Ceramics Dept* Thomas Kendall, MA; *Head Painting & Drawing Dept* Robert Sabin, MA.
Estab 1924; pvt; D&E; nondegree granting program; SC 25; enrl D 778, E 407.
Tuition: $33-$75 depending upon class; no campus res.
Courses: Ceramics; Drawing; Jewelry; Painting; Photography; Weaving.
Children's Classes: Tui varies. Courses—Painting; Drawing; Ceramics; Printmaking; Photography.
Summer School: *Assoc Dir Educ* Kirk Newman. Visiting professionals teach 2 wk summer workshops. Courses—Same as fall and spring.

KALAMAZOO VALLEY COMMUNITY COLLEGE, Department of Art, 6767 W O, 49009. Tel: 616-375-5000. *Instr Art & Head Dept* Drew Krouse, MFA; *Instr* Arleigh Smyavois, MA.
Estab 1968; pub; E; ent req HS dipl or over 19 yrs old; degrees AA and AS; SC 12; enrl D&E 500.
Tuition: $13 per cr hr.
Courses: Ceramics; Drafting; Drawing; Graphic Arts; Graphic Design; Jewelry; Painting; Photography; Sculpture; Textile Design; Two-Dimensional Design.
Summer School: *Dir* Drew Krouse.

WESTERN MICHIGAN UNIVERSITY, Department of Art, 49008. Tel: 616-383-1858. *Chairperson Dept Art* Lawrence John Link, MFA; *Assoc Prof* Andy Argyropoulos, MFA; *Assoc Prof* Joe Delvca, MFA; *Assoc Prof* Joe Frattallone, PhD; *Prof* Charles E Meyer, PhD; *Assoc Prof* Curtis Rhodes, MFA; *Prof* Paul Robbert, MFA; FT faculty 25.
Estab 1904, dept estab 1939; pub; D&E; ent req HS dipl, ACT; degrees BA and BFA 4 yrs, MA 1 yr, MFA 2 yrs; schol; SC 60, LC 9, GC 8; enrl nonmaj 150, maj 502, grad 25.
Tuition: Res—Undergrad $25 per hr, grad $34 per hr; Nonres—Undergrad $58 per hr, grad $74 per hr; campus res room & board $1520 per yr.
Courses: Aesthetics; Architecture; ‡Art Education; ‡Art History; Calligraphy; ‡Ceramics; Collage; Commercial Art; Conceptual Art; Constructions; Drawing; Goldsmithing; ‡Graphic Design; History of Art & Archaeology; ‡Intermedia; ‡Jewelry; Mixed Media; ‡Painting; ‡Photography; ‡Printmaking; ‡Sculpture; Silversmithing; ‡Teacher Training; ‡Textile Design; Video.
Summer School: *Chairperson Dept* John Link. Enrl 300; tui same per hr as acad yr for term of 8 wks beginning May & July for two terms. Courses—Same as above.

LANSING

LANSING COMMUNITY COLLEGE, Performing and Creative Arts Department, 419 N Capital Ave (Mailing Add: PO Box 40010, 48901). Tel: 517-373-7460. *Chairperson Dept* David Machtel, PhD.
Estab 1957, dept estab 1967; pub; D&E; ent req HS dipl; degree AA 2 yrs; schol; SC 60, LC 15; enrl D 758, E 506, nonmaj 460, maj 504, others 300.
Tuition: Res—$8.50 per cr hr; Nonres—$14.50 per cr hr; no campus res.
Courses: ‡Ceramics; ‡Commercial Art; ‡Drawing; ‡Illustration; ‡Interior Design; ‡Jewelry; ‡Painting; ‡Printmaking.

LELAND

LEELANAU SUMMER ART SCHOOL, 49654. (Sponsored by Michigan State University, Art Department).
Estab 1939.
Tuition: $28 per term hr.

LIVONIA

MADONNA COLLEGE, Art Department, 36600 Schoolcraft Rd, 48150. Tel: 313-591-1200, exten 8. *Chairperson Art Dept* Sister M Angeline, PhD; *Instr* Loretta Hubley, MA; *Instr* Anthony Balogh, MA; *Instr* Dayle Kramer; MA; *Instr* Lula Simakas, MA Cand.
Estab 1947; pvt; D&E; ent req HS dipl, portfolio; degrees AA 2 yrs, AB 4 yrs; SC 17, LC 3; enrl D 43, E 22, maj 17.
Tuition: $37 per sem hr; campus res room & board.
Courses: Advertising Design; Art History; Calligraphy; Ceramics; Commercial Art; Drawing; Graphic Arts; Jewelry; Lettering; Mixed Media; Painting; Photography; Printmaking; Sculpture; Teacher Training.
Adult Hobby Classes: Enrl 65; tui $40 per 10 wks. Courses—Painting; Jewelry & Lapidary; Calligraphy.
Summer School: *Dir* Sister M Angeline. Tui $37 per sem hr for summer term beginning May 1. Courses—Printmaking; Watercolor & Acrylics; Art for the Elem Teacher; Calligraphy (noncredit) $40.

SCHOOLCRAFT COLLEGE, Department of Art, 18600 Haggerty Rd, 48151. Tel: 313-591-6400. *Chairperson Dept Art* Robert Dufort, MFA; *Primary Art Faculty:* Lincoln Lao, MFA; James R Black, MFA; Cecilia Kelley, MA.
Estab 1964; pub; D&E; ent req ent exam; degree AA 2 yrs; SC 13, LC 4; enrl D 200, E 60, maj 48.
Tuition: No campus res.
Courses: Art Education; Art History; Ceramics; Costume Design & Construction; Drawing; Film; Graphic Arts; History of Art & Archaeology; Jewelry; Painting; Photography; Printmaking; Sculpture.
Adult Hobby Classes: Courses—Macrame; Acrylic Painting; Stained Glass.

MARQUETTE

NORTHERN MICHIGAN UNIVERSITY, Department of Art and Design, 49855. Tel: 906-227-2194. *Assoc Prof Art & Design & Head Dept* Thomas Cappuccio; *Prof* Richard K Gorski; *Prof* Wolfram F Niessen; *Asst Prof* John D Hubbard; *Asst Prof* James M Quirk; *Assoc Prof* John V Rauch; *Assoc Prof* Marvin R Zehnder.
Estab 1899, dept estab 1964; pub; D&E; ent req HS dipl, ACT; degrees BS, BFA and BA 4 yrs; schol; SC 30, LC 10, GC 18.
Tuition: Res—Undergrad $25 per cr hr, grad $32 per cr hr; Nonres—Undergrad $50 per cr hr, grad $55 per cr hr; campus res room & board $1400 per yr.
Courses: Advertising Design; Art Education; Art History; Ceramics; Commercial Art; Drawing; Film; Goldsmithing; Graphic Arts; Graphic Design; Illustration; Industrial Design; Jewelry; Painting; Photography; Printmaking; Sculpture; Silversmithing.

MIDLAND

MIDLAND CENTER FOR THE ARTS, 1801 W St Andrews, 48640. Tel: 517-631-3250. *Coordr* Gene Sosoille, BA; *Instr* Steven West, BFA; *Instr* Carol Yoshimine, BFA; *Instr* Daniel Wells, BA; *Instrs* Cathy Earle, MA; *Instr* Bernice Sizemore, BA; *Instr* Jim Ardis, BA; *Instr* Val Geidans; *Instr* Niki Diss, BFA.
Estab 1971; pvt; D&E; no ent req; no degrees given; SC 12-20, LC 2; enrl D&E 100.
Tuition: $35 - $55 per sem; no campus res.
Courses: Art History; Ceramics; Graphic Arts; Handicraft (weaving); Jewelry; Mixed Media; Painting; Photography; Printmaking; Sculpture; Silversmithing; Textile Design.
Children's Classes: Enrl 50; tui $25-$30 per sem. Courses—Multimedia and drawing.

MOUNT PLEASANT

CENTRAL MICHIGAN UNIVERSITY, Department of Art, 48859. Tel: 517-774-3025. *Acting Chmn Dept Art* Richard R Kline, MFA; Instrs FT 19, PT 4.
Estab 1892; pub; D&E; ent req HS dipl; degrees BA, BFA and AB 4 yrs; MA; SC 50, LC 9; enrl for univ 16,000.
Tuition: Res—Undergrad $24 per cr hr, grad $32 per cr hr; Nonres—Undergrad $62 per cr hr, grad $71 per cr hr; campus res room & board $2365 per yr.
Courses: Aesthetics; Art Education; Art History; Ceramics; Collage; Commercial Art; Conceptual Art; Constructions; Drawing; Film; Goldsmithing; Graphic Arts; Intermedia; Jewelry; Lettering; Mixed Media; Painting; Photography; Printmaking; Sculpture; Silversmithing.
Summer School: *Dir* Dr Dan Millar.

MUSKEGON

MUSKEGON COMMUNITY COLLEGE, Department of Creative and Performing Arts, 221 S Quarterline, 49443. Tel: 616-773-9131, exten 324. *Chairperson Dept Creative & Performing Arts* Lee Edward Collet, MFA; *Primary Art Faculty:* John Walson, MS; Ken Foster, MFA; Robert Sheardy, MA.
Estab 1926; pub; D&E; ent req HS dipl; degree AA 2 yrs; schol; SC 18, LC 6; enrl D 280, E 60.
Tuition: Res—$14 per cr hr; Nonres—$21 per cr hr; no campus res.
Courses: Art Education; Art History; Ceramics; Costume Design & Construction; Drawing; Film; Interior Design; Painting; Printmaking; Sculpture; Stage Design; Teacher Training; Theatre Course.
Adult Hobby Classes: Tui $14 or $21 per hr. Courses—Ceramics; Painting.
Summer School: *Chairperson Dept Creative & Performing Arts* Lee Edward Collet. Tui $14 per cr hr for term of 7 wks beginning July 5. Courses—Ceramics.

OLIVET

OLIVET COLLEGE, Art Department, 49076. Tel: 616-749-7661. *Chmn & Assoc Prof* Donald Rowe, MFA; *Assoc Prof* H James Hay, MFA; *Prof* William Whitney, MFA.
Estab 1844, dept estab 1870; pvt; D&E; ent req HS dipl; degrees BA 4 yr, MA 1 yr; schol; SC 17, LC 8, GC 10; enrl D 700, nonmaj 200, maj 40, grad 3.
Tuition: $2650 yr, $1325 per sem, $95 per cr hr; campus res room and board $1630 yr.
Courses: Advanced Independent Work; Baroque Art; Basic Design; Drawing; Figurative Sculpture; Graphics; History of Visual Art; Jewelry; Medieval Art; Metalwork; 19th Century Art; Non-Figurative Sculpture; Painting; Printmaking; Primitive Art; Renaissance Art; Research Paper; Sculpture; Silversmithing; 20th Century Art.

PONTIAC

PONTIAC ART CENTER, 47 Williams St, 48053. Tel: 313-333-7849. *Exec Dir* Ian R Lyons, MA; *Instr* Mary Alger, BS; *Instr* Lorraine McCarty, MFA; *Instrs* Sybil Oshinsky, MFA; *Instrs* Eve Szilagyi, BA; *Instr* James Zimmerman, MFA; *Instr* James Gilbert, MFA; *Instr* Carol Goodale, BA.
Estab 1964; pub; D&E; open enrollment; schol; SC 15; enrl 200.
Tuition: Varies; no campus res.
Courses: Ceramics; Drawing; Jewelry; Metalsmithing; Painting; Photography; Sculpture; Watercolor; Weaving.
Children's Classes: Tui $25 per class. Courses—Sculpture; Painting; Drawing.
Summer School: Exec Dir Ian R Lyons. Term of 10 wks beginning June. Courses—Drawing; Jewelry; Painting; Photography; Sculpture; Weaving; Metalsmithing.

PORT HURON

ST CLAIR COUNTY COMMUNITY COLLEGE,* Fine Arts Department, 323 Erie St, 48060. Tel: 313-984-3881. *Discipline Chmn* Patrick Bourke; Instrs FT 4, PT 1.
Estab 1923; pub; D&E; ent req HS dipl, ent exam; degrees AA and AAS 2 yrs; schol; SC 30, LC 5; enrl D 60.
Courses: Advertising Design; Art Education; Ceramics; Commercial Art; Display; Drawing; Graphic Arts; Graphic Design; History of Art & Archaeology; Illustration; Lettering; Painting; Photography; Sculpture; Theatre Arts.

ROCHESTER

OAKLAND UNIVERSITY, Department of Art and Art History, 48063. Tel: 313-377-3375. *Prof Art Hist & Acting Chmn Dept Art & Art Hist* John B Cameron, PhD; *Prof* Carl F Barnes, Jr, PhD; *Prof* Charlotte Stokes, PhD; *Assoc Prof* John Beardman, MFA & MA; *Vis Instr* Janice C Schimmelman, PhD Cand; *Vis Instr* Forrest McGill, PhD; *Vis Instrs* Judith Toth, MFA.
Estab 1957, dept estab 1960; pub; D&E; ent req HS dipl; degree BA 4 yrs; schol; SC 3, LC 9.
Tuition: Res—Undergrad $24.24 per cr hr, grad $33.50 per cr hr; Nonres—Undergrad $63.50 per cr hr; campus res room & board $1548 per yr.
Courses: Art History; History of Art & Archaeology.

SAUGATUCK

OXBOW SUMMER ART WORKSHOPS, 49453. Tel: 616-857-5811. *Workshop Dir* Ellen Lanyon; *Artists-in-Residence:* Keith Achepohl; Cynthia Carlson; Ron Gorchov; Harmony Hammond; Tony Hepburn; Miyoko Ito; Jerry Janosco; Dennis Kowal; James McGarrell; Ed Paschke; Joan Snyder; Juergen Strunck.
Estab 1910; pvt; D&E; ent req over 18 yrs, slides must be submitted; credit toward graduation recognized by most schools; schol; enrl 55 per session, 3 sessions per summer.
Tuition: $475 for 3 wk session, incl room and board.
Courses: Ceramics; Collage; Conceptual Art; Drawing; Graphic Arts; Intermedia; Mixed Media; Painting; Papermaking; Photography; Printmaking; Sculpture; Theatre Arts.

SCOTTVILLE

WEST SHORE COMMUNITY COLLEGE, Division of Humanities and Fine Arts, Box 277, 49454. Tel: 616-845-6211. *Prof Art & Head Dept* Leo Teholiz, MA; *Prof* Floyd Iverson, MA; *Instr* Mrs Pat Monton, Cert; Instrs PT approx 6.
Pub; D&E; ent req HS dipl; degree AA 2 yrs; schol; SC 18, LC 10; enrl D 202, E 81, nonmaj 273, maj 10.

Tuition: Res—$150 per quarter, $10 per cr hr; Nonres—$240 per quarter, $16 per cr hr; no campus res.
Courses: Art History; Calligraphy; Ceramics; Drafting; Drawing; Graphic Design; Lettering; Mixed Media; Painting; Photography; Printmaking; Sculpture; Stage Design; Teacher Training; Theatre Arts.
Adult Hobby Classes: Enrl approx 15; directed by Community Services including art workshops, crafts, photography.
Children's Classes: Enrl approx 15; conducted by Community Services.
Summer School: Dir Leo Teholiz. Enrl approx 12; tui $5 per noncredit class, $10 per cr hr for term of 8 wks beginning June 1. Summer Art Workshop (Outdoor Off Campus Classes). Courses—Pottery; Clay Modeling.

TRAVERSE CITY

NORTHWESTERN MICHIGAN COLLEGE, Art Department, 1701 E Front St, 49684. Tel: 616-946-5650, exten 525. *Instr Art & Chmn Dept* Paul Welch, MA; *Instr* Norman Averill, MA; *Instr* Robert Bach; *Instr* Stephen Ballance, MA; *Instr* Jack Ozegovic, MFA.
Estab 1951, dept estab 1957; pub; D&E; ent req HS dipl; degree AA 2 yrs; schol; SC 40, LC 4; enrl nonmaj 400, maj 75.
Tuition: $11.50 per cr hr per term In-Dist; $19 per cr hr per term In-Serv Area; $21 per cr hr per term In-State; $23 per cr hr per term Out-of-State; campus res room & board.
Courses: Advertising Design; Art Education; Art History; Ceramics; Commercial Art; Drafting; Drawing; Film; Goldsmithing; Graphic Arts; Graphic Design; Illustration; Industrial Design; Jewelry; Lettering; Painting; Photography; Printmaking; Sculpture; Silversmithing; Textile Design.
Summer School: Dir Paul Welch. Tui same as regular session.

UNIVERSITY CENTER

DELTA COLLEGE, Humanities Division, Art Department, 48710. Tel: 517-686-0400. *Prof Art & Chmn Dept* Charles A Breed, MA; *Asst Prof* Larry Butcher, MA; *Assoc Prof* John McCormick, MFA; *Asst Prof* Larry Oughton, MFA; *Assoc Prof* Russell Thayer, MA; *Lectr* Linda Menger, MA; dept has vis profs.
Estab 1960; pub; D&E; ent req open-door policy; degree AA 2 yrs; schol; SC 21, LC 5; enrl D 550, E 100, maj 190.
Tuition: $480 per yr, $16 per cr hr; Out of Dist $840 per yr, $28 per cr hr; Out of State $1140 per yr, $38 per cr hr; campus res $775 per sem.
Courses: Art Education; Art History; Ceramics; Commercial Art; Drawing; Graphic Design; Interior Design; Painting; Photography; Printmaking; Sculpture.

SAGINAW VALLEY STATE COLLEGE, Department of Art and Design, Pierce Rd, 48710. *Prof Art & Design & Chmn Dept* Barron Hirsch, MFA; *Prof* Matthew Zivich, MFA; *Instr* Gayle Leece, BFA; *Instr* Curtis Leece, BFA; *Instr* Paul Davis, MA; *Instr* Martha Yeatman, BA; dept has vis profs for short tenure, less than 1 term.
Estab 1960, dept estab 1968; pub; D&E; ent req HS dipl; degree BA(Art) 4 yrs or less; schol; SC approx 20, LC approx 15; enrl D 200, E 50, maj 37.
Tuition: $22 per cr hr; campus res.
Courses: Advertising Design; Aesthetics; Art Education; Art History; Collage; Commercial Art; Conceptual Art; Constructions; Drawing; Graphic Arts; Graphic Design; Handicrafts (fibre); History of Art & Archaeology; Illustration; Intermedia; Painting; Photography; Printmaking; Sculpture; Teacher Training; Textile Design.
Summer School: Courses vary.

WARREN

MACOMB COUNTY COMMUNITY COLLEGE, Division of Humanities, Art Department, 14500 Twelve Mile Rd, 48093. Tel: 313-779-7210. *Prof* David Barr, MA; *Prof* James Pallas, MFA; *Prof* James Johnston, MA; *Prof* Al Herbert, MA.
Estab 1960, dept estab 1965; pub; D&E; ent req HS dipl, ent exam; degree AA 2 yrs; schol; SC 14, LC 6.
Courses: Advertising Design; Architecture; Ceramics; Commercial Art; Costume Design & Construction; Display; Drafting; Drawing; Graphic Arts; Graphic Design; Handicrafts; History of Art & Archaeology; Illustration; Industrial Design; Jewelry; Painting; Photography; Sculpture; Watercolor.

YPSILANTI

EASTERN MICHIGAN UNIVERSITY, Department of Art, 48197. Tel: 313-487-1268. *Head Dept Art* Kingsley M Calkins, MA.
Estab 1849, dept estab 1901; pub; D&E; ent req HS dipl; degrees BA, BS and BA(Art Educ) 4 yrs, MA(Art Educ) and MFA 2 yrs; schol; SC 55, LC 18; enrl undergrad maj 580, nonmaj 800, grad 220.

Tuition: Res—Undergrad $24.50 per cr hr, grad $37 per cr hr; Nonres—Undergrad $60 per cr hr, grad $90 per cr hr; campus res room & board $1600 per yr.

Courses: Advertising Design, ‡Art Education; Art History; Ceramics; Commercial Art; Conceptual Art; Drawing; Goldsmithing; Graphic Arts; Graphic Design; History of Arts & Archaeology; Illustration; Intermedia; Jewelry; Lettering; Mixed Media; ‡Museum Staff Training; Painting; Photography; Printmaking; Sculpture; Silversmithing; ‡Stage Design; Teacher Training; Textile Design; ‡Theatre Arts; Video.

Summer School: Head Dept Art Kingsley M Calkins. Term of 6 wks beginning June 25.

MINNESOTA

BEMIDJI

BEMIDJI STATE UNIVERSITY, Art Department, 56601. Tel: 218-755-3939. *Chmn* Sally James, BFA; *Prof* Eugene Dalzotto, MFA; *Assoc Prof* Arloene (Westy) James, MFA; *Assoc Prof* Marlin Kaul, MFA; *Assoc Prof* William Kelly, MFA; *Prof* A Keith Malmquist, MFA; *Prof* Russell Sawdey, PhDEd; *Instr* Larry Stene, MFA; occasional vis prof term of one yr.
Estab 1918; pub; D&E; ent req HS dipl, ACT, SAT, PSAT, or SCAT; degrees BA, BS (Teaching) and BS (non-teaching Tech Illustration/Commercial Design) 4 yr, BA offered with any 2 courses; SC 54, LC 17 GC-no grad prog in Art, all undergrad courses can be taken for grad cr under a studio or research number, grad courses offered in Art Educ on demand individual study.
Tuition: Res—Undergrad $10.25 per quarter hr, grad $13 per quarter hr; Nonres—Undergrad $20.25 per quarter hr, grad $24.24 per quarter hour; campus res room and board.
Courses: ‡Art Education; Art History; Ceramics; ‡Commercial Art; Conceptual Art; Drafting; Drawing; Film; Graphic Arts; Graphic Design; Handicrafts (basketry, spinning, weaving, leaded glass, macrame, beading, quilting, batik, trapunto, stitchery, needlepoint); History of Art and Archaeology; Illustration; Industrial Design; Jewelry; Landscape Architecture; Lettering; Painting; Photography; Printmaking; Sculpture; Silversmithing; Teacher Training; Textile Design; Theatre Arts; Video.
Children's Classes: Enrl 20; tui see above. Courses—Art. Preschool children's art classes offered each fall.
Summer School: Dir William Sellon. Tui as above for term of two 5 wk sessions beginning June. Courses—most of regular courses plus special summer session only courses.

COLLEGEVILLE

ST JOHN'S UNIVERSITY, Art Department, 56321. Tel: 612-363-2295. *Head Dept Asst Prof* Hugh Witzmann, MFA; *Asst Prof* Bela Petheo, MFA; *Asst Prof* Jim Hendershot, MFA; *Instr* Alan Reed, MA.
Estab 1863; pvt; D; ent req HS dipl, ent exam; degrees BA Liberal Arts; schol; SC 14, LC 10; enrl D 150.
Tuition: $2820 per yr; campus res $400.
Courses: Aesthetics; Art Education; Art History; Calligraphy; Ceramics; Commercial Art; Costume Design and Construction; Drawing; Graphic Design; History of Art and Archaeology; Jewelry; Landscape Architecture; Mixed Media; Painting; Photography; Printmaking; Sculpture; Silversmithing; Stage Design; Teacher Training.

DULUTH

UNIVERSITY OF MINNESOTA, DULUTH, Department of Art, 55812. Tel: 218-726-8224. *Head Dept* James H Brutger MEd; *Instrs* Thomas Beggs, MFA; *Prof* William Boyce, MEd; *Asst Prof* Joe Boudreau, MFA; *Asst Prof* Leif Brush, MFA; *Asst Prof* Alyce Coker, MEd; *Asst Prof* Thomas Hedin, PhD; vis prof—summer guest workshop conductors.
Enrl D 300, E 100, maj 200, GS 14.
Tuition: Res—Undergrad about $20 per cr hr, grad $26.50 per cr hr.
Courses: Advertising Design; Art Education; Art History; Calligraphy; Ceramics; Commercial Art; Drawing; Film; Graphic Arts; Graphic Design; Jewelry; Lettering; Mixed Media; Museum Staff Training; Painting; Photography; Printmaking; Sculpture; Silversmithing; Textile Design.
Adult Hobby Classes: Courses—Calligraphy; Stained Glass-Beginners and Advanced.
Children's Classes: Saturday art classes.

ELY

VERMILION COMMUNITY COLLEGE, Art Department, 55731. Tel: 218-365-3256, exten 19. *Head Dept Instr* Dan Wood, MAE; *vis prof*—Charlene and Bob Burningham, fibers, winter term.
Estab 1922, dept estab 1964; pub; D&E; ent req HS dipl; degrees AA 2 yr; SC 13; LC 5; enrl D 27, E 38, nonmaj 55, maj 10.
Tuition: Res—Undergrad $495 per yr; Nonres—Undergrad $990 per yr.
Courses: Aesthetics; Ceramics; Display; Drafting; Drawing; History of Art and Archaeology; Lettering; Painting; Photography; Printmaking; Sculpture.
Adult Hobby Classes: Tui $10 per class. Courses—Ceramics; Stained Glass.
Children's Classes: Tui $10 per class. Courses—Crafts; Drawing; Painting.
Summer School: Dir Ray Kenney. Enrl 20 students ea; tui $56 for term of 2 wks beginning June 19th and July 5th. Courses—Photography—Applications in the Arts and Portraits and Darkroom Techniques.

FERGUS FALLS

LUTHERAN BRETHREN SCHOOLS, 56537. Tel: 218-739-3371,72,73. *Head Dept* Rev Joel Lunde, BA.
Estab 1900; den; D&E; ent req HS dipl; questionaire; SC 1, LC 1, enrl D 65, E 20.
Tuition: $450 per sem; campus res room and board $1965.
Courses: Ceramics; Drawing; Painting.

GRAND MARAIS

GRAND MARAIS ART COLONY, 55604. Tel: 218-387-1541. *Head Dept Prof* Birney M Quick, MFA; *Primary Faculty* Byron Bradley, MFA; Harvey Turner, MFA.
Estab 1947; pvt; D&E; ent req open; schol; SC 4; enrl D 125.
Tuition: $400 per sem.
Courses: Drawing; Painting; Printmaking; Sculpture.
Adult Hobby Classes: Courses—Drawing; Painting; Sculpture.
Children's Classes: Sat School.
Summer School: Same as above.

GRAND RAPIDS

ITASCA COMMUNITY COLLEGE,* Highway 169, 55744. Tel: 218-326-9451. *Head Dept Instr* Tyne T Mike.
Estab 1925; pub; D&E; ent req HS dipl; degree AA 2 yr; schol; SC 5, LC 1; enrl D 12, E 2, maj 8.
Tuition: No campus res.
Courses: Aesthetics; Ceramics; Drawing; Painting; Theatre Arts.
Adult Classes: Enrl 16-20; 10 wk. Courses—Ceramics.
Summer School: Enrl 20; term of 4 wk beginning June. Courses—Ceramics.

MANKATO

BETHANY LUTHERAN COLLEGE, Art Department, 56001. Tel: 507-625-2977. *Head Dept Prof* Karen Hageness, BA.
Estab 1927, dept estab 1960; den; D; ent req HS dipl, test scores ACT; degrees AA 2 yr; dipl; schol; SC 2, LC 2; enrl D 36, nonmaj 26, maj 10.
Tuition: $800 per sem, $70 per cr hr; campus res room and board $1300.
Courses: Advertising Design; Art History; Art Structure; Ceramics; Drawing; Interior; Lettering; Painting.

MANKATO STATE UNIVERSITY, Art Department, 56001. Tel: 507-389-6413. *Chmn* John E Spurgin, MFA; *Instrs FT* 17.
Estab 1868, dept estab 1938; pub; D&E; ent req HS dipl; degrees BA, BFA and BS 4 yr, MA and MS 1-1½ yr; SC 42, LC 28, GC 54; enrl D 3000 (total), E 500, nonmaj 1000, maj 225, GS 50.
Tuition: Res—Undergrad $444 per yr, $9.25 per sem cr, grad $540 per yr, $12 per sem cr; Nonres—Undergrad $888 per yr, $18.50 per sem cr, grad $1046 per yr, $23.25 per sem cr; campus res room and board $1148.
Courses: Advertising Design; Art Education; Art History; Calligraphy; Ceramics; Commercial Art; Drawing; Graphic Arts; Graphic Design; History of Art and Archaeology; Illustration; Jewelry; Lettering; Painting; Photography; Printmaking; Sculpture.
Summer School: Tui as above.

MINNEAPOLIS

ART INSTRUCTION SCHOOLS,* 500 S 4th St, 55415. Tel: 612-339-8721. *Dir* Dr A Conrad; *Assoc Dir* Don Jardine.
Estab 1914; pvt.
Courses: Fundamentals of Art and Specialized Art.

AUGSBURG COLLEGE,* Art Department, 731 21st Ave, W, 55485. *Chmn* Philip Thompson; Instrs FT 2, PT 5.
Estab 1869, dept estab 1960; den; D&E; ent req HS dipl; degree BA 4 yr; schol; SC 15, LC 4; enrl D 200, maj 42 others 1700.
Tuition: $3100 per yr; campus res room and board $1500.
Courses: Aesthetics; Art Education; Ceramics; Drawing; Graphic Design; Handicrafts; History of Art & Archaeology; Jewelry; Lettering; Museum Staff Training; Painting; Photography; Sculpture; Stage Design; Teacher Training; Theatre Arts; Weaving.
Summer School: Enrl 250; term of six or four wk beginning last wk May.

MINNEAPOLIS COLLEGE OF ART AND DESIGN,* 133 E 25th St, 55404. Tel: 612-870-3314. *Pres* Dr Jerome J Hausman; Instrs FT 46, PT 14.
Estab 1886; pvt; D&E; ent req HS dipl or GED; degree BFA 4 yr; schol; SC 78, LC 23, enrl D 655, E 400, maj 620.
Courses: Advertising Desing; Audiovisual Production; Aesthetics; Commercial Art; Costume Design & Construction; Drawing; Electronic Art; Fashion Arts Film; Film Animation; Film History; Graphic Arts; Graphic Design; History of Art; Illustration; Painting; Photography; Printmaking; Sculpture; Theatre History.
Adult Classes: Enro 400 per sem. Courses—Fashion Design; Graphic Design; Illustration Painting; Sculpture.
Summer School: Dean Roman J Verostko. Courses—Calligraphy; Drawing; Fashion Design; Graphic Design; Illustration; Painting; Photography; Printmaking; Sculpture; Video/Cinetography.

NORTH HENNEPIN COMMUNITY COLLEGE,* Art Department, 7411 85th Ave N, 55445. Tel: 612-425-4541, exten 152. *Head Dept Instr* Frank Schreiber; Instrs FT 2, PT 4.
Estab 1964; pub; D&E; ent req HS dipl, ent exam; degree AA 2 yr; schol; SC 15, LC 4; enrl D 500, E 100, maj 200, others 100.
Courses: Advertising Design; Aesthetics; Architecture; Audiovisual; Commercial Art; Contemporary Arts; Display; Drawing; Graphic Arts; Graphic Design; History of Art & Archaeology; Illustration; Lettering; Occupational Therapy; Painting; Photography; Stage Design; Theatre Arts.
Adult Hobby Classes: Enrl 30-100; Courses—Painting; Photography; Video.
Summer School: Dir Don Durand. Enrl 700; term of 5 wk beginning June. Courses—Costume; Drawing; Introduction to Arts; Theatre.

UNIVERSITY OF MINNESOTA, MINNEAPOLIS
—School of Architecture and Landscape Architecture,* Institute of Technology, 110 Architecture Bldg, 55455. Tel: 612-373-2198; *Head* Ralph E Rapson; Instrs FT 12, PT 25.
Estab 1912; pub; D&E; ent req completion of recommended first yr col work and selective admis; degrees BArch, BLandscape Arch, BEnviron Design, MArch, MLandscape Arch 4, 5, 6 yrs; schol and fel; SC 20, LC 25, GC 15. 3 options, Architecture (1 yr), City Design (1 yr), Hospital Design (2 yrs).
—Art History, 27 Pleasant St SE, 108 Jones Hall, 55455. Tel: 612-373-3057. *Chmn* Frederick M Asher; *Prof* Frederick A Cooper, PhD; *Prof* Sheila J McNally, PhD; *Prof* Marion J Nelson, PhD; *Prof* Carl D Sheppard, PhD; *Prof* Sidney Simon, PhD; *Prof* Norman W Canedy, PhD; *Prof* Melvin Waldfogel, PhD; *Assoc Prof* Frederick M Asher, PhD; *Assoc Prof* Karal Ann Marling, PhD; *Assoc Prof* Robert Poor, PhD; *Assoc Prof* M Alison Stones, PhD; *Asst Prof* John Steyaert, PhD; *Asst Prof* Michael Stoughton, PhD; *Instr* Frederick T Smith, Master; *vis prof*—Smitrii Sarab'ianov, 19th century Russian art, fall 78.
Pub; D&E; ent req HS dipl; ent exam, GRE required for grad school; degrees BA, 4 yr, MA 2 yr; schol; LC 28; GC 59; enrl D approx 1200 per quarter; E approx 300 per quarter, maj 80, grad 105.
Tuition: Res—Undergrad $254 per quarter, grad $28.50 per cr hr; Nonres—Undergrad $724 per quarter, grad $79.50 per cr hr; campus res available.
Courses: ‡Art History; History of Art & Archaeology; Museum Staff Training.
—Department of Studio Art, 216 21st Ave S (Mailing Add: 208 Art Bldg, West Bank, 55455). Tel: 612-373-3663. *Prof Studio Art & Chmn Dept* Herman Rowan, MFA; *Profs* Bethke, Busa, Hendler, Hoard, MacKenzie, Morrison, Myers and Priede, MFA; *Assoc Profs* Baldwin, Cowette, Hallman, Potratz, Rose and Somberg, MFA; *Asst Profs* Caglioti, Feinberg, Gray, Henkel, Lane, Lucey and Roode, MFA; *vis profs* change quarterly.
Estab 1851, fine arts estab 1939; pub; D&E; ent req HS dipl, PSAT, ACT; degrees BA and BFA 4 yrs, MFA 2-3 yrs; schol; SC 39, LC 7; enrl D 1630, E approx 1000, maj 537, grad 53.
Tuition: Res—$254 per quarter, $28.50 per cr hr; Nonres—$724 per quarter, $79.50 per cr hr; extension $16.50-$28.50 per cr hr; campus res $1300 per yr.

Courses: Advertising Design (Extension only); ‡Ceramics; Commercial Art (Extension only); ‡Drawing; ‡Film; ‡Glassworking; Illustration (Extension only); ‡Painting; ‡Photography; ‡Printmaking; ‡Sculpture.
Summer School: Dir Willard Thompson. Tui $15 per cr hr for term of 5 wk beginning June 12 & July 17. Courses—Ceramics; Drawing; Film; Painting; Photography; Printmaking; Sculpture; Glassworking.

MOORHEAD

CONCORDIA COLLEGE, Art Department, 56560. Tel: 218-299-4623. *Chmn Assoc Prof* Barbara Glasrud, MA; *Prof* Dean B Bowman, MFA; *Prof* Elizabeth Strand, MFA; *Asst Prof* Orland J Rourke, MA; *Asst Prof* Paul F Allen, MFA. Instrs FT 5.
Estab 1891; pvt; D; ent req HS dipl, character references; degrees BA and BM 4 yr independent studio work, work-study program and special studies; schol; SC 10, LC 5; enrl D 150 (Art), maj 40, total 2600.
Tuition: $2995 per yr, $490 per course, student association dues $35; campus res room and board $520 (room) $625 (board).
Courses: Art Education; Art History; Ceramics; Design; Drawing; History of Art and Archaeology; Multi Media; Painting; Printmaking; Sculpture; Teacher Training.
Summer School: Dir Donald Dale. Enrl 40; tui $295 for term of 4 wks beginning May 15 and June 12. Courses—Art History; Art History Travel Seminar; Drawing; Painting; Printmaking.

MOORHEAD STATE UNIVERSITY, Department of Art, 56560. Tel: 218-236-2151. *Chmn* P R Szeitz, MFA; *Assoc Prof Dr* Virginia Barsch, PhD; *Assoc Prof* Dr John Boyd Holland, PhD; *Assoc Prof* Lyle Laske, MFA; *Assoc Prof* Marcel C Stratton, MA; *Prof* John Youngquist, MFA; *Assoc Prof* P J Mousseau, MFA; *Assoc Prof* Donald B McRaven Jr, MFA; *Assoc Prof* Timothy Ray.
Estab 1887; pub; D&E; ent req HS dipl; degrees BA and BS 4 yr, MS additional 1¼ yr; schol; SC 47, LC 20, GC 11; enrl D 4520, maj 175, GS 2.
Tuition: Res—Undergrad $10.25 per cr hr, grad $13 per cr hr; Nonres—Undergrad $20.25 per cr hr, grad $25.25 per cr hr; campus res room and board $592.50.
Courses: Advertising Design; Aesthetics; Art Education; Art History; Ceramics; Collage; Conceptual Art; Constructions; Display; Drawing; Graphic Arts; Graphic Design; History of Art and Archaeology; Illustration; Jewelry; Mixed Media; Painting; Photography; Printmaking; Sculpture; Stage Design; Teacher Training; Theatre Arts; Video.
Summer School: Tui per cr hr for term of 5 wks beginning June. Courses—Basic Drawing; Ceramics; Elements of Art Design; Graphic Design; Painting; Photography; Printmaing.

MORRIS

UNIVERSITY OF MINNESOTA, MORRIS, 56267. Tel: 612-589-4501. *Chmn* W D Spring; *Coordr* Lois Hodgell, MFA; *Coordr* Frederick Peterson, PhD.
Estab 1960, dept estab 1963, pub; D; ent req top 50% in HS, ACT or PSAT; degrees BA 4 yrs; schol; SC 16, LC 8; enrl D 195, nonmaj 150, maj 45.
Tuition: Res—Undergrad $663 per yr; Nonres—Undergrad $1808; campus res room $600.
Courses: Aesthetics; Art Education; ‡Art History; Ceramics; Drawing; Graphic Arts; Painting; Photography; Printmaking; Sculpture; ‡Studio Art; Teacher Training.

NORTHFIELD

CARLETON COLLEGE,* Department of Art, 55057. Tel: 507-645-4431, exten 219. *Chmn* R I Jacobson; Instrs FT 6.
Estab 1921; pvt; degree 4 yr; schol; SC 14, LC 15; enrl maj 30, others 550.
Tuition: $5277 all inclusive; campus res.
Courses: Art History; General Art.

ST OLAF COLLEGE, Art Department, 55057. Tel: 507-663-3248. *Chmn Assoc Prof* Arch Leeam, MA; *Prof* John Maakestad, MFA; *Assoc Prof* Dorothy Divers, MFA; *Assoc Prof* Reidar Dittman, PhD; *Asst Prof* Malcolm Gimse, MFA; *Instr* Malcolm Sowells, MFA; *Prof* Edward Sovik, March.
Estab 1875, dept estab 1932; den; D&E; ent req HS dipl, SAT scores; degrees BA 4 yr; schol.
Tuition: Campus res room and board.
Courses: Aesthetics; Architecture; ‡Art Education; ‡Art History; Calligraphy; Commercial Art; Drafting; Drawing; Film; Graphic Arts; Graphic Design; History of Art and Archaeology; Interior Design; Lettering; Painting; Photography; Printmaking; Sculpture; Stage Design; Teacher Training; Theatre Arts.

Summer School: Dir Lydia Quanbeck. Courses—Production Art; 20th Century Art.

ROCHESTER

ROCHESTER COMMUNITY COLLEGE, Department of Art, 55901. Tel: 507-285-7236. *Head Dept* J A Prom, MFA; *Prof* Terry Dennis, MA; *Prof* Flo Sandok, MS; *Prof* Patricia Kraemer, MA; *Prof* Robert Clausen, MS; *Prof* Phyllis Pinnow, MA; Instrs FT 3, PT 3.
Pub; D&E; degrees AA degrees Rochester combines a consortium of 5 colleges offering upper division and advanced degree work; LC 4; enrl nonmaj 150, maj 30, others 15.
Tuition: Res—$12 per cr hr; Nonres—$24 per cr hr; campus res.
Courses: Advertising Design; Art History; Ceramics; Drawing; Graphic Design; Handicrafts (clay, fibers, metals); Jewelry; Painting; Photography; Printmaking; Sculpture.
Adult Classes: Courses—Clay; Embroidery design seminars; Glass; Stained glass.
Summer School: Enrl 30-60; term of 5 wks. Courses—variable workshops.

SAINT CLOUD

SAINT CLOUD STATE UNIVERSITY,* Department of Art, 56301. Tel: 612-255-4283. *Chmn* Dr James Roy; Instrs FT 14, PT 8.
Pub; D&E; ent req HS dipl; degrees BA, BS, MA(Studio Art) and MS 4 yr; SC 65, LC 15, GC 20; enrl maj 400, SS 60.
Tuition: Res—Undergrad $9.25 per cr hr, grad $11.50, Nonres—Undergrad $23.25 per cr hr, grad $18.50 per cr hr.
Courses: Advertising Design; Aesthetics; Art Education; Ceramics; Commercial Art; Display; Drawing; Glass Blowing; Graphic Arts; Graphic Design; History of. Art & Archaeology; Illustration; Jewelry; Lettering; Museum Staff Training; Painting; Photography; Sculpture; Teacher Training; Textile Design; Weaving.

SAINT JOSEPH

COLLEGE OF SAINT BENEDICT, Art Department, 56374. Tel: 612-363-5785. *Chmn* Miles Bair, MA; *Primary Faculty* Don Bruno, MFA; Sister Thomas Carey, BFA; Sister Dennis Frandrup, MFA; Gordon Goetemann, MFA; Sister Johanna Becker, PhD; Sister Baulu Kuan, MA; Stan Shafer, MFA.
Estab 1913; den; D&E; ent req HS dipl; degrees BA(Art Educ), BA(Art) and BA(Art History) 4 yr, internships and open studio; schol; SC 28, LC 15; enrl D 1500, maj 80.
Tuition: Res—Undergrad and Nonres—Undergrad $2675 per yr; no grad students; campus res room and board.
Courses: Art Education; Art History; Calligraphy; Ceramics; Commercial Art; Constructions; Drawing; Graphic Arts; Graphic Design; History of Art and Archaeology; Jewelry; Mixed Media; Painting; Photography; Printmaking; Sculpture; Teacher Training; Theatre Arts.
Children's Classes: Enrl 30; tui $25 per term. Courses—Mixed and various media.

SAINT PAUL

BETHEL COLLEGE, Department of Art, 3900 Bethel Drive, 55112. Tel: 612-614-6400, exten 6378, 6375. *Chmn* Stewart Luckman, MFA; *Asst Prof* Dale R Johnson, MFA; *Prof* Eugene Johnson, MFA; *Assoc Prof* George Robinson, BFA; *Asst Prof* David Johnson, MFA.
Estab 1871; den; D&E; ent req HS dipl, SAT, ACT, PSAT or NMSQT, evidence of a standard of faith and practice that is compatible to Bethel lifestyle; degrees BS(Art Educ) and BS(Studio Arts) 4 yr; schol; SC 20, LC 12; enrl nonmaj 100, maj 100.
Tuition: Res—Undergrad and Nonres—Undergrad $1375 per sem; campus res room ($315) and board ($250).
Courses: Advertising; Aesthetics; Architecture; Art Education; Art History; Calligraphy; Ceramics; Collage; Commercial Art; Conceptual Art; Constructions; Drawing; Film; Graphic Arts; Graphic Design; Handicrafts (fibers, weaving); History of Art and Archaeology; Illustration; Industrial Design; Jewelry; Lettering; Mixed Media; Painting; Photography; Printmaking; Sculpture; Teacher Training; Textile Design; Video.
Summer School: Dir Kathy Nevins. Tui $250 per ea course taken for cr, $55 for ea course taken for non cr; summer housing $18 per wk, food service available for terms beginning May 23, June 20th and an extended term from June 19 to Aug 11. Courses—Art; Music; Theatre Arts.

COLLEGE OF ST CATHERINE,* Visual Arts Department, 2004 Randolph, 55105. Tel: 612-698-5571, exten 6635. *Chmn* Robert Clark Nelson; *Instrs* FT 6, PT 3.
Pvt; D; W; ent req HS dipl; degree BA(Art) 4 yr; schol.

Courses: Art Education; Arts Core Program; Ceramics; Drawing; Graphic Arts; Graphic Design; History of Art & Archaeology; Jewelry; Lettering; Painting; Photography; Sculpture.
Children's Classes: Summer high school workshop.
Summer School.

HAMLINE UNIVERSITY, Art Department, 55104. Tel: 612-641-2230, 641-2296. *Chmn Prof* Frederick D Leach, PhD; *Primary Faculty* Michael Price, MFA; Leonardo Lasansky, MFA; James Conaway, MFA; Roslye Ultan, MA; Susan Madigan, PhD; Arthur Gould, BFA.
Estab 1854; pvt; D&E; ent req HS dipl; SAT; degrees BA 4 yr, apprentice programs with museums, prof artists, blacksmiths, photography, schol; SC 23, LC 13; enrl D 250, E 30, nonmaj 175, maj 75.
Tuition: $3000 per yr; campus res room and board $675.
Courses: Art Education; Art History; Ceramics; Collage; Conceptual Art; Constructions; Drawing; Graphic Arts; Illustration; Mixed Media; Painting; Photography; Printmaking; Sculpture.
Summer School: Dir Jack Johnson.

MACALESTER COLLEGE,* Department of Art, 1600 Grand Ave, 55105. Tel: 612-647-6279. *Head Dept* Anthony Caponi; *Instrs* FT 4, PT 4.
Estab 1946; den; D; degrees 4 yr; SC 9, LC 8; schol; enrl 20 (aver);
Tuition: Campus res.
Courses: Aesthetics; American Art; Ceramics; Design; Drawing; Graphic Arts; History of Art; Modern & Oriental Art; Painting; Primitive Art; Principals; Processes & Application; Sculpture; Senior Seminar.
Summer School: Two 4 wk sessions June and July.

MINNESOTA MUSEUM OF ART/ART SCHOOL, Education Department, 55101. Tel: 612-227-7613. *Chmn* Alvaro Cardona-Hines; *Coordr* Nell H McClure.
Estab 1926; pub; D&E; SC 12.
Courses: Calligraphy; Ceramics; Drawing; Jewelry; Painting; Photography.
Adult Hobby Classes: Tui $35 for 10 wks. Courses—Calligraphy; Ceramics; Drawing; Painting; Watercolor.
Children's Classes: Tui $25 for 8 wks. Courses—Drawing Imaginary Worlds; Painting; Pottery.
Summer School: Dir Nell McClure.

SCHOOL OF THE ASSOCIATED ARTS, 344 Summit Avenue, 55102. Tel: 612-224-3416 *Dir* Virginia Rahja, MFA; *Dean* Ronald Swenson, MFA; *Primary Faculty* Jerry Lefevre, MFA; Philip Ogle, MFA; John Lenertz, BFA.
Estab 1924; pvt; D; ent req HS dipl; degrees BFA 4 yr; schol; SC 30, LC 8; enrl D 95, maj 95.
Tuition: Res—Undergrad and Nonres—Undergrad $2450 per yr; $1225 per sem; room and board $3200.
Courses: Advertising Design; Art History; ‡Commercial Art; ‡Drawing; ‡Graphic Design; Illustration; Lettering; Mass Communications; ‡Painting; Photography; Production; Sculpture; TV Productions.

UNIVERSITY OF MINNESOTA, Department of Design, 1985 Buford Ave, 55108 (Mailing Add: 240 McNeal Hall). Tel: 612-373-1032. *Head Dept Prof* Gertrude Esteros, PhD; *Prof* Eugene Larkin, MA; *Prof* Marian Bagley, MA; *Asst Prof* Timothy Blade, PhD; *Assoc Prof* Ann Erickson, MA; *Assoc Prof* Homa Amir-Fazli, MA; *Assoc Prof* Richard Abell, MA; *Assoc Prof* Alice Goacher, MA.
Pub; D&E; ent req HS dipl; degrees BS, MS and PhD 4 yr, evening extension 2 yr cert; SC 31; LC 15, GC 33; enrl D 1012 (winter quarter 78), nonmaj 265, maj 747, GS 39, others 21 adult specials.
Tuition: Res—Undergrad $275 per quarter, $23 per cr hr, grad $28.50 per cr hr with appointment; Nonres—Undergrad $784 per quarter, grad $28.50 per cr hr with appointment, $79.50 per cr hr without appointment.
Courses: Art History; Calligraphy (evening school); ‡Costume Design and Construction; Costume History; Decorative Arts; Drawing; Goldsmithing: Handicrafts (jewelry, textile design, weaving off-loom); Housing; ‡Interior Design; Jewelry; ‡Silversmithing; Textile Design.
Summer School: Tui $15 per cr. Courses—Color and Design; Introduction to Design; Materials; 3-D Design Process; Visual Presentation.

SAINT PETER

GUSTAVUS ADOLPHUS COLLEGE,* Art Department, Schaefer Fine Arts Center, 56082. Tel: 507-931-4300, exten 462. *Chmn* Gene D Buckley; *Instrs* FT 4, PT 1, one artist-in-residence.
Estab 1876; den; D; ent req HS grad, ent exam; degree BA 4 yr; schol; SC 27; enrl 2000 (total), 750, art, maj 80.
Tuition: $4300 per yr (comprehensive fee); PT $375 per course.

Courses: Art Education; Basic Design; Bronze Casting; Ceramics; Costume Design & Construction; Drawing; Film History; Film Making; Graphic Design; History of Art; Jewelry; Life Drawing; Painting; Photography; Printmaking; Sculpture; Stage Design; Teacher Training; Textile Design; Theatre Arts; Weaving.
Summer School: Enrl approx 50; two 4 wk terms June to July, July to Aug. Courses—Ceramics; Painting; Photography; Printmaking.

WILLMAR

WILLMAR COMMUNITY COLLEGE,* 56201. Tel: 612-235-2131. *Head Dept* Robert Mattson; *Instrs* FT 1, PT 1.
Estab 1962-63; pub; D&E; ent req HS dipl; degrees AA, AS and AAA 2 yr; SC 8, LC 3; enrl D 50, maj 15.
Courses: Art Education; Ceramics; Display; Drawing; Graphic Arts; Graphic Design; History of Art & Archaeology; Introduction to Studio Practices; Painting; Structure; Teacher Training.
Adult Hobby Classes: Etching; Design; History of Art; Painting.

WINONA

WINONA STATE UNIVERSITY, Johnson and Sanborn Sts, 55987. Tel: 507-457-2133. *Head Dept & Asst Prof* Charles F Evans, MFA; *Asst Prof* Wallace N Johnson, PhD; *Asst Prof* Raymond R Kiihne, MFA; *Asst Prof* Wilfred McKenzie, MFA; *Instr* Judy Schlawin, MS; *Prof* Virginia H Vint, EdD.
Estab 1860; pub; D&E; degrees BA & BS.
Tuition: Res—Undergrad $10.25 per cr hr, grad $13 per cr hr; Nonres—Undergrad $20.25 per cr hr, grad $25.25 per cr hr; plus student fees; campus res $437 per yr single occupancy.
Courses: Art Education; Art History; Ceramics; Commercial Art; Drawing; Graphic Arts; Interior Design; Jewelry; Lettering; Painting; Printmaking; Sculpture.

MISSISSIPPI

BLUE MOUNTAIN

BLUE MOUNTAIN COLLEGE, Art Department, 38610. Tel: 601-685-5711, exten 62. *Chmn Dept* William Dowdy, MA.
Estab 1873, dept estab 1875; den; D&E; ent req HS dipl; degrees BA and BS(Educ) 4 yrs; schol; SC 16, LC 2; enrl D 28, E 12, nonmaj 20, maj 8, others 12.
Tuition: $1080 per yr, $540 per sem, $36 per sem hr; campus res room and board $1030 per yr.
Courses: Art Education; Art History; Commercial Art; ‡Drawing; Jewelry; ‡Painting.
Adult Hobby Classes: Enrl 12; tui $36 per sem hr. Courses—Painting & Drawing.
Summer School: *Dir* William Dowdy. Enrl 20, tui $36 per sem hr for term of 5 wks beginning June 5 and July 10.

BOONEVILLE

NORTHEAST MISSISSIPPI JUNIOR COLLEGE,* Art Department, 38829; *Chmn* Barbara B Curlee; *Instrs* FT 2.
Estab 1948; pub; D&E; ent req HS dipl, ent exam; 2 yr; degrees none; schol; SC 5, LC 3; enrl D 1800, maj 30.
Courses: Aesthetics; Art Education; Art History; Ceramics; Drafting; Drawing; Painting; Teacher Training; Theatre Arts.

CLEVELAND

DELTA STATE UNIVERSITY, Department of Art, Box D-2, 38733. Tel: 601-843-2151. *Chmn Prof* Malcolm M Norwood, MA; *Asst Prof* Sam Glenn Britt, MFA; *Inst* William Carey Lester Jr, MFA; *Instr* Lallah M Perry, MEd (Art); *Instr* Mary Anne Ross, BFA; *Asst Prof* Floyd D Shaman, MA; *Asst Prof* Terry Kay Simmons, MA; *Assoc Prof* Carolyn Rea Stone, PhD; *Asst Prof* Robert Jerry Walden, MFA.
Estab 1924; pub; D&E; ent req HS dipl; degrees BA, BFA and BSE 4 yr, MEd(Art Educ) 1 yr; schol; SC 42, LC 10, GC 30; enrl maj 110.
Tuition: Res—Undergrad and grad $1412 per yr, $709 per sem; Nonres—Undergrad and grad $2160 per yr, $1084 per sem.
Courses: Advertising Design; Aesthetics; Art Education; Art History; Calligraphy; Ceramics; Commercial Art; Costume Design and Construction; Drawing; Fashion Arts; Graphic Arts; Graphic Design; Handicrafts (clay, fibers); Illustration; Interior Design; Lettering; Mixed Media; Painting; Printmaking; Sculpture; Teacher Training; Textile Design.
Children's Classes: Enrl 15 ea class; tui $25 per sem. Two classes ages 6-8, 9-12.

Summer School: Tui $588 for term of 11 wks beginning June 5. Courses—Ceramics; Drawing; Internship in Commercial Design; Introduction to Art; Painting; Sculpture.

CLINTON

MISSISSIPPI COLLEGE,* Art Department, 39056. Tel: 601-924-5131. *Head Dept* Dr Samuel M Gore; *Instrs* D FT 3, PT 2, E PT 2.
Estab 1825; dept estab 1950; den; ent req HS grad; degrees BA, BE (Art) and ME(Art) 4 yr, Freshman Art merit; schol and student assistantships offered; SC 22, LC 3; enrl maj 80, others 300.
Tuition: $645 per sem; campus res $360.
Courses: Art Education; Art History; Ceramics; Commercial Art; Drawing & Painting; Foundry Casting; Interior Design; Sculpture.
Summer School: Courses—Art Appreciation; Art Education; Basic Design; Ceramics; Painting.

COLUMBUS

MISSISSIPPI UNIVERSITY FOR WOMEN, Art Department, 1100 5th Ave S, 39701 (Mailing Add: PO Box W-70 MUW, 39701). Tel: 601-328-4881. *Chmn* Charles E Ambrose, MA; *Prof* Mary Evelyn Stringer, PhD; *Assoc Prof* Eugenia Summer, MA; *Assoc Prof* Elizabeth Dice, MDes; *Assoc Prof* David Frank, MFA; *Assoc Prof* Thomas Nawrocki, MFA; *Asst Prof* Lawrence Feeny, MFA; *Asst Prof* Alan Thurlow, MA.
Estab 1884, pub; D&E; ent req HS DIPL, ACT, SAT; degrees BS, BS and BFA 4 yr, MFA in drawing; painting and printmaking; schol; SC 44, LC 11, GC 43; enrl D 379, E 45, nonmaj 379, maj 200.
Tuition: Res—Undergrad and grad $574 per yr, $287 per sem, $23 per sem hr; Nonres—Undergrad and grad $1324 per yr, $662 per sem hr, $31 per sem hr; campus res room and board $1054.
Courses: ‡Advertising Design; ‡Art Education; Art History; Calligraphy; ‡Ceramics; Collage; ‡Commercial Art; Conceptual Art; Constructions; Costume Design and Construction; Drafting; ‡Drawing; ‡Fashion Arts; Film; ‡Graphic Arts; Graphic Design; Handicrafts (glassblowing, jewelry, metalcrafts, textile, weaving); History of Art and Archaeology; ‡Illustration; ‡Interior Design; Jewelry; Lettering; Mixed Media; ‡Painting, Photography; ‡Printmaking; ‡Sculpture; Silversmithing; Stage Design; Teacher Training; Textile Design; ‡Theatre Arts; ‡Video.
Adult Hobby Classes: Enrl 45; tui $23 per sem hr. Courses—Calligraphy; Ceramics; Drawing; Interior Decorating; Painting.
Summer School: Tui $23 per sem hr for term of 5 wks beginning June 2. Courses—Varies according to demand.

ELLISVILLE

JONES COUNTY JUNIOR COLLEGE,* Division of Fine Arts, Art Department, 39437. Tel: 601-477-3141. *Chmn* Milfred Valentine; *Instrs* FT 2.
Estab 1927; pub; D; ent req HS dipl; degree AA 2 yr; schol; SC 12, LC 4; enrl D 100, E 12, maj 15, others 12.
Courses: Advertising Design; Architecture; Art Education; Ceramics; Commercial Art; Display; Drafting; Drawing; Graphic Arts; History of Art & Archaeology; Lettering; Painting.
Adult Hobby Classes: Enrl 20. Courses—Painting.
Summer School: *Dir* B F Ogletree. Term of 4 wk beginning June. Courses—same as above.

HATTIESBURG

UNIVERSITY OF SOUTHERN MISSISSIPPI, College of Fine Arts, Department of Art, 39401. Tel: 601-266-7281. *Chmn* Dr Jeff R Bowman, EdD; *Instrs* FT 9, PT 4.
Estab 1910; pub; D&E; ent req HS dipl; degrees BA, BFA and MAE; schol; SC 64, LC 41, GC 34; enrl nonmaj 35, maj 150, GS 18.
Tuition: Campus res.
Courses: Aesthetics; ‡Art Education; Art History; Ceramics; ‡Commercial Art; Display; ‡Drawing; Goldsmithing; Graphic Arts; Graphic Design; Handicrafts (weaving); Illustration; Jewelry; Lettering; ‡Painting; Printmaking; ‡Sculpture; Silversmithing; Teacher Training; Textile Design.
Adult Hobby Classes: Courses—Ceramics; Drawing; Painting.
Children's Classes: Courses—Arts & Crafts; Drawing & Painting.
Summer School: Courses—as above.

WILLIAM CAREY COLLEGE, Art Department, 30491. Tel: 601-582-5051, exten 237. *Chmn* Lucile Parker, MFA; *Asst Chmn* Patrice Box-Pope, MFA.
Estab 1906, dept estab 1974; den; D&E; ent req HS dipl; qualifications; degrees BA, BS, BM, MM and MEd 4 yr; schol; enrl D 75, E 25, nonmaj 86, maj 14.
Tuition: Res—Undergrad $2400 per yr (includes boarding), Nonres—Undergrad $1400 per yr; campus res.

Courses: Advertising Design; Art Education; Art History; Ceramics; Drawing; Graphic Arts; Graphic Design; Lettering; Painting; Photography; Printmaking.
Adult Hobby Classes: Courses—Drawing; Painting.

JACKSON

JACKSON STATE COLLEGE,* Department of Art, Lynch at Dalton St, 39207. Tel: 601-948-8533. *Head Dept* Hugh Stevens; Instrs FT 8.
Estab 1949; pub; D; ent req HS dipl; degree BS(Maj in Art) 4 yr; schol; SC 16, LC 7, GC 1; enrl D 486, maj 112.
Tuition: $532 per yr; Nonres—$750 per yr, grad $30 per sem hr; PT $31 per sem hr, PT grad $35.50 per sem hr; campus res $114 per 28 day period.
Courses: Advertising Design; Art Education; Ceramics; Costume Design & Construction; Drawing; Graphic Arts; History of Art & Archaeology; Jewelry; Leather; Painting; Stage Design; Teacher Training; Weaving.
Adult Hobby Classes: Enrl 80; Athenian Art Club activities.
Summer School: Dir Dr Wilbert Greenfield. Tui $117, grad $42; room & board $142.50 Undergrad, $228 grad. Courses—as above.

LORMAN

ALCORN STATE UNIVERSITY, Department of Fine Arts, 39096. Tel: 601-877-3711, exten 255. *Chmn* Joyce Bolden, PhD; *Area Chmn Asst Prof* Constance Alford, MFA; *Asst Prof* Henry Sumpter, MFA.
Estab 1871; dept estab 1973; pub; D&E; ent req HS dipl, score of 11+ ACT; SC 9, LC 3.
Tuition: Res—Undergrad $1500 per yr, $750 per sem; Non-res—Undergrad $2200 per yr, $1100 per sem; campus res $1500.
Courses: Art Education; Art History; Ceramics; Drawing; Handicrafts; Painting.
Children's Classes: Enrl 20, Courses—Drawing; Painting.
Summer School: Enrl 25 per term for term of 10 wks beginning May 28. Courses—Art Education; Fine Arts.

MERIDIAN

MERIDIAN JUNIOR COLLEGE,* Art Department, 5500 Hwy 19 N, 39301. Tel: 601-483-8241. Instrs D FT 1, E FT 1.
Estab 1938; pub; degree AA 2 yr; SC 3, LC 1; enrl 150.
Courses: Ceramics; Design; Drawing & Painting; Independent Study; Printmaking; Sculpture.
Summer School: Enrl 15. Courses—Ceramics; Painting.

MOORHEAD

MISSISSIPPI DELTA JUNIOR COLLEGE,* Department of Fine Arts, 38761. *Chmn* Joe Abrams; *Coordr* Jean Abrams; Instrs FT 2, PT 1.
Estab 1926; pub; D&E; ent req HS dipl, ent exam; degrees AA and AS(Commercial Art) 2 yr; SC 11, LC 2; enrl D 68, E 29, maj 28.
Courses: Advertising Design; Art Appreciation; Ceramics; Commercial Art; Drawing; Graphic Arts; Painting.
Adult Hobby Classes: Enrl 29; Courses—Ceramics; Painting.

POPLARVILLE

PEARL RIVER JUNIOR COLLEGE, 39470. *Instr* Sandra Thames, MA.
Estab 1921; pub; D; ent req HS dipl; enrl D 20, nonmaj 20.
Tuition: Res—Undergrad $260 per yr, $130 per sem, $15 per hr; Nonres—Undergrad $660 per yr, $330 per sem; campus res room and board $651.
Courses: Art Education; Drafting; Photography.

RAYMOND

HINDS JUNIOR COLLEGE,* Department of Art, 39154. Tel: 601-857-5261, exten 302. *Chmn* Bob A Dunaway; Instrs FT 4.
Estab 1918; pub; D&E; ent req ent exam; degree AA 2 yr; SC 5, LC 2; enrl D 400, E 75, maj 60.
Courses: Advertising Design; Ceramics; Commercial Art; Display; Drawing; Lettering; Painting.
Summer School: Term of 5 wk beginning June. Courses—Art Appreciation; Ceramics; Drawing; Introduction to Watercolors.

SCOOBA

EAST MISSISSIPPI JUNIOR COLLEGE, Art Department, Box 176, 39358. Tel: 601-476-5669. *Chmn* Terry Cherry, MA.
Estab 1927; pub; D; ent req HS dipl, ACT; degrees AA 2 yr; schol; SC 5, LC 1; enrl D 650 (total), nonmaj 7, maj 9.

Tuition: Res—Undergrad $1060 per yr, $530 per sem; Non-res—Undergrad $1460 per yr, $730 per sem; campus res room and board $760.
Courses: Advertising Design; Commercial Art; Drawing; Painting; Photography; Printmaking.

TOUGALOO

TOUGALOO COLLEGE, Art Department, 39174. Tel: 601-956-4941, exten 327. *Chmn Dept & Prof* Ronald Schnell, MFA; *Asst Prof* Bruce O'Hara, MFA; *Adj Prof* Anne O'Hara.
Estab 1869, dept estab 1968; pvt; D; ent req HS dipl; degrees BA & BS 4 yr; schol; SC 14, LC 4; enrl D 800, nonmaj 420, maj 28.
Tuition: Res—Undergrad $3000 yr, $1500 per sem; Nonres—Undergrad $1500 yr, $750 per sem; campus res room and board available.
Courses: Art Education; Art History; Commercial Art; Drawing; Graphic Arts; History of Art and Archaeology; Painting; Photography; Printmaking; Sculpture; Photo Journalism.

UNIVERSITY

UNIVERSITY OF MISSISSIPPI, Department of Art, 38677. Tel: 601-232-7193. *Chmn Assoc Prof* James T Quinn, PhD; *Prof* Robert L Tettleton, MEd; *Assoc Prof* John L Winters, MFA; *Assoc Prof* Charles M Gross, MFA; *Asst Prof* Margaret J Gorove, MFA; *Asst Prof* Jere H Allen, MFA; *Asst Prof* Rodger H Wood, MFA; *Asst Prof* Tom Dewey II, PhD; *Instr* Mark W Ackley, MFA; Instrs FT 9, PT 7.
Dept estab 1949; pub; D; ent req HS dipl; degrees BA and BFA 4 yr, MFA 2 yr and MA 1 yr; schol; SC 73, LC 36, GC 46; enrl D 564, nonmaj 250, maj 130, GS 15.
Tuition: Res—Undergrad $351.50 per sem, $25 per cr hr, grad $351.50 per sem, $33 per cr hr; Nonres—Undergrad $739 per sem, $57 per cr hr, grad $739 per sem, $76 per cr hr; campus res room and board $230 (room).
Courses: Advertising Design; Aesthetics; ‡Art Education; ‡Art History; ‡Ceramics; Collage; Commercial Art; Conceptual Art; Drawing; Fashion Arts; Graphic Arts; ‡Graphic Design; Illustration; Industrial Design; Interior Design; Jewelry; ‡Painting; ‡Printmaking; ‡Sculpture.
Summer School: Dir C E Noves. Tui $157 for term of 11 wks beginning June. Courses—Ceramics; Design; Drawing; Painting; Printmaking; Sculpture.

UTICA

UTICA JUNIOR COLLEGE, Humanities Division, 39175. Tel: 601-885-6062. *Head Dept* Dr Bobby Cooper, EdD; *Primary Faculty* Michael McCarty, MFA; Evelyn Quave, BFA.
Estab 1903, dept estab 1976-77; pub; D&E; ent req HS dipl; degrees AA 2 yr; SC 9, LC 1; enrl D 50, E 10, nonmaj 51, maj 9.

MISSOURI

CANTON

CULVER-STOCKTON COLLEGE, Division of Fine Arts, 63435. Tel: 314-288-5221, exten 60. *Head Div* Dr A Wesley Tower; Instrs FT 2.
Estab 1853; pvt; D; ent req HS dipl, ACT or Col Bd Ent Exam; degrees BA(Visual Arts), BS(Art Educ) and BS(Arts Mgt) 4 yrs; schol; SC 16, LC 6; enrl 844, maj 30.
Tuition: $2330; campus res $1390.
Courses: Aesthetics; Art Education; Ceramics; Costume Design & Construction; Drawing; Filmmaking; Graphic Arts; History of Art & Archaeology; Illustration; Jewelry; Museum Staff Training; Painting; Photography; Sculpture; Stage Design; Teacher Training; Theatre Arts; A special pre-teacher training course called SITE (situations for initial teaching experience); Arts Management Program is a double maj in arts and business.
Summer School: Reg Olga Bays. Tui $480 for two 5 wk terms beginning June 8 and Aug 14. Courses—Art Appreciation; Art Education; Ceramics.

CAPE GIRARDEAU

SOUTHEAST MISSOURI STATE UNIVESITY, Department of Art, Normal Ave, 63701. Tel: 314-651-2143. *Chairperson Dept Art* Bill Needle.
Estab 1873, dept estab 1920; pub; D&E; ent req HS dipl; Degrees BS, BS(Educ) and BA 4 yrs, MAT; schol; SC 28, LC 10, GC 18; enrl D 1300.
Tuition: Res—$135 per sem; Nonres—$350 per sem; campus res $1100 per yr.

Courses: Advertising Design; Art Education; Art History; Ceramics; Commercial Art; Crafts; Drawing; Handicrafts; History of Art & Archaeology; Illustration; Jewelry; Lettering; Painting; Photography; Printmaking; Sculpture; Silversmithing; Teacher Training.
Summer School: Chairperson Dept Art Bill Needle. Enrl 164 undergrad, 60 grad; tui $135 for res, $350 for nonres.

CLAYTON

FONTBONNE COLLEGE, Department of Art, 6800 Wydown Blvd, 63119. Tel: 314-862-3456, exten 296. *Prof Art & Chmn Dept* Rudolph E Torrini, MFA; *Assoc Prof & Dir Grad Prog* Henry Knickmeyer, MFA; *Assoc Prof* Kenneth Stout, MFA; *Asst Prof* David Hollowell, MFA; *Asst Prof* Catherine Connor, MFA; *Asst Prof* Virginia Findlay, MA; *Instrs* Frank Ferrario.
Estab 1923; den; D&E; ent req HS dipl; degrees BA and BFA 4 yrs, MFA 2 yrs; schol; SC 11, LC 2; enrl in dept D 60, maj 49, grad 8, others 3 special.
Tuition: $2400 per yr, $1200 per sem, $85 per hr; campus res room & board $775.
Courses: Art Education; Art History; Ceramics; Drawing; Interior Design; Painting; Photography; Printmaking; Sculpture.
Children's Classes: Enrl 25; tui $100 for 5 wks. Courses—Drawing; Design; Sculpture & Ceramics (Junior & Senior High Level).
Summer School: Courses—Sculpture & Ceramics.

COLUMBIA

COLUMBIA COLLEGE,* Art Department, Christian College Ave, 65201. Tel: 314-449-0531. *Chmn Art Dept* Sidney Larson; *Instrs FT* 6, PT 3.
Estab 1851; den; D; ent req HS dipl or equivalent, ACT or SAT, also accept transfer students; degrees AA 2 yrs, BA and BFA 4 yrs; schol; SC 30, LC 4; enrl maj 125.
Tuition: $2500; campus res $1450.
Courses: Advertising Design; Architecture; Art Education; Ceramics; Commercial Art; Costume Design & Construction; Display; Drawing; Fashion Arts; Graphic Design; History of Art & Archaeology; Illustration; Jewelry; Lettering; Painting; Photography; Sculpture; Stage Design; Teacher Training; Textile Design; Theatre Arts.

STEPHENS COLLEGE, Art Department, 65201. Tel: 314-442-2211, exten 302. *Head Art Dept* Gardiner R McCauley, MA; *Primary Art Faculty:* Bruno Andrade, MFA; Louise Luthi, MFA; Nancy P McCauley, MA; Rosalind Moulton, MFA; Nicholas Peckham, MArch; Peter Salter, MFA; Michael Zilka, MFA.
Estab 1833, dept estab 1850; pvt; D&E; ent req SAT or ACT, recommendations, interview; degrees BA 3 or 4 yrs, BFA 3½ or 4 yrs; schol; SC 25, LC 6; enrl D 950, maj 125, others 10.
Tuition: $5275 per yr; Stephens Col Without Walls $265 per course; campus res room and board incl in tui.
Courses: Advertising Design; Aesthetics; Architecture; ‡Art Education; ‡Art History; ‡Ceramics; Commercial Art; Costume Design & Construction (in Theatre Dept); Drafting; Drawing; ‡Fashion Arts (in Fashion Dept); ‡Film (in Commun Dept); Graphic Arts; ‡Graphic Design; ‡Illustration (Fashion Dept); ‡Interior Design; Museum Staff Training (in Humanities Dept); Occupational Therapy (in Psychol Dept); ‡Painting; ‡Photography; ‡Printmaking; ‡Sculpture; ‡Stage Design (Theatre Dept); Teacher Training; ‡Theatre Arts (Theatre Dept); ‡Video (Commun Dept).
Children's Classes: Tui $700 per yr. Stephens Child Study Center, grades K-3, Preschool; includes special creative arts emphasis.
Summer School: Dir Ms Bobbie Burk. Tui $1225 for term of 7 wks beginning May 17. Courses—Color; Drawing & Painting; Graphic Design; Ceramics Sculpture.

UNIVERSITY OF MISSOURI, Art Department, A 126 Fine Arts, 65201. Tel: 314-882-3555. *Chmn Dept* Don Bartlett, MFA.
Estab 1901, dept estab 1912; pub; D&E; ent req HS dipl; degrees BA(Art), BS(Art Educ), MA(Art), MA(Educ), MEd, DEd, PhD and Educ Specialist; SC 76, LC 1, GC 53; enrl nonmaj 1600 sem, maj 250, grad 25.
Tuition: None to Missouri res; student acad fees undergrad $300 per sem, grad $922 per sem; campus res room and board $1220 per yr.
Courses: Advertising Design; Art Education; Calligraphy; Ceramics; Drawing; Graphic Design; Illustration; Jewelry; Lettering; Painting; Photography; Printmaking; Sculpture; Textile Design.
Summer School: Dir Don Bartlett. Enrl 175, tui $161 for term of 8 wks beginning June 12. Courses—Drawing; Watercolor; Ceramics; Printmaking; Jewelry; Sculpture; Design; Art Education.

FAYETTE

CENTRAL METHODIST COLLEGE,* Art Department, 65248. Tel: 816-248-3391, exten 238. *Acting Head* Pat Stapleton; *Instrs FT* 1.
Estab 1855; pvt; D; 4 yr; SC 13, LC 4.
Tuition: Incl room and board $2950.
Courses: Art History; Ceramics; Design; Drawing; Painting; Printmaking; Sculpture; Teacher Education.
Summer School.

FERGUSON

ST LOUIS COMMUNITY COLLEGE AT FLORISSANT VALLEY, Department of Art, 3400 Pershall Rd, 63135. Tel: 314-595-4365. *Asst Prof Art & Chairperson Dept* Sue Eisler, MFA; *Prof* Richard Buckman, MFA; *Assoc Prof* George Bartko, MFA; *Assoc Prof* Charles J Jones, MFA; *Asst Prof* Larry Kozuszek, MFA; *Prof* Edward Menges, MFA; *Asst Prof* Kim Mosley, MFA; *Prof* Frank Stanton, BA; *Instrs* Kermit Ruyle, BA.
Estab 1962; pub; D&E; ent req HS dipl, ent exam; degrees AA and AAS 2 yrs; SC 36, LC 4; enrl maj 70.
Tuition: Res—$17 per cr hr; Nonres—$42 per cr hr; no campus res.
Courses: ‡Advertising Design; Art History; Ceramics; Commercial Art; Drawing; History of Art & Archaeology; Illustration; Lettering; Painting; Photography; Printmaking; Sculpture.
Summer School: Asst Prof & Dir Sue Eisler. Enrl 270; tui $17 per cr hr for term of 8 wks beginning June 13. Courses—Design; Drawing; Figure Drawing; Lettering; Painting.

FULTON

WILLIAM WOODS/WESTMINSTER COLLEGES, Art Department, William Woods College, 65251. Tel: 314-642-2251, exten 323. *Chmn Div Fine Arts & Head Art Dept* George E Tutt, MA; *PT Instrs* Joanne Berneche, BFA; *Instrs* Nick Clapp, BFA; *Asst Prof* Paul Clervi, MA; *Instrs* Gary McCurry, MA; *Instr* Suzanne Sayre, BA; *Asst Prof* Francis Sporer, MA; *Instr* Phyllis Strawn, MA; *Emer Prof* George Latta, MFA; vis prof—Gary Greenburg, ceramics.
Estab 1870; pvt; D; ent req HS dipl, SAT or ACT; degrees BA, BS and BFA 4 yrs; schol; SC 54, LC 6; enrl maj 71.
Tuition: Res—$4750 per yr (incl room and board); Nonres—$3165 per yr; campus res room and board $1530.
Courses: Aesthetics; Art Education; Art History; Art Therapy; Ceramics; Collage; Commercial Art; Costume Design & Construction; Drawing; Handicrafts (weaving); History of Art & Archaeology; Illustration; Interior Design; Jewelry; Occupational Therapy; Painting; Photography; Printmaking; Sculpture; Silversmithing; Stage Design; Teacher Training; Theatre Arts.

JEFFERSON CITY

LINCOLN UNIVERSITY,* Art Department, Lafayette at Dunklin St, 65101. *Instrs FT* 3.
Estab 1927; pub; degrees BS(Art) and BS(Art Educ) 4 yrs; enrl maj 69, others 365.
Tuition: Res—$200 plus $15 per sem hr for over 15 hrs; Nonres—$400 plus $25 per sem hr over 15 hrs; campus res room and board $525 to $540 per sem.
Courses: Teacher Training.

JOPLIN

MISSOURI SOUTHERN STATE COLLEGE, Department of Art, Newman & Duquesne Rds, 64801. Tel: 417-624-8100, exten 263. *Dir Dept Art* Darral A Dishman, MSAE.
Estab 1937; pub; D&E; ent req HS dipl; degrees AA and AS 2 yrs; BA and BSE 4 yrs; schol; SC 22, LC 3; enrl D 425, E 83, nonmaj 360, maj 148, others 16 (over sixty).
Tuition: Res—$175 for 8 cr hrs or more, $17 per cr hr; Nonres—$370 for 8 cr hrs or more, $27 per cr hr.
Courses: Art Education; Art History; Ceramics; Commercial Art; Drawing; Goldsmithing; Handicrafts (survey-arts & crafts); Jewelry; Painting; Photography (Continuing Educ Div); Printmaking; Sculpture; Silversmithing; Teacher Training.
Adult Hobby Classes: Enrl approx 30; tui $1 per hr. Courses—Photography; Tole; Cartooning, plus others; offered by Continuing Educ Div.
Summer School: Dir Art Darral A Dishman. Enrl 15-20 per workshop; tui res $17 per cr hr, nonres $27 per cr hr for term of 2 wks beginning June 5. Courses—Watercolor; Jewelry; Silversmithing; Arts/Crafts; Pottery; Drawing; Printmaking.

KANSAS CITY

AVILA COLLEGE, Art Department, 11901 Wornall Rd, 64145. Tel: 816-942-8400. *Art Coordr* Myron Brody, MFA; *Asst Prof* Michael Burns, MA; *Asst Prof* Sister Colette Doering, MA; *Prof* Sister Margaret Reinhart, MA; *Instr* Jan Norman, MAE; *Instr* Joel Vogt, MA; *Instr* Carol Zastoupil, MFA; *Instr* Martha Crow, MFA.
Estab 1963; den; D&E; ent req HS dipl, SAT and PSAT Scores; degree BA 4 yrs; schol; SC 35, LC 4; enrl D 140, E 20, nonmaj 120, maj 40.
Tuition: $2200 per yr, $1100 per sem, D $65 per cr hr, E $45 per cr hr.
Courses: Art Education; Art History; Calligraphy; Ceramics; Drawing; Lettering; Mixed Media; Occupational Therapy; Painting; Photography; Printmaking; Sculpture; Teacher Training; Textile Design.
Summer School: Dir Myron Brody.

KANSAS CITY ART INSTITUTE, 4415 Warwick Blvd, 64111. Tel: 816-561-4852. *Pres* John W Lottes, BFA; *Chmn Crafts* Kenneth Ferguson, MFA; *Chmn Design* Victor Papanek; *Chmn Painting/Printmaking* Wilbur Niewald, MFA; *Chmn Photography* Lloyd Schnell, BFA; *Chmn Sculpture* Dale Eldred, MFA; *Chmn Found* Steven Whitacre, MFA; *Chmn Lib Arts* George Burris, MA.
Estab 1885; prov; D&E; ent req HS dipl, portfolio interview; degree BFA 4 yrs; schol; SC 9 maj areas, LC 104 lib arts; enrl D 592, E 200, nonmaj 200, maj 592.
Tuition: $2950 per yr, $1475 per sem, $100 per cr hr; campus res room and board $750.
Courses: Advertising Design; Art History; ‡Ceramics; Commercial Art; Display; Drawing; Film; Graphic Arts; ‡Graphic Design; History of Art & Archaeology; Illustration; Industrial Design; Interior Design; Landscape Architecture; Mixed Media; ‡Painting; ‡Photography; ‡Printmaking; ‡Sculpture; ‡Textile Design; Video.
Adult Hobby Classes: Enrl 200 tui $100 per cr hr. Courses—Ceramics; Fiber; Painting; Printmaking; Photography.
Children's Classes: High School Only. Tui $48 per sem. Courses—Ceramics; Painting; Drawing; Photography.
Summer School: Summer Studio Workshops. Tui $600 for term of 6 wks beginning June 19. Courses—Ceramics; Fiber; Painting; Printmaking; Design; Photography; Sculpture.

MAPLE WOODS COMMUNITY COLLEGE, Department of Art and Art History, 2601 NE Barry Rd, 64156. Tel: 816-436-6500, exten 79. *Instr & Head Dept* Helen Mary Turner, M Sec Ed; PT Instrs 6-8.
Estab 1969; pub; D&E; Sat; ent req HS dipl or GED; degree AA 2 yrs; schol; SC 12, LC 2; enrl D 100, E & Sat 50.
Tuition: Res—$142-$274 per sem, $12-$23 per cr hr; Nonres state—$586 per sem, $49 per cr hr; no campus res.
Courses: Art Education; Art History; Ceramics; Commercial Art; Drawing; Handicrafts (Batik); Jewelry; Painting; Photography; Printmaking; Sculpture; Silversmithing.
Adult Hobby Classes: Enrl 30; tui same as above. Courses—Stained Glass.
Children's Classes: Sat and Summer Classes. Enrl 30; tui $30 per 6 wks.
Summer School: Dir Helen Mary Turner. Tui same as above for 8 wks beginning June 1. Courses—Ceramics; Silver; Batik; Painting.

UNIVERSITY OF MISSOURI-KANSAS CITY,* Department of Art and Art History, 5100 Rockhill Rd, 64110. Tel: 816-276-1501. *Chmn* Lee Anne Miller; Instrs FT 12, PT 1.
Estab 1933; pub; D&E; ent req contact Admis Office; enrl maj 210.
Tuition: $300 per sem; Nonres—$600.
Courses: Art History; Drawing; Graphic Design; Painting; Printmaking; Sculpture.
Summer School: 1 term. For information contact Admis Office.

KIRKSVILLE

NORTHEAST MISSOURI STATE UNIVERSITY, Division of Fine Arts, Art Department, 63501. Tel: 816-665-5121, exten 7196. *Head Div Fine Arts* Dean Dale Jorgenson; *Assoc Prof* Helen Babbit, MFA; *Prof* Mary Belle Martin, EdD; *Assoc Prof* Kent McAlexander, MFA; *Asst Prof* Ed McEndarfer, MFA; *Instr & Gallery Dir* Tru McRae, MFA; *Asst Prof* William Murray, MA; *Prof* William Unger, MFA; *Asst Prof* James Pauls, MFA.
Estab 1867; pub; D&E; ent req HS dipl, portfolio; degrees BSE(Art Educ) and BA(Commercial, Studio) 4 yrs, MA(Art Educ) 5 yrs; schol; SC 27, LC 8, GC 8; enrl D 220, nonmaj 45, maj 175, grad 12.
Tuition: $150 per sem, plus $20-$40 per cr hr; campus res.
Courses: Advertising Design; Aesthetics; ‡Art Education; Art History; Ceramics; ‡Commercial Art; Constructions; Drawing; ‡Graphic Arts; Graphic Design; Handicrafts (Macrame); Illustration; Lettering; Museum Staff Training; ‡Painting; Photography; ‡Printmaking; ‡Sculpture; ‡Teacher Training; Textile Design.
Adult Hobby Classes: Art Appreciation for Sr Citizens. Enrl 35; tui free.

Summer School: Enrl 80-100; tui $15 per hr for term of two 5 wk sessions beginning June & July.

LIBERTY

WILLIAM JEWELL COLLEGE, Art Department, 64068. Tel: 816-781-3806. *Head Dept* David B Johnson; Instrs FT 1, PT 3.
Estab 1950; ent req HS grad; SC 4, LC 1.
Courses: Calligraphy; Ceramics; Design; Drawing; Painting.

MARYVILLE

NORTHWEST MISSOURI STATE UNIVERSITY, Department of Art, 64468. Tel: 816-582-7141, exten 178. *Chmn Dept Art* Robert Sunkel, MFA; *Assoc Prof* Lee Hageman, MFA; *Assoc Prof* Donald Robertson, MA; *Asst Prof* Kenneth Nelsen, MFA; *Asst Prof* Russell Schmaljohn, MS; *Asst Prof* Philip Van Voorst, MFA; *Asst Prof* Norman Weil, MFA; *Instr* Philip Laker, MA.
Estab 1905, dept estab 1915; pub; D&E; ent req HS dipl; degrees BFA, BSE and BA 4 yrs; schol; SC 74, LC 19; enrl D 450, E 50, nonmaj 350, maj 150.
Tuition: Res—$190 per sem, $22 per hr; Nonres—$835 per sem, $44 per hr; campus res $350 (room only).
Courses: ‡Art Education; Art History; Ceramics; Drawing; Fibers; Goldsmithing; Jewelry; Painting; Pewtersmithing; Photography; Printmaking; Sculpture; Silversmithing; Teacher Training.
Summer School: Chmn Dept Art Robert Sunkel. Two-week short courses varying from summer to summer; cost is hourly rate listed above. Courses—(Summer 78) Pewtersmithing; Weaving; Ceramics; Printmaking; Art Education.

NEOSHO

CROWDER COLLEGE,* Department of Art, 64850. Tel: 417-451-3223. *Instr* Richard Boyt; Instrs FT 1, PT 5.
Estab 1964; pub; D&E; ent req HS grad or equivalent; degrees AA and AAS 2 yrs; schol; enrl D 1000, E 300, maj 15, others 100.
Courses: Ceramics; Commercial Art; Drawing; History of Art; Introduction to Visual Arts; Painting; Photography; Weaving.
Summer School: Dean of the Col J Cavanough. Term of 8 wks beginning in June. Courses—Varied academic courses.

NEVADA

COTTEY COLLEGE,* Fine Arts Division, 64772. Tel: 417-667-5547. *Pres* Evelyn Milam; *Chmn* Harry Chew; Instrs FT 3.
Estab 1884; pvt; D; W; ent req HS grad, AC Board; degree AA 2 yrs; SC 15, LC 4; enrl maj 12-15, total 369.
Courses: Art Appreciation; Art History; Ceramics; Design; Drawing; Enameling; Fabric; Metal Craft; Mosaics; Painting; Printmaking; Wood.

SAINT CHARLES

LINDENWOOD COLLEGES,* Art Department, 63301. Tel: 314-723-7152, exten 241. *Chmn Dept* W Dean Eckert; Instrs FT 5, PT 4.
Estab 1827; pvt; D&E; ent req HS dipl, ent exam; degrees BA, BS, BFA 4 yrs, MA; schol; SC 42, LC 24; enrl D 200, E 100, maj 45, continuing educ 25.
Tuition: $2600 per yr.
Courses: Art Education; Ceramics; Drawing; History of Art & Archaeology; Museum Staff Training; Painting; Photography; Printmaking; Sculpture; Teacher Training.

SAINT JOSEPH

MISSOURI WESTERN STATE COLLEGE, Art Department, Downs Dr, 64507. Tel: 816-233-7192, exten 422. *Asst Prof Art & Chmn Dept* Jane Nelson, MFA; *Instr* Susan Conn, MA; *Instr* Jean Harmon, MFA; *Asst Prof* Jim Estes, MA; *Assoc Prof* Jack Hughes (John T), MFA; *Instr* Mark Lavetelli, MA; *Instr* Ralph Schaller, MFA.
Estab 1969; pub; D&E; ent req HS dipl, GED, ACT; degrees BS(Art Educ) and BA(Art) 4 yrs; schol; SC 25, LC 8; enrl D 355, E 100, nonmaj 120, maj 70.
Tuition: Res—$402 per yr, $201 per sem, $21.50 per cr hr; Nonres—$782 per yr, $391 per sem, $42 per cr hr; campus res room and board $930 per yr.
Courses: ‡Art Education; Art History; Ceramics; Collage; Commercial Art; Composition (Design); Conceptual Art; Constructions; Costume Design & Construction; Drafting; Drawing; Goldsmithing; Graphic Arts; Graphic Design; Handicrafts (macrame, stained glass, weaving); History of Art & Archaeology; Jewelry; Mixed Media; Painting; Photography;

Printmaking; Sculpture; Silversmithing; Stage Design; ‡Teacher Training; Theatre Arts; Tools & Techniques; Two & Three-Dimensional Design.
Adult Hobby Classes: Tui $1 per noncredit hr, $21.50 per cr hr, sr citizens free. Courses—Oil, Acrylic & Watercolor Painting; Drawing; Macrame; Stain Glass, Weaving; Ceramics.
Summer School: Chmn Art Dept Jane Nelson. Tui res $95.50 5 or more cr hrs, nonres $190.50 5 or more cr hrs for term of 8 wks beginning June 2. Courses—Introduction to Art; Art Education; Painting; Ceramics; Drawing; Printmaking; Sculpture; Photomedia; Two-Dimensional Design.

SAINT LOUIS

ART-MART STUDIO,* 9983 Manchester Rd, 63122. Tel: 314-822-3900. *Dir* Jim W Harmon; *Instrs* D PT 11, E PT 6.
Estab 1955; pvt; SC 17.
Courses: Graphics; Painting; Portrait Painting; Sculpture.
Children's Classes: Sat AM.

MARYVILLE COLLEGE, Art Department, 13550 Conway Rd, 63141. Tel: 314-434-4100, exten 283. *Prof Art & Fine Arts Area Coordr* B Kent Addison, MA; *Assoc Prof* Charles F Jamieson, MFA; *Assoc Prof* Virginia O'Meara, MA; *Instr* Nancy Rice, MFA; *Prof* Rodney M Winfield.
Estab 1872, dept estab 1961; pvt; D&E; ent req HS dipl, ACT or SAT; degrees BA and BFA 4 yrs; schol; SC 74, LC 6; enrl D 150, E 30, nonmaj 60, maj 90.
Tuition: $2500 per yr, $1250 per sem, $85 per cr hr; campus res room and board $1400 per yr.
Courses: Advertising Design; Art History; Calligraphy; ‡Ceramics; Commercial Art; Drafting; Drawing; Graphic Arts; Graphic Design; ‡Interior Design; Jewelry; ‡Painting; Photography; ‡Printmaking; ‡Sculpture.

NOTRE DAME COLLEGE,* Art Department, 320 E Ripa Ave, 63125. Tel: 314-544-0455, exten 36. *Dir* Sister Angelee Fuchs; *Instrs* FT 2, PT 2.
Estab 1954; pvt; D&E; ent req HS dipl, ACT; degrees Teacher Cert, BA 3-4 yrs; schol; SC 23, LC 6; enrl D 25, maj 25.
Adult Hobby Classes: Courses—Ceramics; Crafts; Fabric Design.
Summer School: Dir Sister Angelee Fchs. Courses—Crafts; Painting.

SAINT LOUIS COMMUNITY COLLEGE AT FOREST PARK, Department of Art, 5600 Oakland, 63110. Tel: 314-644-9351. *Chmn Dept Art* Mary L Fifield, MFA; *Assoc Prof* Leon Anderson, MFA; *Assoc Prof* James Hogan, BA; *Assoc Prof* Kimball Wells, MFA; *Instr* Bruce Pasley, MFA; *Instrs* PT 12.
Estab 1962, dept estab 1963; pub; D&E; ent req HS dipl; degrees AA and AAS 2 yrs; schol; SC 36, LC 6; enrl D 100, E 100, nonmaj 75, maj 125.
Tuition: $600 per yr, $300 per sem, $17 per cr hr; no campus res.
Courses: Advertising Design; Art Appreciation; Art History; Ceramics; Color; ‡Commercial Art; Design; Drawing; Figure Drawing; ‡Fine Arts Transfer Program; Graphic Design; Illustration; Lettering; Painting; Photography; Printmaking.
Summer School; Dir Mary L Fifield. Enrl 100; tui $17 per cr hr. Courses—Same as those above.

SAINT LOUIS COMMUNITY COLLEGE AT MERAMEC, Art Department, 11333 Big Bend Blvd, 63122. Tel: 314-966-7632. *Chairperson Art Dept* Ruth Hensler; *Primary Art Faculty:* Fred R Allen, MFA; Garth Bell, AM; David Durham, BFA; John Ferguson; Peter Hoell, BFA; John Nagel, BA; Christine Scavotto, MA; Patrick Shuck, MFA; Mary Sprague, AM; Ronald Thomas, MFA; Sam Wayne, MA; Yvette Woods, BFA.
Estab 1964; pub; D&E; ent req HS dipl; degree AA 2 yrs; schol; SC 15, LC 2.
Tuition: $17 per cr hr; no campus res.
Courses: Advertising Design; Art History; Ceramics; Commercial Art; Drawing; Illustration; Interior Design; Painting; Photography; Printmaking; Sculpture.
Summer School: Chairperson Art Dept Ruth Hensler. Tui $17 per cr hr for term of 9 wks beginning June 12. Courses—Design; Drawing; Figure Drawing; Ceramics; Photography; Sculpture; Art History; Art Appreciation.

UNIVERSITY OF MISSOURI-SAINT LOUIS, Art Department, 8001 Natural Bridge, 63121. Tel: 314-453-5975. *Assoc Prof Art & Chairperson Dept* Sylvia Solochek Walters, MFA; *Assoc Prof* Michael D Taylor, PhD; *Asst Prof* Mary Wilson, PhD; *Instrs* Marie Schmitz, MA; *Asst Prof* James Smith, MFA; *Assoc Prof* Christopher D Roy, PhD.

Estab 1963; pub; D&E; ent req HS dipl; degree BA(Art Hist); SC 10, LC 20; enrl maj 80.
Tuition: $385 per sem; no campus res.
Courses: Art Education; Art History; Ceramics; Drawing; Graphic Design; History of Art & Archaeology; Painting; Printmaking.
Summer School: Courses—Introduction to Art; Primitive Art; Women Artists; Introduction to Painting; Abstract Painting & Drawing; Drawing the Landscape.

WASHINGTON UNIVERSITY
—School of Fine Arts, Lindell & Skinker, 63130. Tel: 314-889-6500.
Dean Sch Roger DesRosiers, MFA; *Assoc Dean Sch* Barry Schactman, MFA; *Asst Dean Sch* Kim Strommen, MFA; *Chairperson 3D Dept* James Sterritt, MFA; *Chairperson 2D Dept* Peter Marcus, MFA; *Chairperson Design Dept* Richard Brunell, BFA; *vis prof*—Gregory Kepes, 77-78.
Estab 1853; pvt; D; ent req HS dipl, SAT or ACT, portfolio; degrees BFA 4 yrs, MFA 2 yrs; schol; SC 62, LC 10, GC 31; enrl 390, nonmaj 5, maj 325, grad 60.
Tuition: $4300 per yr, $2150 per sem, $165 per cr hr; campus res room and board $1750 per yr.
Courses: ‡Advertising Design; Aesthetics; Architecture; Art Education; Art History; Calligraphy; ‡Ceramics; Commercial Art; ‡Conceptual Art; Costume Design & Construction; Drawing; ‡Fashion Arts; Goldsmithing; Graphic Arts; ‡Graphic Design; History of Art & Archaeology; ‡Illustration; Intermedia; ‡Jewelry; Lettering; Mixed Media; ‡Painting; ‡Photography; ‡Printmaking; ‡Sculpture; ‡Silversmithing; Teacher Training; Textile Design; Theatre Arts; Video.
Children's Classes: Sat and Summer Classes for High School Students.
Summer School: Prof Barry Schactman. Courses—Drawing; Printmaking; Metalsmithing; Sculpture; Painting; Graphic Communications.
—School of Architecture, Box 1079, 63130. Tel: 314-889-6200. *Dean Sch* C Michaelides, MArch.
Estab 1910; pvt; D; degrees BA(Archit) 4 yrs, MArch & Urban Design 1-1½-2 yrs, MArch 2-4 yrs; schol; SC 28, LC 58, GC 42; enrl 330, maj 190, grad 140.
Tuition: $4300 per yr; campus res room and board varies.
Courses: ‡Architecture.
Summer School: Dir Michael Nelson. Tui varies. Courses—Fundamentals of Design; Structural Principles; Independent Study; Advanced Architectural Design.

SPRINGFIELD

DRURY COLLEGE,* Art and Art History Department, 65802. Tel: 417-869-0511. *Chmn Dept* John H Simmons; *Instrs* FT 2, PT 1.
Estab 1873; den; degree 4 yrs; schol; SC 12, LC 5; enrl 200.
Courses: General Art; Teacher Training.

SOUTHWEST MISSOURI STATE UNIVERSITY, Department of Art, 901 S National, 65802. Tel: 417-831-1561, exten 204. *Head Dept* James L Richardson; *Instrs* FT 22, PT 9.
Estab 1901; D&E; ent req HS grad, ent exam; degrees BFA, BS(Educ, Educ Comprehensive) and BA 4 yrs; schol; SC 31, LC 14; enrl maj 450, others 2000, total 12,000.
Tuition: $180, nonres $270; campus res $405 per sem.
Courses: Art Appreciation; Art Education; Art History; Ceramics; Drawing; Fibers; Graphic Design; Jewelry & Silversmithing; Painting; Photography & Cinematography; Printmaking & Lithography; Sculpture & Bronze Casting; Teacher Training (with Dept of Educ).
Summer School: Dir Dean Russell Keeling. Enrl total 3500; special workshops available during summer session; tui $20 per cr hr; 4, 5 and 8 wk sessions. Courses—Selected from the above curriculum.

UNION

EAST CENTRAL JUNIOR COLLEGE,* Art Department, PO Box 529, 63084. Tel: 314-583-5193. *Head Dept* Larry Pogue; *Instrs* FT 1, PT 6.
Estab 1968; pub; D&E; ent req HS dipl, ent exam; degrees AA and AAS 2 yrs; schol; SC 8, LC 8; enrl D 370, E 120, maj 37.
Tuition: $120 per sem.
Courses: Art Appreciation; Art Education; Commercial Art; Drawing; Graphic Design; Handicrafts; History of Art & Archaeology; Introduction to Art; Painting; Printmaking; Sculpture.

WARRENSBURG

CENTRAL MISSOURI STATE UNIVERSITY, Art Department, 64093. Tel: 816-429-4480. *Prof Art & Head Dept* Edwin C Ellis, MFA; *Assoc Prof* Richard Monson, MFA; *Asst Prof* John R Haydo, MFA; *Prof* Richard Luehrman, PhD; *Asst Prof* Margaret Peterson, MFA; *Asst*

Prof Harold M Reynolds, EdD; *Asst Prof* Kenneth Meredith, EdD; *Assoc Prof* Edward R Lewis, MFA.
Estab 1871; pub; D & a few E classes; ent req HS dipl Missouri Sch & Col Ability Test, ACT; degrees BS, BSE and BFA 4 yrs; MSE 1 yr; schol; SC 40, LC 14, GC 7; enrl D 251, nonmaj 180, maj 251.
Tuition: Res—$115 per quarter; Nonres—$315 per quarter; campus res room and board $675.
Courses: Advertising Design; Art Education; Art History; Calligraphy; Ceramics; Commercial Art; Drawing; Graphic Arts; History of Art & Archaeology; Illustration; Interior Design; Lettering; Painting; Printmaking; Sculpture; Teacher Training.
Summer School: Head Dept Edwin C Ellis. Tui $115 for term of 10 wks beginning June 2. Courses—Drawing; Design; Painting; Ceramics; plus Grad Studio Courses.

WEBSTER GROVES

WEBSTER COLLEGE, Art Department, 470 E Lockwood Blvd, 63119. Tel: 314-968-0500, exten 358. *Chairperson Art Dept* Kathleen J Regier, PhD; *Asst Prof* Michael Beresford, MFA; *Assoc Prof* Jack Canepa, MFA; *Asst Prof* Susan Hacker, MFA; *Assoc Prof* Leon Hicks, MFA; *Assoc Prof* Sister Gabriel Mary Hoare, MA; *Instr.-Lectr* Paul Hrusovsky, MA; *Assoc Prof* Thomas Lang, MFA; *Lectr* Jan Sultz, MFA; *Assoc Prof* Phil Sultz, BFA.
Estab 1915, dept estab 1946; pvt D&E; ent req HS dipl, SAT or ACT; degrees BA and BFA 4 yrs; schol; SC 60, LC 15; enrl 424, nonmaj 318, maj 100.
Tuition: $2850 per yr, $90 per cr hr; campus res room and board $1380 per yr.
Courses: ‡Art Education; ‡Art History; ‡Ceramics; Collage; Conceptual Art; ‡Drawing; Film; History of Art & Archaeology; ‡Painting; ‡Photography; ‡Printmaking; ‡Sculpture; Teacher Training.
Summer School: Undergrad Dean Charles Madden. Tui $90 per cr hr for term of 6 or 8 wks beginning June 19. Courses—Vary each summer.

MONTANA

BILLINGS

EASTERN MONTANA COLLEGE,* Art Department, 1500 N 30th St, 59101. Tel: 406-657-2011. *Head* Ben C Steele; *Instrs* D FT 3, E FT 3.
Estab 1927; pub; ent req HS grad; degrees BS(Educ) and BA(Liberal Arts) 4 yrs; affiliated with Univ of Montana; SC 19, LC 1.
Tuition: Res—$483; Nonres—$1455.
Courses: Ceramics; Commercial Illustration; Crafts; Design; Drawing; Graphics; History of Art; Lettering & Layout; Metalwork & Jewelry; Painting; Sculpture.
Summer School: Usually 6 courses with emphasis on courses for teachers.

ROCKY MOUNTAIN COLLEGE, Art Department, 1511 Poly Dr, 59102. Tel: 406-245-6151, exten 263. *Assoc Prof Art & Chmn Dept* Robert Morrison, MA; *Assoc Prof* Kathleen Joyce, PhD; *Instr* Patricia Cherewick, MFA.
Estab 1878, dept estab 1957; pvt; D; ent req HS dipl, ACT; degrees BA and BS 4 yrs; schol; SC 12, LC 5; enrl 112, nonmaj 40, maj 30, others 5.
Tuition: $1650 per yr, $825 per sem, $65 per cr hr; campus res room and board $1210 per yr.
Courses: Art Education; Art History; Ceramics; Drawing; Graphic Arts; Graphic Design; Illustration; Painting; Photography; Printmaking; Sculpture; Stage Design; Teacher Training.
Adult Hobby Classes: Enrl 100; tui $20 for 5 wks. Courses—Crafts, Picture-Framing, Painting.

BOZEMAN

MONTANA STATE UNIVERSITY
—School of Art, Haynes Hall, 59717. Tel: 406-994-4501. *Dir Sch* William C Alexander, MFA; vis profs vary each quarter.
Estab 1893; pub; D; ent req HS dipl; degrees BA 4 yrs, MAA 2 yrs; SC 38, LC 19, GC 13; enrl maj 300, grad 19.
Tuition: Res—$558 per yr; Nonres—$1925 per yr; campus res room and board.
Courses: ‡Architecture; Art Education; Art History; Ceramics; ‡Drafting; Drawing; ‡Film; Graphic Arts; Graphic Design; Interior Design; Jewelry; Lettering; Painting; ‡Photography; Printmaking; Sculpture; Silversmithing; Teacher Training; ‡Theatre Arts; ‡Video.
Summer School: Dir Dr Rex Dahl. Courses—Vary each summer according to demand.
—School of Architecture,* Creative Arts Complex. Tel: 406-994-4255. *Dir Sch* Ilmar Reinvald; Instrs FT 14, PT 1.
Pub; degree BArch 5 yrs; LabC 15, LC 14; enrl maj 300.

Tuition: Res—$557.85 for 3 quarters; Nonres—$1368; campus res room and board about $1371 for 3 quarters.
Courses: Architecture.

DILLON

WESTERN MONTANA COLLEGE,* Art Department, 710 S Atlantic, 59725. Tel: 406-683-7312. *Chmn Dept* Don Walters; *Instrs* FT 3.
Estab 1897; pub; D&E; ent req HS dipl; degrees BS 4 yrs, MA; schol; SC 15, LC 6, GC 21.
Courses: Advertising Design; Aesthetics; Art Education; Ceramics; Commercial Art; Drafting; Drawing; Graphic Arts; Graphic Design; Handicrafts; History of Art & Archaeology; Illustration; Industrial Design; Jewelry; Lettering; Painting; Photography; Sculpture; Stage Design; Teacher Training; Theatre Arts.
Summer School: Chmn Dept Don Walters. Term of 4½ and 9 wks beginning June. Courses—Same as regular yr.

GREAT FALLS

COLLEGE OF GREAT FALLS,* Department of Art, 1301 20th St S, 59405. Tel: 406-452-9584. *Dean of Studies* Francis W Dirocco; *Head Dept* Jack N Franjevic; *Instrs* FT 2, PT 2.
Estab 1933; den; D&E; degrees 4 yrs; SC, LabC, LC; enrl varies 1200-1300.
Courses: Art Education; Ceramics; Crafts; Design; Drawing & Painting; Jewelry; Photography; Printmaking; Sculpture; Silversmithing; Textile Design.
Summer School: Dir Richard Gretch; 6 wks.

HAVRE

NORTHERN MONTANA COLLEGE,* Department of Art, 611 16th St, 59501. Tel: 406-265-7821, exten 231. *Assoc Prof* James Brownson; *Instrs* FT 2.
Estab 1929; pub; D&E; ent req HS dipl; degrees AA 2 yrs, BS(Educ) and BA 4 yrs, MSc(Educ); schol; SC 15, LC 5, GC 9; enrl D 425, grad 7.
Courses: Art Education; Ceramics; Commercial Art; Drafting; Drawing; Graphic Arts; Painting; Sculpture; Teacher Training.
Children's Classes: Enrl 60; tui $1 enrl fee. Courses—Drawing; Painting; Sculpture; Ceramics.
Summer School: Dir Dr Lee Spuhler. Enrl 700 col, 47 art classes; term of 8 wks. Courses—Ceramics; Sculpture; Art Appreciation; Art Education.

MILES CITY

MILES COMMUNITY COLLEGE, Department of Fine Arts and Humanities, 2715 Dickinson St, 59301. Tel: 406-232-3031. *Head Dept* LaRayne DeJulis, MA; *Instr* Sydney R Sonneborn, MA; *Instr* Tom Bay, MA; *Instr* Fred McKee, MFA.
Estab 1937, dept estab 1967; pub; D&E; ent req HS dipl, ACT; degrees AA 2 yrs, cert; schol; SC 17, LC 1; enrl D 36, E 23, nonmaj 55, maj 4.
Tuition: Res—$302.50 per yr; Nonres—$722.50 per yr; no campus res.
Courses: Advertising Design; Ceramics; Drawing; Jewelry; Painting; Photography; Stage Design; Teacher Training; Theatre Arts.
Adult Hobby Classes: Enrl minimum of 8; tui $30 per 3 cr course. Courses—Painting; Jewelry Making; Photography; Macrame; Ceramics.

MISSOULA

UNIVERSITY OF MONTANA, Department of Art, 59812. Tel: 406-243-4181. *Chmn Dept Art* Laurence Karasek, RASD; *Prof* Rudy Autio, MFA; *Prof* Bruce Walter Barton, MA; *Prof* Don Bunse, MFA; *Prof* James Dew, MA; *Assoc Prof* Joel Bernstein, PhD; *Assoc Prof* Stephen Connell, MA; *Assoc Prof* Richard Reinholtz, MEd; *vis prof*—Mary Warner, painting, 77-78.
Pub; D&E; ent req HS dipl; degrees BA and BFA 4 yrs, MA and MFA 2 yrs; SC 28, LC 20, GC 10; enrl D 850, E 30.
Tuition: Res—$204.50 per quarter (12-18 cr hrs); Nonres—$660.50 per quarter (12-18 cr hrs).
Courses: Aesthetics; Art Education; Art History; Ceramics; Drawing; Handicrafts (Fiber); History of Art & Archaeology; Jewelry; Lettering; Painting; Photography; Printmaking; Sculpture; Silversmithing.
Summer School: Chmn Laurence Karasek. Term of 4 wks. Courses—Vary due to availability of funds and instructors; normally painting, art education, photography.

NEBRASKA

CHADRON

CHADRON STATE COLLEGE, Division of Fine Arts, Tenth & Main Sts, 69337. Tel: 308-432-4451, exten 317. *Chmn Div Fine Arts* Harry E Holmberg, EdD; *Assoc Prof* Noel Gray, EdD; *Asst Prof* John Dillon, MFA; *Instr* Richard Bird, MFA.
Estab 1911, div estab 1935; pub; D&E; ent req HS dipl; degrees BSE and BA 4 yrs; schol; SC 20, LC 4, GC 2; enrl D 195, nonmaj 155, maj 40.
Tuition: Res—$15.50 per hr; Nonres—$27.50 per hr; campus res room and board $400.
Courses: Aesthetics; Art Education; Ceramics; Commercial Art; Drafting; Drawing; Glass Blowing; Graphic Arts; History of Art; Jewelry; Lettering; Painting; Sculpture; Teacher Training; Theatre Arts; Weaving.
Adult Hobby Classes: Tui $10 per hr. Courses—Variable on demand.
Summer School: Dir Harry E Holmberg. Tui same as above. Courses—Usually 4 to 6 courses on semi rotation basis.

CRETE

DOANE COLLEGE, Department of Art, 68333. Tel: 402-826-2161, exten 273. *Assoc Prof Art & Head Dept* Richard Terrell, MFA; *Instr* Michael Hershey, MFA.
Estab 1872, dept estab 1958; pvt; D; ent req HS dipl; degree BA 4 yrs; schol; SC 6, LC 5, enrl 150, nonmaj 140, maj 10.
Tuition: $2335 per yr; campus res room and board $1130 per yr.
Courses: Art Education; Art History; Ceramics; Drawing; Film; Graphic Design; Jewelry; Painting; Printmaking; Sculpture; Stage Design.

HASTINGS

HASTINGS COLLEGE,* Art Department, 68901. Tel: 402-463-2402. *Prof Art & Chmn Dept* Gary E Coulter; *Instrs* FT 3.
Estab 1925; den; ent req HS grad; degree BA 4 yrs; schol; SC 16, LC 5; enrl maj 50, others 350.
Tuition: $2400; campus res room and board $1350.
Courses: Art Education; Art History; Ceramics; Composition; Drawing & Painting; Printmaking; Sculpture.
Summer School: Acad Dean Dr A L Langvardt. Enrl 25; tui $175 per unit for 6 wks beginning June.

KEARNEY

KEARNEY STATE COLLEGE, Department of Art, 68847. Tel: 308-236-4221. *Prof Art & Chmn Dept* Jack Karraker, MFA; *Assoc Prof* John N Dinsmore, EdD; *Asst Prof* Charles J Eastman, MFA; *Asst Prof* Elmer Holzrichter, MA; *Instr* Mary A Reed, MA; *Assoc Prof* Keith Lowry, MFA; *Prof* Raymond W Schultze, MFA; *Asst Prof* James M May, MA; *Prof* Gary E Zaruba, EdD; *Prof* Larry D Peterson, EdD; Instrs PT 4.
Estab 1903; pub; D&E; ent req HS dipl, SAT or ACT recommended; degrees BFA, BA, BA(Educ) 4 yrs, MA(Educ-Art); schol; SC 23, LC 10, GC 16; enrl D 970, E 30, nonmaj 800, maj 170, grad 30.
Tuition: Res—$15.50 per cr hr; Nonres—$27.50 per cr hr; campus res $489 per yr.
Courses: Aesthetics; ‡Art Education; ‡Art History; ‡Ceramics; ‡Drawing; ‡Painting; Photography; ‡Printmaking; ‡Sculpture; ‡Teacher Training; ‡Textile Design.
Summer School: Second summer session 8 wks; tui $15.50 per cr hr. Courses—Basic Art Curriculum.

LINCOLN

NEBRASKA WESLEYAN UNIVERSITY, Art Department, 50th & St Paul, 68504. Tel: 402-466-2371. *Asst Prof Art & Head Dept* Betty Wallace, MFA; *Asst Prof* James Engeseth, MFA; vis profs—Nadine McHenry, Robert Wilson, Harry Orlyk, Jeanne James, 1977-78.
Estab 1888, dept estab 1890; pvt; D&E; ent req HS dipl, ent exam; degrees AA 2 yrs, BA and BS 4 yrs; schol; SC 22, LC 4; enrl nonmaj 300, maj 30.
Tuition: $1250 per sem.
Courses: Advertising Design; Art Education; Art History; Art Marketing; Ceramics; Commercial Art; Design; Drawing; History of Art & Archaeology; Jewelry; Museum Staff Training; Painting; Photography; Printmaking; Sculpture; Silversmithing.

UNIVERSITY OF NEBRASKA-LINCOLN, Department of Art, 207 Nelle Cochrane Woods Hall, 68588. Tel: 402-472-2631. *Chmn Dept* Dan F Howard, MFA; *VChmn Dept* Collins, PhD; *Chmn Grad Comt* Robert Spence, PhD; *Chief Acad Adv* Peter Worth, ARCA; vis profs—on irregular basis; Instrs FT 20, PT 19.
Estab 1869, dept 1912; pub; D&E; ent req HS dipl; degrees BA, BFA and BFA(Educ) 4 yrs, MFA 2-3 yrs; schol; SC 71, LC 27, GC 45; enrl D 1950, E 175, nonmaj 600, maj 565, grad 25.
Tuition: Res—$318.50 per sem, $21 per cr hr; Nonres—$750.50 per sem, $57 per cr hr; campus res room and board $1335 per yr.
Courses: Advertising Design; ‡Art Education; ‡Art History; ‡Ceramics; Commercial Art; ‡Drawing; Film; ‡Graphic Design; Handicrafts (weaving); Illustration; Lettering; Mixed Media; ‡Painting; ‡Photography; ‡Printmaking; ‡Sculpture; Teacher Training; Two & Three-Dimensional Design.
Summer School: Dir Alan Seagren. Enrl 250; two 5 wk sessions beginning June and Aug. Courses—Drawing; Design; Ceramics; Printmaking; Painting; Art History; Special Problems & Topics.

NORFOLK

NORTHEAST TECHNICAL COMMUNITY COLLEGE, Department of Art, 801 E Benjamin Ave, 68701. Tel: 402-371-0608, exten 245. *Chmn Dept* Patrick Keating, MA; *Instr* Mary Ann Clark, MFA; *Instr* Rebecca Low, MFA; *Instr* Bonnie Mercer, BA; *Instr* Dan Craig, AS; vis prof—Electra Malone, watercolor, spring.
Estab 1928; pub; D&E; ent req HS dipl; degree AA 2 yrs; schol; SC 5, LC 5; enrl D 150, E 50, nonmaj 100, maj 50.
Tuition: Res—$165 per sem, $11 per cr hr; Nonres—$265 per sem, $18 per cr hr; campus res room and board $1000 per yr.
Courses: Art Education; Art History; Drawing; Graphic Design; Painting; Photography.
Summer School: Dir Patrick Keating. Tui $165 for term of 5 wks beginning June 1. Courses—Design; Photography.

OMAHA

COLLEGE OF SAINT MARY,* Art Department, 1901 S 72nd St, 68124. Tel: 402-393-8800, exten 53. *Chmn Dept* Tom Schlosser; Instrs FT 2.
Estab 1923; pvt; D&E; W; ent req HS dipl; degrees BA and BS 4 yrs; schol; SC 11, LC 5; enrl D 278 in Art, maj 18, special 2.
Tuition: FT $74 per cr hr; campus res $612.50 per sem.
Courses: Aesthetics; Art Education; Ceramics; Design; Drawing; Graphic Arts; History of Art & Archaeology; Jewelry; Lettering; Painting; Photography; Printmaking; Sculpture; Teacher Training.

CREIGHTON UNIVERSITY, Fine and Performing Arts Department, 2500 California St, 68178. Tel: 402-449-2509. *Chmn Dept* Donald A Doll; *Primary Art Faculty* Bob Bosco, MFA; Suzanne Dieckman, PhD; Alan Garfield, MA; Bill Hutson, MA; Lee Lubbers, PhD; Joellen Meglin, MFA; Valerie Roche, ARAD; John Thein, MFA; *Artist-in-Residence* Joseph Brown, theatre/poetry, 1977-78; Instrs PT 8.
Estab 1878, dept estab 1966; den; D&E; ent req HS dipl, regular col admis exam; degrees BA and BFA 4 yrs; schol; SC 87, LC 16; enrl univ 4797, dept 888, nonmaj 850, maj 38, cert prog 24.
Tuition: $2840 per yr, $89 per cr hr; campus res room and board $1380 per yr.
Courses: Advertising Design; Aesthetics; Art Education; Art History; Ceramics; Collage; Costume Design & Construction; Design; Drawing; Foundry; History of Art & Archaeology; Intaglio; Lithography; Painting; Photography; Pottery; Printmaking; Sculpture; Studio Fundamentals; Teacher Training; Theatre Arts.
Adult Hobby Classes: Enrl variable; tui $2 per class. Courses—Life Drawing.
Summer School: Dir Donald A Doll. Enrl 60; tui $63 per cr hr for term of 5 wks beginning June 12. Courses: Introductory & Intermediate Ceramics; Advanced Ceramics; Collage; Etching & Sculpture; Drawing; Painting; Photography; Figure Modeling for Sculpture; Watercolor.

UNIVERSITY OF NEBRASKA AT OMAHA, Department of Art, 60th & Dodge Sts (Mailing Add: Box 688, 68101). Tel: 402-554-2420. *Prof Art & Chmn Dept* J V Blackwell, Doctorate; *Prof* Peter Hill, MFA; *Prof* Thomas H Majeski, MFA; *Prof* Sidney Buchanan, MA; *Assoc Prof* Henry Serenco, MFA; *Asst Prof* Larry Bradshaw, MFA & MA; *Asst Prof* Tricia Hollins, MFA; *Asst Prof* Donald B Doe, Doctorate; *Asst Prof* Dorothy Habel, Doctorate; *Vis Instr* David McLeod, MFA; Instrs PT 2.
Estab 1908, dept estab 1910; pub; D&E; ent req HS dipl, ACT or SAT; degrees BA and BFA 4 yrs; schol; SC 27, LC 11, GC 7.
Tuition: Res—Undergrad $20 per cr hr, grad $18 per cr hr; Nonres—Undergrad $54 per cr hr, grad $48.25 per cr hr; no campus res.

Courses: Aesthetics; Architecture; ‡Art Education; ‡Art History; ‡Ceramics; ‡Drawing; Jewelry; ‡Painting; ‡Printmaking; ‡Sculpture.
Summer School: Prof J V Blackwell. Tui same as above for term of 5 wks beginning June 11 and July 14. Courses—Art History Survey; Elementary Painting; Drawing; Art History.

SCOTTSBLUFF

NEBRASKA WESTERN COLLEGE, Division of Language and Arts, 1601 E 27th ST NE, 69361. Tel: 308-635-3603, exten 260. *Chairperson Div* Helen Burnstad, Masters; *Instr* Roy D Doerfler, Master.
Estab 1926; pub; D&E; ent req HS dipl; degrees AA and AS 2 yrs; schol; SC 8, LC 3; enrl D 100, E 230, nonmaj 90, maj 11.
Tuition: Res—$150 per sem, $12.50 per cr hr; Nonres—$237 per sem, $19.75 per cr hr; campus res room and board.
Courses: Art Appreciation; Art Education; Art History; Design Fundamentals; Drawing; Painting; Photography; Theatre Arts.
Adult Hobby Classes: Enrl 230; tui $15 per course. Courses—Carving; Macrame; Pottery; Watercolor & Oil Painting; Weaving; Drawing; Sculpture; Stained Glass.
Summer School: Registrar Pat Lee. Courses—Few in Art.

SEWARD

CONCORDIA COLLEGE, Art Department, 800 N Columbia, 68434. Tel: 402-643-3651. *Prof Art & Head Dept* William R Wolfram, MFA; *Prof* Richard Wiegmann, MFA; *Prof* Donald Dynneson, MFA; *Prof* Renhold P Marxhausen, MFA.
Estab 1894; den; D&E; ent req HS dipl; degrees BS and BA 4 yrs; schol; SC 8, LC 4; enrl nonmaj 30, maj 40.
Tuition: $2740 per yr, $1370 per sem, $40 per cr hr; campus res, room $252, board $298.
Courses: Art Education; Art History; Ceramics; Drawing; Handicrafts; History of Art & Archaeology; Painting; Photography; Printmaking; Sculpture; Teacher Training.
Summer School: Dir Dr Orville Walz. Tui $40 per cr hr for term of 2½ wks beginning June 6. Courses—Fundamentals of Art.

WAYNE

WAYNE STATE COLLEGE,* Art Department, 68787. Tel: 402-375-2200, exten 235. *Chmn Dept* Richard D Lesh; Instrs FT 3.
Estab 1910; pub; ent req HS grad; degrees BA and BFA; schol; SC 21, LC 8; enrl maj 65, others 700, total 2200.
Tuition: Res—$15.50 per cr hr; Nonres—$27.50 per cr hr.
Courses: Art History; Ceramics; Design; Drafting (architectural & mechanical); Drawing & Painting; Graphic Arts; Handicrafts; Jewelry; Sculpture; Teacher Training; Watercolor.
Summer School: Pres Lyle Seymour. Two sessions, Apr 28-June 15, June 16-Aug 4.

NEVADA

LAS VEGAS

UNIVERSITY OF NEVADA, LAS VEGAS, Department of Art, 4505 Maryland Parkway, 89154. Tel: 702-739-3237. *Chmn Dept* Bill S Leaf, MFA; *Prof* Rita Deanin Abbey, MFA; *Assoc Prof* Thomas J Holder, MFA; *Assoc Prof* Michael L McCollum, MFA; *Asst Prof* Nils W Ramstedt, Jr, PhD; *Asst Prof* Robert E Brown, MFA; *Asst Prof* David J Lurie, MFA; *Instr* Claudia L King, MA.
Estab 1955, pub; D&E; ent req HS dipl, ACT; degrees BA and BFA 4 yrs; schol; SC 32, LC 18; enrl all courses 551, maj 95.
Tuition: $750 per sem, $21 per cr hr; campus res room and board $770-$804 per sem.
Courses: Art History; Ceramics; Conceptual Art; Drawing; Film; Intermedia; Painting; Photography; Printmaking; Sculpture.
Summer School: Dir Summer Sessions Paul Aizley. Tui $23 per cr hr for 5 wks beginning June 12 and July 17. Courses—Vary with each session.

RENO

UNIVERSITY OF NEVADA, RENO,* Art Department, 89507. Tel: 702-784-6682. *Chmn Dept* James C McCormick, Jr; Instrs FT 7.
Estab 1940; pub; ent req HS grad and 16 units; degree BA 4 yrs; schol; SC 20, LC 14, GC 5; enrl maj 120, others 800.
Courses: Art Education; Ceramics; Drawing; History of Art; Painting; Photography; Printmaking; Sculpture; Stitchery; Textile Design.
Summer School.

NEW HAMPSHIRE

CONCORD

ST PAUL'S SCHOOL,* Art Department, Art Center in Hargate, 325 Pleasant St, 03301. Tel: 603-225-3341, exten 58. *Head Dept* Thomas R Barrett; Instrs FT 3, PT 3.
Estab 1967; pvt; D; independent secondary boarding school, HS dipl; SC 8, LC 1; all students boarding (496,227 registrations).
Courses: Aesthetics; Architecture; Ceramics; Drawing; Graphic Arts; History of Art & Archaeology; Painting; Photography; Sculpture; Woodworking.
Summer School: Dir Philip C Bell. Term of 6 wks beginning June 22. Courses—Advanced Studies Program; Introduction to Creative Arts.

DURHAM

UNIVERSITY OF NEW HAMPSHIRE,* College of Liberal Arts, Department of the Arts, 03824. *Chmn* Arthur Balderacchi; Instrs FT 19.
Estab 1941; pub; ent req portfolio; degrees BA and BFA 4 yrs; schol; SC 33, LC 20; enrl maj 260, others 1000.
Tuition: Res—$1000; Nonres—$2990; campus res.
Courses: Art History; Ceramics; Drawing; Graphics; Painting; Photography; Sculpture.
Summer School: Dir Dr Edward Durnall. Enrl 1200; tui $35 per cr and reg fee for 4, 6, 8 wk sessions beginning June.

HANOVER

DARTMOUTH COLLEGE,* Department of Art, 03755. Tel: 603-646-2306. *Chmn* Ashley Bryan; *VChmn* John Jacobus; Instrs FT 11, PT 3.
Estab 1906; pvt; degree AB 4 yrs; schol & fel; SC 16, LC 26; enrl 1500.
Tuition: Incl campus res fee, $1510 per term; operating 4 terms on yr-round basis.
Courses: African & Afro-American Arts; African Art & The Festival; Arts of Traditional West Africa; Color Theory; History of Architecture; Photography; Three-Dimensional Design.

MANCHESTER

MANCHESTER INSTITUTE OF ARTS AND SCIENCES,* 148 Concord St, 03104. Tel: 603-623-0313. *Exec Dir* James K Boatner; Instrs PT 30.
Estab 1898; pvt; D&E; ent req none; studios 16; enrl 1800.
Courses: Ballet; Creative Fibres; Design; Drawing; Early American Decorating; Jewelry & Silversmithing; Languages; Modern Dance; Painting; Photography; Pottery; Printmaking; Sculpture; Sewing; Theatre; Watercolor; Weaving.

NOTRE DAME COLLEGE, Art Department, 2321 Elm St, 03104. Tel: 603-623-1846. *Assoc Prof* Sister Liliosa Shea, MFA; *Prof* Frank Oehlschlaeger, MFA; *Asst Prof* Armand Szainer; *Lectr* Gloria Martin, MFA; *Instrs* William Dobe; *Lectr* Fred Dobrowolski, MFA; *Lectr* Jean Nelson, AB.
Estab 1950, dept estab 1965; pvt; D&E; ent req HS dipl; degrees BA(Fine Arts), Commercial Art & Art Educ 4 yr; schol; SC 20, LC 6; enrl nonmaj 24, maj 87.
Tuition: Undergrad $2000 yr, $1000 per sem, $150 PT; Grad $180 PT; campus res room and board $650 yr.
Courses: Advertising Design; ‡Art Education; Art History; Art Therapy; Calligraphy; Ceramics; ‡Commercial Art; Display; Drafting; Drawing; Graphic Arts; Graphic Design; Handicrafts; Illustration; Lettering; Painting; Printmaking; Sculpture; Teacher Training.

SAINT ANSELM'S COLLEGE,* Department of Fine Arts, 03102. Tel: 603-669-1030. *Chmn* Joseph E Scannell; Instrs FT 2.
Estab 1889; pvt; D&E; ent req HS dipl, relative standing, SAT, interview; degree BA 4 yrs; SC 2, LC 9, art hist sem 1; enrl approx 1500.
Courses: Art History; Photography; Studio.
Summer School: Enrl approx 10 students per course. Courses—History of American Art Seminar; Still Photography.

NASHUA

ARTS AND SCIENCE CENTER,* 14 Court St, 03060. Tel: 603-882-1506. *Admin Asst* Eleanor Fleming; Instrs PT 35-40.
Estab 1958; pub; D&E; no ent req; no degrees, noncredited; SC, LC.
Tuition: No campus res.
Courses: Ceramics; Drawing; Enameling; Jewelry; Macrame; Painting; Photography; Sculpture; Theatre Arts; Weaving.
Adult Hobby Classes: Tui varied. Courses—Hand-Built Pottery; Stained Glass.

Children's Classes: Tui varied. Courses—Drawing; Painting; Jewelry; Pottery; Puppet Making; Preschool Art; Sculpture.
Summer School: Dir Eleanor Fleming. Tui varied for ten 5 wk terms from June to July.

RIVIER COLLEGE, Art Department, S Main St, 03060. *Chmn Dept* Sister Marie Couture, MA; *Primary Art Faculty:* Jafar Shoja, MFA; Sister Theresa Couture, MA; Michael Brodeur, MFA; Lynne Johnson, MFA.
Estab 1933, dept estab 1940; pub; D&E; ent req HS dipl, SAT, certain HS equivalencies, preliminary evidence of artistic ability; degrees BA, BS and BFA 4 yrs, AA and AS 2 yrs; schol; SC 47, LC 8; enrl D 221, E 57, nonmaj 12, maj 266.
Tuition: $1100 per sem, $60-$75 per cr hr; room and board $660 per sem; fee for sem studio course $15.
Courses: Advertising Design; Aesthetics; ‡Art Education; Art History; Art Therapy; Calligraphy; ‡Ceramics; Commercial Art; Conceptual Art; Constructions; Display; Drawing; Fashion Arts; Film; Film Graphics; Graphic Arts; ‡Graphic Design; Handicrafts (loom weaving, stitchery); Illustration; Interior Design; Jewelry; Lettering; Mixed Media; ‡Painting; Photography; Printmaking; ‡Sculpture; Teacher Training; Textile Design.
Summer School: Dir Summer Session Sister Eunice Fluet. Enrl 15; tui $325 for term of 3 wks beginning July 10. Precollege Art Program—a noncredit prog meeting from 9 AM to 12 AM and 1 PM to 4 PM 5 days a week with specific purpose of helping art school aspirants to prepare portfolios for use in application process.

NEW LONDON

COLBY-SAWYER COLLEGE,* Art Department, 03257. Tel: 603-526-2010, exten 229. *Head Dept* Donald L Campbell; Instrs FT 5.
Estab 1928; pvt; D; W; degrees AA 2 yrs, AB 4 yrs; schol; SC 9, LC in History of Art 4; enrl 250.
Courses: Ceramics; Composition; Drawing; Painting; Photography; Printmaking; Sculpture; Three-Dimensional Design; Visual Studies.

PETERBOROUGH

SHARON ARTS CENTER,* RFD 2, Box 361, 03458. Tel: 603-924-3582. *Dir* Carl Jackson; Instrs PT 10.
Estab 1947; pvt; D&E; ent req none; schol; SC 20. Classes yr round.
Courses: Ceramics; Drawing; Fashion Arts; Graphic Arts; Jewelry; Lettering; Painting; Patchwork & Applique; Textile Design; Weaving.
Children's Classes: Courses—Pottery.

PLYMOUTH

PLYMOUTH STATE COLLEGE,* Art Department, 03264. Tel: 603-536-1550, exten 201. *Head Dept* Mary C Taylor; Instrs FT 8.
Estab 1871; pub; D&E; ent req HS grad; references; health record; transcript, SAT, CEEB, ACT; degrees BS and BA 4 yrs; schol; SC 17, LC 8; enrl D 2900, maj 170.
Tuition: Res—$700; Nonres—$2050; campus res $1310 double, $1410 single.
Courses: Art Education; Ceramics; Children's Workshop; Drawing; Graphic Arts; History of Art; Painting; Screen Painting; Sculpture; Teacher Training.
Summer School: Dir Dr Julian Schlager. Tui $35 per cr hr for term of 6 wks. Courses—Varied.

RINDGE

FRANKLIN PIERCE COLLEGE,* Art Department, 03461. Tel: 603-899-5111. Instrs FT 4, PT 2.
Estab 1962; pvt; D&E; ent req HS dipl; degree BA(Creative & Performing Arts) 4 yrs; schol; SC 20, LC 2.
Tuition: Approx $3500; campus res approx $1000.
Courses: Ceramics; Drawing; Glassblowing; Graphics; History of Art; Jewelry & Metalcraft; Painting; Photography; Primitive Woodworking; Sculpture; Stage Design; Stained Glass.
Summer School: Dir Anthony Tremblay.

NEW JERSEY

BLACKWOOD

CAMDEN COUNTY COLLEGE, Department of Art, PO Box 200, 08012. Tel: 609-227-7200. *Chmn Dept Art* William Marlin, EdD; *Asst Prof Art* Joseph Conroy, MFA; *Asst Prof Art* Lawrence Delliho, MA.
Estab 1966; ent req HS dipl or equivalent; degree AA 2 yrs; SC 12, LC 10; enrl 100.

Tuition: Res—$250 per sem; Nonres—$300 per sem.
Courses: Art History; Art Therapy; Calligraphy; Design; Drawing; Lettering; Painting; Sculpture.

CALDWELL

CALDWELL COLLEGE,* Art Department, 07006. Tel: 201-228-4424. *Chmn Dept* Sister M Gerardine; Instrs FT 4, PT 5.
Estab art maj 1964; pvt; D; W; ent req HS grad, ent exam, art portfolio; degree BA 3-4 yrs; schol; SC 24, LC 12; enrl maj 70, dept 90.
Courses: Advertising Design; Aesthetics; Art Education; Ceramics; Commercial Art; Drawing; Graphic Arts; History of Art & Archaeology; General Crafts Workshop includes leather carving, weaving, chip carving, batik, enameling; Jewelry; Lettering; Metal Workshop; Painting; Photography; Sculpture; Teacher Training.
Summer School: Dir Sister M Regina. Term of 3 wks beginning June. Courses—Drawing; Printmaking.

CAMDEN

RUTGERS UNIVERSITY, CAMDEN, Camden College of Arts and Sciences, Art Department, 311 N Fifth St, 08102. Tel: 609-757-6242. *Chmn* John Giannotti; Instrs FT 5, PT 8. Pub; D; ent req HS dipl, must qualify for regular col admis, portfolio; degree BA(Art) 4 yr; SC 24, LC 13; art enrl D 475, maj 90.
Courses: Aesthetics; Bronze Casting; Calligraphy; Ceramics; Drawing; Environmental Design; Etching; Gallery Operations; Graphic Arts; Graphic Design; History of Art & Archeology; Lithography; Painting; Photography; Sculpture; Serigraphy.

CONVENT STATION

COLLEGE OF SAINT ELIZABETH,* Art Department, 07961. Tel: 201-539-1600. *Chmn Dept* Sister Ann Haarer; Instrs FT 3.
Estab 1899, art dept 1956; den; D&E; W; ent req HS dipl, ent exam; degree BA 4 yrs; schol; SC 17, LC 4; enrl D art dept 250, maj 27.
Tuition: $2400 per yr; campus res $1550.
Courses: Art Education; Ceramics; Color & Design; Drafting; Drawing; Graphic Arts; Handicrafts; History of Art & Archaeology; Interior Design; Jewelry; Leather Work; Lettering; Painting; Sand Casting; Sculpture; Stitchery; Teacher Training.
Summer School: Dir Sister Mary Kathleen. Tui $67 per cr for PT students. Courses—Art Education; Painting.

DOVER

COUNTY COLLEGE OF MORRIS,* Art Department, Rte 10, Center Grove Rd, 07801. Tel: 201-361-5000, exten 361. *Head Dept* Dr Joyce R Dorr.
Estab 1970; pub; D&E; ent req HS dipl; degree AA(Humanities/Art) 2 yrs; SC 15, LC 3; enrl maj 263.
Tuition: $400 per yr for Morris County res.
Courses: Advertising Design; Ceramics; Drawing; History of Art & Archaeology; Painting; Photography; Sculpture.

FLEMINGTON

GRAZIANO STUDIOS OF FINE ARTS INC, Summer Art Workshop, RD 3, Box 672, 08822 (Mailing Add: 1413 Highland Ave, Plainfield, NJ 07060). Tel: 201-755-1442. *Dir-Instr* Florence Mercolino Graziano, PhD.
Estab 1968, workshop estab 1974; pvt; E (during summer at Flemington Art Workshop D); ent req individual basis acceptance; enrl 10-15.
Tuition: $85 per wk beginning July 11; no campus res.
Courses: Drawing; Graphic Arts; Mixed Media; Model Painting; Portraiture; Printmaking; Watercolor.

GLASSBORO

GLASSBORO STATE COLLEGE,* Department of Art, Rte 322, 08028. Tel: 609-445-7081. *Chairperson* Daniel Chard; Instrs FT 22, PT 5.
Estab 1925; pub; D&E; ent req HS dipl, ent exam, portfolio and SAT; degrees BA 4 yrs, MA; enrl D 6100, E 5000, maj 300, grad students 100.
Tuition: $660 per yr.
Courses: Aesthetics; Art Education; Batik; Ceramics; Drawing; Enameling; Graphic Arts; Handicrafts; History of Art & Archaeology; Jewelry; Lettering; Painting; Photography; Sculpture; Stage Design; Teacher Training; Textile Design; Theatre Arts.

HACKETTSTOWN

CENTENARY COLLEGE FOR WOMEN,* Fine Arts Division, Art Department, 07840. Tel: 201-852-1400. Instrs FT 2, PT 2.
Estab 1874; pvt; D; W; degree AA(Fine & Applied Arts) 2 yrs; SC 11, LC 2; enrl maj 50, others 365, total 678.

JERSEY CITY

JERSEY CITY STATE COLLEGE,* Art Department, 2039 Kennedy Memorial Blvd, 07305. Tel: 201-547-3214. *Chmn* Raymond Statlander; Instrs FT 22, PT 8.
Estab 1952; pub; D&E; ent req HS dipl; degrees BA 4 yrs, MA; schol; SC 40, LC 15, GC 31; enrl D&E approx 500, maj approx 500, grad students approx 80. Internships in museums, public schools and commercial firms and businesses.
Courses: Advertising Design; Aesthetics; Art Education; Ceramics; Commercial Art; Drawing; Graphic Arts; History of Art; Illustration; Jewelry; Lettering; Painting; Photography; Sculpture; Stage Design; Teacher Training; Textile Design; Theatre Arts; Weaving.
Summer School: Term of 6 wks beginning June 25. Courses—Art & Society; Aesthetics of the Visual Arts; Cultural Resources of the Metropolitan Area; Figure Sculpture/Sculpture Studio; Relief Printing/Intaglio Printing; Special Problems; Weaving/Lettering Design.

SAINT PETER'S COLLEGE,* Fine Arts Department, Kennedy Blvd, 07306. Tel: 201-333-4400, exten 276. *Chmn* Oscar G Magnan; Instrs FT 4, PT 12.
Estab 1963; den; D&E; ent req HS grad; degrees BA, BA in Cursu Classico, BS 4 yrs; schol; SC 4, LC 13; enrl D 650, E 250, maj 20.
Tuition: $70 per cr hr; no campus res.
Courses: Art History; Drawing & Painting; Film; Music; Sculpture.
Summer School: Term of 5 wks beginning June. Courses—Film History; Introduction to Music; Introduction to Visual Arts; Primitive Art; Visual Arts in America.

LAKEWOOD

GEORGIAN COURT COLLEGE, Department of Art, Lakewood Ave, 08701. Tel: 201-364-2200, exten 48. *Prof Art & Head Dept* Sister M Christina Geis, MFA; *Assoc Prof* Douglas L McIlvain, MA; *Asst Prof* Sister M Phyllis Breimayer, MA; *Lectr* Carol Reilly, PhD.
Estab 1908, dept estab 1924; pvt; D; ent req HS dipl, col board scores, portfolio; degree BA 4 yrs; schol; SC 18, LC 11; enrl in dept 220, nonmaj 170, maj 50.
Tuition: Res—Undergrad $3550 per yr; Nonres—Undergrad $2150 per yr; campus res room and board $1250 per yr.
Courses: Advertising Design; Art Education; Art History; Basic Design; Ceramics; Commercial Art; Drafting; Drawing; Fashion Arts; Handicrafts (weaving); History of Art & Archaeology; Illustration; Introduction to Art Therapy; Jewelry; Painting; Photography; Printmaking; Sculpture; Teacher Training.
Summer School: Enrl 30; tui $60-$65 for term of 6 wks beginning June 26. Courses—Ceramics; Painting; Sculpture.

RALYN ART CENTER,* 316 Main St, 08701. Tel: 201-363-7500. *Dir* Ralph F Salisbury; Instrs PT 4.
Estab 1964; pub; D&E; no ent req; no degrees; enrl approx 50.
Courses: Drawing; Oils; Sculpture; Watercolors.
Children's Classes: Enrl approx 30. Courses—Drawing; Painting.

LAWRENCEVILLE

RIDER COLLEGE,* Department of Fine Arts, 08648. Tel: 609-896-0800, exten 385. *Acting Chmn* Larry Capo; Instrs FT 3.
Estab 1966; pvt; D&E; ent req HS dipl; degree BA(Fine Arts) 4 yrs; SC 9, LC 4; enrl D 3500, E 5169 (fall, spring and summer), maj 100.
Tuition: $2550 per yr; campus res $1425 per yr.
Courses: Ceramics; Costume Design & Construction; Drawing; Graphic Arts; Graphic Design; History of Art & Archaeology; Painting; Sculpture; Stage Design.
Summer School: Dir Dominick A Iorio.

LAYTON

PETERS VALLEY CRAFTSMEN, INC, Star Rte, 07851. Tel: 201-948-5200. *Exec Dirs* Judy and Dennis McCarthy; Resident Artists, Dick Sexstone, Barbara Mail, Thom Collins, Tom Neugebauer, Wendy Holmes, Suzanne Adams, Bob Margh and Howard Werner; vis artists—Bob Natalini, fine metals and Sandy Noyes, photography; Instrs PT 60.
Estab 1970; pvt; D; ent req previous craft experience for some courses; no degrees granted; enrl 350; internship—fall, winter, spring; weekend workshops—fall, spring.
Tuition: Summer School $75 weekly; campus res room and board $70-$80 weekly.
Courses: Blacksmithing; Ceramics; Fabric Printing; Goldsmithing; Jewelry; Mixed Media; Photography; Silversmithing; Weaving; Woodworking.

MADISON

DREW UNIVERSITY,* Art Department, 07940. *Chmn* Martyvonne Dehoney; Instrs FT 3, PT 5.
Estab 1866; pvt; D; ent req HS dipl, ent exam; degree BA 4 yrs; schol; SC 12, LC 14; dept enrl D 230, E 40.
Courses: Aesthetics; Ceramics; Drawing; History of Art & Archaeology; Intaglio & Relief; Lithography & Silk Screen; Painting; Photography; Sculpture.
New York Semester on Art. Evening Printmaking Workshops in cooperation with The Printmaking Council of NJ; noncredit.
Summer School: Dean & Dir Robert K Ackerman. Courses—Art Appreciation; Studios.

MONTCLAIR

MONTCLAIR ART MUSEUM, Art School, 3 South Mountain Ave (Mailing Add: PO Box X, 07042). Tel: 201-746-5555. *Dir* Kathryn E Gamble; *Registr* Patricia P Barnes; *Instrs* Frances McQuillan, Tom Vincent, Paul Ortlip, Tim Gaydos, Miriam Beerman and Edwin Havas; *Children's Classes Instr* Deborah Healy, Grant Peterson and Diana S Naspo.
Art sch estab 1924; pvt; D&E; ent req desire to study art; no degree or cert granted; schol; SC 17; enrl D 150 per term, E 50 per term.
Tuition: Young People $40 for 12 sessions; Adults $65 for 12 sessions.
Courses: Aesthetics; Art Education; Collage; Constructions; Drawing; Graphic Arts; Graphic Design; Mixed Media; Painting; Printmaking; Sculpture; Watercolor.

MONTCLAIR STATE COLLEGE,* Fine Arts Department, 07043. Tel: 201-893-4308. *Dean* Dr Donald Mintz; *Chmn* Dr Charles Martens; Instrs FT 26, PT 8.
Estab 1908; pub; ent req HS grad and exam, interview, portfolio; degrees BA 4 yrs, MA; state schol and other schol to res; SC 35, LC 18; enrl maj 300, grad maj 175.
Courses: Art Education; Art History; Ceramics; Drawing; Filmmaking; Metalwork; Jewelry; Painting; Photography; Printmaking; Sculpture; Textiles; Theatre Arts; TV as Art; Urban Cultural Design.

NEW BRUNSWICK

RUTGERS, THE STATE UNIVERSITY OF NEW JERSEY, Federated College Departments, 08903. Tel: 201-932-1766. *Chmn* Dr Bille Pickard-Pritchard.
—**Cook College,*** Department of Landscape Architecture, Blake Hall. Tel: 201-932-9317. *Chmn* Roy H DeBoer.
Courses: Film & Video; Landscape Architecture.
—**Douglass College,*** Walters Hall. Tel: 201-932-9856, 932-9857. *Acting Chmn* Virginia L Bush; Instrs FT 15, PT 12.
Estab 1918; W; Degrees BS(Studio, Educ, Art Hist) 4 yrs; schol; SC 28, LC 27; enrl 1000, maj 150.
Courses: Art Education; Ceramics; Design; Drawing; Environmental Art; Film & Video; Graphics; History of Art; Mixed Media; Painting; Photography.
—**Livingston College,*** Lucy Stone Hall. Tel: 201-932-4160, 932-4161. *Acting Chmn* Robert Cook; Instrs FT 15, PT 8.
Estab 1969; degrees BA(Studio, Educ, Art Hist) 4 yrs; schol; SC 37, LC 16; enrl 1000, maj 190.
Courses: Art Education; Ceramics; Commercial Art; Crafts; Design; Drawing; Environmental Art; Film & Video; Glassblowing; Graphics; History of Art; Performance; Photography; Weaving.
—**Mason Gross School of the Arts,** Graduate Program in Visual Arts, 358 George St. Tel: 201-932-9289. *Dean* John Bettenbender, MFA; *Assoc Prof Art & Acting Grad Dir* Markel Bruce Berger, MFA; *Prof* Leon Golub, MFA; *Prof* John Lake Goodyear, MDes; *Assoc Prof* Gary Kuehn, MFA; *Prof* Daniel Newman, BA; *Prof* Bille Pickard-Pritchard, PhD; *Assoc Prof* Peter Stroud, MFA.
Estab 1766; sch estab 1976; pub; D; ent req HS dipl, BFA or equivalent, portfolio; degree MFA 2 yrs; schol; SC 26, LC 10, GC 37; enrl 60, grad 60.
Tuition: Res—Grad $540 per sem; Nonres—Grad $780 per sem; campus res $900 per yr.
Courses: Ceramics; Conceptual Art; Drawing; Film; Intermedia; Mixed Media; Painting; Photography; Printmaking; Sculpture; Video.

—**Rutgers College,** * Voorhees Hall. Tel: 201-932-7041, 932-7839. *Chmn* Matthew Baigell; Instrs FT 12, PT 15.
Estab 1766; degree BA(Studio, Educ, Art Hist) 4 yrs; schol; SC 32, LC 33; enrl 1000, maj 125.
Tuition: Res—$300 per term; Nonres—$600 per term.
Courses: Art & the Computer; Art Education; Drawing; Film & Video; Foundry/Metal; Graphic Arts; History of Art; New Materials & Techniques Design; Painting; Photography.
—**University College,** * Humanities Department, New Jersey Hall. Tel: 201-932-7239. *Chmn* William Walling.
Courses: Art History.
—**Graduate Program in Art History,** Voorhees Hall. Tel: 201-932-7041. *Dir* Martin Eidelberg, PhD; *Primary Art Faculty* Dr Matthew Baigell; Dr Olga Berendsen; Dr John Kenfield; Dr Elizabeth McLachlan; Dr Barbara Lane; Dr Joan Marter; Dr Tod Marder; Dr Jack Spector; Dr James Stubblebine.
Estab 1766, prog estab 1970; pub; D; degrees MA 2 yrs, PhD approx 5 yrs; schol; GC 15 per yr; enrl grad 60.
Tuition: Res—Grad $35 per cr hr; Nonres—Grad $45 per cr hr; campus res.
Courses: ‡History of Art & Archaeology.

NEWARK

NEWARK SCHOOL OF FINE AND INDUSTRIAL ART,* 550 High St, 07102. Instrs D PT 42, E PT 28.
Estab 1882; pub; 3-4 yrs; enrl D 300, E 300.
Courses: Advertising Design; Ceramics; Fashion Illustration; Fine Arts; Industrial Design; Interior Design; Painting; Pictorial Illustration; Sculpture; Textile Design.

RUTGERS UNIVERSITY, NEWARK,* Newark College of Arts and Sciences, Art Department, Bradley Hall, 392 High St, 07103. *Prof Art & Chmn Dept* Vivian E Browne; Instrs FT 6, PT 3.
Pub; D; ent req HS dipl, or as specified by col and univ; degree BA 4 yrs; schol; sem enrl D 486, maj 102.
Courses: Aesthetics; Art Education; Ceramics; Drawing; Environmental Design; Graphic Arts; History of Art & Archaeology; Painting; Photography; Sculpture; Teacher Training.
Summer School: Courses offered vary from year to year.

NUTLEY

NUTLEY ART CENTER, 200 Chestnut St, 07110. Tel: 201-661-2280. *Owner-Dir* Vivian Noyes Fikus, Commercial Artist; *Teacher* Clara Karlan, Design; *Teacher* William Yeager, Teaching Degree; *Teacher* Evelyn Riddle; *Teacher* Marie Hochman.
Estab 1969; pvt; D&E; no ent req; no degrees granted; schol; SC 6; enrl D 40, E 25.
Tuition: Adults $33 - $35 per term (7 sessions); Children $21 - $28 per term (7 sessions).
Courses: Commercial Art; Drawing; Graphic Arts; Graphic Design; Handicrafts (macrame, puppetry); Illustration; Lettering; Mixed Media; Painting; Portraiture; Printmaking; Sculpture; Teacher Training.
Summer School: Tui $25 for term of 4 wks beginning July and Aug.
Courses—Drawing; Painting; Crafts; Portraiture; Beginners Sculpture.

OCEAN CITY

CULTURAL ARTS CENTER OF OCEAN CITY, 409 Wesley Ave, 08226. Tel: 609-399-7628 or 399-6111, exten 280. *Exec Dir* Frances J Taylor; *Head Teaching Staff* Lorraine Watson; *Instr* Ray Dougherty, MFA; *Instr* Florence Deeley, BFA; *Instr* Shirley Waldron, BA; *Instr* Linda Cliff, BA; *Instr* Phoebe Shih; *Instr* Willard S Randall.
Estab 1966; pub; D&E; no ent req; SC 40, LC 1; enrl D 400, E 400.
Tuition: Approx $40 per course; no campus res.
Courses: Acrylics; Art History; Ceramics; Chinese Brush; Drawing; Macrame; Mixed Media; Painting; Photography; Sculpture; Sumi; Watercolor; Woodcarving.
Adult Hobby Classes: Tui $40 per class.
Children's Classes: Enrl 235 (1977); tui $35 per class. Courses—Young Peoples Art; Pottery for Young People; Macrame for Young People.
Summer School: Tui $40 for term of 4-6 wks beginning June.

OCEAN CITY SCHOOL OF ART, 409 Wesley Ave, 08226. Tel: 609-399-7628 or 399-6111, exten 280. *Exec Dir* Frances J Taylor; *Head Teaching Staff* Lorraine Watson; *Instr* Jacqueline Davidson; *Instrs* Attilio Sinagra; *Instr* William Hopkins; *Instr* Scott Griswold; *Instrs* Dorothy Pere; *Instr* Martin Jackson; vis instr—Oliver Grimley, drawing, 6 wks.
Estab 1974; pvt; D&E; no ent req; Cert 3 yrs; schol; SC 14, LC 1; enrl D 1, E 8.
Tuition: $480 per yr, $160 per sem.

Courses: Art History; Ceramics; Chinese Brush; Drawing; Mixed Media; Painting; Photography; Portrait; Sculpture; Sumi; Watercolor.
Summer School: *Exec Dir* Frances J Taylor. Courses—Same classes offered during summer plus workshops and demonstrations.

PRINCETON

PRINCETON UNIVERSITY, 08540. Tel: 609-452-3000.
Pvt; degrees 4 yrs; schol and fel.
—**Department of Art and Archaeology,** 104 McCormick Hall. Tel: 609-452-3780. *Prof Art & Archaeol & Chmn Dept* John Rupert Martin, PhD; *Prof* David R Coffin, PhD; *Prof* Robert Koch, PhD; *Prof* Sam Hunter, MFA; *Prof* John Plummer, PhD; *Prof* Richard Barnhart, PhD; *Prof & Chmn Prog Classical Archaeol* T Leslie Shear, PhD; *Prof & Chmn Prog Chinese & Japanese Art & Archaeol* Wen Fong, PhD.
Estab 1746; pvt; degrees AB, MFA, PhD; schol; LC 14, GC 9; enrl 761, maj 35, grad 50.
Tuition: Res—Undergrad $4650 per yr, grad $4750 per yr; campus res room and board $1705 per yr; total budget $7495 per yr.
Courses: Art History; History of Art & Archaeology; Program II, the Visual Arts Program, offered to undergraduates only, and in conjunction with art history department and course work.
—**School of Architecture and Urban Planning,** * Architecture Bldg. *Dean* Robert L Geddes; Instrs FT 20
Estab 1919; pvt; D; high ent req; degrees AB, 4 yrs, MArch, MArch & Urban Planning, PhD(Arch), PhD(Urban Planning); schol and fel; Sc 6, LC 13, GC 6, seminars 17; new degrees in urban planning; enrl undergrad 120, grad 50.

RIDGEWOOD

RIDGEWOOD SCHOOL OF ART AND DESIGN, 83 Chestnut St, 07450. Tel: 201-444-7100. *Dir* Robert Crawford.
Estab 1961; pvt; D&E; ent req HS dipl; SC 35, LC 2; enrl D 150, E 50.
Tuition: $1800 per yr; no campus res.
Courses: Advertising Design; Art History; Ceramics; Commercial Art; Drawing; Fashion Arts; Graphic Design; Illustration; Lettering; Painting; Photography; Printmaking; Sculpture.

SOUTH ORANGE

SETON HALL UNIVERSITY, Department of Art and Music, South Orange Ave, 07079. Tel: 201-762-9000. *Chmn* Petra T D Chu, PhD; *Prof* Louis de Crenascol, LDD; *Asst Prof* Barbara Kaufman, MA; *Asst Prof* Edwin Havas; *Asst Prof* Anthony Triano; *Asst Prof* William K Burno, MA; *Asst Prof* F Ming Chang; *Prof* Julius Zsaho, PhD; Instrs FT 8, PT 6.
Estab dept 1968; pvt; D&E; degrees BA 4 years; SC 8.
Courses: Architecture; Art History; Commercial Art; Drawing; Illustration; Mixed Media; Painting; Sculpture.

TRENTON

TRENTON STATE COLLEGE, Art Department, Pennington Rd, 08625. Tel: 609-771-2652. *Prof Art & Chmn Dept* Norval C Kern, EdD; *Prof* Henry Ahrens, EdD; *Prof* Howard Goldstein, EdD; *Prof* Joseph Shannon, EdD; *Asst Prof* Wendell Brooks, MFA; *Asst Prof* Christina Craig, MA; *Assoc Prof* Ilse Johnson, MFA; *Asst Prof* Charles Kumnick, MFA; *Asst Prof* Mark Lehman, MFA; *Asst Prof* Hiroshi Murata, MFA; *Asst Prof* Bruce Rigby, MFA; Instrs FT 16, PT 12.
Estab 1855; pub; D&E; ent req HS dipl; degree BA 4 yrs; schol; SC approx 40, LC 10, GC 11; enrl nonmaj 300, maj 450.
Courses: ‡Advertising Design; ‡Art Education; Art History; ‡Art Therapy; Calligraphy; Ceramics; Drawing; Fashion Arts; Graphic Arts; Illustration; ‡Interior Design; Jewelry; Lettering; Painting; Photography; Printmaking; Sculpture; Silversmithing; Teacher Training; Textile Design.

UNION

KEAN COLLEGE OF NEW JERSEY, Fine Arts Department, Morris Ave, 07083. Tel: 201-527-2307. *Chmn Fine Arts Dept* Robert B Coon, EdD; *Coordr Interior Design* H Bernard Lipscomb III, MA; *Coordr Art Educ* Pearl Greenbert, EdD; *Coordr Visual Commun* W Martin Holloway, MFA; *Coordr Specialized Studio* Leonard Pierro, MA; *Coordr Art Hist* Virginia Stotz, MA; Faculty FT 22.
Estab 1855; pub; D&E; ent req HS dipl, portfolio interview for art maj; degree BA 4 yrs; schol; SC 58, LC 37, GC 24; enrl FT 383, PT 236, maj 656, grad 37.
Tuition: Res—$704 per yr, $352 per sem; Nonres—$1408 per yr, $704 per sem; campus res and board $1549 per yr.

Courses: Advertising Design; Aesthetics; ‡Art Education; ‡Art History; Ceramics; ‡Commercial Art; Display; Drafting; Drawing; Film; Graphic Arts; Graphic Design; Illustration; ‡Interior Design; Jewelry; Lettering; Museum Staff Training; Occupational Therapy; Painting; Photography; Printmaking; Sculpture; Textile Design.
Summer School: Asst Dir Mrs Madsen. Tui $22 per cr for term of 6 wks beginning June 26. Courses—Introduction to Art; Drawing; Two and Three-Dimensional Design; Life Drawing; Sculpture; Painting; Printmaking; Jewelry; Ceramics; Lettering; Introduction to Interior Design; Art in Education; Watercolor; Art History; Pre-Columbian Art.

WAYNE

WILLIAM PATERSON COLLEGE,* Division of Fine and Performing Arts, Art Department, 300 Pompton Rd, 07470. Tel: 201-881-2402. Instrs FT 20, PT 2.
Dept estab 1958; pub; degree BA 4 yrs; SC 9, LC 9; enrl maj undergrad 160, grad 65, E nonmaj 150.
Courses: Ceramics; Drawing; Enameling; Graphic Arts; Jewelry; Lapidary; Mechanical Drawing; Metal; Painting; Photography; Sculpture; Teacher Training; Textile Design; Theatre Arts.
Summer School: Term of 6 wks beginning June.

WEST LONG BRANCH

MONMOUTH COLLEGE, Department of Art, Norwood & Cedar Aves, 07764. Tel: 201-222-6600, exten 346. *Chmn Dept Art* Arie van Everdingen, MFA; *Assoc Prof* Vincent DiMattio, MFA; *Asst Prof* Carolyn Bloomer, MA; *Asst Prof* Edward Jankowski, MFA; *Assoc Prof* Alfred Provencher, MA; *Assoc Prof* Martin Ryan, MA; *Instr* David Stanley, MA.
Estab 1933; pvt; D&E; ent req HS dipl, portfolio for transfer students; degrees BA(Art), BFA and BA(Art Educ) 4 yrs; schol; SC 25, LC 8; enrl in dept D 108, E 6, nonmaj 80, maj 108, audits 6.
Tuition: $2950 per yr, $1475 per sem, $89-$91 per cr hr; campus res room and board $600.
Courses: Aesthetics; Appreciation of Art; ‡Art Education; Art History; ‡Ceramics, Drawing; Goldsmithing; Graphic Arts; Handicrafts (macrame, papermaking); History of Art & Archaeology; ‡Painting; Photography; Printmaking; ‡Sculpture; Silversmithing; Teacher Training.
Summer School: Dean Kenneth C Streibig. Enrl approx 80; tui $89 per cr hr for 3 or 6 wk courses beginning June 5. Courses—Art Appreciation; Painting; Sculpture; Ceramics; History of Art; Crafts; Studio Art for Non-Art Majors; Independent Study; The Creative Process.

NEW MEXICO

ALBUQUERQUE

AMERICAN CLASSICAL COLLEGE, 614 Indian School Rd NW, 87102. Tel: 505-843-7749. *Dir* Dr C M Flumiani; *Instrs* FT 2.
Estab 1970; pvt; D; ent req ent exam; 3 yrs; no degrees; schol.
Tuition: FT $100 mo.
Courses: Advertising Design; Aesthetics; Art Education; Commercial Art; Drawing; History of Art & Archaeology; Painting; Sculpture.

SOUTHWESTERN SCHOOL OF ART, 1504 B Wyoming NE, 87112. Tel: 505-299-0316. *Owner-Dir* Ted C Hogsett, BS; *Asst Dir* Doug Dean; *Teacher* Anne Gordon; *Teacher* Helen Weaver, MA; *Teacher* Tina Fuentes, MA.
Estab 1974; pvt; D&E; no ent req; cert; SC 7, LC 8; enrl D 20, E 46; eight wk course starting Apr 10 and ending June 3, 1978.
Tuition: Eight wk sessions $35 plus tax; children's classes eight wk sessions $25 plus tax; no campus res.
Courses: Art History; Drawing; Painting; Printmaking.

UNIVERSITY OF NEW MEXICO
—**College of Fine Arts,** 87131. Tel: 505-277-2111. *Acting Dean Col* Donald C McRae, MA.
Estab 1935; pub.
—**Department of Art.** Tel: 505-277-5861. *Chmn Dept* Nicolai Cikovsky, Jr, PhD; dept has vis profs.
D&E; ent req HS dipl; degrees BA and BFA 4 yrs, MA(Studio) 2 yrs, MFA 3 yrs, MA(Art Hist) 2 yrs, PhD 3 yrs; SC 50, LC 39, GC 49; enrl D 806, nonmaj 200, maj 606, grad 150.
Tuition: Res—undergrad $260 per sem, grad $246 per sem; Nonres—undergrad $758 per sem, grad $744 per sem; campus res room and board.
Courses: Art Education (with Col of Educ); Art History; Ceramics; Drawing; Jewelry; Painting; Photography; Printmaking; Sculpture.
Summer School: Term of 8 wks beginning approx June 1.

—**Tamarind Institute,** 108 Cornell Ave SE. Tel: 505-277-3901. *Dir* Clinton Adams; *Tech Dir* John Sommers, Tamarind Master Printer; *Studio Mgr* Stephen Britko, Tamarind Master Printer; *Asst Dir* Judith Booth.
The Institute is a professional lithography workshop with a 2 yrs program leading to certificate as Tamarind Master Printer; vis artists; research; and publications.
Tuition: Res—$21.50 - $24; Nonres—$63 - $71.50.
—**School of Architecture.** Tel: 505-277-2903. *Dean* Morton Hoppenfeld; Instrs FT 10, PT 3.
Degrees 4 & 6 yrs; SC 23, LC 10, GC 6; enrl 400.

LAS CRUCES

NEW MEXICO STATE UNIVERSITY, College of Arts and Sciences, Art Department, Box 3572, 88003. Tel: 505-646-1705. *Prof Art & Head Dept* Christiane L Joost-Gaugier, PhD; *Prof* Peter Voris, MFA; *Prof* Lee Richards, EdD; *Prof* W C Miles, MFA; *Prof* Richard Wickstrom, MFA; *Prof* Ken Barrick, MA; *Prof* John Moffitt, PhD; vis prof—John Torreano, every spring; Instrs PT 4.
Estab 1975; pub; D&E; ent req HS dipl; degrees BA, BFA and BS(Art Educ) 4 yrs, MA(Studio), MA(Art Hist) and MS(Art Educ) 2 yrs; SC 52, LC 25, GC 53; enrl maj 100, grad 22.
Tuition: Res—$608 per yr, $304 per sem; Nonres—$1744 per yr $872 per sem.
Courses: Architecture; Art Education; Art History; Ceramics; Commercial Art; Conceptual Art; Drawing; Graphic Arts; Graphic Design; Handicrafts (weaving); History of Art & Archaeology; Jewelry; Museum Staff Training; Painting; Photography; Printmaking; Sculpture; Silversmithing.
Summer School: Tui $105 for term of 6 wks. Courses—Drawing; Painting; Ceramics; Sculpture; Art Appreciation.

LAS VEGAS

NEW MEXICO HIGHLANDS UNIVERSITY, Department of Fine Arts, 87701. Tel: 505-425-711, exten 359. *Chmn Dept Fine Arts* Grady Greene, PhD; *Prof* Ray Drew, MA; *Prof* Harry M Leippe, MA; *Asst Prof* Carolyn Powers, MA; *Asst Prof* Benton Patten, EdD; *Asst Prof* Nancy Rosnow, MFA.
Estab 1898; pub; D&E; ent req HS dipl, ACT, Early Admis Prog, GED; degrees BA 4 yrs, MA 1 yr; schol; Sc 24, LC 8, GC 12; enrl nonmaj approx 55, maj 51, grad 4.
Tuition: Res—$348 per yr, $116 per quarter; Nonres—$1056 per yr, $352 per quarter; campus res room and board.
Courses: Art Education; Art History; Calligraphy; Ceramics; Constructions; Drawing; Graphic Arts; Jewelry; Lettering; Painting; Photography; Printmaking; Sculpture; Silversmithing; Stage Design; Teacher Training; Theatre Arts.
Adult Hobby Classes: Courses—Weaving; Painting; Ceramics.
Summer School: Dean Dr Sigfredo Maestas. Tui same as above. Courses—Mostly studio plus core curriculum, depending upon staffing.

PORTALES

EASTERN NEW MEXICO UNIVERSITY, Department of Art and Education, 88130. Tel: 505-562-2652. *Head Dept* Chris Gikas; Instrs FT 4, PT 4.
Estab 1934; pub; D&E; ent req HS grad with C average or GED, ACT; degrees BA, BS and BUnivStudies 4 yrs; schol; SC and LC 52, GC 19; enrl FT 4000.
Tuition: Fees (12 or more hrs) res—$234.50 per sem; Nonres—$518 per sem; room and board $445 per sem.
Courses: Art Education; Commercial Art; Fine Arts; Painting; Sculpture.
Summer School: Dir Chris Gikas; 8 wks.

RUIDOSO

CARRIZO ART AND CRAFT WORKSHOPS, Carrizo Canyon Rd (Mailing Add; PO Drawer A, 88345). Tel: 505-257-2375. *Dir* Hilma Greggerson Collier, MS; Instrs PT 20.
Estab 1956; pvt; D; ent req art interest; SC 19; enrl 300; Summer School.
Tuition: $90 to $165 for 2 wk workshop; campus res room and board $140 to $270 for 2 wks.
Courses: Calligraphy; Goldsmithing; Jewelry; Mixed Media; Painting; Sculpture; Silversmithing; Stained Glass.
Adult Hobby Classes: Tui $125 for 2 wks. Courses—Stained Glass.

SANTA FE

BARNA POTTERY,* Tesuque Dr, 87574. Tel: 505-982-8232. *Dir* Iris Barna; Instrs FT 2, PT 4.

Estab 1960; pvt; D&E; ent req HS dipl; SC 3.
Tuition: No campus res.
Courses: Aesthetics; Ceramics; Display; History of Art & Archaeology; Needle Work; Sculpture.
Apprenticeship in European Style Pottery, 1 yr, room and part board.

COLLEGE OF SANTA FE, Visual Arts Department, St Michael's Dr, 87501. Tel: 505-982-6011. *Dir Visual Arts Dept* Winona Garmhausen, MFA; *Primary Art Faculty:* Ronald Berger, MFA; Leona Zastrow, MA; Meridel Rubenstein, MFA; Ruth Askans, BFA.
Estab 1947, dept estab 1974; pvt; D&E; ent req HS dipl or GED; degree BA(Visual Arts); schol; SC 26, LC 20; enrl D 150, E 50, nonmaj 50, maj 100, others 20 sr citizens.
Tuition: $57 per sem hr plus general fees; campus res room and board $280-$410 per yr.
Courses: ‡Art Education; ‡Art History; Ceramics; Drawing; Goldsmithing; Handicrafts (weaving, woodcarving; woodworking); Jewelry; Painting; Photography; Printmaking; Sculpture; Silversmithing; Teacher Training.
Summer School: Dir Winona Garmhausen. Enrl 60; tui $57 per sem hr for term of 4 or 8 wks beginning May 15. Courses—Drawing; Painting; Printmaking; Outdoor Sketching; Art History; Photography; Jewelry.

INSTITUTE OF AMERICAN INDIAN ARTS,* Cerrillos Rd, 87501. Tel: 505-988-3261. *Arts Dir* Henry Gobin; Instrs FT 12.
Estab 1962; pvt; D; ent req HS dipl; degree AA(Fine Arts) 2 yrs; SC 18, LC 11; enrl 263.
Courses: Advertising Design; Ceramics; Commercial Art; Costume Design & Construction; Drawing; Fashion Arts; Graphic Arts; Graphic Design; Handicrafts; History of Art & Archaeology; Jewelry; Lettering; Museum Staff Training; Painting; Sculpture; Traditional Indian Techniques; Two & Three-Dimensional Design.

SANTA FE WORKSHOPS OF CONTEMPORARY ART, Box 1344, 87501. Tel: 505-983-5573. *Adv Dir* Geraldine Price, BFA; Instrs PT 9.
Estab 1959, Santa Fe 1971; pvt nonprofit; D; ent req age 18 or over; credit for each 8 wks of study; schol; SC 6, LC 2, GC 8; classes held year-round.
Tuition: $500 each 8 wks, PT $25 per wk; campus res.
Courses: Art Therapy; Drawing; Painting; Photography; Printmaking; Sculpture; Silk Screen; Teacher Training; Video; Weaving.

SILVER CITY

WESTERN NEW MEXICO UNIVERSITY, Department of Art, College Ave, 88061. Tel: 505-538-6517. *Acting Chmn Dept Art* Cecil Howard, MFA; *Prof* Dorothy McCray, MFA; *Prof* Gary Core, MFA; *Prof* Polly Hughes, MA; vis artists and teachers during the summers.
Pub; D&E; ent req HS dipl; degrees BA and BS 4 yrs; SC 10, LC 7; enrl D 200, nonmaj 160, maj 40.
Tuition: Campus res room and board.
Courses: Aesthetics; Art Education; Art History; ‡Ceramics; Collage; Constructions; Drawing; Graphic Design; Handicrafts (weaving, stained glass); ‡Jewelry; Mixed Media; ‡Painting; ‡Printmaking; ‡Sculpture; Silversmithing; Teacher Training; Textile Design.
Adult Hobby Classes: Courses—Ceramics; Stained Glass; Lapidary; Silversmithing.
Summer School: Dir Summer Sessions Dr Phill Cook. Courses—Ceramics; Weaving; Metalsmithing; Glassblowing; Painting.

NEW YORK

ALBANY

COLLEGE OF ST ROSE, Division of Art, Western Ave, 12203. Tel: 518-471-5185. *Chmn* Patricia Clahassey, EdD; *Primary Faculty* Karene Faul, MFA; Edward McCartan, MA; Leonard LaRoux, MFA; Margaret M O'Donnell, MA; Paul Mauren, MFA.
Estab 1920, dept estab 1970; pvt; D&E; ent req HS dipl, SAT or ACT, rank in top 2/5 of class; degrees BS(Art) and BS(Art Educ) 4 yr, MS in Art Educ; schol; SC 21, LC 7, GC 8; enrl nonmaj 200, maj 111, GS 14.
Tuition: Undergrad $2310 per yr, $1165 per sem, $75 per cr hr; grad $77.50 per cr hr; campus res room and board $1340.
Courses: Advertising Design; Aesthetics; ‡Art Education; Art History; Calligraphy; Ceramics; ‡Drawing; Graphic Arts; Handicrafts (fibers, weaving); Illustration; Jewelry; ‡Painting; Photography; ‡Printmaking; Sculpture; Teacher Training.
Adult Hobby Classes: Enrl 20; tui $57.50 per cr hr. Courses—some continuing education courses ea sem.

JUNIOR COLLEGE OF ALBANY, Fine Arts Division, 12208. Tel: 518-445-1711. *Chmn* Martin J Gieschen, MFA; *Primary Faculty* Jesse Collins, MFA; Ruth Funk, MA; Willie Marlowe, MFA; Frances Martin, MA; Timothy Martin, MFA; William Schade, MFA; Leo Bouchard; William Claus, MA; William Kammer, BA.
Estab 1957, dept estab 1970; pvt; D&E; ent req HS dipl, references, records, SAT; degrees AA, AS and AAS 2 yr; schol; SC 43, LC 16 (art); enrl D 867 (total), 156 (art), E 823 (total).
Tuition: $1930 per yr; no campus res.
Courses: Advertising Design; Art Education; Art History; Ceramics; Commercial Art; Drawing; Graphic Arts; Graphic Design; Handicrafts (weaving); Illustration; Interior Design; Jewelry; Mixed Media; Painting; Photography; Printmaking; Sculpture; Serigraphy; Special Education; State Design; Theatre Arts.
Summer School: Dir Dean Laura Evans. Courses—varies.

STATE UNIVERSITY OF NEW YORK AT ALBANY, Art Dept, 1400 Washington Ave, 12222. Tel: 518-457-8487. *Chmn Dept* Richard Callner, MAFA; *Prof* Richard Stankieqica; *Prof* Dennis Byng, MS; *Prof* Thom O'Connor, MFA; *Prof* Mojmir Frinta, MFA; *Prof* William Wilson, MFA; *Prof* Edward Cowley, MA; *Assoc Prof* Robert Cartmell, MFA.
Estab 1848; pub; D&E ent req HS dipl and portfolio; degrees BA (36 hr major), 4 yrs, BA (60 hr maj), 4 yr; MA (30 hr maj), 1½ yr: schol; SC 43, LC 20, GC 33; enrl D 750, E 400, nonmaj 600, maj 150, grad 45.
Tuition: Res—Undergrad $3100-$3250 yr, $25 credit, $1800-$2000 for commuter, grad 4700 per sem, $58.50 hr; Nonres—Undergrad $3650-$3850 yr, $40 cr hr, grad $900 per sem, $75 hr; campus residence room and board $740 per yr.
Courses: Aesthetics; Art History; Calligraphy; Collage; Constructions; ‡Drafting; History of Art & Archaeology; Intermedia; Mixed Media; ‡Painting; ‡Photography; ‡Printmaking; ‡Sculpture; Theatre Arts; Plastics.
Adult Hobby Classes: Courses—All studio areas.
Summer School: Asst Dean Grad Studies Paul Saimond. Enrl 350; term of 3 - 6 wk beginning July 1.

ALFRED

NEW YORK STATE COLLEGE OF CERAMICS AT ALFRED UNIVERSITY,* Division of Art & Design, 14802. Tel: 607-871-2442. *Head Dept* Tony Hepburn; Instrs FT 20.
Estab 1900, degrees BFA and MFA 4 yr; enrl maj undergrad 250, grad 25, others 250. Two yr of foundation study and two yr of upper level studio.
Courses: Art Education; Ceramics; Design; Glass; Painting; Photography; Printmaking; Sculpture.
Summer School: Dean Lewis Butler.

AMHERST

DAEMEN COLLEGE, Art Department, 14226. Tel: 716-839-3600, exten 241. *Head Dept & Assoc Prof* Margaret E Bacon, EdD; *Prof* Sister M Jeanne File, PhD; *Prof* James K Y Kuo, MA; *Assoc Prof* James A Allen, MFA; *Assoc Prof* Dennis Barraclough, MFA; *Asst Prof* Bruce E Marzahn, MFA; *Asst Prof* Carol Townsend, MFA; *Asst Prof* Elizabeth Simon, MFA; *Adj Prof* J Carl Burke, MFA.
Estab 1947; pvt; D&E; ent req HS·dipl, art portfolio; degrees BFA (Ceramics, Graphic Design, Painting, Printmaking, Sculpture), BS(Art) and BS(Art Educ) 4 yr; SC 55; enrl D 1200, nonmaj 1100, maj 100.
Tuition: Res—Undergrad $2087.50 per sem, $82 per cr hr; Nonres—Undergrad $1337.50 per sem, $82 per cr hr; campus res room and board $1500.
Courses: Advertising Design; Aesthetics; Art Education; Art History; Calligraphy; Ceramics; Commercial Art; Drawing; Graphic Arts; Graphic Design; Handicrafts (fibers); Museum Staff Training; Painting; Photography; Printmaking; Sculpture; Silversmithing; Teacher Training; Theatre Arts.
Summer School: Dir Terry Brancato.

ANNANDALE-ON-HUDSON

BARD COLLEGE,* Division of Art, Music, Drama & Dance, 12504. Tel: 914-758-6072. *Chmn & Dir Proctor Art Center* Matt Phillips; *Chmn Drama & Dance* William Driver; *Chmn Music* Benjamin A Boretz; Instrs FT 8, PT12
Estab 1865; pvt; degree BA 4 yr; schol; enrl 600.
Courses: Criticism & History of Art; Drawing; Painting; Printmaking; Sculpture; Stage Design; Woodcut.

AURORA

WELLS COLLEGE, Department of Art, Division of the Arts, 13026. Tel: 315-364-7232. *Div Chmn* Nancy Wynn, MA; *Prof* Sheila Edmunds, PhD; *Prof* Hannelore Glasser, PhD; *Assoc Prof* William E Roberts Jr, MA; *Instr.* Pat Knadjian, MFA.
Estab 1868; pvt; D; ent req HS dipl; credit-by-examination programs; degrees BA 4 yr; SC 19, LC 20; enrl D 500 (total), nonmaj 122, maj 18.
Tuition: Res—Undergrad $5190 per yr; Nonres—Undergrad $3480 per yr; campus res.
Courses: Aesthetics; ‡Art History; Ceramics; ‡Drawing; Film; ‡History of Art and Archaeology; ‡Painting; Photography; Printmaking; Teacher Training; ‡Theatre Arts.

BAYSIDE

QUEENSBOROUGH COMMUNITY COLLEGE, Department of Art and Design, 11364. Tel: 212-631-6395. *Chmn & Assoc Prof* Dr Lola B Gellman, PhD; *Assoc Prof* Priva Gross, PhM; *Assoc Prof* John Hawkins, MFA; *Lectr* Robert Rogers, BA; *Assoc Prof* Paul Tschinkel, MFA; *Asst Prof* Kenneth Walpuck, PhD; *Asst Prof* Heinz Wipfler, MA.
Estab 1958, dept estab 1978; pub; D&E; ent req HS dipl, placement exams; degrees AA, AS and AAS; schol; SC 21, LC 14; enrl D 9000, E 4000.
Tuition: Res—Undergrad $387.50 per sem, $35 per cr; Nonres—Undergrad $712.50 per sem, $55 per cr; no campus res.
Courses: Advertising Design; Art History; Ceramics; Color Theory; Design (2nd and 3rd dimensional); Drawing; History of Art and Archaeology; Painting; Photography; Sculpture.
Adult Hobby Classes: Enrl 15; tui $40 to $60 per course. Courses—Antiques; Arts & Crafts for Children; Calligraphy; Interior Design; Jewelry; Stained Glass.
Summer School: Tui $35 per cr for term of 7 wks beginning June 19th. Courses—Ceramics; Drawing; Photography; Watercolor.

BINGHAMTON

ROBERSON CENTER FOR THE ARTS AND SCIENCES, 30 Front St, 13905. Tel: 607-772-0660. *Asst Dir* Laura B Martin; *Instrs* PT 25.
D&E; no degrees. Young People's Art Center; Roberson School of Ballet.
Tuition: Fees vary per instruction.
Courses: Art Experience, Crafts, Jewelry; Mixed Media; Painting & Drawing; Photography; Pottery; Sculpture; Silk Screen; Theatre Arts; Weaving.
Children's Classes: Tui varies per class. Courses—Craft Workshops; Jewelry; Painting & Drawing; Pottery; Sculpture.

STATE UNIVERSITY OF NEW YORK AT BINGHAMTON, Department of Art and Art History, 13901. Tel: 607-798-2111. *Chmn Dept Art & Art Hist* Stanley Ferber, PhD; *Instrs* FT 20.
Estab 1950; pub; d; ent req HS dipl, Regents Schol, ACT or SAT; degrees BA 4 yrs, MA 1-2 yrs, PhD varies; schol; SC 18, LC 32, GC 63; enrl 679, nonmaj 400, maj 82, grad 45.
Tuition: Res—Undergrad $508.50 per sem, grad $739.50 per sem; Nonres—undergrad $808.50 per sem, grad $939.50 per sem (tuition and fees incl); campus res room and board $1500 per yr.
Courses: Advertising Design; Architecture; ‡Art History; Collage; Conceptual Art; Constructions; ‡Drawing; Film (Cinema Dept); ‡Graphic Arts; ‡Graphic Design; History of Art & Archaeology; Mixed Media; Museum Staff Training; ‡Painting; ‡Photography; ‡Printmaking; ‡Sculpture; Video (Cinema Dept).
Summer School: Office of Vice President for Academic Affairs.

BRIARCLIFF MANOR

BRIARCLIFF COLLEGE,* Art Department, 10510. Tel: 914-941-6400. *Chmn* Dr Harold C Simmons; *Instrs* FT 5, PT 1.
Estab 1903; pvt; D; W; ent req 16 academic subjects incl 4 English, SAT and English Composition; degrees AA, BA and BS 2-4 yrs; schol; SC 46, LC 22; enrl 400.
Courses: Archaeology; Art History; Ceramics; Design; Drawing; Film Making; Painting; Photography; Printmaking; Sculpture.
Summer School: Dir Bruce LaRose. SC 3.

BROCKPORT

STATE UNIVERSITY OF NEW YORK COLLEGE AT BROCKPORT,* Department of Art, 204 Fine Arts Bldg, 14220. Tel: 716-395-2209. *Chmn* Richard R Arnold; *Instrs* FT 15.
Pub; D; ent req HS dipl, ent exam; degrees BA and BS 4 yr; schol; SC 23, LC 29 (Art History); enrl 8188, maj 200, grad 2000.

Courses: Ceramics; Drawing; History of Art; Jewelry; Painting; Photography; Printmaking; Sculpture.

BRONX

HERBERT H LEHMAN COLLEGE, Department of Art, Bedford Park Blvd West, 10468. Tel: 212-960-8256. *Chmn & Assoc Prof* William McGee, MAT; *Asst Prof* Theo Stavropoulos, BFA; *Asst Prof* George Corbin, PhD; *Asst Prof* Kent Floeter, MFA; *Asst Prof* Pearl Hale, MS; *Asst Prof* William Sellers, MFA; *Prof* Richard Ziemann, MFA; *Instrs* FT 12, PT 3.
Estab 1968; pub; D&E; ent req HS dipl; degrees BA and BFA 4 yr, MA and MFA 2 yr, BFA program and MFA program can major in Graphic Arts; Painting; Sculpture; SC 18, LC 29, GC 31; enrl nonmaj 100, maj 150, GS 40.
Tuition: $35 per cr, Nonres—Undergrad $40 per cr upper division; grad $75 per cr New York City res; $95 per cr out of state; no campus res.
Courses: Aesthetics; Art Education; Art History; Ceramics; Collage; Color; Color Theory; Conceptual Art; Constructions; Drawing; Design (basic, intermediate, advanced); Graphic Arts; Mixed Media; Painting; Photography; Printmaking; Sculpture; Teacher Training.
Summer School: Dean Chester Robinson. Enrl approx 60; tui as above for term of 6 wks beginning June 9th. Courses—Art History; Graphic Arts; Painting.

MANHATTAN COLLEGE, Fine Arts Department, Manhattan College Parkway, 10471. Tel: 212-548-1400. *Chmn* George L McGeary, EdD; *Asst Prof* John Ornelia, PhD.
Estab 1848; pvt; D&E; ent req HS dipl; degrees BA 4 yr; schol; SC 22, LC 17; enrl D 3000 (total), maj 12.
Tuition: Undergrad $1300 per sem, $80 per cr; campus res room & board $800.
Courses: Aesthetics; Art Education; Art History; Ceramics; Drawing; Film; Graphic Arts; History of Art and Archaeology; Jewelry; Museum Staff Training; Painting; Photography; Printmaking; Sculpture, Teacher Training.

BRONXVILLE

CONCORDIA COLLEGE, 10708. Tel: 914-337-9300. *Head Dept* Florence Halter.
Estab 1881; pvt; D; ent req HS dipl, SAT or ACT; degrees BA and BS 4 yr; schol; SC 4, LC 2.
Tuition: $1995 per yr; campus res room and board $1250.
Courses: Art Education; Art History; Ceramics; Drawing; Handicrafts; History of Art and Archaeology; Painting; Photography; Sculpture; Teacher Training.
Adult Hobby Classes: Courses—Painting.

SARAH LAWRENCE COLLEGE,* Department of Art, 10708. Tel: 914-337-0700, exten 301. *Head Dept* A Uchima; *Instrs* FT 1, PT 7.
Estab 1928; pvt; D; ent req HS dipl; degree AB 4 yr; schol; SC 10; enrl 170.
Courses: Architecture; Ceramics; Drawing; Graphic Arts; History of Art & Archaeology; Painting; Photography; Sculpture; Stage Design; Theatre Arts.
Summer School: Dir Mr Wentworth and Mr Cogan.

BROOKLYN

BROOKLYN MUSEUM ART SCHOOL,* 188 Eastern Pkwy, 11238. Tel: 12-638-4486. *Dir* David O'Lenick; *Registrar* Marge Stevens; *Instrss* FT 5, PT 66.
Estab 1898; pub; D&E; FT and PT; Max Beckmann Memorial schol and foreign and work schol for advanced painting and ceramics; enrl approx 900, HS prog 75.
Courses: Ceramics; Drawing; Etching; Lithography; Jewelry; Museum & Galley Tours; Painting; Printmaking; Sculpture; Stained Glass; Weaving; Welding; Woodworking.
Summer School: Tui $10 per class, $5 per lab for 2 terms beginning July 5 - July 28 and August 1 - August 29. Courses—Ceramics; Construction; Drawing; Graphics; Jewelry; Painting; Sculpture; Stained Glass; Weaving.
High School Summer Program: Tui $10 per course beginning July-August. Courses—Ceramics; Drawing; Jewelry; Printmaking; Stained Glass; Sculpture.

KINGSBOROUGH COMMUNITY COLLEGE (City University of New York), Department of Art, 2001 Oriental Blvd, 11235. Tel: 212-394-5718. *Chmn* Thomas I Nonn, PhD; *Assoc Prof* Jack Bolen, MFA; *Assoc Prof* Peter Hanssen, MFA; *Asst Prof* Anthony Martin, MFA; *Asst Prof* Elizabeth Parker, PhD; *Assoc. Prof* Michael Sherker, EdD; *Prof* Frederic Thursz, MFA.

Estab 1965, dept estab 1972; pub; D&E; ent req HS dipl; degrees AS 2 yr; SC 10, LC 8; enrl maj 135.
Tuition: $675 per yr; no campus res.
Courses: Art History; Ceramics; Drawing; Graphic Arts; Graphic Design; History of Art and Archaeology; Intermedia; Mixed Media; Painting; Printmaking; Sculpture; Theatre Arts.
Summer School: Courses—Art.

LONG ISLAND UNIVERSITY,* Brooklyn Center, Art Department, 385 Flatbush Ave Exten, 11201. Tel: 212-834-6060. *Chmn* Nathan Resnick; Instrs FT 3, PT 3-4.
Pvt; D&E; ent req HS dipl, ent exam; degrees BA and BS 4 yr; schol; SC 5, LC 3.
Tuition: $90 per cr.
Courses: Art Workshops, Drawing; History of Art; History of the Motion Picture; Introduction to Media Art; Painting; Photography; Visual Experience.
Summer School: Tui $90 per cr for term of two 6 wk sessions beginning June and July. Courses—Drawing; Painting; Photography.

PRATT INSTITUTE
—**School of Art & Design,*** 215 Ryerson St, 11205. Tel: 212-636-3600.
Dean Bruce Sharpe; *Chmn Art Educ* Andrew Phelan; *Chmn History of Art* Philip Schmidt; *Chmn Film* Robert Nickerson Manning; *Chmn Fashion Design* Marion Lillard; *Chmn Industrial Design* Giles Aurelli; *Chmn Interior/Environmental Design* R Guy McGinnis; *Chmn Painting & Drawing* Jack Sonenberg; *Chmn Photography* Philip Perkis; *Chmn Printmaking* Vasilios Toulis; *Chmn Sculpture* Richard Budelis; *Chmn Theatre Arts* George New.
Pub: D; enrl 4400
Courses: Art Education; Ceramics; Communication Design; Drawing; History of Art; Film; Fashion Arts; Industrial Design; Interior/Environmental Design; Painting; Photography; Printmaking; Sculpture; Theatre Arts.
—**School of Architecture.***
Acting Dir Warren Gran; *Chmn Curriculum* William Katavolos; *Chmn Faculty Affairs* Rosaria Piomelli; *Chmn Resources* Sidney Shelov; *Chmn Student Affairs* Michael Trencher.
Degrees BS, BProf Studies, 4 yr, BArch 5 yr, MArch 1 yr, MS(Urban Design), 1 yr; MS(Planning), 2 yr; BArch/MS(Urban Design) BArch/MS(Planning), 6 yr.
Courses: Architecture; History of Art & Architecture; Landscape Architecture; Materials; Structures; Design.

BROOKVILLE

SCHOOL OF THE ARTS, C W POST CENTER OF LONG ISLAND UNIVERSITY, Art Department, 11548. Tel: 516-299-2464. *Dean* Julian Mates, PhD; *Chmn & Assoc Prof* Arnold Simonoff; *Prof* James Lewicki; *Prof* Stanley Brodsky, EdD; *Prof* Arthur Silver, BArch; *Assoc Prof* Robert Yasada, MFA; *Assoc Prof* Donald Yaloe, MFA; *Assoc Prof* Jerome Zimmerman, MFA; *Assoc Prof* Joyce Rosa, PhD.
Dept estab 1957; pvt; D&E; ent req HS dipl, portfolio; degrees BA(Art Educ), BA(Art Hist) and BA(Studio) and BFA 4 yr, MA(Photography), MA(Studio), MS(Art Ed) and MFA(Art or Design) 2 yr; schol; SC 70, LC 15, GC 40; enrl D 2000, E 450, nonmaj 2000, maj 250, GS 150, others 50.
Tuition: $1530 per sem; Undergrad and Nonres—Undergrad $90 per cr hr; grad and Nonres—grad $90 per cr hr; campus res room and board.
Courses: ‡Advertising Design; Aesthetics; ‡Art Education; ‡Art History; Ceramics; Collage; Commercial Art; Conceptual Art; Constructions; Drawing; Film; ‡Fine Arts; Graphic Arts; Graphic Design; Handicrafts (ceramics, enameling, jewelry, weaving); Illustration; Intermedia; Jewelry; Lettering; Mixed Media; Painting; Photography; Printmaking; Sculpture; Stage Design; Teacher Training; Theatre Arts; Video.
Summer School: Dir & Prof Arnold Simonoff. Tui Undergrad $90 per cr, grad $98 per cr for 3 summer sessions beginning May 22 - June 23, June 26 - July 28 and July 31 - September 1.

BUFFALO

STATE UNIVERSITY OF NEW YORK COLLEGE AT BUFFALO, Fine Arts Department, 1300 Elmwood Ave, 14222. Tel: 716-862-6014. *Chmn* Francis R Kowsky, PhD.
Estab 1875, dept estab 1961; pub; D&E; ent req HS dipl; degrees BA(Art), BA(Art History) and BFA 4 yr; SC 34, LC 17, GC 6; enrl maj 250 (Art).
Tuition: Res—Undergrad lower division $375 per sem, $25 per cr hr, upper division $450 per sem, $30 per cr hr; Nonres—Undergrad lower division $600 per sem, $40 per cr hr, upper division $750 per sem, $50 per cr hr; campus res available double $375 per sem, single $562.50 per sem.

Courses: Art History; Drawing; Graphic Arts; History of Art and Archaeology; Museum Staff Training; Painting; Photography; Printmaking; Sculpture.

STATE UNIVERSITY OF NEW YORK, UNIVERSITY CENTER AT BUFFALO,* Department of Art and Art History, Bethune Hall, 2917 Main St, 14214. Tel: 716-831-5251. *Chmn* Willard R Harris; Instrs FT 21, PT 14.
Estab 1894; pub; D&E; ent req HS dipl, portfolio, acceptance by univ; degrees BA and BFA 4 yr, MFA 2 yr; MAH 1 yr; schol, grad, fel; SC, LC, GC; enrl D 260, E 150, grad 60.
Courses: Art Education; Art History; Design; Drawing; Intaglio; Lithography; Painting; Photography; Sculpture; Serigraphy; Visual Communications.
Summer School: Courses—Design Workshops; Drawing; Painting; Photo/Film Workshops; Printmaking Workshops; Sculpture.

VILLA MARIA COLLEGE OF BUFFALO, Art Department, 240 Pine Ridge Rd, 14225. Tel: 716-896-0700, exten 324. *Chmn* James W Jipson, MFA; *Lectr* Irene Adamski; *Lectr* Lee Mitchell, BFA; *Lectr* Andy Topolski, MFA; *Assoc Prof* Katherine Verney, MA; *Lectr* William Wahler, *Lectr* Linda Weglewski, BFA.
Estab 1961; pvt; D&E; ent req HS dipl or equivalency; degrees AA, AAS and AS 2 yr; schol; SC 27, LC 3; enrl D 450, E 100, maj 90.
Tuition: $1650 per yr, $825 per sem, $60 per cr hr; no campus res.
Courses: Advertising Design; Art History; Ceramics; Commercial Art; Drafting (mechanical); Drawing; Graphic Arts; ‡Graphic Design; ‡Interior Design; Lettering; Painting; Photography; Printmaking; Sculpture; Textile Design.
Adult Hobby Classes: Courses—Arts and Crafts; Drawing; Painting; Photography; Quilting.
Summer School: Enrl 10 to 20; Tui $180 per cr, $60 per noncr for term of 6 wks beginning June 28. Courses—Drawing; Etching; Gumprinting; Painting; Photography; Silkscreen, Special Photo Processes Workshop.

CANANDAIGUA

COMMUNITY COLLEGE OF THE FINGER LAKES, Visual Performing Arts Dept, Lincoln Hill Campus, 14424. *Acting Chmn* Thomas F Insalaco, MFA; *Prof* Wayne Williams, MFA; *Instr* John Fox, MFA; Instrs FT 3, PT 5.
Estab 1966; pub; D&E; ent req HS dipl; degrees AA 2 yrs; SC 14, LC 2; enrl D 60, nonmaj 700, maj 50.
Tuition: Res—Undergrad $78 per cr hr; Nonres—Undergrad $156 per cr hr; no campus res.
Courses: Advertising Design; Art History; Ceramics; Commercial Art; Drawing; Graphic Arts; Graphic Design; Illustration; Painting; Photography; Printmaking; Sculpture; Stage Design; Theatre Arts.
Summer School: Courses—most of above.

CANTON

ST LAWRENCE UNIVERSITY, Department of Fine Arts, 13617. Tel: 315-379-5180. *Chmn* J Michael Lowe, MFA; *Prof* Harlan H Holladay, PhD; *Prof* Clayton V Fowler, PhD; *Assoc Prof* Guy Berard, MFA; *Assoc Prof* Roger Bailey, MFA; vis prof—Paul D Schweizer, Art History and Curator, 1977-78.
Estab 1856; pvt; D; ent req HS dipl; degrees BA; SC 16, LC 13; enrl maj 41.
Tuition: $3395 per yr, $1697.50 per sem; campus res room and board $1540.
Courses: Art History; Ceramics; Drawing; Painting; Photography; Printmaking; Sculpture; Teacher Training.
Summer School: Dir James Van Ness.

CAZENOVIA

CAZENOVIA COLLEGE, Art Program, 13035. Tel: 315-655-3466, exten 246. *Dir* John Aistars, MFA; *Instr* Constance Simon, MFA.
Estab 1824; pvt; D&E; ent req HS dipl; degrees AA, AS and AAS 2 yr; schol; SC 18, LC 2; enrl nonmaj 21.
Tuition: Res $3165 per yr, $90 per cr hr; campus res room and board $1785.
Courses: ‡Advertising Design; Advertising Layout; Art History: Basic Design; Ceramics; Drawing; Fashion Arts; Figure Drawing; Graphic Arts; History of Art and Archaeology; Illustration; Lettering; Painting; Photography; Printmaking; Typography.

CHAUTAUQUA

CHAUTAUQUA INSTITUTION, Box 28, 14722. Tel: 716-357-4411, 357-5635, exten 232, 233, 234. *Head Painting & Drawing* Revington

Arthur; *Head Ceramics* James Achuff; *Head Sculpture* H Richard Duhme Jr; *Head Photography* George Gambsky; *Head Weaving* Ruth Holroyd.
Estab 1874; pub; D (summers only); schol; SC 26, LC 7; enrl D 500.
Tuition: $164 per 9 wk session, $28 per wk, $6.50 per one session (only as an extension); campus res (9 wks) $360.
Courses: Art History; Calligraphy; Ceramics; Drawing; Fashion Arts; Handicrafts (batik, quilting, weaving); Interior Design; Jewelry; Painting; Photography; Printmaking; Sculpture; Theatre Arts.

CLAYTON

THOUSAND ISLANDS MUSEUM CRAFT SCHOOL, 13624. Tel: 315-686-4123. *Admin* Richard V Palmer; *Asst Admin* Joseph Perrucio. Instrs PT 20.
Estab 1964; D&E; ent req an interest in arts and crafts; no degrees but transfer credit; schol; SC 21; enrl D 210, E 10.
Tuition: $95 plus $20 registration fee for each wk course.
Courses: Acrylic Painting; Advanced EA; Bird Carving; Ceramics; China Painting; Decoy Carving; Jewelry; Quilt Making.
Summer School: July 3-August 25. Courses—Country Painting; Creative Stitchery; Enameling; Loom Techniques; Pattern Weaving; Pottery; Reverse Painting on Glass; Rug Hooking; Water Color Painting; Weaving.

CORNING

CORNING COMMUNITY COLLEGE, Division of Humanities, 14830. Tel: 607-962-9238. *Chmn & Prof* John M Runyon, MFA; *Assoc Prof* Charles R Ringsmuth, MFA; *Instr* John Frisenda, MFA; *Instr.* Horst Werk, MFA; Instrs FT 2, PT 2.
Estab 1958; dept estab 1963; pub; D&E; ent req HS dipl, SAT; degrees AA, AS, AAS 2 yr; SC 8, LC 6.
Courses: Advertising Design; Art History; Ceramics; Drawing; Graphic Arts; Graphic Design; Handicrafts; History of Art and Archaeology; Jewelry; Painting; Printmaking; Silversmithing; Textile Design.
Summer School: Acting Dir Nan Lanning.

CORTLAND

STATE UNIVERSITY OF NEW YORK COLLEGE AT CORTLAND, Art Department, 13045. Tel: 607-753-4316. *Chmn* J Catherine Gibian, MA; *Prof* Steven Barbash, MFA; *Prof* Gerald DiGiusto, BFA; *Assoc Prof* George Dugan, MFA; *Prof* John Jessiman, MFA; *Prof* Barbara Kuhlman, MA; *Asst Prof* David Simon, PhD; *Assoc Prof* James Thorpe, MFA.
Estab 1868, dept estab 1948; pub; D&E; ent req HS dipl, all college admissions standards based on high school average or scores from SAT, ACTP or Regent's tests; degrees BA 4 yr; schol; SC 40, LC 10; enrl D 5300 (total), 1200 (art), maj 80.
Tuition: Res—Undergrad $750 Freshman & Sophomore, $900 Junior and Senior; Nonres—Undergrad $1200 Freshman & Sophomore, $1500 Junior & Senior; other college fee & activity assessment $95; campus res $750 (room) and $664 (board).
Courses: Aesthetics; Art Education; Art History; Ceramics; Design; Drawing; Film; Goldsmithing; Graphic Arts; Handicrafts (enameling, jewelry, metalwork, weaving); History of Art and Archaeology; Jewelry; Painting; Photography; Printmaking; Sculpture; Silversmithing; Textile Design.
Summer School: Dean Andrew Banse. Enrl approx 40; term of 6 wks beginning June 26. Courses—one Studio and one Art History.

ELMIRA

ELMIRA COLLEGE, Art Department, 14901. Tel: 607-734-3911, exten 354. *Primary Art Faculty* William Lee, MFA; Douglas Holtgrewe, MFA; Peter Chamberlain, MFA; Mark Schmidt, MFA.
Estab 1855, pvt; D&E; ent req HS dipl; degrees AA, AS, BA, BS and MEduc; schol; SC 26, LC 15, GC 8; enrl D 250, E 125, maj 35, GS 6.
Tuition: $3420 per yr; campus res room and board $5030.
Courses: Architecture; Art Education; Art History; Ceramics; Costume Design and Construction; Drawing; Graphic Arts; History of Art & Archaeology; Jewelry; Painting; Photography; Printmaking; Sculpture; Silversmithing; Stage Design; Teacher Training; Theatre Arts.

FOREST HILLS

CATAN-ROSE INSTITUTE OF ART,* 72 112th St, 11375. Tel: 212-263-1962. *Pres & Dir* Richard Catan-Rose; Instrs FT 5, PT 9.
Estab 1943; pvt; D&E; ent req HS grad, no ent req for adult or children's classes; Assoc Cert 2 yrs, Cert 4 yrs; schol.

Courses: Advertising Design; Applied Art; Architecture; Art History; Basic Art; Calligraphy; Cartooning; Crafts; Drawing; Fashion Illustration; Film; Fine Arts & Design; Illustration; Industrial Design; Interior Design; Lettering; Painting—Watercolor, Oil, Acrylic, Pastels; Printmaking; Photography; Sculpture; Stage Design; Textiles; Weaving.
Summer School: 7 and 11 wks. Foundation courses—Indoor and Outdoor, Fine Arts, Advertising, Interiors, and Graphic Arts.

FREDONIA

STATE UNIVERSITY COLLEGE, Department of Art, 14063. Tel: 716-673-3537. *Chmn* Emmitt L Christian, MFA; *Assoc Prof* Marvin Bjurin, MFA; *Assoc Prof* Carole Harrison, MFA; *Assoc Prof* John Hughson, MFA; *Prof* William Proweller, PhD; *Assoc Prof* Daniel Reiff, PhD; *Asst Prof* David Small, MFA.
Estab 1925, dept estab approx 1950; pub; D&E; ent req HS dipl; degrees BFA 4 yr; SC 30, LC 10, GC 5; enrl nonmaj 200-250, maj 115, GS 5, others 5.
Tuition: Res—Undergrad $750, grad $900 per yr; Nonres—Undergrad $1200, grad $1500 per yr; campus res.
Courses: Aesthetics; Art History; ‡Art History; ‡Ceramics; Conceptual Art; Drawing; Graphic Arts; Graphic Design; ‡History of Art and Archaeology; Mixed Media; ‡Painting; ‡Photography; ‡Printmaking; ‡Sculpture.

GARDEN CITY

ADELPHI UNIVERSITY,* Department of Art, 11530. Tel: 516-294-8700, exten 387, 388. *Chmn* Grace R Cantone; Instrs FT 8, PT 5.
Estab 1896; pvt; degrees 4 yr; SC 40, LC 10; enrl maj 90, others 600.
Courses: Advertising Design; Color Media, Materials; Crafts; Fashion Design; Graphics; History of Art; Interior Design; Painting & Drawing; Photography; Sculpture & Ceramics; Teaching Methods & Training; Two-Dimensional Design.
Summer School: Two 5 wk sessions; D&E. Courses—Creative Crafts Workshops.

NASSAU COMMUNITY COLLEGE,* Art Department, Stewart Ave, 11530. Tel: 516-742-0600, exten 258. *Chmn* Dr Leon Frankston; Instrs FT 13. PT 23.
Estab 1962; Affiliated with State University of New York. pub; D&E; degrees AA and AAS 2 yr; enrl maj 350.
Courses: Advertising Design; Ceramics; Costume Design; Drawing; Fashion Illustration; Gallery Survey; General Crafts; Graphics; Handcrafts; Interior Design; Painting; Photography; Sculpture.
Summer School: Two 5 wk terms.

GENESEO

STATE UNIVERSITY OF NEW YORK COLLEGE AT GENESEO,* College of Arts & Science, Department of Art, 14454. Tel: 716-245-5415. Instrs FT 10, PT 4.
Estab 1871; pu; D&E; ent req HS dipl, ent exam; degree BA(Art) 3-4 yrs; SC 35, LC 7; enrl D 1000, E 1150, maj approx 100.
Courses: Art Appreciation; Art Education; Ceramics; Drawing; Fashion Arts; Graphic Arts; Handicrafts; History of Art; Jewelry; Modern Architecture; Modern Painting; Painting; Photography; Sculpture; Textile Design; Wood Design.
Summer School: Courses—varies.

GENEVA

HOBART & WILLIAM SMITH COLLEGES,* Art Department, 14456. Tel: 315-789-5500. *Prof* Alvin I Sher; Instrs FT 5.
Estab approx 1800; pvt; D; ent req HS dipl, ent exam; degrees BA and BS 4 yr; schol; SC 15, LC 8; enrl D 1600.
Tuition: Approx $3870 per yr; campus res approx $1730.
Courses: Aesthetics; Architecture; Drawing; Graphic Arts; History of Art & Archaeology; Painting; Photography; Sculpture; Theatre Arts.

HAMILTON

COLGATE UNIVERSITY, Department of Fine Arts, 13346. Tel: 315-824-1000, exten 633. *Chmn & Prof* Jim Loveless, MFA; *Prof* Eric Von Schaack, PhD; *Assoc Prof (Gallery Dir)* Edward Bryant, MA; *Asst Prof* Alan Paulson, MFA; *vis prof*—Edward Fry, Art History, 76-78.
Estab 1819, Dept estab 1905; pvt; D; ent req HS dipl, CEEB or ACT; degrees BA 4 yr; schol; SC 15, LC 26; enrl D 650, maj 45.
Tuition: $4095 per yr; campus res room and board $745 and $910.

Courses: Architecture; Art History; Drawing; Film; Graphic Arts; History of Art & Archaeology; Painting; Photography; Printmaking; Sculpture; Video.

HEMPSTEAD

HOFSTRA UNIVERSITY,* Department of Fine Arts, 11550. Tel: 516-560-3231. *Chmn* David D Porinchak; *Chmn Art History & Humanities Dept* Dr R Myron; *Instrs* FT 14, PT 3.
Estab 1935; pvt; D&E; ent req good secondary school record, coll ent board exam; degrees BA and BS (Art Educ) 4 yr; schol; SC 32, LC 1, GC 3.
Tuition: $1500 per sem; PT $100 per cr hr.
Courses: Color & Design; Current Gallery Developments (lecture); Etching; Fundamentals of Applied Design, 2 & 3-D; Fundamentals of Graphic Expression; General Crafts; Lithography; Metalsmithing; Painting; Photography; Pottery; Sculpture; Serigraphy; 3-D Design; 2-D Representation; Woodcut.
Summer School: Dean University College H Lichtenstein.

HERKIMER

HERKIMER COUNTY COMMUNITY COLLEGE, Humanities Division, 13350. Tel: 315-866-0300, exten 51. *Chmn* Peter P Clarke, PhD; *Assoc Prof* Guido Correro, MA; *Asst Prof* Mirle Prul, MA; Instrs FT 2, PT 1.
Estab 1966; pub; D&E; ent req HS dipl, SAT or ACT; degrees AA, AS and AAS 2 yrs; SC 8, LC 4; enrl D 329 (total), maj 16.
Tuition: Res—Undergrad $275 per sem, $23 per cr hr; Nonres—Undergrad $550 per sem, grad $46 per cr hr; no campus res.
Courses: Art History; Drawing; Film; Museum Staff Training; Painting; Photography; Theatre Arts; Video.
Adult Hobby Classe: Tui varies. Courses—Jewelry Making; Studio in Painting.
Children's Classes: Courses—Workshop in Television.
Summer School: Dir Violet Towne. Courses—various depending on the year.

HIGHLAND FALLS

LADYCLIFF COLLEGE, Art Department, 10928. Tel: 914-446-4747. *Chmn & Assoc Prof* Adrienne Pregno, MA; *Asst Prof* Don Gray, MA; *Asst Prof* Roselaine Perkis, MA; *Lectr* John E Davis, BA; *Lectr* Ellen Twardowski, MPS; *Lectr* Roy Hyrkin, MA.
Estab 1933; pvt; D&E; ent req HS dipl, HS record; degrees BA and BS 4 yr, field experience in Art Therapy, Crafts, Museum Work to Upperclassmen in good academic standing; schol; SC 55, LC 10; enrl D 50, E 20, nonmaj 25, maj 30.
Tuition: $68 per cr hr; campus res room and board.
Courses: Advertising Design; Architecture; ‡Art Education; Art History; Art Therapy; Ceramics; Commercial Art; Conceptual Art; Drafting; Drawing; Fiber; ‡Graphic Arts; Graphic Design; ‡Handicrafts (enameling, pottery, weaving); History of Art and Archaeology; Jewelry; Lettering; Metal Working; Mixed Media; ‡Museum Staff Training; Painting; Photography; Printmaking; Sculpture; Teacher Training.
Children's Classes: Enrl 30 per sem; tui $20-$35 per 8 classes. Courses—Crafts; Drawing; Macrame; Papier Mache; Working with Clay.
Summer School: Dir Julianne Schmidt. Enrl 20; tui $68 per cr for term of 4-6 wks beginning May 22. Courses—Cloisonne Enameling; Crafts; Drawing; Jewelry; Metal Working; Painting; Photography; Pottery; Printing; Weaving.

HOUGHTON

HOUGHTON COLLEGE, Art Department, 14744. Tel: 716-567-2211, exten 140. *Chmn* Donald L Bailey, DA (Music); *Asst Prof* Roger Richardson, MFA; *Asst Prof* Georgiana D Sentz, MS; *vis prof*—Dr M A Landis, Art Education, 1977-78.
Estab 1883; den; D&E; schol; SC 8, LC 6.
Tuition: $2418 per yr; campus res room and board $1350.
Courses: Art Education; Art History; Ceramics; Collage; Drawing; Graphic Arts; Graphic Design; History of Art and Archaeology; Painting; Printmaking.
Summer School: Dir Paul Johnson. Tui $234 for term of 3 wks beginning May 9th. Courses—Art and Christianity.

ITHACA

CORNELL UNIVERSITY
—**College of Architecture,** Art and Planning, Department of Art, 14853. Tel: 607-256-3558. *Dean Col* Kermit C Parsons; *Assoc Prof Art & Chmn*

Dept Zevi Blum, BArch; *Prof* Victor Colby, MFA; *Prof* Jack L Squier, MFA; *Prof* Kenneth Evett, MA; *Assoc Prof* Arnold Singer; *Assoc Prof* Gillian Pederson-Krag, MFA; *Assoc Prof* Steve Poleskie, BS; *Prof* Jason Seley, BA.
Estab 1868, dept estab 1921; pvt; D; ent req HS dipl, portfolio interview, HS transcript, SAT; degrees BFA 4 yrs, MFA 2 yrs; schol; SC 25, LC 1, GC 4; enrl maj 100, grad 13; special students 2.
Tuition: $4800 per yr, $2400 per sem; campus res.
Courses: For Department—Aesthetics; Drawing; ‡Painting; ‡Photography; ‡Printmaking; ‡Sculpture.
Summer School: Dir Arnold Singer. Term of 3 wks beginning June 27. Courses—Painting; Drawing; Photography; Printmaking; Sculpture.
—**College of Arts and Sciences,** * Department of the History of Art, 14850. Tel: 607-256-4905. *Chmn* Stanley O'Connor; *Instrs* FT 12.
Estab 1939; LC 64, GC 12.
Courses: Archaeology; Architecture; Art Criticism; History of Art; Techniques & Materials.
—**New York State College of Human Ecology,** * Department of Design and Environmental Analysis, Tel: 607-256-2168. *Prof & Chmn Dept* Rose Steidl; *Instrs* FT 23.

ITHACA COLLEGE, Art Department, Danby Road, 14850. Tel: 607-274-3011, exten 3330. *Dean* Tom Longin; *Chmn* Harry McCue, MFA; *Prof* Salvatore Grippi; *Prof* Robert Richenburg; *Asst Prof* Gary Wojcik, MFA; *vis prof*—David Smith, MFA; lecturer.
Estab 1892, dept estab 1968; pvt; D&E; ent req HS dipl, SAT scores, review of portfolio; degrees BA and BFA 4 yr; SC 10; enrl nonmaj 200, maj 40.
Tuition: $5400 per yr; campus res room and board.
Courses: Art History; Calligraphy; Conceptual Art; Constructions; Drawing; Film; Intermedia; Mixed Media; Occupational Therapy; Painting; Photography; Printmaking; Sculpture; Stage Design; Theatre Arts; Video.

JAMAICA

ST JOHN'S UNIVERSITY,* Department of Fine Arts, Grand Central & Utopia Pkwys, 11439. Tel: 212-969-8000, exten 249. *Chmn* Edward J Manetta; *Instrs* FT 9, PT 6.
Pvt; D; ent req HS dipl, ent exam, portfolio review; degrees BFA and BS 4 yr; schol; SC 24; LC 9; enrl D 1300, maj 100.
Tuition: $105 per sem hr; no campus res.
Courses: Advertising Design; Ceramics; Display (Internship); Drawing; Graphic Arts; Graphic Design; Handicrafts; Jewelry; Museum Staff Training (Internship); Photography; Sculpture; Teacher Training.
Saturday Scholarship program: Courses—Art; Music.
Summer School: Dir Dr Mahdesian.

JAMESTOWN

JAMESTOWN COMMUNITY COLLEGE, Art Department, 14701. *Chmn* William Disbro, MA; *Asst Prof* John Hiester, MA; *Asst Prof* William Disbro, MA; *vis prof*—Susan Kepecs, sculpture, 1977-78; Instrs PT 5.
Estab 1950, dept estab 1970; pub; D&E; ent req open; degrees AA 60 cr hrs; schol; SC 11, LC 1; enrl D 310, E 254.
Tuition: Res—Undergrad $300 per sem, $20 per cr hr; Nonres—Undergrad $600 per sem, $40 per cr hr.
Courses: Advertising Design; Art History; Calligraphy; Ceramics; Drawing; Film; Painting; Photography; Printmakng; Sculpture; Stage Design; Theatre Arts; Video.
Summer School: Enrl 25; tui $60 for term of 6 wks beginning last wk of June. Courses—Ceramics; Photography.

LAKE PLACID

LAKE PLACID SCHOOL OF ART, Center for Music, Drama and Art, 12946. Tel: 518-523-2591. *Dir* Brian Gormley, MA; *Chmn Ceramics Dept* John R Thompson, MA; *Chmn Painting Dept* Harry Bartnick, MFA; *Chmn Photography Dept* Helmmo Kindermann, MFA; *Chmn Printmaking Dept* James J Catalano, MFA; *Instr* Martin Anderson, MFA; *Instr* Colette Stemple, MFA.
Estab 1972; pvt; D&E; ent req HS dipl, portfolio; degrees dipl 2 yr; schol; SC 25, LC 2; enrl D 35, E 75, maj 35.
Tuition: $1710 per yr, $855 per sem; other $250 per course (subject to change, fall 78); campus res room and board $375.
Courses: Art History; ‡Ceramics; ‡Drawing; ‡Painting; ‡Photography; ‡Printmaking; Sculpture.
Adult Hobby Classes: Enrl 75; tui $45 per 6 wks. Courses—Batik; Calligraphy; Ceramics; Drawing; Framing; Painting; Photography; Printmaking; Silversmithing; Studio Skills.

Children's Classes: Courses—Creative Arts (gallery, music, theater, visual arts); Mixed Media.
Summer School: Enrl 60; tui $250 for term of 6 wks beginning June 19th. Courses—Ceramics; Drawing; Painting; Photography; Printmaking. Intensive visiting artist workshops in all departments.

LARCHMONT

ADAMY'S PLASTICS & MOLD-MAKING WORKSHOPS, 10538. Tel: 914-834-6276. *Dir* George E Adamy, MFA; Instrs FT 1, PT 1.
Estab 1968; pvt; D&E; SC 13, LC 2, GC 13; enrl D 20, E 30.
Tuition: From $25 for 3 hr open-ended sessions to $225 for 10 sessions advanced courses. Individual arrangements for special projects or commissions, and for lectures and demonstrations of other schools, museums, art organizations; no campus res.
Courses: Collage: Constructions; Mold-Making; Museum Staff Training; Painting; Plastics; Printmaking; Sculpture; Teacher Training.
Adult Hobby Classes: As Above.

LOCH SHELDRAKE

SULLIVAN COUNTY COMMUNITY COLLEGE, Division of Commercial Art, 12759. Tel: 914-434-5750, exten 215. *Chmn & Assoc Prof* Joe Hopkins, MFA; *Assoc Prof* L J Agnew, MED; *Asst Prof* Bud Wertheim, BA; *Instr* Thomas Ambrosino, BPS.
Estab 1962, dept estab 1965; pub; D&E; ent req HS dipl, high school equivalency; degrees AAS 2 yr; SC 15-20, enrl D 150, E 30, nonmaj 12, maj 150.
Tuition: $1240 per yr, $299 for PT.
Courses: Advertising Design; Art History; Calligraphy; ‡Commercial Art; Display; Film; Graphic Arts; Graphic Design; History of Art and Archaeology; Lettering; Photography; Theatre Arts; Video.
Summer School: Dir Allan Dampman. Courses—varied.

MALDEN BRIDGE

MALDEN BRIDGE SCHOOL OF ART, 12115. Tel: 518-766-3666. *Dir & Instrs* Betty Warren; *Instr* John Lancaster; *Instr* Michael Lancaster; Instrs FT 2, PT 5.
Estab 1965; pvt; D; ent req students who are seriously interested in developing their skills and knowledge; schol; SC 6; enrl D 55.
Tuition: Res—Undergrad $500 per wk summer session, $350 per month; Nonres—Undergrad $375 per 6 wk session, $275 per month, $225 PT; room available.
Courses: Ceramics; Drawing; Painting; Sculpture.

NEW PALTZ

STATE UNIVERSITY OF NEW YORK COLLEGE AT NEW PALTZ,* 12561.
—**Studio Art Department.** *Chmn* Maurice Brown; Instrs 26.
Pub; degrees BFA and MFA 4 yr; enrl total 8000.
Courses: Ceramics; Gold & Silversmithing; Painting; Photography; Printmaking; Sculpture.
—**Art Education Department.** *Chmn* Susan Wisherd; Instrs 5.
Degrees BS (Art Educ) and MS (Art Educ).
Summer School: Dir Robert Davidson. 8 wk sem.

NEW ROCHELLE

COLLEGE OF NEW ROCHELLE, School of Arts and Sciences, Art Department, 10801. Tel: 914-632-5300. *Head Dept* Sister Mary Jane Robertshaw, MFA; *Primary Faculty* Jack Bosson, MFA; Dr Charles Daly, EdD; Theresa Eppridge, MFA; Irene Kutsky, MFA; Dr William Maxwell, EdD; Anne Terhune, PhD candidate.
Estab 1904, dept estab 1929; pvt; D; ent req HS dipl, SAT recommended, college preparatory program in high school; degrees BA, BFA and BS 4 yr; schol; SC 52, LC 14, GC 21; enrl D 340, nonmaj 35, maj 207, GS 98.
Tuition: $2700 per yr, $1350 per sem, $80 per cr; campus res room and board $2000 (room and board).
Courses: Advertising Design; Aesthetics; ‡Applied Design; Art Psychology; ‡Art Education; ‡Art History; Ceramics; Design, 2nd and 3rd Dimensional; Drafting; Drawing; Fashion Arts; Film; Graphic Arts; Illustration; Interior Design; Jewelry; Mixed Media; Painting; Photography; Printmaking; Sculpture; ‡Studio Arts; Teacher Training; Textile Design; Theatre Arts; Video; Weaving.
Summer School: Dir Steven Sweeney. Enrl 300; tui $80 per cr for two terms of 5 wks beginning June 1. Courses—Advertising Design/Layout; Applied Design Independent Study; Art of North America; Ceramics; Ceramic Sculpture; Creative Watercolor; Creative Workshop in Mixed Media; Designing Educational Media; Drawing; Drawing and Composition; Enameling; Figure and Portrait Painting; Fine Arts,

Independent Study; History of Medieval Art; Jewelry; Loomless Weaving; Photography; Relief Process; Sculpture, Thesis Project/Art Education; Weaving.

HARRIET FeBLAND'S ADVANCED PAINTERS WORKSHOP, Premium Point, 10801. Tel: 914-235-7322. *Dir* Harriet FeBland; *Primary Art Faculty* Bernard Kassoy, Hortense Kassoy; Manuel Barradas.
Estab 1962; pvt; D&E; ent req review of previous work, paintings or sculpture; schol; SC 6, LC 1, GC 4; enrl D 115, E 35, GS 115, others 35.
Tuition: Nonres—adult professional school $145 per sem (15 wks), $65 lect and critiques (5 wks).
Courses: Collage; Constructions; Drawing; Painting; Sculpture; Wood Carving.

NEW YORK

ABBE INSTITUTE,* School of Fine Arts, 100 Fifth Ave, 10011. Tel: 212-924-4364. Instrs D FT 3, PT 5.
Estab 1938 (reopened 1947); pvt; 4 yr; enrl D 60, E 60.
Courses: Display; Drawing & Painting; Fashion Illustration; Illustration; Interior Decoration.

ABBEY SCHOOL OF JEWELRY & ART METAL DESIGN, 305 Seventh Avenue, 10001. Tel: 212-691-1080. *Dir* John R Sharpe; *Instr* Arthur Kutcher; *Instr* Lawrence Kallenberg, MA; *Instr* Janet Vitkavage, BA; *Instr* Rob Klausner, BA; *Instr* Dina Panagoupolous, BA; Instrs FT 7, PT 3.
Estab 1963; pvt; D&E; ent req 17 yrs of age, manual dexterity, good vision; degrees certificate of completion of programs of study; SC 25; enrl D 35, E 38.
Tuition: No campus res.
Courses: Drawing; Jewelry; Silversmithing.
Adult Hobby Classes: Tui $175 per course. Courses—Basic Wax Modeling Techniques; Chainmaking; Finishing Techniques for Jewelry; Handbuilt Jewelry; Jewelry Repair; Lost Wax Casting; Ring Making; Rubbermold Making & Cutting; Silversmithing; Soldering.
Summer School: Same programs offered on a year round basis.

ABINGDON SQUARE PAINTERS, INC, 740 Greenwich, 10014. Tel: 212-243-7343. *Dir* Harriet Fitzgerald; *Pres* Edith P Nolan; Instrs 2.
Estab 1948; pvt; D; ent req must show serious intentions; no academic accreditation; a cooperative of professional artists and students offering instruction to beginning and advanced students; studio facilities available 24 hrs per day; enrl limited to 15.

ART STUDENTS LEAGUE OF NEW YORK,* 215 W 57th St, 10019. Tel: 212-347-4510. *Exec Dir* Stewart Klonis; Instrs FT 53.
Estab 1875; pvt; no ent req; schol; LC; enrl D 1200, E 600, Sat 450 (adults and children).
Courses: Anatomy; Fine Arts Calligraphy; Fine Arts Illustration; Graphics; Painting; Sculpture; Textile Design.
Summer School: In New York City-enrl 750 beginning June; In Woodstock-enrl 80 beginning July.

BALLARD SCHOOL,* Young Women's Christian Association, 610 Lexington Ave, 10022. Tel: 212-755-4500. *Dir* Madeleine J Douet; Instrs PT 7.
Estab 1870, pvt; D&E.
Tuition: $60 for 12 lessons for 12 wk.
Courses: Chinese Brush Work; Drawing & Sketching; Landscape Painting; Life; Oil Painting; Portrait Painting; Sculpture; Watercolor.

CHILDREN'S AID SOCIETY, Visual Arts Center, 209 Sullivan Street, 10012. Tel: 212-254-3074. *Dir* Allen M Hart.
Estab 1853, dept estab 1968; D&E; SC 7; enrl D 200, E 175.
Tuition: Adults—$55 per sem, Children—$32-$42 per sem; no campus res.
Courses: Aesthetics; Art Education; Art History; Cabinetmaking; Ceramics; Collage; Constructions; Drawing; Handicrafts (enameling, puppet making); Jewelry; Mixed Media; Painting; Photography; Pottery; Silversmithing;|Teacher Training.
Adult Hobby Classes: Tui $55 per sem; Courses—Cabinetmaking; Ceramics; Drawing; Enameling; Painting; Photography; Pottery.
Children's Classes: $32-$42 per sem. Courses—Dance; Drawing; Enameling; Mixed Media; Painting; Photography; Puppet Making; Woodwork.

CLAYWORKS, Pottery Department, 332 E Ninth St, 10003. Tel: 212-677-8311. *Primary Faculty* Alix Leff; Susan Claflin; Rima Walker; Darby Ortolano; Helaine Sorgen.
Estab 1973; pvt; D&E; no ent req; SC 3; enrl D 5, E 10.

Tuition: $75 per sem, $35 per mo, $1.25 per hr.
Courses: Ceramics; Handicrafts (macrame).
Adult Hobby Classes: Enrl 5; tui $75 per 12 wks. Courses—Pottery (wheel and handbuilding).
Children's Classes: Enrl 5; tui $36 per 6 wks. Courses—Pottery (wheel and handbuilding) 5-10 and 10-14 yr age groups.
Summer School: Courses—vary according to student demand and interest.

COLUMBIA UNIVERSITY, W 114th to 121st Sts, 10027. Tel: 212-280-1754.
—**School of Architecture,*** Avery Hall. *Dean* James Stewart Polshek; Instrs FT 29, PT 50.
Estab 1881; pvt; degrees MArch (3 yr, minimum ent req BA or BS), MSArch & Urban Design (1 yr, minimum ent req BArch), MSPlanning (2 yrs, minimum ent req BA, BS, BArch or BCE), MSArchTech (1 yr, minimum ent req BArch or BCE), MSHistoric Preservation (1½ yrs, minimum ent req BA, BS or BArch), MSHealth Services Planning & Design (1 yr, minimum ent req BArch); schol and fel; normal enrl 350.
Tuition: $2160 per term; campus res.
Courses: Architectural Technology; Architecture; Architecture & Urban Design; Health Services Planning & Design; Historic Preservation; Urban Planning.
—**Department of Art History and Archaeology,*** 811 Schermerhorn Bldg.
Prof Art Hist & Archaeol & Chmn Dept Alfred Frazer; Instrs FT 24, PT 28. Pvt.
—**Columbia College***
Pvt; M; degree BA 4 yrs.
Courses: Western Art; Lectures; Discussions and seminars. See subject area listing under Graduate Dept.
—**School of General Studies***
Pvt; degree BS 4 yrs; courses, lectures and seminars. See subject area listing under Graduate Dept.
—**Graduate Department.*** *Chmn* Alfred Frazer.
Pvt; degrees MA 2 yrs, MPhil 4 yrs, PhD 7 yrs; schol and fel; courses, lectures and seminars.
Courses: Art & Archaeology of South Eastern Asia; Asian Art & Archaeology; Classical Art & Archaeology; History of Western Art; Near Eastern Art & Archaeology; Primitive & Pre-Columbian Art & Archaeology.
—**Division of Painting and Sculpture,** 305 Dodge Hall, 116th & Broadway. *Ch n Div* Leon Goldin, MFA; *Prof* Andre Racz, BA; *Asst Prof* Jean L..der, MFA; *Asst Prof* David Lund, BA; *Asst Prof* Sahl Swarz, BA; *Lectr* Tony Harrison, BA.
Estab 1754, div estab 1945; pvt; D&E; ent req BA in conjunction with School of General Studies, slide folio for MFA; degree MFA 2 yrs; schol; SC 22, LC 1, GC 5; enrl nonmaj 250, maj 5, grad 30.
Tuition: $150 per point; campus res.
Courses: Drawing; Painting; Printmaking; Sculpture.
Summer School: Dir Summer Session Peter D Shamonsey. Enrl 10 - 15; tui $119 per point for term of 6 wks beginning May 23. Courses—Painting & Drawing.
—**Barnard College,*** Department of Art History, 606 W 120th St. Tel: 212-280-2118. *Chmn* Barbara Novak; Instrs FT 4, PT 4.
Estab 1923; pvt; W; degree 4 yrs; schol; enrl maj 29, total 1930.
Tuition: $2060 per term; campus res.
Courses: History of Art & Painting.
—**Teachers College,*** Department of Art and Education, 525 W 120th St. Tel: 212-865-6000. *Chmn* William J Mahoney; Instrs FT 6, PT 6.
Estab 1888; pvt; ent req Bachelor's degree; degrees MA, MEduc, PhD; schol and fel; grad courses in Teacher Educ; enrl 225.
Tuition: $129 per point, unless otherwise stated.
Courses: Art Appreciation; Crafts; Design; Graphics; Painting; Sculpture; Teacher Education.
Summer School: Two 6 wk sessions beginning early June; tui $129 per point.

COOPER UNION SCHOOL OF ART, Cooper Square, 10003. Tel: 212-254-6300, exten 286,287,288. *Dean* George Sadek, MFA.
Estab 1859; pvt; D&E; ent req HS dipl, ent exam; degrees BFA 4 yr; schol.
Tuition: no tuition.

CRAFT STUDENTS LEAGUE OF THE YWCA, 610 Lexington Ave, 10022. Tel: 212-755-4500, exten 57,58,59,60. *Dir* Margaret-Ann Murphy, MA.
Dept estab 1932; D&E; SC 50; enrl E 3500.
Courses: Calligraphy; Ceramics; Drawing; Goldsmithing; Handicrafts (basketry, bookbinding, enameling, lapidary, macrame, silk screen, stained glass, weaving).
Adult Hobby Classes: Tui $75-$111 per sem of 12 wks. Courses—Decoupage; Picture Framing; Woodworking.
Summer School: Same as above.

EMANU-EL MIDTOWN YM-YWHA,* 344 E 14th St, 10003. Tel: 212-674-7200. *Dir* Charles Eanet; Instrs PT 12.
Estab 1906; pvt; D&E; no ent req; SC 30; enrl D 250 PT.
Courses: Ceramics; Drawing; Painting; Photography.

FASHION INSTITUTE OF TECHNOLOGY, Art & Design Division, 10001. Tel: 212-760-7700. *Dean* Robert W Gutman, BFA; *Chmn Interior Design* A Cimonetti, BFA; *Chmn Fashion Design,* B Zamkoff, BFA; *Chmn Advertising Design* T Giaccone, BFA; *Chmn Fine Arts* F Shapiro, BFA; *Chmn Illustration* R Ahntholz, AAS; *Chmn Photography* H Berg, AAS; *Chmn Display Design* H Christie, AAS; *Chmn Textile Design* H Jacobs, BFA; *Chmn Jewelry Design* M Strump, AAS.
Estab 1951; pub; D&E; ent req HS dipl, ent exam; degrees AAS 2 yr, BFA 4 yr; schol; SC 317, LC 26; enrl D 3019, E 5612, maj 3019.
Tuition: Res—Undergrad $370 per sem; Nonres—Undergrad $695 per sem; campus res room and board $1994 per yr.
Courses: ‡Advertising Design; Aesthetics; Art History; Calligraphy; Ceramics; Collage; ‡Commercial Art; ‡Costume Design and Construction; ‡Display; Drafting; Drawing; Fashion Arts; ‡Goldsmithing; Graphic Arts; Graphic Design; Handicrafts; History of Art and Archaeology; Illustration; ‡Interior Design; ‡Jewelry; Lettering; Mixed Media; ‡Painting; ‡Photography; ‡Printmaking; Restoration and Conservation; ‡Sculpture; ‡Silversmithing; Stage Design; ‡Textile Design; Theatre Arts; Video.
Summer School: Dean Richard Meagher. Enrl 2900; tui $45 to $60 per course for term of 3, 5 and 7 wks beginning June. Courses—as above.

FORDHAM UNIVERSITY, Division of the Arts, 10023. Tel: 212-956-4774. *Chmn* Paul Brach, MFA; *Assoc Prof* Andree Hayum, PhD.
Estab 1968; pvt; D&E; ent req HS dipl; degree BA 4 yr; schol; SC 18, LC 25; enrl D 900, E 1750, maj 56.
Tuition: $77 per cr hr; campus res available uptown.
Courses: Aesthetics; Costume Design & Construction; Drawing; Graphic Arts; History of Art & Archaeology; New Media & Concepts; Painting; Photography; Sculpture; Stage Design; Teacher Training; Theatre Arts.
Summer School: *Dir* Dr Levak. Four terms per summer for 5 ks each.

GERMAIN SCHOOL OF PHOTOGRAPHY,* 225 Broadway, 10007. Tel: 212-964-4550. Instrs FT 10, PT 30.
Estab 1947; pvt; D&E; ent req HS dipl; degree cert 1 yr; schol.
Tuition; Varies.
Summer School: Courses—variety of short courses at our main school in NYC and branch school in Kingston, Jamaica, W.I.

GOETZ ART SCHOOL (formerly located Oklahoma City, Okla), 535 Bedford Center Rd, 10504. Tel: 914-234-9417. *Dir* Richard V Goetz; *vis prof*—Henry Hensche, Frank Mason, oil.
Estab 1946; pvt; D&E; SC 6, LC 2; enrl D 70, E 50.
Tuition: Monthly; no campus res.
Courses: Aesthetics; Drawing; Mixed Media, Painting (figure, landscape, portrait, still life).
Summer School: Enrl 50-70; tui $75 per wk for term of 4 wks beginning June 1.

GREENWICH HOUSE POTTERY, School of Ceramics, 16 Jones St, 10014. Tel: 212-242-4106. *Dir* Jane Hartsook, MFA; Instrs 17.
Estab 1902, dept estab 1948; pvt; D&E; no ent req; no degrees; schol; SC 32; enrl D 200, E 94.
Tuition: $100 per sem (adult); $40 & $50 per sem (children); no campus res.
Courses: Ceramics; Glazing Chemistry; Sculpture.
Adult Hobby Classes: Enrl 200; tui $100 per sem.
Children's Classes: Enrl 94; tui $40 & $50 per sem.
Summer School: Tui $100 per term of 6 wks beginning June 5 to July 14th. Courses—advanced classes in Ceramics; special seminars; workshop seminars.

HENRY STREET SETTLEMENT, Visual Arts Program, 466 Grand St, 10002. *Dir* Renata Karlin, PhD.
Estab 1895; pvt; D; no ent req; schol; SC 18; enrl D 60, E 60.
Tuition: $25-$65 per course.
Courses: Advertising Design; Art Education; Calligraphy; Ceramics; Commercial Art; Drawing; Film; Graphic Arts; Graphic Design; Jewelry; Mixed Media; Painting; Photography; Printmaking; Sculpture; Textile Design; Video.
Children's Classes: Courses—Leather Crafts; Pottery; Tie Dye.
Summer School: As during school year. Instrs FT 6, PT 8.

HUNTER COLLEGE, Art Department, 695 Park Ave, 10024. Tel: 212-570-5709. *Chmn & Prof* Lyman Kipp; *Prof* Robert Swain; *Prof* Wayne Dynes, PhD.
Estab 1890, dept estab 1935; pub; D&E; ent req HS dipl; degrees BA and BFA 4 yr; SC 20-25, LC 10, GC 14-20; enrl D 250 (including evening), maj 250, GS 250.

Tuition: Undergrad $387 per sem, $35 per cr, freshmen and sophomores; $462.50 per sem, $40 per cr, juniors and seniors; grads $750 per sem, $75 per cr; no campus res.
Courses: Art Education; Art History; Ceramics; Conceptual Art; Costume Design and Construction; Drafting; Drawing; Graphic Arts; Graphic Design; History of Art and Archaeology; Lettering; Mixed Media; Painting; Photography; Printmaking; Sculpture; Teacher Training; Textile Design.

JOHN JAY COLLEGE OF CRIMINAL JUSTICE, Art Department of Art, Music and Philosophy, 10019. Tel: 212-489-3557. *Head Dept Prof* Robert P Montgomery, ThD; *Assoc Prof* Laurie Schneider, PhD; *Assoc Prof* Marlene Park, PhD; *Asst Prof* Irene Gordon, PhD; *Asst Prof* John Dobbs; BFA; *Asst Prof* Helen Ramsaran, MFA; *Lectr* John Russell, BFA; Instrs FT 6, PT 4.
Estab 1964, dept estab 1971; pub; D&E; ent req HS dipl; degrees BA and BS 4 yr; SC 5, LC 6; enrl D 180, E 180.
Tuition: Res—Undergrad $387.50 per sem, $35 per cr, grad $462.50 per sem, $40 per cr; Nonres—Undergrad & grad $712.50 per sem, $55 per cr; no campus res.
Courses: Art History; Drawing; Film; Painting; Sculpture.

MAYER SCHOOL OF FASHION DESIGN,* Art Department, 64 W 36th St, 10018. *Dir* Herbert Mayer; Instrs FT 4, PT 13.
Estab 1931; pvt; D&E; ent req ent exam; 9 mo cert in Designing, Patternmaking, Draping, Fashion Drawing, Dressmaking, Grading; SC 11; enrl D 110, E 350.
Courses: Drawing; Dressmaking; Fashion Arts; Fashion Design; Fashion Draping; Patternmaking.
Summer Session.

MECHANICS INSTITUTE,* 20 W 44th St, 10036. Tel: 212-687-4279. *Dir* John I McCormick; Instrs FT 3.
Estab 1820; pvt; E; 3 yr; enrl 2042.
Tuition: Free in subjects related to work of those employed during day.
Courses: Architectural Drafting; Jewelry Design.

NATIONAL ACADEMY SCHOOL OF FINE ARTS, 5 E 89th St, 10028. Tel: 212-369-4880. *Dir* Alice G Melrose; *Instrs* D FT 12, E FT 3.
Estab 1826; pvt; no ent req; schol; SC 12; enrl 170; reg by month.
Courses: Compstition-Portraiture; Drawing; Graphic Arts Workshop; Life Sketch Class; Painting-Oil & Watercolor; Sculpture.
Summer School: May and August.

NEW YORK INSTITUTE OF PHOTOGRAPHY,* 263 9th Ave, 10001. Tel: 212-255-5150.
Estab 1910; individualized instruction; D&E; 12 mo; admission any Monday; normal enrl 500. Approved by New York State; approved for Veterans. Home study course.
Courses: Airbrush Technique; Commercial; Motion Picture Production; Natural Color Photography; Oil Coloring; Portrait Retouching.

NEW YORK SCHOOL OF INTERIOR DESIGN, 155 E 56th Street, 10022. Tel: 212-753-5365. *Pres* Arthut Satz, MFA; *Dean* Kerwin E Dettler, MS; Robert Murray, BFA.
Estab 1916; pvt; D&E; ent req HS dipl; portfolio and interview for 3 yr design or BFA program; schol; SC 25, LC 8; enrl D 700, E 300, nonmaj 865, maj 135.
Tuition: $2400 per yr, $1200 per sem, $70 per cr; no campus res.
Courses: Architecture; Art History; Drafting; Drawing; Graphic Design; Interior Design; Photography.
Summer School: Enrl 200; tui $70 per credit for term of 6 wks beginning July 9th. Courses—variety of lecture & studio courses.

NEW YORK STUDIO SCHOOL OF DRAWING, PAINTING AND SCULPTURE, 8 West 8th Street, 10011. Tel: 212-673-6466. *Dean* Mercedes Matter, BA; *Assoc Dean* William Wright, BA.
Estab 1964; pvt; D; ent req HS dipl, portfolio of recent work; schol; SC 13, LC 2; enrl D 80, GS 40.
Tuition: $2400 per yr, $1200 per sem; no campus res (available in summer only).
Courses: Art History; Drawing; Painting; Sculpture.
Adult Hobby Classes: Enrl 20; tui $125 per 12 wks. Courses—Drawing.
Summer School: Dir William Wright. Enrl 60-80; tui $750 for term of 8 wks beginning June 19th. Courses—Art History; Drawing; Painting; Sculpture.

NEW YORK UNIVERSITY,* Institute of Fine Arts, 1 E 78th St, 10021. Tel: 212-988-5550. *Chmn* Jonathan M Brown.
Pvt; D&E; degrees; schol and fel; enrl 400 GS (plus those maintaining matriculation).
Courses: Conservation & Technology of Works of Art; History of Art & Archaeology; Museum Training.

—School of Education, Department of Art Education & Division of Creative Arts, 80 Washington Sq E, 10003. Tel: 212-598-3478. *Chmn* Howard Conant; *Instrs* FT 10, PT 15.
Pvt; D&E; ent req coll board ent exam, 85% HS average, portfolio, interview; degrees BS, EdD, MA and PhD; schol and fel; SC 26, LC 13, (undergrad), SC 11, LC 15 (grad); enrl maj 115 (undergrad), GS 130.
Courses: Aesthetic Foundations of the Arts; Art Teacher Training; Art Therapy; Design & Graphics; Drawing & Painting; History of Art; Modern Art & Modern Design Seminars; Philosophy of Art; Sculpture; Technological Experiments in the Arts.

92nd STREET YMHA & YWHA, Art Department, 10028. Tel: 212-427-6000, exten 815. *Dir* Janet Bryant. Instrs PT 25.
Estab 1935; pvt; D&E; enrl 500.
Tuition: $60-$125 per sem of 4 mo.
Courses: Art Lectures; Art Tours; Calligraphy (English & Hebrew); Crafts; Drawing; Jewelry & Metalcraft; Painting; Paper-Making; Pottery; Sculpture; Textiles & Arts.
Children's Classes: Tui $50-$110 per sem of 4 mo, level elementary through advanced.
Summer School: June and July. Courses—as above.

PACE UNIVERSITY,* Dyson School of Liberal Arts, Art and Music Department, Pace Plaza, 10038. Tel: 212-285-3000. *Chmn* Peter Fingesten; Instrs FT 4, PT 5.
Estab 1950; pvt; D&E; ent req HS dipl, ent exam; 4 yr, no art major; SC 4, LC 20; enrl D 200, E 150, 700-800 yr art only.
Tuition: PT $80 per cr; campus res.
Courses: Architecture; Ceramics; Drawing; Graphic Design; History of Art & Archaeology; Leather; Macrame; Painting; Sculpture; Silver.
Summer School: Three summer sessions. Courses—Art and Architecture Design.

PARSONS SCHOOL OF DESIGN, 66 Fifth Avenue, 11215. Tel: 212-741-8910. *Dean* David C Levy, PhD.
Estab 1896; pvt; D&E; ent req HS dipl, portfolio; degrees BFA AAS and MFA 2 yr; schol; SC 200, LC 400, GC 25; enrl D 1200, E 2000, maj 100%, GS 25, others 40.
Tuition: $3400 per yr, $100 per cr; campus res room and board $2000.
Courses: ‡Advertising Design; Aesthetics; Architecture; ‡Art Education; Art History; Calligraphy; ‡Ceramics; ‡Commercial Art; Conceptual Art; Constructions; Costume Design and Construction; Display; Drafting; Drawing; ‡Environmental Design; ‡Fashion Arts; Film; ‡Goldsmithing; Graphic Arts; ‡Graphic Design; ‡Handicrafts (weaving); History of Art and Archaeology; ‡Illustration; ‡Industrial Design; ‡Interior Design; ‡Jewelry; Landscape Architecture; Lettering; Mixed Media; ‡Painting; ‡Photography; ‡Printmaking; ‡Sculpture; ‡Silversmithing; ‡Teacher Training; Textile Design.
Adult Hobby Classes: Enrl 1000; tui $100 per course. Courses—varied.
Summer School: Dir Bertram Katz. Enrl 500; tui $200 for term of 4 wks, beginning July 1. Courses—all regularly offered.

PELS SCHOOL OF ART, Department of Commercial Art, 2109 Broadway at 73rd Street, 10023. Tel: 212-873-4283. *Dir* Albert Pels, DFA; *Dean & Instr* Richard Beltran, BA; *Instr* Peter English, BFA; *Instr* Patricia Dillard, BFA; *Instr* Paul Fortenberry, MA.
Estab 1945; pvt; D&E; ent req 2 yrs HS, portfolio; degrees cert of completion 2 yr; schol; SC 6; enrl D 150, E 30, maj-all.
Tuition: $1600 per yr, $160 per mo, PT $160-$85, $1.60 per hr; no campus res.
Courses: ‡Advertising Design; Calligraphy; ‡Commercial Art; Drawing; Graphic Arts; Graphic Design; ‡Illustration; Interior Design; Layouts; Lettering; Mechanicals; Painting; ‡Paste-ups; Textile Design.
Children's Classes: Courses—Drawing; Painting.
Summer School: Enrl 80; tui $195 for term of 8 wks.

DONALD PIERCE SCHOOL OF PAINTING,* 463 West St, 10014. Tel: 212-242-5089. *Dir* Donald Pierce; Instrs FT 1.
Estab 1948; pvt; D; ent req over 16 yr of age; winter session Sept-May.
Courses: Acrylic; Drawing; Oil Painting; Watercolor.

PRATT-PHOENIX SCHOOL OF DESIGN, 160 Lexington Ave, 10016. Tel: 212-685-2973. *Dir* Roslyn Goldfarb, MFA.
Estab 1892; pvt; D; ent req HS dipl, portfolio interview; degrees AOS 2 yrs; schol; D 150.
Tuition: $100 per cr; no campus res.
Courses: Advertising Design; Art History; Calligraphy; Commercial Art; Drawing; Fashion Arts; Graphic Arts; Graphic Design; Illustration.
Summer School.

RIVERSIDE CHURCH ARTS AND CRAFTS, Riverside Drive at 120th St, 10027. Tel: 212-749-8140. *Admin* Dr. John R Moyer, EdD; Instrs PT 36.

Estab 1930; den; D&E; ent req must be 16 yrs of age; no degrees; SC 30; enrl approx 500 (fall and spring sem), 200 (summer).
Tuition: Approx $50 per sem per course, lab and reg fees added; no campus res.
Courses: Calligraphy; Ceramics; Drawing; Handicrafts (basketry, batik & tie-dye, bookbinding, chair caning, dance, early American decoration, fix-it-yourself, gardening, guitar, knitting/crochet, lampshades, macrame, needle arts, picture framing, quiltmaking, rugmaking, sewing, stained glass, weaving, yarn spinning.)
Summer School: Approx 200; tui $40 + lab & reg fees for term of 8 wks beginning June. Courses—generally same as regular year.

UMBERTO ROMANO SCHOOL OF CREATIVE ART,* 162 E 83rd St, 10028. Tel: 212-288-9621. *Dir & Instr* Umberto Romano.
Estab 1933; pvt; D.
Courses: Drawing; Graphic Arts; Painting; Sculpture.

SCHOOL FOR CREATIVE MOVEMENT IN THE ARTS, 265 W 87 Street, 10024. Tel: 212-724-3102. *Directors* Jack & Hattie Wiener, BA's; *Instr* Mary Newhouse, AB; *Instr* Barbara Ann Simpson, MFA; *Instr* Elaine Telsey Wechsler, MA; Instrs PT 4.
Estab 1972; pvt; schol; SC 4 (pre-school), 2 (school age), 1 (teen-age); enrl D 50 (maximum of 8 students in a class, age 3-17).
Tuition: Pre-school $85 per 17 wk term (45 min classes); School-age $90 to $120 per 17 wk term (1¼ and 1 ½ hr classes); Teen-agers $155 per 17 wk term (2 hr classes); no campus res.
Courses: Collage; Constructions; Drawing; Graphic Arts; Mixed Media; Painting; Printmaking.

SCHOOL OF VISUAL ARTS,* 209-213 E 23rd St. 10010. Tel: 212-679-7350. *Dir* Silas H Rhodes; Instrs 300.
Estab 1947; pvt; degree BFA 4 yr; enrl 3000.
Courses: Advertising Design; Airbrush; Audio Visual Art; Children's Book Illustration; Decorative Illustration; Drawing & Painting; Fashion Illustration; Film Art & Editing; Graphics; Journalistic Art; Layout-Lettering; Magazine Illustration; Paste-ups & Mechanicals; Photography; Photo Retouching; Production; Sculpture; Technical Illustration; Textile Design; Typographic Design. Note: This school is a professional art school in higher education. Qualified graduates may complete their studies for a degree at several colleges and universities in New York and out-of-state.

SCULPTURE CENTER,* 167 E 69th St, 10021. Tel: 212-737-9870. Instrs PT 10.
Estab 1933; pvt; D&E; no ent req; no degree; schol.
Courses: Sculpture.
Adult Hobby Classes: Sculpture.

STUDIO WORKSHOP, 3 West 18th Street, 10011. Tel: 212-243-0219. *Dir* Richard Rapaport; *Assoc Dir* Robert Streppone. Instrs FT 2, PT 4.
Estab 1967; pvt; D&E; no ent req; schol; SC 8, LC 8; enrl D 400, E 350.
Courses: Ceramics; Conceptual Art; Drawing; Enameling; Glaze Chemistry; Jewelry; Mixed Media; Occupational Therapy; Painting; Pottery; Sculpture; Silversmithing; Teacher Training; Watercolor.
Adult Hobby Classes: Tui $85 per 2½ months. Courses—as above.
Children's Classes: Tui $65 per 2½ months. Courses—as above.
Summer School: Courses—as above.

TOBE-COBURN SCHOOL FOR FASHION CAREERS, LTD,* 851 Madison Ave, 10021: Tel: 212-879-4644. *Pres & Dir* Avon Lees Jr; Instrs FT 9, PT 15.
Estab 1937; pvt; D; W; 2 yr course for HS grad, 1 yr course for those with 2 or more yr col; classroom study alternates with periods of work in stores or projects in fashion field; partial schol; degree AA (Occupational Studies); enrl 200.
Courses: Display; Fabrics; Fashion History; Fashion Promotion; Fashion Retailing; Merchandising; Salesmanship.

TRAPHAGEN SCHOOL OF FASHION, 257 Park Ave S, 10010. Tel: 212-673-0300. *Dir* Wanda Wdowka; *Chmn Design Dept* Marion Roller, BA; *Instrs* Harold Silverman, BA; *Instrs* Gabrielle Jean-Bart, BA; *Instr* Elena Braithewaite, BA; *Chmn Fashion Illustration* Elsbeth Edwards; *Chmn Interior Design & Dec* Jean Pierre Pique, BA.
Estab 1923; pub; D&E; ent req HS dipl, personal interview; degrees cert 2 yr, co-op BA prog with NY Institute of Technology issuing degrees; schol; enrl D 300 max, E 150.
Tuition: $2150 per yr, $1075 per sem, $14.33 per day, $2.38 per hr; no campus res.
Courses: Costume Design and Construction; Fashion Arts; Interior Design; Lettering.
Summer School: Enrl 15 per class; tui $350 per term of 6 wk. Courses—Draping; Dressmaking; Fashion Art; Interior Design; Patternmaking; Samplemaking.

OAKDALE

DOWLING COLLEGE,* Department of Art, Idle Hour Blvd. 11769. Tel: 516-589-6100, exten 246. *Div Coordr* Niel Peper; Instrs FT 7, PT 17 Pvt; D&E; ent req HS dipl; degrees BA (Visual Art & Speech, Drama), BS and BBA 4 yr; schol; enrl D 1100, E 500.
Tuition: $86 per cr hr; campus res $900 room.
Courses: Advertising Design; Aesthetics; Architecture; Art Education; Ceramics; Commercial Art; Drafting—Architectural; Drawing; Enameling; Graphic Arts; Graphic Design; Handicrafts; History of Art & Archaeology; Painting; Photography; Sculpture; Silversmithing; Stage Design; Teacher Training; Theatre Arts.
Adult Hobby Classes: Courses—Composition; Drawing; Painting.
Summer School: Dean Dr. John McConkey.

OLD WESTBURY

NEW YORK INSTITUTE OF TECHNOLOGY, Fine Arts Department, Wheatley Road, 11568. Tel: 516-686-7543. *Chmn* Dr Frances Lassiter, PhD; *Assoc Prof* William Haney, MFA; *Assoc Prof* Marvin Horowitz, MFA; *Assoc Prof* Shirley Marein, MFA; *Assoc Prof* John Murray, MFA; *Assoc Prof* Hans Schroeder, MFA; *Adjunct Assoc Prof* Phoebe Helman, MFA; *Adjunct Assoc Prof* Roger Williams, MFA.
Estab 1910, dept estab 1963; pvt; D; ent req HS dipl, portfolio review; degrees BFA 4 yr; schol; SC 11, LC 85; enrl D 527, nonmaj 100, maj 427.
Tuition: $2200 per yr, $70 per cr; no campus res.
Courses: ‡Advertising Design; Art History; Calligraphy; Collage; Commercial Art; Conceptual Art; Constructions; Display; Drawing; Film; ‡Graphic Arts; Graphic Design; History of Art and Archaeology; Illustration; Industrial Design; ‡Interior Design; Lettering; Mixed Media; ‡Painting; Photography; ‡Printmaking; ‡Sculpture; ‡Teacher Training; Textile Design.
Summer School: Tui $70 per cr for term of 5 wks. Courses—Drawing; Interior Design; Painting; Sculpture.

STATE UNIVERSITY OF NEW YORK COLLEGE AT OLD WESTBURY, Communicative & Creative Arts Department, Box 210, 11568. Tel: 516-876-3000, 876-3056. *Chmn* Luis Camnitzer; *Primary Faculty* Marc Bomse; Chris Griffin.
Estab 1968, dept estab 1969; pub; D&E; ent req HS dipl, skills proficiency exam, GED, special exception-inquire through admissions; degrees BA (Communicative & Creative Arts) 4 yr; SC 10, LC 10; enrl D&E 277.
Tuition: Res—Lower Division $375 per sem, $25 per cr hr, upper division $450 per sem, $30 per cr hr; Nonres—lower division $600 per sem, $40 per cr hr, upper division $750 per sem, $50 per cr hr; campus res room and board $1400 per yr.
Courses: Art History; Collage; Conceptual Art; Drawing; Graphic Arts; Intermedia; Mixed Media; Painting; Photography; Printmaking; Sculpture.
Summer School: Dir Marc Bomse. Courses—Photography.

ONEONTA

HARTWICK COLLEGE, Art Department, 13820. Tel: 607-432-4200 ext 520. *Prof* Roberta Griffith, MFA; Instrs FT 5, PT 8.
Estab 1927; pvt; D; ent req HS dipl; enrl dept 930, nonmaj 930, maj 65.
Tuition: $4100 per yr; campus res $1750.
Courses: Art Education; Art History; Ceramics; Drawing; Handicrafts (weaving, fiber); Jewelry; Painting; Photography; Printmaking; Sculpture; Silversmithing; Teacher Training; Video.

STATE UNIVERSITY OF NEW YORK COLLEGE AT ONEONTA, Department of Art, 13820. Tel: 607-431-3718. *Chmn* James Mullen, MA; Instrs FT 11.
Estab 1889; pub; D&E; ent req HS dipl, regents schol exam, SAT and ACT; degrees BA (Studio Art, Art History) 4 yr, Coll at Oneonta offers prog leading to MA (Museum History, Folk Art, Conservation & Restoration of Works of Art) in conjunction with the New York State Historical Association at Cooperstown, NY 13326 (Dr Bruce R Buckley, SUNY Dir); SC 31, LC 22; enrl D 660, E 35, maj 123, approx 25-30 at Cooperstown Center.
Tuition: Lower division $650, $21.50 per hr; upper division $800, $26.75 per hr; tui higher for nonres; campus res $1231.
Courses: Ceramics; Drawing; Graphic Arts; History of Art & Archaeology; Jewelry; Museum Staff Training (Cooperstown Programs); Painting; Photography; Sculpture; Stage Design (Dept of Speech & Theatre); Textile Design; Theatre Arts (Dept of Speech & Theatre).
Adult Hobby Classes: Offered only on a subscription basis at normal tuition rates through the Office of Continuing Education.
Children's Classes: Dir Dr Robert Porter. Enrl varies between 20-40 per yr. Offered only through the Upper Catskill Study Council, Sat Able and Ambitious Prog.

Summer School: Dir Dr Robert Nichols. Tui same as in reg session for two 6 wk terms beginning June and July. Courses—(depending on demand) Art Criticism; Art History; Studio Courses.

OSWEGO

STATE UNIVERSITY OF NEW YORK COLLEGE AT OSWEGO, Art Department, 13126. Tel: 315-341-2111. *Chmn* T C Eckersley, MFA; Instrs FT 19.
Estab 1861; pub; D&E; ent req HS dipl, SAT or NYS regents scholarship exam; degrees BA 4 yr, MA 2 yr; SC 31, LC 9; enrl maj 225, GS 5.
Tuition: Res—Undergrad lower division $375 per sem, upper division $450 per sem; Nonres—Undergrad lower division $600 per sem, upper division $750 per sem; campus res room $750 and board $600.
Courses: Aesthetics; Art History; Ceramics; Drawing; Environmental Design; Graphic Arts; Graphic Design; Jewelry; Museum Staff Training; Painting; Photography; Printmaking; Restoration and Conservation; Sculpture; Silversmithing.
Adult Hobby Classes: Tui $25 per person. Classes—Glass Media.
Summer School: Dir Lewis C Popham III. Tui $25.85 lower division per cr hr; NYS res $30.85 upper division per cr hr.

PLEASANTVILLE

PACE UNIVERSITY, Department of Fine Arts, 10603. Tel: 914-941-6400, exten 740. *Chmn & Prof* Brenda Bettinson; *Prof* John Mulgrew, MA; Beth Treadway, MA.
Estab 1906, dept estab 1978; pvt; D&E; ent req HS dipl, SAT scores, review by admissions committee and dept interview; degrees BS (Fine Arts) 4 yr; schol.
Tuition: Campus res room and board.
Courses: Art History; Ceramics; Drawing; Graphic Arts; Graphic Design; Interior Design; Painting; Photography; Printmaking; Sculpture.

POTSDAM

STATE UNIVERSITY OF NEW YORK COLLEGE AT POTSDAM, Department of Fine Arts, 13676. Tel: 315-268-5040. *Chmn* Mark H Sandler, PhD; *Prof* John Riordan, PhD; *Prof* William Gambling, MA; *Prof* Arthur Sennett, MFA; *Assoc Prof* James Sutter, MFA; *Assoc Prof* Steven Sumner, MFA; *Asst Prof* George Green, MFA; *Asst Prof* Joseph Hildreth, MFA; *vis prof*—James Czarnecki, Art Historian, 1978-79.
Estab 1948; pub; D&E; ent req HS dipl, SAT; portfolio review recommended; degrees BA 4 yr, special program Empire State studio sem in New York City, study in London (Jr yr).
Tuition: Res—Undergrad lower division $750 per yr, $375 per sem, $25 per cr hr, upper division $900 per yr, $450 per sem, $30 per cr hr; Nonres—Undergrad lower division $1200 per yr, $600 per sem, $40 per cr hr, upper division $1500 per yr, $750 per sem, $50 per cr hr; no grad students; campus res room and board $750 room and $676 (10 meals per wk).
Courses: Art Education; ‡Art History; ‡Ceramics; Drawing; Goldsmithing; ‡Graphic Arts; Jewelry; ‡Painting; ‡Photography; ‡Printmaking; ‡Sculpture; Silversmithing; Teacher Training.
Summer School: Dir Frank Dunn. Enrl max 25 per class; term of 3-6 wks. Courses—Masterpieces of World Art; Photo Workshop; Pottery Workshop; Sculpture Workshop.

POUGHKEEPSIE

DUTCHESS COMMUNITY COLLEGE,* Department of Visual Arts, 1 Pendell Rd, 12601. Tel: 914-471-4500, exten 339. *Head Dept* William M Brown; Instrs FT 10, PT 3.
Estab 1957; pub; D&E; ent req HS dipl; degree AAS (Commercial Art); schol; SC 24, LC 22; enrl D 660, E 340, maj 100.
Courses: Ceramics; Commercial Art; Drawing; Glass; Graphic Arts; History of Art & Archaeology; Illustration; Jewelry; Leather; Lettering; Metal; Painting; Photography; Plastic; Sculpture; Textile Design; Weaving; Wood.

VASSER COLLEGE, Art Department, 12601. Tel: 914-452-7000, exten 2642. Instrs FT 13, PT 4.
Estab 1861; pvt; D; ent req HS grad, ent exam; degree BA (maj in Art History only, no maj in Studio Art) 4 yr; schol; SC 8, LC; enrl maj 90, others 2400.
Tuition: $3875 per yr; campus res $1825.
Courses: Architecture; Drafting; Drawing; History of Art; Painting; Sculpture.

PURCHASE

MANHATTANVILLE COLLEGE, Art Department, 10577. Tel: 914-946-9600. *Head Dept Prof* John Ross, BFA; *Assoc Prof* Louis Trakis, BFA; *Assoc Prof* Mathew Broner, MFA.
Estab 1841; pvt; D&E; ent req HS dipl, portfolio, interview; degrees BA and BFA 4 yr, MAT 1 yr, special program MATA (Masters of Art in Teaching Art); schol; SC 25, LC (Art Hist) 10, GC 7 or 8; enrl D 180, nonmaj 90, maj 90, GS 10.
Tuition: Res—Undergrad $5400 per yr, $2700 per sem, grad $420 to $460 per course per sem; Nonres—Undergrad $3500 per yr, $1750 per sem; other application fee $20; campus res room and board.
Courses: Advertising Design; Art Education; Art History; Book Design; Calligraphy; Collage; Commercial Art; Constructions; Design; Drawing; Graphic Arts; Graphic Design; History of Art and Archaeology; Lettering; Metal Sculpture; Mixed Media; Painting; Photography; Printmaking; Sculpture; Teacher Training; Textile Design.
Summer School: Dir Mary Thompson. Courses—Art History; Drawing; Painting; Photography; Sculpture.

STATE UNIVERSITY OF NEW YORK COLLEGE AT PURCHASE, Division of Visual Arts, 10577. Tel: 914-253-5014. *Dean* Robert H Gray.
Estab 1966; pub; the campus provides facilities for a large Museum of Visual Arts and some 150,000 gross sq ft along with instruction in film, theatre, dance, music and the various fields in the visual arts.
Courses: Aesthetics; Architecture; Art Education; Drafting; Drawing; Graphic Arts; Graphic Design; History of Art & Archaeology; Industrial Design; Landscape Architecture; Painting; Photography; Sculpture; Stage Design; Theatre Arts.

RIVERDALE

COLLEGE OF MOUNT SAINT VINCENT,* Fine Arts Department, West 263rd St and Riverdale Ave, 10471. Tel: 212-549-8000. *Chmn* Donald M Reynolds Instrs FT 6, PT 2.
Estab 1847; pvt; D&E; ent req HS grad, col board, HS record; degrees BA, BS and BS(Art Education) 4 yr; schol; SC 25, LC 8; enrl D 950, E 50.
Tuition: $1250 per sem; room and board $875 per sem.
Courses: Advertising Design; Art Education; Ceramics; Drawing; Graphic Arts; History of Art; Jewelry; Lettering; Painting (oil and water); Photography; Sculpture; Design; Teacher Training.
Summer School: Dir Margaret Higgins. Tui $60 per cr, $5 reg fee for term of 6 wks beginning June. Courses—Ceramics; Photography; Watercolor; (course offerings vary in summer).

ROCHESTER

NAZARETH COLLEGE OF ROCHESTER, Art Department, 14610. Tel: 716-586-2525, exten 259. *Head Dept & Assoc Prof* Sister Magdalen LaRow, MFA; *Assoc Prof* Margaret Crawford, MFA; *Asst Prof* Mary Jane Edwards, MFA; *Instr* Monte England, MFA; *Instrs* Paulette Myers, MFA; *Instr* Ronald Netsky, MFA; *Instr* Susan Rowley, MST, *Asst Prof* Helen Jennette, MS.
Estab 1926, dept estab 1936; pvt; D&E; ent req HS dipl; degrees BA and BS 4 yr; schol; SC 40, LC 15, GC 6; enrl D 180, E 74, nonmaj 50, maj 180, GS 48.
Tuition: Undergrad $1350 per sem, $72 per cr hr; Nonres—grad $82 per cr hr; campus res room and board $1580 per yr.
Courses: ‡Art Education; ‡Art History; Ceramics; Drawing; Goldsmithing; Jewelry; Painting; Photography; Printmaking; Sculpture; Silversmithing; Textile Design.
Children's Classes: Enrl 20; tui $100 per 4 wks. Courses—Pre-college Art Program.
Summer School: Dir Elaine Hayden. Enrl 60; tui $72/82 per cr hr for term of 6 wks beginning July 5th. Courses—Grad and undergrad.

ROCHESTER INSTITUTE OF TECHNOLOGY
—**College of Fine and Applied Arts,** One Lomb Memorial Dr, 14623. Tel: 716-464-2646. *Dean College & Dir School for American Craftsmen* Dr Robert H Johnston.
   School of Art and Design. *Chmn Fine Arts* Philip W Bornarth; *Chmn Environmental Design* Craig J McArt; *Chmn Found Studies* Ronald E Padghan; *Chmn Communications Design* R Roger Remington; Faculty 31 FT, PT 5. Estab 1829; pvt; ent req HS grad, ent exam, portfolio; degrees AAS, BFA, MFA, MST, 4 - 5 yr; enrl 500. Tui $3096; campus res available. Courses—Art Education (grad only); Communication Design; Painting; Printmaking.
   School of American Craftsmen. Faculty FT 10. Estab 1946; pvt; ent req HS grad, ent exam; portfolio, Jr yr abroad with above academic record; degrees AAS, BFA, MFA, MST 4-5 yr; enrl 140. Tui $3096;

campus res available. Courses—Ceramics; Glassblowing; Metalcrafts & Jewelry; Weaving & Textile Design; Woodworking & Furniture Design. Summer School: College of Continuing Education, two 5 wk terms.
—**College of Graphic Arts and Photography.** *Dean* Lothar K Engelmann, PhD; *Assoc Dean* John L Kronenberg, BS.
School of Photographic Arts and Sciences. Acting Dir David A Engdahl. Tui $3096 per yr.
School of Printing. Dir Mark F Guldin. Tui $3096 per yr.
Graphic Arts Research Center, Dir Herbert E Phillips
School of Photographic Arts and Sciences.

UNIVERSITY OF ROCHESTER,* Department of Fine Arts, Morey Hall, 424, 14627. Tel: 716-275-4284. *Chmn* Archibald M Miller; *Instrs* D FT 13, PT 8, E PT 3.
Estab 1902; degrees 4 yr; schol; SC 25, LC 25; enrl maj 45, others 900.
Tuition: $4050 per yr.
Courses: Dance; History & Criticism of Art; Painting; Photography; Sculpture.

SANBORN

NIAGARA COUNTY COMMUNITY COLLEGE,* Fine Arts Division, 3111 Saunders Settlement Rd, 14303. Tel: 716-731-3271, exten 158. *Chmn* Donald R Harter; *Instrs* FT 6, PT 6.
Estab 1965; pub; D&E; ent req HS dipl; degree AS(Fine Arts) 2 yr; SC 12, LC 4; enrl D 400, E 120, maj 140.
Courses: Aesthetics; Ceramics; Design; Drawing; History of Art & Archaeology; Lettering & Typography; Life Drawing; Painting; Photography; Printmaking; Sculpture; Serigraphy; Visual Communications.
Summer School: Dir Judith Shipengrover. Enrl 30; term of 6-7 wk beginning June. Courses—same as regular yr.

SARATOGA SPRINGS

SKIDMORE COLLEGE,* Department of Art, 12866. Tel: 518-584-5000. *Chmn* Earl B Pardon; *Instrs* FT 21, PT 1.
Estab 1911; pvt; ent req HS grad, 16 cr, ent exam, portfolio; degrees BA and BS 4 yr; schol; SC 32, LC 18; enrl maj 255, 2000 total.
Tuition: $4295 per yr; dormitory room and board $2035 per yr or apartment $1315 per yr.
Courses: Art Education; Art History; Design; Drawing; Enameling; Film Making; Graphic Design; Jewelry; Lettering; Painting; Photography; Pottery; Printmaking; Screen Printing; Sculpture; Weaving.
Summer School: Dir Richard Upton. Enrl 60 for 6 wk. Courses—Ceramics; Drawing; Film Making; Painting; Photography.

YADDO, Box 395, 12866. *Pres* Newman E Wait Jr; *Exec Dir* Curtis Hornack.
Estab 1926; the country estate of the late Mr & Mrs Spencer Trask; pub; ent req open to all who have achieved some measure of prof accomplishment, applications must be received by Feb 1st, work must be shown to an admission committee, invitations are issued by April 15th for periods up to 2 months; no cash grants; enrl limited number.
Tuition: Room board and studio space for limited number.
Courses: Music Composition; Visual Art; Writing.

SCHENECTADY

UNION COLLEGE,* Department of the Arts, Union St, 12308. Tel: 518-370-6201. *Chmn & Prof* Hugh Allen Wilson; *Instrs* FT 8.
Estab 1795; pvt; D; ent req HS dipl, ent exam; degree BA with emphasis in music, art or drama 4 yr; schol; SC 14, LC 4; enrl maj 52.
Tuition: $4600 per yr.
Courses: Drawing; Graphic Arts; Graphic Design; Painting; Photography; Sculpture; Stage Design; Theatre Arts.

SEA CLIFF

STEVENSON ACADEMY OF TRADITIONAL PAINTING, Sea Cliff 11579. Tel: 516-676-6611. *Head Dept & Instr* Harold Ransom Stevenson; *Asst Instrs* Alma Gallanos; *Instrs* FT 2.
Estab 1960; pvt; E; ent req determinative personal interview; SC 3, LC 5; enrl 89.
Tuition: $80 per 10 wk sem, one evening per wk; $400 per 10 wk sem, five evenings per wk; 4 sem per yr; no campus res.
Courses: Artistic Anatomy; Basic course in academic study of form; Drawing; Illustration; Painting.
Summer School: Enrl 55; tui $68-$204 per term of 8 wks beginning June 1. Courses—Artistic Anatomy; Drawing; Painting.

SENECA FALLS

EISENHOWER COLLEGE, Humanities Division, 13148. Tel: 315-568-7172. *Chmn* Dr Sandra Saari, PhD; *Asst Prof* Susan Sauvageau, MFA; *Asst Prof* Peter Slusarski, MA; *Prof* Edmund Demers, PhD; *Instrs* FT 3, PT 1.
Estab 1965, dept estab 1968; pvt; D; ent req HS dipl, SAT, CEEB or ACT; degrees BA 4 yr; schol; SC 14, LC 15; enrl D 80-90, nonmaj 400, maj 15.
Tuition: $3000 per yr, room board and general fee $4785; campus res, room and board.
Courses: Art History; Calligraphy; Ceramics; Drawing; Graphic Arts; Painting; Sculpture.

SOUTHAMPTON

SOUTHAMPTON COLLEGE OF LONG ISLAND UNIVERSITY, Fine Arts Division, 11968. Tel: 516-283-4000, exten 241-243. *Assoc Dean* Donald L Wyckoff, PhD; *Prof* Robert Skinner, PhD; *Prof* Robert Shaughnessy, PhD; *Assoc Prof* Robert Munford, MFA; *Prof* Marie Wynn, MFA; *Assoc Prof* Yosh Higa, MGA; *Prof* Colonius Davis, PhD.
Estab 1963; pvt; D&E; ent req HS dipl and portfolio review; degrees BFA, BA Art Educ, BA(Fine Arts), 4 yr; MA Art Educ; schol; SC 36, LC 17, GC 11; enrl D 398, E 20, nonmaj 100, maj 280, grad 20, others 18.
Tuition: $1487.50 yr; campus res room and board $2690.
Courses: ‡Advertising Design; Aesthetics; ‡Art Education ‡Art History; Calligraphy; ‡Ceramics; Collage ‡Commercial Art; Constructions; Drafting; Drawing; Fashion Arts; Film; Graphic Arts; Handicrafts (jewelry, weaving, basketry, enameling); History of Art & Archaeology; Illustration; ‡Jewelry; Lettering; Museum Staff Training; Occupational Therapy; ‡Painting; ‡Photography; ‡Printmaking; ‡Sculpture; Silversmithing; Stage Design; ‡Teacher Training; Textile Design; Theatre Arts.
Adult Hobby Classes: Courses: Various Crafts; Painting; Drawing; Photography.
Children's Classes: 8 wk summer children's program.
Summer School: Dir Donald L Wyckoff. Tui $96 per cr hr for term of 3 wks beginning July. Courses—Various.

SPARKHILL

ST THOMAS AQUINAS COLLEGE, Art Department, Route 340, 10976. Tel: 914-359-6400, exten 273. *Chmn* Carl Rattner, MFA; *Primary Faculty* Sister Adele Myers, MFA; Sister Elizabeth Slenker, MFA; Roger Howrigan, MFA.
Estab 1952, dept estab 1969; pvt; D&E; ent req HS dipl; degrees BA and BS 4 yr; schol; SC 20, LC 10; enrl D 1100, maj 50.
Tuition: $1400 per yr; campus res.
Courses: Advertising Design; Art Education; Art History; Calligraphy; Ceramics; Commercial Art; Drawing; Handicrafts; Jewelry; Painting; Photography; Printmaking; Sculpture; Teacher Training; Textile Design; Theatre Arts; Video.
Summer School: Dir Dr Joseph Keane. Tui $180 for 3 cr course. Courses—varies 6-9 art courses including Ceramics; Painting; Photography.

STATEN ISLAND

STATEN ISLAND INSTITUTE OF ARTS AND SCIENCES,* Staten Island Museum, 75 Stuyvesant Pl, 10301. Tel: 212-727-1135. *Cur* Freda Esterly; *Instrs* FT 1, PT 2.
Estab 1881; pvt (with added support from New York City); no degrees.
Courses: Drawing (Life Class); Handicrafts; History of Art & Archaeology; Painting.
Adult Courses: Late afternoon and evening.
Children's Classes: During the day.

WAGNER COLLEGE,* Department of Art, 631 Howard Ave, 10301. Tel: 212-390-3192. *Chmn* William Levitt Jr; *Instrs* FT 5, PT 6.
Estab 1948; den; D&E; ent req HS grad; degree BA(Art or Art Educ) 4 yr; schol; SC 20, LC 6; enrl maj 130, others 2500.
Tuition: $2850 per yr (based on 12 to 18 cr per sem); campus res; room and board $1650 per yr.
Courses: Art Education; Art History; Black Art History; Ceramics; Crafts Design; Drawing; Experiments; Film Making; Mixed Media; Painting; Photography; Printmaking; Sculpture; Three-Dimensional Design; Two-Dimensional Design.
Summer School: Two sessions of 4 wks. Special 2 wk course (3 cr,)—Exploring Art in New York.

STONE RIDGE

ULSTER COUNTY COMMUNITY COLLEGE, Department of Visual Arts, 12484. Tel: 914-687-7621, exten 76. *Head Dept & Coordr* Allan Cohen, MFA; *Asst Prof* John A Locke III, MFA; *Instr* Joyce Veldhuis, MFA.
Estab 1963; pub; D&E; ent req HS dipl, SAT; degrees AA 2 yr; SC 17, LC 6; enrl D 250, E 100, nonmaj 305, maj 45.
Tuition: Res—Undergrad $375 per sem, $27 per cr; Nonres—Undergrad $750 per sem, $54 per cr; no campus res.
Courses: Advertising Design; Aesthetics; Art History; Drawing; Fashion Arts; Life Drawing & Anatomy; Painting; Photography; Theatre Arts; Two Dimensional Design; Three Dimensional Design.
Summer School: Enrl 75; $27 per cr for term of 6-8 wks beginning June 78. Courses—Drawing; Painting.

STONY BROOK

STATE UNIVERSITY OF NEW YORK AT STONY BROOK, Art Department, 11794. Tel: 516-246-7070. *Chmn* Melvin H Pekarsky, MA; *Prof* Jacques Guilmain, PhD; *Prof* Lawrence Alloway; *Prof* Nina Mallory, PhD; *Prof* George Koras; *Prof* Leopoldo Castedo; *vis prof*—Janet Fish, painting, spring 78.
Estab 1957; pub; D&E; ent req HS dipl, SAT; degrees BA(Art History) and BA(Studio Art) 4 yr; schol; SC 30, LC 1; enrl D 1289.
Tuition: Res—Undergrad lower division $750 per yr, $375 per sem, $25 per cr hr, upper division $900 per yr, $450 per sem, $30 per cr hr; grad $1400 per yr, $700 per sem, $58.50 per cr hr; *Nonres*—Undergrad lower division $1200 per yr, $600 per sem, $40 per cr hr, upper division $1500 per yr, $750 per sem, $50 per cr hr; grad $1800 per yr, $900 per sem, $75 per cr hr; campus res room and board.
Courses: Art History; Ceramics; Costume Design and Construction; Drawing; History of Art and Archaeology; Occupational Therapy; Painting; Photography; Printmaking; Sculpture; Silversmithing; Stage Design; Theatre Arts.
Summer School: Courses—selected number of regular offerings.

SUFFERN

ROCKLAND COMMUNITY COLLEGE,* Art Department, 145 College Rd, 10901. Tel: 914-356-4650, exten 285. *Chmn* J P Murphy; Instrs FT 6, PT 18.
Estab 1965; pub; D&E; ent req open; degree AAS 2 yr; SC plus apprenticeships; enrl D 900, E 300, maj 200.
Tuition: No campus res.
Courses: Advertising Design; Art Appreciation; Art Therapy; Color Production; Drawing; Electric Art; Graphic Arts; Graphic Design; History of Art; Lettering; Painting; Photography; Sculpture.
Adult Hobby Classes: Tui depends on enrl. Courses—varied.
Children's Classes: Courses—Overseas programs.
Summer School: Courses—Art History; Drawing; Graphic Techniques; Painting; Sculpture.

SYRACUSE

SYRACUSE UNIVERSITY, College of Visual and Performing Arts, School of Art, 200 Crouse College, 13210. Tel: 315-423-2611. *Dean* August L Freundlich, PhD; *Chmn* Sylvia Wyckoff, MFA; *Chmn* Arthur Pulas, MFA; *Chmn* Jerome Malinowski, MFA; *Chmn* Ainslie Burke, MFA; *Chmn* Michael Andres, PhD; *Chmn* Donald Waterman, MFA; *Chmn* Tom Allen, MFA; *Interim Dir* Joseph Scala, MFA; Instrs FT 62, PT 15.
Estab 1873; pvt; D&E; ent req HS dipl, portfolio review; degrees BID 5 yr, BFA 4 yr, MFA, MID and MS 2 yr; schol; SC 200, LC 25, GC 50; enrl D 1097, E 250, maj 1097, GS 186.
Tuition: Campus res.
Courses: Advertising Design; Aesthetics; Art Education; Art History; Ceramics; Commercial Art; Conceptual Art; Constructions; Costume Design and Construction; Drawing; Editorial Design; Fashion Arts; Film; Goldsmithing; Graphic Arts; Graphic Design; Handicrafts, (weaving); Illustration; Industrial Design; Intermedia; Interior Design; Jewelry; Mixed Media; Museum Staff Training; Painting; Photography; Printmaking; Sculpture; Silversmithing; Selected Studies; Stage Design; Teacher Training; Textile Design; Theatre Arts; Video.
Children's Classes: Courses—General Art.
Summer School: Enrl 100. Courses—Ceramics; Drawing; Film; Freshman's core program; Painting; Sculpture; Textile Arts; Visual Communications.

TARRYTOWN

MARYMOUNT COLLEGE, Art Department, 10591. Tel: 914-631-3200. *Chmn* Bianca Haglich, MA; *Asst Prof* Jane Henle, PhD; *Assoc Prof* John Hull; *Assoc Prof* Robert J Lee; *Prof* John Lochtefeld, MFA.

Estab 1918; pvt; D&E; ent req HS dipl, CEEB; degrees BA and BS; schol; SC 40, LC 15; enrl D 46, maj 46.
Tuition: Res—Undergrad $5725 per yr; Nonres—Undergrad $3425 per yr; campus res room and board $2300 per yr + $50 refundable room damage deposit.
Courses: Advertising Design; Art Education; Art History; Ceramics; Commercial Art; Costume Design and Construction; Drawing; Fashion Arts; Graphic Arts; Graphic Design; Handicrafts (stitchery, weaving); History of Art and Archaeology; Illustration; Interior Design; Jewelry; Lettering; Mixed Media; Painting; Photography; Printmaking; Sculpture; Teacher Training; Textile Design.
Summer School: *Dir* Margaret Ellen Flannelly. Tui $67 per cr. Courses—American Architecture; Mixed Media (Art, Vision and Form); Raku—Japanese Ceramics.

TROY

RENSSELAER POLYTECHNIC INSTITUTE,* 12181. Tel: 518-270-6460.
—**School of Architecture.** *Dean* Patrick J Quinn, Instrs FT 17, PT 7.
Estab 1929; pvt; D; degrees BArch, BS, March and MS 4-5 yrs; schol; enrl 230.
Tuition: $4025; campus res.
Courses: Architecture; Building Science.
—**School of Humanities and Social Science,** Department of Art. *Chmn* Ernest F Livingstone.
Courses: Ceramics; Color & Design; Drawing; Painting; Sculpture.

RUSSELL SAGE COLLEGE,* Visual and Performing Arts Department, 203 Second St, 12180. Tel: 518-270-2000. *Chmn* Marjorie Semerad; Instrs FT 6, PT 5.
Pvt; W; ent req HS grad; degree fine arts and divisional maj in Music, Art and Drama 4 yr; enrl 20-40 ea class.

EMMA WILLARD SCHOOL, ARTS DIVISION, Pawling Ave, 12181. Tel: 518-274-4440, exten 482. *Chmn* Carolyn Anderson, MA; *Chmn Art Dept* Leonard T Beecher, MA; *Instr Studio Arts* Katherine Kresieher, BA; *Instr Studio Arts* Chris Weaver, BA.
Estab 1814, dept estab 1969; pvt; D&E; ent req HS dipl, SAT; schol.
Tuition: $5900 including room and board; day student $2905 per yr; campus res.
Courses: Aesthetics; Art History; Ballet; Calligraphy; Ceramics; Collage; Conceptual Art; Constructions; Costume Design and Construction; Dance-modern; Drafting; Drawing; Graphic Arts; Graphic Design; Handicrafts (weaving); History of Art and Archaeology; Illustration; Intermedia; Jewelry; Lettering; Music-theory and individual Instrsuction; Painting; Photography; Printmaking; Sculpture; Spanish; Stage Design; Textile Design; Theatre Arts.
Summer School: For teachers. Studio 78.

UTICA

MOHAWK VALLEY COMMUNITY COLLEGE, Advertising Design and Production, 1101 Sherman Drive, 13501. Tel: 315-792-5446. *Pres* George H. Robertson, PhD; *Head Dept and Prof* Milton Richards; PhD; *Assoc Prof* Virginia M Juergensen, MFA; *Asst Prof* Paul Bowers, MFA; *Instr* James O'Looney, BA; *Instr* James Mannino, BS; *Instr* Reginald Case, MFA; *Instr* Henry Godlewski, BA; Instrs FT 6, PT 7.
Estab 1947, dept estab 1955; pub; D&E; ent req HS dipl; degrees AAS 2 yr; SC 18 (over 2 yr period), LC 6 (over 2 yr period); enrl D 260, E varies, maj 260.
Tuition: $642 per yr; campus res.
Courses: ‡Advertising Design; ‡Advertising Management; ‡Drawing; ‡Graphic Arts; Photography.
Adult Hobby Classes: Tui varies per quarter. Courses—Air Brush; Painting; Photography; Sketching; Watercolor.

MUNSON-WILLIAMS-PROCTOR INSTITUTE,* School of Art, 310 Genesee St, 13502. Tel: 315-797-000. *Dir* John R Manning; *Dir Emer* William C Palmer; Instrs FT 12, PT 10.
Estab 1941; pvt; enrl adults 650, HS students 75, children 700, (350 summer, 350 winter).
Courses: Ceramics; Dance; Drawing; Enameling; Graphic Arts; Introduction to Visual Arts; Metal Arts; Painting; Photography; Pottery; Sculpture.
Summer School: Four morning classes per wk for 4 wk, classes on Tues & Thurs afternoon or E for 4 wk.

WATERTOWN

JEFFERSON COMMUNITY COLLEGE,* Art Department, PO Box 255, 13601. Tel: 315-782-5250. *Pres* James E McVean; *Prof* Klaus Ebeling; Instrs FT 1.

Estab 1963; pub; D&E; 2 yr; SC 2, LC 1; enrl 850 (total).
Courses: Art Appreciation; Art History; Sculpture Studio; Two-Dimensional Studio.

WHITE PLAINS

COLLEGE OF WHITE PLAINS OF PACE UNIVERSITY,* Division of Arts and Letters, 78 N Broadway, 10603. Tel: 914-682-7070. *Chmn* Carol B Gartner; Instrs PT 2.
Pvt; D&E; ent req HS dipl; degree no art major 4 yr; SC 4, LC 4.
Courses: Art Education; Drawing; Graphic Arts; History of Art & Archaeology; Painting; Photography; Stage Design; Theatre Arts.
Summer School: Dir Sister M Berchmanns Coyle. Courses—Painting.

WESTCHESTER ART WORKSHOP, County Center, 10607. Tel: 914-682-2481. *Dir* Paul E Lohner, MA; *Coordr* Jean Mucher, BA.
Estab 1926; pub; D&E; ent req no special req; no degrees; SC 60 per sem—3 sem per yr; enrl D 450, E 250, others 700 (no credits given for courses).
Tuition: $63 per 3 hr, $42 per 2 hr; two 14 wk sem and one 7 wk sem; no campus res.
Courses: Calligraphy; Ceramics; Drawing; Handicrafts; Interior Design; Jewelry; Painting; Photography; Printmaking; Sculpture; Silversmithing.
Children's Classes: Courses—Ceramics; Handcrafts; Jewelry; Painting.
Summer School: Enrl 700; tui same for term of 7 wks beginning June 26th. Courses—same.

YONKERS

ELIZABETH SETON COLLEGE, Art Department, 10701. Tel: 914-969-4000. *Chmn & Assoc Prof* Sister Margaret Beaudette, MFA; *Assoc Prof* Sister Regina Kraft, MFA; *Assoc Prof* Sister Catherine Murphy, MA.
Estab 1960; pvt; D&E & weekends, ent req HS dipl; degrees AS, AAS and AOS; schl; SC 15, LC 3; enrl D 30, E 20, maj 25.
Tuition: Res—Undergrad $3700 per yr; Nonres—Undergrad $2100 per yr; campus res room and board $1600 per yr.
Courses: Advertising Design; Art History; Calligraphy; Ceramics; Drawing; Fashion Arts; Film; Interior Design; Jewelry; Lettering; Painting; Printmaking; Sculpture.
Adult Hobby Classes: Enrl 60. Courses—Etching; Frame making; Painting.

NORTH CAROLINA

ASHEVILLE

UNIVERSITY OF NORTH CAROLINA AT ASHEVILLE, Department of Art and Music, University Heights, 28804. Tel: 704-258-0200. *Prof* S Tucker Cooke, MFA; *Primary Art Faculty* Jos Vandermeer, MFA; Elma Johnson, MFA; Tony Bradley, MFA.
Estab 1927, dept estab 1965; pub; D&E; ent req HS dipl, ent exam; degrees BA 4-5 yr; schl; SC 20, LC 5; enrl D 1,280, E 300, non-maj 50, maj 40.
Tuition: Res—Undergrad $460 yr, $230 sem, $17 part time; Nonres—Undergrad $1115 yr, $90 part time; campus res room.
Courses: Art Education, Art History; Ceramics; Costume Design & Construction; Drawing; Graphic Arts; Intermedia; Jewelry; Mixed Media; Painting; Printmaking; Sculpture; Stage Design; Theatre Arts.
Summer School: Dir S Tucker Cooke; Courses—varies.

BELMONT

SACRED HEART COLLEGE, Department of Art, Main Street, 28012. Tel: 704-825-5146. *Chmn* Sister M Theophane Field, MFA.
Estab 1935, dept estab 1966; pvt & den; D; ent req; HS dipl, ent exam; degrees BA and BS 4 yr, AA 2 yr; SC 30, LC 3; enrl maj 27, others 50.
Tuition: Res—Undergrad $2960 yr, $55 per sem hr; Nonres—Undergrad $1610 yr; campus res room & board.
Courses: ‡Art Education; Art History; Ceramics; Collage; Commercial Art; Constructions (3-D); Drawing; Graphic Arts; Graphic Design; Jewelry; Mixed Media; Painting; Photography; Printmaking; Sculpture; Teacher Training; Textile Design.

BOONE

APPALACHIAN STATE UNIVERSITY,* Department of Art, 28608. Tel: 704-262-2220. *Chmn* L F Edwards; Instrs FT 12, PT 2.
Estab 1960; pub; D; ent req; HS dipl, ent exam; BA and BS(commercial design, art educ, studio art), 4 yr; schl; SC 38, LC 10, GC 12; enrl D 1000, maj 236, grad 5.

Courses: Art Appreciation; Art Education; Ceramics; Commercial Art; Drawing; Fabric Design; Graphic Arts; Graphic Design; Handicrafts; History of Art & Archaeology; Jewelry; Lettering; Painting; Photography; Sculpture; Teacher Training.
Summer School: Dir L F Edwards. Enrl 300; term of 2, 4 & 6 wk beginning May-Aug. Courses—As above.

BREVARD

BREVARD COLLEGE, Division of Fine Arts, 28712. Tel: 704-883-8292. *Chmn* Dr John D Upchurch; *Assoc Professor* Timothy G Murray, MACA; *Instr* Cheryl Harrison.
Estab 1853; den; D&E; ent req HS dipl; degrees AFA 2 yr; schl; SC 12, LC 2.
Tuition: Res—Undergrad $1275 yr; Nonres—Undergrad $1475 yr.
Courses: Art History; Ceramics; Drawing; Film; Graphic Arts; Graphic Design; Painting; Photography; Printmaking; Sculpture; Theatre Arts.
Summer School: Courses—Varies from yr to yr.

CHAPEL HILL

UNIVERSITY OF NORTH CAROLINA AT CHAPEL HILL, Department of Art & Art History, 104 Ackland Art Ctr 003A, 27514. Tel: 919-933-2015. *Prof* William R Kenan, Jr; *Assoc Chmn for Studio Art* Richard W Kinnaird, MFA; *Prof* Donald B Kuspit, PhD; *Prof* Frances Huemer, PhD; *Prof* John W Dixon Jr, PhD; *Prof* Marvin Saltzman, MFA; *Prof* Robert Howard, MA; *Prof* Robert Barnard, MFA; *vis prof*—Hohn A Hertzman, Art History. Fall 77 - Spring 78.
Estab 1789; dept estab 1951; pub; ent req HS dipl; degrees MA and MFA 2 yr, PhD 4 or more yr, AB and BFA 4 yr; schl; SC 22, LC 35, GC 25; enrl D 1457, nonmaj 1167, maj 290, grad 63.
Tuition: Res—Undergrad $264.50 per sem, grad (full load) $262.50 per sem; Nonres—Undergrad $1119.50 per sem, grad (full load) $1117.50 per sem.
Courses: Art Education; Art History; Ceramics; History of Art & Archaeology; Museum Staff Training; Painting; Printmaking; Sculpture.
Summer School: Dir Arthur S Marks. Courses—Basic Art History & Studio Art Courses in Painting, Printmaking, Ceramics & Sculpture.

CHARLOTTE

QUEENS COLLEGE,* Art Department, 1900 Selwyn Ave, 28207. Tel: 704-332-7121. *Head* John D McClanahan; Instrs FT 3, PT 1.
Estab 1857; den; W; degrees granted; ent schl; SC 19, LC 7.
Courses: Ceramics; Commercial Art; Fine Arts; History of Art.

UNIVERSITY OF NORTH CAROLINA-CHARLOTTE, Creative Arts Department, UNCC Station, 28213. Tel: 704-597-2471. *Chmn of Creative Arts* Jack Beasley, MA; *Asst Prof* Rod MacKillop, MFA; *Assoc Prof* Eric Anderson, MFA; *Assoc Prof* Esther Hill, MA; *vis prof*—several different workshop leaders in various media.
Estab 1965, dept estab 1971; pub; D&E; ent req HS dipl; SAT; Col Boards; degrees BCA 4 yr; SC 25, LC 3; enrl D 600, nonmaj 425, maj 175.
Tuition: Res—Undergrad $220 per sem; Nonres—Undergrad $1500 per sem; campus res.
Courses: Architecture; Art Education; Ceramics; Costume Design & Construction; Drawing; Graphic Arts; Handicrafts (metal & weaving); Painting; Photography; Printmaking; Sculpture; Silversmithing; Stage Design; Teacher Training; Theatre Arts.

CULLOWHEE

WESTERN CAROLINA UNIVERSITY, Department of Art, Belk Bldg, 28723. Tel: 704-293-7210. *Assoc Prof* Evan R Firestone, PhD; *Asst Prof* William C Buchanan, MFA; *Assoc Prof* Dr Lee P Budahl, PhD; *Asst Prof* Joan F Byrd, MFA; *Assoc Prof* Dr Perry Kelly, EDD; *Asst Prof* William R Lidh, MFA; *Asst Prof* Theodore P Matus, MFA; *Asst Prof* David Nichols, MFA; *Asst Prof* F Duane Oliver, MA; *Assoc Prof* James E Smith, MFA.
Estab 1889, dept estab 1968; pub; D&E; ent req HS dipl, SAT and C Average in HS; degrees BFA, BA and BSE 4 yr, Art honors studio; SC 36, LC 12; enrl nonmaj 1200 (sem), maj 150.
Tuition: Res—Undergrad $556 yr, $275 per sem; Nonres—Grad $2222 yr, $1111 per sem; campus room & board $1010 yr.
Courses: Advertising Design; Art Education; Art History; Calligraphy; Ceramics; Commercial Art; Drawing; Film; Graphic Arts; Graphic Design; Handicrafts (weaving); History of Art and Archaeology; Illustration; Jewelry; Painting; Photography; Printmaking; Sculpture; Teacher Training.

Summer School: Dir Dr Jerry Rice. Tui $14 per sem hr for summer beginning June 19. Courses—Workshops in Primitive Pottery, Wheel Throwing & Techniques; Glassblowing; Introductory Studio Courses.

DALLAS

GASTON COLLEGE,* Art Department, New Dallas Highway, 28034. Tel: 704-922-3136, exten 205. *Head* Franklin U Creech; Instrs FT 3, PT 2.

Estab 1965; pub; D&E; ent req HS dipl; degrees AA and AFA 2 yr; SC 22, LC 3; enrl D 140, E 50, maj 50.
Courses: Art Education; Ceramics; Drawing; Graphic Arts; Handicrafts; History of Art & Archaeology; Jewelry; Painting; Sculpture; Stage Design; Theatre Arts.
Adult Hobby Classes: Courses—Ceramics; Jewelry; Macrame; Weaving.
Summer School: Dir Franklin U Creech. Enrl 20; term of 11 wk beginning June. Courses—Design; Drawing; Painting; Pottery; Sculpture.

DAVIDSON

DAVIDSON COLLEGE, Art Department, Main St, 28036. Tel: 704-892-2000. *Chmn* Herb Jackson, MFA; *Asst Prof* Larry L Ligo, PhD; *Instr* Russell Warren, MFA.

Estab 1837, dept estab 1950; pvt & den; D; ent req Col Boards, HS transcripts; degrees BA and BS 4 yr; schol; SC 12, LC 9; enrl nonmaj 300, maj 6.
Tuition: $5000 yr (comprehensive fee); campus res room & board fee included in tuition.
Courses: Aesthetics; Art History; Collage; Conceptual Art; Drawing; Graphic Design; History of Art & Archaeology; Painting; Printmaking; Theatre Arts.

DURHAM

DUKE UNIVERSITY, Department of Art, 112 East Duke Bldg, 27708. *Chmn & Prof Art Dept* Sidney D Markman, PhD; *Asst Prof* Vernon Pratt, MFA; *Instr* Frank Smullin, MFA; *Assoc Prof* W K Stars, MA; *Prof* Elizabeth Sunderland, PhD; *Asst Prof* Rona Goffen, PhD.

Pvt; D; ent req HS dipl & ent exam; degrees MA 4 yr; SC 7 LC 30 GC 10; enrl D 496, nonmaj 467, maj 29.
Tuition: Campus res available.
Courses: Art Education; Art History; Ceramics; Conceptual Art; Drawing; Painting; Photography; Printmaking; Sculpture.

NORTH CAROLINA CENTRAL UNIVERSITY, Art Department, Fayetteville St, 27707. Tel: 919-683-6391, 683-6062. *Chmn* Lana T Henderson, PhD; *Prof* Robert Kennedy, MFA; *Prof* Carlyle Johnson, MFA; *Prof* Isabell Levitt, MFA; *Prof* Henry Michaux, EdD; *Prof* Mercedes Thompson, MA; *Prof* Norman Pendergraft, MA; *Prof* Melvin Cnever, MA.

Estab 1910, dept estab 1944; pub; D&E; ent req HS dipl, SAT; degrees in Art Education, Visual Communications and Studio Art, 4 yr; SC 30, LC 11; enrl D 120, E 30, nonmaj 1678, maj 120.
Tuition: Res—Undergrad $421.50 yr; Nonres—Undergrad $1800 yr; campus residence res $2041.50 yr, nonres $2854.50 yr.
Courses: ‡Advertising Design; ‡Art Education; Art History; Ceramics; Commercial Art; Drawing; Graphic Arts; Illustration; Jewelry; Lettering; Painting; Printmaking; Sculpture; Teacher Training; Crafts.
Summer School: Dir Dr W Maynor. Tui $225 for term of 9 wk. Courses—Art Appreciation; Crafts; Basic Drawing; Basic Design; Basic Painting.

ELIZABETH CITY

ELIZABETH CITY STATE UNIVERSITY, Department of Art, Parkview Dr, 27909. *Chmn* Dr Vincent J de Gregorio, PhD; *Assoc Prof* Dr Mohinder S Gill, EDD; *Instr* Dan M Pearce, MED; *Instr* Eugene O'Neal, MFA.

Estab 1891, dept estab 1961; pub; D&E; ent req HS dipl, evaluation of art portfolio by Chmn of Dept of Art; degrees BS 4 yr, Advance courses in Studio and History of Art; SC 27, LC 18; enrl D 1650, E 455, nonmaj 1500, maj 55.
Tuition: Res—Undergrad $340.50 yr; Nonres—Grad $1082.50; campus res room & board $552 yr.
Courses: Art Education; Art History; Ceramics; Drawing; Graphic Arts; Handicrafts; History of Art and Archaeology; Lettering; Mixed Media; Painting; Printmaking; Sculpture; Teacher Training.
Summer School: Dir Edyth B Cole. Enrl 950; tui $45 per credit for term of 4½ wk beginning May 22. Courses—Most courses programmed during regular academic yr.

FAYETTEVILLE

FAYETTEVILLE STATE UNIVERSITY,* Murchison Rd, 28391. *Chmn* Harvey C Jenkins; Instrs FT 4.
Estab 1877; pub; D&E; ent req HS dipl, ent exam; enrl D 60, E 20.
Tuition: Res—Undergrad $1647.50 yr; Nonres—Undergrad $3073.50 yr.
Courses: Advertising Design; Aesthetics; Art Education; Arts & Crafts; Ceramics; Drawing; Graphic Arts; Handicrafts; History of Art & Archaeology; Leather Craft; Lettering; Painting; Photography; Sculpture; Weaving.
Summer School: Dir Dr Ronald Smith. Courses—Art in Childhood Education; Arts & Crafts; Basic Photography; Drawing; Survey of Art.

METHODIST COLLEGE,* Art Department, Raleigh Rd, 28301. Tel: 919-488-7110, exten 257. Instrs FT 2.
Estab 1960; den; D&E; ent req HS dipl, SAT; degrees BA and BS 4 yr; schol; SC 6, LC 4, enrl D 650, maj 12.
Tuition: $1500 yr; campus res room & board $1240.
Courses: Art Education; Drawing; Enameling; Graphic Arts; Handicrafts; History of Art & Archaeology; Painting; Paper Work; Sculpture; Weaving.
Summer School: 3 terms, 3 wk early session, 5 wk main session, 6 wk directed study. Courses—Art Appreciation; Painting; Sculpture; others as needed.

GOLDSBORO

GOLDSBORO ART CENTER. 901-A East Ash St, 27530. Tel: 919-736-3335. *Primary Faculty* A Peter Hollis; Colleen Lane; Freda Kyle, BA; Arlyene Lusk, BA; Russell Knap, BFA; Gerald Boyles, BFA; Phil Kleinert, BFA; Jim Norman, BFA; *vis prof*—Ouida Canaday, workshop, 5 days; Instrs PT 14.
Estab 1971; pub; D&E; no ent req; schol; SC 25; enrl D 150, E 60, others 210.
Tuition: $5 for adults; $15 for children per quarter.
Courses: Calligraphy; Ceramics; Drawing; Handicrafts; Painting; Printmaking.
Adult Hobby Classes: Enrl 180 per quarter; tui $5 per adult per quarter. Courses—Ceramics; Calligraphy; Design; Drawing; Interior Design; Painting; Pottery; Printmaking.
Children's Classes: Enrl 30 per quarter; tui $15 per quarter. Courses—Calligraphy; Discovering Art; Drawing; Painting; Pottery.

GREENSBORO

NORTH CAROLINA AGRICULTURAL AND TECHNICAL STATE UNIVERSITY,* Art Department, 312 N Dudley St, 27411. Tel: 919-379-7993, 379-7645. *Chmn* LeRoy F Holmns; Instrs FT 4, PT 1.
Estab: 1930; pub; SC 29, LC 7; enrl maj 150.
Courses: Art Design; Art Education; Art History; Arts & Crafts; Ceramics; Commercial Art; Graphic Arts; Painting & Drawing; Three-Dimensional Design; Two-Dimensional Design.
Summer School: 6 wk & 2 wk session.

UNIVERSITY OF NORTH CAROLINA AT GREENSBORO,* Art Department, 27412. Tel: 919-379-5248. *Head* Dr Joan Gregory; Instrs FT 22, PT 4.
Dept estab 1935; pub; ent req HS grad, ent exam; degrees BA, BFA, MEd and MFA 4 yr; SC 22, LC 6, GC 8; enrl maj 500, others 4500.
Tuition: Res—$364 yr; Nonres—$2082 yr; campus res room & board $1110 - $1580.
Courses: Advertising Design; Ceramics; Drawing; Fibers; Graphic Arts; Lettering; Painting; Photography; Sculpture; Teacher Training.
Summer School: Dir Dr Jean Eason. Enrl 225; beginning May-June & July-Aug. Courses—Ceramics; Drawing & Picture Composition; Life Drawing; Mechanical Drawing; Moldmaking-Metal Casting; Sculpture; Watercolor.

GREENVILLE

EAST CAROLINA UNIVERSITY,* School of Art, 27834. Tel: 919-758-6665. *Dean* Dr Wellington B Gray; *Chmn Drawing & Painting* Metz Tran Gordley, MFA; *Chmn Sculpture* Robert S Edmiston, MFA; *Chmn Art Educ* William H Holley, EdD; *Chmn Printmaking* Donald R Sexauer, MA; *Chmn Ceramics* Charles F Chamberlain, MFA; *Chmn Design* Sara Edmiston, MA; *Chmn Communication Arts* Arthur Robert Rasch, MA; *Chmn Interior Design* Melvin S Stanforth, MFA; *Chmn Art History* Frances P Daugherty, PhD; Instrs FT 33, PT 12.
Estab 1946; pub; ent req HS dipl, 15 units, Col Board Exam; degrees AB, BS, BFA, MA and MFA 4 yr; SC 131, LC 29, GC 112; enrl maj 736.
Tuition: Res—$141; Nonres—$965; campus res.

Courses: Art Education; Art History; Ceramics; Communication Arts; Design; Interior Design; Painting; Printmaking; Sculpture.
Summer School: Dir Dr Susan McDaniel; *Art Dir* Dr Wellington B Gray. Enrl 8183; 10 wk beginning June.

HIGH POINT

HIGH POINT COLLEGE, Fine Arts Department, Montlieu Ave, 27262. Tel: 919-885-5101. *Assoc Prof* Raiford Porter, MFA.
Estab 1924, dept estab 1956; pvt & den; D&E; ent req HS dipl, SAT; degrees AB and BS 4 yr; schol; SC 16, LC 6; enrl nonmaj 400, maj 35.
Tuition: Res—Undergrad $2600 yr, $1300 per sem; Nonres—Undergrad $1450 yr, $725 per sem; campus res room & board.
Courses: Advertising Design; Aesthetics; Art Education; Art History; Ceramics; Costume Design and Construction; Drawing; Film; History of Art & Archaeology; Museum Staff Training; Painting; Printmaking; Sculpture; Stage Design; Teacher Training; Theatre Arts.
Summer School: Dean David Cole. Courses—general college courses.

JAMESTOWN

GUILFORD TECHNICAL INSTITUTE, Commercial Art Department, PO Box 309, 27260. Tel: 919-454-1126, exten 224. *Head* Norman D Faircloth, MEd Art; *Instr* Jerry E Painter, BFA; *Instr* Ralph E Calhoun, MEd Art; *Instr* Linda L Orr, BFA; *Instr* F Eugene Stafford, BFA; *Instr* N Jeanne Ward, AAS.
Estab 1964; pub; D&E; ent req HS dipl, English and math placement; degrees AAS 2 yr; schol; SC 20 LC 4; enrl D 70, E 60.
Tuition: Res—Undergrad $2.75 hr up to $45.50 per quarter; Nonres—Undergrad $16.50 hr up to $204.50 per quarter, no campus res available.
Courses: Advertising Design; Art History; ‡Commercial Art; Drafting; Drawing; Graphic Arts; Illustration; Lettering; Painting; Photography; Video.
Adult Hobby Classes: Tui $5 per quarter. Courses—Variety of subjects.

LAURINBURG

ST ANDREWS PRESBYTERIAN COLLEGE,* Art Program, 28352. Tel: 919-276-3652, exten 313. Instrs FT 2.
Estab 1960; den; D; ent req HS dipl, SAT, 2.6 grade point average, 12 academic units; degrees BA, MS and BM 4 yrs or 32 courses; schol; SC 14, LC 2; enrl D 852, maj 15-20.
Courses: Aesthetics; Art Education; Drawing; Graphic Arts; Graphic Design; History of Art & Archaeology; Painting; Sculpture; Stage Design.
Summer School: Studio courses offered.

LEXINGTON

DAVIDSON COUNTY COMMUNITY COLLEGE, Language-Fine Arts, Old Greensboro Rd (Mailing Add: Box 1287, 27292). Tel: 704-249-8186, exten 247. *Chmn* Antoinette Wike, MA; *Instr* Camille Lawrence, MA; *Instr* Katherine Montgomery, MA; Instrs FT 2, PT 3.
Estab 1963; dept estab 1966; pub; D&E; ent req; HS dipl; degrees AFA and AA 2 yr; schol; SC 14, LC 4; enrl D 100, E 30, nonmaj 195, maj 35.
Tuition: Res—Undergrad $39 per quarter; no campus res available.
Courses: Art Education; Art History; Basic Design; Ceramics; Drafting; Handicrafts (general); Independent Studio; Painting; Photography; Printmaking; Sculpture.
Adult Hobby Classes: Courses—Variety taught through continuing education.

MARS HILL

MARS HILL COLLEGE, Art Department, 28754. *Chmn* Joe Chris Robertson, MFA; *Prof* Stephen Wing, MA; *Assoc Prof* Gordon Mahy, MFA.
Estab 1856, dept estab 1932; pvt & den; D&E; ent req HS dipl, ent exam; degrees BA 4 yr; schol; SC 9, LC 6; enrl D 130, nonmaj 88, maj 42.
Tuition: Undergrad $3300 yr, $1650 per sem (included room/board allowance).
Courses: Advertising Design; Aesthetics; ‡Art Education; ‡Art History; Ceramics; ‡Graphic Arts; ‡Painting; Photography; Printmaking; Sculpture; Teacher Training; Theatre Arts.
Summer School: Dir of Admissions Dr John Hough. Enrl 400; tui $450 for term of 6 wk beginning May 31-July 6. Courses—Art Education; Pottery; Photography; Aesthetics.

MISENHEIMER

PFEIFFER COLLEGE,* Art Program, 28109. Tel: 704-463-3111. *Dir* James Haymaker; Instrs FT 1, PT 1.
Estab 1965; den; D; ent req HS dipl; schol; SC 4, LC 4; enrl D 125.
Tuition: $1870 yr; other fees $350; campus res $1300.
Courses: Art Education; Ceramics; Drawing; History of Art & Archaeology; Painting; Sculpture; Teacher Training.

MOUNT OLIVE

MOUNT OLIVE COLLEGE, Department of Art, Breazeale Ave. Tel: 919-658-2502.
Estab 1951; den; D&E; degrees AA and AS; schol; SC 5, LC 3.
Tuition: Res—Undergrad $2650 yr; campus res.
Courses: Art Appreciation; Art History; Ceramics; Color & Design; Drawing; Painting; Three-Dimensional Design.

PEMBROKE

PEMBROKE STATE UNIVERSITY,* Art Department, PO Box 66, 28372. Tel: 919-521-4510. Instrs FT 5.
Estab 1941; pub; ent req CEEB scores, HS record, scholastic standing in HS grad class, recommendation of HS guidance counselor and principal; degrees BA and BS 4 yr; SC 30, LC 12; enrl maj 80.
Courses: Art Education; Art History; Ceramics; Commercial Art; Design; Drawing & Painting; Graphic Arts; Photography & Crafts; Sculpture.
Summer School: Variety of courses.

PENLAND

PENLAND SCHOOL OF CRAFTS, 28765. Tel: 704-765-2359. *Dir* William J Brown, MFA.
Estab 1929; pvt; D (summer only); ent req age 18, fall and spring sessions require portfolio and resume; No degrees granted but credit may be obtained through agreement with East Tennessee State Univ; Special program requiring portfolio and resume offered in fall and spring; schol; SC 10-20; enrl D approx 100.
Tuition: $70 wk term of 2-3 wk; campus res room & board $80 wk.
Courses: Ceramics; Handicrafts (various); Jewelry; Painting; Photography; Printmaking; Sculpture; Silversmithing; Textile Design.

RALEIGH

MEREDITH COLLEGE,* Department of Art, 27611. Tel: 919-833-6461, exten 257. *Chmn* Leonard White; Instrs FT 3, PT 4.
Estab 1898; den; D&E; W; ent req HS dipl; degrees AB 4 yr; schol; SC 15, LC 5; enrl D 250, E 40, maj 50, others 10.
Tuition: $2100 yr; room & board $1100 yr.
Courses: Art Education; Ceramics; Commercial Art; Costume Design & Construction; Drawing; Graphic Arts; Graphic Design; History of Art; Painting; Photography; Sculpture.
Adult Hobby Classes: Courses—Painting; Sculpture; Art History.
Summer School: Dir John Hiott; courses variable.

NORTH CAROLINA STATE UNIVERSITY AT RALEIGH,* School of Design, 27607. Tel: 919-737-2201. *Dean* Claude E McKinney; *Dir Landscape Architecture* Arthur L Sullivan; *Dir Architecture* John Loss; *Dir Product Design Program* Vincent M Foote; *Dir Basic Design* Michael Pause; Instrs FT 4, PT 3.
Estab 1948; pub; ent req col board, ent exam; degrees BEnvDesign (in Architecture, Landscape Architecture, Product Design & Product Design, Visual Design Option), MArch, MLandscape Arch, MUrb Design, MProduct Design 4-6 yr; enrl Architecture 354, Landscape Architecture 77, Product Design 105, special students 10.
Tuition: Res—Approx $524.30; Nonres—Approx $2170.30.

ST MARY'S COLLEGE, 900 Hillsborough St, 27611. Tel: 919-828-2521. *Chmn of Dept & Assoc Prof* Margaret Click Williams, MFA; *Instr* Betty Adams, MAT.
Estab 1842; pvt & den; D; ent req HS dipl, SAT or SSAT; degrees HS dipl, AA; schol; SC 11, LC 2; enrl D 150.
Tuition: Undergrad $2735 yr; campus res room & board $1920 yr.
Courses: Art History; Ceramics; Drawing; Graphic Arts; Painting; Printmaking; Stage Design; Theatre Arts.
Summer School: Dean of the College Robert J Miller. Enrl Varies; tui $200 for term of 3-5 wk beginning May or June. Courses—Varies courses each year, no courses offered in Art for 1978.

STATESVILLE

MITCHELL COMMUNITY COLLEGE, Visual Art Department, East Broad St, 28677. Tel: 704-873-2201, exten 202. *Acting Chmn* Donald Everett Moore, MA; Instrs PT 8.
Estab 1852, dept estab 1974; pub; D&E; ent req HS dipl, HS transcripts, Placement Test; degrees AA and AFA 2 yr; schol; SC 12-15, LC 5; enrl D 85, E 25, nonmaj 60, maj 25.
Tuition: Nonres—Undergrad $150 yr, $50 per sem, $8 per course part time; no campus res available.
Courses: Art History; ‡Ceramics; Collage; Drawing; Graphic Arts; Handicrafts; Intermedia; Jewelry; Mixed Media; ‡Painting; Photography; Printmaking; ‡Sculpture.
Adult Hobby Classes: Tui $8 per 10 wk. Courses—Continuing education courses in art & crafts available.
Summer School: Acting Chmn Donald Everett Moore. Enrl 50; tui $50 for term of 10 wk beginning June 6. Courses—Varies, but same as courses listed above.

SYLVA

SOUTHWESTERN TECHNICAL INSTITUTE, Commercial Art & Advertising Design, Webster Rd, 28779 (Mailing Add: PO Box 95, Sylva, 28779). Tel: 704-586-4091 exten 33. *Head Dept* Bob Clark, MS; *Instrs* Eugenia Johnson, MA; Instrs FT 2, PT 3.
Estab 1964, dept estab 1967; pub; D; ent req HS dipl; degrees AAS; schol; SC 19, LC 14; enrl D 40, maj 40.
Tuition: Res—Undergrad $39 quarterly; Nonres—Undergrad $198 quarterly; no campus res.
Courses: ‡Advertising Design; Art History; Calligraphy; ‡Commercial Art; Display; Drafting; Drawing; Fashion Arts; Graphic Arts; Graphic Design; Illustration; Lettering; Painting; Photography.
Adult Hobby Classes: Enrl 30; tui $3.25 per quarter hr. Courses—Painting.

WILMINGTON

UNIVERSITY OF NORTH CAROLINA AT WILMINGTON, Art Department, PO Box 3725, 28406. Tel: 919-791-4330, exten 277. *Chmn* Dr Claude F Howell; *Asst Prof* Ralph Michael Goins, MA; *Asst Prof* Ann Louise Conner, MA; *Lectr* Christie R Pattison, MA; *Instrs* Bertram F Bradshaw, MA.
Estab 1789, dept estab 1952; pub; D&E; ent req HS dipl, ent exam; degrees BCA 4 yr; schol.
Courses: Art Education; Art History; Drawing; History of Art & Archaeology; Jewelry; Mixed Media; Painting; Printmaking.
Adult Hobby Classes: Courses—Painting; Drawing.
Summer School: 2 sessions. Courses—Various Art Classes each summer.

WILSON

ATLANTIC CHRISTIAN COLLEGE, Art Department, 27893. Tel: 919-237-3161. *Chmn* Edward Brown, MFA; *Assoc Prof* Norbert Irving, MFA; *Asst Prof* Thomas Marshall, MA; *Asst Prof* Chris Wilson, MFA; *Prof* Edward Brown, MFA; vis prof—Various part time instructors in art history and weaving.
Estab 1903, dept estab 1950; pvt; D&E; ent req HS dipl, ent exam; degrees BS, BA and BFA 4 yr; SC 13 LC 8; enrl D 68, E 5, nonmaj 68, others 8 (part time).
Tuition: Undergrad $1510 yr, $755 per sem; campus res room & board $950 yr.
Courses: Advertising Design; Art Education; Art History; Ceramics; Commercial Art; Display; Drawing; Graphic Arts; Graphic Design; Handicrafts (weaving); History of Art & Archaeology; Illustration; Museum Staff Training; Painting; Photography; Printmaking; Sculpture; Teacher Training; Textile Design; Theatre Arts.
Adult Hobby Classes: Tui $75 audit per term. Courses—any adult can audit any studio class.
Summer School: Dir Edward Brown. Enrl varies; tui $150 per course for term of 5 wk beginning May 29-June 30 & July 4-Aug 10. Courses: Art Survey; Drawing; Art Education Lab.

WINGATE

WINGATE COLLEGE,* Division of Fine Arts & Foreign Language, 28175. Tel: 704-233-4241. *Chmn Div* Kenneth C Murray; Instrs FT 3.
Estab 1896, dept estab 1958; den; D&E; ent req HS grad; degrees AA and AS 2 yr; schol; enrl D 608, E 50.
Tuition: $1100 (includes room & board).
Courses: Art Appreciation; Arts & Crafts; Ceramics; Cinema; Composition; Drafting; Gallery Tours; History of Art; Introduction to Fine Arts; Painting; Photography; Sketching.
Children's Classes: Courses in art.

Summer School: Pres Dr Thomas E Corts. Term of 5 wk beginning 1st wk June. Courses—all regular class work available if demand warrants.

WINSTON-SALEM

ARTS AND CRAFTS ASSOCIATION,* INC, 610 Coliseum Dr, 27106. Tel: 919-723-7395. *Pres* S O McSwain; *Mgr* Frances H Malcolm. Estab 1953.
Offers classes on all levels of skill in art and craft areas to both adults and children; classes offered in four sessions; children's classes on Sat mornings; workshops with outstanding artists and craftsmen. Invitational Summer Art Honors Program for junior-senior high students. Student shows in Hanes Gallery.

SALEM ACADEMY AND COLLEGE,* Art Department, 27108. Tel: 919-723-7961, exten 349. *Assoc Prof* William Mangum; Instrs FT 3, PT 3.
Den; D; W; ent req HS Dipl; degrees BA 4 yr; schol; enrl D 642, maj 44.
Tuition: $4500 yr includes room & board.
Courses: Art Education; Ceramics; Drawing; Graphic Arts; History of Art; Painting; Sculpture.

WAKE FOREST UNIVERSITY, Department of Art, Box 7232, 27109. Tel: 919-761-5310, 761-5303, 761-5302. *Chmn & Asst Prof* Robert Knott, PhD; *Lectr* Marvin S Coats, MFA; *Instr* Gary A Cook, MFA; *Asst Prof* Brian Legakis, PhD; *Instr* Andrew Polk III, MFA.
Estab 1834, dept estab 1968; pvt; D; ent req HS dipl, SAT; degrees BA 4 yr; schol; SC 14, LC 28; enrl D 250, nonmaj 200, maj 50.
Tuition: Res—Undergrad $3970 yr, $1985 per sem, $85 per cr, grad $2750 yr, $90 per cr; Nonres—Undergrad $2750 yr, $85 per credit; campus res room & board $1220 (no dormitory facilities are available on campus for grad students).
Courses: Aesthetics; Architecture; Art History; Drawing; Graphic Arts; Graphic Design; History of Art & Archaeology; Painting; Printmaking; Sculpture.
Summer School: Dir Percival Perry. Enrl 25; tui $35 per cr, $45 per hr grad, for term of two 5 wk sessions beginning May 22 & June 26. Courses—Painting; Design; Drawing.

WINSTON-SALEM STATE UNIVERSITY, Art Department, 27102. Tel: 919-761-2090. *Chmn* Hayward L Ourbre, MFA; *Prof* James T Diggs, MA; *Asst Prof* Mitzi Shewhake, MFA; *Assoc Prof* Roland S Watts, MFA.
Estab 1892, dept estab 1970; pub; D&E; ent req HS dipl; degrees BA 4 yr; SC 10, LC 7; enrl D 65, nonmaj 275, maj 65.
Tuition: Campus res room & board.
Courses: Art Education; Art History; Drawing; Graphic Arts; Painting; Sculpture.

NORTH DAKOTA

DICKINSON

DICKINSON STATE COLLEGE, Department of Art, Division of Fine Arts and Humanities, 58601. Tel: 701-227-2312. *Chmn and Assoc Prof* Dennis Edward Navrat, MFA; *Assoc Prof* Donald L Duda, MA; *Assoc Prof* Clinton A Sheffield, MA; vis prof—periodic visiting artists and workshops.
Estab 1918, dept estab 1959; pub; D&E; ent req HS dipl, out-of-state, ACT, minimum score 18 or upper-half of class; degrees BA, BS and BCS 4 yr, AA 2 yr; schol; SC 36, LC 8; enrl D approx 150 per quarter, nonmaj 120 maj 30.
Tuition: Res—Undergrad $486 yr, $162 per quarter, $13.50 per quarter hr, $17 extension per quarter hr; Nonres—Undergrad $1047 yr, $349 per quarter, $29.08 per quarter hr, $17 extension per quarter hr; campus res room & board $1000 yr.
Courses: Advertising Design; ‡Art Education; Art History; ‡Ceramics; Costume Design & Construction; Display; Drawing; Goldsmithing; Graphic Design; Handicrafts (leather, enameling, mosaic); Intermedia; Interior Design; ‡Jewelry; Lettering; ‡Painting; Photography; ‡Printmaking; ‡Sculpture; Silversmithing; Stage Design; Teacher Training; ‡Theatre Arts; Color; Serigraphy; Plastics; Foundry.
Adult Hobby Classes: above classes available for credit or audit.
Summer School: Vice Pres for Academic Affairs Dr Paul Larsen. Enrl approx 200; tui same as above for term of 2, 4, 2 wk beginning May 30. Courses: Basic Art; Photography; Watercolor; other division offerings.

GRAND FORKS

UNIVERSITY OF NORTH DAKOTA,* College of Fine Art, Visual Arts Department, 58202. Tel: 701-777-2257. *Chmn* Ronald Schaefer; Instrs D FT 10, GTA 4.

Estab 1883; pub; degrees offered 4 yrs; SC 30, LC 4, GC 14; enrl maj 120, others 1000.
Tuition: Campus res room & board.
Courses: Art History; Ceramics; Commercial Art; Design; Drawing; Elementary Art; Figure Drawing; Graphic Arts; Lab School; Painting; Sculpture; Teacher Training; Welding.
Summer School: Chmn Ronald Schaefer.

JAMESTOWN

JAMESTOWN COLLEGE,* Art Department, 58401. Tel: 701-253-2333. *Chmn* Robert Carter; Instrs FT 1, PT 1.
Pvt; D; ent req HS dipl; degrees BA and BS 4 yr, directed study and individual study in Advanced Studio Areas, private studios and junior and senior majors, schol; SC 13, LC 4; enrl 146, maj 8.
Tuition: $2490; campus res & board $1375.
Courses: Art Education; Art History; Drawing; Figure Drawing; Painting; Printmaking; Two-Dimensional Design.
Summer School: Dir Dr Andresen. 6 wk term beginning June.

MAYVILLE

MAYVILLE STATE COLLEGE,* Art Department, 58257. Tel: 701-786-2301. Instrs FT 1.
Estab 1890; pub; degrees offered, 4 yr; SC 20, LC 4.
Courses: Teacher & Professional Training.
Summer School: Variety of courses.

MINOT

MINOT ART GALLERY, Art School, ND State Fairgrounds (Mailing Add: PO Box 325, 58701). Tel: 701-838-4445. *Dir* Galen R Willert, BS; Instrs PT 2.
Estab 1970; pub; D&E.
Courses: Art History; Ceramics; Drawing; Framing; Graphic Design; Lettering; Matting; Painting; Printmaking; Sculpture; Textile Design.

MINOT STATE COLLEGE,* Division of Fine Arts, 58701. Tel: 701-838-6101, exten 363. *Chmn* C R Schwieger; Instrs FT 3, PT 2.
Estab 1913; pub; degrees BA and BS 4 yr; SC 30; enrl per quarter 300, maj 75.
Tuition: Res $153; Nonres $332; campus res.
Courses: Advanced Ceramics; Advanced Graphics; Advertising; Art History; Ceramics; Crafts; Design; Drawing; Graphics; Jewelry; Painting; Photography; Sculpture; Silk Screen; Weaving.

VALLEY CITY

VALLEY CITY STATE COLLEGE, Art Department, 58072. Tel: 701-845-7561. *Instr* David Behlke, MFA; Instrs FT 2.
Estab 1890, dept estab 1921; pub; D&E; ent req HS dipl, ACT; degrees BS and BA 4 yr, AA 2 yr; schol; SC 20, LC 3; enrl D 1000, E 200, nonmaj 120, maj 30.
Tuition: Res—Undergrad $372 yr, $124 per quarter, $10.33 per credit; Nonres—Undergrad $933 yr, $311 per quarter, $25.92 per credit; campus res room & board $966 yr.
Courses: Art Education; Art History; Ceramics; Commercial Art; Drawing; Graphic Arts; Graphic Design; Painting; Printmaking; Sculpture; Teacher Training.
Adult Hobby Classes: Enrl 10-15; tui $12.50 per quarter. Courses—Watercolor; Drawing.

WAHPETON

NORTH DAKOTA STATE SCHOOL OF SCIENCE, Department of Art, 6th St N, 58075. Tel: 701-671-2231. *Dir* Mary Sand, BA.
Estab 1903, dept estab 1970; pub; D&E.
Courses: Art Education; Drawing; General Craft; Graphic Design; Handicrafts; Lettering; Occupational Therapy; Painting.
Adult Hobby Classes: Enrl 15; tui $30. Courses—Painting.
Summer School: Dir Mary Sand. 2 wk term, 3 hr per day. Courses: Teacher's Art Workshop.

OHIO

ADA

OHIO NORTHERN UNIVERSITY,* Department of Art, 45810. Tel: 419-634-9921, exten 222. *Chmn* Thomas L Gordon; Instrs FT 4.
Pvt; D; ent req, HS dipl, ent exam; degrees BA and BFA 4 yr; schol; SC 30, LC 8; enrl maj 30.

Tuition: $4086 yr (including room & board), part-time $76 per quarter hr.
Courses: Aesthetics; Art Education; Ceramics; Costume Design & Construction; Drawing; Graphic Arts; History of Art & Archaeology; Jewelry; Lettering; Painting; Sculpture; Stage Design; Teacher Training; Theatre Arts.
Summer School: Dir Dr Bernard Linger.

AKRON

UNIVERSITY OF AKRON, Department of Art, 44325. Tel: 216-375-7010. *Dept Head* Warren A Wolf, MFA.
Estab 1926; pub; D&E; ent req HS dipl; degrees BA, BS and BFA 4 yr, AA 2 yr; schol; SC 25, LC 7, GC 8; enrl D 943, E 129, nonmaj 698, maj 245.
Tuition: Res—Undergrad $930 yr, grad $24 per credit; Nonres—Undergrad $3366 yr, grad $24 per credit; campus res.
Courses: ‡Advertising Design; ‡Art History; ‡Ceramics; Collage; Commercial Art; ‡Drawing; ‡Goldsmithing; ‡Graphic Design; Handicrafts (weaving); Illustration; ‡Jewelry; ‡Painting; ‡Photography; ‡Printmaking; ‡Sculpture; ‡Silversmithing; Textile Design.
Summer School: Dir Dr Carrino. Tui by credit for term of 6 wk. Courses—all of the above.

ASHLAND

ASHLAND COLLEGE,* Art Department, College Ave, 44805. Tel: 419-289-4005. *Acting Chmn* Albert W Goad; Instrs FT 7, assoc 1.
Estab 1878; den; D&E; ent req HS dipl, portfolio for BFA program; degrees BA, BS and BFA 4 yr; schol; enrl D 2000, maj 50, minors 40.
Tuition: $3253 yr; campus res $1400 yr.
Courses: Art Education; Ceramics; Drawing; Graphic Arts; Graphic Design; Crafts; History of Art; Painting; Photography; Sculpture; Stage Design; Teacher Training; Theater Arts.

ATHENS

OHIO UNIVERSITY, College of Fine Arts, School of Art, 45701. Tel: 614-594-5667/594-5668. *Dean* Henry H Lin; *Assoc Dean* James H Conover; *Dir* Eric Forrest; Instrs FT 27, PT 24.
Estab 1936; pub; D&E; ent req secondary school dipl-portfolio; degrees BFA, MA and MFA 4-5 yr; schol and fel; SC 88, LC 30, LGC 29, SGC 50; enrl maj 573, others 1718.
Courses: Art Education; Art History; Ceramics; Drawing; Fibers; Glass; Graphic Design; Illustration; Painting; Photography; Printmaking; Sculpture.
Summer School: Two 5 wk sessions beginning June-July and July-Aug; 18 quarter hr maximum per session; SC, LC, GC.

BEREA

BALDWIN-WALLACE COLLEGE,* Department of Art, 44017. Tel: 216-826-2900, exten 2152. *Chmn* Dean Drahos; Instrs FT 5, PT 1.
Estab 1845; den; D&E; degrees AB 4 yr; SC 23 LC 12; enrl 1900; maj 65.
Tuition: $3132 yr; PT $68 per cr hr; campus res $1479. Courses: Art Education; Ceramics & Crafts; Design & Color; Drawing; History of Art; Painting; Photography; Printmaking; Sculpture.
Summer School: Tui $51 per cr hr.

BOWLING GREEN

BOWLING GREEN STATE UNIVERSITY, School of Art, Fine Arts Bldg, 43403. Tel: 419-372-2787. *Dir* Joseph R Spence, PhD; *Head Weaving & Fibers* Kathleen Hagan, MFA; *Head Design* Carl Hall, MFA; *Head Jewelry & Metals* Harold Hasselschwert, MA; *Head Drawing & Graphics* Thomas Hilty, MFA; *Head Ceramics* Charles Lakofsky, MA; *Dir Grad Studies* Robert Mazur, MFA; *Head Art History* Willard Misfeldt, PhD; *Head Painting* Robert Stiuson, MFA.
Estab 1910, dept estab 1946; pub; D&E; ent req ACT (undergrad), GRE (grad); degrees BA, BS & BFA 4 yr, MA 1 yr, MFA 2 yr; schol; SC 53, LC 14, GC 33; enrl D 2460, E 150, nonmaj 995, maj 629, grad 33, others 40.
Tuition: Res—Undergrad $858 yr, $286 per quarter, $29.50 per cr hr, grad $990 yr, $330 per quarter, $30 per cr hr; Nonres—Undergrad $1980 yr, $686 per quarter, $67 per cr hr, grad $1368 yr, $456 per quarter, $40 per cr hr; plus other fees; campus res room & board $4356 yr.
Courses: Advertising Design; ‡Art Education; ‡Art History; Art Therapy; Calligraphy; ‡Ceramics; Collage; Commercial Art; Conceptual Art; Constructions; Display; ‡Drawing; ‡Environmental Design; Glass Working;

Goldsmithing; ‡Graphic Arts; Graphic Design; Handicrafts (weaving, fibers); Illustration; ‡Jewelry; Lettering; Mixed Media; ‡Painting; Photography; ‡Printmaking; ‡Sculpture; Silversmithing; ‡Teacher Training.
Summer School: Dir Dr Joseph R Spence. Courses—Special workshops vary each summer, usual courses in Drawing; Painting; Sculpture; Jewelry; Photography; Printmaking; Art History.

CANTON

CANTON ART INSTITUTE, 1001 Market Ave North, 44702. Tel: 216-453-7666. *Dir* Joseph R Hertzi; *Administrative Asst* Shirley A Allen; *Curator* Manuel J Albacete; *Registrar* Thelma Dittmar; *Administrative Secretary* Verna R Blyer.
Pub; D&E; SC 28; enrl D 322, E 984, others 1306.
Courses: Ceramics; Drawing; Mixed Media; Painting; Photography; Sculpture; Textile Design.

MALONE COLLEGE,* Division of Fine Arts, Dept of Art, 515 25th St NW, 44709. Tel: 216-454-3011. *Head* Mary Louise Robson; Instrs PT 3.
Estab 1956; den; D&E; ent req HS dipl, ent exam; degrees BA, BS (educ) and BS (music) 4 yr; schol; SC 20, LC 2; enrl D 75, maj 30.
Tuition: $76 per cr hr; campus res approx $1134.
Courses: Advertising Design; Art Education; Ceramics; Drawing; Graphic Arts; Graphic Design; History of Art & Archaeology; Jewelry; Leather; Lettering; Painting; Photography; Sculpture; Teacher Training; Textile Design.
Summer School: Enrl 850; tui $76 cr for term of 5 wk beginning June 15 and July 15. Courses—Art Education; Music and Art in the Western World.

CINCINNATI

ART ACADEMY OF CINCINNATI,* Eden Park, 45202. Tel: 513-721-5205. *Dir* Roger Williams, MFA; *Primary Art Faculty* Anthony Batchelor, Dipl; William Burk, MFA; Walter Driesbach, Dipl; April Foster, MFA; Stewart Goldman, BFA; Laurence W Goodridge, MFA; Calvin Kowal, MS; Barron Krody, Dipl; Anne Miotke, MFA; William Sontag, BS; Jane T Stanton, MA; Instrs PT 7.
Estab 1887; pvt; D&E; ent req HS grad; cert, BS collaboration with Univ of Cincinnati, BFA with Northern Kentucky State Col, 4-5 yr; schol; enrl 150.
Tuition: $1760 yr, $55 per cr hr; plus other fees.
Courses: Art History; Communication Design; Drawing; Graphic Arts; Graphic Design; Illustration; Painting; Photography; Printmaking; Sculpture.
Summer School: Supvr Anne Miotke. Enrl 64; tui $55 per cr hr for term of 8 wk beginning June 4

CENTRAL ACADEMY OF COMMERCIAL ART, 2326 Upland Pl, 45206. Tel: 513-961-2484. *Pres* Jackson Grey Storey; *Dean of Education* Michael G McGuire; *Instr* Garrent W Hamm; *Instr* Robert A Trau.
Estab 1931; pvt; D; ent req HS dipl; portfolio; SC 211; enrl D 96.
Tuition: $1700 yr, $850 per sem; campus res room & board $1150 yr.
Courses: Advertising Design; Calligraphy; Color; Commercial Art; Composition; Drawing; Fashion Illustration; Finished Art; Keyline; Illustration; Layout; Letterhead; Lettering; Life Class Mediums; Logotype; Magic Marker; Mediums; Package Design; Painting; Perspective; TV Storyboard; others.

CINCINNATI ART MUSEUM, Education Department, Eden Park, 45202. Tel: 513-721-5204, exten 70, 71. *Curator* Kenneth R Trapp, MA.
Estab 1881; pvt; D&E; ent req must be museum member; schol; SC 3; enrl D 150, E 60-80.
Courses: Drawing; Museum Staff Training; Painting.
Adult Hobby Classes: Enrl 60-80; tui $10 per adult.
Children's Classes: Enrl 150; tui $6 per child. Courses—Drawing; painting; sculpture; plus others.
Summer School: Enrl 200; tui $10 (adult), $6 (child) for term of 12 wk beginning June. Courses—Watercolor; Drawing; plus others.

EDGECLIFF COLLEGE, Art Department, 2220 Victory Parkway, 45206. Tel: 513-961-3770. *Chmn & Dir of BFA & BA Fine Arts Track* Ann Beiersdorfer, MA; *Dir of BA Handcrafts Track* Josiane Guglielmi-Trageser, MA; *Dir of BA Art Educ and Art Therapy Tracks* Sister M Rosine Allgeyer, MFA; *Dir of BA History of Art Track* James Kennedy, MA; vis prof—permanent artist-in-residence, Paul Chidlaw, painting.
Estab 1935; den; D&E; ent req HS dipl, portfolio for acceptance as an art major by end of sophomore yr; degrees BFA and BA 4 yr; schol; SC 20, LC 16; enrl D 120, nonmaj 30, maj 90.
Tuition: $68 per cr hr; campus res room & board $765 per sem.
Courses: Aesthetics; Art Education; Art History; Art Therapy; Ceramics; Collage; Constructions; Costume Design & Construction; Drawing; Fashion Arts; Graphic Arts; Graphic Design; Handicrafts; History of Art & Archaeology; Intermedia; Interior Design; Jewelry; Mixed Media; Paint-

ing; Printmaking; Sculpture; Stage Design; Teacher Training; Textile Design; Theatre Arts; Video.
Summer School: Dir Ann Beiersdorfer.

AL GABLE ADVERTISING ART SCHOOL, Division of Advertising Design School, Inc. 2617 Vine St, Upper Level, 45219. Tel: 513-861-6421. *Dir* Ronald L French; *Instr* Teresa Dave, BS(Art Educ); Instrs FT 2.
Estab 1958; pvt; D&E; ent req HS dipl, personal interview with portfolio; degrees Cert of Completion 2 yrs (day) 3 yrs (night); enrl D 20, E 10.
Tuition: Day—22 months (average) $139 per month, $50 registration night—33 months (average) $45 per month, $20 registration no campus res.
Courses: Advertising Design; Commercial Art; Drawing; Fashion Arts; Graphic Design; Illustration; Lettering; Painting; Photography.
Our curriculum is on a continuous course basis. We cover all areas of advertising art.

OHIO VISUAL ART INSTITUTION (formerly Gebhart Art School), 124 E Seventh St, 45202. Tel: 513-241-4338. *Dir* James E Price; *Primary Art Faculty* William A Leonard, Nikki Howard, Buddy Johnson, Marcia Raney; Instrs FT 7, PT 9.
Estab 1947; pvt; D&E; ent req HS dipl, review of portfolio; enrl D 90, E 40.
Tuition: Undergrad $2000 yr; no campus res available.
Courses: Advertising Design; Art History; Commercial Art; Drawing; Film; Graphic Arts; Graphic Design; Illustration; Industrial Design; Interior Design; Photography.

UNIVERSITY OF CINCINNATI,* College of Design, Architecture and Art, 45221. Tel: 513-475-4934. *Dean* Bertram Berenson; Instrs FT 77, PT 30.
Estab 1922; pub; full-time programs; also cooperative programs whereby students spend alternate periods in classroom and in establishments in his chosen profession; degrees BArch, BCommunity Planning, BS(Design) (with major in fashion design, graphic design, industrial design and interior design), BFA, BFA(Art Educ), BA(Art History), MFA, 2 yr, MFA(Art educ), 1 yr, MA(Art History), 1 yr, MS(Arch), 1 yr; EdD; enrl 1800.
Tuition: Res—$900 yr (full time), Nonres—$2100 yr.
Children's Classes: Sat classes available.

CLEVELAND

CASE WESTERN RESERVE UNIVERSITY, Department of Art, Mather House, 11201 Euclid Ave, 44106. Tel: 216-368-4118. *Assoc Prof & Chmn* Walter S Gibson, PhD; *Prof* Harvey D Buchanan, PhD; *Assoc Prof* Edward J Olszewski, PhD; *Assoc Prof* Anita Rogoff, MS; *Asst Prof* Inabelle Levin, PhD; *Asst Prof* Carol Nathanson, PhD; *Prof* Henry S Robinson, PhD; vis prof—John Cooney BA, also adjunct prof from curatorial staff of Cleveland Museum of Art.
Estab 1875; pvt; D; ent req HS transcript, SAT or ACT, TOEFL for foreign students; degrees BS, MS, BA, MA and PhD; schol; SC 24, LC 55, GC 73; enrl D 644, grad 75.
Tuition: Undergrad & grad $163 per cr hr; campus res room & board.
Courses: ‡Art Education; ‡Art History; Ceramics; Drawing; Film; Handicrafts (enameling); ‡History of Art & Archaeology; Jewelry; Museum Staff Training; Painting; Photography; Textile Design.
Summer School: An occasional introductory course in Art History.

CLEVELAND INSTITUTE OF ART, 11141 E Blvd, 44106. Tel: 216-421-4322. *Pres* Joseph McCullough, MFA; *Primary Art Faculty* Julian Stanczak; Jerome Aidlin; Carroll Cassill; Marco DeMarco; Viktor Schreckengost; Robert Palmer; Sandra August; vis prof—Kenneth Dingwall, painting, spring 1978.
Estab 1882; pvt; D&E; ent req HS dipl, admissions application, HS transcript, portfolio of art work; degrees BFA 5 yr, BS (educ with Case Western Reserve Univ) 4 yr; schol; SC 115, LC 28; enrl D 522, E 239, nonmaj 244, maj 277, others 39(PT & Art Educ).
Tuition: Undergrad $1165 yr; campus res room & board $1835 yr.
Courses: Aesthetics; Art Education; Art History; Calligraphy; ‡Ceramics; ‡Drawing; ‡Enameling; Film ‡Glass; ‡Graphic Design; ‡Illustration; ‡Industrial Design; ‡Jewelry; ‡Medical Illustration; ‡Painting; ‡Photography; ‡Printmaking; ‡Sculpture; ‡Silversmithing; ‡Textile Design; ‡Weaving.
Children's Classes: Enrl 151; tui $30 per session. Courses—Art Basics; Crafts; Design; Drawing; Painting; Printmaking; Photography; Ceramic Sculpture.
Summer School: Dean of Faculty Robert Weitzel. Enrl 145; tui $260 for term of 6 wk beginning June 19. Courses—Design; Watercolor; Drawing; Sculpture; Printmaking; Jewelry and Metalsmithing; Photography; Ceramics.

CLEVELAND STATE UNIVERSITY, Art Department, 2307 Chester Ave (Mailing Add: 1983 E 24th St, 44115). Tel: 216-687-2090 or 687-2089. *Prof & Chmn* Jan van der Meulen, PhD; *Assoc Prof* Thomas E Donaldson, PhD; *Assoc Prof* June E Hargrove, PhD; *Assoc Prof* Marvin H Jones, MA; *Assoc Prof* Gene Kangas, MFA; *Assoc Prof* Walter C Leedy Jr, PhD; *Assoc Prof* Bobby Louise Rowe, PhD; *Assoc Prof* Richard D Schneider, MA; *Assoc Prof* Thomas C Silver, MFA; vis prof—Martha Ehrlich.
Dept estab 1972; pub; D&E; ent req HS dipl; degrees BA 4 yr; schol; SC 26, LC 32.
Courses: Art Education; Art History; Ceramics; Conceptual Art; Constructions; Drawing; Environmental Art; Graphic Arts; Graphic Design; History of Art & Archaeology; Painting; Photography; Printmaking; Sculpture; Teacher Training; Urban.

COOPER SCHOOL OF ART,* 2341 Carnegie Ave, 44115. Tel: 216-241-1486. Instrs FT & PT 32.
Estab 1936; pvt ent req HS grad, art portfolio and personal interview; dipl; 3 yr program, 9 quarters to complete; schol; SC; enrl 500.
Courses: Advertising; Art History; Design; Drawing; Fashion; Film; Graphic Design; Illustration; Painting; Photography; Portrait; Printmaking; Watercolor.
Summer School: 3 sessions starting in June.

CUYAHOGA COMMUNITY COLLEGE,* 700 Carnegie Ave, 44115. Tel: 216-241-5966, exten 462. *Dean* Curtis Jefferson (Metro Campus); *Dean* Dr Martin L Krauss (Western Campus); *Dean* Dr William R Williams (Eastern Campus); Instrs FT 9, PT 17.
Estab 1964; pub; D&E; ent req HS dipl, ent exam; degrees AA 2 yr; schol; SC 28, LC 8.
Courses: Art Education; Ceramics; Commercial Art; Drafting; Drawing; Graphic Arts; Graphic Design; History of Art & Archaeology; Illustration; Occupational Therapy; Painting; Photography; Sculpture; Textile Design; Theatre Arts.
Summer School: Variety of courses.

COLUMBUS

COLUMBUS COLLEGE OF ART AND DESIGN,* (of the Columbus Gallery of Fine Arts), 44 N Washington Ave, 43215. Tel: 614-224-9101. *Dean* Joseph V Canzani; *Asst Dean* Mary T Kinney; Instrs 48.
Estab 1879; pvt D&E; ent req HS grad, art portfolio; degrees BFA 4 yr; schol; approved for Veterans.
Courses: Advertising Design; Advertising-Merchandising; Fashion Illustration; Fine Arts; Graphics; Industrial Design; Interior Design; Magazine Illustration; Packaging Design; Painting; Photography; Sculpture.

OHIO DOMINICAN COLLEGE, Art Department, 1216 Sunbury Rd, 43219. Tel: 614-253-2741. *Chmn Dept* Juris Kakis, MA; *Assoc Prof* Melvyn J Rozen, MFA.
Estab 1911; den; D&E; ent req HS dipl; degrees BA 4 yr, also student may obtain a secondary education cert or special training certificate, K-12; schol; SC & LC 7-9 per sem; enrl D 139, E 105, maj 17.
Tuition: $2730 yr, $1365 per sem, $90 per sem hr; campus res room and board $1540.
Courses: Art Education; Art History; Ceramics; Drawing; Film; Graphic Arts; Painting; Photography; Printmaking; Sculpture; Teacher Training; Textile Design; Theatre Arts; Video.
Summer School: Dir Joe Stotski. Tui $90 per cr hr for term of 7 wk beginning June. Courses—Varies.

OHIO STATE UNIVERSITY
—School of Architecture,* 190 W 17th Ave, 43210. *Dir* Laurence C Gerchkens; Instrs FT 32, PT 19.
Estab 1899; pub; degrees BSArch, BSLand Arch, MArch, MCP 4-6 yrs; enrl Architecture 396, Landscape Architecture 131, City & Regional Planning 145.
Courses: Architecture; City & Regional Planning; Landscape Architecture.
—College of the Arts, 305 Mershon Auditorium, 30 W 15th Ave. Tel: 614-422-5171. *Dean* Col Andrew J Broekema, PhD.
Univ estab 1870, col estab 1968; pub; D&E; ent req HS dipl; degrees BA, BAEd, BFA, BS and BSID 4 yrs, MA, MFA, PhD; schol; SC 106, LC 192, GC 208; enrl D 3678, E varies, nonmaj 2598, maj 998, grad 164.
Tuition: Res—Undergrad $810 per yr, $270 per quarter, grad $990 per yr, $330 per quarter; Nonres—Undergrad $1860 per yr, $620 per quarter, grad $2040 per yr, $680 per quarter; campus res room and board $1475 per yr.
Courses: ‡Art Education; ‡Art History; ‡Ceramics; ‡Costume Design & Construction; ‡Drawing; Graphic Arts; Graphics of Communication;

Graphic Design; ‡Handicrafts (weaving); ‡History of Art & Archaeology; Illustration; ‡Industrial Design; ‡Interior Design; Mixed Media; ‡Painting; Printmaking; ‡Sculpture; ‡Stage Design; ‡Teacher Training; Textile Design; ‡Theatre Arts.
Adult Hobby Classes: Enrl 450 per quarter; tui $9 per quarter. Saturday School, art experiences in all media for local adults.
Children's Classes: Enrl 450 per quarter; tui $9 per quarter. Saturday School, art experience in all media for local children.
Summer School: Regular University offerings during the summer at regular cost per quarter.
Department of Art. *Chmn Dept* Robert Stull, MA; Instrs FT 36, PT 34. Degrees BA, BFA, MA, MFA; SC 56, LC 6, GC 30. Courses: Ceramic Art; Drawing; General Fine Arts; Grapics; Painting; Sculpture.
Department of Art Education, Hopkins Hall 340. Tel: 614-422-7183. *Chmn Dept* Kenneth A Marantz, EdD; *Prof* Arthur Efland; *Assoc Prof* Robert Arnold; *Assoc Prof* Donald Duncan, MFA; *Assoc Prof* Nancy MacGregor, PhD; *Assoc Prof* Ross Norris; *Asst Prof* Rogena Degse, PhD; *Asst Prof* Charles Wieder, MA.
Estab 1907; pub; D&E; ent req HS dipl; degrees BAEd, MA, PhD; schol; SC 6, LC 10, GC 16; enrl maj 95, grad 83. Tuition: Res—Undergrad $305 per quarter, grad $370 per quarter; Nonres—Undergrad $675 per quarter, grad $740 per quarter; graduated fee structure from 1 to 8 quarter hrs; campus res room and board. Courses: Art Appreciation; Art Criticism; ‡Art Education; Film; Goldsmithing; Graphic Design; Handicrafts (bookmaking); ‡Jewelry; Mixed Media; Photo Criticism; Silversmithing; ‡Teacher Training.
Department of Industrial Design. *Chmn Dept* Charles A Wallschlaeger, MFA; Instrs FT 11, PT 4.
Degrees BSID, MA; SC 29, LC 1, GC 15.Courses: Product Design; Space & Enclosure Design; Visual Communication Design.
Department of the History of Art. *Chmn Dept* Howard Crane, PhD, Instrs FT 15, PT 20.
Degrees BA, BFA, MA, PhD; LC 37, GC 52. Courses: History of Art.

CUYAHOGA FALLS

STUDIOS OF JACK RICHARD CREATIVE SCHOOL OF DESIGN,* 2250 Front St, 44221. Tel: 216-929-1575. *Dir* Jack Richard; Instrs FT 1; guest demonstrators.
Estab 1960; pvt; D&E; schol; SC 4, LC 10; enrl D 50-60, E 50-60.
Courses: Aesthetics; Art Education; Ceramics; Drawing; Illustration; Occupational Therapy; Painting; Photography; Sculpture.
Adult Hobby Classes: Enrl 100-120 per session; tui $7 per class. Courses—Drawing; Painting.
Summer School: Dir Jack Richard. Tui $68.75 for term of 8 wk beginning June. Courses—Design; Drawing; Painting.

DAYTON

SINCLAIR COMMUNITY COLLEGE,* Department of Art, 444 W Third St, 45402. Tel: 513-226-2500. *Chmn* John Polston; Instrs FT 3, PT 14.
Estab 1973; pub; D&E; ent req HS dipl, ent exam; degrees AA 2 yr.
Tuition: $10 per cr hr; no campus res available.
Courses: Advertising Design; Ceramics; Commercial Art; Drawing; Painting; Sculpture; Theatre Arts.

WRIGHT STATE UNIVERSITY, Art Department, Colonel Glenn Highway, 45435. Tel: 513-837-2896. *Chmn* Dr Edward Levine, PhD; *Asst Chmn* Kimmerly Kiser, MFA; *Assoc Prof* Raymond Must, MA; *Assoc Prof* Earnest Koerlin, MFA; *Asst Prof* Martha Dunkelman, PhD; *Asst Prof* David Leach, MFA; *Asst Prof* Robert Sibbison, MFA; *Asst Prof* William Spurlock, PhD; *Asst Prof* Thomas Macaulay, MFA; vis prof—Barbara Kruger, painting & drawing, winter 1977-1978; Alan Newman, photography, winter.
Estab 1964, dept estab 1965; pub; D&E; ent req HS dipl; degrees BA and BFA 4 yr; schol; SC 15, LC 10, GC 5; enrl D 70, E 41, nonmaj 10, maj 95, others 6.
Tuition: Res—Undergrad $290 yr, $345 14-18 hr, $28 per cr hr, grad $345 yr, $350 14-18 hr, $34 per cr hr; Nonres—Undergrad $620 yr, $675 14-18 hr, $57 per cr hr, grad $675 yr, $680 14-18 hr, $63 per cr hr; campus res room & board $320 per quarter (double room).
Courses: Art History; Drawing; Film; Graphic Arts; Graphic Design; Painting; Photography; Printmaking; Sculpture.
Summer School: Chmn Dr Edward Levine. Tui same as above for term of 10 wk beginning June 13. Courses—Art History; Drawing; Sculpture; Foundations; Photography; Printmaking.

DELAWARE

OHIO WESLEYAN UNIVERSITY, Fine Arts Department, S Sandusky St, 43015. *Chmn & Assoc Prof* Justin Kronewetter, MFA; *Prof* Jarvis Stewart, PhD; *Prof* Everett Haycock, MA; *Assoc Prof* Robert Engle, MA; *Assoc Prof* Marty Kalb, MfA; *Asst Prof* Betty Heald, MFA; *Asst Prof* James Johnson, MFA.
Estab 1841, dept estab 1864; pvt; D&E; ent req HS dipl, SAT or ACT; degrees BA and BFA 4 yr; enrl D 1200, nonmaj 1075, maj 125.
Tuition: Undergrad $3950 yr; campus res room & board $1680 yr.
Courses: Aesthetics; Art Education; Art History; Ceramics; Commercial Art; Drafting; Drawing; Film; Interior Design; Jewelry; Painting; Photography; Printmaking; Sculpture; Teacher Training; Textile Design; Theatre Arts.
Children's Classes: Enrl 55; tui $5 per 5 wk, Saturday Art School, Art Educ Lab School. Courses—Various media.
Summer School: A limited selection of regular courses offerings plus a special six week traveling seminar to the American southwest.

FINDLAY

FINDLAY COLLEGE, Art Department, 1000 N Main St, 45840. Tel: 419-422-8313, exten 277. *Asst Prof* Doug Salveson, MFA.
Estab 1882; pub; D&E; ent req HS dipl; degrees AA 2 yr, BA and BS 4 yr; schol; SC 21, LC 4; enrl maj 30.
Tuition: Undergrad $930 per quarter, $63 per quarter hr; campus res room & board $1270 yr.
Courses: Advertising Design; Aesthetics; Art Education; Art History; Ceramics; Collage; Drawing; Graphic Design; History of Art & Archaeology; Illustration; Lettering; Painting; Photography; Printmaking; Sculpture; Teacher Training; Theatre Arts.
Adult Hobby Classes: Enrl 10-20; tui $50 per quarter. Courses—Ceramics.
Summer School: Dir Jack Lizotte.

GAMBIER

KENYON COLLEGE, Art Department, 43022. Tel: 614-427-2244. *Chmn & Asst Prof* Eugene J Dwyer, PhD; *Prof* Joseph Slate, BFA; *Assoc Prof* Martin Garhart, MFA; *Asst Prof* Barry Gunderson, MFA; *Asst Prof* Mark Levy, PhD; *Asst Prof* Patricia McCulloh, MFA; *Asst Prof* Carla Steiger, MFA.
Estab 1824, dept estab 1965; pvt; D; ent req HS dipl; degrees BA and BFA; schol; SC 15, LC 10; enrl D 450, nonmaj 250, maj 60.
Tuition: Res—Undergrad $5700 yr; campus res available.
Courses: Art History; Drawing; History of Art & Archaeology; Painting; Photography; Printmaking; Sculpture.

GRANVILLE

DENISON UNIVERSITY, Dept of Art, Box M, 43023. *Chmn & Prof* George Bogdanovitch, MFA; *Asst Prof* Marilyn Hook, MFA; *Prof* Eric E Hirshler, PhD; *Asst Prof* Christopher Bunge, MFA; *Asst Prof* Michael Jung, MFA; *Lectr* Mary K Campbell; Instrs PT 2.
Estab 1830; pvt; D; ent req HS dipl, SAT and ent exam; degrees BA and BFA; schol; SC 28, LC 19; enrl D 2100.
Tuition: Res—Undergrad $3695 yr; campus res room & board $1480 yr.
Courses: Aesthetics; Art History; Ceramics; Collage; Conceptual Art; Constructions; Drawing; Graphic Arts; Graphic Design; History of Art & Archaeology; Illustration; Intermedia; Museum Staff Training; Painting; Photography; Printmaking; Sculpture.

HIRAM

HIRAM COLLEGE,* Art Department, 44234. Tel: 216-569-3211, exten 243/244. *Chmn* Paul A Rochford; Instrs FT 4, PT 2.
Estab 1850; pvt; D; ent req HS dipl; degrees AB 4 yr; schol; SC 19, LC 12; enrl D 1300, maj 65.
Tuition: $3337 yr; campus res $1164 yr.
Courses: Aesthetics; Art Education; Ceramics; Drawing; Fabrics; Film Making; Graphic Arts; Graphic Design; History of Art & Archaeology; Lettering; Painting; Photography; Sculpture; Teacher Training; Theatre Arts.
Summer School: Dir Paul A Rochford, Enrl 180. Courses—Vary.

HURON

BOWLING GREEN STATE UNIVERSITY, Firelands College, Division of Humanities, Art Department, 901 Rye Beach Rd, 44839. Tel: 419-433-5560. *Chmn Art Dept* Julius T Kosan, MFA; Instrs FT 1, PT 3.
Estab 1907, col estab 1966; pub; D&E; ent req HS dipl, SAT; degree AA 2 yrs; schol; SC 12, LC 3; enrl D 1200.
Tuition: $906 per yr; $302 per quarter; $30.50 per cr hr; no campus res.

Courses: Art Education; Art History; Drawing; Enameling; History of Art & Archaeology; Painting; Photography; Teacher Training; Theatre Arts.
Summer School: Tui $30.50 per cr hr for term of 5 wks beginning June 18. Courses—Art Education; Studio Courses.

KENT

KENT STATE UNIVERSITY,* College of Fine and Professional Art, School of Art, 44242. Tel: 216-672-2193. *Dir* Dr Stuart Schar; Instrs FT 43, PT 10.
Estab 1913; pub; degrees BA, BFA, BS, MA, MFA and MEduc 4 yr; schol; enrl maj 900.
Tuition: Res—Undergrad $225 per quarter; Nonres—Undergrad $625.
Courses: Art Education; Art History; Cinematography; Ceramics; Drawing; Enameling; Glass; Graphic Design; Industrial Design; Jewelry; Painting; Printmaking; Sculpture; Weaving.
Summer School: Includes special Blossom-Kent Art Program.

MARIETTA

MARIETTA COLLEGE,* Art Department, 45750. Tel: 614-373-4643. *Chmn* M Jeanne Tasse; Instrs FT 4, PT 1.
Estab 1835; pvt; degree AB 4 yr; grants in aid and student loans; SC 20, LC 7; enrl maj 75, total col enrl approx 1600.
Courses: Ceramics; Costume Design; Drafting; Drawing; Graphic Arts; Lettering; Painting; Sculpture; Teacher Training; Television; Theatre Arts.

MOUNT SAINT JOSEPH

COLLEGE OF MOUNT ST JOSEPH, Art Department, Delhi and Neeb Roads, 45051. Tel: 513-244-4309. *Chmn & Assoc Prof* Sister Ann Austin Mooney, MFA; *Asst Prof* Sharon Kesterson Bollen, MA; *Assoc Prof* Betty Brothers, MAT; *Prof* John R Nartker, MFA; *Assoc Prof* Daniel Mader, MA; vis prof—Five.
Estab 1920; den; D&E; ent req HS dipl, National Testing Scores; degrees BA and BFA 4 yr, AA 2 yr; schol; SC 35, LC 4; enrl D 80 plus, nonmaj 35, maj 80.
Tuition: Res—Undergrad $2208 yr; campus res $730 per sem.
Courses: ‡Art Education; Art History; ‡Ceramics; ‡Drawing; Graphic Design; Handicrafts (batik, enameling plus others); ‡Interior Design; ‡Jewelry; Lettering; Occupational Therapy; ‡Painting (art therapy); ‡Photography; ‡Printmaking; ‡Sculpture; ‡Silversmithing.

NEW CONCORD

MUSKINGUM COLLEGE,* Art Department, 43762. Tel: 614-826-8101. *Chmn* Louis O Palmer; Instrs FT 3.
Estab 1837; pvt; D; ent req HS dipl, ent exam, specific school standards; degrees BA, BS and BMusic 4 yr; schol; SC 13; LC 6; enrl D 300, maj 14.
Tuition: $3250 yr; campus res $1411 yr.
Courses: Aesthetics; Art Education; Ceramics; Commercial Art; Drawing; Graphic Arts; History of Art & Archaeology; Jewelry; Museum Staff Training; Painting; Sculpture; Teacher Training; Theatre Arts.

OBERLIN

OBERLIN COLLEGE, Department of Art, 44074. Tel: 216-775-8181. *Chmn* Paul B Arnold, MFA; *Prof* Richard E Spear, PhD; *Prof* Forbes J Whiteside, MFA; *Assoc Prof* John Pearson, MFA; *Assoc Prof* Athena Tacha, D Univ Paris; *Asst Prof* William E Hood, PhD; *Asst Prof* Ann W Epstein, PhD; *Asst Prof* Kathleen Nicholson, PhD; *Asst Prof* Daphne Rosenzweig, PhD.
Estab 1833, dept estab 1917; pvt; D; ent req HS dipl, SAT; degrees BA 4 yr, MA 2 yr; schol; SC 28, LC 38, number of advanced undergrad and grad courses, 13; enrl D approx 600, nonmaj 60, maj 61, Grad 9.
Tuition: Undergrad & grad $3975 yr; campus res room & board $1665.
Courses: Art History; Drawing; History of Art and Archaeology; Painting; Printmaking; Sculpture.

OXFORD

MIAMI UNIVERSITY, School of Fine Arts, Art Department, Heistand Hall, 45056. Tel: 513-529-6121, 6310. *Chmn & Prof Asst* Robert B Butler, MFA; *Prof* John Michael, DEd; *Prof* Peter Dahoda, MFA; *Prof* Derwin W Edwards, MA; *Prof* Judith P George, MFA; *Prof* Harold R Truax, DEd; *Prof* Robert Wolfe Jr, MFA; *Assoc Prof* Joseph L Cox III, MFA; *Assoc Prof* Crossan H Curry, MFA; *Assoc Prof* Willis H Davis, MA; *Assoc Prof* Thomas J Gilmore, MA; *Assoc Prof* W Alex McKibben, MFA; *Assoc Prof* Edward L Talbott, MFA; *Assoc Prof* Helen V Worrall, MFA; *Asst Prof* Lon L Beck, MFA; *Asst Prof* Kathryn L Cot-

noir, MFA; *Asst Prof* Philip M Joseph, MFA; *Asst Prof* James C Kaufman, MFA; *Asst Prof* E James Killy, MFA; *Asst Prof* Edward K Montgomery, MFA; *Asst Prof* Jerry W Morris, DEd; *Asst Prof* Sandra P Packard, DEd; *Asst Prof* M Ellen Patton, MFA; *Asst Prof* Barry A Rosenberg, MFA; *Asst Prof* Michael H Stuckhardt, DEd; *Asst Prof* Gary Wheeler, MFA; *Sr Instr* Jane E Toadvine, MA; *Lectr* Carlos de Azevedo, MA; *Instr* Marion Cooley, MA; *vis asst prof*—Catherine Waller, MFA; *vis instr* Judith L Ott, MA.
Estab 1809, dept estab 1929; pub; D&E; ent req HS dipl, ACT or SAT, Class rank; degrees BFA and BS(Art) 4 yr, MFA 2 yr, MA(Art) or (Art Education) and Med(Art Education) one year; schol; SC 49, LC 35, GC 20; enrl D 2309, nonmaj 1890, maj 419, GS 32.
Tuition: Res—Undergrad $528 per sem, grad $603 per sem; Nonres—Undergrad $650 per sem; campus res room and board $2546.
Courses: ‡Advertising Design; Architecture; ‡Art Education; Art History; Calligraphy; ‡Ceramics: Collage; Commercial Art; Display; ‡Drawing; Graphic Arts: ‡Graphic Design; History of Art and Archaeology; Illustration; ‡Jewelry; Lettering; Museum Staff Training; ‡Painting; Photography; ‡Printmaking; ‡Sculpture; ‡Silversmithing; Stitchery; ‡Teacher Training; ‡Textile Design; Weaving.
Children's Classes: Enrl 70; tui $5 per sem. Courses—General Art.
Summer School: Dir Peter Dahoda, MFA. Tui $68.25 per one wk, no credit; Undergrad for credit $68.25, Grad $79.50 for credit; Nonres $97.50 per one wk; room and board 1 to 5 days $8.50 per single, $6 double; 6-10 days $8 for single, $5.50 for double; 11 or more days $7.50 for single, $5 for double. Courses—varied workshops.

PAINESVILLE

LAKE ERIE COLLEGE/GARFIELD SENIOR COLLEGE,* Art Department, 44077. Tel: 216-352-3361, exten 248, 305. Instrs FT 3, PT 4.
Estab 1856; pvt; ent req col board exam; degrees BA and BFA 4 yr; SC 20, LC 7; total enrl 800.
Courses: Art Education; Ceramics; Design; History & Appreciation of Art; Introductory Art; Painting; Sculpture.

SPRINGFIELD

SPRINGFIELD ART CENTER, 107 Cliff Park Rd, 45501. Tel: 513-325-4673. *Dir* Patricia D'Arcy Catron; Instrs PT approx 20.
Estab 1951; pvt; D&E; schol; enrl D approx 600.
Courses: Ceramics; Drawing; Jewelry; Painting; Photography; Sculpture.
Tuition: No campus res available.
Adult Hobby Classes: Tui $45 per quarter. Courses—Gourmet Cooking; Batik; Weaving.
Children's Classes: Tui $25 per quarter. Courses—Drawing; Art Experiences; Pottery and Sculpture.

WITTENBERG UNIVERSITY, Art Department, Crabill Art Center, 818 N Fountain Ave, 45501. Tel: 513-327-6311. *Prof* John O Schlump, MA; *Assoc Prof* Don Dunifon, MFA; *Assoc Prof* George Ramsay, MFA; *Asst Prof* Jack Osbun, MFA; *Asst Prof* Richard Hagelberger, MFA; *Instrs* Jack Mann, MA.
Estab 1842; pvt and den; D&E; ent req HS dipl, class rank, transcript, SAT or ACT test results, recommendations and if possible, a personal interview; degrees AB and BFA 4 yr; schol; SC 30, LC 17; enrl D 350, nonmaj 270, maj 80.
Tuition: Nonres—Undergrad $3072 yr; campus res room & board $1560 yr.
Courses: Advertising Design; Aesthetics; ‡Art Education; ‡Art History; ‡Ceramics; ‡Commercial Art; Drawing; ‡Graphic Arts; Graphic Design; History of Art & Archaeology; ‡Illustration; Industrial Design; Interior Design; Jewelry; ‡Painting; Photography; ‡Printmaking; ‡Sculpture; ‡Teacher Training.
Summer School: Assoc Dean of the College Dr Richard Ortquist. Enrl 400; tui $250 for term of 7 wk beginning June 14. Courses—Art in the Elementary School; Fundamental of Art; Painting.

TIFFIN

HEIDELBERG COLLEGE,* 44883. Tel: 419-448-2000. *Head Prof* George Keester; Instrs FT 3.
Estab 1850; pvt; D; ent req HS dipl, each applicant's qualifications are considered individually; degrees AB 4 yr; Independent study, honors work available; schol; SC 22, LC 9; enrl 200, maj 24.
Tuition: $1670 per sem, $127 per sem hr; campus res $1340.
Courses: Advertising Design; Aesthetics; Art Education; Ceramics; Chip Carving; Commercial Art; Copper Enameling; Display; Drawing; Graphic Arts; Graphic Design; History of Art & Archaeology; Illustration; Jewelry; Lettering; Metal Tooling; Mosaic; Museum Staff Training; Painting; Sculpture; Stage Design; Teacher Training; Theatre Arts.

Summer School: Dir Dr Roy Bacon. 6 wk beginning June. Courses—Practical Arts; Materials and Methods in Teaching.

TOLEDO

TOLEDO MUSEUM OF ART,* School of Design, Box 1013, 43697. Tel: 419-255-8000. *Asst Dir* Charles F Gunther; Instrs FT 13, PT 5.
Estab 1919; pvt; D&E; degrees in cooperation with Univ of Toledo 4 yr; schol.
Courses: Ceramics; Design; Drawing; Glass Craftsmanship; History of Art & Appreciation; Interior Design; Metalsmithing; Painting; Printmaking; Sculpture.
Adult Hobby Classes: Enrl 1200 per quarter. Meet PM and E.
Children's Classes: Enrl 2000 per quarter. Free classes for children on Sat in art and music.

WESTERVILLE

OTTERBEIN COLLEGE,* Department of Visual Arts, 43081. Tel: 614-882-3000. Instrs FT 3.
Pvt; ent req HS dipl; degrees BA 4 yr; schol; SC 11, LC 4; enrl D 1400, maj 32.
Courses: Architecture; Art Education; Art Psychotherapy; Bronze Casting; Ceramics; Drawing; Graphic Design; Handicrafts; History of Art & Archaeology; Macrame; Painting; Photography; Sculpture; Stage Design; Teacher Training; Theatre Arts.

WILBERFORCE

CENTRAL STATE UNIVERSITY,* Department of Art, 45384. Tel: 513-376-6610. *Chmn* Hayward R Dinsmore; Instrs FT 3.
Estab 1856; D; ent req HS dipl; degrees BA and BS 4 yr; SC 20, LC 8; enrl D 175, maj 45, others 130.
Courses: Advertising Design; Art Education; Ceramics; Drawing; Graphic Arts; History of Art & Archaeology; Lettering; Painting; Sculpture; Teacher Training.
Summer School: Chmn H R Dinsmore. Enrl maj 20, others 100; Term of 12 wk beginning June 16, two sessions. Courses—Art for the Elementary Teacher; Art History; Black Artists; Introduction to Art; Painting; Sculpture.

WILBERFORCE UNIVERSITY, Art Department, 45384. Tel: 513-376-2911. *Head Dept & Asst Prof* Edward G Hill, MA; *Instr* James Padgett, MFA; *Instr* Richard Wheatley, BA.
Estab 1856, dept estab 1973; pvt; D; ent req HS dipl; degrees BA, BS and BS (Ed) 4 yr; SC 22, LC 5; enrl D 26, Maj 26.
Courses: Advertising Design; Art Education; Art History; Ceramics; Commercial Art; Drawing; Fashion Arts; Handicrafts; History of Art and Archaeology; Painting (mural); Photography; Printmaking; Sculpture; Teacher Training.

WILLOUGHBY

SCHOOL OF FINE ARTS, Visual Arts Department, 38660 Mentor Ave, 44094. Tel: 216-951-7500. *Dir* James Savage, BM; *Visual Arts Coordinator & Gallery Dir* Doris Foster, BFA.
Estab 1957; pvt; D&E; schol; SC 24; enrl D 252, E 240.
Tuition: $35-$60 per sem; no campus res available.
Courses: Ceramics; Drawing; Intermedia; Mixed Media; Painting; Photography; Stage Design; Theatre Arts.
Adult Hobby Classes: Tui $55-$60 per sem. Courses—Ceramics; Photography; Drawing; Painting.
Children's Classes: Tui $35-$45 per sem. Courses—Ceramics; Photography; Drawing; Painting; Ceramic Sculpture.
Summer School: Dir James Savage. Tui $25-$70 for term of 6 wk beginning June 19. Courses—Same as above.

WOOSTER

COLLEGE OF WOOSTER, Department of Art, University St, 44691. Tel: 216-264-1234, exten 388. *Chmn* Thalia Gouma-Peterson, PhD; *Prof* Arnold Lewis, PhD; *Instr* Mary Breckenridge, MA; *Prof* Donald MacKenzie, PhD; *Assoc Prof* George Olson, MFA; *Instr* Clayton Lee, AB; *Instr* Rebecca Seeman, MFA.
Estab 1866; den; D&E; ent req HS dipl, plus interview; degrees BA 4 yr; SC 13, LC 19; enrl D Approx 225 per quarter, maj 40.
Tuition: Res—Undergrad $3990 yr; campus res $1260 yr.
Courses: Architecture; Art Education; Art History; Ceramics; Constructions; Drawing; Graphic Arts; History of Art & Archaeology; Painting; Photography; Printmaking; Sculpture; Stage Design; Teacher Training; Theatre Arts.

An art center operated by the community, for children and adults is housed in the same area and is supported in part by the College, but no degree program is offered and its program is non-College oriented.

YELLOW SPRINGS

ANTIOCH COLLEGE, Department of Art, 45387. Tel: 513-767-7331, exten 464. *Chmn* Allan L Jones, MFA; *Assoc Prof* James W Jordan, MFA; *Assoc Prof* John P Rritterskamp, MFA; *Assoc Prof* Karen Shirley, MFA; *Asst Prof* Janis Crystal Lipzin, MFA; *Instr* Nancy Rexroth, MFA.
Estab 1853; pvt; D&E; ent req HS dipl; degrees BA & BFA 5 yr; SC 48, LC 10; enrl D 665 per quarter, nonmaj 100, maj 50.
Tuition: Res—Undergrad $6020 yr (including room & board plus other fees), grad $1875 per quarter full time, $937.50 per quarter part time plus other fees; Adult Degree Completion Program, approx $2100.
Courses: Aesthetics; Art Education; ‡Art History; ‡Ceramics; Conceptual Art; Constructions; Drafting; ‡Drawing; ‡Film; ‡Graphic Arts; History of Art; ‡Painting; ‡Photography; ‡Printmaking; ‡Sculpture.

YOUNGSTOWN

YOUNGSTOWN STATE UNIVERSITY, Art Department, Fine and Performing Arts, 410 Wick Ave, 44555. Tel: 216-746-1851. *Prof* Jon Naberezny, MA; *Assoc Prof* Richard Mitchell, MFA; *Assoc Prof* Russell Maddick, MFA; *Assoc Prof* Joseph Babisch, MA; *Assoc Prof* Elaine Juhasz, MEd; *Assoc Prof* James Lepore; MFA; *Assoc Prof* James Lucas, MFA; *Asst Prof* Jaroslav Ryska, PhD; *Assoc Prof* R Ulrich, MA; *Asst Prof* Michael Walusis, MFA; *Asst Prof* Louis Zona, DA; *Instr* Dan Fantauzzi, MFA; *Instr* Michael Moseley, MFA; *Assoc Prof* Alfred Bright, MA; vis prof—Alfred Leslie, oil painting, fall quarter 1977.
Estab 1908, dept estab 1952; pub; D&E; ent req HS dipl; degrees AB, BFA and BS 4 yr; SC 44, LC 26, GC 8; enrl D&E 1250, maj 300, grad 15.
Tuition: Res—Undergrad & grad $678 yr, $226 per quarter; $19 per hr; Nonres—Undergrad & grad $1278 yr, $426 per quarter, $37 per hr; no campus res available.
Courses: ‡Art Education; ‡Art History; Ceramics; ‡Commercial Art; Drawing; Graphic Arts; ‡Graphic Design; Illustration; Interior Design; Jewelry; Lettering; Museum Staff Training; ‡Painting; Photography; ‡Printmaking; ‡Sculpture; Teacher Training.
Adult Hobby Classes: Tui $35 per 8 wk. Courses—Painting; Drawing; Photography; Ceramics; Weaving; Calligraphy.
Summer School: Dir Jon Naberezny. Tui same as above for term of 5½ wk beginning June 15-July 20, second term, July 21-Aug 24. Courses—Same as Above.

ZANESVILLE

ZANESVILLE ART CENTER,* 1145 Maple Ave, 43701. Tel: 614-452-0741. *Dir* Dr Charles Dietz; Instrs PT 8.
Estab 1936; pvt; D&E; ent req conference; schol; SC 12; enrl D 135, E 70.
Courses: Ceramics; Drawing; Handicrafts; Macrame; Needlepoint; Painting; Sculpture.
Adult Hobby Classes: Courses—Macrame; Needlepoint.
Children's Classes: Enrl 60. Courses—Drawing; Painting.

OKLAHOMA

ADA

EAST CENTRAL UNIVERSITY, Art Department, 74820. Tel: 405-332-8000, exten 353. *Chmn & Assoc Prof* Dee J Lafon, MFA; *Assoc Prof* Bob O Barker, MFA; *Instr* Robert Sieg, MFA; *Instr* Paul Pfrehm, MFA; vis prof—Don Cook, photography, spring.
Estab 1909; pub; D&E; ent req HS dipl, ATC; degrees BA and BA(Educ) 4 yr, MEd 33 hrs, post graduate work, public service program; schol; SC 22, LC 10, GC 8; enrl D 222, E 105, nonmaj 103, maj 80, GS 3, others 36.
Tuition: Res—Undergrad lower division $12.45 per cr hr, upper division $13.45 per cr hr, grad $15.25 per cr hr; Nonres—Undergrad lower division $31.20 per cr hr, upper division $35.20 per cr hr, grad $39.25 per cr hr; campus res.
Courses: ‡Art Education; Art History; ‡Ceramics; Conceptual Art; ‡Drawing; Film; Graphic Arts; Jewelry; Mixed Media; ‡Painting; Photography; ‡Printmaking; ‡Sculpture; Silversmithing; ‡Teacher Training; Wood Design.
Adult Hobby Classes: Enrl 25 average; tui $30. Courses—Drawing; Painting; Silk Screen.

Summer School: Dir Dr Stephenson. Courses—Ceramics; Drawing; Painting; Printmaking.

ALVA

NORTHWESTERN OKLAHOMA STATE UNIVERSITY, Art Department, 73717. Tel: 405-327-1700, exten 243. *Chmn* Don Bellah, BFA.
Estab 1897; pub; D; ent req HS dipl; degrees BA(Art), BA(Educ) and standard certificate 4 yr, grad study for master of teaching degree 18 grad hrs available; SC 28, LC 6, GC 3; enrl D 50-80, nonmaj 50, maj 30, GS 3.
Tuition: Res—Undergrad lower division $12.45 hourly, upper division $13.45 hourly, grad $15.25 hourly; Nonres—Undergrad lower division $31.20 hourly, upper division $35.20 hourly, grad $39.25; other correspondence and extension $16.50; campus res room and board $960 per yr.
Courses: Advertising Design; ‡Art Education; Art History; Ceramics; Commercial Art; Drawing; Graphic Arts; History of Art and Archaeology; Painting; Printmaking; Sculpture; Textile Design.
Summer School: Enrl 40; tui same as above for term of two 5 wk sessions beginning May 31 to July 1 and July 6th to Aug 9th. Courses—vary each summer.

BETHANY

BETHANY NAZARENE COLLEGE, Art Department, 6729 NW Expressway, 73008. Tel: 405-789-6400, exten 327. *Head Dept & Asst Prof* Nila West Murrow, MTchg; *Assoc Prof* Melvin Unruh, MMusEd; vis prof—Gene Hartsell, commercial art, fall.
Estab 1920; den; D&E; ent req HS dipl, ACT; SC 13, LC 7; enrl D 51 E 6, nonmaj 38, maj 13.
Tuition: $42 per hr; campus res room and board $1180 per yr.
Courses: Aesthetics; Art Education; Art History; Ceramics; Commercial Art; Drawing; Handicrafts (variety incl macrame, quilting); Painting; Sculpture; ‡Teacher Training.

CHICKASHA

UNIVERSITY OF SCIENCE AND ARTS OF OKLAHOMA,* Arts Department, 73018. Tel: 405-224-3140, exten 311; Instrs FT 2, PT 1.
Estab 1909; pub; D; degree 124 hr req for grad; SC 26, LC 3; enrl maj 57, others 180.
Courses: Commercial Art; Design; History of Art; Jewelry & Crafts; Painting & Drawing; Pottery & Modeling; Sculpture & Ceramic Sculpture; Teacher Training.
Summer School.

CLAREMORE

CLAREMORE COLLEGE, Art Department, College Hill, 74017. Tel: 918-341-7510, exten 318. *Dir* Fred R Warford, EdD; *Instr* Grace McCoy, MFA; *Instr* Rowe Lee-Mills, BA; *Instr* Sam Hildebrand, BFA.
Estab 1971; pub; D&E; ent req HS dipl, ACT; degrees AA and AS 2 yr; schol; SC 22, LC 3; enrl D 126, E 60, nonmaj 146, maj 40.
Tuition: Res—Undergrad $9.50 per hr; Nonres—Undergrad $25 per hr; campus res room and board res $1604; nonres $2100.
Courses: Art History; Ceramics; Drawing; Graphic Arts; Lettering; Painting; Photography; Printmaking; Sculpture.
Adult Hobby Classes: Tui $20 per 8 wk course. Courses—Landscape; Portrait Painting.
Children's Classes: Tui $9.50 per hr. Courses—Children's Art.
Summer School: Tui $9.50 per hr for term of 8 wks beginning June 5th. Courses—Advanced Ceramics; Art Appreciation; Drawing; Painting.

DURANT

SOUTHEASTERN OKLAHOMA STATE COLLEGE,* Art Department, 74701. Tel: 405-924-0121, exten 2411; Instrs FT 4.
Estab 1909; pub; ent req HS grad, col exam; degrees BA, BS and MEduc 4-5 yrs; enrl 330 (art).
Tuition: $176.
Courses: Applied Design; Ceramics; Crafts; Design; History of Art; Modeling—Clay; Painting—Oil and Watercolor; Perspective Drawing; Pictorial Composition.

EDMOND

CENTRAL STATE UNIVERSITY,* Art Department Bldg, 73034. Tel: 405-341-2980, exten 201, 202. *Chmn* Kathryn Alcorn; Instrs FT 10, PT 4.
Estab 1890; pub; D&E; ent req HS dipl, health exams, IQ test, schol tests; degrees BA, BS and MEduc 3-4 yr; schol; enrl maj 280, grad 20, dept 1168, school 10,000.
Tuition: Available at Office of Admissions.

Courses: Advertising Design; Art Appreciation; Art Education; Art in America; Arts & Crafts; Ceramics; Commercial Art; Design; Etching & Lithography; Figure Drawing; History of Art; Jewelry & Metal Design; Modeling; Painting; Perspective & Composition; Puppetry & Related Arts; Sculpture; Studio Art; Teacher Training; Watercolor; Weaving.

ENID

PHILLIPS UNIVERSITY, Department of Art, University Place, 73701. Tel: 405-237-4433. *Head Dept and Prof* John Randolph, MFA; *Assoc Prof* Jim Bray, MA; *Assoc Prof* Paul Denny Jr, MFA; *Asst Prof* Susan Appel, MA; *Instr* Elbert Wheeler, MA; *Instr* Meme Wheeler, BAE; Instrs FT 4, PT 2.
Estab 1907, dept estab 1909; den; D&E; ent req HS dipl; degrees MBA and ME 5 yr, BA, BS and BFA 4 yrs; schol; SC 20, LC 6; enrl D 45, E 18, nonmaj 20, maj 25, others 18.
Tuition: Res & nonres—Undergrad $50 per hr; campus res room and board $3000.
Courses: Advertising Design; Art Education; Art History; Ceramics; Commercial Art; Constructions; Drawing; Goldsmithing; Graphic Arts; Graphic Design; Handicrafts; History of Art and Archaeology; Jewelry; Lettering; Painting; Sculpture; Silversmithing; Teacher Training.
Adult Hobby Classes: Enrl 18; tui $50 per course. Courses—Ceramics; Jewelry.
Summer School: Enrl 15; tui $50 for term of one cr hr. Courses—varies.

LANGSTON

LANGSTON UNIVERSITY, Art Department, General Delivery, 73050. Tel: 405-466-2231. *Chmn* Wallace Owens, MFA; *Asst Prof* Juanita Cotton, MA(Art); *Instr* Edwin Helm, MA(Art).
Estab 1897, dept estab 1928; pub; D&E; ent req HS dipl; degrees BA(Art Educ) and BA(Arts & Science); enrl D 51, nonmaj 20, maj 31.
Tuition: Res—Undergrad $370, Nonres—Undergrad $405; campus res room and board $950 per yr.
Courses: Art Education; Art History; Ceramics; Commercial Art; Drawing; Graphic Arts; History of Art and Archaeology; Jewelry; Lettering; Mixed Media; Painting; Photography; Printmaking; Sculpture; Silversmithing; Teacher Training; Theatre Arts.
Summer School: Tui $96 for term of 8 wks beginning June 5th. Courses—Drawing; Painting; Public School Art.

LAWTON

CAMERON UNIVERSITY,* Art Department, 2800 Gore Blvd, 73501. Tel: 405-248-2200, exten 66. *Chmn* Jack Bryan; Instrs FT 5, PT 2.
Estab 1970; pub; D&E; ent req HS dipl; degree BA 4 yr; schol; SC 22, LC 5; enrl D 417, E 90, maj 60.
Tuition: $12.45 per hr per sem; campus res $531 per sem.
Courses: Art Education; Ceramics; Drawing; Graphic Arts; Graphic Design; History of Art & Archaeology; Jewelry; Painting; Sculpture.
Summer School: Courses—Art Education; Ceramics; Graphics; Jewelry; Painting.

MIAMI

NORTHEASTERN OKLAHOMA A&M COLLEGE, Art Department, 74354. Tel: 918-542-8441, exten 263. *Chmn* Kathryn Paige, MA; *Chmn Fine Arts* Kenneth Richards. Instrs FT 1, PT 1.
Estab 1919; pub; D&E; ent req HS dipl; degrees AA 2 yr; schol; SC 11, LC 1.
Tuition: Res $9.50 per hr; Nonres $25 per cr hr; campus res room and board.
Courses: Art Education; Calligraphy; Costume Design and Construction; Drafting; Drawing; History of Art and Archaeology; Lettering; Mixed Media; Painting; Sculpture; Stage Design; Theatre Arts.

NORMAN

UNIVERSITY OF OKLAHOMA,* School of Art, 73069. Tel: 405-352-2691. *Dir* Joe F Hobbs; Instrs FT 15, PT 1.
Estab 1911; pub; degrees BFA, M (Art Educ) and MFA 4 yr; schol; SC 27, LC 22, GC 12; enrl maj 350, others 1200.
Courses: Advertising Design; Art Education; Ceramic Design; Drawing; Film; Graphics; History of Art; Metal Design; Painting; Product Design; Sculpture.

OKLAHOMA CITY

OKLAHOMA CITY UNIVERSITY,* Art Department, 73106. Tel: 405-525-5461. *Chmn* Brunel D Faris; Instrs FT 2, PT.
Estab 1904; den; D&E; degrees 4 yr; schol; LC 2; enrl maj 50.

Tuition: Men $2727, women $2767 per yr, includes books, lab fee estimates, meals and room.
Courses: Advertising Art; Ceramics; Design; Figure Drawing; Graphics; History of Art; Jewelry; Painting; Sculpture; Teacher Training; Watercolor.
Summer School: *Dir* Jack Daivs. Enrl 300; tui $55 per cr hr for two 6 wk sessions June to July, July to August.

OKMULGEE

OKLAHOMA STATE UNIVERSITY, School of Technical Training, 4th and Mission, 74447. Tel: 918-756-6211. *Head Dept* Carlisle J Waugh, BS; *Instr* Paul A Gresham, MFA; *Instr* Gary Borchert, BA; *Instr* H Allen Shaw Jr, BFA; *Instr* Ira Eaker, BA; *Instr* Larry Rose; Instr FT 5, PT 1.
Estab 1948; dept estab 1970; pub; D&E; ent req HS dipl or 17½ yrs of age; degrees 2 yr dipl, degree granting technical school; schol; SC 12, LC 1; enrl D 130, E 18.
Tuition: Res—Undergrad $735 per yr, $245 per trimester; Nonres—Undergrad $444.25 per trimester; campus res $1100 per yr.
Courses: Advertising Design; Art Education; Commercial Art; Drafting; Drawing; Goldsmithing; Graphic Arts; Graphic Design; Illustration; Jewelry; Landscape Architecture; Lettering; Photography.
Summer School: Tui same as above per trimester beginning June 1st to last of Sept.

SHAWNEE

OKLAHOMA BAPTIST UNIVERSITY,* College of Liberal Art, Art Department, 74801. *Head Dept* Leroy Bond; Instrs FT 2, PT 1.
Estab 1926; den; degree BA 4 yr; schol; SC 10, LC 1; enrl maj 29, others 22.
Tuition: $1300 per yr; campus res.
Courses: Teacher Training.

STILLWATER

OKLAHOMA STATE UNIVERSITY, Art Department, Gardiner Hall, 74074. Tel: 405-624-6016. *Chmn* Herbert Gottfried, PhD.
Estab 1890, dept estab 1928; pub; D&E; ent req HS dipl; degrees BA, BA(Art Educ), BFA, 4 yr; SC 20, LC 4; enrl D 850, E 60, nonmaj 810, maj 100.
Tuition: Res—Undergrad $13.25 - $15.50 per cr hr; Nonres—Undergrad $28.75 - $33.25 per cr hr; campus res room and board $1218.
Courses: Art History; Ceramics; Drawing; Graphic Design; Jewelry; Lettering; Painting; Printmaking; Sculpture.
Summer School: *Dir* Herbert Gottfried. Tui same as fall and spring.

TAHLEQUAH

NORTHEASTERN OKLAHOMA STATE UNIVERSITY, 74464. Tel: 918-456-5511, exten 405. *Chmn* Dr Tom Cottrill, EdD; *Primary Faculty* Dr Kathleen Schmidt, EdD; Jerry Choate, MFA; R C Coones, MFA.
Estab 1889; pub; D&E; ent req HS dipl; degrees BA and BA (Educ) 4 yr; schol; enrl nonmaj 50, maj 30, GS 10.
Tuition: Campus res room and board.
Courses: Art Education; Art History; Ceramics; Commercial Art; Costume Design and Construction; Drafting; Drawing; Graphic Arts; Jewelry; Lettering; Painting; Photography; Printmaking; Sculpture; Silversmithing; Stage Design; Teacher Training; Theatre Arts.
Adult Hobby Classes: Courses—Indian Art; Silversmithing.
Summer School: Regular summer session.

TULSA

UNIVERSITY OF TULSA,* Department of Art, 600 S College Ave, 74104. Tel: 918-939-6351, exten 202. *Head Dept* Bradley E Place; Instrs FT D 8, PT E 6, 3 grad teaching asst.
Estab 1898; pvt; degrees BA, BS, BFA, MA, MFA and MTA 4 yr; schol; SC 20, LC 13, GC 22; enrl maj 160, others 400.
Tuition: $850 per sem; campus res.
Courses: Advertising Design; Ceramics; Drawing & Painting; Graphic Arts; Handicrafts; Industrial Design; Sculpture; Teacher Training; Technical Illustration; Television (Speech Department).
Summer School: *Dir* Bradley E Place. Enrl 150; two sessions June and July.

WARNER

CONNORS STATE COLLEGE,* Art Department, 74469. Tel: 918-463-2931. *Head Dept* Jack Best; Instrs FT 1, PT 1.

Estab 1908; pub; D; ent req HS dipl; degree AA 2 yr; SC 8, LC 1; enrl 120.
Courses: Advertising Design; Drafting; Drawing; Graphic Arts; Graphic Design; History of Art & Archaeology; Painting.

WEATHERFORD

SOUTHWESTERN OKLAHOMA STATE UNIVERSITY, Art Department, 73096. Tel: 405-772-6611, exten 5000. *Chmn* Richard H Taflinger, MFA; *Instr* Denny Carley, MA; *Asst Prof* Montee Hoke, MA; *Instr* R Park Lang, MA; *Asst Prof* Leroy Schultz, MT; *Instr* James A Terrell, MA; *Asst Prof* Warren D Waggoner, MFA.
Estab 1901, dept estab 1941; pub; D&E; ent req HS dipl; degrees BA (Art), BA (Art Educ) and BA (Commer Art) 4 yr; SC 35, LC 8, GC 43; enrl D 5000.
Tuition: Varies; campus res.
Courses: Advertising Design; Art Education; Art History; Ceramics; Commercial Art; Drawing; Graphic Arts; Graphic Design; History of Art and Archaeology; Illustration; Jewelry; Lettering; Mixed Media; Painting; Sculpture; Teacher Training.
Summer School: Courses—Ceramics; Drawing; Elements of Art; Fundamentals of Art; Introduction to Clay; Jewelry; Metal I & II; Painting I, II, III, V.

OREGON

ALBANY

LINN BENTON COMMUNITY COLLEGE,* Art Department, 6500 SW Pacific Blvd, 97321. Tel: 503-928-2361. *Chmn Humanities Div* Kenneth D Cheney; Instrs FT 5, PT 1.
Estab 1968; pub; D&E; ent req open entry; degrees AA, AS and AGS 2 yrs; SC 14, LC 2; enrl D 2000, E 4000.
Tuition: In-state, in-dist $333 per yr.
Courses: Advertising Design; Aesthetics; Ceramics; Commercial Art; Display; Drafting; Drawing; Graphic Arts; Graphic Design; Handicrafts; History of Art & Archaeology; Illustration; Jewelry; Lettering; Painting; Photography in Motion Pictures; Sculpture & Architecture; Stitchery; Textile Design; Theatre Arts; Weaving.
Adult Hobby Classes: Tole Painting; Watercolor & Painting.

ASHLAND

OREGON COLLEGE OF ART,* 30 S First St, 97520. Tel: 503-482-0113. *Pres* Dr Richard K Walsh; Instrs FT 2, PT 5.
Estab 1971; pvt; D; ent req HS dipl, portfolio; degrees Bachelor of Professional Arts or cr transfer for AA or BA at adjacent Southern Oregon State Col 4 yrs; schol; SC 24, LC 5; enrl D 40.
Courses: Advertising Design; Art Education; Ceramics; Commercial Art; Costume Design & Construction; Drawing; Fashion Arts; Graphic Arts; Graphic Design; History of Art & Archaeology; Illustration; Jewelry; Lettering; Painting; Sculpture; Teacher Training; Textile Design; Theatre Arts.

SOUTHERN OREGON STATE COLLEGE, Department of Art, Siskiyou Blvd, 97520. Tel: 503-482-6386. *Chairperson Dept Art* Wesley G Chapman, PhD; vis prof—Lynn Brown, sculpture, fall, winter, spring.
Estab 1926; pub; D&E; ent req HS dipl; degrees BA or BSArt Educ, BA or BSArt 4 yrs; schol; SC 48, LC 11, GC 1; enrl D 120, E 30, nonmaj 100, maj 75.
Tuition: Res—undergrad $233 per yr, grad $356 per yr; Nonres—undergrad $656 per yr; campus res room and board.
Courses: Advertising Design; Art Education; ‡Art History; Calligraphy; ‡Ceramics; Commercial Art; ‡Crafts; ‡Drawing; Graphic Design; Illustration; ‡Jewelry; Lettering; ‡Painting; Photography; ‡Printmaking; ‡Sculpture; ‡Teacher Training; Watercolor; ‡Weaving.
Summer School: Dir Dr Esby McGill.

BEND

CENTRAL OREGON COMMUNITY COLLEGE, Department of Art, College Way, 97701. *Asst Prof Art* Tom Temple, MA(Art); *Asst Prof Art* Douglas C Smith, MA(Art).
Estab 1949; pub; D&E; ent req HS dipl; degrees AA, AS, Cert; schol; enrl in col D 1500, E 2000.
Tuition: In-dist $125 per yr, out-of-dist $195 per yr, out-of-state $600 per yr; campus res room and board $1200 per yr.
Courses: Calligraphy; Ceramics; Drawing; Painting; Photography; Printmaking; Stage Design; Theatre Arts.

Summer School: Dir Dick Friedman. Enrl 350; term of 8 wks beginning June 19.

COOS BAY

COOS ART MUSEUM, 515 Market Ave, 97420. Tel: 503-267-3901. *Educ Dir* Jo Reid; Instrs PT 8.
Estab 1966; pvt; D&E; SC 7; enrl D 15, E 100.
Courses: Calligraphy; Children's Craft & Stitchery; Display; Drawing; Jewelry; Lettering; Painting; Sculpture; Spinning; Stitchery; Weaving.
Adult Hobby Classes: Enrl 100; tui for 10 wks, nonmem $18, mem $15.
Children's Classes: Enrl 40.
Summer School: Dir Jo Reid. Tui same as above; Courses—Children's Craft, Drawing & Painting.

CORVALLIS

OREGON STATE UNIVERSITY, College of Liberal Arts, 97331. Tel: 503-754-2511. *Dean Col* Gordon W Gilkey.
 Department of Art, Fairbanks Hall. Tel: 503-754-1745. *Chmn Dept* John H Rock; Instrs FT 20; PT 2.
Estab 1908; pub; D&E; ent req HS grad; degrees BA, BS(Art) and BFA 4 yrs; schol; SC 40, LC 15; enrl 1400.
Tuition: Res—$213 per quarter term; Nonres—$700 per quarter term.
Courses: Advertising Design; Ceramics; Design; Drawing; Elementary Art Education; Fabric Design; History of Art; Illustration; Jewelry & Metal Design; Painting; Photography; Printmaking; Sculpture; Secondary Art Education.
Summer School: An 8-11 wk-term is conducted with similar offerings to those listed above. The equivalent to one quarter term of work may be accomplished. Tui undergrad $191, grad $286 (res & nonres).
—**Department of Architecture and Landscape Architecture,** AG Hall, Tel: 503-754-2606. *Chmn Dept* John R Stewart; Instrs FT 9.
Architecture estab 1947, Landscape Architecture estab 1908, combined department 1971; pub; D&E; ent req HS dipl; degrees Liberal Studies, BS or BA with major emphasis in each area 4 yrs; SC 36, LC 12; enrl nonmaj 200, maj 150.
Tuition: Res—undergrad $738 per yr, grad $1164 per yr; Nonres—undergrad $1311 per yr, grad $2487 per yr; campus res.
Courses: Architectural Design & Drawing; Architectural Design Studios; Architecture; Construction & Materials; Drafting; Drawing; Graphics & Delineation; History & Theory; Housing & Architectural Philosophy; Influence of Man on His Physical Environs; Interior Design; Landscape Architecture; Landscape Design Studios; Landscape Design & Theory; Maintenance & Construction; Plant Materials & Composition.

EUGENE

MAUDE KERNS ART CENTER, 1910 E 15th Ave, 97403. *Dir* Carol Wood; Instrs PT 25.
Estab 1955; pvt; D&E; schol; SC 45; enrl D&E 450.
Tuition: $38-$45 per class per quarter.
Courses: Calligraphy; Ceramics; Graphic Arts; Handicrafts; Jewelry; Painting; Photography; Stitchery.
Adult Hobby Classes: Enrl 420; Courses—As above.
Children's Classes: Enrl 50; tui $20. Courses—Ceramics; Drawing.
Summer School: Courses varied.

LANE COMMUNITY COLLEGE, Art and Applied Design Department, 4000 E 30th Ave, 97405. Tel: 503-747-4501, exten 306. *Chmn Dept* Roger Cornell McAlister, MFA; *Primary Art Faculty:* Bruce Wild, MFA; Bill Blix, MFA; Harold Hoy, MFA; Bruce Dean, MFA; Craig Spilman, MFA; Alda Vinson, MA; Dan White, MFA; vis prof—Kathleen Shanahan, painting, drawing, design, 1977-78.
Estab 1964, dept estab 1967; pub; D&E; ent req HS dipl; degrees AA, AS 2 yrs; SC 42, LC 4; enrl D 300, E 75, nonmaj 240, maj 60.
Tuition: Res—$130 per sem, $10.90 per cr hr; Nonres—$545 per sem; no campus res.
Courses: Art History; Ceramics; Drafting; Drawing; Goldsmithing; Graphic Arts; Jewelry; Painting; Photography; Printmaking; Sculpture, especially Metal Casting; Silversmithing.
Summer School: Dir Roger Cornell McAlister. Tui $10.90 per cr hr. Courses—Drawing; Painting; Sculpture.

UNIVERSITY OF OREGON, School of Architecture and Allied Arts Department of Fine and Applied Arts, 97403. Tel: 503-686-3610. *Dept Head* Robert C James, MFA; vis prof—Tim Corkery, painting, 77-78; Milton Halberstadt, photography, winter/spring 78.
Pub; D; degrees BA, BS 4 yr; BFA 5 yr, MFA 2 yr minimum after BFA or equivalent; schol; enrl D 1500, nonmajors 367, maj 926, other 231.
Tuition: Res—Undergrad $738 yr; grad $1175 yr; Nonres—Undergrad $2487, grad $1312; campus res room and board $1400 per yr.

Courses: Calligraphy; Ceramics; Drafting; Drawing; Goldsmithing; Graphic Design; Jewelry; Painting; Photography; Printmaking; Sculpture; Silversmithing; Video.
Summer School: Dir Robert James. Tui $252 for term of 8 wk beginning June 20.

LA GRANDE

EASTERN OREGON STATE COLLEGE, Division of Humanities, 97850. Tel: 503-963-2171, exten 252. *Chairperson Div Humanities* Dr Mary Jane Loso; *Assoc Prof Art* Thomas Morandi, MFA; *Assoc Prof Art* Ian Gatley, MA; *Asst Prof Art* Robin Alexander, PhD; *Asst Prof Art* Thomas Dimond, MFA.
Estab 1929; pub; D&E; ent req HS dipl; degrees BA/BS in Art, BA/BS in Sec Educ with Endorsement in Art, BA/BS in Elem Educ with Specialization in Art, 4 yrs; SC 32, LC 8, GC 2.
Tuition: Campus res room and board.
Courses: Aesthetics; ‡Art Education; Art History; Calligraphy; Ceramics; Drawing; Glassblowing; Lettering; Painting; Photography; Printmaking; Sculpture; Stage Design; Teacher Training; Textile Design; Theatre Arts.
Summer School: Dir Dr Richard Hiatt. Term of 4 - 8 wks. Courses—Two or three a summer, beginning level.

McMINNVILLE

LINFIELD COLLEGE, Art Department, 97128. Tel: 503-472-4121, exten 274. *Prof Art & Chmn Dept* Steven Karatzas, MFA; *Prof* Patricia Fields, MFA; *Prof* Randall Jelinek, MFA; vis prof—Roger Feldman, drawing, spring sem 1978.
Estab 1849, dept estab 1964; pvt; D; ent req HS dipl; degrees BA 4 yrs, ME 2 yrs; schol; SC 16, LC 2; enrl nonmaj 150, maj 20.
Tuition: $1400 per sem, $55 per hr; campus res room and board $1450 per yr.
Courses: Advertising Design; Art Education; Art History; Calligraphy; Ceramics; Commercial Art; Constructions; Costume Design & Construction; Drawing; Film; Graphic Arts; Graphic Design; Interior Design; Lettering; Mixed Media; Painting; Photography; Printmaking; Sculpture; Stage Design; Teacher Training; Textile Design; Theatre Arts; Video.
Summer School: Tui $430 for 5 sem hrs/5 wk block, Block I June 12-July 14, Block II July 17 - Aug 18.

MONMOUTH

OREGON COLLEGE OF EDUCATION,* Art Department, 97361. Tel: 503-838-1220, exten 340. *Chmn Dept* Daniel G Cannon; Instrs FT 11.
Estab 1856; pub; D&E; degrees BA and BS 4 yrs; SC 63, LC 17, GC 6; enrl total 3500.
Tuition: (all 3 terms) Res—undergrad $684; Nonres—undergrad $1953.
Courses: Art Education; Art History; Contemporary Problems; Crafts; Design; Drawing & Composition; Environmental Design; Individual Studies; Lettering; Life Drawing; Light Image (Photography); Mixed Media; Oil & Acrylic Painting; Printmaking; Sculpture; Textile Design; The Art Idea: Visual Thinking; Visual Learning & Communication; Watercolor.
Summer School: Chmn Daniel G Cannon. Tui undergrad $171 for 12-21 hrs, grad $253 for 9-16 hrs. Courses—As above.

PORTLAND

JUDSON BAPTIST COLLEGE, Department of Visual Arts, 9201 NE Fremont St, 97220. Tel: 503-252-5563. *Assoc Prof Art & Head Dept Visual Arts* David S Johnson, MFA; *Instr* Janet Otter, BA.
Estab 1956, dept estab 1964; den; D&E; ent req HS dipl, CEEB, references; degrees AA and AS 2 yrs; schol; SC 5, LC 2; enrl D 66, E 15, nonmaj 60-65, maj 12-15.
Tuition: Res—$3390 per yr; Nonres—$2070 per yr; campus res room and board $1320.
Courses: Advertising Design; Art Appreciation; Art History; Basic Design; Calligraphy; Drawing; Painting.

LEWIS AND CLARK COLLEGE, Department of Art, 0615 SW Palatine Hill Rd, 97219. Tel: 503-244-6161, exten 321. *Prof Art & Chmn Dept* Ken Shores, MFA; *Assoc Prof* Norman Paasche; *Asst Prof* Stewart Buettner, PhD; *Asst Prof* Raymond S Barnes, MFA.
Estab 187, dept estab 1946; pvt; D; ent req HS dipl; degrees BS and BA 4 yrs; schol; SC 10, LC 2.
Courses: Art History; Calligraphy; Ceramics; Drawing; Graphic Arts; History of Art & Archaeology; Painting; Printmaking; Sculpture.
Summer School: Dir Sid Eiders.

PORTLAND ART MUSEUM, Museum Art School, 1219 SW Park Ave, 97205. Tel: 503-226-4391. *Acting Dean* Harry Widman, MFA; *Instr* Manuel Izquierdo; *Instr* George Cummings; *Instr* Jack Myers; *Instr* George Johanson; *Instr* Jack McLarty; *Instr* Edward Malin; *Instr* William Grand; Instrs FT 14, PT 29.
Estab 1909; pvt; D&E; ent req HS dipl plus home drawing test; degree BFA 4 yrs; schol; SC 17, LC 7; enrl D FT 146, PT 50, E 248.
Tuition: $1898 per yr, $949 per sem; no campus res.
Courses: Advertising Design; Art History; Calligraphy; Ceramics; Commercial Art; Drawing; Fashion Arts; Graphic Arts; Graphic Design; Illustration; Lettering; Painting; Photography; Printmaking; Sculpture.
Adult Hobby Classes: Enrl 248; tui $81 per sem. Courses—Life Drawing; Graphic Design; Painting; Sculpture; Ceramics; Calligraphy; Printmaking.
Children's Classes: Enrl 120; tui $70 per sem. Courses—General Art.
Summer School: Acting Dean Harry Widman. Tui $70 for 6 wks beginning June 19.

PORTLAND STATE UNIVERSITY, Department of Art and Architecture, PO Box 751, 97207. Tel: 503-229-3515. *Prof Art Hist & Head Dept Art & Architecture* Leonard B Kimbrell, PhD; *Prof* Raymond Grimm, MA; *Prof* James L Hansen, Dipl; *Prof* Frederick H Heidel, MFA; *Prof* Robert Kasal, MA; *Prof* Louis Ocepek, MA.
Estab 1955; pub; D&E; ent req HS dipl; degrees BS and BA(Art) 4 yrs, MST, MAT(Art) 1 yr, MFA(Painting, Ceramics, Sculpture) 2 yrs; schol; enrl E 2000, nonmaj 1300, maj 600, grad 30, others 70.
Tuition: Res—undergrad $179 per term, grad $311 per term; Nonres—undergrad $710 per term; campus res.
Courses: ‡Advertising Design; Architecture; Art Education; ‡Art History; Calligraphy; ‡Ceramics; Conceptual Art; ‡Drawing; Goldsmithing; Graphic Arts; ‡Graphic Design; History of Art & Archaeology; ‡Jewelry; Lettering; ‡Painting; Photography; Printmaking; ‡Sculpture; Silversmithing; Teacher Training.
Summer School: Enrl 4 - 500; term of 8 - 12 wks beginning June 28. Courses—Vary, two centers, one in Portland and one at Cannan Beach, The Haystack Program.

REED COLLEGE,* Department of Art, 97202. Tel: 503-771-1112. *Chmn Dept* Charles S Rhyne; Instrs FT 4, PT 1.
Estab 1911; pvt; D; degree BA 3-5 yrs; schol; SC 7, LC 5; enrl D 1150, E 15.
Tuition: $460 per yr; campus res $1650 per yr.
Courses: Aesthetics; Calligraphy & Paleography; Drawing; History of Art & Archaeology; Painting; Sculpture.

SCHOOL OF THE ARTS AND CRAFTS SOCIETY, 616 NW 18th St, 97209. Tel: 503-228-4741. *Dir* Bridget Beattie McCarthy; Instrs PT 40.
Estab 1906; pvt; D&E; no ent req; no degrees; schol; SC and LC 50; enrl D 225-250, E 200-225.
Tuition: All courses cost $67 per ten wk period; classes vary in laboratory fees; no campus res.
Courses: Calligraphy; Ceramics; Drawing; Handicrafts; Jewelry; Photography; Printmaking; Silversmithing; Textile Design.
Children's Classses: Enrl 25; tui $36 per 10 wks. Courses—Pottery; Jewelry; Cartooning; Art Adventures.

ROSEBURG

UMPQUA COMMUNITY COLLEGE, Art Department, PO Box 967, 97470. Tel: 503-672-5571, exten 44. *Coordr* Joel Lynn Boyel, Jr, MFA; *Instr* Robert Bell, MFA; *Instr* Marie Rasmussen, MA; *Instr* Christine Westergaard, MFA.
Estab 1964; pub; D&E; ent req HS dipl; degree AA 2 yrs; schol; SC 5, LC 2; enrl D 160, E 80, maj 12.
Tuition: $132 per term (10 wks); no campus res.
Courses: Art History; Ceramics; Drawing; Painting; Photography; Theatre Arts.
Adult Hobby Classes: Courses—Ceramics; Drawing; Painting; Photography.

SALEM

CHEMEKETA COMMUNITY COLLEGE, Department of English and Humanities, 4000 Lancaster Dr NE (Mailing Add: PO Box 14007, 97309). Tel: 503-399-5000. *Assoc Dir* Thomas Gill, MFA; *Instr* Robert Bibler, MFA.
Estab 1969, dept estab 1975; pub; D&E; ent req none; degree AA 2 yrs; schol; SC 9, LC 3; enrl D 125, E 75.
Tuition: Res—$13 per cr hr, $130 quarterly; Nonres—$19.50 - $48.50 per cr hr, $195 - $485 quarterly; no campus res.
Courses: Art History; Calligraphy; Ceramics; Drafting; Drawing; Film; Painting; Photography; Printmaking; Theatre Arts.

Adult Hobby Classes: Enrl 150-200; tui 75¢ per contact hr.
Summer School: Assoc Dir Thomas Gill. Term of 8 wks.

PENNSYLVANIA

ALLENTOWN

CEDAR CREST COLLEGE,* Art Department, 18104. Tel: 215-437-4471. *Chmn Dept* Ryland W Greene; Instrs FT 3, PT 2.
Estab 1867; pvt; D&E; ent req HS dipl, CEEB; degrees BA, BS, Interdisciplinary Fine Arts Maj (art, theatre, music, dance, creative writing), 4 yrs; schol; SC 11, Art History courses 4; enrl 750.
Courses: Aesthetics; Art Education; Ceramics; Comparative Study of Art; Drawing; History of Art; Jewelry; Metal Forming; Painting; Sculpture; Theatre Arts.
Cooperative Summer School with Muhlenberg College; courses—Ceramics; Jewelry-Metalsmithing.

BETHLEHEM

LEHIGH UNIVERSITY, Department of Fine Arts, Chandler-Ullman Hall, Bldg 17, 18015. Tel: 215-691-7000, exten 525. *Asst Prof Art & Chairperson Pro Tempore Dept Fine Arts* Ricardo Viera, MFA; *Prof* Richard J Redd, MFA; *Assoc Prof* Carlos J Alvare, MArch, MCP; *Asst Prof* Gary M Burnley, MFA; Instrs PT 4.
Estab 1925; pvt; D&E; ent req HS dipl, SAT, CEEB; degree BA 4 yrs; SC 22, LC 16; enrl D&E 700.
Tuition: $3825 per yr, $1912.50 per sem; campus res room and board.
Courses:‡Architecture; ‡Art History; Ceramics; Costume Design & Construction; Drafting; Drawing; ‡General Art; History of Art & Archaeology; Mixed Media; Museum Staff Training; Painting; Photography; Printmaking; Restoration & Conservation; Sculpture.
Summer School: Dir Dr Norman Sam. Courses—Teacher Training.

MORAVIAN COLLEGE, Department of Art, South Campus, 18018. Tel: 215-865-0741. *Prof Art & Chmn Dept* Rudy S Ackerman, DEd; *Assoc Prof* Daniel Tereshko, MFA; *Instr* Michael Gaston, MFA; *Instr* Michael Gaston, MFA; *Assoc Instr* Charlene Engel, PhD; *Photographer in-Residence* Judy Ross, MA; *Ceramist in-Residence* Renzo Faggioli, Master Craftsman.
Estab 1807, dept estab 1963; pvt; D&E; ent req HS dipl; degrees BA and BS 4 yrs; SC 15, LC 8; enrl D 350, E 15, nonmaj 1200, maj 50.
Tuition: $5000 per yr.
Courses: ‡Art History; ‡Ceramics; ‡Drawing; Film; Jewelry; ‡Painting; ‡Photography; Printmaking; Sculpture; Silversmithing; Textile Design.
Summer School: Tui $250 for term of 6 wks. Courses—Same as during regular terms.

BLOOMSBURG

BLOOMSBURG STATE COLLEGE, Department of Art, Blakeless Center for the Humanities, 17815. *Prof Art & Chmn Dept* Percival R Roberts III, EdD; *Asst Prof* Karl Beamer, MFA; *Assoc Prof* Stewart Nagel, MFA; *Assoc Prof* Barbara J Strohman, MFA; *Asst Prof* Charles Thomas Walter, PhD; *Asst Prof* Robert Koslosky, MA; *Asst Prof* Gary F-Clark, MA; *Asst Prof* John Cook, MA; *Assoc Prof* Kenneth T Wilson, MA; vis prof—Walter Nichols, drawing, painting, 1977-78.
Estab 1839, dept estab 1940; pub; D&E; ent req HS dipl; degrees BA(Art Studio) and BA(Art Hist) 4 yrs; schol; SC 7, LC 12; enrl D 1800, E 200, maj 75.
Tuition: Res—$410 per sem; Nonres—$750 per sem; campus res.
Courses: Aesthetics; Art Education; Art History; Ceramics; Crafts; Drawing; General Design; Goldsmithing; History of Art & Archaeology; Jewelry; Museum Staff Training; Painting; Printmaking; Sculpture; Silversmithing; Stage Design; Textile Design; Theatre Arts; Weaving.
Children's Classes: Enrl 25; tui $10 per sem; Sat classes for children.
Summer School: Dean Richard O Wolfe. Enrl 200-300; tui $43 per cr hr. Courses—Vary.

BRYN MAWR

BRYN MAWR COLLEGE,* Department of the History of Art, 19010. Tel: 215-525-1000, exten 249, 250. *Chmn Dept* Charles Dempsey; Instrs FT 6, PT 1.
Estab 1913; pvt; W (men in grad sch); degrees BA 4 yrs, MA, PhD; schol and fel; LC 10, GC 8; enrl maj 20, grad 30, others 150.
Tuition: $4625; campus res.
Courses: History of Art.

HARCUM JUNIOR COLLEGE,* Department of Fine Arts, 19010. Tel: 215-525-4100; exten 215. *Chmn Dept* Martin Zipin; Instrs FT 1, PT 5.
Estab 1915; pvt; D&E; W; ent req HS dipl; degree AA 2 yrs; schol; SC 7, LC 1; enrl D 40, E 8, maj 10.
Courses: Commercial Art; Drawing; Fashion Arts; Graphic Design; History of Art & Archaeology; Lettering; Painting; Sculpture.

CARLISLE

DICKINSON COLLEGE, Fine Arts Department, High St, 17013. Tel: 717-243-5121, exten 344. *Prof Art & Chmn Fine Arts Dept* Dennis Akin, MFA; *Asst Prof* Sharon Latchaw/Hirsch, PhD; *Asst Prof* Dennis Clive, MFA; *Asst Prof* Caroline Bruzelius, PhD.
Estab 1773, dept estab 1940; pvt; D; ent req HS dipl, SAT; degrees BA and BS 4 yrs; SC 7, LC 11; enrl 250, nonmaj 185, maj 65.
Tuition: $2060 per sem; Campus res room and board $885 per sem, $1770 per yr.
Courses: ‡Art History; Ceramics; Drawing; Film; ‡Mixed Media; Painting; Photography; Printmaking; Sculpture.
Summer School: Dir Peggy Garrett. Tui $295 per course for term of 5½ wks beginning May 31. Courses—Same as above.

CHAMBERSBURG

WILSON COLLEGE,* Department of Fine Arts, 17201. Tel: 717-264-4141, exten 353. *Chmn Dept* Josephine M Harris; Instrs FT 3, PT 2.
Pvt; W; ent exam; degree BA(Studio, Art Hist, Dance, Drama) 4 yrs; SC 16, LC 19, seminars in studio, art history, dance, drama, enrl maj 18.
Courses: Dance Composition & Performance; Drawing & Painting; Elements of Staging; Graphic Arts; Independent Study; Problems in Acting; Sculpture.

CHELTENHAM

CHELTENHAM ART CENTRE, 439 Ashbourne Rd, 19012. Tel: 215-ES9-4660. *Dir* G Noble Wagner.
Estab 1938; pvt nonprofit; D&E; SC 83, LC 2, enrl total 1800.
Courses: Ceramics; Collage; Drawing; Handicrafts; Jewelry; Mixed Media; Painting; Photography; Printmaking; Sculpture; Theatre Arts.

CHEYNEY

CHEYNEY STATE COLLEGE,* Department of Art, 19319. *Chmn Dept* Samuel L Curtis; Instrs FT 7.
Estab 1937; pub; D&E; ent req HS dipl, ent exam; degree BA 4 yrs; schol; SC 16, LC 4.
Courses: Aesthetics; Art Therapy; Ceramics; Drawing; Graphic Arts; Handicrafts; History of Art & Archaeology; Painting; Sculpture.

CLARION

CLARION STATE COLLEGE, Department of Art, 16214. Tel: 814-226-6000, exten 379. *Chmn Dept Art* Robert D Hobbs, EdD; *Prof* Francis C Baptist, EdD; *Assoc Prof* Alfred B Charley, MFA; *Assoc Prof* William T Edwards, Jr, EdD; *Assoc Prof* William E Grosch, MEd; *Asst Prof* Charles G Pearce, MEd; *Asst Prof* Andor S P-Jobb, MFA; *Assoc Prof* Eugene A Seelye, MA.
Estab 1867; pub; D&E; ent req HS dipl; degree BA(Art) yrs; SC 4, LC 21, GC 1; enrl D&E 925 (one sem), maj 25.
Tuition: Campus res room and board.
Courses: Art Education; Art History; Ceramics; Drawing; Graphic Arts; Graphic Design; Handicrafts (arts & crafts course); Jewelry; Painting; Sculpture; Three-Dimensional Design.
Adult Hobby Classes: Continuing Education. Tui $35-$50 for 12 wk course. Courses—Drawing; Ceramics; Patchwork; Applique & Quilting.
Summer School: Dir Dr Charles Schontz.

CRESSON

MOUNT ALOYSIUS JUNIOR COLLEGE, Art Department, Rte 22, 16630. Tel: 814-886-4131, exten 40. *Assoc Prof* Hettie Jane Osborne; Instrs FT 4.
Estab 1939; den; D&E; ent req HS dipl, SAT, ACT, health record, art portfolio and interview; degree AA 2 yrs; schol; SC 10, LC 12; enrl D 153, E 8, maj 23.
Tuition: $75 per cr; campus res room and board $1400 per yr.
Courses: Advertising Design; Art Education; Art History; Calligraphy; Ceramics; Commercial Art; Display; Drawing; Figure Drawing; Graphic Design; Lettering; Occupational Therapy; Painting; Photography; Printmaking; Sculpture; Textile Design; Two & Three-Dimensional Design.

DALLAS

COLLEGE MISERICORDIA, Art Department, 18612. Tel: 717-675-2181, exten 234. *Asst Prof Art & Chmn Dept* Ralph G Kaleshefski, MA; *Instrs* Sarah Davis Elliott, MFA; *Asst Prof* Martha Rochester Kaleshefski, MFA; *Asst Prof* Sister Flora Mulhearn, MA; *Asst Prof* Sister Elaine Tulanowski, MA.
Estab 1924, dept estab 1965; pvt; D&E; ent req HS dipl; degrees AAS, BA, BS, BM, BS(Nursing); schol; SC 35, LC 10; enrl D 40, nonmaj 25, maj 40, others 4 extension.
Tuition: $68 per cr; campus res room and board.
Courses: Aesthetics; ‡Art Education; Art History; Calligraphy; Ceramics; Drawing; History of Art & Archaeology; Painting; Photography; Printmaking; Sculpture; Teacher Training; Theatre Arts.
Summer School: Dir Sister Mary Glennon. Tui $68 per cr. Courses—Change every summer depending on need.

EASTON

LAFAYETTE COLLEGE,* Department of Art, 18042. Tel: 215-253-6281, exten 328. *Head Dept* Dr Joseph W Gluhman; *Instrs* FT 3, PT 2.
Estab 1827; pvt; D&E; ent req HS dipl, ent exam, selective admis; degrees BS and AB 4 yrs; schol; SC 8, LC 12; enrl D 300, E 250, maj 4.
Courses: Art History; Drawing; History of Architecture; Painting; Printmaking; Sculpture; Two & Three-Dimensional Design.
Summer School: Dir Earl G Peace.

EDINBORO

EDINBORO STATE COLLEGE, Art Department, 16444. Tel: 814-732-2406. *Chmn Art Dept* Richard H Laing, DEd; *Chmn 2-Dimensional Area* Ian Short, MFA; *Chmn 3-Dimensional Area* Jerry Valley, MFA; *Chmn Crafts* Donna Nicholas, MFA; *Chmn Art Hist* Barthwell Farmer, MA; *Chmn Art Educ* Dorn Howlett, MA; *Dir Galleries* Mary Jane Kidd, MFA; *Cur Coll* L Rosenfeld, MA; FT Faculty 48.
Estab 1857; pub; D&E; ent req HS dipl, SAT; degrees BSEd, BFA and BA 4 yrs, MEd 1 yr, MFA 2 yrs; schol; SC 86, LC 30, GC 20; enrl D 850 art maj, nonmaj 6000, grad 25.
Tuition: Res—Undergrad $1854 per yr, $425 per sem, grad $475 per sem, $51 per cr hr; Nonres—Undergrad $2604 per yr, $800 per sem, grad $890 per sem, $75 per cr hr; campus res.
Courses: Aesthetics; Art Education; Art History; Ceramics; Communications Graphics; Conceptual Art; Drawing; Film; Graphic Design; History of Art; Illustration; Jewelry; Lettering; Mixed Media; Painting; Photography; Printmaking; Sculpture; Silversmithing; Teacher Training; Textile Design.
Summer School: Dir Dr Richard H Laing. Courses—Painting; Drawing; Jewelry; Printmaking; Weaving; Textile Design; Sculpture.

ERIE

MERCYHURST COLLEGE, Department of Art, 501 E 38th St, 16501. Tel: 814-864-0681. *Dir* Ernest Mauthe, MA; *Prof* Joseph Pizzat, EdD; *Assoc Prof* Edward Higgins, MS; *Assoc Prof* Daniel Burke, MEd; *Instrs* PT 4.
Estab 1926, dept estab 1950; pvt; D&E; ent req HS dipl, Col Boards, portfolio review; degree BA 4 yrs; schol; SC 45, LC 12; enrl D 100, E 30, maj 100.
Tuition: $2575 per yr; campus res room and board $1330 per yr.
Courses: Advertising Design; Art Appreciation; Art Education; Art Foundations; Art History; Ceramics; Child Art; Commercial Art; Contemporary Art Theories; Creative Arts for Adolescents and Children; Creativity; Drawing; Fibers/Fabrics; Independent Study; Individualized Studio; Jewelry; Painting; Photography; Printmaking; Sculpture; Senior Seminar; Teaching Internship; Television Internship.
Adult Hobby Classes: 6-8 wks. Courses—Drawing; Painting; Crafts.
Summer School: Dir Ernest Mauthe. Tui $160 per course for term of 5-6 wks beginning June/July. Courses—Vary.

GETTYSBURG

GETTYSBURG COLLEGE, Department of Art, 17325. Tel: 717-334-3131, exten 243. *Prof & Head* Ingolf J Qually, MFA; *Prof* Norman L Annis, MFA; *Instr* Carol D Small, MA.
Estab 1832, dept estab 1956; pvt; D; ent req HS dipl, ent exam; degrees BA 4 yr; schol; SC 10, LC 15; enrl D 300.
Tuition: $3960 yr; campus res room and board $5490 per yr.
Courses: Aesthetics; ‡Art History; Basic Design; ‡Drawing; Figure Drawing; ‡Painting; ‡Print ‡Printmaking; ‡Sculpture.

GLENSIDE

BEAVER COLLEGE, Department of Fine Arts, Easton & Church Rds, 19038. Tel: 215-884-3500. *Chmn Dept Fine Arts* Jack Davis, MA; *Assoc Prof* Judith Brodsley, MFA; *Prof* Jean Francksen, BFA; *Asst Prof* Ron Kalla, MEd; *Asst Prof* Ann Williams, MFA.
Estab 1853; pvt; D&E; ent req HS dipl, SAT, ACT, portfolio review; degrees BA and BFA 4 yrs, MA(Educ) 1 yr; schol; SC 40, LC 18; enrl in col D FT 607, PT 178, nonmaj in dept 20, maj in dept 126.
Tuition: $3400 per yr, $1700 per sem, $420 per course; campus res room and board $1800.
Courses: Advertising Design; Aesthetics; ‡Art Education; ‡Art History; ‡Ceramics; Commercial Art; Drawing; ‡Graphic Design; Illustration; ‡Interior Design; ‡Jewelry; ‡Painting; Photography; ‡Printmaking; Teacher Training; Weaving.
Summer School: Chmn Jack Davis. Enrl approx 200; tui $55 per cr hr for term of 7 wks beginning June 12. Courses—Painting; Printmaking; Ceramics; High School Program.

GREENSBURG

SETON HILL COLLEGE, Department of Art, 15601. Tel: 412-834-2200, exten 388. *Chmn Dept* Stuart R Thompson, PhD; *Primary Art Faculty:* Josefa Filkosky, MFA; Raymond DeFazio, MEd; Laura Bench, MFA; Mary Janice Grindle, BA; Rosalie O'Hara, ML; 1 PT Instrs.
Estab 1918, dept estab 1950; den D&E; ent req HS dipl, review portfolio; degree BA 4 yrs; SC 20, LC 6; enrl D 78, maj 78.
Tuition: $2370 per yr; campus res room and board $1300 per yr.
Courses: Aesthetics; ‡Art Education; ‡Calligraphy; ‡Ceramics; Costume Design & Construction; ‡Drawing; Fashion Arts; ‡Film; Goldsmithing; Handicrafts (fabrics); ‡Jewelry; Lettering; ‡Painting; ‡Photography; ‡Printmaking; ‡Sculpture; Silversmithing; Stage Design; Teacher Training; Textile Design; Theatre Arts; Video.
Summer School: Dir Continuing Educ Vivian Henderson. Courses—Clay; Raku; Photography; Metalsmithing; Fabrics.

GREENVILLE

THIEL COLLEGE, Department of Art, College Ave, 16125. Tel: 412-588-7700, exten 415. *Assoc Prof Art & Chmn Dept* Ronald A Pivovar, MFA; *Assoc Prof* Alvin S Dunkle, MA; *Assoc Prof* Richard L Hayes, MA; *Asst Prof* William F DeWolf, PhD(Art Educ).
Estab 1866, dept estab 1965; pvt; D&E; ent req HS dipl, interviews; degree BA 4 yrs; schol; SC 15, LC 11; enrl D 275, nonmaj 200, maj 75.
Tuition: Res—$2105 per yr; Nonres—$1425 per yr, $96 per cr hr; Jan interim term $487; campus res room and board $1380 per yr.
Courses: Art Education; Art History; Ceramics; Drawing; Graphic Arts; History of Art & Archaeology; Jewelry; Painting; Printmaking; Sculpture; Silversmithing; Stage Design; Teacher Training; Theatre Arts.
Summer School: Asst Acad Dean Richard Houpt. Tui $288 per course for term of 4 wks beginning June 5. Courses—Jewelry; Crafts Workshop; Extended Studies.

HAVERFORD

HAVERFORD COLLEGE,* Fine Arts Department, 19041. Tel: 215-649-9600, exten 266. *Chmn Dept* Christopher Cairns; *Instrs* FT Haverford 3, FT Bryn Mawr 1.
Col estab 1833, dept estab 1969; pvt; D; M; ent req HS dipl; programs in cooperation with Bryn Mawr College Fine Arts Department; degree BA 4 yrs; schol; SC Haverford 10, Bryn Mawr 5, LC Haverford 1, Bryn Mawr 12, GC in History of Art at Bryn Mawr; enrl maj 15.
Tuition: $4330 per yr, special students $550 per course per sem; campus res $1950.
Courses: Drawing; Graphic Arts; History of Art & Archaeology; Painting; Photography; Sculpture.

MAINLINE CENTER OF THE ARTS, Old Buck Rd & Lancaster Ave, 19041. Tel: 215-LA5-0272. *Admin Dir* Eleanor Daitzman; *Primary Art Faculty* Gerald Kolpan, BFA; Angie Arlen, BFA; George Gansworth, BFA; Itzhaic Sankowsky, MA; Robert Finch, BFA; Cyril Gardner, BFA; Tom Ewing, BFA; Richard Leiberman, BFA.
Estab 1937; pvt; D&E; ent req all students must be members of the Arts Center; SC 45; enrl D 300, E 250.
Tuition: $25 to $70 for 8-15 wks; no campus res.
Courses: Art History; Calligraphy; Cartoon & Caricature; Ceramics; China Painting; Collage; Commercial Art; Conceptual Art; Constructions; Decorative Arts; Drawing; Film; Goldsmithing; Graphic Arts; Graphic Design; Handicrafts (weaving, basketry, batik, tie-dyeing); Illustration; Jewelry; Lettering; Mixed Media; Painting; Photography; Printmaking; Sculpture; Silversmithing; Soft Sculpture; Theatre Arts.
Children's Classes: Enrl 150; tui $40 for 15 wks. Courses—General Arts; Pottery.

Summer School: Admin Dir Eleanor Daitzman. Tui varies, classes begin June 12 and June 19. Courses—Same as above.

HUNTINGDON

JUNIATA COLLEGE,* Department of Art, Moore St, 16652. Tel: 814-643-4310. *Chmn Dept* Alex McBridge; Instrs FT 1, PT 1.
Estab 1876; pvt; D; ent req HS dipl; degree BA 4 yrs; schol; SC 12, LC 3; enrl 300, maj 10.
Tuition: $3990 inclusive; campus res.
Courses: Aesthetics; Art Education; Ceramics; Drawing; Graphic Arts; History of Art & Archaeology; Painting; Photography; Teacher Training; Theatre Arts.
Summer School: Dir Dr Hartman. Courses—Art History; Ceramics; Studio Art.

INDIANA

INDIANA UNIVERSITY OF PENNSYLVANIA,* Department of Art and Art Education; 15701. Tel: 412-357-2530. *Chmn Dept* Benjamin T Miller; Instrs FT 22.
Univ estab 1875, dept estab 1906; pub; D&E; ent req HS grad and col ent board exam; degrees BS(Art Educ), BA(Humanities with Art Concentration) 4 yrs, MEd, MA; enrl undergrad 400, grad 70, total school 10,500.
Courses: Art Education; General Art; Professional Art; Teacher Training; Children's Visual Imagery, evenings; Adult Evening Classes.

JOHNSTOWN

UNIVERSITY OF PITTSBURGH AT JOHNSTOWN, Department of Fine Arts, 15904. Tel: 814-266-9661, exten 378. *Asst Prof Humanities & Chmn Dept Fine Arts* Richard Channin, PhD.
Estab 1927, dept estab 1976; pub; D&E; ent req HS dipl, SAT; degree BA(Humanities) 4 yrs; schol; SC 3, LC 6; enrl nonmaj 85.
Tuition: Campus res room and board.
Courses: Art History; Drawing; History of Art & Archaeology; Painting.

KUTZTOWN

KUTZTOWN STATE COLLEGE,* School of Art, Art Education and Fine Arts Departments, 19530. Tel: 215-683-3511, exten 309. *Dean* Dr Evan J Kern; Instrs 35.
Estab 1866; pub; ent req Col Board Ent Exam, HS record; degrees BS(Art Educ) and BFA(Advertising, Painting; Sculpture) 4 yrs, MEd(Art Educ); enrl art 850, total 5000.
Tuition: Res—grad $42 per sem hr; Nonres—$46 per sem hr.
Courses: Teacher Education.
Summer School: Dean Dr Evan J Kern.

LANCASTER

FRANKLIN AND MARSHALL COLLEGE, Art Department, 17604. Tel: 717-291-4199. *Chmn Dept* Folke T Kihlstedt, PhD; *Asst Prof* James Peterson, MFA; *Asst Prof* Linda Cunningham, MFA; *Asst Prof* Andrew J Cosentino, PhD; *Adj Prof* Diana Galis, PhD; *Resident Prof* Betsy Fahlman, MA.
Estab 1966; pvt; D&E; ent req HS dipl, SAT; degrees BA and BS 4 yrs; schol; SC 10, LC 20; enrl in col D 2011, E 605.
Tuition: Res—$5695 per yr; Nonres—$4130 per yr.
Courses: Architecture; Art History; Drawing; History of Art & Archaeology; Painting; Printmaking; Sculpture.
Summer School: Dir Richard Schneider. Tui $300 for course, two 5 wk sessions beginning June 7. Courses—Drawing; Painting; Sculpture; Architecture; Drawing.

LEWISBURG

BUCKNELL UNIVERSITY, Department of Art, 17837. Tel: 717-524-1307. *Head Dept* Gerald Eager, PhD; *Primary Art Faculty* Neil Anderson, MFA; William Lasansky, MFA; James Turner, PhD.
Estab 1846; pvt; D; ent req HS dipl; degree BA 4 yrs; schol; SC 19, LC 20, GC 30; enrl D 500, nonmaj 450, maj 50, grad 2.
Tuition: $4000 per yr; campus res room and board.
Courses: Art History; Drawing; Graphic Arts; History of Art & Archaeology; Painting; Printmaking; Sculpture.
Summer School: Dir Summer Session Hugh McKeegan. Enrl 50; tui $200 per course for term of 3 or 6 wks beginning June 5. Courses—3 Studio Courses; 3 Lecture Courses.

MANSFIELD

MANSFIELD STATE COLLEGE, School of Fine and Applied Arts, Art Department, 16933. Tel: 717-662-4092. *Prof Art & Chmn Dept* Jay D Kain, PhD; *Prof* Steve Bencetie, DEd; *Prof* Jim Cecere, DEd; *Assoc Prof* Ernest Frombach, MEd; *Asst Prof* Dale Witherow, MFA; *Asst Prof* Lissa Hunter, MFA; *Asst Prof* Sam Thomas, MEd; *Asst Prof* Tom Loomis, MA; *Asst Prof* Stan Zujkowski, MS.
Estab 1857; pub; D; ent req HS dipl, SAT, portfolio and interview; degrees BA(Studio Art, BA(Art Hist) and BSE(Art Educ) 4 yrs; SC 26, LC 18; enrl D 700, maj 90.
Tuition: Res—$950 per yr, $475 per sem; Nonres—$1780 per yr, $950 per sem; campus res.
Courses: Aesthetics; Art Education; Art History; Ceramics; Drawing; Handicrafts; Jewelry; Painting; Photography; Printmaking; Sculpture; Silversmithing; Teacher Training; Textile Design.
Children's Classes: Tui $5 per sem for Sat classes.
Summer School: Dir Dr Jay D Kain. Term of 3-6 wks beginning June 12. Courses—Studio Courses; Art History.

MEADVILLE

ALLEGHENY COLLEGE, Art Department, 16335. Tel: 814-724-3371. *Prof Art & Head Dept* Richard Kleeman, MFA; *Prof* Carl F Heeschen, MA; *Prof* Anne Philbin, MFA; *Instr* Sharon Sitt, PhD; *Gallery Dir* Martha Holt, MFA.
Estab 1815, dept estab 1930; pvt; D; ent req HS dipl, ent exam; degrees BA and BS 4 yrs; schol; SC 17, LC 7; enrl 450, maj 15.
Tuition: $3300 per yr, $1100 per sem; campus res room and board $1280 per yr.
Courses: Art History; Ceramics; Drawing; Graphic Arts; History of Art & Archaeology; Lettering; Painting; Photography; Printmaking; Sculpture.

MERCERSBURG

MERCERSBURG ACADEMY,* Department of Fine Arts, 17236. Tel: 717-328-2151. *Chmn Dept* William C Fowle; Instrs FT 2, PT 5.
Estab 1972; pvt; D; ent exam req; secondary school, granting HS dipl; schol; SC 4, LC 3; enrl 100.
Courses: Ceramics; Drawing; Graphic Arts; Graphic Design; Handicrafts; History of Art & Archaeology; Painting; Photography; Pottery; Sculpture; Stage Design; Textile Design; Theatre Arts; Weaving.

MIDDLETOWN

PENNSYLVANIA STATE UNIVERSITY, CAPITOL CAMPUS, Department of Humanities, 17057. Tel: 717-787-7742. *Instr* Troy Thomas, MFA; *Asst Prof* Elenor Ebersole, EdD; *Prof* Irwin Richman, PhD; Instrs PT 10.
Estab 1965; pub; D&E; ent req 2 yrs of col or CLEP; degrees BHum 2 yrs, MHum 1½-2 yrs; schol; SC 7, LC 15; enrl D&E 60, grad 40.
Tuition: Res—$1250 per yr; Nonres—$2700 per yr; campus res room and board $700.
Courses: Aesthetics; Architecture; Art Education; Art History; Ceramics; History of Art & Archaeology; Mixed Media; Painting; Photography; Sculpture; Theatre Arts; Video.

MILLERSVILLE

MILLERSVILLE STATE COLLEGE, Art Department, 17064. Tel: 717-872-5411, exten 253. *Dir* R Gordon Wise, EdD; *Primary Art Faculty:* Kent Carson, PhD; Dom Fanani, EdD; John Ground, MFA; Ike Hay, MFA; Robert Hustrad, MFA; Robert Lowing, MFA; Robert Lyon, MEd; Sheba Sharrow, MFA; Ronald Sykes, EdD.
Estab 1855, dept estab 1965; pub; D&E; ent req HS dipl; degrees BS(Art Educ) and BA(Art) 4 yrs, MEd(Art Educ) 1 yr; SC 65, LC 10, GC 64; enrl maj 282, grad 14.
Tuition: Res—Undergrad $900 per yr, $450 per sem, $33 per cr hr, grad $45 per cr hr; Nonres—Undergrad $1600 per yr, $800 per sem, $60 per cr hr, grad $65 per cr hr; campus res room and board $975 per yr.
Courses: Art Education; Art History; Calligraphy; Ceramics; Drafting; Drawing; Film; Graphic Arts; Illustration; Jewelry; Lettering; Painting; Photography; Printmaking; Sculpture; Silversmithing; Teacher Training; Textile Design.
Summer School: Dir Ronald Sykes. Enrl 300; tui $200 for term of 5 wks, two 5 wk sessions beginning June and July. Courses—All Studio.

MOUNTAINHOME

DREISBACH ART GALLERY, Rte 191, 18342. *Owner* C I Dreisbach; Instrs FT 1.
Estab 1958; pvt; D (summers only); no ent req; enrl 200.

Tuition: $7 per day.
Courses: Painting.

NEW KENSINGTON

PENNSYLVANIA STATE UNIVERSITY AT NEW KEN-SINGTON,* 3550 Seventh St, 15068. Instrs FT 1.
Estab 1968; pub; D; ent req col boards; 2 yr (option for 4 yr at Main Campus at University Park); schol; SC 3-4, LC 1 per sem.
Tuition: No campus res.
Courses: Art Education; Design; Drawing; History of Art; Painting; Theatre Arts; Watercolor.

NEW WILMINGTON

WESTMINSTER COLLEGE,* Art Department, 16142. Tel: 412-946-8761 Exten 366. *Head Dept* Nelson E Oestreich; Instrs 3.
Estab 1852; den; D; degrees BS and BA(Fine Arts, Educ) 4 yrs; enrl maj 50, total 1500.
Tuition: $3940 incl campus res.

NEWTOWN

BUCKS COUNTY COMMUNITY COLLEGE, Fine Arts Department, Swamp Rd, 18940. Tel: 215-968-5861, exten 236. *Chairperson Fine Arts Dept* Bruce Katsiff, MFA; *Primary Art Faculty* Robert Dodge, Frank Dominguez, Jack Gevins, Alan Goldstein, Paul Keene, Nancy Hellebrand, Catherine Jansen, Diane Lindenheim, Marlene Miller, Frank McConnell, Stephen Ripper, Carlotte Schatz and Helen Weisz.
Estab 1965; pub; D&E; ent req HS dipl; degree AA; enrl D&E 8000 (school).
Courses: Advertising Design; Art History; Calligraphy; Ceramics; Collage; Conceptual Art; Constructions; Drawing; Graphic Arts; Graphic Design; History of Art & Archaeology; Illustration; Jewelry; Painting; Photography; Printmaking; Sculpture; Silversmithing.

PHILADELPHIA

ANTONELLI SCHOOL OF PHOTOGRAPHY, 1210 Race St, 19107 (Mailing Add: PO Box 1767, 19105). Tel: 215-563-8558. *VPres* Joseph B Thompson, BS; *Teacher* Donald W Beetham, BA; *Teacher* Robert D Golding, BFA; *Teacher* Robert J Salgado, BS; *Teacher* Gilbert H Weiss, BS; *Teacher* Quentin R Whitmore, BA(Art Educ).
Estab 1938; pvt; D&E; ent req HS dipl; enrl D 196, E 60.
Tuition: No campus res.
Courses: Photography.

ART INSTITUTE OF PHILADELPHIA, 1818 Cherry St, 19103. Tel: 215-567-7080. *Pres* Philip Trachtman, BFA; *Coordr Interior Design* Charles Agnew, BA; *Coordr Commercial Art* Charles Ellis; *Primary Art Faculty:* Pedra Kosit, MFA; Alice Gripman, BFA; Linda Grossman, BFA; William Hooper, MFA.
Estab 1966; pvt; D; ent req HS dipl, portfolio; degree AST 3 yrs; SC 30, LC 8; enrl 200.
Tuition: $1800 per yr, $900 per sem; no campus res.
Courses: ‡Advertising Design; Art History; ‡Commercial Art; Conceptual Art; Drafting; Drawing; ‡Fashion Arts; Graphic Arts, ‡Graphic Design; ‡Illustration; ‡Interior Design; Lettering; Mixed Media; Painting; Photography; Printmaking.
Summer School: *Dir* Philip Trachtman. Courses—as above.

DREXEL UNIVERSITY,* Nesbitt College, Department of Design, Newbitt Hall, 33rd & Market Sts, 19104. Tel: 215-895-2390. *Dean* Marjorie E Rankin; *Head Dept Design* Mary Epstein; Instrs FT 10, PT 10.
Estab 1891; pvt; ent req col board exam; degrees BS 4 yrs, MS and cooperative plan; schol; SC 39, LC 9; enrl maj 300, others 414.
Courses: Design & Merchandising; Fashion Design; Interior Design.
Summer School: *Dean* Marjorie E Rankin. Enrl 159; term of 6 or 12 wks.

SAMUEL S FLEISHER ART MEMORIAL, (administered by the Philadelphia Museum of Art), 715-721 Catharine Street, 19147. Tel: 215-922-3456. *Admin* Thora E Jacobson; *Primary Art Faculty* Martin Jackson; Filomena Dellaripa; Frank Gasparro; Tom Gaughan; Mac Fisher.
Estab 1898; pvt; E; no ent req; no degrees; LC 1, enrl E 2000.
Courses: Ceramics; Drawing; Painting; Photography; Printmaking; Sculpture.
Adult Hobby Classes: Enrl 2000.
Children's Classes: Enrl 500; no tui; Courses—Drawing; Painting; Sculpture.

Summer School: Courses—Ceramics; Drawing; Painting; Photography; Printmaking; Sculpture; Welding.

HUSSIAN SCHOOL OF ART, INC,* Commercial Art Department, 1300 Arch St, 19107. Tel: 215-563-5726. *Pres* Ronald Dove; Instrs FT 3, PT 15.
Estab 1946; pvt; D; ent req HS dipl, portfolio interview; 4 yrs; no degree; enrl 148.
Tuition: No campus Res.
Courses: Advertising Design; Commercial Art; Drawing; Graphic Arts; Graphic Design; History of Art & Archaeology; Illustration; Lettering; Painting; Photography.

LA SALLE COLLEGE, Department of Fine Arts, 20th St & Olney Ave, 19141. Tel: 215-951-1000. *Assoc Prof Art & Chmn Dept Fine Arts* George K Diehl, PhD; *Asst Prof* Thomas Ridington, MFA; *Asst Prof* James Hanes; *Lectr* Herman Gundersheimer, PhD; *Lectr* James Lang, MFA.
Estab 1865, dept estab 1972; den; D&E; ent req HS dipl; degree BA 4 yrs; SC 2; enrl D 15, maj 15.
Tuition: Res—$3500 per yr; Nonres—$2730 per yr; campus res room and board.
Courses: Art History; Painting; Printmaking.

MOORE COLLEGE OF ART, 20th & Race Sts, 19103. Tel: 215-568-4515. *Pres* Herbert Burgart, DEd; *Chmn Advert Design* Vincent Faralli, Dipl; *Chmn Art Educ* Gladys Novick, MA; *Chmn Ceramic Design* Jack Thompson, MFA; *Chmn Fashion Design* Nancy McGee, MFA; *Chmn Fashion Illustration* Mildred Ivins, Dipl; *Chmn Art Hist* Lewis Greenberg, MA; *Chmn Illustration* Beth Krush, Dipl; *Chmn Interior Design* Joseph Beluch, BArch; *Chm Painting* David Bowman, MFA; *Chmn Photography* Robert Cohen, MFA; *Chmn Printmaking* Charles Fahlen, MFA and William Walton; *Chmn Sculpture/Metalsmithing* Gerald Crimmins, MFA and Richard Posniak, MFA; *Chmn Textile Design* Deborah Warner, MFA.
Estab 1844; pvt; D&E; ent req HS dipl, portfolio, SAT; degrees BA, BS and BFA 4 yrs; enrl in col D 475, E 70, nonmaj 75, maj 475.
Tuition: Res—$4750 per yr; Nonres—$3200 per yr; PT students $110 per cr; campus res room and board $1550 per yr.
Courses: ‡Advertising Design; ‡Art Education; ‡Art History; ‡Ceramics; Drawing; ‡Fashion Arts; ‡Fashion Design; ‡Fashion Illustration; Goldsmithing; History of Art & Archaeology; ‡Illustration; ‡Interior Design; ‡Jewelry; Lettering; Mixed Media; ‡Painting; ‡Photography; ‡Printmaking; ‡Sculpture; Silversmithing; Stage Design; Teacher Training; ‡Textile Design; Theatre Arts.
Children's Classes: Enrl 202; tui $50 per sem. Courses—General Art.
Summer School: *Dean* Hilda Schoenwetter. Term usually 4-6 wks.

PENNSYLVANIA ACADEMY OF THE FINE ARTS, Broad & Cherry Sts, 19102. Tel: 215-972-7624. *Dean* Ephraim Weinberg, MAE; Instrs FT 31.
Estab 1805; pvt; D&E; ent req HS dipl, portfolio; degree BFA coordinated program with Univ of Pennsylvania or Philadelphia Col Art, 5 yrs; schol; SC 11, LC 3; enrl D 400, E 150.
Tuition: $1400 per yr, $700 per sem; campus res $980 per yr (women only).
Courses: Art History; Drawing; Painting; Printmaking; Sculpture.
Summer School: *Registr* Tish Byrne. Enrl 175; tui $75-$262.50 for term of 4 - 6 wks beginning June 13. Courses—Life, Portrait, Still Life & Landscape Painting & Drawing.

PHILADELPHIA COLLEGE OF ART, Broad & Spruce Sts, 19102. Tel: 215-893-3151. *Pres* Thomas F Schutte, PhD; *Dean Faculty* Nathan Knobler, MA; *Prof* Walter Erlebacher, MID; *Dept Chairpersons: Assoc Prof* Arlene Gostin, MA; *Asst Prof* Wayne Bates, MFA; *Asst Prof* Al Johnson, MArch; *Prof* Robert McGovern, BA; *Assoc Prof* Michael Rossman, MFA; *Assoc Prof* Hans Allemann, BA; *Assoc Prof* Robert Stein, MFA; *Assoc Prof* Steve Tarantal, MFA; *Special Adj Prof* Noel Mayo, BA; *Prof & Assoc Dean Liberal Arts* Patricia Cruser, MA; *Assoc Prof* Cynthia Carlson, MFA; *Assoc Prof* Gerald Nichols, MFA; *Assoc Prof* Gerald Greenfield, MFA; *Asst Prof* Michael Lasuchin, MFA.
Estab 1876; pvt; D&E; ent req HS dipl, portfolio, SAT; degrees BFA and BS 4 yrs, MA 5 yrs; schol; SC 339, LC 74, GC 5; enrl D 1160, E 720, grad 11.
Tuition: $3696 per yr; campus res room and board $1100 per yr.
Courses: Advertising Design; Art Education; Art History; Calligraphy; Ceramics; Drawing; Film; Glassblowing; Graphic Arts; Graphic Design; Illustration; Industrial Design; Interior Design; Jewelry; Painting; Photography; Printmaking; Sculpture; Silversmithing; Teacher Training; Textile Design; Woodworking.
Children's Classes: Enrl 350; tui $65 per sem. Courses—Drawing; Design; Painting; Printmaking; Jewelry; Ceramics; Photography & Film.

Summer School: Dir Robert Stein. Enrl 225; tui $325, additional $75 for weekend trips, term of 5 wks beginning June 26. Courses—Pre-College Program.

PHILADELPHIA COLLEGE OF TEXTILES AND SCIENCE,* School of Textiles, School House Lane & Henry Ave, 19144. Tel: 215-843-9700. *Acting Pres* Donald B Partridge; *Dir Sch* Fred Fortess; *Dir Evening & Summer Sch* Peter Mills.
Estab 1884; pvt; no ent req; degree BS 4 yrs; schol; enrl D 1065, E 784.
Tuition: $1400.
Courses: Apparel Design; Apparel Management; Basic Design; Business Administration; Chemistry; Chemistry & Dyeing; Drawing; Fabric Design; Fashion Textile Retailing; Knitted Design; Life Science; Management & Marketing; Print Design; Textile Engineering; Textile Quality Control & Testing; Weaving Design.

PHILADELPHIA COMMUNITY COLLEGE, Department of Fine Arts, 34 S 11th St, 19107. Tel: 215-972-7210. *Dir Div Humanities* William Baker, MA; *Assoc Prof* Wallace Peters, MA; *Assoc Prof* Valern Seligsohn, MFA; *Asst Prof* Diane Burko, MFA; *Asst Prof* Robert Paige, MFA.
Estab 1967; pub; D&E; ent req HS dipl, portfolio; degree AA 2 yrs; SC 10, LC 6; enrl D 80 art maj.
Tuition: $500 per yr; no campus res.
Courses: Art History; Ceramics; Drawing; Graphic Design; Painting; Photography.

ST JOSEPH'S COLLEGE, Fine Arts Program, 54th & City Ave, 19131. Tel: 215-879-7604. *Dir Prog* Frank Olley, PhD; *Lectr* Robert Wilde, PhD; *Lectr* Dennis Weeks, MFA; *Lectr* Rev Dennis McNally, MA; *Lectr* Lynn Denton, MFA; *Lectr* Betsy Anderson, MA; *Lectr* Danny Baker, BA; *Lectr* Peg Schofield, MFA; *Lectr* Don Scioli, BA.
Estab 1851; prog estab 1975; den; D&E; ent req HS dipl; SC 15, LC 4; enrl D 150, E 30.
Tuition: Res—$4500 per yr; Nonres—$2200 per yr; campus res room and board.
Courses: Aesthetics; Art Education; Art History; Ceramics; Drawing; Film; Painting; Photography; Printmaking; Stage Design; Theatre Arts.

STUDIO SCHOOL OF ART AND DESIGN, 1424 Spruce St, 19102. Tel: 215-PE5-0908. *Dir* Janet R Goodfriend, Dipl; *Asst Dir* John Koomar; *Primary Art Faculty* Nicholas Leslie; Andrew Theis; Preston Williamson; Margaret DeBaeeke, BFA; Curtis Lawton.
Estab 1959; pvt; D; ent req HS dipl, interview, portfolio; SC 8, LC 4; enrl 41.
Tuition: $1100 per yr, $550 per sem, $115.80 monthly, $1.15 per hr; no campus res.
Courses: ‡Advertising Design; Art History; Color Theory; ‡Commercial Art; Drawing; ‡Graphic Arts; ‡Graphic Design; ‡Illustration; Lettering; Mixed Media; Painting; Photography.

TRACEY-WARNER SCHOOL, 401 N Broad St, 19108. Tel: 215-574-0402. *Pres* Lewis H Warner; *Instr* Louise Boyce; Instrs FT 9, PT 3.
Estab 1956; pvt; D; ent req HS dipl; degrees AA 2 yr, dipl or cert; enrl D 125.
Tuition: $990 per sem; no campus res.
Courses: Advertising Design; Art Education; Art History; ‡Costume Design and Construction; ‡Draping Design; Fashion Arts; Handicrafts; ‡Illustration; Jewelry; Pattern Drafting; Pattern Grading; Textiles.

TYLER SCHOOL OF ART OF TEMPLE UNIVERSITY,* Beech & Penrose Aves, 19126. Tel: 215-224-7575. *Dean* Dr Jack Wasserman; Instrs FT 58, PT 6.
Estab 1935; pub; D&E; ent req HS grad, SAT, portfolio; degrees BFA 4 yrs, MFA, MEd (2 yrs work in all arts req before specializing); grad asst and schol; enrl D 650, E 250; Rome Branch, Jr yr or grad study.
Courses: Animated Film; Art Education; Art History; Ceramics; Drawing; Graphic Design; Metalsmithing; Painting; Photography; Printmaking; Sculpture; Silkscreen Printing; Typography; Weaving.
Summer School: Assoc Dean Don Lantzy. Courses—Ceramics; Drawing; Metalsmithing; Painting; Photography; Printmaking; Sculpture; Watercolor; Weaving.

UNIVERSITY OF PENNSYLVANIA,* Graduate School of Fine Arts, 19174. Tel: 215-243-8321. *Dean* Peter Shepeard.
Estab 1874; pvt; ent req ent exam; degrees granted; schol and fel; GC.
Tuition: Grad $4396; campus res available.
—Department of Architecture. *Chmn* Peter McCleary; *Chmn Grad Group* G Holmes Perkins; Instrs FT 7, PT 25.
Degrees MArch, PhD; LC 10, GC 9; enrl 160.
Courses: Architectural Design & Construction.
—Department of City and Regional Planning. *Chmn* William Grigsby; Instrs FT 11, PT 8.
Degrees MCP, PhD; LC 21, GC 4; enrl 100.

—Department of Landscape Architecture and Regional Planning. *Chmn* Ian L McHarg; Instrs FT 8, PT 5.
Degrees MLA, MRP; LC 7, Design Courses 4; enrl 60.
—Department of Fine Arts. *Co-Chmn* Robert Engman and Neil G Welliver; Instrs FT 7, PT 4.
Degrees BFA, MFA; SC 21, LC 5, GC; enrl 60.
Courses: Graphics; Painting; Sculpture.

PITTSBURGH

ART INSTITUTE OF PITTSBURGH,* 526 Penn Ave, 15222. Tel: 412-471-5651. *Pres* John A Johns; Instrs D FT 53, PT 16, E FT 6, PT 3.
Estab 1921; pvt; ent req HS grad; degrees AA 2 yrs, Dipl; enrl D 1500, E 150.
Courses: Airbrush Technique; Fashion Illustration; Interior Design; Photography; Photography-Audiovisual-Multimedia Visual Communications.
Commercial Art Prep School: 6 wk summer FT; Teenage summer classes, 6 wk ½ day; Sat teenage classes. Free 2 wk art instructors workshop.

CARLOW COLLEGE,* Art Department, 3333 Fifth Ave, 15213. *Chmn Dept* Richard Devlin; Instrs FT 2, PT 3.
Estab 1945; den; D&E; ent req HS dipl, col boards, HS record; degrees in Art, Art Educ, Art Therapy Preparation, 4 yrs; schol; SC 17, LC 6; enrl 200, maj 42.
Courses: Aesthetics; Art & Psychology; Art Education; Art Therapy; Batik; Ceramics; Drawing; Graphic Arts; History of Art & Archaeology; Jewelry; Lettering; Metalcraft; Painting; Photography; Sculpture; Teacher Training; Theatre Arts; Weaving.
Summer School: Acad Dean Sister Elizabeth McMillan. Enrl approx 40; term of 6 wks beginning June. Courses—Art Fundamentals; Ceramics.

CARNEGIE-MELLON UNIVERSITY,* College of Fine Arts, 5000 Forbes Ave, 15213. Tel: 412-621-2600, exten 427. *Dean* Akram Midani.
Estab 1905; pvt; ent req coll board ent exam plus auditions or portfolio; degrees granted 4-5 yr; schol and fel.
Tuition: $3100; campus res available.
Summer School: Includes some pre-college courses term of 6 wk.
—Department of Architecture. *Acting Head* Robert S Taylor; Instrs FT 23, PT 5.
Degrees GC, MArch first and second degree, PhD in conjunction with School of Urban and Public Affairs; enrl 206.
Courses: Architecture.
—Department of Design. *Head* Joseph Ballay; Instrs FT 11, PT 6.
Degrees GC, MFA Design; enrl 162.
Courses: Design Theory; Graphic Design; Illustration; Industrial Design; Interior Environments.
—Department of Art. *Head* Orvill Winsand; Instrs FT 22, PT 3.
Degrees GC MFA, DA; enrl 235.
Courses: Art Education; Crafts; Painting; Printmaking; Sculpture.
—Department of Drama. *Head* Walter Eysselinck; Instrs FT 24, PT 1.
Degrees GC, MFA, PhD; enrl 223.
Courses: Stage Design.

CHATHAM COLLEGE,* Department of Art, Woodland Rd, 15232. Tel: 412-441-8200. *Chmn* Shirley Stark; Instrs FT 3, PT 2.
Estab 1869; pvt; W; ent req HS grad; degree BA 4 yrs; SC 17, LC 7.
Tuition: $5250 incl res fees.
Courses: Basic Photography; Ceramics; Drawing; Graphic Arts; History of Art; Painting; Sculpture.

IVY SCHOOL OF PROFESSIONAL ART, University Ave, 15214. Tel: 413-323-3200. *Pres/Dir* Morris B Kirshenbaum, BS; *Dean* Irwin Rosen, BFA; *Primary Art Faculty* Philip Mendlow, MFA; Paul Grafius, BFA; Richard Horton, BFA; Norman Rice, BA; Frank Sparrow, Dipl; Abe Weiner, BFA.
Estab 1960; pvt; D; ent req HS dipl, portfolio, letters of recommendations; Dipl 2 yrs (in process AST degree, 2 yrs); enrl 300.
Tuition: $675 per quarter; no campus res.
Courses: ‡Advertising Design; Art History; Calligraphy; Collage; ‡Commercial Art; Display; Drawing; Exhibition Design; Fashion Arts; Film; ‡Graphic Design; ‡Illustration; Intermedia; Interior Design; Lettering; Mixed Media; ‡Painting; ‡Photography; ‡Printmaking; ‡Sculpture; Stage Design; Textile Design; Video.

LA ROCHE COLLEGE, Department of Graphic Arts & Design, 9000 Babcock Blvd, 15237. Tel: 412-931-9333. *Area Coordr* Harvey R Levenson, MS; *Primary Art Faculty* Grant Dinsmorg, MFA; Mack Taylor, BFA; Instrs PT 15.
Estab 1963; dept estab 1965; pvt; D&E; ent req HS dipl; degrees BA and BS 4 yrs; SC 25, LC 15; enrl D&E 200, nonmaj 20, maj 180.
Tuition: $4200 per yr; campus res room and board $2200 per yr.

Courses: Advertising Design; Aesthetics; Art History; Calligraphy; Ceramics; Commercial Art; Display; Fashion Arts; ‡Graphic Arts; ‡Graphic Design; Illustration; Industrial Design; Interior Design; Lettering; Painting; Photography; Sculpture.
Summer School: Dir Betsey Devon. Tui $70 cr.

UNIVERSITY OF PITTSBURGH, Henry Clay Frick Fine Arts Bldg, 15260.
—**Department of Fine Arts.*** Tel: 412-624-4121. *Chmn* Millard F Hearn; Instrs FT 12.
Estab 1927; pvt; D; degrees, undergrad maj in Art History, grad prog MA and PhD in Western and Oriental Art History; schol and fel; LC 34, GC 5; enrl 1200.
Tuition: $695 per term, PT $62 per cr hr.
—**Department of Studio Arts.*** Tel: 412-624-4118. *Chmn* Virgil D Cantini; Instrs FT 8.
Estab 1968; pvt; D; undergrad maj in Studio Arts; LC 34; enrl 1500.
Courses: Painting; Graphics; Sculpture.

RADNOR

CABRINI COLLEGE,* Department of Fine Arts, Eagle & King of Prussia Rds, 19087. Tel: 215-687-2100, exten 53. *Chmn Dept* Sister Salesia LeDieu; Instrs FT 1, PT 1.
Estab 1957; den; D&E; ent req ᵸHS dipl, satisfactory average and rank in secondary school class, SAT, recommendations; degrees BA, BS and BSEd 4 yrs, no art major; schol; SC 11, LC 4, courses available through Eastern Col 4; enrl D 74, E 20.
Courses: Art Education; Ceramics; Design & Composition; Drawing; History of Art & Archaeology; Painting; Teacher Training.
Summer School: Dir Sister Julia Toto. Enrl 350; term of 6 wks beginning May and July. Courses offered vary according to demand.

ROSEMONT

ROSEMONT COLLEGE,* Division of the Arts, 19010. Tel: 215-527-0200. *Chmn Div* Patricia M Nugent; Instrs FT 4, PT 10.
Estab 1925; pvt; D; W (exchange with Villanova Univ); ent req HS dipl, ent exam; degrees BA(Studio Art, Art Hist) and BFA(Studio Art) 4 yrs; schol; 6 hr Studio Art, 3 hr Art History; enrl total col 705, art 300, grad approx 15.
Tuition: $2875; campus res $1725.
Courses: Aesthetics; Art Education; Ceramics; Dance; Design; Drawing; Graphic Arts; History of Art & Architecture; Lettering; Music; Painting; Photography; Sculpture; Teacher Training; Theatre.

SCRANTON

INTERNATIONAL CORRESPONDENCE SCHOOLS, School of Interior Design, Oak St, 18515. Tel: 717-342-7701, exten 254. *VPres Educ* Robert G Donovan; *Dir* Elaine G Thomas, BS; Instrs FT 2, PT 3.
Estab 1890, Sch Interior Design estab 1969; pvt; ent req HS dipl; enrl 3000.
Courses: Interior Decoration & Design; Principles of Interior Design; Elements of Interior Design; Room Decor.

MARYWOOD COLLEGE,* Art Department, 2300 Adams Ave, 18509. Tel: 717-343-6521, exten 252. Instrs FT 5, PT 4.
Estab 1926; pvt; D&E; ent req HS dipl, portfolio and interview; degrees AB and BS(Art Educ) 4 yrs; schol; SC 28, LC 7, GC 12; enrl maj 98, grad 17.
Courses: Advertising Design; Aesthetics; Art Education; Art Seminar; Ceramics; Design I & II; Drawing I & II; Enameling; Graphic Arts; Handicrafts; History of Art (I, II, Contemporary); Illustration & Fashion; Jewelry; Lettering; Metalcraft; Painting; Philosophy of Art; Photography; Sculpture I & II; Teacher Training; Theatre Arts; Weaving & Textile Designs.
Summer School: 6 wk term beginning June. Courses—Art for the Elementary Teacher; Ceramics; Chinese Brush Painting; Design Research; Directed Readings; Graduate Figure Drawing; History of Art; Painting; Printmaking; Sculpture; Special Class Arts & Crafts.

SELINSGROVE

SUSQUEHANNA UNIVERSITY,* Department of Art, 17870. Tel: 717-374-2345. *Assoc Prof Art* George R Bucher; Instrs FT 1, PT 1.
Estab 1858; den; D&E; ent req Col Ent Exam Board tests, HS class standing, personal interview; degrees BA, BS and BMus 4 yrs; enrl 1400.
Tuition: $3156 incl fees; campus res $1346.
Courses: Art History & Appreciation; Graphic Design; Painting; Theatre Arts.

SHIPPENSBURG

SHIPPENSBURG STATE COLLEGE, Art Department, Prince St, 17257. Tel: 717-532-6307. *Chmn Art Dept* Harry D Bentz, EdD; *Primary Art Faculty* Harry Kirk, MEd; Betsy Farmer, PhD; William Hynes, MEd; George Waricher, MEd.
Estab 1871, dept estab 1920; pub; D&E; ent req HS dipl; degree BS(Elem Educ); schol; internships; SC 13, LC 4; enrl D 400, E 100, nonmaj 600, grad 15, others 20 continuing educ.
Tuition: Res—$400 per sem; Nonres—$750 per sem; PT $33-$63 per cr hr; campus res room and board $504 per sem.
Courses: Art History; Ceramics; Drawing; Graphic Arts; Handicrafts (arts & crafts); Lettering; Painting; Printmaking; Sculpture; Teacher Training; Textile Design.
Adult Hobby Classes: Enrl 25; tui $15 per course. Courses—Basic Watercolor; Ceramics.
Summer School: Dir Dr Harry D Bentz. Tui $33 per cr hr for term of 3 - 6 wks beginning June 5. Courses—Arts & Crafts; Introduction to Art; Ceramics; Creative Experiences in Art.

SLIPPERY ROCK

SLIPPERY ROCK STATE COLLEGE,* Department of Art, 16057. Tel: 412-794-7271. *Chmn Dept* Jon D Wink; Instrs FT 9.
Pub; D&E; ent req HS dipl; degree BA(Art) 4 yrs; SC 27, LC 3; enrl maj 55.
Tuition: $800 per yr; campus res $1008 per yr.
Courses: Art Education; Ceramics; Drawing; Graphic Arts; History of Art & Archaeology; Jewelry; Painting; Photography; Sculpture; Textile Design.
Summer School: Tui $33 per cr hr.

SWARTHMORE

SWARTHMORE COLLEGE, Department of Art, 19081. Tel: 215-544-7900, exten 315. *Chairperson Dept Art* T Kaori Kitao, PhD; *Assoc Prof* Eric Carlson, PhD; *Asst Prof* Alison Kettering, PhD; *Asst Prof* Constance Cain Hungerford, PhD; *Asst Prof* (part-time) Kit-Yin Tieng Snyder, MA; *Asst Prof* Michael Knutson, MFA; *Asst Prof* Daniel Black, MFA; vis prof—Leo Rubenfien, photography; C Franklin Sayre, Oriental art.
Estab 1864, dept estab 1925; pvt; D; ent req HS dipl, SAT, CEEB; degree BA 4 yrs; schol; SC 14, LC 33; enrl nonmaj 500, maj 25.
Tuition: $3880 per yr; campus res room and board $1800 per yr.
Courses: Aesthetics; Architecture History; Art History; Ceramics; Drawing; Film; Graphic Arts; History of Art & Archaeology; Mixed Media; Painting; Photography; Printmaking; Sculpture.

UNIONTOWN

PENNSYLVANIA STATE UNIVERSITY, FAYETTE CAMPUS, College of Arts and Architecture, Department of Art, Hwy 119 N, 15401. Tel: 412-437-2801, exten 29. *Assoc Prof Art & Chmn Dept* Zeljko Kujundzic, MFA; *Asst Prof* Gloria De Paolis, MA; *Asst Prof* V Romanek, PhD; *Asst Prof* D Drost.
Estab 1968; pub; D&E; ent req HS dipl.
Tuition: $393 per 10 wk term.
Courses: Architecture; Art History; Ceramics; Drafting; Drawing; Painting; Sculpture; Teacher Training.

UNIVERSITY PARK

PENNSYLVANIA STATE UNIVERSITY, UNIVERSITY PARK
—**College of Arts and Architecture,** 111 Arts Bldg, 16802. Tel: 814-865-2591. *Dean Col* Walter H Walters, PhD; *Head Dept Architecture* Raniero Corbelletti, MS; *Head Dept Art* Lawrence Edwards, MFA; *Head Dept Art Hist* Hellmut Hager, PhD; *Head Dept Landscape Architecture* David Young, MLA; *Head Dept Music* Robert Baisley, MA; *Head Dept Theatre & Film* Douglas Cook, MA; Instrs FT 115, PT approx 12.
Univ estab 1855, col estab 1963; pub; D&E; ent req HS dipl, standardized testing; degrees BS, BArch, BA, BFA and BMus 4 yrs, BLA 5 yrs, MA, MFA, MS, MMus, PhD; schol; SC 189, LC 126, GC 75; enrl in col 26,000 gen students in electives annually, maj 1281, grad 189.
Tuition: Res—Undergrad $1263 for 3 terms, grad $1347 for 3 terms; Nonres—Undergrad $2643 for 3 terms, grad $2727 for 3 terms; campus res room and board $1509 per yr.
Courses: ‡Architecture; ‡Art History; ‡Ceramics; Constructions; Costume Design & Construction; Drafting; ‡Drawing; ‡Film; Graphic Arts; ‡Graphic Design; ‡Landscape Architecture; ‡Painting; ‡Photography; ‡Printmaking; Restoration & Conservation; ‡Sculpture; Stage Design; ‡Theatre Arts; Video.

Department of Art History, 229 Arts Bldg. Tel: 814-865-6326. *Prof Art Hist & Head Dept* Hellmut Hager, PhD; *Prof* Anthony Cutler, PhD; *Prof* Eugenio Battisti, Perfeziamento, Rome; *Prof* Roland Flesicher, PhD; *Assoc Prof* Dawson Kiang, PhD; *Assoc Prof* Bertrand Davezac, PhD; *Prof* George Mauner, PhD; *Assoc Prof* Jeanne C Porter, PhD.
Dept estab 1956; pub; ent req HS dipl; degrees BA 4 yrs, MA 3 yrs, PhD 6 yrs; LC 50, GC 40; enrl maj 30, grad 40.
Tuition: Res—Undergrad $383 per sem, grad $449 per sem; Nonres—Undergrad $801 per sem, grad $909 per sem; campus res.
Courses: History of Art & Archaeology.

WASHINGTON

WASHINGTON AND JEFFERSON COLLEGE, Art Department, S Lincoln St, 15301. Tel: 412-222-4400. *Chmn Art Dept* Paul B Edwards, MA; *Prof* Hugh H Taylor, MA; *Instr* Patricia Maloney, MFA.
Estab 1787, dept estab 1959; pvt; D&E; ent req HS dipl, SAT, achievement tests; degrees BA 4 yrs, MA; schol; SC 14, LC 8; enrl D 162, E 18, nonmaj 139, maj 23, others 15.
Tuition: $2300 per yr; campus res room and board $1425 per yr.
Courses: Art History; Ceramic Sculpture; Ceramics; Drawing; Graphic Arts; Painting; Printmaking; Restoration & Conservation; Sculpture.
Adult Hobby Classes: Tui $25 for 8 wks.
Summer School: Dir Dr William W Leake. Tui $70 per cr hr for term of 4 wks beginning June 13. Courses—Full range.

WAYNE

WAYNE ART CENTER, 413 Maplewood Ave, 19087. Tel: 215-688-3553. *Pres* Linda Rodgers; *Instr* Tom Ewing; *Instr* Edward Lis; *Instr* Mary Richardson Miller; *Instr* David Day; *Instr* Joanne Cleveland; *Instr* Dan Miller; *Instr* Vera Cianfrani.
Estab 1930; pvt; D&E; no ent req; SC 15; enrl D 130, E 50, others 40.
Courses: Calligraphy; Collage; Drawing; Jewelry; Mixed Media; Painting; Photography; Printmaking; Sculpture.
Adult Hobby Classes: Tui $65 for 15 wk sem, yearly dues $15. Courses—As Above.
Children's Classes: Tui $30 for 10 wk sem, yearly dues $6. Courses—Painting; Drawing; Sculpture.
Summer School: Pres Linda Rodgers. Tui $30 for 6 wks beginning June. Courses—Same as above with Landscape Painting.

WILKES-BARRE

WILKES COLLEGE, Department of Art, S River St, 18703. Tel: 717-824-4651, exten 486, 480 & 368. *Chmn* William H Sterling, PhD; *Prof* Chester Colson, MS; *Assoc Prof* Berenice D'Vorzon, MA; *Asst Prof* Herbert Simon, MA; *Asst Prof* Richard Fuller, MA; *Asst Prof* Allan Maxwell, MFA.
Estab 1947; pvt; D&E; ent req HS dipl, SAT; degrees BA 4 yr; schol; SC 18, LC 6; enrl D 115, E 40, nonmaj 80, maj 75.
Tuition: Undergrad $2700 yr, $1350 per sem, $90 per cr hr; campus res room and board $1450.
Courses: Aesthetics; Art Education; Art History; Batik; Ceramics; Drawing; Fiber Design; Handicrafts (weaving); Jewelry; Painting; Photography; Printmaking; Sculpture; Stage Design; Teacher Training; Theatre Arts.
Summer School: Dir John Meyers. Enrl variable; tui $70 per cr hr for term of 5-8 wk beginning June 8. Courses—Variable.

WILLIAMSPORT

LYCOMING COLLEGE, Art Department, 17701. Tel: 717-326-1951, exten 260. *Assoc Prof Art & Chmn Dept* Roger Douglas Shipley, MFA; *Asst Prof* Jon Robert Bogle, MFA; *Asst Prof* Ruane Helen Miller, MFA; *PT Instrs* Terry Wild, BFA and Katharine L Fetters, BS.
Estab 1812; pvt; D&E; ent req HS dipl, ACT or SAT; degree BA 4 yrs; schol; SC 20, LC 7; enrl D 620, E 80, nonmaj 668, maj 32.
Tuition: $2700 per yr; campus res room and board $1300 per yr.
Courses: Advertising Design; Art History; Ceramics; Color Theory; Drawing; Graphic Arts; History of Art & Archaeology; ‡Painting; Photography; ‡Printmaking; ‡Sculpture.
Summer School: Assoc Prof Roger Douglas Shipley. Enrl 10; tui $500 room & board for term of 6 wks beginning June 5. Courses—Photography; Painting; Printmaking.
Mini Term: Tui room & board $420. Courses—Photography; Color Theory; Silkscreen Printing.

WILLIAMSPORT AREA COMMUNITY COLLEGE, Department of Engineering and Design, 1005 W Third St, 17701 Tel: 717-326-3761. *Dir Dept* Dr Paul L McQuay; *Asst Prof* Lloyd Cotner; *Asst Prof* William Dittmar, BA; *Asst Prof* William Ealer, BSB; *Asst Prof* Walter Hartman; *Instr* Jackie Welliver, CET; *Instr* Joseph Mark, AIA; *Asst Prof* Dale

Metzker; *Instr* Harold Newton; *Instr* Fred Schaefer, Jr; *Asst Prof* Dale Straub, BS; *Asst Prof* Chalmer Van Horn, BS.
Estab 1965; pub; D&E; ent req HS dipl, placement test; degree AA 2 yrs; schol; enrl D 2903, E 2909.
Tuition: No campus res.
Courses: Advertising Design; Architecture; Calligraphy; Commercial Art; Constructions; Drafting; Drawing; Graphic Arts; Illustration; Landscape Architecture; Lettering; Restoration & Conservation.
Summer School: Coordr Thomas E Vargo.

YORK

YORK ACADEMY OF ARTS, 625 E Philadelphia St, 17403. Tel: 717-848-1447. *Educ Dir* Florian Suitak, MA.
Estab 1952; pvt; D; ent req HS dipl, portfolio; enrl 270.
Tuition: $1377 per yr, $459 per trimester, $45.90 per class; no campus res.
Courses: Advertising Design; Art History; Calligraphy; ‡Commercial Art; Display; Drawing; ‡Fine Arts; Graphic Arts; Graphic Design; Illustration; ‡Interior Design; Lettering; Painting; Pastel Painting; Photography; Printmaking; Television & Film Art; Textile Design.
Adult Hobby Classes: Enrl 100; tui $30 for 8 wks. Courses—Art for Beginners; Painting; Portraiture; Watercolor; Calligraphy; Photography.
Children's Classes: Enrl 50; tui $24 for 8 wks. Courses—Drawing & Painting.
Summer School: Enrl 50; term of 4 wks beginning June 14. Courses—Drawing & Painting Workshop, tui $78; Oil Painters Workshop, tui $120.

YORK COLLEGE OF PENNSYLVANIA, Country Club Road, 17405. Tel: 717-846-7788. *Head Dept & Prof* Heinz Hosch, MA; *Instr* Otto H Tomasch, MA; *Asst Prof* Siham A Osman, PhD; *Sculptor-in-resident* Zoel Burickson.
Estab 1941; pvt; D&E; ent req HS dipl, SAT or ACT; degrees BA 4 yrs and AA 2 yrs; SC 17, LC 7.
Tuition: Undergrad $1880 per yr, $940 per sem, $51 per cr hr; campus res room and board $1358.
Courses: Art History; Drawing; Painting; Sculpture.
Adult Hobby Courses: Enrl 40; Tui $51 per cr hr. Courses—any or all.
Summer School: Dir Merris Harvey. Enrl 15, tui $46 per cr hr 1978, $51 per cr hr 1979 for term of 2 five wk session beginning June 19 and July 24.

RHODE ISLAND

BRISTOL

ROGER WILLIAMS COLLEGE, Art Department, Old Ferry Road, 02809. Tel: 401-255-1000. *Coordr* Carol J Hathaway, MA; *Instr* James Cathers, MFA; *Instr* Charlotte Spencer, MA.
Estab 1948; dept estab 1967; pvt; D&E; ent req HS dipl; degrees BA 4 yr, AA 2 yr, Apprenticeship and Senior Teaching; SC 18 LC 8, enrl D 1800, E 1500, maj 38.
Tuition: Res $2600 per yr; campus res room and board $1560.
Courses: Aesthetics; Architecture; Art Education; Art History; Ceramics; Costume Design and Construction; Drafting; Drawing; Film; Handicrafts (leather, macrame, weaving, evening only); History of Art and Archaeology; Painting; Photography; Printmaking; Restoration and Conservation; Sculpture; Stage Design; Teacher Training; Theatre Arts.
Summer School: Dean Edwin Wilde. Courses—Ceramics; Design; Drawing; Painting; Weaving.

KINGSTON

UNIVERSITY OF RHODE ISLAND,* Department of Art, Fine Arts Center, 02881. Tel: 401-792-2131, 792-5821. *Chmn Prof* Richard Fraenkel; Instrs FT 14, PT 3.
Estab 1892; pub; D (exten E&D); ent req same as require for Col of Arts & Sciences; degrees BA and BFA 4 yr; schol; SC 21 (3 cr ea), studio seminars 24 (no grad prog offered), LC 23; enrl maj 165 others 900.
Tuition: Res free; nonres $1145.
Courses: Art History; Drawing; Filmmaking; Graphic Design; Painting; Photography; Printmaking; Sculpture.
Summer School: Dean Dr Frank Woods. Enrl 200; Two terms. Courses—Art History; Design; Painting; Photography; Printmaking; Sculpture.

NEWPORT

SALVE REGINA THE NEWPORT COLLEGE, Art Department, Ochre Point Ave, 02840. Tel: 401-847-6650, exten 217. *Head Dept* Sister Arlene Woods, RSM, MFA; *Primary Faculty* Sister Michaeline Lewnadowski, MFA; David Jorgensen, MFA.
Estab 1947; den; D&E; ent req HS dipl, ent exam; degrees BA 4 yr; SC 28, LC 8; enrl D 95 (dept), nonmaj 84, maj 11.
Tuition: Res—Undergrad $2200 per sem, $80 per cr (day), $45 per cr (night), grad $80 per cr; Nonres—Undergrad $1350 per sem, $80 per cr (day), $45 per cr (night); grad $80 per cr; campus res room & board $850 per sem.
Courses: Advertising Design; Aesthetics; Art Education; Art History; Calligraphy; Ceramics; Drawing; Illustration; Painting; Photography; Printmaking; Teacher Training.
Summer School: Dir Sister Mary McAuliff. Tui $80 for one cr, $45 non-credit, term varies with number of credits involved. Courses—Art Appreciation; Photography as a Resource for the Painter; Quilting; Religious Art Workshop; Sculpture; Sketching in Newport; Stone Carving (Calligraphy).

SCHOOL OF THE ART ASSOCIATION OF NEWPORT, 76 Bellevue Ave, 02840. Tel: 401-847-0179. *Admn* Jemison Faust.
Estab 1913; D&E; no ent req; no degrees (col cr given through Roger Williams Col (Open Division); schol; SC 14, LC 3; enrl D 160 (total).
Tuition: $54 per course per sem, 12 wk sem, classes meet 3 hr per wk.
Courses: Advertising Design; Art History; Collage; Commercial Art; Drawing; Graphic Design; Handicrafts (weaving); Mixed Media; Painting; Printmaking; Sculpture; Stage Design; Theatre Arts.
Children's Classes: Enrl 50; tui $36 per sem. Courses—Drawing; Multimedia; Painting.
Summer School: Enrl 160; tui $36 per term of 4 wks beginning July 10 to Aug 3, classes meet twice a wk. Courses—as above.

PROVIDENCE

BROWN UNIVERSITY, Department of Art, 02912. Tel: 401-863-2421. *Chmn* Kermit S Champa, PhD; *Chmn Studio Division* Walter Feldman, MFA.
Pvt; D; degrees BA 4 yr, MA/PhD in Art History; SC 8-10, LC 10-14, GC 10-12; enrl maj 70, GS 45.
Tuition: Res—Undergrad $7140 per yr, $3570 per sem, $632 per unit, grad depends on boarding arrangements; Nonres—Undergrad & grad $5050 per yr; campus res room and board.
Courses: Art History; Drawing; History of Art and Archaeology; Painting; Printmaking; Sculpture.

PROVIDENCE COLLEGE, Department of Fine Arts, River Avenue, 02918. Tel: 401-865-2401. *Chmn* Richard N Elkington, MFA; *Prof* Rev Lawrence M Hunt, OP, PhD; *Primary Faculty* James Baker, MFA; Rev Adrian G Dabash, OP, MFA; Suzanne H D'Avanzo, MA; Jon DiCicco, MFA (Educ); Alice H Hauck, MA; Nancy E Garner, MA; Rev Richard A McAlister, OP, MFA; Kathryn McCauley Morton, MA.
Estab 1917; dept estab 1969; pvt; D&E; ent req HS dipl, portfolio needed for transfer students; degrees BA 4 yr; SC 49, LC 8; enrl D 464, E 250, nonmaj 399, maj 65.
Tuition: Res and Nonres—Undergrad $2852 per yr, grad $153 per course; campus res room and board $1780 per yr.
Courses: Architecture; ‡Art Education; Art History; Calligraphy; ‡Ceramics; Drafting; ‡Drawing; Handicrafts (soft and hard); Lettering; ‡Painting; ‡Photography; ‡Printmaking; ‡Sculpture; Stage Design; Teacher Training.
Summer School: Dir Rev James M Murphy, OP. Tui $111 for term of 6 wks beginning June 19 to July 27. Courses—Art History; Calligraphy; Ceramics; Drawing; Painting; Photography; Printmaking; Soft and Hard Crafts.
A summer program is offered to our students at Pietrasanta, Italy. *Dir* Richard A McAlister, OP. Courses—Art History; Languages; Literature; Religious Studies; Studio.

RHODE ISLAND COLLEGE, Art Department, 02908. Tel: 401-456-8054. *Chmn* Harriet E Brisson, MFA; *Asst Prof* Samuel B Ames, MFA; *Prof* John DeMelim, MFA; *Asst Prof* Krisjohn O Horvat, MFA; *Instrs* Roberta Houllahan, MFA; *Asst Prof* Mary Ball Howkins, PhD; *Assoc Prof* David M Hysell, PhD; *Asst Prof* Richard A Kenyon, MS; *Assoc Prof* Pauline Ladd, MFA; *Assoc Prof* Curtis K LaFollette, MFA; *Asst Prof* Betty E Ohlin, MA; *Assoc Prof* Enrico Pinardi, MFA; *Prof* Angelo V Rosati, MA; *Prof* Donald C Smith, AM; *Assoc Prof* Ronald M Steinberg PhD; *Assoc Prof* Lawrence F Sykes, MS.
Estab 1854, dept estab 1969; pub; D&E; ent req HS dipl, CEEB and SAT; degrees BA (Art History), BA(Studio) and BS(Art Educ) 4 yr, MAT 1 yr; SC 31, LC 10, GC 5; enrl D 443, E approx 50, nonmaj approx 228, maj 188, GS 30.

Tuition: Res—Undergrad $625 per yr, grad $35 per cr; Nonres—Undergrad $1513 per yr, grad $45 per cr; campus res room & board $1610.
Courses: Aesthetics; ‡Art Education; ‡Art Education; Art History; Ceramics; Drawing; Fiber; Film; Graphic Design; Metal; ‡Painting; ‡Photography; ‡Printmaking; ‡Sculpture; Teacher Training.
Children's Classes: Enrl 165; tui $75 per 20 wks. Courses—Ceramics; Drawing; Life Drawing; Painting; Printmaking.
Summer School: Dir & Assoc prof Richard A Kenyon. Enrl approx 150; tui $35 per cr, nonres $46 per cr for term of 6 wks beginning June 26th. Courses—Ceramics; Drawing; Fiber; Painting; Photography.

RHODE ISLAND SCHOOL OF DESIGN,* 2 College St, 02903. Tel: 401-331-3507. *Pres* Lee Hall; *Chmn Div of Fine Arts* Gilbert A Franklin, BFA; *Chmn Div of Arch Studies* Friedrich St Florian, Dipl Ing in Arch, MS in Urban Design; *Chmn Div of Design* Thomas Sgouros, BFA; *Head Photography* Albert P Beaver; *Head Painting & Printmaking* Roland J Belhumeur, MFA; *Head Arch* Derek Bradford, Dipl Arch, MLA; *Head Glass* Dale Chihuly, MFA; *Head Program in Landscape* J Michael Everett, March; *Head Dept of Sculpture* Leuren Ewing, MFA; *Head Prog in Interior Arch* Charles B Fink, BArch; *Head Dept of History of Art* Gregor Goethals, MA; *Head Program in Industrial Design* Marc S Harrison, MFA; *Head Program in Printmaking* Lawrence Heyman, MFA; *Acting Head Dept of Apparel Design* Lorraine Howes; *Head Dept of Illustration* David Macaulay, BArch; *Head Dept of Textile Design* Alice Marcoux; *Head Dept of Graphic Design* Thomas Ockerse, MFA; *Head Dept of Ceramics* Jacquelyn Ione Rice, MFA; *Instrs* FT 97, PT 55.
Estab 1877; pvt; endowed; ent req HS grad; degrees BArch; BID; BFA; BLandscape Arch; MA(Art Educ); MAT; MFA nad MID 4-5 yrs; schol, grants-in-aid to res, student loans, fel; enrl D 1353, E 650.
Tuition: $3775 per yr plus fees; room & board $1650 prep; campus res and approved housing.
Courses: Apparel Design; Architecture; Ceramics; Film Studies; Graphic Design; Ilustration; Industrial Design; Interior Architecture; Jewelry & Metalsmithing; ‡Landscape Architecture; Painting & Printmaking; Photography; Sculpture (Glass); Teacher Education (grad level only); Television Studies; Textile Design; Wood & Furniture Design.
Summer School: Dir Bruce Helander. Enrl 800, tui $400 average. Courses—Pre-Col Foundation Program; Summner Program in Provincetown, Mass; Transfer Session; Workshops in several fine arts and design area.

WARWICK

RHODE ISLAND JUNIOR COLLEGE,* Department of Art, 400 East Ave, 02886. Tel: 401-825-2267. *Chmn* Rita C Lepper; *Instrs* FT 10, PT 2.
Estab 1964; pub; D&E; ent req HS dipl, ent exam, equivalency exam; degrees AA, AS and AAS 2 yr; schol; SC 16, LC 3, seminar 1; enrl D4600.
Courses: Ceramics; Commercial Art; Crafts; Drafting (Vocational-Technical Div); Drawing; Graphic Arts; Graphic Design; History of Art & Archaeology; Painting; Photography; Sculpture.
Continuing Education School: Dean John G Marmaras. Term of 6 wks. Courses—Beginning and Advanced Studio; Ceramics; Commercial Art and Photography; Life Drawing.

SOUTH CAROLINA

AIKEN

UNIVERSITY OF SOUTH CAROLINA AT AIKEN, 171 University Parkway, 29801. Tel: 803-648-6851, exten 153. *Head Dept* Jane Winer, MFA; Instrs FT 1, PT 4.
Estab 1961, dept estab 1970; pub, D&E; ent req HS dipl, GED; SAT; SC 15, LC 5, enrl D 100, E 50, nonmaj 80, maj 20.
Tuition: Res—Undergrad $810 per yr, $27 per sem hr, grad $1020 per yr, $34 per sem hr; Nonres—Undergrad $1950 per yr, $65 per sem hr, grad $2550 per yr, $85 per sem hr; no campus res.
Courses: Advertising Design; Art Education; Art History; Ceramics; Commercial Art; Conceptual Art; Drawing; History of Art and Archaeology; Illustration; Painting; Photography; Printmaking; Stage Design; Theatre Arts.
Summer School: Tui varies. Courses—varies.

CHARLESTON

BAPTIST COLLEGE AT CHARLESTON,* Department of Art, Hwy 78 at I-26, 29411. Tel: 803-797-4911. *Chmn* Joseph Ward; Instrs FT 2.
Estab 1960, den; D&E, ent req GED or HS dipl; degrees BA and BS 4 yr; schol; SC 14, LC 2; enrl D 80, E 71, maj 15.
Tuition: $1070 per yr, PT (9 hr) $535 per sem; campus res $1570 per yr.

Courses: Art Education; Batik; Ceramics; Drawing; Graphic Arts; History of Art & Archaeology; Painting; Papier Mache; Sculpture; Teacher Training; Theatre Arts (Drama Dept); Weaving.
Summer School: Enrl 1500; two 5 wk sessions beginning June. Courses—same as above.

COLLEGE OF CHARLESTON,* Department of Fine Arts, 66 George St, 29401. Tel: 803-722-0181. *Chmn* Dr Diane Chalmers Johnson; Instrs FT 14, PT 5.
Estab 1966; pub; D&E; ent req HS dipl; degree BA(Fine Arts) 4 yr; SC 36, LC 24.
Tuition: $550 per yr; nonres $1450.
Courses: Aesthetics; Architecture; Costume Design & Construction; Drawing; Graphic Arts; History of Art & Archaeology; Painting; Sculpture; State Design; Theatre Arts.

CLEMSON

CLEMSON UNIVERSITY,* College of Architecture, Department of History and Visual Studies, Lee Hall, 29631. Tel: 803-656-3081. *Head Dept* Thomas E McPeak; Instrs FT 10, PT 2.
Estab 1967; pub; D; ent req available on request; degree MFA 60 hr; GC 24, SC 40, LC 29 (undergrad courses for service to pre-architecture and other Univ requirements); enrl approx 1500 annually, grad maj 10.
Courses: Art and Architectural History; Ceramics; Drawing; Graphic Design; Painting; Photography; Printmaking; Sculpture.

CLINTON

PRESBYTERIAN COLLEGE, Fine Arts Department, 29325. Tel: 803-833-2820, exten 296. *Head & Assoc* Robert Jolly.
Estab 1880, dept estab 1960; den; D&E; ent req HS dipl with C average, SAT; degrees BA 4 yr; schol; SC 8, LC 5, enrl D 200, nonmaj 190, maj 10.
Tuition: $2250; campus res room and board $1265.
Courses: ‡Art Education; Art History; Drawing; ‡Painting; Printmaking; Sculpture.
Summer School: *Dean* Dr Fred Chapman. Enrl 150; tui $50 per cr hr for term of 5 wk beginning June 5. Courses—Art Appreciation; Painting.

COLUMBIA

BENEDICT COLLEGE,* Visual Art Studies, Taylor and Harden Sts, 29204. Tel: 803-779-4930, exten 354. Instrs FT 2.
Estab 1870; pvt; D; ent req HS dipl; degree BA(Teaching of Art) and general art major 4 yr; schol; SC 11, LC 6.
Courses: Art Education; Arts & Crafts; Ceramics; Drawing; Graphic Arts; Graphic Design; History of Art & Archaeology; Lettering; Painting; Photography; Sculpture; Teacher Training.
Summer School: Term of 5 wk beginning June. Courses—Art Appreciation plus 4 others.

RICHLAND ART WORKSHOP OF THE COLUMBIA MUSEUM OF ART,* 1112 Bull St, 29201. Tel: 803-799-2810. *Dir* Dr J R Craft; Instrs FT 3, PT 5.
Estab 1950 (operates as service of the Columbia Museum of Art); D&E; no ent req.
Courses: (Youths and adults) Ceramics; Crafts; Figure Drawing; Graphics; Jewelry; Painting; Photography; Sculpture.

UNIVERSITY OF SOUTH CAROLINA, Department of Art, Sloan College, 29208. Tel: 803-777-4236. *Chmn & Prof* John O'Neil, EdD; *Chmn Art History* John Bryan, PhD; *Chmn Art Education* Truman Teed, EdD; *Chmn Art Studio* Harry Hansen, MFA; *Instrs* Jim Crumer, EdD; *Instr* Randy Mack, PhD; *Instr* Annie Quinsac, PhD; *Instr* Philip Mullen, PhD.
Estab 1811, dept estab 1924; pub; D&E; ent req HS dipl; degrees BA, BFA and BS 4 yr, MFA 2 yr, MA and MAT one yr; schol; SC 100, LC 20, GC 25; enrl D 5000, E 400, maj 600, GS 180.
Tuition: Res $366; Nonres $846 per sem; campus res room and board $500 (room).
Courses: ‡Advertising Design; Aesthetics; ‡Art Education; ‡Art History; ‡Ceramics; Conceptual Art; ‡Drawing; Film; Goldsmithing; ‡Graphic Arts; Illustration; ‡Interior Design; Jewelry; Lettering; Museum Staff Training; ‡Painting; Photography; ‡Printmaking; Restoration and Conservation; ‡Sculpture; Silversmithing; Teacher Training; Textile Design; Video.
Children's Classes: Enrl 60; tui $25 per child. Courses—Saturday morning art classes.

Summer School: Enrl 200; tui $30 per cr for term of 5 wks beginning June 2 and July 10. Courses—Art Education; Art History; Ceramics; Drawing; Glassblowing; Painting; Printmaking; Sculpture.

DUE WEST

ERSKINE COLLEGE,* Department of Art, 29639. Tel: 803-379-2131. *Head Dept* Felix Bauer.
Estab 1839; den; D; ent req; degree 4 yr; SC 3, LC 1; enrl approx 80 per sem.
Summer School: Courses—Art Appreciation; Art for Teachers, K-6.

GAFFNEY

LIMESTONE COLLEGE,* Art Department, 29340. Tel: 803-489-7698, exten 164. *Head Dept* James A Cox; Instrs FT 2.
Estab 1845; pvt; D&E; ent req HS dipl ent exam; degrees BS (Educ, Studio) 4 yr; schol; SC 19, LC 9; enrl D 112, maj 42, others 3.
Courses: Aesthetics; Art Education; Ceramics; Drawing; History of Art & Archaeology; Jewelry; Painting; Printmaking (Wood-Block & Silk-Screen); Sculpture; Teacher Training; Theatre Arts.
Summer School: *Dir* Dr Nelson. Term of 6 wk beginning June. Courses—Art Appreciation; Ceramics; Drawing & Painting.

GREENVILLE

BOB JONES UNIVERSITY, School of Fine Arts, 29614. Tel: 803-242-5011, exten 239. *Dean* Dwight Gustafson, DMus; *Chmn* Emery Bopp, MFA; *Primary Faculty* David Appleman, MA; Kathy Bell, MA; Carl Blair, MFA; Lorrainne Edwards, MA; Darrel Koons, MA; Harrell Whittington, MA.
Estab 1927, dept estab 1945; pvt; D; ent req HS dipl; letters of recommendation; degrees BA and BS 4 yr, MA 1-2 yrs; SC 29, LC 12, GC 10; enrl D 235; nonmaj 122, maj 108, GS 5.
Tuition: $1062 per yr, $531 per sem; campus res room and board $1638.
Courses: Advertising Design; Aesthetics; Art Education; Art History; Calligraphy; Ceramics; Collage; Commercial Art; Conceptual Art; ‡Costume Design and Construction; Drawing; Film; Graphic Arts; Graphic Design; Handicrafts (batik, leather tooling, weaving); History of Art and Archaeology; Illustration; Lettering; Painting; ‡Photography; Printmaking; Restoration and Conservation; Sculpture; ‡Stage Design; Teacher Training; Theatre Arts. Other—elective courses available from the Division of Cinema and the Dept of Dramatic Production.

FURMAN UNIVERSITY, Department of Art, 29613. Tel: 803-294-2074, 2000. *Chmn* Richard Olof Sorensen, PhD; *Assoc Prof* Thomas E Flowers, MFA; *Asst Prof* Glen E Howerton, MA.
Estab 1826; den; D&E; degrees BA 4 yr, MA with concentration in art one yr or more, MA program in Education with an emphasis in art; SC 17-18, LC 7, GC varies; enrl D 35-40, E 10-20, nonmaj 10, maj 30, GS 3, others 15.
Tuition: $2592 per yr, $81 per cr hr; room and board $1724.
Courses: Advertising Design; Aesthetics; Art Education; Art History; Calligraphy; Ceramics; Classical Art History; Construction; Drawing; Graphic Arts; Handicrafts; Internship in Ad Design; Internship in Museum; Lettering; Medieval Art History; Oriental Art History; Painting; Printmaking; Primitive & Prehistoric; Modern Art History; Renaissance Art History; Sculpture; Stage Design; Teacher Training.
Adult Hobby Classes: Courses—Basketry; Calligraphy.
Summer School: *Dir* Dr Hazel Harris. Courses—Art Education; Drawing; Printmaking; others on demand.

GREENVILLE COUNTY MUSEUM OF ART,* Museum School of Art, 420 College St, 29601. Tel: 803-271-7570. *Dir* Sharon H Whitley; Instrs FT 1, PT 18.
Estab 1960; pub; D&E; no ent req; degrees AAA and AFA 2-3 yrs; schol; SC 12, LC 2, GC 6; enrl D 200, E 100.
Courses: Advertising Design; Crafts; Drawing; History of Art; Painting; Philosophy of Art; Photography; Pottery; Printmaking; Sculpture; Video; Weaving.
Children's Classes: Enrl approx 15 per course, ages 6-12. Courses—Mixed-media.
Summer School: Enrl approx 300 per sem; 4 wk term. Courses—same as regular sem.

GREENWOOD

LANDER COLLEGE,* Department of Visual Studies, 29646. Tel: 803-229-5521, exten 231. *Coordr Visual Studies* Robert Harold Poe; Instrs FT 3, PT 2.
Estab 1872; pub; D&E; ent req HS dipl; degree BA (Art) 4 yr; schol; SC 25, LC 5; enrl D 235, E 60, maj 35.
Tuition: $560 per yr; nonres $600 per yr; campus res $1200 to $1400.

Courses: Advertising Design; Aesthetics; Art Education; Ceramics; Commercial Art; Drawing; Graphic Arts; Graphic Design; History of Art & Archaeology; Illustration; Painting; Sculpture; Teacher Training.

HARTSVILLE

COKER COLLEGE,* Art Department, 29550. Tel: 803-332-1381, exten 417. *Head Dept* R Nickey Brumbaugh; *Instrs* FT 2 PT 1.
Estab 1908, pvt; D&E; ent req HS dipl, ent exam; degrees AB and BS 4 yr; schol; SC 29; LC 8; enrl D 545, maj 29.
Tuition: $2082 per yr; campus res (room and board) $1280 per yr.
Courses: Art Education; Ceramics; Commercial Art; Crafts; Drawing; Graphic Arts; Handicrafts; History of Art; Painting; Photography; Sculpture.
Summer School: Term of 5 wk. Courses—Art Appreciation; Art Education.

NEWBERRY

NEWBERRY COLLEGE, Department of Art, College Street, 29108. Tel: 803-276-5010, exten 289. *Head Dept & Asst Prof* Kenneth David Brown, MA; *Instr* Cathy Cherry Crowell, MA.
Estab 1856, dept estab 1973; den; D&E; ent req HS dipl, SAT; degrees AB(Art) 4 yrs of 126 hrs, two courses in independent study; financial aid available; SC 35, LC 2; enrl D 114, nonmaj 106, maj 9, others one adult audit.
Tuition: $3675 per yr includes room and board; campus res available.
Courses: Art History; Ceramics; Costume Design and Construction; ‡Drawing; Mixed Media; ‡Painting; ‡Printmaking; Sculpture; Stage Design; Theatre Arts.
Summer School: Courses—Crafts; Drawing; Painting.

ORANGEBURG

SOUTH CAROLINA STATE COLLEGE, Art Program, 29115. Tel: 803-536-7174. *Dir* Leo F Twiggs, EdD; *Prof Asst* Donald J Zurlo, MFA; *Asst Prof* James L McFadden; *Instr* Terry J Hunter, MFA.
Dept estab 1972; D&E; ent req HS dipl; degrees BA and BS 4 yr, MA and MS approx 2 yr; SC 15, LC 7; enrl D 73, nonmaj 8, maj 73.
Tuition: Res $300 per sem, nonres $650 per sem; campus res.
Courses: Art Education.
Summer School: *Dir* Dr A S Belcher. Tui $34 per cr hr. Courses—Art Appreciation; Arts and Crafts for Children.

ROCK HILL

WINTHROP COLLEGE,* Department of Art, 29733. Tel: 803-323-2126. *Chmn* Edmund Lewandowski, *Instrs* FT 8.
Estab 1886; pub; degree BVA.
Tuition: $75 per sem; non-res $200; PT $6.25, non-res $16.75.
Courses: Art Education; Ceramics; Crafts; Graphic-Advertising Design; Painting; Photography; Printmaking; Sculpture.
Summer School: Two 5 wk terms beginning June.

SPARTANBURG

CONVERSE COLLEGE,* Division of the Fine Arts, Department of Art, 29301. Tel: 803-585-6421, exten 251. *Chmn* Mayo MacBoggs; *Instrs* FT 4, PT 2.
Estab 1889; pvt; D&E; W (men accepted in Arts & Music); ent req 16 units or equivalent; degrees BA and BFA 4 yr; schol; SC 25, LC 12.
Courses: Ceramics; Drawing; Graphic Arts; History of Art; Interior Design; Painting; Photography; Sculpture.

ART ASSOCIATION SCHOOL, 385 S Spring St, 29301. Tel: 803-583-1399. *Dir* Marcia Gelband, BA; *Educ Chmn* Elaine Wagner, BFA.
Estab 1970; D&E (Spring Sem Apr 3-June 9); no ent req; continuing education units in cooperation with University of South Carolina in Spartanburg; SC 25; enrl D 200, E 300 (adult, young adult and children's classes).
Tuition: $35-$50 for 10 wk sem.
Courses: Ceramics; Drawing; Film; Graphic Arts; Handicrafts (Weaving); Mixed Media; Painting; Printmaking; Sculpture; Textile Design.

SOUTH DAKOTA

ABERDEEN

NORTHERN STATE COLLEGE, Art Department, 57401. Tel 605-622-2514. *Chmn* Jim Gibson, MFA.

Estab 1907; pub; D&E; ent req ACT; degrees AA, BA, BS, BSEd and MSEd; SC 40, LC 12, GC 10; enrl D 400, E 100, maj 85, GS 1.
Tuition: $75 per cr; non-res $29 per cr; campus res.
Courses: Art Education; Art History; Ceramics; Commercial Art; Drawing; Jewelry; Mixed Media; Painting; Printmaking; Sculpture; Teacher Training.
Adult Hobby Classes: Tui $14.50. One class.
Summer School: Enrl 25, tui same. Courses—same.

BROOKINGS

SOUTH DAKOTA STATE UNIVERSITY, Art Department, Solberg Hall, 57006. Tel: 605-688-4103. *Head Dept* Fredrick W Bunce, PhD; *Prof* Richard Edie, MFA; *Asst Prof* Dennis Guastella, MFA; *Asst Prof* Gerald Kruse, MFA; *Assoc Prof* Helen Morgan, MAE; *Assoc Prof* Mel Spinar, MFA; *vis prof*—Chris Martens, sculpture, spring 1978.
Estab 1881, pub; D&E; ent req HS dipl, ent ACT; degrees BA and BS 126 sem crs; SC 28, LC 8.
Courses: Advertising Design; Art Education; Art History; Calligraphy; Ceramics; Commercial Art; Drawing; Graphic Arts; Graphic Design; History of Art and Archaeology; Intermedia; Lettering; Museum Staff Training; Painting; Printmaking; Sculpture; Textile Design.

HURON

HURON COLLEGE,* Art Department, 57350. Tel: 605-352-8721, exten 272. *Instrs* FT 2.
Pub; D; ent req HS dipl, ent exam; degrees BA and BS 4 yr; schol; SC 9, LC 2, enrl D 580.
Courses: Art Education; Drawing; Graphic Arts; Graphic Design; History of Art & Archaeology; Painting; Photography; Sculpture; Teacher Training.
Summer School: Courses—Drawing Techniques; Three Dimensional Design.

MADISON

DAKOTA STATE COLLEGE,* Division of Fine and Applied Art, 57042. Tel: 605-256-3551, exten 219. *Instrs* FT 2.
Estab 1881; pub; D; ent req HS dipl, ACT; degree BS 4 yr; schol; SC 16, LC 5; enrl D 120, maj 20.
Courses: Art Education; Ceramics; Drawing; History of Art & Archaeology; Jewelry; Painting; Sculpture; Teacher Training.
Summer School: Term of 8 wk beginning June.

MITCHELL

DAKOTA WESLEYAN UNIVERSITY,* Department of Art, University Blvd, 57301. Tel: 605-996-5685. *Head Dept* Milton Kudlacek; *Instrs* FT 1.
Estab 1885; den; ent req upper half of HS class; degree 4 yr; schol; SC, LC; enrl 200.
Tuition: $1625 per yr; room & board $1080.
Courses: General Art.
Summer School: Courses—varied.

SIOUX FALLS

AUGUSTANA COLLEGE,* Art Department, 57102. Tel: 605-336-5426. *Head Dept* John Carlander; *Instrs* FT 4.
Estab 1860; den; D&E; ent req HS dipl, ent exam; degrees BA and MAE 4 yr; schol; SC 14, LC 3; enrl total 1861.
Tuition: $2700; campus res $1140.
Courses: Art Education; Ceramics; Drawing; Etching; History of Art; Lithography; Painting; Sculpture.
Summer School: *Dir* Dr Arthur Olsen. Term of 8 wk beginning June. Courses—Arts; Crafts; Drawing.

SIOUX FALLS COLLEGE,* Division of Fine Arts, Department of Art, 1501 S Prairie St, 57101. *Chmn* Jay Olson; *Instrs* FT 1.
Estab 1883; pub; degrees BA with maj in Art or Art Educ 4 yr; schol; SC, LC; enrl 1000.
Tuition: $2000 per yr; campus res.
Courses: Art Education; Art History; Crafts; Design & Illustration; Drawing; Painting.
Summer School: Courses—Crafts; Design; Drawing; Education.

SPEARFISH

BLACK HILLS STATE COLLEGE,* Art Department, 57783. Tel: 605-642-6272. *Chmn* Dr Victor Weidensee; *Instrs* FT 4.

Estab 1883; pub; D; ent req HS dipl, transcripts, ACT, physical exam; degree BA 4 yr; schol; SC 15, LC 4; enrl maj 50.
Tuition: $16.50 per sem hr; non-res $36 per sem hr; campus res $1814.50.
Courses: Art Education; Ceramics; Commercial Art; Drafting; Drawing; Lettering; Painting; Photography; Sculpture.
Summer School: Courses—Art in Our Lives; Drawing; Painting; School Arts & Crafts.

SPRINGFIELD

UNIVERSITY OF SOUTH DAKOTA, SPRINGFIELD, 57062. Tel: 605-369-2264. *Head Dept* Ed Gettinger; Instrs FT 1.
Estab 1881, pub; D; ent req HS dipl; degrees AA, AS and AAS 2 yr; schol; SC 12, LC 2; enrl D 70, maj 14, grad 70.
Courses: Ceramics; Drawing; Graphic Design; Lettering; Painting; Sculpture; Technical Illustration.
Adult Hobby Classes: Enrl 15, Courses—Ceramics: Painting.
Summer School: Enrl 20; term of 5 wk beginning June. Courses—Art Appreciation; Design; Drawing; Independent Study; Painting.

VERMILLION

UNIVERSITY OF SOUTH DAKOTA, Department of Art, 57069. Tel: 605-677-5636. *Chmn* John A Day, MFA.
Estab 1862; dept estab 1933; pub; D&E; ent req HS dipl; degrees BS (Art Educ) and BFA 4 yr; schol; SC 50, LC 10, GC 10; enrl D 450, nonmaj 340, maj 100, GS 10.
Tuition: Res—Undergrad $17.50 per hr, grad $28.75 per hr; Nonres—Undergrad $41 per hr, grad $55 per hr; campus res room and board $520.
Courses: Advertising Design; Aesthetics; ‡Art Education; Art History; ‡Ceramics; Costume Design and Construction; Drawing; Film; ‡Graphic Arts; Graphic Design; History of Art and Archaeology; Lettering; ‡Painting; ‡Photography; ‡Printmaking; ‡Sculpture; Stage Design; Textile Design; Theatre Arts.
Summer School: Courses—varies.

YANKTON

MOUNT MARTY COLLEGE, Art Department, 57078. Tel: 605-668-1011, 668-1574. *Head Dept & Instr* Sister Kathleen Hickenbotham, MFA; *Asst Prof* Michael Gontesky, MFA; *Instr & Res Artist* Sister Leonarda Longen, MFA; *Lectr* Sister Kathleen Courtney, MA.
Estab 1936; den; D; ent req HS dipl; degrees BA 4 yr; schol; SC 17, LC 5; enrl 9.
Tuition: $60 per cr hr; campus res room and board $400.
Courses: ‡Advertising Design; ‡Art Education; Art History; Calligraphy; Ceramics; ‡Commercial Art; Drawing; Film; Graphic Arts; Handicrafts; ‡Painting; ‡Photography; ‡Printmaking; ‡Sculpture.
Summer School: *Dir* Sister Jacqueline Ernster. Tui $60 per cr hr for term of 4 wks beginning June and July. Courses—Ceramics; Photography I & II.

YANKTON COLLEGE,* Department of Art, 57078. Tel: 605-665-3661. *Head Dept* Jerome Gallagher; Instrs PT 3.
Estab 1881; pvt; den; ent req HS grad; degree 4 yr; schol; SC, LC.
Tuition: $2340 per term; PT $65 per cr hr; room & board $1250 per term.
Courses: Ceramics; Drawing; Foundations; History of Art; Painting (Oil & Acrylic); Sculpture; Weaving.

TENNESSEE

ATHENS

TENNESSEE WESLEYAN COLLEGE,* Department of Art, PO Box 40, 37303. Tel: 615-745-5906. *Chmn* Robert Jolly.
Estab 1857, dept estab 1966; den; D&E; ent req HS dipl; degrees BA and BS 4 yr; SC 7, LC 5; enrl total 500, maj 10.
Tuition: $1440 yr; campus res $1320.
Courses: Art Education; Design; Drawing; History of Art; Painting; Sculpture.
Summer School: *Acad Dean* Dr Robert Evans. Enrl 360; term of 5 wk beginning June. Courses—Public school art courses.

CHATTANOOGA

UNIVERSITY OF TENNESSEE AT CHATTANOOGA, Department of Art, Vine St, 37401. Tel 615-755-4178. *Head & Prof* George Cress, MFA; *Prof* Jim Collins, MFA; *Asst Prof* E Alan White; MFA; *Asst Prof* Stephen S LeWinter, MA.
Estab 1928; pub; D&E; ent req HS dipl, ACT or SAT, health exam; degrees BA and BS 4 yr; SC 11, LC 13, GC 1; enrl D 420, E 80, nonmaj 500, maj 130, grad 6, others 14.
Tuition: Res—Undergrad $256 per sem, grad $274 per sem; Nonres—Undergrad $450 per sem, grad $81 per hr; campus res $460 per sem.
Courses: Art Education; Art History; Ceramics; Commercial Art; Drawing; Graphic Design; Painting; Printmaking; Sculpture.
Adult Hobby Classes: Tui $60 per 6 wk. Courses—Stained Glass.
Summer School: Tui $256 for term of 5 wk.

CLARKSVILLE

AUSTIN PEAY STATE UNIVERSITY, Department of Art, College St, 37040. Tel: 615-648-7011. *Prof Art & Chmn Dept* Charles T Young, EdD; *Primary Art Faculty* T Max Hochstetler, MFA; Olen Bryant, MFA; Yeung Ha, MFA; Philancy N Holder, MA; Algar Dole, MFA; Gerard Tenney, BA; Lewis Burton, MA.
Estab 1927, Dept estab 1930; pub; D&E; ent req HS dipl; degrees BFA, BA and BS 4 yrs, AA 2 yrs; GC 3; enrl D 615, E 75, nonmaj 475, maj 140.
Tuition: Res—$456 per yr; Nonres $1392 per yr; campus res room and board $1215 per yr.
Courses: Advertising Design; Aesthetics; Art Education; Art History; Calligraphy; Ceramics; Commercial Art; Drafting; Drawing; Graphic Arts; Graphic Design; Handicrafts (weaving); History of Art & Archaeology; Illustration; Lettering; Mixed Media; Painting; Photography; Printmaking; Sculpture; Stage Design; Teacher Training; Textile Design; Theatre Arts.
Adult Hobby Classes: Courses—Italic Handwriting; Painting; Crafts.
Summer School: *Chmn Dept Art* Charles T Young. Enrl 125; tui $134 for term of 6 wks beginning June 14. Courses—Art Appreciation; Painting; Art Education.

CLEVELAND

CLEVELAND STATE COMMUNITY COLLEGE, Department of Art, Adkisson Dr, 37311. *Assoc Prof & Dept Coordr* Jere L Chumley, MA; *Instr* Cathy Smith, MS.
Estab 1967; pub; D&E; ent req HS dipl or GED; degrees AA and AS 2 yrs; SC 6, LC 5; enrl D 107, E 28, nonmaj 76, maj 59.
Tuition: Res—$252 per yr, $84 per quarter, $7 quarter hr; Nonres—$1182 per yr, $396 per quarter, $33 quarter hr; no campus res.
Courses: Art Appreciation; Art Education; Art History; Arts & Crafts; Basic Design; Ceramics; Commercial Art; Drawing; Printmaking; Sculpture.
Adult Hobby Classes: Enrl 35; tui $10-25 per course. Courses—Painting; Ceramics; Macrame, all offered through Community Serv Div.
Summer School: *Dir* Jere L Chumley. Enrl approx 12 per class; tui $84 per quarter, $7 quarter hr for two 5 wk sessions beginning June 13. Courses—Painting; Ceramics; Art Appreciation; Arts & Crafts.

COLLEGEDALE

SOUTHERN MISSIONARY COLLEGE,* Art Department, 37315. Instrs FT 3, PT 1.
Estab 1969; den; D&E; ent req HS dipl, ent exam; degrees BA(art) and BA(art educ) 4 yr; LC 3; enrl maj 34.
Tuition: $2670 yr.
Courses: Advertising Design; Art Education; Ceramics; Drawing; Graphic Arts; Graphic Design; Handicrafts; History of Art & Archaeology; Industrial Design; Landscape Architecture; Painting; Photography; Sculpture; Teacher Training; Textile Design.

COLUMBIA

COLUMBIA STATE COMMUNITY COLLEGE, Department of Art, 38401. Tel: 615-388-0120. *Head Dept Art* Fred Behrens, MFA.
Estab 1966; pub; D&E; ent req open door institution; degrees AA and AS 2 yrs; schol; SC 17, LC 4; enrl D 230, nonmaj 215, maj 12 to 15.
Tuition: $252 per yr, $33 per hr; no campus res.
Courses: ‡Art Education; Art History; ‡Art Studio; Ceramics; Drawing; Film; History of Art & Archaeology; Painting; Photography; Printmaking.

Summer School: Dir Fred Behrens. Enrl 30 to 40; tui $84 for term of 5 wks beginning June. Courses—Art Appreciation & School Art.

FRANKLIN

HARRIS SCHOOL OF ADVERTISING ART, INC,* Route 8, Battlewood Estates, Hillsboro Rd, 37064. Tel: 615-794-8544. Instrs FT 3.
Estab 1932; pvt; D; ent req HS dipl; 2, 3 and 4 yr cert; SC, LC; enrl 75. A small personal school with professional standards offering a practical curriculum, personalized to each student's individuality. Two, three and four yr cert courses in advertising art.
Courses: Airbrush Rendering; Artistic Anatomy; Composition & Design; Figure Drawing & Painting; Head Drawing & Painting; Lettering & Typography; Lithography; Mechanical Art & Paste-Up; Perspective Drawing; Photoengraving; Printing Processes; Still Life Painting.

GATLINBURG

ARROWMONT SCHOOL OF ARTS AND CRAFTS, Parkway (Mailing Add: Box 567, 37738). Tel: 615-436-5860. *Dir* Ray Pierotti.
Estab 1945; pvt; D&E (operate mostly in summer with special programs for fall, winter and spring); ent req HS dipl; no degrees granted, though credit is offered for courses through the Univ of Tennessee, Knoxville and other similar institutions; schol; SC 44-50, GC 30; enrl D 1000.
Tuition: $75 per wk, 1 or 2 wks sessions; campus res room and board $80-$100 per wk.
Courses: Ceramics; Conceptual Art; Display; Drawing; Fiber Sculpture; Glassblowing; Goldsmithing; Graphic Arts; Graphic Design; Interior Design; Jewelry; Metalsmithing; Painting; Papermaking; Photography; Sculpture; Silversmithing; Textile Design.

GREENEVILLE

TUSCULUM COLLEGE,* Division of Creative Arts & Humanities, 37743. Tel: 615-639-2861. *Dir* J Clement Allison; Instrs FT 2.
Col estab 1794; den; D; ent req HS dipl; degrees BA and BS 4 yrs; schol; SC 25, LC 3; enrl D 445, maj 18.
Tuition: $1920 per yr; campus res $1491.
Courses: Art Education; Ceramics; Drawing; Glassblowing; History of Art & Archaeology; Life Drawing; Painting; Printmaking; Sculpture; Two & Three-Dimensional Design.
Adult Continuing Education Classes: Enrl 14. Courses—Painting.

JACKSON

LANE COLLEGE,* Art Department, 545 Lane Ave, 38301. Tel: 901-424-4600. *Assoc Prof* Phyllis Carol Shieber; Instrs FT 1.
Den; D; ent req HS dipl; 4 yr; no art major; schol; SC 8, LC 3; enrl 165.
Courses: Art Education; Ceramics; Drawing; History of Art & Archaeology; Painting.

UNION UNIVERSITY, Department of Art, Hwy 45 Bypass (Mailing Add: Union University Box 2078, 38301). Tel: 901-668-1818. *Chmn Dept Art* Grove Robinson, MFA; *Assoc Prof* Patricia Pinson, PhD; *Assoc Prof* Meredith Luck, MFA; *PT Instr* Elizabeth Emison, BA.
Estab 1824, dept estab 1958; den; E&E; ent req HS dipl, ACT; degrees BA and BS 4 yrs; schol; SC 20, LC 5; enrl D 200, E 40, maj 28.
Tuition: $45-$65 per sem hr;; campus res room and board $466 per sem.
Courses: Advertising Design; Art Appreciation; Art Education; Art History; ‡Ceramics; Commercial Art; Drawing; Goldsmithing; Handicrafts; Jewelry; Lettering; ‡Painting; Photography; Printmaking; ‡Sculpture; Silversmithing; Teacher Training.
Summer School: Dir Grove Robinson. Enrl 50; tui $65 per hr for term of 5 wks beginning June and July.

JEFFERSON CITY

CARSON-NEWMAN COLLEGE,* Art Department, 37760. Tel: 615-475-9061, exten 242. *Chmn Dept* R Earl Cleveland; Instrs FT 2-3.
Col estab 1851, art maj 1963; den; D&E; ent req HS dipl; degree BA(Art) 4 yrs; schol; SC 26, LC 7; enrl maj 36.
Tuition: $1700 per yr, studio fees $5-$25; campus res $1350.
Courses: Aesthetics; Art Education; Ceramics; Drawing; Graphic Arts; History of Art & Archaeology; Lettering; Painting; School & Recreation Crafts; Sculpture; Stage Design; Teacher Training; Theatre Arts.
Summer School: Chmn R Earl Cleveland. Courses—Art Appreciation; Teacher Workshops; Travel Study in Europe.

JOHNSON CITY

EAST TENNESSEE STATE UNIVERSITY, Fine Arts Department, Box 23740A, 37601. Tel: 615-929-4247. *Prof Art & Chmn Dept Fine Arts* William Radford Thomas, PhD; *Instr* Spencer Crawford, MFA;

Assoc Prof Gerald Edmundson, MA; *Instrs* Debra Gold, MFA; *Instr* Teresa Lonier, MFA; *Assoc Prof* James Mills, PhD; *Assoc Prof* George Moldovan, MA; *Instr* Al Park, MFA; *Prof* John Pav, PhD; *Assoc Prof* John Steele, MA; *Asst Prof* Charles Thompson, MFA; *Instr* Harrison Vaughan, MA.
Estab 1909, dept estab 1949; pub; D&E; ent req HS dipl, ACT or SAT; degrees BA, BS and BFA 4 yrs; MA, MFA; schol; SC 102, LC 30, GC 46; enrl D approx 1400.
Tuition: Res—Undergrad $14 per quarter hr, $154 per quarter, grad $16 per quarter hr, $167 per quarter; Nonres—Undergrad $26 per quarter hr, $312 per quarter; campus res room and board approx $550 per quarter.
Courses: ‡Art Education; ‡Art History; ‡Ceramics; ‡Drawing; Enameling; Goldsmithing; ‡Graphic Design; ‡Jewelry; Lettering; ‡Painting; ‡Photography; Printmaking; ‡Sculpture; Silversmithing; Weaving.
Summer School: Dir Dr William Radford Thomas. Tui $154 for term of 4 wks beginning June 13 and July 17. Courses—Same as above.

KNOXVILLE

UNIVERSITY OF TENNESSEE, KNOXVILLE
—**Department of Art,** 927 Volunteer Blvd, 37916. Tel: 615-974-3408. *Head Dept Art* Donald F Kurka, PhD; *Prof* Dale G Cleaver, PhD; *Assoc Prof* Fred Martinson, PhD; *Assoc Prof* Fred Moffatt, PhD; *Assoc Prof* Lanier Surpthe, PhD; *Prof* Walter Stevens, MFA; *Prof* Richard Clarke, MFA; *Prof* Byron McKeeby, MFA; 17 Additional FT Faculty.
Estab 1794, dept estab 1951; pub; D&E; ent req HS dipl; degrees BA and BFA 4 yrs; MFA 2 yrs; schol; SC 51, LC 23, GC 50; enrl D 1500, E 250, nonmaj 300, maj 350, grad 15.
Tuition: Res—Undergrad $16 per quarter hr, grad $22 per quarter hr; Nonres—Undergrad $38 per quarter hr, $52 per quarter hr; campus res room and board $1300 per yr.
Courses: ‡Advertising Design; ‡Art History; ‡Commercial Art; Constructions; ‡Drawing; Film; Graphic Arts; Graphic Design; ‡History of Art & Archaelogy; Lettering; ‡Painting; ‡Printmaking; ‡Sculpture.
Summer School: Prof William Kennedy. Enrl 400; term of 3 sessions beginning June and Aug. Courses—Same as above.
—**Crafts and Interior Design Department,** 13th & Cumberland Ave, 37916. Tel: 615-974-2360. *Prof & Head Dept* Robbie G Blakemore, PhD; *Asst Prof* Sandra J Blain, MFA; *Asst Prof* Richard H Daehnert, MFA; *Asst Prof* James F Darrow, EdD; *Prof* Joseph Falsetti, MA; *Assoc Prof* Walter J Moran, MS; *Assoc Prof* Ray Pierotti, MM.
Estab 1794, dept estab 1936; pub; D&E; ent req HS dipl; degree BS 4 yrs; SC 44, LC 5, GC 55; enrl maj 394, grad 73.
Tuition: Res—Undergrad $150 per quarter, grad $160 per quarter; Nonres—Undergrad & grad $460 per quarter; prog & serv fee $15.
Courses: Aesthetics; Ceramics; Display; Drafting; Fabric Structures; Interior Design; Jewelry; Mixed Media; Textile Design; Wood Design.

MARYVILLE

MARYVILLE COLLEGE,* Division of Fine Arts, Art Section, 37801. Tel: 615-982-9132. *Head* Thelma Roper Bianco; Instrs FT 2, PT 1.
Estab 1937; den; degrees 4 yrs; schol; SC 10, LC 5.
Courses: Art Education; American Art History; Ancient & Medieval Art History; Ceramic Sculpture; Contemporary Art History; Drawing & Composition; Enameling; Jewelry; Printing; Printmaking & Fabric Design; Renaissance Art History; 17th - 19th Century Art History; Visual Theory & Design; Weaving.
Children's Classes: Courses—Art Education; Crafts.

MEMPHIS

MEMPHIS ACADEMY OF ARTS, Overton Park, 38112. Tel: 901-726-4085. *Pres* Jameson M Jones, PhD; *Dean* Phillip S Morris, MFA; Instrs FT 17, PT 10.
Estab 1936; pvt; D&E; ent req HS dipl; degrees BFA and cert 4 yrs; schol; enrl D 240, E 300.
Tuition: $750 per sem; no campus res.
Courses: Advertising Design; Aesthetics; Art History; Calligraphy; Ceramics; Commercial Art; Drawing; Enameling; Illustration; Jewelry; Lettering; Painting; Photography; Printmaking; Sculpture; Silversmithing; Textile Design.
Adult Hobby Classes: Enrl 200; term of 16 wks. Courses—Painting; Metal Arts; Photography; Watercolor; Sculpture; Pottery; Drawing.
Children's Classes: Enrl 250; tui $60 for 25 wks. Courses—Drawing; Painting; Jewelry; Pottery; Sculpture; Photography.
Summer School: Enrl 500; tui $50 per cr hr for term of 6 wks beginning early June. Courses—Drawing; Metal Arts; Painting; Photography; Weaving; Printing & Dyeing; Watercolor; Sculpture.

MEMPHIS STATE UNIVERSITY, Department of Art, 38152. Tel: 901-454-2216. *Chmn Dept Art* Dana D Johnson, EdD.

Estab 1912; pub; D&E; ent req HS dipl, SAT; degrees BA and BFA 4 yrs, MA and MAT 1 yr, MFA 2 yrs; SC 100, LC 40, GC 30; enrl D 2200, maj 400, grad 80.
Tuition: Campus res.
Courses: Advertising Design; Art Education; Art History; Ceramics; Commercial Art; Display; Drawing; Graphic Design; History of Art & Archaeology; Illustration; Intermedia; Interior Design; Jewelry; Lettering; Museum Staff Training; Painting; Photography; Printmaking; Sculpture; Teacher Training; Textile Design.
Summer School: Dir Dr Dana D Johnson.

SOUTHWESTERN AT MEMPHIS, Department of Art, 2000 N Parkway, 38112. Tel: 274-1800-321. *Prof Art & Chmn Dept* Lawrence K Anthony, MFA; *Asst Prof* Peter Bowman, MFA; *Asst Prof* Murray Riss, MFA; *Asst Prof* Anne Robbins, MA; *Instr* Rosemary Dougherty, BFA; *Instr* William Womack, BFA; *Asst Prof* George Apperson, PhD; *Lectr* John Whitlock, PhD.
Estab 1848, dept estab 1940; pvt; D&E; ent req SAT or ACT, 13 acad credits, 16 overall; degree BA 4 yrs; SC 17, LC 12; enrl D 250, nonmaj 240, maj 10.
Tuition: $3400 per yr; campus res room and board $1620 per yr.
Courses: Aesthetics; Architecture; Art History; Calligraphy; Drawing; Film; History of Art & Archaeology; Museum Staff Training; Painting; Photography; Printmaking; Sculpture; Textile Design; Theatre Arts.
Summer School: Dir Dr John Streety. Tui $65 per cr hr for term of 4 or 6 wks beginning June 5 and July 3. Courses—Painting; Art History.

MURFREESBORO

MIDDLE TENNESSEE STATE UNIVERSITY, Art Department, Box 25, 37132. Tel: 615-898-2455. *Chmn Art Dept* Lon Nuell, EdD; *Asst Prof* David Bigelow, MFA; *Asst Prof* Charles Jansen, EdS; *Asst Prof* Kenneth J Catbagan, MFA; *Assoc Prof* Klaus Kallenberger; *Assoc Prof* Marilyn Dafoe, MSEd; *Assoc Prof* David LeDoux, MFA; *Asst Prof* Oliver Fancher, MFA; *Asst Prof* Phillip Vander Weg, MFA; *Assoc Prof* James S Gibson, MFA; *Asst Prof* Janet Higgins, MFA.
Estab 1911, dept estab 1952; pub; D&E; ent req HS dipl; degrees BS (Art Educ), BA and BFA 4 yrs; schol; SC 62, LC 10, GC 35; enrl nonmaj 900, maj 200, grad 5.
Tuition: Res—Undergrad $221 per sem, grad $241 per sem; Nonres—Undergrad $689 per sem, grad $709 per sem; campus res room and board $198 per sem.
Courses: ‡Advertising Design; ‡Art Education; ‡Ceramics; ‡Commercial Art; Drawing; Goldsmithing; ‡Jewelry; ‡Painting; ‡Printmaking; ‡Sculpture; ‡Silversmithing; Textile Design.
Children's Classes: Creative Art Clinic for Children; enrl 45; tui $25 per term.
Summer School: Chmn Art Dept Dr Lon Nuell. Enrl 200; tui $468 for term of 10 wks beginning June 6. Courses— Art Education; General Studio.

NASHVILLE

FISK UNIVERSITY, Art Department, PO Box 2, 37203. Tel: 615-329-8685. *Chmn Art Dept* Earl Hooks, MA; *Asst Prof* Stephanie Pogue, *Cur* Robert Hall, MA.
Estab 1867, dept estab 1935; pvt; D; ent req HS dipl, SAT; degrees BS and BA 4 yrs; SC 10, LC 3; enrl 120, nonmaj 90, maj 30.
Tuition: $2350 per yr; campus res room and board.
Courses: Aesthetics; Art History; Ceramics; Drawing; Museum Staff Training; Painting; Photography; Printmaking; Sculpture.

GEORGE PEABODY COLLEGE FOR TEACHERS, Art Faculty, 21st Ave S, 37203. Tel: 615-327-8178 or 327-8001. *Assoc Prof & Chairperson* Michael L Taylor, MFA; *Assoc Prof* Michael Samford, MFA; *Assoc Prof* Robert E Pletcher, EdD; *Prof* John M Frase, MFA; *Asst Prof & Cur Cohen Mus* Alan Vaughan, MA.
Estab 1875, faculty estab 1914; pvt; D&E; ent req HS dipl, SAT; degrees BS 4 yrs, BSMS 5 yrs, MS 2 yrs; schol; SC 14, LC 5, GC 15; enrl in col D approx 2000, nonmaj 700, maj 50, grad 10.
Tuition: Undergrad $2700 per yr, $1350 per sem, $60 per sem hr; Grad $3200 per yr, $1600 per sem, $70 per sem hr; campus res room and board.
Courses: Aesthetics; Art Education; Art History; Calligraphy; Ceramics; Collage; Conceptual Art; Constructions; Drawing; Film; Goldsmithing; Graphic Arts; Graphic Design; Intermedia; Jewelry; Mixed Media; Painting; Photography; Printmaking; Sculpture; Silversmithing; Teacher Training.
Summer School: Chairperson Michael L Taylor. 10 wk regular sessions.

TENNESSEE BOTANICAL GARDENS AND FINE ARTS CENTER, Cheekwood, Cheek Rd, 37205. Tel: 615-352-5310. *Dir* John Henry Nozynski, MFA; *Cur Educ* Roberta Mathews, BFA.

Estab 1960; pvt; D&E; SC 10-15, LC 5-10.
Courses: Ceramics; Collage; Commercial Art; Drawing; Graphic Arts; Handicrafts (pottery-enamelwork, batik-stitchery); Jewelry; Painting; Printmaking; Sculpture; Textile Design.
Adult Hobby Classes: Courses—As above.
Children's Classes: Enrl approx 100; tui $25-$40 per quarter. Courses—Painting; Drawing; Sculpture; Jewelry; Art History; Watercolor.
Summer School: Dir Roberta Mathews.

VANDERBILT UNIVERSITY, Department of Fine Arts, West End Ave at 23rd St (Mailing Add: Box 1801, Station B, 37235). Tel: 615-322-2831. *Chmn Dept* F Hamilton Hazlehurst, PhD; *Prof* Thomas B Brumbaugh, PhD; *Assoc Prof* Ljubica D Popovich, PhD; *Assoc Prof* Robert L Mode, PhD; *Assoc Prof* Milan Mihal, PhD; *Assoc Prof* Donald Evans, MFA; *Assoc Prof* Christine Hasenmueller, PhD; *Asst Prof* James R. Ramsey, PhD; *Asst Prof* Lamar Lynes, MFA.
Estab 1873, dept estab 1944; pvt; D; ent req HS dipl, ent exam; degrees BA 4 yrs, MA (Art Hist) 1-2 yrs; schol; SC 8, LC 35, GC 30; enrl nonmaj 2000 maj 75, grad 5.
Tuition: $3650 per yr, $1825 per sem, $152 per sem hr; campus res room and board $1900 per yr.
Courses: ‡Art History; Drawing; Film; History of Art & Archaeology; Multimedia Design; Painting; Photography.
Summer School: Dean Robert Donaldson. Tui $92 per sem hr for two 4 wk terms beginning June 6. Courses—Vary.

WATKINS INSTITUTE,* School for Adults, 601 Church, 37219. Tel: 615-242-1851. Instrs PT 7.
Estab 1913; pvt; D&E; noncredit adult educ program, must be 17 yrs of age or older; no degree; SC 4, LC 1; enrl D 125, E 200.
Courses: Art Education; Commercial Art; Drawing; Painting; Photography.

SEWANEE

UNIVERSITY OF THE SOUTH,* Department of Fine Arts, 37375. Tel: 615-598-5780. *Chmn Dept* James Edward Carlos; Instrs FT 3, PT 1.
Pvt; D; ent req ent exam; degree BA 4 yrs; schol; SC 25, LC 20; enrl 450, maj 25.
Tuition: $1600 per sem; room and board $655 per sem.
Courses: Art History; Drawing; Painting; Photography; Printmaking; Sculpture.

TEXAS

ABILENE

ABILENE CHRISTIAN UNIVERSITY,* Art Department, 79601. Tel: 915-677-1911, exten 674. Instrs FT 5, PT 2.
Estab 1906; den; D&E; ent req upper 3/4 HS grad class or at 15 standard score ACT composite; degrees BA, BFA and BS(Educ) 4 yr; SC 24, LC 8; enrl maj 54.
Courses: Commercial Art; Design; Drawing; History of Art; Painting; Pottery; Sculpture; Teacher Training.
Summer School: 5 1/2 wk beginning June.

HARDIN-SIMMONS UNIVERSITY,* Department of Art, 79601. Tel: 915-677-7281, exten 220. *Head Dept* Ira M Taylor; Instrs FT D 2, PT E 3.
Estab 1891; den; ent req HS grad; degrees BA and BS 4 yr; schol; SC 17, LC 10, GC 4; enrl maj 50.
Tuition: $45 per sem hr; campus res with room and board $452 to $517.
Courses: Art History; Ceramics; Crafts; Design; Drawing & Painting; Printmaking; Sculpture; Teacher Training.
Summer School: Enrl 70; 12 wk (2 terms) beginning June.

McMURRY COLLEGE, Art Department, 79605 (Mailing Add: Box 8, McMurry Station, Abilene, 79605). Tel: 915-692-4130, exten 307. *Head Dept & Assoc Prof* Sherwood E Suter, MFA; *Asst Prof* Robert Howell, MFA; *Lectr* J Robert Miller, BS.
Estab 1923; pvt; D&E; ent req HS dipl; degrees BA and BS 4 yr; schol; SC 19, LC 1; enrl D 80, E 8, nonmaj 50, maj 27.
Tuition: Res—Undergrad $2770 per yr, $1385 per sem (incl room & board), $54 per sem hr; Nonres—Undergrad $1620 per yr, $810 per sem, $54 per sem hr; campus res room & board $1000 per yr plus $60 for air cond.
Courses: Art Education; Art History; Ceramics; Design (freshmen); Drawing; Jewelry; Lettering; Painting; Printmaking; Teacher Training.
Summer School: Dir Dr Paul Jungmeyer. Enrl 25; tui $54 per sem hr for term of 6 wks beginning June into first wk of July.
Courses—Ceramics; Design; Painting.

ALPINE

SUL ROSS STATE UNIVERSITY, Art Department, 79830. Tel: 915-837-3461, exten 250. *Head Dept & Assoc Prof* Miriam A Lowrance, MA; *Prof* Roy E Dodson, EdD; *Asst Prof* Charles R Hext, MFA.
Estab 1920, dept estab 1922; pub; D&E; ent req HS dipl, ACT or SAT; degrees BA and BFA 4 yr; MA(Ed in Art) 1½ yr; schol; SC 21, LC 3, GC 19; enrl D 183, E 32, nonmaj 170, maj 45-60, GS 32.
Tuition: Res \$122 per sem, nonres \$662 per sem; campus res room & board \$768.
Courses: Advertising Design; Aesthetics; ‡Art Education; Art History; Ceramics; Commercial Art; Drawing; Graphic Arts; Handicrafts (fibers, weaving); History of Art and Archaeology; Illustration; Jewelry; Mixed Media; Painting; Photography; Printmaking; Sculpture; Silversmithing; Teacher Training; Textile Design.
Adult Hobby Classes: Enrl 75; Tui \$20 per 3 - 4 wks. Courses—Ceramics; China Painting; Drawing; Jewelry; Macrame; Painting.
Summer School: Tui \$56 for term of 6 wks. Courses—Art Education; Ceramics; Crafts; Fibers; Jewelry; Painting; Sculpture.

ALVIN

ALVIN COMMUNITY COLLEGE, Art Department, 77511. Tel: 713-331-6111. *Chmn* Ziya Sever, MA.
Estab 1949; D&E; ent req HS dipl; degrees AA 2 yr.
Tuition: Res approx \$84 per sem, approx \$40 PT; nonres approx \$250 per sem, approx \$125 PT; no campus res.
Courses: Art Appreciation; Ceramics; Drawing; Graphic Design; Painting; Watercolor.
Summer School: Enrl 20 or less; term of 12 wks beginning May 31. Courses—Art Appreciation; Design; Drawing; Watercolor.

AMARILLO

AMARILLO COLLEGE, Art Department, 2200 South Washington, 79178 (Mailing Add: PO Box 447, 79178). Tel: 806-376-5111, exten 397. *Chmn* Denny Fraze, MFA; *Asst Prof* David Cale, MFA; *Instr* Tom Glover, MFA.
Estab 1926; pub; D&E; ent req HS dipl, CEEB; degrees AA 2 yr; schol; SC 18, LC 2; enrl dept D 142, E 60.
Tuition: Res—Undergrad \$125 per sem, Nonres—Undergrad \$200 per sem; no campus res.
Courses: Art History: Ceramics; Drawing; Jewelry; Painting; Printmaking; Sculpture; Silversmithing.

ARLINGTON

UNIVERSITY OF TEXAS AT ARLINGTON, Department of Art, 144 Fine Arts Building, 76019. *Chmn* Vincent J Bruno, PhD.
Estab 1895, dept estab 1933; pub; D&E; ent req HS dipl; degrees BFA 4 yr; SC 60, LC 7.
Courses: ‡Advertising Design; ‡Art Education; ‡Art History; ‡Ceramics; ‡Commercial Art; Drawing; ‡Fashion Arts; ‡Film; ‡Goldsmithing; ‡Jewelry; Metalsmithing; ‡Painting; Papermaking; ‡Photography; ‡Printmaking; ‡Sculpture; ‡Silversmithing.

AUSTIN

AUSTIN COMMUNITY COLLEGE, Department of Commercial Art and Fine Arts, 12th & Rio Grande, 78701. Tel: 512-476-6381, exten 27, 29. *Head Dept* Luis Guerra, MFA; *Primary Faculty* David Wahlgren, MFA; David Olds, MFA; Ro Thompson, BFA; Clark Bradley, BFA; Carol Ivey, BFA; David Elliott, BFA; Madelon Umlauf, MFA.
Estab 1973/74; pub; D&E; ent req HS dipl, or GED; degrees AA 2 yrs; special problems course which allows students to specialize or get college cr for free lancing with live job situations; enrl approx \$250 per sem.
Tuition: Res—Undergrad \$10 per cr hr; Nonres—Undergrad \$30 per cr hr; other adult Continuing Education non-cr courses \$1 per hr.
Courses: Advertising Design; Art History; Calligraphy; Commercial Art; Drafting; Drawing; Fashion Arts; Film; Graphic Arts; Graphic Design; Illustration; Lettering; Mixed Media; Painting; Photography; Printmaking; Stage Design; Theatre Arts; Typography; Video.
Adult Hobby Classes: Tui \$1 per hr. Courses—Drawing; Macrame; Painting; Weaving.
Summer School: Enrl 250; tui \$10 per cr hr for term of 11 wks beginning June 5th. Courses—varied.

CONCORDIA LUTHERAN COLLEGE,* Department of Art, 3400 Interregional, 78705. *Head Dept* Virginia Erickson; Instrs PT 1.

Estab 1925; den; D; ent req HS dipl; degree AA 2 yr; schol; SC 1, LC 1; enrl D 350.
Tuition: \$660 per yr; campus res \$1010.
Courses: Art Fundamentals; Drawing; Painting.

UNIVERSITY OF TEXAS, University Station, 78712.
—**School of Architecture,*** PO Box 7908, 78712. Tel: 512-471-1922. *Dean* Harold Box; Instrs FT 20, PT 10.
Estab 1910, pub; ent req 16 cr incl 3½ Math, 1 Science; degree 5-6 yr; enrl 387.
Tuition: \$50 per sem; Nonres—\$40 per sem hr.
Courses: ‡Architecture.
—**College of Fine Arts,*** Department of Art, *Dean* Peter M Garvie. Instrs FT 49, PT 4.
Estab 1938; degree 4 yr; SC 78, LC 21; enrl maj 1000, others 1162.
Tuition: \$50; Nonres \$40 per sem hr.
Courses: Ceramics; Commercial Art & Illustration; Crafts; Design; Drawing; Graphic Arts; History & Criticism of Art; Painting; Pictorial Composition; Sculpture; Teacher Education with College of Education.
Summer School: Two 6 wk terms.

BEAUMONT

LAMAR UNIVERSITY, Art Department, PO Box 10027, 77710. Tel: 713-838-7427. *Head Dept & Prof* Robert C Rogan, DEd; *Prof J Robert Madden, MFA; Prof* Jerry Newman, MFA; *Prof* Robert O'Neill, MFA; *Instr* Billie C Edwards, MA; *Instr* Philip Fitzpatrick, MFA; *Instr* Lynne Lokensgard, MA; *Instr* Meredith M Jack, MFA.
Estab 1923, dept estab 1951; pub; D&E; ent req HS dipl; degrees BA and BS 4 yr; schol; SC 50, LC 10; enrl D 589, E 45, nonmaj 160, maj 200.
Tuition: Res—Undergrad \$85.50 for 3 sem hrs; Nonres—Undergrad \$155.50 for 3 sem hrs; campus res.
Courses: Advertising Design; ‡Art Education; Art History; Ceramics; ‡Commercial Art; Drawing; Fashion Arts; Film; Graphic Arts; ‡Graphic Design; Handicrafts (weaving); History of Art and Archaeology; Illustration; Jewelry; ‡Painting; Photography; Printmaking; Sculpture.
Children's Classes: Enrl 77; tui \$12.50 per 2 wks. Courses—Children's Workshop.
Summer School: Tui \$55.50 per 3 cr hrs for term of 6 wks, beginning May 30th.

BELTON

MARY HARDIN-BAYLOR COLLEGE,* Art Department, 76513. Tel: 817-939-5811, exten 44. *Chmn* Ted L Austin; Instrs FT 2.
Estab 1845; den; D&E; ent req upper half of HS grad class; degrees BA, BFA and BS 4 yr; schol; SC 6, LC 1 and 1 independent learning course per sem. D classes studio, E classes Art History.
Courses: Art Education; Art History; Ceramics; Design; Drawing; Graphics; Jewelry; Painting.
Summer School: Dir Ted L Austin. Sem of 5 wk, from 1 to 4 hrs cr. Courses—Crafts; Independent Learning.

BIG SPRING

HOWARD COLLEGE, Art Department, Birdwell Lane, 79720. Tel: 915-267-6311, exten 72. *Chmn* Kathleen Weber, MEd; *Instr* Susan King, MA; *Instr.* David Norvella, BFA.
Estab 1948, dept estab 1972; pub; D&E; ent req HS dipl, ACT; degrees AA; schol; SC 5, LC 1; enrl D 70, E 20, nonmaj 60, maj 10.
Tuition: Res—Undergrad \$100 per sem, \$3 per hr; Nonres—Undergrad \$300 per sem; campus res room and board \$500.
Courses: Advertising Design; Art Education; Art History; Ceramics; Drawing; Handicrafts (weaving); History of Art and Archaeology; Illustration; Interior Design; Lettering; Teacher Training; Textile Design.
Adult Hobby Classes: Enrl 150; tui \$12 per 6 wks; Courses—Needlepoint; Pottery; Quilting; Stained Glass.
Children's Classes: Enrl 20, tui \$15 per 6 wks. Courses—General Art.

BROWNSVILLE

TEXAS SOUTHWEST COLLEGE,* Fine Arts Department, 83 Fort Brown, 78520. *Chmn* Jean Serafy; Instrs FT 2, PT 1.
Estab 1973; pub; D&E; ent req HS dipl; degree AA (Fine Arts) 2-3 yrs; schol; SC 10, LC 10; enrl D 300, E 100.
Courses: Art Education; Ceramics; Design I and II; Drawing; Graphic Design; History of Art & Archaeology; Painting; Sculpture.
Adult Hobby Classes: Courses—Ceramics; Drawing.
Summer School: Term of 16 wk. Courses—Art Appreciation.

BROWNWOOD

HOWARD PAYNE UNIVERSITY,* School of Fine and Applied Arts, Department of Art, Howard Payne Station, 76801. Tel: 915-646-2502, exten 245. *Dean* Charles A Stewart; Instrs FT 4.
Estab 1889; den; D&E; ent req HS dipl, ent exam; degrees BA, BFA (Studio or Art Educ) and BS 4-5 yr; SC 18, LC 12; enrl D 200, E 69, maj 3.
Tuition: $42 per sem hr; campus res $895-$930.
Courses: Advertising Design; Aesthetics; Art Education; Ceramics; Commercial Art; Drawing; History of Art & Archaeology; Metalcrafts; Painting; Photography; Sculpture; Teacher Training.
Adult Hobby Classes: Enrl 30; tui $35 per course: Courses—Metalcrafts; Painting; Weaving.
Summer School: Enrl 75; tui term of 6 wk beginning June. Courses—Art Education; Crafts; Painting.

CANYON

WEST TEXAS STATE UNIVERSITY, Art Department, 79016. Tel: 806-656-2291. *Head Dept* Steven L Mayes, MFA; *Asst Prof* Margie Adkins, MFA; *Prof* Emilio Caballero, EdD; *Instr* Margaret Campbell, MEd; *Asst Prof* David Rindlisbacher, MFA; *Assoc Prof* Darold Smith, MFA; *Instr* Jerri Warren, MEd; *vis prof*—Ellen Fox, art history, spring 1978.
Estab 1910; pub; D&E; ent req HS dipl; degrees BA, BS, BFA and MA; schol; SC 70, LC 23, GC 50; enrl maj 120, GS 23.
Tuition: Res $64 per sem, $50 PT; Nonres $640 per sem, $360 PT; foreign students $224. There are additional fees all students must pay; campus res $1000.
Courses: Advertising Design; Aesthetics; Art Education; Art History; Ceramics; Commercial Art; Drawing; Goldsmithing; Graphic Arts; Graphic Design; Handicrafts (macrame, rugs); History of Art and Archaeology; Illustration; Interior Design; Jewelry; Painting; Printmaking; Sculpture; Silversmithing; Teacher Training; Textile Design.
Summer School: Courses—as above.

COLLEGE STATION

TEXAS A&M UNIVERSITY,* College of Architecture and Environmental Design, 77843. *Dean* Raymond D Reed; Instrs FT 55.
Estab 1905; pub; D; ent req SAT; CEEB, Achievement, HS average; degrees BEnviron Design; BS(Landscape Arch); DEnviron Design; MArch; MLandscape; MPlanning 4 yr; enrl maj Arch 820, total 1500.
Tuition: Res $4 per sem cr hr; nonres $40 per sem cr hr; fees approx $652.

COMMERCE

EAST TEXAS STATE UNIVERSITY, Department of Art, 75428. Tel: 214-468-2584. *Head Dept* Charles E McGough, MA; *Chmn Painting* Karl Umlauf, MFA; *Chmn Ceramics* James Watral, MFA; *Chmn Graphics* Lee Baxter Davis, MFA; *Chmn Advertising* Jack Unrult, BPA; *Chmn Education* Dick Meyer, EdD; *vis prof*—Gregor Geisman, ceramics, 1977-78.
Pub; D&E; ent req HS dipl, ACT or SAT; degrees BA, BS and BFA 4 yr, MFA 2 yr, MA and MS 1½ yr; we have a special program called the Post Masters/MFA which is worked out on an individual basis; schol; SC 64, LC 19, GC 19; enrl maj 300, GS 34.
Tuition: Res $13 per sem hr; Nonres $48 per sem hr; campus res room & board $1000 yr.
Courses: ‡Advertising Design; Aesthetics; ‡Art Education; Art History; ‡Ceramics; Collage; ‡Commercial Art; Conceptual Art; Constructions; Costume Design and Construction; Drafting; ‡Drawing; Fashion Arts; Film; ‡Graphic Arts; ‡Graphic Design; History of Art and Archaeology; ‡Illustration; Industrial Design; Intermedia; Interior Design; ‡Jewelry; Lettering; Mixed Media; ‡Painting; Photography; ‡Printmaking; ‡Sculpture; Silversmithing; Stage Design; ‡Teacher Training; Theatre Arts; Video; ‡Watercolor.
Adult Hobby Classes: Enrl average 15; tui $77.25 per sem; Courses—Bonzai; Ceramics; Drawing; Painting; Watercolor.
Summer School: Enrl average 15; tui $52.25 for term of 2 to 6 wks beginning June 2. Courses—Art Education; Ceramics; Design; Drawing; Graphics; Hobby Styled Courses; Graphics; Painting.

CORPUS CHRISTI

DEL MAR COLLEGE, Department of Art, Ayers at Baldwin, 78404. Tel: 512-882-6231, exten 216. *Chmn & Prof* Joseph A Cain, MA; *Assoc Prof* Ronald Dee Sullivan, MA; *Asst Prof* Jan R Ward, MA; *Asst Prof* W E Lambert, MFA; *Instr* Baxter Coffee, MFA; *Instrs* Rodrigo Benavides, BFA; *Instr* John Freeman, MFA; *Instr* Gerald LaPorte, BFA; *Instr* June McKinley, BFA.

Estab 1935; pub; D&E; ent req HS dipl, SAT score or any accepted test including GED; degrees AA 2 yr (Studio Art Educ and Art History); schol; SC 10, LC 3; enrl D 500, E 100, nonmaj 400, maj 126.
Tuition: Res $4 per sem hr, $25 minimum; Nonres $17 per sem hr, $200 maximum; foreign students $14 per sem hr, $200 minimum; plus other fees; no campus res.
Courses: Advertising Design; Aesthetics; Architecture; Art Education; Art History; Collage; Commercial Art; Display; Drawing; Graphic Arts; Handicrafts; Handweaving; History of Art and Archaeology; Lettering; Painting; Photography; Printmaking; Sculpture; Textile Design.
Summer School: Tui same. Courses—As above.

CORSICANA

NAVARRO COLLEGE,* Art Department, Box 1170, 75110. Tel: 214-874-6501. *Dir* Margaret Hicks; Instrs FT 1, PT 1.
Estab 1946; pub; D&E; ent req HS dipl, ent exam, special permission; degrees AA, AS, A Gen Educ and A Appl Sci 60 sem hr; schol; SC 11, LC 1; enrl D 50, maj 15.
Courses: Advertising Design; Commercial Art; Drawing; Illustration; Lettering; Painting; Photography.
Adult Hobby Classes: Enrl 20. Courses—Painting.

DALLAS

SOUTHERN METHODIST UNIVERSITY, Division of Fine Arts, 75275. Tel: 214-692-2489. *Chmn* Eleanor Tufts, PhD; *Chmn Studio Art* Arthur Koch, MFA; *Chmn Art History* Annemarie Carr, PhD; *Chmn Art Education* Jon Hardwick, EdD.
Estab 1917; pvt; D&E; ent req selective admission; degrees BFA 4 yr, MFA 2 yr; MA 1½ yr; schol; SC 45, LC (art history) 65, (art education) 29; enrl D 291, maj 191, GS 53.
Tuition: $2760 per yr, $1380 per sem, $115 per hr; campus res room $700 & board $880.
Courses: ‡Art Education; ‡Art History; ‡Ceramics; ‡Drawing; ‡Graphic Design; Jewelry; Museum Staff Training; ‡Painting; ‡Photography; ‡Printmaking; ‡Sculpture; Teacher Training.
Children's Classes: Enrl 100; tui $55 per course. Courses—Ceramics; Drawing; Painting; Photography; Printmaking; Sculpture.
Summer School: Dir George Zeiss. Tui $115 per cr hr for term of 5 wks. Courses—Art Education; Introduction to Art History; Ceramics; Drawing; Painting; Printmaking; Sculpture.

DENTON

NORTH TEXAS STATE UNIVERSITY, Department of Art, 76203. Tel: 817-788-2071. *Chmn & Prof* D Jack Davis, PhD; *Grad Coordr* Margaret O Lucas, D Ed; *Undergrad Coordr* Claudia W Betti, MFA.
Estab 1890, dept estab 1930; pub; D&E; ent req HS dipl; degrees BA and BFA in Art 4½ yr, MA and MFA 2 yr; schol; SC 151, LC 20, GC 55; maj 1200, GS 109.
Tuition: $50 per sem hr, non-res $40 per sem hr; campus res.
Courses: ‡Advertising Art; ‡Art Education; ‡Art History; Ceramics; Costume Design and Construction; Drawing; Graphic Design; Handicrafts (weaving); Illustration; ‡Interior Design; Jewelry; Lettering; Museum Staff Training; ‡Painting; ‡Photography; ‡Printmaking; ‡Sculpture; Silversmithing; Teacher Training; Textile Design; Video.
Summer School.

TEXAS WOMAN'S UNIVERSITY, Department of Art, 76201 (Mailing add: Box 22995, TWU Station, 76204). Tel: 817-382-8923. *Chmn & Prof* Donald E Smith, PhD; *Prof* Warren V Casey, MA; *Asst Prof* A E Green, MFA; *Instr* William E Meek, BFA; *Prof* J Brough Miller, MFA; *Prof* John F Rios, MA; *Asst Prof* Shirlee Shaver, BA; *Dir & Instr* Mark S Smith, MFA; *Instr* Linda Stuckenbruck-Smith, MFA; *Assoc Prof* Winifred S Williams, MS; *Instr* Lee Candler Young, MBA.
Estab 1901; pub; D&E; ent req HS dipl, (ent exam to MA-portfolio recommended); degrees BA, BS and BFA 4 yr, MA 1 yr; schol; SC 21, LC 34, GC 17; enrl D 297, E 79, nonmaj 214, maj 161, GS 76, others 300 undergrad.
Tuition: Res $4 per sem hr, $50 minimum; Nonres $40 per sem hr, campus res $470 - $1000 for room only; meal plan available at extra charge.
Courses: Advertising Design; Art Education; Art History; Calligraphy; Ceramics; Collage; Commercial Art; Conceptual Art; Constructions; Costume Design and Construction; Drafting; Drawing; Fashion Arts; Goldsmithing; Graphic Arts; Graphic Design; Handicrafts (fibers, printed textiles); Illustration; Interior Design; Jewelry; Lettering; Mixed Media; Painting; Photography; Printmaking; Sculpture; Silversmithing; Teacher Training; Textile Design.
Adult Hobby Classes: Enrl 32; tui as above. Courses—Ceramics; Painting; Beginning Weaving.

Summer School: Enrl 112; tui same as above for term of 6 wks beginning June 7. Courses—as above.

EDINBURG

PAN AMERICAN UNIVERSITY, Art Department, 78539. Tel: 512-381-3141. *Head Dept* Dr Nancy Moyer Prince, PhD; *Chmn Art Education* Dr Norman Browne, EdD; *Chmn Painting* E E Nichols, MFA; *Chmn Printmaking* Philip Field, MFA; *Chmn Ceramics* Richard Hyslin, MA; *Chmn Metals* Jerry Bailey, MFA; *Chmn Advertising Design* Rosario Laudicina, MA; *Chmn Art History* Sandra Swenson, MA.
Estab 1927, dept estab 1972; pub; D&E; ent req open, immunization; degrees BA and BFA 4 yr; schol; SC 43, LC 14; enrl D 1200, E 150; nonmaj 500, maj 175.
Tuition: Res $56 to $167 (graduating scale depending on number of hours); nonres $46 to $887; foreign $206 to $367; campus res room and board $1000.
Courses: ‡Advertising Design; ‡Art Education; Art History; ‡Ceramics; Drafting; Drawing; Goldsmithing; Graphic Arts; Graphic Design; Illustration; ‡Jewelry; Lettering; ‡Painting; Photography; ‡Printmaking; ‡Sculpture; ‡Silversmithing.
Summer School: Enrl 20 students per class; tui $31 to $78 for term of 6 wks beginning June 2 to July 11. Courses—Art Appreciation; Beginning Painting; Ceramics; Design; Drawing; Elementary Art Ed; Metals; Photography; Sculpture.

EL PASO

UNIVERSITY OF TEXAS AT EL PASO, Department of Art, 79968. Tel: 915-747-5181. *Head Dept* Dr Clarke H Garnsey; *Instrs FT* 10.
Estab 1939; pub; D&E; degrees BA 4 yr and BFA 5 yr; schol; SC 24, LC 7, GC 7; enrl 750.
Courses: Art Education; Art History; Ceramics; Design; Drawing; Graphics; Jewelry; Painting; Sculpture & Modeling; Silversmithing.
Adult Hobby Classes through Extension Div; fees vary from class to class.
Summer School: Two terms June to July and July to August.

FORT WORTH

TEXAS CHRISTIAN UNIVERSITY,* School of Fine Arts, Art Department, 76129. *Dean* George T Tade; *Chmn & Prof* Anthony Jones; *Instrs FT* 9, *PT* 9.
Estab 1909; pvt; degrees BA, BFA, BSEd, MFA and MA (American Studies & Museum Training) undergrad 4 yr, grad 2 yr minimum; schol and grad fel; SC 35, LC 10, GC; enrl maj 150, others 450.
Tuition: $80 per sem hr; campus res.
Courses: Art Education; Art History & Criticism; Ceramics; Commercial Art; Drawing, Design & Painting; Graphics; Metals; Sculpture.
Summer School.

TEXAS WESLEYAN COLLEGE,* Department of Art, PO Box 3277, 76105. Tel: 817-534-0251, exten 289. *Chmn* Donald W Bellah; *Instrs FT* 1, *PT* 2.
Den; D&E; ent req HS dipl; degree BA 4 yr; schol; SC, LC.
Tuition: $54 per hr; campus res $621 per sem.
Courses: Art Education; Ceramics; Drawing; History of Art & Archaeology; Painting; Printmaking; Teacher Training.
Summer School: Tui $175 for term of 5 wk beginning in June. Courses—Basic Art.

HOUSTON

HOUSTON BAPTIST COLLEGE,* Department of Fine Arts, 7502 Fondren Rd, 77036. Tel: 713-774-7661, exten 253. *Chmn* Gary M Horton; *Instrs FT* 2.
Estab 1963; den; D&E; ent req HS dipl, ent exam; degrees BA & BS; schol; SC 7, LC 9; enrl D 1300, maj 35.
Tuition: $1650 per yr.
Courses: Art Education; Ceramics; Drawing; Graphic Arts; History of Art & Archaeology; Painting; Sculpture; Teacher Training.

HOUSTON SCHOOL OF COMMERCIAL ART, INC, 821 Chelsea, 77002. Tel: 713-523-2564. *Head Dept & Instr* Ellen Chadick, Cert; *Instr* Susan Johnson, BFA; *Instrs FT* 2, *PT* 1.
Estab 1974; pvt; D&E; ent req previous education or training for Accelerated Commercial Art Course; enrl D 40 - 45, E 12 - 15.
Tuition: Accelerated Commercial Art $65 per month, $1500 total; Commercial Art $135 per month, $2300 total; no campus res.
Courses: Advertising Design; Commercial Art; Graphic Arts; Graphic Design; Illustration.

MUSEUM OF FINE ARTS, School of Art, 3815 Garrott, 77006 (Mailing Add: PO Box 5826, 77005). Tel: 713-529-7659. *Dir* Kenneth R Jewesson, MFA; *Instr* Arthur Turner, MFA; *Instr* Robert Weimerskirch, MFA equiv; *Instr* Sandra Parmer Zilker, MFA; *Instr* Ben Woitena, MFA; *Instr* WIlliam Dennard, MFA; *Instr* Suzanne Manns, BFA; *Dean (Jr School)* Norma R Ory, BFA.
Estab 1926; pvt; D&E; ent req none, (preferably HS grad in Adult School); degrees cert of completion 3 yr (90 hrs); schol; SC 41, LC 12; enrl D 328, E 244, nonmaj 365, maj 207, others 189 enrolled in 4 wk lecture series.
Tuition: Full Time $385.50 per sem, PT $115 each for Studio Courses, $65 ea for Art History; no campus res.
Courses: Art History; ‡Ceramics; Drawing; ‡Jewelry; ‡Painting; ‡Printmaking; ‡Sculpture; Visual Fundamentals.
Children's Classes: Enrl 259; tui $55 (age 4 to 12), $80 (age 12 to 18 yrs). Courses—(Ages 4-12) General curriculum-all media; (13-18 yrs) Ceramics; Drawing; Jewelry; Painting; Photography.
Summer School: Enrl 217 (adult), 283 (Jr school); tui $85 per course PT, $230 FT for term of 6 wks beginning June 6. Courses—same as above but no Art History in summer.

RICE UNIVERSITY, Department of Art and Art History, 77001. (Mailing Add: PO Box 1892, Houston). Tel: 713-528-4141, exten 357. *Chmn & Assoc Prof* Philip Oliver-Smith, PhD; *Prof* Katherine T Brown, MFA; *Prof* William A Camfield, PhD; *Prof* Neil Havens, MA; *Prof* John O'Neil, MFA; *Prof* David G Parsons, MS; *Assoc Prof* Chester A Boterf, MFA; *Assoc Prof* Geoffrey Winningham, MFA; *Asst Prof* Basilios Poulos, MFA; *Asst Prof* John F Scott, PhD; *Asst Prof* Walter M Widrig, PhD; *Asst Prof* Dadi Wirz, Cert; *Lectr* Carol Luce Badner, MFA; *Lectr* Brian Huberman; *Vis Lectr* Thomas McEvilley, PhD.
Estab 1912, dept estab 1966-67; pvt; D; ent req HS dipl, CEEB, also evaluations of HS counselors and teachers and an interview are required; degrees BA 4 yr, BFA 5 yr for additional studio work; schol; SC 23, LC 30, GC (BFA) 5; enrl D 125, nonmaj 75, maj 50, GS 4 (BFA).
Tuition: $2500 per yr, $1250 & $115 fees per sem; grad $2500 for first six sem; PT (by special permission) $100 per hr + $50 registr fees; campus res room and board $1950.
Courses: Art History; Constructions; Drawing; Film; History of Art and Archaeology; Painting; Photography; Printmaking; Sculpture; Theatre Arts; Video.
Adult Hobby Classes: Tui $200 per class. Courses—Photography.

SAN JACINTO COLLEGE NORTH, Art Department, 77015. Tel: 713-458-4050. *Chmn* Al Clinkinbeard, MFA; *Instr* Lydia Bodnar-Balahutrak, MFA.
Estab 1972; pub; D&E; ent req HS dipl; degrees AA 2 yr; schol; SC 16, LC 1; enrl D 93, E 35, nonmaj 20, maj 40.
Tuition: Res—Undergrad $96 per yr, $48 per 12 hrs, $25 for 6 hrs; Nonres—Undergrad $400 per yr, $200 per sem, $120 per 6 hrs; no campus res.
Courses: ‡Advertising Design; Calligraphy; Commercial Art; Drawing; Fashion Arts; Graphic Arts; Graphic Design; Illustration; Interior Design; Lettering; Painting; Photography; Sculpture; Textile Design.
Adult Hobby Classes: Enrl 15; tui $49 per 60 hrs. Courses—Oil Painting.
Children's Classes: Enrl 15, tui $35 per 2 wks. Courses—Awareness workshop.

TEXAS SOUTHERN UNIVERSITY,* Department of Art, 3201 Wheeler Ave, 77004. Tel: 713-527-7011, exten 7326. *Head Dept* Dr John T Biggers; *Instrs FT* 6, *PT* 1.
Estab 1949; pub; D&E; ent req HS dipl; degrees BFA and BArt Educ 5 yr; schol; SC 31, LC 12, GC 4; enrl maj 85, other 100.
Courses: Advertising Design; Aesthetics; Art Education; Ceramics; Commercial Art; Drawing; Graphic Arts; Graphic Design; History of Art & Archaeology; Lettering; Painting; Sculpture; Teacher Training; Textile Design; Weaving.
Summer School: Enrl average 100 for term of 6 wk beginning June.
Courses—Art Appreciation in Educational Program; Advanced Crafts for Teachers; Basic Art for Elementary Teachers; Exhibition; Mural Painting in School; Problems in Art Education; Problems in Secondary Art Education; Research Projects.

UNIVERSITY OF HOUSTON, Department of Art, 77004. Tel: 713-749-2601. *Chmn & Prof* George R Bunker, BA; *Instrs FT* 27, *PT* 18.
Estab 1927; pub; D&E; ent req HS dipl, SAT; degrees BA(Art History) and BFA 4 yr, MFA 2 yr; schol; SC open-varies; enrl D 1500, E 200.
Tuition: $4 per cr hr for res, minimum of $50 plus fees; campus res.
Courses: Advertising Design; Art Education; ‡Art History; Calligraphy; Ceramics; Commercial Art; Drafting; ‡Drawing; Goldsmithing; ‡Graphic Design; History of Art and Archaeology; Illustration; ‡Interior Design; ‡Jewelry; Lettering; Museum Staff Training; ‡Painting; Photography; ‡Printmaking; ‡Sculpture; Silversmithing; Video.

HUNTSVILLE

SAM HOUSTON STATE UNIVERSITY, Art Department, 77341. Tel: 713-295-6211, exten 2181. *Head Dept & Prof* Gene M Eastman, MFA; *Prof* L Gaddis Geeslin, MFA; *Prof* Charles A Pebworth, MA; *Prof* Stanley E Lea, MFA; *Prof* Gene E Jackson, MFA; *Assoc Prof* Harry J Ahysen, MFA; *Assoc Prof* Evelyn E Anderson, MFA; *Asst Prof* William J Breitenbach, MFA; *Asst Prof* Kenneth L Zonker, MA; *Asst Prof* Jimmy H Barker, MFA; *Instrs* Darryl L Patrick, MA; *vis prof*—Dan Glidden, illustration, spring.
Estab 1879, dept estab 1937; pub; D; ent req HS dipl, ACT or SAT; degrees BAT and BFA 4 yrs, MFA 2 yrs minimum; schol; SC 29, LC 7, GC 14; enrl dept D 980, nonmaj 755, maj 225, GS 14.
Tuition: Res $300 per yr, $150 per sem, $50 per hr; Nonres $1200 per yr, $600 per sem; campus res room & board $550.
Courses: ‡Advertising Design; ‡Art Education; Art History; Ceramics; Drawing; ‡Handicrafts (fibers); Illustration; ‡Painting; ‡Printmaking; ‡Sculpture.
Summer School: Enrl varies; tui $73 per term of 6 wks beginning May 30th. Courses—advanced and graduate.

HURST

TARRANT COUNTY JUNIOR COLLEGE, NORTHEAST CAMPUS, 76053. Tel: 817-281-7860. *Chmn* Arnold Leondar, MA; *Asst Prof* Richard Hlad, MA; *Asst Prof* Martha Gordon, MFA; *Instr* Roger Tufts, MEd.
Estab 1967, dept estab 1968; pub; D&E; ent req HS dipl, GED, admission by individual approval; degrees AA and AAS 2 yr; SC 19, LC 3; enrl D 250, E 200, nonmaj 200, maj 250.
Tuition: Res $4 per hr, minimum $25 per sem; nonres $3 per sem hr; other $40 per sem hr; no campus res.
Courses: Advertising Design; Art Education; Art History; Ceramics; Collage; Commercial Art; Constructions; Drawing; History of Art and Archaeology; Jewelry; Mixed Media; Painting; Photography; Printmaking; Sculpture; Silversmithing.
Adult Hobby Classes: Enrl 20; for 8 wks. Courses—Stained Glass; Tole Painting.
Summer School: Enrl 20; tui $25 for term of 6 wks beginning May 24, 25. Courses—Art Education; Ceramics; Design; Drawing; Painting; Photography.

INGRAM

HILL COUNTRY ARTS FOUNDATION,* Box 176, 78025. Tel: 512-367-5121. *Co-Chmn* Ro Dillard and Eleanore Collier; *Instrs* PT 20.
Estab 1959, pub; D; no ent req; no degrees; schol; SC 20, enrl 440.
Courses: Ceramics; Costume Design & Construction; Drawing; Macrame; Needle Weaving; Painting; Photography; Sculpture; Stage Design; Stitchery; Theatre Arts; Writer's Workshop.
Children's Classes: Enrl 39; 4 wk sessions. Courses—Creative Arts and Crafts.

KINGSVILLE

TEXAS A&I UNIVERSITY, Art Department, 78363 (Mailing Add: Box 157, Kingsville, 78363). Tel: 512-595-2619. *Chmn* Dr Richard Scherpereel; *Assoc Prof* William Renfrow; *Assoc* Maurice Schmidt; *Asst* Ralph Magruder; *Instr* Jose Martinez; *Instr* Janet Gracia; *Instr* Mark Anderson; *vis instr* Jerry Teagarden.
Estab 1925, dept estab 1930; pub; D&E; ent req HS dipl; degrees BFA and BA 4 yr; SC 21, LC 5, GC 2; enrl D 700, nonmaj 300, maj 400, art maj 150, GS 20.
Tuition: Res—Undergrad $250 per sem, grad $300 per sem; Nonres—Undergrad $900 per sem, grad $1000; campus res.
Courses: Advertising Design; Art Education; Art History; Ceramics; Collage; Drawing; Graphic Arts; Intermedia; Lettering; Painting; Printmaking; Sculpture; Teacher Training.
Summer School: Courses—full schedule.

LEVELLAND

SOUTH PLAINS COLLEGE,* Art Department, College Ave, 79336. Tel: 806-894-4921, exten 242. *Chmn* Harley B Bulls; *Instrs* FT 3.
Estab 1958; pub; D&E; ent req HS dipl; degree AA 2 yr; SC 1, LC 5; enrl D 186, E 51, maj 154.
Tuition: In-dist $4 per sem hr; Out-of-dist $4 per sem hr; out-of-state $20 per sem hr; foreign $14 per sem hr.
Courses: Advertising Design; Ceramics; Commercial Art; Drafting; Drawing; Graphic Arts; Graphic Design; History of Art; Lettering; Painting; Photography; Sculpture; Teacher Training.

Adult Hobby Classes: Enrl varies; tui same as above. Courses—China Painting; Flower arranging; Gift Wrapping; Oil painting; Photography; Tole Painting.

LUBBOCK

TEXAS TECH UNIVERSITY, Department of Art, 79409. Tel: 742-3825. *Chmn* James Broderick MA; *Prof* Don Durland, MA; *Prof* Paul Hanna, MFA; *Prof* Reid Hastie, PhD; *Prof* Jim Howze, MS; *Prof* Clarence Kincaid, DED; *Prof* Lynwood Kreneck, MFA; *Prof* Bill Lockhart, DEd; vis prof—James Bolton, painting, 1977-1978.
Estab 1925, dept estab 1967; pub; D&E; ent req HS dipl, SAT or ACT test; degrees BA, BFA and BSE 4 yr, MAE 36 hrs, MFA 60 hrs, min, PhD 54 hrs beyond MA min; schol; SC 80 undergrad, 23 grad, LC 27 undergrad, 17 grad, GC 46; enrl D 1450, nonmaj 700, maj 700, GS 42.
Tuition: Variable for res and non-res; campus res room and board.
Courses: ‡Advertising Design; Aesthetics; ‡Art Education; Art History; Ceramics; Drawing; Film; Goldsmithing; Graphic Arts; Graphic Design; Handicrafts (enameling, weaving); History of Art and Archaeology; Illustration; ‡Interior Design; Jewelry; Lettering; Mixed Media; Painting; Photography; Printmaking; Sculpture; Silversmithing; Teacher Training; Textile Design; Video.
Summer School: *Dir* Bill Lockhart and *Dir* James Hanns. Courses—same as academic year.

MARSHALL

WILEY COLLEGE,* Department of Fine Arts, Roseborough Springs Rd, 75680. Tel: 214-938-8341. *Head Dept* Cherry Lou Violette, Instrs FT 4, PT 2.
Estab 1873; den; D&E; ent req HS dipl; degrees no art major; schol; SC 16, LC 2; enrl D 56.
Tuition: $50 per hr, plus special fees; campus res $500-$794 per yr.
Courses: Advertising Design; Art Education; Ceramics; Commercial Art; Decoupage; Drawing; Enameling; Fashion Arts; Graphic Arts; Graphic Design; History of Art & Archaeology; Painting; Teacher Training; Theatre Arts; Weaving.
Summer School: *Dir* Dr David R Houston. Tui $50 per hr for term of 8 wk beginning June. Courses—as required.

MIDLAND

MIDLAND COLLEGE, Art Department, 79701. Tel: 915-684-7851. *Chmn* Stan Jacobs, MFA; *Primary Faculty* Denny Pickett, MFA; Marilyn Todd, MA; Sara Gilstrap, MA.
Estab 1972; pub; D&E; ent req HS dipl; degrees AA and AAA 2 y; schol; SC 28, LC 4; enrl D 70, E 80, nonmaj 125, maj 25.
Tuition: Res—Undergrad $48 per 12 hr + $36 fees; Nonres—Undergrad $200 per 12 hr plus $36 fee; no campus res.
Courses: ‡Advertising Design; Aesthetics; Art Education; Art History; ‡Ceramics; Collage; ‡Commercial Art; Constructions; Drafting; ‡Drawing; Fashion Arts; Film; Graphic Arts; Graphic Design; Handicrafts; Illustration; Interior Design; ‡Jewelry; Lettering; Mixed Media; ‡Painting; ‡Photography; ‡Printmaking; ‡Sculpture; Silversmithing; Stage Design; Teacher Training; Textile Design; Theatre Arts; Video.
Adult Hobby Classes: Tui $20 per 6 wk. Courses—Drawing; Painting.
Summer School: Same as regular term.

NACOGDOCHES

STEPHEN F AUSTIN STATE UNIVERSITY, Art Department, Box 3001, 75962. Tel: 713-569-4804. *Chmn* Jon D Wink, MFA.
Estab 1923; pub; D&E; ent req HS dipl, ACT score 18; degrees BFA 4 yrs, MFA 2 yr, MA 1 yr; SC 28, LC 11, GC 11; enrl D 461, nonmaj 270, maj 216, GS 30.
Tuition: Res—Undergrad $60 per 15 hr, grad $50 per 12 hr; Nonres—Undergrad $600 per 15 hr, grad $480 per 12 hr; campus res room and board.
Courses: Advertising Design; Art Education; Art History; Ceramics; Commercial Art; Drawing; Goldsmithing; Graphic Arts; Graphic Design; Illustration; Jewelry; Lettering; Mixed Media; Painting; Printmaking; Sculpture; Silversmithing.

ODESSA

UNIVERSITY OF TEXAS OF PERMIAN BASIN, Art Discipline, 79762. Tel: 915-367-2133. *Chmn & Assoc Prof* Stanley Marcus, EdD; *Asst Prof* Pam Price, MFA.
Estab 1972; pub; D; ent req Associate degree or 60 college credits; degrees BA 2 yr (we are an upper level institution); schol; SC 45, LC 10; enrl nonmaj 10, maj 30.
Tuition: campus res.

Courses: Ceramics; Commercial Art; Painting; Printmaking; Sculpture. Summer School Courses—varied.

PASADENA

SAN JACINTO COLLEGE, Art Department, 77505. Tel: 713-479-1501, exten 230. *Chmn* Charles R Brown, MAE; *Instr* William C Balusek, MFA; *Instr* Douglass Sweet, MFA; *Instr* Joe Slovacek, Dipl.
Estab 1961; pub; D&E; ent req HS dipl, GED or individual approval; degrees AA and AS 2 yrs; SC 5, LC 1; Enrl D 230, E 45, nonmaj 120, maj 155.
Tuition: Res $60 per sem; Nonres $135 per sem; no campus res.
Courses: Advertising Design; Calligraphy; Commercial Art; Drafting; Drawing; Graphic Arts; Graphic Design; Interior Design; Lettering; Painting; Photography; Sculpture; Theatre Arts.
Summer School: Enrl 25; tui $25 for term of 6 wks beginning June 5th. Courses—Design; Painting Workshop.

PLAINVIEW

WAYLAND BAPTIST COLLEGE,* Department of Art, Box 54, 1900 W Seventh, 79072. Tel: 806-296-5521, exten 46. *Chmn* Dr Robert E Bicknell; Instrs FT 1.
Den; D&E; ent req HS dipl, ent exam; degrees BA and BS 4 yr; schol; SC 15, LC 2; enrl D 81, E 24, maj 10.
Tuition: $37 per cr hr.
Courses: Aesthetics; Art Education; Ceramics; Drawing; Graphic Arts; Graphic Design; History of Art & Archaeology; Illustration; Jewelry; Lettering; Museum Staff Training; Painting; Photography; Sculpture; Teacher Training.
Summer School: Courses—vary each micro term.

ROCKPORT

SIMON MICHAEL SCHOOL OF FINE ARTS, 510 E King, 78382 (Mailing Add; PO Box 1283, Rockport, 78382). Tel: 512-729-6233. *Head Dept* Simon Michael; Instrs FT 1.
Estab 1947; pvt; D; no ent req; no degrees; enrl D 200, others professionals and beginners.
Courses: Architecture; Drawing; Landscape Architecture; Mixed Media; Painting; Sculpture; Summer School Workshops; Summer Travel Workshops.
Summer School: Enrl varies; tui varies for workshop for term of 1 wk. Courses—Painting.

SAN ANGELO

ANGELO STATE UNIVERSITY, Art and Music Department, ASU Station, 76901. *Coordr & Assoc Prof* Dr Robert Prestiano; *Chmn Art and Music* Dr Charles Robison, PhD.
Estab 1963, dept estab 1976; pub; D&E; ent req HS dipl; degrees BA with Art Major and BA with Art Major and Teaching Certification, special topics courses which change subject with each offering; SC 13, LC 8; enrl D 400 (art), E 50, nonmaj 320, maj 80.
Tuition: Res $59.50 per sem hr; nonres $49.50 per sem hr; campus res room and board $1130.
Courses: Architecture; Art Education; Art History; Ceramics; Commercial Art; Creative Design; Drawing; Graphic Arts; History of Contemporary Art; History of Italian Renaissance; Painting; Printmaking; Sculpture; Stage Design.
Summer School: Tui as above for term of 17 wks beginning June 10. Courses—Art History; Introduction to Art; Studio Courses, ie Design and Drawing.

SAN ANTONIO

INCARNATE WORD COLLEGE, Humanities and Fine Arts, 4301 Broadway, 78201. Tel: 512-828-1261, exten 234. *Chmn* B C O'Halloran, PhD; *Assoc Prof* Bill Reily, MFA; *Asst Prof* Eloise Stoker, MA; *Instrs* Sister Martha Ann Kirk, MA; *Lectr* Nancy Pawel, BS.
Estab 1881, dept estab 1964; den; D; ent req HS dipl, ent exam, degrees BA 4 yrs; schol; SC 14, LC 9; enrl D 119, nonmaj 44, maj 75.
Tuition: Undergrad $60 per hr; grad $65 per hr; campus res room and board $1260.
Courses: Art Education; Art History; Ceramics; Drawing; History of Art and Archaeology; Mixed Media; Museum Staff Training; Painting; Printmaking; Sculpture; Teacher Training.

OUR LADY OF THE LAKE UNIVERSITY, Fine Arts Division, Department of Art, 78285. Tel: 512-434-5711. *Dir* Richard Slocum, MA; *Prof* Sister M Tharsilla Fuchs, MA; *Asst Prof* Sister Jule Adele Espey, PhD; *Asst Prof* Sister Dorcas Mladenka, MA; Instrs FT 1, PT 2.
Estab 1911, dept estab 1920; den; D&E; ent req HS dipl, completion of GED tests, 35 on each test or average of 45 on tests; degrees BA(Art); schol; SC 12, LC 3; enrl nonmaj 145, maj 21.
Tuition: Res & nonres undergrad $60 per sem hr cr; res & nonres grad $65 to $74 per hr cr; English as a foreign language program $560 per sem, campus res room and board $275 to $425.
Courses: Art Education; Art History; Cinema; Design; Drawing; Painting; Photography; Practicum in Art; Printmaking; Problems.
Adult Hobby Classes: Enrl varies; tui varies. Courses—varies.
Summer School.

ST MARY'S UNIVERSITY OF SAN ANTONIO, Department of Fine Arts, 2700 Cincinnati Ave, 78284. Tel: 512-433-2311. *Dir* Margaret Ivy; Instrs FT 6, PT 3.
Estab 1852; den; D&E; ent req HS dipl, ent exam; degree BA 4 - 5 yrs; schol; SC 10, LC 20; enrl D 60, maj 58.
Tuition: $60 per sem hr, $15 lab fee per course; campus res $340 - $640 per sem (room and board).
Courses: Aesthetics; Art Education; Ceramics; Cinema-Arts; Drafting; Drawing; Graphic Design; History of Art & Archaeology; Lettering; Painting; Photography; Sculpture; Teacher Training; Theatre Arts.
Adult Hobby Classes: Enrl 75 - 100; tui $25. Courses—vary.
Summer School: Courses—vary.

SAN ANTONIO ART INSTITUTE, 6000 North New Braunfels, 78209. (Mailing Add: PO Box 6092, San Antonio 78209). Tel: 512-824-0531. *Exec Dir* Jack A Rodgers, MA; *Coordr* Kent Rush, MA; *Primary Faculty* Jerry G Alexander, MFA; Carl Embrey, MFA; Reginald M Rowe, MFA.
D&E; no ent req.
Tuition: $110 per sem; no campus res.
Courses: Art History; Ceramics; Design 3-D; Drawing; Figure Modeling; Graphic Arts; Life Drawing; Painting; Photography; Printmaking; Sculpture; Tutorial Critique; Watercolor.
Children's Classes: Tui $54 per 12 wks for 3 - 5 and 6 - 10 age.

SAN ANTONIO COLLEGE,* Art Department, 1300 San Pedro Ave, 78284. Tel: 734-7311, exten 226. *Chmn* Mel Casas; Instrs FT 11, PT 3.
Estab 1955; pub; D&E; ent req HS dipl, ent exam; degrees AA and AS 2 yr; SC 32, LC 3; enrl D 1000 - 1300, E 250 - 450.
Tuition: $14 per sem hr res; no campus res.
Courses: Advertising Design; Architecture; Art Education; Display; Drawing; History of Art & Archaeology; Illustration; Industrial Design; Jewelry; Lettering; Painting; Photography; Sculpture.

TRINITY UNIVERSITY,* Art Department, 715 Stadium Dr, 78284. Tel: 512-736-7216. *Chmn* William A Bristow; Instrs FT 7, PT 5.
Estab 1869; pvt; D&E; ent req HS dipl, ent exam, CEEB, SAT; degree BA(Art) 4 yr; schol; SC 38, LC 13; enrl D&E 1358, maj approx 75.
Tuition: $2352 per yr; campus res $1440 room & board.
Courses: Advertising Design; Art Education; Ceramics; Commercial Art; Drawing; Fashion Arts; Graphic Arts; Graphic Design; History of Art & Archaeology; Illustration; Painting; Sculpture; Teacher Training.
Summer School: Tui $90 per sem hr for term of 5 wk beginning June & July. Courses—regular, reduced schedule.

UNIVERSITY OF TEXAS AT SAN ANTONIO, Division of Art and Design, FM 1604, 78285. Tel: 512-691-4352. *Prof Art & Dir Div Art & Design* Ronald Binks, MFA; *Asst Prof* Ronald M Cohen, MFA; *Assoc Prof* Charles T Field, MFA; *Instr* Alvin Martin, AM; *Assoc Prof* Robert J Mullen, Dr; *Asst Prof* Randa A Newland, MFA; *Asst Prof* Felipe Reyes, MFA; *Assoc Prof* Judith B Sobre, Dr; vis profs—Kazuya Sakai, painting, James Newberry, photography and Stephen Reynolds, ceramics, 1977-78.
Pub; D&E; ent req HS dipl, ACT, grad, GRE; degrees BFA 4 yrs, MFA 2 yrs; schol; SC 31, LC 25, GC 17; enrl maj 200, grad 35.
Tuition: $50 per sem (12 hrs or under); no campus res.
Courses: Art History; Ceramics; Drawing; History of Art & Archaeology; Painting; Photography; Printmaking; Sculpture.
Summer School: Tui $25 per sem. Courses—Art History; Ceramics; Drawing; Painting; Photography; Printmaking; Sculpture.

SAN MARCOS

SOUTHWEST TEXAS STATE UNIVERSITY, Department of Art, 78666. Tel: 512-245-2184. *Dean* Ralph Harrel; *Chmn* Brian G Row, MFA.
Estab 1903, dept estab 1916; pub; D&E; ent req HS dipl, ACT score minimum of 15; degrees BS(Commercial Art), BS(Education), BS(Education all-level) and BFA(Commercial & Studio) 4 yr; SC 26, LC 8, GC 6; enrl D 1800, nonmaj 1338, maj 462, GS 27.
Tuition: Res $396 for total of 30 hrs, $65.50 for one hr; nonres $1476 for total of 30 hrs, $55.50 for one hr; campus res room and board $590.

Courses: Art Education; Art History; Calligraphy; Ceramics; Commercial Art; Drawing; Graphic Arts; Graphic Design; Jewelry; Lettering; Mixed Media; Painting; Printmaking; Sculpture; Textile Design.
Summer School: Tui $85 for 6 hrs for term of 5 wks beginning June 5th. Courses—as above.

SEQUIN

TEXAS LUTHERAN COLLEGE,* Department of Art, 78155. Tel: 512-379-4161, exten 58. *Chmn* Elmer P Petersen; *Instrs* FT 2.
Estab 1961; den; D; ent req HS dipl; degree BA(Art) 4 yr; SC 18, LC 3; enrl 1000, maj 23.
Tuition: Campus res.
Courses: Art Education; Ceramics; Drawing; History of Art; Painting; Sculpture; Teacher Training. Workshops on Metal Jewelry; Photography; Stained Glass; Welding offered for ½ cr.
Summer School: Courses—varied.

SHERMAN

AUSTIN COLLEGE, Art Department, 75090. Tel: 214-892-9101, exten 251. *Chmn & Prof* Carl R Neidhardt, PhD; *Assoc Prof* Vernon Fisher, MFA; *Asst Prof* Julie Bozzi, MFA.
Estab 1848; pvt; D; ent req ent exam plus acceptance by admission committee; degrees BA 4 yr, MA 5 yr; schol; SC 9, LC 5, GC 8; enrl D 340, maj 60, GS 5.
Tuition: $2800 per yr, $1400 per sem, $400 per course; we anticipate approx 6% increase next year; campus res room and board $1300.
Courses: Art Education; Art History; Drawing; Graphic Design; Painting; Photography; Printmaking.
Summer School: Tui Undergrad $280 per course, grad $300 per course for term of 7 wks beginning June 2, 1978. Courses—Introduction to Art; One Art History course.

TEXARKANA

TEXARKANA COLLEGE, Art Department, Texarkana, 75501. Tel: 214-838-4541. *Chmn* William Caver; *Prof* Ralph Caver, MFA; *Assoc Prof* Mary Lone, MA; *Instrs* FT 2, PT 2.
Estab 1927; D&E; ent req HS dipl; schol.
Tuition: $230 per yr, $115 per sem; no campus res.
Courses: Art Education; Ceramics; Drafting; Drawing; History of Art and Archaeology; Painting; Sculpture; Teacher Training; Weaving.
Adult Hobby Class: Enrl 30, tui $38 per term. Courses—Ceramics.
Summer School: Tui $50 for term of 6 wks beginning May 31. Courses—Art Education; Ceramics; Design; Drawing; Painting.

TYLER

TEXAS EASTERN UNIVERSITY, Department of Art, 3900 University Blvd, 75701. Tel: 214-566-1471, exten 289. *Chmn & Assoc Prof* William B Stephens, EdD; *Asst Prof* Donald Van Horn, MFA; *Assoc Prof* Kenneth Casstevens, EdD.
Estab 1973; pub; D&E; ent req AA degree or 60 hrs of college study; degrees BA and BFA in Art; schol; SC 28, LC 6, GC 11.
Tuition: Res $172.50 per sem; Nonres $322.50 per sem.
Courses: Aesthetics; Art Education; Art History; Ceramics; Drawing; Graphic Arts; Graphic Design; History of Art and Archaeology; Interior Design; Mixed Media; Painting; Photography; Printmaking; Sculpture; Stage Design; Teacher Training.
Summer School: Tui res $76, nonres $151. Courses—varies.

VICTORIA

VICTORIA COLLEGE, 2200 Red River, 77901. *Head Dept* Larry Shook, MA; *vis prof*—Nancy Bandy.
Estab 1925; pub; D&E; ent req HS dipl; SC 9, LC 3; enrl D 100, E 40, nonmaj 40, maj 100.
Tuition: Res—$100 per sem; Nonres—$200 per sem; no campus res.
Courses: Art Education; Art History; Commercial Art; Display; Drafting; Drawing; Graphic Design; Printmaking; Sculpture; Teacher Training.
Summer School: Courses—as above.

WACO

BAYLOR UNIVERSITY, Department of Art, 76703. Tel: 817-772-3724. *Chmn* J B Smith, EdD; *Chmn Crafts Curriculum* Paul Kemp, MFA; *Chmn Painting* John McClanahan, MFA; *Chmn Printmaking* Berry Klingman, MFA; *Chmn Commercial Design* Charles Isoline, MA; *Chmn Art History* William M Jensen, PhD; *Lectr* Vernie Logan, MA.

Estab 1845, dept estab 1870; den; D&E; ent req HS dipl, ent exam ACT tests; degrees AB 4 yr, BS(Art Educ) 4 yr; BFA 5 yr; schol; SC 58, LC 12, GC 4; enrl D 300, E 30, nonmaj 200, maj 100, GS 2.
Tuition: $1650 per yr, $55 per sem hr; campus res room and board $2900.
Courses: ‡Advertising Design; Aesthetics; ‡Art Education; Art History; Ceramics; Constructions; Drawing; Graphic Arts; Handicrafts (metal); History of Art & Archaeology; Jewelry; Lettering; ‡Painting; Photography; ‡Printmaking; Sculpture; Silversmithing; Teacher Training.
Summer School: Dean Lee Dunham. Enrl 75; tui $165 per term for term of 6 wks beginning May 29 & July 5. Courses—Art Education; Art History; Ceramics; Commercial Design; Crafts; Design; Painting.

MCLENNAN COMMUNITY COLLEGE, Art Department, 1400 College, 76708. Tel: 817-756-6551, exten 282. *Instrs* Barney Fitzpatrick, MFA; *Instrs* John Chatmas, MFA; *Instrs* FT 2.
Estab 1965; pub; D&E; ent req HS dipl; degrees AA 2 yr; SC 8, LC 3; enrl D 35, nonmaj 10, maj 25.
Tuition: Res $80 per sem; Nonres $360 per sem; no campus res.
Courses: Art Appreciation; Art History; Color; Design; Drawing; Painting; Sculpture.
Adult Hobby Classes: Tui depends on the class. Courses—Ceramics; Drawing; Jewelry; Painting; Sculpture; Stained glass.
Summer School: Tui $60. Courses—Design; Drawing.

WEATHERFORD

WEATHERFORD COLLEGE, Department of Humanities and Art, Park Ave, 76086. Tel: 817-594-5471, exten 32. *Head Dept of Art* Myrlan Coleman, MA; *Chmn Humanities* Jack Harvey, MA; *Instr* Donna Miller, BA.
Estab 1856, dept estab 1959; pub; D&E; ent req HS dipl; degrees AA; SC 10, LC 4; enrl D 58, nonmaj 30, maj 16, others 12.
Tuition: Res—Undergrad $4 per sem hr, grad $14 per sem hr. minimum $200; Nonres—Undergrad $17 per sem hr, maximum $200; campus res.
Courses: Advertising; Aesthetics; Art Education; Art History; Ceramics; Commercial Art; Constructions; Drawing; Graphic Design; History of Art and Archaeology; Illustration; Intermedia; Mixed Media; Painting.
Summer School: Term of May 24 and July 10.

WHARTON

WHARTON COUNTY JUNIOR COLLEGE, Art Department, 77488. Tel: 713-532-4560, exten 52. *Chmn* Bruce F Turner, PhD; *Instr* Morna Nation, BFA.
Pub; D&E; ent req HS dipl, GED; degrees 2 yrs; SC 8, LC 2; enrl D 90, E 15.
Tuition: Campus res.
Courses: Art Education; Art History; Ceramics; Drawing; History of Art and Archaeology; Painting; Sculpture; Teacher Training.

WICHITA FALLS

MIDWESTERN STATE UNIVERSITY, Department of Art, 76308. Tel: 817-692-6611. *Chmn* Thomas G Crossnoe, MA; *Assoc Prof* Richard M Ash III, MFA; *Asst Prof* Larry H Davis, MFA; *Asst Prof* Raymond Stefanelli, MFA; *Asst Prof* Donald Harter, MFA; *Instrs* Robert Greer, MA.
Estab 1926; pub; D&E; ent req HS dipl, ACT, SAT; degrees BA, BFA and BSE 4 yr; SC 20-30, LC 406, enrl D 300 per sem, E 30-50 per sem; nonmaj 60, maj 125, others 10.
Tuition: Res $176 per sem based on 15 hr load; nonres $716 based on 15 hr load; campus res room and board $480.
Courses: ‡Advertising Design; ‡Art Education; Art History; ‡Ceramics; ‡Commercial Art; Drawing; ‡Goldsmithing; ‡Graphic Arts; ‡Graphic Design; Handicrafts (fibers); ‡Jewelry; ‡Painting; ‡Photography; ‡Printmaking; ‡Sculpture; ‡Silversmithing.
Summer School: Enrl 100-150; tui $70 for 6 hrs for term of 6 wks beginning June 1. Courses—same as full year with minor variations.

UTAH

CEDAR CITY

SOUTHERN UTAH STATE COLLEGE, Department of Art, 84720. Tel: 801-586-9481. *Chmn* Glen Dale Anderson; *Instrs* FT 4, PT 2.
Estab 1897; pub; D&E; ent req HS dipl ent exam; degrees BA and BS 4 yr; schol; ent req HS dipl, ent exam; degrees BA and BS 4 yr; schol; SC 29, LC 6; enrl D 300, E 80, maj 60, minors 45.
Tuition: $360 per yr; campus res room & board $552-702.

Courses: Advertising Design; Art Education; Ceramics; Commercial Art; Drawing; Graphic Arts; Graphic Design; History of Art & Archaeology; Illustration; Lettering; Painting; Sculpture; Teacher Training.
Summer School: (Special Program) Tui $120 for term of 8 wk beginning June. Courses—Art History; Ceramics; Drawing; Painting.

LOGAN

UTAH STATE UNIVERSITY, College of Humanities and Arts, 84322. Tel: 801-752-4100. Estab 1889; pub; degrees granted 4 yr; schol
—**Department of Landscape Architecture.*** Tel: 801-752-4100, exten 7346. *Head* Richard Toth; Instrs FT 6, PT 4. Enrl 155.
—**Department of Art.*** Tel: 801-752-4100, exten 7538. *Head* Dr Ray W Hellberg, PhD; *Prof* Ralph T Clark, MFA; *Prof* Jon Anderson, MFA; *Prof* Harrison Groutage, MFA; *Asst Prof* Tetsuo Kusama, MFA; *Prof* Moishe Smith, MFA; *Assoc Prof* Adrian VanSuchtelen, MFA; *Prof* Larry Elsner, MFA.
Estab 1890; D&E; ent req HS dipl, HS transcript & ACT; degrees BS, BA, BFA, MFA and MA; schol; enrl D 340, maj 340, grad 24.
Tuition: Res—Undergrad & grad $185 yr; Nonres—Undergrad & grad $472 yr; campus available.
Courses: ‡Advertising Design; ‡Art Education; ‡Ceramics; ‡Drawing; ‡Illustration; ‡Painting; ‡Photography; ‡Printmaking; ‡Sculpture; ‡Textile Design.
Summer School: *Head* Dr Ray W Hellberg. Courses—Beginning Design; Beginning Drawing; Basic Photography; Basic Ceramic Handbuilding; Basic Ceramic Wheelthrow; Intermediate Ceramics; Landscape Painting; Basic Watercolor; Intermediate Sculpture; Individual Projects; Advanced Ceramic Studio; Drawing Studio; Art Studio; Painting Studio; Photo Studio; Advanced Sculpture and Metalsmithing; Ceramics Studio; Printmaking Studio.

OGDEN

WEBER STATE COLLEGE, Art & Photography Department, 3750 Harrison Blvd, 84408. Tel: 801-399-5941, exten 462. *Chmn & Prof* Richard J Van Wagoner, MFA; *Assoc Prof* Arthur R Adelmann, MFA; *Assoc Prof* Dale W Bryner, MFA; *Asst Prof* David N Cox, MFA; *Lectr* Susan Makov Denza, MFA; *Prof* Charles M Groberg, MFA; *Prof* James R McBeth, MFA; *Asst Prof* Samuel H Moya, MA.
Estab 1933, dept estab 1937; pub; D&E; ent req HS dipl, ACT; degrees cert 1 yr, AA, AS 2 yr, BA, BS, 4 yr; schol; SC 66, LC 17; enrl D 2464, E 694, nonmaj 700, maj 251.
Tuition: Res—Undergrad $174 per quarter; Nonres—Undergrad $361.50 per quarter. Campus res room and board $1259 yr or apartment $408.
Courses: Advertising Design; ‡Art Education; Art History; Ceramics; ‡Commercial Art; Drawing; Film; Goldsmithing; ‡Graphic Arts; ‡Graphic Design; ‡Illustration; Jewelry; Lettering; Painting; ‡Photography; Printmaking; Sculpture; Silversmithing; Teacher Training; Textile Design.
Summer School: *Dir* Richard J Van Wagoner. Tui $174 for term of 8 wk beginning June 19. Courses: Introduction to Art; Drawing; Design; Ceramics; Sculpture; Metalsmithing; Jewelry Design; Painting.

PROVO

BRIGHAM YOUNG UNIVERSITY, Department of Art and Design, C-502 HFAC, 84602. Tel: 801-374-1211, exten 4266. *Chmn* Robert L Marshal, MFA; Instrs FT 25.
Estab 1875; dept estab 1893; den; D&E; ent req HS dipl or ACT; degrees BA and BFA 4 yr, MFA 2 yr and MA 1½ yr; schol; SC 61, LC 19, GC 20; enrl D 6545, E 1563, maj 550, GS 30.
Tuition: Res—Undergrad $1260 per yr, $420 per sem, PT $43 per cr hr, grad $1410 per yr, $470 per sem, PT at $48 per cr hr; Nonchurchmember—Undergrad $1890 per yr, $630 per sem, PT at $65 per cr hr, grad $2115 per yr, $705 per sem, PT at $72 per cr hr; campus res room and board $1820.
Courses: Art Education; ‡Art History; ‡Ceramics; ‡Drawing; ‡Graphic Design; ‡Handicrafts (fibers, metals, wood); ‡History of Art and Archaeology; ‡Illustration; ‡Industrial Design; ‡Jewelry; Lettering; ‡Painting; ‡Printmaking; ‡Sculpture; ‡Teacher Training.

SAINT GEORGE

DIXIE COLLEGE, Art Department, 84770. Tel: 801-673-4811, exten 297. *Head Dept & Coordr* Gerald Olson, MS; Glen Blakely, MFA.
Estab 1911; pub; D&E; ent req HS dipl, ACT; degrees AA and AS 2 yr; schol; SC 24, LC 7, GC 1; enrl D 400, maj 30.
Tuition: Res—Undergrad $147 per quarter; Nonres—Undergrad $297 per quarter; campus res $100-$140 per quarter.

Courses: Advertising Design; Art Education; Art History; Ceramics; Commercial Art; Costume Design and Construction; Drafting; Drawing; Film; History of Art and Archaeology; Illustration; Interior Design; Painting; Photograph; Printmaking; Sculpture; Teacher Training; Textile Design; Theatre Arts; Video.
Adult Hobby Classes: Enrl 20; tui $50 per quarter. Courses—Ceramics; Oil Painting; Wood Carving.
Summer School: Courses—Basic Design; Basic Drawing.

SALT LAKE CITY

UNIVERSITY OF UTAH, Art Department, AAC 161, 84112. Tel: 801-581-8678. *Prof* Robert S Olpin, PhD; *Prof* Dorothy Bearnson, MA; *Prof* Angelo Caravaglia, TC; *Assoc Prof* Paul Davis, MFA; *Prof* Alvin Gittins, BA; *Assoc Prof* Richard Johnston, MFA; *Assoc Prof* Robert Kleinschmidt, MFA; *Asst Prof* Raymond Morales, BA; *Assoc Prof* Frank Anthony Smith, MFA; *Prof* V Douglas Snow, MFA; *Prof* Lennox Tierney; *Assoc Instr* Julie Connell, MFA; *Prof Emer* George S Dibble, MA; *Asst Prof* Nathan Winters, PhD.
Estab 1850, dept estab 1888; pub; D&E; ent req HS dipl, degrees BA and BFA 4 yr, MA and MFA 2 yr; schol; SC 79, LC 57, GC 27; enrl D 3624, E 465, nonmaj 1347, maj 350, GS 10.
Tuition: Res—Undergrad $196.50 (10 hrs or more) per quarter, grad $68.50 (for 1 or 2 cr hrs); grad $294.75 (10 hrs or more) per quarter, $102.75 (for 1 or 2 cr hr); Nonres—Undergrad $491.50 (10 hrs or more) per quarter, $155.50 (for 1 or 2 cr hrs), grad $737.25 (10 hrs or more) per quarter, $233.25 (1 or 2 cr hr); campus res room & board.
Courses: Advertising Design; Art Education: ‡Art History; ‡Ceramics; Commercial Art; Drawing; Film; Goldsmithing; Graphic Arts; ‡Graphic Design; ‡Handicrafts (fibers); Illustration; Jewelry; ‡Painting; Photography; ‡Printmaking; ‡Sculpture; ‡Silversmithing; Teacher Training.
Summer School: *Dir* V Douglas Snow. Tui $196.50 for res for term of 6 wks, $491.50 for nonres for 6 wks beginning July 10th-Aug 19th. Courses—Art History; Ceramics; Drawing; Fibers; Life Drawing; Painting; Photography; Sculpture; Small Metals & Jewelry.

WESTMINSTER COLLEGE,* Department of Art, 1840 S 13th E 84105. Tel: 801-484-7651, exten 66. *Acting Chmn* Philip A Day Jr; Instrs FT 2, PT 5.
Estab 1875; pvt; D; ent req HS dipl ent exam acceptable HS grade point average; degrees BA and BS 4 yr; schol; SC 25, LC 2; enrl D 900-1000, maj 25.
Tuition: $1700 per yr, campus res approx $605.
Courses: Art Education; Ceramics; Drawing; History of Art & Archaeology; Jewelry; Painting; Photography; Printmaking; Sculpture; Teacher Training; Weaving.

VERMONT

BENNINGTON

BENNINGTON COLLEGE,* 05201. Tel: 802-442-5401. *Pres* Gail Thain Parker; Instrs FT 70.
Estab 1932; pvt; degrees AB and MA 4 yr; schol.
Courses: Architecture; Ceramics; Drawing; Graphic Arts; History of Art; Painting; Photography; Sculpture.

BURLINGTON

UNIVERSITY OF VERMONT,* College of Arts & Sciences, Department of Art, 05401. Tel: 802-655-2014. *Chmn* Richard Janson; Instrs 16. Pub; D&E; degrees BA and BS 4 yr; enrl 650.
Courses: Art Education; Art History; Ceramics; Design; Drawing; Fine Metal Crafts; Painting; Photography; Printmaking; Sculpture.
Summer School: *Dir* John Bushey. 8 wks beginning May to Aug. Courses—University of Vermont-Shelburne Museum program in American Art; Design; History.

CASTLETON

CASTLETON STATE COLLEGE, Art Department, 05735. Tel: 802-468-5611. *Head Dept & Assoc Prof* Charles R Anderson, BFA; *Assoc Prof* Warren Kimble, BFA; *Prof* Lawrence N Jensen, EdE; *Instr* William Ramage, MFA.
Estab 1787; pub; D&E; ent req HS dipl, ACT, SAT, CEEB; degrees BA and BS 4 yr, A/SBA 2 yr (business with art concentration); SC 31, LC 3, GC varies; enrl D 1400, E 1000, nonmaj 300, maj 63, GS 5.
Tuition: Res—Undergrad & grad $670 per yr, $335 per sem, $28 per cr; Nonres—Undergrad and grad $2100 per yr, $1050 per sem, $88 per cr; campus res room & board $1445.

Courses: Advertising Design; Art Education; Art History; Calligraphy; Commercial Art; Costume Design and Construction; Drawing; Graphic Arts; Graphic Design; Handicrafts (general crafts); Illustration; Lettering; Painting; Photography; Printmaking; Sculpture; Teacher Training; Theatre Arts; Typography.
Summer School: Dir Dr Walter Reuling. Courses—Crafts; Drawing; Painting; Photography; Watercolor.

JOHNSON

JOHNSON STATE COLLEGE,* Division of Humanities, 05656. Tel: 802-635-2356, exten 221. *Chmn* John Duffy; Instrs FT 5, PT 2.
Pub; D&E; ent req HS dipl; degree BA 4 yr; schol; Vermont res only; SC 19, LC 4; enrl D 400.
Tuition: Res—$335 per sem; Nonres—$1050 per sem; campus res room & Board $722.50.
Courses: Aesthetics; Art Education; Ceramics; Drawing; Graphic Arts; History of Art & Archaeology; Painting; Photography; Sculpture; Teacher Training.

MIDDLEBURY

MIDDLEBURY COLLEGE,* Department of Art, Johnson Building, 05753. Tel: 802-388-2762. *Chmn* Robert F Reigg; Instrs FT 6, PT 1.
Estab 1942; pvt; D; ent req exam and cert; degree AB; SC 8, LC 14; enrl maj 15, others 350.
Tuition: $5750 per yr includes campus res.
Courses: Art History; Design; Drawing & Painting; Printmaking; Sculpture.

MONTPELIER

VERMONT COLLEGE OF NORWICH UNIVERSITY, Philosophy, Religion and Fine Arts Department, College Street, 05602. Tel: 802-229-0522, exten 28. *Chmn* Dr Edward Suftin, PhD; *Assoc Prof* Harold Krauth, MA; *Asst Prof* Earl Fechter, MFA; *Instr* Brian Webb, PhD; *Instr* Dean Perkins, PhD.
Pvt; D&E; ent req HS dipl; degrees AA; enrl D 65 (studio art), E 8, nonmaj 65.
Tuition: Campus res.
Courses: Art Education; Art History; Design; Drawing; Painting; Photography; Printmaking.

POULTNEY

GREEN MOUNTAIN COLLEGE,* Department of Art, 05764. Tel: 802-287-9305. *Pres* Raymond A Withey; Instrs FT 2.
Estab 1834; pvt; W; degree AA 2 yr; SC 8, LC 3, enrl maj 63.
Courses: Advertising Design; Display; Drawing; Lettering; Painting.

STOWE

WRIGHT SCHOOL OF ART,* 05672. Tel: 802-253-4305. *Dir* Stanley Marc Wright; Instrs FT 2.
Estab 1949; SC 5, LC 4; enrl 50.
Tuition: $40 per wk.
Children's Classes: Four Sat AM $5 per lesson, June to Sept. Courses—Drawing; Painting.

VIRGINIA

ARLINGTON

MARYMOUNT COLLEGE OF VIRGINIA, Admissions Office, 2807 N Glebe Rd, 22207. Tel: 703-524-2500, exten 58. *Chmn* Robert Draghi, PhD; *Asst Prof* Marie Gabrielle Berg, RSHM, MFA; *Artist-in-Residence* John Chapman Lewis; *Instr* Pamela Stoessell, MFA; *Vis Lectr* Wilfred Brunner, MFA; *Vis Lectr* Judy Didoha, MA; *Vis Lectr* Oscar Fitzgerald, PhD; *Vis Lectr* Elizabeth Nightlinger, MA.
Estab 1950; pvt; D&E; ent req HS dipl, SAT results, letter of recommendation; degrees BA 3 yrs, AA 2 yrs; SC 14, LC 20.
Tuition: $2475 per yr, $1237.50 per sem; $80 per cr hr; continuing education $40 per cr; campus res room and board $1625.
Courses: Art Education; ‡Art History; Ceramics; ‡Commercial Art; Costume Design and Construction; Display; Drawing; Fashion Arts; Graphic Arts; Graphic Design; ‡History of Art and Archaeology; ‡Interior Design; Painting; Sculpture; Textile Design; ‡Theatre Arts.
Adult Hobby Classes: Courses—any course in fine arts.

Summer School: Dir James J Kelly. Tui $80 per cr for term of 5 wks beginning May 15.

BLACKSBURG

VIRGINIA POLYTECHNIC INSTITUTE AND STATE UNIVERSITY,* College of Arts and Sciences, 24061. Tel: 703-951-5421. *Head Dept* Dean Carter; Instrs FT 8, PT 2.
Estab 1969; pub; degrees BA 4 yr; SC 17, LC 7.
Tuition: $675.

BRISTOL

SULLINS COLLEGE,* Art Department, 24201. Tel: 703-669-6112. *Chmn* Guy H Benson; Instrs FT 1, PT 4.
Estab 1870; pvt; D; W; ent req HS grad; degree AFA 2 yr; schol; SC 12, LC 1; enrl maj 30, others 15.
Courses: Advanced Painting; Beginning Design; Beginning Drawing & Painting; Ceramics; History of Art; Independent Studio Study; Interior Design; Jewelry; Photography; Sculpture; Set Design; Weaving.

VIRGINIA INTERMONT COLLEGE, Moore St, 24201. Tel: 703-669-6101. *Chmn* Tedd Blevins, MFA; *Primary Faculty* Marvin Tadlock, MFA; David Braun, MFA; Instrs FT 3.
Estab 1884; den; D&E; ent req HS dipl, review of work; degrees BA (Art) and BA (Art Educ) 4 yr, AA 2 yr; schol; SC 15, LC 4; enrl D 35, non maj 110.
Tuition: $1850 per yr, $45 per hr; campus res room & board $1350 to $1850.
Courses: ‡Advertising Design; ‡Art Education; Art History; Calligraphy; ‡Ceramics; Collage; ‡Commercial Art; Costume Design and Construction; Drawing; Fashion Arts; Film; Graphic Arts; Graphic Design; Illustration; Lettering; Mixed Media; Painting; Photography; Printmaking; Sculpture; Teacher Training.

BUENA VISTA

SOUTHERN SEMINARY JUNIOR COLLEGE, 24416. Tel: 703-261-6181. *Chmn* Leroy U Rudasill Jr, MA.
Estab 1867; pvt; D; ent req HS dipl, SAT or ACT; degrees AA, AS and AFA 2 yr; SC 10, LC 5; enrl D 185, nonmaj 175, maj 10.
Tuition: Res—Undergrad $4300 per yr; Nonres—Undergrad $2700 per yr.
Courses: Art Education; Art History; Ceramics; Display; Drawing; Graphic Arts; Handicrafts (macrame); Interior Design; Jewelry; Painting; Printmaking; Sculpture.

CHARLOTTESVILLE

HOLDEN SCHOOL OF ART AND DESIGN, 2246 Ivy Rd, 22901. Tel: 804-295-9357. *Dir* E Lee Armentrout, BA; *Dir Commercial Art* W R Beane, BS; *Dir Fine Art* Catherine Williams, MFA; Instrs FT 4, PT 3.
Estab 1928, dept estab 1964; pvt; D; ent req HS dipl, portfolio; enrl D 78, maj 78.
Tuition: $1350 per yr, $745 per sem; campus res.
Courses: Advertising Design; Architecture; Art History; ‡Commercial Art; Drafting; Drawing; Graphic Arts; History of Art and Archaeology; ‡Illustration; ‡Interior Design; Lettering; Mixed Media; Painting; Printmaking.

UNIVERSITY OF VIRGINIA, McIntire Department of Art, Fayerweather Hall, 22903. Tel: 804-924-3057, 924-3541. *Chmn & Assoc Prof* Keith P F Moxey, PhD; Faculty FT 16.
Estab 1819, dept estab 1951; pub; D; ent req HS dipl; degrees BA(Studio and Art History), MA(Art History) and PhD (Art History); SC 20, LC 13, GC 18; enrl D 1534, maj 104, GS 27 res, 18 nonres.
Tuition: Res—Undergrad $804 per yr, grad $864 per yr, $432 per sem; Nonres—Undergrad $1939 per yr, $969.50 per sem, grad $1939 per yr, $969.50 per sem; campus res.
Courses: Art History; Drawing; Graphic Arts; Graphic Design; Painting; Photography; Printmaking; Sculpture.
Summer School: Dir Alton L Taylor. Enrl varies; tui $38 per sem hr for term of July 13th to August 8th. Courses—Art History (History of Art I, Artists & Masterpieces, Great Traditions of Asian Art); Studio (Introduction to Photography, Drawing I & II, Painting I).

DANVILLE

AVERETT COLLEGE, Art Department, 24541. Tel: 804-793-7811. *Coordr & Prof* Maud F Gatewood, MA; *Assoc Prof* Robert Marsh, MFA; *Instr* Diane Kendrick MFA; *Instr* Richard Gantt, MFA; Instrs FT 3, PT 1.

Estab 1859, dept estab 1930; pvt; D&E; ent req HS dipl; degrees AB; schol; SC 13, LC 5; enrl D 1000, nonmaj 250, maj 25.
Tuition: $55 per sem hr; campus res room & board $3600.
Courses: Advertising Design; Art Education; Art History; Ceramics; Commercial Art; Drawing; Fashion Arts; History of Art and Archaeology; Illustration; Jewelry; Lettering; Painting; Printmaking; Sculpture; Teacher Training; Textile Design.

FAIRFAX

GEORGE MASON UNIVERSITY, Department of Fine and Performing Arts, 22030. Tel: 703-323-2450. *Head Dept & Prof* Sam di Bonaventura, DMA; *Assoc Prof* Barbara Chabrowe, PhD; *Asst Prof* E Walter Kravitz, MFA; *Asst Prof* Carol C Mattusch, PhD; *Asst Prof* P B North, PhD; *Asst Prof* N W Ward, MFA; *Asst Prof* A Castro, MFA; Instrs FT 6, PT 2.
Estab 1948, dept estab 1966; pub; D&E; ent req HS dipl, SAT or CEEB; degrees BA; SC 16, LC 15; enrl nonmaj 200, maj 96.
Tuition: $384 per sem; Nonres $744 per sem; campus res.
Courses: Art Education; ‡Art History; Ceramics; Drafting; Drawing; Film; Graphic Arts; History of Art and Archaeology; Painting; Printmaking; Sculpture; Stage Design; ‡Studio Art; Theatre Arts.
Summer School: Courses—Art Appreciation; Visual Thinking.

FARMVILLE

LONGWOOD COLLEGE,* Art Department 23901. Tel: 804-392-9359. *Chmn* Barbara L Bishop, Instrs FT 9, PT 1.
Estab 1839; pub; D; ent req HS grad; degrees BA and BS 4 yr; schol; SC 32, LC 10, GC 1; enrl 700 (art), 2200 (total).
Courses: Art Education; Art History & Appreciation; Ceramics; General Crafts; Drawing & Composition; Enamels; Filmmaking; Jewelry & Metals; Painting; Photography; Printmaking & Graphic Design; Sculpture; Weaving.
Children's Classes: Enrl 20; one class per sem.
Summer School: Courses—Studio and workshops.

FREDERICKSBURG

MARY WASHINGTON COLLEGE, Art Department, 22401. Tel: 703-373-7250. *Chmn & Assoc Prof* Barbara Meyer, PhD; *Prof* Pauline G King, PhD; *Prof* Cornelia Oliver, PhD; *Instr* Joseph Dreiss, MA; *Prof* Paul C Muick, PhD; *Assoc Prof* John Lamph, MFA; *Assoc Prof* Teruo Hara, MFA; *Asst Prof* Joseph DiBella, MFA.
Estab 1904; pub; D&E; ent req HS dipl, ent exam; degrees BA and BS 4 yrs; schol; SC 18, LC 20; enrl maj 50.
Tuition: Campus res room & board.
Courses: Art Education; Art History; Ceramics; Constructions; Costume Design and Construction; Drawing; Graphic Arts; History of Art and Archaeology; Painting; Photography; Printmaking; Sculpture; Stage Design; Theatre Arts.

HAMPTON

HAMPTON INSTITUTE,* Art Department, 23368. Tel: 703-723-6581, exten 406. Instrs FT 7, PT 2.
Estab 1869; pvt; D; ent req HS grad; degrees BA, BS, BFA and MA(Art Educ, Fine Arts) 4 yr; schol; SC 22, LC 7, GC 9; enrl maj 53, others 300, GS 5.
Tuition: Campus res.
Courses: Advanced Commercial Art; Ceramics; Design; Egg Tempera; History of Art; Metalwork & Jewelry; Painting (incl fresco); Photography; Teacher Training.
Summer School: Courses—Advanced Workshop in Ceramics; Art Education Methods; Art Methods for the Elementary School; Basic Design; Ceramics; Commercial Art; Design; Drawing and Composition; Graphics; Metalwork & Jewelry; Painting; Understanding the Arts.

HARRISONBURG

JAMES MADISON UNIVERSITY, Art Department, 22801. Tel: 703-433-6216. *Head Dept* J David Diller, PhD; *Prof* Martha B Caldwell, PhD; *Prof* Jerry L Coulter, MFA; *Prof* Crystal Theodore, EdD; *Assoc Prof* Kenneth J Beer, MA; *Asst Prof* Rebecca Hawkins, MFA; *Asst Prof* Philip James EdD; *Asst Prof* Kathleen Arthur, PhD.
Estab 1908; pub; D&E; ent req HS dipl, graduates must submit portfolio; undergrads selected largely on academic merit; degrees BA(Art Hist), BS and BFA(Studio) 4 yr, MA 1½ to 2 yrs; schol; SC 31, LC 21, GC 22; enrl D&E 1254 (total), maj 175, GS 13.
Tuition: Res—Undergrad $400 per sem, grad $30 per sem hr; Nonres—Undergrad $650 per sem hr, grad $47 per sem hr; campus res room & board $1426.

Courses: Advertising Design; Aesthetics; Art Education; Art History; Ceramics; Drafting; Drawing; Goldsmithing; Industrial Design; Jewelry; Interior Design; Museum Staff Training; Painting; Photography; Printmaking; Sculpture; Silversmithing; Teacher Training; Textile Design.
Summer School: Dir Dr Elizabeth Finlayson. Tui Res—Undergrad $16 per cr hr, grad $30 per cr hr; Nonres—Undergrad $33 per cr hr, grad $47 per cr hr for term of 8 wks beginning June 12th.
Courses—Art Appreciation; Art Criticism (grad level); Art Education; Ceramics (undergrad level); Drawing; Graphics & Painting; Painting; Photography; Printmaking; Sculpture.

HOLLINS

HOLLINS COLLEGE, Art Department, 24020. Tel: 703-362-6521. *Chmn & Assoc Prof* William G White, MFA; *Asst Prof* Nancy Dahlstrom MFA; *Prof* Frances Niederer, PhD; *Prof* Lewis Thompson, MFA; *Assoc Prof* W L Whitwell, MFA.
Estab 1842; pvt; D; ent req HS dipl; degrees BA 4 yr; schol; SC 13; enrl D 395, maj 66.
Tuition: $3825 per yr; campus res room and board $1525 per yr.
Courses: Aesthetics; ‡Art History; Drawing; ‡History of Art and Archaeology; Museum Staff Training; ‡Painting; ‡Photography; ‡Printmaking; ‡Sculpture; ‡Teacher Training.

LEXINGTON

WASHINGTON AND LEE UNIVERSITY, Department of Fine Arts, 24450. Tel: 703-463-9111, exten 190, 350.
Head Dept Dr Gerard Maurice Doyon, PhD; Dr Pamela H Simpson, PhD; *Prof* I-Hsiung Ju, MA; Isabel McIlvain, MFA; Dr Herman W Taylor, Jr, PhD; *Prof* Marid Pellicciaro, MA.
Estab 1742, dept 1920; pvt; D; ent req HS dipl, SAT, 3 CEEB, one English CEEB plus essay on skills in English, English composition test, entrance requirements most rigorous in English, required of all, including art majors, and all others deemed necessary in individual cases; degrees BA 4 yr; schol; SC 14, LC 26; enrl D 1200 (in college) nonmaj 200, maj 4 to 6.
Tuition: $3100 per yr; campus res room and board and tuition, average cost $4600 per yr.
Courses: ‡Art History; Drawing; History of Art and Archaeology; Museum Staff Training; Painting; Printmaking; Sculpture; Stage Design; Theatre Arts; other—study Art Abroad—Taiwan, Greece, France.

LYNCHBURG

LYNCHBURG COLLEGE, Art Department, 24501. Tel: 804-845-9071, exten 295. *Chmn & Prof* W Donald Evans; *Asst Prof* Virginia Irby Davis, MEd; *Asst Prof* Charles E Worsham, MA; *Asst Prof* Thelma L Twery, BA.
Estab 1903, dept estab 1948; pvt; D&E; ent req HS dipl; degrees BA and BS 4 yr; SC 26, LC 16, GC 2; enrl D 400, E 50, nonmaj 410, maj 40.
Tuition: Res—Undergrad $4050 per yr; Nonres—Undergrad $2600; campus res room and board.
Courses: Aesthetics; Architecture; Art Education Art History; Ceramics; Drawing; Film; Graphic Arts; Graphic Design; Handicrafts (mixed); History of Art and Archaeology; Occupational Therapy; Painting; Photography; Printmaking; Sculpture; Teacher Training; Theatre Arts.
Summer School: Courses—Art Education; Art History and Appreciation; Crafts; Photography.

RANDOLPH-MACON WOMAN'S COLLEGE,* Department of Art, 24503. Tel: 804-846-7392, exten 366. *Chmn* Elliott R Twery; Instrs FT 3-4.
Estab 1891; pvt; D; W; degree BA 4 yr; schol; SC 18, LC 15; enrl maj 35, others 305.
Tuition: $4100 includes campus res.
Courses: American Painting; Filmmaking; Printmaking I & II; Sculpture & Ceramics.

MC LEAN

MCLEAN ARTS CENTER, Art Department, 1437 Emerson Ave, 22101. Tel: 703-790-0861, 365-3048. *Head Dept* John Bryans.
Estab 1955; pvt; D&E; SC 1; enrl D 37, E 6.
Tuition: $55 for 10 lessons for adults; $35 for children; no campus res.
Courses: Drawing; Painting.
Adult Hobby Classes: Enrl 28, tui $55 per 10 lessons. Courses—Drawing; Emphasis on watercolor; Painting.
Children's Classes: Enrl 15; tui $35 per 10 lessons. Courses—Drawing; Painting.

NORFOLK

NORFOLK STATE COLLEGE, Fine Arts Department, 23504. Tel: 804-623-8844. *Head Dept* Rod A Taylor, PhD.
Estab 1935; pub; D&E; ent req HS dipl; degrees BA(Art Education), BA(Fine Arts) and BA(Graphic Design) 4 yrs; SC 50, LC 7; enrl D 355, E 18, nonmaj 200, maj 155.
Tuition: Res—Undergrad $265 per sem, $22 per hr, grad $308 per sem, $27 per hr; Nonres—Undergrad $432 per sem, $32 per hr; grad $435 per sem, grad $40 per hr; campus res room and board $576.
Courses: Advertising Design; ‡Art Education; Art History; Calligraphy; Ceramics; Collage; Commercial Art; Drawing; ‡Graphic Arts; Graphic Design; Handicrafts (general crafts); History of Art and Archaeology; Jewelry; Lettering; Mixed Media; ‡Painting; Photography; Printmaking; Sculpture; Teacher Training.
Adult Hobby Classes: Enrl 30. Courses—Ceramics; Crafts.
Children's Classes: Enrl 45; tui none. Courses—all areas, at A.M.
Summer School: Courses—Ceramics; Crafts; Graphics; Painting; Photography; Sculpture.

OLD DOMINION UNIVERSITY, Art Department, 23508. Tel: 804-489-6213. *Chmn Art History* Evelyn G Dreyer; *Chmn Studio* Kenneth G Daley, MFA; *Prof* Charles K Sibley; *Prof* Victor E Pickett; *Prof* Parker G Lewley; *Prof* Alexander B Jackson, *vis prof*—Gael Bennett, drawing, 77-78.
Pub; D&E; ent req HS dipl, SAT; degrees BA(Art Hist), BA(Studio), BS(Art Educ) and BFA 4 yrs; schol; SC 43, LC 12, GC 6; enrl D 250, E 86, maj 233, GS 2.
Tuition: Campus res.
Courses: ‡Art Education; Art History; Ceramics; Color; Drawing; Goldsmithing; Graphic Arts; Graphic Design; Handicrafts (fibers); History of Art and Archaeology; Painting; Photography; Printmaking; Sculpture; Silversmithing; Teacher Training; Textile Design; Three-D Design; Two-D Design.
Adult Hobby Classes: Courses—Bounty Rainbow Program (selection and costs varied).
Children's Classes: Courses—Bounty Rainbow Program (selection and cost varied).
Summer School: Courses—Art History; Studio.

VIRGINIA WESLEYAN COLLEGE, Art Department of the Humanities Division, 23502. Tel: 804-461-3232. *Head Dept* Barclay Sheaks, BFA; *Asst Prof* Neil Britton, MFA; *Instr* Myrna Andursky, MA; *Instr* Charles Flynn, MFA; *Instr* F D Cossitt, MFA.
Pvt, den; D&E; ent req HS dipl, SAT; degrees BA(Liberal Arts) 4 yr; schol; SC 21, LC 8; enrl E 20.
Tuition: $2750 per yr; campus res room & board $1350.
Courses: Art Education; Art History; Ceramics; Collage; Conceptual Art; Constructions; Drawing; Graphic Arts; Handicrafts (fabric enrichment, weaving); Jewelry; Mixed Media; Painting; Printmaking; Sculpture; Teacher Training.

PETERSBURG

RICHARD BLAND COLLEGE, Rte 1, Box 77A, 23803. Tel: 804-732-0111 exten, 220. *Pres* Clarence Maze Jr, PhD; *Asst Prof* Susan G Brown, BFA.
Estab 1960, dept estab 1963; pub; D&E; ent req HS dipl, SAT; recommendation of HS counselor; degrees AA, AA(Fine Arts), AS and AS(Business) 2 yr; SC 3, LC 3; enrl D 73.
Tuition: Res—Undergrad $480 per yr, $240 per sem, $22 per hr; Nonres—Undergrad $810 per yr, $405 per sem, $33 per hr; no campus res.
Courses: Art Appreciation; Art History; Basic Design; Drawing; Painting; Sculpture.
Adult Hobby Classes: Courses—Interior Design; Yoga.
Children's Classes: Enrl approx 20; tui $22 per hr; Courses—Art for Children; Children's Gymnastics.
Summer School: *Dir* John B McNeer. Enrl approx 300; tui $22 per hr for term of 6 wks beginning June 7th. Courses—varied.

VIRGINIA STATE COLLEGE, Fine Arts Department, 23803. Tel: 804-520-6328. *Head Dept* Dr A D Macklin, EdD; *Asst Prof* Eugene Vango, MFA; *Asst Prof* Doris Woodson, MFA; *Asst Prof* Everett Winrow, MAE; *Instr* Charles Flynn, MA.
Estab 1883; dept estab 1935; pub; D&E; ent req HS dipl; degrees BS 4 yrs; SC 16, LC 6, GC 2; enrl D 400, E 60, nonmaj 302, maj 98.
Tuition: Res—Undergrad and grad $738 per yr; Nonres—Undergrad & grad $1198 per yr; campus res room and board $764.
Courses: Advertising Design; Aesthetics; Art Education; Art History; Ceramics; Drawing; History of Art and Archaeology; Jewelry; Lettering; Painting; Printmaking; Sculpture.

Adult Hobby Classes: Enrl 20; tui $105 per course. Courses—Batik; Ceramics; Jewelry; Macrame; Painting; Printmaking.
Summer School: *Dir* Dr S A Madden. Enrl 20; tui $120 for term of 6 wks, beginning June 19. Courses—Basic Art; Ceramics; Crafts; Jewelry.

RADFORD

RADFORD COLLEGE, Art Department, PO Box 5791, 24142. Tel: 703-731-5475. *Chmn & Prof* Dr G Lynn Gordon, DEd; *Prof* Dr Paul W Frets, DA; *Prof* Dr Noel G Lawson, PhD; *Asst Prof* Jerry H Krebs, MFA; *Asst Prof* Pam F Lawson, MFA; *Asst Prof* Dr Fred Thayed, DEd; *Asst Prof* Dr Heliede Salam, Phd.
Estab 1910, dept estab 1936; pub; D&E; ent req HS dipl, SAT; degrees BA, BS(non-teaching) and BS(teaching) 4 yrs, MS one year; schol; SC 52, LC 12, GC 26; enrl D 191, E 18, nonmaj 978, maj 191, GS 28, others 15.
Tuition: Res—$2454 per yr, $818 per quarter, $25 per quarter hr; Nonres—$867 per yr, $289 per quarter, $25 per quarter; Out-of-State—$3054 per yr, $1018 per quarter, $25 per quarter hr; campus res room & board.
Courses: Advertising Design; Architecture; ‡Art Education; ‡Art History; Calligraphy; Ceramics; Commercial Art; Drawing; Goldsmithing; Graphic Arts; Graphic Design; Handicrafts (enameling, raku, weaving); History of Art and Archaeology; Illustration; Jewelry; Lettering Painting; Photography; Printmaking; Sculpture; Silversmithing; Teacher Training; Textile Design.
Summer School: Enrl 421; tui as above. Courses—all labs plus Art Appreciation; Art Education.

RICHMOND

UNIVERSITY OF RICHMOND, Department of Art, 23173. Tel: 804-285-6246. *Head Dept & Assoc Prof* Charles W Johnson Jr, PhD; *Assoc Prof* Demetrios Mavroudis, EdD; *Asst Prof* Jeanne Begien Campbell; *Instr* Anne P Frederick, MA; *Instr* Harvey McWilliams, MFA.
Pvt; D&E; ent req HS dipl, CEEB; degrees BA and BS 4 yr; SC 29, LC 15.
Courses: Art Education; Art History; Ceramics; Drawing; Graphic Arts; Graphic Design; Handicrafts (variety); History of Art and Archaeology; Painting; Printmaking; Sculpture.
Summer School: *Dir* Dr Max Graeber. Courses—Art Appreciation; Independent Study.

VIRGINIA COMMONWEALTH UNIVERSITY,* School of the Arts, 325 N Harrison St, 23284. Tel: 804-770-7261. *Dean* Murry N DePillars; Instrs FT 139, PT 53.
Estab 1838; pub; D&E; ent req portfolio; degrees BFA and BM 4 yr, MA, MM, MAE, MFA and MME 2 yrs; schol, fel, grad assistantships; enrl 2130 (art), 17,500 (total).
Tuition: Res—Undergrad and grad $730; Nonres—Undergrad and grad $1460; art fees approx $35 each sem.
Courses: Art Education; Art History; Ceramics; Communication Arts & Design; Fabric Design; Fashion Design; Furniture Design; Interior Design; Jewelry; Painting & Printmaking; Photography; Sculpture.
Children's Classes: Full summer school offerings.

STAUNTON

MARY BALDWIN COLLEGE, Department of Art, Frederick and New Streets, 24401. Tel: 703-885-0811, exten 394. *Head Dept & Prof* Ulysse Desportes, Dr Univ of Paris; *Assoc Prof* Mary Tuck Echols, PhD.
Estab 1842; pvt; D&E; ent req HS dipl; degrees BA 4 yrs; schol; SC 16, LC 18; enrl D 173, E 32, nonmaj 172, maj 33, others 4 non-credit.
Tuition: Res—Undergrad $5120 per yr, $2560 per sem; Nonres—Undergrad $3520 per yr, $2760 per sem; campus res room & board $1600.
Courses: Advertising Design; Aesthetics; Art Education; Art History; Ceramics; Collage; Commercial Art; Conceptual Art; Constructions; Costume Design and Construction; Display; Drawing; Film; Graphic Arts; Graphic Design; Handicrafts (fabric arts, weaving); History of Art and Archaeology; Illustration; Interior Design; Lettering, Mixed Media; Museum Staff Training; Painting; Photography; Printmaking; Sculpture; Stage Design; Teacher Training; Theatre Arts; Video.

SWEET BRIAR

SWEET BRIAR COLLEGE, Art History Dept, 24595. Tel: 703-381-5451. *Prof* Ruth M Firm, PhD; *Assoc Prof* Aileen Laing, PhD; *Asst Prof* Susan Bandes, PhD; *Instr* Diane Moran, MA.
Estab 1901, dept estab 1930; pvt; D; ent req HS dipl; degrees BA 4 yr; schol; LC 18; 3; enrl D 135, nonmaj 101, maj 16.
Tuition: $5300 including room and board.

Courses: Architecture; Art History; History of Art and Archaeology; Art Studio Department. Courses—Drawing; Graphic Arts; Mixed Media; Painting; Photography; Printmaking; Sculpture.

WILLIAMSBURG

COLLEGE OF WILLIAM AND MARY, Department of Fine Arts, 23185. Tel: 804-253-4385. *Chmn & Assoc Prof* Miles Chappell, PhD; *Prof* Carl Roseberg, MFA; *Assoc Prof* Henry Coleman, MA; *Assoc Prof* Paul Helfrich, MFA; *Asst Prof* Marlene Jack, MFA; *Asst Prof* W D Barnes, MFA; *Instr* W D Houghland, AIA; *Assoc Prof* J D Kornwold, PhD; *Prof* R K Newman, PhD.
Estab 1693, dept estab 1936; pub; D; ent req HS dipl; degrees BA 4 yr; SC 20, LC 22; enrl D 5000, nonmaj 693, maj 64.
Tuition: Res—$34 per sem hr; Nonres—$83 per sem hr; campus res $640 - $840 per yr.
Courses: ‡Architecture; ‡Art History; Ceramics; Drawing; Graphic Arts; Painting; Sculpture.
Summer School: Dir Paul Clem. Courses—Art History; Design; Painting; Sculpture.

WISE

CLINCH VALLEY COLLEGE OF THE UNIVERSITY OF VIRGINIA, 24293. Tel: 703-328-2431. *Chmn* J Glenn Blackburn, PhD; *Assoc Prof* Betty J Gilliam, MFA.
Estab 1954, dept estab 1968; pub; D&E; ent req HS dipl, SAT or ACT; degrees baccalaureate (BA and BS) 4 yr; schol; SC 9, LC 4.
Tuition: Res—Undergrad $500 per yr, $250 per sem; Nonres—Undergrad $700 per yr, $350 per sem; campus res room & board $900.
Courses: Art Education; Art History; Ceramics; Costume Design and Construction; Drafting; Drawing; Film; History of Art and Archaeology; Painting; Photography; Sculpture; Stage Design; ‡Teacher Training; Theatre Arts.
Adult Hobby Classes: Tui $21 per hr. Courses—Christmas wrapping; Flower arranging.
Summer School: Dir Dr George E Culbertson. Tui $23 per sem hr for two terms of five wks beginning June 5th and July 10th.

WASHINGTON

BELLEVUE

BELLEVUE COMMUNITY COLLEGE,* Art Department, 98007. Tel: 206-641-2358. *Chmn* Robert Purser; Instrs, FT 2, PT 2-3.
Estab 1966; pub; D&E; no ent req; degree AA 2 yr; SC 15, LC 5; enrl 300, maj 60.
Tuition: No campus res.
Courses: Drawing; Graphic Design; History of Art & Archaeology; Painting; Photography; Sculpture; Textile Design.
Adult Hobby Classes: Enrl 600; Courses—Ceramics; Design; Drawing; Jewelry; Painting; Photography; Sculpture.

BELLINGHAM

WESTERN WASHINGTON UNIVERSITY, College of Fine and Performing Arts, Art Department, 89225. Tel: 206-676-3660, 3661. *Chmn* Thomas Schlotterback, PhD; Instrs, FT 15, PT 6.
Estab 1899; pub; D&E; ent req HS dipl, ent exam; degrees BA, BA(Educ); BFA and MEd 4 yr; enrl D 1500.
Tuition: Res—Undergrad $206, grad $228 quarterly; Nonres—Undergrad $661, grad $752 quarterly; SE Asian Veterans $162 per quarter; campus res room & board approx $515 per quarter.
Summer School: Tui $197 for term of 9 wks. Terms of 3 wk, 6 wk, 9 wks and regular sessions, full-time students.

BREMERTON

OLYMPIC COLLEGE, Art Department, 98310. Tel: 206-478-4511, exten 4866. *Chmn* Robert J Dietz, PhD; *Primary Faculty* LaDeane V Tate, MA; Mel R Wallis, MA; Jack W Crouse, MA; Kenneth V Crow, MA.
Estab 1946; pub; D&E; ent req HS dipl; degrees AA, AS and ATA 2 yr; schol; LC 3; enrl D 125, E 75.
Tuition: Res—Undergrad $102 per quarter, $10.20 per cr; Nonres—Undergrad $396 per quarter, $39.60 per cr; no campus res.
Courses: Art History; Calligraphy; Ceramics; Drawing; Jewelry; Painting; Photography; Printmaking; Sculpture.
Adult Hobby Classes: Courses—Painting; Stained Glass.

CHENEY

EASTERN WASHINGTON UNIVERSITY, Department of Art, 99004. Tel: 509-359-2493. *Chmn* Gregory W Hawkins, PhD.
Estab 1886; pub; D; ent req appropriate evidence of ability to succeed academically; degrees BA, BEd and BFA 4 yrs, MA and MEd 1 to 2 yrs; schol; SC 58, LC 21, GC 18; enrl D 600, nonmaj 200, maj 200, GS 20.
Tuition: Res—Undergrad $591 per yr, $197 per quarter, $12 PT, grad 14 per hr; Nonres—Undergrad $1983 per yr, $661 per quarter, $12 PT, grad $14 per hr; campus res room & board $1245.
Courses: Aesthetics; ‡Art Education; ‡Art History; ‡Ceramics; ‡Conceptual Art; Drawing; Film; Illustration; Intermedia; ‡Jewelry; Museum Staff Training; ‡Painting; ‡Photography; ‡Printmaking; ‡Sculpture; ‡Silversmithing; ‡Teacher Training; ‡Textile Design; Video.

ELLENSBURG

CENTRAL WASHINGTON UNIVERSITY,* Department of Art, 98926. Tel: 509-963-2665. *Chmn* George Stillman, Instrs, FT 15.
Estab 1891 pub; D; ent req GPA 2; degrees BA, MA and MFA 4-5 yrs; enrl maj 300, others 4500.
Tuition: $17 per quarter hr; campus res.
Courses: Art Education; Commercial Art; Crafts; Design; Drawing; History of Art; Jewelry; Painting; Photography; Pottery; Printmaking, Sculpture.
Summer School.

LONGVIEW

LOWER COLUMBIA COLLEGE, 1600 Maple, 98632. Tel: 206-577-2334. *Instr* Martha Boentgen, MFA; *Instr* Arthur Miller, MA.
Estab 1934; pub; D&E; ent req HS dipl; degrees AAS 2 yrs; schol; SC 36, LC 8; enrl D 128; E 81.
Tuition: Res—Undergrad $291 per yr, $9.70 per hr; Nonres—Undergrad $1188 per yr, $39.60 per hr; no campus res.
Courses: Art History; Calligraphy; Ceramics; Drawing; Graphic Arts; History of Art and Archaeology; Mixed Media; Painting; Printmaking; Sculpture.
Adult Hobby Classes: Enrl 40; tui $29.10 per quarter. Courses—Recreational Painting.

MOSES LAKE

BIG BEND COMMUNITY COLLEGE, Art Department, 98857. Tel: 509-762-5351. *Chmn* Stephen Tse, MFA; *Asst Instr* Lorraine Garcia.
Estab 1962; pub; D&E; ent req HS dipl; degrees AA 2 yr; SC 8, LC 1; enrl D 325, E 60, maj 10 to 15.
Tuition: Res—Undergrad $249 per yr, $83 per quarter, $8.30 PT; Nonres—Undergrad $681 per yr, $227 per quarter, $22.70 PT; campus res room and board.
Courses: Art History; Basic Design; Ceramics; Drawing; Graphic Arts; Lettering; Painting.
Summer School: Dir Mike Lang. Tui $8.30 per cr hr for term of 6 wks. Courses—Drawing; Ceramics; Painting.

MOUNT VERNON

SKAGIT VALLEY COLLEGE,* Department of Art, 2405 College Way, 98273. Tel: 206-424-1031. *Chmn* Orville K Chatti; Instrs, FT 2, PT 6.
Estab 1926; pub; D&E; ent req open; degree AA 2 yr; schol; SC 32, LC 1; enrl D 1300, E 3200, maj 50.
Courses: Art Appreciation; Ceramics; Crafts; Design; Drawing; Jewelry; Painting; Photography; Printmaking; Sculpture; Stained Glass.

PULLMAN

WASHINGTON STATE UNIVERSITY, Fine Arts Department, 99164. Tel: 509-335-8686. *Chmn* Ross Coates, PhD; *Prof* Gaylen C Hansen, MFA; *Prof* Keith Monaghan, MA; *Assoc Prof* Robert Helm, MFA; *Assoc Prof* Fran Ho, MFA; *Assoc Prof* Arthur Okazaki, MA; *Asst Prof* Jo Hockenhull, MA; *Asst Prof* Patrick Siler, MA.
Estab 1890, dept estab 1925; pub; D&E; ent req HS dipl; degrees BA (Fine Arts) 4 yr, MFA 2 yr; schol; SC 29, LC 13, GC 25; enrl D 1593; E 131, maj 220, GS 25.
Tuition: Res—Undergrad $330 per sem, grad $370; Nonres—Undergrad $1197 per sem; grad $1369; campus res room and board $1540.
Courses: Advertising Design; Art History; Calligraphy; Ceramics; Drawing; Graphic Design; Illustration; Jewelry; Lettering; Museum Staff Training; Painting; Photography; Printmaking; Sculpture.

Summer School: Enrl varied; tui $27 per cr hr for term of four 2 wk workshops beginning June 19 to August 11. Courses—varied.

SEATTLE

BURNLEY SCHOOL OF PROFESSIONAL ART, INC. 905 East Pine St, 98122. Tel: 206-322-0596. *Dir* Jess D Cauthorn; *Primary Faculty* Fred Griffin, BFA; James Scott, BFA; Gary Nelson; William Cumming; Marilyn Nordell, BFA; Gail Merrick.
Estab 1946; pvt; D; ent req HS dipl, portfolio approval; degrees prof dipl; SC 2: enrl D 150.
Tuition: $600 per yr; no campus res.
Courses: Advertising Design; Commercial Art; Fashion Arts; Film; Graphic Arts; Graphic Design; Illustration; Lettering; Video.
Summer School: Enrl 60; tui $480 per term of 12 wks beginning May 15.

CORNISH INSTITUTE OF ALLIED ARTS, 710 East Roy, 98102. Tel: 206-323-1400. *Pres* Melvin Strauss; *Chmn Fine Arts* Craig Langager; *Chmn Design* Victor Baumgartner. Instrs FT 14, PT 80.
Estab 1914; pvt; D&E; ent req HS dipl, portfolio review, Fine Arts, Design, personal interview; degrees BAA and BFA 4 yr; schol; SC 57, LC 6; enrl nonmaj 156 PT, maj 245 FT.
Tuition: Res $1800 per yr, $900 per sem, $70 per cr; no campus res.
Courses: Advertising Design; Aesthetics; Art History; ‡Ceramics; Commercial Art; Conceptual Art; Constructions; Costume Design and Construction; Drafting; Drawing; Graphic Arts; ‡Graphic Design Illustration; Industrial Design; ‡Interior Design; ‡Jewelry; Lettering; ‡Painting; Photography; ‡Printmaking; ‡Sculpture; Theatre; Theatre Arts.
Adult Hobby Classes: Enrl 249; tui $70 per cr. Courses—Design; Fine Arts.
Children's Classes: Enrl 318; tui from $32.
Summer School: Tui $500 (full-time) for term of 9 wks beginning June 19th. Courses—Design; Fine Arts; Theatre.

FACTORY OF VISUAL ART, 4649 Sunnyside N, 98103. Tel: 206-632-8177. *Dir* Mickey Gustin, MA; *Primary Faculty* Jeffrey Bishop, MFA; Steve McClelland, MFA; Gayle Sullivan, MFA; Steve Soltar, MFA; Charles Draney, MFA; Peggy Van Bianchi, MFA; Mike Saito, MFA.
Estab 1968; pvt; D&E; ent req open; degrees cert 2 yr min; schol; SC 54, LC 1; enrl D&E 350 (aver qtr).
Tuition: $132 per quarter per 6 hr course; no campus res.
Courses: Art History; Calligraphy; Ceramics; Bookbinding; Costume Design and Construction; Drawing; Dye Processes; Enameling; Goldsmithing; Jewelry; Mixed Media; Painting; Papermaking; Photography; Photography Silk Screen; Printing; Printmaking; Sculpture; Silversmithing; Spinning; Stained Glass; Textiles; Weaving.
Children's Classes: Enrl 45 per quarter, tui $2 per hr. Courses—Ceramics; Drawing; Jewelry; Painting.
Summer School: Tui same as above for term of 10 wks beginning June 19th. Courses—short workshops with local and visiting artists.

NORTH SEATTLE COMMUNITY COLLEGE, Humanities Division, Art Department, 9300 Burke Ave N, 98103. Tel: 206-634-4513. *Acting Chmn Art Dept* John Constantine, MFA; *Instr* Elroy Christenson, MFA; *Instr* David J Harris, MFA.
Estab 1970; pub; D&E; ent req HS dipl; degree AA 2 yrs; schol; SC 27, LC 7; enrl D 150, E 65.
Tuition: Res—$100 per quarter; Nonres—$250 per quarter; no campus res.
Courses: Art History; Ceramics; Collage; Drawing; History of Art & Archaeology; Interior Design; Jewelry; Painting; Photography; Printmaking; Sculpture.
Adult Hobby Classes: Courses—Drawing; Painting.
Summer School: Tui $100 for term of 8 wks beginning June 20. Courses—Drawing; Introduction to Art.

SEATTLE CENTRAL COMMUNITY COLLEGE,* 1718 Broadway, 98122. Tel: 206-587-3800.
Estab 1970; pub; D&E; ent req HS dipl, ent exam; 2 yrs; schol.
Tuition: No campus res.
—Division of Humanities. Tel: 206-587-3877. *Chmn* John Doty; Instrs FT 3, PT 2.
SC 15, LC 5; enrl D 70, E 50; degree AA.
Courses: Art History; Fine Arts (Painting); Sculpture.

SHORELINE COMMUNITY COLLEGE, Humanities Division, 16101 Greenwood Ave North, 98133. Tel: 206-546-4101. *Chmn* Wayne McQuire; *Prof* John Kirk, MFA; *Prof* Mike Larson, BA; *Prof* Denis Ostermeyer, MFA; *Prof* Chris Simons, MFA.
Estab 1964; pub; D&E; ent req HS dipl, college entrance exam; degrees AA and AFA; SC 9, LC Art Hist survey; enrl D 5500.

Tuition: Res—Undergrad $83 per quarter, $8.30 per quarter hour; Nonres—Undergrad $227 per quarter, $22.70 per quarter hr; no campus res.
Courses: ‡Advertising Design; Art History; Ceramics; ‡Commercial Art; Drawing; History of Art; Illustration; Lettering; Painting; Photography; Sculpture; Stage Design; Teacher Training; Theatre Arts.
Summer School: Term of 8 wk summer session beginning June 19th to August 11th. Courses—Ceramics; Design; Drawing; Photography.

UNIVERSITY OF WASHINGTON, School of Art DM-10, 98195. Tel: 206-543-0970. *Dir* Richard Arnold; *Assoc Dir* Eugene Pizzuro.
Estab 1878; pub; D&E; ent req must meet U of W Admission req; degrees BFA 5 yr, BA 4 yr, MA, PhD and MFA; schol; SC 113, LC 84 GC 30; enrl D&E 3662, maj 1010, GS 109.
Tuition: Res—Undergrad $220, grad 247; Nonres—Undergrad $798, grad $912; campus res room & board $1254-$1869.
Courses: Advertising Design; ‡Art Education; ‡Art History; ‡Ceramics; Drawing; ‡Fabric Surface Design; Film; ‡General Art; ‡Graphic Design; Handicrafts (bookbinding, leather, paper); ‡Industrial Design; ‡Interior Design; Jewelry; Metal Design; ‡Painting; Photography; ‡Printmaking; ‡Sculpture; Silversmithing; Teacher Training; ‡Textile Design; Video.

SPOKANE

FORT WRIGHT COLLEGE OF THE HOLY NAMES, School of Art, W 4000 Randolph Rd, 99204. Tel: 509-328-2970, exten 55. *Chmn* Paula Turnbull, MFA; *Instr* Terry Buckendorf; MFA; *Instr* Doug Coffin, MFA; *Assoc Prof* Charles Palmer, MFA; *Instr* Dorothy Altman SNJM, MA; *Instr* Henry Hawkins Lyman Jr, MFA.
Estab 1889; pvt; D&E; ent req not req for class attendance; degrees BA 4 yr and BFA; schol; SC 13, LC 7; enrl D 529 (total), maj 24.
Tuition: $2335 per yr; campus res room & board $1550 plus activity fee.
Courses: Ceramics; Drawing; Goldsmithing; Jewelry; Painting; Sculpture; Silversmithing; Textile Design.

GONZAGA UNIVERSITY,* School of Arts and Sciences, Department of Art, Boone Ave, 99258. *Chmn* Robert Gilmore; Instrs FT 3, PT 3.
Estab 1962; pvt; D&E; ent req HS dipl; degrees BA 4 yr, grad cert in art; SC 20, LC 5, GC 12; enrl D 250 incl maj 50, grad 8, others 80.
Tuition: $1295 per sem; campus res $720.
Courses: Art Education; Ceramics; Commercial Art; Drawing; History of Art & Archaeology; Painting; Printmaking; Sculpture; Teacher Training.
Summer School: Dir Bud Hazel. 6 wk beginning June. Courses—Ceramics; Drawing; Painting; Printmaking; 20th Century Art History.

SPOKANE FALLS COMMUNITY COLLEGE, Creative & Performing Arts, 99204. Tel: 509-456-6100. *Chmn* Donald Nepean; *Dept Chmn* Jo Fyfe and Jac Rogers; *Primary Faculty* Gayle Anderson; Gary Ayers; Margaret Gregg; George Heimdal; Ralph Hoover, Dick Ibach; Ken Keefer; Jeanette Kirishian; Lee Knouse; Kathy Peterson; Lloyd Pierce; Chuck Roadruck.
Estab 1963; pub; D&E; ent req HS dipl, GED; degrees AAA 3 yr, and AA 2 yr; schol; SC 41, LC 5; enrl D 600, E 200.
Tuition: Res—$104 per quarter; Nonres—$403 per quarter, no campus res.
Courses: Advertising; Design; Architecture; Art History; Batik; Calligraphy; Ceramics; ‡Commercial Art; Display; Drawing; Illustration; Interior Design; Intro to Art; Jewelry; Lettering; Mixed Media; Package Design; Painting; ‡Photography; Printmaking; Sculpture; Vol Design; Weaving.
Summer School: Dir Lowell Jacobs. Courses—Batik; Ceramics; Color & Design; Faceting; Interior Design; Intro to Art; Lettering; Oil Painting; Watercolor; Weaving.

WHITWORTH COLLEGE, Art Department, Hawthorne Road, 99251. Tel: 509-466-1000. *Coordr & Assoc Prof* Pauline Haas, MFA; *Assoc Prof* J Russell Larson, MEd; *Assoc Prof* Walter Grosvenor, MAT.
Pvt; D&E; ent req HS dipl; degrees BA and BS 4 yr, MA, MAT & MEd 2 yr; schol; SC 18, LC 3.
Tuition: Campus res room & board.
Courses: Art Education; Art History; Ceramics; Drawing; Handicrafts (batik, general, textile arts); Jewelry; Lettering; Painting; Photography; Printmaking; Sculpture.
Summer School: Dir Alvin Quall. Courses—Art Ed Methods; Ceramics; Painting; Photography; Textile Arts.

TACOMA

FORT STEILACOOM COMMUNITY COLLEGE, Fine Arts Department, 9401 Far West Drive, 98499. Tel: 206-964-6717. *Chmn* Hal Buckner, MFA; Instrs FT 3; PT 4.
Estab 1966, dept estab 1972; pub; D&E; ent exam; degrees AA 2 yr; SC 20, LC 5; enrl D 350.

Tuition: $87.50 per term; no campus res.
Courses: Art History; Ceramics; Drafting; Drawing; Fashion Arts; Film; Interior Design; Painting; Photography; Printmaking; Sculpture; Stage Design; Theatre Arts.
Summer School: Courses—Ceramics; Drawing; Painting.

PACIFIC LUTHERAN UNIVERSITY, Department of Art, 98447. Tel: 206-531-6900, exten 392. *Chmn* Walt Tomsic, MFA; *Artist-in-Residence* Dennis Cox, MFA; *Artist-in-Residence* Thomas Torrens, MFA; *Prof* Lars Kittleson, MFA; *Prof* Ernst Schwidder, MFA; *Prof* George R Elwell, MFA; *Prof* George Roskos, MFA; *Prof* David Keyew, MFA; *vis prof*—Sande Percival, fibers, spring 78.
Estab 1890, dept estab 1971; den; D&E; ent req HS dipl, Washington Pre-College Test or ACT; degrees BA, BAEd and BFA 4 yr; schol; SC 20, LC 12; enrl D 1000, E 50, maj 50.
Tuition: $75 per hr; campus res room & board $1300.
Courses: ‡Advertising Design; Architecture; ‡Art Education; ‡Art History; Ceramics; ‡Commercial Art; ‡Drawing; ‡Film; ‡Graphic Arts; ‡Graphic Design; Handicrafts (fibers); History of Art and Archaeology; Illustration; Jewelry; Mixed Media; ‡Painting; ‡Photography; ‡Printmaking; ‡Sculpture; ‡Teacher Training; Textile Design.
Summer School: Dir Dr Richard Moe. Enrl 100, tui $54 per sem hr for term of 4 wks, 2 terms beginning mid June and mid July. Courses—Bronze Casting Workshop; Color Slide workshop; Landscape Painting Workshop; Plato to Pop (art history/theory); Watercolor Workshop.

UNIVERSITY OF PUGET SOUND,* Art Department, 1500 N Warner St, 98416. Tel: 206-759-3521. *Chmn* Bill D Colby; *Instrs* FT 11, PT 5.
Estab 1935; den; D&E; ent req HS grad; degrees BA, MA and MFA 4 yr; SC 41, LC 11, GC 23, undergrad 177.
Tuition: $3100 per yr; $1550 per sem; Campus res room and board $1500.
Courses: Art History; Ceramics; Composition & Design; Drawing; Graphic Arts; Jewelry; Lettering; Painting; Sculpture; Teacher Training.
Summer School: 9 wks beginning June.

WALLA WALLA

WALLA WALLA COMMUNITY COLLEGE,* Department of Art, 500 Tausick Way, 99362. *Dir* Kenneth R MacKintosh; *Instrs* PT 3.
Estab 1967; pub; D&E; ent req HS dipl; degrees AA 2 yr; SC 3, LC 1.
Tuition: $250 per yr; no campus res.
Courses: Art Education; Ceramics; Drawing; Painting.
Adult Hobby Classes: Tui $25; Courses—Tole Painting.

WHITMAN COLLEGE,* Art Department, Boyer Ave, 99362. Tel: 509-529-5100. *Chmn* Richard J Rasmussen; *Instrs* FT 3, PT 1.
Pvt; D; ent req HS dipl, ent exam; degree BA 4 yrs; SC 15, LC 8; enrl D 225, maj 10.
Courses: Aesthetics; Art Education; Ceramics; Drawing; History of Art & Archaeology; Painting; Sculpture; Stage Design.

WENATCHEE

WENATCHEE VALLEY COLLEGE, Art Department, 1300 5th St, 98801. Tel: 509-662-1651. *Instr* Robert Graves, MFA; *Instr* Daryl Dietrich, MA; *Instr* Gary Basquett, BA.
Estab 1939; pub; D&E; ent req HS dipl, open door policy; degrees AA 2 yr; schol; LC 4; enrl D 550, E 200, maj 45.
Tuition: Res—Undergrad $291 per yr, $97 per quarter, $9.70 per cr hr; Nonres—Undergrad $1188 per yr, $396 per quarter; campus res and board.
Courses: Art History; Ceramics; Collage; Drafting; Drawing; Graphic Arts; Interior Design; Jewelry; Lettering; Painting; Printmaking; Sculpture; Silversmithing.
Summer School: Dir Dr Ed Hill.

WEST VIRGINIA

ATHENS

CONCORD COLLEGE, Art Department, 24712. Tel: 304-384-3115, exten 277. *Head Dept & Prof* Maynard R (Jim) Coiner, MFA; *Assoc Prof* Gerald C Arrington, MFA; *Asst Prof* Sheila M Chipley, EdD.
Estab 1872, dept estab 1925; pub; D&E; ent req HS dipl; degrees BA and BS 4 yr; schol; SC 32, LC 3; enrl nonmaj 200, maj 60, D 60.
Tuition: Res—$159, per sem; Nonres—$609 per sem; campus res room and board $690 per yr.

Courses: ‡Advertising Design; ‡Art Education; Art History; Calligraphy; Ceramics; Collage, ‡Commercial Art; Constructions; Drawing; Graphic Arts; Graphic Design; Handicrafts; History of Art and Archaeology; Illustration; Jewelry; Lettering; Printmaking; Sculpture; Teacher Training.
Summer School: Tui $80 for term of 5 wks beginning June 10. Courses—varied.

BETHANY

BETHANY COLLEGE, Art Department, 26032. Tel: 304-829-7541. *Chmn* Walter L Kornowski, MFA; *Asst Prof* Wesley Wagner; *Lectr* Joel Collins.
Estab 1840, dept estab 1958; den; D; ent req HS dipl; degrees BA and BS 4 yrs; schol; SC 27, LC 7; enrl D 136, nonmaj 106, maj 30.
Tuition: Res—Undergrad $4900 per yr, $2450 per sem, $132 per hr; Nonres—Undergrad $3420 per yr, $1710 per sem, $50 per hr grad $107 per hr over 16 hrs; campus res room and board, $495 for room, $765 for board.
Courses: ‡Advertising Design; ‡Art Education; Art History; Calligraphy; Ceramics; ‡Commercial Art; Drawing; Graphic Design; Illustration; Jewelry; Lettering; Mixed Media; Painting; Photography; Printmaking; Sculpture; ‡Teacher Training.
Summer School: Dir Joseph M Kurey. Tui $50 per hour for two 5 week summer terms and an 11 wk independent study period. Courses—Independent studies; Seminars; Tutorials.

BUCKHANNON

WEST VIRGINIA WESLEYAN COLLEGE, Department of Fine Arts, College Avenue, 26201. Tel: 304-473-8181. *Chmn* William Baily Oldaker, MFA; *Assoc Prof* Stephen D Tinelli, MA; *Assoc Prof* Ralph Cook, DAEd; *Instr* Nancy Brown Smith, MFA; *Instr* Pricilla Emery, MA; *Asst Prof* Michael Thiedeman, MFA.
Estab 1890; den; D&E; ent req HS dipl; ent exam; degrees BA and MA (Teaching); schol; SC 12, LC 6; enrl nonmaj 100, maj 40, GS 3.
Tuition: $2240 per yr, $1170 per sem, $100 per hr; campus res room & board $1144.
Courses: Art Education; Art History; Ceramics; Drawing; Graphic Arts; Graphic Design; History of Art and Archaeology; Jewelry; Painting; Photography; Printmaking; Sculpture; Teacher Training; Theatre Arts.
Summer School: Dir Dr Kenneth Welliver. Courses—Art Education; Art History; Studio Arts.

CHARLESTON

MORRIS HARVEY COLLEGE,* Art Department, 2500 MacCorkle Ave, 25304. Tel: 304-346-9471. *Head Dept* Henry C Keeling; *Instrs* FT 3.
Estab 1888, pvt, D&E; ent req usual col res; degree 4 yr; SC 16, LC 3; enrl maj 58, others 600.
Tuition: Res—$700 per sem; Non-res fee $300.
Courses: Advanced Studio; Art Appreciation; Art Education; Art History; Ceramics; Design; Painting; Printmaking; Sculpture.
Summer School: Enrl 100 each term; tui $39 per cr hr 2 terms of 10 wks, 1st term June, 2nd term July.

ELKINS

DAVIS AND ELKINS COLLEGE,* Department of Art, 26241. Tel: 304-636-3439, exten 51. *Chmn* Robert C Wever; *Instrs* FT 1, PT 2.
Den; D; ent req HS dipl; degree BA 4 yr; schol; SC 15, LC 5; enrl maj 12.
Tuition: $3100 per yr; campus res $1350.
Courses: Art Education; Ceramics; Drawing; Graphic Arts; History of Art; Painting; Sculpture; Teacher Training.
Adult Hobby Classes: Enrl 90.
Summer School: 2, 4 and 6 wk terms beginning July. Special summer workshop in mountain crafts. Courses—Basketry; Caning; Pottery; Weaving.

FAIRMONT

FAIRMONT STATE COLLEGE, Art Department, 26554. Tel: 304-367-4000. *Chmn* Mr. Wellock; *Primary Faculty* Dr Stephen Smigocki, PhD; James Brooks, MFA; John Clovis, MFA; Barry Snyder, MFA.
Pub; D&E; ent req HS dipl; degrees BA (Art Educ) 4 yr; schol; enrl D 30, nonmaj 20, maj 10.
Tuition: Res—Undergrad $149 per sem, $16 per cr hr; Nonres—Undergrad $599 per sem, $54 per cr hr; campus res room and board.
Courses: Advertising Design; ‡Art Education; Art History; Ceramics; Commercial Art; Drawing; Graphic Arts; Painting; Photography; Printmaking; Sculpture; Watercolor Painting.

Children's Classes: Enrl 60, tui $15 per student. Courses—offered in summer and after regular school in evening.

GLENVILLE

GLENVILLE STATE COLLEGE, Department of Art, High St, 26351. Tel: 304-462-7361, exten 243, 244. *Chmn* David Harry, MA; *Asst Prof* James W Rogers, MFA; *Instr* George D Harper, MA; *Prof* Gary Gillespie, PhD; *Prof* Charles C Scott, MFA.
Estab 1872, dept estab 1952; pub; D&E; ent req HS dipl; degrees AB 4 yr, AA 2 yr; schol; SC 25, LC 3; enrl D 128, E 55, nonmaj 25, maj 60.
Tuition: Res—Undergrad $310 per yr, $155 per sem, $12 per hr; Nonres—Undergrad $1210 per yr, $605 per sem, $50 per hr; campus res room and board.
Courses: Art Education; Art History; ‡Ceramics; Drawing; Graphic Arts; Jewelry; Lettering; ‡Painting; Photography; Printmaking; Sculpture; Textile Design; Weaving.
Summer School: Dir Charles C Scott. Enrl 15-20, tui res $36, nonres $150 for term of 3-6 wks beginning June 12th. Courses—Pottery Workshop.

HUNTINGTON

MARSHALL UNIVERSITY,* Department of Art, 16th St and Third Ave. 25701. Tel: 304-696-6760. *Chmn* June Q Kilgore, Instrs FT.
Estab 1903; pub; ent req HS grad; degrees AB, MA and MS(Art Educ, Studio) 4 yr; enrl maj incl grad $275.
Tuition: Res—$172.20 per sem; Nonres—$647.20; campus res.
Courses: Art Education; Ceramics; Design; Drawing; Graphic Processes; History of Art; Painting; Sculpture.
Summer School: Tui $68 for 6 sem hr; nonres $305.60 for two 5 wk terms.

INSTITUTE

WEST VIRGINIA STATE COLLEGE,* Art Department, 25112. Tel: 304-766-3196. *Acting Chmn* Della Brown Taylor; Instrs FT 5.
D&E; ent req HS dipl; degrees AB (Art) and BSEd (Art) 4 yr; schol SC 26, LC 11.
Tuition: Res—$50 per yr; Nonres—$350; campus res $1050.52.
Courses: Art Education; Ceramics; Commercial Art; Drawing; Graphic Arts; History of Art; Jewelry; Painting; Photography; Sculpture; Stage Design; Teacher Training; Textile Design; Theatre Arts.
Children's College: Tui $10 per 10 wk course.
Summer School: Enrl 50; tui nonres $58 for two 5 wk terms. Courses—flexible.

MONTGOMERY

WEST VIRGINIA INSTITUTE OF TECHNOLOGY,* Fine and Applied Arts Department, 25136. Tel: 304-442-9581. *Head Dept* Arthur Ray Pierce.
Estab 1896; pub; ent req HS grad; degrees AS, BA and BS 2-4 yrs; schol; enrl 2750 (total).
Courses: Art Appreciation; Ceramics; Design; Painting.

MORGANTOWN

WEST VIRGINIA UNIVERSITY, Division of Art, Creative Arts Center, 26506. Tel: 304-293-3140. *Chmn & Prof* Urban Couch, MFA; *Prof* Robert Anderson, MFA; *Prof* Peter Charles, MFA; *Prof* John Clarkson, MA; *Prof* Michael Dupree, MF; *Prof* Ben Freedman, MA; *Prof* Clifford Harvey, BFA; *Prof* Stephen Lawson, MFA; *Prof* Tom Nakashima, MFA; *Prof* Margarte Rajam, PhD; *Prof* James Risser, MFA; *Prof* Bernie Schultz, MA; *Prof* William Thomas, PhD.
Estab 1867, dept estab 1950; pub; D&E; ent req HS dipl; degrees BA(Art Educ) and BFA 4 yr, MA(Art) and MFA(Art) 2-4 yrs; grad degrees; enrl D 250, maj 250, GS 50.
Tuition: Res—Undergrad $201.50 per sem, grad $216.50; Nonres—Undergrad $691.50 per sem, grad $716.50; campus res.
Courses: ‡Art Education; Art History; Basic Design; ‡Ceramics; Drawing; ‡Graphic Design; ‡Painting; Photography; ‡Printmaking; ‡Sculpture.

SHEPERDSTOWN

SHEPERD COLLEGE,* Art Department, 25443. Tel: 304-876-2511, exten 294. *Chmn* Guy Frank; Instrs FT 4, PT 2.
Estab 1872; pub; D; ent req HS dipl; degrees BA, BA(Educ) and BS 4 yr; SC 16, LC 7; enrl maj 80.
Tuition: $342 per yr; campus res $1340 per yr.

Courses: Aesthetic Criticism; Applied Design; Art Education; Ceramics; Commercial Art; Design; Drawing; General Crafts; Graphic Arts & Printmaking; History of Art; Jewelry; Lettering; Painting; Sculpture; Teacher Training.
Summer School: Dir Dr H Schlossberg. Tui $71 for two 5 wk sessions beginning June. Courses—offered on demand.

WEST LIBERTY

WEST LIBERTY STATE COLLEGE, Art Department, West Liberty, 26074.
Tel: 304-336-8019. *Chmn* Bernie K Peace, MFA; *Prof* Ernest D Comiskey, MFA; *Assoc Prof* Karen Rychlewski, MFA; *Asst Prof* R Paul Padgett, MA; *Instr* Neora Koval, MA.
Estab 1836; pub; D&E; ent req HS dipl, score of 14 of ACT test or upper three fourths of HS class; degrees BA and BS 4 yrs; schol; SC 40, LC 5; enrl D 855; E 140; nonmaj 900, maj 95, others 14.
Tuition: Res—Undergrad $312 per yr, $156 per sem, approx $16 per cr hr; Nonres—Undergrad $1212 per yr, $606 per sem, approx $51 per cr hr; campus res room and board.
Courses: Advertising Design; Art Education; Art History; Ceramics; Collage; ‡Commercial Art; Display; Drawing; Film; Graphic Arts; Graphic Design; Handicrafts (general crafts); History of Art and Archaeology; Illustration; Jewelry; Lettering; Mixed Media; Painting; Photography; Printmaking; Sculpture; Stage Design; ‡Teacher Training; Theatre Arts.
Summer School: Dir Alfred R de Jaager. Tui res $15 per sem hr; nonres $42 per sem hr. Courses—Art Education; Drawing; Painting; Special Education.

WISCONSIN

APPLETON

LAWRENCE UNIVERSITY, Department of Art, 54911. Tel: 414-739-3681. *Chmn* E Dane Purdo; Instrs FT 6.
Estab 1847; ent req HS performance, CEEB scores, recommendation; Degree BA 4 yr; SC 8, LC 17.
Tuition: $5300 includes room and board per 3 term yr.
Courses: Art Education; Art History; Ceramics; Design; Drawing & Composition; Metalwork; Painting; Photography; Printmaking; Sculpture.

BELOIT

BELOIT COLLEGE,* Department of Art, 53511. Tel: 608-365-3391, exten 677, 678. *Head Dept* Jarrett W Strawn; Instrs FT 4, PT 1.
Estab 1847; pvt; D&E; ent req top third of class, 3 yr foreign language, 4 yr English, SAT or ACT score encouraged but not required; degrees BA, BS & MAT 4 yr (8 terms modified tri-sem) SC 14, LC 10; enrl maj 85, gen col enrl 1525.
Tuition: $3300 plus $1280 room and board for two terms.
Courses: American Art; Baroque; Ceramics; Design; Drawing; Far Eastern Art; Filmmaking; Graphics; History of Art I & II;. Independent Studies; Modern Architecture; Modern Art; Painting; Photography; Renaissance; Sculpture; Seminar in Art.
Children's Classes: Enrl 20; tui fall terms only $5-$10.
Summer Session: Part of normal tri-sem prog.

DE PERE

ST NORBERT COLLEGE,* Art Department, 54115. *Head Dept* X G Colevechio; Instrs FT 4.
Estab 1898; pvt-den; D; ent req HS dipl, ent exam; degree BA 4 yr; schol; SC 19; LC 5; enrl D 60, maj 60.
Tuition: $2650 per yr; campus res $1194-$1584 includes room & board.
Courses: Art Education; Ceramics; Drawing; Filmmaking; Graphic Arts; Graphic Design; History of Art; History of Environmental Aesthetics; Jewelry; Painting; Photography; Sculpture; Teacher Training.
Summer School: Dir John Giovannini. Term of 6 wk beginning July.
Courses—Art Education: Ceramics; Drawing; History of Art; Painting; Sculpture.

EAU CLAIRE

UNIVERSITY OF WISCONSIN-EAU CLAIRE,* Department of Art, Park and Garfield Aves, 54701. Tel: 715-836-3278. *Chmn* Charles Campbell; Instrs FT 16, PT 1.
Estab 1916; pub; D&E; ent req HS dipl, ent exam; degrees BA and BFA 4 yr; schol; SC 31, LC 12; enrl maj 250.
Tuition: $1774 per yr, $287 monthly; campus res $858.50.

Courses: Advertising Design; Art Education; Ceramics; Drawing; Graphic Arts; Graphic Design; History of Art; Metalsmithing; Painting; Sculpture; Teacher Training; Weaving.
Adult Hobby Classes: Courses—Ceramics; Pottery.
Summer School: Term of 8 wk beginning June 11.
Courses—Art Appreciation; Art Education; Art History; Drawing; Painting; Pottery.

FOND DU LAC

MARIAN COLLEGE, Art Department, 45 S National Ave, 54935 (Mailing Add, 475 Gillett St, Fond du Lac). Tel: 41-921-3900, exten 254. *Coordr* Sister Mary Neff, MA; *Instr.* Sister Jean Brenner, MA; *Prof* Sister Maetha Schouse, MA; *Chmn Arts and Letters* Sister Mary Christine Fellerhoff, MA.
Estab 1936; pvt; E; ent req HS dipl, ACT or SAT; degrees BA and BA(Art Educ) 4 yr; schol; SC 20, LC 12; enrl D 107, E 35 maj 6.
Tuition: $1750 per yr, $875 per sem; campus res room & board.
Courses: Art Education.
Children's Classes: Courses—In Relationship with Art Education.

GREEN BAY

UNIVERSITY OF WISCONSIN-GREEN BAY,* Visual Arts Option. College of Creative Communication, 54302. *Head Dept* Robert Pum; Instrs FT 5, PT 2.
Estab 1970; pub; D&E; ent req HS dipl, ent exam; degrees BA and BS 4 yr; SC 29, LC 3; enrl D 5500.
Courses: Aesthetics; Art Education; Ceramics; Drawing; Graphic Arts; Jewelry; Painting; Photography; Sculpture; Stage Design; Teacher Training; Theatre Arts.
Summer School: Courses—varies.

KENOSHA

UNIVERSITY OF WISCONSIN-PARKSIDE, Fine Arts Division. Art Discipline, 53140. Tel: 414-553-2457. *Chmn* Rollin Jansky, MS; *Coordr & Assoc Prof* John Satre Murphy, MFA; *Assoc Prof* Dennis Bayuzick, MFA; *Asst Prof* David V Holmes, MFA; *Asst Prof* Dale Kohlstedt, MFA.
Estab 1965; pub; D&E; ent req HS dipl; degrees BA and BS 4 yr; SC 25, LC 6.
Tuition: Res—Undergrad $348.50 per sem, $38.25 per hr; Nonres—Undergrad $1214.50 per sem, $110.50 per hr; no campus res.
Courses: Aesthetics; Art Education; Art History; Calligraphy; Ceramics; Drawing; Film; Jewelry; Life Modeling; Painting; Printmaking; Sculpture; Silversmithing; Teacher Training; Textile Design.
Summer School: Tui $34 res, $101 nonres for term of 8 wks beginning mid June. Courses—varies from summer to summer.

LA CROSSE

UNIVERSITY OF WISCONSIN-LA CROSSE,* Art Department, 1725 State St, 54601. Tel: 608-784-6050, exten 257. *Chmn* Leonard R Stach; Instrs FT 9.
Estab 1905; pub; D&E; ent req HS dipl; degrees BA and BS 4 yr; schol; SC 25, LC 5; enrl 7600 (total).
Courses: Art Education; Ceramics; Drawing; Graphic Arts; History of Art & Archaeology; Jewelry; Painting; Sculpture; Theatre Arts.

VITERBO COLLEGE, Art Department, 815 S Ninth, 54601. Tel: 608-784-0040. *Chmn* Sister Carlene Unser, MA; *Assoc Prof* Tim Crane, MFA; *Assoc Prof* Steve Bigler, MFA; *Asst Prof* Jim Knipe, MFA; *Instrs* Sister Donna Weber, MA.
Estab 1890; pvt; D&E; degrees BA and BAEd 4 yr; SC 10 - 12, LC 6; enrl D 55, maj 55.
Tuition: $1990 per yr; campus res room and board $1285.
Courses: Advertising Design; ‡Art Education; Art History; Ceramics; Commercial Art; Costume Design and Construction; Drawing; Fibers; Graphic Arts; Illustration; Painting; Photography; Printmaking; Sculpture; Teacher Training; Theatre Arts; Weaving.
Summer School: Tui $40 per sem hr. Courses—Art Methods for Elementary Teachers; Painting; Weaving.

MADISON

EDGEWOOD COLLEGE, Art Department, 855 Woodrow St, 53711. Tel: 608-257-4861, exten 207. *Prof* Sister Alice O'Rourke, PhD; *Chmn* Sister M Teresita Kelly OP, MFA; John C Barsness, MFA; Sister Lorraine Heinz, MFA; Sister Margaret Mary Majewski, PhD; Sister M Stephanie Stauder, MFA.

Estab 1941; den; D&E; ent req HS dipl, SAT; degrees BA or BS 4 yr; institutional grants based on financial needs; SC 20, LC 4; enrl D&E 500 (total); nonmaj 70, maj 20.
Tuition: $2200; campus res.
Courses: Art Education; Art History; Ceramics; Constructions; Drawing; Film; Graphic Arts; Graphic Design; Lettering; Painting; Photography; Printmaking; Sculpture; Teacher Training.
Summer School: Dir Dr Joseph Schmiedicki. Tui $86 per cr. Courses—varied.

MADISON AREA TECHNICAL COLLEGE, Communication Arts; 53703. Tel: 608-266-5058. *Chmn* Charles M Haycock, MA; *Primary Faculty* Owen Kampen BS; Don Trudell, MFA; William Feeny, MA; Bruce Ellinger, BS; John Fritsch, MFA; Roberta Meyer, MFA; Joann Hayes, BS.
Estab 1911; pub; D&E; ent req HS dipl; degrees AA 2 yr, commercial art-layout-design; schol; SC 45, LC 12; enrl D 5300, E PT 23,000.
Tuition: $7.60 per cr, average $204; no campus res.
Courses: Advertising Design; Aesthetics; Architecture; Art History; Calligraphy; Ceramics; ‡Commercial Art; Conceptual Art; Display; ‡Drafting; Drawing; Fashion Arts; Film; Goldsmithing; ‡Graphic Arts; History of Art and Archaeology; Illustration; ‡Interior Design; Jewelry; ‡Landscape Architecture; Lettering; Mixed Media; ‡Occupational Therapy; Painting; ‡Photography; Printmaking; Sculpture; Video.
Adult Hobby Classes: Enrl 1000; tui $0.19 per hour. Courses—all of usual.
Summer School: Tui $7.60 per cr for 6 wks. Courses—selected art.

UNIVERSITY OF WISCONSIN, MADISON
—**School of Education,*** Department of Art, 6241 Humanities Bldg, 455 N Park, 53706. Tel: 608-262-1660. *Chmn* Phillip M Hamilton; Instrs FT 40, PT 18.
Estab 1911; pub; degrees BS(Art, Art Educ), 4 yrs, MA(Art, Art Educ), MFA(Art), PhD(Art Educ); undergrad schol, grad schol and fel; SC 47, LC 2, GC 19; enrl maj 850.
Courses: Art Education; Art Metal; Ceramics; Design; Drawing; Etching; Glassblowing; Lithography; Painting; Photography; Photo-Offset; Relief Printing; Sculpture; Serigraphy; Stage Design & Lighting; Typography; Watercolor; Woodworking.
—**College of Letters and Science,** Department of Art History, 800 University Ave. Tel: 608-263-2340. *Prof Art Hist & Chmn Dept* Jane C Hutchison, PhD; *Prof* Robert Beetem, PhD; *Instr* Barbara Buenger, MA; *Prof* James Dennis, PhD; *Prof* Frank Horlbeck, PhD; *Asst Prof* Narciso Menocal, PhD; *Assoc Prof* Warren Moon, PhD; vis lectr—Nina Nickolaevna Kalitina, spring 78.
Estab 1848, dept estab 1925; pub; D; ent req HS dipl; degrees BA 4 yrs, MA 1 yr, PhD 3 yrs; schol; LC 37, GC 4; enrl in dept 2372, maj 61, grad 24.
Tuition: Res—Undergrad $367 per sem, $30.55 per cr, grad $519 per sem, $65 per cr; Nonres—Undergrad $1342 per sem, $111.80 per cr, grad $1636 per sem, $75.75 per cr; campus res room and board $1285 per yr.
Courses: Architecture; ‡Art History; Museum Staff Training.
Summer School: Prof & Chmn Jane C Hutchison. Term of 8 wks beginning June 19. Courses—Ancient &・Medieval Art; Renaissance to Modern Art; Roman Art; Netherlandish Painting of the 17th Century; American Painting.
—**School of Family Resources and Consumer Sciences,** Environment, Textiles, and Design Program Area, 1300 Linden Dr. Tel: 608-262-3190, 262-2651. *Prof & Prog Coordr* Emma M Jordre, MS; *Prof* Robert P Bartholomew, MFA; *Asst Prof* Virginia T Boyd, PhD; *Asst Prof* James Buesing, MA; *Assoc Prof* Jane Graff, MA; *Lectr* Candy Hafermann, MFA; *Assoc Prof* Roger M Kramer, MS; *Assoc Prof* Patricia K Mansfield, MS; *Asst Prof* Joyce O Marquess, MFA; *Prof* Agatha A Norton, MS; *Lectr* Ruth C Morrissey, PhD Cand; *Lectr* Suzanne B Scott, MS; *Assoc Prof* Mary G Stieglitz, PhD; *Asst Prof* Otto Charles Thieme, MFA; *Lectr* Betsy Tuttle, MFA; *Lectr* Gail C Winkler, MS.
D&E; ent req HS dipl; degrees BS 4 yrs, MS 2 yrs; schol; SC 23, LC 3, GC 300; enrl in dept D 862-978, E 53, grad 25.
Tuition: Res—Undergrad $367 per sem, grad $519 per sem; Nonres—Undergrad $1342 per sem, grad $1636 per sem; guest student, res $157.75, nonres $645.25; campus res.
Courses: Apparel Design; Costume Design & Construction; Handicrafts (weaving); Interior Design; Retailing; Textile Design; Textile Science; Textiles & Clothing.
Summer School: Tui $30.25 - $112.25 per cr hr for term of several lengths. Courses—Designing for the Elderly; Experimental Textile Design; Interior Design; Weaving; Human Factors in Design; Visual Representation for Designers; Physiology of Textiles & Clothing.

MARINETTE

UNIVERSITY OF WISCONSIN CENTER, Marinette County, Bay Shore Rd, 54143. Tel: 715-735-7477. *Head Dept & Assoc Prof* James La Malfa, MFA.
Estab 1850, dept estab 1946; pub; D&E; ent req HS dipl; degrees AA 2 yrs; schol; SC 6 - 8, LC 2 - 3; enrl D 65, maj 10.
Tuitions: Res—Undergrad $317.50 per sem; Nonres—Undergrad $1151.50 per sem; campus res room and board $630.
Courses: Art History; Ceramics; Color Photography; Drawing; Painting; Photography; Printmaking; Sculpture; Survey of Art; Watercolor.
Summer School: Dir William A Schmidtke. Tui $23 per cr for term of 6 wks, beginning June 12th. Courses—Beginning and advanced photography plus courses in other disciplines.

MENOMONIE

UNIVERSITY OF WISCONSIN-STOUT, Art Department, 54751. Tel: 715-232-1141. *Head Dept Prof* Orazio Fumagalli, PhD; *Prof* Todd Boppel, MFA; *Assoc Prof* Doug Cumming, MFA; *Assoc Prof* James McCormick, MFA; *Assoc Prof* William Schulman, ABD; *Assoc Prof* John Perri, MFA; *Assoc Prof* Charles Wimmer, MFA.
Estab 1893, dept estab 1965; pub; E; ent req HS dipl; degrees BA (Art) and BS (Art Educ) 4 yrs, emphasis Interior or Industrial Design 4 yr; SC 60; LC 6; enrl D 24; nonmaj 400, maj 275.
Tuition: Res—Undergrad $363 per sem, $29.25 per cr hr, grad $424.50 per sem, $58.50 per cr hr; Nonres—Undergrad $866 per sem, grad $849 per sem; campus res room & board $705 per yr.
Courses: Aesthetics; ‡Art Education; Art History; Ceramics; Conceptual Art; Constructions; Display; Drawing; Fashion Arts; Goldsmithing; Graphic Arts; Graphic Design; History of Art and Archaeology; Illustration; ‡Industrial Design; Jewelry; Mixed Media; Painting; Printmaking; Sculpture; Silversmithing; ‡Teacher Training.
Children's Classes: Courses—Sat classes in Art (Media changes and Drama).
Summer School: Enrl varies with class; tui res $144, nonres $432 for term of 8 wks beginning June 12th through August 4th. Courses—Drawing 100/500; Fundamentals of Design; Painting; Sculpture.

MILWAUKEE

ALVERNO COLLEGE,* Art Department, 3401 S 39 St, 53215. Tel: 414-671-5400, exten 255. *Chmn Arts & Humanities Div* Susan Siefert; Instrs FT 4, PT 3.
Estab 1948; pvt; D&E; W only in degree prog; ent req GPA, class rank and ACT or SAT; degree BA 4 yr (or 128 cr); schol; SC 20, LC 5; enrl D 200, E 50, maj 35.
Tuition: $2200 per yr; campus res $1100 per yr.
Courses: Art Education; Ceramics; Drawing; Enameling (Cloisonne); General Crafts; History of Art; Introduction to Visual Art; Metal Working; Painting; Printmaking; Sculpture; Stage Design; Teacher Training; Weaving.
Summer School: Term June to August. Courses—Art Education; Studio Art.

CARDINAL STRITCH COLLEGE, Art Department, 53217. Tel: 414-352-5400, exten 331. *Head Dept & Prof* Sister M Thomasita Fessler, DFA; *Prof of Art* Irene Kilmurry, MS; *Assoc Prof* Claudia M Gorecki, MS; *Assoc Prof* John Tryba, MAE; *Instr* Mildred Tryba, BA; *Instr* Sister Madonna Balestrieri, MA; *Lectr* Marianne Rodwell, BS; *Lectr* Paul Calhoun; *Lectr* Marilyn Drucker; *Lectr* Frances Üllenberg.
Estab 1937 den; D&E; ent req HS dipl, ent exam; degrees BA and BFA 4 yr, AA 2 yr; schol; SC 29, LC 17; enrl maj 98.
Tuition: Undergrad $1100 per sem, $60 per cr hr 1-6 hr, $85 per cr hr, $7 and up per hr; grad $70 per cr hr 1-6 hr, $90 per cr hr $7 and up; campus res room and board $1120-$1270 per yr.
Courses: Advertising Design; Aesthetics; Art Education; Art History; Calligraphy; Ceramics; Collage; Commercial Art; Constructions; Costume Design and Construction; Drawing; Graphic Arts; Graphic Design; Handicrafts (weaving); Jewelry; Lettering; Mixed Media; Painting; Photography; Printmaking; Sculpture; Teacher Training; Textile Design.
Adult Hobby Classes: Courses—Enameling.
Children's Classes: Tui $35 per child. Courses—Traditional media plus various crafts.
Summer School: Term of 6 wks beginning June 19th. Courses—Composition; Drawing; Sculpture; possible college credit for summer foreign tour.

CONCORDIA COLLEGE, Art Department, 53208. Tel: 414-344-3400. *Chmn* William L Chandler, MS (Art).
Estab 1881, dept estab 1971; den; D&E; ent req HS dipl; degrees AA 2 yrs; SC 6, LC 1; enrl nonmaj 50, maj 5.

Tuition: $950 per sem, $65 per hr; campus res room & board $760 per sem.
Courses: Art History; Crafts; Drawing; Painting; Sculpture.

MILWAUKEE AREA TECHNICAL COLLEGE, Graphic & Applied Arts Division, 53203. Tel: 414-278-6432. *Head Dept* Harold A Milbrath, MFA; *Instr* Howard Austin, BFA; *Instr* William Bonfiay, MA; *Instr* William Crandall, MA; *Instr* Leland Felber, BE; *Instr* Geraldine Geischer, MFA; *Instr* Chris Hansen, BA; *Instr* Hans Krommenhoek, MEA; *Instrs* Jos Niesl, *Prof* Commercial Artist.
Estab 1912, dept estab 1958; pub; D&E; ent req HS dipl; degrees AA 2 yrs; financial aid; enrl D 150 (Comm Art), 90 (Crafts), E 50 (Comm Art), 100 (Crafts).
Tuition: $400 per yr, $200 per sem; tui and fees approx $12 per cr; no campus res.
Courses: ‡Advertising Design; Calligraphy; Ceramics; ‡Commercial Art; Display; Drawing; Film; Graphic Design; Illustration; Jewelry; Lettering; Photography; Silversmithing.
Adult Hobby Classes: Tui $12 per cr.

MILWAUKEE SCHOOL OF THE ARTS, 207 N Milwaukee St, 53202. Tel: 414-276-7889. *Dir* Jack H White, BFA; *Chmn Foundations Dept* Joseph Mendla, MFA; *Chmn Fine Arts Dept* C W Peckenpaugh, BFA; *Chmn Design Dept* Frank Lukusavitz, BFA; Instrs FT 8, PT 17.
Estab 1974; pvt; D&E; ent req HS dipl, portfolio, letter of intent, medical report; degrees BFA and MSA 4 yr; schol; enrl D 100, E 75; nonmaj 40, maj 60.
Tuition: $1600 per yr, $800 per sem, PT proportionate; no campus res.
Courses: ‡Advertising Design; Art History; ‡Drawing; ‡Illustration; ‡Industrial Design; ‡Interior Design; ‡Painting; Photography; ‡Printmaking; ‡Sculpture.
Adult Hobby Classes: Enrl 75; tui $75 per course. Courses—Advertising; Drawing; Illustration; Painting; Printmaking; Sculpture.

MOUNT MARY COLLEGE, Art Department, 53222. Tel: 414-258-4810. *Chmn* Sister Regine Collins, MA; *Prof* Sister M Remy Revor, MFA; *Assoc Prof* Sister M Rosemarita Heubner, MFA; *Asst Prof* Joseph Rozman, MFA; *Asst Prof* Suzanne Harker, MA; *Instr* Sister M Angelee Fuchs, MA; *Instr* Deirdre Lee Kozlowski, MS; Instrs FT 6, PT 9.
Estab 1913, dept estab 1929; den; D&E; ent req HS dipl; degrees BA 4 yr; schol; SC 22, LC 12; enrl D 200, E 30; nonmaj 50, maj 150.
Tuition: $1375 per yr (includes board), $950 per sem, $79.50 per cr; campus res room and board (board $950, rooms vary average $450).
Courses: Art Education; Art History; Art Therapy; Calligraphy; Ceramics; Costume Design and Construction; Drafting (arch); Drawing; Enameling; Fashion Arts; Film; Goldsmithing; Graphic Arts; Handicrafts (fiber arts, weaving); Illustration; Interior Design; Jewelry; Occupational Therapy; Painting; Photography; Printmaking; Sculpture; Silversmithing; Stage Design; Teacher Training; Textile Design.
Summer School: Dir Sister Ellen Lorenz. Enrl 120; tui $65 per cr for term of 6 wks beginning June 19th. Courses—Art Therapy; Ceramics; Design; Drawing; Environmental Design; Fiber Arts; Photography, Watercolor.

UNIVERSITY OF WISCONSIN-MILWAUKEE,* School of Fine Arts, Department of Art, 53201. Tel: 414-963-4200. *Dean* Robert W Corrigan; Instrs FT 35, PT 3.
Degrees BS (Art), BS (Art Educ), BFA (Art), BFA (with Teachers cert), MS (Art), MS (Art Educ), MFA (Art), MFA (with Teachers Cert); enrl 860 art maj.
Courses: Art Education; Art Metal; Ceramics; Design; Drawing & Painting; Graphics; Photography; Sculpture; Visual Communication; Weaving.

OSHKOSH

UNIVERSITY OF WISCONSIN-OSHKOSH,* Department of Art, 54901. Tel: 414-424-2222. *Chmn* Michael Brandt; Instrs FT 25.
Estab 1871; pub; D&E; ent req HS dipl; degrees BA, BAE and BS (Art) 4 yr; schol to grad students; SC 56, LC 14, GC 31; enrl D 10,500, E 2500, maj 300, grad 15, minors 50.
Tuition: Res—Undergrad $340.50 per sem, grad $400.50 per sem; PT undergrad $28.45 per cr, PT grad $44.58 per cr; Nonres—Undergrad $1149.50 per sem, grad $1175 per sem; PT undergrad $95.70 per cr, PT grad $130.58 per cr; campus res.
Courses: Advertising Design; Art Education; Ceramics; Commercial Art; Drawing; Graphic Arts; History of Art & Archaeology; Jewelry; Lettering; Museology; Painting; Photography; Sculpture; Teacher Training; Textile Design; Woodcraft.

PLATTEVILLE

UNIVERSITY OF WISCONSIN-PLATTEVILLE,* Department of Art, 53818. Tel: 608-342-1781. *Head Dept* Thomas C Hendrickson; Instrs FT 7.
Estab 1866, pub; D&E; ent req HS dipl, ent exam; degrees BA and BS 4 yr; SC 30, LC 5, GC 3; enrl maj 105.
Tuition: $684 per yr, non-res $1055 per yr.
Courses: Aesthetics; Architecture; Art Education; Ceramics; Drafting; Drawing; Graphic Arts; History of Art & Archaeology; Industrial Design; Jewelry; Painting; Photography; Sculpture; Stage Design; Teacher Training; Theatre Arts.
Summer School: *Dir* Harold Hutchinson. Enrl 2200; term of 8 wk beginning June 15. Courses—total dept offering.

RIPON

RIPON COLLEGE,* Art Department, 54971. Tel: 414-748-8110. *Chmn* Dr Erwin Breithaupt; Instrs FT 3.
Estab 1851; pvt; D; ent req grad from accredited secondary school, SAT or ACT is recommended, but not required; degree AB 4 yr; schol and financial aid; SC 13, LC 8; enrl maj 20.
Tuition: $4790 comprehensive fee.
Courses: Art History; Design; Drawing; Multi-Media; Painting; Printmaking.

RIVER FALLS

UNIVERSITY OF WISCONSIN-RIVER FALLS, Art Department, 54022. Tel: 715-425-3266. *Chmn* Mary Barrett, MFA; *Prof* William Ammerman, MFA; *Assoc Prof* Pat Clark, MFA; *Prof* Walter Nottingham, MFA; *Prof* Kurt Wild, MFA; *Prof* John Buschen, PhD; *Asst Prof* Douglas Johnson, MFA; *Asst prof* Terrance Schubert, MFA; *Asst Prof* Don Miller, MFA; Instrs FT 10, PT 5.
Estab 1874, dept estab 1958; pub; D; ent req HS dipl degrees BA, BS (Ed), BFA and BS (LB Arts) 4 yrs; schol; SC 26, LC 18, GC 3; enrl nonmaj 250, maj 191.
Tuition: Res—Undergrad $240.11 per quarter; Nonres—Undergrad $779.95 per quarter; campus res room & board.
Courses: Aesthetics; ‡Art Education; Art History; Ceramics; Costume Design and Construction; Drawing; Film; Glass-hot & cold; Graphic Design; History of Art and Archaeology; Jewelry; Painting; Photography; Printmaking; Sculpture; Silversmithing; Stage Design; Textile Design; Weaving.
Summer School: Term of 8 wks beginning June 12th to Aug 4th. Courses—Art Education; Clay; Clay Sculpture; Drawing; Fiber; Introduction to Art; Silkscreen & Lith.

STEVENS POINT

UNIVERSITY OF WISCONSIN-STEVENS POINT, Department of Art, College of Fine Arts, 2100 Main St, 54481. Tel: 715-346-2669. *Head Dept & Prof* Henry M Runke, MFA; *Prof* Norman Keats, MFA; *Prof* Herbert Sandmann, MFA; *Prof* Richard Schneider, MFA; *Prof* Colleen Garvey, MFA; *Assoc Prof* David L Smith, MFA; *Assoc Prof* Gary Hagen, MFA; *Assoc Prof* Daniel Fabiano, MFA; *Asst Prof* Wayne Halverson, MA; *Asst Prof* Gail Fountain, MFA.
Estab 1894; pub; D&E; ent req HS dipl; degrees BA (Fine Arts), BS (Art Educ) and BS (Fine Arts); enrl D 866, nonmaj 666, maj 200.
Tuition: Campus res room & board.
Courses: Architecture; ‡Art Education; Art History; Ceramics; Drawing; Goldsmithing; Graphic Arts; Graphic Design; Handicrafts (varied-glass, leather, wood); Jewelry; Lettering; Painting; Printmaking; Sculpture; Silversmithing; Teacher Training; Textile Design.
Children's Classes: Art Workshop.
Summer School: *Dir* M J Difford. Term of 8 wks beginning June 12th. Courses—Art Metal; Design; Drawing; Layout and Lettering.

SUPERIOR

UNIVERSITY OF WISCONSIN-SUPERIOR, Department of Art, 54880. Tel: 715-392-8101, exten 368. *Chmn* Mel Olsen, MFA; *Assoc Prof* William Morgan, MFA; *Assoc Prof* James Grittner, MFA; *Prof* Arthur Kruk, EdD; *Asst Prof* Marjorie Whitsitt, PhD; *Asst Prof* Leonard Petersen, MFA; *Asst Prof* John Freeman, MFA; *Asst Prof* W Pope Wright, MFA.
Estab 1896, dept estab 1930; pub; D&E; ent req HS dipl; degrees MA 5 - 6 yrs, BFA with certif 5 yr, BS and BFA 4 yr; schol; enrl D 250, E 100 - 125, nonmaj 100, maj 150, GS 30.
Tuition: Res—Undergrad $244.34 per sem, grad $293.34; Nonres—Undergrad $821.67 per sem, grad $859, 34 per sem; campus res room and board.

Courses: Advertising Design; ‡Art Education; ‡Art History; ‡Ceramics; Collage; Commercial Art; Conceptual Art; ‡Costume Design and Construction; ‡Drawing; ‡Film: ‡Graphic Arts; ‡Handicrafts (batik, general crafts survey); ‡Jewelry; Mixed Media; ‡Occupational Therapy, †Painting; ‡Photography; ‡Printmaking; ‡Sculpture; ‡Silversmithing; ‡Stage Design; ‡Teacher Training; ‡Textile Design; Theatre Arts; Video.
Adult Hobby Classes: Tui $40 per quarter approx. Courses—Batik; Blacksmithing; Photography; Rosemaling; Spinning; Stained Glass.
Summer School: Tui varies for term of 8 wks beginning June 12th. Courses—All Studios + noncredit ethnic and folk arts institute.

WHITEWATER

UNIVERSITY OF WISCONSIN-WHITEWATER, College of the Arts, Department of Art, 53190. Tel: 414-472-1324. *Dean* Raymond E Light; Instrs FT 18.
Estab 1868; pub; D&E; ent req HS dipl; degrees BA and BS (Art, Art Educ, Art History) 4 yr; SC 41, LC 18; enrl D 270, maj 270.
Tuition: $701 per yr; campus res $1322.
Courses: Advertising Design; Aesthetics; Art Education; Ceramics; Commercial Art; Drawing; Graphic Arts; Graphic Design; Handicrafts; History of Art & Archaeology; Illustration; Jewelry; Lettering; Painting; Sculpture; Teacher Training; Textile Design; Weaving.
Summer School: Tui $50 per cr for term of 8 wk beginning June.

WYOMING

CASPER

CASPER COLLEGE, 125 College Drive, 82601. Tel: 307-268-2110. *Acting Head* James L Gaither, MEd; *Primary Faculty* Wilhelm Ossa, MFA; Ed Gothberg, MFA; Stephen Naegle, MFA; Lynn Munns, MFA.
Pub; D&E; ent req HS dipl; degrees AA 2 yrs; schol LC 2; enrl D 3870.
Tuition: Res—Undergrad $144 per sem, $13 PT; Nonres—Undergrad $450 per sem, $40 PT; campus res room and board $507 per sem.
Courses: Advetising Design; Aesthetics; Art History; Ceramics; Collage; ‡Commercial Art; Drafting; Drawing; ‡Handicrafts (weaving); Illustration; Jewelry; ‡Painting; Photography; ‡Sculpture; Silversmithing; Textile Design; Theatre Arts; Video.

CHEYENNE

LARAMIE COUNTY COMMUNITY COLLEGE, Division of Humanities, 82001. Tel: 307-634-5853, exten 132. *Div Chmn* Thomas Neal, MA; *Instr* Walter O Sills, MA; *Instr* Carolyn Palmer, MA; *Instr* Barry Pendley, MA; *Instr* Betsy LaRowe, MA; *Instr* Marilyn Werkele, MA; *Instr* Beth Corwin, MA; *Instr* Douglas Piper, BA.
Estab 1969; pub; D&E; ent req HS dipl; degrees AA; schol; SC 19, LC 3; enrl D 80, E 180, nonmaj 150, maj 10.
Tuition: Res—Undergrad $300 per yr, $150 per sem, $13 per hr; Nonres—Undergrad $600 per yr, $300 per sem, $13 per hr; no campus res.
Courses: Advertising Design; Art History; Ceramics; Drafting; Drawing; Goldsmithing; Graphic Arts; Graphic Design; Jewelry; Painting; Photography; Sculpture; Silversmithing; Stage Design; Theatre Arts; Watercolor (separate classes for opaque and transparent techniques).
Adult Hobby Classes: Tui $13 per cr hr. Courses—all of the above.
Summer School: Tui $13 per cr hr for term of 8 wks beginning May 26. Courses—Ceramics; Drawing; Jewelry; Painting; Watercolor.

LARAMIE

UNIVERSITY OF WYOMING, Art Department, PO Box 3138, University Station, 82071. Tel: 307-766-3371. *Head Dept* Carl Niederer, BS; *Prof* Joseph Deaderickm, MFA; *Prof* Richard Evans, MA; *Prof* Victor Flach, MFA; *Prof* James T Forrest, MS; *Assoc Prof* F David Reif, MFA; *Asst Prof* Jean O Schaefer, PhD; *Asst Prof* John Van Alstine, MFA; Instrs FT 8, PT 2.
Estab 1886, dept estab 1946; pub; D; ent req HS dipl; BA, BS and BFA 4 yrs, MFA 3 yrs, MA and MAT 2 yrs; schol SC 23, LC 6, GC 13; enrl D 120, nonmaj 600, maj 120 GS 21.
Tuition: Res $434 per yr, nonres $1400 per yr; campus res $859 per yr.
Courses: Advertising Design; Art History; Ceramics; Commercial Art; Drawing; Graphic Arts; Graphic Design; Lettering; Painting; Printmaking; Sculpture.
Adult Hobby Classes: Courses—Ceramics; Stained Glass through extension service.
Summer School: Tui $105/$250 for term of 8 wks beginning June 5.

POWELL

NORTHWEST COMMUNITY COLLEGE, 82435. Tel: 307-764-6507. *Head Dept & Coordr* Ken Fulton, MA; *Asst Prof* John Banks, MA; *Instr* Malcolm Tervo, BA.
Estab 1946, dept estab 1952; pub; D&E; ent req HS dipl, res-none, nonres-ACT; degrees AA 2 yr; schol; SC 12, LC 4; enrl D 130, E 222; nonmaj 317; maj 35.
Tuition: Res—Undergrad $130 per sem, $11 per cr; Nonres—Undergrad $350 per sem, $33 per cr; campus res room & board $1171.
Courses: Advertising Design; ‡Art Education; Ceramics; ‡Commercial Art; Drawing; ‡Graphic Arts; Handicrafts (leather, weaving); ‡Jewelry; Lettering; ‡Painting; ‡Photography; ‡Printmaking; Sculpture; Silversmithing.
Adult Hobby Classes: Courses—Basic Painting; Ceramics; Drawing; Tole; Watercolor.

RIVERTON

CENTRAL WYOMING COLLEGE, Art Center, 82501. Tel: 307-856-9291. *Head Dept* Willis R Patterson, MFA; *Primary Faculty* Sallie Wesaw, MFA; Jerry Antolik, MA.
Estab 1966; pub; D&E; ent req HS dipl, GED; degrees AA 2 yrs; schol; SC 20, LC 2; enrl D 300, E 500, nonmaj 50, maj 15, others 20.
Tuition: $225 per yr, $112.50 per sem, $11.25 per hr; special workshops, fees variable; campus res room and board $1138.
Courses: Ceramics; Constructions; Drafting; Drawing; Handicrafts (lapidary, weaving); Jewelry; Mixed Media; Painting; Photography; Printmaking; Sculpture; Silversmithing; Stage Design; Stained Glass; Textile Design.
Adult Hobby Classes: Tui $10 per hr. Courses—Figure Drawing; Macrame; Tole Painting.
Children's Classes: Tui variable. Courses—Drawing; Music; Painting; Pottery; Sculpture; Theatre.
Summer School: Dir Dr Don Jeanroy. Enrl 150; tui varies; term varies. Courses—Special Workshops as scheduled plus pottery and painting.

ROCK SPRINGS

WESTERN WYOMING COLLEGE,* Art Department, 82901. Tel: 307-382-2121, exten 152. *Head Dept* Gary Grubb; Instrs FT 2, PT 4.
Estab 1959; pub; D&E; ent req HS dipl; degree AA 2 yr; schol; SC 12, LC 1; enrl D 125, E 40, maj 20.
Courses: Ceramics; Drawing; Handicrafts; History of Art & Archaeology; Painting; Photography; Sculpture; Theatre Arts.
Adult Hobby Classes: Enrl 100. Courses—Crafts; Drawing; Painting; Pottery.

SHERIDAN

SHERIDAN COLLEGE,* Art Department, 82801. Tel: 307-674-4421. *Chmn & Prof* Richard Martinsen; Instrs FT 4.
Estab 1951; pub; D&E; ent req HS grad; degree AA, AS and AAS 2 yr; enrl maj 10.
Courses—Ceramics; Design; Drawing; Life Drawing; Painting; Sculpture.
Adult Hobby Classes: Noncredit.

TORRINGTON

EASTERN WYOMING COLLEGE,* Art Department, 3200 West C St, 82240. Tel: 307-532-4191, exten 31. *Head Dept* Sue Milner; Instrs FT 1 PT 2.
Estab 1948; pub; D&E; ent req varied; degrees AA and AAS 2 yr; schol; SC 3, LC 1; enrl D 40, E 15, maj 2.
Courses: Ceramics; Drawing; Graphic Arts; History of Art & Archaeology; Painting; Photography ; Sculpture.
Children's Classes: Enrl 25; 4 wks in summer. Courses—General subjects.

AMERICAN SAMOA

PAGO PAGO

AMERICAN SAMOA COMMUNITY COLLEGE,* PO Box 2609, 96799. Instrs PT 1.
Estab 1970; pub; D; ent req HS dipl, 18 yrs; degrees AA and AS 2 yr; enrl D 10.
Courses—Ceramics.

PUERTO RICO

MAYAGUEZ

UNIVERSITY OF PUERTO RICO, MAYAGUEZ,* Department of Humanities, 00708. Tel: 809-832-4040, exten 3156, 3170. *Assoc Dir* Dr Luis E Baco; Instrs FT 7.
Estab 1970; pub; D; ent req HS dipl; degrees BA(Art Theory) and BA (Plastic Arts) 4 yr; SC 67, LC 8; enrl 345, maj 86.
Courses: Seminar in Romanesque Art.

PONCE

CATHOLIC UNIVERSITY OF PUERTO RICO, Department of History & Fine Arts, 00731. Tel: 809-844-4150, exten 253. *Head Dept & Coordr* Julio Micheli, MFA; *Prof* Ana Basso Bruno, MFA; *Prof* Adrian N Ramirez, MA; *Prof* Mahir Laracuente, MM; *Prof* Hufty E Rawson, BFA; Instrs FT 4, PT 1.
Estab 1948, dept estab 1964; den; D; ent req HS dipl; degrees BA 4 yrs; schol; SC 22, LC 4; enrl D 50 maj.
Tuition: $1200 per yr min + fees, $35 per cr hr; campus res room & board.
Courses: Advertising Design; Aesthetics; Art Education; Art History; ‡Ceramics; Conceptual Art; Constructions; Drawing; Graphic Design; ‡Painting; ‡Printmaking; ‡Sculpture.

RIO PIETRAS

UNIVERSITY OF PUERTO RICO, Department of Fine Arts, Ponce de Leon Ave, (Mailing Add: 21847 Rio Piedras, 00931). *Head Dept* Luis Hernandez Cruz, MA; *Primary Faculty* Enrique Sanua Gutierrez, PhD; Juan Jose Barragan Tanta, PhD; Federico Barreda Y Monge, PhD; Susana Herrero, MA; John Balossi, MA; Magdalana Ferdinandy, PhD; Jose Buscaglia Guillermety, MA.
Estab 1902, dept estab 1950; pub; D; ent req HS dipl; degrees BA 4 yrs; schol; enrl D 200, maj 45.
Tuition: $75; campus res.
Courses: Aesthetics; Architecture; Art History; Conceptual Art; Graphic Arts; History of Art and Archaeology; Mixed Media; Painting; Printmaking; Sculpture; Video.

SAN GERMAN

INTER AMERICAN UNIVERSITY OF PUERTO RICO, Department of Performing Arts (Bellas Artes in Spanish), 00753. Tel: 892-1095-253, 279. *Chmn* Robert M Fitzmaurice, PhD; *Assoc Chmn* Noemi Ruiz, MFA; *Assoc Prof* V Jaime Asencio hijo, MA; *Asst Prof* Jaime Carrero, MA; *Assoc Prof* Genoveva Comas, MS; *Instr.* Raul Acero, MFA; *Instr.* Gloria de Duncan, MA; *Instr* Carmen Vazquez de Guy, MA; *Instr* Joyce Anne Wlodarczyk, MFA; *vis prof*—Rolando Lopez Dirube, sculpture; Instrs FT 6, PT 5.
Estab 1912, dept estab 1947; pvt; D; ent req HS dipl; college board, presentation of portfolio; degrees BA 4 yr; schol; SC 20, LC 12; enrl D 135, maj 135.
Tuition: $600 per sem plus $15 health fee, plus $5 activity fee; some courses subject to $15 lab fee; campus res room & board $1020.
Courses: Art Education; Art History; Calligraphy; Ceramics; Drawing; Experimental Design in Native Media; Graphic Arts; Handicrafts (leather, macrame, metals); Painting; Photography; Printmaking; Sculpture; Teacher Training.
Children's Classes: Enrl 15; tui $45 per course. Courses—Photography; Pottery.
Summer School: Courses—Art Appreciation; Basic & Advanced Photography.

SAN JUAN

INSTITUTE OF PUERTO RICAN CULTURE, (Escuela de Artes Plasticas),* El Morro Grounds, 00905. Tel: 809-725-1522. (Mailing Add: Institute de Cultura Puertorriquena, Aptdo 4184, San Juan 00936.) *Dir* Felix Rodriguez Baez; *Prof* Maria Socorro Cruz, PhD; *Prof* Arturo

Davila, PhD; *Prof* Victoria Espinoso, PhD; *Prof* Antonio Marforell; *Prof* Myanda Baez; *Prof* Rafael Lopez Del Compo; *Prof* Tomas Batista.
Estab 1971; pub; D; ent req HS dipl, ent exam; degrees BA 4 yr; schol; SC 38, LC 12, GC 10; enrl D 160.
Tuition: None.
Courses: Aesthetics; Art Education; Art History; Calligraphy; ‡Ceramics; Drawing; ‡Graphic Arts; History of Art & Archaeology; ‡Painting; Photography; Printmaking; ‡Sculpture; Teacher Training.
Summer School: Courses—Basic Drawing; Painting; Sculpture.

VIRGIN ISLANDS

CHRISTANSTED SAINT CROIX

ST CROIX SCHOOL OF THE ARTS, INC, PO Box 1086, 00820. Tel: 809-772-3767. *Dir* Dorothy F Raedler, Instrs PT 12.
Estab 1970; pvt; D; ent req recommendation; schol; SC 27, enrl D 203.
Courses: Batik, Ceramics; Dance; Drawing; Fashion Arts; Jewelry; Macrame; Needle Crafts; Painting; Sculpture; Silk Screen; Theatre Arts.

CANADIAN ART SCHOOLS

ALBERTA

BANFF

BANFF CENTRE SCHOOL OF FINE ARTS,* T0L 0C0. Tel: 403-762-3391. *Head Art Div* Takao Tanabe; *Dir* David Leighton; Instrs PT 20.
Estab 1933; summer school and winter studio program; ent req Senior matriculation and art school for cr courses; schol; enrl Art Div 200, others 1200. All media, studio and location in scenic Canadian Rockies.

CALGARY

ALBERTA COLLEGE OF ART, Southern Alberta Institute of Technology, 1301 16th Ave NW, T2M 0L4. Tel: 403-284-8651. *Head Alberta Col Art* Kenneth G Sturdy, DLC, DA; *Asst Head* James Ulrich, MA; *Opers Supvr* Kenneth Craig, MVA; *Sr Instrs* Richard Edwards, NCC, ATC; *Sr Instrs* Walter Drohan, RCA; *Sr Instrs* F Palmer, RCA; *Sr Instrs* Frank Vervoort, ACA; approx 20 guest lectr per yr in all disciplines.
Estab 1926; pub; D&E; ent req HS dipl, admis test; Dipl in Visual Arts, 4 yrs; schol; SC approx 250, LC 14, GC 7; enrl D 600, E 500, nonmaj 210, maj 321, grad 11, others 58.
Tuition: $144 per yr; campus res $500 per yr.
Courses: Advertising Design; Aesthetics; Art History; Calligraphy; Ceramics; Collage; Conceptual Art; Constructions; Costume Design & Construction; Creative Movement & Visual Design; Display; Drawing; Film; Goldsmithing; Graphic Arts; Graphic Design; Handicrafts (Metals, Textiles, Ceramics); Illustration; Intermedia; Jewelry; Lettering; Mixed Media; Painting; Photography; Printmaking; Sculpture; Silversmithing; Textile Design.
Adult Hobby Classes: Enrl 500; tui $95 for 20 wks. Courses—Drawing; Design; Painting; Printmaking; Media Extension; Watercolor; Portraiture; Showcard Lettering; Textiles; Jewelry; Ceramics; Sculpture; Stained Glass.
Children's Classes: Enrl 140; tui $35 for 20 wks. Courses—Painting; Sculpture; Ceramics; Mixed Media; Puppetry; Advanced Painting for Teenagers.

MOUNT ROYAL COLLEGE,* 4825 Richard Rd SW, T3E 6K6. *Chmn* Richard V Peterson; Instrs FT 6, PT 8.
Estab 1910; pub; D&E; ent req HS dipl; dipl 1-2 yrs; schol; SC 12, LC 17.
Tuition: $14 per cr hr.
Courses: Architecture; Ceramics; Display; Drafting; Drawing; Graphic Arts; Graphic Design; History of Art & Archaeology; Lettering; Painting; Photography; Sculpture; Stage Design.

UNIVERSITY OF CALGARY,* Department of Art, 2920 24th Ave NW, T2N 1N4. Tel: 403-284-5252. *Head* V R Brosz; Instrs FT 28, PT 7.
Estab 1965; pub; D&E; ent req HS dipl; degree BFA 4 yrs; SC 25, LC 10, GC 12; enrl D 167, E 58, all maj.
Tuition: $279.25 half-yr, $558.50 full-yr.
Courses: Art Education; Ceramics; Graphic Arts; Graphic Design; History of Art; Painting; Photography; Sculpture.
Summer School: Dir V R Brosz. 2 terms of 6 wks, May, June & July. Courses—Art History; Ceramics; Design; Drawing; Graphics; Painting.

EDMONTON

UNIVERSITY OF ALBERTA, Department of Art and Design, 88th Ave & 112th St, T6G 2C9. Tel: 604-432-3261. *Prof Art & Design & Chmn Dept* D Haynes, Dipl, ACA; *Prof & Assoc Chmn Dept* J Freeman, MVA; vis prof—P Hide, sculpture, 8 months.
Estab 1905; pub; D&E; ent req HS dipl; degrees BFA 4 yrs, MVA 2 yrs; SC 51; enrl 1518 total undergrad, maj 126, grad 22.
Tuition: Undergrad $550 per yr, $250 per term; grad $625 per yr; campus res.
Courses: Art History; Drawing; Film; Graphic Arts; Graphic Design; Industrial Design; Painting; Photography; Printmaking; Sculpture; Video.
Summer School: Chmn D Haynes. Tui $170 full course for term of 6 wks beginning July 4. Courses—Art; Art History.

LETHBRIDGE

UNIVERSITY OF LETHBRIDGE, Department of Art, 4401 University Dr, T1K 3M4. Tel: 403-329-2691. *Assoc Prof Art & Chmn Dept* Larry E Weaver, MFA; *Assoc Prof* Pauline McGeorge, MFA; *Assoc Prof* Herb Hicks, MFA; *Assoc Prof* Charles Crane, MA(Art Hist); *Asst Prof* Bill McCarroll, MFA; *Asst Prof* Alan Barkley, MFA; vis lectr—4-8 for 2-3 days each.
Estab 1967; pub; D&E; ent req HS dipl; degrees BA and BFA 4 yrs; schol; SC 26, LC 9.
Courses: ‡Art Education; Art History; ‡Ceramics; Conceptual Art; Constructions; Drawing; History of Art & Archaeology; Mixed Media; ‡Painting; Photography; ‡Printmaking; ‡Sculpture; Theatre Arts; Video.

RED DEER

RED DEER COLLEGE,* Department of Art and Design, T4N 5H5. Tel: 403-346-3376. *Chmn Fine & Performing Art* Ian Cook; Instrs FT 4, PT 4.
Estab 1973; pub; D&E; ent req HS dipl, portfolio; dipl in art & design 2 yrs; SC 13, LC 1; enrl D FT 40, E PT 60.
Tuition: $250 per yr plus cost of materials.
Courses: Ceramics; Commercial Art; Drawing; Graphic Arts; Graphic Design; History of Art & Archaeology; Painting; Photography; Sculpture; Stage Design; Theatre Arts.
Adult Hobby Classes: Enrl 80. Courses—Batik; Painting; Weaving.
Children's Classes: Enrl 40. Courses—Ceramics; Painting.
Summer School: Dir Ian Cook. Tui $50 per course. Courses—Introductory Ceramics; Outdoor Landscape Painting.

BRITISH COLUMBIA

NELSON

SELKIRK COLLEGE, Kootenay School of Art Division, 2001 Silverking Rd, V1L 1C8. Tel: 604-352-6601, exten 23. *Dir* D O MacGregor, BFA; *Chief Instrs* M R Levitt, BFA; *Chief Instr* E H Underhill, MA; *Instrs* A Bain, MFA; *Instr* S Kresta, Dipl; *Instr* G Mackie, Dipl; *Instr* J Campbell, Dipl; *Instr* A Farrell, BFA; *Instr* M Zmur, Dipl.
Estab 1960; pub; D&E; ent req HS dipl, portfolio; no degrees, 2 yr cert, 3 yr dipl, 10 month graphic design; enrl D 110, E 30, maj 35.
Tuition: $15 mo, $1 per day; no campus res.

Courses: Advertising Design; ‡Applied Design; Art Education; Art History; ‡Ceramics; Collage; Commercial Art; Conceptual Art; Constructions; Display; Drawing; Graphic Arts; ‡Graphic Design; Handicrafts; Illustration; Jewelry; Lettering; Museum Staff Training; ‡Painting; Photography; ‡Printmaking; ‡Sculpture; Silversmithing.

VANCOUVER

UNIVERSITY OF BRITISH COLUMBIA

—**Department of Fine Arts,** 2075 Wesbrook Mall, V6T 1W5. Tel: 604-228-5650. *Head & Prof* George Knox, PhD; *Prof* Alan Sawyer, PhD; *Assoc Prof* James O Caswell, PhD; *Assoc Prof* W Herbert Gilbert, BA; *Assoc Prof* Roy Kiyooka; *Assoc Prof* Mary Morehart, PhD; *Assoc Prof* Lionel A J Thomas, RCA; *Asst Prof* Marvin Cohodas, PhD; *Asst Prof* Rhodri Windsor Liscombe, PhD; *Asst Prof* Moritaka Matsumoto, PhD; *Asst Prof* Debra Pincus, PhD; *Asst Prof* Richard Reid, BFA; *Asst Prof* George Rosenberg, MA; *Vis Prof*—Richard Prince, sculpture, 1977-78; Instrs FT 5.
Estab 1914, dept estab 1955; pub; D&E; ent req HS dipl; degrees BA 4 yr, BFA 4 yr, MA 2 yr, PhD, unspecified; schol; SC 18, LC 26, GC 14; enrl D 1560, E 119, maj 192, grad 42.
Tuition: Undergrad $572 yr, $125 per 3 unit course; grad $812 first yr, $437 second yr; campus res room and board varies.
Courses: ‡Art History; Drawing; Film; History of Art & Archaeology; Painting; Photography; Printmaking; Sculpture; Video.
Summer School: Dir Dr Norman Watt. Tui $125 per 3 unit course. Courses—varies.
—**School of Architecture,*** Tel: 604-228-2779. *Dir* Robert MacLeod, Instrs FT 11.
Estab 1946; pub; degrees BArch, MArch, 3 yr; enrl 227.
Tuition: $716 session.
Courses: Architecture.

VANCOUVER COMMUNITY COLLEGE, LANGARA CAMPUS, Department of Fine Arts, 100 W 49th Ave, V5Y 2Z6. Tel: 604-324-5511. *Chmn Dept Fine Arts* Barry Holmes, Dipl Art; *Instr* Catherine Broderick, MFA; *Instr* Gordon Caruso, Dipl Art; *Instr* Gerald Formosa, Dipl Art; *Instr* Don Hutchinson, Dipl Art; *Instr* Michael Minot, Nat Dipl; *Instr* Barbara Shelly, MA.
Estab 1970; pub; D&E; ent req HS dipl, portfolio; Fine Arts Dipl 2 yrs; schol; SC 7, LC 1; enrl D 120.
Tuition: $125-$150 per sem, plus $5 material fees per each $25; no campus res.
Courses: Art History; Ceramics; Design; Drawing; Fabric Arts; Painting; Printmaking; Sculpture.
Adult Classes: Enrl 15 per class; tui $25 per sem. Courses—Drawing; Design; Ceramics; Fabric Arts.

VANCOUVER SCHOOL OF ART, 249 Dunsmuir St, V6B 1X2. Tel: 604-681-9525. *Prin* Robin C Mayor; *Dean* Tom Hudson.
Estab 1925; pub; D; ent req HS dipl plus presentation of folio of art work; Dipl in Art 4 yrs; SC 20, LC 8; enrl 450, maj 300, grad 9.
Tuition: $371 per yr; grad $125 per sem, $31 monthly; no campus res.
Courses: Advertising Design; Art History; Calligraphy; Ceramics; Commercial Art; Conceptual Art; Drawing; Film; Graphic Design; History of Art & Archaeology; Illustration; Interior Design; Lettering; Mixed Media; Occupational Therapy; Painting; Photography; Printmaking; Sculpture; Video.
Adult Hobby Classes: Enrl 450; tui $371 per yr.
Summer School: Dean Summer Inst Tom Hudson. Enrl 150-170; tui $75 for one month beginning June 12 or July 10. Courses—Film Animation; Ceramics; Painting; Drawing; Lithography; Photography; Intaglio, Child Art.

VICTORIA

UNIVERSITY OF VICTORIA, Department of Visual Arts, PO Box 1700, V8W 2Y2. Tel: 604-477-6911. *Prof Drawing & Painting & Chmn Dept Visual Arts* Donald Harvey, ATD; *Asst Prof* Mowry Baden, MA; *Asst Prof* Ruth S Beer, MVA; *Assoc Prof* Pat Martin Bates, Dipl Royale; *Assoc Prof* Roland Brener, Post Dipl AD; *Assoc Prof* John P Dobereiner, MFA; *Assoc Prof* George W Tiessen, MFA; dept has an extensive prog of vis artists.
Estab 1963; pub; D; ent req HS dipl; degree BFA 4 yrs; enrl 210, nonmaj 18, maj 16.
Tuition: Campus res.
Courses: Drawing; ‡Painting; Photography; ‡Printmaking; ‡Sculpture.
Summer School: Courses—Drawing; Painting; Printmaking; Photography.

MANITOBA

WINNIPEG

UNIVERSITY OF MANITOBA

—**School of Art,** R3T 2N2. Tel: 204-474-9303. *Head & Prof* Alfred E Hammer, MFA; *Chmn Drawing* Alex Bruning, MA; *Chmn Painting* Don Reichert, BFA; *Chmn Ceramics* Robert W Archambeau, MFA; *Chmn Sculpture* Michael Bigger, MFA; *Chmn Photography* David DeVries, MFA; *Chmn Graphic Design* Norman Schmidt, BFA; *Chmn Printmaking* William Pura, MFA; *Chmn Art History* Eileen Kelly, MA; *Chmn Foundations* Steve Higgins, MFA.
Estab 1950; pub; D; ent req HS dipl and portfolio; degrees BFA 3 yr, BFA Honors 4 yr, Dipl in Art 4 yr; SC 35, LC 16; enrl D 350.
Tuition: $550 yr plus materials; campus residence $880 per yr.
Courses: ‡Art History; Calligraphy; ‡Ceramics; ‡Drawing; ‡Graphic Arts; ‡Graphic Design; ‡Painting; ‡Photography; ‡Printmaking; ‡Sculpture.
Summer School: Dir Alfred E Hammer. Tui $100 for term of 6 wk beginning July 5. Courses—Drawing; Painting; Art History.
—**Faculty of Architecture.*** Tel: 204-474-9286. *Dean* J M Anderson; *Asst to Dean* Peter E Forster; *Head Dept Environmental Studies* Carl R Nelson, Jr; *Head Dept Arch* Kum-Chew Lye; *Head Dept Landscape Arch* Alexander Rattray; *Head Dept Interior Design* Joan M Harland; *Head Dept City Planning* V J Kostka; Instrs FT 47, PT 6 E PT 2.
Estab 1913; pub; ent req for Environmental Studies—Senior Matriculation with 60% average, for Arch—degree of Bach of Environmental Studies or equivalent, for Interior Design—Senior Matriculation or Bach of Environmental Studies, for Landscape Arch—Bach of Environmental Studies or equivalent; degrees Arch 6 yr, LandsArch 5 yr, Int Des 4 yr, City Planning GC 2 yr; schol; enrl Environmental Studies 243, Arch 127, Int des 268, City Planning GC 44.
Courses: Environmental Studies; Architecture; Landscape Architecture; Interior Design; City Planning GC.

NEW BRUNSWICK

EDMUNDSTON

COLLEGE SAINT-LOUIS-MAILLET, Department of Visual Arts, E3V 2S8. Tel: 506-735-8804. *Prof* George Widiez; *Prof* Yvette Bisson; *Prof* Lise Bourque, MFA; *Prof* Jaques Martin, BFA; vis prof—Roland Breucker, painting & theatrical sets, winter.
Estab 1946, dept estab 1968; pub; D&E; ent req HS dipl; degree BA(Fine Arts) 4 yrs; schol; SC 12, LC 1; enrl D 20, E 11, nonmaj 25, maj 6.
Tuition: $620 per yr; campus res room and board $475 per yr.
Courses: Art History; Ceramics; Drawing; Painting; Sculpture.
Children's Classes: Enrl 60; tui $20 per sem. Courses—Painting.

FREDERICTON

DEPARTMENT OF YOUTH, RECREATION AND CULTURAL RESOURCES, New Brunswick Craft School, Hut 3, Woodstock Rd, E3B 5H1. Tel: 506-453-2305. *Dir* George F Fry.
Estab 1946; pub; D; ent req HS dipl, questionnaire and interview; Dipl 3 yrs; enrl 30.
Tuition: $300 plus materials for New Brunswick students; $500 plus materials for others; no campus res.
Courses: Art History; ‡Ceramics; Drawing; ‡Jewelry; Photography; ‡Silversmithing; ‡Textile Design; ‡Weaving; ‡Wood.
Adult Hobby Classes: Tui $30 for 10 wks. Courses—Photography; Creative Weaving; Body Covering.
Summer School: Dir Sonsa Cudebec. Enrl 1500; tui $5 for 1 day beginning July-Aug; Courses—Summer Craft School.

UNIVERSITY OF NEW BRUNSWICK,* Faculty of Education, Art Education Section, E3B 5A3. Tel: 506-455-8901, exten 251. *Head* Thomas R Smith.
Univ enrl 5000, educ 200.
Courses: Art & Child Development; Art Education for Elementary Teachers; Pottery & Clay Sculpture; Evening Pottery Course.
Children's Classes: Sat AM.
Summer School: Courses—Art for Children.

MONCTON

UNIVERSITE DE MONCTON,* Department of Visual Arts, E1A 3E9. Tel: 506-855-2070. Instrs FT 3.
Estab 1967; pub; D&E; ent req HS dipl; degree BA(Fine Arts) 4 yrs; SC 7, LC 3; enrl D 80, E 40, grad 10.

Courses: Aesthetics; Art Education; Ceramics; Drawing; History of Art & Archaeology; Painting; Photography; Sculpture; Teacher Training.

SACKVILLE

MOUNT ALLISON UNIVERSITY, Fine Arts Department, E0A 3C0. Tel: 506-536-2040, exten 492. *Prof Fine Arts & Head Dept* Virgil Hammock, MFA; *Prof* E B Pulford, BFA; *Assoc Prof* John Asimakos; *Assoc Prof* M J A Crooker, MA; *Assoc Prof* Thomas Henderson, MFA; *Assoc Prof* David Silverberg, BA; *Asst Prof* Harold Feist, MFA; *Lectr* Thaddeus Holownia; extensive vis artists prog.
Estab 1858; pub; D&E; ent req HS dipl; degree BFA 4 yrs; SC 17, LC 5; enrl D 55.
Tuition: Campus res.
Courses: Art History; Drawing; Intermedia; ‡Painting; ‡Photography; ‡Printmaking; ‡Sculpture.
Summer School: High School Workshop; Adult Workshop; Photography.

NOVA SCOTIA

HALIFAX

NOVA SCOTIA COLLEGE OF ART AND DESIGN, 5163 Duke St, B3J 3J6. Tel: 902-422-7381, exten 122. *Pres* Garry Neill Kennedy, MFA; *Chmn Design Div* Frank Fox, ARCA; *Chmn Craft Div* Ian Austen, BD; *Chmn Studio Div* Terence Johnson, MFA; *Chmn Art Educ Div* Harold Pearse, MA; *Chmn Art Hist Div* Dennis Young, BA; approx 20 vis profs a year.
Estab 1887; pvt; D&E; ent req HS dipl, portfolio or project req; degrees BFA, BD(Environ Planning or Common Design) and BA(Art Educ) 4 yrs, MFA and MA(Art Educ) 2 yrs; SC 67, LC 31, GC 8 each sem; enrl D 433, E 188, grad 17.
Tuition: $435 per sem; no campus res.
Courses: Art Education; Art History; Ceramics; Conceptual Art; Constructions; Drawing; Goldsmithing; Graphic Arts; Graphic Design; History of Art & Archaeology; Jewelry; Mixed Media; Painting; Photography; Printmaking; Sculpture; Silversmithing; Teacher Training; Textile Design; Video; Weaving.
Adult Hobby Classes: Tui $10-$80 per sem. Courses—Drawing; Painting; Spinning & Dyeing; Jewelry; Fabrics; Ceramics; Photography.
Children's Classes: Tui free. Courses—Art.
Summer School: *Dean* James Davies. Tui $435 for term of 13 wks beginning May 15.

NOVA SCOTIA TECHNICAL COLLEGE, Faculty of Architecture, Spring Garden Rd (Mailing Add: PO Box 1000, B3J 2X4). *Dean* Peter Manning, PhD; *Prof* J Philip McAleer, PhD; *Asst Prof* J Bradford, MArch; *Asst Prof* L W Richards, MArch; *Assoc Prof* H Stubsjoen, MScArch; *Prof* O Biskaps, MArch.
Estab 1911, faculty estab 1961; pvt; D; ent req previous 2 yrs at univ; degrees BArch 4 yrs after previous 2 at univ, MArch 1 yr minimum; schol; SC many, LC many, GC several; enrl approx 200, maj 200, grad 2.
Courses: Architecture; Art History; Constructions; Drafting; Photography.

ONTARIO

DOWNSVIEW

YORK UNIVERSITY,* Department of Visual Arts, Fine Arts Bldg, 4700 Keele St, M3J 1P3. *Dean Faculty Fine Arts* J G Green; Instrs FT 28, PT 13.
Estab 1969; pub; D&E; ent req HS dipl, interview and portfolio evaluation; degree BA(Hons), 4 yrs; SC 26, LC 17; enrl D over 400, maj 400, others approx 120.
Courses: Drawing; Graphic Arts; Graphic Design; History of Art & Archaeology; Painting; Photography; Sculpture.

GUELPH

UNIVERSITY OF GUELPH, Fine Art Department, N1G 2W1. Tel: 519-824-4120, exten 2413. *Chmn Fine Art Dept* Thomas Tritschler, PhD; Instrs FT 13.
Estab 1966; pub; D; ent req HS dipl; degrees BA 3 yrs, BA(Hons) 4 yrs; SC 24, LC 27; enrl 959, maj 225.
Tuition: $342 per sem; campus res.
Courses: Drawing; History of Art & Archaeology; Painting; Printmaking; Sculpture.

HAMILTON

McMASTER UNIVERSITY,* Department of Art and Art History, 1280 Main St W, L8S 4L8. Tel: 416-522-9140. *Chmn Dept* P H Walton; Instrs FT 9, PT 2.
Estab 1934; degrees BA(Studio & Art Hist), Hons BA(Studio & Art Hist) 3-4 yrs; SC 12, LC 29; enrl 85.
Tuition: Campus res.
Courses: History of Art; Studio Art Program.

KINGSTON

QUEEN'S UNIVERSITY,* Department of Art, K7L 3N6. Tel: 613-547-6172. *Head Dept* Joseph Polzer; Instrs FT 17, PT 5.
Estab 1932; pub; D&E; ent req Grade XIII; degrees BA 3 yrs, BA(Hons) and BAE 4 yrs, MA(Conservation); SC 16, LC 25; Summer School.
Tuition: University admission and fees apply; campus res.
Courses: Design; Drawing; History of Art; History of Technique; Painting; Printmaking; Sculpture.

LONDON

UNIVERSITY OF WESTERN ONTARIO,* Department of Visual Arts, N6A 3K7. Tel: 519-679-2440. *Chmn* J L Barrio-Garay; Instrs FT 10, PT 1.
Estab 1967; pub; D&E; ent req HS dipl, ent exam, portfolio and interview; degree Hons BA(Visual Arts) 3 - 4 yrs; SC 11, LC 15; Enrl maj 160.
Tuition: $765.
Courses: Drawing; History of Art & Archaeology; Museum Staff Training; Painting; Photography; Printmaking; Sculpture.
Summer School: Enrl limited; term of 6 wks beginning July. Courses—Visual Arts.

OTTAWA

CARLETON UNIVERSITY,* Department of Art History, Colonel By Dr, K1S 5B6. Tel: 613-231-2700. *Chmn* Dr D G Burnett; Instrs FT 5, PT 3.
Estab 1964; D&E; ent req HS dipl; degrees BA 6 Hons 3 - 4 yrs; Schol; SC 2, LC 25, GC 3; enrl D over 700, maj 135.
Courses: Architecture; History of Art & Archaeology; Museum Staff Training.
Adult Hobby Classes: Courses—Ceramics; Drawing; Painting.
Summer School: *Chmn* Dr D G Burnett. Courses—Art History.

REXDALE

HUMBER COLLEGE OF APPLIED ARTS AND TECHNOLOGY,* Creative and Communication Arts Division, Humber College Blvd, M9W 5L7. Tel: 416-676-1200. *Dean* Jack Ross; Instrs FT 53, PT 24
Estab 1967; pub; D&E, ent req HS dipl, mature student status, one yr of employment plus 19 yrs of age; 2 & 3 yr dipl courses; no degrees; SC 300, LC 75, GC 6; enrl grad 50, PT students 25.
Courses: Advertising Design; Architecture; Batik; Ceramics; Commercial Art; Display; Drafting; Drawing; Film/TV Production; Furniture Design; Graphic Arts & Design; Handicrafts; History of Art & Archaeology; Illustration; Industrial Design; Interior Design; Jewelry; Journalism; Landscape Architecture; Leathercraft; Lettering & Typography; Macrame; Packaging Design; Painting; Photography; Printing Processes; Sculpture; Stage Design; Studio Methods; Theatre Arts; Weaving; Wood Crafts.
Adult Hobby Classes: Enrl 210. Courses—Crochet Batik; beginning classes in most of regular courses.
Children's Classes: Enrl 87. Courses—Beginning Arts & Crafts; Painting.
Summer School: *Dean Creative Arts* Jack Ross. Term of 10-16 wks beginning May & June. Courses— Beginning and advanced classes in most of regular courses.

SOUTHAMPTON

SOUTHAMPTON ART SCHOOL, 20 Albert St, N0H T10. *Dir & Resident Artist* Edna Johnson; *Instr* Herbert Ariss; *Instr* Corbett Gray; *Instr* John Mattar.
Estab 1958 as a summer school; pub; D, July and Aug.
Tuition: Adults $80 per wk; students (14-18) $60 per wk; children (10-13) $25 per wk, half days only; no campus res.
Courses: Art Education; Drawing; Mixed Media; Painting; Photography.

TORONTO

GEORGE BROWN COLLEGE OF APPLIED ARTS AND TECH-NOLOGY,* Box 1015, Station B, M5T 2T9. Tel: 416-967-1212. *Subject Supvr* H Greville; Instrs FT9, PT 10.
Estab 1970; pub; D&E part-time only; ent req HS dipl, ent exam; dipl and specialist cert 2-3 yrs; SC 20, LC 4, GC 5; enrl D 145, E 90.
Courses: Advertising Design; Commercial Art; Graphic Design; History of Art & Archaeology; Lettering.

ONTARIO COLLEGE OF ART, 100 McCaul St, M5T 1W1. Tel: 416-362-5311. *Pres* Paul D Fleck, PhD; *Chmn Dept Found Studies* David Hall-Humpherson, AOCA; *Chmn Dept Commun & Design* Beresford Mitchell, AOCA; *Chmn Dept Design* Joan Burt, BArch, MRAIC; *Chmn Dept Exp Art* Gustav Weisman; *Chmn Dept Fine Art* Eric Freifeld; *Chmn Dept Photo/Elec Arts* Richard Hill, PhilM; *Chmn Dept Lib Arts Studies* Thomas Gordon, MA; *Chmn Dept Technol Studies* Michael Harmes; *Coordr Gen Studies Prog* David Chavel, AOCA, OSA; *Sr Adv* Mary Egan Haines, BID, AXA.
Estab 1876; pub; D&E; ent req HS dipl, interview; degrees Assoc of Ont Col Art, Dipl 4 yrs; schol; SC approx 450; enrl D 1235, E 1270, grad 35.
Tuition: $575 per yr, $60 per course; yearly fees for applicants outside Canada $1500; no campus res.
Courses: Advertising Design; Aesthetics; Art History; Batik; Ceramics; Collage; Color; Commercial Art; Conceptual Art; Costume Design; Display; Drafting; Drawing; Environmental Design; Fashion Arts; Film; Glass Coloring & Forming; Goldsmithing-Metal Work; Graphic Arts; Graphic Design; History of Art & Archaeology; Illustration; Industrial Design; Interior Design; Jewelry; Mixed Media; Multimedia Printing; Painting; Photography; Printmaking; Sculpture; Silversmithing-Metal Work; Stage Design; Textile Design; Theatre Arts; Typography; Video.
Children's Classes: Enrl 30; tui $15 per course. Courses—Design Explorations (a Sat course for secondary school students).
Summer School: Asst Registr PT Studies Linda Frampton. Enrl 700; tui $90 per course for term of 3 wks every day or 15 wks every evening, beginning May 8 to Aug 18. Courses—Drawing; Painting; Watercolor; Graphics; Color; Textiles; Ceramics; Environmental Design; Art History.

THREE SCHOOLS,* 296 Brunswick Ave, M5S 2M7. Tel: 416-920-8370. *Pres* John Sime.
—New School of Art (full-time day school). *Dir* Gordon Rayner; Instrs PT 20.
Estab 1962; pvt; D; ent interview; 1 - 4 yrs in contemporary visual arts; no degree enrl 100.
—Artists Workshop (part-time school). *Dir* Barbara Wood; Instrs PT 70.
Estab 1951; D&E; enrl 2000. course of 11 wks; children's art classes for 25 wk program; visual and performing arts and crafts.
Courses: Ceramics; Drawing; Filmmaking; Graphic Design; Hand Bookbinding; Illustration; Painting; Photography; Printmaking; Sculpture; Textile Arts.
—New School of Theatre (full-time day school). *Dir* James H Burt; Instrs PT 7.
Estab 1974; D; ent interview; enrl 30; 26 wk academic yr.
—Hockley Valley School (summer school). *Dir* John Sime; visual and performing arts and crafts, children's art classes and nursery; Month of July in the Country; enrl 100 per wk.
Estab 1962.
—Other Place (part-time evening school). *Dir* Barbara Wood; lecture courses in the arts and allied subjects; E; Instrs PT 20.
Estab 1973; course of 10 wks.

TORONTO SCHOOL OF ART, 225 Brunswick Ave, M5S 2M6. Tel: 416-921-3986. *Dir* Barbara Barrett, BA; *Primary Art Faculty:* Frances Gage; Fortunato Aglialoro; Larry Middlestadt; Jo Manning; George Hawken; Maureen Swann; June Drutz; Patricia Clemes; vis prof—Dainis Miezajs, watercolor.
Estab 1969; pvt; D&E; no ent req; dipl and credits; schol; enrl D&E 200.
Tuition: $450 per yr, $230 per sem, $54 for 12 wks; no campus res.
Courses: Drawing; Graphic Arts; Mixed Media; Painting; Printmaking; Sculpture.

UNIVERSITY OF TORONTO
—Department of Fine Art,* Sidney Smith Hall, M5S 1A1. Tel: 416-928-6272. *Chmn* F E Winter; Instrs FT 17, PT 1.
Estab 1934; pub; degrees 3-4 yrs; LC, GC.
Tuition: Campus res.
Courses: History of Art.
—School of Architecture, 230 College St. Tel: 416-928-2573. *Prof Architecture & Dir Sch* Blanche Lemco van Ginkel, MCP; *Assoc Prof* John Hall, OSA/CSGA.
Estab 1948; pub; D; ent req HS dipl, portfolio of work and interview; degrees BArch 5 yrs, MArch 1 yr for Studio/minimum 2 yrs for research; SC 5, LC 33, GC 11; enrl 299, nonmaj 6, maj 293, grad 13.

Tuition: Res—Undergrad $750 per yr, grad $956 per yr; Nonres—Undergrad $1606 per yr, grad $1950 per yr; campus res.
Courses: Architecture; Drawing; Photography.
Department of Architecture. *Chmn* Peter Prangnell; Instrs FT 20, PT 12.
Degree 5 yrs; GC; enrl 250. Tuition: $822.
Department of Urban and Regional Planning. *Chmn* Dr Alan Waterhouse; Instrs FT 6, PT 8.
Degree GC 2 yrs, 1 yr dipl GC; enrl 38. Tuition: $605.
—Department of Landscape Architecture, 230 College St, M5S 1A1. Tel: 416-978-3103. *Chmn & Assoc Prof* William Rock, Jr, MLA; *Assoc Prof* Ed Fife, MLA; *Assoc Prof* Jerry Englar, MLA; *Prof* Richard Strong, MLA; *Vis Asst Prof* Larry Diamond, MLA; *Asst Prof* James Belisle, MArch, MLA; *Vis Lectr* David McWhirter BLA; various vis prof.
Estab 1827, dept estab 1965; pub; D; ent req grade 13 dipl; degrees BLA 4 yr; schol; enrl 140, nonmaj 6, maj 140.
Tuition: Nonres—Undergrad $950; campus res room and board.
Courses: Aesthetics; Architecture; Art History Constructions; Drafting; Drawing; Film; Graphic Arts; Landscape Architecture; Landscape Planning; Planting Design; Landscape Architecture Technology.

WATERLOO

UNIVERSITY OF WATERLOO, Fine Arts Department, University Ave, N2L 3G1. Tel: 519-885-1211. *Chmn Dept* A M Urquhart, BFA; *Assoc Prof* Nancy-Lou Patterson, BA; *Prof* Virgil Burnett, MA; *Assoc Prof* Don MacKay, MFA; *Asst Prof* Art Green, BFA; *Asst Prof* Basia Irland, MFA; *Asst Prof* Eve Kliman, PhD; *Asst Prof* Jan Uhde, PhD.
Estab 1958, dept estab 1968; pub; D&E; ent req HS dipl; degrees BA 3 yrs, BA(Hons) 4 yrs; SC 32, LC 27; enrl maj 75.
Tuition: $783 per yr; campus res.
Courses: Art History; Calligraphy; Ceramic Sculpture; Drawing; Film; Illustration; Painting; Photography; Printmaking; Sculpture.

WINDSOR

UNIVERSITY OF WINDSOR,* Fine Arts Department, Huron Church Rd at College, N9B 3P4. Tel: 519-253-4232, exten 359. *Chmn Dept* Antonio P Doctor; Instrs FT 9, PT 7.
Estab 1960; pub; D&E; ent req HS dipl, grade 13, adult; degrees BA, Hons BA and BFA 3 - 4 yrs; schol; SC 22, LC 18; enrl D 137, E approx 110, maj 192, others 10.
Tuition: $770 per yr.
Courses: Drawing; History of Art & Archaeology; Painting; Printmaking; Sculpture.
Summer School: Head Antonio P Doctor. Enrl 118; tui $125 for studio courses, $125 for art history for term of 6 wks beginning July. Courses—Art Fundamentals; Art History Survey; Basic Drawing; Beginning Painting; Ceramics; Intermediate Drawing; Printmaking; Sculpture.
European Summer Program: Head Antonio P Doctor. Enrl 10; tui $145 per course, students must take 2 courses, 6 wks beginning July - Aug. Courses—Intermediate Drawing; Printmaking & Independent Studio Work in Drawing & Printmaking.

PRINCE EDWARD ISLAND

CHARLOTTETOWN

HOLLAND COLLEGE,* Commercial Design Department, PO Box 878, C1A 7N8. Tel: 902-892-4191, exten 226. *Chmn Dept* Henry Purdy; Instrs FT 2, PT 2.
Estab 1969; pub; D&E; ent req HS dipl, interview; Dipl Commercial Art 3 yrs; schol; enrl D 40, E 70.
Courses: Advertising Design; Art Education; Commercial Art; Display; Drawing; Graphic Arts & Design; Illustration; Industrial Design; Lettering; Painting; Photography; Sculpture; Stage Design; Textile Design.
Adult Hobby Classes: Enrl 70.

QUEBEC

MONTREAL

CONCORDIA UNIVERSITY, SIR GEORGE WILLIAMS CAMPUS,* Department of Fine Arts, 1435 Drummond St, H3G 1M8. Tel: 514-879-4132. *Dean Faculty Fine Arts* Alfred Pinsky; Instrs FT and PT 29.

D&E; degrees BFA, BA, post-BFA Dipl in Art Educ, 1 yr full-time leading to teaching cert, MA(Art Educ), 1 yr full-time, MFA (Studio or Art Hist), 2 yr full-time; 5 yr res req for full and part-time students. Noncredit E courses in Life Drawing, Painting and Portrait Sculpture; experimental children's art classes (4 - 16 yrs of age).
Courses: Art Education; Art History; Crafts; Design; Film; Graphic Design; Graphics; Painting; Photography; Sculpture; Theatre Arts.

McGILL UNIVERSITY
—**Department Art History,** 853 Sherbrooke West, H3A 2T6. Tel: 514-392-4977. *Chmn & Prof* W O Judkins, PhD; *Prof* G Galvaris, PhD; *Assoc Prof* R Bertos, PhD; *Assoc Prof* R Bergmann, PhD; *Asst Prof* T Glen, PhD; *Lectr* R Langstadt.
Pvt; D; ent req HS dipl, or CEGEP Dipl; degrees BA 3 yr, MA 2 yr, PhD 2 yr; teaching assistantships; SC 2, LC 7, GC 4, Seminars 2.
Tuition: Being revised; campus res available.
Courses: Fundamentals of Drawing & Painting; ‡History of Art & Archaeology.
—**School of Architecture,*** 3484 University St. *Dir* Derek Drummond; Instrs FT 10, PT 9.
Estab 1896; ent req ent exam; degrees BArch 6 yr; fel; SC 12, LC 7.
Courses: Architectural Design; Drawing; History of Art & Architecture.

MONTREAL MUSEUM OF FINE ARTS,* School of Art and Design,
3430 Ave du Musee, H3G 2C7. *Dean* Richard S Halliday; Instrs FT and PT 28.
Estab 1940; pvt; D&E; ent req HS grad, portfolio; Dipl in Visual Arts, Animation Design & Interior Design, 3 yrs; Continuing Education Evening Courses; Children's Sat Art Classes; Enrl 450.

UNIVERSITE DU QUEBEC A MONTREAL, FAMILLE DES ARTS,* Pavillon des Arts, 1199 Rue Bleury, H3C 3P8 Tel: 514-282-7001.
Estab 1969; ent req 2 yrs after HS; degree Baccalauréat spécialisé 3 yrs; programs offered: Environmental Design; Graphic Design; History of Art; Plastic Art (Engraving, Sculpture, Painting); Plastic Art Teaching.
Courses: Aesthetics; Anatomy; Architectural Drafting; Ceramic Sculpture; Design; Drawing; Etching & Engraving; Fresco; Graphic Techniques; Modeling; Mural Painting; Painting; Perspective; Stone & Wood Carving; Teacher Training.

QUEBEC

UNIVERSITE LAVAL CITE UNIVERSITAIRE,* Ecole des Arts Visuels (School of Visual Arts), Faculté des Arts, G1K 7P4. Tel: 418-656-7631. Instrs FT 27, PT 16.
Estab 1970; pub; D; ent req 2 yrs col; 3 yrs for Baccalauré at en Arts plastiques or Bacallauréat en Communication graphique plus 1 yr for cert in art teaching; enrl 300.
Courses: Drawing; Engraving; Film Animation; Graphic Design; Graphics; Illustration; Lithography; Painting; Photography; Sculpture; Silk Screen; Stained Glass; Tapestry.

TROIS RIVIERES

UNIVERSITY OF QUEBEC, TROIS RIVIERES,* Fine Arts Section, PO Box 500, G9A 5H7. Tel: 819-376-5330. *Dir* Christian Demers; Instrs FT 9, PT 9.
Estab 1969; pub; D&E; ent req ent exam or DEC; degree specialized baccalaureat in fine arts, 3 yrs; SC 12, LC 8, GC 28; enrl D 150, E 100.
Tuition: $50 per course plus $15 for inscription; no campus res.
Courses: Aesthetics; Art Administration; Art Education; Basic Design; Ceramics; Drafting; Drawing; Glass; Graphic Arts; History of Art & Archaeology; Painting; Sculpture; Weaving.
Adult Hobby Classes: Enrl 100. Courses—Painting; Weaving.
Summer School: *Dir* Henri-Georges St-Louis. Tui $50 per course of 3 wks.

SASKATCHEWAN

REGINA

UNIVERSITY OF REGINA.
—**Department of Visual Arts,*** S4S 0A2. Tel: 306-584-4872. *Head* J C Nugent; Instrs FT 11.
Pub; ent req HS grad; degrees BA(Art) 3 yrs, BFA 4 yrs, MFA 2 yrs, Cert 2 yrs; enrl 200.
Tuition: $292 per sem.
Courses: Drawing; Film; Graphics; History of Art; Painting; Pottery; Sculpture.
—**Faculty of Education,*** Department of Art Education. Tel: 306-584-4546. Instrs FT 3, PT 1.
Estab 1965; pub; D&E; ent req HS dipl, matriculation or degree for maj in art; degrees BEd, BA, MEd, 5 yrs; schol; LC 6; enrl D 160, E 20, maj 10, night teachers in field.
Courses: Aesthetics; Art Education.
Children's Classes: Sat.
Summer School: *Exten Courses* H Kindred; *Dean Educ* Dr Toombs. 1973 enrl 500-1000; term of 3 to 6 wks, beginning May.

SASKATOON

UNIVERSITY OF SASKATCHEWAN, SASKATOON CAMPUS,* Department of Art, S7N 0W0. *Prof Art & Head Dept* Don Rogers; Instrs FT 15, PT 4.
Estab 1936; pub; D; ent req HS grad; degrees BA(Art) 3 yrs - 15 classes, BAHons(Art Hist) 4 yrs - 20 classes, BFA 4 yrs - 20 classes, MA(Studio Art) 2 yrs grad prog, BEd(Art) available from Col Educ; schol; SC, LC, GC; open studio prog; enrl approx 850, BFA prog 130, grad 5.
Tuition: $120 per class, 5 classes per acad yr, 1 class during Intersession and 1 class during summer school.
Courses: Art Education; Drawing; History of Western Art; Painting; Photography; Pottery; Printmaking; Sculpture; Survey Studio - Art History Seminars.
Summer School: Emma Lake Campus and Saskatoon Campus; courses change each yr.

Art Schools Abroad

ARGENTINA

BUENOS AIRES

ESCUELA NACIONAL DE BELLAS ARTES 'MANUEL BEL-GRANO'* (National Schoool of Fine Arts 'Manuel Belgrano'), Cerrito 1350. *Dir* Maria L San Martin; Instrs PT 120.
Estab 1799; pub; D&E; ent req ent exam, 3 yr secondary school; degree, Maestro Nacional de Artes Visuales, 4 yrs; SC 13; enrl D 476, E 276.
Courses: Art Education; Composition System & Analysis of Works; Drawing; Engraving; History of Art; Painting; Sculpture.

ESCUELA SUPERIOR DE BELLAS ARTES DE LA NACION ERNESTO DE LA CARCOVA* (National Superior School of Fine Arts Ernesto de la Carcova), Tristan Achaval Rodriguez 1701 Avenida Costanera Sur esquina Brasil). Tel: 31-5144, 31-4419. *Rector & Prof* Jorge E Lezama; *Secy* Ines B Meseguer; Instrs PT 24.
Estab 1923; pub; D; ent exam, 1st and 2nd fine arts schools dipl; degree, Superior Professor granted in the chosen subject, 4 yrs; SC 4, LC 2; enrl 85. No tui.
Courses: Aesthetics; Ceramics; Costume Design & Construction; Drawing; Graphic Arts; Graphic Design; History of Art & Archaeology; Illustration; Lettering; Movie Design; Mural Painting; Painting; Sculpture; Stage Design; TV Design; Teacher Training.

AUSTRALIA

DARLINGHURST

NATIONAL ART SCHOOL,* Department of Technical Education, NSW, Forbes St, 2010. Tel: 310266. *Head* H Abbott; *Head Div Fine Arts* Peter Laverty; *Head Div Design* Philip Hickie.
Estab first classes 1918; pub; D&E; ent req ent exam, higher school cert; degree, ASTC(Associateship of Sydney Technical College), 5 yrs; schol; enrl FT 939, PT 3064, day and evening.
Courses: Ceramics; Commercial Art; Costume Design & Construction; Graphic Design; Illustration; Industrial Design; Interior Design; Painting; Sculpture.
Adult Hobby Classes: Courses—Ceramics; Drawing; Painting; Sculpture.
Children's Classes: Various subjects.

MELBOURNE

VICTORIAN COLLEGE OF THE ARTS,* School of Art, 234 St Kilda Rd, 3004. Tel: 62-5061. *Dir* Lenton Parr; *Dean Sch Art* William Kelly; Lectrs FT 6, PT 1.
Estab first classes 1973 (previously National Gallery of Victoria Art School, estab 1868); pub; D; ent req for dipl matriculation or equivalent, for grad dipl, dipl or equivalent; degrees 3 yr dipl arts, 2 yr grad dipl fine art; enrl dipl 68, grad dipl 12. Tui free.
Courses: Painting; Printmaking; Sculpture.

AUSTRIA

SALZBURG

INTERNATIONAL SUMMER ACADEMY OF FINE ARTS, Kaigasse 2, A-5010 (Mailing Add: PO Box 18, Salzburg, A-5010). *Pres* Hermann Stuppack.
Pub; D.

Tuition: $250 per 5 wks beginning July 23rd. Courses—Architecture; Bronze Casting; Calligraphy; Etching; Free Painting; Goldsmith's Craft; Lithography; Mural Painting; Photography; School of Vision; Sculpture; Stage Design.

VIENNA

HOCHSCHULE FÜR ANGEWANDTE KUNST IN WIEN* (University of Applied Art in Vienna), Stubenring 3, A-1011. Tel: 0222-72 21 91. *Rector* Johannes Spalt, Instrs FT 106, PT 28.
Founded 1868; pub; D; dipl(MA) 4 - 5 yrs; enrl 650.
Courses: Architecture; Art Appreciation; Art History; Art Teacher Education; Bookbinding; Calligraphy; Cartooning; Ceramics; Design; Drawing; Fashion Illustration; History of Culture & Civilization; History of Interiors; Illustration; Jewelry/Enameling; Lettering; Metalcraft; Mosaics; Painting; Pictorial Composition; Pottery; Printmaking; Sculpture; Weaving.

BELGIUM

ANTWERP

NATIONAAL HOGER INSTITUUT VOOR BOUWKUNST EN STEDEBOUW* (National Higher Institute of Architecture and Town Planning), Mutsaertstraat 31, 2000. Tel: 32.41.61. *Dir* F DeGroodt; Instrs 17.
Estab 1663; pub; ent req complete high school; Architectural Degree, 5 yrs.

NATIONAAL HOGER INSTITUUT VOOR SCHONE KUNSTEN-ANTWERPEN* (National Higher Institute of Fine Arts), Mutsaertstraat 31. Tel: 335619. *Dir* M Macken; Instrs 49.
Estab 1663; pub; ent req practical exam & general formation of HS (16 yrs); 5 & 6 yrs for National Higher Institute of Fine Arts, knowledge of Dutch, French, English or German languages is required.

BRUSSELS

ACADEMIE ROYALE DES BEAUX-ARTS, ECOLE SUPERIEURE DES ARTS DECORATIFS ET ECOLE SUPERIEURE D'-ARCHITECTURE DE BRUXELLES,* (Royal Academy of Fine Arts, Brussels), 144 ru du Midi, B-1000. Profs 54, Assts 6.
Founded 1711; D&E; 3, 4 & 6 yr degrees; advanced courses; schol and awards.
Representative Courses: Advertising; Aesthetics; Architecture; Decorative Arts; Design; Drawing; Engraving; Graphic Arts; History of Architecture; History of Art; History of Costume; Painting; Plastic Arts; Sculpture.

ECOLE DES ARTS ET METIERS D'ETTERBEEK,* 78, Rue General Tombeur, B-1040. Tel: 02.733.75.99. *Dir* J Ado Baltus; Instrs FT 22.
Estab 1919; pub; E; no ent req for first yr, then exam req to go on; cert after 4 yrs, dipl after 2 more yrs; classes in French; SC 25, LC 1. Tui free; no campus res.
Courses: Advertising Design; Cabinet Construction; Ceramics; Display; Drafting; Drawing; Enamel; Graphic Arts; History of Art & Archaeology; Illustration; Jewelry; Lettering; Painting; Photography; Pottery; Sculpture; Tapestry & Weaving; Wrought Iron.

ECOLE NATIONALE SUPERIEURE D'ARCHITECTURE ET DES ARTS VISUELS* (National School of Architecture and Decorative Arts), 21 abbaye de la Cambre, B1-1050. *Dir* Robert L Delevoy; *Instrs* FT 24.
Estab 1926; 4 & 5 yrs; schol; enrl 300.
Courses: Architecture; Cinematography; Decorative Arts; Experimental Animation; Industrial Design.

BULGARIA

SOFIA

NIKOLAJ PAVLOVIC HIGHER INSTITUTE OF FINE ARTS,* rue Sipka 1. *Rector & Prof* U Mineko; *Pro-Rector & Prof* V Joncev; *Pro-Rector & Prof* P Cuhovski; *Pro-Rector & Assoc Prof* G Petrov; *Dean Fine Arts & Prof* D Dobrev; *Dean Applied Arts & Assoc Prof* S Serafimov.
First founded 1896; reorganized as an Institute 1954. 427 students.

BURMA

MANDALAY

STATE SCHOOL OF FINE ARTS,* East Moat Rd. Tel: 176. *Prin* U Kan Nyunt; *Instrs* FT 18.
Estab 1953; pub; D&E; ent req Middle School dipl, ent exam; dipl 3 yrs; schol; SC, LC, GC; enrl 1969-70 D 179, E 50.
Courses: Drawing; Commercial Art; Painting; Sculpture.

CHINA, REPUBLIC OF

TAIPEI

NATIONAL TAIWAN ACADEMY OF ARTS,* Pan-chiao Park. Tel: 220. *Pres* Chu Tsun-I; *Instrs* FT 82, PT 168.
Estab 1955; pub; D&E; ent req ent exam with HS dipl, Music Dept with jr HS dipl; D 3 yrs, Music 5 yrs, E 4 yrs; degree; schol open to Chinese student only.
Courses: Chinese Music; Cinema & Drama; Fine Arts—Arts Education, Chinese Arts, Drawing, Western Arts; Graphic Arts—Photography, Printing; Industrial Arts—Ceramics, Commercial Art, Industrial Design; Music (incl Dancing); Radio & Television.

COLOMBIA

BOGOTA

UNIVERSIDAD JAVERIANA, Facultad de Arquitectura y Diseno (Javeriana University Faculty of Architecture and Design), Carrera 7, 40-62. Tel: 2455102 or 2458983. *Acad Dean* Pedro P Polo Verano, BA Arch; *Head Architecture* Juan Ferroni, BA Arch; *Head Industrial Design* Romulo Polo, BA Ind Design; *Head Advertising Art* Fabio Puerta, BA: *Head Architectural Drafting* Jorge Ulloa, BA Arch; *Head of Means of Expression* Ramon Munoz, BA Arch; *Head Hist & Inst Aesthetic Investigations* Jaime Salcedo, BA Arch; *Head Urban Studies* Jorge Londono, MS Town Planning; *Head Construction* Alfonso Delgado, BA Arch.
Estab 1623, faculty estab 1951; den; D; ent req HS dipl, ent exam, personal interview; degrees Technician in Advertising Art or Architectural Drafting, 3 yrs, BA(Arch) and BA(Indust Design), 5 yrs; SC 1 per sem, LC 5 per sem; enrl 813, maj 813.
Tuition: $450 per sem; no campus res.
Courses: ‡Advertising Design; ‡Architecture; Art History; Calligraphy; Commercial Art; Constructions; ‡Drafting; Drawing; Graphic Arts; History of Art & Archaeology; ‡Industrial Design; Lettering; Photography; Restoration & Conservation.

CZECHOSLOVAKIA

PRAGUE

AKADEMIE VYTVARNYCH UMENI* (Academy of Fine Arts), U Adademie 172, 7. *Rector & Prof* Miloys Axman; 16 members.
Founded 1799.

VYSOKA SKOLA UMELECKOPRUMYSLOVA* (Academy of Applied Arts), nam Krasnoarmejcu 80, 1. *Rector & Prof* Jan Simota.
Founded 1885; enrl 310.

DENMARK

AARHUS

SCHOOL OF ARCHITECTURE IN AARHUS, Nørreport 20, 8000. Tel: 06-13 08 22. *Rector & Prof* Nils-Ole Lund; *Instrs* FT 84, PT 8.
Estab 1965; pub; D; ent req HS dipl; degree cand arch, 6 yrs; enrl 1000.
Tuition: The running of the school is paid by the state, and so the tuition is free.
Courses: ‡Architecture; Furniture; ‡Industrial Design; ‡Interior Design; ‡Landscape & Garden Architecture; ‡Physical & Economic Planning; ‡Restoration and Conservation; ‡Town Planning; ‡Town Renewal.

COPENHAGEN

DEN GRAFISKI HoJSKOLE* (Graphic College of Denmark), Julius Thomsengade 3 B. *Dir* Leif Monies.
Courses: Drafting; Graphics; Layout; Reproduction Techniques.

DET KONGELIGE DANSKE KUNSTAKADEMI* (The Royal Danish Academy of Fine Arts), Kongens Nytorv 1, 1050 K. *Dir Sch Architecture* Tobias Faber; *Dir Sch Painting, Sculpture & Graphic Arts* Ole Schwalbe.
Estab 1754; under supervision of Ministry of Cultural Affairs; cert 5 yrs. Foreigners may be admitted to the Academy as temporary students. They are not admitted as beginners in the different subjects, but may take part in voluntary instruction at the School of Painting and Sculpture and may also join advanced classes at the School of Architecture, e.g., the special subjects such as furniture designing, town-planning, garden-planning, etc. Most produce independent work for approval for entrance. No summer school.
Courses: Architecture; Painting; Sculpture.

ENGLAND

BIRMINGHAM

CITY OF BIRMINGHAM POLYTECHNIC,* Art and Design Centre, Perry Barr, B42 2SU. Tel: 021 356-6911. *Head Dept Art* T Scott; *Head Dept Hist of Art & Complementary Studies* P J Barlow; *Head Dept Fashion & Textiles* D Tomlinson; *Head Dept Three-Dimensional Design* R W Potter.
Pub; ent req vary according to course; grad 4-5 yrs.
Courses: Architecture; Art Education; Fashion & Textiles—Embroidery, Fashion, Printed Textiles, Women Textiles; Fine Art—Painting, Printmaking, Sculpture; History of Art & Complementary Studies; Pre-Diploma & Foundation Studies; Three-Dimensional Design—Ceramics, Furniture, Industrial Design, Interior Design, Jewelry & Silversmithing, Painting & Decorating, Theatre Design; Town Planning; Visual Communication—Graphic Design, Photography.

BRIGHTON

BRIGHTON POLYTECHNIC, Faculty of Art and Design, Grand Parade. Tel: 0273-64141. *Dean Faculty* R Plummer, ARCA; *Head Dept Art Hist* R Haynes, MPhil; *Head Dept Combined Arts* P D Rose, ATD; *Head Dept Fine Art* G Irwin; *Head Dept Three-Dimensional Design* J Crook; *Head Dept Visual Communication* J V Lord.
Estab dept 1970; pub; D&E; ent req 18 years of age by October 1 and completion of foundation course in art and design or 2 GCE O level and 2 GCE A levels or 3 GCE A levels or equivalent qualification; degrees 3 yr degree in expressive arts; fine art; graphic design; interior design; wood, metal, ceramics and plastics; 4 yr degree in fashion textile design and administration; enrl PT D&E 704, grad 327, others 894.
Adult Hobby Classes: Available.
Summer School: Offered by Brighton Polytechnic. Tui £70 for one term beginning Sept 10. Courses—Drawing; Bookbinding; Pottery; Printmaking.

LEICESTER

LEICESTER POLYTECHNIC* (Incorporating the Former Leicester College of Art and Design), Priory St, CV1 5FB. Tel: (0203) 24166. *Dean* D C Broadhead; *Head Dept Art* C Saxton; *Head Dept Industrial*

Design A Brickwood; *Head Dept Graphic Design* A Harrison; *Head Dept Art Hist & Commun* D Phillips; *Head Centre for Media Studies* N Stair; Instrs FT 3000, PT 2500.
Estab 1870 designated as a Polytechnic 1969; pub; D&E; ent req HS dipl or equivalent and selection procedure; 3 yrs (following 1 yr Foundation Course); BA(Hons), MA in Art and Design (2nd degree equivalent).
Courses: Architecture; Art Education; Art Teacher Training; Ceramics; Commercial Art; Contour Fashion (Foundation Garment, Leisurewear and Lingerie Design); Costume Design & Construction; Drawing; Fashion; Fashion Art; Furniture; Glass; Graphics; History of Art & Archaeology; Illustration; Industrial Design; Interior Design; Jewelry; Lettering; Painting; Photography; Sculpture; Silver; Textile Design; Textile Technology; Three-Dimensional Design.

LONDON

CENTRAL SCHOOL OF ART AND DESIGN,* Southampton Row, WC1B 4AP. Tel: 01-405-1825. *Prin* Michael Pattrick; Instrs FT 44, PT 156.
Estab 1896; controlled by Inner London Education Authority; ent req submission of work; Foundation Course (1 yr, Textile Design & Graphic Design), Central School Dipl; enrl 470.
Courses: Ceramics; Enameling; Etching; Graphic Design; Industrial Design; Jewelry Design; Painting; Printmaking; Sculpture; Stained Glass; Textile Design; Theatre Design.

CHELSEA SCHOOL OF ART,* Manresa Rd, SW 3 6LS. Tel: 01-352-4846. *Prin* Frederick Brill; Instrs D FT 20, PT 50, E PT 10.
Estab 1895; ent req acad qualifications, ent exam, submission of work, interview; dipl, cert 3 - 4 yrs; enrl 250.
Courses: Graphics; Painting; Printed Surface Design; Sculpture.

CITY & GUILDS OF LONDON ART SCHOOL,* 122-4 Kennington Park Rd, SE 11. *Chmn* Sir Edward Chadwycke-Healey; Instrs 17.
Estab 1879; full and part-time courses; D, E & Sun classes.
Courses: Engraving; Lettering; Lithography; Painting; Sculpture; Woodcarving.

HEATHERLEY SCHOOL OF FINE ART,* 33 Warwick Square, SW1V 2AH. *Prin* John Walton.
Estab 1845; all aspects of art study, including Printing and Sculpture; pre-dipl work, vocational and nonvocational courses; nonselective; studio space available; special courses arranged by negotiation; educational advice supplied.

ROYAL ACADEMY SCHOOLS, ROYAL ACADEMY OF ARTS, Burlington House, Piccadilly, W1V ODS. Tel: 01-734-9052, Sch Exten 40. *Keeper* Peter Greenham, CBE, BA, RA; *Cur* Walter Woodington, RP, RBA; acad has vis tutors.
Estab 1768; pvt; D; ent req cand for all courses should be under 25 yrs of age, though exceptions are sometimes made; degrees Royal Acad Schs Postgrad Dipl, Royal Acad Schs Dipl Advanced Studies and Royal Acad Schs Dipl, 3 yrs.
Tuition: Courses £ 650 yr; Postgrad Course £ 750 per yr; no campus res.
Courses: Painting (Fine Art); Printmaking (as a second subject); Sculpture.

ROYAL COLLEGE OF ART,* Kensington Gore, SW7 2EU. Tel: 01-584-5020. *Rector* Lord Esher; Instrs FT 38, PT 79.
Estab 1837; pub; D; ent exam; 2-3 yrs postgrad degrees, MA(RCA), MDes(RCA), PhD(RCA); enrl 600.
Courses: Automotive Design; Ceramics & Glass; Design Methodology; Environmental Design; Fashion Design; Film & Television; Furniture Design; General Studies; Graphic Design; Graphic Information; Illustration; Industrial Design; Jewelry Design; Painting; Photography; Printmaking; Sculpture; Silversmithing; Textile Design, Knitted, Printed, Woven & Tapestry.

SAINT MARTINS SCHOOL OF ART, 107-111 Charing Cross Rd, WC2H ODU. Tel: 01-437-0058. *Prin* Ian Simpson, ARCA; *Head Painting & VPrin* Frederick Gore, RA; *Head Sculpture* Frank Martin, FRBS, RAS; *Head Fashion Design* Lydia Kemeny, ARCA; *Head Graphic Design* Gordon Ransom, ARCA; *Head Complementary Studies* Simon Pugh, MA; *Head Found Studies* Ken Bale, ARCA.
Estab 1854; pub; D&E; ent req HS dipl, ent exam, portfolio; degrees BA(Hons) in Fine Art and Graphic Design, 3 yrs, BA(Hons) in Fashion/Textiles Design, 3 or 4 yrs, MA(Fashion Design), 1 yr; SC 12, GC 1; enrl D 650, E 580, grad 10.
Tuition: £ 705 per yr, Found Studies £ 390 per yr; no campus res.

Courses: ‡Advertising Design; Art History; ‡Commercial Art; Conceptual Art; ‡Constructions; ‡Costume Design & Construction; Drawing; ‡Fashion Arts; ‡Film; ‡Graphic Arts; ‡Graphic Design; ‡Illustration; ‡Painting; ‡Photography; ‡Printmaking; ‡Sculpture; ‡Textile Design; Video.

SLADE SCHOOL OF FINE ART,* University College London, Gower St, WC1E 6 BT. *Dir & Prof* Lawrence Gowing.
4 yr; course leads to Univ of London BA(Fine Arts), 2 yr postgrad course leads to Univ of London higher dipl in Fine Arts, 2 yr postgrad course also leads to dipl in Film Studies and research facilities lead to Univ of London MPhil or PhD(Fine Art or Film Studies); enrl 180.
Courses: Drawing; Engraving; Etching; Lithography; Painting; Sculpture; Silk-Screen Printing; Study of the Film; Theatre Design.

MANCHESTER

MANCHESTER POLYTECHNIC, Faculty of Art and Design, Cavendish St, All Saints, M15 6BR. Tel: 061-228 6171. *Dir* Sir Alex Smith, PhD; *Dean Faculty* B C C Hirst, HonADF, ATD; *Head Dept Visual Studies* G W Hoverstadt, ATD; *Head Dept Commun Arts & Design* A L J Connolly, ATD AssocSIAD; *Head Dept Environ Design* M H Darke, DiplArch, FRIBA; *Head Dept Fine Arts* D Wain-Hobson, ARCA; *Acting Head Dept Indust Design* C MacGregor, DA, MSIAD; *Head Dept Printing Technol* P R Fletcher, MIOP, MSIAD; *Head Dept Textiles-Fashion* A Levy, DesRCA, FSIAD.
Estab 1838, faculty estab 1970; pub; D&E; ent req high potential creative ability in art and design, 18 yrs of age, completion of full-time Found course; degrees BA(Hons) in Graphic Design, Fine Art, Interior Design, Indust Design, Wood - Metal - Ceramics, Embroidery, Fashion and Printed-Woven Textiles, 3 yrs, BA(Landscape) 3 yrs, BA(Hons) in Architecture, 4 yrs, MA in Graphic Design, Fine Art and Textiles - Fashion, 1 yr, MA in Interior Design and Indust Design 2 yrs, nondegrees Dipl in Landscape Architecture and Foundation course, 1 yr, Dipl in Architecture, 2 yrs, Dipl in Theatre and Printing Technology, 3 yrs; enrl 1562.
Tuition: BA Courses Home Students £ 500 per yr, Overseas Students, 650 per yr; MA Courses Home Students £ 650 per yr, Overseas Students £ 750 per yr.
Courses: Architecture; Ceramics; Fashion Arts; Film; Foundation Course in Art & Design; Graphic Design; Illustration; Industrial Design; Interior Design; Jewelry; Landscape Architecture; Painting; Photography; Printing Technology; Printmaking; Sculpture; Silversmithing; Textile Design.

NOTTINGHAM

TRENT POLYTECHNIC,* Department of Art and Design, Burton St, NG1 4BU. Tel: 0602-48248. *Dir* R Hedley; Instrs FT 72, PT 60.
Estab 1843 (Govt School of Design); pvt; ent req exam GCE on 0 and A levels, or equivalent; dipl, 4 yrs; enrl FT 500.
Courses: Architectural Ceramics; Creative Photography; Fashion - Textiles; Fine Art; Furniture Design; Graphics; Interior Design; Textiles Technology; Theatre Design.

OXFORD

UNIVERSITY OF OXFORD, Ruskin School of Drawings and Fine Art, 74 High St, OX1 4BG. Tel: 0865- 47825. *Ruskin Master of Drawing* Philip Morsberger, MA; *Head Painting* Timothy Gibbs, MA; *Head Printmaking* Edward Bernstein, MFA; *Deputy Head Painting* John Newberry, MA.
Estab 1249, dept estab 1871; pvt; D&E; ent req HS dipl, University entrance exam plus portfolio; degrees BFA 3 yr; SC 5, LC 2; enrl D 60, maj 60.
Tuition: £ 1050 yr; other expenses 2700; campus res room and board available.
Courses: Art History; Drawing; Illustration; ‡Painting; ‡Printmaking; Sculpture; Anatomy.

FRANCE

AIX-EN-PROVENCE

INSTITUTE FOR AMERICAN UNIVERSITIES, Fine Arts in Aix, Avignon and Canterbury, 27 Place de l'Universite, 13625. Tel: 42-23.39.35. *Pres* Herbert Maza, Doctorate; *Lectr* Geoffrey Rubins, Doctorate; *Lectr* Elena Colin, MA; Instrs PT 7.
Estab 1957, fine arts estab 1960; pvt; D; ent req HS dipl; cert granted; schol; SC 5, LC 2; enrl 35, nonmaj 30, maj 5.
Tuition: $1980 per yr, $1045 per sem $70 per cr hr; campus res room and board $1300 per yr.

Courses: ‡Art History; Ceramics; Clay Modeling; ‡Drawing; History of Art & Archaeology; Iron Work; ‡Painting; ‡Sculpture; Stained Glass; Theatre Arts.
Summer School: Dir Art in Provence Elena Colin. Enrl 12; tui $595 for term of 6 wks beginning June 16. Courses—Studio Painting & Drawing in Avignon.

LEO MARCHUTZ SCHOOL OF PAINTING AND DRAWING INC, 6 bis rue Mazarine, 13100. Tel: 42-26-34-97. *Dir & Prof* William M Weyman, BFA; *Prof* Samuel Bjorklund, MFA; *Prof* John Gaparach.
Estab 1972; pvt; D; ent req interest in painting or art hist; cert of study; schol; SC 3, LC 2; enrl 15.
Tuition: $1740 for winter (8 months); no campus res.
Courses: Art Criticism; Art History; Drawing; Painting.
Summer School: Dir William M Weyman. Enrl 15; tui $540 for term of 6 wks beginning June 16. Courses—Painting; Drawing; Art History; Art Criticism.

FONTAINEBLEAU

FONTAINEBLEAU SCHOOL OF FINE ARTS, Palais de Fontainebleau, 77305. Tel: 422-25-39. (American Office: Fontainebleau Schools, 1083 Fifth Ave, New York, NY 10028. Tel: 212-348-2297). *Dir & Prof Architecture* Marion Tournon-Branly; *Prof* P Devinoy; *Prof* G Benoit; *Prof* L G Noviant; *Instr* C Roux-Dorlut; *Prof* R Pechere; *Instr* J Grocholski; *Instr* Louis-René Petit; *Cur* C Samoyault; vis profs—Y M Froidevaux, B Lossky, Paolo Soleri and B Baschet.
Estab 1923; pvt; D; summer school only; ent req five yr basic background in course applied for; no age limitations; cert for successful completion of course; schol; SC 9, LC 5, GC 5; enrl 25-45.
Tuition: $1550 for the summer, includes room and board and registration fee.
Courses: Architecture; Art Education; Art History; Drafting; Drawing; Graphic Arts; Graphic Design; History of Art & Archaeology; Landscape Architecture; Painting; Sculpture; Stained Glass.

LACOSTE

SARAH LAWRENCE COLLEGE, Village des Arts en France du Sarah Lawrence College, 84710 (Mailing Add: Bronxville, NY 10708). Tel: 90-75-82-07. *Dir* Bernard Pfriem; *Primary Art Faculty:* Yasuo Mizui; Evert Lindfors; Crystal Woodward, MA(Art Psychother); Instrs FT 10.
Col estab 1928, art prog in France estab 1970; pvt; D&E; summer June 25 to Aug 5, fall sem Sept 5 to Dec 15; ent req HS dipl, recommendations, open to all qualified students and graduates of all institutions; SC 8, LC 2; enrl summer 60, fall 30.
Tuition: $3200 for fall sem, $1500 for summer term of 6 wks.
Courses: Art History; Drawing; Painting; Photography; Printmaking; Sculpture.

PARIS

ECOLE DU LOUVRE* (School of the Louvre), 34 Quai du Louvre, 75001. *Prin* E de Margerie; Instrs 41.
Estab 1881; degrees for postgrads, 3 yrs; LC.
Summer School: For 4 wks.

ECOLE NATIONALE SUPERIEURE DES ARTS DECORATIFS* (National College of Decorative Arts), 31 ru d'Ulm, 5e. Tel: DAN 76-79. *Dir* M Tourliere.
Estab 1766 as the Royal School of Design; ent req ent exam, entrants must be between 17 (min) and 25 (max) yrs old and must have previous training; dipl, 4 yrs.
Courses: Advertising & Graphic Arts; Decorative Art; Design for Modern Industry; Interior Decoration; Jewelry; Metalwork; Mural Painting; Sculpture; Stage Design; Textiles.

ECOLE NATIONALE SUPERIEURE DES BEAUX-ARTS* (National College of Fine Arts), 17, Quai Malaquais, 6e. *Dir* J Bertin; Instrs 200.
Founded 1648; enrl 10,000.
Courses: Architecture; Drawing; Engraving; Painting; Sculpture.

PARIS AMERICAN ACADEMY, 9 rue des Ursulines, 75005. *Chmn Dept* Gregg Conway; *Prof* Guayo; *Prof* D'Hauterive; *Prof* Henri Goetz; *Head Fashion Dept* Paul McDonough.
Estab 1966; pvt; D&E; no ent req.
Courses: Ceramics; Drawing; History of Art & Archaeology; Painting; Photography; Sculpture; Theatre Arts.
Summer School: Term July - Aug. Courses—same as regular session.

UNIVERSITE DE PARIS I A LA SORBONNE, INSTITUT D'ART ET D'ARCHEOLOGIE* (University of Paris I at the Sorbonne, Institute of Art Archaeology) 3 rue Michelet, 75006. *Dir* J Deshayes.
Ent req exam, BA, BS, Dipl Classical Literature; degrees BA or Dipl Doctorates in Archaeology, 2 yrs; enrl 300.

STRASBOURG

SCHILLER COLLEGE, EUROPE UNIVERSITY, Art Department, 161 rue Melanie, 67000. *Chmn* Erik Vandemeulebroecke, MFA; Instrs FT 1, PT 3; *guest artists*—Roger Cochard, Diplome; Paul Burghoffer, Diplome; Camille Claus.
Estab 1963, dept estab 1974; pvt; D&E; ent req HS dipl, for grad students BFA or equivalent plus submission of portfolio; degrees BFA 4 yr, MFA 2 yr; schol; SC 12; enrl maj undergrad 10, grad 6.
Tuition: Res—Undergrad $5180 includes tuition room and board per yr; Nonres—Undergrad $2980 includes tuition per yr; PT student fee per cr $100; campus res room & board.
Courses: Aesthetics; ‡Art History; ‡Drawing; ‡Painting; ‡Printmaking; ‡Sculpture; ‡Theatre Arts.

GERMANY, FEDERAL REPUBLIC OF

BERLIN

STAATLICHE HOCHSCHULE FÜR BILDENDE KÜNSTE BERLIN* (State College of Fine Arts), Hardenbergstrasse 33, 12. Tel: 31 03 31. *Dir & Prof* Konrad Sage; Instrs 182.
Estab 1696; pub; D&E; ent req HS dipl, ent exam; degree, Dipl, Ing, architecture only.
Courses: Advertising Design; Architecture; Art Education; Ceramics; Commercial Art; Costume Design & Construction; Drawing; Fashion Arts; Graphic Arts; Graphic Design; Illustration; Industrial Design; Landscape Architecture; Lettering; Painting; Sculpture; Stage Design; Textile Design.

DUSSELDORF

STAATLICHE KUNSTAKADEMIE, DUSSELDORF,* Hochschule für Bildende Künste (State Academy of Art), Eiskellerstrasse 1, D-4000. Tel: 1.09.91. *Dir & Prof* Norbert Kricke; Instrs FT 37, PT 8.
Estab 1773; pub; ent req exam, submission of portfolio, degrees 4 yrs; cert; schol & fel; enrl (summer terms) c 650.
Courses: Applied Graphic Arts; Architecture; Art Education; Film; Fine Graphic Arts; Painting; Sculpture; Stage Design.

HAMBURG

HOCHSCHULE FÜR BILDENDE KÜNSTE* (College of Fine Arts), D 2000 Hamburg 76, Lerchenfeld 2. Tel: 22811. *Pres* Dr Freiherr von Buttlar.
Courses: Architecture; Art Education; Art History; Ceramics; Drawing; Film; Furniture Design; Graphic Arts; Industrial Design; Metalwork; Painting; Photography; Sculpture; Textile Design; Topography; Video; Weaving.

HEIDELBERG

SCHILLER COLLEGE-EUROPE,* Fine Arts Department, Central Administration, 6900 Heidelberg, Friedrich-Ebert-Anlage 4, 69. Tel: 06221-12046. *Acad Dean* J G Eggert; Instrs 144.
Estab 1964; pvt; D&E; instruction in English; ent req HS dipl; degrees AA, BA, MA, BFA, MFA, BM, MM, ABA, BBA; enrl 650 (student body composed of students from 45 various countries). Study Centers in Heidelberg, London, Madrid, Paris and Strasbourg.
Courses: Ceramics; Drawing; European Art History; Painting; Printmaking; Sculpture; Stage Design; Theatre Arts.
Academic-Yr-Abroad and Interim Programs.
Summer School: Enrl 160; 6 wk prog beginning end of June.

KARLSRUHE

STAATLICHE AKADEMIE DER BILDENDEN KÜNSTE* (State Academy of Fine Arts), Reinhold-Frank-Strasse 81-83, 75. *Prof & Rector* Klaus Arnold; Instrs 15.
Founded 1854.

MUNICH

AKADEMIE DER BILDENDEN KÜNSTE* (Academy of Fine Arts), Akademiestrasse 2. Tel: 33 85 21. *Pres & Prof* Reipka; Instrs FT 16, PT 4.

Estab 1770, re-estab 1808, merged with Academy of Fine Arts 1946. Studies limited to 10 sem; degrees; dipl; schol for foreigners; schol of German Academy's Exchange Program and the Bavarian State Department of Education.

Courses: Architecture; City Planning; Furniture Design; Graphic Arts; Interior Decoration; Jewelry Design; Painting; Sculpture; Stagecraft; Textile Design.

NUREMBERG

AKADEMIE DER BILDENDEN KÜNSTE IN NÜRNBERG (Academy of Fine Arts in Nuremberg), Bingstrasse 60, D-8500. Tel: 0911-40 50 61. *Prof* Günther Voglsamer.

Estab 1662; pub; D; ent req HS dipl; Sch Cert Exam Art; SC 11; enrl 301.

Tuition: No fee; no campus res.

Courses: Advertising Design; Art Education; Drawing; Goldsmithing; Graphic Arts; Graphic Design; Illustration; Interior Design; Jewelry; Painting; Printmaking; Sculpture; Silversmithing; Textile Design.

STUTTGART

STAATLICHE AKADEMIE DER BILDENDEN KÜNSTE* (State Academy of Fine Arts), Am Weissenhof 1, 7. Tel: 0711 221161. *Prof & Rector* Dr Wolfgang Kermer; *Prof & Pro-Rector* Hans Gottfried von Stockhausen; Instrs 70.

Estab 1869; pub; D; ent req Abitur for Art Educ, practical experience in applied arts, ent exam for all classes; dipl in art educ; SC, LC, GC; enrl approx 900.

Courses: Art Education; Art History; Ceramics; Furniture Design; Graphic Arts; Interior Decoration; Painting; Product Design; Sculpture; Stage Design; Textile Design.

GUATEMALA

GUATEMALA CITY

ESCUELA NACIONAL DE ARTES PLASTICAS* (National School of Plastic Arts), 8a Avenida 12044 zona 1. Tel: 25667. *Escultor* Max Saravia Guai; Instrs PT 15.

Estab 1920; pub; E; ent req Primary Sch dipl (to have a degree 3 yrs of HS); degrees, Bachiller, Maestro en pintura, escultura, grabado, 3 yrs; SC 13, LC 2; enrl 150.

Tuition: Free.

Courses: Advertising Design; Architecture; Artistic Naked; Ceramics; Commercial Art; Drafting; Graphic Arts; History of Art & Archaeology; Mural Painting-Laboratory; Painting; Painting Restoration; Sculpture.

Children's Classes: Enrl 20; tui free. Courses—Painting.

INDIA

BARODA

MAHARAJA SAYAJIRAO UNIVERSITY OF BARODA,* Faculty of Fine Arts, University Rd, Pushpa-Baug, 2. Tel: 64721, 64238. *Dean Faculty Fine Arts* Dr Ratan Parimoo.

Estab 1949.

Courses: Advertising Art; Art History; Lithography; Painting; Photography; Sculpture; Woodcrafts.

VARANASI

BANARAS HINDU UNIVERSITY,* College of Music and Fine Arts, Uttar Pradesh, 221005. Tel: 64491. *Dean Faculty Arts* Dr V P Singh; *Dean Faculty Music & Fine Arts* Dr K S Kulkarni; Instrs FT 5.

Estab 1950; a Constituent Col of Banaras Hindu Univ; ent req aptitude test in Dipl; dipl in Fine Arts, degrees in Painting (BFA), Sculpture (BFA), Applied Arts (BAA), 3 yrs.

IRAQ

BAGHDAD

ACADEMY OF FINE ARTS, Department of Plastic Arts, Al-Waziriya. Tel: 22026. *Chmn Dept & Prof* Ismail Al-Shaikhli; vis prof—Roman Artimofisky, painting, yr.

Estab 1967; pub; D; ent req exam; degrees BA 4 yrs, MA 2 yrs; SC 20, LC 20, GC 12.

Tuition: Free.

Courses: Aesthetics; Art Education; Art History; Calligraphy; Ceramics; Commercial Art; Display; Drafting; Drawing; Graphic Arts; Graphic Design; History of Art & Archaeology; Interior Design; Painting; Photography; Sculpture; Teacher Training; Textile Design.

IRELAND

DUBLIN

NATIONAL COLLEGE OF ART AND DESIGN,* Kildare St, 2. Tel: 682911. *Dir* Jonah Jones; Instrs FT 42, PT 18.

Estab 1746; pub; D&E; ent req HS dipl, ent exam; degree Associate of National Col Art, 4 yrs; schol to Irish citizens; SC 3; enrl D 250, E 600.

Courses: Advertising Design; Aesthetics; Art Education; Ceramics; Costume Design & Construction; Display; Drafting; Drawing; Fashion Arts; Graphic Arts; Graphic Design; History of Art & Archaeology; Illustration; Industrial Design; Jewelry; Lettering; Painting; Photography; Sculpture; Stage Design; Teacher Training; Textile Design.

Adult Hobby Classes: Enrl 300. Courses—Same as above.

ITALY

BOLOGNA

ACCADEMIA DI BELLE ARTI E LICEO ARTISTICO* (Academy of Fine Arts), via Belle Arti 54. *Prof & Dir* Enzo Pasqualini.

FLORENCE

ACCADEMIA DI BELLE ARTI* (Academy of Fine Arts), via Ricasoli 66.
Founded 1801.

ROSARY COLLEGE,* Graduate School of Fine Arts at Schifanoia Villa, via Boccaccio, 123, 50133. Tel: 055-576-297. *Dean* Sister Jean Richter; Instrs PT 20.

Estab 1948; pvt; affiliated with Rosary College, River Forest, Ill; D; ent req BFA(Art) or BA(Art); degrees MA, MFA, 1-3 yrs; schol; enrl 40.

Tuition: $1800 per sem, $150 per cr hr.

Courses: Art History; Art Restoration (3 yrs); Painting; Printmaking; Sculpture.

Summer School: Tui $600, plus cost of travel. Courses—Italian Romanesque Art & Architecture (field trip).

STUDIO ART CENTERS INTERNATIANAL, 40 via de' Ginori, 50129. Tel: (055) 26-39-48. *Dir & Dean Painting & Drawing* Jules Maidoff, MA; *Co-Dir SACI Prog* William Darr, MFA; *Primary Art Faculty:* Piero Colacicchi, Dipl Sculpture; Claudio B Curri; Tamio Fujimura, MFA; Kathleen Knipple, MFA; Margherita Licht, PhD; Martino Maringoni; Dennis Olsen, MA; Leonardo Passeri; vis artists & critics—Luca Alinari, Giuliano Ghelli, Renato Bittoni, Dino Carini, Bruno Canova, Dino Pasquali, Vanni Bramante and Livio Orazio Valentini.

Initiated by Drake Univ 1969, incorporated 1976; academically affiliated with Drake Univ and other sch progs; offers fully accredited progs, with credits readily transferable to other schools; the program is divided into fall and spring terms, as well as a special 3 wk summer session; ent req above freshman level of college and in good acad standing (at least 2.0 based on 4.0 scale), noncollege students above the age of 18; schol; enrl limited to 40 students; school has own residence facilities.

Courses: Art History; Fine Arts; Drawing; Painting; Printmaking; Serigraphy; Fabric Design; Weaving; Sculpture; Ceramics; Jewelry; Metalwork & Enameling; Graphic Design; Photography; Etruscology & Restoration; Painting Restoration.

MILAN

ACCADEMIA DI BELLE ARTI DI BRERA* (Academy of Fine Arts of Brera), Palazzo di Brera, via Brera 28. *Pres* Dr Dott A de Micheli; Instrs FT 13.

Estab 1776; ent req submission of work; dipl, 4 yrs; enrl approx 255.

Courses: Decoration; Painting; Sculpture.

NAPLES

ACCADEMIE DE BELLE ARTI E LICEO ARTISTICO* (Academy of Fine Arts), via Bellini 36. *Prof & Dir* Constanza Lorenzetti. Founded 1838.

PERUGIA

ACCADEMIA DI BELLE ARTI* (Academy of Fine Arts), Piazza San Francesco 5, 06100. *Pres* Avv V Parlavecchio; *Prof Architecture & Dir* P Frenguelli; *Prof & Coordr* G F Bissietta.
D&E; cert.
Courses: Architecture; Decoration; History of Modern & Ancient Art; History of the Theatre; Painting; Sculpture; Theory of Art; Stage Craft.
Summer School: Courses—Art; Art History; Art Tours; Bronze Casting; Ceramics; Engraving; Fresco; Landscape Marble & Stone Work; Painting; Restoration; Sculpture.

RAVENNA

ACCADEMIA DE BELLE ARTI RAVENNA ITALIA* (Academy of Fine Arts), Loggetta Lombardesca, Via Roma, 48100. Tel: 23935 30178. *Dir & Prof* Raffaele De Grada; *Gen Secy* Rag Gianfranco Bustacchini; Instrs FT 8, PT 3.
Pub; D; ent req ent exam; degree, specializzazione mosaico, 4 yrs; SC 4, LC 4.
Tuition: Free for foreigners; no campus res.
Courses: Mosaics.

ROME

ACCADEMIA DE BELLE ARTIE LICEO ARTISTICO* (Academy of Fine Arts), via Ripetta 218-222, 00186. Tel: 688.834, 688.861. *Prof & Dir* Marcello Avenali; Instrs FT 42, PT 26.
Founded 1470, licensed 1873 and 1924; no ent req except with degree, 21 yrs of age; dipl, 4 yrs; SC, LC; enrl 1975.
Courses: Adult Hobby Classes; Architecture; Art of Engraving; Artistic Anatomy; Decoration; History of Art; History of Costumes (Popular & Folk); History of Movies & Theatre; Interior Decorating; Ornamental Modeling; Painting; Scene Painting; Scenery Technique; School of Modeling; School of the Nude in Art; Sculpture; Techniques of Art with Marble

AMERICAN ACADEMY IN ROME, Via Angelo Masina 5, 00153. *Dir* Henry A Millon; *Prof in Charge Classical Studies* Frank E Brown. Estab 1894; ent req Rome Prize Competition; Fels.
The American Academy of Rome is *not* a school; it offers no courses of instruction and maintains no teaching staff; it is simply a place where the Rome Prize Fellows (in architecture, landscape architecture, painting, sculpture, music composition, classics, post classical studies, art history) work and live. Information about these fellowships must be obtained from: Secretary, American Academy in Rome, 41 E 65th St, New York, NY 10021.

BRITISH SCHOOL AT ROME, Via Gramsci 61, 00197. *Dir* David Whitehouse, PhD; *Chmn Faculty Painting* Frederick Brill; *Chmn Faculty Sculpture* Paul De Monchaux; *Chmn Faculty Printmaking* Andrew Freeth.
Estab 1911; pvt; ent req ent by competition; schol; Postgrad Inst with facilities for artists; school provides working and living accommodations for its scholars.

INSTITUTO CENTRALE DEL RESTAURO* (Central Institute for the Restoration of Works of Art), Piazza San Francesco di Paola 9, 00186. Tel: 960161. *Dir* Dr Giovanni Urbani; Instrs FT 15.
Estab 1939; pub; D&E; ent req secondary school dipl (license) or equivalent; dipl to conduct or practice restoration, 3 yrs; SC 7; enrl 24 students, 24 brokers. Tui free.
Courses: Art Education; Chemistry; History of Antique, Medieval & Modern Art; Law Governing Antique & Fine Arts; Natural Science; Physics; Techniques of Restoration.

VALDOTTAVO

STUDIO CAMNITZER-PORTER, Melchiade 1, Prov de Lucca. Tel: 0583-835781. (American Office: Studio Camnitzer-Porter, 11 Cherrywood Lane, Locust Valley, NY 11560. Tel: 516-671-9630). *Dir & Instrs* Luis Camnitzer; *Instrs* Swietlan Kraczyna, MFA.
Estab 1975; pvt; D & E; the studio is a summer school; ent req portfolio; enrl 12 per session (first session: June 27-July 24; second session: July 27-Aug 22).
Tuition: $520 per session; campus res and room $120 per session.
Courses: Photography; Printmaking

VENICE

ACCADEMIA DI BELLE ARTI E LICEO ARTISTICO* (Academy of Fine Arts), Dorsoduro 1050. *Pres* Conte Ing Alessandro Passi. Founded 1750.

JAPAN

KANAZAWA CITY

KANAZAWA BIJUTSU KOGEI DAIGAKU* (Kanazawa College of Art), 11-1, Kodachino 5-chome, 920. Tel: 0762-62-3531. *Pres* Mamoru Osawa; Instrs FT 47, PT 55.
Estab 1950; pub; D; ent req HS dipl, ent exam; degree MFA, 4 yrs; schol; SC 40, LC 86; enrl D 530, maj 20, grad 530, others 20; Summer School.
Courses: Advertising Design; Aesthetics; Art Education; Ceramics; Commercial Art; Drafting; Drawing; Graphic Arts; Graphic Design; Handicrafts; History of Art & Archaeology; Illustration; Industrial Design; Lettering; Museum Staff Training; Painting; Photography; Sculpture; Teacher Training; Textile Design.
Adult Hobby Classes: Enrl 150; no tui; series of Sat lectures for citizens on various topics of arts and crafts.

KYOTO

KYOTO CITY UNIVERSITY OF FINE ARTS,* School of Art, 50, Hiyoshi-cho, Imakumano, Higashiyama-ku. *Dir* Takeshi Umehara; *Head Dept* Ryuken Sawa; Instrs FT 60, PT 41.
Estab 1880; ent req exam for HS grad; 2 yr (postgrad); degrees, 4 yrs; enrl 125.
Courses: Design; Japanese Painting; Lacquer; Oil Painting; Pottery; Sculpture; Textile Design.

MEXICO

CHOLULA

UNIVERSITY OF THE AMERICAS,* Art Department, Apdo Postal 100, Department B-1, Sta Catarina Martir. Tel: 47-06-55, exten 128. *Chmn* Jorge Duron; Instrs FT 8, PT 3.
Estab 1947; pvt; D&E; ent req HS dipl, for advanced standing presentation of portfolio and/or transparencies; degrees BA(Fine Arts, Art Hist), BFA(Painting, Sculpture, Graphics, Photography), 3 yrs, MFA(Painting, Sculpture); grad schol; SC 32, LC 25, GC 10; enrl approx 200 per quarter.
Courses: Aesthetics; Conservation & Restoration Techniques; Design; Drawing; Graphic Arts; History of Art & Archaeology; Mexican Crafts; Painting; Photography; Sculpture.

GUADALAJARA

UNIVERSIDAD DE GUADALAJARA,* Cursos de Verano/Cursos de Invierno, Apdo Postal 1-2543, Belen 120. *Dir* Jorge Martinez Lopez; *Prof & Dean Sch Arts* Rafael Zamarripa Castañeda; *Dean Faculty Architecture* Arq Vicente Pérez Carabias; Instrs FT 13.
Cursos de Verano estab 1947, Cursos de Invierno estab 1972; pub; D; ent req HS dipl; no degree; SC 10, LC 3, GC 8.
Courses: Ceramics; Drawing; History of Art & Archaeology; Painting; Sculpture.

MEXICO CITY

ESCUELA NACIONAL DE ARTES PLASTICAS* (National School of Plastic Arts), Academia 22. *Master Plastic Arts* Roberto Garibay Sida; Profs 109.
Founded 1781; enrl 750.
Courses: Commercial Art; Drawing; Engraving; Painting; Sculpture.

SAN MAGUEL DE ALLENDE

INSTITUTO ALLENDE* (Allende Institute). *Pres & Dir* Stirling Dickinson; *Adminr* Nell Fernandez; *Dean Faculty* James Pinto; *Dean Students* William Parker; *Head Grad Studies* Fred Samuelson; *Head Writing Center* Robert Somerlott; Instrs FT 25, PT 15.
Estab 1938; pvt, inc with the Univ Guanajuato; ent req HS grad; degrees, BA, BFA, MA, MFA, 3-4 yrs; schols plus assistantships and working schols; enrl approx 1500 per yr.
Courses: Archaeology; Art History; Botany; Drawing & Painting; Enameling; Fiction; Graphic Arts; History of Mexico; Intensive Spanish; Leather Work; Lost Wax; Nonfiction; Photography; Poetry; Psychology; Sculpture; Silverwork; Sociology; Textile Design; Weaving.
Adult Hobby Classes: (noncr), courses as above, all seasons.
Summer School: Dir Stirling Dickinson. 10 wk term starting June.

NETHERLANDS

AMSTERDAM

GERRIT RIETVELD ACADEMIE, Fred Roeskestraat 96, 1076 ED. Tel: 020-720406/731869. *Dir* Simon H den Hartog; Instrs FT 15, PT 95.
Estab 1924; pub; D&E; ent req HS dipl, review of portfolio; dipl granted, 5 yrs; enrl D 500, E 380.
Tuition: Depends on income of parents; maximum $220 per yr; no campus res.
Courses: ‡Advertising Design; ‡Animation; Art History; ‡Ceramics; Costume Design & Construction; ‡Drawing; ‡Fashion Arts; ‡Glass Design; ‡Graphic Arts; ‡Graphic Design; ‡Illustration; ‡Industrial Design; ‡Interior Design; ‡Jewelry; Lettering; ‡Painting; ‡Photography; ‡Printmaking; ‡Sculpture; ‡Silversmithing; ‡Stage Design; ‡Textile Design; ‡Theatre Arts; Video.

RIJKSAKADEMIE VAN BEELDENDE KUNSTEN* (State Academy of Fine Arts), Stadhouderskade 86. Tel: 79.78.11. *Dir* Dr J van Riemsdijk.
Courses: Fine Arts; History of Art; Scenography; Visual Communication.

THE HAGUE

KONINKLIJKE ACADEMIE VAN BEELDENDE KUNSTEN (Royal Academy of Fine Arts), Prinsessegracht 4. Tel: 070-643835. *Dir* J J Beljon.
Estab 1682; Ministry of Education; D&E; ent req HS dipl; LC 6.
Tuition: 150 Dutch guilders; no campus res.
Courses: Advertising Design; Costume Design & Construction; Drawing; Environmental Design; Fashion Arts; Graphic Arts; Graphic Design; Illustration; Industrial Design; Interior Design; Painting; Sculpture; Textile Design.

STICHTING DE VRIJE ACADEMIE PSYCHOPOLIS VOOR BEELDENDE KUNSTEN* (Foundation The Free Academy Psychopolis for Audio-Visual Arts—International Art Laboratory) De Gheijnstraat 129, PO Box 6390. Tel: 070-638968. *Dir* George Lampe; Instrs PT approx 40.
Estab 1947, resorting under the Ministry of Culture and The Residence The Hague, Fine Arts; no ent req, must be at least 17 yrs of age; no dipl.
Courses: Art in Architecture; Ceramics; Costume Design & Construction; Drawing; Fashion Arts; Glass; Graphic Arts; Graphic Design; Illustration; Jewelry; Painting; Photography; Sculpture; Textile Design; Theatre Arts; Woodwork.

ROTTERDAM

ACADEMIE VAN BEELDENDE KUNSTEN (Academy of Fine Arts), G J de Jonghweg 4. Tel: 3110.366244, Exten 31. *Dir* Klaas de Jong; *V-Dir* P Geurts and B Bos; *V-Dir E Course* A Aan de Wiel.
Estab 1773; pub; D&E; ent req HS dipl; SC 6; no campus res.
Courses: Advertising Design; Art History; Ceramics; Collage; Commercial Art; Conceptual Art; Constructions; Costume Design & Construction; Display; Drawing; Fashion Arts; Film; Graphic Arts; Graphic Design; Illustration; Interior Design; Lettering; Mixed Media; Painting; Photography; Printmaking; Sculpture; Teacher Training; Video.

NEW ZEALAND

AUCKLAND

UNIVERSITY OF AUCKLAND, School of Fine Arts, 20 Whitaker Place, Private Bag. *Prof* J D Saunders, DipFA(Hons)NZ, DipIndustDesign, NDD, MSIA, FNZSID, FRSA; *Prof* Paul J. Beadle, MFIM, (Hon) MNZSID, MNZSSP, FRSA.

Estab 1881, sch estab 1950; pub; D; ent req univ ent; degrees BFA 4 yrs, MFA 2 yrs;
Tuition: On application (varies).
Courses: Advertising Design; Aesthetics; Art History; Commercial Art; Conceptual Art; Drawing; Graphic Arts; Graphic Design; Handicrafts (fiber); Industrial Design; Intermedia; Jewelry; Lettering; Mixed Media; Painting; Photography; Printmaking; Sculpture; Silversmithing; Video.
Summer School: Organized by Continuing Educ Dept. Courses—Photography; Printmaking (others from time to time).

NORWAY

OSLO

STATENS KUNSTAKADEMI* (State Art Academy), Uranienborgvien 2. *Rector & Prof* Alf-Jorgen Aas; *Adminr* Conrad Løwø; Instrs FT 5, PT 6.
Estab 1909; ent req exam; 4 yrs; no tui.
Courses: Drawing; Modeling; Painting.

PHILIPPINES

MANILA

PHILIPPINE COLLEGE OF ARTS AND TRADES, Graphics Department, Ayala Blvd corner San Marcelino St. *Head Graphics Dept* Diosdado Nicdao, Jr. MMgt; *Instr.* Silvino Lopez, BS(Indust Educ); *Instr* Leopoldo Ludovice, BS(Indust Educ); *Instr.* Oscar Pecson, BS(Fine Arts).
Estab 1901, dept estab 1971; pub; D&E; ent req HS dipl; degree BS(Indust Educ), (Art Educ Maj); schol; LC 1; enrl D 15, E 5.
Tuition: 145 per sem; no campus res.
Courses: Art Education; Ceramics; Drafting; Drawing; Graphic Arts.
Summer School: Dir Diosdado Nicdao, Jr.

POLAND

CRACOW

AKADEMIA SZTUK PIEKNYCH* (Academy of Fine Arts), Plac Matekji, 13. *Prof & Rector* Marian Konieczny.
Courses: Advertising; Conservation of Works of Art; Graphic Arts; Interior Decoration; Painting; Posters; Scenography; Sculpture; Textile Design; Town Planning.

LODZ

PANSTWOWA WYZSZA SZKOLA SZTUK PLASTYCZNYCH (Higher School of Art and Design), 121 Wojska Polskiego Str. 91-726. *Rector & Reader* Weislaw Garbolinski; *V-Rector & Reader* Jerzy Derkowski; *V-Rector & Reader* Benon Liberski; *Head Gen Studies Dept & Sr Tutor* Ryszard Hunger; *Head Graphic Arts Dept & Prof* Stanislaw Fijalkowski; *Head Indust Design Dept & Reader* Jan Finkstein.
Estab 1946; pub; D; ent req HS dipl; degree MA 5 yrs; enrl 70.
Courses: Advertising Design; Art History; Drawing; Fashion Arts; Graphic Arts; Graphic Design; Industrial Design; Jewelry; Painting; Photography; Printmaking; Sculpture; Silversmithing; Textile Design.

WARSAW

AKADEMIA SZTUK PIEKNYCH* (Academy of Fine Arts), Krakowskie Przedmiescie 5.
Courses: Conservation of Works of Art; Graphic Arts; Interior Architecture; Painting; Pedagogical; Sculpture; Textiles; Theatre Set Design.

PORTUGAL

LISBON

ESCOLA SUPERIOR DE BELAS ARTES* (School of Fine Arts), Largo da Biblioteca Publica. *Dir* Joaquim Correia.
Estab 1836.

OPORTO

ESCOLA SUPERIOR DE BELAS ARTES* (Higher School of Fine Arts), av Rodriques de Freitas. *Dir* Carlos Ramos.
Estab 1836.

ROMANIA

CLUJ-NAPOCA

INSTITUTUL DE ARTE PLASTICE ION ANDREESCU* (Institute of Plastic Arts Ion Andreescu), Piata Libertatii 31, 3400. Tel: 951-11577. *Rector* L Feszt; *Dean* E Bacila; Instrs FT 61, PT 6.
Estab 1949; pub; D; ent req HS dipl, ent exam; licensed for fine art with the mention of the specialty, 4 yrs; schol; SC 24, LC 21, GC 6; enrl 252, maj 5. Tui free.
Courses: Advertising Design; Aesthetics; Art Education; Ceramics; Commercial Art; Costume Design & Construction; Drawing; Graphic Arts; Graphic Design; History of Art & Archaeology; Industrial Design; Lettering; Painting; Photography; Sculpture; Teacher Training; Textile Design.

SCOTLAND

EDINBURGH

EDINBURGH COLLEGE OF ART,* Lauriston Place, EH3 9DF. *Prin* J T Hunter.
Estab 1907.
Courses: Architecture; Crafts; Design; Drawing; Painting; Planning; Sculpture.

SOUTH AFRICA, REPUBLIC OF

PORT ELIZABETH

PORT ELIZABETH SCHOOL OF ART OF THE COLLEGE FOR ADVANCED TECHNICAL EDUCATION,* Private Bag 6011, 6000. *Head Sch Art* G H H Nesbit; Instrs FT 18, PT 7.
Estab 1882; pub; D; ent req HS dipl; National Dipl(Art, Design, Photography), Higher National Dipl, 3 yrs; enrl 140.
Tuition: Campus res.
Courses: Advertising Design; Art Education; Ceramics; Commercial Art; Costume Design & Construction; Drawing; Fashion Arts; Graphic Arts; Graphic Design; History of Art & Archaeology; Illustration; Lettering; Painting; Photography; Sculpture; Teacher Training (with Univ of Port Elizabeth); Textile Design.

SPAIN

BARCELONA

ESCUELA SUPERIOR DE BELLAS ARTES DE SAN JORGE* (Barcelona School of Fine Arts), Calle Europa S/N, Ciudad Universitaria. *Prof & Dir* Frederico Mares Deulovol.

MADRID

ESCUELA DE ARTES DECORATIVAS (School of Decorative Arts), Héroes del 10 de Agosto, 5, Madrid, I, Espana. Tel: 2 26-67-74. *Head Dept* Jose Luis Mercado Segoviano, Director General; Jose Luis Fuentes Otero, Jefe De Estudios.
Pvt; D&E; ent req HS dipl; degrees Cursos de "Tecnicos en Decoración de Interiores," schol; SC 3, LC 4; enrl major and grad students.
Tuition: No campus res.
Courses: Advertising Design; Art Education; Art History; Drawing; Interior Design.
Adult Hobby Classes: Tui $35 per month. Courses—Cursos de Técnicos en Decoración de Inferiores (Interior decoration and Technology).

Children's Classes: Tui $35 per month. Courses: Cursos de Dibujo y Pintura Infantil (Drawing, Painting).

ESCUELA NACIONAL DE ARTES GRAFICAS* (Madrid School of Graphic Arts), Calle Jesus Maestro, 3. *Dir* Luis Gimeno Soldevilla; Instrs FT 32.
Estab 1911; 3 yrs; enrl 223.
Courses: Graphic Arts.

SEVILLE

ESCUELA SUPERIOR DE BELLAS ARTES DE SANTA ISABEL DE HUNGRIA DE SEVILLE* (Seville School of Fine Arts), Gonzaldo Bilbao 7-9. *Dir* Jose Hernandez Diaz.
Founded 1940; enrl 106 students.
Courses: Fine Arts.

VALENCIA

ESCUELA SUPERIOR DE BELLAS ARTES DE SAN CARLOS* (Valencia School of Fine Arts), Calle del Museo 2. *Dir* Daniel de Neuda Llisiona; Instrs 26.
Estab 1765; affiliated with the Univ of Valencia; 5 yrs; schol; enrl 300.
Summer School: 8 wks from July to Sept.

SWEDEN

GOTHENBURG

GÖTEBORG UNIVERSITET* (Gothenburg University), Vasaparken, 41124. *Prof & Dean Faculty Arts* P Aström.
Estab 1891; pub; ent req HS exam; 3-4 yrs; enrl 8000.

KONSTINDUSTRISKOLAN I GOTËBORG* (Gothenburg School of Design), Kristinelundsgatan 6-8, 411 37. Tel: 160517 or 208765. *Prin* Gösta Andren; Instrs D FT 20, PT 32, E PT 33.
Estab 1848; pub; ent req ent exam and artistic talent; 4 yrs; enrl 500.

STOCKHOLM

KUNGL. KONSTHOGSKOLAN* (Royal Academy Art School), Fredsgatan 12, Box 16 317, 103 26. *Dir* Sven Ljungberg; Instrs FT 19.
Estab 1735; affiliated with the Royal Swedign Academy of Fine Arts. 5 yrs; no fees. Foreign students can be accepted as guest students for one year at a time and generally not more than two years in all, or as special students following parts of the instruction, all in very limited numbers, on presentation of testimonials to prove they have been enrolled as regular students of some foreign Art Institute of the same status (University). Applicants are required to submit specimens of their work. The Academy cannot secure accommodations for its students.
Courses: Architecture; Drawing; Graphic Art; Painting; Restoration; Sculpture.

SWITZERLAND

GENEVA

ECOLES D'ART DE GENEVE* (Geneva Schools of Art), 9, Bd Helvetique, 1205. *Dir* M Michel Rappo.
Estab 1748.
—Ecole des Beaux-Arts (School of Fine Arts). Tel: 29.05.10. Head M Jean-Luc Daval.
Founded 1748; ent req HS grad; ent exam; dipl.
Courses: Audiovisual Expression; Design; Engraving; Modeling; Painting; Perspective; Sculpture.
—Ecole des arts Decoratifs (School of Decorative Arts), 15, Bd James-Fazy. Tel: 31.37.57. Head M Claude Malinjod.
Founded 1876; ent req HS grad, ent exam; cert.
Courses: Ceramics; Enameling; Graphics; Industrial Art; Interior Design; Jewelry.

LAUSANNE

LAUSANNE COLLEGE OF ART AND DESIGN, Ave Elysée 4, CH 1006. Tel: 021 27 75 23. *Prin* Jacques Monnier-Raball, Lic és Lett; *Dean*

Léon Prebandier; *Head Fine Arts* Hansjörg Gisiger; *Head Gen Artistic Studies* Janos Urban; *Head Graphic Design Dept* Werner Jeker; *Head Indust Design Dept* Claude Dupraz.
Estab 1821; pub; D; ent req HS dipl; Dipl granted, 5 yrs; SC 27, LC 15, GC 42
Tuition: 557.50 Fr.S; no campus res.
Courses: Advertising Design; Aesthetics; Art Education; Art History; Calligraphy; Commercial Art; Conceptual Art; Constructions; Display; Drafting; Drawing; Film; Graphic Arts; Graphic Design; History of Art & Archaeology; Illustration; Industrial Design; Intermedia; Lettering; Mixed Media; Painting; Photography; Printmaking; Sculpture; Semiology; Teacher Training; Video.

USSR

TALLINN

EESTI NSV RIIKLIK KUNSTIINSTITUUT* (State Art Institute of the Estonian SSR), Tartu Maantee 1, 200001. *Rector* J Vares; *Asst Rector* P Tarvas; *Dean* L Habicht; *Dean* H Parmas; Instrs FT 95, PT 14.
Estab 1914; pub; ent req secondary educ, preliminary training in art; 5-6 yrs; degrees; schol; SC, LC. Children's Classes.
Courses: Architecture; Ceramics; Design; Fashion; Glass; Graphics; Interior Decoration; Leather; Metalwork; Painting; Scene Decoration; Sculpture; Textiles.

ART INFORMATION

State Arts Councils

This Directory of State Arts Councils was compiled by the American Council for the Arts, 570 Seventh Avenue, New York, N.Y. 10018. Permission to include the listing in the American Art Directory is gratefully acknowledged by the Editors.

NATIONAL ENDOWMENT FOR THE ARTS

Regional Coordinators

Dale Kobler
Pacific States
P.O. Box 15187
San Francisco, CA 94115
415-921-9008

Mrs. Frances Poteet
Lower Plains Area
601 East Austin, Suite 1410
Alamo, TX 78516
512-787-6756

John Wessel
Mid-Atlantic States
110 West 15th Street
New York, NY 10011
212-989-6347

Rudolph Nashan
Northeastern States
30 Savoy Street
Providence, RI 02906
401-274-4754

Charles Springman
Gulf States
630 North Blount Street, Apt. 4
Raleigh, NC 27604
919-832-0047

Terry Melton
Northwest States
728 Rural Avenue South
Salem, OR 97302
503-581-5284

Mrs. Bertha Masor
Great Lakes States
4200 Marine Drive
Chicago, IL 60513
312-525-6748

Gerald Ness
Mid-South States
2130 P Street, NW, Apt 422
Washington, DC 20037
202-293-9042

Joanne Soper
North Plains States
3510 Lindenwood
Sioux City, IA 51104
712-258-2014

Regional Organizations of State Arts Agencies

Mid-America Arts Alliance

Henry Moran, Executive Director
G-50, Crown Center 3

2440 Pershing
Kansas City, MO 64108
816-421-1388

Western States Arts Foundation

Richard Harcourt, President
428 E 11th Avenue, Suite 201
Denver, CO 80203
303-832-7979

Affiliated State Arts Agencies of the Upper Midwest

Robert Altman
430 Oak Grove Street, Suite 402
Minneapolis, MN 55403
612-871-6392

Southern Arts Federation

Anthony Turney, Executive Director
225 Peachtree Street, Suite 1104
Atlanta, GA 30303
404-577-7244

The Arts Exchange

Clinton Baer, Executive Director
16 Whipple Building
Lebanon, NH 03766
603-448-4353

New England Foundation for the Arts

Thomas Wolf, Director
8 Francis Avenue
Cambridge, MA 02138
617-492-2914

National Assembly of State Arts Agencies

Anne Goekjian
1010 Vermont Avenue, NW, Suite 516
Washington DC 20002
202-347-6352

National Assembly of Community Arts Agencies

John Blaine, Director
Cultural Arts Council of Houston
c/o Houston Coliseum
Houston, TX 77001

UNITED STATES

Alabama State Council on the Arts and Humanities

Mr. Aubrey D. Green, Chairman
P.O. Drawer G
York, AL 36952
Home: 205-392-5211

M. J. Zakrzewski, Executive Director
449 South MacDonough Street

Montgomery, AL 36130
Home: 205-277-2221
Office: 205-832-6758

Alaska State Council on the Arts

Mrs. Jean Mackin, Chairman
1114 Nenana
Fairbanks, AK 99701
Home: 907-452-2094

Roy H. Helms, Executive Director
619 Warehouse Avenue, Suite 220
Anchorage, AK 99501
Office: 907-279-1558

Arizona Commission on the Arts and Humanities

Lewis J. Ruskin, Chairman
5800 Foothills Drive
Scottsdale, AZ 85253
Home: 602-948-6080
Office: 602-271-5882

Louise C. Tester, Executive Director
6330 North Seventh Street
Phoenix, AZ 85014
Office: 602-271-5882

The Office of Arkansas State Arts and Humanities

Hardy Little, III, Chairman
P.O. Box 6
Jonesboro, AR 72401
Office: 501-935-3813

Dr. Sandra Perry, Executive Director
Continental Building, Suite 500
Main and Markham Streets
Little Rock, AR 72201
Home: 501-565-4991
Office: 501-371-2539

California Arts Council

Peter Coyote, Chairman
115 I Street
Sacramento, CA 95814
Office: 916-445-1530

Gloria Flores, Acting Director
115 I Street
Sacramento, CA 95814
Office: 916-445-1530

The Colorado Council on the Arts and Humanities

Dean Robert B. Yegge, Chairman
Yegge, Hall & Evans
1340 Denver Club Building
Denver, CO 80202
Offices: 303-222-2855

Robert N. Sheets, Executive Director
770 Pennsylvania Street
Denver, CO 80203
Home: 303-333-3974
Office: 303-892-2617, 892-2618

Connecticut Commission on the Arts

June K. Goodman, Chairperson
1 Lakeside Road
Danbury, CT 06810
Home: 203-744-4454
Office: 203-566-4770

Anthony S. Keller, Executive Director
340 Capitol Avenue
Hartford, CT 06106
Home: 203-523-0330
Office: 203-566-4770

Delaware State Arts Countil

Mr. Gene Derrickson, Chairman
Wilmington State Office Building
Ninth and French Streets
Wilmington, DE 19801
Home: 302-798-6228
Office: 302-571-3540

Donald Schulman,
Wilmington State Office Building
Ninth and French Streets
Wilmington, DE 19801
Office: 302-571-3540

District of Columbia Commission on the Arts

Ms. ViCurtis Hinton, Chairman
1310 Farragut Street, Northwest
Washington, DC 20011
Home: 202-882-5757
Office: 202-629-2824

Larry Neal, Executive Director
1012 14th Street NW, Suite 1203
Washington, DC 20005
Office: 202-724-5613

Fine Arts Council of Florida

Mrs. Jo Surran, Chairman
9 Cantabriari
Florissant, MO 63033
Home: 314-921-7754

Dr. John K. Urice, Executive Director
Fine Arts Council of Florida
Department of State, The Capitol
Tallahassee, FL 32304
Home: 904-386-1909
Office: 904-488-2980

Georgia Council for the Arts and Humanities

Mrs. Isabelle Watkins, Chairman
3920 Club Drive, Northeast
Atlanta, GA 30319
Home: 404-233-6589

John Bitterman, Executive Director
225 Peachtree Street, Northeast, Suite 1600
Atlanta, GA 30303
Office: 404-656-3990

Hawaii State Foundation on Culture and Humanities

Masaru Yokouchi, Chairman
2180 Main Street, Suite 616
Wailuku, Maui, HI 96793
Home: 808-244-4662
Office: 808-244-7991

Alfred Preis, Executive Director
250 South King Street, Room 310
Honolulu, HI 96813
Home: 808-988-3155
Office: 808-548-4145

Idaho State Commission on the Arts and Humanities

Donna Bray, Acting Chairman
1314 Deakin
Moscow, ID 83843
Home: 208-882-2135
Office: 208-882-8500

Carl Petrick, Executive Director
506 North Fifth Street, Annex 3
Boise, ID 83720
Office: 208-384-2119

Illinois Arts Council

William M. DuVall
Borg Warner Corporation
200 S. Michigan Blvd
Chicago IL 60604
Office: 312-322-8656

Clark Mitze, Executive Director
111 North Wabash Avenue, Room 720
Chicago, IL 60602
Office: 312-435-6750

Indiana Arts Commission

Kathy Martin, Chairman
St. Mary-of-the-Woods College
Terre Haute, IN 47876
Office: 812-535-4141

Janet I. Harris, Executive Director
155 East Market, Suite 614
Indianapolis, IN 46204
Office: 317-633-5649

Iowa State Arts Council

H. Mel Willits, Chairman
6231 Washington
Des Moines, IA 50322
Office: 515-288-1955

Jack E. Olds, Executive Director
State Capitol Building
Des Moines, IA 50319
Home: 515-279-9572
Office: 515-281-4451

Kansas Arts Commission

Martha D. Nichols, Chairman
2401 Drury Lane
Shawnee Mission, KS 66208
Home: 913-362-6755

John A. Reed, Executive Director
509-A Kansas Avenue
Topeka, KS 66603
Office: 913-296-3335

The Kentucky Arts Commission

Albert Smith, Chairman
The Logan Leader
Russellville, KY 42276
Office: 502-726-9507

Ms. Nash Cox, Executive Director
100 West Main
Frankfort, KY 40601
Home: 502-223-5211
Office: 502-564-3757

Louisiana State Arts Council

Mrs. Peggy Towers, Chairman
9677 West Tampa Drive
Baton Rouge, LA 70815
Home: 504-927-0563

Al Head, Executive Director
Division of the Arts
P.O. Box 44247
Baton Rouge, LA 70804
Office: 504-389-6291

Maine State Commission on the Arts and Humanities

Phillip Isaacson, Chairman
2 Benson Street
Lewiston, ME 04240
Home: 207-783-2207

Alden G. Wilson, Executive Director
State House
Augusta, ME 04330
Office: 207-289-2724

Maryland Arts Council

James Burgess
108 Lakeview Drive
Salisbury, MD 21801
Office: 301-546-3261

Kenneth Kahr, Executive Director
15 West Mulberry Street
Baltimore, MD 21201
Office: 301-685-6740

Massachusetts Council on the Arts and Humanities

Vernon R. Alden, Chairman
The Boston Company
1 Boston Place

Boston, MA 02108
Office: 617-722-7030

Anne Hawley, Director
One Ashburton Place
Boston, MA 02108
617-727-3668

Michigan Council for the Arts

Walter R. Boris, Chairman
Executive Vice President, Consumers Power Co.
212 West Michigan Ave.
Jackson, MI 49201
Home: 517-783-5691
Office: 517-788-1111

E. Ray Scott, Executive Director
1200 Sixth Avenue
Executive Plaza Room P160
Detroit, MI 48226
Home: 313-961-1314
Office: 313-256-3735

Minnesota Arts Board

Sandy Hale, Chairman
1833 Girard Avenue South
Minneapolis, MN 55403
Home: 612-377-3878
Office: 612-874-1335

Stephen Sell, Executive Director
314 Clifton Avenue
Minneapolis, MN 55403
Office: 612-874-1335

Mississippi Arts Commission

Mrs. W. A. Middleton, Chairman
316 Fairgrounds
Winona, MS 38967
Home: 601-283-1116

Mrs. Lida Rogers, Executive Director
Box 1341
Jackson, MS 39205
Office: 601-354-7336
Home: 601-584-6870

Missouri State Council on the Arts

Mrs. Rosalyn Kling
8092 Blue Springs Lane
St Louis, MO 63131
Home: 314-432-3405

J. Robert Sulmar, Interim Director
727 North First Street
St Louis, MO 63102
Office: 314-241-7900

Montana Arts Council

Ms. Maxine M. Blackmer, Chairman
635 Hastings Avenue
Missoula, MT 59801
Home: 406-549-0457

David E. Nelson, Executive Director
235 East Pine Street
Missoula, MT 59801
Office: 406-543-8286

Nebraska Arts Council

Wallace A. Richardson, Chairman
1000 NBC Center
Lincoln, NE 68508
Office: 402-475-7011

Robert Pierle, Executive Director
8448 West Center Road
Omaha, NE 68124
Office: 402-554-2122

Nevada State Council on the Arts

Thomas E. Ogg
5350 St Andrews
Reno, NV 89502
Home: 702-825-1314

James D. Deere, Executive Director
4600 Keitzke Lane
Suite 134, Building 2
Reno, NV 89502
Home: 702-323-5207
Office: 702-784-6231

New Hampshire Commission on the Arts

R. Alden Burt, Chairman
Box 82
Lebanon, NH 03766
Home: 603-448-2062

John G. Coe, Executive Director
Phoenix Hall
40 North Main Street
Concord, NH 03301
Office: 603-271-2789

New Jersey Council on the Arts

Mrs. Barbara Furst
Llewellyn Park
West Orange, NJ 07052
Office: 201-325-1100

Al Kochka, Executive Director
109 West State Street
Trenton, NJ 08608
Office: 609-292-6130

New Mexico Arts Commission

Mrs. Helen Azar, Chairman
7604 Arroyo del Oso, North East
Albuquerque, NM 87109
Home: 505-296-7771

Bernard B. Lopez, Executive Director
Lew Wallace Building
Capitol Complex
Santa Fe, NM 87503
Office: 505-827-2061

New York State Council on the Arts

Mrs. Kitty Carlisle Hart, Chairman
80 Centre Street
New York, NY 10013
Office: 212-488-5222

Robert L. Mayer, Executive Director
80 Centre Street
New York, NY 10013
Office: 212-488-5222

North Carolina Arts Council

H. Martin Lancaster, Chairman
P.O. Box 916
Goldsboro, NC 27530
919-735-7275

Mary Regan, Executive Director
Department of Cultural Resources
Raleigh, NC 27611
Office: 919-733-5896

North Dakota Council on the Arts and Humanities

John Hove, Chairman
North Dakota State University
Minard 320
Fargo, ND 58102
Office: 701-237-7143

Glenn Scott, Director
North Dakota State University
Minard 309D
Fargo, ND 58102
Office: 701-237-7674

Ohio Arts Council

John Henle, Chairman
Chamber of Commerce
50 West Broad Street

Columbus, OH 43215
Home: 614-885-7810
Office: 614-221-1321

Wayne P. Lawson, Acting Director
50 West Broad Street, Suite 2840
Columbus, OH 43215
Office: 614-466-2613

Oklahoma Arts and Humanities Council

John B. Wagner, Chairman
3514 S. Husband
Stillwater, OK 74074
Home: 405-372-6878
Office: 405-373-0848

Ben Di Salvo, Executive Director
2101 North Lincoln, Room 640
Jim Thorpe Building
Oklahoma City, OK 73105
Home: 405-528-1558
Office: 405-521-2931

Oregon Arts Commission

Peter Koehler, Chairman
Evans Product
1121 South West Salmon
Portland, OR 97205
Office: 503-222-5592

Peter de C. Hero, Executive Director
835 Summer Street, North East
Salem, OR 97301
Office: 503-378-3625

Commonwealth of Pennsylvania Council on the Arts

Hiram Hershey, Chairman
c/o 2001 North Front Street
Harrisburg, PA 17102
Office: 717-787-6883

Otis B. Morse, Executive Director
2001 North Front Street
Harrisburg, PA 17102
Office: 717-787-6883

Rhode Island Council on the Arts

Donald Jaldrich, Vice President
Rhode Island Hospital Trust National Bank
P.O. Box 1558
Providence, RI 02901
Office: 401-278-8108

Robin Berry, Executive Director
334 Westminster Mall
Providence, RI 02903
Office: 401-277-3880

South Carolina Arts Commission

Kenneth R. Brown, Chairman
P.O. Box 22213
Columbia, SC 29222
Office: 809-765-8246

Rick George, Executive Director
Boylston House
829 Richland Street
Columbia, SC 29201
Office: 803-758-3442

South Dakota State Fine Arts Council

Dr. Wayne Knutson, Chairman
College of Fine Arts
University of South Dakota
Vermillion, SD 57069
Home: 605-624-3293
Office: 605-677-5481

Mrs. Charlotte Carver, Executive Director
108 West 11 Street
Sioux Falls, SD 57102
Home: 605-332-7257
Office: 605-334-7651

Tennessee Arts Commission

Mrs. W. Glenn Bullock, Chairman
7100 Sherwood Drive
Knoxville, TN 37919
Home: 615-584-1975

Tom Bacchetti, Executive Director
222 Capitol Hill Building
Nashville, TN 37219
Office: 615-741-1701

Texas Commission on the Arts and Humanities

Dr. George S. Heyer, Jr, Chairman
100 East 27th Street
Austin, TX 78705
Office: 512-472-6736

Maurice D. Coats, Executive Director
P.O. Box 13406, Capitol Station
202 West 13th Street
Austin, TX 78711
Home: 512-836-6942
Office: 512-475-6593

Utah State Division of Fine Arts

Connie Jo M. Hepworth, Chairman
3714 East 3800 South
Salt Lake City, UT 84109
Home: 801-278-3331

Ruth R. Draper, Executive Director
609 East South Temple Street
Salt Lake City, UT 84102
Home: 801-582-4144
Office: 801-533-5895

Vermont Council on the Arts

Brian Lloyd, Chairman
311 North Street
Burlington, VT 05401
Home: 802-864-4171

Ellen McCulloch-Lovell, Executive Director
136 State Street
Montpelier, VT 05602
Office: 802-828-3291

Virginia Commission of the Arts and Humanities

Peter A. G. Brown, Chairman
Colonial Williamsburg Foundation
Williamsburg, VA 23185
Office: 804-229-1000

Jerry T. Haynie, Executive Director
400 East Grace Street, First Floor
Richmond, VA 23219
Office: 804-786-4492

Washington State Arts Commission

Mary E. Dunton, Acting Chairman
Fort Wright College
West 4000 Randolph Road
Spokane, WA 99204
Office: 509-328-2970

James L. Haseltine, Executive Director
1151 Black Lake Blvd.
Olympia, WA 98504
Home: 206-866-4157
Office: 206-753-3860

West Virginia Arts and Humanities Council

Mrs. Pat S. Pappas, Chairman
12 Fairview Heights
Parkersburg, WV 26101
Home: 314-428-1123

James B. Andrews, Executive Director
Science and Cultural Center
Capitol Complex
Charleston, WV 25305
Home: 304-562-9186
Office: 304-348-3711

Wisconsin Arts Board

Joel Skornicka, Chairperson
97 Bascom Hall
University of Wisconsin-Madison
Madison, WI 53706
Office: 608-263-5510

Jerrold B. Rouby, Executive Director
123 West Washington Avenue
Madison, WI 53702
Home: 608-233-6105
Office: 608-266-8106

Wyoming Council on the Arts

James Boyle, Chairman
706 South 14th Street
Laramie, WY 82070
Office: 307-745-5346

John Buhler, Executive Director
State of Wyoming
Cheyenne, WY 82002
Office: 307-777-7742

UNITED STATES TERRITORIES

American Samoa Arts Council

Mr. Palauni M. Tuiasosopo, Administrator
Office of the Governor
GAS American Samoa
Pago Pago 96799
Home: (overseas) 633-4060
Office: (overseas) 633-4116

Insular Arts Council of Guam

Lara Souder, Chairman
Office of the Governor
P.O. Box 2950
Agana, GU 96910
Office: (overseas) 729-2466

Peter Guerrero, Program Director
Office of the Governor
P.O. Box 2950
Agana, GU 96910
Office: (overseas) 729-2466

**Institute of Puerto Rican Culture
(Instituto del Cultura Puertorriquena)**

Arq. Carlos Sanz, Chairman
Apartado Postal 4184
San Juan, PR 00905
Office 809-723-2115

Luis M. Rodrigues Morales, Executive Director
Apartado Postal 4184
San Juan, PR 00905
Office: 809-723-2115

Virgin Islands Council on the Arts

Rita L. Forbes, Chairman
Box 217
Christiansted, St. Croix, VI 00820
Office: 809-773-0046

Stephen J, Bostic, Executive Director
Caravelle Arcade
Christiansted, St. Croix, VI 00820
Office: 809-773-3075, Exten 3

CANADA PROVINCIAL ARTS COUNCILS

Alberta

Walter H. Kassa, Assistant Deputy Minister for Cultural
    Development
Department of Culture, Youth and Recreation
Government of Alberta

11th Floor, CN Tower
10004 104th Avenue
Edmonton, AB T5J OK5

British Columbia

Honorable Erney Hall, Provincial Minister
Parliament Buildings
Victoria, BC

Manitoba

Mary Elizabeth Bayer
Assistant Deputy Minister
Department of Tourism, Recreation and Cultural Affairs
555 Main Street
Winnipeg, MB R3B 1C3
Office: 204-944-2237

New Brunswick

Honorable Brenda Robertson
Ministry of Youth and Social Services
Government of New Brunswick
Fredericton, NB

Newfoundland

John C. Perlen, Director of Cultural Affairs
Governments of Newfoundland & Labrador
Newfoundland Arts and Culture Center
P.O. Box 1854
St. John's, NF

Nova Scotia

Louis Stephen
Coordinator of Cultural Services
Department of Recreation
Province of Nova Scotia
P.O. Box 864
Halifax, NS

Northwest Territories

Carl Abrahamson
Liaison Office
Arts and Crafts Section
Department of Industry and Development
Government of Northwest Territories
P.O. Box 1320
Yellow Knife, NT

Ontario

Louis Applebaum, Executive Director
Province of Ontario Council for the Arts
151 Bloor Street West, Fifth Floor
Toronto, ON M5S LT6
Office: 416-961-1660

Prince Edward Island

Doyles B. Boylan
Department of the Environment and Tourism
P.O. Box 2000
Charlottetown, PEI

Quebec

Louis O'Neill
Ministre des Affairs Culturelles
955 St Louis Road
Quebec, PQ

Saskatchewan

Joy Cohnstaedt, Executive Director
Saskatchewan Arts Board
200 Lakeshore Drive
Regina, SK S4S OA4

Yukon

Michael P. Herron, Chairman
Yukon Arts Council
P.O. Box 4297
Whitehorse, YT

Directors and Supervisors of Art Education in School Systems

Compiled from a survey made by the National Art Education Association under the direction of Dr. John J. Mahlmann, Executive Director.

ALABAMA

John B. Hall
Art Specialist
State Department of Education
State Office Building
Room 607
Montgomery, Alabama 36130

ALASKA

Marilou Madden
Educational Program Support
Alaska Department of Education
Pouch F
Juneau, Alaska 99811

ARIZONA

Raymond G. Van Diest
Fine Arts Specialist
Arizona Department of Education
1535 West Jefferson Street
Phoenix, Arizona 85007

ARKANSAS

Jerry C. Swope
Supervisor of Art Education
Arch Ford Education Building
Capitol Mall
Little Rock, Arkansas 72201

CALIFORNIA

Louis P. Nash
Consultant Arts and Humanities Education
California State Department of Education
721 Capitol Mall
Sacramento, California 95814

COLORADO

No position

CONNECTICUT

Robert J. Saunders
Art Education Consultant
State Department of Education
P.O. Box 2219
Hartford, Connecticut 06115

DELAWARE

Mr. James R. Gervan
Supervisor of Art and Music Education
Department of Public Instruction
Townsend Building
Dover, Delaware 19901

DISTRICT OF COLUMBIA

Director (position open)

Mrs. Marie B. Williams
Supervisory Director of Art
Public Schools of D.C.
14th & Jackson Streets, N.E.
Room 117
Washington, D.C. 20017

FLORIDA

Neil Mooney
Art Consultant
State Department of Education
108 Miles Johnson Building
Tallahassee, Florida 32304

GEORGIA

Ruth Gassett
Consultant, Art Education
Education Annex
156 Trinity Street, S.W.
Atlanta, Georgia 30303

HAWAII

Stanley I. Yamamoto
Program Specialist, Art Education
Room 1201
1270 Queen Emma Street
Honolulu, Hawaii 96804

IDAHO

Bert A. Burda
Fine Arts Representative
Len B. Jordan Office Building
State Department of Education
Boise, Idaho 83720

ILLINOIS

Larry L. Emmons
Art Education Specialist
Illinois Office of Education
100 North First Street
Springfield, Illinois 62777

INDIANA

Ann Timberman
Art Consultant
State Department of Public Instruction
Division of Curriculum
120 West Market
Indianapolis, Indiana 46204

IOWA

Dr. Laura Magee
Consultant, Arts Education
Curriculum Division

Department of Public Instruction
Grimes State Office Building
Des Moines, Iowa 50319

KANSAS

No position

KENTUCKY

Mrs. Ruth West
Consultant, Art Education
Division of Program Development
Kentucky Department of Education
Frankfort, Kentucky 40601

LOUISIANA

Mrs. Myrtle Kerr
State Supervisor of Art
P.O. Box 44064
Baton Rouge, Louisiana 70804

MAINE

Virgilio Mori
Arts Coordinator
State of Maine Department of Education
Augusta, Maine 04330

MARYLAND

Harold H. Lott
Consultant of Art
State Department of Education
International Towers Building
P.O. Box 8717, BWI Airport
Baltimore, Maryland 21240

MASSACHUSETTS

William E. Farrington
Senior Supervisor of Art Education
State Department of Education
182 Tremont Street
Boston, Massachusetts 02111

MICHIGAN

Dr. Barbara Carlisle
Fine Arts Specialist
Michigan Department of Education
P.O. Box 30008
Lansing, Michigan 48909

MINNESOTA

Robert M. Paul
Art Coordinator
State Department of Education
Division of Instruction
Room 639, Capitol Square
St. Paul, Minnesota 55101

MISSISSIPPI

Miss Sandra Nicola
Art Education Consultant
State Department of Education
P.O. Box 771
Jackson, Mississippi 39205

MISSOURI

Richard L. Stokes
Supervisor of Art
State Department of Education
Division of Instruction
Section of Fine Arts
Jefferson City, Missouri 65101

MONTANA

Robert Crebo
Arts in Education Program
Office of the Superintendent of Public Instruction
State Capitol Building
Helena, Montana 59601

NEBRASKA

J. Stephen Lahr
State Art Consultant
Nebraska Department of Education
Sixth Floor Box 94987
Lincoln, Nebraska 68509

NEVADA

Tom Summers
Consultant in Humanities
Nevada Department of Education
Capitol Complex
Carson City, Nevada 89710

NEW HAMPSHIRE

John Michael Gray
Consultant, Arts Education
Department of Education
64 North Main Street
Concord, New Hampshire 03301

NEW JERSEY

Al Kochka
Executive Director
New Jersey State Council on the Arts
27 West State Street
Trenton, New Jersey 08625

NEW MEXICO

Helen M. Thompson
Arts Specialist
State Department of Education
State Capitol Building
Santa Fe, New Mexico 87503

NEW YORK

No position

NORTH CAROLINA

Doc McCulloch
State Art Supervisor
Division of Cultural Arts
State Department of Public Instruction
Raleigh, North Carolina 27611

NORTH DAKOTA

Harold Michelson
Director of Secondary Education
North Dakota Public Instruction
Capitol Building
Bismarck, North Dakota 58501

OHIO

Jerry Tollifson
Supervisor, Art Education
Department of Education
Ohio Departments Building
Room 815
65 South Front Street
Columbus, Ohio 43215

OKLAHOMA

Ms. Peggy Long
Fine Arts Specialist

State Department of Education
2500 N. Lincoln
Oklahoma City, Oklahoma 73105

OREGON

Dr. Delmer Aebischer
Basic Education Section
State Department of Education
942 Lancaster Drive, North East
Salem, Oregon 97310

PENNSYLVANIA

Clyde M. McGeary
Chief, Division of General Education
Bureau of Curriculum Services
Box 911
Harrisburg, PA 17126

RHODE ISLAND

Arlene I. Wilson
Consultant, Program Development
Rhode Island Department of Education
Roger Williams Building
Hayes Street
Providence, Rhode Island 02908

SOUTH CAROLINA

Thomas A. Hatfield
Supervisor of Art
South Carolina Department of Education
705 Rutledge Building
Columbia, South Carolina 29201

SOUTH DAKOTA

Dr. Joyce Levin
Director of Curriculum
Division of Elementary and Secondary Education
Office Building, Suite 3
Pierre, South Dakota 57501

TENNESSEE

Robert Daniel
Supervisor of Instruction in Arts
Building 307
11th Avenue
Smyrna, Tennessee 37167

TEXAS

Ida Nell Williams
Art Consultant
Texas Education Agency
201 East 11th Street
Austin, Texas 78711

UTAH

Charles B. Stubbs
State Specialist in Art Education
250 East Fifth South
Salt Lake City, Utah 84111

VERMONT

Miss M. Rita Pfeifer
Arts Consultant
Department of Education
Montpelier, Vermont 05602

VIRGINIA

Mrs. Shirlee C. Loomer
Assistant Supervisor of Art Education
State Department of Education
Richmond, Virginia 23216

WASHINGTON

William Radcliffe, Jr.
Supervisor of Art Programs
State Office of Public Instruction
P.O. Box 527
Olympia, Washington 98501

WEST VIRGINIA

Virginia Walker
Curriculum Development Specialist, Art
West Virginia Department of Education
Capitol Complex B-318
Charleston, West Virginia 25305

WISCONSIN

Earl L. Collins
Supervisor, Art Education
Coordinator-Statewide Arts and Humanities
126 Langdon Street
Madison, Wisconsin 53702

WYOMING

Candace Noble
Coordinator, Foreign Language, Bilingual
    Education and Fine Arts
State Office Building West
Cheyenne, Wyoming 82002

PUERTO RICO

Carmen Tuya
Director, Visual Arts Program
Commonwealth of Puerto Rico
Department of Education
Hato Rey, Puerto Rico 00919

VIRGIN ISLANDS

Douglas Covey
Supervisor of Art
Department of Education
P.O. Box 1
Christiansted, St. Croix, Virgin Islands 00820

SCHOOL SYSTEMS OF 500,000 & OVER IN POPULATION

Birmingham Public Schools

Mrs. Lila J. Wells
Supervisor of Art
P.O. Box 114
Birmingham, Alabama 35201

Phoenix Union High School District

Mrs. Dorothy Johnson Bergamo
Chairman, Department of Performing Arts
Trevor G. Browne High School
7402 W. Catalina Drive
Phoenix, Arizona 85033

Long Beach Unified School District

Sherry E. Swan
Art Consultant, Fine Arts Education
701 Locust Avenue
Long Beach, California 90814

Los Angeles Unified School District

Pauline D. James
Instructional Specialist, Art
Instructional Planning Division A-327
Administrative Offices
450 N Grand
Los Angeles, California 90015

San Diego Unified School District

Dr. Leven C. Leatherbury
Curriculum Specialist, Art Education
San Diego Unified School District
4100 Normal Street
San Diego, California 92103

San Francisco Unified School District

Herbert R. Simon
Director of Creative Art
135 Van Ness Avenue
San Francisco, California 94102

Dade County Public Schools

Charles M. King
Art Supervisor
1410 Northeast Second Avenue
Miami, Florida 33132

Lee County Public Schools

Mrs. Margaret A. Bare
Coordinator of Fine Arts
School Annex, 3308 Canal Street
Fort Myers, Florida 33902

De Kalb County Schools

Mrs. Sara Jo Sirmans
Supervisor of Art
2860 Guinevere Drive, North East
Atlanta, Georgia 30345

Chicago Public Schools

Helen M. Joyner
Art Consultant
228 North LaSalle Street
Chicago, Illinois 60601

Indianapolis Public Schools

Ted A. Moore
Supervisor of Art
120 East Walnut Street
Indianapolis, Indiana 46204

Davenport Community School District

Lars H. Souder
Coordinator of Art Education
1001 Harrison
Davenport, Iowa 52803

Des Moines Independent Community School District

Ruth Mobberly
Art Education Supervisor
1800 Grand Avenue
Des Moines, Iowa 50307

Baltimore City Public Schools

Richard L. Micherdzinski
Director of Art
Oliver and Eden Streets
Baltimore, Maryland 21213

Prince George's County Public Schools

Dr. Leroy Gaskin
Supervisor of Art, K-12
Instructional Services Center
Upper Marlboro, Maryland 20870

Boston Public Schools

Miss Elizabeth H. Gilligan
Director of Fine Arts
26 Court Street
Boston, Massachusetts 02108

Chicopee Public Schools

Miss Margaret L. Mannix
Supervisor of Art
244 Oak Street
Holyoke, Massachusetts 01040

Benton Harbor Public Schools

Mr. Charles Murray
Art Department Chairman
870 Colfax Avenue
Benton Harbor, Michigan 49022

Detroit Public Schools

James Jennings
Supervisor, Department of Art Education
842 Schools Center
5057 Woodward
Detroit, Michigan 48202

Flint Board of Education

Maurice D. Frost
Coordinator of Fine Arts
942 East Sixth Street
Flint, Michigan 48503

Wayne Community School District

Miss Suan Price
Coordinator of Visual Arts and Physical Education
3712 Williams Street
Wayne, Michigan 48184

Osseo Senior High School District

Eugene Waldowski
Art Teacher
317 Second Avenue, N.W.
Osseo, Minnesota 55369

Kansas City Public Schools

Leonard Pryor
District Coordinator, Fine and Performing Arts
Room 808
1211 McGee Street
Kansas, Missouri 64106

Raytown Consolidated School District 2

Miss Jean Harrison
Art Coordinator, Kindergarten—12
10500 East 60th Terrace
Raytown, Missouri 64133

St. Louis Public Schools

Dr. Marie L. Larkin
Supervisor of Art
5329 Columbia Avenue
St. Louis, Missouri 63139

Buffalo Public Schools

John M. Gaylord
Director of Art Education
Room 709 C City Hall
Buffalo, New York 14202

Rochester City School District

Burt A. Towne
Director of Arts and Humanities
13 Fitzhugh Street S.
Rochester, New York 14614

Cincinnati Public Schools

Donald P. Sowell
Instructional Consultant, Art Education
230 East Ninth Street
Cincinnati, Ohio 45202

Columbus Public Schools

Mrs. Kay McGill
Director of Fine and Performing Arts
270 East State Street
Columbus, Ohio 43215

Toledo Board of Education

Miss Beverly Domalski
Director of Art
Toledo Public Schools
Manhattan & Elm
Toledo, Ohio 43608

Willoughby-Eastlake City Schools

Mrs. Uarda Overbaugh
Art Consultant
Willoughby-Eastlake City Schools
Royalview Elementary School
31500 Royalview Drive
Willowick, Ohio 44094

The School District of Philadelphia

Jack Bookbinder
Director of Art Education
Board of Education
21 & Parkway
Philadelphia, Pennsylvania 19103

Austin Independent School District

Sherilyn Howze
Art Coordinator
6100 Guadalupe
Austin, Texas 78752

Houston Independent School District

Mrs. Mary Pearl Temple
Director of Art Education
3830 Richmond Avenue
Houston, Texas 77027

Federal Way School District 210

Scott Pepper
Art Consultant
31455 28th Avenue South
Federal Way, Washington 98002

Seattle School District 1

Mr. Henry W. Petterson
Art Specialist
815 Fourth Avenue N.
Seattle, Washington 98107

Milwaukee Public Schools

Gordon Borchardt
Director of Art Education
P.O. Drawer 10K
Milwaukee, Wisconsin 53201

SCHOOL SYSTEMS OF 100,000 TO 499,999

Bessemer Public Schools

Margaret K. Elm
Art Consultant
417 South 18th
Bessemer, Alabama 35020

Jefferson County Board of Education

Mr. DeLeon Fancher
Assistant Art Supervisor
1009 North 21 St
Birmingham, Alabama 35203

Gadsden City Schools

Mrs. Ma Lou Smith
Art Specialist
P.O. Box 184
Gadsden, Alabama 35902

Opelika Public Schools

Roslyn B. Stern
Art Consultant
P.O. Box 311
Opelika, Alabama 36801

Tuscaloosa City Schools

Mrs. Ronna Lasser
Art Teacher - Coordinator, Elementary
1100 21st Street E.
Tuscaloosa, Alabama 35401

Anchorage School District

Dr. Ruth Keitz
Art Coordinator
2503 Blueberry
Anchorage, Alaska 99503

Mesa Public Schools

Dr. Edna Gilbert
Arts Director
Mesa Public Schools
14 West Second Avenue
Mesa, Arizona 85202

Phoenix Elementary District 1

Miss Betty Lou Richards
Art Director
125 East Lincoln
Phoenix, Arizona 85004

Prescott Elementary Schools

Ella F. Fisher
Supervisor of Art Education
Prescott Elementary Schools
146 South Granite Street
Prescott, Arizona 86301

Tucson Elementary Schools

Sunnyside School District 12
Rubina F. Gallo
Los Ninos Elementary School
Elementary Art Consultant
470 West Valencia Road
Tucson, Arizona 85704

Tucson Public Schools District 1

Dr. Nik Krevitsky
Director of Art and Educational Materials Center
Thomas L. Lee Instructional
Resource Center
2025 East Winsett Street
Tucson, Arizona 85712

Alameda Unified School District

Miss Olivia Krause
Supervisor of Art Education
400 Grand Street
Alameda, California 94501

Alhambra City Schools

Mrs. Ann Wollen
Art Consultant
15 West Alhambra Road
Alhambra, California 91801

Alum Rock Union Elementary School District

Alex Salazar
Program Coordinator of Cultural Arts

Director of Curriculum
2930 Gay Avenue
San Jose, California 95127

Bakersfield City School District

Mrs. Mary K. Mueller
Consultant, Art Education
Education Center
1300 Baker Street
Bakersfield, California 93305

Baldwin Park Unified School District

Kathryn McIlreath
Art Specialist
Baldwin Park USD
3699 North Holly Avenue
Baldwin Park, California 91706

Berkeley Unified School District

Philip St. Martin
Chairman, Art, Industry and Design
Berkeley High School
Berkeley, California 94709

Burbank Unified School District

Harold R. Bucklin
Coordinator of Elementary Education
245 East Magnolia Boulevard
Burbank, California 91504

Campbell Elementary School District

Mrs. Marcia Wells
Art Consultant
155 North Third Street
Campbell, California 95008

Campbell Union High School District

Ross C. Deniston
Art Supervisor
Camden High School
2075 Camden Avenue
San Jose, California 95124

Compton City School District

Kenneth Gregg
Staff Teacher Art
Mrs. Billie Jackson
Staff Teacher Art
Compton Unified School District
604 South Tamarind Avenue
Compton, California 90220

Kenneth R. Gregg
Staff Teacher, Art
Area Instructional Services
1623 E. 118th Street
Los Angeles, California 90059

Compton Union High School District

Leonard F. Fisher
District Curriculum Assistant, Art
417 West Alondar Boulevard
Compton, California 90220

Danville Unified School District

Arthur H. Dougherty
Fine Arts Coordinator
599 Old Orchard Drive
Danville, California 94526

Escondido Union School District

Rex Hamilton
Fine Arts Specialist
Fifth & Maple
Escondido, California 92025

Fresno City Unified School District

Mr. Ralph E. Gomas
Art Coordinator
Education Center Tulare M

3132 East Fairmont
Fresno, California 93721

Fullerton Elementary School District

Mrs. Gelsomina Barton
Fine Arts Coordinator
1401 West Valencia Drive
Fullerton, California 92633

Garden Grove Unified School District

Bernard M. Jones, Jr.
Art Specialist
10331 Stanford Avenue
Garden Grove, California 92640

Glendale Unified School District

Mrs. Audrey A. Welch
Arts Coordinator
223 North Jackson Street
Glendale, California 91206

Hudson School District

Mrs. Lona Hoffman
Consultant
15959 East Gale Avenue
La Puente, California 91745

La Mesa-Spring Valley School District

Jean A. Shour
Art Coordinator
4750 Date Avenue
La Mesa, California 92041

Montebello Unified School District

Mrs. Jewel Bishop Starkey
Consultant, Art
123 South Montebello Boulevard
Montebello, California 90640

Monroe Valley Unified School District

Dr. Robert Banister
District Art Supervisor
13911 Perris Boulevard
Sunnymead, California 92388

Mt. Diablo Unified School District

Mr. James E. Snowden
Curriculum Specialist in Art and Industrial Education
1936 Carlotta Drive
Concord, California 94519

Newport-Mesa Unified School District

Jenean Romberg
Newport-Mesa School District
1601 Sixteenth Street
Newport Beach, California 92660

Novato Unified School District

Lee Hilton
Curriculum Specialist, Art
1015 Seventh Street
Novato, California 94947

Oakland Unified School District

Stanley H. Cohen
Art Consultant
1025 Second Avenue
Oakland, California 94606

Ocean View School District

Mrs. Rose Clark
Resource Teacher, Art
7972 Warner Avenue
Huntington Beach, California 92647

Palo Alto Unified School District

Mrs. Kathryn M. Alexander
Art Consultant
25 Churchill Avenue
Palo Alto, California 94306

Pasadena City Unified School District

Norman E. Schmidt
Director of Program/Art Education
351 South Hudson
Pasadena, California 91109

Pasadena Secondary School District

Sr. Alberta Curran
St. Andrew High School
42 Chestnut Street
Pasadena, California 91103

San Jose Unified School District

Mr. William Shelley
Supervisor of Art Education
1605 Park Avenue
San Jose, California 95126

San Lorenzo Unified School District

Thomas R. Phillips
Music and Fine Arts Coordinator
15510 Usher Street
San Lorenzo, California 94580

San Mateo City School District

Richard Sperisen
Art Consultant & Director
School Design
P.O. Box K
San Mateo, California 94402

Santa Barbara High School District

Janice Y. Lorber
Art Department
700 E. Anapamu Street
Santa Barbara, California 93103

Santa Clara Unified School District

Miss Janet E. Tellefsen
Art Consultant
P.O. Box 397
Santa Clara, California 95052

Santa Monica Unified School District

Richard Wagnon
Supervisor of Music and Art
Joan F. Vaupen
Art Teacher, Curriculum Assistant
Art Office, Santa Monica Bd. of Education
1723 Fourth Street
Santa Monica, California 90401

San Mateo Union High School District

Gregg MacGibbon
Art Curriculum Council Chairman
Crestmoor High School
300 Piedmont Avenue
San Bruno, California 94066

Sweetwater Union High School District

Mr. Frank Buzga
District Art Committee Chairman
Sweetwater Union High School District
1130 Fifth Avenue
Chula Vista, California 92011

Ventura Unified School District

Howard Quam
Coordinator Instructional Media Services
120 East Santa Clara
Ventura, California 93001

School District 12, Adams County

Dr. Norma Goecke
Music and Art Subject Specialty
11285 Highline Drive
Denver, Colorado 80233

Aurora Public Schools

Richard D. Schafer
Art Consultant
1085 Peoria Street
Aurora, Colorado 80011

Arapahoe County School District 6

Dr Judy Rogers
Consultant in Art Education, K-12
6558 South Acoma Street
Littleton, Colorado 80120

Boulder Valley Public School District

Buck Owens
Art Resource
P.O. Box 9011
Boulder, Colorado 80302

Colorado Springs Public Schools, District 11

Robert Simpich
Director, Art Education
1115 North El Paso Street
Colorado Springs, Colorado 80903

Jefferson County School District R-1

Larry T. Schultz
Coordinator of Art
809 Quail Street
Lakewood, Colorado 80215

Poudre School District R-1

Miss Sylvia B. Maxey
Art Coordinator
2407 La Porte Street
Fort Collins, Colorado 80521

Bristol Public Schools

Mrs. Carol Jackowicz
Department Head
Box 1601
Bristol, Connecticut 06010

East Hartford Board of Education

Donald E. Hallquist
Supervisor/Fine and Performing Arts
110 Long Hill Drive
East Hartford, Connecticut 06108

Fairfield School System

Mr. Peter Clarke
Art Coordinator
c/o Andrew Warde High School
Fairfield, Connecticut 06430

Greenwich Board of Education

Harold L. Krevolin
Coordinator Art/Music
290 Greenwich Avenue
Greenwich, Connecticut 06830

Hartford Public Schools

Paul J. Dilworth
Supervisor, Department of the Arts
249 High School
Hartford, Connecticut 06103

Meriden Public Schools

Thomas F. Potter
Supervisor of Art

Board of Education
22 Liberty Street
Meriden, Connecticut 06450

Milford Public Schools

Frank J. Vespi
Department Head
Elementary Art Department
Ellis Hill Annex, Building 3
Milford, Connecticut 06460

New Canaan Public Schools

Mrs. Bernice D. Hall
Chairman Art K-12
New Canaan, Connecticut 06849

New Haven Public Schools

Margaret F. Ring
Supervisor of Art
765 Elm Street
New Haven, Connecticut 06511

Norwalk Public Schools

Dr. Donald Rogers
Art Department Head
Board of Education Offices
105 Main Street
Norwalk, Connecticut 06852

Stamford Public Schools

John C. Nerreau
Coordinator of Art
Hoyt School
1500 High Ridge Road
Stamford, Connecticut 06903

Newark School District

Harley S. Hastings
Supervisor of Music and Art
Newark School District
83 East Main Street
Newark, Delaware 19711

Wilmington Public Schools

Robert C. Moore
Supervisor of Art Education
Wilmington Public Schools
1400 Washington Street
Wilmington, Delaware 19899

Broward County School System

Mrs. Jeanette McArthur
Director of Art Education
1320 S.W. Fourth Street
P.O. Box 8369
Fort Lauderdale, Florida 33312

Duval County School Board

William H. Dodd
Supervisor of Art Education
1701 Davis Street
Jacksonville, Florida 32209

Escambia County School Board

Miss Mary Jo Burgess
Supervisor of Art
5502 Lillian Highway
Pensacola, Florida 32506

Hillsborough County Board of Public Instruction

Dorothy Kennedy
Supervisor Art and Humanities
Instructional Services Center
707 East Columbus Drive
Tampa, Florida 33602

Lee County Public Schools

Mrs. Margaret A. Bare
Coordinator of Fine Arts
School Annex
3308 Canal Street
Fort Myers, Florida 33902

Manatee County School System

Mrs. Eleanor H. Paul
Acting Art Supervisor
5886 17th Street, West
Bradenton, Florida 33507

The Okaloosa County School System

Collis V. Porter
Art Supervisor
120 Lowery Place
Fort Walton Beach, Florida 32548

Palm Beach County Public Schools

Mrs. Jo D. Kowalchuk
Supervisor
School Board of Palm Beach County
South Administrative Offices
505 South Congress Avenue
Boynton Beach, Florida 33435

Panama City Public Schools

Art Davis
Art Coordinator
Bay County Schools
1855 Liddon Road
Panama City, Florida 32401

School Board of Pinellas County, Florida

Phyllis M. Thurston
Art Supervisor
100 North Greenwood
Clearwater, Florida 33515

Polk County School Board

Joe P. Mitchell
Coordinator of Art Instruction
P.O. Box 391
Bartow, Florida 33830

St. Lucie County School Board

Mr. Harold Supank
2909 Delaware Avenue
Fort Pierce, Florida 33450

Sarasota County School Board

Mary Francis MacDonald
Supervisor of Art Education
2418 Hatton Street
Sarasota, Florida 33577

Volusia County Board of Public Instruction

Mrs. Dorothy Johnson
Art Supervisor
P.O. Box 1910
Daytona Beach, Florida 32015

Atlanta Public Schools

David Walker
Coordinator, Arts and Humanities Center
1280 Peachtree Street, N.E.
Atlanta, Georgia 30309

Callaway Educational Association

Carolyn Ann Page
Art Director
Dallis Street
La Grange, Georgia 30240

Clark County School District

Jane D. Deason
Visual Art Supervisor
Box 1708
Athens, Georgia 30601

Clayton County Board of Education

Mrs. Martha Ellen Stilwell
Curriculum Coordinator, Art, Music
120 Smith Street
Jonesboro, Georgia 30236

Eastman Public Schools

Earl W. Woodward
Art Supervisor, Title III
Cultural Enrichment Project
Eastman, Georgia 31023

Fulton County School District

Miss Emory Rose Wood
Director of Art Education
786 Cleveland Avenue, S.W.
Atlanta, Georgia 30315

Macon Public Schools

Miss J. Elizabeth McElroy
Art Supervisor, Area 4
Hunt School
990 Shurling Drive
Macon, Georgia 31201

Peach City Schools

Mrs. Jean D. Pervis
Art Consultant
Fort Valley High School
Knox Valley, Georgia 31031

Walton County Public Schools

Mrs. Perry Nelle Darby
Art Consultant
Walton City Board of Education
Monroe, Georgia 30655

Kamehameha Schools

Mrs. Frances Pickens
Art Instructor, Senior High School Division
Bernice Pauahi Bishop Estate
Kapalama Heights
Honolulu, Hawaii 96817

Independent School District of Boise City

Robert Wand
Supervisor of Art
1207 Fort Street
Boise, Idaho 83702

Arlington Township High School District 214

Edward Fischer
District Coordinator of Arts, Music and Student Teaching
Township High School District 214
799 West Kensington Road
Mount Prospect, Illinois 60056

Cicero Elementary District 99

Emil R. Proska
Art Coordinator
5110 West 24th
Cicero, Illinois 60650

Champaign County Schools

Mrs. Josephine W. Payne
Elementary Art Consultant Champaign Unit 4
2035 South New Street
Champaign, Illinois 61820

Danville Community Consolidated School District 118

William B. Handley
Director of Fine Arts
516 North Jackson Street
Danville, Illinois 61832

Elgin Public Schools, District U-46

Mrs. Corinne Loeh
Director of Art Education
4 South Gifford Street
Elgin, Illinois 60120

District 65 Schools, Evanston

Tom Harris
Director of Fine Arts
1314 Ridge Avenue
Evanston, Illinois 60201

Granite City Community Unit 9

Eugene L. Aiassi
Administrative Consultant of Art Education
2545 Westmoreland Drive
Granite City, Illinois 62040

Moline Public Schools

Karl Haytcher
Coordinator of Art
1619 Eleventh Avenue
Moline, Illinois 61265

Oak Park Elementary Schools

Floyd Freerksen
970 Madison
Oak Park, Illinois 60302

District 15 Schools, Palatine

Mrs. Josephine L. Heyden
Art Chairperson
789 North Inverway
Palatine, Illinois 60067

Rockford Public Schools

Paul Pullin
Supervisor of Art
201 South Madison Street
Rockford, Illinois 61101

Rock Island Public Schools

Richard T. Klatt
Director of Art
1400 25th Avenue
Rock Island, Illinois 61201

Waukegan Unit School District 60

Martha D. Wasylik
Director of Art Education K-12
Unit School District 60
Lincoln Center
1201 North Sheridan Road
Waukegan, Illinois 60085

Western Springs Public Schools

Wesley R. Buchwald
Supervisor of Art
Area B
4815 South Karlov Avenue
Western Springs, Illinois 60632

Anderson Public Schools

Doris Noel
Supervisor of Art
528 West 11th Street
Anderson, Indiana 46016

Bartholomew Consolidated School Corporation

Karl McCaꞧ
Supervisor of Art Education
Senior High School
Columbus, Indiana 47201

Bedford Public Schools

Jim Blyeth
Chairman
North Lawrence Art Department
2222 West Eighth Street
Bedford, Indiana 47421

Evansville-Vanderburgh School Corporation

Harry C. Friley
Director of Education Resources/Art Education
1 South East Ninth Street
Evansville, Indiana 47708

Fort Wayne Community Schools

Mr. Gene P. Porter
Consultant for Art
1230 South Clinton Street
Fort Wayne, Indiana 46802

Gary Public Schools

Mrs. John A. Mohamed
Supervisor of Art K-12
620 East 10th Place
Gary, Indiana 46408

Hammond Public Schools

Robert Lee Fischer
Curriculum Consultant
524 173rd Street
Hammond, Indiana 46320

Kokomo-Center Township Consolidated School Corporation

James Osborne
Coordinator of Art Education
100 West Lincoln Road
Kokomo, Indiana 46901

Marion Community Schools

George Kind
Art Coordinator
Marion High School
716 West 26th Street
Marion, Indiana 46952

Michigan City Area Schools

Mrs. Kay Behrndt
Director of Art
609 Lafayette Street
Michigan City, Indiana 46360

Muncie Community Schools

Miss Beulah Book
Supervisor of Art, K-12
Research and Planning Building
600 N. Mulberry Street
Muncie, Indiana 47305

New Castle Community Schools

Mrs. Shirley A. Liby
Director of Art and Media
Media Center
522 Elliott Avenue
New Castle, Indiana 47362

Richmond Community Schools

Edward L. Loar
Coordinator of Art Education
Administration Building
300 Whitewater Boulevard
Richmond, Indiana 47374

South Bend Community School Corporation

Kenneth Geoffroy
Coordinator of Fine Arts
635 South Main Street
South Bend, Indiana 46623

Vigo County School Corporation

Mrs. Harriet McCullough
Elementary School Art Supervisor
961 Lafayette Avenue
Terre Haute, Indiana 47804

Metropolitan School District of Washington Township

Max I. Briggs
Chairman, Art Department
North Central High School
1801 East 86th Street
Indianapolis, Indiana 46240

Cedar Rapids Community School District

Archie E. Bauman
Project Leader for Art Education
346 Second Avenue, S.W.
Cedar Rapids, Iowa 52404

Sioux City Community School District

Robert J. Patnaud
Division Head
Art Department
1221 Pierce Street
Sioux City, Iowa 51105

Unified School District 500, Kansas City

E. Eileen Hughes
Director of Art
2019 Tauromee
Kansas City, Kansas 66102

Shawnee Mission Public School District 512

Peter Perdaris
Supervisor of Art
7235 Antioch Road
Shawnee Mission, Kansas 66204

Unified School District 501, Shawnee County

Donna D. Pauler Held
Instructional Specialist Art K-12
Supervisor of Art
1601 Van Buren
Topeka, Kansas 66612

Unified School District Wichita, 259

William W. King
Director of Art Education
640 North Emporia
Wichita, Kansas 67214

Jefferson County Public Schools

Norma E. Brown
Art Supervisor
Brown Education Center
675 River City Mall
Louisville, Kentucky 40202

Caddo Parish School System

Mrs. Zelphia B. Layton
Supervisor of Related Arts Education
1961 Midway
P.O. Box 3700
Shreveport, Louisiana 71108

Calcasieu Parish School System

Brad Daigle
Supervisor, Music and Art
1732 Kirkman Street
Lake Charles, Louisiana 70601

New Orleans Public Schools

Shirley Trusty Corey
Supervisor of Cultural Resources
4100 Touro Street
New Orleans, Louisiana 70122

Ouachita Parish School System

Henry Camp
Fine Arts Coordinator
P.O. Box 1642
Monroe, Louisiana 71201

Allegany County Public Schools

Harry R. Mandel
Supervisor of Art Education
108 Washington Street
Cumberland, Maryland 21502

Anne Arundel County Public Schools

Mary E. Wellham
Coordinator of Art
Board of Education
2644 Riva Road
Annapolis, Maryland 21401

Baltimore County Public Schools

James B. Laubheimer
Coordinator of Art
John L. Crossin
Supervisor of Art
Patricia A. Agee
Art Specialist
Board of Education of Baltimore County
Towson, Maryland 21204

Carroll County Public School System

Dr. Warren W. Shelley
Supervisor of Art and Music
Carroll County Board of Education
55 North Court Street
Westminster, Maryland 21157

Charles County Board of Education

Ann S. Richardson
Supervisor of Art
La Plata, Maryland 20646

Frederick County Public Schools

Carroll H. Kehne, Jr.
Supervisor of Art
115 East Church Street
Frederick, Maryland 21701

Howard County Public Schools

H. Eugene Miller
Supervisor, Art and Music
Howard County Board of Education
Clarksville, Maryland 21029

Montgomery County Public Schools

Emil Hrebenach
Coordinator Secondary Art
850 Hungerford Drive
Rockville, Maryland 20850

Washington County Public Schools

Mr. Clyde H. Roberts
Supervisor of Art
Box 730
Hagerstown, Maryland 21740

Bourue Public Schools

Jeremiah M. Lyon
Art Director
Bourue High School
Bourue, Massachusetts 02532

Brockton Public Schools

Pasquale F. Morano
Director of the Arts
50 Summer Street
Brockton, Massachusetts 02402

Cambridge School Department

Rita W. Ritterbush
Director of Art
1700 Cambridge Street
Cambridge, Massachusetts 02138

Fall River Public Schools

Edmond St. Laurent
Director of Fine Arts
417 Rock Street
Fall River, Massachusetts 02720

Framingham Public Schools

Neal Cotton
Director of Art
50 Lawrence Street
Framingham, Massachusetts 01701

Braintree Public Schools

Margaret D. Puffer
Director of Art
Braintree Public Schools
Ten Tremont Street
South Braintree, Massachusetts 02185

Greenfield Public Schools

Mrs. Shirley A. Crowell
Art Coordinator
197 Federal Street
Greenfield, Massachusetts 01301

Lexington Public Schools

Paul A. Ciano
Coordinator of the Visual Arts
Education Department K-12
Lexington Public Schools
Lexington, Massachusetts 02173

Lowell Public Schools

Thomas McGuire
Director of Art
Lowell, Massachusetts

Lynn Public Schools

Marjorie Clancy
Art Department
42 Franklin Street
Lynn, Massachusetts 01902

Medford Public Schools

Frances Fanning
Art Director
25 Hall Avenue
Medford, Massachusetts 02155

New Bedford Public Schools

Raymond G. Bisaillon
Art Education Director
County Street Administration Building
455 County Street
New Bedford, Massachusetts 02740

Newton Public Schools

Dr. Al Hurwitz
Visual and Related Arts
100 Walnut Street
Newtonville, Massachusetts 02160

Pittsfield Public Schools

Mrs. Winifred Bell
Art Coordinator, K-12

Pittsfield Public Schools
P.O. Box 1187
Pittsfield, Massachusetts 01201

Barnsville Public Schools

Deborah A. Barrows
Elementary Art Specialist
Box 424
Centerville, Massachusetts 02632

Quincy Public Schools

Mr. Walter E. Lunsman, Director
Art and Humanities Department
Quincy Public Schools
Coddington Street
Quincy, Massachusetts 02169

Somerville Public Schools

Charles Khirallah
Director of Art
City Hall Annex
Somerville, Massachusetts 02143

Springfield Public Schools

Robert L. Drummond
Director of Fine and Industrial Arts
195 State Street
Springfield, Massachusetts 01103

Weymouth Public Schools

Philip S. Dolan
Crafts and Design Instructor
Weymouth South High School
360 Pleasant Street
South Weymouth, Massachusetts 02190

Waltham School Department

Paul D. Shea
Art Director
Waltham Public Schools
Waltham, Massachusetts 02154

Worcester Public Schools

Marilyn Goodman
Acting Director of Art
31 Elizabeth Street
Worcester, Massachusetts 01605

Ann Arbor Public Schools

Mrs. Ruth L. Beatty
Coordinator of Art
Public School Administration Building
2555 South State
Ann Arbor, Michigan 48104

Battle Creek Public Schools

Max D. Misner
Art Consultant
Willard Library Building
Battle Creek, Michigan 49016

Bay City Public Schools

Jane D. Miller
Coordinator
Bay City, Michigan 48706

Benton Harbor Public Schools

Charles Murray
Art Department Chairman
870 Colfax Avenue
Benton Harbor, Michigan 49022

Dearborn Public Schools

Donald Boughner
Art Resource Teacher
4824 Lois Avenue
Dearborn, Michigan 48126

East Detroit Public Schools

Donald Olesklewicz
Chairman, Art Department
15550 Couzens
East Detroit, Michigan 48021

Farmington Public Schools

Mrs. Beverly L. Ellis
Chairman, Elementary Arts Consultant
32500 Shiawassee
Farmington, Michigan 48024

Garden City Public Schools

Donald L. Beatty
Deputy Superintendent
1333 Radcliff Street
Garden City, Michigan 48135

Grand Rapids Public Schools

Mrs. Vee Matusko
Supervisor of Art
143 Bostwick, N.E.
Grand Rapids, Michigan 49502

Kalamazoo Public Schools

Doris M. Miller
Consultant for Elementary Art
1220 Howard Street
Kalamazoo, Michigan 49001

Lansing School District

Peggy King
Director of Art Instruction
3426 South Cedar Street
Lansing, Michigan 48910

Midland Public Schools

James Hopfensperger
Coordinator of Art
600 E. Carpenter Street
Midland, Michigan 48640

City of Pontiac School District

Otha Whitcomb
Art Specialist
Franklin Elementary School
661 Franklin Road
Pontiac, Michigan 48513

Portage Public Schools

Al Kushner
Chairman, Art Department
Portage Public Schools
Portage, Michigan 49081

Port Huron Area School District

Sally Westrick Gregg
Director, Art Education
509 Stanton Street
Port Huron, Michigan 48060

Roseville Public Schools

Curt Winnega
Chairman, Art Department, Secondary Schools
Brablec High School
Roseville, Michigan 48066

Saginaw City School District

Richard A. Foulds
Supervisor, Art Education
550 Millard Street
Saginaw, Michigan 48607

Anoka-Hennepin Independent School District 11

Jean Thurston
Art Coordinator

Educational Service Center
1129 Hanson Boulevard
Anoka, Minnesota 55303

Independent School District 709, Duluth

Sheldon Johnson
Supervisor of Art
Board of Education Building
Lake Avenue and Second Street
Duluth, Minnesota 55802

Minneapolis Public Schools

Dr. Eugenia M. Oole
Consultant in Art
807 North East Broadway
Minneapolis, Minnesota 55413

Independent School District 281, Robbinsdale Area

Pearl Halverson
Elementary Art Coordinator
4148 Winnetka Avenue, North
Minneapolis, Minnesota 55427

Osseo Senior High School District

Eugene Waldowski
Art Teacher
317 Second Avenue, N.W.
Osseo, Minnesota 55369

Rochester, District 535

Kenneth Bauman
Elementary Art Consultant
463 Northern Heights Drive, N.E.
Rochester, Minnesota 55901

St. Louis Park Public Schools

Robert Anderson
Department Chairman
Art Education
6425 West 33rd Street
St. Louis Park, Minnesota 55426

Independent School District 621, Mounds View

Ellsworth E. Erickson
District Art Coordinator
Art Research, Resource Center
3555 North Victoria
St. Paul, Minnesota 55172

Independent School District 625, St. Paul

Stephen Conger
Supervisor of Art
Independent School District 625
Saint Paul Public Schools
360 Colborne
St. Paul, Minnesota 55102

Independent School District 624, White Bear Lake

Franklin J. Zeller
Art Coordinator
Bellaire Elementary School
White Bear Lake, Minnesota 55110

Jackson Public Schools

Mary Dell Burford
Supervisor of Art
Elementary Schools
1593 West Capital Street
Jackson, Mississippi 39203

Berkeley Public Schools

Arthur B. Kennon
Elementary Art Coordinator
6001 Berkeley Drive
Berkeley, Missouri 63134

Ferguson-Florissant School District

Mrs. Alice P. Ulbright
Coordinator of Art Education
655 January Avenue
Ferguson, Missouri 63135

Independence School District

Louis H. Braley
Art Consultant
1231 South Windsor
Independence, Missouri 64055

Parkway School District

Jerrel L. Swingle
Art Coordinator
Parkway School District
455 North Woods Mill Road
Chesterfield, Missouri 63017

Kirkwood Public Schools

Mrs. Chris Murphy
Art Instructor K-5
230 Quan Avenue
Kirkwood, Missouri 63122

North Kansas City

Katherine Smith
Elementary Art Supervisor
2000 North East 46th Street
Kansas City, Missouri 64116

The School District of St. Joseph

Marie Corcoran
Art Consultant
School District of St. Joseph
Tenth and Felix Streets
St. Joseph, Missouri 64501

Ritenour Consolidated School District

Mrs. Verneta Sevier
District Art Coordinator
Ritenour Consolidated School District
2420 Woodson Road
St. Louis County, Missouri 63114

School District of Springfield R12

Bill Stockstill
Coordinator of Art
Secondary Schools
Parkview High School
516 West Meadows
Springfield, Missouri 65804

School District 2, Billings

Archie Elliot
Director of Art Education
101-Tenth Street West
Billings, Montana 59102

School District 1, Great Falls

James D. Poor
Supervisor of Art
1100 Fourth Street South
Great Falls, Montana 59401

Lincoln Public Schools

Roger Dean Van Deventer
Art Consultant K-12
Public School Administration Building
P.O. Box 82889
Lincoln, Nebraska 68501

Omaha Public Schools

Gerald Pabst
Supervisor
3902 Davenport Street
Omaha, Nebraska 68131

Ralston Public Schools

Mrs. Judith C. Pittack
Elementary Art Supervisor
79th and Seymour
Ralston, Nebraska 68127

Las Vegas City Schools

Mrs. Marjorie A. Phillips
Phil Leger
Robertson High School
Las Vegas, New Mexico 87701

Manchester School Union 37

Leonard R. Armstrong
Director of Art
88 Lowell Street
Manchester, New Hampshire 03104

Cherry Hill Public Schools

Yvonne L. Bieberbach
Art Coordinator
1155 Marklress Road
Cherry Hill, New Jersey 08034

Clifton Public Schools

Richard Ebert
Director of Music, Art and Elementary Education
Clifton Public Schools
745 Clifton Avenue
Clifton, New Jersey 07013

East Orange Public School System

Bernice E. Magnie
Director of Art
21 Winans Street
East Orange, New Jersey 07017

Elizabeth Public Schools

Eddie Smith
Board of Education
500 North Broad Street
Elizabeth, New Jersey 07202

Public Schools of Jersey City

Claire J. Warlikowski
Acting Supervisor of Art
30 Montgomery Street
Jersey City, New Jersey 07306

Middletown Township Public Schools

Wayne Ehlers
Middletown Township Public Schools
59 Tindall Road
Middletown, New Jersey 07748

Newark Public Schools

Dr. Ruth K. Assarsson
Director of Art Education
Department of Art Education
15 State Street
Newark, New Jersey 07102

Paterson Board of Education

Edward B. Epstein
Supervisor of Fine Arts
Board of Education
33 Church Street, B-4
Paterson, New Jersey 07505

Summit Public Schools

Arthur E. DeBrito
Chairman, Art Department K-12
Summit Public Schools
Summit, New Jersey 07901

Trenton Public Schools

John T. Cunningham
Director of Fine Arts
Board of Education
Nine South Stockton Street
Trenton, New Jersey 08611

Wayne Public Schools

Gayle Jones Reed
Art Coordinator
50 Nellis Drive
Wayne, New Jersey 07470

Albany Public Schools

Margaret M. Smith
Director of Art Education
Albany Board of Education
Academy Park
Albany, New York 12207

Binghamton City School District

Anne Greiner
Chairman Art Department
31 Main Street
Binghamton, New York 13905

Brentwood Public Schools

Manuel R. Vega
Coordinator of Art and Administrative Assistant
Brentwood Public Schools
Administration Building
Third Avenue and Fourth Street
Brentwood, New York 11717

Union Free School District 10

Mr. Sidney Cumins
District Art Consultant
80 Hauppauge Road
Commack, New York 11725

Connetquot City School District 7

Eugene Lissandrello
Related Arts Chairman
Connetquot High School
District Central Office
780 Ocean Avenue
Bohemia, New York 11716

East Meadow Public Schools

Phyllis B. Nelson
Director of Art Education
Curriculum Center
Meadowbrook Elementary School
East Meadow, New York 11554

City School District of Elmira

Mervin Slotnick
Director of Art
Administration Building
951 Hoffman Street
Elmira, New York 14905

Farmingdale Public Schools

Roger Hartford
Department Chairman
Farmingdale Senior High School
Lincoln Street
Farmingdale, New York 11735

Kenmore-Town of Tonawanda Public Schools

Robert Freeland
Art Supervisor K-12
1500 Colvin Boulevard
Kenmore, New York 14223

Levittown Union Free School District

Casimir Cetnarowski
Supervisor of Art
Board of Education Offices

North Village Green
Levittown, New York 11756

Lindenhurst Public Schools

Mrs. Barbara Payne
Elementary Art Coordinator K-6
E. W. Bower School
Montauk Highway

Massapequa Public Schools

Morris Brewer
Coordinating Chairman, Art
Administrative Wing, Massapequa High School
4925 Merrick Road
Massapequa, New York 11758

Middle Country Central School District 11

Henry Lechowicz
Art Coordinator
Seldon, New York 11784

Mount Vernon Public Schools

Dr. C. Andrew Randall
Supervisor of Music and Art
Education Center
165 North Columbus Avenue
Mt. Vernon, New York 10553

Community School District New Rochelle

Mortimer H. Slotnick
Arts and Humanities Consultant
515 North Avenue
New Rochelle, New York 10801

New York City Public Schools

George Kaye
Acting Director of Art
Board of Education
131 Livingston Street
Brooklyn, New York 11201

North Syracuse Central Schools

Roger E. Hyndman
Coordinator of Art Education
Lawrence Road Curriculum Center
North Syracuse, New York 13212

School District of Niagara Falls

Donald Banks
Supervisor of Fine Arts
607 Walnut Avenue
Niagara Falls, New York 14301

Oceanside Union Free School District

Paul C. Olivia
Director of Art Education
145 Merle Avenue
Oceanside, New York 11572

Central School District 4, Plainview-Old Bethpage

Charles Burge
Art Coordinator
John F. Kennedy High School
Plainview, New York 11803

Rome City School District

Guy Nasci
Director of Art
108 E. Garden Street
Rome, New York 13440

Schenectady Public Schools

Edwin G. Weinheimer
Supervisor of Art
108 Union Street
Schenectady, New York 12305

Sewanhaka Central District 2

Michael A. Russo
Art Coordinator
Floral Park Art Department
210 Locust Street
Floral Park
Long Island, New York 11001

Smithtown Public Schools

Richard Mello
Art Coordinator
Smithtown Central School District 1
St. James
Long Island, New York 11780

South Huntington, Union Free School District 13

Mrs. Maree Galvin
Coordinator of Art, K-6
31 Walt Whitman Road
Huntington Station, New York 11746

Three Village Central School District 1

Edward T. Goebel
Director of Art
Three Village Central School District 1
Nicoll Road
Setauket, New York 11733

Wappingers Central School District

Anthony J. Caccamo
Director of Art Education
Wappingers Central School District
John Jay High School
Route 52
Hopewell Junction, New York 12533

White Plains Public Schools

John Ruddley
Westchester County Supervisor of Art
Department of Parks, Recreation and Conservation
County Center
White Plains, New York 10606

Yonkers Public Schools

Mrs. Ellen Kruger
Supervisor of Art
Board of Education
Yonkers, New York 10701

Charlotte-Mecklenburg Schools

Mrs. Elizabeth Mack
Acting Director
P.O. Box 149
Charlotte, North Carolina 28201

Durham City Schools

Jessie D. Kearney
Director of Art
P.O. Box 2246
Durham, North Carolina 27702

Greensboro Public Schools

Elizabeth H. Bell
Art Supervisor
712 North Eugene Street/Drawer V
Greensboro, North Carolina 27402

Fort Bragg Schools

Miss Claudia J. Sailor
Art Coordinator
Fort Bragg Dependents Schools
Drawer A
Fort Bragg, North Carolina 28307

Wake County Public School System

Rose Melvin
Supervisor of Visual Arts
1600 Fayetteville Road
Raleigh, North Carolina 27603

Wayne County Schools

Joyce Thigpen
Supervisor of Cultural Arts
P.O. Drawer 27
Goldsboro, North Carolina 27530

Winston-Salem/Forsyth County Schools

Antony Swider
Coordinator of Art Education
P.O. Box 2513
Winston-Salem, North Carolina 27102

Fargo Public Schools

Vince Lindstrom
Cultural Resources Center
Creative Arts Studio
1430 Seventh Street South
Fargo, North Dakota 58102

Akron Public Schools

Brian B. Heard
Director of Art Education
70 North Broadway
Akron, Ohio 44308

Berea City Schools

Charles Armstrong
Art Supervisor
390 Fair Street
Berea, Ohio 44017

Canton City Schools

Mari Niarchos
Art Consultant (K-12)
618 High Avenue, N.W.
Canton, Ohio 44703

Cleveland Public Schools

Ronald N. Day
Directing Supervisor of Art
1380 East Sixth Street
Cleveland, Ohio 44114

Cuyahoga Falls City Schools

Ronald Simon
Head, Art Department
c/o Falls High School
2300 Fourth Street
Cuyahoga Falls, Ohio 44221

Dayton Public Schools

Armand Martino
Supervisor of Art
Dayton Board of Education
Service Building
4280 North Western Avenue
Dayton, Ohio 45427

Findlay Public Schools

Alexander Baluch
Coordinator of Fine Arts
1001 Blanchard Avenue
Findlay, Ohio 45840

Kettering City School District

Robert Thygerson
Supervisor, Music and Fine Arts
Kettering City School District
3490 Far Hills Avenue
Kettering, Ohio 45429

Lima City School District

Joan Hebden
Director of Art
515 South Calumet Avenue
Lima, Ohio 45804

Mansfield City Schools

Lois Beveridge
Art Resource Teacher
145 West Park Boulevard
Mansfield, Ohio 44902

Mentor Public Schools

Ted Keller
Supervisor of Art
Mentor High School
6477 Center Street
Mentor, Ohio 44060

Parma City Schools

Wanda Ullman
Coordinator of Art
6726 Ridge Road
Parma, Ohio 44129

Warren City Schools

James G. Friend
Supervising Teacher of Art
1360 Autumn Drive, N.W.
Warren, Ohio 44458

Washington Local Schools

Sandy Sheperd
Art Coordinator
5201 Douglas Road
Toledo, Ohio 43613

Youngstown City Schools

Andrew Nadzam
Supervisor of Art
20 West Wood Street
Youngstown, Ohio 44503

Enid Public Schools, Independent 57

Eldon Ames
Art Supervisor
111 South Taylor
Enid, Oklahoma 73701

Tulsa Public Schools

Mrs. Bobbie Jean Brophy
Supervisor of Art
3027 South New Haven
Tulsa, Oklahoma 74145

Beaverton School District 48

Omer Gosnell
Productions Specialist
Curriculum Specialist
P.O. Box 200
Beaverton, Oregon 97005

Bend Public School District 1

Richard G. Dedlow
Art Specialist
Administrative School District 1
1 South West Broadway
Bend, Oregon 97701

Eugene Public Schools, District 4J

Mrs. Freda Young
Art Education Coordinator
200 North Monroe
Eugene, Oregon 97402

David Douglas School District

Joseph B. Kleven
Supervisor of Art
2900 South East 122nd Avenue
Portland, Oregon 97236

Area IV Portland Public Schools

Austin O. Myers
Consultant
Area IV Curriculum Center
Barlow School
3700 South East 92nd
Portland, Oregon 97226

Portland Public Schools

Roberta J. Caughlan
Project Manager
Eco-Aesthetics Continuum
Portland Public Schools
7700 S.E. Reed College Place
c/o Dunway School
Portland, Oregon 97202

Salem Public Schools, District 24J

Don Walton
Art Resource Teacher
P.O. Box 87
Salem, Oregon 97308

Abington School District

Louis S. Mohollen
Supervisor of Art
Abington School District
1841 Susquehanna
Abington, Pennsylvania 19001

Allentown Public Schools

W. Valgene Routch
Fine Arts Coordinator
31 South Penn Street
Allentown, Pennsylvania 18105

Altoona Area School District

Calvin E. Folk
Supervisor of Art
1415 Seventh Avenue
Altoona, Pennsylvania 16603

Armstrong School District

Charles Milton Hanna
Department Chairman
Fourth and Tenth
Ford City, Pennsylvania 16226

Bethlehem Area School District

Dr. Frederick G. Gilmartin
Art Coordinator
Bethlehem Schools
2307 Rodgers Street
Bethlehem, Pennsylvania 18018

Bristol Township Public Schools

Joseph Pavone
Supervisor of Art
63 Manor Circle
Bristol, Pennsylvania 19007

Chambersburg Area School District

Mrs. Joyce S. Wyatt
Elementary Art Department Chairman
511 South Sixth Street
Chambersburg, Pennsylvania 17201

Chester Upland School District

Robert E. Vaughan
Director of Fine Arts

Chester Upland School District
18th and Melrose
Chester, Pennsylvania 19013

Erie School District

Paul G. Grack
Coordinator of Fine Arts
1511 Peach Street
Erie, Pennsylvania 16501

Harrisburg City School District

Ray P. Firestone
Associate Director, Art Education
1201 North Sixth Street
Harrisburg, Pennsylvania 17102

Hazelton Area School District

Albert Sarkas
Supervisor of Art
Green and Laurel Streets
Hazelton, Pennsylvania 18201

Greater Johnstown School District

Sara Jane Stewart
Supervisor of Art
Chestnut Building
501-509 Chestnut Street
Johnstown, Pennsylvania 15906

School District of Lancaster

Albert B. Minnich
Director of Art and Industrial Arts
225 West Orange Street
Lancaster, Pennsylvania 17604

New Castle Public Schools

Jesse W. Badger
Director of Art Education
Administration Building
Corner of North and East Streets
New Castle, Pennsylvania 16101

Pennsbury School District

Karl C. Schantz
Art Teacher, Quarry Hill School
Pennsbury School District
Fallsington, Pennsylvania 19054

Pittsburgh Public Schools

Ruth M. Ebken
Director of Art
Board of Public Education
341 South Bellefield Avenue
Pittsburgh, Pennsylvania 15213

Reading School District

Earl A. McLane
Director of Art
Administration Building
Eighth & Washington Streets
Reading, Pennsylvania 19601

Scranton Public Schools

Terrence Gallagher
Supervisor of Art
425 North Washington Avenue
Scranton, Pennsylvania 18503

Upper Darby School District

Judson G. Snyder
District Art Supervisor
Upper Darby, Pennsylvania 19084

Warren County School District

James Hill
Elementary Art Supervisor

Market Street Elementary School
Market and Second Streets
Warren, Pennsylvania 16365

West Chester Area School District

Dr. Richard Ciganko
Art Supervisor
Henderson Senior High School
Lincoln & Montgomery Avenue
West Chester, Pennsylvania 19380

West Shore School District

Mrs. Eleanor P. Stanton
Coordinator of Art
1833 Bridge Street
New Cumberland, Pennsylvania 17070

Williamsport Area School District

Dr. June E. Baskin
Supervisor of Art
Transeau Educational Center
845 Park Avenue
Williamsport, Pennsylvania 17701

Pawtucket School Department

Mrs. Veronica M. Farrell
Art Director
Administration Building
Park Place
Pawtucket, Rhode Island 02860

Providence School System

Mrs. Catherine W. Hill
Supervisor of Art
50 Washington Street
Providence, Rhode Island 02903

Warwick School Department

Dorothy Desmond
Department Head, Elementary Art
Box 507 Conimicut Station
34 Warwick Lake Avenue
Warwick, Rhode Island 02889

Charleston County School District

Hans A. Pawley
Director of Fine Arts
Charleston County School District
3 Chisolm Street
Charleston, South Carolina 29401

Darlington County

June McCauley
Art Supervisor
St. John's High School
Darlington, South Carolina 29532

Florence School District 1

James H. Rash
Art Supervisor
109 West Pine Street
Florence, South Carolina 29501

Greenville County School District

Robert Strother
Art Coordinator
Box 2848, 301 Camperdown Way
Greenville, South Carolina 29602

Greenwood School District 50

Mrs. Ray Young
Art Supervisor
P.O. Box 248
Greenwood, South Carolina 29646

Spartanburg County School District 7

Betty Jane Bramlett
Art Coordinator
Spartanburg City Schools

P.O. Box 970
Spartanburg, South Carolina 29301

Rapid City Public Schools

Diana M. Tollefson
Bureau of Indian Affairs
Cheyenne-Eagle Butte High School
Eagle Butte, South Dakota 57625

Chattanooga Public Schools

C. E. Blevins
Resource Teacher
3100 Rossville Boulevard
Chattanooga, Tennessee 37407

Knoxville City Schools

Mrs. Billie Connatser
Supervisor of Art
101 East Fifth Avenue
Knoxville, Tennessee 37917

Knox County Board of Education

Mrs. VaLera Lewis
Supervisor of Art
Fort Hill Building
Box 2188
Knoxville, Tennessee 37902

Metropolitan Nashville Davidson County Public Schools

James D. Hughes
Supervisor, Art Education
2601 Bransford Avenue
Nashville, Tennessee 37204

Abilene Public Schools

Scott Darr
Art Consultant
P.O. Box 981
Abilene, Texas 79604

Corpus Christi Independent School District

Neva G. Christian
Art Coordinator
1045 Hamlin
Corpus Christi, Texas 78411

El Paso Independent School District

Edwa Steirnagle
Art Consultant
Department of Fine Arts/223/Arizona
El Paso, Texas 79930

Edgewood Independent School District

Mrs. Isabel DeLaGarza
Art Supervisor
5358 West Commerce Street
San Antonio, Texas 78237

Fort Worth Independent School District

Ted C. Couch
Program Director, Art Education
3210 West Lancaster Street
Fort Worth, Texas 76107

Galveston Independent School District

Mignon Weisinger
Art Supervisor
Secondary Schools
Ball High Schools
4115 Avenue O
Galveston, Texas 77558

Goose Creek Consolidated Independent School District

Tommy F. Seale
Director of Music, Art and Crafts
P.O. Box 30
Baytown, Texas 77520

Killeen Independent School District

Hazel Watson
Assistant Superintendent for Instruction
P.O. Box 967
Killeen, Texas 76541

Midland Independent School District

Bill R. Cormack
Coordinator of Fine Arts
702 North "N"
Midland, Texas 79701

North East Independent School District

Maxine Allert
Consultant, Art Education
10333 Broadway
San Antonio, Texas 78286

Pasadena Independent School District

Katherine Reid
Supervisor of Art
3010 Bayshore Drive
Pasadena, Texas 77502

Amarillo Independent School District

Betty Jane Foster
Director of Art Education
910 West Eighth Avenue
Amarillo, Texas, 79101

Richardson Independent School District

Mrs. Madge S. Barnett
Secondary Art Supervisor
1233 Ottawa Drive
Richardson, Texas 75080

San Angelo Independent School District

Mrs. Velma Jo Whitfield
Art Supervisor
100 North Magdalen Street
San Angelo, Texas 76901

Spring Branch Independent School District

Mrs. Altharetta Yeargin
Art Coordinator
955 Campbell Road
Houston, Texas 77024

Wichita Falls Independent School District

Walter Ehlert
Supervisor of Art
1105 Halliday Street
Wichita Falls, Texas 76301

Davis County School District

Ivan Cornia
Art Supervisor
David County School District
Farmington, Utah 84025

Granite School District

Delbert W. Smedley
Supervisor, Art Education
340 East 3545 South
Salt Lake City, Utah 84115

Jordan School District

David R. Roberts
Art Consultant
Jordan School District
9361 South 400 East
Sandy, Utah 84070

Ogden City School District

Norman L. Skanchy
Principal, Horace Mann School
1300 Ninth Street
Ogden, Utah 84404

Salt Lake City Board of Education

Russell E. Bjorklund
Specialist in Art
440 East First South
Salt Lake City, Utah 84111

Barre City Schools

Helen D. Cate
Art Supervisor
Barre City Schools
Barre City, Vermont 15641

Alexandria City Public Schools

Joseph J. Adgate
Coordinator, Art, K-12
418 South Washington Street
Alexandria, Virginia 22313

Chesapeake Public Schools

Mrs. Edith G. Franklin
Supervisor of Art Education
School Administration Building
P.O. Box 15204
Chesapeake, Virginia 23320

Fairfax County Public Schools

Dr. Beverly A. Heinle
Art Curriculum Specialist
10700 Page Avenue
Fairfax, Virginia 22030

Hampton City Schools

Leroy Hubbard
Supervisor of Art
Thomas Street School Board Annex
1300 Thomas Street
Hampton, Virginia 23369

Arlington County Public Schools

Dr. Richard G. Wiggin
Supervisor of Art
1426 North Quincy Street
Arlington, Virginia 22207

Henrico County Public Schools

W. Randolph Cheatham
Coordinator of Art
P.O. Box 40
Highland Springs, Virginia 23075

Newport News Public Schools

Lee Montgomery
Acting Supervisor of Art
12465 Warwick Boulevard
Newport News, Virginia 23606

Norfolk City Schools

Kay White Baker
Director
School Administration Building
800 East City Hall Avenue
Norfolk, Virginia 23510

Pittsylvania County Schools

Jeffrey R. Guenther
Supervisor of Art
Pittsylvania County Schools
Chatham, Virginia 24531

Portsmouth Public Schools

Mr. John Backley
Supervisor Fine Arts
Portsmouth Public Schools
253 Constitution Avenue
Portsmouth, Virginia 23704

Prince William County Public Schools

Gary DiVeechia
Supervisor of Art
P.O. Box 389
Manassas, Virginia 22110

Richmond City Public Schools

Dale Nelson
Supervisor of Elementary Arts
Richmond Public Schools
301 North Ninth Street
Richmond, Virginia 23219

Roanoke City Public Schools

Mrs. Leslie Willett
Art Supervisor
P.O. Box 13145
Roanoke, Virginia 24009

Bellevue Public Schools

Lewis G. McCord
Coordinator of Art Education
310 102nd, South/West Area
Bellevue, Washington 98004

Clover Park School District 400

James D. Blanchard
Supervisor of Art
5214 Steilacoom Boulevard, S.W.
Lakewood Center, Washington 98499

Edmonds School District 15

Jerry Conrad
Consultant Teacher in Art
3800 196th Street S.W.
Lynnwood, Washington 98036

Everett School Dictrict 2

Patrick Maher
Supervisor of Industrial and Fine Arts
Auditorium Building
2400 Colby Avenue
Everett, Washington 98201

Highline School District 401

Marie Dunstan
Art Coordinator
Highline School District 401
15675 Ambaum Boulevard, S.W.
Seattle, Washington 98166

Kent School District 415

Dr. Jim Barchek
12033 South East 256th
Coordinator of Art
508 North Central Avenue
Kent, Washington 98031

Lake Washington School District 414

Chester Potuzak
Coordinator of Fine/Performing Arts
410 First Street
Kirkland, Washington 98033

Renton School District 403

Hal Chambers, Art Resource Teacher
1525 North Fourth Street
Renton, Washington 98055

Spokane Public Schools

Mrs. Shirley A. Tupper
Coordinator of General Programs
West 825 Trent Avenue
Spokane, Washington 99201

Tacoma Public Schools

Jack D. Motteler
Assistant in Curriculum, Art
Tacoma Public Schools
P.O. Box 1357
Tacoma, Washington 98401

Vancouver School District 37

Jack W. Francis
Supervisor, Creative Arts Department
605 North Devine Road
Vancouver, Washington 98661

Yakima School District 7

Richard S. Williams
Director of Art Education
Company Seven
501 South Seventh Street
Yakima, Washington 98901

Cabell County Public Schools

Libby K. Caligan
Director of Art
620 20th Street
Huntington, West Virginia 25709

Kanawha County Schools

Ruby Stanfield
Consultant of Art K-12
200 Elizabeth Street
Charleston, West Virginia 25311

Marion County Board of Education

Mrs. Sara Adams
Supervisor of Art
200 Gaston Avenue
Fairmont, West Virginia 26554

Monongalia County Schools

Wilbur V. Bauer
Coordinator of Art Education
48 Edgewood Street
Morgantown, West Virginia 26505

Appleton Public Schools

Matt V. Kahnke
Elementary Art Coordinator

Harold Carlson
Secondary Art Coordinator
120 East Harris Street
Appleton, Wisconsin 54911

Kenosha Unified School District 1

Sam P. Christy
Coordinator of Art
4001 60th Street
Kenosha, Wisconsin 53140

Madison Metropolitan School District

Frank C. Lindl
Fine Arts Coordinator
545 West Dayton Street
Madison, Wisconsin 53703

Milwaukee Public Schools

Mr. Kent Anderson
Curriculum Specialist, Art
P.O. Drawer 10K
Milwaukee, Wisconsin 53201

Racine Unified Schools

Dr. Helen F. Patton
Director of Art Education K-12
2220 Northwestern Avenue
Racine, Wisconsin 53404

Sheboygan Area School District

Allen Hanson
Art Supervisor
830 Virginia Avenue
Sheboygan, Wisconsin 53081

Waukesha City Schools Joint District 1

Roland Schrupp
K-12, Art Learning Specialist
222 Maple Avenue
Waukesha, Wisconsin 53186

School District of West Allis-West Milwaukee

Kenneth B. Cottingham, Supervisor
9333 West Lincoln Avenue
West Allis, Wisconsin 53227

Laramie County School District 1

Margaret L. Albert
2810 House Avenue
Cheyenne, Wyoming 82001

Guam Department of Education

Adriano B. Pangelinan, Assistant Professor of Art
University of Guam
Fine Arts
P.O. Box Ek
Agana, Guam 96910

Art Magazines

Note — A for Annuals; M for Monthlies; W for Weeklies; Q for Quarterlies.

African Arts/Arts D'Afrique (Q)—John Povey, Ed; African Studies Center, University of California, 405 Hilgard Ave, Los Angeles, CA 90024   Yearly 14.00

American Art Journal (Bi-A)—Jane Van N. Turano & Lawrence Fleischman, Ed; Kennedy Galleries, 40 W. 57th St, Fifth Floor, New York, NY 10019   Yearly 12.00

American Art Review (Bi-M)—Thomas R. Kellaway, Ed. & Publ; Box 65007, Los Angeles, CA 90065   Yearly 18.00

American Artist (M)—David Preiss, Ed; 1515 Broadway, New York, NY 10036   Yearly 15.00

American Graphic Artists of the Twentieth Century (Irreg)—Brooklyn Museum, Eastern Parkway, Brooklyn, NY 11238   4.00

American Journal of Archaeology (Q)—Jerome J. Pollitt, Ed; Archaeological Institute of America, 260 W. Broadway, New York, NY 10013   Yearly 15.00

Antiques (M)—Wendell Garrett, Ed; 551 Fifth Ave, New York, NY 10017   Yearly 18.00

Appollo Magazine (M)—Denys Sutton, Ed; 22 Davies St, London, W. 1, England   Yearly 48.00

Archaeology (Bi-M)—Phyllis Pollak Katz, Ed; Archaeological Institute of America, 260 W. Broadway, New York, NY 10013   Yearly 15.00

Architectural Record (M)—Walter F. Wagner, Jr, Ed; 1220 Avenue of the Americas, New York, NY 10020   Yearly 12.00

Art Bulletin (Q)—Howard Hibbard, Ed; 16 East 52nd St, New York, NY 10022

Art Direction (M)—Don Barron, Ed; 19 West 44th St, New York, NY 10036   Yearly 12.50

Artforum (M)—Joseph Masheck, Ed; 667 Madison Avenue, New York, NY 10021   Yearly 22.50

The Art Gallery Magazine (M except Aug. & Sept)—William C. Bendig & Jay Jacobs, Ed; Ivoryton, CT 06442   Single 1.50 Yearly 13.00

Art in America (Bi-M)—Elizabeth C. Baker, Ed; 150 East 58th St, New York, NY 10022   Yearly 16.50

Art Index (Q)—David J. Patten, Ed; The H. W. Wilson Co, 950 University Ave, New York, NY 10452   Subscription on service basis. Write for rates.

Art International (Bi-M)—James Fitzsimmons, Ed. & Publ; Via Maraini 17-A, Lugono, Switzerland   Yearly 36.00

Art Journal (Q)—Diane Kelder, Ed; 16 East 52nd St, New York, NY 10022   Yearly 8.00

Artmagazine (Q)—Pat Fleisher, Ed; 234 Eglinton Avenue East, Toronto, Ont. M4P 1K5   Yearly 10.00

Art Material Trade News (M)—C. Edwin Shade, Ed; (National Art Material Trade Asn), Syndicate Magazines Inc, 6 East 43rd St, New York, NY 10017   Yearly 18.00

Art News (M Sept-May, Q June-Aug)—Milton Esterow, Ed; 750 Third Ave, New York, NY 10017   Yearly 18.00

Artist (M)—Peter Garrard, Ed; 155 West 15th St, New York, NY 10011   Yearly 8.00

Artist's Proof (A)—Fritz Eichenberg, Ed; Pratt Center for Contemporary Printmaking, 831 Broadway, New York, NY 10013   Membership price 12.50

Artscanada (Bi-M)—Anne Brodgley, Ed; 3 Church St, Toronto, Ontario, M5E 1M2   Yearly 17.00

Arts Magazine (10 Issues)—Richard Martin, Ed; 23 East 26th St, New York, NY 10010   Yearly 20.00

Artweek (Weekly Sept-May, Bi-M June-Aug)—Cecile N. McCann, Ed; 1305 Franklin St, Oakland, CA 94612   Yearly 12.50

CA Magazine (Bi-M)—Richard S. Coyne, Ed; 410 Sherman Ave (P.O. Box 10300), Palo Alto, CA 94303   Single 3.00 Annual 18.00

California Design (Triennial)—E. M. Moore, Ed; California Design Program, 300 East Green St, Pasadena, CA 91101   Yearly 7.50

Ceramics Monthly (M)—Spencer Davis, Ed; Professional Publications, Inc, Box 12448, Columbus, OH 43212   Yearly 8.00

Cimaise (Bi-M)—Jean Robert Arnaud, Ed; Wittenborn & Co, 1018 Madison Ave, New York, NY 10021   Yearly 36.00

Connoisseur, The (M)—Bevis Hillier, Ed; National Magazine Co, Ltd, Chestergate House, Vauxhall Bridge Rd, London, SW1V 1HF, England   60.00

Contemporary American Painting and Sculpture (Bi-A)—Allen S. Weller, Ed; University of Illinois Press, Urbana, IL 61801

Craft Horizons (Bi-M)—Mrs. Rose Slivka, Ed; 44 West 53rd St, New York, NY 10022   Yearly 10.00

Design Quarterly (Q)—Mildred Friedman, Ed; Walker Art Center, Vineland Place, Minneapolis, MN 55403   Yearly 5.00

Gazette des Beaux-Arts (10 issues)—Daniel Wildenstein, Dir; Imprimeries Runies, 33, Avenue de la Gare, CH-1001, Lausanne, Switzerland   Yearly 24.00

Graphic Design (Q)—Masura Katzumie, Ed; Wittenborn & Co, 1018 Madison Ave, New York, NY 10021   Single 7.25 Yearly 24.50

Graphis Annual (A)—Walter Herdeg, Ed; Dufourstrasse 107, CH-8008 Zurich, Switzerland   Single 37.50

Graphis Magazine (Bi-M)—Walter Herdeg, Ed; Dufourstrasse 107, CH-8008 Zurich, Switzerland   Yearly 39.00

High Performance (Q)—Linda Frye Burnham, Ed; 240 S Broadway, Fifth Floor, Los Angeles, CA 90012   Yearly 8.00

House & Garden (M)—Mary Jane Pool, Ed; 350 Madison Ave, New York, NY 10017   Yearly 10.00

House & Home (M)—John F. Goldsmith, Ed; 1221 Avenue of the Americas, New York, NY 10020   Yearly 12.00

House Beautiful (M)—Wallace Guenther, Ed; 250 West 55th St, New York, NY 10019   Yearly 10.00

Illustrator Magazine (Q)—Don L. Jardine, Ed; 500 South Fourth St, Minneapolis, MN 55415   Yearly 4.00

Illustrators Annual: The Annual of American Illustration (A-Fall)—Don Barron, Ed; Published for Society of Illustrators by Hastings House, Publishers, 10 E. 40th St, New York, NY 10016   Yearly 24.50

Industrial Design (6 Issues)—George T. Finley, Ed; 1515 Broadway, New York, NY 10036   Yearly 17.00

Interior Design (M)—Sherman R. Emery, Ed; 150 East 58th St, New York, NY 10022   Yearly 14.00

Interiors (M)—C. Ray Smith, Ed; 1515 Broadway, New York, NY 10036   Yearly 15.00

International Poster Annual (Bi-A)—Arthur Niggli, Ed; Texts in English, French and German; Hastings House, Publishers, 10 E. 40th St, New York, NY 10016   Yearly 16.00

Journal of Aesthetics & Art Criticism (Q)—John Fisher, Ed; Temple University, Department of Philosophy, Philadelphia, PA 19122   Membership 10.00 (Non-members 15.00)

Society of Architectural Historians Journal (Q)—Christian F. Otto, Ed; 1700 Walnut St, Room 716, Philadelphia, PA 19103   Yearly 20.00 (membership)

Kunst und das schoene Heim (M)—Karl Thiemig, Ed; Wittenborn & Co, 1018 Madison Ave, New York, NY 10021   Single 2.00 Yearly 20.00

Kunstwerk (Bi-M)—Klaus Juergen-Fischer, Ed; Wittenborn & Co, 1018 Madison Ave, New York, NY 10021   Yearly 12.50

Landscape Architecture (Q)—Grady Clay, Ed; 1190 E. Broadway, Louisville, KY 40204   Yearly 12.00

Leonardo: Art Science and Technology (Q)—Frank J. Malina, Ed; Pergamon Press, Inc, Journals Dept, Maxwell House, Fairview Park, Elmsford, NY 10523 (and Headington Hill Hall, Oxford 0X3 OBW, England)   Yearly 66.00

Marsyas (Bi-A)—Paul Yule & Andrew Clark, Eds; Institute of Fine Arts, New York University, 1 E. 78th St, New York, NY 10021   Single 8.00

Metropolitan Museum of Art Bulletin (Q)—Katharine H. B. Stoddert, Ed; Fifth Ave. at 82nd St, New York, NY 10028   Yearly 11.50

Mobilia (M)—Mette Bratvold, Ed; Wittenborn & Co, 1018 Madison Ave, New York, NY 10021   Single 3.00 Yearly 27.50

Modern Publicity: International Advertising Art (A)—Ella Moody, Ed; The Viking Press, 625 Madison Ave, New York, NY 10022   Issue 12.50

Museum News (Bi-M)—Ellen C. Hicks, Ed; American Association of Museums, 1055 Thomas Jefferson St, NW, Washington, DC 20007   Yearly 12.00

National Endowment for the Arts. Guide to Programs (1-2/yr)—National Endowment for the Arts, Superintendent of Documents, U.S. Government Printing Office, Washington, DC 20402   1.00

National Sculpture Review (Q)—Theodora Morgan, Ed; 777 Third Avenue, New York, NY 10017   (Non-members 5.00)

New Jersey Music and Arts Magazine (10 Issues)—Ruthann Williams, Ed; 572 Main Street, Chatham, NJ 07928   Yearly 6.00

Old-Time New England (Q)—Abbott Lowell Cummings, Ed; The Society for the Preservation of New England Antiquities, 141 Cambridge St, Boston, MA 02114   Single .75 Yearly 5.00

Opus International (Bi-M)—Editions Georges Fall, 15 Rue Paul Fort, Paris (75014) France   Yearly 15 F.

Pantheon (Q)—Dr. Erich Steingraeber, Ed; Wittenborn & Co, 1018 Madison Ave, New York, NY 10021   Yearly 25.00

Penrose Annual (A)—10 E. 40th St, New York, NY 10016   Price varies

Photographis: International Annual of Advertising & Editorial Photography (A)—Walter Herdeg, Ed; Dufourstrasse 107, CH-8008 Zurich, Switzerland   Single 37.50

Pictures on Exhibit (Bi-M)—Charles Z. Offin, Ed; 30 E. 60th St, New York, NY 10022   Yearly 6.00

Praxis (3/yr)—Ronald Reimers, Ed; 2125 Hearst Ave, Berkeley, CA 94709   Yearly 8.00 Individual; 14.00 Institutions

Print, American Graphic Design Magazine (Bi-M)—Martin Fox, Ed; 355 Lexington Ave, New York, NY 10017   Yearly 20.00

Pro: The Voice of the Cartooning World (M)—Arnold L. Wagner, Ed. & Publ; 1130 N. Cottage, Salem, OR 97301   Yearly 10.00

Progressive Architecture (M)—John Morris Dixon, Ed; 600 Summer St, Stamford, CT 06904   Yearly 7.00

Royal Society of Arts Journal (M)—J. S. Skidmore, Ed; 6 John Adam St, Adelphi, London W.C.2, England   Yearly 11.55

School Arts Magazine (M Sept-June)—George F. Horn, Ed; 50 Portland St, Worcester, MA 01608   Yearly 10.00

Sculpture International (Bi-A)—Pergamon Press, Maxwell House, Fairview Park, Elmsford, NY 10523   Yearly 33.00

Southwest Art Magazine (M except July)—Vicki Baucum, Ed; P.O. Box 13037, Houston, TX 77019   Yearly 15.00

Southwestern Art (Q)—John H. Jenkins, Ed; Box 1763, Austin, TX 78767   Yearly 8.50

Stained Glass (Q)—Dr. Norman L. Temme, Ed; 1125 Wilmington Ave, St. Louis, MO 63111   Yearly 8.00

Structure (Irreg)—Joost Baljeu, Ed; Wittenborn & Co, 1018 Madison Ave, New York, NY 10021   Yearly 2.75

Structurist (A)—Eli Bornstein, Ed; Wittenborn & Co, 1018 Madison Ave, New York, NY 10021   Per Issue 5.00

Studio International (6/yr)—Richard Cork, Ed; Studio International Publications Ltd, 14 W. Central St, London WC1A 1JH, England Yearly 30.00 Students; 34.00 Individuals

Vingtieme Siecle (XX e Siecle) (Bi-A)—Gino di San Lazzaro, Ed; Wittenborn & Co, 1018 Madison Ave, New York, NY 10021 Single 18.50 Yearly 35.00

Washington International Arts Letter (10 Issues)—Daniel Millsaps, Ed. & Publ; P.O. Box 9005, Washington, DC 20003 Yearly 16.00 Individual; 32.00 Institutions

Werk (M)—Lucius Burckhardt & Diego Peverelli, Ed; Association of Swiss Architects; Wittenborn & Co, 1018 Madison Ave, New York, NY 10021 Yearly 6.00 Individual; 32.00 Institutions

Newspapers Carrying Art Notes

With name of art editor or critic.

ALABAMA

Alabama Journal, Montgomery—Bill Myrick
Birmingham News—Oliver Roosevelt
Fayette County Broadcaster, Fayette—Jack Black
The Huntsville Times—Alan Moore
The Mobile Press Register—Gordon Tatum, Jr.
Tuscaloosa News—Dr. J. Fred Goossen

ALASKA

Anchorage Times—Connie Godwin
Daily News, Anchorage—Molly B. Jones
The Daily Sitka Sentinel—Sandy Poulson

ARIZONA

Arizona Daily Star, Tucson—Max Hillyard
Arizona Living, Phoenix—Ann Dutton
Arizona Republic, Phoenix—Thomas Goldthwaite
Mesa Tribune—Ruth Wiley
The Phoenix Gazette—Jim Newton
Scottsdale Daily Progress—Kyle H Lawson & Barbara Perlman
Tempe Daily News—Jan Young
Tucson Citizen—Sheldon Reich & Robert M. Quinn
Verde Independent, Cottonwood—Eugene N. Marten

ARKANSAS

The Arkansas Democrat, Little Rock—Ray White
Arkansas Gazette, Little Rock—Bill Lewis
Paragould Daily Press—Kathy Craft
Stuttgart Daily Leader—Calvin Mannen

CALIFORNIA

The Anaheim Bulletin—Angele Haddad
Berkeley Daily Gazette—William Haigwood
The Claremont Courier (Montclair Courier, Upland Courier, The Newspaper), Claremont—Thelma O'Brien
Contra Costa Times, Walnut Creek—Carol Fowler
Daily Pilot, Costa Mesa—Jackie Hyman
Escondido Daily Times-Advocate—Kathlyn Russell
Fresno Bee—David Hale
Fullerton News Tribune—Sue Campbell
The Hanford Sentinel—Ruth J. Gomes
Independent-Journal, San Rafael—Ada Garfinkel
Independent Press-Telegram, Long Beach—Elise Emery
La Jolla Light—Edith Gay Fall
Los Angeles Herald Examiner—Pamela J King
Los Angeles Times—Charles Champlin
Los Gatos Times-Observer—George R. Kane
Modesto Bee—Leo Stutzin
Monterey Peninsula Herald—Irene Lagorio
The Oakland Tribune—Charles Shere
Pacific Sun, Mill Valley—Tom Cervenak
Palo Alto Times—Paul Emerson
Palos Verdes Peninsula News—Reid L. Bundy
Pasadena Star News—Larry Palmer
Redlands Daily Facts—Josephine Reay
The Richmond Independent—William Haigwood
Riverside Press—John F. Muncie
Sacramento Bee—Charles Johnson
Sacramento Union—Richard Simon

Salinas Californian—Helen Manning
San Bernardino Sun-Telegram—Rosemary Hite
San Diego Evening Tribune—Jan Jennings
San Diego Union—Richard R Reilly
San Francisco Chronicle—Alfred Frankenstein
San Francisco Examiner—Alexander Fried & Arthur Bloomfield
San Jose Mercury-News—Janos Gereben
San Mateo Times—Vera Graham
San Rafael Independent-Journal—Ada Garfinkel
Santa Ana Register—Gary Lycan
Santa Barbara News-Press—Richard Ames
Santa Monica Evening Outlook—Barry Brennan
Turlock Daily Journal—Carl Baggese

COLORADO

Boulder Daily Camera—Ina Posey
Colorado Springs Gazette Telegraph—John Fetler
Colorado Springs Sun—E Thomas McClanahan
The Daily Transcript—Elizabeth M Wilkinson
The Denver Magazine—Blair Chotzinoff
Denver Post—James Mills
Pueblo Chieftain—Dr Mildred Monteverde
Pueblo Star Journal—Dr Mildred Monteverde
Rocky Mountain News, Denver—Duncan Pollock

CONNECTICUT

The Bridgeport Post & Sunday Post—Betty Tyler
Danbury News-Times—Millie Siegel
The Darien Review—Ray Yates
East Hartford Gazette—Phyllis M. Charest
The Greenwich Time—Dorothy Friedman
The Hartford Courant—Jolene Goldenthal
Meriden Journal—Tom Potter
The New Britain Herald—Judith W. Brown
New Canaan Advertiser—Dean Hadley
New Haven Register—Shirley Gonzales
New London Day—Raymond K. Bordner
New Milford Times—Frank Merkling
The News-Times, Danbury—Millie Siegel
The Stamford Advocate—Bella O'Hara
Waterbury American—Katherine Davidson
The West Hartford News—Shirlee Westbrook
Westport News—Shelley List

DELAWARE

Wilmington Morning News—Otto Dekom
Wilmington Evening Journal—Ruth Jillyo Kaplan
Wilmington Sunday News Journal—Edith De Shazo

DISTRICT OF COLUMBIA

Washington Post—Paul Richard & Jo Ann Lewis
The Washington Star—Benjamin Forgey

FLORIDA

Boca Raton News—Mary Crowe Dorst
Clearwater Sun—Lisa Velders & Norman Morgan
Florida Times-Union, Jacksonville—Judy Wells Martin
Fort Lauderdale News—Shubert Jonas
Gainesville Sun—Diane Chun

Jacksonville Journal—Elihu Edelson
Key West Citizen—Earl Adam
The Ledger, Lakeland—Jeff Kline
The Miami Beach Sun-Reporter—Josephine A. Bruun
The Miami Herald—Ellen Edwards
Miami News—Bill Von Maurer
Orlando Sentinel Star—Mary Joyce
Palm Beach Daily News, West Palm Beach—Millie Wolff
Palm Beach Post—Charles Calhoun
The St. Augustine Record—Fred Whitley
St. Petersburg Independent—Jeannette Crane
St. Petersburg Times—Charles Benbow
Sarasota Herald-Tribune—Marcia Corbino
Sarasota Journal—R. N. Robertson
Tallahassee Democrat—Mary Ann Lindley
The Tampa Times—Robert L. Martin
Tampa Tribune—Joanne M. Rodriguez
Venice Gondolier—Dorothy E. Lippstreuer
Winter Park Sun Herald—Nancy Long

GEORGIA

Athens Banner-Herald—Masie Underwood
Athens Daily News—Douglas Matyka
The Atlanta Journal & Constitution, Mount Berry—Clyde Burnett
Columbus Enquirer—Harry E. Franklin
Columbus Ledger—Edge R. Reid
Savannah News & Press—Marshall L. Reed

HAWAII

The Honolulu Advertiser—Web Anderson
The Maui News—Roy Nickerson
The Star Bulletin, Honolulu—Jean Charlot

IDAHO

The Idaho State Journal, Pocatello—Joan La Liberte
The Idaho Statesman, Boise—Julie T. Monroe
Lewiston Morning Tribune—Bruce Spottleson
Times-News, Twin Falls—Richard G. High

ILLINOIS

Chicago Daily News—Franz Schulze
The Chicago Sun-Times—Frank Schulz
Chicago Tribune—Alan G. Artner
Clinton Journal-Public—Donald C. Kemp
The Courier, Champaign—Mrs. Stephen Tager
Daily Courier-News—Peter Powell & Howard Elliott
Decatur Herald & Review—William Ward
Galesburg Register-Mail—Isabelle Buncher
The Herald Whig, Quincy—Betty Moritz
Joliet Herald-News—Lorrie Gawla
The Lake Forester, Highland Park—Dorothy Andries
Marion Daily Republican—Oldham Paisley
Monmouth Daily Review Atlas—Martha Hamilton
Pantagraph, Bloomington—Tony Holloway
Peoria Journal Star—Gerald (Jerry) Klein
The Pioneer Press, Wilmette—Dorothy Andries
Rockford Morning Star—David Zimmerman
Rockford Register-Republic—David Zimmerman
The Sunday Register-Star, Rockford—David Zimmerman

INDIANA

Anderson Daily Bulletin—Donna Douglas
Anderson Herald—Holly Miller
The Brown County Democrat, Nashville—Bruce Gregory Temple
Evansville Courier—Jeanne Suhrheinrich
Evansville Press—Gail McLeod
Gary Post-Tribune—John Forwalter
Indianapolis News—Marion Simon Garmel
The Indianapolis Star—Corbin Patrick
Journal-Gazette, Fort Wayne—Laura Pipino
Lafayette Journal & Courier—Chris Huber
Lafayette Leader—Rebecca Sawyer
LaPorte Herald-Argus—Maxine Ford
Muncie Evening Press—Robert Loy
The Muncie Star—Nancy Millard
New Albany Tribune—Patricia Cornwell

News-Sentinel, Fort Wayne—Gene Porter
South Bend Tribune—Johnathon J. White
The Terre Haute Tribune-Sta—Beatrice Biggs

IOWA

The Ames Daily Tribune—Pam Witmer
The Anamosa Eureka—James Andrew Mayer
The Anamosa Journal—James Andrew Mayer
Cedar Rapids Gazette—Charles Stroh
The Charles City Press—Dividicus Noman
Cherokee Daily Times—Tom Miller
Des Moines Register—Nicholas G. Baldwin
Fairfield Daily Ledger—Olive Schanfeldt
The Fort Dodge Messenger—Lois Johnson
Iowa City Press Citizen—Starla Smith
Marshalltown Times-Republican—Lois Jacobs
Mason City Globe-Gazette—Thomas Thoma
The Sioux City Journal—Jane Hunwardsen
The Times-Democrat, Davenport—Julie Jensen

KANSAS

Atchison Daily Globe—Margaret Schwein
Clay Center Dispatch—H. E. Valentine
The Daily Reporter, Independence—Georgia High
The Hutchinson News—Kathy Brown
Russell Daily News—Harold L. "Prince" Elmquist
Topeka Capital-Journal—Peggy Greene
The Wichita Eagle-Beacon—Dorothy Wood

KENTUCKY

Berea Citizen—Barbara H. Bordelon
Lexington Herald Leader—John Alexander
Louisville Courier-Journal—Sarah Lansdell

LOUISIANA

Alexandria Town Talk—Verdis Dowdy
The Courier, New Orleans—S. Joslyn Fosberg
East Bank Guide, Metairie—Mrs. Byron J. E. Hoover
Monroe News Star World—Ms. J. C. Huntley
The Morning Advocate, Baton Rouge—Anne K. Price
The Shreveport Journal—Larry Shor
The Shreveport Times—Jim Montgomery
The State Times, Baton Rouge—Cara Lu Salam
States-Item—Roger Green
The Times Picayune, New Orleans—George E. Jordan

MAINE

Bangor Daily News—Robert H. Newall
The Camden Herald—Mary Sullivan
The Courier-Gazette, Rockland—Ivy W. Dodd
Lewiston Daily Sun—A. Kent Foster
Maine Sunday Telegram, Portland—Robert S. Niss
Portland Newspaper Evening Express—Robert S. Niss
Portland Press Herald—Robert S. Niss
Rockland Courier-Gazette, Inc—Flora G. Cullen
Waterville Morning Sentinel—Tony Betts

MARYLAND

The Annapolis Evening Capital—Marie Bailey
Baltimore News-American—R. P. Harriss
Baltimore Sun—Barbara Gold
Hagerstown Daily Mail—Harry Warner
Hagerstown Morning Herald—Harry Warner, Jr.

MASSACHUSETTS

Amherst Record—Frances Chastain
The Berkshire Courier, Great Barrington—Stephen Seche
The Berkshire Eagle, Pittsfield—Winifred Bell
The Boston Globe—Robert Taylor
Boston Herald American—Robert Garrett
The Boston Phoenix—Kenneth Baker
Brockton Enterprise-Times—Dorothy Dale
Cambridge Chronicle—Ann Philips
The Concord Patriot—Ann Chang
Daily Hampshire Gazette, Northampton—Martha Beaver
The Daily Sentinel-Enterprise, Fitchburg—Kay Tobin
Falmouth Enterprise—William J. Adelman
Gloucester Daily Times—Barbara H. Erkkila

Greenfield Recorder—Daniel Weck
The Inquirer & Mirror, Nantucket—Mary Kennedy Wright
The Lowell Sun—Ann Schecter
Malden Evening News—J. William Breslin
Malden Sun Times—Allen Swartz
The Marblehead Messenger—David Ramsay
New Bedford Standard-Times—Richard Pacheco
Quincy Patriot Ledger—Jon Lehman
Provincetown Advocate—Richard Hornak
The Real Paper, Cambridge—Carol Eron
Salem Evening News—James M. Shea
The Southbridge Evening News—Linda Megathlin
Springfield Daily News—Tom Hart
Springfield Sunday Republican—Arnold Friedman
Springfield Morning Union—Arnold Friedman
Standard Times, New Bedford—Earl J. Dias
Wellesley Townsman—Herbert S. Austin
Westfield Evening News—Deborah Baker
The Worcester Gazette—David D. Oswell
The Worcester Telegram—Marilyn W. Spear

MICHIGAN

Alpena News—Betty Werth
The Ann Arbor News—Jean Paul Slusser
Birmingham Eccentric—Corinne Abatt
Cheboygan Daily Tribune—Joyce Leslie
Detroit Free Press—Marsha Miro
Detroit News—Joy Hakanson (Mrs. Raymond L. Colby)
Enquirer and News, Battle Creek—James A. Dean
The Flint Journal—James E. Harvey
Kalamazoo Gazette—Victor W. Rauch
Grand Rapids Press—Bernice Winslow Mancewicz
Jackson Citizen Patriot—Ray Dennis
Lansing State Journal—Paul Palmer
Macomb Daily, Mount Clemens—George Hagan
Muskegon Chronicle—Christine Valmassei
The Oakland Press—Sue Hegenbarth
The Saginaw News—James W. Henderson
Towne Courier, East Lansing—Phyllis Thomas

MINNESOTA

Duluth Herald—James F. Hefferman
Mankato Free Press—David Graham Hage
Minneapolis Star—Peter Altman
Minneapolis Tribune—Robert Lundegaard
News Tribune, Duluth—James F. Hefferman
Owatonna People's Press—Bruce Benidt
Rochester Post-Bulletin—Pauline Walle
St. Paul Dispatch—John H. Harvey
St. Paul Pioneer Press—Robert L. Protzman
Winona Daily News—Carolyn Kosidowski

MISSISSIPPI

Clarion Ledger, Jackson—O. C. McDavid
Columbus Commercial Dispatch—Patrick K. Lynn
Greenwood Commonwealth—Harry W. Merritt
Jackson Daily News—O. C. McDavid
Laurel Leader-Call—J. W. West
Meridian Star—Nancy Duvergne Smith
Oxford Eagle—Nina Goolsby

MISSOURI

The Kansas City Star—Donald Hoffman
Maryville Daily Forum—Muriel M. Alcott
The National Catholic Reporter, Kansas City—Harry J. Cargas
St. Joseph News-Press—James Day
St. Louis Globe-Democrat—John Brod Peters
St. Louis Post-Dispatch—E. F. Porter, Jr.
Southeast Missourian, Cape Girardeau—Judith Ann Crow
Springfield Daily News—Ed Albin
Springfield Leader & Press—Ed Albin
Times, Kansas City—Donald Hoffmann

MONTANA

Anaconda Leader—Sally Campbell
Billings Gazette—Kathryn Wright
Bozeman Chronicle—Florence Trout

The Daily Inter Lake, Katispell—Marlin Hanson
The Montana Standard, Butte—Kathleen Cook
The Sidney Herald—Ted Scherf

NEBRASKA

Lincoln Journal—Helen J. Haggie
Omaha World-Herald—Judy Van Wagner

NEVADA

Henderson Home News—Barbara Lauer
Las Vegas Review-Journal—A. Wilber Stevens
Las Vegas Sun—Steve Lesnick

NEW HAMPSHIRE

Keene Sentinel—Ernest Hebert
Manchester Union Leader—George Woodbury
The Nashua Telegraph—Deborah Ladd
The New Hampshire Times, Corcord—Steve Sherman

NEW JERSEY

Courier News, Bridgewater—Donald Rubincam
Courier-Post, Camden—Edith De Shazo
Daily Journal, Elizabeth—Joseph Bakes
The Daily Register, Red Bank—Carol Jacobson
Homes News, New Brunswick—Doris E. Brown
Hunterdon Review, White House Station—Rachel Mullen
Newark Star-Ledger—Eileen Watkins
Nutley Sun—Michael C. Gabriele
Paterson Evening News—Abe J. Greene
Princeton Packet—Elaine P. Heinemann & Susan Santangelo
The Record, Hackensack—David Spengler
Summit Herald—Betty McAndrews
Town Topics, Princeton—Helen Schwartz
Verona-Cedar Grove Times, Verona—Brian Donadio

NEW MEXICO

The Albuquerque Journal—William Lea Hoffman
The Albuquerque Tribune—Keith Raether
Gallup Independent—Nancy Mueller
The New Mexican, Santa Fe—Don Fabricant
The Taos News—Billie Blair

NEW YORK

Albany Times Union—Fred Lebrun
Buffalo Courier-Express—Katy Kline
The Buffalo Evening News—Anthony Bannon
Clinton Courier—William Boynton
The Daily Freeman, Kingston—Tobie Geertsema
East Hampton Star—Phyllis Braff
Elmira Star-Gazette—Salle Richards
Elmira Sunday Telegram—Salle Richards
Evening News, Newburgh—Al Rhoades
The Freeman's Journal, Cooperstown—Jane S. Johnson
Goshen Independent Republican—Janet Schwerdt
Hamilton County News, Speculator—George List, Jr.
The Ithaca Journal—Jack Sherman
Jamestown Post-Journal—William M. Flynn
The Knickerbocker News, Albany—C. Robie Booth
Long-Islander—Kay Meyer
Middletown Times Herald-Record—Maybelle Mann
Nassau Star, Long Beach—Dr. Irwin S. Grodner
New York Post—Emily Genauer
The New York Times—Hilton Kramer
News, New York—Al Paladini
Niagara Gazette, Niagara Falls—Jack Foran
Oneonta Star—Jessie Nichols
The Post-Star, Glens Falls—Don A. Metivier
Potsdam Courier & Freeman—Betsy Baker
Poughkeepsie Journal—Jeffrey Borak
The Press, Binghamton—Gerald Handte
Red Hook Rhinebeck, Hyde Park—Jean C. McGregor
Rochester Democrat & Chronicle—Sally Eauclaire
Saratogian, Saratoga Springs—Shelley Riley
Schenectady Union-Star—Marjorie Feiner
The Skaneateles Press—Mrs. J. Lee Wood
Staten Island Advance—Elaine Boies
Syracuse Herald American—Ann Hartranft-Temple
Tarrytown Daily News—Thomas Flynn
Times Record, Troy—Doug deLisle

The Times-Union, Rochester—Rosemary Teres
Utica Daily Press—Jonas Kover
The Village Voice, New York—John Perreault
The Villager, New York—different contributors

NORTH CAROLINA

Asheville Citizen-Times—Richard VanKleeck
The Chapel Hill Newspaper—Paquita Jurgensen
The Charlotte News—Mary Estes
Charlotte Observer—Alan Oren
The Daily Reflector, Greenville—Jerry S. Raynor
The Durham Morning Herald—John Coit, Blue Greenberg & R. C. Smith
The Durham Sun — Susan Wenzel
Greensboro Daily News—Patricia Krebs
The Greensboro Record—Abe D. Jones, Jr.
The Hickory Daily Record—Marjorie Lee Millholland
The News and Observer, Raleigh—Guy E. Munger, Jr.
The Sun-Journal, New Bern—Jonathan Segal
Wilmington Star News—Bill Stover
Winston-Salem Journal & Sentinel—Beverly Wolter

NORTH DAKOTA

The Forum, Fargo—Carol Knapp
Grand Forks Herald—Ken Retallic
Times Record, Valley City—Mark E. Bowden

OHIO

Akron Beacon Journal—Carolyn Carr
The Athens Messenger—Heidi Knapp
Cincinnati Enquirer—Owen Findsen
Cincinnati Post—Ellen Brown
Cleveland Plain Dealer—Helen B. Cullinan
Cleveland Press—Dick Wootten
Columbus Dispatch—Frances Piper
Dayton Daily News—Betty Dietz Krebs
Dayton Journal Herald—Walt McCaslin
Mansfield News Journal—Ellen McClarran
News-Herald, Willoughby— W. C. Miller, III
North Canton Sun—Thomas V. Sell
Painesville Telegraph—Peggy Samartini
Springfield News-Sun—James Hays
The Times Recorder, Zanesville—Dr. Charles Dietz
The Toledo Blade—Louise Bruner
The Toledo Times—Joseph V. Knack
Youngstown Vindicator—Clyde Singer

OKLAHOMA

Bartlesville Examiner Enterprise—Jim Wood
Daily Armoreite, Ardmore—Rusty Lang
The Daily Oklahoman, Oklahoma City—Bruce Westbrook
Lawton Constitution—Bill Crawford
Morning Press, Lawton—Bill Crawford
Muskogee Daily Phoenix & Times Democrat—Joan Morrison
Norman Transcript—Jack Craddock
Oklahoma City Times—Jon Denton
The Oklahoma Journal, Oklahoma City—Nancy Gilson
Stillwater News-Press—James C. Stratton
The Tulsa Tribune—Caroline Johnson
The Tulsa World—Maurice de Vinna

OREGON

Corvallis Gazette-Times—Saundra Donaldson
Eugene Register-Guard—Fred Crafts
The Oregon Journal, Portland—Andy Rocchia
Oregon Statesman, Portland—Ron Cowan
Portland Scribe—Paul Sutinen
World, Coos Bay—J. Paul Baron

PENNSYLVANIA

Bethlehem Globe-Times—Len Barcousky
Chestnut Hill Local—Marguerite Stork
The Daily Intelligencer, Doylestown—Donald P. Davis
The Daily Pennsylvanian, Philadelphia—Erika Wallace
The Daily Republican, Phoenixville—Joseph P. Ujobai
Erie Times-News—Fred Livingston
The Evening Chronicle, Allentown—Albert Hofammann
Harrisburg Patriot-News—Robert J. Evans

Intelligencer Journal, Lancaster—James L. Kinter
Kutztown Patriot—Ade-Rolfe Floreen
Lock Haven Express—Sarah Loria
The News, Aliquippa—R. A. Palket
News-Tribune, Beaver Falls—Nadine Huff
Philadelphia Evening & Sunday Bulletin—Nessa R. Forman
Philadilphia Inquirer—Victoria Donahoe
The Pittsburgh Post-Gazette—Donald Miller
Pittsburgh Press—Maureen Meister
Reading Eagle—Toni Cowan
The Scranton Times—Daniel L. Cusick
The Scranton Tribune—Mrs. Gene Brislin
Times-Leader, Wilkes Barre—Roy Morgan
Union County Journal, Lewisburg—John C. P. Boylan
York Daily Record—Walt Partymiller
York Dispatch—Jean Farlow

RHODE ISLAND

The Evening Bulletin, Providence—Bradford F. Swan
Narragansett Times, Wakefield—Arline M. Aissis
Newport Daily News—William Kutik
Providence Journal—Bradford F. Swan
Warwick Beacon—Joan Christian & Tom Izzo
The Westerly Sun—Charles W. Utter

SOUTH CAROLINA

The Charleston News & Courier—Michael Tyzack
Columbia Record—Richard Smurthwaite
Georgetown Times—Cathy McConnell
Greenville News, Piedmont—Elizabeth Anne George
The Greenville Piedmont—Miriam Goodspeed
Index-Journal, Greenwood—Ann M. Tuck
Rock Hill Evening Herald—Bud Newcomb
The State, Columbia—William Starr
The Sumter Daily Item—Bob Williams

SOUTH DAKOTA

Rapid City Journal—Ruth Brennan
Sioux Falls Argus-Leader—Ralph Green
Vermillion Plain Talk—Mary Arnold
Yankton Press & Dakotan—James Lyle Van Osdel

TENNESSEE

Chattanooga News-Free Press—Jim Hazard
Chattanooga Times—Wes Hasden
The Commercial Appeal, Memphis—Guy Northrop
Johnson City Press Chronicle—Walter Miller
Kingsport Times-News—Margy Clark
Knoxville Journal—Stephen Horne
Knoxville News-Sentinel—Frank Weirich
Nashville Banner—Julie Pursell
The Nashville Tennessean—Clara Hieronymus
The Oak Ridger, Oak Ridge—Bonnie Van Gilder
Press Scimitar, Memphis—Jane Sanderson
Winchester Herald-Chronicle—Dorothy C. Drewry

TEXAS

Abilene Reporter—News—Danny Goddard
Amarillo Daily News—Bette Thompson
Amarillo Globe-Times—Bette Thompson
Amarillo Sunday News-Globe—Bette Thompson
The Austin American Statesman—Margaret Taylor Dry
Beaumont Enterprise—Linda Lange
Beaumont Journal—Linda Lange
Caller-Times, Corpus Christi—Maurice Schmidt
Canyon News—Ann Melin
Dallas Morning News—Janet Kutner
Dallas Times Herald—Lorraine Haacke
El Paso Herald Post—Betty Pierce
The El Paso Times—Edna Gundrsen
Fort Worth Press—Drenda William
Fort Worth Star-Telegram—Diane Bonelli
The Houston Chronicle—Ann Holmes
The Houston Post—George Christian
Kerrville Daily Times—Leah Feleman
The Lubbock Avalanche-Journal—William D. Kerns
The Odessa American—Jerry Ashley
Orange Leader—Gayle Standridge
Plainview Herald—Myrna Smith
San Angelo Standard Times—Ann Ward Rogers

San Antonio Express & News—Ron White
The San Antonio Light—Glenn Tucker
Waco Tribune-Herald—D. Craig Boate

UTAH

Box Elder News and Journal, Brigham City—Sara Yates
The Deseret News, Salt Lake City—Charles Nickerson
Provo Daily Herald—Charlene R. Winters
Salt Lake Tribune, Salt Lake City—George S. Dibble
Springville Herald—Pat Conover

VERMONT

Addison County Independent, Middlebury—Celine Slator
The Bennington Banner—Judson Brown
The Sunday Rutland Herald, Barre—Steven J. Wallach
Sunday Times Argus, Barre—Steven J. Wallach

VIRGINIA

The Alexandria Gazette—Terry Jemison
Charlottesville Daily Progress—Ruth Latter
The Ledger-Star, Norfolk—John Levin & Cornelia Justice
Lynchburg News—Mrs. Cecil Mullan
Richmond Times-Dispatch—F. D. Cossitt
The Roanoke Times—Ann Weinstein
The Times-Herald, Newport News—H. Reid
Virginia Gazette, Williamsburg—Jim Spencer
The Virginian-Pilot, Norfolk—F. D. Cossitt
World News, Roanoke—Ann Weinstein

WASHINGTON

The Daily Olympian, Olympia—Robert Lee Eskridge
The Goldendale Sentinel—David M. Wilhelms
Longview Daily News—Bob Peterson
Pierce County Herald, Puyallup—Lori Price
Seattle Post-Intelligencer—R. M. Campbell
The Seattle Times—Deloris Tarzan
The Spokane Community Press—Chuck Potter
Spokesman-Review, Spokane—Gladys E. Guilbert
The Spokane Daily Chronicle—Cynthia Gilbert
Tacoma News Tribune—Eve Reynolds
Walla Walla Union-Bulletin—Marianna Jones
Yakima Herald-Republic—James Gosney

WEST VIRGINIA

The Advertiser, Huntington—Angela Green
Bluefield Daily Telegraph—David Lee Williams
The Charleston Daily Mail—Mel Verost
The Charleston Gazette—Della Brown Taylor
The Huntington Herald Dispatch—Susan-Margaret Jones

WISCONSIN

Beloit Daily News—Minnie Mills Enking
Capital Times, Madison—Rob Fixmer
Green Bay Press-Gazettte—Daphne Tobit
The Milwaukee Journal—James M. Auer
The Milwaukee Sentinel—Dean Jensen
Northwestern, Oshkosh—Mary Zimmerman
The Post Crescent, Appleton—David Wagner
Sheboygan Press—Shirley Jarvis
Wausau Daily Herald—Barbara Lundquist & Jamie Orcutt
Wisconsin State Journal, Madison—Donald K. Davies

WYOMING

Laramie Daily Boomerang—Sandra E. Guzzo
Northern Wyoming News, Worland—Helen Turner
Wyoming Eagle, Cheyenne—Rosalind Routt

PUERTO RICO

El Mundo, San Juan—Antonio J. Molina

CANADA

ALBERTA

Calgary Herald—Nancy Tousley
The Edmonton Journal—Bob Harvey

BRITISH COLUMBIA

Columbian, New Westminster—Margherita Leech
Vancouver Province—Art Perry
Vancouver Sun—Andrew Scott
Victoria Colonist—Erith Smith
Victoria Daily Times—J. Gibson

MANITOBA

Winnipeg Free Press—John W. Graham
Winnipeg Tribune—Jan Kamienski

NEWFOUNDLAND

The Evening Telegram, St. John's—Peter Bell

NOVA SCOTIA

Dartmouth Free Press—John H. Colville
Halifax Mail-Star—Gretchen Pierce

ONTARIO

The Globe & Mail, Toronto—James Purdie
Kitchener-Waterloo Record—Carol Jankowski
The London Free Press—Lenore Crawford
Ottawa Citizen—Kathleen Walker
The Ottawa Journal— W. Q. Ketchum
St. Catharines Standard—Linda Turner
Sarnia Observer—Geoffrey H. Lane
The Spectator, Hamilton—Grace Inglis
Toronto Star—Gary Michael Dault
The Windsor Star—John Laycock

QUEBEC

Montreal Gazette—Virginia Nixon
Mediart, Montreal—Normand Theriault
Montreal Le Devoir—Christian Allegre
Montreal Photo-Journal—Marcel Huguet
The Montreal Star—Henry Lehmann & Georges Bogardi
La Presse, Montreal—Giles Toupin
Quebec City Le Soleil—Paul Roux
Sherbrooke La Tribune—Rene Bethiaume

Scholarships and Fellowships

OFFERED BY	AMOUNT	OPENED TO	DURATION	WHEN OFFERED
Abilene Fine Arts Museum,* Oscar Rose Park, Box 1858, Abilene, TX 79605	$500	Art students		Annually
Academy of Art College 625 Sutter St, San Francisco, CA 94102	$1875	Full-time B average 2nd year student	One year	Annually
Academy of the Arts, Harrison & South Sts, Easton, MD 21601	$100 per year	High school students going to art school, only to Talbot Resident	One year	Annually
Adirondack Lakes Center for the Arts, Blue Mountain Lake, NY 12812	Up to $30	7th to 12th grade students	Summer session	
Alaska Artists' Guild, Ltd, PO Box 1888, Anchorage, AK 99501	$500	Senior high school students for continuing education in art field	One time	Annually
Alaska Association for the Arts,* PO Box 2786, Fairbanks, AK 99707	$200 minimum	High school or college students	One year	Annually
Albert Pels School of Art, Inc, 2109 Broadway, New York, NY 10023	$1600 per year	High school seniors	One year (renewable)	Annually
	$1600 per year	Enrolled student working scholarship	One year	Annually
Alberta Association of Architects,* 217 Revillon Bldg, Edmonton AB T5J 1B2, Canada	$250	Architectural technology students at Northern and Southern Alberta Institutes of Technology	One year	Annually
Alberta College of Art, Southern Alberta Institute of Technology, 1301 16th Ave. NW Calgary, AB T2M 0L4, Canada	$15,000 (total)	Students Registered in A.C.A. programmes	One year	Annually
Alberta Culture, Visual Arts, Government of the Province of Alberta, Edmonton, AB, Canada T5J 0K5	$100 - $750, (total) $15,000	Residents of Alberta	One year	Annually
Alice Lloyd College, Pippa Passes, KY 41844	Variable	Anyone - Appalachian preferred	One or two years	Annually
Allied Artists of America, Inc, 1083 Fifth Ave, New York, NY 10028	$200	Any students attending National Academy School of Fine Arts	One year	Annually
Lyman Allyn Museum, 100 Mohegan Ave, New London, CT 06320	$45 for childrens' art classes	Needy children	One year	Annually
Amarillo Art Center, Box 447, Amarillo, TX 79178	Variable	Primarily to disabled or deprived children and young adults	Each semester	
American Academy, 41 E 65th St, New York, NY 10021	$6000, plus residency	Citizens of the US	One year	Annually
American Academy and Institute of Arts and Letters, 633 W 155th St, New York, NY 10032	$3000 awards	Painters, sculptors, graphic artists (cannot be applied for)		Annually
American Academy of Art, 220 S State St, Chicago, IL 60604	$5000	High school seniors		Annually
American Antiquarian Society, 185 Salisbury St, Worcester, MA 01609	Up to $1666 per month (NEH Fellowships)	Qualified scholars in American history and culture to 1877	Six months - one year	Annually
	Up to $1800 (Daniels Fellowships)	Qualified scholars in American history and culture to 1877	One to three months	Annually
American Numismatic Society, Broadway at 155th St, New York, NY 10032	$3500 Fellowship	Graduate student	One year	Annually
	(12) $750 grants	Graduate students and junior members of faculty	June 12 - August 11	Annually

OFFERED BY	AMOUNT	OPENED TO	DURATION	WHEN OFFERED
American Oriental Society, Secretary, 329 Sterling Memorial Library, Yale Station, New Haven, CT 06520	$5000 for the study of the history of Chinese painting	Students who have completed 3 years of Chinese language study at a recognized university, or the equivalent, and all requirements for a PhD in Chinese painting studies, except for travel, the written dissertation and its defense	1 year	July 1st to June 30th
American-Scandinavian Foundation, Exchange Division, 127 E 73rd St, New York, NY 10021	$500 - $5000	Applicants with BA degree (Unrestricted fields) for Denmark, Finland, Iceland, Norway and Sweden	Up to one year	Annually
American Society of Interior Designers Educational Foundation,* 730 Fifth Ave, New York, NY 10019	Variable	Interior design students and teachers	One year	Annually
American Watercolor Society, 1083 Fifth Ave, New York, NY 10028	Variable	Art schools and colleges for further award to outstanding students of water-color painting	One year	Annually
Archaeological Institute of America, 260 W Broadway, New York, NY 10013	Variable - $7000 and up	Students of Aegean, Italian, or Meso-potamian archaeology	One year	Annually
Arizona State University, Department of Art, Tempe, AZ 85281	$1500 - $4000, also tuition waivers	Qualified Graduate Students—admitted students in the graduate program	Semester or academic year	Annually, semi-annually
Arkansas Arts Center, MacArthur Park, Little Rock, AR 72203	Varies as to class	Qualified applicant	By semesters	
Arkansas State University, Fine Arts Center, State University, AR 72467	$460, full tuition scholarship, 6 awarded annually	1st and 2nd semester freshmen	One year	Annually
Armstrong Museum of Art and Archaeology,* Olivet College, Olivet, MI 49076	Variable	Prospective college students and college students	One - two years	Annually
Arrowmont School of Arts and Crafts, Box 567, Gatlinburg, TN 37738	Varies from $250 to full tuition internships	Everyone	One to five weeks	Annually
Art Association of Richmond,* McGuire Memorial Hall, Whitewater Blvd, Richmond, IN 47374	$350	High school senior studying art	One year	Annually
The Art Barn,* 143 Lower Cross Rd, Greenwich, CT 06830	$200	Children		Semiannually
Art Center College of Design, 1700 Lida St, Pasadena, CA 91103	$645	Third term students	Continuous	Each semester
Art Gallery of Ontario, Grange Park, Toronto, ON M5T 1G4, Canada	Varied subsidized grants, Gallery pays 85%	Secondary school students	One year - 25 week course	Annually
Art in Architecture, Joseph Young, 1434 S Spaulding Ave, Los Angeles, CA 90019	$200 - $500	Graduate students	One year	Annually
Art Institute of Boston, 700 Beacon St, Boston, MA 02215	$50 to $925	Accepted or enrolled students at the Art Institute	One - three years	Annually
Art Institute of Ft Lauderdale,* 3000 E Las Olas Blvd, Ft Lauderdale, FL 33316	Variable	Graduating high school seniors	Two years	Annually
Art Students League of New York,* 215 W 57th St, New York, NY 10019	Tuition $4000 Traveling Scholarships (2)	League students	One year	Annually
Artists' Guild, c/o Art Museum of the Palm Beaches, Inc, PO Box 2300, West Palm Beach, FL 33402	$300	High school graduate art student of South Florida	One Year	For the Norton Gallery and School of Art.
Arts and Crafts Center of Pittsburgh,* Mellon Park, Pittsburgh, PA 15232	Nominal	Underprivileged qualified students, Pittsburgh residents only	One term	Each term
Arts and Crafts Society of Portland,* 616 NW 18th Ave, Portland, OR 97209	Work exchange scholarships for school tuition	Students in financial need	Per term	Per term
Arts and Science Center,* 14 Court St, Nashua, NH 03060	For education classes at the Center (4 semesters)	Qualified qpplicants	Ten weeks	Quarterly
Arts Club of Washington,* 2017 Eye St NW, Washington, DC 20006	$600	Students at local universities or colleges only	One year	Annually
Arts Council of Spartanburg County, Inc, 385 South Spring St, Spartanburg, SC 29301	Varies	Resident of Spartanburg County	One year	As decided by Board of Governors
Association of Medical Illustrators,* 6650 Northwest Hwy, Chicago, IL 60631	$100	2nd year medical illustration students	One year	Annually
Atlanta College of Art, 1280 Peachtree St NE, Atlanta, GA 30309		Needy students		Annually

OFFERED BY	AMOUNT	OPENED TO	DURATION	WHEN OFFERED
Atlantic Christian College, Art Department, Wilson, NC 27893	Determined by Art Faculty	All Art students	Determined by Art faculty	Anytime during the year
Ball State University, 1500 University Ave, Muncie, IN 47306	$2800 graduate assistantship ($385 summer term)	Degree candidate in Art Department	One year (renewable)	Annually
	$3225 fellowship ($440 summer term)	Doctoral candidate in Art Department	One year (renewable)	Annually
Bassist Institute,* 923 SW Taylor St, Portland, OR 97205	$2000	Students	One and two years	Annually
Battle Creek Civic Art Center, 265 Emmett St, Battle Creek, MI 49017	$15 - $25 per person each term	Public and parochial school students in the greater Battle Creek area only	Per term	Each Semester
Beloit College,* Department of Art, Beloit, WI 53511	Variable	Qualified students	One year (renewable)	Annually
Berry College, Art Department, Mt Berry, GA 30149	Varies	Freshman art majors	One year	Semi-annually
Birmingham-Bloomfield Art Association, 1516 S Cranbrook Rd, Birmingham, MI 48009	Full, dependent upon course cost	Local high school art students	Per term	Per term (variable)
Blue Mountain College, Dept of Art, Blue Mountain, MS 38610	$135	Art majors	One year	Annually
Bob Jones University, School of Fine Arts, Wade Hampton Blvd, Greenville, SC 29614	$50 to $150 per month	Undergraduate students with demonstrated financial need and satisfactory school record	One semester (renewable)	Semi-annually
Boston Architectural Center,* 320 Newbury St, Boston, MA 02115	Variable	Qualified attending students		Annually
Bradley University,* Layton School of Art, Peoria, IL 61606	Undergraduate $2600; 8 graduate assistantships of $1200 each	Any student in or entering the art program	One year (renewable)	Annually
Briarcliff College,* Art Department, Elm Rd, Briarcliff Manor, NY 10510	$500 per year	Entering freshmen and transfer students	Four years	Annually
Brigham Young University, Harris Fine Arts Center, Provo, UT 84601	Tuition	Qualified freshman applicants, transfer and continuing students	One year	Annually
British Government, Marshall Scholarships. Apply: British Consulate-General, San Francisco, 120 Montgomery St, San Francisco, CA 94104. Closing date for applications Oct 22.	(30) in the order of 1750 a year. In certain circumstances a marriage allowance is also payable.	US citizens. Available to college or university graduates under 26 years of age for study of any subject leading to the award of a British University degree. Candidates may apply either in region in which they live or where they received at least two years of college training.	Two years (with possibility of extension for a third year).	Annually
Brockton Art Center,* Art Workshops, Oak St, Brockton, MA 02401	$50	Needy children	Per term	Per term
Brooklyn Museum Art School, 188 Eastern Parkway, Brooklyn, NY 11238	(20) Max Beckmann Memorial Scholarships covering tuition and registration fees	College art majors and professional art school students completing their undergraduate studies by June 1978.	One year	
	(5) Robert Smithson Memorial Scholarships covering tuition and registration fees.	College art majors and professional art school students completing their undergraduate studies by June 1978.	One year	
Bucknell University,* Department of Art, Lewisburg, PA 17837	$2000 plus tuition	Registered graduate students	One year (renewable)	Annually
Burnley School of Professional Art, Inc, 905 East Pine St, Seattle, WA 98122	Semester tuition	Students who have completed one semester in School. Financial need is not considered	Can be won as many times as student is enrolled in school	Fall/Spring Semesters
C W Post Center of Long Island University, Art Department, Northern Blvd, Greenvale, NY 11548.	Up to ½ year	Undergraduates	Four years	Semi-annually
	$1800 plus tuition	Graduate assistants	Two years	Semi-annually
	$23 per credit	Graduates other than assistants	Two years	Semi-annually
Caldwell College Art Department, Caldwell, NY 07006	$500 - $2100 Grants: $100 and up	Academically qualified Economically qualified	One year One year	Renewable annually Renewable annually
California College of Arts and Crafts, 5212 Broadway, Oakland, CA 94618	Variable. Scholarships, loans, grants	Grants, loans, employment open to all students. Scholarships open to continuing students who have attended for two or more consecutive semesters and are currently enrolled	One year	Annually
California Institute of the Arts, School of Art, 24700 McBean Pkwy, Valencia, CA 91355	Varies	Everyone	One year	Annually
California State University, Chico* Art Department, Chico, CA 95929	$1000	Art students	One year	Annually

OFFERED BY	AMOUNT	OPENED TO	DURATION	WHEN OFFERED
California State University, Hayward,* Art Dept, 25800 Hillary St, Hayward, CA 94542	Variable ($100 - $300 annually)	Any art student	One year	
Campbellsville College, Department of Fine Arts, Campbellsville, KY 42718	$100 per semester	All applicants who can show proficiency	Four years (renewable)	Semi-annually
Canadian Society for Education Through Art, Faculty of Education, University of Regina, Regina, SK, S4S 0A2 Canada	$500 (six)	High school graduates	One year	Annually
Cardinal Stritch College, 6801 N Yates Rd, Milwaukee, WI 53217	(2) $200 (total of $400)	Art Concentrators of present undergraduate students of freshman, sophomore, and junior status.	One year (may apply a second year).	Annually
Carrizo Art & Craft Workshops, Drawer A, Ruidoso, NM 88345	Tuition plus $305	Young adults	Two weeks	Annually
Catholic University of America,* 620 Michigan Ave NE, Washington, DC 20017	(2) half-tuition scholarships	BA and MFA students	One year	Annually
Catholic University of Puerto Rico,* Department of History and Fine Arts, Ponce, PR 00731	(1) Full tuition	Low income freshmen with art talent	Four years	Biennially or every four years
Cazenovia College, Cazenovia, NY 13035.	$100 - $1000	Advertising Design Majors	Academic year (renewable)	Annually
Centenary College of Louisiana,* Department of Art, Centenary Blvd, Shreveport, LA 71104	Varied from full tuition to nominal amounts	Outstanding students	One year	Annually
Central Wyoming College,* Art Center, Riverton, WY 82501	Tuition	Anyone with artistic potential regardless of age, race, or sex	One year	Annually
Chabot College,* Humanities Division, 25555 Hesperin Blvd, Hayward, CA 94545	$100 annually from California Art Society	Fine arts majors	One year	Annually
Chadron State College, Division of Fine Arts, Chadron, NE 69337	Up to full in-state tuition for first year; $100 each semester for subsequent years	No restrictions		Annually
Charles River Creative Arts Program,* 56 Centre St, Dover, MA 02030	$2000	Those needing financial aid	One year	Annually
Charles Stewart Mott Community College,* Fine Arts Division, 1401 E Court St, Flint, MI 48503	Up to $450	Current art students		Annually
Cherokee National Historical Society, Inc, PO Box 515, Tahlequah, OK 74464	Variable	Graduate level students of Cherokee descent studying for the museum and archival professions		
Carolina Art Association, Gibbes Art Gallery, 135 Meeting St, Charleston, SC 29401	$10 to $100	Art students	Per session	Several times a year
The Charleston Art Gallery of Sunrise, 755 Myrtle Rd, Charleston, WV 25314	Tuition	Underprivileged and competition winners	One year	Annually
Chautauqua Art Center Summer School, Wythe Ave, Chautauqua, NY 14722	$2000.	Any non-professionals.	One year	Annually
Cherokee National Historical Society, Inc, PO Box 515, TSA-LA-GI, Tahlequah, OK 74464	Open	Cherokee graduate students in museum related fields	Variable	
Cheyenne Artists Guild, Inc, 1010 E 16th St, Cheyenne, WY 82001	$200	Senior high school students of Cheyenne only	One year	Annually
Chicago Public School Art Society, Art Institute of Chicago, Michigan Ave at Adams St, Chicago, IL 60603	$85	Children who are involved in Society's Art Form program	Per semester	Semi-annually
Claremore Junior College, Art Department, College Hill, Claremore, OK 74017	$150	Art majors	Academic year	Annually
Cleveland Institute of Art, 11141 East Boulevard, Cleveland, OH 44106	$1000 per student	Qualified students	One year	Annually
Cleveland State University, Department of Art, Euclid Ave at E 24th St, Cleveland, OH 44115	Tuition	Any student, based on merit	One year	Annually
Coe College Art Galleries, 1221 First Avenue NE, Cedar Rapids, IA 52402	Variable	Incoming freshman students	One year	Annually

OFFERED BY	AMOUNT	OPENED TO	DURATION	WHEN OFFERED
Colby Community College, Art Department, 1255 S Range, Colby, KS 67701	$100 up to Full tuition and fees	Any applicant, juried portfolio	Two years	Annually
Colby-Sawyer College, New London, NH 03257	Approximately $350	Entering and upperclass students	One year	Annually
College of Art and Design, Center for Creative Studies, 245 E Kirby St, Detroit, MI 48202	Varies	Current students and high school seniors	One year	Annually
College of Mount St Joseph,* Art Department, Mount Saint Joseph, OH 45051	One year $1920	High school graduates. Special scholastic scholarship	One year	Annually
College of New Rochelle,* Castle Pl, New Rochelle, NY 10801	Variable, depending on need	Incoming freshman with portfolio	Four years renewable	Annually
College of St Catherine,* Visual Arts Department, 2004 Randolph, St. Paul, MN 55105	Variable	Art majors	One year	Annually
College of Saint Mary, 72nd & Mercy Road, Omaha, NE 68124	$1000 per year	High school graduates	Four years	Annually
College of the Ozarks, Art Department, 610 Johnson St, Clarksville, AR 72830	$200	Art majors	One year (Renewable)	Annually
Colorado State University Art Department, G100 Visual Arts Building, Fort Collins, CO 80523	$3000	MFA students	Two to three years	April
Colorado Women's College, Montview* at Quebec, Denver, CO 80220	Variable	Art students	One year	Annually
Columbia College, Eighth and Rogers, Columbia, MO 65201	Up to $1000 plus work study	Students showing talent and/or need	One year	Annually
Columbia University,* School of the Arts, 617 Dodge, New York, NY 10027	Variable	All registered students in competition		Annually
Community Arts Council of Chilliwack, Box 53, Chilliwack, BC, Canada V2P 6H7	$300	Those seeking higher education in the fine arts	One year	Annually
Compton Community College,* Art Department, 1111 E Artesia Blvd, Compton, CA 90224	$200 - $300	Art majors	One year	Annually
Concordia College, Art Department, Moorhead, MN 56560	Up to $1500	Entering freshmen and upper classmen	One year	Annually
Contemporary Arts Museum, 5216 Montrose, Houston, TX 77006	$120 - $125	Underprivileged	Semester basis	
Cooper School of Art,* 2341 Carnegie Ave SW, Cleveland, OH 44115	Full and partial tuition, total $12,000	High school seniors	One year (renewable)	Annually
Coppini Academy of Fine Arts, 115 Melrose Pl, San Antonio, TX 78212	Senior $400 Junior $100 - $250	Ages 21 - 30 Ages 16 - 20		Annually Annually
Corcoran School of Art,* 17th & New York Ave NW, Washington DC 10006	William Wilson Corcoran Scholarship	Students from area high schools	Summer course	Annually in April
	Rohsheim Memorial Award	Outstanding first year students	One semester	Annually in May
	Kenneth Stubbs Memorial Award	Outstanding drawing students	One semester	Annually in May
	Mary Lay Thom Sculpture Prize	Outstanding sculpture students	One semester	Annually in May
	Eugene Weisz Memorial Scholarship	Outstanding painting students	One semester	Annually in May
	Sarah Pickens Roberts Memorial Award	Student whose work is judged most promising	One semester	Annually in May
	Cash prizes in Final Annual Graduation Exhibition	Prize-winning students		Annually in May
Cornell College, Mt. Vernon, IA 52314	$3400	Selected on recommendation of Art Dept. Also based on need		Annually
Cornish Institute of Allied Arts, 710 E Roy, Seattle, WA 98103	Variable amounts, tuition scholarships	Registered full-time students	One year	Annually
Craft Center,* 25 Sagamore Rd, Worcester, MA 01605	$60	People in need	Ten week semester	Annually
Cranbrook Academy of Art, Bloomfield Hills, MI 48013	$50,000 annually	Students enrolled in Architecture, Ceramics, Design, Fiber, Metalsmithing, Painting, Photography, Printmaking, and Sculpture at Cranbrook Academy of Art.	One year	Annually

OFFERED BY	AMOUNT	OPENED TO	DURATION	WHEN OFFERED
Creighton University, Fine Arts Department, 2500 California St, Omaha, NE 68178	$250	Alternates between visual and performing arts major		Annually
Davidson County Art Guild, West Center St, Lexington, NC 27292	$100	Davidson County art student	One year (renewable)	Annually
Dayton Art Institute, Forest & Riverview Ave, Dayton, OH 45405	$2000 - $3000 (total)	Qualified students		Semiannually
Dean Junior College,* Visual and Performing Arts Department, 99 Main St, Franklin, MA 02038	Variable	Full-time students	One year	Annually
Delaware Art Museum,* 2301 Kentmere Pkwy, Wilmington, DE 19806	Variable	Public school pupils	One year	Semiannually
Delta State University, Art Department, Box D-2, Cleveland, MS 38733	Smith-Patterson Award ($100)	Senior art students with 3.5 or above average and high attainment in studio work		Annually
	Maxine Boggan Holcombe Scholarship ($100)	Junior level art education major with scholarship and accomplishment in studio work		Annually
	Malcolm Norwood Scholarship ($300)	Entering freshman student who is an art major at DSU and shows outstanding art work in the annual Crosstie Festival		Annually
Detroit Artists' Market, 1452 Randolph St, Detroit, MI 48226	$1000	Any qualified student who is attending the specific school whose turn it is to receive the scholarship; given on rotating basis to Center for Creative Studies, Wayne State University and Cranbrook Academy of Art	One year	Annually
Dickinson State College,* Department of Art, Dickinson, ND 58601	$500 TMI Systems Design Corporation Scholarship	Any art or business student	One year	Annually
	$100 Tom Niemitaló Memorial Art Scholarship	Any art major or minor	One year	Annually
	$100 DSC Alumni Foundation Scholarships	Freshmen	One year	Annually
Douglas Art Association Little Gallery, 300 11th St, Box 256, Douglas, AZ 85607	$200	Local students	One year	Annually
Drake University, Des Moines, IA 50311	$50 - $300 (total of $18,000)	Art majors	One year (renewable)	Annually
Dumbarton Oaks Research Library and Collection, 1703 32nd St NW, Washington, DC 20007	Variable	Graduate students and post-doctoral scholars of Byzantine studies, Pre-Columbian studies and History of Landscape Architecture.	One year	Annually
Dunedin Fine Arts & Cultural Center, 1143 Michigan Blvd, Dunedin, FL 33528	Variable	Students sixth grade and above with sincere interest and/or talent and financial need.	5, 8 and 10 weeks depending upon length of class	Year round, per quarter
Dutchess Community College,* Department of Visual Arts, 1 Pendell Rd, Poughkeepsie, NY 12601	$250	Second-year students	One year	Annually
East Central Junior College,* Art Department, Box 529, Union, MO 63084	$110	Students	One year	Annually
East Mississippi Junior College, Art Department, Box 176, Scooba, MS 39358	Determined on merit basis	All students in art major curriculum	One year	Annually
East Tennessee State University, Carroll Reece Museum, Johnson City, TN 37601	$3000	High school seniors and college students	One year	Annually
Eastern Arizona College, Church St, Thatcher, AZ 85552	Tuition (resident)	Anyone	One year	Annually
Edgecliff College,* Art Department, 2220 Victory Pkwy, Cincinnati, OH 45206	$1760	Graduating high school seniors	Four years	Annually
Edinboro State College, Department of Art, Edinboro, PA 16412	$3000	BFA or equivalent	One year	Annually
El Camino College,* Division of Fine Arts, 16007 Crenshaw Blvd, Via Torrance, CA 90506	$300 per year	Junior standing and transfer to an accredited school for more art training	One year	Annually
Eliot McMurrough School of Art,* 306 Fifth Ave, Indialantic, FL 32903	Work scholarships	Those in need who are already enrolled	One term	Semi-annually

OFFERED BY	AMOUNT	OPENED TO	DURATION	WHEN OFFERED
El Paso Museum of Art, 1211 Montana Ave, El Paso, TX 79902	$500	Junior and senior high school students of El Paso	Per year	
Erie Art Center, 338 W Sixth St, Erie, PA 16507	Generally for amount of tuition	Anyone demonstrating financial need	One term	Quarterly
Essex Institute, 132 Essex St, Salem, MA 01970	Fellowships arranged through Boston University American Studies program	Graduate students in American Studies	One year	Annually
Fairmont State College, Department of Art, Fairmont, WV 26554	$300 per year	Qualified by portfolio submission	Four years	Annually
Fashion Institute of Technology, 227 W 27th St, New York, NY 10001	Variable	All students who qualify	Renewable	Annually
Harriet FeBlands Advanced Painters Workshop, Premium Point, New Rochelle, NY 10801	Tuition for one semester	Winners of the FeBland Group Annual Exhibition "Scholarship Award	Semester	Annually
Findlay College, Art Department, 1000 N Main St, Findlay OH 45840	Variable	All students	One year (renewable)	Annually
Fine Arts Center of Clinton, 119 W Macon St, Clinton, IL 61727	Tuition only	Qualified students		Annually
Fletcher Farm Craft School, Ludlow, VT 05149	(4) $50 and (2) $100	Vermont Teachers of Arts & Crafts	Two or four weeks	Annually
Flint Institute of Arts, DeWaters Art Center, 1120 E. Kearsley St, Flint, MI 48503	Partial	Gifted children	One semester	
Florida Gulf Coast Art Center, Inc, 222 Ponce de Leon Blvd, Clearwater, FL 33516	Variable	Junior and senior high school students in Pinellas County	Summer	Annually
Florida State University, Tallahassee, FL 32306	Assistantships $1500 - $2800 Fellowships $4200 - $5000	Graduate students in art Graduate students in art history	One year One year	Annually Annually
Fort Hays State University, Hays, KS 67601	$12,000	Graduate students and art students	One year	Annually
Fort Wright College of the Holy Names, Department of Art, W 4000 Randolph Rd, Spokane, WA 99204	(2) $600; (2) $300; (3) $200	Students admitted to the FWC School of Art	One year (Renewable)	Annually, April 20 of each year
Franklin and Marshall College, Lancaster, PA 17604	Variable	Students with pronounced talent		Annually
Freer Gallery of Art, 12th & Jefferson Dr, SW, Washington, DC 20560	Variable	PhD candidate from University of Michigan in Oriental art field; PhD candidate in field of Chinese art	Variable	No set formula
Fresno Arts Center, 3033 E Yale Ave, Fresno, CA 93703	$900	School students	Each class session (3)	
Friends University, Art Department, 2100 University Ave, Wichita, KS 67213	$300 per year	All art majors	One to four years	
Furman University, Art Department, Greenville, SC 29613	Mattie Hipp Cunningham Scholarship $1350	Art major selected by the faculty of Art Department	One year (can be repeated in unusual circumstances)	Once every third year
The Gallery/Stratford, 54 Romeo St, North Stratford, ON N5A 3C7, Canada Ela Moll Memorial Fund	$150	Graduating high school students for further art education in Perth County	One year	Annually
Georgetown College, Georgetown, KY 40324	$250 - $450 plus financial aid on a need basis	All graduates of accredited school secondary schools. A portfolio is required for an art grant but not for admission to the program	As long as academic progress is being made	Semi-annually
Grand Canyon College,* Art Department, 3300 W Camelback Rd, PO Box 11097, Phoenix, AZ 85061	Up to 50%	Majors accepted into degree program	One year (renewable)	Annually
Grants for Graduate Study Abroad. Write: Counselling and Correspondence Unit, Institute of International Education, 809 United Nations Plaza, New York, NY 10017		Note: People in the arts may apply for any of these awards (Fulbright-Hays and Foreign Governments, ITT International Fellowships, Lusk Memorial Fellowships, Lade Memorial Fellowships), but they must be affiliated with an educational institute abroad while pursuing their studies.		One academic year
Greater Fall River Art Association*, 80 Belmont St, Fall River, MA 02720	$100	Students entering Art Department of Southeastern Massachusetts University	One year	Annually

OFFERED BY	AMOUNT	OPENED TO	DURATION	WHEN OFFERED
Elizabeth Greenshields Foundation, 1814 Sherbrooke St W, Montreal, PQ, H3H 1E4, Canada	Various (30)	Nationals of any country for study in any country in painting and sculpture	One year	No closing date
Greenville College, Department of Art, Greenville, IL 62246	Variable	Anyone (dependent on family need and high school academic standing)	Full year	Annually
Greenwich House Pottery & Ceramic School, 16 Jones St, New York, NY 10014	Tuition	Adults and children with talent	One semester (renewable)	Semi-annually
John Simon Guggenheim Memorial Foundation, 90 Park Ave, New York, NY 10016	Adjusted to needs of fellows	Citizens or permanent residents of U.S., Canada, other American states, Caribbean, Philippines, and French, Dutch, and British possessions in Western Hemisphere, normally 30 to 45 years of age	One year	Annually
Solomon R Guggenheim Museum, 1071 Fifth Ave, New York, NY 10028	Curatorial Fellowship $7500. Funds available for visits to museums in major cities throughout the country.	Graduate student interested in a curatorial career (MA in art history required, PhD preferred).	One year	Annually in Sept
	Summer Volunteer Program (2) $500 stipends	Returning interns	Summer	Annually
	(2-3) $500 scholarships	Scholarship students meeting college work/study requirements.	Summer	Annually
	Volunteer Work Experience Program (1) $500	One skilled intern in the photography department	Fall or Spring Semester	Annually
Harding College, Department of Art, Searcy, AR 72143	$125	Art majors	One semester	Each semester
Harford Community College,* Humanities Division, 401 Thomas Run Rd, Bel Air, MD 21014	$50	Student matriculating in an art program	One year	Annually
Hastings College,* Art Department, Hastings, NE 68901	$200 - $500	All art majors	Four years	Annually
Haystack Mountain School of Crafts, Deer Isle, ME 04627	$600 (16)	Candidates with one year or more graduate specialization in crafts	Six weeks	Annually
Herron School of Art, Indiana University-Purdue University at Indianapolis, 1701 N Pennsylvania St, Indianapolis, IN 46202	Scholarships, total per year $10,000. Also various financial aid available through Indiana University	Any student	One year	Annually
Hinckley School of Crafts, Hinckley, ME 04944		College art students	Six weeks	Annually, summer
Historical Society of Delaware*, Market St, Wilmington, DE 19801	Summer internship program	College juniors interested in museum and historical society work	Summer	Annually
Historical Society of York County, 250 E. Market St, York PA 17403	$100 - $200	Summer interns	Six weeks	Annually
Honolulu Academy of Arts,* Studio Program, 900 S. Beretania St, Honolulu, HI 96814	$880 (year's tuition)	Students who successfully completed first year study	One year	Annually
Hope College, Art Department, Rusk Building, Holland, MI 49423	$1500.	Art majors	One year	Annually
Howard University,* Department of Art, College of Fine Arts, Sixth & Fairmont Sts NW, Washington, DC 20001	Up to $2000	Students	One year	Annually
Henry E Huntington Library and Art Gallery, San Marino, CA 91108	$600 per month	Scholars (not to candidates for advanced degrees)	One to twelve months	Annually. Applications received Oct. 1 - Dec. 31 for awards beginning the following June
	NEH Fellowships up to $1,667 per month	Same as above	Six to twelve months	
Hutchinson Art Association, 321 E. First St, Hutchinson, KS 67501	$250	Junior college art students	One year	Annually
Incorporated E A Abbey Scholarships for Mural Painting in the USA, 1083 Fifth Ave, New York, NY 10028	$6000 scholarship for study in mural painting in US and abroad	US citizens not more than 35 years of age	One year	Biennially
Indiana State University, Department of Art, Terre Haute, IN 47809	$2000	MFA, MS, MA	One year	Annually
Industrial Designers Society of America, 1750 Old Meadow Rd, McLean, VA 22101	Walter Dorwin Teague Research Fund; depends on amount required for research projects	Practicing designers	One year	Annually
Institute of American Indian Arts,* Cerrillos Rd, Santa Fe, NM 87501	Full - board, room, all materials plus two years high school	Any native American	Two years	Annually

OFFERED BY	AMOUNT -	OPENED TO	DURATION	WHEN OFFERED
Institute of Contemporary Art, University of Pennsylvania, 34th & Walnut Sts, Philadelphia, PA 19104	Cost of fall lecture series	Applicants	One year	Annually
Institute of Puerto Rican Culture,* Apartado 4184, San Juan, PR 00905	Variable	Artists, writers, and scholars	One year	Annually
Instituto Allende, San Miguel de Allende, Guanajuato, Mexico	Full tuition of $380 per quarter, renewable	Registered full-time students		Quarterly from Jan. 1st
InterAmerican University, San German, PR 00753	Variable	All with talent		Annually, semi-annually
Interlochen Arts Academy, Interlochen, MI 49463	Up to $2000	Anyone, based on need and merit	One Year	Annually
International Museum of Photography, 900 East Ave, Rochester, NY 14607	$7200 (3)	Post-masters degree	One year	Annually
Ivy School of Professional Art, University Ave, Pittsburgh, PA 15214	Tuition	Teens - Saturday classes	One year	Annually
James Madison University,* Duke Fine Arts Center, Main at Grace St, Harrisonburg, VA 22801	$2400 - $3000	Graduate students in the Department of Art	One Year	Annually
Jamestown College, Art Department, Jamestown, ND 58401	$400	Entering freshmen art majors	One year (renewable to total of $1600).	Annually
Jersey City State College, 2039 Kennedy Blvd, Jersey City, NJ 07305	Full tuition and fees	Incoming freshmen and community college graduates on the basis of academic ability and potential contribution to the College as evidenced by SAT scores and class rank.	One year	
	Margaret Williams Scholarship in Fine and Performing Arts	To be awarded at the discretion of the College's Scholarship Committee.		
	The Charlotte and Hugo Prins Simons Scholarship in Art	To be awarded at the discretion of the College's Scholarship Committee.		
Junior Arts Center, 4814 Hollywood Blvd, Los Angeles, CA 90027	Tailored to students' needs	Promising artists	To fulfill project	As requested
Junior College of Albany, Dept of Fine Arts, 74 New Scotland Ave, Albany, NY 12208	(6) $400	Professional art students (Apply to Martin J Gieschen, 140 New Scotland Ave, Albany, NY 12208)	One semester	Each semester
Kalamazoo Institute of Arts, 314 S Park St, Kalamazoo, MI 49007	Tuition	Area school children	One semester	Semi-annually
Kansas City Art Institute, 4415 Warwick Blvd, Kansas City, MO 64111	Varies	Demonstrated need	One year	Annually
Kansas State University, Department of Art, Manhattan, KS 66506	$3000 Teaching Assistantships	Students working for Master's degree	Nine months	Annually
	Variable scholarship awards	Freshman - senior undergraduates	One year	Annually
Kappa Pi International Honorary Art Fraternity, Box 7843, Midfield, Birmingham, AL 35228	$500	Student members	One year	Annually
Kearney State College, School of Fine Arts & Humanities, Art Department, Kearney, NE 68847	$200 tuition waiver	Entering freshmen	One year	Annually
Kent State University, School of Art, New Art Bldg, Kent, OH 44242	(22) $2900	Graduate assistants	One year	Annually, (March - Sept)
	(15) Ranging from full tuition and fees to partial remissions	Students	One year	Annually, Fall Quarter, Spring Quarter
Maude Kerns Art Center, 1910 E 15th Ave, Eugene, OR 97403	(4) tuition only, work scholarships	Qualified applicant	One term	Each term
Lafayette Art Center,* 101 S Ninth St, Lafayette, IN 47901	Up to $500	Eligible students, low income and merit	One semester (24 sessions)	Semi-annually
Laguna Gloria Art Museum, PO Box 5568, Austin TX 78763	$50 to $75	Financially needy art school applicants		
Lahaina Arts Society, 649 Wharf St, Lahaina, HI 96761	$1000 per year	High school seniors	One year	Annually
Lake Michigan College, Art Department, 2755 E Napier Ave, Benton Harbor, MI 49022	$300 (three per year)			
Lake Placid School of Art, Center for Music, Drama and Art, Saranac Ave, Lake Placid, NY 12946	Tuition waiver (work-study)	Full-time students who show financial need (Annual summer scholarships offered to Union of Independent Colleges of Art students)	One year	Annually

OFFERED BY	AMOUNT	OPENED TO	DURATION	WHEN OFFERED
Las Vegas Art Museum, Sponsored by Las Vegas Art League, 3333 W. Washington, Las Vegas, NV 89107	Membership and tuition to any class	Graduating high school seniors, each high school in area	One year	Annually
Le Musee Regional de Rimouski, 35 ouest Saint-Germain, Rimouski, PQ, Canada G5L 4B4	$500	Artists - groups	One year	Annually
Lindenwood Colleges,* Art Department, St Charles, MO 63301	$500 - $2000	Art majors	One year	Annually
Little Gallery of Arts, 155 E Main, Vernal, UT 84078	$100	High school seniors	One year	Annually
Loch Haven Art Center, Inc,* 2416 N Mills Ave, Orlando, FL 32803	Varies (class tuition)	Qualified applicants	Ten-week class	Each quarter
Los Angeles County Museum of Art, 5905 Wilshire Blvd, Los Angeles, CA 90036	Modern and Contemporary Art Council New Talent Award $2000	Local artists under 36	One year	Annually
Louisville School of Art, 100 Park Rd, Anchorage, KY 40223	$5250 (annual total)	Students doing quality work	One semester	Semi-annually
Loyola Marymount University, Malone Art Gallery, 7101 W 80th St, Los Angeles, CA 90045	Related to financial status	Financially deprived	One semester	Semi-annually
MacDowell Colony, Inc, Peterborough, NH 03458 (applications obtainable: The MacDowell Colony, Inc, 680 Park Ave, New York, NY 10021	Resident fellowships to professional writers, painters, sculptors, filmmakers, printmakers, and composers provide board, room, use of studio for maximum of three months. A token charge of $10 per diem is waived in cases of need.	Nationals of any country	One to two months (summer) One to three months (winter)	
McMurry College, Art Department, Sayles Blvd & S 14th St, Abilene, TX 79605	$2000	Art students who show special ability	One year	Annually
McNeese State University,* Department of Visual Arts, 4000 Ryan St, Lake Charles, LA 70609	$300	Sophomore majors and up	One year and renewable	
McPherson College, Art Department, 1600 E Euclid, McPherson, KS 67460	$400 per year	Entering students who plan to major in art	One year (renewable if student does satisfactory work to total of $1600).	Annually
Madonna College,* Art Department, 36600 Schoolcraft Rd, Livonia, MI 48150	Robert Svoboda Scholarship $2500	Student interested in art or journalism	One year	Annually
Malden Bridge Art School, Malden Bridge, NY 12115	(2) full tuition (1) $100	Anyone	One year	Annually
Manatee Junior College,* Department of Art, 26th St W, Brandenton, FL 33505	Full tuition (3)	Students majoring in art; preference given to Fla. residents; sophomore	One year	Annually
Manitoba Association of Architects, Winnipeg MB, Canada R3B 0W9	$300	Architecture students enrolled at the University of Manitoba only	One year	Annually
Mankato State University, Art Department, Mankato, MN 56001	$300	Outstanding undergraduate, based upon performance academically and creatively	Unlimited	Annually
Maple Woods Community College, Art & Art History Department, 2601 NE Barry Road, Kansas City, MO 64156	Varies	Art students	One semester	Annually
Marion Art Center, Main St, Marion, MA 02739	$250	High school seniors	One year	Annually
Maryland College of Art & Design, 10500 Georgia Ave, Silver Spring, MD 20902	Limited half scholarships for first year	Freshman Foundation students	One year	Annually, Aug/Sept
The Memphis Academy of Arts,* Overton Park, Memphis, TN 38112	$50,000 (total)	High school graduates and college transfers	One year	Annually
Mercyhurst College, 501 E 38th St, Erie, PA 16501	Open	All freshmen art or art education applicants	One year (renewable)	Annually
Merrick Art Gallery, Fifth Ave & 11th St, New Brighton, PA 15066	$25	New Brighton high school art students		Annually
Mesa College, Grand Junction, CO 81501	Tuition scholarships (4)	One each class - freshman, sophomore, junior, senior	Continuous with annual review	Annually
Mesa Community College,* Department of Art, 1833 W Southern Ave, Mesa, AZ 85202	Six at $100 cash	Area students	One year	Annually

OFFERED BY	AMOUNT	OPENED TO	DURATION	WHEN OFFERED
Metropolitan Museum of Art, The Main Bldg, Fifth Ave at 82nd St, New York, NY 10028	Variable	Scholars researching art historical fields relating to Metropolitan Museum of Art collections	One year	Deadline Jan. 13 Awards letters sent on March 1
Metropolitan Museum & Art Centers, 1212 Anastasia Avenue, Coral Gables, FL 33134	Approximately $100 per year	Children		
Midland College, Dept of Art, 3600 N Garfield, Midland, TX 79701	Full tuition and fees	Full time student (12 hrs) art major, at least 6 credits per semester	One semester continuing for one additional semester	Semi-annually
	$100 per semester	Any student in art	One semester	Semi-annually
Midway Studios, University of Chicago, 6016 S Ingleside, Chicago, IL 60637	Partial tuition awards	Outstanding entering graduate students	Awarded & renewed annually	Deadline: Jan. 15
Miles Community College, Art Department, 2715 Dickinson St, Miles City, MT 59301	$180	Drama and visual art students	One year	Annually
Millikin University Art Department, 1184 W Main, Decatur, IL 62522	$500 - $1000	Qualified students	Four years	Annually
Mills College, Art Department, 5000 MacArthur Blvd, Oakland, CA 94613	Alumnae grants (covers tuition) & Assistantships	Mills graduate students		Annually
	Eleanor Crum Award in Ceramics	Graduating MFA's		Annually
	Catherine Morgan Trefethen Award	Graduating students		Annually
	Aurelia Henry Reinhardt Faculty Purse	Graduating seniors for further study		Annually
Milwaukee School of the Arts, 207 N Milwaukee St, Milwaukee, WI 53202	Varying amounts	Full-time students of MSA attending one or more semesters—based on merit and performance	Split over 2 semesters	Annually
Minot Art Association, Minot Art Gallery, Box 325, Minot, ND 58701	$200 to attend the International Art Camp at Peace Gardens, ND	High school students (2)	One week	Annually
Mississippi University for Women, Columbus, MS 39701	$100 - $300	Undergraduates	One year	Annually
	Student Assistantships $1,000	Graduates	One year (renewable)	Annually
	Tuition Fellowships	Graduates	One year (renewable)	Annually
Missouri Southern State College, Art Department, Newman & Duquesne Rds, Joplin, MO 64801	$250 (2) and $200 (2) and $400 (1)	Top quality students with art skills	One year	Annually
Missouri Western State College,* Art Department, 4525 Downs Dr, St Joseph, MO 64507	Varies	Any qualifying student majoring in art	By semester	By semester
Mitchell Community College, Art Department, E Broad St, Statesville, NC 28677	(2) full tuition	Full time students—one high school (competition & recommendations); one sophomore, already enrolled	One year	Annually
Mobile Art Association, Inc, c/o Vasco Geer, Jr, 30 Alverson Rd, Mobile, AL 36608	$500	Second year art students	One year	Annually
Monroe City-County Fine Arts Council, 1555 S. Raisinville Rd, Monroe, MI 48161	$300	County residents	One year	Annually
Montalvo Center for the Arts, PO Box 158, Saratoga, CA 95070	$75 single per month, $90 double per month (a limited number of resident scholarships).	Qualified artists, with specific projects	Three months (may be extended an additional three months)	
Montana State University, School of Art, Bozeman, MT 59715	$3600	Graduate students	10 months	Annually - April
Montclair Art Museum, Art School, 3 S Mountain Ave, Montclair, NJ 07042	Tuition	Adults or children	One year	Upon request
Montclair State College, School of Fine and Performing Arts, Upper Montclair, NJ 07043	$3000	Qualified graduate students	One year	Annually
Monterey Peninsula College, Div of Creative Arts, 980 Fremont St, Monterey, CA 93940	Central Coast Art Association (2) $250 scholarships (first year); $100 in subsequent years	A transferring student to a 4-year institution after completion of courses at MPC upon proof of registration	Four years	Each spring to be used the following fall.
	Monterey Peninsula Museum of Art (3) $500 per semester scholarships (renewable), work scholarships	Students enrolled at MPC in the Art Dept major	Renewable for the period of a student's full-time enrollment at MPC in the Art Department	
	Peter Mark Fry $100	Art or drama major, must be a sophomore and demonstrate talent—selection made by Art or Drama faculty.		

OFFERED BY	AMOUNT	OPENED TO	DURATION	WHEN OFFERED
Monterey Peninsula Museum of Art, 559 Pacific St, Monterey, CA 93940	$500 per semester (2)	Local college students	1 semester with a possible renewal	Semi-annually
Montgomery Museum of Fine Arts,* 440 S McDonough St, Montgomery, AL 36104	$100	Any student	One year	Annually
Moore College of Art, Philadelphia, PA 19103	Partial and full tuition scholarships	Undergraduates and entering freshmen	One year	Annually
Mount Aloysius Junior College, Cresson, PA 16630	$300 - $500	Anyone eligible for entry with art portfolio and interview	Two years	Annually
Mount Marty College, 1100 W Fifth, Yankton, SD 57078	Up to $500	Especially talented students		Annually
Mount Saint Clare College,* Art Department, 400 N Bluff, Clinton, IA 52732	$300, other financial aid available	Incoming freshmen and students already enrolled	One year; renewable if work merits it	Annually
Mount Wachusett Community College, Art Department, Teaching Faculty Association (TFA), Gardner, MA 01440	Approximately $100	Art majors in transfer	One year	Annually
Mulvane Art Center, Washburn University, Topeka, KS 66621	$3000	Qualified students	One year plus	Annually
Municipal Art Society of Baltimore City, c/o Mr. Beverley C. Compton, Jr, Alex Brown & Sons, 135 E Baltimore St, Baltimore, MD 21202	Traveling scholarship	Senior students of the Graduate School, Maryland Institute, Baltimore	One year	Annually
Murray State University, Art Department, 15th St, Murray, KY 42071	$100 to $250 (one to five given)	Incoming freshmen		Annually
	$200 (Clara M Eagle Scholarship)	Freshmen, sophomores or juniors majoring in art at Murray State University		Annually
Museum of Fine Arts, Houston School of Art, 1001 Bissonnet St, Houston, Tex 77005	Variable	Students, on basis of portfolio	One year	Annually
Museum Without Walls, RCEDA Inc, PO Box 45, Morris Ave, Friendsville, MD 21531	$400,000 (total)	Community college students in areas where program circulates	Two years	Semi-annually
Muskegon Community College, Department of Art, 221 S Quarterline Rd, Muskegon, MI 49442	$200	Any art student		Each semester
Mystic Seaport, Inc, Mystic, CT 06355 (In cooperation with University of Connecticut)	$1.35 per course	Graduate students and teachers or other professionals who wish to broaden their backgrounds	June - August	Annually
National Collection of Fine Arts, Smithsonian Institution, Washington, DC 20560	$9000, plus $1000 for travel	Advanced students in art history. Deadline: Jan 15	Sept 3 - July 31	Deadline Jan 15
	Limited stipend	College seniors, graduate students in art history and studio art.	9 weeks, commence in June	Deadline, Feb 15
National Endowment for the Arts, 2401 E St, NW, Washington, DC 20506	Up to $10,000	Artists of exceptional talent	One year	Annually
National Gallery of Art, Constitution Ave at Sixth St NW, Washington, DC 20565 (Note: Applications for the following fellowships are accepted only in the form of recommendations from the chairman of a graduate department of art history)	David E. Finley Fellowship	Ph.D. candidates	Two years, plus eight months at the National Gallery	Annually (deadline Dec. 31)
	Samuel H. Kress Fellowships (2)	Ph.D. candidates	One academic year	Annually (deadline Dec. 31)
	Chester Dale Fellowships (4)	Ph.D candidates	One academic year	Annually (deadline Dec. 31)
	Robert H. and Clarice Smith Fellowship	Ph.D. candidates or holders	One academic year	Annually (deadline Dec. 31)
Nazareth College of Rochester,* Art Department, 4245 East Ave, Rochester, NY 14610	Variable	Qalified high school graduates, ie, B+ average, total score of 1200 CEEB, and/or impressive art portfolio	One year (renewable)	Annually
New Mexico Highlands University, Dept of Fine Arts, Las Vegas, NM 87701	Up to $325 for academic year	All undergraduates	One academic year	Annually
	$2160 plus three quarters of full tuition, graduate assistantship	Graduate students only	One academic year	Annually
New Mexico State University, Art Department, Box 3572, Las Cruces, NM 88003	$2000 - $4000 (graduate assistantships)	Graduate students	One - two years	Annually
New York Institute of Technology, Fine Arts Department, Wheatley Rd, Old Westbury, NY 11568	$2200	High school seniors	One year	Annually

OFFERED BY	AMOUNT	OPENED TO	DURATION	WHEN OFFERED
New York School of Interior Design, 155 E 56th St, New York, NY 10022	$1120 maximum per term	Design students; preference given to second and third year students	One semester (renewable)	Annually (deadline May 1)
New York Studio School of Drawing, Painting & Sculpture, 8 W Eighth St, New York, NY 10011	$25,000	Students enrolled for one year who qualify on the basis of need by semester	By semester	Each semester
North Park College, Fine Arts Division, 5125 N Spaulding, Chicago, Il 60625	$300 $500	Sophomore art majors Junior art majors	One year One year	Annually Annually
North Shore Art League,* 620 Lincoln, Winnetka, IL 60093	$1500	Art Institute of Chicago students	One year	Annually
Northeast Missouri State University, Division of Fine Arts, Kirksville, MO 63501	Varying amounts	High school seniors; other awards available to junior college graduates	One year (renewable)	Annually
Northeastern A&M College, Art Department, 1 Street NE, Miami, OK 74354	Three usually given	Art majors	One year	Annually
Northeastern Illinois University, Art Department, St Louis at Bryn Mawr Ave, Chicago, IL 60625	$476 (2 terms)	Board of Governors Talent Scholarships available to gifted art students	Two terms	Annually
Northeastern Oklahoma State University, Division of Arts & Letters, Tahlequah, OK 74464	Up to 15 hours general tuition (3)	Undergraduates	One semester, subject to continuation	
Northern Illinois University Department of Art, DeKalb, IL 60115	Jack Arends Scholarship	Art majors with 3.0 overall Grad Point Average, one year residence at NIU, portfolio, and 3 recommendations (2 from Art Department)		Annually
	James P Bates Memorial Scholarship	Rotated among majors in the various areas of the Art Department	One year	Annually
	Richard Keefer Scholarship	Art majors, rotated among four areas—Art History and Art Education; Drawing, Painting, and Printmaking; Crafts; Design and Photography	One year	Annually
	Talented Student Scholarship	Graduate or undergraduate, incoming freshmen, with 12 or more hours per semester	One year	Annually
	Cora B Miner Scholarship	Preferably to student from DeKalb County, with interest in realistic art	One year	Annually
Northern Michigan University,* c/o Prof Cappuccio, Marquette, MI 49855	$500	Sophomore art and design majors who have been majors in NMU art dept at least one semester	One year	Annually
Northern Montana College,* Department of Art, 611 16th St, Havre, MT 59501	$50	An art major or minor who has demonstrated high art ability and who is in need of financial aid	No limit established	Annually
Northwest Nazarene College, Holly at Dewey, Boise, ID 83651	Variable	Fine arts majors	One year	Annually
Northwestern College, Art Department, Orange City, IA 51041	$100	Art majors upon acceptance of portfolio	One year	Annually
Oak Ridge Community Art Center,* PO Box 105, Oak Ridge, TN 37830	Varies according to class	Anyone	One quarter	Quarterly
Oakland City College, Oakland City, IN 47660	Variable	Outstanding ability shown in art (competitive)	One year (renewable)	Annually
	$900	Entering freshmen	One year (renewable)	Annually
Oakland Museum,* 1000 Oak St, Oakland, CA 94607	$1000	California artists	One year	Annually
Oberlin College, Department of Art, Oberlin, OH 44074	$3,150, plus tuition remission (3 graduate assistantships)	Graduates with BA degrees who qualify	One year (renewable)	Annually
	Kress Art History Fellowship of up to $3500, plus tuition remission (1 or 2)	Graduates with BA degrees who qualify	One year (renewable)	Annually
Occidental College,* Art Department, 1600 Campus Rd, Los Angeles, CA 90041	Open	Art majors who can demonstrate financial need	Renewable for four years	Annually
Ocean City School of Art—Ocean City Cultural Arts Center, 409 Wesley Ave, Ocean City, NJ 08226	$40	Members and students of the Art Center	One semester	Each semester
Ohio State University, Department of the History of Art, 154 W 12th Ave, Columbus, OH 43210	$2700 for first year to $3645 for fourth year	Students who demonstrate accomplishment and evidence of potential excellence in teaching, scholarship and/or research in History of Art	Eight quarters for students in MA program; 14 quarters for students in PhD program	Annually

OFFERED BY	AMOUNT	OPENED TO	DURATION	WHEN OFFERED
Ohio State University, Graduate School, Division of Art Education, Columbus, OH 43210	$3600 plus tuition	All MA and PhD candidates (special minority fellowships are also awarded)	One calendar year	Annually, Feb deadline
Ohio University School of Art, Athens, OH 45701	Tuition scholarship assistantships	Undergraduate students Graduates	One year (renewable)	Annually
Oklahoma Art Center, 3113 Pershing Blvd, Oklahoma City, OK 73107	$150	Young Talent in Oklahoma winners	One year	Annually
Oklahoma Baptist University, 500 W University, Shawnee, OK 74801	Variable	Rising sophomore, junior or senior visual art student	One year	Annually
Oklahoma City University, NW 23rd at N Blackwelder, Oklahoma City, OK 73106	$2500 (Mrs Iva B Kelley Art Scholarship)	Oklahoma residents (5 years) junior standing, 57 hours, art majors	One or two years	Annually
Old Dominion University, Hampton Blvd, Norfolk, VA 23508	$500	All art students	One year	Annually
Ontario Arts Council, Kitchener Waterloo Art Gallery, 43 Benton St, Kitchener, ON N2G 3H1, Canada	Up to $1500	Ontario artists	One year	Annually
	Up to $4000	Ontario artists	One year	Annually
Ontario College of Art, 100 McCaul St, Toronto, ON M5T 1W1, Canada	Variable	Students only	One year	Annually
Oregon College of Art, 30 S First St, Ashland, OR 97520	$100 to $450	High school and college transfer students—based on competitive portfolios of artwork	Academic year	Annually
Otero Junior College,* Art Department, 18th & Colorado, La Junta, CO 81050	$300	Colorado residents with artist promise	One year	Annually
Otis Art Institute,* 2401 Wilshire Blvd, Los Angeles, CA 90057	Variable	Students enrolled at Otis in the BFA or MFA degree programs	Academic year	Annually
Ottumwa Heights College, Ottumwa, IA 52501	$300	Full-time students in art, drama, and/or music	One year, renewable second year	Annually
Our Lady of the Lake University, 411 SW 24th St, San Antonio, TX 78285	Variable	Majors in art	Variable	Annually
Palomar College, San Marcos, CA 92069	$75 Lake San Marcos Art League Award	Returning sophomore majoring in art		June
	$50 Catherine Ann (Tim) Sawday Memorial Scholarship	Deserving student majoring in art or science		June
	$100 San Dieguito Art Guild Scholarship	Graduate planning to pursue a career in painting		June
	$300 Fallbrook Art Association	Art major continuing on to a 4-year accredited art school		June
	$150 Showcase of the Arts - Evelyn Surface Memorial	Two awards - one for art student returning to Palomar and one for a graduating art student going on to a 4-year institution		June
Palos Verdes Art Center and Museum, 5504 W Crestridge Rd, Rancho Palos Verdes, CA 90274	Class fees	High school students in Palos Verdes	One semester	
Pan American University, Department of Art, Edinburg, TX 78539	$100 tuition scholarship (12 hors per semester for 2 semesters)	Art majors with 2.5 average (4.00 system), 30 hours completed study	One year	Annually
	$300 Lemont-Wilcox	Any art major	One year	Annually
Parsons School of Design, 65 Fifth Avenue, New York, NY 10028	$200,000	All financially eligible, matriculated students	Academic year	Annually
Pasadena City College, Art Department, 1570 E Colorado Blvd, Pasadena, CA 91106	$1000 (2)	All our students majoring in art		Annually
Pennsylvania Academy of the Fine Arts, Broad & Cherry Sts, Philadelphia, PA 19102	Scholastic Magazine Art Award (1) 1 year tuition	High school seniors	One year	Annually
	Full and half tuition scholarships	2nd, 3rd & 4th year Academy students	One year	Annually
	Cresson European Travel Scholarship and tuition - $3300	3rd, 4th year Academy students	Three months	Annually
	Schiedt & Ware Travel Scholarship - $2000	3rd, 4th year Academy students	Three months	Annually
Peoria Art Guild, 1831 N Knoxville Ave, Peoria, IL 61603	$18 - $30	Students who would benefit from artistic instructions, but who would be otherwise unable to afford art classes	8 - 10 weeks	4 times each year

OFFERED BY	AMOUNT	OPENED TO	DURATION	WHEN OFFERED
Pittsfield Art Association,* PO Box 385, Pittsfield, MA 01201	$1000	Art major		Annually
Pitzer College,* Department of Art, 1050 N Mills Ave, Claremont, CA 91711	Variable	Qualified students		Annually
Place des Arts, 166 King Edward St, Coquitlam, BC, Canada V3K 4T2	Up to $400 through the Coquitlam Fine Arts Council	Any artist living within the area	One year	Annually
The Ponca City Art Association, Box 1394, Ponca City, OK 74601	$50 (2)	Outstanding art student, one boy and one girl	One year	Annually
Pontiac Art Center, 47 Williams St, Pontiac, MI 48053	$20 and $50 (tuition for children and adults)	All	Ten-week terms	All year
Portland Art Museum, Museum Art School, 1209 SW Park St, Portland, OR 97205	$8140	Enrolled students	One school year	Annually
Portland School of Art of the Portland Society of Art, 97 Spring St, Portland, ME 04101	$200	Greater Portland resident (entering)	One year	Annually
	$200	State of Maine outside of Greater Portland (entering)	One year	Annually
	$200 (2)	Qualified students	One year	Annually
Pratt Graphics Center, extension of Pratt Institute, 160 Lexington Ave, New York, NY 10016	Tuition up to a period of one year	Talented artists	Up to one year	September thru July
Presbyterian College, Department of Visual Arts, Clinton, SC 29325	$200	All art students	One year	Annually
Prince Rupert Art Club, c/o Ms. Johan C. Woodland, Corresp. Secy, Court House, Prince Rupert, BC, Canada V8J 2J6	$100	Any deserving amateur or student	Summer course	Annually
Providence Art Club, 11 Thomas St, Providence, RI 02903	Tuition and fees (3)	Rhode Island School of Design students	One year	Annually
Provincetown Workshop, A School of Painting and Drawing,* 492 Commercial St, Provincetown, MA 02657	$285 (20)	Students of art schools	One season	Annually, summers
Quincy Art Center,* 1515 Jersey St, Quincy, IL 62301	Approximately $250 annually	Underprivileged children	One year	Semi-annually
Quincy College,* Art Department, 1831 College Ave, Quincy, IL 62301	Variable	Art student majors	One year	Annually
Rensselaer County Historical Society,* 59 Second St, Troy, NY 12180	$1000 funded by NYSCA summer museum intern program	Senior Russell Sage students		Annually, if funded
Ricks College, Department of Art, Rexburg, ID 83440	$100 - $300	Art majors	One year	
Ringling School of Art, Sarasota, FL 33580	$400	Upper class students only	One year	Annually
Rio Hondo College,* Fine Arts Department, 3600 Workman Mill Rd, Whittier, CA 90608	$100	Second year art students	One year	Annually
Riverside Art Center and Museum, 3425 Seventh, Riverside, CA 92501	$200 per year	Based on need and talent	$50 per quarter	Quarterly
Roberson Center for the Arts and Sciences, 30 Front St, Binghamton, NY 13905	Variable, covering the class fee only	Talented and interested students in art, music, dance	One semester	
Rockport Art Association, The Old Tavern, 12 Main St, Rockport, MA 01966	$100	Graduation senior in the Rockport, Mass, high school who is majoring in art at a university, college, or a full time art school	First year	Annually
Rocky Mountain School of Art, 1441 Ogden St, Denver, CO 80218	$379.50 quarterly (job scholarship only)	Five students every two years	Two years	
Rogue Valley Art Association*, P.O. Box 763, Medford, OR 97501	$200	Students	Summer classes	Annually
Rosary College, Director of Foreign Studies, River Forest, IL 60305	$500 - $1000 each (15) $1000 - $2000	Nationals of US for study in Florence, Italy, for study in painting, sculpture, printmaking, art history and art restoration at Rosary College Graduate School of Fine Arts, Villa Schifanoia, to men and women qualified for graduate study in fine arts who hold BA or equivalent and have knowledge of Italian	One - two years	

OFFERED BY	AMOUNT	OPENED TO	DURATION	WHEN OFFERED
Roswell Museum and Art Center, 11th & Main Sts, Roswell, NM 88201	Grant provides home, studio, maintenance, materials, and stipend. Stipend varies according to family size.	Painters, sculptors, printmakers, weavers, and ceramicists	Grant period can vary — usually six - twelve months	Information supplied upon request, please specify media.
Royal Architectural Institute of Canada, Suite 1104, 151 Slater St, Ottawa, ON K1P 5H3, Canada	Andre Francou Scholarship $2000	Graduate students of the School of Architecture at the University of Montreal		Annually
	Ernest Wilby Memorial Scholarship $500	A student entering the year before the final year of the main architectural course at a Canadian School of Architecture who shows definite promise and talent in his work and who requires financial assistance		Annually
Royal Canadian Academy of Arts, 601 - 11 Yorkville Avenue, Toronto, Ont., Canada M4W 1L3	Varying amounts through RCA Trust Fund	Applicants	One year	Annually
Saginaw Art Museum,* 1126 N Michigan Ave, Saginaw, MI 48602	Tuition for art classes	All students	One year	Annually
St Louis Community College at Forest Park, Art Department, 5600 Oakland Ave, St Louis, MO 63110	Varies	Art students	One semester	Annually
St. Thomas Aquinas College,* Art Department, Rte 340, Sparkill, NY 10976	Variable	All eligible applicants	One year	Semi-annually
Salem Art Association, Bush Barn Art Center, 600 Mission St, Salem, OR 97301	Amount of a class tuition	Any person of any age	Ten-week term	Quarterly
Salmagundi Club, 47 Fifth Ave, New York, NY 10003	Scholarship Membership prorated over four-year period	Qualified applicants, artists under 30 years of age, three examples of work to be submitted for approval by committee	Four years	
Sam Houston State University, Art Department, Huntsville, TX 77340	Approx $3287 (teaching fellowship)	Art majors with BFA or equivalent, with 60 or more hours in art	One year (renewable)	Annually
San Bernardino Art Association, Inc,* PO Box 2272, 1640 E Highland, San Bernardino, CA 92406	$400	High school art seniors		Annually
San Diego State University,* Department of Art, San Diego, CA 92182	$500-$1000	Upper division students	One year	Annually
San Francisco Art Institute, 800 Chestnut St, San Francisco, CA 91433	Tuition scholarships		Academic year	March for coming academic year
San Jacinto College North, Department of Art, 5800 Uvalde, Houston, TX 77049	Varies upon need (North Shore Area Art League scholarship)	Any full-time student	Fall and Spring	Annually
Santa Cruz Art League, Inc, 526 Broadway, Santa Cruz, CA 95060	$500	Between ages 13-18	One year	Annually
Santa Fe Workshops of Contemporary Art, Box 1344, Santa Fe, NM 87501	Half-tuition work-scholarships ($250)	Over 17-years old—motivated to learn and work in painting, drawing, sculpture, printmaking, photography, and art therapy	Summer 8-week programs	Annually
Santa Rosa Junior College, Department of Art, 1501 Mendocino Ave, Santa Rosa, CA 95401	$500	Art students	One semester or one year	
Saskatchewan Arts Board*, 200 Lakeshore Dr, Regina, SK S4S 0A4, Canada	$1000 grants	Saskatchewan artists		Semi-annually
School Art League of New York City, 1 Times Square, New York, NY 10036	$100,000 annually	High school students	One year (to be continued at the discretion of the granting institutions)	Annually
School for Creative Movement in the Arts, 265 W 87th St, New York, NY 10024	Maximum of half off tuition—$50-$80 per term	Children only from 2¾ to 17 years based on financial need and interest	One or two terms	Semi-annually
School of American Research, PO Box 2188, Santa Fe, NM 87501	$5500	Doctoral and postdoctoral scholars; limited to 3 scholars per year	11 months	Annually
School of Fashion Design, 136 Newbury St, Boston, MA 02116	Varies	Fulltime students who have completed at least one semester	One year	Annually
School of Fine Arts, 38660 Mentor Ave, Willoughby, OH 44094	Tuition	Talent plus need	One year	Annually
School of the Art Association of Newport, 76 Bellevue, Newport, RI 02840	Half or full tuition	Anyone with need		

OFFERED BY	AMOUNT	OPENED TO	DURATION	WHEN OFFERED
School of the Art Institute of Chicago, Michigan Ave at Adams St, Chicago, IL 60603	Variable	Full-time degree students in need	One year	Annually
School of the Associated Arts, 344 Summit Ave, St Paul, MN 55102	Variable	Students	One year	Annually
School of the Museum of Fine Arts, 230 The Fenway, Boston, MA 02115	$150 to $2000 per year	All diploma or degree matriculating students determined eligible by CCS/ACT needs analysis	Academic year	Annually
	$40,000 awarded in varying amounts rs (approx 15 annually)	Graduates of the School of the Museum of Fine Arts	Flexible (average one year)	Annually
School of the Wichita Art Association,* 9112 E Central, Wichita, KS 67206. Awarded through public school system and various service organizations	$2000	Art students of the Wichita area	One year	Annually
School of the Worcester Art Museum,* 55 Salisbury St, Worcester, MA 01608	Up to full tuition depending on financial need	Matriculating students at the School of the Worcester Art Museum only; accepted applicants will be considered upon receipt of tuition deposit	One academic year	Annually (deadline Apr. 1)
Scottsdale Artists' League, P.O. Box 1071, Scottsdale, AZ 85252	Variable	Various schools, colleges and universities in Arizona	One year	Annually
Norman Seibert Printmaking Scholarship, Corvallis, OR 97331	Full in-state tuition	All printmaking majors	Three academic terms	Annually
Selkirk College,* Kootenay School of Art Division, 2001 Silverking Rd, Nelson, BC, V1L 1C8, Canada	Variable	Students of Kootenay School of Art	One year	Annually
Seward County Community College, Department of Fine Arts & Communications, Liberal, KS 67901	Tuition and books	Art majors	One year (renewable)	Annually
Shasta College, Art Department, Old Oregon Trail, Redding, CA 96001	Various	Art students		
Sheldon Memorial Art Gallery, Lincoln, NE 68508	$4000	University of Nebraska graduate students	One year	Annually
Skowhegan School of Painting and Sculpture, Skowhegan, ME 04976	10 full scholarships $1950 each	Qualified US art students 18 years of age and over	Nine weeks July & Aug	Annually
	35 partial scholarships	Qualified US art students 18 years of age and over	Nine weeks July & Aug	Annually
	Cash purchase prizes in Final Exhibition, scholarships to winter art schools	Current Skowhegan students		
Smithsonian Institution, Office of Fellowships & Grants, Washington, DC 20560	$12,000	Post-doctoral scholars in American art history, Oriental art history	Six months to one year	Deadline: Jan 15
	$7000	Doctoral candidates in American art history, Oriental art history	Six months to one year	Deadline: Jan 15
Society of Architectural Historians, 1700 Walnut St, Rm 716, Philadelphia, PA 19103	One or two given to participate in annual tour	Outstanding students engaged in graduate work in architecture, architectural history, city planning or urban history, landscape or history of landscape design and current member of the Society of Architectural Historians		Annually
	Alice Davis Hitchcock			Annually
	Book Award			
	Founders' Award			Annually
South Bend Art Center, 121 N Lafayette Blvd, South Bend, IN 46601	$300	Qualified applicants		Semi-annually
South Carolina Arts Commission, 829 Richland St, Columbia, SC 29201	$130,000 in grant funds annually	Arts organizations and artists	One year	Quarterly
	$12,000 fellowship funds	Resident artists	One year	Annually, Deadline: Apr 1.
South County Art Association, 1319 Kingstown Rd, Kingston, RI 02881	$500	High school seniors majoring in art	One year	Annually
South Dakota State University, Memorial Art Center, Medary Ave at Harvey Dunn St, Brookings, SD 57006	$200	Art students at University	One year	Annually
South Florida Art Institute of Hollywood, 1301 S Ocean Drive, Hollywood, FL 33019	$8000 yearly	Elementary, senior and junior high school graduates	One, two and four years	Annually

OFFERED BY	AMOUNT	OPENED TO	DURATION	WHEN OFFERED
South Plains College, Art Department, College Ave, Levelland, TX 79336	Variable	Talented, needy students	One year	Annually
Southampton College of Long Island University, Art Department, Southampton, NY 11968	$1,000	Students	Four years	Annually
Southeast Missouri State University, Department of Art, Cape Girardeau, MO 63701	(2) full year scholarships; (1) half-year scholarship	Art department majors		Annually
Southeastern Center for Contemporary Art, 2721 Robinhood Rd, Winston Salem, NC 27106	$2000	Southeastern artists	For their use	Every two years
Southern Baptist College, Humanities-Art Department, College City, AR 72476	$200	High school seniors and others seeking admittance, by portfolio	One semester (renewable)	Semi-annually
	Variable	Most outstanding art student		Annually
Southern Baptist College,* Walnut Ridge, AR 72476	Variable	Most outstanding art student annually		Annually
Southern Illinois University at Edwardsville, Department of Art and Design, School of Fine Arts and Communications, Edwardsville, IL 62026	Stipend and tuition waiver	Graduate students accepted for admission		Annually
Southern Oregon State College, Art Department, Ashland, OR 97520	$300	Art major	One year	Annually
Southern Utah State College,* Department of Art, Cedar City, UT 84720	Tuition and supplies $256	Residents of Utah and nonresidents Sophomores, juniors and seniors	One year Two years	Annually and quarterly Annually
Southwest Craft Center, 300 Augusta St, San Antonio, TX 78205	Class tuition and supplies	Deserving students	Two - sixteen weeks	Quarterly
Southwest Missouri State University,* Department of Art, 901 S National, Springfield, MO 65802	$240	Art majors and graduating seniors of Southwest Missouri State University	One year	Annually
Spiva Art Center, Inc, Newman & Duquesne Rds, Joplin, MO 64801	Variable	Prospective college art students	One year (renewable)	
Spokane Falls Creative Art Gallery, W 3410 Fort Wright Dr, Spokane, WA 99204	$3000	Anyone	Quarterly	Quarterly
Springfield Art Center, 107 Cliff Park Rd, Springfield, OH 45501	$25 - $100	Children, some adults, by semester		
Springfield College, 263 Alden St, Springfield, MA 01109	Variable	Qualified students based on financial need	One year	Annually
State University Center, Department of Art and Art History, Binghamton, NY 13901	Variable graduate assistantships and teaching assistantships	Incoming and resident graduate students	To a maximum of 4 years, renewable yearly	Annually, April
Stephens College, Art Department, Columbia, MO 65201	$500 - $2000	Varies—contact admissions office for information and details		
Sterling College, Sterling, KS 67579	$500	Any art students	One year	Annually
Studio Workshop, 3 W 18th St, New York, NY 10011	To be determined	Anyone	One year	Annually and semi-annually
Sul Ross State University, Art Department, Alpine, TX 79830	$300	Entering art major	One year	Annually
Summervail Workshop for Art & Critical Studies, Box 1114, Vail, CO 81657	Tuition only, $135 per class	Any qualified student. Must submit three letters of reference, current resume, and 10 slides of recent work	Three weeks; 2 to 3 three-week sessions per summer	Annually
Summit Art Center, 68 Elm St, Summit, NJ 07901	$35 - $55 per session	Students in need	Fifteen-week session	Per session
Sunbury Shores Arts and Nature Centre, Inc, 139 Water St (P.O. Box 100), St. Andrews, NB, Canada	Approximately $1000	High school students	Summers	Annually
Swain School of Design, 19 Hawthorn St, New Bedford, MA 02740	$12,000	All	One year	Annually
Syracuse University, Joe and Emily Lowe Art Gallery, Sims Hall, Syracuse, NY 13210	Teaching assistantships, fellowships	Museology and art students	One year	Annually
Margaret Fort Tahern Gallery, Austin Peay State University Art Department, Clarksville, TN 37040	$300 (total)	High school art seniors in central Tennessee	One year	Annually

OFFERED BY	AMOUNT	OPENED TO	DURATION	WHEN OFFERED
Tampa Bay Art Center,* 320 North Blvd, Tampa, FL 33606		Low socioeconomically handicapped; elementary age, high school age, retired citizens		Quarterly
Tarrant County Junior College, Northeast Campus, Department of Art, 828 Harwood Road, Hurst, TX 76053	$50 tuition award	Art students at freshman-sophomore levels	One semester	Semi-annually
Texarkana College,* Art Department, Texarkana, TX 75501	$100	Art majors	One year	Annually
Texas Southern University,* Department of Art, 3201 Wheeler Ave, Houston, TX 77004	$2000	All art students with completion of one year's course work in art at TSU may apply	Four years	Annually
Texas Tech University, Department of Art, Box 4720, Lubbock, TX 79409	Variable	All undergraduate and graduate art students	One or two semesters	
Three Schools,* New School of Art, 296 Brunswick Ave, Toronto, ON M5S 2M7, Canada	Up to $200	Students who have completed one year or more	One year	Annually
Louis Comfort Tiffany Foundation,* 1083 Fifth Ave, New York, NY 10028	$2000 (maximum)	US citizens of demonstrated talent	One year	Annually
Toledo Museum of Art,* Monroe St at Scottwood Ave, Toledo, OH 43609	Variable	Graduate students	One year	Annually
Toronto School of Art,* 225 Brunswick Ave, Toronto, ON M5S 2M6, Canada	Variable	Students chosen by staff	One year	
Traphagen School of Fashion, 257 Park Ave S, New York, NY 10010	$2150 Famous Alumni Scholarship	Second year students	One year	Annually
	$2150 School Art League, New York City Scholarship	First year students		Annually
	$2150 National Scholastic Magazine Scholarship	First year students		Annually
	$2150	First year students (two years) Flemington Fur Co. Competition (open to high school juniors and seniors in NY, NJ, CT, DE, MD, and PA)		Annually
Above scholarships are renewable upon performance each year				
Truro Center for the Arts at Castle Hill, Inc, Castle Rd, Box 756, Truro, MA 02666	4 working scholarships in exchange for tuition; no housing — ceramacists preferred	Preferably between 17 and 21 years	June 21 - September 7	Annually
Tucson Museum of Art, Inc, 235 W Alameda, Tucson, AZ 85701	$2000	Talented needy and minority students	One year	Annually
Tufts University in Affiliation with The Boston Museum of Fine Arts School, Cohen Arts Center, Medford, MA 02155	Variable	According to need and ability		Annually
Tullahoma Fine Arts Center, 401 S Jackson, Tullahoma, TN 37388	$200	Motlow Community College Art major	One year	Annually
Tusculum College,* Department of Art, Greeneville, TN 37743	$400 - $800	Students in upper 40% of their class who show leadership talent, art talent	One year	Annually
Umpqua Community College, Department of Art, PO Box 967, Roseburg, OR 97470	$132	New or returning art majors	One term	Annually
Union University,* Department of Art, Jackson, TN 38301	Variable	Those demonstrating talent and promise	One year (renewable)	
US Government Grants for Graduate Study Abroad under the Fulbright-Hays Act. Write: Counselling and Correspondence Unit, Institute of International Education, 809 United Nations Plaza, New York, NY 10017	Variable	Graduate students who are U.S. citizens with B.A. degree or in the creative and performing arts, 4 years of professional study and/or experience, and who have a knowledge of the language of the country for which application is made.	One year	Annually
University of Alaska at Anchorage,* Dept of Art, 2533 Providence Ave, Anchorage, AK 99504	$250 plus state aid	All art students		Annually
University of Alabama, Department of Art, PO Box 1247, Huntsville, AL 35807	$645 per year	Art major with 2.0 average on 3.0 scale	One year	Annually
University of Alaska, Fairbanks,* Department of Art, Fine Arts Complex, Fairbanks, AK 99701	In or out of state tuition	Art students, incoming and continuing	One year	Annually

OFFERED BY	AMOUNT	OPENED TO	DURATION	WHEN OFFERED
University of Arizona, College of Fine Arts, Department of Art, Tucson, AZ 85721	Variable	Students enrolled in Art program UA	One year	Annually
University of Arkansas, Fayetteville, AR 72701	$2070-$2421 Assistantships	Graduate students	Two years of more	Annually
	$100-$300 scholarships	Sophomore, junior or senior art students enrolled in the Art Department at the University of Arkansas	One year	Annually
University of California, Santa Barbara,* Art Department, Santa Barbara, CA 93106	Variable	Graduate students approved by the Art Department chairman	Academic year	Annually
University of Chicago, Cochrane-Woods Art Center, 5540 S Greenwood Ave, Chicago, IL 60637	Full and partial tuition fellowships and, in rare cases, stipends	The best qualified entering and continuing graduate students	Academic year	Annually, mid-Feb
University of Colorado at Boulder,* Fine Arts Department, Boulder, CO 80309	In-state tuition $2500 plus tuition waiver	Undergraduates Graduate students	One year One year	Annually Annually
University of Delaware, Newark, DE 19711 (in cooperation with Winterthur Museum)	Up to ten fellowships covering tuition, travel and a $3,000 stipend.	College graduates in one of the humanities, social sciences, or American studies	Two years	Annually
University of Denver School of Art, University Park, Denver, CO 80208	Variable; several $1500 annual, renewable "University Scholars" merit awards; graduate student assistantships in addition to scholarships	Graduate students, eligible when accepted for admission; undergraduate, one through the National Scholastic Competition, others.	Varying	Quarterly and annually for different types
University of Hartford, Hartford Art School, 200 Bloomfield Ave, West Hartford, CT 06117	$1000	Competition scholarship award	One year	Annually
University of Idaho, Department of Art & Architecture, Moscow, ID 83843	$400 (Novah Southon Tisdale Scholarship)	All majors in art, undergraduate and graduate, based on ability alone		Annually in the Spring for Fall semester
	$400 (Commemorative Art Scholarship)	Upper division undergraduates in art, based on need and ability		Annually in the Spring for Fall semester
University of Illinois, Urbana-Champaign,* Champaign, IL 61820	$2500	Graduate students and applicants with BA degree	Nine months	Annually
	$3000	Graduate students and applicants with BA degree	Eleven months	Annually
University of Illinois, Urbana-Champaign, College of Fine and Applied Arts, 110 Architecture Bldg, Urbana, IL 61801	$2500	Graduates of the College of Fine and Applied Arts of the University of Illinois, College of Fine and Applied Arts, Urbana-Champaign and to graduates of similar institutions of equal educational standing	One academic year	Annually
University of Iowa, School of Art and Art History, Iowa City, IA 52242	Graduate College Scholarships up to $2000 Ford Foundation B.F.A. and M.F.A. Scholarships up to $2000 Paula P. Grahame Scholarship up to $1500 Kress Foundation Fellowship in Art History $3500, Travel Grants to $1200 Assistantships $3800 - $4200	All scholarships listed available to graduate students and some undergraduate students	One year (renewable)	Annually
University of Kansas, School of Education, School of Fine Arts, 109 Bailey Hall, Lawrence KS 66045	Variable	Undergraduates in Art Education	One academic year (renewable)	Annually
University of Lethbridge,* Department of Art, Lethbridge, AB, Canada	Variable	Qualified students		Annually
University of Louisville, Allen R Hite Art Institute, Louisville, KY 40208	Variable (tuition only)	Art and art history students	One year (renewable)	Annually
University of Maryland, College Park,* Art Department, College Park, MD 20742	$100 - $3100	Students with excellent scholarship and teaching promises	One year	Annually
		Graduate students in the Museum Training Program	One year	Annually
University of Massachusetts, Amherst,* College of Arts and Sciences, Department of Art, Amherst, MA 01002	$1200 - $2000 assistantships $2800 University Fellowships	Graduate students Graduate students with a 3.5 QPA or better	One - two years One - two years	Annually Annually

OFFERED BY	AMOUNT	OPENED TO	DURATION	WHEN OFFERED
University of Michigan, Ann Arbor,* History of Art Department, Ann Arbor, MI 48109	Charles L Freer Scholarship in Oriental Art. Amounts vary up to $2400 plus fees	Graduate student beginning advanced work in Oriental art	One year	Annually
	Charles L Freer Fellowships in Oriental Art. $400 per month	Advanced graduate students in Oriental art—residence at Freer Gallery, Washington, DC	One year	Annually
	Samuel H Kress Foundation Scholarship and Fellowship. Amounts vary up to $2400 plus fees	Advanced graduate students	One year	Annually
	Graduate Fellowships offered by Horace H Rackham School of Graduate Studies. Amounts vary up to $2400 plus fees	Graduate students	One year	Annually
	Teaching Fellowships approx $4000 per academic year	Graduate students of the second year and beyond	Maximum of three years	Annually
	Regional Museum Internships. Stipend approx $2500 plus fees	Advanced graduate students	One year	Annually
University of Minnesota, Duluth, School of Fine Arts, Duluth, MN 55812	$500 scholarships (7)	Undergraduates	One year	Annually
	Assistantships (9)	Graduate students	One year	Annually
University of Minnesota, Minneapolis, Department of Studio Art, Minneapolis, MN 55455	Variable, up to $200 for materials	Qualified undergraduates	One year	Winter or Spring
	Up to $3500 plus tuition	Graduate students		Winter
University of Mississippi Department of Art, Fine Arts Center, University, MS 38677	$1700	Graduate students in art	Nine months	Annually
University of Nebraska-Lincoln, Department of Art, Woods Hall, Lincoln, NE 68588	Thomas Coleman Memorial Scholarship in Printmaking, $150 each	Outstanding graduate and undergraduate student in prints	Singular	Annually
	Francis Vreeland Award in Art, 3 awards of $500 each	Outstanding graduate and undergraduate students in studio art	Singular	Annually
University of Nevada, Department of Art, 4505 Maryland Parkway, Las Vegas, NV 89154	$1000	Entering freshmen only	Four years, renewable upon demonstration of satisfactory progress	Annually
University of New Mexico,* College of Fine Arts, Albuquerque, NM 87131	$2500 and $2700 $3100 and $3300	Graduate students	One academic year	Annually
University of North Carolina, Dept of Art & Music, University Heights, Asheville, NC 28804	$300 (Norman Sultan Scholarship)	Outstanding student majoring in art with financial need	One year	Annually
University of North Carolina-Chapel Hill, Department of Art, 104 Ackland Art Center 003A, Chapel Hill, NC 27514	Emily Pollard Fellowship, $4000	Art History Graduate students only	One year	Annually
	Samuel H Kress Fellowships, $3500			
	Rockefeller Foundation Fellowship, varies $3500-$6000			
University of North Carolina at Greensboro, Greensboro, NC 27412	Variable	University art students	Up to four years	Annually
	$900-$1000 graduate assistantships in the Art Dept.	Graduates	Semester	Semi-annually
University of Notre Dame, Graduate School, Art Department, Notre Dame, IN 46556	Tuition $3600 Stipend $2500	Teaching assistants chosen by faculty	Up to two years	Annually
University of Oregon, Eugene, OR 97403	$100 - $300 (20 units)	Students with one year residence	One year	Annually
	$2500 - $2800 (14 units) graduate assistantships	Qualified students at graduate level; nonresident must submit photographic exhibit of recent work (most reserved for 2nd year of residence)	One year	Annually
University of Pittsburgh,* Schenley Plaza, Pittsburgh, PA 15260	$3140-TA, $3350-TF, $3500-Mellon Tuition scholarships	Fine arts graduate students (art history)	One year (renewable)	Annually
University of San Diego,* Art Department, Alcala Park, San Diego, CA 92110	$1500	Art students at University of San Diego	One year	Annually
University of Southern California, Idyllwild School of Music and the Arts, PO Box 38, Idyllwild, CA 92349	$20,000	Students with proven ability and need	Ten-week summer program	Annually
University of Southern California, University Park, Los Angeles, CA 90007	Graduate teaching assistantships Contact Department of Fine Arts	Fine art students, graduate and undergraduate	One year	Annually
	Graduate fellowships. Contact The Graduate School			
	Financial assistance in general. Contact Director of Student Aid			

OFFERED BY	AMOUNT	OPENED TO	DURATION	WHEN OFFERED
University of Tennessee-Knoxville, Tyson Art Center, 927 Volunteer Blvd, Knoxville, TN 37916	Variable	Undergraduate students who are enrolled	One quarter; occasionally one year	Quarterly during academic year
	Variable	Students who are applying to the Graduate School for admission and are planning to work for the MFA degree in the art department		
University of Texas at San Antonio, Art Department, 4242 Piedras Dr E, Suite 250, San Antonio, TX 78284	$100	Art students in good standing	One semester	Each semester
University of Texas of the Permian Basin,* Faculty of Art, Odessa, TX 79762	$800	Qualified students	One year	Annually
University of Utah, Museum of Fine Arts, 10 Art & Architecture Center, Salt Lake City, UT 84112	$100	Docents	One year	Annually
University of Washington, School of Art, Seattle, WA 98195	Approx $40,000	Art majors	One year and quarterly	Annually and quarterly
University of West Florida, Faculty of Art, Pensacola, FL 32504	Out-of-state tuition waiver $1575, yearly one-half in-state tuition $375, yearly	Students with grade point averages of 3.0 during their first two college years	One year, renewable	Annually
University of Windsor, Fine Arts Department, Huron Church Rd at College, Windsor, ON, Canada N9B 3P4	Variable	Fine arts students, other university students	One year	Annually
University of Wisconsin-Eau Claire,* Financial Aids Office, Eau Claire, WI 54701	Variable	Qualified students	One year	Annually
University of Wyoming, University Station, Box 3138, Laramie, WY 82071	$1950	Both in-state and out-of-state students	One year (renewable)	Annually
Valley City State College, Art Department, Valley City, ND 58072	$300	Any full time art major	One year	Annually
Vancouver Community College, Langara Campus,* Department of Fine Arts, 100 W. 49th St, Vancouver, BC V5Y 2Z6, Canada	$15 - $300	Any art student taking any academic and studio courses	One year	Annually
Ventura College,* Fine Arts Department, 4667 Telegraph Rd, Ventura, CA 93003	Various amounts	All art students	One year	Annually
Virginia Museum of Fine Arts, Richmond, VA 23221	Student Fellowship $1500 Graduate Fellowship $3600 Professional Fellowship $2400	Virginians who were born in the State, or who have resided in it for a period of at least five years; must be involved in the arts.	One year	Annually, Deadline Apr 1
Virginia Polytechnic Institute and State University, Blacksburg, VA 24061	$150	Art majors who are rising seniors	One year	Annually
Visual Art's Center of the Children's Aid Society, 209 Sullivan St, New York, NY 10012	Variable	Depending on economic situation	One year	Semi-annually
Waldorf College,* Art Department, Forest City, IA 50436	Variable with need	Art majors	One year	Annually
Washington and Lee University, Lexington, VA 24450	Varies according to need	Art majors, college men only	One year (renewable up to four years)	Annually
Washington State University, Fine Arts Department, Pullman WA 99163	$200 - $500	Art majors	One year	Annually
Washington University, St Louis, MO 63130	$200 - $4800	Full-time students in the School of Fine Arts	One year (usually renewable)	Annually
Wayland Baptist College Department of Art, Box 54, 1900 W Seventh, Plainview, TX 79072	Various amounts	Everyone majoring or minoring in art	Semester	Semi-annually
Weber State College, Art Department, 3750 Harrison Blvd, Ogden, UT 84403	Tuition waiver	All art majors	One year	Annually
Wenatchee Valley College Department of Applied and Fine Arts, Fifth St, Wenatchee, WA 98801	$252 (4)	Best qualified applicants		
West Georgia College,* Art Department, Carrollton, GA 30117	Various	Art majors	One year	Annually

OFFERED BY	AMOUNT	OPENED TO	DURATION	WHEN OFFERED
West Shore Community College, Division of Humanities & Fine Arts, 2240 W Sugar Grove Road, Scottville, MI 59454	$150 - $500	Qualified full-time, talented art students	One year	Annually
West Texas State University, Department of Art, Box 16, WT Station, Canyon, TX 79016	Up to $500	High school seniors and transfer students	One year	Annually
West Virginia University, Art Department, Morgantown, WV 26506	$2000	MFA degree students	One year (renewable)	Annually
Western Illinois University Art Department, West Adams, Macomb, IL 61455	(4) Assistantships, $290 per month	Graduate applicants with required credentials		Annually or semi-annually
	Tuition waivers (5 to 10) Talent grants, $100 to $300 each (4 to 10)	Students matriculating or new students with outstanding records or portfolios		Annually or semi-annually
Western Montana College, 710 S Atlantic, Dillon, MT 59725	$100	A promising art student in second, third or fourth year at WMC	One year	Annually
Western Wyoming College Art Department, Rock Springs, WY 82901	Tuition	High school graduates with strong interest in the arts	One year	Annually
Westmar College,* Art Department, Le Mars, IA 51031	Variable	Those of outstanding artistic ability and those who can demonstrate financial need		Annually
Whitworth College, Art Department, W Hawthorne Rd, Spokane, WA 99251	Maximum $200	Art majors, students enrolling with art emphasis, undeclared majors	One year	Annually
William Woods College, Fulton, MO 65251	$100 and up	Art majors and Art Therapy majors	One year, renewable	Annually
Williams College,* Department of Art, Williamstown, MA 01267	$3000 Hubbard Hutchinson Memorial Scholarship	Williams senior for two years of graduate work	Two years at $3000 a year	Annually
	Cadwallader Evans III Memorial Scholarship	Williams student beginning junior year and majoring in English or art	One year (may be extended second year)	Annually
	Edith Weston Andrews Scholarship	Williams student majoring in art or music	One year (may be extended second year)	Annually
	Beatrice Stone Scholarship	Williams student majoring in art or music	One year (may be extended second year)	Annually
Windward Artists Guild, PO Box 851, Kailua, HI 96734	$100	High School students of Windward Oahu		Annually
Henry Francis du Pont Winterthur Museum, Winterthur, DE 19735	Variable	Graduate students in art conservation and connoisseurship	Two or three years	Annually
Wittenberg University, Springfield, OH 45501	$2000 - $3000	All art students	One year	Annually
Catharine Lorillard Wolfe Art Club, 802 Broadway, New York, NY 10003	$100 each	Art Students League and National School of Design students	One year	Annually
Wright State University, Art Department, Col Glenn Highway, Dayton, OH 45431	Variable	Art majors	Variable	Annually and quarterly
Charles A Wustum Museum of Fine Arts, 2519 Northwestern Ave, Racine, WI 53404	$500 to other institutions, $400 to our own classes	Residents of Racine		Annually
Xavier University of Louisiana, Art Deparment, Palmetto & Pine Sts, New Orleans, LA 70125	Full or part tuition	Any student accepted by University	One year (renewable)	Annually
Yale Center for British Art and British Studies, Box 2120 Yale Station, New Haven, CT 06520	Open	Advanced scholars in British Art	Three months and up	Annually in Nov
Yale University, School of Art, 180 York St, New Haven, CT 06520	Per need	Eligible students	Academic year	Annually
York Academy of Arts,* 625 E Philadelphia St, York, PA 17403	$4293	Open to students who have successfully completed one year of study, based on financial need and academic standing	One year	Annually
Young Harris College, Department of Art, Young Harris, GA 30582	$1,700	Art majors	One year	Annually
Joseph Young/Art in Architecture, 1434 S Spaulding Ave, Los Angeles, CA 90019	$900 (based on talent)	Qualified graduate students	One year	

Open Exhibitions
National, Regional and State-Wide

ALABAMA

DIXIE ANNUAL, Montgomery. Annual, Spring. All two-dimensional works on paper except photographs. Open to artists of 13 states—Ala, Ark, Fla, Ga, Ky, La, Miss, Mo, NC, SC, Tenn, Tex & Va. Jury, prizes awarded in the form of museum purchases. Fee $7, two works per artist; maximum 5 ft by 5 ft. Entries & entry cards due six weeks prior to the opening of the exhibition. For further information write Registrar, Montgomery Museum of Fine Arts, 440 S McDonough St, Montgomery, AL 36104.

WATERCOLOR SOCIETY OF ALABAMA JURIED COMPETITION, Birmingham. Annual, Sept. All aqueous media applied to paper. Open to all US artists. Jury, cash awards, purchase awards. Fee $10 per entry, limit two entries. Deadline Aug. 29. Exhibit Sept. 10 - Oct. 8. For information write Hazel Brough, 17 Elmira Dr, Tuscaloosa AL 35401.

ALASKA

ALL ALASKA JURIED EXHIBITION, Anchorage. Annual, Feb, Anchorage; Mar, Fairbanks; Apr, Juneau. Paintings, prints, drawings, sculpture, & photography. Open to Alaska residents only. Jury, cash awards. No fee, two items per category. Entries due Jan. For further information write Anchorage Historical & Fine Arts Museum, 701 West Seventh Ave, Anchorage, AK 99501.

EARTH, FIRE AND FIBER CRAFT DESIGN JURIED EXHIBIT, Anchorage. Annual, Oct, Nov, Fairbanks; Dec, Juneau. Open to all crafts media, pottery, jewelry, metal, wood, weaving, etc. Open to Alaska residents only. Juried, cash awards. No fee, two items per category. For further information, write Anchorage Historical and Fine Arts Museum, 701 W Seventh Ave, Anchorage, AK 99501.

ARIZONA

DOUGLAS ART ASSOCIATION TWO FLAGS ART FESTIVAL. Annual, May. Open to all artists of US & Mex. Cash awards, prizes & purchase awards. Entry fee $3, limit two, 20% comn. For further information write Douglas Art Association, Box 256, 300 11th St, Douglas, AZ 85607.

HEARD MUSEUM GUILD, Phoenix. Annual, Nov-Dec. All original arts & crafts. Open to Indians of NAm, Indian students & those of Indian descent. Cash awards & ribbons. Fee 20% comn. Entry forms & work due Oct 9-Nov 6. For further information write Chmn, Heard Museum Guild Indian Arts & Crafts Exhibit, 22 E Monte Vista Rd, Phoenix, AZ 85004.

TUCSON MUSEUM OF ART/ARIZONA CRAFTS. Biennial, odd numbered years, Mar-Apr. All craft media. Open to Arizona residents. Jury, purchase, cash and exhibition awards totaling $3,000. Fee $4 per entry. For entry due dates and further information write Gerrit Cone, Assistant Museum Director, Tucson Museum of Art, 235 W Alameda, Tucson, AZ 85701.

TUCSON MUSEUM OF ART/ARIZONA'S OUTLOOK. Biennial, even numbered year Mar-Apr. Painting, sculpture, graphics, drawings and photography. Open to Ariz. residents. Jury, purchase and exhibition awards totaling $3,000. Fee $4 per entry. For entry due dates and further information write Gerrit Cone, Assistant Museum Director, Tucson Museum of Art, 235 W Alameda, Tucson, AZ 85701.

ARKANSAS

ARKANSAS ARTS CENTER DELTA ART EXHIBITION, Little Rock. Annual, Oct-Nov. All paintings & sculpture (not over 500 pounds). Open to artists born in or residing in Ark, La, Miss, Mo, Okla, Tenn & Tex. Jury, $1000 Grand Award, $3000 purchase awards. Fee $5, limit two. Entry cards and 35mm slides due August 11. For further information write Townsend Wolfe, The Arkansas Arts Center, MacArthur Park, PO Box 2137, Little Rock, AR 72203.

ARKANSAS ARTS CENTER PRINTS: DRAWINGS & CRAFTS EXHIBITION, Little Rock. Annual, May-June. Prints in all media; drawings in all media (except watercolors); photographs in color and/or monochrome; crafts in metal, clay, textile, glass, wood, plastics & combined media. Open to artists born in or residing in Ark, La, Miss, Mo, Okla, Tenn & Tex. Jury, awards & $2000 purchase prizes. Fee $5, limit two. Dates for entry cards and work due to be announced. For further information write Townsend Wolfe, Director, The Arkansas Arts Center, MacArthur Park, PO Box 2137, Little Rock, AR 72203.

ARKANSAS ARTS CENTER TOYS DESIGNED BY ARTISTS EXHIBITION, Little Rock. Annual, Dec-Jan. Toys in all media. Open to all artists. $1000 in purchase awards. Fee $5. Jury, limit 3. Dates for entry cards and work due to be announced. For further information write Townsend Wolfe, Director, The Arkansas Arts Center, MacArthur Park, PO Box 2137, Little Rock, AR 72203.

FORT SMITH ART CENTER.* Annual, Mar. Painting, watercolor, drawing. Open to artists of Ark, Kans, La, Mo, Okla, Miss, Tenn & Tex. Jury, prizes & purchase awards. Fee $5. Entry cards & work due Feb. For further information write Registrar, Fort Smith Art Center, 423 N Sixth St, Fort Smith, AR 72901.

CALIFORNIA

ALL-CALIFORNIA PRINT EXHIBITION,* Los Angeles. Annual, Jan. All prints. Open to living Calif artists. Jury, over $1500 awards. Fee, limit on entries. Fees, forms & work due Nov 18. For further information write Betty Anderson, Los Angeles Printmaking Society, 1028 Mission St, South Pasadena, CA 91030.

LOS ANGELES PRINTMAKING SOCIETY NATIONAL PRINT EXHIBITION.* Annual, Nov. Prints excluding mono or photographs. Open to all US citizens residing in US. Cash awards, purchase awards. Fee $5 for 2 slides, 20% comn. Entry cards & slides due July 1, work due Oct 30. For further information write J. Bockman, 18330 Black Hawk, Northridge, CA 91324.

MANY MEDIA MINI EXHIBITION,* Redlands. Annual, Oct. All media, original work, total size not to exceed 15 inches in any direction (no photography). Open to all Calif artists. Fee $3 per entry, limit three. For further information write Redlands Art Association, 12 E Vine St, Redlands, CA 92373.

NATIONAL WATERCOLOR SOCIETY,* Los Angeles. Annual, Nov. All water-based media. Open to all US artists. Jury, purchase awards & cash awards. Fee $10; work due Sept 24. For further information write Faith Fellman, Secy, 1300 S Orange Dr, Los Angeles, CA 90019.

SAN BERNARDINO ART ASSOCIATION INLAND EXHIBITION.* Annual, Oct. Oil, acrylic, watercolor, mixed, collage, graphics (no sculpture or photography). Open to all Calif artists. Cash awards & purchase awards. Fee $3 per entry, limit two, 30% comn. Entry cards & work due Sept 30. For further information write San Bernardino Art Association, PO Box 2272, San Bernardino, CA 92406.

SAN FRANCISCO ANNUL ARTS FESTIVAL. Open to artists of the nine Bay area counties. Purchase awards. For further information write Elio Benvenuto, Arts Commission—City and County of San Francisco, 165 Grove St, San Francisco, CA 94102.

SANTA CRUZ ART LEAGUE.* Annual, Apr. Oil, watercolor & mixed media, representational art only. Open to all Calif residents. Jury. Fee $4 per entry, limit three in each medium. For further information write Santa Cruz Art League, 526 Broadway, Santa Cruz, CA 95060.

WATERCOLOR XI, Riverside. Annual, Apr, at Riverside Art Center & Museum. Transparent watercolor. Open to all California artists who submit paintings in transparent watercolor. Juried, with $350, $250, $150 awards, and other cash awards, and honorable mentions. Fee $4 per painting, total of three, one hung. Entries due mid-March, date to be announced. For further information write Elizabeth Hopkins, Pres, Watercolor West, PO Box 213, Redlands, CA 92373.

COLORADO

FOOTHILLS ART CENTER/NORTH AMERICAN SCULPTURE EXHIBITION, Golden. Annual, Apr-May. Sculpture in a permanent media. Open to any living artist in the US, Mexico or Canada. Juried by slides, $5000 in cash awards. Details not yet confirmed. For further information write Marian Metsopoulos, Foothills Art Center, 809 15th St, Golden, CO 80401.

FOOTHILLS ART CENTER/REGIONAL OIL EXHIBITION, Golden. Annual, Mar-Apr. Oil. Open to states surrounding Colorado. Juried by slides, with cash awards. Details not yet confirmed. For further information write Marian Metsopoulos, Foothills Art Center, 809 15th St, Golden, CO 80401

FOOTHILLS ART CENTER/ROCKY MOUNTAIN NATIONAL WATERMEDIA EXHIBITION, Golden. Annual, Aug-Sept. Watermedia on paper. Open to all artists living in the US. Juried by slides, with $9000 cash prizes. Details not yet confirmed. For further information write Marian Metsopoulos, Foothills Art Center, 809 15th St, Golden, CO 80401.

FOOTHILLS ART CENTER/THREADS UNLIMITED V, Golden. Annual, June-July. All fibers. Open to states surrounding Colorado as well as Colorado. Juried by slides, with cash awards. Details not yet confirmed. For further information write Marian Metsopoulos, Foothills Art Center, 809 15th St, Golden, CO 80401.

CONNECTICUT

CONNECTICUT SOCIETY OF WOMEN PAINTERS,* West Hartford. Annual, May. All original work. Open to women who reside in Conn. Cash awards. Fee $5 mem, $8 non-mem, per entry, limit two. Entry cards & work due Apr 27 & 28, St Joseph College, West Hartford. For further information write Vincenza Uccello, Chmn, 207 Branford St, Hartford, CT 06112.

NEW HAVEN PAINT AND CLAY CLUB.* Annual, Mar-Apr. Oil, watercolor, acrylic, graphics & sculpture. Open to artists from the New Eng states & NY. Prizes & purchase awards. Fee $6 for first entry, $4 for second, 15% comn. Entry cards & work due Feb 24. For further information write Sunni Cretella, 57 Seaview Ave, Branford, CT 06405.

SILVERMINE GUILD OF ARTISTS NATIONAL PRINT EXHIBITION, New Canaan. Biennial, Mar (next show, 80). All print media. Open to all artists. Jury, purchase prizes. Fee; two works per artist allowed. For further information write Exhib Secy, Silvermine Guild of Artists, Inc, 1037 Silvermine Rd, New Canaan, CT 06840.

SILVERMINE GUILD OF ARTISTS NEW ENGLAND EXHIBITION OF PAINTING AND SCULPTURE, New Canaan. Annual, June. All painting & sculpture. Open to artists of the six New Eng States of NY, NJ & Pa. Jury; more than $6000 in cash awards. Fee. For further information write Exhib Secy, Silvermine Guild of Artists, Inc, 1037 Silvermine Rd, New Canaan, CT 06840.

SLATER MEMORIAL MUSEUM, Norwich. Annual, Mar-Apr. All media. Open to all resident Conn artists. Jury, prizes. Fee $4 per piece, limit two; sculpture limited to 200 pounds. For further information write The Slater Memorial Museum, 108 Crescent St, Norwich, CT 06360.

DELAWARE

DELAWARE ART MUSEUM ANNUAL CONTEMPORARY CRAFTS EXHIBITION, Wilmington. Annual, Nov-Dec. Ceramics, fibers, metals, wood, leather and glass; must be original designs executed by the entrants. Open to craftsmen in Delaware and the northeastern US, (includes Md, DC, NJ, Pa, NY, and New England). Juried by slides, with cash prizes awarded by judge and purchase prizes made by the Museum. Fee $8 per person, with limit of three works per person. Details not yet established, make inquiries in August. For further information write to Education Department, Delaware Art Museum, 2301 Kentmere Parkway, Wilmington, DE 19806.

FLORIDA

BOCA RATON CENTER FOR THE ARTS, Annual, Feb. Original painting & sculpture. Open to all artists. Jury. Entries due Feb. to be delivered by hand only. For further information write Boca Raton Center for the Arts, 801 W Palmetto Park Rd, Boca Raton, FL 33432.

BOYNTON BEACH FESTIVAL OF THE ARTS ANNUAL, Boynton Beach. Annual, Mar. Oil, watercolors, ceramics, sculpture, graphics, crafts, mixed media, jewelry. Open to all original artwork, professional and amateur. Juried, submit three slides/photographs, over $1000 in prizes for professionals and ribbons for amateurs. Fee $15 professional, $12 amateur. Entries due February 15. For further information write Laura Mudryk, 128 E Ocean Ave, Boynton Beach, FL 33435.

FALL FESTIVAL OF ARTS AND CRAFTS, Panama City. Annual, Nov, Indoor, Municipal Auditorium. All media, must be original arts and crafts. Open to national. Fee $20. For further information write Chairman, Fall Festival, Panama Art Association, PO Box 883, Panama City, FL 32401.

LATIN QUARTER ART GALLERY,* Tampa. Annual, Feb. All media. Open to all artists. Jury, prizes. Fee $5 one entry, $8 two entries. Entry cards & work due Jan, all work must be hand delivered. For further information write Oscar Aguayo, PO Box 5287, Tampa, FL 33675.

MIAMI GRAPHICS BIENNIAL, Miami. Biennial, next exhibition 1979. Graphics. Open to all artists in the US. Juried with honor, purchase awards. Fee $10. Entry date not yet determined. For further information write to Metropolitan Museum & Art Centers, 1212 Anastasia Ave, Coral Gables, FL 33134.

NATIONAL MINIATURE ART SHOW ANNUAL, Clearwater. Annual, Jan. All media, fine art and sculpture, no crafts. Open to all artists in US and abroad. Juried, $1000 in prizes. Fee $7 for up to three works; $11 for up to six. Entry cards and checks by November 18, works due November 25. For further information write Mr. Leslie Chepren, 10993 Dorothy Lane, Largo, FL 33540.

SOCIETY OF THE FOUR ARTS EXHIBITION OF CONTEMPORARY AMERICAN PAINTINGS, Palm Beach. Annual, Dec. Oils, watercolor, drawings, mixed, & flat collages completed since Jan, 77. Open to artists residing in the US. Cash awards. Fee $3, limit 2 entries (fee refunded if entry accepted); comn 10%. Specific dates on which entry cards & work are due announced in prospectus available upon request in Sept. For further information write The Society of the Four Arts, Four Arts Plaza, Palm Beach, FL 33480.

GEORGIA

ATLANTA PLAYHOUSE THEATRE AND GEORGIA TECH STUDENT INTERNATIONAL DOGWOOD FESTIVAL ART SHOW, Atlanta. Annual, Mar-Apr (Atlanta Dogwood Festival). Any hanging work of art suitable; oils, tempera, drawings, graphics, sculptures, collages (and may include photography this year). Open to all artists in the US/international. Juried by slides, judged for awards, with purchase awards and prizes. Fee $7. Entries due February 20. For further information write Ida S Borochoff, Artistic Director, Atlanta Playhouse Theatre, Ltd, PO Box 1253, Atlanta, GA 30301.

OUTDOORS IN GEORGIA ANNUAL WILDLIFE SHOW, Atlanta. Annual, Oct. Painting (oils and acrylics), watercolor, drawing (pen and ink/charcoal/pencil/pastel), prints (engravings/woodcuts/etchings), photography, sculpture. Open to wildlife artists in Georgia. Juried, cash prizes for first place, ribbons for second and third place. Fee $25 to reserve 5 x 10 ft space. Entries due after April 20. For further information write Liz Carmichael Jones, Georgia Department of Natural Resources, Room 720, 270 Washington St SW, Atlanta, GA 30334.

HAWAII

ART HAWAII 1978, Honolulu. Annual, Dec. All-media. Open to all artists residing in Hawaii. Juror. Fee $3 per entry, limited to five. Slide entries due by Sept. 30. For further information write Selden Washington, Asst Dir, Honolulu Academy of Arts, 900 S Beretania St, Honolulu, HI 96814.

HAWAII NATIONAL PRINT EXHIBITION, Honolulu. Biennial, Sept-Oct, 1979. All media except monoprints. Open to all artists living in the US. Jury. Fee $8 per artist, three entries per artist. Entries due no later than July 1. For further information write Joseph Feher, Honolulu Academy of Arts, 900 S Beretania St, Honolulu, HI 96814.

ILLINOIS

ART INSTITUTE OF CHICAGO. Biennial. All media, not over 7 x 10 x 5 ft or weigh over 1000 pounds. Open to artists, 18 or over, legal residents of 130 mile radius of Chicago. Jury, awards. Fee none. For further information write Painting & Sculpture Dept, The Art Institute of Chicago, Michigan & Adams, Chicago, IL 60603.

NORTH SHORE ART LEAGUE NEW HORIZONS IN ART, Chicago. Annual, May. Painting, sculpture, graphics, photog. Open to Ill artists. Cash awards, purchase awards & ribbons. Fee 15% comn. Entry cards & work due early May. For further information write North Shore Art League, 620 Lincoln Ave, Winnetka, IL 60093.

ROCKFORD AND VICINITY ANNUAL JURIED SHOW. Annual Feb or Mar. Oil, watercolor, sculpture and graphic arts. Open to artists within 200 miles of Rockford. Fee: $10 per entry (two pieces), $5 to members. Entries due in January. For further information, write Rockford Art Association, 737 N Main St, Rockford, IL 61103.

INDIANA

ANDERSON·FINE ARTS CENTER WINTER SHOW, Anderson. Annual, Jan-Feb. Watercolors and prints. Open to artists currently residing in Ind, Ill, Ky, Ohio and Mich. Juried by a professional outside the region, $1000 in cash and purchase awards. Fee $5 for two entries. Entry forms due December 23, works due first week in January. For further information write Joseph B Schenk, Director, Anderson Fine Arts Center, 226 W Eighth St, Anderson, IN 46016.

BALL STATE UNIVERSITY DRAWING & SMALL SCULPTURE SHOW, Muncie. Annual, May-June. Drawings & small sculpture. Open to all artists in the United States. One judge, awards. Sculptures judged solely by slides which are due around February 1. (Actual date varies slightly from year to year. Drawings must be sent to the Art Gallery for judging. Due around end of March; actual date varies slightly from year to year also.) For further information & prospectus write Art Gallery, Ball State University, Muncie, IN 47306.

EVANSVILLE MUSEUM OF ARTS & SCIENCE MID-STATES ART EXHIBITION. Annual, Nov. Painting, sculpture, watercolor, graphic arts, collage & mobiles (no photographs). Open to artists within a radius of 200 miles from Evansville or any resident of the State of Indiana. Jury, awards. Handling fee is $5 for one entry or $8 for limit of two entries. Entries due in Oct. For further information write Art Comt, Evansville Museum of Arts & Science, 411 SE Riverside Dr, Evansville, IN 47713.

EVANSVILLE MUSEUM OF ARTS & SCIENCE MID-STATES CRAFT EXHIBITION. Annual, Feb. Ceramics, textiles, metal work, wood, enamel, glass & others. Open to artists within a radius of 200 miles from Evansville or any resident of the State of Indiana. Jury, awards. Fee $5 for three objects or less. Entries due Jan. For further information write Craft Comt, Evansville Museum of Arts & Science, 411 SE Riverside Dr, Evansville, IN 47713.

HOOSIER SALON,* Indianapolis. Annual, Jan-Feb. All media & sculpture. Open to Indiana artists, native or by residence in the state for one yr minimum. Jury, awards $4000-$5000. Fee $7.50. Entry due early Jan. For further information write Hoosier Salon, 951 N Delaware, Indianapolis, IN 46202.

INDIANAPOLIS MUSEUM OF ART INDIANA ARTISTS EXHIBITION. Biennial, Feb 79. Painting & sculpture, and works on paper. Open to artists who reside or have resided in Indiana. Jury, awards. Fee $5 per entry, limit two per artist. Entries due early or mid-Jan. For further information write Registrar, Indianapolis Museum of Art, 1200 W 38th St, Indianapolis, IN 46208.

INDIANAPOLIS MUSEUM OF ART INDIANA CRAFTS EXHIBITION. Biennial, Mar-Apr, 80. Hand-crafted articles. Open to past or present Indiana residents. Jury, awards. Fee $5 per artist, limit two. Entries due early or mid-Feb. For further information write Registrar, Indianapolis Museum of Art, 1200 W 38th St, Indianapolis, IN 46208.

LAFAYETTE ART CENTER. Biennial, May-July 1979. Further details not available. For further information write Lafayette Art Center, 101 S Ninth St, Lafayette, IN 47901.

LAFAYETTE ART CENTER FIESTA. Annual, Sept. All media and crafts. Open to all midwest artists and craftsmen. Juried, over $600 in prizes. Fee $20. Entry slides of work due by July 15. For further information write Lafayette Art Center, 101 S Ninth St, Lafayette, IN 47901.

MICHIANA REGIONAL ART EXHIBITION, South Bend. Biennial, Apr-May, 78. Painting, sculpture, graphics & crafts. Open to artists in Mich & Ind, or former residents. Jury, awards. Fee $7, limited to two entries. Entries due one month in advance (Mar). For further information write Art Center Inc, 120 S St Joseph St, South Bend, IN 46601.

WABASH VALLEY EXHIBITION, Terre Haute. Annual, Mar. All media. Open to artists within a 160 mile radius of Terre Haute. Jury, awards. Fee $4 for first entry, $3 for second and third, limit to three. Entries due Feb. For further information write Curator, the Sheldon Swope Art Gallery, 25 S Seventh St, Terre Haute, IN 47807.

IOWA

DES MOINES ART CENTER ANNUAL. Annual, spring. Printings, drawings, prints, sculpture, crafts. Open to anyone living in Iowa above high school age. Juried, best work $250, 2 adult painting $100, 2 student $50, special ceramic award $250, 1 adult $100 and a student $50 in sculpture, prints, drawings, and crafts. No fee. For further information write Des Moines Art Center, Greenwood Park, Des Moines, IA 50312.

IOWA CRAFTS ANNUAL, Mason City. Annual, Oct-Nov. Open to any and all craft media, such as clay, fiber, metals and others. Open to all artists, craftspersons residing within the State of Iowa. Juried by submission of the work, up to $800 in cash awards. No fee. Entry deadline 5 PM October 1. For further information write Richard Leet, Director, Charles H MacNider Museum, 303 Second St SE, Mason City, IA 50401.

NORWEGIAN-AMERICAN MUSEUM NATIONAL ROSEMALING EXHIBITION, Decorah. Annual, July. Rose painting on wood. Open to anyone who has been resident of the US for last five years. Jury, $25 blue ribbon, $15 red ribbon, $10 white ribbon. Fee $2.00 per entry. Entries due July 15. For further information write Norwegian-American Museum, 502 W Water St, Decorah, IA 52101.

SIOUX CITY ART CENTER. Annual, Fall. Paintings. Open to residents of Iowa, Nebr, Minn & SDak. One-man jury, up to $1200 in purchase & cash awards. Entries due Sept-Oct. For further information write Dir, Sioux City Art Center, 513 Nebraska St, Sioux City, IA 51101.

KANSAS

WATERCOLOR SOCIETY EXHIBITION,* Wichita. Annual, Dec. Transparent aqueous on paper. Open to all artists living in Kans. Cash awards, prizes & purchase awards. Fee $5; comn 20%. Entry cards due before Oct 1 & work due Oct 1. For further information write Lucinda Foster, Pres, Kansas Watercolor Society, 600 Longford Lane, Wichita, KS 67206.

KENTUCKY

J B SPEED ART MUSEUM ANNUAL, Louisville. Annual, Sept. In annual rotation: painting, sculpture, graphics, crafts. Open to artists in Kentucky, Indiana, Ohio, Illinois, Missouri, Tennessee, Virginia, West Virginia. Juried, no special awards, purchase commitments. No fee. Entries due August 5. For further information write Mrs. Reva Crumpler, J B Speed Art Museum, PO Box 8345, Louisville, KY 40208.

LOUISIANA

LOUISIANA WATERCOLOR SOCIETY INTERNATIONAL,* Baton Rouge. Annual, Dec-Jan. Water based, recent original paintings on paper. Open to all artists. Cash awards & purchase prizes. Fee $3 per entry, no limit to number of entries. Work due Dec 1. For further information write Jean Williams, Secy, 785 Brehm Pl, Jefferson, LA 70121.

NEW ORLEANS MUSEUM OF ART. Biennial, Spring. Focus on contemporary art by prof artists from thirteen-state region of Southeastern US. Single juror, purchase awards. No fee. For further information write Artists' Biennial, New Orleans Museum of Art, PO Box 19123, Lelong Ave, City Park, New Orleans, LA 70179.

MAINE

WILLIAM A FARNSWORTH ART MUSEUM OPEN SHOW, Rockland. Annual, Feb-Apr. All media included. Open to all resident Maine artists. Juried, prizes and awards. No fee. Entries due approximately February 15-24. For further information write Marius B Peladeau, Director, William A Farnsworth Library and Art Museum, Box 466, Rockland, ME 04841.

OGUNQUIT ART CENTER NATIONAL PAINTING EXHIBITION. Annual, June-Sept. Oil, watercolor, mixed (originals only). Open to all US artists. Cash awards. Fee $10, 25% comn. Entry cards due June 1 & work due June 5. For further information write Mrs F Nims, The Ogunquit Art Center, Hoyt's Lane, Ogunquit, ME 03907.

MARYLAND

ACADEMY OF THE ARTS MARYLAND ART EXHIBITION, Easton. Annual, Apr-May. All painting, collages, graphics, sculpture. Open to artists born or residing in Md, students at Md art schs & members of Acad. Jury, cash prizes & purchase awards. No fee. Entry cards due April 9 & work due April 14 & 15. For further information write The Academy of the Arts, PO Box 605, Easton, MD 21601.

BALTIMORE MUSEUM OF ART BIENNIAL EXHIBITION. Biennial, during the even year. All media (slides or photographs of work not acceptable). Open to artists born or currently residing in Md. Jury, prizes & awards. No fee. Entries due as announced, usually 3 mo. before exhib. For further information write Mrs Alice C Steinbach, Dir Pub Info, Baltimore Museum of Art, Art Museum Dr, Baltimore, MD 21218.

CUMBERLAND VALLEY ANNUAL PHOTOGRAPHIC SALON, Hagerstown. Annual, Feb. Photographs. Open to residents & former residents of the Cumberland Valley region. Jury, prizes & awards. Fee $5.00. Entries due Jan 15. For further information write Washington County Museum of Fine Arts, PO Box 423, Hagerstown, MD 21740.

CUMBERLAND VALLEY ARTISTS ANNUAL EXHIBITION, Hagerstown. Annual, June. Open media. Open to residents & former residents of the Cumberland Valley region. Jury, prizes & awards. Fee $10.00. Entries due May 15. For further information write Washington County Museum of Fine Arts, PO Box 423, Hagerstown, MD 21740.

MASSACHUSETTS

BERKSHIRE ART ASSOCIATION,* Pittsfield. Annual, Oct. All painting, pastels, graphics, collages, sculpture. Open to artists of New Eng & NY only. Cash awards, prizes & purchase awards. Fee $6. Entry cards & work due on published date in Sept. For further information write Mrs Glenn L Jorn, Pres, 101 Patricia Ave, Dalton, MA 01226.

BOSTON PRINTMAKERS.* Annual, location & dates change yearly. All print media except monotypes. Open to all American and Canadian printmakers. Jury, awards. Fee $5 each, limit two, 33⅓% Comn. For further information write Mrs S M Rantz, Secy, 299 High Rock St, Dept A, Needham, MA 02192.

CULTURAL AFFAIRS COMMISSION NATIONAL PRINT EXHIBITION,* Springfield. Annual, May. All print, no monotypes. Open to all US artists. Jury, purchase prizes and one-man show award. Fee $4, limit two. Entry cards and work due Apr 19. For further information write Prof Josephine L Cecco, Springfield College, 263 Alden St, Springfield, MA 01109.

GREATER FALL RIVER ART ASSOCIATION NATIONAL.* Annual, May. Painting, graphics, sculpture, pottery, blown glass, textiles. Open to all artists in the US & Can. Jury, prizes & purchase awards. Fee $5 per entry. Entry cards & slides due Apr 12. For further information write Bernice Goldsmith, 80 Belmont St, Fall River, MA 02720.

MARION ART CENTER BISTATE SHOW.* Annual, Aug-Sept. Painting, print, sculpture, photog. Open to artists of Mass & RI. Jury, prizes. Fee $5 for two entries. Entry cards & fee due Aug 15 & work due Aug. 23. For further information write Marion Art Center, Front St, Marion, MA 02738.

NEW ENGLAND ARTISTS TRADITIONAL OPEN SHOW,* Fall River. Annual. Paintings, graphics. Jury, cash awards. Fee $3. Entries due Nov. For further information write Mrs Edward A Doyle, Dir, 80 Belmont St, Fall River, MA 02720.

SPRINGFIELD ART LEAGUE NATIONAL EXHIBITION. Annual, Apr-May. Painting, mixed, graphics, sculpture. Open to all artists residing in US. Jury, cash awards. Fee $8. Entry cards & work due Mar 23. For further information write Sally A. Johnson, Exhib Chairwoman, 131 Maple St, Longmeadow, MA 01106.

SPRINGFIELD ART LEAGUE NON-JURIED EXHIBITION.* Annual, Nov-Dec. Oil, watercolor, mixed, graphics, sculpture. Open to all artists, hand-delivered work only. Non-juried. Fee $8. Entry cards & work due Oct. For further information write Sally A. Johnson, Exhib Chairwoman, 131 Maple St, Longmeadow, MA 01106.

MICHIGAN

HARTLAND ART COUNCIL ART SHOW.* Annual, June. Open to all Mich artists. Jury, prizes & purchase awards. Fee. For further information write William Nelson, Pres, Hartland Art Council, Box 126, Hartland, MI 48029.

MICHIGAN PAINTERS-PRINTMAKERS EXHIBITION,* Grand Rapids. Biennial (with craftsmen show in off yrs), Sept-Oct. Paintings & prints (No competition 76, to resume in 78). Open to Mich residents. Jury, prizes to $3000. Fee $2 per work, limit of three works. Entries due Aug 14-24 (except Aug 20). For further information write Miss Idamarie Holmer, Grand Rapids Art Museum, 230 E Fulton, Grand Rapids, MI 49502.

MID-MICHIGAN ANNUAL EXHIBITION,* Midland. Annual, Feb. All media & mixed media (painting, drawing, prints, sculpture, plastics, ceramics, textiles, jewelry, enameling, metalwork, woodwork, photography). Open to Mich artists 18 yrs and over, only original work completed within the past 2 yrs. Jury, prizes & awards. Fee $5 per artist, limit three entries; no fee for MAC members. Entries due Jan. For further information write The Midland Art Council of Midland Center for the Arts, Inc, 1801 W St Andrews, Midland, MI 48640.

WORKS IN PROGRESS SERIES, Detroit. Annual or semi-annual, Feb 1979 and Sept 1979. One-person or small group shows, any media. Open to all Michigan artists. Jury, occasional purchases. No fee. Resume and slides (no maximum) by October 1978. For further information write Department of Modern Art, DIA, 5200 Woodward Avenue, Detroit, MI 48202.

MINNESOTA

ROCHESTER ART CENTER. Annual, June. All media. Open to artists and craftspeople of Minnesota. Non-juried, no prizes. Fee $10 for space rental. Entries due May 26. For further information write to B J Shigaki, Dir, 320 E Center, Rochester, MN 55901.

WHITE BEAR ARTS COUNCIL & LAKEWOOD COMMUNITY COLLEGE NORTHERN LIGHTS, White Bear Lake. Annual, Apr. Paintings, sculpture, drawings, no prints. Open to artists in Minnesota, Wisconsin, Iowa, North Dakota and South Dakota. Juried, prizes, ribbons, money awards and purchase awards. Fee $5 first entry, $3 second entry, two entries per artist. Entries due approximately two weeks before show, date to be decided. For further information write White Bear Arts Council, Box 8715, White Bear Lake, MN 55110.

MISSISSIPPI

LAUREN ROGERS MUSEUM OF ART BIENNIAL, Laurel. May, 1979. All media painting competition, no sculpture. Open to residents of Miss, Tenn, W Va, Ky, NC, SC, Va, Ga, Fla, Ark, Tex. Juried, purchase awards with top award of $900, other lesser awards, together totaling $3000. Fee $5, maximum of three entries (color slides). Entries due March 1. For further information write Biennial, Lauren Rogers Museum of Art, PO Box 1108, Laurel, MS 39440.

MISSOURI

NATIONAL WILDLIFE ART SHOW (formerly Midwest Wildlife Art Show), Kansas City. Annual, Mar. Acrylics, drawings, oils, pastels, sculpture, watercolors, decoy carvings and wood carvings. Open to professional wildlife artists of the US. Juried, ribbons. Fee and donated original piece of artist's work to the Sponsor Ducks Unlimited. Entries due November 15. For further information write David Wells, Chairman, 1901 Erie, North Kansas City, MO 64116.

WATERCOLOR USA, Springfield. Annual, late Spring, early Summer. Any aquamedia (paint composed of water-soluble pigment) executed on paper or a paper-like support. Open to living, adult artists, 18 years of age or older, residing in the continental US. Jury, approximately $10,000 in cash, purchase awards and patron purchases. Handling fee $6. Entry deadline varies from year to year. For further information write William C Landwehr, Dir, Springfield Art Museum, 1111 E Brookside Dr, Springfield, MO 65807.

MONTANA

YELLOWSTONE ART CENTER'S ANNUAL ART AUCTION, Billings. Annual, Apr-May. All media. Open to any artist in US. Prizes Best of Show $300, and three Honorable Mentions $100 each. Fee $5. Entries due two months previous to auction. For further information write to Yellowstone Art Center, 401 N 27th St, Billings, MT 59101.

NEBRASKA

JOSLYN ART MUSEUM BIENNIAL, Omaha. Biennial, held in even-numbered yrs, late winter or spring. Painting, sculpture, graphics. Open to artists in Ark, Colo, Ill, Ind, Iowa, Kans, La, Mich, Minn, Mo, Mont, Nebr, NMex, NDak, Ohio, Okla, SDak, Tex, Wisc & Wyo. Jury, awards. Entries due as announced. For further information write Joslyn Biennial, Joslyn Art Museum, 2200 Dodge St, Omaha, NE 68102.

NORTH PLATTE VALLEY ARTISTS' GUILD,* Scottsbluff. Annual, Apr. All media. Open to residents of Mont, Nebr, NDak, SDak & Wyo. Prizes, puchase awards & ribbons. Fee $5 per entry for adults & $1.50 for youths; 30% Comn. Entry cards due Mar 10, work due Mar 17. For further information write North Platte Valley Artists' Guild, PO Box 1041, Scottsbluff, NE 69361.

NEVADA

LAS VEGAS ART LEAGUE NATIONAL ART ROUND-UP.* Annual, Apr. All painting, graphics, textiles, sculpture, ceramics, jewelry. Open to all artists. $2000 in cash awards, purchase awards & ribbons. Fee $8 for one or two entries, 20% comn. Entry cards & color slides (2x2 in) due Feb 1, work due Mar 18. For further information write Las Vegas Art League, 3333-6 W Washington, Las Vegas, NV 89107.

NEW JERSEY

ART CENTER OF NEW JERSEY, East Orange. Annual, Mar-Apr. Oil, watercolor, graphics, sculpture. Open to artists of Conn, NJ, NY & Pa. Jury, prizes. Fee $6 for one, $10 for two entries; 25% comn. Entry cards due Mar work due Mar 16 - 18. For further information write Art Center of New Jersey, 16 Washington St, East Orange, NJ 07017.

HUNTERDON ART CENTER NATIONAL PRINT EXHIBITION, Clinton. Annual, Mar-Apr. All print media except monotype. Open to all artists in the US. Jury, purchase awards. Fee $10 for 1 or 2 prints includes insurance & return of work, mem $8. For further information write A S Marsh, Hunterdon Art Center, 7 Center St, Clinton, NJ 08809.

MINIATURE ART SOCIETY OF NEW JERSEY,* Nutley. Annual, May. Original miniature art work (no crafts). Open to all artists. Jury, prizes & purchase awards. Fee $8, limit three (mem seven). Entry cards due Feb 13, work due Feb 23. For futher information write Nutley Art Center, 200 Chestnut St, Nutley, NJ 07110.

NEW JERSEY CHAPTER AMERICAN ARTISTS' PROFESSIONAL LEAGUE,* West Orange. Annual, Nov. Oil, watercolor, mixed graphics. Open to all realistic artists. Cash awards. Fee members $3 for one entry, $5 for two, non-members $5 for one, $7 for two. Entry cards due Sept & work due Oct 21. For further information write Mrs Patricia Sprouls, 188 Kaywin Dr, Paramus, NJ 07652.

NEW JERSEY WATERCOLOR SOCIETY, alternate yrs Morris Museum, Morristown & Monmouth Museum, Lincroft. Annual, Nov-Dec. Watercolor, casein, tempera. Open to all present or former residents of NJ. Jury, awards. Fee subject to yearly decision of board. For further information write John C Bermingham, 249 So Main St, Wharton, NJ 07885.

PAINTERS & SCULPTOR SOCIETY OF NEW JERSEY.* Annual. Oil, watercolor, casein, acrylic, graphics, sculpture. Open to all artists in US & Can. Fee $7. Entries due May 8. For further information write Suzan Sanford, 267 Parker Ave, Clifton, NJ 07011.

SIDNEY ROTHMAN-THE GALLERY, Barnegat Light. Annual, June-September. All media. Open to professionals, national scope. Personal jury, no prizes; this is a show sale. No fee. Entries due early May. For further information write Sidney Rothman-The Gallery, Box 17, Barnegat Light, NJ 08006.

WESTFIELD ART ASSOCIATION,* Cranford. Annual, Mar-Apr. All painting, original work only. Open to all NJ residents. Jury, prizes & cash awards. Fee $5 per entry. Work due Mar 18. For further information write Mrs Elven Sheahan, 721 Clark St, Westfield, NJ 07090.

NEW MEXICO

MUSEUM OF ALBUQUERQUE. Biennial, Apr 1979. Arts and crafts. Open to artists and craftspeople of New Mexico. Regular exhibition schedule altered due to completion of new museum building. Entry due May 1978. For further information write Ellen J Landis, Curator of Art, Museum of Albuquerque, PO Box 1293, Albuquerque, NM 87103.

MUSEUM OF NEW MEXICO, Santa Fe. Biennial (New Mexico Biennial held alternate yrs), Feb-Mar Apr-May. All media. Open to artists of Southwest. Jury, awards. For further information write Don Strel, Div Dir, Museum of Fine Arts, Museum of New Mexico, PO Box 2087, Santa Fe, NM 87501.

NEW MEXICO ART LEAGUE SMALL PAINTING SHOW, Albuquerque. Annual, Feb. All media. Open to all artists. Jury, prizes. Fee $6 per entry, limit two. Entry cards and work due Jan 10. For further information write New Mexico Art League, 3401 Juan Tabo NE, Albuquerque, NM 87111.

NEW MEXICO ARTS AND CRAFTS FAIR, Albuquerque. Annual, last weekend in June. All media except home arts or crafts. Open to all NMex artists & craftsmen 18 yrs and older. Jury. Fee $60 each booth. $7.50 entry fee. Entry forms & 3 samples of work due mid-February. For further information write New Mexico Arts & Crafts Fair, PO Box 30044, Albuquerque, NM 87190.

NEW YORK

AMERICAN WATERCOLOR SOCIETY, New York. Annual, Apr. 1979 Watercolor, watermedia. Jury, cash awards with medals. Fee $8. Submission can be by slides. For further information write The American Watercolor Society, 1083 Fifth Ave, New York, NY 10028.

ART DIRECTORS CLUB,* New York. Annual Exhibition of Advertising & Editorial Art & Design, Spring. Open to advertising or editorial materials, promotion, posters, packaging & others. Jury, medals & certificates. Fee $2 per proof; $7.50 each TV film. Entries due Dec. For further information write The Art Directors Club, 488 Madison Ave, New York, NY 10022.

AUDUBON ARTISTS, New York. Annual, Jan-Feb. Oil, watercolor, graphics, sculpture, casein, polymer. Open to all artists. Jury, awards. Fee $8, one entry per artist. Entry due Jan. For further information write Secy, Audubon Artists, 1083 Fifth Ave, New York, NY 10028.

WOLF AND MARY BRAUN FUND YOUNG DESIGNERS COMPETITION, New York, NY. Annual. Open to students of product package design in credited schools in the United States and Canada. Jury, awards. For further information write W Braun Company 260 Fifth Ave, New York, NY 10001.

CHAUTAUQUA EXHIBITION OF AMERICAN ART. Annual, July. Oil, acrylic, watercolor, prints, drawing, mixed-media. Open to all artists residents of US & territories. Jury, cash prizes. Fee $6 for one entry, $10 for two. Entry slides (juried by slide only) due Apr 8 & work due May 31. For further information write Chautauqua Art Association, Box 1365, Chautauqua, NY 14722.

COOPERSTOWN ART ASSOCIATION NATIONAL EXHIBITION. Annual, July-Aug. Painting, graphics, sculpture & crafts (no photography). Open to any adult in the US. $3000 in prizes. Fee $7.50 each entry, 20% comn. Mailed entries due in the hands of agent by June 7. Hand delivered entries June 15, 16, 17 only. For further information write Cooperstown Art Association, 22 Main St, Cooperstown, NY 13326.

EVERSON MUSEUM OF ART NATIONAL CERAMIC EXHIBITION,* Syracuse. Biennial, Nov-Dec. Ceramics. Open to potters & enamelists in the US & Can. Jury, purchase prizes. Fee. For further information write Everson Museum of Art, 401 Harrison St, Syracuse, NY 13202.

HUDSON VALLEY ART ASSOCIATION, INC, White Plains. Annual, May. School of realism only, oil, watercolors, graphics, sculpture, pastel. Open to all artists, over 18 years, in this school of art. Double juried show, juried for selection and prizes, monetary and gold medals in each media. Fee $10. Entries due week prior to exhibition. For further information write Joan Rudman, Secretary, 274 Quarry Road, Stamford, CT 06903.

KNICKERBOCKER ARTISTS EXHIBITION,* New York. Annual, Oct. Oil, watercolor, acrylic, casein, graphics, sculpture. Open to all artists. Jury, prizes. Fee $10. Work due Oct 16. For further information write Ann Kovach, 100-36 Bellaire Pl, Bellaire, NY 11429.

LONG BEACH ART ASSOCIATION.* Annual, May. All media. Open to all adults. Jury, prizes. Fee $6 per entry, $10 for two. Entry cards & work due Apr 21. For further information write Long Beach Art Association, PO Box 70, Island Park, NY 11558.

NATIONAL ACADEMY OF DESIGN, New York. Annual, Feb-Mar. Oil, sculpture, watercolors, graphics. Open to all artists. Jury, awards. No fee. Entry due Feb. For further information write National Academy of Design, 1083 Fifth Ave, New York, NY 10028.

NATIONAL ART LEAGUE SPRING EXHIBITION,* Douglaston. Annual, May. Oil, watercolor, casein, pastels, black/whites, graphics, and small sculpture. Open to all artists and sculptors. Juried, cash awards, prizes and ribbons. Fee $7 non members, $5 members; 20% comm. Entry

cards and work due May 6. For further information write Philip Beaman, Exhibit Chairman, National Art League, 44-21 Douglaston Pkwy, Douglaston, NY 11363.

NATIONAL ARTS CLUB OPEN WATERCOLOR EXHIBITION, New York. Annual, usually in Nov. Watercolor only. Open to all. Juried, cash awards, material awards, one-man show awards. Fee $10. Details not yet confirmed. For further information write Moses Worthman, AWS, 3027 Brighton Fifth St, Brooklyn, NY 11235.

NATIONAL SCULPTURE SOCIETY, New York. Annual, Mar. Sculpture only. Open to all American sculptors on a juried basis. Jury prizes & awards. No fee. Write for prospectus approx Jan 1. For further information write National Sculpture Society, 777 Third Avenue, New York, NY 10017.

NATIONAL SOCIETY OF PAINTERS IN CASEIN & ACRYLIC, New York. Annual, Dec. Casein and Acrylic. Open to all artists. Jury, $2500 cash awards & medals. Fee $7. Entries due Nov. For information write to Lily Shuff, 155 West 68th Street, New York, NY 10023.

PASTEL SOCIETY OF AMERICA NATIONAL JURIED ALL PASTEL SHOW, New York. Annual, Sept-Oct. Pastel media. Open to all artists. Juried, $4000 in cash prizes, plus material awards, scholarships. Fee $10 first entry, $5 second, limit two paintings. Entry date September 14, out-of-towners may send slides, deadline July 15. For further information write Richard Pionk, Chairman, 1349 Lexington Avenue, New York, NY 10028.

SOCIETY OF AMERICAN GRAPHIC ARTISTS, New York. Biennial. All prints except monotype. Open to all printmakers. Jury, awards. Fee $5, limit one (30 inches maximum). For further information write Society of American Graphic Artists, 1083 Fifth Ave, New York, NY 10028.

SUFFOLK COUNTY ARTISTS LEAGUE,* Babylon. Annual, Mar. Oils, watercolor, acrylic, sculpture. Open to all artists. Jury, cash awards. Fee $4 per entry, limit two. For further information write Mario Grimaldi, Dir, Suffolk County Artists League, 39 E Main St, Babylon, NY 11702.

SUMI-E SOCIETY OF AMERICA EXHIBITION, New York. Annual, Spring. Oriental brush painting only; subjects must be original. Open to all artists. Jury, prizes. Fee $7.50 for non-mem, limit 2. For further information write Mrs Resly Reis 58-35 251 St Little Neck, NY 11362.

CATHARINE LORILLARD WOLFE ART CLUB, New York. Annual, Nov-Dec. Oil, watercolor, pastel, graphics, sculpture. Jury, money prizes. Fee. For further information and prospectus write Toni Heaney, 29 Emerson Court, Westbury, NY 11590.

NORTH CAROLINA

NORTH CAROLINA ARTISTS EXHIBITION, Raleigh. Annual, Dec-Jan. Painting, graphics, sculpture, photography, crafts. Open to natives & residents of NC. Cash awards, prizes & purchase awards. Fee $5 per artist, limit two works. Entry cards & work due Oct. For further information write Cur of Art, North Carolina Museum of Art, 107 E Morgan St, Raleigh, NC 27601.

SOUTHEASTERN CENTER FOR CONTEMPORARY ART, Winston-Salem. Annual competition - media as specified. Open to all artists, 18 years & older, residing in the 11 southeastern states. Jury, purchase awards. Fee $5. For further information write Southeastern Center for Contemporary Art (SECCA), 750 Marguerite Drive, Winston-Salem, NC 27106.

NORTH DAKOTA

MINOT STATE COLLEGE NATIONAL PRINT & DRAWING EXHIBITION. Annual, Feb. All prints, drawings. Open to all US artists. Purchase awards. Fee $5 for 2 slide entries. Slides due Dec 8. For further information write National Print & Drawing Exhibition, Art Department, Minot State College, Minot, ND 58701.

NATIONAL ART EXHIBITION BIENNIAL, Valley City. Biennial, Apr. All media. Open to all artists. Juried, approximately $1500 in prizes. Fee $5, limit of two works per artist. Entries due March 18, 1979; no slides required. For further information write 2nd Crossing Gallery, Box 1319, Valley City State College, Valley City, ND 58072.

NORTH DAKOTA PRINT & DRAWING EXHIBITION, Grand Forks. Annual, Apr. All prints & drawings. Open to all US artists. Jury, purchase awards. Fee $5. Work due Mar 1. For further information write North Dakota Annual, Visual Arts Dept, University of North Dakota, Grand Forks, ND 58201.

OHIO

BUTLER INSTITUTE OF AMERICAN ART MIDYEAR SHOW, Youngstown. Annual, July-Aug. Oil, watercolor, acrylic, casein. Open to artists of the US. Jury, awards. Fee $8. Entry cards & work due June. For further information write Butler Institute of American Art, 524 Wick Ave, Youngstown, OH 44502.

MARIETTA COLLEGE CRAFTS NATIONAL. Annual. Crafts & sculpture. Open to craftspeople in the US. Jury, $5000 in awards & prizes. Fee $10. Slides due Sept 9. For further information write Arthur Howard Winer, Dir, MCCN, Marietta College, Marietta, OH 45750.

MARIETTA NATIONAL, MARIETTA COLLEGE INTERNATIONAL COMPETITION (formerly Mainstreams). Annual, April-May. Open to all painters & sculptors. Jury, prizes & purchase awards. Fee $10, limit five. Entry cards due Feb. 2. For further information write William Gerhold, Dir, Marietta National, Marietta College, Marietta, OH 45750.

MASSILLON MUSEUM OHIO FINE ARTS EXHIBITION. Biennial, Mar (next 79). Oil, watercolor, polymer, acrylic. Open to residents of Ohio & former residents. Jury, prizes & purchase awards. Fee $3. Work due Feb. 4. For further information write Miss Mary Merwin, The Massillon Museum, 212 Lincoln Way E, Massillon, OH 44646.

OHIO ARTISTS & CRAFTSMEN SHOW, Massillon. Biennial, July-Aug 78 (next 80). Print, drawing, photography, all crafts & sculpture. Open to all present & former residents of Ohio. Prizes & purchase awards. Fee $3, 10% comm. Work due June 11. For further information write Miss Mary Merwin, The Massillon Museum, 212 Lincoln Way E, Massillon, OH 44646.

OHIO CERAMIC, SCULPTURE & CRAFT SHOW, Youngstown. Annual, Jan-Feb. Ceramic, enamel, sculpture and craft. Open to present & former Ohio residents. Jury, purchase awards. Entry fee. Entries due Nov 2-Dec 10. For further information write: Butler Institute of American Art, 524 Wick Ave, Youngstown, OH 44502.

OHIO SELECTION, Dayton. All mediums. Open to artists residing in Ohio. Juried/invitational exhibition. Slides due early September for jurying, approximately 7 artists then invited to exhibit 8 - 10 works each. Perspectus available May. For further information write Registrar, Dayton Art Institute, PO Box 941, Dayton, OH 45401.

OKLAHOMA

GREEN COUNTRY ART ASSOCIATION DOGWOOD ART FESTIVAL,* Poteau. Annual, Easter-Mothers Day. Paintings & sculpture only. Open to artists of Ark, Kans, Mo, Okla & Tex. Jury. Fee. Entry cards due Apr 2, work due Apr 14. For further information write Eloise J Schellstede, Pres, Green Country Art Association, 1825 E 15th St, Tulsa, OK 74104.

GREEN COUNTRY ART ASSOCIATION PLUS 65 ART SHOW,* Tulsa. Annual, Mar. Paintings & sculpture only. Open to artists of Ark, Kans, Mo, Okla & Tex. No fee to artists 65 yrs & older or mem, others $10; 10% comn. Entries due Mar 5-17. For further information write Eloise J Schellstede, Pres, Green Country Art Association, 1825 E 15th St, Tulsa, OK 74104.

NATIONAL COMPETITION FOR AMERICAN INDIAN ARTISTS,* Tulsa. Annual, May. Painting, sculpture & graphics. Open to artists of American Indian descent living in the US. Jury, prizes. No fee. Entries due first Sat in Apr. For further information write Dr Donald G Humphrey, Dir, Philbrook Art Center, 2727 S Rockford Rd, Tulsa, OK 74114.

OKLAHOMA ART CENTER EIGHT STATE EXHIBITION OF PAINTING & SCULPTURE, Oklahoma City. Biennial, Sept-Oct. Painting & sculpture. Open to residents of Ark, Colo, Kans, La, Mo, NMex, Okla & Tex. Jury, purchase awards. Fee $5. Entries due by Aug. For further information write, Oklahoma Art Center, 3113 Pershing Blvd, Oklahoma City, OK 73107.

OKLAHOMA ART CENTER NATIONAL PRINT & DRAWING EXHIBITION, Oklahoma City. Annual, Apr. Prints & drawings. Open to any resident of the US. Jury, awards. Fee $5. For further information write Oklahoma Art Center, 3113 Pershing Blvd, Oklahoma City, OK 73107.

THE OKLAHOMA MUSEUM OF ART ARTISTS' SALON, Oklahoma City. Annual, Spring. All media of painting, graphics and sculpture. Open to all U.S. artists. Jury, cash awards. Fee $3 per item entered. Prospectus will be sent upon request. Usual deadline for all entries between Mar 15 and Apr 1 (varies each year). For further information write James K Reeve, Dir, 7316 Nichols Road, Oklahoma City, OK 73120.

PHILBROOK ART CENTER OKLAHOMA ANNUAL,* Tulsa. Annual, Apr. Painting, sculpture & graphics. Open to residents of Okla or former residents who have lived in the state at least one year. Jury, prizes. Fee $1 per entry. Entries due first Sat in Mar. For further information write Dr Donald G Humphrey, Dir, Philbrook Art Center, 2727 S Rockford Rd, Tulsa, OK 74114.

OREGON

COOS ART MUSEUM CRAFT EXHIBITION, Coos Bay. Annual, July. Crafts or functional art. Open to persons anywhere in the US. Juried/invitational show, cash prizes and merit awards. Fee $5 for two craft items. Entries due one month in advance of show. For further information write Maggie Karl, Coos Art Museum, 515 Market Ave, Coos Bay, OR 97420.

COOS ART MUSEUM PAINTING AND SCULPTURE EXHIBITION, Coos Bay. Annual, Nov. Painting, sculpture/non-functional art. Open to persons anywhere in the US. Juried/invitational show, cash prizes and merit awards. Fee $7.50. Entries due one month in advance of show. For further information write Maggie Karl, Coos Art Museum, 515 Market Ave, Coos Bay, OR 97420.

COOS ART MUSEUM PHOTOGRAPHY EXHIBITION, Coos Bay. Annual, Apr. Photography. Open to persons anywhere in the US. Juried/invitational show, cash prizes and merit awards. Fee $10 for three prints. Entries due one month in advance of show. For further information write Maggie Karl, Coos Art Museum, 515 Market Ave, Coos Bay, OR 97420.

PENNSYLVANIA

AMERICAN COLOR PRINT SOCIETY,* Philadelphia. Annual, Mar. All print media in color. Open to all printmakers working in color. Jury, awards. Fee $2.75. Entry due Feb. For further information write American Color Print Society, 2022 Walnut St, Philadelphia, PA 19103.

CARNEGIE INSTITUTE THREE RIVERS ARTS FESTIVAL, Pittsburgh. Annual, May. Painting, sculpture, crafts, photographs, banners & prints. Open to all artists within Western Pa. and surrounding communities. Fee, 25% comn. Entry cards & slides due Mar 31. For further information write Barbara L Widdoes, Exec Dir, Three Rivers Arts Festival, 4400 Forbes Ave, Pittsburgh, PA 15213.

PRINT CLUB BIENNIAL INTERNATIONAL OPEN EXHIBITION, Philadelphia. Biennial, Spring. Prints (limited edition only). Open to all. Juried, purchase awards; prizes become part of The Print Club collection at the Philadelphia Museum of Art. No fee. Entry details to be announced. For further information write Ofelia Garcia, Director, The Print Club, 1614 Latimer St, Philadelphia, PA 19103.

WASHINGTON & JEFFERSON COLLEGE NATIONAL PAINTING SHOW, Washington. Annual, Mar-Apr. All painting. Open to any US artist, 18 yrs old. Prizes & purchase awards. Fee $3 for one or two slide entries. Entry cards & slides due Jan, work due Mar. For further information write Paul B Edwards, Art Dept, Washington & Jefferson College, Washington, PA 15301.

RHODE ISLAND

ART ASSOCIATION OF NEWPORT.* Annual, July. Oil, watercolor, prints, drawings, photographs (alternate with small sculpture). Open to all American artists. Jury, awards. Fee $7 ($7 for 2 photographs). Entry due early June. For further information write Art Association of Newport, 76 Bellevue Ave, Newport, RI 02840.

PROVIDENCE ART CLUB. Three open shows every year, scheduled at different times & varied from season to season; for instance, an open small sculpture show, an open drawing or print show, or perhaps a painting or craft show. For further information write Mrs Tore Dalenius, Providence Art Club, 11 Thomas St, Providence, RI 02903.

PROVIDENCE WATERCOLOR CLUB.* Annual, Oct-Nov. Watercolor. Open toNew Eng artists. Cash awards, prizes & ribbons. Fee $8. Work due Oct 14. For further information write Barbara Besson, 6 Thomas St, Providence, RI 02906.

SOUTH COUNTRY ART ASSOCIATION ANNUAL OPEN SHOW, Kingston. Annual, Apr. All media. Open to all professional artists. Jury, cash awards. Fee $3 per entry, limit 3 per artist. Entries due first Fri & Sat in Apr. For further information write South County Art Association, Helme House, 1319 Kingstown, RI 02881.

TENNESSEE

BROOKS MEMORIAL ART GALLERY MID-SOUTH EXHIBITION,* Memphis. Biennial, date for next exhibition not set. Paintings, drawings, sculpture, prints. Open to artists residing within 250 air miles of Memphis. Jury, awards. For further information write Mid-South Exhibition, Brooks Memorial Art Gallery, Overton Park, Memphis, TN 38112.

DULIN NATIONAL PRINT & DRAWING COMPETITION,* Knoxville. Annual, May. Prints & drawings. Open to all artists living & working in the US. Prizes. Fee $5. Entry cards due mid-Mar, work due later Mar. For further information write Dulin Gallery of Art, 3100 Kingston Pike, Knoxville, TN 37919.

HUNTER ANNUAL EXHIBITION, Chattanooga. Annual, Mar. Painting and drawing. Open to artists in Ala, Ark, Fla, Ga, Ky, La, Miss, NC, SC, Tenn, Va. Jury, $6,000 in purchase awards. Fee $5. Entries due in February. For further information, write Hunter Museum of Art, Bluff View, Chattanooga, TN 37403.

MISSISSIPPI RIVER CRAFT SHOW, Memphis. Biennial, Sept-Oct. Open to craftsmen residing within the ten mid-continent states bordering the Mississippi River. For further information write Mississippi River Craft Show, Brooks Memorial Art Gallery, Overton Park, Memphis, TN 38112.

SOUTHERN WATERCOLOR SOCIETY ANNUAL EXHIBITION, Memphis. Annual, Feb to be held in Denton, Texas. Watercolor. Open to all artists living in 18 southern states, plus Washington, DC. Juried, $5000 awards. Fee $15 members, $20 non-members. Slides due November 15. For further information write Southern Watercolor Society, PO Box 12250, Memphis, TN 38112.

TENNESSEE ALL-STATE ARTISTS EXHIBITION,* Nashville. Annual, Nov. Oil, mixed, pastel, watercolor, graphics & sculpture. Open to all artists residing in Tenn. Purchase awards. Fee $3 per entry; 10% comn. Entry cards & work due Sept 25-Oct 13. For further information write Watkins Institute, Sixth & Church, Nashville, TN 37219.

TENNESSEE ART LEAGUE & PARTHENON OF NASHVILLE CENTRAL STATES ART EXHIBITION.* Annual, May. Painting, graphics, sculpture. Open to artists of Ala, Ark, Ga, Ky, Miss, NC, SC, Tenn, Va & other areas within 300 miles of Nashville. Jury, purchase awards & prizes. Fee $3 per entry, limit three. Work due Mar 25-Apr 2. For further information write Central States Art Exhibition, The Parthenon, Nashville, TN 37203.

TEXAS

AMARILLO ART CENTER EXHIBITION. Biennial, Oct 1979. Any two-dimensional work. Open to all artists in Texas, New Mexico, Oklahoma, Colorado and Kansas. Juried, purchase prizes and awards variable.

Fee may be waived for 1979. Entries due summer of 1979. For further information write Jerry Daviee, Curator, Amarillo Art Center, Box 447, Amarillo, TX 79178.

DEL MAR COLLEGE DRAWING & SMALL SCULPTURE SHOW,* Corpus Christi. Annual, May. Any drawing or small sculpture. Open to all US artists. Jury, prizes & purchase awards. Fee $5 per entry, no limit. Entry cards and work due Mar 25. For further information write Joseph A Cain, Chmn, Dept of Fine Arts, Del Mar College, Corpus Christi, TX 78404.

EL PASO MUSEUM OF ART NATIONAL SUN CARNIVAL. Biennial, Dec. All painting. Open to any US citizen residing in the US and its territories. Jury, purchase awards. For further information write Secy to Cur of Collections, El Paso Museum of Art, 1211 Montana, El Paso, TX 79902.

RIO GRANDE VALLEY ARTS & CRAFTS EXPOSITION,* Brownsville. Annual, Nov. All media. Open to all artists & craftsmen. Fee $25, no comn. Entry cards due Oct & work due Nov. For further information write Mrs Tencha Sloss, Gen Chmn, Brownsville Art League, PO Box 3404, Brownsville, TX 78520.

TEXAS FINE ARTS ASSOCIATION ANNUAL EXHIBITION,* Austin. Annual, May-June. Oil, acrylic, watercolor, drawing, sculpture & mixed media. Open to all artists residing in US. Jury, prizes, cash awards & purchase awards of approximately $5000. Fee $5 (no fee for member's first slide). Slides due Feb 1, work due Apr. For further information write Mrs John D Haltom, Exec Dir, PO Box 5023, Austin, TX 78763.

TEXAS WATERCOLOR SOCIETY EXHIBITION,* San Antonio. Annual, May. Transparent or opaque watercolor on paper; entries must be framed under plastic. Open to present & former residents of Tex. Cash awards, purchase awards. Fee $7.50 per painting for non-mem, 10% comn. Entry cards & work due Jan 10. For further information write Mary Lou Lewis, Exhib Chmn, 204 Ridgemont, San Antonio, TX 78209.

WEST TEXAS NATIONAL WATERCOLOR SHOW, Lubbock. Annual, Dec-Jan. Watercolor. Open to all artists in US. Over $3500 in purchase prizes & awards. Fee $5 per entry, no limit. All will be by slides only; deadline for slides April 20th. For further information write The Museum, Texas Tech University, Lubbock, TX 79409.

UTAH

SPRINGVILLE MUSEUM OF ART ANNUAL NATIONAL APRIL SHOW. Annual, Apr. Paintings, drawings and prints. Open to all artists in the US. Juried, approximately $2000 cash prizes and purchase awards. Fee $4 per work, limit 2 works per artist. Entries are pre-juried by slides. Prospectus available. For further information write Springville Museum of Art, 126 E 400th South, Springville, UT 84663.

UTAH STATEWIDE COMPETITION AND EXHIBIT,* Salt Lake City. Annual, June through Labor Day. Painting, drawing, watercolor. Open to residents of Utah. Jury, $1000 purchase award, other awards as merited. Fee $2. Entries due approx May 15 (varies each yr). For further information write Utah State Division of Fine Arts, 609 E South Temple St, Salt Lake City, UT 94108.

VIRGINIA

AMERICAN DRAWING EXHIBITION,* Norfolk. Biennial, Jan-Feb (odd years). Drawing. Open to all adult artists residing in the US. Jury, awards. Entries due Nov. For further information write American Drawing Biennial, Chrysler Museum at Norfolk, Olney Rd & Mowbray Arch, Norfolk, VA 23510.

IRENE LEACHE MEMORIAL EXHIBITION,* Norfolk. Biennial, Mar-Apr (even years). All painting & drawing media (pastels not acceptable). Open to artists residing in Va, NC, SC, Ga, Md, WVa and DC. Jury, cash awards. Fee $10; limit three; 20% comn; Entry & cards due Jan 12. For further information write Irene Leache Memorial Exhibition, Chrysler Museum of Norfolk, Olney Rd & Mowbray Arch, Norfolk, VA 23510.

NATIONAL SEAWALL ART SHOW, Portsmouth. Annual, May. All original oil, acrylic, watercolor, graphics, photography, sculpture & crafts. Open to all artists. Over $5,100 in cash awards, prizes, purchase awards & ribbons. Fee $13.00 & $17.00. Deadline for entry is May 1.

Entries due May & work due first day of show; artist must be present. For further information write Donna Morris, Portsmouth Seawall Art Show, 430 High Street, Portsmouth, VA 23704

RICHMOND CRAFT FAIR. Annual, Nov. US designer crafts, no oil/painting/kits, etc. Open to US designer craftsmen. Juried, 5 color slides, $2500 in purchase prize, and cash awards. Fee $3 slide, $30 booth, 15% comn. Entry slides due June 1. For further information write Ruth T Summers, Director, Hand Work Shop, Inc., 316 N 24th St, Richmond, VA 23223.

ROANOKE FINE ARTS CENTER JURIED ARTIST EXHIBITION. Annual, Nov. All media, except craft. Open to Virginia artists. Juried, purchase prizes and Certificates of Distinction. Fee $10, limit of three entries. For further information write Roanoke Fine Arts Center, PO Box 8162, 301 23rd St SW, Roanoke, VA 24014.

VIRGINIA ARTISTS, Richmond. Biennial, May-June (odd years). Original paintings, drawings, watercolor, collages & sculpture. Jury, awards. Limit three works. Entries due Jan 1. For further information write Virginia Museum of Fine Arts, Boulevard & Grove Aves, Richmond, VA 23221.

VIRGINIA CRAFTSMEN, Richmond. Biennial, Mar-Apr. Personally designed crafts in metal, textile, wood, ceramics & leather. Open to natives & residents of Va & those former residents who lived in Va for three years. Jury, awards. Limit of three works. Entries due by Jan. For further information write Virginia Museum of Fine Arts, Boulevard & Grove Aves, Richmond, VA 23221.

VIRGINIA DESIGNERS, Richmond. Biennial, Jan-Feb. Magazine & newspaper advertisements, brochures, folders, catalogues, programs, posters & others. Open to natives & residents of Va & those former residents who lived in Va for three years. Jury, awards. Fee $5, limit of ten panels. Entries due by Nov. For further information write Virginia Museum of Fine Arts, Boulevard & Grove Aves, Richmond, VA 23221.

VIRGINIA PHOTOGRAPHERS, Richmond. Biennial, Oct-Nov. Monochrome & color photographic prints & color transparencies. Open to natives & residents of Va & those former residents who lived in Va for three years. Jury, awards. Fee $5 for non-mem (mem free); limit five prints & five transparencies. Entries by Aug. For further information write Virginia Museum of Fine Arts, Boulevard & Grove Aves, Richmond, VA 23221.

WASHINGTON

FOOTPRINT, NW INTERNATIONAL SMALL FORMAT PRINT EXHIBITION, Seattle. Annual, June. Original prints (no photo or monotypes). Open to all living artists. Juried, approximately $3000 prizes. Fee $6 in US, $8 outside US. Entries due January 1. For further information write Footprint, 702 First Avenue, Seattle, WA 98104.

NEW PHOTOGRAPHICS, Ellensburg. Annual, Apr-May. Photography. Open internationally. Juried, no prizes. No fee. Entry slides due March. For further information write Central Washington University, Art Department, Ellensburg, WA 98926.

NORTHWEST CRAFTS EXHIBITION, Seattle. Biennial, Oct-Nov (odd years). Crafts in all media. Open to craftspeople presently working or residing in the states of Washington, Oregon, Idaho, Montana, Wyoming, and Alaska. Juried with awards. No entry fee. Entries due September. For further information write Henry Art Gallery, University of Washington, Seattle, WA 98195.

NORTHWEST WATERCOLOR SOCIETY EXHIBITION,* Bellevue. Annual, Apr. Water based painting on paper. Open to all artists living in Alaska, Idaho, Mont, Ore, Wash & BC. Cash awards, purchase prizes. Fee $5 30% comn. For further information or prospectus write Northwest Watercolor Society, 2829 140th Ave, Bellevue, WA 98005.

WEST VIRGINIA

HUNTINGTON GALLERIES—EXHIBITION 280: PAINTING, SCULPTURE AND CRAFTS. Biennial, Mar - Apr (79). Open to artists above high school age, living within 280 miles of Huntington. Jury, awards. Fee, Slide entries due Dec. 4, 1978, accepted work due Jan. 29, 1979. For further information write Exhibition 280, Program Coordinator, Huntington Galleries, 2033 McCoy Rd, Huntington, WV 25701.

WISCONSIN

LAKEFRONT FESTIVAL OF ARTS, Milwaukee. Annual. June. Multi-media. Open to professional artists and craftsmen from across the country. Juried, $5000 in prizes. Fee $8 for 1978. Entries due mid-March. For further information write Rosalie Goldstein, Milwaukee Art Center, 750 N Lincoln Memorial Dr, Milwaukee, WI 53202.

STEVENS POINT FINE ARTS EXHIBITION.* Annual, Oct. Painting, drawing, graphics. Open to all artists residing in Wis. Jury, $500 top award, other cash & purchase awards. Fee $10. Entry cards & work due Oct 21. For further information write Mrs James Delzell, 1124 Ridge Rd, Stevens Point, WI 54481.

WYOMING

AMERICAN NATIONAL MINIATURE SHOW, Laramie. Annual Oct. Paintings and all drawings in all media. Open to all US artists. Cash awards and ribbons. Size limit framed, 10 x 12. For further information write Laramie Art Guild, 603½ Ivinson Avenue, Laramie, WY. 82070.

WESTERN STATES ART EXHIBITION,* Cody. Annual, June - July. Oil, watercolor, graphics, pastels, sculpture, ceramics & other (all work-must be suitable for hanging). Open to all artists. Cash awards & ribbons. Fee $5 prof, $3.50 amateur for each work, limit three. For further information write Cody County Art League, PO Box 1524, Cody, WY 82414.

CANADA

CONCOURS D'ART GRAPHIQUE QUÉBÉCOIS, Sherbrooke, Québec. Biennial, June - Aug. 1979. Prints, drawings, all media. Open to all artists residing in Québec. Juried, $2000 in prizes. No fee. Entries due February 28. For further information write Graham Cantieni Directeur Artistique, Centre Culturel, Université de Sherbrooke, Sherbrooke, PQ, Canada J1K 2R1.

MUSEUM OF NORTHERN BRITISH COLUMBIA, PRINCE RUPERT MUSEUM ART GALLERY. Annual, and biennial, Summer, late Spring, Christmas. Mixed, mainly oil, tempera, etc, but includes sculpture in different media and crafts. Open to local and regional artists. Juried for photography or school art. For further information write Museum Art Gallery Coordinator, Box 669, Prince Rupert, BC, Canada, V8J 3S1.

SOUTHWEST 39, Windsor. Annual, March. All media. Open to artists of the Southwestern Ont Region. Jury prizes. Fee $3. Entries due Feb 7. For further information write The Art Gallery of Windsor, 445 Riverside Dr W, Windsor, ON, Can N9A 6T8.

WESTERN ONTARIO EXHIBITION,* London. Annual, May. All painting media, sculpture, prints, drawings, wall hangings (batik or woven). Open to all residents of Southwestern Ont. Jury, prizes & awards. No fee. Entries due early Apr. For further information write Secy, Annual Western Ontario Exhibition, London Art Gallery, 305 Queen's Ave, London, ON, Can N6B 1X2.

Traveling Exhibitions Booking Agencies

ALABAMA ART LEAGUE,* Montgomery Museum of Fine Arts, 440 S McDonough St, Montgomery, AL 36104. *Pres* A Phillip Coley. Exhibit—approx. 25-30 drawings, prints and small paintings selected from the annual juried exhibit by juror. No rental fee; in-state, pulled via trailer by Art League member; out-of-state, arrangements can be made. Catalog available.

ALBERTA ART FOUNDATION, 11th Floor, CN Tower, 10004-104 Ave, Edmonton, AB, Canada, T5J 0K1. *Coordinator/Consultant* W Tin Ng.
Exhibits—Printmakers of Alberta, 19 prints by contemporary Alberta artists. Other exhibitions can be arranged if interested parties write and indicate space available. Requests giving an advance notice of 4 months would be appreciated. No rental fee. Transportation arrangements—the Foundation will pre-pay one way and the borrower is responsible to pay for returning the exhibitions. Catalogs available.

AMARILLO ART CENTER, 2200 South Van Buren, Box 447, Amarillo, TX 79178. *Dir* Thomas A Livesay.
Exhibits—American Images, photographs from the Farm Security Administration, currently the exhibit is circulating with assistance from the National Endowment for the Humanities. Exhibit booked through April, 1980. Full description in *Humanities* magazine, Spring, 1977. Rental fee $150 through 1980; $250 after Jan. 1981. Catalogs available.

AMERICAN ABSTRACT ARTISTS,* 218 W. 20th St, New York, NY 10011. *Pres* Leo Rabkin.
Traveling shows available. No set rental fees.

AMERICAN FEDERATION OF ARTS, 41 E. 65th St, New York, NY 10021. *Dir* Wilder Green.
Approximately 30 exhibitions circulated in the U.S. and abroad—Painting, sculpture, graphic arts, photography, design and crafts. Exhibitions and catalogues organized by AFA with guest curators for museums, colleges, schools and art centers. AFA Chapter Members are entitled to reduced participation fees.

THE AMERICAN INSTITUTE OF GRAPHIC ARTS, 1059 Third Ave, New York, NY 10021. *Exec Dir* Caroline Hightower.
Annual exhibitions of Best Books and Communication Graphics, plus rotating exhibitions of Covers, Insides, Illustration, Packaging, and one man shows or special projects. Slide shows available as well. For information contact Travelling Show Co-ordinator.

AMERICAN WATERCOLOR SOCIETY, 1083 Fifth Avenue, New York, NY 10028. *Chmn Traveling Exhibitions* Edmond J FitzGerald.
Two exhibitions of fifty paintings each are selected by the Jury of Awards from our annual exhibitions for a one-year circuit. One exhibition is framed, the other uniformly matted (28 x 36 or 24 x 30, depending on the size of the painting). Several prizewinners from the annual are included in each group. The framed show weighs about 1500 lbs, the matted, about 200 lbs. The AWS annuals are all juried, member and non-member, exhibitions, held each April in New York. Requests cannot be considered until the following October. Rental fee of $200 per two week (minimum) booking. Exhibiting organizations pay on-going shipping. AWS carries limited insurance during the circuit. Two of the Annual Exhibition Catalogs (containing traveling exhibition listings and itineraries) are provided, plus publicity information and several black and white photographs of prize winning paintings.

ANCHORAGE HISTORICAL AND FINE ARTS MUSEUM, 121 W. Seventh Ave, Anchorage, AK 99501. *Dir* R. L. Shalkop.

Circulation of exhibitions in Alaska only. No rental fee; transportation variable. No catalogs available.

ARKANSAS ARTS CENTER, State Services, MacArthur Park, PO Box 2137, Little Rock, AR 72203. *Dir State Services* June Freeman.
Exhibits—Arkansas Weavers' Work—14 works of varied sizes; Crafts—13 works; Disfarmer of Heber Springs—44 works; George Fisher Cartoons—24 black and white cartoons, panel of text; Images in Black and White—24 black and white prints (11 x 14 framed), 2 panels of text; Young Arkansas Artists—20 in each part; Inez Whitfield Watercolors—34 works; Old Roots, New Directions: Arkansas Blues Today—24 (15 x 19 framed), 45-minute cassette tape; Shapes—10 works of varied sizes; Ten Intaglio Prints; Ten West Coast Artists—10 works (average size 30 x 22); Texture—10 works (average size 25 x 34); Watercolor—16 works of varied sizes; Works by Robert Andrew Parker—12 works (average size 21 x 28); Make-A-Place. Instate rental fees: free, $25 or $50 plus transportation; out-of-state rental fees double. No catalogs available.

ARKANSAS STATE UNIVERSITY, Drawer AAAA, Art Department, Box 846, State College, AR 72467. *Coordinator of Traveling Exhibitions* Donn Hedman.
Faculty Traveling Exhibit—11 participating artists, 50 two-dimensional pieces—oils, watercolors, prints, drawings, 25 three-dimensional pieces—sculpture, ceramics, jewelry. Works range from traditional to contemporary. No rental fee, shipping one way. Catalogs available.

ASSOCIATED AMERICAN ARTISTS, 663 Fifth Ave, New York, NY 10022. *Dir Traveling Exhibitions* Robert Koo.
Original prints in all media by artists of many countries. Etchings, lithographs, woodcuts, serigraphs, intaglios, stencils, in black and white, and in color.
Group Exhibitions: American Master Prints; Authors! Authors!; Prints by Jack Coughlin and Sidney Chafetz; New Talent in Printmaking.
One-Man Shows: John Taylor Arms, Mario Avati, Milton Avery, Will Barnet, Thomas Hart Benton, John Steuart Curry, Fritz Eichenberg, Lyonel Feininger, Rockwell Kent, Armin Landeck, Raphael Soyer, Paul Wunderlich.
Private and public organizations and institutions having facilities for the care of the fine prints eligible. Rental fees from $100 to $250. For additional information, please write or call 212-755-4211.

ASSOCIATION OF SCIENCE-TECHNOLOGY CENTERS (ASTC), 1016 Sixteenth St, NW, Washington, DC 20036. *Exec Dir* Michael Templeton.
Exhibits—approx 20 museum quality exhibitions, predominantly science and technology oriented, but also including crafts, photography, and cultural exhibitions. The three exhibits described here are representative. Theme and Variation—Holography by Anait, consists of 22 large and small holographic panels, and is a stunning example of the use of lasers to create artistic sculpture. It uses about 100 running feet. The participation fee for a 6-week booking is $425 to ASTC members, $525 to non-members. A catalog and description of holography are supplied.
Threadlines Pakistan consists of 300 examples of the contemporary textile industry in Pakistan. It uses from 2,000 - 4,500 sq ft and 200/300 feet of wall space. The participation fee for a 6-week booking is $150 to ASTC members, $250 to non-members. A documentary film and a brochure accompany the exhibit.
Medical Photography by Lennart Nilsson consists of 44 photographs of human internal organs by the famed Swedish photographer. The exhibit requires 120 running feet. The participation fee for a 6-week booking is $250 to ASTC members, $400 to non-members. Brochures accompany this exhibit.

Small rental fees are charged. Lendee institutions are responsible for the cost of inbound shipping unless otherwise specified. Shipping arrangements are made by ASTC. Catalogs are available with complete descriptions of exhibitions circulated by ASTC.

BALTIMORE MUSEUM OF ART, Art Museum Drive, Baltimore, MD 21218. *Coordinator of Traveling Exhibitions* Susan Cumins.
Exhibitions available only to institutions within Maryland. Six to seven exhibitions per year, up to 30 pieces in each. 1977-78—Georges Rouault: Miserere; What's in a Face? How to Look at Portraits; Charles Carroll of Carrollton and the American Revolution; Maryland through the Stereoscope; Oceanic Images: Figurative Art of New Guinea; Western Maryland Artists. 1978-79—Personal Realities: Five Ways of Seeing; Period Needlework in America; East Baltimore: Tradition and Transition; Focus on Fiber; The Anatomy of an Artwork. Rental fee $75 per 4-week booking; it includes transportation, installation, printed brochures and posters. Catalogs available.

BURCHFIELD CENTER, 1300 Elmwood Ave, Buffalo, NY 14222. *Dir* Dr Edna M Lindemann.
Exhibition—Burchfield Wallpapers, includes approx. 30 framed pieces of the original Burchfield wallpaper produced by the Birge Co, 1921-29, up to 4 original paintings by the artist for wallpapers, one of three panels of original watercolor for Riviera scenic paper, two panels (96 x 72 in.) of two of the original Burchfield papers, Modernistic Pattern and Stylized Flowers in Diagonal Pattern, mounted on masonite and one panel mounted on masonite of The Birches and of the 1973 reproduction of the Sunflowers. A copy of the 35mm sound/color film, The Sites of a City: Charles Burchfield's Buffalo, (exclusive property of the Burchfield Center), included in rental. Rental fee: $850 plus transportation. In New York State travel arrangements are made through GANYS; others by arrangement. Catalogues available at $4 each.

BURNABY ART GALLERY, 6344 Gilpin St, Burnaby, BC, Canada V5G 2J3. *Dir* Jack Hardman.
Exhibits—Don Portelance—Oils and Acrylics, framed, crated exhibition for smaller gallery; Cast Metal Sculpture—10 Vancouver Sculptors small cast metal works, packed in cases to be used as plinths; Peter Ochs—Sculpture in Wood, suitable for smaller gallery; Joe Plaskett—British Columbia Series of Pastels recently rediscovered from 1958; Leighton Davis—large exhibition of recent watercolors; Douglas Cardinal—Architect, Plans, Photographs & Models of major Canadian architect. No rental fee except for Douglas Cardinal ($250). Transportation to be paid to next exhibition center. Catalogs available for Cast Metal Sculpture and Douglas Cardinal.

C W POST ART GALLERY, C W Post College, Long Island University, Greenvale, NY 11548. *Dir* Joan Vita Miller.
Exhibits—Gertrude Stein and her Friends. A photographic exhibition consisting of 28 (30 x 40) photographic enlargements from Yale University's Beinecke Rare Book and Manuscript Library. The collection gives the viewer insight into the stimulating world of art and literature of an era inhabited by such luminaries as Picasso, Matisse, Braque, Renoir, Gris, Picabia and Vellotton. Fifty illustrated catalogs (20 pages) with an introduction by James Mellow, former New York Times art critic will be included.
C W Post Permanent Collection. An exhibition of contemporary graphics selected from the permanent collection represents a variety of styles comprising 20th century printmaking. No catalog available.
Rental fee is $250 per month. Transportation to be arranged.

CAMPBELL MUSEUM, Campbell Place, Camden, NJ 08101. *Museum Asst* Bess Brock.
Exhibit—18th century porcelain and silver soup tureens and accompanying catalogs. No rental fee. All transportation costs paid by Campbell Museum.

CENTER FOR CREATIVE PHOTOGRAPHY, 843 East University Blvd, Tucson, AZ 85719. *Center Asst/Exhib* Marnie Gillett.
Exhibits—Ansel Adams—A Survey. 40 framed prints personally selected by Adams to represent his long and distinguished career in photography. 100 running feet. Rental fee $500 per month.
Ansel Adams—Photographs of the Southwest: 1928-1968. 100 framed prints. This exhibition is a landmark as it culminates 40 years of work by Adams in the Southwest states. 200 running feet. Rental fee $1,000 per month.
Evidence by Mike Mandel and Larry Sultan. An exhibition of 79 photographs selected from government agencies, educational institutions and corporations. Rental fee $400 per month.
Ralph Gibson, Photographer. 26 black and white photographs—autobiographical probings of an unfamiliar terrain of dreams and the subconscious. Rental fee $350 per month.

Exhibits are shipped framed and ready for installation, with a press packet included. Transportation and full insurance coverage against theft and damage are the additional responsibility of the renter.

CHEROKEE NATIONAL MUSEUM, PO Box 515, TSA-LA-GI, Tahlequah, OK 74464. *Exec V Pres* M A Hagerstrand.
Temporary exhibitions arranged with small institutions to their needs and desires and our capabilities and schedule. Subjects available are Cherokee history and culture and limited Indian art on the Trail of Tears theme. Rental fees arranged for each exhibit. No catalogs available.

CLEMSON UNIVERSITY, College of Architecture, Rudolph Lee Gallery, Clemson, SC 29631. *Coordinator of Educational Media and Exhibits* Tom Dimond.
Exhibits—Foundry Art, 50 wooden patterns for industrial machines; photographs demonstrating casting process; SC Architecture, 114 black and white photo murals describing 300 years of South Carolina architecture. Rental fee and transportation arrangements on request.

CONTEMPORARY CHRISTIAN ARTISTS, PO Box 68, Normal, IL 61761. *Dir* Tom R Toperzer.
Exhibitions of art by Christian artists—one-person, group, thematic, media, exhibitions ranging in scale. Rental fees plus transportation one way. Catalogs available.

DELAWARE ART MUSEUM, 2301 Kentmere Parkway, Wilmington, DE 19806. *Coordinator Traveling Exhibitions* Susan Hall Brooks.
Three types of loan material available to the public—exhibitions (mounted reproductions ready for hanging); portfolios (slightly smaller pictures suitable for classroom); and slides (for supplementing your exhibition, class lecture). The material includes photography, reproductions, original works of art, records of recent exhibitions. Please call or write for additional information. No rental fee for instate schools; out-of-state institutions annual fee of $25, mailing charges additional. Catalogs available.

EDMONTON ART GALLERY, 2 Sir Winston Churchill Square, Edmonton, AB, Canada T5J 2C1. *Exten Cur* Ray Ouellet.
Exhibits—William Tilland—Landscape Photographs (28 photographs 14 x 18, 42 running feet); rental fee $150.
William Leroy Stevenson (26 oil paintings, most 24 x 30, 120 running feet); rental fee $200.
Violet Owen—Drawings and Paintings (20 works, 100 running feet); rental fee $150.
Alan Reynolds—Drawings by a Sculptor (20 drawings, 4 photographs, 16 x 20, 100 running feet); rental fee $100.
Signey Tillim—Adam and Eve Drawings (38 works 14 x 18, 80 running feet); rental fee $200.
The John Henry Hinton Photographs—China 1894-1918 (70 prints from original negatives, framed 14 x 18, 210 running feet); rental fee $200.
Rental fees, as noted with each exhibit. Crates provided. Exhibiting center pays one-way shipping charges. Insurance cost included in rental fee. Catalogs or posters available.

EDO COMPREHENSIVE EXHIBITION SERVICES, 453 Sycamore Road, Santa Monica, CA 90402. William Osmun. Tel: 213 454 8041.
Exhibits—Amish Quilts, about 1880-1930; Jasper Johns/Screenprints, 1968-1978; Herbert Bayer: Photographic Works, 1925-1936; Pictures of a Floating World, Japanese Woodcuts, late 18th-mid-19th centuries; Serge Lifar Collection of Ballet Set and Costume Designs, 1904-mid-1940s; Photographs of Moholy-Nagy, mid-1920s-mid-1940s; The Sensuous Line, Indian Drawings of the 17th, 18th, and 19th centuries from the Paul F Walter Collection; Navajo Blankets 1850s-1890s from the Collection of Anthony Berlant; Indians in Washington, DC, Portrait photographs 1858-1890; Brooke Alexander, A Decade of Print Publishing, 1968-1978; Indonesian Textiles. Rental fees $850 - $3,000, participant pays one-way transportation. Catalogs available.

ESMARK, INC, 55 E Munroe, Chicago, IL 60603. *Asst Mgr Corporate Affairs* Liz Sode. A collection of Currier & Ives prints capturing early American life—650 original Currier & Ives lithographs and memorabilia broken into four groups each providing a cross-section of Currier & Ives works. They are loaned by contract as complete units.
The Legacy of Currier & Ives is a 16 mm sound and color, 23 minute film providing an extraordinary perspective of the nation's growth during its westward expansion. Over 200 prints from the Esmark Collection are shown in this movie which is made available for use in classrooms and meetings of civic and service organizations through Public Relations Dept, Esmark, Inc. 55 E Monroe, Chicago, IL 60603.

FISK UNIVERSITY MUSEUM, 18th and Jackson Sts, PO Box 2, Nashville, TN 37203. *Cur* R Hall.

William H Johnson exhibit (matted, 17 prints); Works by Contemporary Afro-Americans (20 paintings, prints and photographs). Works on Paper (17 prints and drawings by Afro-Americans); Rental fee and transportation paid by exhibitor.

FLORIDA ARTIST GROUP, INC, 115 Lee Circle, Englewood, FL 33533. *Pres* Leah B Lasbury.
Jury chosen Annual Exhibition of Members Show (34-45 entries) is available following the Spring Exhibition (May). Also, from the local areas other traveling exhibitions are available throughout the year (includes paintings, graphics, sculpture, assemblages). No rental fees; self-financed, hopefully, with help from the galleries and museums. Catalogs available of the Spring Annual.

FORT HAYS STATE UNIVERSITY, Department of Art, Hays, KS 67601. *Chmn* John C Thorns, Jr.
Varied exhibitions available depending upon the desire of the individual renting the exhibition. Rental fee: $50 plus shipping charges. No catalog available.

FRENCH CULTURAL SERVICES, Exhibitions Department, 972 Fifth Ave, New York, NY 10021, *Head Photography Exhibitions* Christian Leprette. Tel: 212-737-9700, exten 716/717.
Exhibits—Andre Villers: "Diurnes", a photographic (black and white) and montage essay done in collaboration with Picasso; Etienne Bertrand Weill—Metaforms (color and black & white); Collection Kahn—Autochromes, first color photographs (Tonkin, Ireland); Americans in France—Margi Ide Brockman, Richard W Golden; Jaydie Putterman; French Photography 1975-1976—50 black and white photographs; Color from France—Philippe de Croix, Florence Gruere, Jean-Philippe Jourdrin, Lilian Rovers; Andre Kertesz and France; Serve Louvat/Jean de Bire—a collection of 50 turn-of-the-century sepia prints; Andre Naggar—color photography; Cartier-Bresson—black and white film strip narrated in English.
Documentary Exhibits—Pictures of American Independence (from the collection of the Chateau de Blerancourt)—64 photographic panels; Victor Segalen 1878-1919 (115 photographs); 19th & early 20th century French Illustrators (original drawings from the Artine Artinian Collection); Posters of the 1890s—original turn-of-the-century posters from France; French Women—59 black & white and color panels; Tendencies of French Contemporary Architecture—96 photographs; Churches and Cathedrals—81 black & white photographs; Cinema—80 years of French movies; Le Metropolitain—68 black & white and color photographs about the Paris Subway yesterday, today and tomorrow; Normandy—19 color photographs.
No rental fees, but one-way shipping costs plus insurance paid by exhibitor. Press releases available upon request. Catalog available.

GUND COLLECTION OF WESTERN ART, One Erieview Plaza, Cleveland, OH 44114 (Mailing Add: 14 Nassau St, PO Box 449, Princeton, NJ 08540). *Exec Dir* Diane Mitnaul.
Exhibit—Late 19th and early 20th century American Western Art (emphasis on Frederic S Remington, Charles M Russell, includes several Bierstadts, Farneys, A J Millers), 70 pieces. Collection is loaned to any interested museum or facility which meets security standards. No rental fee, exhibitor pays cost of insurance and shipping. Catalog available.

HOFSTRA UNIVERSITY, Emily Lowe Gallery, Hempstead, NY 11550. *Dir* Kevin E Consey.
Exhibit—The Art of Boxing, 18th, 19th and 20th century prints, drawings, paintings and sculpture with boxing as the subject matter. Included are works by Riggs, Bellows, Cruikshank, Rowlandson, Currier & Ives, and Nieman, a total of 57 works. Rental fee of $500 for 6-8 week period; includes 100 catalogs.

HUDSON RIVER MUSEUM, 511 Warburton Ave, Trevor Park-on Hudson, Yonkers, NY 10701. *Registrar* Judy Matson.
Exhibit—Lee Friedlander—Photographs, 150 black and white photographs with an illustrated book (137 black and white reproductions). Rental fee is $1,000 for a four week period. Photographs are framed and under plexiglas and will be crated for shipping. Included in the fee are 25 free copies of the book, all expenses of insurance and crating and one-way transportation. Framed size of each photograph is 14 x 18 inches. Bookings in 1979 are still available.

ILLINOIS STATE UNIVERSITY,* Normal, IL. 61761. The University Museums, *Dir* Roslyn A Walker-Oni.
Two exhibits—Development of the Figure Concept in Graphic Art Work by Children from Different Countries, 65 originals, requiring display space of 180-240 running feet, insurance $650; The Development of Spatial Relations in the Graphic Art Work by Children from Different Countries, 59 originals requiring display space of 180-240 running feet,

insurance $590. Rental fee: $100 plus return transportation. Explanatory text includes script, a list notating age, sex, size, country, title and accession number.

INDEPENDENT CURATORS INCORPORATED, 1740 N Street NW, Washington, DC 20036 and 799 Broadway, New York, NY 10003. *Coordinator, New York* Anne Cohen de Pietro.
Exhibits—From Self-Portrait to Autobiography, 45 works and videotapes, approx 120 running feet, includes work by Acconci, L Anderson, Antin, Beckley, Jonas, Oppenheim, Welch, Wilke. Rental fee $1,800 (includes one performance).
Numerals—Mathematical Concepts in Contemporary Art, 40 works, mainly drawings by artists, architects, composers and choreographers whose work is based on serial progressions and number system. Rental fee $1,000.
New Work/New York—22 works by 8 young New York artists, paintings, painted wall sculptures, recent prints and unique books. Rental fee $1,000 (blanket-wrap).
Artists' Books USA—major survey of printed and hand-made books or book-objects from the past decade, 135 books (half to be displayed in cases provided by ICI, the remainder suitable for exhibition or library use). Rental fee $350.
Rental fees stated above are for 4-week period. Exhibitor pays incoming shipping. Catalogs available.

INTERNATIONAL BUSINESS MACHINES CORPORATION, Armonk, NY 10504. *Mgr Design and Arts Programs* NA Costantino.
Exhibit—Models of inventions of Leonardo da Vinci. No rental fee. Transportation costs assumed by IBM on loans to museums, universities, colleges and public libraries. Catalog on request.

INTERNATIONAL EXCHANGE PRINT EXHIBITIONS, Portland Art Museum, 1219 SW Park Avenue, Portland, OR 97205. *Cur Prints & Drawings* Gordon W Gilkey. Tel: 503-226-2811.
Exhibits of about 100 each contemporary original graphic arts from abroad with new exhibits imported each year. Prorated expenses plus one-way transportation. Catalogs on request.

INTERNATIONAL EXHIBITIONS FOUNDATION, 1729 H Street NW, Suite 310, Washington, DC 20006. Tel: 202-298-7010. *President* Mrs John A Pope.
Organizes and circulates art exhibitions throughout the United States, Canada, and Europe. Exhibitions in the fields of painting, sculpture, photography, drawings, prints, architecture, and decorative arts are available. Approximately 50 percent are special loan exhibitions from abroad. All exhibitions are accompanied by scholarly catalogues published by the Foundation in conjunction with the tours. Many exhibitions are also supplemented by educational, interpretive materials such as slides, film, and photomurals. Exhibitions are available to museums and galleries for a wide range of rental fees plus transportation charges to the next exhibitor.

INTERNATIONAL MUSEUM OF PHOTOGRAPHY, 900 East Ave, Rochester, NY 14607. Tel: 716-271-3361. *Dir* Robert Doherty.
Exhibits—Eugene Atget; Harry Callahan/City (50 prints); Contemporary Photographers VI; Contemporary Photographers VII; Bruce Davidson; Robert Doisneau; Robert Frank; Lewis Hine II; Eadweard Muybridge; Arnold Newman; Photo/Graphics; W Eugene Smith; Tulsa/Larry Clark; Jerry Uelsmann; West of the Rockies; Carl Toth; Josef Sudek; Gary Hallman; Mark Cohen; A Panorama of the American Movie Still Photograph; Roy Stryker, The Humane Propagandist; Arthur Rothstein, My Land, My People; Stephen Livick; Vedutie Della Camera. Rental for one month periods, cost includes insurance and one-way transportation. Slide sets relating to the history of photography are also available. For further information on exhibitions or slides write to the museum's Office of Extension Activities, above address.

KIAH MUSEUM,* 505 W. 36th St, Savannah, GA 30311. *Asst Cur* Nancy H Walker.
Headquarters for National Conference of Artists student traveling shows. These projects have been spearheaded at the Kiah Museum with student NCA members taking part from at least 20 states and 17 foreign countries. Some of the art received in exchange from foreign students, and from each other, has been matted, acetate covered and organized. Exhibits—International Student Artists Show, 52 pieces of acrylics, pencil, pen and inks, lithographs and watercolors from 18 countries; Hawaiian Show, 25 pieces of tree bark, shell and sand designs; African Collection, 35 pieces of watercolors, pen and inks, and crayons from Mawuli School, HoGhana, West Africa; American Collection, 30 pieces of watercolors, lithographs, pencil sketches, pen and inks and mixed media. No rental fees, but exhibitor is responsible for transportation and insurance expenses. Catalogs available.

MIDTOWN GALLERIES, INC, 11 E 57th St, New York, NY 10022. *Dir* Mrs Alan D Gruskin.
Exhibitions arranged—group or one man shows of drawings, watercolors, oils by contemporary American artists. Available to museums, universities, colleges and art centers. Rental fees plus transportation. Rental fee cancelled upon museum purchase. Inquiries invited.

MORRIS-JUMEL MANSION, West 160 St & Edgecombe Ave, New York, NY 10032. *Exec Dir* Jane Sullivan Crowley.
Slide presentations: The Royal Visit; Restoration of Morris Jumel; Morris-Jumel Colonial Herb Garden; NYC's Historic Heritage. Rental fee is a donation to Morris-Jumel Mansion.

MUSEUM OF FINE ARTS, 255 Beach Drive North, St Petersburg, FL 33701. *Asst Dir* Alan DuBois.
Twentieth Century American Photography—up to 70 framed images including works by such photographers as Abbott, Adams, Avedon, Bourke-White, Bullock, Callahan, Caponigro, Cunningham, Evans, Frank, Friedlander, Haas, Halsman, Morgan, Newman, Penn, Porter, Kertesz, Laughlin, Siskind, Sommer, W E Smith, H H Smith, Steichen, Strand, B Weston, E Weston, Vestal, White, Uelsman, and others. Sizes range from 9 x 12 to 30 x 40 inches. No rental fee to qualified museums; shipping and insurance expenses are borne by the borrower. Catalogs in preparation.

MUSEUM OF MODERN ART, 11 W 53rd St, New York, NY 10019.
Exhibition Program: Coordinator of Exhibitions Richard L Palmer; *Admin Asst* Marie Frost.
A number of exhibitions directed by members of the Museum's curatorial staff are offered to other qualified museums on a participating basis. These exhibitions are generally either full-scale projects or reduced versions of shows initially presented at The Museum of Modern Art. Although exhibitions are not necessarily available at all times in all media, the traveling program does cover the entire range of the Museum's New York program—painting, sculpture, drawings, prints, photography, architecture and design. Participating fees usually begin at $750 for smaller exhibitions and range up to several thousand dollars for major exhibitions. Tour participants are also asked to cover prorated transport costs.
International Program: Dir, International Prog Waldo Rasmussen.
The primary function of the program is to encourage cultural exchange in all the visual arts on a broad international level. Exhibitions of painting, sculpture, drawings, prints, photography, architecture, design, and film are circulated by the Museum to foreign countries under the auspices of The International Council of The Museum of Modern Art. Exhibitions representing art of other countries or cultures are also prepared for showing in the U.S. Rental fee plus transportation from preceding exhibitor. Programs with overseas libraries and visiting foreign specialists.
Circulating Film Program: Assoc Dir, Dept of Film Margareta Akermark.
Programs drawn from the Museum's international archive of films are available to educational institutions in the U.S. for study purposes. The films exemplify or illustrate the history, development and technique of the motion picture. Rental fee plus transportation. The 1973 Catalogue and recent Supplements list more than 500 titles ranging from films of the 1890's to recent independent productions.

MUSEUM WITHOUT WALLS,* 104 Morris Ave, PO Box 197, Friendsville, MD 21531. *Dir Museum* Richard Kibbey
A large collection, including photographs from all periods, woodcuts, engravings, etchings, lithographs, silkscreens, monotypes, watercolors, drawings, paintings, and sculpture; access to a great deal more, ranging from folk art to antique maps and toys. Current exhibits—Jacob Riis: Turn-of-the-Century Photographer; Lewis Hine Early Twentieth Century Photographer; The Graven Image, illustrates how an artist conceives of and produces an intaglio print, complete with drawings and numerous states of prints, including the final version; The Human Image, selections from 500 years of printmaking; Contemporary Silkscreen Prints; Artists' Themes from Literature and Theatre; Interpretations of Architecture and Man-Made.

MYSTIC SEAPORT, INC, Greenmanville Ave, Mystic CT 06355. *Public Affairs Dept* Patricia E Kelly.
3, 5, or 8 panel exhibit system, can include slide show, can be prepared to deal with—Mystic Seaport in general; 19th century New England—fisheries, life ashore, whaling, children who went to sea; wooden ships and boats; ship preservation. Exhibits can include photographs, museum objects, brochures, posters. Usually limited to 100-mile radius. Rental fees and transportation arrangements negotiable. Catalogs available.

NATIONAL SOCIETY OF PAINTERS IN CASEIN & ACRYLIC, 1083 Fifth Ave, New York, NY 10028. *Contact* A E S Peterson, 27 Holbrook NE, Rumford, RI 02916.

Exhibit—35 paintings in casein & acrylic. No rental fee; available to colleges, libraries, museums. Exhibitor must pay one-way transportation costs. Catalogs available.

NEWFOUNDLAND MUSEUM, Duckworth St, St John's, NF, Canada. *Exten Officer* Walter Peddle.
Atlantic Conquest—graphic portrayal of the development of aviation in Newfoundland from 1919-1939; Atlantic Cable—Newfoundland's role in the development of a transatlantic cable. No rental fee; transportation arrangements made by the museum. Catalogs not available.

NEWPORT HARBOR ART MUSEUM, 850 San Clemente Dr, Newport Beach, CA 92660. *Director* Thomas H Garver; *Curator of Exhibitions* Betty Turnbull.
Organizes and circulates exhibitions of the art of our time, with the emphasis on American art of the last 30 years. Exhibitions are usually circulated by letter directly to other art institutions, but inquiries are always encouraged from any museum looking for exhibitions dealing with painting, sculpture and photography, with an emphasis on modern and contemporary art.

OAKLAND UNIVERSITY, Meadow Brook Art Gallery, Rochester, MI 48063. *Cur* Kiichi Usui.
Art in Architecture—42 photographic murals, 32 wall labels, 5 boxes for transportation. The exhibition was originally presented with the cooperation of the General Services Administration, Washington, DC, funded by Michigan Council for the Arts. No rental fee, but exhibitor is responsible for transportation and insurance coverage in the amount of $11,535.
Winoru Yamasaki slide presentation, 160 slides (2 Carousel trays) and recorded tape. Rental fee $35.00, the exhibitor is responsible for transportation and insurance. Catalogs available at printers' cost, $1.75.

OLD BERGEN ART GUILD, 43 W 33rd St, Bayonne, NJ 07002. *Dir* William D Gorman; *Assoc Dir* Jan Gary.
Over 70 group and one-man traveling exhibits—Oils, watercolors, caseins and graphics in all styles by contemporary American artists. Available to museums, art centers, universities, colleges, and libraries. No fee, except for one-way express charge. Send stamped, addressed envelope for free catalog.

OWATONNA ARTS COUNCIL, PO Box 134, Owatonna, MN 55060. *Cur* Silvan Durben.
The Marianne Young World Costume Collection. This collection includes 98 garments from 25 countries and is complete with accessories such as hats, jewelry, gloves and boots. The collection includes caftans, saris, coats, kimonos and French originals. Examples of the gowns in the collection include: a dress from South Africa made completely of white ostrich feathers; a long gown from Pakistan covered with mirrors held in place by embroidery; a bright blue poncho cape from Bali (used in formal dances) is painted in gold, yellow and shocking pink; a wine-red caracul skin coat from Afghanistan is embroidered in gold with black caracul edging. The costumes, all in her own petite size, were collected by Marianne Young during 50 years of travel. Rental fee is $300, transportation is provided one way in Minnesota. Transportation to other states is negotiable. Brochure available on request.

PAINE ART CENTER AND ARBORETUM, 1410 Algoma Blvd, Oshkosh, WI 54901. *Cur Coll* Janet Rothe.
The Wisconsin Octagon House—a graphic exhibition of how the octagon house came into being in Wisconsin about 1855-1865. The Octagon House was inspired by a New York phrenologist, Orson S Fowler's book—A Home for All. Dissatisfied with the current revivalist style of houses, Fowler offered a more economical, convenient and comfortable "octagonal" alternative. Rental fee $500, plus transportation. Catalogs available.

PHILADELPHIA MUSEUM OF ART, 26th & Parkway, PO Box 7646, Philadelphia, PA 19101. *Head Dept Rights & Reproduction* Lois Glewwe.
30,000 2 x 2 inch color slides available for sale. Catalogs available on request. Film Library. 100 16mm, optical sound films available for rent to educational institutions and art organizations. Catalogs available on request from Division of Education.

PORTLAND ART MUSEUM, 1219 SW Park Ave, Portland, OR 97205. *Dir* Donald Jenkins; and *Cur* Dr William Chiego.
Turkish Miniatures and Related Decorative Arts, from the collection of Edwin Binney 3rd. Turkish miniature paintings and manuscripts; also includes examples of ceramics, textiles, and metal work. Available after February 1979. Rental fee under $10,000. Catalogs available.

PRATT GRAPHICS CENTER, 160 Lexington Avenue, New York, NY 10016. *Dir* Andrew Stasik.

Exhibition of graphic arts—original prints, available to art schools, universities, art associations. Current shows—Contemporary Graphic Protest and the Grand Tradition; A Survey of Intaglio Printmaking; Photography in Printmaking; Sixth International Miniature Print Exhibition; The Presidency—Irreverent and Relevant; Five Contemporary Masters of the Black and White Print; The Black Experience in Prints; The Figure and Machine in the Print Today; Monotypes; Contemporary Serigraphs; New Directions in Printmaking; The Collagraph—A New Print Medium; Contemporary American Fine Arts Posters; Puerto Rican Graphics; Against the Wall; Doris Lanier; Forerunners of the American Print Renaissance 1920/50; The Butcher, the Baker, the Candlestick Maker; Images of Labor; Funny? Minimum rental fee.

ROTHMANS OF PALL MALL CANADA, LTD, 75 Dugglaw Road, Toronto, Ontario, Canada, M6A 2W4. Tel: 416-789-7711. Michael P Ney.
Contemporary Canadian paintings, prints, drawings, and Eskimo sculpture—approx 300 works. Works from the collection available for circulating exhibitions to major public institutions in Canada. Presently circulating is Los Mayas, on a two-year tour schedule including 14 museums.

SANFORD MUSEUM AND PLANETARIUM, 117 East Willow, Cherokee, Iowa 51012. *Dir* Robert W Howe.
Virginia Herrick Quilt Block Exhibit—a large collection of quilt block patterns (some common & uncommon); Oscillons—electronic abstractions by Ben Laposky—photographs of works completed by one of the pioneers of computer art in North America and the world; Midwest Indians and Frontier Photography—early photographs of Indians connected with Iowa and the surrounding states, 1869-1900. Rental fee plus shipping charges to be paid by exhibitor.

SECESSION GALLERY OF PHOTOGRAPHY, 510 Fort St, Victoria, BC, Canada. (Mailing Add: PO Box 5207, Station B, Victoria, BC, Canada, V8R 6N4). *Dir* Tom Gore.
While we do not have prepackaged exhibitions available, we are prepared to assemble and curate exhibitions for travel consisting of work by Western Canadian photographers. Rental fee and transportation by negotiation. No catalogs available.

SEGY GALLERY, 50 W 57th St, New York, NY 10019. *Dir* Ladislas Segy.
Exhibits—African sculptures, masks, statues, some utensils, in wood, ivory and bronze. 30 African sculptures for 3 weeks period. 5 circuits each season. Rental fee: $450 for 3 weeks, insurance and one way transportation included. Art and Science Museums, art departments and galleries of universities and colleges, college Student Unions, art clubs, libraries and others eligible. Catalog on request. Mr. Segy is available for lectures on African and Modern Art. Conditions upon request.

SMITHSONIAN INSTITUTION TRAVELING EXHIBITION SERVICE (SITES), Washington, DC 20560. *Dir* Dennis A Gould. *Sr Exhibits Coordinator* Anne R Gossett. *Project Coordinator-International Program* Eileen Rose.
200 exhibitions—Architecture, cultural history, decorative arts, design, environment, paintings, prints & drawings, photography, science & technology. Available to educational, scientific, cultural and on occasion, commercial institutions. Educational materials and program activities supplement the exhibits. Catalogs, posters and brochures accompany specific exhibits. †Annual catalog "Update" available.
†Quarterly newsletter "Siteline" available now. "Update" catalogue available in Fall 1978.

SOCIETY OF AMERICAN GRAPHIC ARTISTS, 1083 Fifth Ave, New York, NY 10028. *Pres* Stanley Kaplan.
55th SAGA National Traveling Print Exhibition (147 prints); 56th SAGA National Traveling Print Exhibition (50 prints). Rental fee $100 for one month; 50 catalogs to each institution.

SOUTHERN ASSOCIATION OF SCULPTORS, INC, Art Department, University of Alabama, Huntsville, AL 35801. *Pres* Jeff Bayer.
Annual national competitive traveling sculpture exhibitions of 15 to 30 pieces of sculpture. Fee: $500 plus shipping for one direction with each institution receiving 200 illustrated catalogs. Exhibition booked a year in advance and tours for one year.

MAURICE SPERTUS MUSEUM OF JUDAICA, 618 S Michigan Ave, Chicago, IL 60605. *Museum Registrar* Mary Dannerth.
Exhibitions—The Jews of Sandor, 25 photographs, 1 lead photograph, 1 map panel, 1 synagogue floor plan panel and label copy. This photographic essay details the lives of the Jews of Sandor, an agrarian village in Iraqi Kurdistan, which ceased to exist as a unit when its people emigrated to Israel in 1950. The exhibition reveals life in this agrarian community, which until its assimilation into Israeli society, had changed little since Babylonian times. Rental fee $250 including insurance and 10

catalogs for 3 months. Additional catalogs $1.00 (selling price $1.50). Transportation costs will be borne by borrower.
The Jews of Yemen, 71 photographs, 1 map, 8 panels of explanatory copy; 1 eight-track cartridge of Yemenite dance music. This photographic essay depicts the sudden flight of the Jews from Yemen/Aden to Israel and reveals this largely unfamiliar aspect of Jewish culture. The majority of the photographs were taken in Aden and Israel during the period 1949-1950 in the course of Operation Magic Carpet. The remainder document certain aspects of the Yemenite Jews in Israel from 1950 to 1960. Rental fee of $750 includes insurance and 30 catalogs for 3 months. Additional catalogs $3.00 (selling price $5.00). Transportation charges extra. Additional components—a film of Boi Temen Dance Festival, approx 25 min in length; cost $50. Special arrangements may be made to borrow a limited number of pertinent artifacts (jewelry, textiles, household objects).

STATE UNIVERSITY OF NEW YORK COLLEGE AT POTSDAM,* Pierrepont Ave, Potsdam, NY 13676. *Dir Art Gallery* Benedict Goldsmith; *Cur* Dr Roland Gibson.
Exhibits—Roland Gibson Collection of Contemporary Japanese Art, 25-30 paintings, sculpture objects and prints; College Collection of Contemporary Prints, 15-25 prints. Available for use by neighboring institutions, within 100 mile radius.

SYRACUSE UNIVERSITY, Joe and Emily Lowe Art Gallery, Sims Hall, Syracuse, NY 13210. *Dir* Joseph Scala.
Record Album Art—The Recording Artist. Consists of approx 150 pieces of original work that has led to the images on record albums today. There are paintings, graphics, photo transparencies, sculpture and dye transfer prints. Looks best with 350 linear feet. Among the pieces are Charles Gardner's—Peer Gynt Suites Nos 1 & 2; Joseph Stelmach's—Prokofiev Symphony No 5; John Lennon's—Mind Games; Ignacio Gomez's—The Beatles Rock & Roll Music; and Jimmy Wachtel's—The Rockin' and Rollin' 50s and 60s. A small but popular segment of the show is devoted to original art by the recording stars themselves—Diane Keaton, Richard Havens and Patti Smith, among others. Rental fee is $1,000, plus prorata shipping one way and insurance. Catalogs are available at $3.00 each.

TEXAS FINE ARTS ASSOCIATION, 3809 W 35th St, Austin, TX 78703. *Exec Dir* Mrs John D Haltom.
Approx 7 exhibitions containing 19-20 paintings each. Travel throughout Texas only. Rental fee: $85 plus out-going freight. Catalogs and biographic material available.

TUSKEGEE INSTITUTE,* Tuskegee Institute, AL 36088. George W Carver Museum *Dir Art Gallery* Stefania Jarkowski.
Exhibits—William H Johnson, Black artist, 20 works in oil, gouache, watercolor and ink collection of 35 contemporary Polish posters, all posters are matted and covered with acetate; collection of 48 watercolors by the contemporary leading artists of Poland, all paintings are matted and covered with acetate. All exhibitions' starting dates available Sept, 1976. No catalogs available.

UNIVERSITY OF ILLINOIS, Continuing Education and Public Service/Visual Arts, 123 Fine Arts Building, Champaign, IL 61820. Prof Ted Zernich.
Exhibitions—Photography, approx 60 running feet; Drawing—approx 100 running feet; Painting—approx 200 running feet; Printmaking—approx 60 running feet; Instructional materials average 60 feet. Rental fee of $40 provides 10 weeks of exhibition materials over 12 months. Participating institutions pay all shipping and insurance costs. Catalogs available.

UNIVERSITY OF MARYLAND ART GALLERY, Art Sociology Building, College Park, MD 20742. *Dir* Dr Eleanor Green.
Exhibits—Graphic Images of Japan—contemporary Japanese graphic art woodblocks, etchings, silkscreen, lithographs and mixed media prints (57 prints, traditional themes to avant-garde motifs); Treasury Department Mural Studies from the 1930s and 1940s, 120 sketches and finished studies in many media. A selection from this extensive collection can be arranged for exhibition. Rental fee and transportation can be arranged. Handout sheets for Japanese prints, and full catalog for Treasury Department mural studies available.

UNIVERSITY OF REGINA, Norman Mackenzie Art Gallery, Regina, SK, Canada S4S 0A2.
Exhibitions are for circulation only within Canada. Exhibitions developed by the extension department's Community Program are exhibited throughout the province.

UNIVERSITY OF SHERBROOKE, Cultural Center Art Gallery, Sherbrooke, PQ, Canada J1K 2R1. *Artistic Dir* Graham Cantieni.

Exhibit—Works on Paper by artists working in the Eastern Townships, total of 30 works in all media. Rental fee $150 plus transportation charges to next center. Catalogs available.

VAN ARSDALE ASSOCIATES, INC, PO Box 1965, Winter Park, FL 32790. *Pres* Dorothy T Van Arsdale.
Exhibits—Approx 20 exhibitions of painting, sculpture, drawings, prints, photographs, textiles, both foreign and American, usually about 25 to 50 pieces. Rental fees from $195 to $600 for 4-week booking period. The exhibitor is responsible for outgoing shipping. Annual catalog available plus occasional exhibition catalogs.

VIRGINIA POLYTECHNIC INSTITUTE AND STATE UNIVERSITY, Owens Hall, Department of Art, Blacksburg, VA 24061. *Head Dept* Prof Dean Carter.
Faculty exhibition. No rental fee, but borrower must pay freight both ways and insurance. No catalog.

WASHINGTON STATE ART SERVICES, Museum of Art, Washington State University, Pullman, WA 99164. *Dir* Harvey West.
Wide range of 2-dimensional art objects. Each exhibit includes approx 20-30 art works ranging from works on paper to special installations. Rental fee available on request. Catalogs for certain exhibits.

WESTERN ASSOCIATION OF ART MUSEUMS, Mills College, Box 9989, Oakland CA 94613. Traveling Exhibitions Dept.
Approx 30-50 exhibits—Varied media, exhibition themes. Rental fee: $300 to $2000. Catalog on request.

WESTERN MONTANA COLLEGE ART GALLERY,* Dillon, MT 59725. *Dir* Jim Corr.
Two exhibits, 30 pieces of work each, matted and covered with acetate—Drawings, prints, watercolors and some photographs. One crate of approx. 30 pounds. Geared to the small schools who often have difficulty obtaining art shows. No rental fee. May be shipped by bus or mailed parcel post. No catalogs.

WESTMINSTER COLLEGE ART GALLERY,* New Wilmington, PA 16142. *Gallery Dir* Robert Godfrey.
Exhibits—The Figure in Recent American Painting, 24 large to medium size paintings; In Praise of Space - The Landscape in American Art, 58 large to small size paintings, drawings, watercolors by contemporary painters; The Figure in Recent American Drawings, 50 framed drawings by 25 contemporary artists; Recent American Narrative Painting; The Portrait in Recent American Painting. Rental fee: approx $700 within 500 mile radius and includes transportation, insurance, installation (if requested) and 100 catalogs.

WINNIPEG ART GALLERY, 300 Memorial Blvd, Winnipeg, MB, Canada, R3C 1V1. *Asst Cur Exten Services* Jane Christiani.
Exhibitions—Steranko—Comics; Canadian Political Cartoons; L L Fitzgerald—A Retrospective; Ministic Sculpture; Looking South; Artists Prints and Multiples; Photographs by Clayton Bailey, Joanne Jackson Johnson and David McMillan; The Railway—Patron of the Arts in Canada; Photographs by Ron Webber; H Eric Bergman—Wood Engravings; British Watercolors; Graphics from British Columbia; Cape Dorset—Eskimo Prints Series III; The Catch; Contemporary Canadian Graphics; Salvador Dali—Aliyah; Honore Daumier—Lithographs; Hommage a Albert Dumouchel; Kathe Kollwitz—Etchings and Lithographs; Oskar Laske—Etchings and Lithographs; Oskar Laske—Watercolors; Winston Leathers' Cosmic Variations; Manitoba Graphics; Modern European Graphics; W J Phillips—Woodcuts and Wood Engravings; Gino Severini—Flowers and Masks; Gordon Smith—Graphics. Rental fees vary from $75 to $150 and include insurance and shipping costs. Catalogs may be included, but this varies.

INDEXES

Personnel Index

Aach, Herb, *Pres,* Artists Technical Inst, New York, NY

Aakhus, Turid, *Librn,* Kunstindustrimuseet I, Oslo, Norway

Aasma, Karin, *Cur Exhib,* Rohsska Konstslojkmuseet, Goteborg, Sweden

Abbe, Ronald, *Assoc Cur,* Housatonic Museum of Art & *Mem Faculty,* Housatonic Community College, Bridgeport, CT

Abbey, Norm, *Area Chmn Photography,* Pasadena City College, CA

Abbey, Rita Deanin, *Prof,* Univ Nevada, Las Vegas

Abbott, H, *Head,* Nat Art School, Darlinghurst, Australia

Abbott, Julie, *Asst,* Artists Gallery of Vancouver, BC

Abbott, Sidney M, *Cur,* Ancient and Honorable Artillery Co of Massachusetts, Boston

Abd el Aal, Mrs Saniyeh, *First Cur,* Egyptian Museum, Cairo

Abd el-Salam el-Nawawy, Ibrahim, *First Sub-Dir,* Egyptian Museum, Cairo

Abee, Thelma M, *Asst to Dir,* Hickory Museum of Art, NC

Abel, John P Van, *Secy,* Canton Art Inst, OH

Abell, Richard, *Assoc Prof,* Univ Minnesota, Saint Paul

Aber, Robert, *Pres Bd,* Roberson Center, Binghamton, NY

Abeshouse, Jordan, *Pres,* New Haven Paint & Clay Club, CT

Abid, Ann B, *Librn,* St Louis Art Museum, MO

Abita, Salvatore, *Dir,* Museo Villa Pignatelli, Museo De Capodimonte, Naples, Italy

Abney, James K, *Pres,* Harrison County Historical Museum, Marshall, TX

Abou-Ghazi, Dr Dia, *Dir & Librn,* Egyptian Museum, Cairo

Abrahamson, Roy, *Chmn Art Educ,* Southern Illinois Univ, Carbondale

Abrams, Jean, *Coordr,* Mississippi Delta Junior College, Moorhead

Abrams, Joe, *Chmn,* Mississippi Delta Junior College, Moorhead

Abrams, Tobi, *Instr,* Felician College, Chicago, IL

Absher, Henry, *VPres,* Hickory Museum of Art, NC

Abt, Jeffrey, *Cur Coll-Exhib,* Wichita Art Museum, KS

Acero, Raul, *Instr,* Inter American Univ Puerto Rico, San German

Acha, Juan, *Coordr,* Museo de Arte Moderno, Mexico City, Mexico

Achenbach, Nancy F, *Exec Dir,* Northern Virginia Fine Arts Association, Alexandria

Achepohl, Keith, *Artist-in-Residence,* Oxbow Summer Art Workshops, Saugatuck, MI

Achuff, James, *Head Ceramics,* Chautauqua Institution, NY

Ackerman, Gerald M, *Prof & Chmn Dept,* Pomona College, Claremont, CA

Ackerman, Robert K, *Dean & Dir Summer School,* Drew Univ, Madison, NJ

Ackerman, Rudy S, *Prof Art & Chmn Dept,* Moravian College, Bethlehem, PA

Ackerson, Mrs LeRoy, *Secy,* Central Iowa Art Association, Marshalltown

Ackley, Mark W, *Instr,* Univ Mississippi, University

Acorn, Eleanor, *Head Librn,* John M Cuelenaere Library, Prince Albert, SK

Acquavella, William, *VPres,* Art Dealers Association of America, see National and Regional Organizations

Adachi, Kenji, *Dir,* Tokyo Kokuritsu Kindai Bijutsukan, Japan

Adair, Charlene, *Secy,* Five Civilized Tribes Museum, Muskogee, OK

Adams, Anne, *Registrar,* Amon Carter Museum of Western Art, Fort Worth, TX

Adams, Ansel, *Pres,* Friends of Photography, Carmel, CA

Adams, Betty, *Instr,* St Mary's College, Raleigh, NC

Adams, Mrs. Bobbe, *Librn,* Silvermine Guild of Artists Gallery, New Canaan, CT

Adams, Charles, *Chmn Dept Humanities,* Central Florida Community College, Ocala

Adams, Clinton, *Dir,* Tamarind Inst, Univ New Mexico, Albuquerque

Adams, Douglas, *Assoc Prof,* Morehead State Univ, KY

Adams, Fletcher P, *Dir,* Vesper George School of Art, Boston, MA; *Secy,* Boston Watercolor Society, Scituate, MA

Adams, Franklin, *Assoc Prof,* Tulane Univ, New Orleans, LA

Adams, J B, *Secy,* Artists' Fellowship, New York, NY

Adams, James R C, *Prof & Head Dept,* Manchester College, North Manchester, IN

Adams, Mrs Kenneth, *VPres,* Canton Art Inst, OH

Adams, Laurie, *Office Adminr,* Hunterdon Art Center, Clinton, NJ

Adams, Robert, *Asst Prof,* Alabama A&M Univ, Huntsville

Adams, Ruth, *Admin Asst,* Brattleboro Museum and Art Center, VT

Adams, Sarah, *Libr Asst,* Lake Placid School of Art Gallery, NY

Adams, Suzanne, *Resident Artist,* Peters Valley Craftsmen, Layton, NJ

Adams, Virginia, *Assoc Prof,* College of Notre Dame of Maryland, Baltimore

Adams, W Howard, *Asst to Dir Nat Prog,* Nat Gallery of Art, Washington, DC

Adams, Wesley A, *Deputy Dir Finance & Admin,* Winterthur Museum and Gardens, DE

Adamski, Irene, *Lectr,* Villa Maria College of Buffalo, NY

Adamson, Jim, *Instr,* Sierra College, Rocklin, CA

Adamy, George E, *Dir,* Adamy's Plastics & Mold Making Workshops, Larchmont, NY

Addison, B Kent, *Prof Art & Fine Arts Area Coordr,* Maryville College, Saint Louis, MO

Addkison, Andry, *Instr,* California College of Arts and Crafts, Oakland

Addleson, Miss E S J, *Cur,* Durban Art Gallery, South Africa

Adelman, Jean, *Librn,* Univ Pennsylvania Museum, Philadelphia

Adelmann, Arthur R, *Assoc Prof,* Weber State College, Ogden, UT

Adhemar, Helene, *Cur,* Orangerie & Jeu de Paume Galleries, Musee du Louvre, Paris, France; *Chief Conservator,* Musee du Jeu de Paume, Paris, France

Adkins, Cary, *Instr,* Grand Canyon College, Phoenix, AZ

Adkins, Margie, *Asst Prof,* West Texas State Univ, Canyon

Adkins, Marjorie R, *Chief Fine Arts Div,* Chicago Public Library, IL

Adlin, Nelson, *Prof,* Community College of Baltimore, MD

Adolph, Dr Hubert, *Cur,* Osterreichische Galerie, Vienna, Austria

Agar, Eunice, *Chairperson Studio Arts Dept & In Charge Gallery,* Simon's Rock Early College, Great Barrington, MA

Agee, William C, *Dir,* Museum of Fine Arts, Houston, TX

Agha, Miss Zubeida, *Exec Dir,* Art Gallery Society of Contemporary Art, Rawalpindi, Pakistan

Aglialoro, Fortunato, *Mem Faculty,* Toronto School of Art, ON

Agnew, Charles, *Coordr Interior Design,* Art Inst of Philadelphia, PA

Agnew, L J, *Assoc Prof,* Sullivan County Community College, Loch Sheldrake, NY

Agualia, Robert, *Cur,* Roberson Center, Binghamton, NY

Aguayo, Oscar, *Exec Dir,* Latin Quarter Art Gallery, Tampa, FL

Ague, Ann, *Regional Librn,* Orange County Public Library, Garden Grove, CA

Aguet, Henry, *Chmn Design Prog,* Herron School of Art, Indiana Univ-Purdue Univ, Indianapolis

Ahearn, Martin R, *Pres,* Rockport Art Association, MA

Ahearn, Mary M, *Mgr Tavern Door Card Shop,* Rockport Art Association, MA

Ahmad, Mrs Nafisa, *Secy,* Art Gallery Society of Contemporary Art, Rawalpindi, Pakistan

Ahmad, Sufi, *Assoc Prof,* Saint Francis College, Fort Wayne, IN

Ahmad, Waseem, *Chemist,* Lahore Museum, Pakistan

Ahnell, Dr Emil G, *Chmn,* Kentucky Wesleyan College, Owensboro

Ahntholz, R, *Chmn Illustration,* Fashion Inst of Technology, New York, NY

Ahrens, Henry, *Prof,* Trenton State College, NJ

Ahrens, Kent, *Cur,* Randolph-Macon Woman's College Art Gallery, Lynchburg, VA

Ahysen, Harry J, *Assoc Prof,* Sam Houston State Univ, Huntsville, TX

Aiches, Alan, *Dir,* St. Johns Art Gallery, Wilmington, NC

Aidekman, Mrs Alex, *Pres,* Summit Art Center, NJ

Aidlin, Jerome, *Instr,* Cleveland Inst of Art, OH

Aiken, Joyce, *Prof,* California State Univ, Fresno

Aiken, O S, *Treas,* Florence Museum, SC

Aiken, Roger, *Instr,* Colorado College, Colorado Springs

Aird, David, *Dir,* Musee Historique de Vaudreuil, PQ

Aistars, John, *Dir,* Cazenovia College, NY

Aitken, George T, *Supt,* Williams College Museum of Art, Williamstown, MA

Aizley, Paul, *Dir Summer School,* Univ Nevada, Las Vegas

Akalay, Dr Z, *Librn,* Topkapi Saray Museum, Istanbul, Turkey

Aker, George, *Pres,* Sierra Arts Found, Reno, NV

Akin, Dennis, *Prof Art & Chmn Fine Arts Dept,* Dickinson College, Carlisle, PA

Akus, Julian, *Chmn,* Eastern Connecticut State College, Williamantic

Albacete, Manuel J, *Cur,* Canton Art Inst, OH

Alber, Dr Zofia, *Far Eastern Art,* Museum Narodowe W Krakowie, Cracow, Poland

Alberetti, Robert, *Chmn,* Western Connecticut State College, Danbury

Alberici, Dr Clelia, *Dir,* Civiche Raccolte de Arte Applicata & *Dir,* Racotta della Stampe Achelle Bertarelli, Museo d'Arte Antica, Milan, Italy

Albertoni, Juan Carlos, *Courses & Conferences,* Centro de Arte y Communicacion, Buenos Aires, Argentina

Albright, Ripley, *Asst Cur Prints & Drawings,* Brooklyn Museum, NY

Alcorn, Kathryn, *Chmn,* Central State Univ, Edmond, OK

Aldao, Dr Federico, *Dir,* Museo Nacional de Arte Decorativo Buenos Aires, Argentina

Alder, Gale, *Architectural Historian,* Nat Trust for Historic Preservation, Washington, DC

Alder, Sebastian, *Dir,* La Jolla Museum of Contemporary Art, CA

Alderette, R, *Mem Faculty,* Golden West College, Huntington Beach, CA

Aldrich, Ann, *Treas,* South County Art Association, Kingston, RI

Aldrich, Larry, *Founder & Pres,* Soho Center for Visual Artists, New York, NY

Aldridge, C Clay, *Registrar,* Nat Infantry Museum, Fort Benning, GA

Alexander, Jerry G, *Instr,* San Antonio Art Inst, TX

Alexander, Robin, *Asst Prof Art,* Eastern Oregon State College, La Grande

Alexander, Suzanne, *Asst to Cur,* Courtauld Inst of Art Galleries, London, England

Alexander, William C, *Dir School Art,* Montana State Univ, Bozeman

Alexson, F, *VPres,* Saskatoon Gallery and Conservatory Corp, SK

Alf-Jorgen, *Rector & Prof,* Statens Kunstakademi, Oslo, Norway

Alford, Constance, *Area Chmn & Asst Prof,* Alcorn State Univ, Lorman, MS

Alger, John R F, *Asst Dir,* McAllen International Museum, TX

Alger, Mary, *Instr,* Pontiac Art Center, MI

Al-Hilali, Neda, *Assoc Prof,* Scripps College, Claremont, CA

Ali, Mrs Nusrat, *Display Officer,* Lahore Museum, Pakistan

Alinder, James, *Exec Dir,* Friends of Photography, Carmel, CA

Alkema, Chester, *Assoc Prof,* Grand Valley State Colleges, Allendale, MI

Allan, Janet, *Mgr,* Lahaina Arts Society, HI

Allara, Pamela, *Asst Prof,* Tufts Univ, Medford, MA

Allemann, Hans, *Assoc Prof & Dept Chairperson,* Philadelphia College of Art, PA

Allen, Carl M, *Dir Exhib,* Ashland College Arts and Humanities Gallery, OH

Allen, Douglas, *Mem Jury,* Society of Animal Artists, see National and Regional Organizations

Allen, Fred R, *Mem Faculty,* Saint Louis Community College at Meramec, MO

Allen, Georgia K, *Exec Dir,* Arts Council of Spartanburg County, SC

Allen, Greg, *Gallery Asst,* Rio Hondo College Art Gallery, Whittier, CA

Allen, Hubert L, *Cur Classical Archaeology,* World Heritage Museum, Univ Illinois at Urbana-Champaign, Urbana

Allen, J Clyff, *Preparator,* B R Larsen Gallery, Brigham Young Univ, Provo, UT

Allen, James A, *Assoc Prof,* Daemen College, Amherst, NY

Allen, Jere H, *Chmn Gallery Comt & Asst Prof,* Univ Mississippi, University

Allen, Jerry, *Visual Arts Coordr,* King County Arts Commission, Seattle, WA

Allen, Margaret, *Secy,* Univ Western Ontario, London

Allen, Mary Zane, *Gallery Mgr,* Univ Wisconsin-Milwaukee Union Art Gallery

Allen, Max I, *Prof,* Manchester College, North Manchester, IN

Allen, Paul F, *Prof,* Concordia College, Moorhead, MN

Allen, Reginald, *Cur,* Gilbert & Sullivan Coll, Pierpont Morgan Library, New York, NY

Allen, Shirley A, *Asst,* Canton Art Inst, OH

Allen, Terry, *Assoc Prof,* California State Univ, Fresno

Allen, Tom, *Chmn,* Syracuse Univ, NY

Allendorfer, Harry C, Jr, *Dir Maritime Preservation,* Nat Trust for Historic Preservation, Washington, DC

Alley, James, *Instr,* Interlochen Arts Acad, MI

Alley, Perry, *Treas,* Hudson Valley Art Association, White Plains, NY

Allgeyer, Sister M Rosine, *Dir BA Art Educ & Art Therapy,* Edgecliff College, Cincinnati, OH

Allgrove, Joan, *Keeper Textiles,* Whitworth Art Gallery, Univ Manchester, England

Alling, Clarence, *Gallery Dir,* Waterloo Municipal Galleries, IA

Allison, Donn C, *Dir,* Zigler Museum, Jennings, LA

Allison, Mrs Donn C, *Cur Promotions & Pub Relations,* Zigler Museum, Jennings, LA

Allison, Glenn, *Cur Exhib,* Univ British Columbia, Vancouver

Allison, J Clement, *Dir,* Tusculum College, Greeneville, TN

Alloway, Lawrence, *Dir Art Gallery & Prof,* State Univ New York at Stony Brook

Almquist, Robert, *Head Dept,* Lewis-Clark State College, Lewiston, ID

Alpert, Diane, *Cur Coll,* Indiana State Museum, Indianapolis

Alsdorf, James W, *Chmn Bd Trustees,* Art Inst of Chicago, IL

Al-Shaikhli, Ismail, *Chmn Dept & Prof,* Acad of Fine Arts, Baghdad, Iraq

Alstadt, Drenda, *Secy,* Mid-Southern Watercolorists, Little Rock, AR

Alstars, John, *Dir Art Prog,* Cazenovia College Gallery, NY

Alter, Forrest, *Head Art, Music & Drama Dept,* Flint Public Library, MI

Altman, Dorothy, *Instr,* Fort Wright College of the Holy Names, Spokane, WA

Altman, Patricia B, *Cur Textiles & Folk Art,* Museum of Cultural History, Univ California, Los Angeles

Alton, Susanna D, The American Federation of Arts, see National and Regional Organizations

Altschuler, Franz, *Asst Prof,* Morehead State Univ, KY

Alvare, Carlos J, *Assoc Prof,* Lehigh Univ, Bethlehem, PA

Alvarez, Juan, *Cur Exhib,* Anchorage Historical and Fine Arts Museum, AK

Amadei, Daniel, *Chief Exten Serv,* Montreal Museum of Fine Arts, PQ

Amaya, Mario, *Dir,* Chrysler Museum at Norfolk, VA

Ambach, Gordon M, *Exec Deputy Comr Educ,* State Education Dept, Albany, NY

Ambrose, Charles E, *Dir Gallery, Cur Mus & Permanent Collection & Chmn Art Dept,* Mississippi Univ for Women, Columbus

Ambrosiani, Bjorn, *Keeper Mus Dept,* Statens Historiska Museum, Stockholm, Sweden

Ambrosino, Thomas, *Instr,* Sullivan County Community College, Loch Sheldrake, NY

Ambrosio, Katie, *Mgr,* Carmel Mission Basilica, CA

Ameen, Lula, *Asst Prof,* Nicholls State Univ, Thibodaux, LA

Americano, Dr Alvaro, *Exec Secy,* Museu de Arte Moderna Brazil, Rio De Janerio

Amerson, L Price, *Cur,* Univ California Nelson Gallery, Davis

Ames, Amyas, *Chmn,* Lincoln Center for the Performing Arts, New York, NY

Ames, John H, *Pres,* Nebraska Art Association, Univ Nebraska Art Gallery, Lincoln

Ames, M M, *Dir,* Univ British Columbia Museum of Anthropology, Vancouver

Ames, Madge, *Treas,* Kennebec Valley Art Association, Hallowell, ME

Ames, Samuel B, *Chmn Gallery Comt,* Art Center Gallery & *Asst Prof,* Rhode Island College, Providence

Ames, Walter, *Chmn Bd,* Timken Art Gallery, San Diego, CA

Amiet, Pierre, *Cur Oriental Antiquities,* Musee du Louvre, Paris, France

Amiot, Theresa, *Asst Prof,* College of Our Lady of the Elms, Chicopee, MA

Amir-Fazli, Homa, *Assoc Prof,* Univ Minnesota, Saint Paul

Amirsoltani, Karen, *Mem Faculty,* Ray-Vogue Schools, Chicago, IL

Ammerman, William, *Prof,* Univ Wisconsin-River Falls

Ammons, Betty, *Asst Librn,* United Methodist Historical Society, Baltimore, MD

Amory, Robert, Jr, *Secy & Gen Counsel,* Nat Gallery of Art, Washington, DC

Amos, Robert, *Asst to Dir & Librn,* Art Gallery of Greater Victoria, BC

Amrhein, John K, *Librn,* Rohrbach Library, Kutztown State College, PA

Amundson, Dale, *VRepresentative,* Le Front des Artistes Canadiens, Winnipeg, MB

Amussen, Theodore S, *Editor,* Nat Gallery of Art, Washington, DC

Amylon, Kristin A, *Asst Dir Coll,* Rockwell-Corning Museum, Corning, NY

Amyx, Chester, *Chmn Fine Arts Div & Summer School,* Cuesta College, San Luis Obispo, CA

Ananian, Elissa, *Prof,* Salem State College, MA

Anazawa, Kazuo, *Deputy Dir,* Tokyo Kokuritsu Kindai Bijutsukan, Japan

Anderle, Donald F, *Chief Art & Archit,* New York Public Library, NY

Andersen, Frithjof Meidell, *Hon Consul Pres,* Vestlandske Kunstindustrimuseum, Bergen, Norway

Andersen, Greta, *Assoc Conservator,* William Hayes Fogg Art Museum, Cambridge, MA

Andersen, Jeffrey W, *Dir & Librn,* Lyme Historical Society, Old Lyme, CT

Andersen, Wayne, *Chmn Comt Visual Arts,* Massachusetts Inst of Technology, Cambridge

Anderson, Mrs A Douglas, *Dir Educ Serv,* Univ Nebraska Art Gallery, Lincoln

Anderson, Alice, *VPres,* Winnipeg Sketch Club, MB

Anderson, Berneal, *Registrar,* Joslyn Art Museum, Omaha, NE

Anderson, Betsy, *Lectr,* Saint Joseph's College, Philadelphia, PA

Anderson, Bruce, *Dir,* Mason City Public Library, IA

Anderson, Carolyn, *Coordr,* Colorado State Univ, Fort Collins

Anderson, Carolyn, *Chmn Arts Div,* Emma Willard School, Troy, NY

Anderson, Charles R, *Head Dept & Assoc Prof,* Castleton State College, VT

Anderson, Cheryl, *Cur Educ Serv,* Shaker Community, Pittsfield, MA

Anderson, Donald B, *Pres Bd Trustees,* Roswell Museum and Art Center, NM

Anderson, Eric, *Assoc Prof,* Univ North Carolina, Charlotte

Anderson, Evelyn E, *Assoc Prof,* Sam Houston State Univ, Huntsville, TX

Anderson, Gary, *Chmn,* Transylvania Univ, Lexington, KY

Bakes, Alan, *VChmn Bd,* Visual Arts Ontario, Toronto

Balboni, Armand, *Asst Prof,* Springfield College, MA

Baldelli, Raymond J, *Instr,* Guilford Art and Music School, CT

Balderacchi, Arthur, *Chmn Dept Arts,* Univ New Hampshire, Durham

Baldwin, Ben, *VPres,* Maui Historical Society, Wailuku, HI

Baldwin, Harold L, *Cur Photographic Gallery,* Middle Tennessee State Univ, Murfreesboro

Baldwin, Russell W, *Dir,* Boehm Gallery, Palomar Community College, San Marcos, CA

Baldwin, W Donald, *Pres,* Royal Architectural Inst of Canada, see National Organizations in Canada

Bale, Ken, *Head Found Studies,* Saint Martins School of Art, London, England

Balentine, Anne M, *Corresp Secy,* Arizona Watercolor Association, Phoenix

Bales, Cecille, *Chmn Bd,* Thomas Gilcrease Inst of American History and Art, Tulsa, OK

Bales, Jewel, *Treas,* Arizona Watercolor Association, Phoenix

Bales, Richard, *Asst to Dir Music,* Nat Gallery of Art, Washington, DC

Balestrieri, Sister Madonna, *Instr,* Cardinal Stritch College, Milwaukee, WI

Balf, Oliver, *Mem Faculty,* Montserrat School of Visual Art, Beverly, MA

Balhatchet, Clara, *Adv,* Mystic Art Association, CT

Balke, Mrs M N, *Chief Librn,* Nat Gallery of Canada, Ottawa, ON

Balkind, Alvin, *Chief Cur,* Vancouver Art Gallery, BC

Ball, George W, *Chmn Bd Trustees,* Asia Soc, New York, NY

Ballaine, Jerrold, *Assoc Prof & Co-Chmn Dept,* Univ California, Berkeley

Ballance, Stephen, *Instr,* Northwestern Michigan College, Traverse City

Ballard, Lockett Fored, Jr, *Dir,* Litchfield Historical Society, CT

Ballay, Joseph, *Head,* Carnegie-Mellon Univ, Pittsburgh, PA

Ballentine, Dikka, *Co-Chairwoman,* Lake Region Art Association, Devils Lake, ND

Ballentine, Don M, *Head Dept,* Atlanta Area Technical School, GA

Ballinger, Barbara, *Clerical Asst,* Ball State University Art Gallery, Muncie, IN

Ballinger, K A, *Pres,* Anderson Park Art Gallery, Invercargill, New Zealand

Balogh, Anthony, *Instr,* Madonna College, Livonia, MI

Balossi, John, *Mem Faculty,* Univ Puerto Rico, Rio Pietras

Baltus, J Ado, *Dir,* Ecole des Arts et Metiers D'Etterbeek, Brussels, Belgium

Balusek, William C, *Instr,* San Jacinto College, Pasadena, TX

Banach, Dr Jerzy, *Polish Iconography,* Muzeum Narodowe W Krakowie, Cracow, Poland

Bandes, Susan, *Asst Prof,* Sweet Briar College, VA

Bandy, Nancy, *Vis Prof,* Victoria College, TX

Bane, Mackey, *Cur,* Southeastern Center For Contemporary Art, Winston-Salem, NC

Bannerjee, N R, *Dir,* Nat Museum of India, New Delhi

Banks, John, *Asst Prof,* Northwest Community College, Powell, WY

Banks, Lloyd, *VPres,* Florida Gulf Coast Art Center, Clearwater

Banse, Andrew, *Dean of Summer School,* State Univ New York College at Cortland

Bantens, Robert J, *Asst Prof,* Univ South Alabama, Mobile

Baptie, Sue M, *Dir,* Vancouver City Archives, BC

Baptist, Francis C, *Prof,* Clarion State College, PA

Baragwanath, Albert K, *Senior Cur,* Museum of the City of New York, NY

Barati, George, *Exec Dir,* Villa Montalvo Center for the Arts, Saratoga, CA

Baratte, John, *Dir,* Univ Miami, Coral Gables, FL

Barbash, Steven, *Prof,* State Univ New York, College At Cortland

Barber, James, *Dir,* Plymouth City Museum and Art Gallery, England

Barber, Ronald L, *Asst Dir,* Museum of the Philadelphia Civic Center, PA

Barbic, Vesna, *Chief Cur,* Atelier Ivan Mestrovic, Galerije Grad Zabreba, Yugoslavia

Barbour, Arthur, *Mem Staff,* Rehoboth Art League, Rehoboth Beach, DE

Barclay, John T, *Pres,* Colorado Inst of Art, Denver

Barde, Alex, *Asst Prof,* Pittsburg State Univ, KS

Bardes, Leo N, *Div Dir,* College of San Mateo, CA

Bardi, P M, *Dir,* Museu de Arte de Sao Paulo, Brazil

Bardo, Pamela P, *Cur Decorative Arts,* New Orleans Museum of Art, LA

Baren, Mrs Paul, *Adminr,* Katonah Gallery, NY

Bargar, Mrs Robert, *Secy,* Chautauqua Gallery of Art, NY

Barile, Margaret R, *Asst Librn,* North Carolina State Univ Design Library, Raleigh

Barker, Bob O, *Assoc Prof,* East Central Univ, Ada, OK

Barker, Garry, *Exec Dir,* Kentucky Guild of Artists and Craftsmen, Berea

Barker, Jimmy H, *Asst Prof,* Sam Houston State Univ, Huntsville, TX

Barker, R Mildred, *Cur Manuscripts,* Shaker Museum, Poland Spring, ME

Barkley, Alan, *Asst Prof,* Univ Lethbridge, AB

Barksdale, A Beverly, *Gen Mgr,* Cleveland Museum of Art, OH

Barksdale, Clarence C, *Chmn,* Arts and Education Council of Greater St Louis, MO

Barlow, P J, *Head Dept History Art & Complementary Studies,* City of Birmingham Polytechnic, England

Barna, Iris, *Dir,* Barna Pottery, Santa Fe, NM

Barnard, Robert, *Prof,* Univ North Carolina at Chapel Hill

Barnes, Barry R, *Head Dept,* College of the Siskiyous, Weed, CA

Barnes, Bruce, *Dept Head Genealogy & Whaling,* New Bedford Free Public Library, MA

Barnes, Carl F, Jr, *Prof,* Oakland Univ, Rochester, MI; *Pres,* International Center of Medieval Art, New York, NY

Barnes, Gary, *Asst Prof,* Arkansas Tech Univ, Russellville

Barnes, Gordon, *Pres,* Canadian Guild of Potters, see National Organizations in Canada

Barnes, Jairus B, *Dir History Mus,* Western Reserve Historical Society, Cleveland, OH

Barnes, Muriel, *Treas,* Artist-Craftsmen of New York, NY

Barnes, Patricia P, *Registrar,* Montclair Art Museum, NJ

Barnes, Raymond S, *Asst Prof,* Lewis and Clark College, Portland, OR

Barnes, Sharron, *Asst Prof,* Gulf Coast Community College, Panama City, FL

Barnes, W D, *Asst Prof,* College of William and Mary, Williamsburg, VA

Barnet, Will, *Adv Bd Mem,* Famous Artists School, Westport, CT; *Artist Trustee,* Visual Artists and Galleries Association, see National and Regional Organizations

Barnett, Betty, *Educ Dir,* Arts Place II, Oklahoma Art Center, Oklahoma City

Barnett, Ed Willis, *Pres & Dir,* Alabama Museum of Photography, Birmingham

Barnett, Elliott B, *Pres,* Fort Lauderdale Museum of the Arts, FL

Barnett, Peter, *Asst Prof,* Earlham College, Richmond, IN

Barnett, Col W W, Jr, *Secy,* Hill Country Arts Found, Ingram, TX

Barney, Lary D, *Supvry Park Ranger,* Scotts Bluff Nat Monument, Gering, NE

Barnhart, Richard, *Prof,* Princeton Univ, NJ

Barnitz, Downing, *Assoc Prof,* Florida Southern College, Lakeland

Barnwell, F Edward, *Cur/Registrar & Librn,* Columbia Museums of Art and Science, SC

Barnwell, John, *Pres,* Miniature Art Society of New Jersey, Nutley

Baro, Gene, *Consult Cur Prints & Drawings,* Brooklyn Museum, NY

Baron, Nicholas B, *Art Research Dir,* American Art Society, Los Angeles, CA

Baron, Raymond, *Conf Dir & Publns Dir,* American Council for the Arts, see National and Regional Organizations

Baron, Stewart, *Design Coordr,* San Jose State Univ, CA

Barons, Richard, *Cur,* Roberson Center, Binghamton, NY

Barr, David, *Prof,* Macomb County Community College, Warren, MI

Barr, Laura, *Secy-Treas,* Hutchinson Art Association, KS

Barrachini, Dr Clara, *Dir,* Museo Nazionale di Villa Guinigi, Lucca, Italy

Barraclough, Dennis, *Prof,* Daemen College, Amherst, NY

Barradas, Manuel, *Mem Faculty,* Harriet FeBland's Advanced Painters Workshop, New Rochelle, NY

Barradell, Mrs D, *Cur,* Lloydminster Barr Colony Museum Committee, SK

Barragar, Roberta, *Assoc Prof,* Pierce College, Woodland Hills, CA

Barreto, Ricardo, *Admin Asst-Art Historian,* Intermuseum Conservation Association, see National and Regional Organizations

Barrett, Barbara, *Dir,* Toronto School of Art, ON

Barrett, Cheryl, *Adv,* Mystic Art Association, CT

Barrett, Mary, *Chmn,* Univ Wisconsin-River Falls

Barrett, Mrs Roger, *First VPres,* Arts Club of Chicago, IL

Barrett, Thomas R, *Head Art Dept,* St Paul's School, Concord, NH

Barrick, Ken, *Prof,* New Mexico State Univ, Las Cruces

Barrie, Diana, *Asst Prof,* Univ Northern Iowa, Cedar Falls

Barrio-Garay, J L, *Chmn,* Univ Western Ontario, London

Barry, Anne Meredith, *Chmn Bd,* Visual Arts Ontario, Toronto; *Pres,* Society of Canadian Artists, see National Organizations in Canada

Barry, Robert E, *Coordr Gallery,* Southeastern Massachusetts Univ, North Dartmouth

Barsch, Virginia, *Assoc Prof,* Moorhead State Univ, MN

Barsdale, Mary K, *Secy,* Alaska Association for the Arts, Fairbanks

Barsha, Carol, *Painter,* Regis College, Weston, MA

Barsness, John, *Mem Faculty,* Edgewood College, Madison, WI

Bartel, Marvin, *Prof Art & Chmn Dept,* Goshen College, IN

Barter, Judith, *Cur,* Amherst College Art Collection, MA

Barth, Charles, *Assoc Prof Art & Chmn Dept,* Mount Mercy College, Cedar Rapids, IA

Bartholomew, Martha L, *Prog Coordr,* Muckenthaler Cultural Center, Fullerton, CA

Bartholomew, Robert P, *Prof,* Univ Wisconsin, Madison

Bartholomew, Terese Tse, *Cur Indian Art,* Asian Art Museum, San Francisco, CA

Bartko, George, *Assoc Prof,* Saint Louis Community College at Florissant Valley, Ferguson, MO

Bartle, Dorothy B, *Cur Cons & Fire Museum,* Newark Museum, NJ

Bartle, Wilmot T, *Admin Asst,* Newark Museum, NJ

Bartlett, Christopher, *Dir,* Towson State Univ Art Gallery, MD

Bartlett, Dolores, *Pres,* Arts and Crafts Association of Meriden, CT

Bartlett, Don, *Chmn Dept & Dir Summer School,* Univ Missouri, Columbia

Bartlett, William F, *Mem Jury,* Society of Animal Artists, see National and Regional Organizations

Bartley, Anne, *Secy,* American Council for the Arts, see National and Regional Organizations

Bartner, Howard C, *Instr,* Johns Hopkins Univ, Baltimore, MD

Bartnick, Harry, *Chmn Painting Dept,* Lake Placid School of Art, NY

Barton, Bruce Walter, *Prof,* Univ Montana, Missoula

Barton, Ruth, *Reference Librn,* Detroit Public Library, MI

Bartz, James R, *Chmn Art Educ,* Wichita State Univ, KS

Barwick, Kent, *Exec Dir,* Municipal Art Society of New York, NY

Barzun, Jacques, *Pres,* American Academy and Institute of Arts and Letters, see National and Regional Organizations

Baschet, B, *Vis Prof,* Fontainebleau School of Fine Arts, France

Basham, Pet, *Secy,* Socorro Art League, NM

Basicevic, Dimitrije, *Chief Cur,* Galerija Benko Horvat, Galerije Grada Zabreba, Yugoslavia

Basner, Paul, *Treas,* Canton Art Inst, OH

Basquett, Gary, *Instr,* Wenatchee Valley College, WA

Bass, Harry W, Jr, *Pres,* American Numismatic Society, see National and Regional Organizations

Bassen, Irmgard, *Regional Librn,* Orange County Public Library, Garden Grove, CA

Bassett, Dr D A, *Dir,* Nat Museum of Wales, Cardiff

Bassett, Jerry, *Exhib Coordr,* Univ South Florida/Galleries Program, Tampa

Bassett, Mary, *Librn,* Brandywine River Museum, Chadds Ford, PA

Bassist, Donald H, *Pres,* Bassist Inst, Portland, OR

Bassist, Norma, *Librn,* Bassist Inst, Portland, OR

Bastian, Mrs Kenneth, *Secy,* Cedar Rapids Art Center, IA

Bastian, Susan, *Asst to Cur,* Univ Notre Dame Art Gallery, IN

Bastien, Suzanne, *Pres,* Centre D'Art de Victoriaville, PQ

Basu, Sukanta, *Restorer,* Nat Gallery of Modern Art, New Delhi, India

Batchelor, Anthony, *Mem Faculty,* Art Academy of Cincinnati, OH

Batchelor, Elisabeth, *Conservator,* Cincinnati Art Museum, OH

Bateman, Mrs W E, Jr, *Art Dir,* Fannie Mebane Ralph Library and Gallery, Bel Haven, NC

Bates, Dorothy, *Mem Faculty,* Charles Stewart Mott Community College, Flint, MI

Bates, Henry E, *City Librn,* Milwaukee Public Library, WI

Bates, Pat Martin, *Assoc Prof,* Univ Victoria, BC

Bates, Raymond E, *Instr,* Modesto Junior College, CA

Bates, Wayne, *Chairperson & Asst Prof,* Philadelphia College of Art, PA

Batham, Shri R N, *Guide Lectr,* Nat Gallery of Modern Art, New Delhi, India

Batis, Robert, *Dir,* Charles B Goddard Center for the Visual and Performing Arts, Ardmore, OK

Batista, Tomás, *Prof,* Inst of Puerto Rican Culture, San Juan

Battenberg, John, *Sculpture Coordr,* San Jose State Univ, CA

Battisti, Eugenio, *Prof,* Pennsylvania State Univ, University Park

Battisto, Caroline A, *Mem Faculty,* Norwich Art School, CT

Batto, Mrs E B, *Cur & Mgr,* Frontier Times Museum, Bandera, TX

Batty, Mrs John T, *Asst Dir,* Stockbridge Historical Society, MA

Batzka, Stephen, *Asst Prof,* Manchester College, North Manchester, IN

Bauber, Joel, *Instr,* Columbia College, CA

Baudouin, Frans, *Keeper Art,* Historical Museum City of Antwerp, Rubenianum; *Cur,* Openluchtmuseum Voor Beeldhouwkunst Middelheim & *Dir,* Museum Mayer Van Den Bergh, Antwerp, Belgium

Bauer, Felix, *Head Dept,* Erskine College, Due West, SC

Bauer, Dr J, *Cur Folk Art,* Bayerisches Nationalmuseum, Munich, Germany

Bauer, Lynn, *VChmn,* Municipal Art Commission, Kansas City, MO

Bauer, Margaret, *Educ Prog Coordr,* Burchfield Center, Buffalo, NY

Bauer, Richard G, *Dir,* Schumacher Gallery, Capital Univ, Columbus, OH

Bauer, Dr Sofie, *Librn,* Stadelsches Kunstinstitut, Frankfurt Am Main, Germany

Bauerle, Babette, *Libr Asst,* Bryn Mawr College, PA

Baum, Dr Elfriede, *Cur,* Osterreichische Galerie, Vienna, Austria

Baum, Ellen, *Funding Chair,* Women in the Arts Found, New York, NY

Baum, Peter, *Dir,* Wolfgang-Gurlitt-Museum, Linz, Austria

Baumann, Dr F, *Dir,* Kunsthaus Zurich, Switzerland

Baumann, Richard, *Cur Renaissance & Modern Art,* Univ Missouri Museum of Art and Archaeology, Columbia

Baumberger, Evelyn, *Librn,* South Dakota State Univ, Brookings

Baumgartner, Victor, *Chmn Design Dept,* Cornish Inst of Allied Arts, Seattle, WA

Baxter, Colles, *Asst Cur Prints,* Smith College Museum of Art, Northampton, MA

Bay, Tom, *Instr,* Miles Community College, MT

Bayard, Ivy, *Librn,* Temple Univ, Philadelphia, PA

Bayer, Jeffrey, *Pres,* Southern Association of Sculptures, see National and Regional Organizations; *Chmn & Prof,* Univ Alabama, Huntsville

Bayless, Stephen, *Head Dept,* Georgia Southern College, Statesboro

Bayliss, George V, *Dean Sch & Dean Summer School,* University of Michigan, Ann Arbor

Bays, Olga, *Mem Faculty,* Culver-Stockton College, Canton, MO

Bayuzick, Dennis, *Assoc Prof,* Univ Wisconsin-Parkside, Kenosha

Beach, Dorothy, *Librn,* Trinity College Library, Washington, DC

Beacock, E Stanley, *Dir,* London Public Library and Art Museum, ON

Beadle, Ernst, *Artist Trustee,* Visual Artists and Galleries Association, see National and Regional Organizations

Beadle, Paul J, *Prof,* Univ Auckland, New Zealand

Beal, Graham W J, *Cur,* Walker Art Center, Minneapolis, MN

Beale, Arthur, *Chief Conservator,* William Hayes Fogg Art Museum, Cambridge, MA

Bealmer, William, *Exec Dir,* Springfield Art Association of Edwards Place, IL

Beam, Kenneth M, *Adminr,* Chrysler Museum at Norfolk, VA

Beam, Philip C, *Mem Faculty,* Bowdoin College, Brunswick, ME

Beaman, Hope S, *Dir,* Green Hill Art Gallery, Greensboro, NC

Beaman, John R, Jr, *Treas,* Green Hill Art Gallery, Greensboro, NC

Beamer, Karl A, *Dir,* Haas Gallery of Art & *Asst Prof,* Bloomsburg State College, PA

Bean, D A, *Judge, Pres Bd Dir,* Kitchener-Waterloo Art Gallery, ON

Bean, Jacob, *Cur Drawings,* Metropolitan Museum of Art, New York, NY

Beane, W R, *Dir Commercial Art,* Holden School of Art and Design, Charlottesville, VA

Bear, James A, Jr, *Cur-Dir,* Monticello, Charlottesville, VA

Bear, Marcelle, *Treas,* Florida Artist Group, St Augustine

Bearce, Jeana, *Assoc Prof,* Univ Maine at Portland-Gorham, Gorham

Bearden, Romare, *Artist Trustee,* Visual Artists and Galleries Association, see National and Regional Organizations

Beardman, John, *Assoc Prof,* Oakland Univ, Rochester, MI

Beardsley, Beulah, *Secy,* Denver Artists Guild, CO

Beardsley, Edward, *Dir Mus,* Univ California Art Galleries, Riverside

Beardsley, Theodore S, Jr, *Dir,* Hispanic Society of America, New York, NY

Bearnson, Dorothy, *Prof,* Univ Utah, Salt Lake City

Beasley, Jack, *Chmn Creative Arts,* Univ North Carolina, Charlotte

Beasley, Richard, *Mem Faculty,* Northern Arizona Univ, Flagstaff

Beauchamp, Barbara, *Staff Asst,* Stephen Foster Center, White Springs, FL

Beauchamp, Toni, *Asst to Dir,* Univ Houston Gallery, TX

Beaudette, Sister Margaret, *Chmn & Assoc Prof,* Elizabeth Seton College, Yonkers, NY

Beaudoin, James, *Dir,* Dickinson State College, ND

Beaudoin, Paul-Emile, *Dir,* Musee Kateri Tekakwitha, Caughnawaga, PQ

Beaulé, Marc, *Secy,* Association des Graveurs du Quebec, Montreal

Beaumont, Maria Alice, *Dir & Cur Painting,* Museu Nacional De Arte Antiga Lisbon, Portugal

Beaver, Albert P, *Head Photography,* Rhode Island School of Design, Providence

Beaver, Susan, *Coordr,* Eye Level Gallery, Halifax, NS

Bebee, Andrea K, *Librn,* Univ Washington Henry Art Gallery, Seattle

Becher, Liselotte, *Librn,* Staatliche Graphische Sammlung, Munich, Germany

Becht, Mary, *Secy,* Erie Art Center, PA

Beck, Dorys L, *Asst to Dir,* Fresno Arts Center, CA

Beck, Dr Herbert, *Dir,* Liebieghaus, Museum alter Plastik, Frankfurt, Germany

Beck, Lon L, *Asst Prof,* Miami Univ, Oxford, OH

Beck, Robert A, *Pres,* New Jersey Historical Society Museum, Newark

Beckelman, John, *Instr,* Coe College, Cedar Rapids, IA

Becker, Sister Johanna, *Mem Faculty,* College of Saint Benedict, Saint Joseph, MN

Beckman, Julie, *CETA Dir in Training,* Tennessee Valley Art Center, Tuscumbia, AL

Beckman, Thomas, *Registrar,* Milwaukee Art Center, WI

Beckos, Barbara, *Cur Educ,* Everson Museum of Art, Syracuse, NY

Beckwith, Barbara, *Secy,* Tyler Art Gallery, State Univ New York at Oswego

Beckwith, Claudia, *Gallery Coordr,* Virginia Polytechnic Inst & State Univ Art Gallery, Blacksburg

Beckwith, J G, *Keeper Archit & Sculpture,* Victoria and Albert Museum, London, England

Beczkeiwicz, Ania, *Lectr,* Marian College, Indianapolis, IN

Bedard, Rodrique, *Conservator,* Montreal Museum of Fine Arts, PQ

Bedini, Silvio A, *Deputy Dir,* Nat Museum of History and Technology, Washington, DC

Beebe, Mary L, *Exec Dir & Librn,* Portland Center for the Visual Arts, OR

Beebee, Robert, *Librn II,* San Antonio Public Library, TX

Beech, Olive Ann, *Chmn Bd,* Wichita Art Association, KS

Beecher, Leonard T, *Chmn Art Dept,* Emma Willard School, Troy, NY

Beedle, R K, *Dir Restoration,* Jekyll Island Museum, GA

Beelke, Ralph, *Head Dept Creative Arts,* Purdue Univ, West Lafayette, IN

Beene, Patricia C, *Asst to Dir,* Southern Illinois Univ, Carbondale

Beer, Kenneth J, *Assoc Prof,* James Madison Univ, Harrisonburg, VA

Beer, Ruth, *Asst Prof,* Univ Victoria, BC

Beeren, Dr W A L, *Dir,* Museum Boymans-Van Beuningen, Rotterdam, Netherlands

Beerman, Miriam, *Instr,* Montclair Art Museum, NJ

Beetem, Robert, *Prof,* Univ Wisconsin, Madison

Beetham, Donald W, *Teacher,* Antonelli School of Photography, Philadelphia, PA

Bernstein, Rebecca, *Exec Dir,* Art Barn, Greenwich, CT

Berreth, David S, *Asst Dir,* Univ Wisconsin-Madison Mem Union

Berry, Barbara J, *Secy,* Univ Mississippi Gallery, University

Berry, Betty, *Mem Faculty,* Ouachita Baptist Univ, Arkadelphia, AR

Berry, Ethan, *Mem Faculty,* Montserrat School of Visual Art, Beverly, MA

Berry, Michele K, *Secy,* Society of North American Artists, see National and Regional Organizations

Berry, Nancy, *Cur Educ,* Southern Methodist Univ, Dallas, TX

Berry, Rosann S, *Exec Secy,* Society of Architectural Historians, see National and Regional Organizations

Berry, William, *Assoc Prof,* Boston Univ, MA

Berryman, Cara, *Exhib Coord,* Wilkes College, Wilkes-Barre, PA

Bersch, Mary John, *Prof,* College of Notre Dame of Maryland, Baltimore

Bertagnolli, Janet L, *Registrar,* Illinois State Univ, Normal

Bertelli, Dr Carlo, *Dir,* Pinacoteca di Brera, Milan, Italy

Bertelli, Dr Ilaria Toesca, *Dir,* Galleria e Museo del Palazzo Ducale, Mantua, Italy

Bertheux, W, *Head Dept Applied Art,* Stedelijk Museum-Amsterdam, Netherlands

Bertin, J, *Dir,* Nat College of Fine Arts, Paris, France

Bertolli, Robert, *Prof,* Boston State College, MA

Bertos, R, *Assoc Prof,* McGill Univ, Montreal, PQ

Bertrand, J Rayburn, *Pres Found,* Univ Southwestern Louisiana Art Center, Lafayette

Best, Cookie, *Dir,* Las Vegas Art League, NV

Best, Eileen, *Secy,* Ontario Crafts Council, Toronto

Best, Jack, *Head Dept,* Connors State College, Warner, OK

Best, William R, *Dir,* Thomas Gilcrease Inst of American History and Art, Tulsa, OK

Bertheaux, W, *Head Dept Applied Art,* Stedelijk Museum-Amsterdam, Netherlands

Betensky, Rose Hart, *Pres,* American Society of Contemporary Artists, see National and Regional Organizations

Bethel, Audrey, *Exec Dir,* Arts and Crafts Center of Pittsburgh, PA

Beti, Dr Luciano, *Dir,* Galleria Delgi Uffizi, Florence, Italy

Betsch, Dr William E, *Mem Faculty,* Univ Miami, Coral Gables, FL

Bettenbender, John, *Dean,* Mason Gross School of the Arts, Rutgers, The State Univ New Jersey, New Brunswick

Betti, Claudia W, *Undergrad Coordr,* North Texas State Univ, Denton

Bettinson, Brenda, *Chmn & Prof,* Pace Univ, White Plains, NY

Beville, Henry B, *Chief Photographic Lab,* Nat Gallery of Art, Washington, DC

Bex, Florent, *Dir,* Internationaal Cultureel Centrum, Antwerp, Belgium

Beyer, Victor, *Cur Sculpture,* Musee du Louvre, Paris, France

Bhowmik, S K, *Dir,* Museum and Picture Gallery, Baroda, India

Bialosky, Marshall, *Prof & Chmn,* California State Univ, Dominguez Hills

Bianchi, Robert, *Asst Cur Egyptian & Classical Art,* Brooklyn Museum, NY

Bibler, Richard, *Instr,* Monterey Peninsula College, CA

Bibler, Robert, *Instr,* Chemeketa Community College, Salem, OR

Bice, Megan, *Educ Cur,* Art Gallery of Windsor, ON

Bickford, Christopher P, *Dir,* Connecticut Historical Society Library, Hartford

Bicknell, Robert E, *Chmn,* Wayland Baptist College, Plainview, TX

Biddle, James, *Pres,* Nat Trust for Historic Preservation, Washington, DC

Biddle, Livingston L, Jr, *Chmn,* Nat Endowment for the Arts, see National and Regional Organizations

Biddle, Martin, *Dir,* Univ Pennsylvania Museum, Philadelphia

Bienemann, Bruce, *Asst Dir,* Sioux City Art Center, IA

Biers, Jane C, *Cur Ancient Art,* Univ Missouri Museum of Art and Archaeology, Columbia

Biesboer, Dr P, *Cur Ancient Art,* Frans Halsmuseum, Haarlem, Netherlands

Bigbee, Nelle, *First VPres,* Tennessee Valley Art Center, Tuscumbia, AL

Bigelow, David, *Asst Prof,* Middle Tennessee State Univ, Murfreesboro

Bigger, Michael, *Chmn Sculpture,* Univ Manitoba, Winnipeg

Biggers, John T, *Head Dept,* Texas Southern Univ, Houston

Biggs, Lorraine, *VPres Bd Dir,* Copper Village Museum and Arts Center, Anaconda, MT

Bigler, Steve, *Assoc Prof,* Viterbo College, La Crosse, WI

Bilaitis, Richard J, *Gallery Coordr,* Wayne State Univ Art Gallery, Detroit, MI

Bilderback, Norman C, *Dir Exhib,* California Museum of Science and Industry, Los Angeles

Bilinski, Donald, *Dir,* Polish Museum of America, Chicago, IL

Bilisoly, Mrs Frank Nash, *Secy,* Irene Leache Mem, Norfolk, VA

Bilk, Marjorie, *Librn,* Moore College of Art, Philadelphia, PA

Billeter, Dr E, *VDir,* Kunsthaus Zurich, Switzerland

Billmeyer, Dr Fred W, Jr, *Secy,* Inter-Society Color Council, see National and Regional Organizations

Binai, Paul F, *Cur Exhib,* Carnegie Inst Museum of Art, Pittsburgh, PA

Bindler, Nathan, *Assoc Prof,* Augusta College, GA

Binegger, Uli, *Art-Cur in Charge Serigraphed Reproductions,* Muiska-Museum, Munich, Germany

Bingaman, Elizabeth, *Films Specialist,* Minneapolis Public Library and Information Center, Minneapolis, MN

Bingham, Lois A, *Chief Office of Exhib Abroad,* Nat Collection of Fine Arts, Washington, DC

Bingham, Olivia, *Secy,* Crossett Art League, AR

Binkert, June, *Pres Bd Trustees,* Burnaby Art Gallery, BC

Binkley, Donald, *Coordr Exhib,* Omniplex, Oklahoma City, OK

Binks, Ronald, *Prof Art & Dir Div Art & Design,* Univ Texas at San Antonio

Binns, Patti, *Secy,* Kern County Museum, Bakersfield, CA

Bionomann, Bruce A, *Asst Dir,* Sioux City Art Center, IA

Birch, Cathy Leffel, *Educ Serv,* Rockwell-Corning Museum, Corning, NY

Birch, Virginia, *Secy,* Arts and Crafts Association of Meriden, CT

Bird, Richard, *Head Dept,* Ricks College, Rexburg, ID

Bird, Richard, *Instr,* Chadron State College, NE

Birdman, Jerome, *Dean,* School of Fine Arts, Univ Nebraska, Omaha

Birdsall, James, *Treas,* Owatonna Arts Center, MN

Birdsall, Virginia, *Performing Arts Chmn,* Owatonna Arts Center, MN

Birgili, Turhan, *Cur Photography,* Istanbul Arkeoloji Muzeleri, Turkey

Birnbaum, Mildred, *Gallery Dir,* Art Barn, Greenwich, CT

Birnie, Adelaide R, *Bursar,* Montclair Art Museum, NJ

Bisaillon, Ed, *Dir,* Hastings Museum, NE

Biscow, Phoebe, *Secy,* Art Barn, Greenwich, CT

Bishop, Barbara L, *Chmn Art Dept & Dir,* Longwood College, Farmville, VA

Bishop, Budd, *VPres,* Intermuseum Conservation Association, see National and Regional Organizations

Bishop, Budd Harris, *Dir,* Columbus Gallery of Fine Arts, OH

Bishop, Dottie, *Asst Prof,* Olivet Nazarene College, Kankakee, IL

Bishop, Janice, *Admin Asst,* Ontario Association of Art Galleries, Toronto

Bishop, Jeffrey, *Mem Faculty,* Factory of Visual Art, Seattle, WA

Bishop, Minor, *Secy,* Fine Arts Found of New York, NY

Bishop, Dr Robert, *Dir,* Museum of American Folk Art, New York, NY

Bishop, Ron, *Asst Dir,* Univ Nebraska Art Galleries, Omaha

Bissietta, G F, *Prof & Coordr,* Accademia di Belle Arti, Perugia, Italy

Bisson, Yvette, *Prof,* College Saint-Louis-Maillet, Edmundston, NB

Bissoodnov, Vladimir I, *Art Secy,* State Museum of Oriental Art, Moscow, USSR

Bisttram, Emil, *Pres,* Taos Art Association, NM

Bitner, William L, III, *Assoc Comm Instructional Services,* State Education Dept, Albany, NY

Bitz, Gwen, *Asst Registrar,* Walker Art Center, Minneapolis, MN

Bjarnhof, Mette, *Restorer, Dept Painting & Sculpture,* Statens Museum for Kunst, Copenhagen, Denmark

Bjarnhof, Steen, *Restorer Acting for Chief Restorer, Dept Painting & Sculpture,* Statens Museum for Kunst, Copenhagen, Denmark

Bjerre, Henrik, *Restorer Acting for Chief Restorer, Dept Painting & Sculpture,* Statens Museum for Kunst, Copenhagen, Denmark

Bjone, Helen, *VPres,* Sheyenne Valley Arts and Crafts Association, Fort Ransom, ND

Bjorkland, Marilyn, *Registrar,* Minneapolis Inst of Arts, MN

Bjorklund, Samuel, *Prof,* Leo Marchutz School of Painting and Drawing, Aix-en-Provence, France

Bjorkman, Donald, *Assoc Prof,* California Polytechnic State Univ, San Luis Obispo

Björkvik, Halvard, *Dir,* Norsk Folkemuseum, Oslo, Norway

Bjornsson, Arni, *Cur,* Thjodminjasafn, Reykjavik, Iceland

Bjurin, Marvin, *Assoc Prof,* State Univ of New York, College at Fredonia

Bjurstrom, P, *Head Prints & Drawings Dept,* Nationalmuseum, Stockholm, Sweden

Black, Daniel, *Asst Prof,* Swarthmore College, PA

Black, James R, *Mem Faculty,* Schoolcraft College, Livonia, MI

Black, Joe V, *Pres Bd Trustees,* Zigler Museum, Jennings, LA

Black, Mary, *Cur Painting & Sculpture,* New York Historical Society, NY

Black, Patti Carr, *Dir,* Old Capitol Museum, Mississippi Dept of Archives and History, Jackson

Black, Richard, *Prof,* Drake Univ, Des Moines, IA

Blackburn, J Glenn, *Chmn,* Clinch Valley College of Univ Virginia, Wise

Blackburn, Robert, *Dir,* Printmaking Workshop, New York, NY

Blackim, Dave, *Chmn,* Hutchinson Community Junior College, KS

Blackmun, Barbara Winston, *Chairperson Art Dept,* San Diego Mesa College, CA

Blacksberg, Leslie, *Cataloger,* Hebrew Union College, Los Angeles, CA

Blackwell, J V, *Prof Art & Chmn Dept,* Univ Nebraska at Omaha

Blackwood, C Roy, *Instr,* Southeastern Louisiana Univ, Hammond

Blade, Timothy, *Asst Prof,* Univ Minnesota, Saint Paul

Blaesing, William, *Cur Exhib,* Charles A Wustum Museum of Fine Arts, Racine, WI

Blain, Bradley, *Cur,* Kitchener-Waterloo Art Gallery, ON

Blain, Sandra, *VPres,* Southern Highland Handicraft Guild, Asheville, NC

Blain, Sandra J, *Asst Prof,* Univ Tennessee, Knoxville

Blain, Wilfred, *Admin Officer,* Ottawa Public Library, ON

Blaine, Martha, *Indian Archives*, Oklahoma Historical Society, Oklahoma City

Blair, C, *Keeper Metalwork*, Victoria and Alberta Museum, London, England

Blair, Carl, *Mem Faculty*, Bob Jones Univ, Greenville, SC

Blair, Jean, *Second VPres*, Monmouth Museum and Cultural Center, Lincroft, NJ

Blair, Laurel G, *Cur*, Blair Museum of Lithophanes and Carved Waxes, Toledo, OH

Blair, Mary, *VPres*, Brattleboro Museum and Art Center, VT

Blair, Thomas E, *Mgr*, California State Fair & Exposition Art Show, Sacramento, CA

Blake, Hortense, *Dir*, Clinton Art Association Gallery, IA

Blake, Peter, *Chmn*, Boston Architectural Center, MA

Blakely, Glen, *Mem Faculty*, Dixie College, Saint George, UT

Blakely, Dr Phyllis R, *Assoc Archivist*, Public Archives of Nova Scotia, Halifax

Blakemore, Robbie G, *Head Dept & Prof*, Univ Tennessee, Knoxville

Blalock, Dorothy, *VPres*, Nicholas Roerich Museum, New York, NY

Blanchard, Henry J, *Dir*, Centre Cultural de Shawinigan, PQ

Blanton, Paul, *Head Dept*, Univ Idaho, Moscow

Blasage, Margaret, *Dir Publns*, Art Inst of Chicago, IL

Blasdel, Dr Hugo G, *Exec Dir*, Nat Architectural Accrediting Board, see National and Regional Organizations

Blattberg, Rebecca, *Treas*, Chicago Art Dealers Association, IL

Bledsoe, Jane K, *Asst Dir*, Art Galleries, Long Beach, CA

Blehel, Howard, *Vis Prof*, Springfield College, MA

Bleibtreu, Dr Hermann K, *Dir*, Museum of Northern Arizona, Flagstaff

Blench, Brian, *Keeper Decorative Arts*, Glasgow Museum and Art Galleries, Scotland

Blenderman, Dr Al, *Pres*, Sioux City Art Center, IA

Blevins, Dr, *Head Dept*, Indiana State Univ, Evansville

Blevins, Tedd, *Chmn*, Virginia Intermont College, Bristol

Blickman, Mrs J H, *Recording Secy*, Museum of Arts and Sciences, Daytona Beach, FL

Blindheim, Charlotte, *Head Viking Age Dept*, Universitetets Samling Av Nordiske Oldsaker, Oslo, Norway

Blindheim, Martin, *Head Medieval Age Dept*, Universitetets Samling Av Nordiske Oldsaker, Oslo, Norway

Bliss, Harry E, *Assoc Prof*, Palomar College, San Marcos, CA

Blitzer, Charles, *Asst Secy History & Art*, Smithsonian Institution, Washington, DC

Bliven, Shirley, *Dir*, Arts for Living Center, Burlington, IA

Blix, Bill, *Mem Faculty*, Lane Community College, Eugene, OR

Blizard, William, *Chmn Art Dept & In Charge*, Babson Library Art Gallery, Springfield College, MA

Blizzard, Alan, *Prof*, Scripps College, Claremont, CA

Bloch, Dr E Maurice, *Dir & Cur*, Grunwald Center for the Graphic Arts, Univ California, Los Angeles

Bloch, Milton J, *Dir*, Mint Museum of Art, Charlotte, NC

Bloch, Dr Peter, *Dir Dept of Sculpture*, Staatliche Museen Preussischer Kulturbesitz, Berlin, Germany

Block, Abby, *Pres*, North Shore Art League, Winnetka, IL

Blocker, Merrie, *Dir*, DeCordova School, DeCordova and Dana Museum and Park, Lincoln, MA

Blodgett, Fritz, *Instr*, Sierra College, Rocklin, CA

Bloedel, Flora, *Secy*, Williams College Museum of Art, Williamstown, MA

Blogg, Irene, *Pres*, Sculptor's Society of Canada, see National Organizations in Canada

Blokhuis, S M, *Head Educ Dept*, Stedelijk Museum De Lakenhal, Netherlands

Blom, Arthur, *Instr*, Grand Valley State College, Allendale, MI

Blomstrann, Lois L, *Asst to Dir*, New Britain Museum of American Art, CT

Bloom, Susan, *Cur*, Queens Museum, Flushing, NY

Bloomer, Carolyn, *Asst Prof*, Monmouth College, West Long Branch, NJ

Bloomer, Harlan, *Dir*, Nichols Gallery, Mankato, MN

Bloomer, Jerry M, *Secy-Registrar & Librn*, R W Norton Art Gallery, Shreveport, LA

Bloss, Meredith, *Librn*, New Haven Free Public Library, CT

Blosser, John, *Head Dept & Instr*, Hesston College, KS

Blovits, Larry, *Assoc Prof*, Aquinas College, Grand Rapids, MI

Blum, Harlow B, *Head Dept*, Monmouth College, IL

Blum, Kristin E, *Exec Dir*, Hoosier Salon Patrons Association, Indianapolis, IN

Blum, Zevi, *Assoc Prof Art & Chmn Dept*, Cornell Univ, Ithaca, NY

Blume, Peter F, *Cur*, Allentown Art Museum, PA

Blumenthal, Arthur, *Cur*, Dartmouth College Museum and Galleries, Hanover, NH

Blumenthal, Elizabeth, *Instr*, Johns Hopkins Univ, Baltimore, MD

Blumenthal, Gloria, *Slide Librn*, Hebrew Union College, Los Angeles, CA

Blunk, Robert Jr, *Assoc Prof*, Pittsburg State Univ, KS

Blyer, Verna R, *Admin Secy*, Canton Art Inst, OH

Boardman, Patricia Hanify, *Art Therapist*, Regis College, Weston, MA

Boatner, James K, *Exec Dir*, Manchester Inst of Arts and Sciences, NH

Bob, Murray L, *Dir*, James Prendergast Library Association, Jamestown, NY

Bobo, Paul, *Art Librn*, Univ Oklahoma, Norman

Bobowick, Mrs Matthew, *First VPres*, Bridgeport Art League, CT

Bock, Dr Henning, *Dir*, Picture Gallery, Staatliche Museen Preussischer Kulturbesitz, Berlin, Germany

Bockstoce, John R, *Cur Ethnology*, New Bedford Whaling Museum, MA

Bocz, George R, *Prof*, Florida State Univ, Tallahassee

Bodem, Dennis R, *Dir*, Jesse Besser Museum, Alpena, MI

Bodnar, Mrs N, *Pres*, Ukrainian Arts and Crafts Museum, Edmonton, AB

Bodnar, Peter David, III, *Mem Faculty*, Louisville School of Art, Anchorage, KY

Bodnar-Balahutrak, Lydia, *Instr*, San Jacinto College North, Houston, TX

Boe, Alf, *Dir*, City of Oslo Art Collection, Norway

Boegen, Anne, *Work with Children and Young Adults*, Miami-Dade Public Library, FL

Boehm, Ann, *Pres*, Midland Art Council of the Midland Center for the Arts, MI

Boehm, Mary, *Treas*, Breezewood Found Museum and Garden, Monkton, MD

Boehmer, Ron, *Art Coordr*, Lynchburg Fine Arts Center, VA

Boelke, Walter, *Mem Faculty*, Western Connecticut State College, Danbury

Boentgen, Martha, *Instr*, Lower Columbia College, Longview, WA

Boerlin, Dr Paul-Henry, *Cur Paintings*, Offentliche Kunstsammlung Kunstmuseum Basel, Switzerland

Boersma, Dr J W, *Cur Archaeology*, Groninger Museum Voor Stad En Land, Netherlands

Boethius, Lena, *Asst Cur Deposit Dept*, Goteborgs Konstmuseum, Sweden

Boeve, Edgar G, *Assoc Prof Art & Chmn Dept & Dir Summer School*, Calvin College, Grand Rapids, MI

Bogdanovitch, George, *Chmn & Prof*, Denison Univ, Granville, OH

Boggs, Arlene A, *Secy, Registrar & Librn*, Illinois State Univ, Normal

Bogh, Lone, *Restorer, Dept Painting & Sculpture*, Statens Museum for Kunst, Copenhagen, Denmark

Bogle, Jon Robert, *Dir, Art Center Gallery & Asst Prof*, Lycoming College, Williamsport, PA

Bogle, Michael, *Textile Conservator*, Merrimack Valley Textile Museum, North Andover, MA

Bohanon, Gloria, *Asst Prof*, Los Angeles City College, CA

Bohlsen, Darrell A, *Dir*, Sangre De Cristo Arts & Conference Center, Pueblo, CO

Bohrnstedt, Wayne R, *Dean Div*, Univ Redlands, CA

Boigon, Irving, *VPres*, Royal Architectural Inst of Canada, see National Organizations in Canada

Boileau, Andree, *Mgr*, Musee Historique de Vaudreuil, PQ

Boiten, Dr E A J, *Cur Mediaeval & Later History*, Groninger Museum Voor Stad En Land, Netherlands

Bol, Dr Peter, *Dir*, Liebieghaus, Museum alter Plastik, Frankfurt, Germany

Bolan, Suzanne, *Cur Decorative Arts*, Philip H & A S W Rosenbach Found Museum, Philadelphia, PA

Boland, Robert M, *Prof*, Berkshire Community College, Pittsfield, MA

Bolas, Gerald D, *Dir*, Washington Univ Gallery of Art, St Louis, MO

Bolden, Joyce, *Chmn*, Alcorn State Univ, Lorman, MS

Bolder, Stuart, *First VPres*, Rochester Historical Society, NY

Bolduc, Pauline, *Dept Head Tech Serv*, New Bedford Free Public Library, MA

Bolen, Jack, *Assoc Prof*, Kingsborough Community College, Brooklyn, NY

Boles, Pat, *Instr*, Monterey Peninsula College, CA

Bolge, George S, *Dir*, Fort Lauderdale Museum of the Arts, FL

Bolin, Judith, *Office Mgr*, San Jose Museum of Art, CA

Bolley, James R, *Mgr*, World Museum/Art Centre, Tulsa, OK

Bolling, Sarah, *Secy*, Associated Artists of Winston-Salem, NC

Bollinger, Irene, *Coordr & Librn*, Craft Resource Centre, Ontario Crafts Council, Toronto

Bolner, Clifton, *Secy*, San Antonio Museum Association, TX

Bolomey, Roger, *Chmn Dept*, California State Univ, Fresno

Bolton, Bruce D, *Mgr*, Society of the Montreal Military & Maritime Museum, PQ

Bolton, James, *Vis Prof*, Texas Tech Univ, Lubbock

Bolton, Shirley L, *Asst Prof*, Univ West Florida, Pensacola

Bolton-Smith, Robin, *Assoc Cur, 18th & 19th Century Painting & Sculpture*, Nat Collection of Fine Arts, Washington, DC

Boltz, Shirley, *Pub Relations Coordr*, Indiana State Museum, Indianapolis

Bolz, Dr Ingeborg, *Cur American Indian Art*, Rautenstrauch-Joest Museum fur Volkerkunde, Museen der Stadt Koln, Germany

Bolz, Sarah, *Cur*, Elizabet Ney Museum, Austin, TX

Bomeisler, Anne, *Mus Asst*, Museum of Cultural History, Univ California, Los Angeles

Bomnert, Thomas, *Mem Faculty*, Charles Stewart Mott Community College, Flint, MI

Bomse, Marc, *Mem Faculty & Dir Summer School*, State Univ New York College at Old Westbury

Bond, Barbara, *Exec Dir*, York Inst Museum, Saco, ME

Bond, Carolyn, *Dir*, Redding Museum and Art Center, CA

Bond, Elisabeth, *Area Coordr*, Northern Illinois Univ, DeKalb

Bond, Leroy, *Head Dept*, Oklahoma Baptist Univ, Shawnee

Bond, Margaret, *Head Pub Relations*, Univ Rochester Mem Art Gallery, NY

Bondurant, Francis G, *Cataloger,* New York Univ Art Collection, NY

Bonebrake, John C, *Secy,* Cleveland Museum of Art, OH

Bonfiay, William, *Instr,* Milwaukee Area Technical College, WI

Bonna, J P, *Asst Conservator,* Musees Saint-Denis, Reim, France

Bonsanti, Dr Giorgio, *Dir,* Galleria e Museo Estense, Modena, Italy

Bonte, Genevieve, *Librn Conservator,* Union Centrale des Arts Decoratifs Paris, France

Bonzelaar, Helen, *Asst Prof,* Calvin College, Grand Rapids, MI

Booke, Elizabeth M, *Pres,* Arts Council, Winston-Salem, NC

Booker, Mrs Edward N, *Pres Bd Dir,* Green Hill Art Gallery, Greensboro, NC

Booker, William, *Asst to Dir,* Dacotah Prairie Museum, Aberdeen, SD

Boon, G C, *Keeper Archeology,* Nat Museum of Wales, Cardiff

Boone, Edward J, Jr, *Admin Asst,* MacArthur Mem, Norfolk, VA

Boone, Garret, *Prof,* Earlham College, Richmond, IN

Boorman, Robert, *Pres,* Lakehead Visual Arts, Thunder Bay, ON

Boorstin, Daniel J, *Librn of Congress,* Library of Congress, Washington, DC

Booth, Abigail, *Coordr,* Bicentennial Inventory of American Paintings, National Collection of Fine Arts, Washington, DC

Booth, Dr Bill R, *Head Dept,* Morehead State Univ, KY

Booth, Elizabeth C, *Head Librn,* Univ Pittsburgh Art Gallery, PA

Booth, Gordon, *Publ Mgr,* Nat Gallery of London, England

Booth, Judith, *Asst Dir,* Tamarind Inst, Univ New Mexico, Albuquerque

Booth, Judy, *Secy,* Santa Monica College Art Gallery, CA

Booth, Louise A T, *Instr,* Morehead State Univ, KY

Booth, Lydia Noble, *Dir,* Guilford Art and Music School, CT

Boothby, Norman B, *Prof,* Tulane Univ, New Orleans, LA

Boots, Dona, *Educ Dir,* Merrick Art Gallery, New Brighton, PA

Boozer, Tom, *Exec Dir,* Arts and Humanities Council of Tuscaloosa County, Tuscaloosa, AL

Bopp, Emery, *Chmn,* Bob Jones Univ, Greenville, SC

Boppel, Todd, *Prof,* Univ Wisconsin-Stout, Menomonie

Borchardt, H, *Dir & VPres,* Lovis Corinth Memorial Found, New York, NY

Borchert, Gary, *Instr,* Oklahoma State Univ, Okmulgee

Borcoman, J, *Cur Photography,* Nat Gallery of Canada, Ottawa, ON

Bordaz, Jacques, *Assoc Cur Palaeolithic Archaeology,* Univ Pennsylvania Museum, Philadelphia

Bordaz, Robert, *Pres,* Union Centrale des Arts Decoratifs, Paris, France

Bordeaux, Jean-Luc, *Dir,* California State Univ Fine Arts Gallery, Northridge

Borden, Jeanne, *Librn,* Rhode Island School of Design, Providence

Borden, Sidney, *Dir,* Inst of Lettering and Design, Chicago, IL

Boretz, Benjamin A, *Chmn Music,* Bard College, Annandale-on-Hudson, NY

Borger, Dr Hugo, *Dir,* Romisch-Germanisches Museum, Museen der Stadt Koln, Germany

Borger, Irene, *Audience Develop Specialist,* Los Angeles Inst of Contemporary Art, CA

Borio, Dr Leonidas Lopes, *Treas,* Museu de Arte Moderna Brazil, Rio de Janiero

Borman, Charles, *Assoc Chmn,* California State Univ, Los Angeles

Borman, R, *Cur,* Bemeentemuseum Arnhem, Netherlands

Bornarth, Philip W, *Chmn Fine Arts,* Rochester Inst Technology, NY

Borneman, Walter R, *Asst to Dir,* Colorado Historical Society, Denver

Boronda, Beonne, *Secy,* Mystic Art Association, CT

Borovicka, Dr Jaroslav, *Asst,* Stadtische Kunsthalle, Dusseldorf, Germany

Borrani, Antonio, *Teacher,* Venice Painting, Drawing & Sculpture Studio, CA

Borrego, Elisa, *Cur & Researcher,* Galeria de la Raza, San Francisco, CA

Borrman, D C, *Adminr,* Walker Art Center, Minneapolis, MN

Bos, B, *VDir,* Academie Van Beeldende Kunsten, Rotterdam, Netherlands

Bosco, Bob, *Mem Faculty,* Creighton Univ, Omaha, NE

Boser, Dr. Renee, *Cur Africa, Textiles,* Museum Fur Volkerkunde Und Schweizerisches Museum·Fur Volkskunde, Basel, Switzerland

Bosman, Edgar C L, *Conservator,* South African Nat Gallery, Cape Town

Bosson, Jack, *Mem Faculty,* College of New Rochelle, NY

Bostick, William A, *Adminr & Secy,* Detroit Inst of Art Collections, MI

Bostwick, Elizabeth, *Librn,* Huntington Galleries, WV

Boterf, Chester A, *Assoc Prof,* Rice Univ, Houston, TX

Bothen, Claes, *Pres,* American Swedish Historical Found Museum, Philadelphia, PA

Bothmer, Bernard V, *Chmn of Dept Egyptian & Classical Art & Keeper of the Wilbour Coll,* Brooklyn Museum, NY

Botsai, Elmer E, *Pres,* American Inst of Architects, see National and Regional Organizations

Bott, Dr Gerhard, *Gen Dir,* Museen der Stadt Koln, Germany

Bott, Patricia Allen, *Secy,* Society of Animal Artists, see National and Regional Organizations

Bott, William, *Trustee,* Attleboro Museum, MA

Bottoms, Nancy, *Treas,* Paducah Art Guild, KY

Botwinick, Michael, *Dir,* Brooklyn Museum, NY

Bouchard, Leo, *Mem Faculty,* Junior College of Albany, NY

Boucher, S Marcelle, *Archivist Conservator,* Marie de L'Incarnation Center and Museum, Quebec, PQ

Boudreau, Elizabeth S, *Asst to Dir,* State Univ New York at Stony Brook Art Gallery

Boudreau, Eulalie, *Dir,* Univ Moncton Galerie D'Art, NB

Boudreau, Joe, *Asst Prof,* Univ Minnesota, Duluth

Boukamp, Mary, *Librn,* Ivy School of Professional Art Galleries, Pittsburgh, PA

Bouler, Sheryl B, *Supvr Junior Mus,* Newark Museum, NJ

Boulet, Roger, *Dir,* Art Gallery of Greater Victoria, BC

Bouloukos, Athanasios, *Chmn Critical Studies,* Massachusetts College of Art, Boston

Boulware, William, *Adj Prof,* Southwestern College, Winfield, KS

Bourke, Sister Celeste Mary, *Mem Faculty,* Siena Heights College, Adrian, MI

Bourke, Patrick, *Discipline Chmn,* Saint Clair County Community College, Port Huron, MI

Bourke, Thomas, *Dir Performing Arts,* Colorado Springs Fine Arts Center, CO

Bourque, Lise, *Prof,* College Saint-Louis-Maillet, Edmundson, NB

Bouslough, Ray, *Arts Specialist,* Davenport Municipal Art Gallery, IA

Bousquet, Jean, *Supvr Music & Arts,* Berkshire Athenaeum, Pittsfield, MA

Bouton, Margaret I, *Chief Educ & Pub Prog,* Nat Gallery of Art, Washington, DC

Bovey, John A, *Archivist,* Provincial Archives of Manitoba, Winnipeg

Bowdish, Leah, *Secy,* Clearwater Art Association, ID

Bowe, Martin, *Dir,* Newfoundland Museum, Saint Johns

Bowen, David, *Instr,* Laguna Beach School of Art, CA

Bower, Gerald, *Asst Prof,* Louisiana State Univ, Baton Rouge

Bowerman, John, *Pres,* Henry S Lane Home, Crawfordsville, IN

Bowers, Harry, *Chmn Photography Dept,* San Francisco Art nst, CA

Bowers, Paul, *Asst Prof,* Mohawk Valley Community College, Utica, NY

Bowie, George L, *Pres,* London Art Gallery Association, ON

Bowles, Thomas A, III, *Dir,* Huntsville Museum of Art, AL

Bowling, Gary, *Mem Faculty,* Sioux City Art Center, IA

Bowling Gary R, *Dir,* Weidler Art Gallery & *Head Art Dept,* Westmar College, Lemars, IA

Bowman, Capt Carl G, *Pres & Exec Dir,* Maritime Museum Association of San Diego, CA

Bowman, David, *Chmn Painting,* Moore College of Art, Philadelphia, PA

Bowman, Dean B, *Prof,* Concordia College, Moorhead, MN

Bowman, Geoffrey, *Printmaking & Photography Coordr,* San Jose State Univ, CA

Bowman, Dr Jeff R, *Chmn,* Univ Southern Mississippi, Hattiesburg

Bowman, Ken, *Instr,* Blackhawk Mountain School of Art, CO

Bowman, Mary J, *Pres,* Minneapolis Inst of Arts, MN

Bowman, Dr Milton, *Registrar Summer School,* Monmouth College, IL

Bowman, Peter, *Asst Prof,* Southwestern at Memphis, TN

Bowman, Ruth, *Cur,* New York Univ Art Collection, New York

Bowne, James D, *Dir,* Sheldon Swope Art Gallery, Terre Haute, IN

Bowron, Edgar Peters, *Cur Renaissance & Baroque Art,* Walters Art Gallery, Baltimore, MD

Bowsfield, Blaire L, *Secy,* Lloydminster Barr Colony Museum Committee, SK

Box, Harold, *Dean,* Univ Texas, Austin

Box-Pope, Patrice, *Asst Chmn,* William Carey College, Hattiesburg, MS

Boyce, Gerald G, *Prof Art & Chmn Fine Arts,* Indiana Central Univ, Indianapolis

Boyce, Louise, *Instr,* Tracey-Warner School, Philadelphia, PA

Boyce, William, *Prof,* Univ Minnesota, Duluth

Boyce, William G, *Dir,* Tweed Museum of Art, Duluth, MN

Boyd, Amy S, *Dir,* Imperial Calcasieu Museum, Lake Charles, LA

Boyd, James D, *Dir,* Dundee Museums and Art Gallery, Scotland

Boyd, John D, *Chmn Studio Arts,* Wichita State Univ, KS

Boyd, Karen W, *Mem Faculty,* Murray State Univ, KY

Boyd, Lakin, *Asst Prof,* Alabama A&M Univ, Huntsville

Boyd, Virginia T, *Asst Prof,* Univ Wisconsin, Madison

Boyer, Dr Ruth, *Instr,* California College of Arts and Crafts, Oakland

Boyesen, L Rostrup, *Dir,* Nordjyllands Kunstmuseum, Aalborg, Denmark

Boykin, Eddie, *Pres,* Abilene Fine Arts Museum, TX

Boylan, William, *Senior Clerk,* Joe and Emily Lowe Art Gallery, Syracuse Univ, NY

Boyle, James M, *Chmn,* Wyoming Council on the Arts, Cheyenne

Boyle, Joel Lynn, *Coordr,* Umpqua Community College, Roseburg, OR

Boyle, Richard J, *Dir Collection,* Pennsylvania Acad of Fine Arts, Philadelphia

Boyle, William J S, *Exec Dir,* Visual Arts Ontario Toronto

Boyles, Gerald, *Mem Faculty,* Goldsboro Art Center, NC

Boynton, Charles, *Treas,* Salt Lake City Art Center, UT

Boynton, Wyman P, *VPres,* John Paul Jones House, Portsmouth, NH

Boyt, Patrick E, *Pres,* Beaumont Art Museum, TX

Boyt, Richard, *Instr,* Crowder College, Neosho, MO

Bozzi, Julie, *Asst Prof,* Austin College, Sherman, TX

Braasem, W A, *Dir,* Westfries Museum, Hoorn, Netherlands

Brabander, W H, *Deputy Managing Dir,* Stedelijk Museum-Amsterdam, Netherlands

Brach, Paul, *Chmn,* Fordham Univ, New York, NY

Bracke, Victor, *Head Dept,* Bakersfield College, CA

Brackenridge, Dr R Douglas, *Pres,* Presbyterian Historical Society, Philadelphia, PA

Bracker, Dr Jörgen, *Cur Classical Archaeology,* Romisch-Germanisches Museum, Museen der Stadt Koln, Germany

Brackett, Cynthia, *Treas,* Pemaquid Group of Artists, Pemaquid Point, ME

Brackett, Woodbury, *Pres,* Lincoln County Cultural and Historical Association, Wiscasset, ME

Bradbury, Ellen, *Cur Pre-Columbian Arts,* Minneapolis Inst of Arts, MN

Bradbury, Mrs Walter I, *Treas,* Greenwich Art Society and Art Center, CT

Bradford, Derek, *Head Archit,* Rhode Island School of Design, Providence

Bradford, J, *Asst Prof,* Nova Scotia Technical College, Halifax

Bradford, William, *Academic Asst,* Courtauld Inst of Art Galleries, London, England

Bradley, Barbara, *Dir Illustration,* Acad of Art College, San Francisco, CA

Bradley, Byron, *Instr,* Grand Marais Art Colony, MN

Bradley, Camille L, *Clerk,* Dept of State Diplomatic Reception Rooms, Washington, DC

Bradley, Clark, *Mem Faculty,* Austin Community College, TX

Bradley, Gail, *Prof,* North Park College, Chicago, IL

Bradley, Gerry M, *Admin Asst,* Lincoln County Cultural and Historical Association, Wiscasset, ME

Bradley, Kim, *Dir,* Portland State Univ, OR

Bradley, Marilynne, *Secy,* St Louis Artists Guild, MO

Bradley, Paul M, *Assoc Dean Continuing Educ,* San Jose State Univ, CA

Bradley, R T, *Dir,* Sarnia Public Library and Art Gallery, ON

Bradley, Sarah, *Asst Dir,* Asia House Gallery, Asia Society, New York, NY

Bradley, Tony, *Mem Faculty,* Univ North Carolina at Asheville

Bradley, Mrs Vernon, *Mem Secy,* Oklahoma Museum of Art, Oklahoma City

Bradman, Susan, *VPres,* Burlington County Historical Society, NJ

Bradshaw, Bertram F, *Instr,* Univ North Carolina at Wilmington

Bradshaw, Brian, *Dir,* Nat Gallery of Rhodesia, Salisbury

Bradshaw, Carolyn Tannehill, *Cur Art,* Thomas Gilcrease Inst of American History and Art, Tulsa, OK

Bradshaw, Glenn R, *Mem Faculty,* Univ Illinois, Urbana-Champaign, Champaign

Bradshaw, Larry, *Asst Prof,* Univ Nebraska at Omaha

Bradt, Bernice, *Publicity & Pub Relations,* Robert McLaughlin Gallery, Oshawa, ON

Bradway, Wallace, *Mus Registrar,* Art Inst of Chicago, IL

Brady, Linda, *Publicity,* Alaska Artists Guild, Anchorage

Bragdon, Edward A, Jr, *Pres,* Society for Preservation of Historic Landmarks, York, ME

Bragg, Nicholas B, *Exec Dir,* Reynolda House, Winston-Salem, NC

Bragg, William S, *Exec Dir,* Glenhyrst Arts Council of Brantford, ON

Braham, Allan, *Keeper,* Nat Gallery of London, England

Braig, Kathryn B, *Asst to Librn,* Mariners Museum, Newport News, VA

Braithewaite, Elena, *Instr,* Traphagen School of Fashion, New York, NY

Braithwaite, Noreen, *Pres,* Redding Museum and Art Center, CA

Brake, Ronald, *Pres,* North Shore Arts Association, Gloucester, MA

Brancato, Terry, *Dir Summer School,* Daemen College, Amherst, NY

Brand, Barbara A, *Adminr,* Hammond-Harwood House, Annapolis, MD

Brandenburg, Dorothy, *Bd Pres,* Univ New Mexico Harwood Found, Taos

Brandenburg, Kurt E, *Exec Dir,* Chester County Historical Society, West Chester, PA

Brandes, Jeff, *Exhib,* Minnesota Museum of Art Permanent Collection Gallery, St Paul

Brandner, Elinora, *Secy & Coordr,* Southeast Alaska Regional Arts Council, Sitka

Brandon, David S, *Cur & Dir,* Loveland Museum, CO

Brandon, Dr Ida, *Dir Summer School,* Bowie State College, MD

Brandon, Kenneth, *Head Dept,* Otero Junior College, La Junta, CO

Brandt, Michael, *Chmn,* Univ Wisconsin-Oshkosh

Brandt, Rex, *Co-Dir,* Brandt Painting Workshops, Corona del Mar, CA

Brandt, Rolf W, *Special Exhib Chmn,* Council of Ozark Artists and Craftsmen, Springdale, AR

Branham, Richard, *Chmn Dept Design,* Univ Kansas, Lawrence

Brannon, Mrs Revelie, *Cur,* Fort Hill, Clemson, SC

Branson, Edward V, *Instr,* Yavapai College, Prescott, AZ

Branson, Paul, *Pres,* Society of Animal Artists, see National and Regional Organizations

Brant, Mary, *Mgr,* Community Arts Center, Fort Wayne Fine Arts Found, IN

Brantley, Michael W, *Educ Serv,* North Carolina Museum of Art, Raleigh

Brantley, Nancy S, *Asst,* Virginia Commonwealth Univ School of Arts Library, Richmond

Brassill, Jo Ann, *Assoc Prof,* Univ Southern Colorado, Belmont Campus, Pueblo

Brauchler, Ken, *Chmn,* State Univ New York at Buffalo

Braucht, June Elder, *Dir,* Monterey Peninsula Museum of Art, CA

Braude, Claire, *Photographer,* Minnesota Museum of Art Permanent Collection Gallery, St Paul

Brauer, Richard, *Cur,* Sloan Galleries, Valparaiso Univ, IN

Braun, David, *Mem Faculty,* Virginia Intermont College, Bristol

Bravakis, Olivia, *Asst Cur,* Wood Art Gallery, Montpelier, VT

Brawley, Robert J, *Chmn Art Dept & Dir Summer School,* Lone Mountain College, San Francisco, CA

Bray, Hazel, *Assoc Cur,* Oakland Museum, CA

Bray, Ina, *VChmn,* King County Arts Commission, Seattle, WA

Bray, Jim, *Assoc Prof,* Philips Univ, Enid, OK

Braybrooke, Valerie V, *Dir,* Univ Mississippi Museum, Oxford

Brazil, Judy, *Instr,* Johnson County Community College, Overland Park, KS

Brazton, Anne, *Art Librn,* Ohio Univ, Athens

Brealey, John, *Conservator Paintings,* Metropolitan Museum of Art, New York, NY

Brearton, Beulah, *Asst Dir,* Stradling Museum of the Horse, Patagonia, AZ

Breay, Sharon, *Second VPres,* Toledo Federation of Art Societies, OH

Breckenridge, James, *Prof,* Northwestern Univ, Evanston, IL; *Pres,* Midwest Art History Society, see National and Regional Organizations

Breckenridge, Mary, *Instr,* College of Wooster, OH

Breed, Charles A, *Prof Art & Chmn Dept,* Delta College, University Center, MI

Breeden, Eve, *Pres,* Art Centre of New Jersey, East Orange

Breen, Mary, *Secy,* Evanston Art Center, IL

Breeskin, Adelyn D, *Consult 20th Century Painting & Sculpture,* Nat Collection of Fine Arts, Washington, DC

Breimayer, Sister M Phyllis, *Asst Prof,* Georgian Court College, Lakewood, NJ

Breitenbach, William J, *Asst Prof,* Sam Houston State Univ, Huntsville, TX

Breithaupt, Dr Erwin, *Dir Art Gallery & Chmn Art Dept,* Ripon College, WI

Bremer, J, *Cur,* Municipal Van Abbemuseum, Eindhoven, Netherlands

Breneisen, Frank, *Chmn Dept,* Morningside College, Sioux City, IA

Brener, Roland, *Assoc Prof,* Univ Victoria, BC

Brennan, Francis E, *Secy,* The American Federation of Arts, see National and Regional Organizations

Brenner, Sister Jean, *Instr,* Marian College, Fond du Lac, WI

Brenner, M Diane, *Mus Archivist,* Anchorage Historical and Fine Arts Museum, AK

Brent, Mrs Allan R, *Dir,* Louisiana Arts and Science Center, Baton Rouge

Breslau, Leo, *Pres,* Nat Art League, Douglaston, NY

Breton, Arthur, *Cur Manuscripts,* Archives of American Art, Washington, DC

Brettell, Ruthann, *Asst to Exec VPres,* American Numismatic Association, see National and Regional Organizations

Breucker, Roland, *Vis Prof,* College Saint-Louis-Maillet, Edmundston, NB

Brewer, Bradley, *Pres,* Museum of Art, Science and Industry, Bridgeport, CT

Brewer, Donald, *Dir,* Univ Southern California Art Galleries, Los Angeles

Brewer, Jack, *Assoc Prof,* Indiana Univ, South Bend

Brewer, Mrs Lawrence, *Chmn,* Liberty Hall Museum, Frankfort, KY

Brewster, Mrs Albert J, III, *Asst Secy,* Stan Hywet Hall Found, Akron, OH

Brezik, Brother Hilarion, *Dir Fine Arts Exhib Prog,* St Edward's Univ, Austin, TX

Brezzo, Steven L, *Asst Dir,* Fine Arts Gallery of San Diego, CA

Brian, Fred, *Mem Faculty,* Illinois Wesleyan Univ, Bloomington

Bricker, Norman, *Exec Secy,* Muckenthaler Cultural Center, Fullerton, CA

Brickus, Viktoras, *Pres,* Canadian Society of Painters in Watercolor, see National Organizations in Canada

Brickwood, A, *Head Dept Industrial Design,* Leicester Polytechnic, England

Bridges, John, *Community Activities Dir,* Pack Mem Public Library, Asheville, NC

Bright, Alfred, *Assoc Prof,* Youngstown State Univ, OH

Bright, Jane, *Pres,* Paducah Art Guild, KY

Briley, John B, *Mgr,* Campus Martius Museum and Ohio River Museum, Marietta, OH

Brill, Frederick, *Prin,* Chelsea School of Art, London, England

Brill, Frederick, *Chmn Faculty Painting,* British School at Rome, Italy

Brill, Marilyn, *VPres Prog,* Miniature Art Society of New Jersey, Nutley

Brill, Robert H, *Research Scientist,* Corning Museum of Glass, Corning, NY

Brill, Wayne, *Instr,* Interlochen Arts Academy, MI

Brillinger, Anne, *Publicity Dir,* Utah Travel Council, Salt Lake City

Brimble, Alan, *Controller,* St Louis Art Museum, MO

Brimer, Denise, *Dir Dance Dept,* Colorado Mountain College, Vail

Brindle, Laurie A, *Gallery Asst,* Boehm Gallery, Palomar Community College, San Marcos, CA

Brink, Quido, *VPres,* Wisconsin Painters and Sculptors, Milwaukee

Brinker, Dr Helmut, *Cur East Asia,* Museum Rietberg Zürich, Switzerland

Brinkerhoff, Dericksen M, *Prof,* Univ California, Riverside

Brinkgreve, C, *Asst Educ Dept,* Frans Halsmuseum, Haarlem, Netherlands

Brinkman, Dr John A, *Dir,* Bergman Gallery, Univ Chicago, IL

Brinson, Loyce, *Secy,* Fannie Mebane Ralph Library and Gallery, Bel Haven, NC

Brinton, Harry, *Dir,* Jacksonville Public Library, FL

Brisch, Dr Klaus, *Dir,* Museum of Islamic Art & Antiquities, Staatliche Museen Preussischer Kulturbesitz, Berlin, Germany

Briseno, Vidal, *Cur,* Contemporary Arts Museum, Houston, TX

Brisson, Harriet E, *Chmn,* Rhode Island College, Providence

Bristol, Lillian, *Coordr Pub Relations,* Montclair Art Museum, NJ

Bristoll, Mrs Harrison, Jr, *Pres,* Historical Society of Kent County, Chestertown, MD

Bristow, James, *Admin Officer,* Winnipeg Art Gallery, MB

Bristow, William A, *Chmn,* Trinity Univ, San Antonio, TX

Britain, William E, *Pres,* Swain School of Design, New Bedford, MA

Britko, Stephen, *Studio Mgr,* Tamarind Inst, Univ New Mexico, Albuquerque

Britow, Julia, *Art Chmn,* Irene Leache Mem, Norfolk, VA

Britt, Sam Glenn, *Asst Prof,* Delta State Univ, Cleveland, MS

Britton, Clark, *Chmn Graphic Design,* Wichita State Univ, KS

Britton, Neil, *Asst Prof,* Virginia Wesleyan College, Norfolk, VA

Broadhead, D C, *Dean,* Leicester Polytechnic, England

Brock, Bess, *Mus Asst,* Campbell Museum, Camden, NJ

Broderick, Catherine, *Instr,* Vancouver Community College, Langara Campus, BC

Broderick, James, *Chmn,* Texas Tech Univ, Lubbock

Brodeur, Danyelle, *Animator,* Dorval Cultural Centre, PQ

Brodeur, Michael, *Mem Faculty,* Rivier College, Nashua, NH

Brodie, Debra, *City Librn,* Hillsboro Public Library, OR

Brodsky, Joyce, *Prof,* Univ Connecticut, Storrs

Brodsky, Stanley, *Prof,* School of the Arts, C W Post Center of Long Island Univ, Brookville, NY

Brodsley, Judith, *Assoc Prof,* Beaver College, Glenside, PA

Brody, Myron, *Art Coordr & Dir Summer School,* Avila College, Kansas City, MO

Brody, Sherry, *Admin Asst for CETA Program,* Los Angeles Inst of Contemporary Art, CA

Broekema, Andrew J, *Dean Col,* Ohio State University, Columbus

Brogden, Stephen R, *Dir,* Univ New Mexico Harwood Found, Taos

Brokaw, Dorothy, *Adminr,* Maryhill Museum of Art, Goldendale, WA

Bromley, Allyn, *Instr,* Leeward Community College, Pearl City, HI

Broner, Mathew, *Assoc Prof,* Manhattanville College, Purchase, NY

Bronowski, V, *Cur,* Musees Communaux Beaux-Arts et Archeologie, Verviers, Belgium

Bronson, Marty, *Dir,* Fashion Inst of Technology, New York, NY

Bronstein, Herbert, *Pub Relations Mgr,* Brooklyn Museum, NY

Brook, Robert A, *Under Secy,* Smithsonian Institution, Washington, DC

Brooke, Anna, *Librn,* Hirshhorn Museum and Sculpture Garden, Washington, DC

Brooke, David S, *Dir,* Sterling and Francine Clark Art Inst, Williamstown, MA

Brookes, Alan, *Asst Prof,* Univ Northern Iowa, Cedar Falls

Brookhart, Doris I, *Head Dept & Asst Prof,* John Brown Univ, Siloam Springs, AR

Brooking, Dolores, *Dir Mus Educ,* Univ Kansas, Lawrence

Brooks, Alan, *Coordr Fine Art,* City College of San Francisco, CA

Brooks, Ben, *Archivist,* Provincetown Art Association and Museum, MA

Brooks, Doug, *Chmn,* Phoenix College, AZ

Brooks, James, *Mem Faculty,* Fairmont State College, WV

Brooks, Jane, *Editor,* Textile Museum, Washington, DC

Brooks, John B, *Cur Crafts & Educ,* Pennsylvania Farm Museum of Landis Valley, Lancaster

Brooks, John H, *Assoc Dir,* Sterling and Francine Clark Art Inst, Williamstown, MA

Brooks, Helen, *Secy,* Rochester Historical Society, NY

Brooks, Wendell, *Asst Prof,* Trenton State College, NJ

Brooks, Whitney L, *VPres,* Litchfield Historical Society, CT

Brooks, Wilma, *Art & Music Dept Head,* Wichita Public Library, KS

Broos, Dr C H A, *Head Prints Dept,* Haags Gemeentemuseum, The Hague, Netherlands

Broos, Mrs John A, Jr, *Pres,* Old Masters Soc, Art Inst of Chicago, IL

Broshahan, Mary Ann, *Pres,* Minot Art Gallery, ND

Brosz, V R, *Head Dept & Dir Summer School,* University of Calgary, AB

Brothers, Betty, *Assoc Prof,* College of Mount Saint Joseph, OH

Brothers, Darrell, *Prof,* Thomas More College, Fort Mitchell, KY

Brouch, Dr Virginia M, *Chmn Summer School,* Florida State Univ, Tallahassee

Broude, Norma, *Assoc Prof,* American Univ, Washington, DC

Broudo, J David, *Head Art Dept,* Endicott College, Beverly, MA

Broudy, Elizabeth, *Prog Coordr,* Univ Iowa Museum of Art, Iowa City

Brouillet, Johanne, *Promotions,* Univ Sherbrooke Cultural Center, PQ

Broun, Dr Elizabeth, *Cur Prints & Drawings,* Univ Kansas, Lawrence

Brouwer, Norman J, *Librn,* South Street Seaport Museum, New York, NY

Brown, Ann Barton, *Cur Coll,* Brandywine River Museum, Chadds Ford, PA

Brown, Barbara M, *Cur Educ & Acting Cur Decorative Arts,* Milwaukee Art Center, WI

Brown, Bennie, Jr, *Librn Archivist,* Gunston Hall Plantation, Lorton, VA

Brown, Betty Jean, *Guard-Preparator,* North Carolina Central Univ, Durham

Brown, C Dudley, *VPres,* Arts Club of Washington, DC

Brown, Mrs C Gaskell, *Keeper of Archaeology,* Plymouth City Museum and Art Gallery, England

Brown, Carole R, *Asst Prof,* Elmhurst College, IL

Brown, Carolyn R, *Educ Asst,* Contemporary Arts Center, Cincinnati, OH

Brown, Charles R, *Chmn,* San Jacinto College, Pasadena, TX

Brown, David, *Cur Italian Renaissance Painting,* Nat Gallery of Art, Washington, DC

Brown, Delores, *Exec Secy,* Montana Historical Society, Helena

Brown, Dick, *Exten Head,* Topeka Public Library, KS

Brown, Dion K, *Mem Faculty,* Polk Community College, Winter Haven, FL

Brown, Dr Donald F, *Dir,* Thomas College Exhibitions, Waterville, ME

Brown, Edward, *Mus Dir, Chmn Dept & Dir Summer School,* Atlantic Christian College, Art Gallery, Wilson NC

Brown, Dr Ellsworth, *Dir,* Tennessee State Museum, Nashville

Brown, Frances E, *Chmn,* Five Civilized Tribes Museum, Muskogee, OK

Brown, Frank, *Arts & Crafts Coordr,* Univ California, Los Angeles

Brown, Frank E, *Prof in Charge Classical Studies,* American Academy in Rome, Italy

Brown, Gale, *Exhib Technician,* Inst and Museum of the Great Plains, Lawton, OK

Brown, Gaye L, *Dir Pub Relations,* Worcester Art Museum, MA

Brown, Georgina, *Exec Dir,* Heritage Museum & Gallery, Leadville, CO

Brown, Dr Gerald F, *Exec Dir,* Paint 'N' Palette Club, Anamosa, IA

Brown, Harold, *Cur Emer,* Bath Marine Museum, ME

Brown, Hilton, *Chmn Dept & Prof Visual Arts,* Goucher College, Towson, MD

Brown, J Carter, *Chmn,* Commission of Fine Arts, Washington, DC; *Dir,* National Gallery of Art, Washington, DC

Brown, James M, *Dir,* Society of the Four Arts, Palm Beach, FL

Brown, Jane, *Workshop & Exhib Coordr,* Sangre De Cristo Arts & Conference Center, Pueblo, CO

Brown, John M, *Gen Mgr,* Bellingrath Gardens and Home, Theodore, AL

Brown, Jonathan M, *Chmn,* New York Univ, New York

Brown, Joseph, *Artist-in-Residence,* Creighton Univ, Omaha, NE

Brown, Judy, *Instr,* Brockton Art Center, MA

Brown, Kandy, *AV Librn,* Beverly Hills Public Library, CA

Brown, Katherine T, *Prof,* Rice Univ, Houston, TX

Brown, Kenneth, *Dir,* Pack Mem Public Library, Asheville, NC

Brown, Kenneth, *Chmn,* South Carolina Arts Commission, Columbia

Brown, Kenneth David, *Head Dept & Asst Prof,* Newberry College, SC

Brown, Kevin, *Registrar & Educ Dir,* Plains Art Museum & Rourke Art Gallery, Moorhead, MN

Brown, Mrs Leonard, *Dir,* Tyringham Inst, MA

Brown, Lynn, *Vis Prof,* Southern Oregon State College, Ashland

Brown, Mrs M M, *Mus Cur,* Sibbald Point Provincial Park, Sutton West, ON

Brown, Mary B, *Pres,* Tennessee Valley Art Center, Tuscumbia, AL

Brown, Maurice, *Chmn,* State Univ New York College at New Paltz

Brown, Mildred B, *Pres,* Paint 'N' Palette Club, Anamosa, IA

Brown Mrs Moreau D, *Chmn,* Lockwood-Mathews Mansion Museum, Norwalk, CT

Brown, Myrtle, *Libr Technician,* Charleston Museum, SC

Brown, Dr Richard F, *Dir,* Kimbell Art Museum, Fort Worth, TX

Brown, Robert E, *Asst Prof,* Univ Nevada, Las Vegas

Brown, Robert W, *Prof,* Glendale College, CA

Brown, Sarah R, *Pres,* Marion Art Center, MA

Brown, Susan G, *Asst Prof,* Richard Bland College, Petersburg, VA

Brown, Suzanne, *Treas,* Pittsfield Art League, MA

Brown, Rev Thomas, *Chmn Art Dept & Dir Summer School,* Quincy College, IL

Brown, Susan, *Cur,* Univ Minnesota Gallery, Minneapolis

Brown, Vee, *Instr,* Young Harris College, GA

Brown, Warren D, *Prof,* Southwestern College, Winfield, KS

Brown, William, *Area Coordr,* Northern Illinois Univ, DeKalb

Brown, William, *Cur Glass,* Zanesville Art Center, OH

Brown, William Archie, *Affiliate,* Emory Univ, Atlanta, GA

Brown, William J, *Dir,* Penland School of Crafts, NC

Brown, William M, *Head Dept,* Dutchess Community College, Poughkeepsie, NY

Brown, Mrs William W, *Secy,* Mattatuck Historical Society, Waterbury, CT

Browne, Cynthia E, *Cataloger,* New Jersey Historical Society Museum, Newark

Browne, Rev Joseph P, *Dir,* Univ Portland, OR

Browne, Norman, *Chmn Art Educ,* Pan American Univ, Edinburg, TX

Browne, Patti, *Exec Dir,* Municipal Art Commission, Kansas City, MO

Browne, Vivian E, *Prof Art & Chmn Dept,* Rutgers Univ, Newark, NJ

Brownfield, John P, *Chmn Art Dept,* Univ Redlands, CA

Brownson, E James, *Assoc Prof,* Northern Montana College, Havre

Brozovich, Tom J, *Mem Faculty,* American River College, Sacramento, CA

Bruce, Gale, *Instr Arts & Crafts,* Palo Alto Junior Museum and Zoo, CA

Bruening Mrs Henry A, *Secy,* Historical Society of Kent County, Chestertown, MD

Bruhm, Thomas P, *Cur,* William Benton Museum of Art, Storrs, CT

Bruijn, J G de, *Librn,* Teylers Museum, Haarlem, Netherlands

Brumbaugh, R Nickey, *Head Dept,* Coker College, Hartsville, SC

Brumbaugh, Thomas B, *Prof,* Vanderbilt Univ, Nashville, TN

Brun, Michael, *Mem Faculty,* Murray State University, KY

Brunell, Richard, *Chairperson Design Dept,* Washington Univ, Saint Louis, MO

Bruner, Ronnald I, *Mem Faculty,* Colby Commity College, KS

Brunhammer, Yvonne, *Cur,* Union Centrale des Arts Decoratifs Paris, France

Bruni, Stephen, *Prog Asst,* Delaware Art Museum, Wilmington

Bruning, Alex, *Chmn Drawing,* Univ Manitoba, Winnipeg

Brunius, Jan, *Dir,* Rohsska Konstslojkmuseet, Goteborg, Sweden

Brunkus, Richard, *Instr,* Albion College, MI

Brunner, Christal, *Reference Librn,* Mexico-Audrain County Library, MO

Brunner, Conrad, *Gallery Asst,* Chautauqua Gallery of Art, NY

Brunner, Wilfred, *Vis Lectr,* Marymount College of Virginia, Arlington

Bruno, Ana Basso, *Prof,* Catholic Univ Puerto Rico, Ponce

Bruno, Don, *Mem Faculty,* College of Saint Benedict, Saint Joseph, MN

Bruno, Santo, *Pres,* Atlanta Art Workers Coalition; *Instr,* Atlanta College of Arts, GA

Bruno, Vincent J, *Chmn,* Univ Texas at Arlington

Bruns, Larry L, *Cur Art,* Bower's Museum, Santa Ana, CA

Brush, Daniel, *Prof,* Georgetown Univ, Washington, DC

Brush, Leif, *Asst Prof,* Univ Minnesota, Duluth

Brutger, James H, *Head Dept,* Univ Minnesota, Duluth

Bruzelius, Caroline, *Asst Prof,* Dickinson College, Carlisle, PA

Bryan, Ashley, *Chmn,* Dartmouth College, Hanover, NH

Bryan, Jack, *Chmn,* Cameron Univ, Lawton, OK

Bryan, John, *Chmn Art History,* Univ South Carolina, Columbia

Bryan, Marlene, *Adminr,* Univ Waterloo, ON

Bryans, John, *Head Dept,* McLean Arts Center, VA

Bryant, Billy J, *Prof,* Northwestern State Univ Louisiana, Natchitoches

Bryant, Edward, *Dir-Cur Gallery & Assoc Prof,* Colgate Univ, Hamilton, NY

Bryant, Faye, *Pres,* Windward Artists Guild, Lihue, Hawaii

Bryant, Janet, *Dir,* 92nd St YM & YWHA, New York, NY

Bryant, Olen, *Mem Faculty,* Austin Peay State Univ, Clarksville, TN

Bryden-Wills, Betty, *Pres,* Ogunquit Art Association, ME

Bryner, Dale W, *Assoc Prof,* Weber State College, Ogden, UT

Bryzek, Dr Anna Rozycka, *Italian Painting,* Muzeum Narodowe W Krakowie, Cracow, Poland

Buch, Hugo Arne, *Cur,* Louisiana Museum of Modern Art, Humlebaek, Denmark

Buchan, David, *Publns Dir,* Art Metropole, Toronto, ON

Buchanan, George, *Deputy Dir,* Glasgow Museums and Art Galleries, Scotland

Buchanan, Harvey D, *Prof,* Case Western Reserve Univ, Cleveland, OH

Buchanan, James V, *Develop Dir,* Columbus Gallery of Fine Arts, OH

Buchanan, John, *Special Asst to Dir,* Metropolitan Museum of Art, New York, NY

Buchanan, John, *Coordr of Mus Develop,* Tennessee State Museum, Nashville

Buchanan, Sidney, *Prof,* Univ Nebraska at Omaha

Buchanan, William C, *Asst Prof,* Western Carolina Univ, Cullowhee, NC

Bucher, Francois, *Prof,* Florida State Univ, Tallahassee

Bucher, George R, *Assoc Prof Art,* Susquehanna Univ, Selinsgrove, PA

Buchholz, Regina, *Assoc Prof,* Loyola Marymount Univ, Los Angeles, CA

Buchwald, Charles, *Treas,* Oklahoma Art Center, Oklahoma City

Buck, Robert T, Jr, *Dir,* Albright-Knox Art Gallery, Buffalo, NY

Buckendorf, Terry, *Instr,* Fort Wright College of the Holy Names, Spokane, WA

Buckley, Denise, *Prof,* Albertus Magnus College, New Haven, CT

Buckley, Gene D, *Chmn,* Gustavus Adolphus College, Saint Peter, MN

Buckley, Margaret, *Librn,* Des Moines Art Center, IA

Buckman, Richard, *Prof,* St Louis Community College at Florissant Valley, Ferguson, MO

Buckner, Hal, *Chmn,* Fort Steilacoom Community College, Tacoma, WA

Budahl, Lee P, *Assoc Prof,* Western Carolina Univ, Cullowhee, NC

Budde, Dr Rainer, *Cur Modern Art,* Wallraf-Richartz Museum, Museen der Stadt Koln, Germany

Budelis, Richard, *Chmn Sculpture,* Pratt Inst School of Art & Design, Brooklyn, NY

Budgehyde, T, *Head Art Dept & Dir Summer School,* Greenfield Community College, MA

Buechhner, Thomas S, *Dir,* Corning Museum of Glass, NY

Buenger, Barbara, *Instr,* Univ Wisconsin, Madison

Buening, Sister Helen, *Chmn,* Benedictine College, Atchison, KS

Bueno, Maria Eugenia Sanchez, *Head Educ Dept,* Museo Nacional de Antropologia, Mexico City, Mexico

Buesing, James W, *Asst Prof,* Univ Wisconsin, Madison

Buettner, Stewart, *Asst Prof,* Lewis and Clark College, Portland, OR

Bufano, Ralph A, *Dir,* Paine Art Center and Arboretum, Oshkosh, WI

Buffington, Mrs Roger, *VPres,* Greater Fall River Art Association, MA

Bugbee, Olive Vandruff, *Cur Art,* Panhandle-Plains Historical Society Museum, Canyon, TX

Bugbeel, Victoria, *Secy,* Atlanta Art Workers Coalition, GA

Buhl, Dr M L, *Keeper Coll Classical Antiquities,* Nat Museum, Copenhagen, Denmark

Buhler, Curt F, *Research Fellow for Texts Emer,* Pierpont Morgan Library, New York, NY

Buhler, John, *Exec Dir,* Wyoming Council on the Arts, Cheyenne

Buhlinger, Ernest, *Secy,* Bassist Inst, Portland, OR

Buisman, J H van Borssum, *Deputy Cur Art Coll,* Teylers Museum, Haarlem, Netherlands

Buitron, Diana M, *Cur Greek & Roman Art,* Walters Art Gallery, Baltimore, MD

Buki, Zoltan, *Cur Fine Arts,* New Jersey State Museum, Trenton

Bulger, Margaret Ann, *Florida Folklife Coordr & Librn,* Stephen Foster Center, White Springs

Bull, Mrs R H, *VPres & Mus Comt Pres,* Peel Museum and Art Gallery, Brampton, ON

Bullard, E John, *Dir,* New Orleans Museum of Art, LA

Bullock, Dr Ray E, *Dir Gallery, Chmn Art Dept & Dir Summer School,* Taylor Univ, Upland, IN

Bullock, Starmanda, *Chmn,* Howard Univ, Washington, DC

Bulls, Harley B, *Chmn,* South Plains College, Levelland, TX

Bumbeck, David A, *Dir,* Middlebury College, VT

Bumgardner, Georgia B, *Cur Graphic Arts,* American Antiquarian Society, see National and Regional Organizations

Bunce, Fredrick W, *Head Dept,* South Dakota State Univ, Brookings

Bunce, William C, *Dir,* Univ Wisconsin-Madison Mem Union

Bunge, Christopher, *Dir Art Gallery & Asst Prof,* Denison Univ, Granville, OH

Bunker, George R, *Chmn & Prof,* Univ Houston, TX

Bunn, Ann, *Cur Educ,* Contemporary Arts Museum, Houston' TX

Bunn, Jennings W, Jr, *Admin Asst,* School of the Ozarks, Point Lookout, MO

Bunnell, Peter C, *VPres,* Friends of Photography, Carmel, CA

Bunse, Dale, *Instr,* Columbia College, CA

Bunse, Don, *Prof,* Univ Montana, Missoula

Burback, Willia M, *Special Asst Educ,* Museum of Modern Art, New York, NY

Burby, Barbara, *Secy,* Mills House Volunteers, Mills House Art Gallery, Garden Grove, CA

Burcaw, G Ellis, *Dir,* Univ Idaho Museum, Moscow

Burch, J Lindsey, *Instr,* Johns Hopkins Univ, Baltimore, MD

Burch, Marlyn, *Pres,* Arts Council of Topeka, KS

Burchard, Charles, *Dean,* Col Architecture, Virginia Polytechnic Inst & State Univ, Blacksburg

Burdayron, Linda, *Animator,* Dorval Cultural Centre, PQ

Burden, Shirley, *VPres,* Los Angeles Art Association and Galleries, CA

Burdick, Marjorie Z, *Secy,* Univ Florida Gallery, Gainesville

Burek, Jim, *Prof,* Louisiana State Univ, Baton Rouge

Burgart, Herbert, *Pres,* Moore College of Art, Philadelphia, PA

Burgess, Eldon R, *Dir,* Mexico-Audrain County Library, Mexico, MO

Burgess, James L, *Asst Prof,* Salisbury State College, MD

Burgess, Larry E, *Cur,* Lincoln Mem Shrine, Redlands, CA

Burghardt, James H, *Librn,* Multnomah County Library, Portland, OR

Burghoffer, Paul, *Vis Prof,* Schiller College, Europe Univ, Strasbourg, France

Burickson, Zoel, *Sculptor-in-Residence,* York College of Pennsylvania

Burk, Ms Bobbie, *Dir Summer School,* Stephens College, Columbia, MO

Burk, C William, *Dir,* Southern Oregon Historical Society, Jackson

Burk, George, *Cur Art Collection & Dir Dept Art,* Nasson College, Springvale, ME

Burk, William, *Mem Faculty,* Art Academy of Cincinnati, OH

Burke, Ainslie, *Chmn,* Syracuse Univ, NY

Burke, Dan, *Registrar,* Univ Utah Museum of Fine Arts, Salt Lake City

Burke, Daniel, *Assoc Prof,* Mercyhurst College, Erie, PA

Burke, Elizabeth, *Head Dept,* Union College, Barbourville, KY

Burke, J Carl, *Adj Prof,* Daemen College, Amherst, NY

Burke, James D, *Drawings & Photographs,* Yale Univ Art Gallery, New Haven, CT

Burke, Jean, *VPres,* Ontario Crafts Council, Toronto

Burkey, Sophia, *Admin Secy,* Southern Alleghenies Museum of Art, Loretto, PA

Burkhart, Ardath, *First VPres,* Hoosier Salon Patrons Association, Indianapolis, IN

Burkhart, Linda, *Admin Asst,* Sanford Museum and Planetarium, Cherokee, IA

Burko, Diane, *Asst Prof,* Philadelphia Community College, PA

Burley, Lina, *Pres,* Boothbay Region Art Gallery, Boothbay Harbor, ME

Burley, William, *Treas,* Boothbay Region Art Gallery, Boothbay Harbor, ME

Burley, William, *Treas,* Maine Art Gallery, Lincoln County Cultural and Historical Association, Wiscasset

Burn, Dr Emilie E, *Head,* Jacksonville State Univ, AL

Burnet, Mrs William, *VPres,* Washington Depot Art Association, CT

Burnett, Dr D G, *Chmn & Dir Summer School,* Carleton Univ, Ottawa, ON

Burnett, Jean C, *Pub Relations Dir,* Wadsworth Atheneum, Hartford, CT

Burnett, Virgil, *Prof,* Univ Waterloo, ON

Burnette, Mrs Robert, *Secy,* Civic Fine Arts Association, Sioux Falls, SD

Burnham, Bonnie, *Dir Art Theft Archive,* International Found for Art Research, see National and Regional Organizations

Burnham, Dahl C, *Treas,* Pioneer Museum and Haggin Galleries, Stockton, CA

Burnham, Dorothy K, *Cur Textiles Dept,* Royal Ontario Museum, Toronto

Burnham, Wesley J, *Chmn Dept Art,* Northwestern Univ, Evanston, IL

Burningham, Bob, *Vis Prof,* Vermilion Community College, Ely, MN

Burningham, Charlene, *Vis Prof,* Vermilion Community College, Ely, MN

Burnley, Gary M, *Asst Prof,* Lehigh Univ, Bethlehem, PA

Burno, William K, *Asst Prof,* Seton Hall Univ, South Orange, NJ

Burns, A Lee, *Instr,* Smith College, Northampton, MA

Burns, Elizabeth B, *Exec Dir,* International Found for Art Research, see National and Regional Organizations

Burns, J Bradley, *Coordr Exhib,* Hunter Museum of Art, Chattanooga, TN

Burns, Joan E, *Prin Art Librn,* Newark Public Library, NJ

Burns, L, *Cur,* Oak Hall, Niagara Falls, ON

Burns, Michael, *Asst Prof,* Avila College, Kansas City, MO

Burns, Suzanne S, *Asst to Dir,* Cummer Gallery of Art, Jacksonville, FL

Burns, Dr William A, *Dir,* Florence Museum, SC

Burnside, Wesley M, *Dir Art Acquisitions,* B R Larsen Gallery, Brigham Young Univ, Provo, UT

Burnstad, Helen, *Chairperson Div,* Nebraska Western College, Scottsbluff

Burollet, Therese, *Dir Mille,* Musee Cognacq-Jay, Paris, France

Burpitt, Martha, *Instr,* Brenau College, Gainesville, GA

Burris, George, *Chmn Liberal Arts,* Kansas City Art Inst, MO

Burroughs, Charles G, *Cur,* Du Sable Museum of African American History, Chicago, IL

Burroughs, Edward, *Dir,* Middletown Fine Arts Center, OH

Burroughs, Margaret R, *Dir,* Du Sable Museum of African American History, Chicago, IL

Burshears, J F, *Dir,* Koshare Indian Museum, La Junta, CO

Burstein, Rose Anne, *Librn,* Sarah Lawrence College Library, Bronxville, NY

Burt, Clyde, *Assoc Prof,* Indiana Univ-Purdue Univ, Fort Wayne, IN

Burt, James H, *Dir,* New School of Theatre, Three Schools, Toronto, ON

Burt, Joan, *Chmn Dept Design,* Ontario College of Art, Toronto

Burt, Marlow, *Exec Dir,* St Paul Council of Arts and Sciences, MN

Burt, Ruth, *Supvr of Standards,* League of New Hampshire Craftsmen, Concord

Burt, Ulla, *Admin Asst to Dir,* La Jolla Museum of Contemporary Art, CA

Burt, Mrs Wallace J, *Second VPres Bd Trustees,* Museum of Arts and Sciences, Daytona Beach, FL

Burtch, Michael, *Educ & Exten,* Robert McLaughlin Gallery, Oshawa, ON

Burton, DR I F, *Pres,* Archives of American Art, Washington, DC

Burton, Lewis, *Cur Art Gallery & Mem Faculty,* Austin Peay State Univ, Clarksville, TN

Busch, Dr Gunter, *Dir,* Kunsthalle Bremen, Germany

Busch, Mary, *Exec Dir,* Friends of the Art Gallery, Vassar College Art Gallery, Poughkeepsie, NY

Busch, P, *Dir,* California State Univ Art Gallery, Chico

Buschen, John, *Prof,* Univ Wisconsin-River Falls

Busey, Bruce, *Prog Dir,* Keokuk Art Center, IA

Bush, Harold, *Treas,* Springfield Art & Historical Society, VT

Bush, Dr Martin H, *Dir,* Wichita State Univ Museum, KS

Bush, Nancy, *VPres,* American Council for the Arts, see National and Regional Organizations

Bush, Renee, *Exhib Cur,* Southern Oregon Historical Society, Jacksonville

Bush, Dr Robert D, *Asst Dir,* Historic New Orleans Collection, LA

Bush, Terry M, *Dir Arts Center,* McLean County Art Association, Bloomington, IL

Bush, Virginia L, *Acting Chmn,* Douglass College, The State Univ New Jersey, New Brunswick

Bushard, Gerri, *Secy,* South Dakota State Univ, Brookings

Bushey, John, *Dir Summer School,* Univ Vermont, Burlington

Bushnell, Marietta P, *Librn,* Pennsylvania Acad of Fine Arts Collection, Philadelphia

Busta, William E, *Dir,* Dacotah Prairie Museum, Aberdeen, SD

Bustacchini, Rag Gianfranco, *Gen Secy,* Accademia de Belle Arti Ravenna Italia

Buster, William R, *Dir Gen,* Kentucky Historical Society Museum, Frankfort

Butcher, Larry, *Asst Prof,* Delta College, University Center, MI

Buten, David, *Dir,* Buten Museum of Wedgwood, Merion, PA

Buten, Mrs Harry M, *Pres,* Buten Museum of Wedgwood, Merion, PA

Butera, Joseph L, *Dir,* Butera School of Art, Boston, MA

Butler, Jeanne F, *Pres Found and Owner House,* American Inst of Architects Found, Washington, DC

Butler, John M, Jr, *Treas,* North Shore Art League, Winnetka, IL

Butler, John P, *Cur of Monies,* School of the Ozarks, Point Lookout, MO

Butler, Joseph G, *Dir & Pres,* Butler Inst of American Art Museum, Youngstown, OH

Butler, Lewis, *Dean Summer School,* New York State College of Ceramics at Alfred Univ

Butler, Marigene, *Conservator,* Philadelphia Museum of Art, PA

Butler, Marigene H, *Secy-Treas & Dir,* Inter-museum Conservation Association, see National and Regional Organizations

Butler, Ona, *Librn,* Harry Thornton Library, Pensacola Museum of Art, FL

Butler, Robert B, *Chmn & Prof Asst,* Miami Univ, Oxford, OH

Butorac, Frank G, *Dir,* Mercer County Community College Library, Trenton, NJ

Butterfield, Thomas F, *Dir Arts,* Virginia Polytechnic Inst & State Univ Art Gallery, Blacksburg

Buttlar, Dr Freiherr von, *Pres,* Hochschule Fur Bildende Kunste, Hamburg, Germany

Butts, H Daniel, III, *Dir,* Mansfield Art Center, OH

Butz, Richard A, *Instr,* Portland School of Art, ME

Buyck, J, *Asst Cur,* Koninklijk Museum Voor Schone Kunsten, Antwerp, Belgium

Byam, Milton S, *Dir,* Queens Borough Public Library, Jamaica, NY

Byers, J Frederick, III, *VPres,* Museum of Modern Art, New York, NY

Byers, Margery, *Chief Office of Pub Affairs,* Nat Collection of Fine Arts, Washington, DC

Byng, Dennis, *Prof,* State Univ New York at Albany

Bynum, Roxye, *Pres,* San Angelo Art Club, TX

Byongsam, Kyongju Mus Han, *Dir,* Nat Museum of Korea, Seoul

Byrd, Al, *Instr,* Sacramento City College, CA

Byrd, Joan F, *Asst Prof,* Western Carolina Univ, Cullowhee, NC

Byrd, Sen Robert C, *Chmn,* US Senate Commission on Art and Antiquities, Washington, DC

Byrne, Janet S, *Cur Prints & Photographs,* Metropolitan Museum of Art, New York, NY

Byrne, Tish, *Registrar Summer School,* Pennsylvania Acad of Fine Arts, Philadelphia

Caballero, Emilio, *Prof,* West Texas State Univ, Canyon

Cable, Dr Paul, *Dir Summer School,* Mercer Univ, Macon, GA

Cabot, Lewis, *Treas,* Museum of American Folk Art, New York, NY

Cabral, Madalena, *Educ Serv,* Museu Nacional de Arte Antiga Lisbon, Portugal

Cacan, Adeline, *Chief Cur,* Musee du Petit Palais (Municipal Museum), Paris, France

Caddell, Foster, *Head Dept,* Foster Caddell's Art School, Voluntown, CT

Cadden, Mrs John F, *VPres,* Strasburg Museum, VA

Caddy, Frank, *VPres/Admin,* Greenfield Village and Henry Ford Museum, Dearborn, MI

Cadigan, Edward, *Coordr Operations,* Mem Univ Newfoundland, Saint Johns

Cadman, Lesley, *Dean Students,* Lake Placid School of Art Gallery, NY

Caffey, Anna Jean, *Registrar,* Stark Museum of Art, Orange, TX

Caflisch, Trudy, *Secy,* Bundner Kunsthaus Chur, Switzerland

Cagle, Marion, *Children's Librn,* Lee County Library, Tupelo, MS

Caglioti, Victor, *Assoc Prof,* Sacred Heart Univ, Bridgeport, CT

Cagwin, Maj Gen Lee (Ret), *VPres,* Monterey Peninsula Museum of Art, CA

Cahill, James, *Prof & Co-Chmn Dept,* Univ California, Berkeley

Cahill, Sally, *Admin Asst,* Guild of South Carolina Artists, Columbia

Cahill, Sarah A, *Admin Asst,* Columbia Museums of Art and Science, SC

Cahn, Walter, *VPres,* International Center of Medieval Art, New York, NY

Cahoon, Herbert, *Cur Autograph Manuscripts & Later Printed Books,* Pierpont Morgan Library, New York, NY

Cain, David, *Instr,* Guilford Art and Music School, CT

Cain, H Thomas, *Cur Anthropology,* Heard Museum, Phoenix, AZ

Cain, J Frederick, *Cur Fine Arts,* Charleston Art Gallery of Sunrise, WV

Cain, Joseph A, *Chmn & Prof,* Del Mar College, Corpus Christi, TX

Cain, Rita, *Secy,* Marion Art Center, MA

Cain, Walker O, *Secy,* American Acad in Rome, New York, NY

Cairns, Christopher, *Chmn Dept,* Haverford College, PA

Cajori, Charles, *Vis Prof,* American Univ, Washington, DC

Calado, Rafael, *Cur Ceramics,* Museu Nacional de Arte Antiga Lisbon, Portugal

Calden, Lisa C, *Registrar,* Univ Wisconsin-Madison Mem Union

Calderwood, Roger D, *Historian, Librn & Registrar,* Victoria Society of Maine Women, Portland

Caldwell, Eleanor, *Area Coordr,* Northern Illinois Univ, DeKalb

Caldwell, Joan G, *Research Cur,* New Orleans Museum of Art, LA

Caldwell, John, *Area Chmn Design,* Pasadena City College, CA

Caldwell, Martha B, *VPres,* Southeastern College Art Conference, see National and Regional Organizations; *Prof,* James Madison Univ, Harrisonburg, VA

Caldwell, Maurice Blaine, *Head,* Truett-McConnell College, Cleveland, GA

Cale, David, *Asst Prof,* Amarillo College, TX

Caleca, Dr Antonino, *Dir,* Pinacoteca Nazionale, Lucca, Italy; *Dir,* Museo Nazionale di San Matteo, Pisa, Italy

Caleff, J, *Dir Gen,* Haaretz Museum, Tel-Aviv, Israel

Calhoun, James, *Music Librn,* Dallas Public Library, TX

Calhoun, Paul, *Lectr,* Cardinal Stritch College, Milwaukee, WI

Calhoun, Ralph E., *Instr,* Guilford Technical Inst, Jamestown, NC

Calhoun, Mrs Wallace, *VPres,* Singing River Art Association, Pascagoula, MS

Calkin, Carleton, *Pres,* St Augustine Historical Society, FL

Calkins, Kingsley M, *Head Art Dept & Dir Summer School,* Eastern Michigan Univ, Ypsilanti

Callaghan, Elizabeth, *Information Officer,* Newfoundland Museum, Saint Johns

Callazzo, Cecelia F, *Secy,* Connecticut Valley Historical Museum, Springfield, MA

Callicott, Duncan P, *Garden Dir,* Tennessee Botanical Gardens and Fine Arts Center, Nashville

Callister, J Herbert, *Cur Textiles & Costumes,* Wadsworth Atheneum, Hartford, CT

Callner, Richard, *Chmn Dept,* State Univ of New York at Albany

Callow, Bette Ray, *Asst Librn,* G Pillow Lewis Mem Library, Memphis Academy of Arts, TN

Calnan, Philippa, *Dir Pub Information,* Los Angeles County Museum of Art, CA

Calo, Maryann, *Cur Prints,* Joe and Emily Lowe Art Gallery, Syracuse Univ, NY

Calverley, Charles, *Trustee,* Attleboro Museum, MA

Calvin, Louise, *Instr,* Transylvania Univ, Lexington, KY

Calzand, Julie, *Dir Prog,* Univ Southwestern Louisiana Union Art Gallery, Lafayette

Camarata, Martin, *Dir Art Gallery & Prof,* California State College Stanislaus, Turlock

Camcioglu, Fehamet, *Cur Lab Preservation,* Istanbul Arkeoloji Muzeleri, Turkey

Cameron, Duncan, *Dir,* Glenbow-Alberta Inst, Calgary, AB

Cameron, Elsa, *Cur Art School,* Fine Arts Museums of San Francisco; *Cur-in-Charge,* De Young Museum Art School, San Francisco, CA

Cameron, Mrs Gary L, *Pres,* Fairfield Public Library and Museum, IA

Cameron, John B, *Prof Art Hist & Acting Chmn Dept Art & Art Hist,* Oakland Univ, Rochester, MI

Cameron, Nomi, *Secy,* Ontario Society of Artists, Toronto

Camfield, William A, *Prof,* Rice Univ, Houston, TX

Cammack, Mrs Luther S, *Workshop Chmn,* Council of Ozark Artists and Craftsmen, Springdale, AR

Camnitzer, Luis, *Chmn,* State Univ New York College at Old Westbury

Camnitzer, Luis, *Dir & Instr,* Studio Camnitzer-Porter, Valdottavo, Italy

Camp, Daniel, *Instr,* Miracosta College, Oceanside, CA

Camp, Edward, *Prof,* Manatee Junior College, Brandenton, FL

Camp, Dr Liselotte, *Pub Relations,* Bayerischen Staatsgemaldesammlungen, Munich, Germany

Camp, Orton P, Jr, *Pres,* Mattatuck Historical Society, Waterbury, CT

Camp, R, *Mem Faculty,* Golden West College, Huntington Beach, CA

Campbell, Charles, *Chmn,* Univ Wisconsin, Eau Claire

Campbell, Donald L, *Head Dept,* Colby-Sawyer College, New London, NH

Campbell, Francis D, Jr, *Librn,* American Numismatic Society, see National and Regional Organizations

Campbell, J, *Instr,* Selkirk College, Nelson, BC

Campbell, J Duncan, *Dir,* Pennsylvania Historical and Museum Commission, Harrisburg

Campbell, Jeanne Begien, *Asst Prof,* Univ Richmond, VA

Campbell, John Cardess, *Instr,* Rudolph Schaeffer School of Design, San Francisco, CA

Campbell, Kitty, *Pub Progs Coordr,* Cornell Univ, Ithaca, NY

Campbell, Mrs L E, *Secy,* Lake Region Art Association, Devils Lake, ND

Campbell, LaVona, *Treas,* Arizona Artist Guild, Phoenix

Campbell, Lorraine, *Secy,* Lakehead Visual Arts, Thunder Bay, ON

Campbell, Margaret, *Instr,* West Texas State Univ, Canyon

Campbell, Marjorie, *Assoc Prof,* Univ Northern Iowa, Cedar Falls

Campbell, Mary K, *Lectr,* Denison Univ, Granville, OH

Campbell, Mary S, *Exec Dir,* Studio Museum in Harlem, New York, NY

Campbell, Nancy, *Admin Asst,* State Univ New York at New Paltz

Campbell, Nina, *Exec Secy,* Marion Art Center, MA

Campbell, Sara, *Cur,* Norton Simon Museum, Pasadena, CA

Campbell, Shirley, *Secy Bd Dir,* Heritage Museum & Gallery, Leadville, CO

Campbell, Theodore, *Dir Summer School,* Univ California, Santa Cruz

Campbell, William P, *Cur American Painting & Index of American Design,* Nat Gallery of Art, Washington, DC

Campeau, Ray, *Dir,* Ketterer Art Center, Bozeman, MT

Campton, Bill, *Cur Exhib,* Boise Gallery of Art, ID

Campus, Joseph J, III, *Treas,* Pensacola Museum of Art, FL

Campuzano, Felipe J Garcia, *Dir,* Museo Regional de Nuevo Leon, Monterrey, Mexico

Canaday, Ouida, *Vis Prof,* Goldsboro Art Center, NC

Canby, Jeanny Vorys, *Cur Egyptian & Ancient Near Eastern Art,* Walters Art Gallery, Baltimore, MD

Candau, Eugenie, *Librn,* Louise Sloss Ackerman Fine Arts Library, San Franciso, CA

Candell, Victor, *Instr,* Provincetown Workshop, MA

Candler, G M, *Deputy Dir,* American Museum in Britain, Bath, England

Canedy, Norman W, *Prof,* Univ Minnesota, Minneapolis

Canepa, Jack, *Assoc Prof,* Webster College, Webster Groves, MO; *Dir,* Loretto-Hilton Center Gallery, Webster College, St Louis, MO

Canfield, Franklin O, *Pres,* Parrish Art Museum, Southampton, NY

Cangialosi, Russell, *Prof,* Los Angeles City College, CA

Caniklioglu, Teoman, *Cur Islamic Coins,* Istanbul Arkeoloji Muzeleri, Turkey

Canner, Suzanne, *Dir Art Therapy,* Dean Junior College, Franklin, MA

Canning, John S, *Pres,* Glenhyrst Arts Council of Brantford, ON

Canning, Mrs Thomas, *Librn,* Creative Arts Center and Gallery, West Virginia Univ, Morgantown

Cannon, Daniel G, *Chmn Dept & Chmn Summer School,* Oregon College of Education, Monmouth

Cannon-Brookes, Dr P, *Keeper Art,* Nat Museum of Wales, Cardiff

Cano, Margarita, *Art Librn,* Miami-Dade Public Library, FL

Canter, Millicent, *Chmn,* Longview Museum and Arts Center, TX

Cantieni, Graham, *Art Dir,* Univ Sherbrooke Cultural Center, PQ

Cantini, Virgil D, *Chmn,* Univ Pittsburgh, PA

Cantlin, Cathy, *Recording Secy,* Art Centre of New Jersey, East Orange

Cantone, Grace R, *Chmn,* Adelphi Univ, Garden City, NY

Cantor, Dorothy, *Educ Dir,* Mattatuck Historical Society Waterbury, CT

Cantrell, Gary, *Music Librn,* Adelphi Univ, Garden City, NY

Cantrick, Margaret, *Asst Librn,* Albright-Knox Art Gallery, Buffalo, NY

Canzani, Joseph V, *Mem Faculty,* Columbus College of Art and Design, OH

Capa, Cornell, *Exec Dir,* International Center of Photography, New York, NY

Capers, Charlotte, *Dir Information & Educ,* Mississippi Department of Archives and History, Jackson

Caplan, Jerry, *Co-Dir,* Chatham College Art Gallery, Pittsburgh, PA

Capo, Larry, *Acting Chmn,* Rider College, Lawrenceville, NJ

Caponi, Anthony, *Head Dept,* Macalester College, Saint Paul, MN

Capozzi, Bro John, *Asst Art Cur,* Saint Bonaventure Univ Art Collection, NY

Cappuccio, Thomas, *Assoc Prof Art & Design & Head Dept,* Northern Michigan Univ, Marquette

Carrabias, Arq Vicente Perez, *Dean Faculty Architecture,* Universidad de Guadalajara, Mexico

Caravaglia, Angelo, *Prof,* Univ Utah, Salt Lake City

Carayanni, Mrs Evdoxia, *Restorer,* Nat Pinakothiki and Alexander Soutzos Museum, Athens, Greece

Carcaba, Hubert W, *VPres,* St Augustine Historical Society, FL

Carden, Mrs Micki, *Pub Relations Coordr,* Miami-Dade Public Library, Miami, FL

Cardman, Cecilia, *First VPres,* Catharine Lorillard Wolfe Art Club, New York, NY

Cardona-Hines, Alvaro, *Chmn Art School & In-Charge Educ Prog for Schools,* Minnesota Museum of Art, St Paul

Cardy, B, *Keeper Conservation,* Manchester City Art Galleries, England

Carettoni, Gianfilippo, *Roman Antiquities,* Museo Nazionale Romano, Italy

Carey, John T, *Prof,* Univ West Florida, Pensacola

Carey, Philip, *Cur,* Roberson Center, Binghamton, NY

Carey, Sister Thomas, *Mem Faculty,* College of Saint Benedict, Saint Joseph, MN

Cargo, Russell A, *Cur,* Waco Art Center, TX

Caric, Olga, *Librn,* Museum of Modern Art, Belgrade, Yugoslavia

Carini, Anselmo, *Assoc Cur Prints & Drawings,* Art Inst of Chicago, IL

Carl, Dora, *Pub Relations Specialist,* Mississippi Museum of Art, Jackson

Carlander, John, *Head Dept,* Augustana College, Sioux Falls, SD

Carlberg, Norman, *Sculptor-in-Residence,* Maryland Inst, Baltimore

Carlbon, Larry, *Pres,* Hunterdon Art Center, Clinton, NJ

Carley, Denny, *Instr,* Southwestern Oklahoma State Univ, Weatherford

Carling, Philip C, *First VPres,* Monmouth Museum and Cultural Center, Lincroft, NJ

Carlos, James Edward, *Dir Gallery of Fine Arts & Chmn Dept,* Univ of the South, Sewanee, TN

Carlson, Cynthia, *Artist-in-Residence,* Oxbow Summer Art Workshops, Saugatuck, MI

Carlson, Cynthia, *Dept Chairperson & Assoc Prof,* Philadelphia College of Art, PA

Carlson, Eleanor, *Chairperson Music Dept,* Southeastern Massachusetts Univ, North Dartmouth

Carlson, Eric, *Assoc Prof,* Swarthmore College, PA

Carlson, Richard, *Educ Cur,* Hudson River Museum, Yonkers, NY

Carlson, Dr Robert E, *Secy,* Chester County Historical Society, West Chester, PA

Carlson, Victor, *Cur Prints & Drawings,* Baltimore Museum of Art, MD

Carlton, Diane, *Clerical Asst,* Museum of the Southwest, Midland, TX

Carmean, E A, *Cur 20th Century,* Nat Gallery of Art, Washington, DC

Carmichael, James H Pete, *Instr,* Friends of the Arts and Sciences, Hilton Leech Studio, Sarasota, FL

Carmichael, Marion, *Catalog Librn,* Stowe-Day Found, Hartford, CT

Carney, Harold E, *Assoc Prof,* Tulane Univ, New Orleans, LA

Cecil, R A, *Asst to Dir,* Wallace Collection, London, England

Cellini, Nicholas, *Fine Arts Librn,* Beverly Hills Public Library, CA

Cerny, Cathy, *Asst to Cur,* Univ Washington Henry Art Gallery, Seattle

Cerny, Charlene, *Cur,* Museum of International Folk Art, Santa Fe, NM

Cervantes, Ms Arcie, *Chairperson Art Comt,* Angelo State Univ Center, San Angelo, TX

Cervantes, James, *Cur Military History,* Heritage Plantation of Sandwich, MA

Cervene, Richard, *Prof,* Grinnell College, IA

Cervenka, Sister Barbara, *Mem Faculty,* Siena Heights College, Adrian, MI

Cetti, Charles, *Chmn Bd Trustees,* Historic Pensacola Preservation Board, FL

Cevc, Dr Anica, *Dir,* Narodna Galerija Yugoslavia, Ljubljana

Chabrowe, Barbara, *Assoc Prof,* George Mason Univ, Fairfax, VA

Chadick, Ellen, *Head Dept & Instr,* Houston School of Commercial Art, TX

Chadwick, William G, *Chmn Bd,* Museum of the Philadelphia Civic Center, PA

Chadwycke-Healey, Sir Edward, *Chmn,* City & Guilds of London Art School, England

Chaffee, Tom, *Asst Prof,* Arkansas State Univ, State University

Chaikin, Hank, *Dir,* Verde Valley Art Association, Jerome, AZ

Chalker, E Gould, *Treas,* Essex Art Association, CT

Challis, A Thomas, *Librn,* Southern Utah State College, Cedar City

Chalmers, Diane, *Chmn,* College of Charleston, SC

Chalmers, E Laurence, Jr, *Pres,* Art Inst of Chicago, IL

Chamberlain, Betty, *Dir,* Art Information Center, New York, NY

Chamberlain, Charles F, *Chmn Ceramics,* East Carolina Univ, Greenville, NC

Chamberlain, E *Keeper Prints,* Fitzwilliam Museum, Univ Cambridge, England

Chamberlain, Merle, *Asst Librn,* Philadelphia Museum of Art, PA

Chamberlain, Peter, *Mem Faculty,* Elmira College, NY

Chambers, Bruce W, *Asst Dir Cur Serv,* Univ Rochester Mem Art Gallery, NY

Champa, Kermit S, *Chmn,* Brown Univ, Providence, RI

Chance, Catherine, *Special Asst Urban Affairs,* Metropolitan Museum of Art, New York, NY

Chandler, Barbara, *Registrar,* Philadelphia Museum of Art, PA

Chandler, E G, *Pres,* Lyme Art Association, Old Lyme, CT

Chandler, William L, *Chmn,* Concordia College, Milwaukee, WI

Chandor, Mary, *Art Cur,* Morris Museum of Arts and Sciences, Morristown, NJ

Chandra, Pramod, *Prof,* Univ Chicago, IL

Chang, F Ming, *Asst Prof,* Seton Hall Univ, South Orange, NJ

Chang, John R, *Deputy Dir,* Vancouver City Archives, BC

Chang, Peter, *Cur Dept Rare Books & Documents,* Nat Palace Museum, Taiwan, Republic of China

Chanlatte, Luis A, *Cur Archaeology,* Univ Puerto Rico, Rio Piedras

Channin, Richard, *Asst Prof Humanities & Chmn Dept Fine Arts,* Univ Pittsburgh at Johnstown, PA

Chao-shen, Chiang, *Acting Deputy Dir & Cur Dept Calligraphy & Painting,* Nat Palace Museum, Taiwan, Republic of China

Chapard, Francoise, *Librn,* Institute de France, Musee Conde, Paris

Chapin, Leslie A, *Treas,* Westfield Athenaeum, MA

Chaplin, George, *Dir, Studio Arts Prog,* Trinity College Austin Arts Center, Hartford, CT

Chapman, Allan D, *Mus Librn,* Robert Goldwater Library of Primitive Art, Metropolitan Museum of Art, New York, NY

Chapman, Delbert, *Treas,* Keokuk Art Center, IA

Chapman, Fred, *Dean Summer School,* Presbyterian College, Clinton, SC

Chapman, Gretel, *Keeper Goucher Coll,* Goucher College Gallery, Towson, MD

Chapman, Mrs John W, *Second VPres,* Everson Museum of Art, Syracuse, NY

Chapman, Vannort S, *VPres,* Star-Spangled Banner Flag House Association, Baltimore, MD

Chapman, Walter, *Instr,* San Diego Mesa College, CA

Chapman, Wesley G, *Chairperson Dept Art,* Southern Oregon State College, Ashland

Chapnick, Mrs Ronald, *Secy,* Fine Arts Association, Willoughby, OH

Chappell, Dr Miles, *Assoc Prof, Chmn Art Dept & In Charge Art Collection,* College of William and Mary, Williamsburg, VA

Chappell, Sally Kitt, *Assoc Prof, Chmn Dept & Dir Summer School,* DePaul Univ, Chicago, IL

Chapu, Philippe, *Cur,* Musee des Monuments Francais, Paris

Charbonneau, M E, *Park Supt,* Sibbald Point Provincial Park, Sutton West, ON

Chard, Daniel, *Chairperson,* Glassboro State College, NJ

Charles, Peter, *Prof,* West Virginia Univ, Morgantown

Charley, Alfred B, *Assoc Prof,* Clarion State College, PA

Charlton, R I H, *Publns Officer,* Ashmolean Museum, Oxford Univ, England

Charron, Daniel C, *Mem Faculty,* Norwich Art School, CT

Chase, W T, *Head Conservator,* Technical Lab, Freer Gallery of Art, Washington, DC

Chassman, Neil A, *Chmn,* Western Illinois Univ, Macomb

Chatlain, Charlotte, *Registrar,* Historic New Orleans Collection, LA

Chatmas, John, *Instr,* McLennan Community College, Waco, TX

Chatt, Orville K, *Chmn,* Skagit Valley College, Mt Vernon, WA

Chauvin, Clarice, *Dir Summer School,* Anna Maria College, Paxton, MA

Chavel, David, *Coordr Gen Studies Prog,* Ontario College of Art, Toronto

Chavez, Olga Joffre, *Asst Dir,* Museo Nacional de Arqueologia, La Paz, Bolivia

Chaw, Gladys, *Librn,* College of San Mateo Library, CA

Chazan, Cindy, *Dir,* Harvey Golden Inst, Saidye Bronfman Centre (YM-YWHA & NHS), Montreal, PQ

Cheever, John, *Secy Academy,* American Academy and Inst of Arts and Letters, see National and Regional Organizations

Cheevers, James W, *Sr Cur,* US Naval Academy Museum, Annapolis, MD

Chegwidden, Dennis D, *Mem Faculty,* Hutchinson Community Junior College, KS

Chehab, Emir Maurice, *Dir & Chief Cur,* Musee Nat, Beirut, Lebanon

Chelimsky, Oscar, *Mem Faculty,* Maryland College of Art and Design, Silver Spring

Chell, Joyce, *Secy,* Ojai Valley Art Center, CA

Cheney, Kenneth D, *Chmn Humanities Div,* Linn Benton Community College, Albany, OR

Cheney, Liana, *Asst Prof,* Univ Lowell, MA

Chenoweth, Mary, *Chmn & Assoc Prof,* Colorado College, Colorado Springs

Cherewick, Patricia, *Instr,* Rocky Mountain College, Billings, MT

Chernow, Burt, *Prof & Chmn Art & Dir,* Housatonic Museum of Art, Housatonic Community College, Bridgeport, CT

Cherry, Terry, *Chmn,* East Mississippi Junior College, Scooba

Chester, Janie K, *Dir,* Saginaw Art Museum, MI

Chestney, Anita H, *Instr,* Grand Canyon College, Phoenix, AZ

Chetham, Charles, *Dir,* Smith College Museum of Art, Northampton, MA

Chevalier, Real, *Treas,* La Societe des Decorateurs-Ensembliers du Quebec, Montreal

Chevallier, B, *Cur,* Musee Nat du Chateau de Fontainebleau, France

Chevian, Margaret, *Asst,* Providence Public Library, RI

Chew, Harry, *Chmn,* Cottey College, Nevada, MO

Chew, Dr Paul A, *Dir,* Westmoreland County Museum of Art, Greensburg, PA

Chiarini, Dr Marco, *Dir,* Galleria Palatina, Florence, Italy

Chick, Lucille, *Staff Secy,* Southern Artists Association, Hot Springs, AR

Chieffo, Clifford T, *Head Art Dept & Cur, Art & History Museum,* Georgetown Univ, Washington, DC

Chieffo, Patricia H, *Assoc Cur,* Art and History Museum, Georgetown Univ, Washington, DC

Chiego, William, *Cur,* Portland Art Association, OR

Chihuly, Dale, *Head Glass,* Rhode Island School of Design, Providence

Child, Kent, *Chmn Humanities Div & Gallery Adv,* Gavilan College, Gilroy, CA

Child, Tim, *Gallery/Educ Coordr,* Thames Arts Centre, Chatham, ON

Childs, Elizabeth, *Cur General Coll,* Valentine Museum, Richmond, VA

Childs, Suse C, *Librn,* The Cloisters, Metropolitan Museum of Art, New York, NY

Chilla, Benigna, *Instr,* Berkshire Community College, Pittsfield, MA

Chilton, W P, *Pres Bd Admin,* Hermitage Found Museum, Norfolk, VA

Chipley, Sheila M, *Asst Prof,* Concord College, Athens, WV

Chipmen, Joseph, *Designer & Preparator,* Wheelwright Museum, Santa Fe, NM

Chiro, Lily, *Admin,* Centre for Experimental Art and Communication, Toronto, ON

Chism, Robert H, *Chmn,* Butler County Community College, El Dorado, KS

Chlebak, George F, *Mem Faculty,* Kansas Wesleyan Univ, Salina

Choate, Jerry, *Mem Faculty,* Northeastern Oklahoma State Univ, Tahlequah

Chock, Vickie, *Lectr,* Leeward Community College, Pearl City, HI

Chodkowski, Henry J, *Prof,* Univ Louisville, KY

Choi, Sunu, *Dir-Gen,* Nat Museum of Korea, Seoul

Chong, Yangmo, *Chief Cur,* Nat Museum of Korea, Seoul

Choolijan, Gladys, *Secy,* Bergen Community Museum, Paramus, NJ

Christensen, Gardell Dano, *Pres,* Wind River Valley Artists Guild, Dubois, WY

Christensen, Maury, *Information Dir,* Utah Travel Council, Salt Lake City

Christenson, Elroy, *Instr,* North Seattle Community College, WA

Christian, Corinne, *Prog Coordr,* Yuma Art Center, AZ

Christian, Emmitt L, *Chmn,* State Univ New York College at Fredonia

Christiansen, J, *Cur Greek & Roman Art,* NY Carlsberg Glyptothek, Copenhagen, Denmark

Christianson, John, *Dir in Charge Acad Relations,* Vesterheim, Decorah, IA

Christie, H, *Chmn Display Design,* Fashion Inst of Technology, New York, NY

Christie, Robert, *Exec Secy-Treas,* Royal Architectural Inst of Canada, see National Organizations of Canada; *Gallery Supvr,* Univ Saskatchewan, Saskatoon

Christison, Muriel B, *Dir,* Univ Illinois, Champaign

Christoph, Peter, *Manuscripts & Spec Coll,* New York State Library, Albany

Christopher, Dr William, *VPres,* Art Association of Richmond, IN

Christophersen, Betty, *VPres,* Paint 'N' Palette Club, Anamosa, IA

Chruscici, Tadeusz, *Dir,* Muzeum Narodowe W Krakowie, Cracow, Poland

Chrysler, Jean, *Librn,* Chrysler Museum at Norfolk, VA

Chrysler, Walter P, Jr, *Pres Bd Trustees,* Chrysler Museum at Norfolk, VA

Chrzanowska, A, *Cur,* Muzeum Narodowe W Wroclawiu, Wroclaw, Poland

Chu, Petra T D, *Chmn Art Dept & Dir,* Student Center Art Gallery, Seton Hall Univ, South Orange, NJ

Chumley, Gail, *Secy to Dir,* Brooks Mem Art Gallery, Memphis, TN

Chumley, Jere L, *Assoc Prof, Dept Coordr & Dir Summer School,* Cleveland State Community College, TN

Church, Elsa, *Cur,* Schenectady County Historical Society, NY

Church, John, *Instr,* Interlochen Arts Academy, MI

Churches, Roger, *Chmn,* Loma Linda Univ, La Sierra Campus, Riverside, CA

Churchill, Shelley E, *Cur,* Spartanburg County Art Association, SC

Churdar, Janice, *Staff Supvr,* Bob Jones Univ Museum and Art Gallery, Greenville, SC

Cianfioni, Emilio, *Conservator,* Dade County Art Museum, Miami, FL

Cianfrani, Vera, *Instr,* Wayne Art Center, PA

Cieckiewicz, Stanislaw, *Mgr,* Panstwowe Zbiory Sztuki na Wawelu, Cracow, Poland

Cig, Dr Kemal, *Dir,* Topkapi Saray Museum, Istanbul, Turkey

Cikovsky, Nicolai, Jr, *Chmn Art Dept,* Univ New Mexico, Albuquerque

Cimonetti, A, *Chmn Interior Design,* Fashion Inst Technology, New York, NY

Cinsneros, Dorothy, *Asst Librn,* Huntington Free Library and Reading Room, Bronx, NY

Citrin, Sharon, *Cur,* Gallery of Prehistoric Paintings, New York, NY

Claflin, Susan, *Mem Faculty,* Clayworks, New York, NY

Clahassey, Patricia, *Chmn,* College of St Rose, Albany, NY

Clain-Stefanelli, Elvira, *Art Advisory Bd,* Society of Medalists, see National and Regional Organizations

Clancy, Justine, *Slide Cur,* Univ California Architecture and Fine Arts Library, Los Angeles

Clapp, Nick, *Instr,* William Woods/Westminster Colleges, Fulton, MO

Clarien, Gary, *Workshop Supvr,* Palo Alto Cultural Center, CA

Clark, A McFadyen, *Chief Canadian Ethnology Serv,* Nat Museum of Man, Ottawa, ON

Clark, Alan B, *Dir,* Albuquerque Public Library, NM

Clark, Alson, *Librn,* Univ California Architecture and Fine Arts Library, Los Angeles

Clark, Bee, *Admin Asst,* Boise Gallery of Art, ID

Clark, Bob, *Head Dept Commercial Art & Advertising Design,* Southwestern Technical Inst, Sylva, NC

Clark, Carol, *Cur Paintings,* Amon Carter Museum of Western Art, Fort Worth, TX

Clark, Carroll, *Editor Office of Publns,* Nat Collection of Fine Arts, Washington, DC

Clark, Charles E, *VPres,* New Hampshire Historical Society, Concord

Clark, D, *Cur,* Edmonton Art Gallery, AB

Clark, Edward, *Vis Prof,* Louisiana State Univ, Baton Rouge

Clark, Edward F, Jr, *County Supvr,* Hudson County Court House, Jersey City, NJ

Clark, Gary F, *Asst Prof,* Bloomsburg State College, PA

Clark, James, *Instr,* San Diego Mesa College, CA

Clark, James M, *Chmn,* Blackburn College, Carlinville, IL

Clark, Joan C, *Pres,* Pottstown Area Artists Guild, PA

Clark, Joe, *Library Assoc,* New Orleans Public Library, LA

Clark, Mark A, *Cur Decorative Arts,* Chrysler Museum at Norfolk, VA

Clark, Mary Ann, *Instr,* Northeast Technical Community College, Norfolk, NE

Clark, Mary Jane, *Registrar,* Dartmouth College Museum and Galleries, Hanover, NH

Clark, N, *Coordr Ottawa Exhib,* Nat Gallery of Canada, Ottawa, ON

Clark, Neill, *Instr,* Atlanta College of Art, GA

Clark, Neill W, *Treas,* Hickory Museum of Art, NC

Clark, Pat, *Assoc Prof,* Univ Wisconsin-River Falls

Clark, Phyllis Blair, *Asst Mus Dir,* College of Wooster Art Center Museum, OH

Clark, Ralph T, *Prof,* Utah State Univ, Logan

Clark, Sarah, *Asst Cur,* Seattle Art Museum Modern Art Pavilion, WA

Clark, Dr Septimus Mendonca, *Asst Exec Dir,* Museu de Arte Moderna Brazil, Rio de Janiero

Clark, Tommy, *Mem Faculty,* Campbellsville College, KY

Clark, Winnifred, *Reference Librn,* Detroit Public Library, MI

Clarke, D, *Journal Exec Ed,* Association of Collegiate Schools of Architecture, see National and Regional Organizations

Clarke, D Sherman, *Cataloger,* Univ Pittsburgh Art Gallery, PA

Clarke, Michael, *Asst Keeper Prints,* Whitworth Art Gallery, Univ Manchester, England

Clarke, Peter P, *Chmn,* Herkimer County Community College, NY

Clarke, Richard, *Prof,* Univ Tennessee, Knoxville

Clarkson, Grant, *Pres,* Peel Museum and Art Gallery, Brampton, ON

Clarkson, John D, *Cur CAC Galleries & Prof,* West Virginia Univ, Morgantown

Claus, Camille, *Vis Prof,* Schiller College, Europe Univ, Strasbourg, France

Claus, William, *Mem Faculty,* Junior College of Albany, NY

Clausen, Robert, *Prof,* Rochester Community College, MN

Clawson, Chip, *Materials Mgr,* Archie Bray Found, Helena, MT

Clay, Langdon F, *Asst Dir Educ,* Univ Rochester Mem Art Gallery, NY

Claypool, Julia B, *Educ Specialist,* Tryon Palace Restoration Complex, New Bern, NC

Clayton, John M, *Univ Archivist & Dir Permanent Art Coll,* Univ Delaware, Newark

Clearwater, James, *Gallery Mgr,* New York Univ Art Collection, NY

Cleary, John R, *Instr,* Salisbury State College, MD

Cleaver, Dale G, *Prof,* Univ Tennessee, Knoxville

Cleaves, Col Haskell, *Pres,* Colonel Black Mansion, Ellsworth, ME

Clem, Paul, *Dir Summer School,* College of William and Mary, Williamsburg, VA

Clemans, H, *Mem Faculty,* Golden West College, Huntington Beach, CA

Clement, Adele, *Secy,* Essex Art Association, CT

Clement, Robert L, Jr, *VPres,* Charleston Museum, SC

Clements, Nora, *Secy,* Society for Preservation of Historic Landmarks, York, ME

Clemes, Patricia, *Mem Faculty,* Toronto School of Art, ON

Clerman, Maurice, *Mem Faculty,* Maryland College of Art and Design, Silver Spring

Clervi, Paul, *Asst Prof,* William Woods/Westminster Colleges, Fulton, MO

Cleveland, Dr Helen B, *Dir,* Chautauqua Gallery of Art, NY

Cleveland, Joanne, *Instr,* Wayne Art Center, PA

Cleveland, John H, Jr, *Exec Dir,* Greater Gary Arts Council, IN

Cleveland, R Earl, *Chmn Dept & Dir Summer School,* Carson-Newman College, Jefferson City, TN

Cleverdon, John H, *Prof,* Univ South Alabama, Mobile

Clewell, E B, *Cur,* Moravian Historical Society, Nazareth, PA

Cliff, Linda, *Instr,* Cultural Arts Center of Ocean City, NJ

Clifford, Deborah, *VChmn Bd,* Vermont State Craft Center at Frog Hollow, Middlebury

Clifford, Ethel, *Secy,* Haystack Mountain School of Crafts Gallery, Deer Isle, ME

Clifford, Paul A, *Cur Pre-Columbian Coll,* Duke Univ Museum of Art, Durham, NC

Clifford, T P C, *Dir,* Manchester City Art Galleries, England

Climer, J E, *Dir & Cur,* Saskatoon Gallery and Conservatory Corp, SK

Cline, Carol, *Exhib Designer,* Panhandle-Plains Historical Society Museum, Canyon, TX

Cline, Kay, *Dir,* Museum on Wheels, Monterey Peninsula Museum of Art, CA

Clinkinbeard, Al, *Chmn,* San Jacinto College North, Houston, TX

Clisby, Roger D, *Chief Cur,* E B Crocker Art Gallery, Sacramento, CA

Clive, Dennis, *Asst Prof,* Dickinson College, Carlisle, PA

Clivengood, Mrs James, *Exec Secy,* Marblehead Arts Association, MA

Close, Gloria W, *Asst Librn,* North Carolina State Univ Design Library, Raleigh

Clothier, George B, *Treas,* Samuel S Fleisher Art Mem, Philadelphia, PA

Clothier, Peter D, *Acting Dir/Dean,* Otis Art Inst, Los Angeles, CA

Cloud, Richard C, *Treas,* Chester County Historical Society, West Chester, PA

Cloudman, Ruth H, *Chief Cur,* Joslyn Art Museum, Omaha, NE

Cloudsley, Donald, *Deputy Dir Support Serv,* Buffalo and Erie County Public Library, Buffalo, NY

Clough, Lynn, *Asst,* Univ Wisconsin, Oshkosh

Clovis, John, *Mem Faculty,* Fairmont State College, WV

Clunie, Margaret B, *Cur,* Bowdoin College Museum of Art, Brunswick, ME

Clyde, Edward J, *Sr Trustee,* Deshong Mem Art Galleries, Cheston, PA

Cnever, Melvin, *Prof,* North Carolina Central Univ, Durham

Coak, Pam, *Architectural Designer,* Glendale Federal Savings and Loan Association, CA, see Corporate Art Holdings

Coates, Ann S, *Cur Slides,* Allen R Hite Art Inst, Univ Louisville, KY

Coates, Ross, *Chmn,* Washington State Univ, Pullman

Coats, Marvin S, *Lectr,* Wake Forest Univ, Winston-Salem, NC

Coblentz, Patricia L, *Asst Dir,* Museum of American Folk Art, New York, NY

Coburn, Bette Lee, *VPres,* Guild of South Carolina Artists, Columbia

Cocchini, Marianne A, *Admin Dir,* Electronic Arts Intermix, New York, NY

Cochard, Roger, *Vis Prof,* Schiller College, Europe Univ, Strasbourg, France

Cochenour, Donnice, *Cur Special Coll,* Inst and Museum of the Great Plains, Lawton, OK

Cochius, Miss J M, *Cur Oriental Ceramics,* Groninger Museum Voor Stad En Land, Netherlands

Cochran, Malcolm, *Exhib Coordr,* Dartmouth College Museum and Galleries, Hanover, NH

Cochran, Thomas C, *VPres,* Historical Society of Pennsylvania, Philadelphia

Cochran, William, *Dean Summer Session,* Solano Community College, Suisun City, CA

Cochrane, Jame, *Pres,* Kingsport Fine Arts Center, TN

Codding, Anthony S, *Dir,* Univ Pennsylvania Inst of Contemporary Art, Philadelphia

Coddington, Dabney M, *Cur Educ,* Tryon Palace Restoration Complex, New Bern, NC

Cody, John V, *Prof,* Boston State College, MA

Coe, Mrs Henry H R, *Chmn,* Buffalo Bill Mem Association, Cody, WY

Coe, Mildred M, *Dir,* Hickory Museum of Art, NC

Coe, Ralph T, *Dir,* William Rockhill Nelson Gallery of Art, Kansas City, MO

Coe, William R, *Cur Amer Section,* Univ of Pennsylvania Museum, Philadelphia

Coerr, DeRenne, *Registrar,* De Young Museum, Fine Arts Museums of San Francisco, CA

Cofer, Alene, *Asst Dir Admin,* Mariners Museum, Newport News, VA

Coffee, Baxter, *Instr,* Del Mar College, Corpus Christi, TX

Coffey, Mrs Dan, *Historian/Librn,* Beverly Historical Society, MA

Coffin, David R, *Prof,* Princeton Univ, NJ

Coffin, Doug, *Instr,* Fort Wright College of the Holy Names, Spokane, WA

Coffman, Barbara, *Secy,* Jordan Historical Museum of the Twenty, ON

Coffman, Terrence J, *Pres & Dir Summer School,* Maryland College of Art and Design, Silver Spring

Cofrances, Mrs Humbert, *Pres,* Frederick Thompson Found, New York, NY

Cogan, Mr, *Dir of Summer School,* Sarah Lawrence College, Bronxville, NY

Cogan, Mrs Jerry, *Chmn,* Spatanburg County Art Association, SC

Coghlan, Gladys M, *Dir Libr,* Historical Society of Delaware, Wilmington

Cogswell, Mrs Dean, *Pres,* Wenham Historical Association and Museum, MA

Cohan, Allan L, *Coordr,* Ulster County Community College Visual Arts Gallery, Stony Ridge, NY

Cohan, Ann Liljengren, *Asst Dir,* David Strawn Art Gallery, Jacksonville, IL

Cohan, Jack, *Mgr,* Jorgensen Auditorium, Univ Connecticut, Storrs

Cohan, Peter S, *Dir,* David Strawn Art Gallery, Jacksonville, IL

Cohan, Zara, *Gallery Dir,* Kean College of New Jersey, Union

Cohen, Allan, *Head Dept & Coordr,* Ulster County Community College, Stony Ridge, NY

Cohen, Charles E, *Chmn & Assoc Prof,* Univ Chicago, IL

Cohen, Edwin, *Head Art Dept,* Purdue Univ, Calumet Campus, Hammond, IN

Cohen, Esther, *Pres,* Peoria Art Guild, IL

Cohen, Harold, *Prof,* Univ California, San Diego, La Jolla

Cohen, Judy, *Cur,* Museum of International Folk Art, Santa Fe, NM

Cohen, Kathleen, *Mem Faculty,* San Jose State Univ, CA

Cohen, Lewis, *Mem Faculty,* Laguna Beach School of Art, CA

Cohen, Mitch, *Cur Registrar,* Davenport Municipal Art Gallery, IA

Cohen, Robert, *Chmn Photography,* Moore College of Art, Philadelphia, PA

Cohen, Ronald M, *Asst Prof,* Univ Texas at San Antonio

Cohn, Anna R, *Cur & Dir,* B'nai B'rith Exhibit Hall, Washington, DC

Cohn, Jane, *Pub Info Dir,* Hudson River Museum, Yonkers, NY

Cohn, Marjorie, *Assoc Conservator,* William Hayes Fogg Art Museum, Cambridge, MA

Cohodas, Marvin, *Asst Prof,* Univ British Columbia, Vancouver

Coiner, Maynard R (Jim), *Head Dept & Prof,* Concord College, Athens, WV

Coke, Charles V, *Assoc Prof,* Northwestern State Univ Louisiana, Natchitoches

Coke, Van Deren, *Dir,* Univ New Mexico Art Museum, Albuquerque

Coker, Alyce, *Asst Prof,* Univ Minnesota, Duluth

Coker, Gylbert, *Cur,* Studio Museum in Harlem, New York, NY

Coker, John, *Dir Fine Arts Events,* Univ South Florida Galleries Program, Tampa

Coker, Robert R, *Treas,* Brookgreen Gardens, Murrells Inlet, SC

Colacicchi, Piero, *Mem Faculty,* Studio Art Centers International, Florence, Italy

Colby, Bill D, *Chmn,* Univ Puget Sound, Tacoma, WA

Colby, Victor, *Prof,* Cornell Univ, Ithaca, NY

Colchin, Helen, *Head Fine Arts Dept,* Public Library of Fort Wayne and Allen County, Fort Wayne, IN

Cole, David, *Dean Summer School,* High Point College, NC

Cole, David C, *Cur,* Fort Meade Museum, Fort George Meade, MD

Cole, Dora Jane, *Pres,* Kauai Museum, Lihue, HI

Cole, Edyth B, *Dir Summer School,* Elizabeth City State Univ, NC

Cole, Elise, *Cur Art Educ,* Ella Sharp Museum, Jackson, MI

Cole, Frederic, *VPres,* Key West Art and Historical Society, FL

Cole, George, *Dir Summer School,* Southern Connecticut State College, New Haven

Cole, Howson W, *Librn,* Virginia Historical Society, Richmond

Cole, Jan, *Librn,* College of the Ozarks Art Department Library, Clarksville, AR

Cole, Sylvan, *Gallery Trustee,* Visual Artists and Galleries Association, see National and Regional Organizations

Coleburn, Sue, *Bookstore Mgr,* Brandywine River Museum, Chadds Ford, PA

Coleman, Collene, *Registrar,* Sheldon Swope Art Gallery, Terre Haute, IN

Coleman, Elizabeth A, *Cur Costumes & Textiles,* Brooklyn Museum, NY

Coleman, Floyd, *Head Art History,* Southern Illinois Univ, Edwardsville

Coleman, Henry, *Assoc Prof,* College of William and Mary, Williamsburg, VA

Coleman, Loring, *VPres,* Concord Art Association, MA

Coleman, Myrlan, *Head Dept Art,* Weatherford College, TX

Coleman, Mrs R H, *Cur,* Liberty Hall Museum, Frankfort, KY

Coleman, Thomas F, *Chmn,* Indiana Univ, Bloomington

Coleman, Victor, *Dir,* Nightingale Arts Association, Toronto, ON

Coleman, William C, *Dir,* Carolina Art Association, Charleston, SC

Coles, Arlo, *Mem Faculty,* Ricks College, Rexburg, ID

Coles, Dr William H, *Secy,* Carolina Art Association, Charleston, SC

Colevechio, X G, *Head Dept,* Saint Norbert College, De Pere, WI

Coley, Betty A, *Librn,* Baylor Univ Art Museum, Waco, TX

Coley, Philip, *Pres,* Montgomery Museum of Fine Arts & Asst Prof, Auburn University at Montgomery, AL

Colgrove, Miss J, *Recording Secy,* Lyceum Club and Women's Art Association of Canada, Toronto, ON

Colier, Will, *Prof,* Santa Rosa Junior College, CA

Colin, Elena, *Lectr & Dir Art Summer School,* Inst for American Universities, Aix-en-Provence, France

Colin, Ralph F, *Admin VPres & Counsel,* Art Dealers Association of America, see National and Regional Organizations

Colker, Edward, *Dir School Art & Design,* Univ Illinois, Chicago Circle

Colket, Meredith, *Exec Dir,* Western Reserve Historical Society, Cleveland, OH

Collens, David, *Cur,* Storm King Art Center, Mountainville, NY

Collet, Lee Edward, *Chairperson Dept Creative & Performing Arts & Dir Summer School,* Muskegon Community College, MI

Collette, Dr Alfred T, *Dir,* Joe and Emily Lowe Art Gallery, Syracuse Univ, NY

Collier, Eleanore, *Co-Chmn,* Hill Country Arts Found, Ingram, TX

Collier, Hilma Greggerson, *Dir,* Carrizo Art and Craft Workshops, Ruidoso, NM

Collier, Ralph, *Pres,* Campbell Museum, Camden, NJ

Collins, Christiane C, *Head Librn,* Adam L Gimbel Library, Parsons School of Design, New York, NY

Collins, Delmar L, *Mgr,* Will Rogers Mem and Museum, Claremore, OK

Collins, Harvey A, *Assoc Prof Art, Chmn Dept & Dir Summer School,* Olivet Nazarene College, Kankakee, IL

Collins, Howard, *VChmn Art Dept,* Univ Nebraska, Lincoln

Collins, Jesse, *Mem Faculty,* Junior College of Albany, NY

Collins, Jim, *Dir Art Gallery & Prof,* Univ Tennessee at Chattanooga

Collins, Joel, *Lectr,* Bethany College, WV

Collins, Lea, *Visual Arts Officer,* Saskatchewan Arts Board, Regina

Collins, Sister M Regina, *Chmn,* Mount Mary College, Milwaukee, WI

Collins, Nicole, *Secy,* Centre Cultural de Shawinigan, PQ

Collins, Dr Reba Neighbors, *Cur & Librn,* Will Rogers Mem and Museum, Claremore, OK

Collins, Sister Regine, *Chmn,* Mount Mary College, Milwaukee, WI

Collins, Susan, *Asst Dir,* Westerly Public Library, RI

Collins, Ted, *VPres,* Eccles Community Art Center, Ogden, UT

Collins, Thom, *Resident Artist,* Peters Valley Craftsmen, Layton, NJ

Collins, William C, *Dir,* Portland School of Art, ME

Collinson, Helen, *Cur,* Univ Alberta Art Gallery and Museum, Edmonton

Colquitt, Carlton, *Dir Develop,* Wheelwright Museum, Santa Fe, NM

Colson, Chester, *Prof,* Wilkes College, Wilkes-Barre, PA

Colt, Priscilla, *Dir,* Univ Kentucky Art Museum, Lexington

Colvert, Richard, *Secy,* Charles B Goddard Center for the Visual and Performing Arts, Ardmore, OK

Colvig, Richard, *Sr Librn in Charge,* Oakland Public Library, CA

Colwill, Stiles T, *Asst Gallery Cur,* Maryland Historical Society Museum, Baltimore

Comas, Genoveva, *Assoc Prof,* Inter American Univ Puerto Rico, San German

Combs-Smith, Andrew, *Educ Dir,* Kentucky Guild of Artists and Craftsmen, Berea

Comer, Eugenia, *Asst Prof,* Augusta College, GA

Comiskey, Ernest D, *Prof,* West Liberty State College, WV

Compton, Beverley C, *Pres,* Municipal Art Society of Baltimore City, MD

Compton, J E, *Assoc Prof,* Florida A&M Univ, Tallahassee

Compton, Julie M, *Head Fine Arts Dept,* Atlanta Public Library, GA

Comstock, Craig, *Pres,* Pacific Grove Art Center, CA

Conan, Vivian, *Dir,* Port Chester Public Library, NY

Conant, Howard, *Dept Head,* Univ of Arizona, Tucson

Conant, Mary, *Pres,* Marblehead Arts Association, MA

Conaway, James, *Exhib Dir Galleries & Mem Faculty,* Hamline Univ, Saint Paul, MN

Concha, Jerry, *Chmn Drawing & Painting,* de Young Museum Art School, San Francisco, CA

Condax, Philip, *Equipment,* International Museum of Photography, Rochester, NY

Condit, Carl W, *Prof Art History & Chmn Dept,* Northwestern Univ, Evanston, IL

Cone, Gerrit C, *Asst Dir,* Tucson Museum of Art, AZ

Conesa, Lillian, *Supvr Processing Center,* Miami-Dade Public Library, Miami, FL

Conforti, Michael, *Cur Decorative Arts,* Fine Arts Museums of San Francisco, CA

Conger, Clement E, *Cur,* Dept of State Diplomatic Reception Rooms; *Cur,* The White House, Washington, DC

Conger, John T, *Mgr Personnel,* Metropolitan Museum of Art, New York, NY

Conger, William, *Assoc Prof,* DePaul Univ, Chicago, IL

Conklin, Mrs David, *VPres,* London Art Gallery Association, ON

Conley, B, *Mem Faculty,* Golden West College, Huntington Beach, CA

Conlon, Donald, *Pres,* Warwick Arts Found, RI

Conlon, James E, *Asst,* Ethnic American Slide Library & *Prof,* Univ South Alabama, Mobile

Conly, Marc, *Asst Dir,* Rocky Mountain School of Art, Denver, CO

Conn, Catherine, *Cur Exhib,* Hudson River Museum, Yonkers, NY

Conn, Susan, *Instr,* Missouri Western State College, Saint Joseph

Connah, Neill W, *Mem Faculty,* Georgia Inst of Technology, Atlanta

Connell, Julie, *Assoc Instr,* Univ Utah, Salt Lake City

Connell, Stephen, *Assoc Prof,* Univ Montana, Missoula

Conner, Ann Louise, *Asst Prof,* Univ North Carolina at Wilmington

Conner, George A, *VPres,* Star-Spangled Banner Flag House Association, Baltimore, MD

Conner, Sister M Rebecca, *Head Dept,* Saint Mary College, Leavenworth, KS

Conner, Neppie, *Chmn Dept & Prof,* Univ Arkansas, Fayetteville

Connery, Mary Catherine, *Asst to Dir,* Oklahoma Art Center, Oklahoma City

Connett, Dee M, *Head Dept,* Friends Univ, Wichita, KS

Connolly, A L J, *Head Dept Commun Arts & Design,* Manchester Polytechnic, England

Connolly, Bruce E, *Head Technical Serv,* New York State College of Ceramics at Alfred Univ

Connolly, G Florence, *Cur Fine Arts,* Boston Public Library, MA

Connolly, Thomas, *Treas,* Artists Guild Inc of New York, see National and Regional Organizations

Connor, Catherine, *Asst Prof,* Fontbonne College, Clayton, MO

Connors, Dorothy, *Adminr,* Metropolitan Museum and Art Centers, Coral Gables, FL

Connors, Mrs John F, *Exec Secy,* Frick Art Museum, Pittsburgh, PA

Conover, James H, *Assoc Dean,* Ohio Univ, Athens

Conover, Louis S, *Treas,* Mobile Art Association, AL

Conover, Robert, *Dir,* Pasadena Public Library, CA; *VPres,* Society of American Graphic Artists, see National and Regional Organizations

Conover, William, *VPres,* Pittsfield Art League, MA

Conrad, *Adminr,* Statens Kunstakademi, Oslo, Norway

Conrad, Dr A, *Dir,* Art Instruction Schools, Minneapolis, MN

Conrad, John, *Instr,* San Diego Mesa College, CA

Conrad, Dr Kurt, *Cur Ethnology,* Saltzburger Museum Carolino Augusteum, Austria

Conrad, Richard, *Dir,* Mills House Art Gallery, Garden Grove, CA

Conrad, Sadie, *Secy,* Kelowna Centennial Museum & Nat Exhibit Centre, BC

Conrad, Theodore, *VPres,* Jersey City Museum Association, NJ

Conragan, Dr A Kirk, *Dir,* Josephine D Randall Junior Museum, San Francisco, CA

Conroy, Joseph, *Asst Prof Art,* Camden County College, Blackwood, NJ

Consey, Kevin E, *Dir,* Hofstra Univ, Hempstead, NY

Constantine, Greg, *Chmn,* Andrews Univ, Berrien Springs, MI

Constantine, H F, *Dir,* Sheffield City Art Galleries, England

Constantine, John, *Chmn Art Dept,* North Seattle Community College, WA

Contini-Bonacossi, Alessandro, *Cur Photographic Archives,* Nat Gallery of Art, Washington, DC

Conway, Mrs Avery H, *Mem Secy,* Berkshire Museum, Pittsfield, MA

Conway, Gregg, *Chmn Dept,* Paris American Academy, France

Conway, Myra Lee, *Chairwoman Graphic Design,* New England School of Art and Design, Boston, MA

Conway, Wallace, *Cur Exhib,* New Jersey State Museum, Trenton

Conzelman, Margaret, *Gallery Mgr,* Detroit Artists Market, MI

Cook, Alan M, *Keeper Pub Serv,* Univ Pennsylvania Museum, Philadelphia

Cook, Bonnie, *Registrar,* San Jose State Univ, CA

Cook, Christopher C, *Dir,* Addison Gallery of American Art, Andover, MA

Cook, Don, *Vis Prof,* East Central Univ, Ada, OK

Cook, Douglas, *Head Dept Theatre & Film,* Pennsylvania State Univ, University Park

Cook, Garnetta, *Head Audiovisual Section,* Illinois State Library, Springfield

Cook, Gary A, *Instr,* Wake Forest Univ, Winston-Salem, NC

Cook, Ian, *Chmn Fine & Performing Art & Dir Summer School,* Red Deer College, AB

Cook, John, *Asst Prof,* Bloomsburg State College, PA

Cook, Dr Kenneth R, *Assoc Provost & Dir Summer School,* Univ Arkansas, Fayetteville

Cook, Mary, *Mus Secy,* Univ Oklahoma Museum of Art, Norman

Cook, Peter W, *Chief Cur,* Bennington Museum, VT

Cook, Dr Phill, *Dir Summer Sessions,* Western New Mexico Univ, Silver City

Cook, Ralph, *Assoc Prof,* West Virginia Wesleyan College, Buckhannon

Cook, Robert, *Acting Chmn,* Livingston College, Rutgers, The State Univ New Jersey, New Brunswick

Cook, Sterling, *Coordr Mus Art Coll,* Miami Univ Art Center, Oxford, OH

Cooke, A Martin, *Supvr Art Instr,* Richmond Art Center, CA

Cooke, Edwy F, *Dir,* Concordia Univ, Montreal, PQ

Cooke, S Tucker, *Prof & Dir Summer School,* Univ North Carolina at Asheville

Cooke, Mrs Thomas Turner, *Regent,* Mt Vernon Ladies' Association, VA

Cooley, Marion, *Instr,* Miami Univ, Oxford, OH

Cooley, Nathan J, *Pres,* Greater Gary Arts Council, IN

Coolidge, Lawrence, *Chmn Trustees,* Longfellow's Wayside Inn, South Sudbury, MA

Coombs, K E, *Secy,* Municipal Art Commission, Kansas City, MO

Coomes, Charles, *Treas,* St Augustine Historical Society, FL

Coon, A W, *VPres Bd,* R W Norton Art Gallery, Shreveport, LA

Coon, Robert B, *Chmn Fine Arts Dept,* Kean College of New Jersey, Union

Coones, R C, *Mem Faculty,* Northeastern Oklahoma State Univ, Tahlequah

Cooney, James E, *Pres Bd Trustees,* Des Moines Art Center, IA

Cooney, John, *Vis Prof,* Case Western Reserve Univ, Cleveland, OH

Cooney, John D, *Research Cur Egyptian Art,* Cleveland Museum of Art, OH

Cooney, Kay, *Secy,* Allied Arts Council, Medicine Hat, AB

Cooney, Dr Stuart, *Dir Summer School,* California State College, Sonoma, Rohnert Park

Coonrod, Craig, *Gallery Coordr,* Rhode Island College Art Center Gallery, Providence

Cooper, Anna, *Librn,* Reynolda House, Winston-Salem, NC

Cooper, Bobby, *Head Dept,* Utica Junior College, MS

Cooper, Brian, *Registrar,* Royal College of Art Exhibitions, London, England

Cooper, Donna, *Librn,* McMichael Canadian Collection, Kleinburg, ON

Cooper, Edward, *Exec Dir,* Cambridge Art Association, MA

Cooper, Frederick A, *Prof,* Univ Minnesota, Minneapolis

Cooper, Ginny, *Children's Librn,* Hillsboro Public Library, OR

Cooper, Mrs Howard, *VChmn,* Massillon Museum, OH

Cooper, Dr John, *Dir Summer School,* California Lutheran College, Thousand Oaks

Cooper, Kathleen, *Cur Educ,* Indiana State Museum, Indianapolis

Cooper, Ken, *Community Serv Dir,* Gavilan College Art Gallery, Gilroy, CA

Cooper, Mario, *Pres,* American Watercolor Society, see National and Regional Organizations

Cooper, Mark, *Mgr Photograph Studio,* Metropolitan Museum of Art, New York, NY

Cooper, Maxine E, *Exec Secy,* Salem Art Association, OR

Cooper, Neloise, *Treas,* Buchanan Arts and Crafts, Buchanan Dam, TX

Cooper, Rhonda, *Registrar & Asst Cur Asian Art,* Dayton Art Inst Galleries, OH

Cooper, Willard, *Prof Art, Chmn Dept & Dir Summer School,* Centenary College of Louisiana, Shreveport

Cooper, William, *VPres,* Historical Society of Kent County, Chestertown, MD

Cope, Dr Garrett, *Second VPres,* Greater Gary Arts Council, IN

Cope, Mary M, *Librn,* Morris Raphael Cohen Library, City College of New York, NY

Copeland, Jane, *Annual Giving Coordr,* Philadelphia Museum of Art, PA

Copeley, William N, *Asst Librn,* New Hampshire Historical Society, Concord

Coplans, John, *Dir,* Akron Art Inst Museum, OH

Coppedge, Arthur, *Coordr of Exhib,* New Muse Community Museum of Brooklyn, NY

Coppock, William D, *Pres,* Cedar Rapids Art Center, IA

Coram, Richard D, *Mem Faculty,* Ottumwa Heights College, IA

Corbeil, John W, *Assoc Prof,* Pierce College, Woodland Hills, CA

Corbeil, Father Wilfrid, *Pres,* Musee D'Art de Joliette, PQ

Corbelletti, Raniero, *Head Dept Architecture,* Pennsylvania State Univ, University Park

Corbin, David C, *Pres,* Stan Hywet Hall Found, Akron, OH

Corbin, George, *Asst Prof,* Herbert H Lehman College, Bronx, NY

Corcoran, Audrey, *Secy,* California State Fair & Exposition Art Show, Sacramento

Corcoran, F, *Chief Educ & Cultural Affairs Div,* Nat Museum of Man, Ottawa, ON

Cordiner, William, *Assoc Prof,* Univ Northern Colorado, Greeley

Core, Gary, *Prof,* Western New Mexico Univ, Silver City

Corey, Peter L, *Dir/Cur,* Sheldon Jackson College Museum, Sitka, AK

Corey, Thomas, *Mem Faculty,* Swain School of Design, New Bedford, MA

Coris, Anna M, *Cur Early Italian Painting,* Nat Gallery of Art, Washington, DC

Corkery, Tim, *Vis Prof,* Univ Oregon, Eugene

Corlette, Suzanne, *Cur Cultural History,* New Jersey State Museum, Trenton

Corley, Suber, *VPres,* Centre for Experimental Art and Communication, Toronto, ON

Cormack, Malcolm, *Cur Paintings,* Yale Center for British Art, Yale University, New Haven, CT

Corn, Wanda, *Assoc Prof,* Mills College, Oakland, CA

Cornelius, Phil, *Area Chmn Ceramics,* Pasadena City College, CA

Cornell, Dorothy, *Dir,* River Vale Public Library, NJ

Cornell, Thomas, *Chmn,* Bowdoin College, Brunswick, ME

Corno, Gene, *Mem Faculty,* Mesa Community College, AZ

Corr, Jim, *Dir,* Western Montana College Art Gallery, Dillon

Correas, Horacio E, *Dir,* Museo Municipal de Bellas Artes Juan B Castagnino, Rosario, Argentina

Correia, Joaquim, *Dir,* Escola Superior de Belas Artes, Lisbon, Portugal

Correro, Guido, *Assoc Prof,* Herkimer County Community College, NY

Corrigan, Paul J, *Instr,* Modesto Junior College, CA

Corrigan, Robert W, *Dean,* Univ Wisconsin-Milwaukee

Corrigan, Ruth R, *Dir Univ Libraries,* Carnegie-Mellon Univ, Pittsburgh, PA

Corriveau, Ramona L, *Pres,* Springfield City Library, MA

Cortright, Elizabeth Rak, *Dir,* Copper Village Museum and Arts Center, Anaconda, MT

Cortright, Florence, *Admin Asst,* Copper Village Museum and Arts Center, Anaconda, MT

Corts, Thomas E, *Pres,* Wingate College, NC

Corwin, Beth, *Instr,* Laramie County Community College, Cheyenne, WY

Cory, John M, *Dir,* New York Public Library, NY

Cory, Ken, *Librn,* Western Montana College Art Gallery, Dillon

Cosentino, Andrew J, *Asst Prof,* Franklin and Marshall College, Lancaster, PA

Cossitt, F D, *Instr,* Virginia Wesleyan College, Norfolk; *Arts Consult,* Virginia Beach Arts Center

Costa, Germana Maria Camarao, *Librn,* Museu de Arte Moderna Brazil, Rio de Janeiro

Costa, Theodore, *Captain & Historian,* Staten Island Ferry Maritime Museum, NY

Costamagna, Alba, *Supvr & Dir Drawings & Prints,* Museo de Capodimonte, Naples, Italy

Costamagna, Marilyn, *Asst Librn,* Brand Library and Art Center, Glendale, CA

Costello, Michael, *Instr,* Univ Lowell, MA

Costigan, Constance C, *Asst Prof,* George Washington University, Washington, DC

Cotner, Lloyd, *Asst Prof,* Williamsport Area Community College, PA

Cotnoir, Kathryn L, *Asst Prof,* Miami Univ, Oxford, OH

Cotter, John L, *Assoc Cur in Charge,* American Historical Archaeology, Univ Pennsylvania Museum, Philadelphia

Cotton, Juanita, *Asst Prof,* Langston Univ, OK

Cottrill, Tom, *Chmn,* Northeastern Oklahoma State Univ, Tahlequah

Couch, Urban, *Chmn & Prof,* West Virginia Univ, Morgantown

Coughlin, Twyla, *VPres,* Southeast Alaska Regional Arts Council, Sitka

Coulling, S H, *Exec Dir,* Oglebay Inst Mansion Museum, Wheeling, WV

Coulter, Gary E, *Chmn Dept,* Hastings College, NE

Coulter, Jerry L, *Prof,* James Madison Univ, Harrisonburg, VA

Couper, Richard C, *Pres,* New York Public Library, NY

Court, Jane, *Information Asst,* Royal Ontario Museum, Toronto

Courtney, Sister Kathleen, *Lectr,* Mount Marty College, Yankton, SD

Courtney, Keith, *Community Relations,* Art Gallery of Hamilton, ON

Courtney, R Howard, *Sales & Rental Chmn,* Peoria Art Guild, IL

Couture, Sister Marie, *Chmn Dept,* Rivier College, Nashua, NH

Couture, Sister Theresa, *Mem Faculty,* Rivier College, Nashua, NH

Couturier, Darrel J, *Assoc Dir,* Couturier Galerie, Stamford, CT

Couturier, Marion B, *Dir,* Couturier Galerie, Stamford, CT

Couvee, D H, *Dir,* Frans Halsmuseum, Haarlem, Netherlands

Couvee-Jampoller, Mrs L, *Cur,* Rijksmuseum Vincent Van Gogh, Amsterdam, Netherlands

Coverstone, Jean L, *Assoc Prof Art, Head Dept & Dir Summer School,* Grace College, Winona Lake, IN

Covey, Victor, *Chief Conservator,* Nat Gallery of Art, Washington, DC

Covi, Dr Dario A, *Dir,* Allen R Hite Art Inst, Univ Louisville, KY

Cowan, Anita, *Asst,* Santa Cruz Public Library, CA

Cowan, Leonore, *Cur Picture Coll,* New York Public Library, NY

Cowardin, Samuel P, III, *Assoc Prof,* Clark Univ, Worcester, MA

Cowen, Allan H, *Assoc Dir,* Arts Council, Winston-Salem, NC

Cowles, Charles, *Cur,* Seattle Art Museum Modern Art Pavilion, WA

Cowles, Gardner, *VChmn,* Museum of Modern Art, New York, NY

Cowley, Edward, *Prof,* State Univ New York at Albany

Cox, Allyn, *Secy,* Associates of the Art Commission, New York, NY

Cox, Mrs C W, *Registrar,* Frick Art Museum, Pittsburgh, PA

Cox, David N, *Asst Prof,* Weber State College, Ogden, UT

Cox, Dennis, *Artist-in-Residence,* Pacific Lutheran Univ, Tacoma, WA

Cox, Elinor, *Recorder,* Miniature Painters, Sculptors and Gravers Society of Washington, DC

Cox, J W S, *Pres,* New England School of Art and Design, Boston, MA

Cox, James, *Gallery Mgr,* Grand Central Art Galleries, New York, NY

Cox, James A, *Head Dept,* Limestone College, Gaffney, SC

Cox, Joseph L, III, *Assoc Prof,* Miami Univ, Oxford, OH

Cox, Lorraine, *Treas,* Nat Hall of Fame for Famous American Indians, Anadarko, OK

Cox, Marvel, *Mem Faculty,* Sioux City Art Center, IA

Cox, Paul, *Chmn,* Orange Coast College, Costa Mesa, CA

Cox, Yvonne, *Textile Conservator,* Isabella Stewart Gardner Museum, Boston, MA

Coxwell, Roy, *Pres,* Desert Caballeros Western Museum, Wickenburg, AZ

Coyle, Sister M Berchmanns, *Dir Summer School,* College of White Plains of Pace Univ, NY

Coyne, Alice, *Corresp Secy,* New Hampshire Art Association, Manchester

Coyne, Kathleen, *Pres,* Victoria Society of Maine Women, Portland

Coz, Beverly, *Cur Exhib,* Nat Portrait Gallery, Washington, DC

Cozzi, Ciriaco, *VPres,* Provincetown Art Association and Museum, MA

Cozzie, Anthony F, *Dir,* Roswell P Flower Mem Library, Watertown, NY

Crabb, Patrick, *Instr,* Santa Ana College, CA

Crabb, Ted, *Dir & Secy,* Univ Wisconsin-Madison Mem Union

Craddick, Jan, *Exec Dir,* Southeast Alaska Regional Arts Council, Sitka

Craffert, D, *Professional Asst,* Pretoria Art Museum, South Africa

Craft, J R, *Dir,* Richland Art Workshop of the Columbia Museum of Art, SC

Cragin, Mrs John, *Secy,* Spiva Art Center, Joplin, MO

Craig, Christina, *Asst Prof,* Trenton State College, NJ

Craig, Dan, *Instr,* Northeast Technical Community College, Norfolk, NE

Craig, James, *Pres,* Community Arts Council of Vancouver, BC

Craig, Kenneth, *Operations Supvr,* Alberta College of Art, Calgary

Craig, Yvonne, *Registrar,* Beaumont Art Museum, TX

Crain, John W, *Dir,* Dallas Historical Society, TX

Crain, Sally, *VPres,* Cumberland Art Society, TN

Cramer, Richard D, *Prof & Head Dept,* Univ California, Davis

Crammer, Dana, *Technical Mgr,* Solomon R Guggenheim Museum, New York, NY

Crandall, James, *Asst Prof,* Pierce College, Woodland Hills, CA

Crandall, William, *Instr,* Milwaukee Area Technical College, WI

Crane, Charles, *Assoc Prof,* Univ Lethbridge, AB

Crane, Frances, *Pres,* Winnipeg Sketch Club, MB

Crane, Howard, *Chmn Dept History of Art,* Ohio State Univ, Columbus

Crane, Tim, *Assoc Prof,* Viterbo College, La Crosse, WI

Crangle, Mrs William, *Pres,* Canajoharie Library and Art Gallery, NY

Crary, Miner D, Jr, *Chmn Bd Trustees,* Heckscher Museum, Huntington, NY

Craven, Roy C, Jr, *Dir,* Univ Florida Gallery, Gainesville

Crawford, Barbara, *In-House Gallery Chair,* Women in the Arts Found, New York, NY

Crawford, Carol, *Pub Relations,* The Exhibitionists, Jamaica, NY

Crawford, David, *Chmn Bd,* Vermont State Craft Center at Frog Hollow, Middlebury

Crawford, Donald D, *Dir,* Lauren Rogers Library and Museum of Art, Laurel, MS

Crawford, J J, *Pres,* Strasburg Museum, VA

Crawford, Margaret, *Assoc Prof,* Nazareth College of Rochester, NY

Crawford, Robert, *Dir,* Ridgewood School of Art and Design, NJ

Crawford, Spencer, *Instr,* East Tennessee State Univ, Johnson City

Crawford, Vaughn E, *Cur in Charge Ancient Near Eastern Art,* Metropolitan Museum of Art, New York, NY

Crawley, Carla, *Cur,* Mount Holyoke College Art Museum, South Hadley, MA

Crawshay, Sir William, *Pres Colonel,* Nat Museum of Wales, Cardiff

Creagan, Daniel A, *Chmn & Assoc Prof,* Spring Hill College, Mobile, AL

Creager, Marile, *Asst Dir,* Tacoma Public Library, WA

Creech, Franklin U, *Head & Dir Summer School,* Gaston College, Dallas, NC

Creeden, Mrs John, *VPres,* Mount Holyoke College Art Museum, South Hadley, MA

Creel, Dana S, *Pres,* Sleepy Hollow Restorations, Tarrytown, NY

Crelly, William R, *Prof,* Emory Univ, Atlanta, GA

Cress, George, *Head & Prof,* Univ Tennessee at Chattanooga

Cressotti, Frank, *Head,* Holyoke Community College, MA

Cresswell, Pearl, *Asst to Cur,* Fisk Univ Museum, Nashville, TN

Cretara, Dominec, *Chmn Fine Arts Dept,* Art Inst of Boston, MA

Crew, Roger T, Jr, *Research Asst,* MacArthur Mem, Norfolk, VA

Crewe, Leonard C, Jr, *Pres,* Maryland Historical Society Museum, Baltimore

Crews, Polly, *Dir,* Fort Smith Art Center, AR

Cridge, Edmund, *Head Media Serv,* Elmer E Rasmuson Library, Univ Alaska Museum, Fairbanks

Crighton, R, *Keeper Applied Arts,* Fitzwilliam Museum, Univ Cambridge, England

Crimmins, Gerald, *Chmn Sculpture/Metalsmithing,* Moore College of Art, Philadelphia, PA

Crimmons, Allen, *First VPres,* Canadian Guild of Potters, see National Organizations of Canada

Crisp, Lynn P, *Asst Librn,* North Carolina State Univ Design Library, Raleigh

Crispino, Luigi, *Chmn Dept,* Franklin College, IN

Criswell, Grover C, *Pres Col,* American Numismatic Association, see National and Regional Organizations

Critchfield, Harry, *Instr,* California College of Arts and Crafts, Oakland

Crockett, Richard B, *Pres Bd Dirs,* Plains Art Museum & Rourke Art Gallery, Moorhead, MN

Cronenwett, Philip N, *Cur,* Jones Library, Amherst, MA

Cronin, Francis X, *Dir Summer School,* Chamberlayne Junior College, Boston, MA

Cronk, Frank, *Assoc Prof,* Univ Idaho, Moscow

Crook, J, *Head Dept,* Three-Dimensional Design, Brighton Polytechnic, England

Crooker, M J A, *Assoc Prof,* Mount Allison University, Sackville, NB

Crosby, Ranice W, *Assoc Prof Art as Applied to Med & Dir Dept,* Johns Hopkins Univ, Baltimore, MD

Crosby, Thomas M, Jr, *Chmn Bd,* Walker Art Center, Minneapolis, MN

Cross, Frank Moore, Jr, *Dir,* Semitic Museum, Harvard Univ, Cambridge, MA

Cross, Vera L, *Dir,* Attleboro Museum, MA

Crossgrove, Robert, *Prof,* Univ Connecticut, Storrs

Crossnoe, Thomas G, *Chmn,* Midwestern State Univ, Wichita Falls, TX

Crouch, Pinny, *Dir,* Ships of the Sea Museum, Savannah, GA

Crouse, Jack W, *Mem Faculty,* Olympic College, Bremerton, WA

Crow, Kenneth V, *Mem Faculty,* Olympic College, Bremerton, WA

Crow, Martha, *Instr,* Avila College, Kansas City, MO

Crowder, Charles, *Dir Music,* Phillips Collection, Washington, DC

Crowe, Angus, *Acting Chmn Interior Design,* New England School of Art and Design, Boston, MA

Crowell, Cathy Cherry, *Instr,* Newberry College, SC

Crowfoot, H L, *Dir,* Jordan Historical Museum of the Twenty, ON

Crowley, Jane Sullivan, *Dir,* Morris-Jumel Mansion, New York, NY

Crowley, Pat, *Dir,* Texas Christian Univ Student Center Gallery, Fort Worth

Crown, William, III, *Treas,* Florida Gulf Coast Art Center, Clearwater

Croydon, Michael, *Prof,* Lake Forest College, IL

Crozier, John, *Librn,* Santa Barbara Museum of Art, CA

Cruger, George, *Head Publ Dept,* Virginia Museum of Fine Arts, Richmond

Crumer, Jim, *Instr,* Univ South Carolina, Columbia

Crumpacker, Anne, *VPres,* Contemporary Crafts Association and Gallery, Portland, OR

Crumpler, Reva, *Communications Officer,* J B Speed Art Museum, Louisville, KY

Cruser, Patricia, *Dept Chairperson & Dean Liberal Arts,* Philadelphia College of Art, PA

Cruz, Luis Hernandez, *Head Dept,* Univ Puerto Rico, Rio Piedras

Cruz, Maria Socorro, *Prof,* Inst of Puerto Rican Culture, San Juan

CuBose, Mrs E H, *Pres,* San Antonio Art League, TX

Cudebec, Sonsa, *Dir Summer School,* Dept of Youth, Recreation and Cultural Resources, Fredericton, NB

Cuhovski, P, *Pro-Rector & Prof,* Nikolaj Pavlovic Higher Institute of Fine Arts, Sofia, Bulgaria

Culbertson, Dr George E, *Dir Summer School,* Clinch Valley College of Univ Virginia, Wise

Culler, Elizabeth, *Registrar & Asst Cur,* Virginia Museum of Fine Arts, Richmond

Culley, Paul T, *Head Technical Reference,* New York State College of Ceramics at Alfred Univ

Culverwell, Albert H, *Dir,* Eastern Washington State Historical Society, Spokane

Cumming, Doug, *Assoc Prof,* Univ Wisconsin-Stout, Menomonie

Cumming, Glen E, *Dir,* Art Gallery of Hamilton, ON

Cumming, William, *Mem Faculty,* Burnley School of Professional Art, Seattle, WA

Cummings, Abbott L, *Exec Dir,* Society for the Preservation of New England Antiquities, Boston, MA

Cummings, Frederick J, *Exec Dir,* Detroit Inst of Art Collections, MI

Cummings, George, *Instr,* Museum Art School, Portland, OR

Cummings, H W, *VPres,* Stained Glass Association of America, see National and Regional Organizations

Cummings, Nancy, *Young People's Coordr,* Clark County Library District Art Activities, Las Vegas, NV

Cummings, Paul, *Cur,* Whitney Museum of American Art, New York, NY

Cummins, Karen, *Asst Dir,* New Jersey State Museum, Trenton

Cunkle, Elisabeth, *Librn,* Anne Bremer Mem Library, San Francisco Art Inst, CA

Cunliffe, Nanette, *Mem Staff,* Rehoboth Art League, Rehoboth Beach, DE

Cunningham, David, *Supvr Exhib Prod,* Glenbow-Alberta Inst, Calgary, AB

Cunningham, John, *Pres & Dir,* Carmel Art Inst, CA

Cunningham, Linda, *Asst Prof,* Franklin and Marshall College, Lancaster, PA

Cunningham, Matthew, *Student Dir,* Sampson Art Gallery, Thiel College, Greenville, PA

Cunningham, Robert, *Asst Dir,* Queensland Art Gallery, Brisbane, Australia

Cunningham, Robert G, *Teacher,* Venice Painting, Drawing & Sculpture Studio, CA

Cunningham, Roland C, *Conservator,* Wadsworth Atheneum, Hartford, CT

Curlee, Barbara B, *Chmn,* Northeast Mississippi Junior College, Booneville

Currier, Mary Ann, *Mem Staff,* Louisville School of Art, Anchorage, KY

Currin, John L, *Counselor & Secy,* American Red Cross, see National and Regional Organizations

Curry, Crossan H, *Assoc Prof,* Miami Univ, Oxford, OH

Curry, David, *Instr,* Sacramento City College, CA

Curry, Larry J, *Cur American Art,* Detroit Inst of Art Collections, MI

Curry, Sylvia, *Pres Bd Dir,* Art Gallery of Windsor, ON

Curtis, Mrs. Floyd E, *Pres,* Phillips County Museum, Helena, AR

Curtis, George H, *Asst Dir,* Harry S Truman Library and Museum, Independence, MO

Curtis, Howard W, *Cur,* Haverhill Public Library, MA

Curtis, John O, *Dir Cur Dept,* Old Sturbridge Village, MA

Curtis, Nelson, *Prof,* Univ Idaho, Moscow

Curtis, Phillip H, *Cur Decorative Arts,* Newark Museum, NJ

Curtis, Roger, *Treas,* North Shore Arts Association, Gloucester, MA

Curtis, Samuel L, *Chmn Dept,* Cheyney State College, PA

Curtis, Tom, *Pres,* Association of American Editorial Cartoonists, see National and Regional Organizations

Curtis, Verna, *Asst Cur,* Milwaukee Art Center, WI

Curtis, Walter D, *Asst Prof,* Univ Arkansas, Fayetteville

Curtiss, Harold M, *Pres,* Sheldon Art Museum, Middlebury, VT

Cushing, Barbara, *Prof,* Univ Maine, Orono

Cushing, John D, *Librn,* Massachusetts Historical Society, Boston

Cushing, Stanley E, *Librn,* Guild of Book Workers, see National and Regional Organizations

Cutler, Anthony, *Prof,* Pennsylvania State Univ, University Park

Cutler, John, *Pres,* Providence Art Club, RI

Cutshaw, Mrs Michael, *Cur,* West Baton Rouge Museum, Port Allen, LA

Cutting, Gregory, *Asst City Librn,* Hillsboro Public Library, OR

Cygan, Henry, *Guide,* Polish Museum of America, Chicago, IL

Czach, Marie, *Dir,* Western Illinois Univ Art Gallery, Macomb

Czarnecki, James, *Vis Prof,* State Univ New York College at Potsdam

Czarniecki, M J, III, *Dir,* Mississippi Museum of Art, Jackson

Czerwinski, Edward, *Develop Mgr,* Brooklyn Museum, NY

Czestochowski, Joseph S, *Dir,* Maryland Inst College of Art, Baltimore

Czichos, Raymond L, *Dir,* Pioneer Town, Wimberley, TX

Czobor, Dr A, *Head Prints & Drawings,* Szepmuveszet Muzeum, Budapest, Hungary

Czuma, Stanislaw, *Cur Indian Art,* Cleveland Museum of Art, OH

Dabash, Adrian G, *Mem Faculty,* Providence College, RI

Daehnert, Richard H, *Asst Prof,* Univ Tennessee, Knoxville

Dafoe, Marilyn, *Assoc Prof,* Middle Tennessee State Univ, Murfreesboro

Dagenais, Margaret, *Prof,* Loyola Univ Chicago, IL

Dages, Alan, *Historic Site Mgr,* New York State Dept of Parks and Recreation, Hudson

Dahl, Rex, *Dir Summer School,* Montana State Univ, Bozeman

Dahlback, Dr Bengt, *Dir,* Nationalmuseum, Stockholm, Sweden

Dahlen, Marilyn, *Secy,* Coquille Valley Art Association, OR

Dahlstrom, Nancy, *Asst Prof,* Hollins College, VA

Dahoda, Peter, *Prof & Dir Summer School,* Miami Univ, Oxford, OH

Dailey, Charles, *Dir,* Inst of American Indian Arts Museum, Santa Fe, NM

Dailey, Dan, *Chmn Fine Arts/3D,* Massachusetts College of Art, Boston

Daily, May Ann, *Dir of Pub Relations,* Walters Art Gallery, Baltimore, MD

Daitzman, Eleanor, *Admin Dir & Dir Summer School,* Mainline Center of the Arts, Haverford, PA

Dake, Dennis, *Coordr Art Educ,* Iowa State Univ, Ames

Dakus, Ms C, *Librn,* Edmonton Art Gallery, AB

Dale, Donald, *Dir Summer School,* Concordia College, Moorhead, MN

Dale, Gary, *Media Center Technical Dir,* Library and Media Center, MINNEAPOLIS College of Art and Design, MN

Dalenius, Marjory, *Gallery Secy,* Providence Art Club, RI

Daley, Kenneth G, *Chmn Studio,* Old Dominion Univ, Norfolk, VA

Dallavis, Sister Olive Louise, *Pres,* Avila College Art Gallery, Kansas City, MO

Dalrymple, Mrs Byron W, *Pres,* Hill Country Arts Found, Ingram, TX

Dalton, Mrs Charles R, *Pres,* Irene Leache Mem Association, Norfolk, VA

Dalton, Mary, *Supvr Media Contact,* Midland Art Council of the Midland Center for the Arts, MI

Daltrop, Georg, *Cur Classical Art (Greek & Roman Sculpture),* Monumenti Musei e Gallerie Pontificie, Vatican City, Italy

DaLuiso, Florence S, *Art Librn,* Lockwood Mem Library, State Univ New York at Buffalo

Daly, Dr Charles, *Mem Faculty,* College of New Rochelle, NY

Daly, Florence, *Pres,* Kennebec Valley Art Association, Hallowell, ME

Daly, Gail F, *Cur Asst,* Dept of State Diplomatic Reception Rooms, Washington, DC

Daly, Russell, *Mem Faculty,* Swain School of Design, New Bedford, MA

Damianos, Sylvester, *Pres,* Pittsburgh Plan for Art, PA

Dampman, Allan, *Dir Summer School,* Sullivan County Community College, Loch Sheldrake, NY

Dana, Carol S, *Secy,* Joe and Emily Lowe Art Gallery, Syracuse Univ, NY

D'Anato, Juliana, *Prof,* Albertus Magnus College, New Haven, CT

Dandenault, Sara, *Asst to Dir,* Battle Creek Civic Art Center, MI

D'Andrea, Jeanne, *Cur Exhib and Publ,* Los Angeles County Museum of Art, CA

Dane, William J, *Supvr Art & Music Dept,* Newark Public Library, NJ

Daner, Judy, *Instr,* Craft Center, Worcester, MA

D'Angelo, George, *Pres,* Philadelphia Art Alliance, PA

Daniel, Betty, *Libr Records,* Washington Univ Gallery of Art, St Louis, MO

Daniel, Keith, *Instr,* Assumption College, Worchester, MA

Daniel, Suzanne, *Asst Prof,* Morgan State Univ, Baltimore, MD

Daniels, Dan, *Dir Pub Relations,* M Grumbacher, Inc, New York, NY see Corporate Art Holdings

Daniels, John P, *Head Educ & State Serv,* John and Mable Ringling Museum of Art, Sarasota, FL

Daniels, Linda M, *Asst,* Providence Public Library, RI

Daniels, Mickey, *Third VPres,* Arizona Watercolor Association, Phoenix

Daniels, Ronald B, *Chief Pub Serv,* Bucknell Univ, Lewisburg, PA

Daniels, Sarah, *AV Cur,* Atlanta College of Art Library, GA

Danielson, J Deering, *Chmn Bd Govs,* Metropolitan Museum and Art Centers, Coral Gables, FL

Danne, Richard, *Pres,* American Inst of Graphic Arts, see National and Regional Organizations

Dannerth, Mary Larkin, *Registrar,* Spertus Museum of Judaica, Chicago, IL

Dannials, Earnie, *Prog Adv,* Univ Southwestern Louisiana Union Art Gallery, Lafayette

Danoff, I Michael, *Assoc Dir,* Milwaukee Art Center, WI

Danson, Dr Edward B, *Pres Bd Trustees,* Museum of Northern Arizona, Flagstaff

Danzker-Birnie, Jo-Anne, *Cur,* Vancouver Art Gallery, BC

Daoud, Rihab, *Librn,* Nat Museum of Damascus, Syria

Dar, Dr Saifur Rahman, *Dir,* Lahore Museum, Pakistan

Darby, Norma, *Acquisitions Comt,* Owatonna Arts Center, MN

d'Argencourt, Louise, *Asst Cur European Art,* Nat Gallery of Canada, Ottawa, ON

D'Arista, Robert A, *Dir, Watkins Gallery & Chmn Art Dept,* American Univ, Washington, DC

Darke, M H, *Head Dept Environ Design,* Manchester Polytechnic, England

Darling, Sharon, *Decorative Arts,* Chicago Historical Society, IL

Darr, William, *Prof,* Drake Univ, Des Moines, IA

Darr, William, *Co-Dir SACI Prog,* Studio Art Centers International, Florence, Italy

Darrow, Cal, *Dir Summer School,* College of Marin, Kentfield, CA

Darrow, Dr Harriett, *Dir Summer School,* Indiana State Univ, Terre Haute

Darrow, James F, *Asst Prof,* Univ Tennessee, Knoxville

Darrow, Paul, *Prof,* Scripps College, Claremont, CA

Daschbach, Catherine, *Treas,* San Bernardino Art Association, CA

da Silva Guimaraes, Margardia Maria Barbosa, *Chief Technical Dept,* Museu Nacional de Belas Artes, Rio de Janeiro, Brazil

Daste, Nowell A, *Head Dept,* McNeese State Univ, Lake Charles, LA

D'Atri, E Lang, *Pres,* Canton Art Inst, OH

Dattell, Michael, *Dir Advertising & Graphic Design,* Acad of Art College, San Francisco, CA

Datus, Jay, *Dir,* Kachina School of Art, Phoenix, AZ

Daube, Mrs Leon, *Pres,* Charles B Goddard Center for the Visual & Performing Arts, Ardmore, OK

Daugherty, Charles, *Asst Prof,* Pomona College, Claremont, CA

Daugherty, Frances P, *Chmn Art History,* East Carolina Univ, Greenville, NC

Daugherty, Marshall, *Chmn,* Mercer Univ, Macon, GA

Daum, Timothy, *Asst Art Librn,* Ohio Univ Seigfred Gallery, Athens

Dauterman, Carl C, *Consult for Decorative Arts,* Univ Illinois, Champaign

D'Avanzo, Suzanne H, *Mem Faculty,* Providence College, RI

Dave, Teresa, *Instr,* Al Gable Advertising Art School, Cincinnati, OH

Davenport, Patricia, *Cur Educ,* El Paso Museum of Art, TX

Davenport, William H, *Cur Oceanian Section,* Univ Pennsylvania Museum, Philadelphia

Davern, Ms Jeremyn, *Pub Affairs Dir,* Grand Central Art Galleries, New York, NY

Davezac, Bertrand, *Assoc Prof,* Pennsylvania State Univ, University Park

Davi, Susan A, *Art & History Ref Librn,* Morris Library, Univ Delaware, Newark

David, Agnes, *Pres,* Associated Artists of Winston-Salem, NC

David, Ann, *Admin Cur,* Winnipeg Art Gallery, MB

David Haas, *Asst Prof,* Univ Northern Colorado, Greeley

David, Honore S, *Chmn Educ Dept,* Dayton Art Inst Galleries, OH

Davidian, David, *Pres,* Art Directors Club, see National and Regional Organizations

Davidock, Peter, *Registrar,* Nat Gallery of Art, Washington, DC

Davids, Ken, *Dir Summer School,* California College of Arts and Crafts, Oakland

Davidson, Bernice, *Research Cur,* Frick Collection, New York, NY

Davidson, Carl Melvin, *Dean Col Fine & Communication Arts,* Loyola Marymount Univ, Los Angeles, CA

Davidson, Chuck, *Communication Design Chmn,* Art Center College of Design, Pasadena, CA

Davidson, Herbert, *Cur Exhib,* Museum of Art, Science and Industry, Bridgeport, CT

Davidson, Jacqueline, *Instr,* Ocean City School of Art, NJ

Davidson, Karen, *Staff Asst,* Busch-Reisinger Museum, Harvard Univ, Cambridge, MA

Davidson, Kay M, *Instr,* Leeward Community College, Pearl City, HI

Davidson, Marilyn, *Secy,* Windward Artists Guild, Lihue, HI

Davidson, Patsy, *Coordr,* Lincoln Community Arts Council, NE

Davidson, Robert, *Dir Summer School,* State Univ New York at New Paltz

Davidson, Robert, *Cur,* Nat Cowboy Hall of Fame, Oklahoma City, OK

Davidson, S Leonard, *Treas,* Inter-Society Color Council, see National and Regional Organizations

Daviee, Jerry M, *Cur Art,* Amarillo Art Center, TX

Davies, Cynthia, *Cur Harvey Coll,* Heard Museum, Phoenix, AZ

Davies, Hugh M, *Dir,* Univ Massachusetts Gallery, Amherst

Davies, James, *Dean Summer School,* Nova Scotia College of Art and Design, Halifax

Davies, W A Twiston, *VPres,* Nat Museum of Wales, Cardiff

Davila, Arturo, *Prof,* Puerto Rican Culture, San Juan

Davis, Jack, *Chmn Dept Fine Arts & Chmn Summer Schools,* Beaver College, Glenside, PA

Davis, Ann Marie, *Co-Dir,* Tyringham Art Galleries, MA

Davis, Art, *Asst Prof,* Grace College, Winona Lake, IN

Davis, Caecilia, *Assoc Chmn Art History,* Tulane Univ, New Orleans, LA

Davis, H Chace, Jr, *Treas,* Peale Museum, Baltimore, MD

Davis, Charles W, *Acting Head,* Univ Alaska, Fairbanks

Davis, Colis, Jr, *Dir Photography,* Hampton Association for the Arts and Humanities, VA

Davis, Colonius, *Prof,* Southampton College of Long Island Univ, NY

Davis, Constance, *Asst Prof,* McNeese State Univ, Lake Charles, LA

Davis, D Jack, *Chmn & Prof,* North Texas State Univ, Denton

Davis, Darwin R, *Dir,* Battle Creek Civic Art Center, MI

Davis, Donald, *Co-Dir,* Tyringham Art Galleries, MA

Davis, Dustin P, *Dir,* Frostburg State College, MD

Davis, Jack, *Chmn Dept Fine Arts,* Beaver College, Glenside, PA

Davis, Jack, *Dir Summer School,* Oklahoma City Univ, OK

Davis, Joan C, *Dir,* Bob Jones Univ, Greenville, SC

Davis, John E, *Lectr,* Ladycliff College, Highland Falls, NY

Davis, Larry H, *Asst Prof,* Midwestern State Univ, Wichita Falls, TX

Davis, Lee Baxter, *Chmn Graphics,* East Texas State Univ, Commerce

Davis, Leo R, *Assoc Prof,* Univ Arkansas, Fayetteville

Davis, Lin, *Librn,* Springfield Art Museum, MO

Davis, Linda, *Secy,* Clark County Historical Society, Springfield, OH

Davis, Marian B, *Cur,* Art Museum, Austin, TX

Davis, Marion, *Librn,* Florida Gulf Coast Art Center, Clearwater

Davis, Marsha, *Secy,* Hockaday Center for the Arts, Kalispell, MT

Davis, Mary B, *Librn,* Huntington Free Library and Reading Room, Bronx, NY

Davis, Nell, *Dir Emer,* Lauren Rogers Library and Museum of Art, Laurel, MS

Davis, Paul, *Instr,* Saginaw Valley State College, University Center, MI

Davis, Paul, *Assoc Prof,* Univ Utah, Salt Lake City

Davis, Robert Spink, *VPres,* Providence Athenaeum, RI

Davis, Sue, *Secy,* Waterloo Art Association, IA

Davis, T Peter, *Develop Dir,* Studio Museum in Harlem, New York, NY

Davis, Virginia Irby, *Asst Prof,* Lynchburg College, VA

Davis, Wayne, *Mem Faculty,* Rudolph Schaeffer School of Design, San Francisco, CA

Davis, Wes, *Dir Univ Center,* Angelo State Univ Center, San Angelo, TX

Davis, William D, *Asst Dir,* Pennsylvania State Univ Museum of Art, University Park

Davis, Willis H, *Assoc Prof,* Miami Univ, Oxford, OH

Daw, Robert H, *Fine Arts Chmn,* Topeka Public Library, KS

Dawkings, Jimmie, *Instr,* Alabama A&m Univ, Huntsville

Dawley, Gisela, *Owner-Instr,* Gisela Dawley Art Studio, Simi Valley, CA

Dawson, Bess, *Dir,* Mississippi Art Colony, Meridian

Dawson, Dr John M, *Dir of Libraries,* Norris Library, Univ Delaware, Newark

Dawson, Nelson L, *Ed History Quarterly,* Filson Club, Louisville, KY

Dawson, Robert, *Dir Pub Relations,* Greenfield Village and Henry Ford Museum, Dearborn, MI

Dawson, Robert, *Chmn,* Massillon Museum, OH

Day, Ann, *Asst Cur Educ Serv,* Univ Utah Museum of Fine Arts, Salt Lake City

Day, David, *Instr,* Wayne Art Center, PA

Day, J Dennis, *Dir,* Salt Lake City Public Library, UT

Day, Jean, *Secy,* Coos Art Museum, Coos Bay, OR

Day, Jill R, *Gallery Coordr,* Rogue Vallery Art Association, Medford, OR

Day, John A, *Chmn,* Univ South Dakota, Vermillion

Day, Maurice, *VPres,* Pemaquid Group of Artists, Pemaquid Point, ME

Day, Melvin N, *Dir,* Nat Art Gallery of New Zealand, Wellington

Day, Patrice Jones, *Develop Officer,* Museum of Fine Arts, Houston, TX

Day, Philip A, Jr, *Acting Chmn,* Westminster College, Salt Lake City, UT

Day, William, *Deputy Dir,* Studio Museum in Harlem, New York, NY

Dayton, Patricia, *Cur Asst CETA,* Anderson Fine Arts Center, IN

Deaderickm, Joseph, *Prof,* Univ Wyoming, Laramie

de Montebello, Philippe, *Dir,* Metropolitan Museum of Art, New York, NY

Demow, Annette, *Secy,* C W Post Center of Long Island Univ, Greenvale, NY

Dempsey, Bruce H, *Dir,* Jacksonville Art Museum, FL

Dempsey, Charles, *Chmn Dept,* Bryn Mawr College, PA

Dempsey, Hugh, *Chief Cur,* Glenbow-Alberta Inst, Calgary, AB

Dempsey, John P, *Assoc Prof,* Univ Alabama in Huntsville

de Narvaez, Martha M, *Cur Manuscripts & Rare Books,* Hispanic Society of America Library, New York, NY

de Nave, F, *Asst Dir,* Stedelijk Prentenkabinet, Antwerp, Belgium; *Asst Dir,* Museum Plantin-Moretus, Antwerp, Belgium

Den Blauwen, Dr A L, *Dir Dept Decorative Arts,* Rijksmuseum Amsterdam, Netherlands

Denby, Gregory, *Preparator,* Univ Notre Dame Art Gallery, IN

Dengate, James, *Cur Numismatics,* World Heritage Museum, Univ Illinois at Urbana-Champaign, Urbana

Dengler, Eartha, *Asst Librn,* Merrimack Valley Textile Museum, North Andover, MA

den Hartog, Simon H, *Dir,* Gerrit Rietveld Academie, Amsterdam, Netherlands

Denison, Cara D, *Assoc Cur Drawings & Prints,* Pierpont Morgan Library, New York, NY

Denison, Jacqueline, *Cur Exhib,* Putnam Museum, Davenport, IA

Dennard, William, *Instr,* School of Art, Museum of Fine Arts, Houston, TX

Denning, Catherine, *Research Asst,* Annmary Brown Memorial, Brown Univ, Providence, RI

Dennis, David, *Installation Coordr,* Univ Iowa Museum of Art, Iowa City

Dennis, James, *Prof,* Univ Wisconsin, Madison

Dennis, Terry, *Prof,* Rochester Community College, MN

Dennison, Keith E, *Dir,* Pioneer Museum and Haggin Galleries, Stockton, CA

Dennison, Nan, *Asst to Dir,* Henry Morrison Flagler Museum, Palm Beach, FL

Denny, Paul, Jr, *Assoc Prof,* Phillips Univ, Enid, OK

Denton, Lynn, *Lectr,* Saint Joseph's College, Philadelphia, PA

Denton, Monroe A, Jr, *Dir,* Muhlenberg College Center for the Arts, PA

Denton, Mrs Spencer, *Dir,* Five Civilized Tribes Museum, Muskogee, OK

Dentzel, Carl, *Pres,* Cultural Heritage Board, City of Los Angeles Municipal Arts Dept, CA

Denza, Susan Makov, *Lectr,* Weber State College, Ogden, UT

de Orlov, Lino S Lipinsky, *Cur History,* John Jay Homestead, Katonah, NY

DePaolis, Gloria, *Asst Prof,* Pennsylvania State Univ, Uniontown

dePeyster, Mrs James A, *VPres,* Society of the Four Arts, Palm Beach, FL

DePillars, Murry N, *Dean,* Virginia Commonwealth Univ, Richmond

De Poorter, Nora, *Asst Keeper,* Rubenianum, Antwerp, Belgium

DePopolo, Margaret, *Librn,* Rotch Library of Architecture and Planning, Massachusetts Inst of Technology, Cambridge

DeRensis, Jean, *Asst Dir/Operations,* Forbes Street Gallery, Carnegie-Mellon Univ, Pittsburgh, PA

Derer, F J, *Exec Secy,* West Bend Gallery of Fine Arts, WI

Derga, Malinda, *Secy,* Paint 'N' Palette Club, Anamosa, IA

der Heiden, Dr Rudiger, *Dir German Baroque Paintings,* Bayerischen Staatsgemaldesammlungen, Munich, Germany

Derkowski, Jerzy, *V-Rector & Reader,* Panstwowa Wyzsza Szkola Sztuk Plastycznych, Lodz, Poland

Dern, Mrs James, *Secy,* Canajoharie Library and Art Gallery, NY

de Roo, Rene, *Cur,* Musees Royaux D'Art et D'Histoire, Brussels, Belgium

Derr, Bernard L, *Chmn Art Dept,* Earlham College, Richmond, IN

de Salas Y Bosch, Xavier, *Dir,* Museo del Prado, Madrid, Spain

De Samper, Hugh, *Dir Press Bur,* Colonial Williamsburg Found, VA

De Saracho, Lorenzo Hurtado, *Pres,* Museo de Bellas Artes, Bilbao, Spain

De Savoye, Janni, *Exec Asst,* Visual Arts Ontario, Toronto

Deshaies, Arthur, *Prof,* Florida State Univ, Tallahassee

Deshaies, Ruth Dryden, *Chmn Art Prog,* Tallahassee Community College, FL

Deshayes, J, *Dir,* Univ Paris I at the Sorbonne, Inst of Art and Archaeology, France

Deshler, I, *Admin Asst,* Association of Collegiate Schools of Architecture, see National and Regional Organizations

de Silva, Dr P H D H, *Dir,* Colombo Nat Museum, Sri Lanka

Desisso, Janet, *Asst Dir,* Store Front Museum, Jamaica, NY

Des Jardins, Doris, *Secy,* Oakland Univ, Rochester, MI

Deslandes, G, *Keeper Art,* Dundee Museums and Art Gallery, Scotland

DeSloover, Rose, *Asst Prof,* Marygrove College, Detroit, MI

DeSota, Raoul, MA, *Assoc Prof,* Los Angeles City College, CA

DeSpain, Joseph, *Instr,* Campbellsville College, KY

Desportes, Ulysse, *Head Dept & Prof,* Mary Baldwin College, Staunton, VA

Despres, Marian A, *Pres Bd Trustees,* Chicago Architecture Found, IL

DesRosiers, Roger, *Dean School,* Washington Univ, Saint Louis, MO

Desser, Maxwell, *Secy,* American Watercolor Society, see National and Regional Organizations

de Suduiraut, S Guillot, *Asst Conservator,* Musee des Beaux-Arts, Tours, France

De Temple, Jean, *Asst Dir,* Ottawa Public Library, ON

Detmer, Mrs Howard F, *VPres,* Victoria Society of Maine Women, Portland, ME

Detmers, William, *Chmn Art Educ Prog,* Herron School of Art, Indiana Univ-Purdue Univ, Indianapolis

de Trezabal, Pilar de la Fuente, *Museography,* Museo de San Carlos, Mexico City, Mexico

Dettler, Kerwin E, *Dean,* New York School of Interior Design, NY

Detwiller, Frederic C, *Archit Historian,* Society for the Preservation of New England Antiquities, Boston, MA

Deulovol, Frederico Mares, *Prof & Dir,* Escuela Superior de Bellas Artes de San Jorge, Barcelona, Spain

Deussen, Claire Isaacs, *Dir,* Junior Art Center, Los Angeles, CA

Deutsch, Mrs Allen, *VPres,* Womens City Club of Cleveland, OH

de Vazquez, Sandra Beliza, *Instr,* Univ de las Americas Galeria de Arte, Cholula, Mexico

DeVeau, Winifred, *Art Dir,* Port Chester Public Library, NY

Devel, Doris C, *Libr Technical Asst,* Boehm Gallery, Palomar Community College, San Marcos, CA

de Villechenon, Mrs M N Pinot, *Chief Conservator,* Musee des Beaux-Arts, Tours, France

Devine, Marge Duffy, *Scribe,* Nat Cartoonists Society, see National and Regional Organizations

Devine, Michael J, *Asst Dir,* Ohio Historical Society, Columbus

Devinoy, P, *Prof,* Fontainebleau School of Fine Arts, France

Devlin, Mary K, *Special Serv Librn,* Univ Portland, OR

Devlin, Richard, *Chmn Dept,* Carlow College, Pittsburgh, PA

Devon, Betsey, *Dir Summer School,* La Roche College, Pittsburgh, PA

De Vos, Dr D, *Cur,* Stedelyke Musea, Bruges, Belgium

De Vos-De Jong, M, *Educ Serv,* Koninklijk Museum Voor Schone Kunsten, Antwerp, Belgium

DeVries, David, *Chmn Photography,* Univ Manitoba, Winnipeg

De Vries, Keith, *Assoc Cur,* Univ Pennsylvania Museum, Philadelphia

Dew, James, *Prof,* Univ Montana, Missoula

Dew, Roderick, *Librn,* Colorado Springs Fine Arts Center, CO

Deward, Ellen F, *Admin Mem & Pub Affairs,* Society for the Preservation of New England Antiquities, Boston, MA

Dewey, Priscilla B, *Dir,* Charles River Creative Arts Program, Dover, MA

Dewey, Tom II, *Asst Prof,* Univ Mississippi, University

de Wiel, A Aan, *VDir E Course,* Academie Van Beeldende Kunsten, Rotterdam, Netherlands

de Wilde, E L L, *Dir,* Stedelijk Museum-Amsterdam, Netherlands

DeWolf, William F, *Asst Prof,* Thiel College, Greenville, PA

Dezutter, Dr W, *Cur,* Stedelyke Musea, Bruges, Belgium

Dhaemers, Robert A, *Prof,* Mills College, Oakland, CA

d'Harnoncourt, Anne, *Cur 20th Century Art,* Philadelphia Museum of Art, PA

D'Hauterive, *Prof,* Paris American Acad, France

Diamond, Larry, *Vis Asst Prof,* Dept Landscape Architecture, Univ Toronto, ON

Diaz, Jose Hernandez, *Dir,* Escuela Superior de Bellas Artes de Santa Isabel de Hungria de Seville, Spain

Di Bartolomeo, Mrs R E, *Secy Comt,* Oglebay Inst Mansion Museum, Wheeling, WV

Dibble, Daniel M, *Pres,* William Rockhill Nelson Gallery of Art, Kansas City, MO

Dibble, George S, *Prof Emer,* Univ Utah, Salt Lake City

Dibble, Thomas Reilly, *Dir,* Southern Vermont Art Center, Manchester

DiBella, Joseph, *Asst Prof,* Mary Washington College, Fredericksburg, VA

Dibner, Martin, *Dir,* Westbrook College, Portland, ME

di Bonaventura, Sam, *Head Dept & Prof,* George Mason Univ, Fairfax, VA

Dice, Elizabeth, *Assoc Prof,* Mississippi Univ for Women, Columbus

DiChiara, Rosemarie, *Asst to Dir,* Mattatuck Historical Society, Waterbury, CT

DiCicco, John, *Mem Faculty,* Providence College, RI

Dick, John Henry, *VPres,* Carolina Art Association, Charleston, SC

Dickenhof, John, *Area Chmn Crafts & Dir Summer School,* Pasadena City College, CA

Dickenson, Sara, *Asst Prof,* Southern Univ in New Orleans, LA

Dickenson, Victoria, *Cur Coll,* Newfoundland Museum, Saint Johns

Dicker, LaVerne, *Cur Photography,* California Historical Society, San Francisco

Dickey, T, *Coordr Exhib & Educ Prog,* Univ Alaska Museum, Fairbanks

Dickinson, Amina, *Prog Dir,* Museum of African Art, Washington, DC

Dickinson, Frank Holdsworth, *Asst Dir,* Dunedin Public Art Gallery, New Zealand

Dickinson, Nancy, *Dir,* Univ California Gallery, Davis

Dickinson, Stirling, *Pres, Dir School & Dir Summer School,* Inst Allende, San Maguel de Allende, Mexico

Dickson, Donna, *Secy,* Wyoming Council on the Arts, Cheyenne

Dickson, Elizabeth, *Pres,* Buck Hill Art Association, Buck Hills Falls, PA

Dickson, James K, *Head Fine Arts Dept,* Enoch Pratt Free Library of Baltimore City, MD

Dickson, Janet S, *Cur Educ,* Yale Univ Art Gallery, New Haven, CT

Dickson, Thyra, *Asst to Dir,* Jacksonville Museum of Arts and Sciences, FL

Didoha, Judy, *Vis Lectr,* Marymount College of Virginia, Arlington

Dieckman, Suzanne, *Mem Faculty,* Creighton Univ, Omaha, NE

Diehl, George K, *Assoc Prof Art & Chmn Dept Fine Arts,* La Salle College, Philadelphia, PA

Diehl, Richard, *Chmn Mus Comt,* Univ Missouri Museum of Anthropology, Columbia

Dienes, Edward, *Pres,* Kentucky Guild of Artists and Craftsmen, Berea

Dierfeldt, Jerome, *Exhib Specialist,* Hastings Museum, NE

Dietemann, Dave, *Coordr,* Colorado State Univ, Fort Collins

Dieterly, Richard, *Secy,* Hunterdon Art Center, Clinton, NJ

Dietrich, Bruce L, *Dir,* Reading Public Museum and Art Gallery, PA

Dietrich, Daryl, *Instr,* Wenatchee Valley College, WA

Dietterle, Mrs George, *Pres,* Monterey Peninsula Museum of Art, CA

Dietz, Charles, *Dir,* Zanesville Art Center, OH

Dietz, Margaret, *Exec Secy,* Arabian Horse Museum, Barnesville, MD

Dietz, Robert J, *Chmn,* Olympic College, Bremerton, WA

Diez, Paul, *Secy,* Museo Romantico Madrid, Spain

Diez, William E, *Second VPres,* Rochester Historical Society, NY

Diezotto, Eugene, *Prof,* Bemidji State Univ, MN

Diffily, Dr John A, *Dir Educ,* Amon Carter Museum of Western Art, Fort Worth, TX

Difford, M J, *Dir Summer School,* Univ Wisconsin-Stevens Point

Diggs, James T, *Prof,* Winston-Salem State Univ, NC

DiGiovanni, Robert, *Prof,* Boston State College, MA

DiGiusto, Gerald, *Prof,* State Univ New York College at Cortland

Di Julio, Max, *Prog Dir,* Loretto Heights College, Denver, CO

Dillard, Patricia, *Instr,* Pels School of Art, New York, NY

Dillard, Ro, *Co-Chmn,* Hill Country Arts Found, Ingram, TX

Dillenbeck, Mildred, *Dir,* Remington Art Museum, Ogdensburg, NY

Diller, J David, *Head Dept,* James Madison Univ, Harrisonburg, VA

Dillon, Douglas, *Chmn Bd Trustees,* Metropolitan Museum of Art, New York, NY

Dillon, Dr Drew, *Dir Summer School,* Flagler College, Saint Augustine, FL

Dillon, John, *Assoc Prof,* Univ Alabama in Birmingham

Dillon, John, *Asst Prof,* Chadron State College, NE

Dillon, Michael, *Cur Exhib,* Tyler Museum of Art, TX

Dillon, Mildred, *VPres,* American Color Print Society, Philadelphia, PA

Dillon, Monika, *Pub Affairs,* Museum of the City of New York, NY

Dillon, Phillis, *Conservator,* Heye Found, New York, NY

Dillon, Virginia, *Circulation Dept Head,* Wichita Public Library, KS

Dillow, Nancy, *Dir,* Univ Regina, SK

Dilts, R F, *Pres,* Saskatoon Gallery and Conservatory Corporation, SK

Dimant, Enrique, *Courses & Conferences,* Centro de Arte y Communicacion, Buenos Aires, Argentina

DiMattia, Ernest A, Jr, *Dir,* Ferguson Library, Stamford, CT

DiMattio, Vincent, *Assoc Prof,* Monmouth College, West Long Branch, NJ

Dimmitt, Richard, *Special Projects & AV Librn,* Orange County Public Library, Garden Grove, CA

Dimond, Thomas, *Asst Prof Art,* Eastern Oregon State College, LaGrande

Dimond, Tom, *Coordr Educ Media & Exhib,* Rudolph E Lee Gallery, Clemson Univ, SC

DiNatale, Paul, *VPres,* New York Society of Architects, NY

Dines, Nicholas, *Dir MLA Prog,* Univ Massachusetts, Amherst

Dingman, Beth, *Regional Develop Dir,* Ontario Crafts Council, Toronto

Dings, Marjorie, *Admin Asst,* Friends of Art, Wellesley College Museum, MA

Dingwall, Kenneth, *Vis Prof,* Cleveland Inst of Art, OH

Dinkelspiel, Edgar N, *Pres,* Long Branch Historical Museum, NJ

Dinngen, Marie DeSales, *Assoc Prof,* Regis College, Weston, MA

Dinsmore, Hayward R, *Chmn,* Central State Univ, Wilberforce, OH

Dinsmore, John N, *Assoc Prof,* Kearney State College, NE

Dinsmore, Marianne, *Librn,* Lyman Allyn Museum, New London, CT

Dinsmorg, Grant, *Mem Faculty,* La Roche College, Pittsburgh, PA

Dionne, Raoul, *Pres,* Univ Moncton Galerie D'Art, NB

Di Peso, Dr Charles C, *Dir,* Amerind Found, Dragoon, AZ

Dippel, R M, *Head Dept Painting & Sculpture,* Stedelijk Museum-Amsterdam, Netherlands

Dirks, John, *Asst Dir,* Museum of Art of Ogunquit, ME

Dirlam, Barbara, *Secy,* International Center of Medieval Art, New York, NY

Dirocco, Francis W, *Dean Studies,* College of Great Falls, MT

Dirube, Rolando Lopez, *Vis Prof,* Inter American Univ Puerto Rico, San German

Disbro, William, *Chmn & Asst Prof,* Jamestown Community College, NY

Discepolo, Lana, *Treas,* Spectrum, Friends of Fine Art, Toledo, OH

Dishman, Darral A, *Dir,* Spiva Art Center, Joplin, MO; *Dir Dept Art & Summer School,* Missouri Southern State College, Joplin

Disney, Russell, *Treas,* Canadian Conference of the Arts, see National Organizations in Canada

DiTeresa, Neil, *Assoc Prof,* Berea College, KY

Dittman, Reidar, *Assoc Prof,* St Olaf College, Northfield, MN

Dittmar, Thelma, *Registrar,* Canton Art Inst, OH

Dittmar, William, *Asst Prof,* Williamsport Area Community College, PA

Ditto, Kay, *Treas,* Arts for Living Center, Burlington, IA

Dittrich, Dr Edith, *Chief Cur,* Museum fur Ostasiatische Kunst, Museen der Stadt Koln, Germany

Divelbess, Diane, *Chairperson & Prof,* California State Polytechnic Univ, Pomona

Divelbiss, Maggie, *Development Mgr,* Sangre De Cristo Arts & Conference Center, Pueblo, CO

Divers, Dorothy, *Assoc Prof,* St Olaf College, Northfield, MN

Dix, Carl, *Pres,* Fort Peck Fine Arts Council, Glasgow, MT

Dixon, Albert G, Jr, *Dir,* San Jose Museum of Art, CA

Dixon, F Eugene Jr, *Pres,* Philadelphia Art Commission, PA

Dixon, Mrs John, *Publicity,* Greenwich Art Society and Art Center, CT

Dixon, John W, Jr, *Prof,* Univ North Carolina at Chapel Hill

Dixon, Stewart S, *VPres,* Chicago Historical Society, IL

Djerf, Linda M, *Registrar,* Univ Minnesota Gallery, Minneapolis

Doak, Banton S, *Assoc Prof,* Florida Southern College, Lakeland

Doak, Gale L, *Instr,* Florida Southern College Lakeland

Dobbs, Gil, *Exhib Adminr,* Western Association of Arts Museums, see National and Regional Organizations

Dobbs, James, *Lectr,* California State Polytechnic Univ, Pomona

Dobbs, John, *Asst Prof,* John Jay College of Criminal Justice, New York, NY

Dobbs, Capt W A, *Pres,* Singing River Art Association, Pascagoula, MS

Dobe, William, *Instr,* Notre Dame College, Manchester, NH

Dobereiner, John P, *Assoc Prof,* Univ Victoria, BC

Dobkin, John, *Adminr,* Cooper-Hewitt Museum, New York, NY

Dobrev, D, *Dean Fine Arts & Prof,* Nikolaj Pavlovic Higher Inst of Fine Arts, Sofia, Bulgaria

Dobrick, Jo-Anne, *Asst Secy,* Chicago Art Dealers Association, IL

Dobrowolski, Fred, *Lectr,* Notre Dame College, Manchester, NH

Dobrowolsky, Stanley, *Secy,* Taras H Shevchenko Museum and Mem Park Found, Oakville, ON

Docking, Gil, *Acting Dir,* Art Gallery of New South Wales, Sydney, Australia

Doctor, Antonio P, *Chmn Dept & Head Summer School & Head European Summer Prog,* Univ Windsor, ON

Doctorow, Erica, *Head,* Fine Arts Library, Adelphi Univ, Garden City, NY

Dodd, Irene, *Head Art Dept & In Charge of Art Gallery,* Valdosta State College, GA

Dodge, Ernest S, *Dir,* Peabody Museum of Salem, MA

Dodge, Robert Dodge, *Mem Faculty,* Bucks County Community College, Newtown, PA

Dodson, Robert G, *Dir,* St Gregory's Abbey and College, Shawnee, OK

Dodson, Roy E, *Prof,* Sul Ross State Univ, Alpine, TX

Dodwell, C R, *Dir,* Whitworth Art Gallery, Univ Manchester, England

Dodworth, Allen, *Dir,* Boise Gallery of Arts, ID

Dodworth, Allen Stevens, *Dir,* Salt Lake Art Center, UT

Doe, Donald B, *Asst Prof,* Univ Nebraska at Omaha

Doelger, William E P, *Secy-Treas,* Society of the Four Arts, Palm Beach, FL

Doerfler, Roy D, *Instr,* Nebraska Western College, Scottsbluff

Doering, Sister Colette, *Asst Prof,* Avila College, Kansas City, MO

Doeringer, Suzannah, *Asst Dir,* William Hayes Fogg Art Museum, Cambridge, MA

Doerr, Mrs Stanley, *Pres,* Central Iowa Art Association, Marshalltown

Dohanos, Stevan, *Chmn Adv Bd,* Famous Artists School, Westport, CT

Doherty, Robert J, *Dir,* International Museum of Photography, Rochester, NY

Doherty, Roger, *Cur Bldgs & Sites,* Colorado Historical Society, Denver

Dohn, Helen, *Secy Mus Coll Div,* Virginia Museum of Fine Arts, Richmond

Dohnalova, Marie, *Asst Librn,* Moravaska Galerie V Brne, Brno, Czechoslovakia

Dohrenwend, D, *Cur Far Eastern Dept,* Royal Ontario Museum, Toronto

Doig, Mrs Thomas G, *Adminr,* Concord Antiquarian Society Museum, MA

Doiron, Mrs Burton, *Co-Chmn,* Beaumont Arts Council, TX

Doksansky, Florence, *Acquisitions Librn,* Rotch Library of Architecture and Planning, Massachusetts Inst of Technology, Cambridge

Dolarian, Ara, *Prof,* California State Univ, Fresno

Dole, Algar, *Mem Faculty,* Austin Peay State Univ, Clarksville, TN

Dole, John S, *VPres, Treas & Gen Counsel,* Council of American Artist Societies, see National and Regional Organizations

Dolese, Peter, *Prog Dir,* Arts Place II, Oklahoma Art Center, Oklahoma City

Dolkhart, Ruth, *Mgr Mem,* Jewish Museum, New York, NY

Doll, Donald A, *Chmn Fine & Performing Arts Dept,* Creighton Univ, Omaha, NE

Doll, Nancy, *Dir,* Keene State College, NH

Dolunay, Necati, *Dir,* Istanbul Arkeoloji Muzeleri, Turkey

Domas, Joseph J, *Secy,* Religious Americana Museum, Ringoes, NJ

Domas, Mrs Joseph J, *Cur,* Religious Americana Museum, Ringoes, NJ

Dominquez, Frank, *Mem Faculty,* Bucks County Community College, Newtown, PA

Domit, Moussa M, *Dir,* North Carolina Museum of Art, Raleigh

Domonkos, Alex, *Instr,* Guilford Art and Music School, CT

Doms, Keith, *Dir,* Free Library of Philadelphia, PA

Donahue, Frank R, *Treas,* Sculpture Center, New York, NY

Donahue, Kenneth, *Dir,* Los Angeles County Museum of Art, CA

Donaldson, Dr Jeff R, *Dir,* Howard Univ Galleries of Art, Washington, DC

Donaldson, P, *Mem Faculty,* Golden West College, Huntington Beach, CA

Donaldson, Robert, *Dean Summer School,* Vanderbilt Univ, Nashville, TN

Donaldson, Shirley, *Gallery Dir,* Coe College Art Galleries, Cedar Rapids, IA

Donaldson, Thomas E, *Assoc Prof,* Cleveland State Univ, OH

Donat, Joseph, *Mem Faculty,* Long Beach City College, CA

Donbaz, Veysel, *Cur Cuneiform Tablet Coll,* Istanbul Arkeoloji Muzeleri, Turkey

Dondy, Emanuel, *Librn Dir,* Mount Vernon Public Library, NY

Donerty, Ann, *Admir,* International Center of Photography, New York, NY

Dong, Betty, *Libr Asst,* Howe Architecture Library, Arizona State Univ, Tempe

Donham, Flora B, *Dir,* Maine Coast Artists, Rockport

Donley, Robert, *Assoc Prof,* DePaul Univ, Chicago, IL

Donnan, Christopher B, *Dir,* Museum of Cultural History, Univ California, Los Angeles

Donnelly, Mary Emmanuel, *Dir Summer School,* College of Notre Dame, Belmont, CA

Donnelly, Thomas A, *VChmn Admin,* Brooklyn Inst of Arts and Sciences, NY

Donnelly, William, *Acad VPres,* de Saisset Art Gallery & Museum, Santa Clara, CA

Donoghue, Mrs F J, *Doll Cur,* Wenham Historical Association and Museum, MA

Donohue, Katharine, *Librn,* Natural History Museum of Los Angeles County, CA

Donovan, Robert G, *VPres Educ,* International Correspondence Schools, Scranton, PA

Dooley, Janet, *Prog Coordr,* Huntington Galleries, WV

Dooley, John B, *Head Librn,* College of San Mateo Library, CA

Dooley, John M, Jr, *Secy & Exhib Chmn,* Philadelphia Sketch Club, PA

Doolittle, Roy W, Jr, *Secy,* Albright-Knox Art Gallery, Buffalo, NY

Doppelfeld, Dieter, *VPres,* Alaska Artists Guild, Anchorage

Doralisa, Duarte P, *Librn,* Museo Nacional de Bellas Artes, Santiago, Chile

Doran, Faye, *Asst Prof,* Harding College, Searcy, AR

Dorcheck, Stephen, *Dir Summer School,* Manatee Junior College, Bradenton, FL

Dorholt, Kingsly, *Dir,* St Cloud State Univ, MN

Dorn, Gordon, *Area Coordr,* Northern Illinois Univ, De Kalb

Dorr, Betsy, *Pres & Cur,* Socorro Art League, NM

Dorr, Dr Joyce R, *Head Dept,* County College of Morris, Dover, NJ

D'Orsi, Sybil, *Treas,* Catharine Lorillard Wolfe Art Club, New York, NY

Dorst, Claire V, *Chmn Art Dept & In Charge Art Gallery,* Florida Atlantic Univ, Boca Raton

Dorst, Mary C, *Gallery Coordr,* Florida Atlantic Univ Art Gallery, Boca Raton

Dorval, Karen A, *Head Fine Arts Dept,* Springfield City Library, MA

Dosal, Arthur M, *Pres,* Latin Quarter Art Gallery, Tampa, FL

Doswell, James T, III, *Cur,* Stephen Foster Center, White Springs, FL

Doty, Robert M, *Dir,* Currier Gallery of Art, Manchester, NH

Doud, Richard K, *Catalog American Portraits Survey Coordr,* Nat Portrait Gallery, Washington, DC

Doudera, Gerard, *Prof,* Univ Connecticut, Storrs

Douet, Madeleine J, *Dir,* Ballard School, New York, NY

Dougal, Mary, *Historic Site Mgr,* Philipse Manor Hall State Historic Site, Yonkers, NY

Dougan, Paul, *Pres,* Salt Lake Art Center, UT

Dougherty, John, *Dir Summer School,* Atlanta College of Art, GA

Dougherty, Ray, *Instr,* Cultural Arts Center of Ocean City, NJ

Dougherty, Richard, *VPres Pub Affairs,* Metropolitan Museum of Art, New York, NY

Dougherty, Rosemary, *Instr,* Southwestern at Memphis, TN

Doughty, K A, *Cur,* South London Art Gallery, England

Douglas, Dean, *Dir,* Univ Montana, Missoula

Douglas, Edwin P, *Instr,* Portland School of Art, ME

Douke, Daniel, *Dir,* California State Univ Fine Arts Gallery, Los Angeles

Douris, George, *VPres,* Philadelphia Sketch Club, PA

Dove, Judy, *Instr,* Friends Univ, Wichita, KS

Dove, Ronald, *Pres,* Hussian School of Art, Philadelphia, PA

Dowdy, William, *Chmn Dept & Dir Summer School,* Blue Mountain College, MS

Dowhie, Leonard, *Instr,* Nicholls State Univ, Thibodaux, LA

Dowley, Francis H, *Prof,* Univ Chicago, IL

Dowling, Susan, *Pres,* Verde Valley Art Association, Jerome, AZ

Downey, Cleta H, *Assoc Cur,* Univ New Mexico Art Museum, Albuquerque

Downie, Sir Harry, *Cur,* Carmel Mission Basilica, CA

Downing, Mrs Harry, *Secy,* John Paul Jones House, Portsmouth, NH

Downing, Jack, *Asst Dir,* Panhandle-Plains Historical Society Museum, Canyon, TX

Downs, Dorothy, *Registrar,* Univ Miami, Coral Gables, FL

Downs, R W, *Mem Faculty,* Univ Miami, Coral Gables, FL

Doyle, Mrs Edward A, *Dir,* Greater Fall River Art Association, MA

Doyle, Leo, *Chmn Dept,* California State College at San Bernardino

Doyon, Gerard Maurice, *Head Dept,* Washington and Lee Univ, Lexington, VA

Drabkin, Stella, *VPres,* American Color Print Society, Philadelphia, PA

Draffin, Nicholas, *Cur Prints & Drawings,* Art Gallery of New South Wales, Sydney, Australia

Draghi, Robert, *Chmn,* Marymount College of Virginia, Arlington

Drahos, Dean, *Chmn,* Baldwin-Wallace College, Berea, OH

Draisner, Donald, *Cur Coll,* Southern Oregon Historical Society, Jacksonville

Drake, Barbara, *VPres,* Peoria Art Guild, IL

Drake, Louise, *Cur Educ,* Dade County Art Museum, Miami, FL

Draney, Charles, *Mem Staff,* Factory of Visual Art, Seattle, WA

Draper, Alexander F, *Adminr,* Heye Found, New York, NY

Draper, Denise, *Mgr Art Sales & Rental,* Fine Arts Gallery of San Diego, CA

Draper, J L, *Chmn Dept Art, Acting Dean & In Charge Art Gallery,* Florida State Univ, Tallahassee

Draper, Ruth R, *Exec Dir,* Utah State Div of Fine Arts, Salt Lake City

Draper, Mrs Sheelagh, *Chief Cur,* Vancouver City Archives, BC

Draper-Bloom, Line, *VPres,* Spectrum, Friends of Fine Arts, Toledo, OH

Drechsler, Carol, *VPres,* Craftsmen's Association of British Columbia, Vancouver

Dreiband, Laurence, *Fine Arts Dept Chmn,* Art Center College of Design, Pasadena, CA

Dreibholz, Ursule, *Paper Conservator,* Yale Univ Art Gallery, New Haven, CT

Dreier, Dr Franz-Adrian, *Dir,* Museum of Arts & Craft, Staatliche Museen Preussischer Kulturbesitz, Berlin, Germany

Dreisbach, C I, *Owner,* Dreisbach Art Gallery, Mountainhome, PA

Dreiss, Joseph, *Instr,* Mary Washington College, Fredericksburg, VA

Dressel, Barry, *Asst Dir,* Peale Museum, Baltimore, MD

Dresye, Sharon, *Registrar,* Potsdam Public Museum, NY

Drew, Frances K, *Librn,* College of Architecture Library, Georgia Inst of Technology, Atlanta

Drew, Harry V, *Dir,* Klamath County Museum, Klamath Falls, OR

Drew, Nancy, *Cur,* Long Beach Museum of Art, CA

Drew, Ray, *Prof,* New Mexico Highlands Univ, Las Vegas

Drewien, Vivian, *VPres & Prog Dir,* Socorro Art League, NM

Drexler, Arthur, *Dir Dept Architecture & Design,* Museum of Modern Art, New York, NY

Dreyer, Evelyn G, *Chmn Art History,* Old Dominion Univ, Norfolk, VA

Driesbach, Walter, *Mem Faculty,* Art Academy of Cincinnati, OH

Driessen, H, *Cur,* Gemeentemuseum Arnhem, Netherlands

Driggers, Jeff, *Art & Music Dept Librn,* Jacksonville Public Library, FL

Dring, Matilda, *Photograph Archivist,* San Francisco Maritime Museum Association, CA

Driscoll, Mrs A T, *VPres,* Southwest Missouri Museum Associates, Springfield

Driscoll, Denis H, *Mem Faculty,* Norwich Art School, CT

Driscoll, John P, *Registrar,* Pennsylvania State Univ Museum of Art, University Park

Driver, Clive E, *Dir,* Philip H & A S W Rosenbach Found Museum, Philadelphia, PA

Driver, William, *Chmn Drama & Dance,* Bard College, Annandale-on-Hudson, NY

Droege, Anthony, *Assoc Prof,* Indiana Univ, South Bend

Drohan, Walter, *Sr Instr,* Alberta College of Art, Calgary, AB

Dronberger, Jane, *Prof,* Hutchinson Community Junior College & *VPres,* Hutchinson Art Association, KS

Drost, D, *Asst Prof,* Pennsylvania State Univ, Uniontown

Drucker, Marilyn, *Lectr,* Cardinal Stritch College, Milwaukee, WI

Drucker, Steven, *Exhibits Chmn,* College of Idaho, Caldwell

Drue, Abby, *VPres,* Atlanta Art Workers Coalition, GA

Druick, D, *Cur Prints,* Nat Gallery of Canada, Ottawa, ON

Drummond, Derek, *Dir,* School of Architecture, McGill Univ, Montreal, PQ

Drutt, Helen Williams, *Gallery Dir,* Moore College of Art Gallery, Philadelphia, PA

Drutz, June, *Mem Faculty,* Toronto School of Art, ON

Dryden, J E, *Senior Archivist,* Provincial Archives of Alberta, Edmonton

Dryer, Mrs A L, *Resident Potter,* Strasburg Museum, VA

Dryfhout, John H, *Supt,* Saint-Gaudens Nat Historic Site, Cornish, NH

Dryfoos, Susan, *Co-Dir,* Gallery of Prehistoric Paintings, New York, NY

Duana, Tanya, *Museum Liaison Chair,* Women in the Arts Found, New York, NY

Duarte, Carlos, *Conservation Dept,* Museo de Bellas Artes, Caracas, Venezuela

Dubberly, Ronald A, *Librn,* Seattle Public Library, WA

Dube, Dr Wolf-Dieter, *Cur 20th Century Art,* Bayerischen Staatsgemaldesammlungen, Munich, Germany

Du Bois, Alan, *Asst Dir,* Museum of Fine Arts of St Petersburg, FL

DuBois, Henry J, *Fine Arts Librn,* California State Univ, Long Beach

Dubon, David T, *Cur Decorative Arts, Medieval & Renaissance,* Philadelphia Museum of Art, PA

DuBose, Lucius B, *Cur,* George Peabody College for Teachers Museum, Nashville, TN

Dubowski, Harriet, *Dir,* Anderson Gallery, Virginia Commonwealth Univ, Richmond

DuCasse, Ralph S, *Prof Art & Chmn Dept,* Mills College, Oakland, CA

Ducey, James, *Preparator,* Univ Illinois, Champaign

Duchac, Kenneth F, *Dir,* Brooklyn Public Library, NY

Duchesneau, Guy P E, *Mgr,* Society of the Montreal Military & Maritime Museum, PQ

Ducommun, Charles E, *VPres,* Los Angeles County Museum of Art, CA

Duda, Donald L, *Assoc Prof,* Dickinson State College, ND

Duda, Yvonne, *Secy,* Minnesota Artists Association, Minneapolis

Dudley, Janice Stafford, *Secy,* MacArthur Mem, Norfolk, Va

Dudley, Peter, *Mem Faculty,* Greenfield Community College, MA

Duenyas, Ester, *Educ Cur,* Hebrew Union College, Los Angeles, CA

Dufault, Ron, *Gallery Cur,* Univ Minnesota, St Paul

Duff, James H, *Dir,* Brandywine River Museum, Chadds Ford, PA

Duffy, John, *Chmn,* Johnson State College, VT

Duffy, Mrs John, *VPres,* Spiva Art Center, Joplin, MO

Dufort, Robert, *Chairperson Dept Art,* Schoolcraft College, Livonia, MI

Dufour, Lydia A, *Cur Iconography,* Hispanic Society of America, New York, NY

Dufour, Paul, *Prof,* Louisiana State Univ, Baton Rouge

Dugan, Alan, *Instr,* Truro Center for the Arts at Castle Hill, MA

Dugan, George, *Assoc Prof,* State Univ New York College at Corland

Dugas, Judge Jacques, *VPres,* Musee D'Art de Joliette, PQ

Dugdale, James, *Mem Faculty,* Joliet Junior College, IL

Duggleby, Mrs S J, *Pub Chmn,* Cody Country Art League, WY

Duhaime, Lucie, *Treas,* New Hampshire Art Association, Manchester

Duhme, H Richard, Jr, *Head Sculpture,* Chautauqua Institution, NY

Duke, Carl F, *Head Dept Art,* Pensacola Junior College, FL

Dumas, Roger F, *Exhib,* Maitland Art Center & Research Studio, FL

Dunaway, Bob A, *Chmn Art Dept & Dir,* Marie Hull Gallery, Hinds Junior College, Raymond, MS

Dunaway, Sherry R, *Secy/Registrar,* Univ Texas Art Gallery, Arlington

Dunbar, John, *Instr,* California College of Arts and Crafts, Oakland

Dunbar, Philip H, *Cur,* Connecticut Historical Society Library, Hartford

Dunbar, Prescott N, *Treas,* New Orleans Museum of Art, LA

Duncan, A B, *Chmn Bd Trustees,* San Antonio Museum Association, TX

Duncan, Donald, *Assoc Prof,* Ohio State Univ, Columbus

Duncan, James, *Dir Summer School,* Riverside City College, CA

Duncan, Jim, *Center Dir,* Univ Southern Colorado, Art Gallery, Pueblo

Dunham, Lee, *Dean Summer School,* Baylor Univ, Waco, TX

Dunifon, Don, *Assoc Prof,* Wittenberg Univ, Springfield, OH

Dunkelman, Martha, *Asst Prof,* Wright State Univ, Dayton, OH

Dunkle, Alvin S, *Assoc Prof,* Thiel College, Greenville, PA

Dunlop, Mrs Edwin, *Trustee,* Attleboro Museum, MA

Dunn, Frank, *Dir Summer School,* State Univ New York College at Potsdam

Dunn, James S, *Asst Dir,* Stamford Museum and Nature Center, CT

Dunn, Laney, *Educ Asst,* Dixon Gallery and Gardens, Memphis, TN

Dunn, McChesney S, *Asst to Dir,* Southeastern Center for Contemporary Art, Winston-Salem, NC

Dunn, Noel L, *Pres,* Southeastern Center for Contemporary Art, Winston-Salem, NC

Duparc, F J, *Asst,* Koninklijk Kabinet Van Schilderijen Mauritshuis, The Hague, Netherlands

Dupraz, Claude, *Head Indust Design Dept,* Lausanne College of Art & Design, Switzerland

Dupree, Michael, *Prof,* West Virginia Univ, Morgantown

Durand, Don, *Dir Summer School,* North Hennepin Community College, Minneapolis, MN

Durben, Silvan A, *Cur,* Owatonna Arts Center, MN

Durham, David, *Mem Faculty,* Saint Louis Community College at Meramec, St Louis, MO

Durham, Walter T, *Pres,* Tennessee Historical Society, Nashville

Durkee, Stephen, *Prof Art & Chmn Dept,* Framingham State College, MA

Durland, Don, *Prof,* Texas Tech Univ, Lubbock

Durnall, Dr Edward, *Dir Summer School,* Univ New Hampshire, Durham

Duron, Jorge, *Chmn,* Univ the Americas, Cholula, Mexico

Durr, Pam, *Instr,* Monterey Peninsula College, CA

Durrant, George D, *Assoc Prof,* Palomar College, San Marcos, CA

Durst, J W, *Cur,* Greenwood Museum, SC

Durston, Louise, *Librn,* Museum of Fine Arts, Santa Fe, NM

Dursum, Brian, *Asst to Dir,* Univ Miami, Coral Gables, FL

Duseck, Bernard, *Prof,* California Polytechnic State Univ, San Luis Obispo

Dusendschon, Noel, *Prof,* Indiana Univ-Purdue Univ, Fort Wayne, IN

Dutton, Richard H, *Head Dept Art,* Indian Hills Community College, Centerville, IA

DuVal, Frank, *Cur Exhib,* Museum Without Walls, Rceda Inc, Friendsville, MD

Duvall, Sue, *Secy,* Blanden Art Gallery, Fort Dodge, IA

Dvorak, Dr Anna, *Librn,* North Carolina Museum of Art, Raleigh

D'Vorzon, Berenice, *Assoc Prof,* Wilkes College, Wilkes-Barre, PA

Dweck, Edward M, *Dir,* Bronx Museum of the Arts, NY

Dwight, Edward H, *Dir,* Munson-Williams-Proctor Inst Museum of Art, Utica, NY

Dwyer, Eugene J, *Chmn & Asst Prof,* Kenyon College, Gambier, OH

Dwyer, Jayne, *Secy,* Ogunquit Art Association, ME

Dwyer, Melva, *Librn,* Univ British Columbia, Vancouver

Dyens, Georges M, *Dir Visual & Fine Arts Dept,* Saidye Bronfman Centre (YM-YWHA & NHS), Montreal, PQ

Dyer, Carlus and Ruth, *Dirs,* Aldrich Museum of Contemporary Art, Ridgefield, CT

Dykes, D W, *Secy,* Nat Museum of Wales, Cardiff

Dykes, Steven E, *VDir Admin & Personnel,* Fine Arts Museums of San Francisco, CA

Dynes, Wayne, *Prof,* Hunter College, New York, NY

Dynneson, Donald, *Prof,* Concordia College, Seward, NE

Dyson, Mrs Raymond, *VPres,* Pensacola Museum of Art, FL

Dyson, Robert H, Jr, *Cur Near Eastern Section,* Univ Pennsylvania Museum, Philadelphia; *Pres,* Archaeological Inst of America, see National and Regional Organizations

Eagan, William R, *Secy-Treas,* Willet Stained Glass Studios, Philadelphia, PA

Eager, E Hartley, *Gallery Adminr,* Maryland Historical Society Museum, Baltimore

Eager, Gerald, *Head Dept,* Bucknell Univ, Lewisburg, PA

Eager, James, *Interim Gallery Coordr,* State Univ New York at New Paltz

Eagerton, Robert, *Chmn Printmaking Prog,* Herron School of Art, Indiana Univ-Purdue Univ, Indianapolis

Eaker, Ira, *Instr,* Oklahoma State Univ, Okmulgee

Eakins, Joyce, *Vis Prof-Artist in Residence,* Colorado Women's College, Denver

Eakle, James, *Dept Head,* Contra Costa College, San Pablo, CA

Ealer, William, *Asst Prof,* Williamsport Area Community College, PA

Ealy, Ophelia, *Gallery Exhib Chmn,* Huntsville Art League and Museum Association, AL

Eanet, Charles, *Dir,* Emanu-el Midtown YM-YWHA, New York, NY

Early, Charles, *Libr Asst,* Univ Notre Dame Architecture Library, IN

Easker, Fred, *Asst Dir,* Cedar Rapids Art Center, IA

Eason, Jean, *Dir Summer School,* Univ North Carolina at Greensboro

Eason, Robert, *Theater Librn,* Dallas Public Library, TX

East, Dennis, *Head of Archives/Manuscripts,* Ohio Historical Society, Columbus

Eastman, Charles J, *Asst Prof,* Kearney State College, NE

Eastman, G, *Secy,* Kitchener-Waterloo Art Gallery, ON

Eastman, Gene M, *Head Dept & Prof,* Sam Houston State Univ, Huntsville, TX

Eaton, Renee Grignard, *Prog,* California Historical Society, San Francisco

Eaton, Judge Richard B, *VPres,* Redding Museum and Art Center, CA

Eayrs, Frederick E, Jr, *Dir of Properties & Coll,* Society for the Preservation of New England Antiquities, Boston, MA

Ebeling, Klaus, *Prof,* Jefferson Community College, Watertown, NY

Eber, Marian, *Admin Asst,* Frederick S Wight Art Galleries, Univ California, Los Angeles

Eberdt, Clarice, *Chmn,* Marycrest College, Davenport, IA

Eberle, Priscilla, *Exec Secy,* Spiva Art Center, Joplin, MO

Ebersole, Elenor, *Asst Prof,* Pennsylvania State Univ, Capitol Campus, Middletown

Ebert, D, *Mem Faculty,* Golden West College, Huntington Beach, CA

Ebie, William D, *Asst Dir,* Roswell Museum and Art Center, NM

Eble, Bernard E, *VChmn Mem Hall Comt,* Louisiana Historical Association, New Orleans

Eccles, John D, *Pres,* Eccles Community Art Center, Ogden, UT

Eccles, Viscount, *Chmn,* British Library Bd, London, England

Echevarria, Sister Carmen, *Mem Faculty,* Saint Mary College, Leavenworth, KS

Echeverria, Felipe, *Asst Prof,* Univ Northern Iowa, Cedar Falls

Echols, Mary Tuck, *Assoc Prof,* Mary Baldwin College, Staunton, VA

Ecke, Evans, *Vis Prof,* Rudolph Schaeffer School of Design, San Francisco, CA

Eckels, Dr Claire, *Chmn,* Harford Community College, Bel Air, MD

Eckersley, T C, *Chmn,* State Univ New York College at Oswego

Eckert, W Dean, *Chmn Dept,* Lindenwood Colleges, Saint Charles, MO

Eckes, Harold, *Coordr Learning Resources,* Los Angeles Trade-Technical College Library, CA

Eckheart, Douglas, *Acting Head Dept,* Luther College, Decorah, IA

Eckstein, Deborah K, *Dir & Dir Summer School,* Dunedin Fine Arts & Cultural Center, FL

Eckstein, Ruth, *Secy,* American Abstract Artists, see National and Regional Organizations

Economou, Helen, *Admin Asst,* Manchester Inst of Arts and Sciences, NH

Edds, Neil, *Dept Head & Pres,* Independence Community Junior College, KS

Eddy, Warren S, *Dir,* Cortland Free Library, NY

Edelson, Gilbert S, *Secy,* Art Dealers Association of America, see National and Regional Organizations

Edelstein, J M, *Chief Librn,* Nat Gallery of Art, Washington, DC

Edens, Marjorie, *Historian/Newsletter Ed,* Southern Oregon Historical Society, Jacksonville

Edick, Mary Deweerd, *Ceramist,* Regis College, Weston, MA

Edie, Richard, *Prof,* South Dakota State Univ, Brookings

Edkins, Barbara B, *Librn,* Phillips Library, Peabody Museum of Salem, MA

Edlhauser, June M, *Coordr Fine Arts,* Milwaukee Public Library, WI

Edmiston, Robert S, *Chmn Sculpture,* East Carolina Univ, Greenville, NC

Edmiston, Sara, *Chmn Design,* East Carolina Univ, Greenville, NC

Edmondson, Mary, *Secy,* Miniature Painters, Sculptors and Gravers Society of Washington, DC

Edmunds, Sheila, *Prof,* Wells College, Aurora, NY

Edmundson, Gerald, *Pres,* Southern Highland Handicraft Guild, Asheville, NC

Edmundson, Gerald, *Assoc Prof,* East Tennessee State Univ, Johnson City

Edwards, Beverly, *Art Workshops Coordr & Dir Summer School,* Brockton Art Center, MA

Edwards, Billie C, *Instr,* Lamar Univ, Beaumont, TX

Edwards, Derwin W, *Prof,* Miami Univ, Oxford, OH

Edwards, Elisabeth, *Chmn Fashion Illustration,* Traphagen School of Fashion, New York, NY

Edwards, G Roger, *Assoc Cur Mediterranean Section,* Univ Pennsylvania Museum, Philadelphia

Edwards, Gerald P, *Cur History,* Thomas Gilcrease Inst of American History and Art, Tulsa, OK

Edwards, James B, *Prof,* Northeast Louisiana Univ, Monroe

Edwards, L F, *Chmn & Dir Summer School,* Appalachian State Univ, Boone, NC

Edwards, Lawrence, *Head Dept Art,* Pennsylvania State Univ, University Park

Edwards, Lorrainne, *Mem Faculty,* Bob Jones Univ, Greenville, SC

Edwards, Marcia, *Pres,* Fort Smith Art Center, AR

Edwards, Mary Jane, *Asst Prof,* Nazareth College of Rochester, NY

Edwards, Paul B, *Chmn Art Dept,* Washington and Jefferson College, Washington, PA

Edwards, Richard, *Instr,* Alberta College of Art, Calgary

Edwards, Robert S, *Secy,* Arts and Education Council of Greater St Louis, MO

Edwards, Sandra, *Receptionist,* Univ New Mexico Art Museum, Albuquerque

Edwards, William T, Jr, *Assoc Prof,* Clarion State College, PA

Efland, Arthur, *Prof,* Ohio State Univ, Columbus

Eftaxias, Lambros, *Chmn,* Benaki Museum, Athens, Greece

Egan, V, *Treas,* Miniature Art Society of New Jersey, Nutley

Egelson, Polly, *Instr,* Brockton Art Center, MA

Egerer, Carl W, *Pres,* South Arkansas Art League, El Dorado

Eggen, J Archer, *Dir Libraries,* St. Paul Public Library, MN

Eggert, J G, *Acad Dean,* Schiller College-Europe, Heidelberg, Germany

Eggum, Arne, *Chief Cur,* City of Oslo Art Collection, Norway

Egherman, Ronald, *Asst Dir Admin,* Univ California, Berkeley

Egleston, Robert, *Cur,* New Haven Colony Historical Society, CT

Egleston, Truman, *Prof,* Boston State College, MA

Ehresman,, Donald, *Chmn Dept History of Archit & Art,* Univ Illinois, Chicago Circle

Ehrhardt, Ursula M, *Instr,* Salisbury State College, MD

Ehrlich, Nancy, *Dir Libr,* Jackson County Historical Society, Independence, MO

Eich, Dr Paul, *Cur,* Stadelsches Kunstinstitut, Frankfurt Am Main, Germany

Eickhorst, William, *Asst Prof,* Univ Maine, Orono

Eide, Joel S, *Dir Art Gallery,* Northern Arizona Univ, Flagstaff

Eide, John, *Instr,* Portland School of Art, ME

Eidelberg, Martin, *Dir,* Graduate Program in Art History, Rutgers, The State Univ New Jersey, New Brunswick

Eiders, Sid, *Dir Summer School,* Lewis and Clark College, Portland, OR

Eifert, Donald A, *Pres,* Society of Medalists, see National and Regional Organizations

Eige, G Eason, *Cur Coll,* Huntington Galleries, WV

Eikelberry, Larry, *Dir Educ,* William Rockhill Nelson Gallery of Art, Kansas City, MO

Eikemeier, Dr Peter, *Cur Netherlandish Paintings,* Bayerischen Staatsgemaldesammlungen, Munich, Germany

Eirk, Katherine, *Conservator,* Nat Collection of Fine Arts, Washington, DC

Eis, Ruth, *Cur,* Judah L Magnes Mem Museum, Berkeley, CA

Eisen, Sylvia, *Dir,* Long Beach Public Library, NY

Eisenman, Alvin, *Prof,* Yale Univ, New Haven, CT

Eisgrau, Evelyn, *VPres,* Women in the Arts Found, New York, NY

Eisler, Sue, *Asst Prof Art, Chairperson Dept & Dir Summer School,* Saint Louis Community College at Florissant Valley, Ferguson, MO

Eisner, Dr Elliot W, *Pres,* Nat Art Education Association, see National and Regional Organizations

Eiteljorg, Harrison, *Chmn Bd Trustees,* Indianapolis Museum of Art, IN

Eitner, Lorenz, *Dir Museum and Art Gallery, Chmn Art Dept & Dir Summer School,* Stanford Univ, CA

Ekdahl, Janis, *Librn,* Vassar College Art Gallery, Poughkeepsie, NY

Ekedal, Ellen, *Dir,* Loyola Marymount Univ, Los Angeles, CA

Ela, Patrick H, *Admin Dir,* Craft and Folk Art Museum, Los Angeles, CA

Elam, Charles H, *Registrar,* Detroit Inst of Art Collections, MI

Elam, Leslie J, *Dir & Secy,* American Numismatic Society, see National and Regional Organizations

Elder, William Voss, III, *Chmn Curatorial Div & Cur Decorative Arts,* Baltimore Museum of Art, MD

Eldot, Eleanor, *Music & Art,* Queensborough Community College Library, Bayside, NY

Eldred, Dale, *Chmn Sculpture,* Kansas City Art Institute, MO

Eldredge, Dr Charles C, *Dir,* Univ Kansas, Lawrence

Eldridge, Maudmae E, *Dir,* South Texas Artmobile, Corpus Christi

Eleazer, Grace, *Cur Coll,* Jacksonville Museum of Arts and Sciences, FL

Elfvin, Mrs John T, *VPres,* Albright-Knox Art Gallery, Buffalo, NY

Elgavish, Dr Joseph, *Dir,* Museum of Ancient Art, Haifa, Israel

Elias, Clifford E, *Secy,* Merrimack Valley Textile Museum, North Andover, MA

Elias, Margery M, *Assoc,* Dezign House III, Cleveland, OH

Elias, Ramon J, *Dir,* Dezign House III, Cleveland, OH

Eliscu, Frank, *Art Adv Bd,* Society of Medalists, see National and Regional Organizations

Elkin, P Bush, *Secy,* Dallas Print and Drawing Society, Dallas Public Library, TX

Elkington, Richard N, *Chmn,* Providence College, RI

Elks, Hazel Hulbert, *Dir,* Free Public Library of Elizabeth, NJ

Ellemers, *Arts Exten Officer/Dir,* Saskatchewan School of the Arts, Saskatchewan Arts Board, Regina

Ellinger, Bruce, *Mem Faculty,* Madison Area Technical College, WI

Ellinger, Dr Ilona, *Prof,* Trinity College, Washington, DC

Elliot, Navar, *Cur Exhib,* Charlotte Nature Museum, NC

Elliot, R Sherrard, *Pres,* Northern Virginia Fine Arts Association, Alexandria

Elliott, David, *Mem Faculty,* Austin Community College, TX

Elliott, J H, Jr, *Dir,* Atlanta Museum, GA

Elliott, James, *Dir,* Univ California, Berkeley

Elliott, James, *Dir,* Wadsworth Atheneum, Hartford, CT

Elliott, Dr L Gene, *Librn,* Bob Jones Univ, Greenville, SC

Elliott, Robbins, *Exec VPres,* Royal Architectural Inst of Canada, see National Organizations of Canada

Elliott, Sarah Davis, *Instr,* College Misericordia, Dallas, PA

Ellis, Anita, *Registrar,* Cincinnati Art Museum, OH

Ellis, Austin T, *Dir,* Moose Jaw Art Museum, SK

Ellis, Carl E, *Dir & Cur Art,* Everhart Museum, Scranton, PA

Ellis, Charles, *Coordr Commerical Art,* Art Inst of Philadelphia, PA

Ellis, Donald, *Dir Archit,* Univ Manitoba Gallery 111, Winnipeg

Ellis, Edwin C, *Prof Art, Head Dept & Dir Summer School,* Central Missouri State Univ, Warrensburg

Ellis, George R, *Cur Africa, Ocenia & Indonesia,* Museum of Cultural History, Univ California, Los Angeles

Ellis, Gilda, *Pres,* Artists Equity Association, see National and Regional Organizations

Ellis, Jackie, *Secy,* Central Wyoming Museum of Art, Casper

Ellis, Nancy L, *Registrar,* Museum of Cultural History, Univ California, Los Angeles

Ellis, Richard, *Educ Coordr,* Junior Arts Center Los Angeles, CA

Ellis, Richard, *Mem Jury,* Society of Animal Artists, see National and Regional Organizations

Ellis, Robert H, Jr, *Registrar,* Kendall Whaling Museum, Sharon, MA

Ellis, W F, *Dir,* Queen Victoria Museum, Launceston, Australia

Ellison, Ralph, *Secy Inst,* American Academy and Inst of Arts and Letters, see National and Regional Organizations

Ellison, Rosemary, *Cur,* Southern Plains Indian Museum, Anadarko, OK; *Acting Cur,* Museum of the Plains Indian, Browning, MT

Ellsworth, Mrs D F, *Secy,* Allied Arts of Seattle, WA

Ellsworth, Linda V, *Historian,* Historic Pensacola Preservation Board, FL

Ellsworth, Margaret, *Chmn,* King County Arts Commission, Seattle, WA

Elrod, James, *Assoc Librn & Head,* Technical Processes, California Inst of the Arts Library, Valencia

Elsey, George M, *Pres,* American Red Cross, see National and Regional Organizations

Elsner, Larry, *Prof,* Utah State Univ, Logan

Elwell, George R, *Prof,* Pacific Lutheran Univ, Tacoma, WA

Ely, Robert V, *VPres,* Roswell Museum and Art Center, NM

Elzea, Rowland, *Cur,* Delaware Art Museum, Wilmington

Emanuel, Dr Meyer, *VPres,* Kennebec Valley Art Association, Hallowell, ME

Embrey, Carl, *Mem Faculty,* San Antonio Art Inst, TX

Emden, Miriam, *Mem Dept Head,* Solomon R Guggenheim Museum, New York, NY

Emerick, Judson J, *Asst Prof,* Pomona College, Claremont, CA

Emerson, Edith, *Pres & Cur,* Violet Oakley Mem Found, Philadelphia, PA

Emerson, John M, *Pres,* Canadian Society for Education Through Art, see National Organizations of Canada

Emerson, Roberta Shinn, *Dir,* Huntington Galleries, WV

Emerson, William R, *Dir,* Franklin D Roosevelt Library and Museum, Hyde Park, NY

Emery, Irene, *Cur Emer,* Textile Museum, Washington, DC

Emery, Pricilla, *Instr,* West Virginia Wesleyan College, Buckhannon

Emily, Catherine, *Pub Information,* Art Research Center, Kansas City, MO

Emison, Elizabeth, *PT Instr,* Union Univ, Jackson, TN

Emmerich, Carl, *Prof,* Eastern Illinois Univ, Charleston

Emmert, Richard, *Gallery Mgr,* Gilpin County Arts Association, Central City, CO

Emmett, Joseph O, *Treas,* Cincinnati Art Club, OH

Edmond, Pierre, *Secy,* Musee Historique de Vaudreuil, PQ

Emrich, Jeanette, *Asst Secy,* Florida Gulf Coast Art Center, Clearwater

Endacott, Pamela, *Instr,* Smith College, Northampton, MA

Endegama, P, *Cur Anthropology,* Colombo National Museum, Sri Lanka

Eng, James, *Instr,* Framingham State College, MA

Engdahl, David A, *Acting Dir,* School of Photographic Arts and Sciences, Rochester Inst Technology, NY

Engel, Charlene, *Assoc Instr,* Moravian College, Bethlehem, PA

Engel, Helen Vanden, *Music Librn,* Grand Rapids Public Library, MI

Engelbrect, Peter, *Treas,* The Exhibitionists, Jamaica, NY

Engelhardt, Jim, *Asst Prof,* Univ Idaho, Moscow

Engelmann, Lothar K, *Dean,* College of Graphic Arts and Photography, Rochester Inst Technology, NY

Engeman, Richard H, *Librn,* Southern Oregon Historical Society, Jacksonville

Engen, Richard, *Dir,* Alaska State Museum, Juneau

Engerman, Jeanne, *Asst Librn,* Hewitt Mem Library, Washington State Historical Society, Tacoma

Engeseth, James, *Asst Prof,* Nebraska Wesleyan Univ, Lincoln

England, Monte, *Instr,* Nazareth College of Rochester, NY

Englar, Jerry, *Assoc Prof,* Dept of Landscape Architecture, Univ Toronto, ON

Engle, G W, *Adminr,* Colorado Springs Fine Arts Center, CO

Engle, Nanene, *Assoc Prof,* Univ Evansville, IN

Engle, Robert, *Assoc Prof,* Ohio Wesleyan Univ, Delaware

Engle, Robert C, *Construction Manager,* Nat Gallery of Art, Washington, DC

Engler, Christine, *Recording Secy,* Society of American Graphic Artists, see National and Regional Organizations

Engler, Toby, *Admin Asst,* Tucson Museum of Art, AZ

Engleson, Richard, *Dir Arts & Sci,* Southwestern Community College, Creston, IA

English, Joseph E, *Adminr,* Nat Gallery of Art, Washington, DC

English, Mark, *Adv Bd Mem,* Famous Artists School, Westport, CT

English, Peter, *Instr,* Pels School of Art, New York, NY

Enman, Tom K, *Dir,* Laguna Beach Museum of Art, CA

Ensign, Charles, *Assoc Prof,* Tift College, Forsyth, GA

Ensign, Walter, *First VPres,* Alaska Association for the Arts, Fairbanks

Ensor, Barbara, *Secy,* Professional Art Dealers Association of Canada, see National Organizations of Canada

Ensor, John H, *Treas,* Star-Spangled Banner Flag House Association, Baltimore, MD

Enyeart, James, *Dir,* Center for Creative Photography, Tucson, AZ

Eppridge, Theresa, *Mem Faculty,* College of New Rochelle, NY

Epstein, Andy, *Dir,* Forbes Street Gallery, Carnegie-Mellon Univ, Pittsburgh, PA

Epstein, Ann W, *Asst Prof,* Oberlin College, OH

Epstein, Mary, *Head Dept Design,* Drexel Univ, Philadelphia, PA

Erb, Sandra, *Secy to Dir,* Fine Arts Gallery of San Diego, CA

Ercilla, Jorge Guillermo Luna, *Regent,* Escuela Superior de Bellas Artes Ernesto de la Carcova, Sculpture Museum, Buenos Aires, Argentina

Eri, Mrs Gyongyi, *Deputy Dir Gen,* Magyar Nemzeti Galeria, Budapest, Hungary

Erichsen, John, *Asst Cur,* Kobenhavns Bymuseum, Copenhagen, Denmark

Erickson, Ann, *Assoc Prof,* Univ Minnesota, Saint Paul

Erickson, Jon T, *Cur Coll,* Heard Museum, Phoenix, AZ

Erickson, Lee, *Secy,* Eureka Springs Guild of Artists and Crafts People, AR

Erickson, Nancy, *Treas,* Allied Arts of Seattle, WA

Erickson, Virgil, *Clerk,* Springfield Art & Historical Society, VT

Erickson, Virginia, *Head Dept,* Concordia Lutheran College, Austin, TX

Eriksen, Svend, *Librn,* Det Danske Kunstindustrimuseum, Copenhagen, Denmark

Erikson, Marianne, *Asst Cur Textiles,* Rohsska Konstslojkmuseet, Goteborg, Sweden

Erlebacher, Walter, *Prof,* Philadelphia College of Art, PA

Erlich, Ruth, *Corresp Secy,* Nat Watercolor Society, Los Angeles, CA

Ermoyan, Arpi, *Exec Dir,* Society of Illustrators, see National and Regional Organizations

Erney, Richard A, *Assoc Dir,* State Historical Society of Wisconsin, Madison

Ernst, E Urban, *Pres,* Pioneer Museum and Haggin Galleries, Stockton, CA

Ernster, Sister Jacqueline, *Dir Summer School,* Mount Marty College, Yankton, SD

Eroh, Agnes, *Asst Prof,* Loma Linda Univ, La Sierra Campus, Riverside, CA

Erpelding, Victoria, *Library Asst,* Elmer Belt Library of Vinciana, Univ California, Los Angeles

Errickson, Betsy, *Asst Cur,* Hopewell Museum, NJ

Ertas, Adnon, *Mem Faculty,* College of DuPage, Glen Ellyn, IL

Esch, Joan L, *Asst Prof,* Mount Holyoke College, South Hadley, MA

Escott, Charles, *Chmn,* West Valley College, Saratoga, CA

Esher, Lord, *Rector,* Royal College of Art, London, England

Eshoo, Robert, *Supvr,* Currier Art Center, Currier Gallery of Art, Manchester, NH

Eskey, Doyle, *Assoc Prof,* Prince George's Community College, Largo, MD

Eskind, Andrew, *Asst Dir,* International Museum of Photography, Rochester, NY

Esler, J K, *Chmn,* Printing and Drawing Council of Canada, see National Organizations of Canada

Esmaili, Dusty, *Asst Cur,* Springville Museum of Art, UT

Esmerian, Ralph, *Chmn,* Museum of American Folk Art, New York, NY

Esparza, Roberto, *Community Relations Coordr,* San Antonio Museum Association, TX

Espejel, Dr Carlos, *Dir,* Museo Nacional de Artes y Industrias Populares, Mexico City, Mexico

Espey, Sister Jule Adele, *Asst Prof,* Our Lady of the Lake Univ, San Antonio, TX

Espinoso, Victoria, *Prof,* Inst Puerto Rican Culture, San Juan

Espinoza, Roberto, *Supt & Preparator,* Yuma Art Center, AZ

Esquibel, George, *Instr,* Sacramento City College, CA

Essers, Dr Volkmar, *Cur,* Kunstsammlung Nordrhein-Westfalen, Dusseldorf, Germany

Estabrook, Reed, *Asst Prof,* Univ Northern Iowa, Cedar Falls

Estell, Robin, *Secy,* Huntsville Art League and Museum Association, AL

Esterly, Freda, *Cur,* Staten Island Inst of Arts and Sciences, NY

Esteros, Gertrude, *Head Dept & Prof,* Univ Minnesota, Saint Paul

Estes, Jim, *Asst Prof,* Missouri Western State College, Saint Joseph

Estes, Maxie Chambliss, *Head Dept,* La Grange College, GA

Estes, Rosemary E, *Registrar,* Museum of Early Southern Decorative Arts, Winston-Salem, NC

Eszlary, Dr E, *Head Old Sculpture,* Szepmuveszet: Muzeum, Budapest, Hungary

Ethier, Louise, *Pres,* Musee D'Art de Saint-Laurent, PQ

Etkin, Mariano, *Music Dept,* Centro de Arte y Communicacion, Buenos Aires, Argentina

Etter, Juanita, *Asst Mgr,* Campus Martius Museum and Ohio River Museum, Marietta

Ettinger, Linda, *Mem Staff,* Arkansas Arts Center, Little Rock

Ettinghausen, Richard, *Consultative Chmn Islamic Art,* Metropolitan Museum of Art, New York, NY

Euell, Julian, *Asst Secy for Public Serv,* Smithsonian Institution, Washington, DC

Eugene, Robert, *Adminr,* Princeton Antiques Bookservice, Atlantic City, NJ

Eustace, Ann L, *Reference,* Nutley Public Library, NJ

Evans, Bob, *Exhib Chmn,* Paducah Art Guild, KY

Evans, Bruce H, *Dir,* Dayton Art Inst Galleries, OH

Evans, Charles F, *Head Dept & Asst Prof,* Winona State Univ, MN

Evans, Christine, *Mgr,* The Foundry, Honolulu, HI

Evans, Donald, *Assoc Prof,* Vanderbilt Univ, Nashville, TN

Evans, Dorothy G, *Dir,* School Art League of New York City, Brooklyn, NY

Evans, Elaine A, *Cur Coll,* Univ Tennessee, Knoxville

Evans, Elizabeth C, Cornell Univ, Ithaca, NY

Evans, Emily, *Asst Librn,* Portland Art Association, OR

Evans, Fran, *Librn,* Prince George Art Gallery, BC

Evans, Howard M, *Dir,* Haystack Mountain School of Crafts, Deer Isle, ME

Evans, Mrs Jack P, *Treas,* Montgomery Museum of Fine Arts, AL

Evans, James, *Asst Gallery Preparator,* Los Angeles Inst of Contemporary Art, CA

Evans, Joanne, *Publicity & Programming,* Joslyn Art Museum, Omaha, NE

Evans, John, *Sales Mgr,* Grand Central Art Galleries, New York, NY

Evans, Laura, *Dir & Dean Summer School,* Junior College of Albany, NY

Evans, Lenore K, *Lectr & Instr Summer School,* Michigan Technological Univ, Houghton

Evans, Linda E, *Prog Dir,* Western Association of Art Museums, see National and Regional Organizations

Evans, Mary L, *Secy,* Chester County Historical Society, West Chester, PA

Evans, Nancy Goyne, *Registrar,* Winterthur Museum and Gardens, DE

Evans, Richard, *Prof,* Univ Wyoming, Laramie

Evans, Robert, *Acad Dean,* Tennessee Wesleyan College, Athens

Evans, Mrs Robert G, *VChmn Bd & Chmn Mem,* Kansas City Art Inst Gallery, MO

Evans, Robert J, *Cur Art,* Illinois State Museum of Natural History and Art, Springfield

Evans, Sondra, *Cultural Arts Coordr,* Mills House Art Gallery, Garden Grove, CA

Evans, W Donald, *Chmn & Prof,* Lynchburg College, VA

Evarts, Wilbur, *Exec Dir,* Paint 'N' Palette Club, Anamosa, IA

Evans, William, *Chmn of Artists in Residence,* The Foundry, Honolulu, HI

Evelyn, Douglas E, *Asst Dir,* Nat Portrait Gallery, Washington, DC

Even, Robert L, *Chmn Art Dept,* Northern Illinois Univ, De Kalb

Everdingen, Arie Van, *Chmn Dept Art,* Monmouth College, West Long Branch, NJ

Everett, J Michael, *Head Prog in Landscape,* Rhode Island School of Design, Providence

Eversole, Mary, *Admin Asst,* Sangre De Cristo Arts & Conference Center, Pueblo, CO

Everts, Connor, *Head Printmaking Dept,* Cranbrook Academy of Art, Bloomfield Hills, MI

Eves, Bruce, *Publ,* Centre for Experimental Art and Communication, Toronto, ON

Evett, Kenneth, *Prof,* Cornell Univ, Ithaca, NY

Ewasaki, Yoshikazu, *Cur Painting,* Tokyo Kokuritsu Kindai Bijutsukan, Japan

Ewaschyshyn, Rev Justin, *Dir,* Basilian Fathers, Mundare, AB

Ewer, John C, *Develop Officer,* Worcester Art Museum, MA

Ewing, Bayard, *Pres & Trustee,* The American Federation of Arts, see National and Regional Organizations

Ewing, George, *Dir,* Museum of New Mexico, Santa Fe

Ewing, Lauren, *Head Dept Sculpture,* Rhode Island School of Design, Providence

Ewing, Tom, *Instr,* Wayne Art Center, PA

Ewing, Tom, *Mem Faculty,* Mainline Center of the Arts, Haverford, PA

Ewing, William, *Dir Exhib,* International Center of Photography, New York, NY

Eyerly, Pauline, *Cur Educ,* Portland Art Association, OR

Eysselinck, Walter, *Head Dept Drama,* Carnegie-Mellon Univ, Pittsburgh, PA

Fabbri, Nancy, *Assoc Prof,* Connecticut College, New London

Faber, Tobias, *Dir,* School of Architecture, Royal Danish Acad of Fine Arts, Copenhagen

Fabiano, Daniel, *Assoc Prof,* Univ Wisconsin-Stevens Point

Fabregas, Rafael, *Pres,* La Casa del Libro, San Juan, PR

Fabrycki, William, *Chmn Dept & Dir Summer School,* Joliet Junior College, IL

Facci, Domenico, *VPres,* Artists Equity Association of New York, NY

Faesy, Robert, *Pres,* Aldrich Museum of Contemporary Art, Ridgefield, CT

Fagaly, William, *Sr Cur Coll,* New Orleans Museum of Art, LA

Faggioli, Renzo, *Ceramist in-Residence,* Moravian College, Bethlehem, PA

Fahey, M Kevin, Jr, *Prog Dir,* Kilcawley Center Art Gallery, Youngstown State Univ, OH

Fahlen, Charles, *Chmn Printmaking,* Moore College ort, Philadelphia, PA

Fahlman, Betsy, *Resident Prof,* Franklin and Marshall College, Lancaster, PA

Fahy, Everett, *Dir,* Frick Collection, New York, NY

Faichney, John, *Art Librn,* Centre for Experimental Art and Communication, Toronto, ON

Fain, Barnet, *Chmn Mus Council,* Rhode Island School of Design Museum of Art, Providence

Fair, Beth, *Vol Coordr,* Palo Alto Cultural Center, CA

Fairbanks, Evelyn, *Exec Dir,* Metropolitan Cultural Arts Center, Minneapolis, MN

Fairbanks, Johnathan, *Cur American Decorative Arts,* Museum of Fine Arts, Boston, MA

Fairbanks, Justin, *Head,* Eastern Arizona College, Thatcher

Fairbrother, D, *VPres Civic Arts,* Community Arts Council of Vancouver, BC

Fairchild, Isabel S, *Dir,* Central Connecticut State College Museum, New Britain

Fairchild, Ruth, *Artist In-Residence,* Kirkland Art Center, Clinton, NY

Faircloth, Norman D, *Head,* Guilford Technical Inst, Jamestown, NC

Faison, Seth S, *VChmn,* Brooklyn Inst of Arts and Sciences, NY

Falana, K A, *Asst Prof,* Florida A&M Univ, Tallahassee

Falgoust, Hymel G, *Prof,* Southeastern Louisiana Univ, Hammond

Falk, Lorne, *Asst Cur,* Banff Centre, AB

Falk, Toby, *Mus Educ Coordr,* Tucson Museum of Art, AZ

Falkler, William A, *Pres,* York Acad of Arts, PA

Falkner, Etta, *Librn,* Old Sturbridge Village, MA

Fallon, Dr Jerome, *Dir Summer School,* Hillsdale College, MI

Falsetti, Joseph, *Prof,* Univ Tennessee, Knoxville

Fanani, Dom, *Mem Faculty,* Millersville State College, PA

Fanata, Katherine, *Circulation,* Long Beach Public Library, NY

Fancher, Oliver, *Asst Prof,* Middle Tennessee State Univ, Murfreesboro

Fantauzzi, Dan, *Instr,* Youngstown State Univ, OH

Faralli, Vincent, *Chmn Advertising Design,* Moore College of Art, Philadelphia, PA

Farber, Manny, *Prof,* Univ California, San Diego, La Jolla

Farinella, Paul J, *Pres,* Munson-William-Proctor Inst Museum of Art, Utica, NY

Faris, Brunel D, *Chmn,* Oklahoma City Univ, OK

Farkas, Ray Lynn, *VPres,* Wallingford Art League, CT

Farlow, Susan, *Asst,* Wellesley College Museum, MA

Farmer, Barthwell, *Chmn Art History,* Edinboro State College, PA

Farmer, Betsy, *Mem Faculty,* Shippensburg State College, PA

Farmer, John David, *Dir,* Birmingham Museum of Art, AL

Farnam, Anne, *Cur,* Essex Inst, Salem, MA

Farnham, Katherine G, *Cur Decorative Arts,* High Museum of Art, Atlanta, GA

Farooqi, Dr Anis, *Deputy Keeper Educ,* Nat Gallery of Modern Art, New Delhi, India

Farquharson, Alexander, *Mem Faculty,* Boston Center for Adult Education, MA

Farquharson, Marion, *Mem Faculty,* Rehoboth Art League, Rehoboth Beach, DE

Farrar, Elaine W, MA, *Instr,* Yavapai College, Prescott, AZ

Farrell, A, *Instr,* Selkirk College, Nelson, BC

Farrell, Mrs B, *Treas,* Edmonton Art Club, AB

Farrell, Mrs H W, *Pres,* Civic Fine Arts Association, Sioux Falls, SD

Farrell, Neal J, *Treas,* Museum of Modern Art, New York, NY

Farrell, Patricia, *Docent,* Chapel Arts Center, Saint Anselm's College, Manchester, NH

Fasake, William E, *Pres,* Schenectady County Historical Society, NY

Fash, Willam L, *Dean,* Georgia Inst of Technology, Atlanta

Fassett, Brian R, *Asst Prof,* Northeast Louisiana Univ, Monroe

Fasulo, Marijo, *Asst Dir,* State Univ New York at Albany

Faude, Wilson H, *Cur,* Mark Twain Mem, Hartford, CT

Faudie, Fred, *Asst Prof,* Univ Lowell, MA

Faukner, Lloyd E, *Chairperson Div,* Modesto Junior College, CA

Faul, Karene, *Mem Faculty,* College of St Rose, Albany, NY

Faulkner, Mrs Clark W, *Secy,* Nebraska Art Association, Univ Nebraska Art Gallery, Lincoln

Faunce, Sarah C, *Cur & Dept Head Paintings & Sculpture,* Brooklyn Museum, NY

Faust, Jemison, *Admnr,* School of the Art Association of Newport, RI

Fava, Dr Anna Serena, *Cur Numismatics,* Museo Civico, Torino, Italy

Favell, Gene H, *Pres,* Favell Museum of Western Art & Indian Artifacts, Klamath Falls, OR

Favell, Winifred L, *VPres & Treas,* Favell Museum of Western Art & Indian Artifacts, Klamath Falls, OR

Fawcett, Mrs Thomas, *Secy,* Old Gaol Museum, York, ME

Fawcett, W Peyton, *Librn,* Field Museum of Natural History, Chicago, IL

Faxon, Susan C, *Dir,* Univ New Hampshire Art Galleries, Durham

Fay, Kathy, *Art Instr,* School of Fashion Design, Boston, MA

Fayman, Mrs Lynn G, *Pres Bd Trustees,* La Jolla Museum of Contemporary Art, CA

Fazio, Beatrice, *Adult Serv Librn,* River Vale Public Library, NJ

Fazzini, Richard, *Cur Egyptian & Classical Art,* Brooklyn Museum, NY

Featherstone, David, *Exec Asst,* Friends of Photography, Carmel, CA

Feaux, Shirley, *Pres,* Huntsville Art League and Museum Association, AL

FeBland, Harriet, *Dir,* Harriet FeBland's Advanced Painters Workshop, New Rochelle, NY

Fechter, Earl, *Asst Prof,* Vermont College of Norwich Univ, Montpelier

Federico, Frank, *Instr,* Dunedin Fine Arts & Cultural Center, FL

Federico, Jean Taylor, *Cur,* DAR Museum, Washington, DC

Federighi, Christine, *Mem Faculty,* Univ Miami, Coral Gables, FL

Fee, S T, *Pres,* Oklahoma Museum of Art, Oklahoma City

Feeny, Lawrence, *Asst Prof,* Mississippi Univ for Women, Columbus

Feeny, William, *Mem Faculty,* Madison Area Technical College, WI

Feher, Joseph, *Sr Cur & Cur Graphic Arts & Studio Prog,* Honolulu Academy of Arts Collection, HI

Feichtneir, Karl, *Manuscripts,* California Historical Society, San Francisco

Feidt, Thorpe, *Mem Faculty,* Montserrat School of Visual Art, Beverly, MA

Feinberg, Jean, *Slide Registry Comt Mem,* Women's Slide Registry, New York, NY

Feinberg, Mildred, *Corresp Secy,* North Shore Art League, Winnetka, IL

Feinblatt, Ebria, *Sr Cur Prints & Drawings,* Los Angeles County Museum of Art, CA

Feiner, Lynn, *Recording Secy,* South County Art Association, Kingston, RI

Feint, Donald, *Mem Faculty,* Cornell Univ, Ithaca, NY

Feist, Harold, *Asst Prof,* Mount Allison Univ, Sackville, NB

Feitelson, Lorser, *Chmn,* Los Angeles Art Association and Galleries, CA

Felber, Leland, *Instr,* Milwaukee Area Technical College, WI

Feldenheimer, Mrs Paul, *Pres Art Association,* Reed College Art Gallery, Portland, OR

Feldman, Aline, *Corresp Secy,* Society of Washington Printmakers, Washington, DC

Feldman, Arthur M, *Dir,* Spertus Museum of Judaica, Chicago, IL

Feldman, Bella, *Instr,* California College of Arts and Crafts, Oakland

Feldman, Edmund B, *Dir Summer School,* Univ Georgia, Athens

Feldman, Eugene P, *Res Dir,* Du Sable Museum of African American History, Chicago, IL

Feldman, Lawrence H, *Cur & Dir,* Univ Missouri Museum of Anthropology, Columbia

Feld, Roger, *Vis Prof,* Linfield College, McMinnville, OR

Feldman, Walter, *Chmn Studio Div,* Brown Univ, Providence, RI

Felker, Wendy, *Admin Asst,* Reynolda House, Winston-Salem, NC

Fell, Dorothy, *Asst Dir,* Womens City Club of Cleveland, OH

Feller, Robert L, *Cur Analytical Lab,* Nat Gallery of Art, Washington, DC

Fellerhoff, Sister Mary Christine, *Chmn Arts & Letters,* Marian College, Fond du Lac, WI

Fellows, Helen, *Cur Coll,* Loveland Museum, CO

Felter, James Warren, *Cur & Dir Exhib,* Simon Fraser Univ Gallery & *Chmn,* Western Canada Art Association, Burnaby, BC

Feltus, Anne, *Publicist,* Museum of Fine Arts, Houston, TX

Fender, Roy, *Gallery Dir,* Western Maryland College, Westminster

Fenimore, Ronald, MA, *Coordr Advertsing Design,* Iowa State Univ, Ames

Fenn, Gale, *Secy,* Fitchburg Art Museum, MA

Fennelly, Raymond J, *Chief Educ,* Museum of Art, Science and Industry, Bridgeport, CT

Fenner, Wilbur, *Chmn,* Cerritos Community College, Norwalk, CA

Fenton, Julia A, *Dir Activities,* Atlanta Art Workers Coalition, GA

Fenton, T, *Dir,* Edmonton Art Gallery, AB

Fenz, Werner, *Cur,* Neue Galerie Am Landesmuseum Joanneum, Graz, Austria

Ferber, Elsie V H, *Cur Art Information,* Nat Gallery of Art, Washington, DC

Ferber, Lee, *Prof,* Drake Univ, Des Moines, IA

Ferber, Linda, *Cur Paintings & Sculpture,* Brooklyn Museum, NY

Ferber, Dr Stanley, *Chmn Dept Art & Art History,* State Univ New York at Binghamton

Ferdinandy, Magdalana, *Mem Faculty,* Univ Puerto Rico, Rio Pietras

Ferguson, Dr Carra, *Mem Faculty,* Georgetown Univ, Washington, DC

Ferguson Charles B, *Dir,* New Britain Museum of American Art, CT

Ferguson, Curt, *Regional Park Supt,* William S Hart Museum, Newhall, CA

Ferguson, John, *Mem Faculty,* Saint Louis Community College at Meramec, St Louis, MO

Ferguson, Dr John L, *Dir,* Arkansas History Commission, Little Rock

Ferguson, Kenneth, *Chmn Crafts,* Kansas City Art Inst, MO

Ferguson, Lorna, *Cur,* Tatham Art Gallery, Pietermaritzburg, South Africa

Ferguson, Marie D, *Dir Develop,* Dayton Art Inst Galleries, OH

Ferguson, Dr R H L, *Pres Councillor,* Auckland City Art Gallery, New Zealand

Ferguson, Robert, *Asst Cur,* Jersey City Museum Association, NJ

Ferguson, Robert J, *Chmn Dept & Dir Summer School,* Henry Ford Community College, Dearborn, MI

Ferguson, Rodney, *Prof,* Southern Univ in New Orleans, LA

Fergusson, Peter J, *Assoc Prof,* Wellesley College, MA

Ferioli, Dr Piera, *Asst to Supt,* Museo Nazionale Romano, Italy

Fernandes, Orlandino Seitas, *Dir,* Museu da Inconfidencia Brazil, Ouro Preto

Fernandez, Dorothy, *Secy,* Douglas Art Association, AZ

Fernandez, Nell, *Adminr,* Instituto Allende, San Maguel de Allende, Mexico

Fernandez, Rafael A, *Cur Prints & Drawings,* Sterling and Francine Clark Art Inst, Williamstown, MA

Fernando, Mrs W M, *Cur Educ & Publ,* Colombo Nat Museum, Sri Lanka

Ferng, Hou-Ran, *Librn,* St John's Univ Art Gallery, Jamaica, NY

Ferrario, Frank, *Instr,* Fontbonne College, Clayton, MO

Ferrario, Paula, *Serials & Rare Books,* Washington Univ Gallery of Art, St Louis, MO

Ferrazza, Mario, *Asst Cur Modern Religious Art Coll,* Monumenti Musei e Gallerie Pontificie, Vatican City, Italy

Ferren, Rae, *Asst Cur,* Guild Hall of East Hampton, NY

Ferrer, Miguel A, *Treas,* La Casa del Libro, San Juan, PR

Ferro, Maximilian L, *Architect,* Society for the Preservation of New England Antiquities, Boston, MA

Ferroni, Juan, *Head Architecture,* Javeriana Univ Faculty of Architecture and Design, Bogota, Colombia

Fessler, Sister M Thomasita, *Head Dept & Prof,* Cardinal Stritch College, Milwaukee, WI

Feszczak, Zenon L, *Design Dir,* Museum of the Philadelphia Civic Center, PA

Feszt, L, *Rector,* Institutul de Arte Plastice Ion Andreescu, Cluj-Napoca, Romania

Fetchko, Peter, *Asst Dir,* Peabody Museum of Salem, MA

Fetter, Katharine L, *PT Instr,* Lycoming College, Williamsport, PA

Fiandaca, Frederick A, *Asst Prof,* Framingham State College, MA

Fichter, Robert, *Assoc Prof,* Florida State Univ, Tallahassee

Fiebich-Ripke, Annemarie, *Cur Restoration,* Saltzburger Museum Carolino Augusteum, Austria

Field, Charles T, *Assoc Prof,* Univ Texas at San Antonio

Field, Frank E, *Pres,* Art Students League of New York Gallery, NY

Field, Sister M Theophane, *Mem Faculty,* Sacred Heart College, Belmont, NC

Field, Philip, *Chmn Printmaking,* Pan American Univ, Edinburg, TX

Field, Mrs R, *Secy,* Maitland Art Center & Research Studio, FL

Field, Dr Richard S, *Cur,* Wesleyan Univ, Middletown, CT

Fields, Dale, *Exec Dir,* Historical Society of Delaware, Wilmington

Fields, Marjorie, *Pres,* Sculpture Center, New York, NY

Fields, Patricia, *Prof,* Linfield College, McMinnville, OR

Fife, Ed, *Assoc Prof,* Dept of Landscape Architecture, Univ Toronto, ON

Fifield, Mary L, *Chmn Dept Art & Dir Summer School,* Saint Louis Community College at Forest Park, MO

Figueroa, Paul C, *Cur Educ,* Carolina Art Association, Charleston, SC

Fijalkowski, Stanislaw, *Head Graphic Arts Dept & Prof,* Panstwowa Wyzsza Szkola Sztuk Plastycznych, Lodz, Poland

Fikus, Vivian Noyes, *Owner-Dir,* Nutley Art Center & *Secy,* Miniature Art Society of New Jersey, Nutley

File, Sister M Jeanne, *Prof,* Daemen College, Amherst, NY

Filkosky, Josefa, *Mem Faculty,* Seton Hill College, Greensburg, PA

Finch, Martin, *VPres,* Association of Medical Illustrators, see National and Regional Organizations

Finch, Robert Finch, *Mem Faculty,* Mainline Center of the Arts, Haverford, PA

Finch, Zaidee, *Secy,* Calgary Artists Society, AB

Findlay, Virginia, *Asst Prof,* Fontbonne College, Clayton, MO

Fine, Ruth, *VPres,* Print Club, Philadelphia, PA

Fine, Ruth E, *Cur,* Alverthorpe Gallery, Jenkintown, PA

Finegan, Don, *Prof,* Univ Northern Iowa, Cedar Falls

Fingesten, Peter, *Chmn,* Pace Univ, New York, NY

Fink, Charles B, *Head Prog Interior Archit,* Rhode Island School of Design, Providence

Fink, Herbert, *Printmaker/Drawer,* Southern Illinois Univ, Carbondale

Fink, Larry, *Vis Prof,* Yale Univ, New Haven, CT

Fink, Lois M, *Research Cur,* Nat Collection of Fine Arts, Washington, DC

Finkel, Kenneth, *Cur Prints,* Library Co of Philadelphia, PA

Finkel, Tina I, *Pres,* Duke Univ Union Graphic Arts Committee, Durham, NC

Finkelpearl, Katherine D, *Librn,* Wellesley College Museum, MA

Finkelstein, Joseph, *Pres,* Schenectady Museum, NY

Finkstein, Jan, *Head Indust Design Dept & Reader,* Panstwowa Wyzsza Szkola Sztuk Plastycznych, Lodz, Poland

Finlay, J C, *Pres,* Association des Musees Canadiens, see National Organizations in Canada

Finlayson, Dr Elizabeth, *Dir Summer School,* James Madison Univ, Harrisonburg, VA

Finlayson, Mona, *Asst Prin,* Nutana Collegiate Inst, Saskatoon, SK

Finley, Gregg, *Cur Canadian History,* New Brunswick Museum, Sain John

Finok, Furman J, *Pres,* Artists' Fellowship, New York, NY

Fiorello, Joseph, *Prof,* Boston State College, MA

Firestone, Evan R., *Assoc Prof,* Western Carolina Univ, Cullowhee, NC

Firm, Ruth M, *Prof,* Sweet Briar College, VA

Firth, Edith G, *Head Canadian History Dept,* Metropolitan Toronto Library Board, ON

Fisch, Robert W, *Cur Arms & Armor,* West Point Museum, NY

Fischer, Barbara, *Children's Room Dept Head,* Wichita Public Library, KS

Fischer, Billie, *Mem Faculty,* Kalamazoo College, MI

Fischer, Dr Eberhard, *Dir,* Museum Rietberg Zürich, Switzerland

Fischer, Erik, *Keeper Dept Prints & Drawings,* Statens Museum for Kunst, Copenhagen, Denmark

Fischer, Henry G, *Lila Acheson Wallace Cur Egyptology,* Metropolitan Museum of Art, New York, NY

Fischer, Michael, *Photographer Office of Registrar,* Nat Collection of Fine Arts, Washington, DC

Fischer, Mrs Robert L, *Secy,* Grand Prairie Art Council, Stuttgart, AR

Fish, Janet, *Vis Prof,* State Univ New York at Stony Brook

Fish, Kaye, *Registrar,* Norton Gallery and School of Art, West Palm Beach, FL

Fish, Mary, *Mem Faculty,* Housatonic Community College, Bridgeport, CT

Fisher, Alleene Lowery, *Dir,* Art School of the Crafts Guild

Fisher, Mrs B C, *Owner,* Westover, Charles City, VA

Fisher, Clare, *Dir,* Once Gallery, New York, NY

Fisher, Fred, *Designer & Asst to Dir,* Univ Illinois, Champaign

Fisher, James, *Dir,* Elizabet Ney Museum, Austin, TX

Fisher, Jay, *Asst Cur Prints & Drawings,* Baltimore Museum of Art, MD

Fisher, John C, *Secy,* Louisiana State Univ Art Museum, Baton Rouge

Fisher, John J, *Journal Ed,* American Society for Aesthetics, see National and Regional Organizations

Fisher, Mac, *Mem Faculty,* Samuel S Fleisher Art Mem, Philadelphia, PA

Fisher, Morgan, *Film & Video Coordr,* Los Angeles Inst of Contemporary Art, CA

Fisher, Nora, *Cur Textiles,* Museum of International Folk Art, Santa Fe, NM

Fisher, Paula, *Recording Secy,* North Shore Art League, Winnetka, IL

Fisher, Rosemary, *Mem Staff,* Arkansas Arts Center, Little Rock

Fisher, Sunny, *Pres,* Crossett Art League, AR

Fisher, Vernon, *Assoc Prof,* Austin College, Sherman, TX

Fiske, Patricia L, *Asst Cur Old World,* Textile Museum, Washington, DC

Fiske, Timothy, *Chmn Educ Div,* Minneapolis Inst of Arts, MN

Fite, Nancy, *Coordr Children's Mus,* Arts and Science Center, Nashua, NH

Fittipaldi, Teodoro, *Supvr,* Museo de Capodimonte, Naples, Italy; *Dir,* Museo Nazionale di San Martino, Naples, Italy

Fitzgerald, Dori B, *Mem & Educ Coordr,* Roanoke Fine Arts Center, VA

Fitzgerald, Harriet, *Dir,* Abingdon Square Painters, New York, NY

Fitzgerald, Oscar, *Vis Lectr,* Marymount College of Virginia, Arlington

Fitzgerald, Sally, *Cultural Affairs Coordr,* Federal Reserve Bank of Boston, MA, see Corporate Art Holdings

Fitzmaurice, Robert M, *Chmn,* Inter American Univ Puerto Rico, San German

Fitzpatrick, Barney, *Instr,* McLennan Community College, Waco, TX

Fitzpatrick, Joseph, *Prof,* Univ Kentucky, Lexington

Fitzpatrick, Philip, *Instr,* Lamar Univ, Beaumont, TX

Fitzpatrick, Robert, *Pres,* California Inst of the Arts, Valencia

Fitzsimmons, Barbara, *VPres,* Clearwater Art Association, ID

Fix, John R, *Mem Staff,* Norwich Art School, CT

Flach, Victor, *Prof,* Univ Wyoming, Laramie

Flagg, Thomas J, *Dean,* Howard Univ, Washington, DC

Flaherty, Michael, *Craftshop Dir,* Univ Southwestern Louisiana Union Art Gallery, Lafayette

Flanigan, Rev James F, *Chmn Art Dept & Chmn Summer School,* Univ Notre Dame, IN

Flannelly, Margaret Ellen, *Dir Summer School,* Marymount College, Tarrytown, NY

Flannery, Louis, *Chief Librn,* Oregon Historical Society, Portland

Flannery, Michael J, *Interlibrary Loan Librn,* Lamson Library, Plymouth State College, NH

Flavin, Patricia, *Clerical Officer,* Hugh Lane Municipal Gallery of Modern Art, Dublin, Ireland

Fleck, Dr Paul D, *Pres,* Ontario College of Art, Toronto

Fleck, Rudolf, *Asst Prof,* Loyola Marymount Univ, Los Angeles, CA

Fleishman, Lawrence A, *Gallery Trustee,* Visual Artists and Galleries Association, see National and Regional Organizations

Fleming, Eleanor, *Admin Asst & Dir Summer School,* Arts and Sciences Center, Nashua, NH

Fleming, Mrs J G, *VPres Policy & Planning,* Community Arts Council of Vancouver, BC

Fleming, Joseph O, II, *Dir Div Fine Arts,* Central Florida Community College Art Collection, Ocala

Fleming, William, *Supt,* Frick Collection, New York, NY

Flesicher, Roland, *Prof,* Pennsylvania State Univ, University Park

Fletcher, Dale T, *Dir,* B R Larsen Gallery, Brigham Young Univ, Provo, UT

Fletcher, Dr Donald B, *Pres,* Redwood Library and Athenaeum, Newport, RI

Fletcher, Martha, *Conservator,* Univ Washington Henry Art Gallery, Seattle

Fletcher, P R, *Head Dept Printing Technol,* Manchester Polytechnic, England

Flick, Hugh M, *Pres,* New York State Historical Association, Cooperstown, NY

Flinn, Elizabeth, *Assoc Mus Educ,* Junior Museum, Metropolitan Museum of Art, New York, NY

Flint, Janet A, *Cur Prints & Drawings,* Nat Collection of Fine Arts, Washington, DC

Flint, Patti, *Pres,* Galesburg Civic Art Center, IL

Flint, Peter, *Vis Prof,* Porterville Community College, CA

Floeter, Kent, *Asst Prof,* Herbert H Lehman College, Bronx, NY

Flood, James W, *Chmn,* Towson State College, Baltimore, MD

Flora, Joseph, *VPres,* Schenectady Museum, NY

Flores, Yolanda, *Secy,* Pontiac Creative Arts Center, MI

Floreth, Dorothy, *Pres Art Assoc,* David Strawn Art Gallery, Jacksonville, IL

Flowers, Thomas E, *Assoc Prof,* Furman Univ, Greenville, SC

Floyd, Margaret, *Asst Prof,* Tufts Univ, Medford, MA

Fluet, Sister Eunice, *Dir Summer School,* Rivier College, Nashua, NH

Flumiani, Dr C M, *Dir,* American Classical College, Albuquerque, NM

Flynn, Barbara, *Prin Librn,* Ontario City Library, CA

Flynn, Brandan, *Keeper Art,* Central Art Gallery, Wolverhampton, England

Flynn, Charles, *Instr,* Virginia Wesleyan College, Norfolk

Flynn, Charles, *Instr,* Virginia State College, Petersburg

Foerster, Bernd, *Dean Art School & Dean Summer School,* Kansas State Univ, Manhattan

Foester, Dr Lloyd, *Acad Dean Summer School,* Bethany College, Lindsborg, KS

Fogel, Dr D, *VPres,* Nicholas Roerich Museum, New York, NY

Fohrman, Darcie Cohen, *Designer,* Spertus Museum of Judaica, Chicago, IL

Foley, Kathy K, *Asst Cur,* Dayton Art Inst Galleries, OH

Foley, Suzanne, *Chief Cur,* San Francisco Museum of Modern Art, CA

Follette, Kent, *Asst Prof,* Loyola Univ of Chicago, IL

Follis, Nancy, *Secy,* Lindenwood Colleges Gallery, St Charles, MO

Folsom, Karl L, *Preparator,* Wine Museum of San Francisco, CA

Folsom, Stan, *Instr,* Brockton Art Center, MA

Fomenko, Mrs Peter, *Pres Bd Dirs,* Zanesville Art Center, OH

Fominaya, Eloy, *Head Dept & Prof,* Augusta College, GA

Fonda, Henry E, *Chairperson,* Nat Council for Arts and Education, see National and Regional Organizations

Fong, Ruby, *Secy,* Univ Calgary, AB

Fong, Wen, *Prof & Chmn Prog Chinese & Japanese Art & Archaeol,* Princeton Univ, NJ; *Special Consult,* Metropolitan Museum of Art, New York, NY

Fontein, Jan, *Cur Asiatic Art,* Museum of Fine Arts, Boston MA

Foote, Marjorie B, *Cur Costumes,* Schenectady Museum, NY

Foote, Vincent M, *Dir Product Design Prog,* North Carolina State Univ at Raleigh

Forbes, Mr, *Deputy Warden Assay Office,* Worshipful Co of Goldsmiths, London, England

Forbes, Anne, *Instr,* Craft Center, Worcester, MA

Forbes, Donna M, *Dir,* Yellowstone Art Center, Billings, MT

Force, Debra J, *Cur,* Insurance of North America, Philadelphia, PA, see Corporate Art Holdings

Ford, Beth M, *Asst Prof,* Florida Southern College, Lakeland

Ford, Charles, *Exhib Coordr,* Jay R Broussard Mem Galleries, Baton Rouge, LA

Ford, Dean Lee, *Dir Summer School,* Santa Ana College, CA

Ford, Harry X, *Pres,* California College of Arts and Crafts, Oakland

Ford, Ingrid, *Mem,* California Historical Society, San Francisco

Ford, Sharon E, *Instr,* Santa Ana College, CA

Ford, William Clay, *Chmn,* Greenfield Village and Henry Ford Museum, Dearborn, MI

Forero, Diego, *Architecture Coordr,* Centro de Arte y Communicacion, Buenos Aires, Argentina

Forester-Hahn, Francoise, *Asst Prof,* Univ California, Riverside

Forge, Andrew, *Dean,* Yale Univ, New Haven, CT

Formosa, Gerald, *Instr,* Vancouver Community College, Langara Campus, BC

Fornemann, Dr Rudolph, *Cur History,* Milwaukee Public Museum, WI

Forney, Darrell E, *Subject Area Rep & Dir Summer School,* Sacramento City College, CA

Forrest, Eric, *Dir,* School of Art, Ohio Univ, Athens

Forrest, James T, *Dir Art Museum & Prof,* University of Wyoming, Cheyenne

Forrest, James Taylor, *Dir,* Bradford Brinton Mem Ranch Museum, Big Horn, WY

Fors, Richard E, *Dir,* John Woodman Higgins Armory, Worcester, MA

Forslund, Inga, *Librn,* Museum of Modern Art, New York, NY

Forst, Miles, *Chmn Intermedia,* Otis Art Inst, Los Angeles, CA

Forster, Mark, *Cur,* Luna County Museum, Deming, NM

Forster, Patricia, *Librn,* Nat Gallery of Victoria, Australia

Forster, Peter E, *Asst to Dean,* Univ Manitoba, Winnipeg

Forte, Marie-Josee, *Conservator,* Musee de L'Oeuvre Notre Dame, Strasbourg, France

Fortenberry, Paul, *Instr,* Pels School of Art, New York, NY

Fortess, Fred, *Dir School,* Philadelphia College of Textiles and Science, PA

Fortson, Kay, *Pres,* Kimbell Art Museum, Fort Worth, TX

Fosdick, Sina, *Exec VPres,* Nicholas Roerich Museum, New York, NY

Foss, Randi, *Librn,* Norsk Folkemuseum, Oslo, Norway

Fossi, Dr Mazzino, *Librn,* Galleria e Museo Estense, Modena, Italy

Foster, April, *Mem Faculty,* Art Academy of Cincinnati, OH

Foster, Arthur J, *Secy,* American Fine Arts Society, New York, NY

Foster, Brian, *Mgr,* Colby Community College Arts Center, KS

Foster, David, *Chmn Art Dept,* Lake Tahoe Community College, South Lake Tahoe, CA

Foster, Doris, *Visual Arts Coordr,* Fine Arts Association, Willoughby, OH

Foster, Edward E, *Chmn,* Saint Mary's College of Maryland, Saint Mary's City

Foster, James W, *Dir,* Honolulu Academy of Arts Collection, HI

Foster, Ken, *Mem Faculty,* Muskegon Community College, MI

Foster, Ralph, *VChmn,* School of the Ozarks, Point Lookout, MO

Foster, Mrs V, *Keeper Costumes,* Manchester City Art Galleries, England

Fostervoll, Kari, *Conservator Textiles,* Kunstindustrimuseet, Oslo, Norway

Foujita, Shin-ichiro, *Cur,* Ohara Bijitsukan, Okayama Prefecture, Kurashiki, Japan

Fountain, Gail, *Asst Prof,* Univ Wisconsin-Stevens Point

Fouste, Dr Bonnie, *Coordr Summer School,* Cypress College, CA

Fowle, William C, *Mem Faculty,* Mercersburg Acad, PA

Fowler, Albert W, *Asst Dir,* Swarthmore College, PA

Fowler, Clayton V, *Prof,* St Lawrence Univ, Canton, NY

Fowler, David, *Chmn Bd Trustees,* Mississippi Museum of Art, Jackson

Fowler, Harry W, *VPres,* American Numismatic Society, see National and Regional Organizations

Fowler, Mrs Theodore, *Acting Librn,* Washington Depot Art Association, CT

Fox, Ellen, *Vis Prof,* West Texas State Univ, Canyon

Fox, Frank, *Chmn Design Div,* Nova Scotia College of Art and Design, Halifax

Fox, Jan Marshall, *Art Coordr,* Univ Wisconsin-Madison Mem Union

Fox, John, *Instr,* Community College of the Finger Lakes, Canandaigua, NY

Fox, Judith, *Asst Dir,* Wellesley College Museum, MA

Fox, Laurie A, *Asst Art Librn,* Ann Bunce Cheney Library, Hartford Art School, West Hartford, CT

Fox, Marcia S, *Publicity Dir,* Silvermine Guild of Artists Gallery, New Canaan, CT

Fox, Thurman O, *Dir Mus,* State Historical Society of Wisconsin, Madison

Foy, Elizabeth J, *Admin Asst,* Nat Gallery of Art, Washington, DC

Fraas, Gayle, *Instr,* Hinckley School of Crafts, ME

Fraccio, William, *Instr,* Propersi Galleries and School of Art, Greenwich, CT

Fraenkel, Richard, *Chmn & Prof,* Univ Rhode Island, Kingston

Fraher, David J, *Coordr Artists in Schools /Dir Poetry Prog,* Wyoming Council on the Arts, Cheyenne

Frampton, Linda, *Asst Registrar PT Studies (Summer School),* Ontario College of Art, Toronto

Francell, Larry, *Dir & Librn,* Wichita Falls Museum and Art Center, TX

Franci, Cortez, *Prof,* Manatee Junior College, Brandenton, FL

Francis, Ellen, *Secy,* Arts for Living Center, Burlington, IA

Francis, Nancy, *Librn,* Eleanor Calvert Mem Library, Kitchener-Waterloo Art Gallery, ON

Francksen, Jean, *Prof,* Beaver College, Glenside, PA

Franco, Robert, *Dir School & Dir Summer School,* Silvermine Guild School of the Arts, New Canaan, CT

Frandrup, Sister Dennis, *Mem Faculty,* College of Saint Benedict, Saint Joseph, MN

Frandsen, Doris, *Dir Exhib,* Waterloo Art Association, IA

Frandsen, Jan Wurtz, *Asst Keeper, Dept Prints & Drawings,* Statens Museum for Kunst, Copenhagen, Denmark

Franjevic, Jack N, *Head Dept,* College of Great Falls, MT

Frank, Ann, *Fine Arts Librn,* Manchester City Library, NH

Frank, Barbara, *Asst Cur Slide Librn,* Univ California Art Galleries, Riverside

Frank, David, *Assoc Prof,* Mississippi Univ for Women, Columbus

Frank, Guy, *Chmn,* Shepherd College, Shepherdstown, WV

Frank, Richard, *Asst Prof,* Augusta College, GA

Frankel, Dextra, *Dir,* California State Univ Art Gallery, Fullerton

Frankel, Robert H, *Asst Dir,* Phoenix Art Museum, AZ

Franken, Bette, *Registrar,* Inst and Museum of the Great Plains, Lawton, OK

Franklin, Carole, *Music Librn,* Pennsylvania State Univ Museum of Art, University Park

Franklin, Ed, *Instr,* Central Florida Community College, Ocala

Franklin, Edith, *First VPres,* Toledo Federation of Art Societies, OH

Franklin, Gilbert A, *Chmn Div Fine Arts,* Rhode Island School of Design, Providence

Franklin, Dr Hardy R, *Dir,* Public Library of the District of Columbia, Washington, DC

Franklin, Martha, *Asst Librn,* Kalamazoo Inst of Art, MI

Franklin, Patt, *Assoc Prof,* Univ Maine at Portland-Gorham, Gorham

Frankova, Dr A, *Chief Dept Expositions,* Statni Zidovske Muzeum Prague, Czechoslovakia

Frankowiak, Robert, *Asst Art Dir,* Milwaukee Public Museum, WI

Franks, Dr Kenny, *Publns,* Oklahoma Historical Society, Oklahoma City

Frankston, Dr Leon, *Chmn,* Nassau Community College, Garden City, NY

Fransen, Hans, *Asst Dir,* South African Nat Gallery, Cape Town

Frantz, Barry, *Mem Faculty,* Cuesta College, San Luis Obispo, CA

Frantz, Richard C, *Cur Exhib,* Manchester Inst of Arts and Sciences, NH

Franzen, Joan C, *Dir,* Skowhegan School of Painting and Sculpture, ME

Frase, John M, *Prof,* George Peabody College for Teachers, Nashville, TN

Fraser, E D, *Cur,* Art Gallery of Windsor, ON

Fraser, John A, *Asst Secy & Treas,* Hall of Fame of the Trotter, Goshen, NY

Frattallone, Joe, *Assoc Prof,* Western Michigan Univ, Kalamazoo

Fray, Florence M, *Asst Dir,* Spokane Public Library, WA

Frayher, Mary, *Secy,* Guild Hall of East Hampton, NY

Frazar, Stanton M, *Dir,* Historic New Orleans Collection, LA

Fraze, Denny, *Chmn,* Amarillo College, TX

Frazer, Alan D, *Registrar,* New Jersey Historical Society Museum, Newark

Frazer, Alfred, *Chmn, Dept Art History & Archaeology & Graduate Dept,* Columbia Univ, New York, NY

Frazer, John, *Prof,* Wesleyan Univ, Middletown, CT

Frazier, Douglas, *Pres,* Artists Association of Nantucket, MA

Frazier, Richard B, *VPres,* Cody Country Art League, WY

Frederick, Anne P, *Instr,* Univ Richmond, VA

Frederick, Charles, *Assoc Prof,* California State Polytechnic Univ, Pomona

Frederick, Kathleen A, *Asst Librn,* Chester County Historical Society, West Chester, PA

Fredericks, Marjorie H, *Prog & Publns,* Newark Museum, NJ

Fredericks, Marshall M, *Second VPres,* Brookgreen Gardens, Murrells Inlet, SC

Fredericksen, Burton, *Cur Paintings,* J Paul Getty Museum, Malibu, CA

Fredricksen, Daniel, *Cur Exhib,* Kenosha Public Museum, WI

Frederikse, Yolanda R, *Chmn,* Immaculata College of Washington, DC

Fredlund, Bjorn, *Cur Old Masters Dept,* Goteborgs Konstmuseum, Sweden

Free, Renee, *Acting Sr Cur & Cur European & American Art,* Art Gallery of New South Wales, Sydney, Australia

Freed, James Ingo, *Dean,* Illinois Inst of Technology, Chicago

Freedman, Ben, *Prof,* West Virginia Univ, Morgantown

Freeman, Gary, *Chmn Sculpture Prog,* Herron School of Art, Indiana Univ-Purdue Univ, Indianapolis

Freeman, J, *Prof & Assoc Chmn Dept,* Univ Alberta, Edmonton

Freeman, John, *Instr,* Del Mar College, Corpus Christi, TX

Freeman, John, *Asst Prof,* Univ Wisconsin-Superior

Freeman, June, *Dir State Serv,* Arkansas Arts Center, Little Rock

Freeman, Mark, *Pres,* National Society of Painters in Casein and Acrylic, see National and Regional Organizations; *Pres,* Audubon Artists, see National and Regional Organizations; *VPres,* Artists Equity Association of New York, NY

Freeman, Susie, *Museum Shop & Volunteer,* Plains Art Museum, Moorhead, MN

Freeman, Tina, *Cur Photography,* New Orleans Museum of Art, LA

Freemen, Jean, *Literary & Theatre Officer,* Saskatchewan Arts Board, Regina

Freer, Harvey, *Dir Coll,* Maryhill Museum of Art, Goldendale, WA

Freer, Raymond A, *Chmn,* Anderson College, IN

Freeth, Andrew, *Chmn Faculty Printmaking,* British School at Rome, Italy

Freifeld, Eric, *Chmn Dept Fine Art,* Ontario College of Art, Toronto

Freitag, Wolfgang, *Librn,* Fogg Art Museum, Cambridge, MA

Freivogel, Dr Max, *Dir,* Museum Zu Allerheiligen, Schaffhausen, Switzerland

Frel, Dr Jiri, *Cur Antiquities,* J Paul Getty Museum, Malibu, CA

French, Denney G, *Secy,* Art Association of Richmond, IN

French, Ray H, *Prof,* DePauw Univ, Greencastle, IN

French, Ronald L, *Dir,* Div of Advertising Design School, Al Gable Advertising Art School, Cincinnati, OH

Frenguelli, P, *Prof Architecture & Dir,* Accademia di Belle Arti, Perugia, Italy

Frenk-Westheim, Mariana, *Coordr,* Museo de Arte Moderno, Mexico City, Mexico

Freshley, Katherine T, *Librn,* Arthur D Jenkins Library, Washington, DC

Frets, Paul W, *Prof,* Radford College, VA

Fretwell, Dr E K, Jr, *Chmn Advisory Comt,* Burchfield Center, Buffalo, NY

Freudenheim, Tom L, *Dir,* Baltimore Museum of Art, MD

Freundlich, August L, *Dean,* Syracuse Univ, NY

Freve, Mrs Claire, *Secy,* Le Comite des Arts D'Arvida, PQ

Frey, Viola, *Instr,* California College of Arts and Crafts, Oakland

Frick, Henry Clay, II, *Pres,* Frick Collection, New York, NY

Fricke, Michele, *Gallery Dir,* Saint Mary's College, Notre Dame, IN

Fridley, Pat, *Secy,* Alaska Artists Guild, Anchorage

Fridley, Russell W, *Dir,* Minnesota Historical Society, Saint Paul

Fried, Walter J, *Chmn,* Guild Hall of East Hampton, NY

Friedenberg, Elizabeth, *Adj Prof,* Centenary College of Louisiana, Shreveport

Friedhoff, Beverly, *Office Mgr,* Civic Fine Arts Association, Sioux Falls, SD

Friedlander, Robert, *Pres,* New York Society of Architects, NY

Friedman, Dick, *Dir Summer School,* Central Oregon Community College, Bend

Friedman, Estelle, *Instr,* Santa Ana College, CA

Friedman, Joan, *Cur Rare Books,* Yale Univ Art Gallery, New Haven, CT

Friedman, John, *Chmn Photography,* De Young Museum Art School, San Francisco, CA

Friedman, Dr Kenneth S, *Exec Dir,* Inst for Advanced Studies in Contemporary Art, San Diego, CA

Friedman, Martin, *Dir,* Walker Art Center, Minneapolis, MN

Friedman, Mildred S, *Editor,* Walker Art Center, Minneapolis, MN

Friedman, Mira, *Cur,* Tel Aviv Museum, Israel

Friedman, Roger J, *Pres,* Lotos Club, New York, NY

Frinta, Mojmir, *Prof,* State Univ New York at Albany

Frisch, Susan, *Curatorial Asst,* Chesterwood, Stockbridge, MA

Frisenda, John, *Instr,* Corning Community College, NY

Fritsch, John, *Mem Faculty,* Madison Area Technical College, WI

Fritschi, Ingeborg, *VPres,* Nicholas Roerich Museum, New York, NY

Fritzmann, Frank J, *Gallery Coordr,* Northeastern Illinois Univ, Chicago

Frizzelle, Jack, *Mgr Pub Information,* Metropolitan Museum of Art, New York, NY

Frodl, Dr Gerbert, *Cur,* Osterreichische Galerie, Vienna, Austria

Froenlich, Olga, *Asst,* Artists Gallery, Vancouver, BC

Frohock, Edith, *Assoc Prof,* Univ Alabama in Birmingham

Froidevaux, N M, *Vis Prof,* Fontainebleau School of Fine Arts, France

Frolich, Brother Gebhard, *Chmn,* Loyola Univ, New Orleans, LA

Frombach, Ernest, *Assoc Prof,* Mansfield State College, PA

Fromer, Seymour, *Dir,* Judah L Magnes Mem Museum, Berkeley, CA

Fromm, Dolores, *Secy,* Kitchener-Waterloo Art Gallery, ON

Fronmuller, Regina Marie, *Head Dept & Dir Summer School,* Springfield College, IL

Fronton, A, *Registrar,* Nat Gallery of Canada, Ottawa, ON

Frontz, Stephanie, *Librn,* Univ Rochester, NY

Frost, Mrs F Daniel, *VPres,* Los Angeles County Museum of Art, CA

Ghez, M Oscar, *Pres & Founder,* Musee D' Art Moderne, Geneva, Switzerland

Ghiz, Ronald, *Assoc Prof,* Univ Maine, Orono

Giaccone, T, *Chmn Advertising Design,* Fashion Inst of Technology, New York, NY

Giannotti, John, *Chmn,* Rutgers Univ, Camden, NJ

Gibb, Pamela, *Coordr,* Ontario Association of Art Galleries, Toronto

Gibbons, Jerry, *Chmn,* Southern Baptist College, College City, AR

Gibbs, Cora Lee, *Cur Educ,* Rhode Island School of Design Museum of Art, Providence

Gibbs, Donald T, *Librn,* Redwood Library and Athenaeum, Newport, RI

Gibbs, Rebecca, *Secy,* Mexico-Audrain County Library, Mexico, MO

Gibbs, Timothy, *Head Painting,* Univ Oxford, England

Gibian, J Catherine, *Chmn Art Dept & In Charge Art Slide Library,* State Univ New York College at Cortland

Gibson, D, *Mem Officer,* Peace Region Arts Society, Spirit River, AB

Gibson, Dorothy, *Pres,* Plastic Club, Philadelphia, PA

Gibson, Ellery B, *Mem Faculty,* Northern Arizona Univ, Flagstaff

Gibson, George, *Managing Ed,* Historical Society of Delaware, Wilmington

Gibson, James S, *Assoc Prof,* Middle Tennessee State Univ, Murfreesboro

Gibson, Jill, *Teacher,* Venice Painting, Drawing & Sculpture Studio, CA

Gibson, Jim, *Chmn,* Northern State College, Aberdeen, SD

Gibson, M, *Exten Officer,* Saskatoon Gallery and Conservatory Corp, SK

Gibson, Walter S, *Assoc Prof & Chmn,* Case Western Reserve Univ, Cleveland, OH

Gieber, P Terry, *Instr Art,* Southwestern Community College, Creston, IA

Gielle, Kenneth, *Instr,* Annhurst College, Woodstock, CT

Gieschen, Martin J, *Chmn,* Junior College of Albany, NY

Giese, David, *Asst Prof,* Univ Idaho, Moscow

Giesy, Alene, *Circ Dept Head,* Topeka Public Library, KS

Giigel, Lewis E, *Dean Div,* El Camino College, Los Angeles, CA

Gikas, Chris, *Dir Art Gallery, Head Dept Art & Dir Summer School,* Eastern New Mexico Univ, Portales

Gilbert, Albert, *VPres,* Society of Animal Artists, see National and Regional Organizations

Gilbert, Gail, *Admin Asst,* Amarillo Art Center, TX

Gilbert, Gail R, *Art Librn,* Allen R Hite Art Inst, Univ Louisville, KY

Gilbert, James, *Instr,* Pontiac Art Center, MI

Gilbert, Mrs James, *Educ & Prog Chmn,* Cody County Art League, WY

Gilbert, Phyllis, *Pres,* Springfield Art Association of Edwards Place, IL

Gilbert, W Herbert, *Assoc Prof,* Univ British Columbia, Vancouver

Gilborn, Craig A, *Dir,* Adirondack Museum of the Adirondack Historical Association, Blue Mountain Lake, NY

Gilfoy, Peggy S, *Cur Ethnographic Art Textiles & Supvr Educ Prog & Serv,* Indianapolis Museum of Art, IN

Gilg, Karen K, *Asst to Cur,* Southern Utah State College, Cedar City

Gilkey, Gordon W, *Dean Col,* Oregon State Univ, Corvallis

Gill, Andrew J, *Exec Dir,* New Muse Community Museum of Brooklyn, NY

Gill, Brendan, *Pres,* Municipal Art Society of New York, NY

Gill, Charles, *Instr,* California College of Arts and Crafts, Oakland

Gill, Johanna, *Chmn Media,* Massachusetts College of Art, Boston

Gill, M S, *Librn,* Lahore Museum, Pakistan

Gill, Mohinder S, *Assoc Prof,* Elizabeth City State Univ, NC

Gill, Phyllis, *Admin Asst Art Galleries,* Univ California, Riverside

Gill, Sarah, *Prof,* Santa Rosa Junior College, CA

Gill, Thomas, *Assoc Dir Art Dept & Assoc Dir Summer School,* Chemeketa Community College, Salem, OR

Gillespie, Bruce, *Treas,* Wayne Art Center, PA

Gillespie, Gary, *Prof,* Glenville State College, WV

Gillespie, Hamp, *VPres,* Triton Museum of Art, Santa Clara, CA

Gillespie, Martha, *Secy,* Roswell Museum and Art Center, NM

Gillette, Dixie M, *Acting Dir,* Univ New Mexico Harwood Found, Taos

Gillette, Gerald W, *Research Historian,* Presbyterian Historical Society, Philadelphia, PA

Gilliam, Betty J, *Assoc Prof,* Clinch Valley College of Univ Virginia, Wise

Gillam, Scott, *Instr,* Atlanta College of Art, GA

Gilliland, James V, *Assoc Art Educ,* State Education Dept, Albany, NY

Gillis, Gaylord W, Jr, *VPres,* Founders Society, Detroit Institute of Arts, MI

Gillis, Verna, *Pres & Exec Dir,* American International Sculptors Symposiums, see National and Regional Organizations

Gilmer, J Mel, *Pres,* Sturdivant Hall, Selma, AL

Gilmor, Jane E, *Dir,* McAuley Gallery & *Assoc Prof,* Mount Mercy College, Cedar Rapids, IA

Gilmore, Jean Allman, *Pub Relations Asst,* Delaware Art Museum, Wilmington

Gilmore, Robert, *Chmn,* Gonzaga Univ, Spokane, WA

Gilmore, Thomas J, *Assoc Prof,* Miami Univ, Oxford, OH

Gilot, Francoise, *Chmn, Painting & Drawing Workshops,* Univ Southern California, Idyllwild Campus

Gil-Roberts, H, *Treas,* Lyme Art Association, Old Lyme, CT

Gilstrap, Sara, *Mem Faculty,* Midland College, TX

Gimbel, Pat, *Asst Dir,* Univ North Dakota Art Galleries, Grand Forks

Gimse, Malcolm, *Asst Prof,* St Olaf College, Northfield, MN

Gingles, Bill, *Dir,* Brenau College, Gainesville, GA

Gingles, Susan, *Instr,* Brenau College, Gainesville, GA

Gingold, Diane J, *Cur,* Montgomery Museum of Fine Arts, AL

Giovannini, John, *Dir Summer School,* Saint Norbert College, De Pere, WI

Gips, Ed, *Dir Mem & Chapter Serv,* American Society of Interior Designers, see National and Regional Organizations

Gipstein, Mrs Edward, *Docent,* Lyman Allyn Museum, New London, CT

Girard, Guy, *Pres,* Association des Graveurs du Quebec, Montreal

Girdler, Reynolds, *Treas,* School Art League of New York City, Brooklyn, NY

Girdner, Walter W, *Chmn Dept,* Pasadena City College, CA

Gisiger, Hansjorg, *Head Fine Arts,* Lausanne College of Art & Design, Switzerland

Gispert, Pedro J, *Cur Art,* Univ Puerto Rico, Rio Piedras

Gitner, Fred J, *Librn,* French Institute Alliance Francaise Library, New York, NY

Gittins, Alvin, *Prof,* Univ Utah, Salt Lake City

Giusti, George, *Instr,* Famous Artists School, Westport, CT

Gladden, Vivian, *Cataloger,* Cleveland Inst of Art, OH

Gladfelter, Lloyd, *Pres,* Sarasota Art Association, FL

Gladstone, Caroline Thiermann, *Volunteer Guides Coordr,* Philadelphia Museum of Art, PA

Glasberg, Jane A, *Pub Relations,* Milwaukee Art Center, WI

Glaser, Walter, *Prof,* California State Polytechnic Univ, Pomona

Glasgow, Lukman, *Dir,* Contemporary Crafts Association and Gallery, Portland, OR

Glasgow, Vaughn, *Chief Cur,* Louisiana State Museum, New Orleans

Glasrud, Barbara, *Chmn & Assoc Prof,* Concordia College, Moorhead, MN

Glasser, Hannelore, *Prof,* Wells College, Aurora, NY

Glassman, Herbert, *Pres Bd Dirs,* Boston Architectural Center, MA

Glassman, Jerome, *Pres,* Mitchell Museum, Mount Vernon, IL

Glasson, Lloyd, *Assoc Prof,* Hartford Art School, Univ Hartford, West Hartford, CT

Glattley, Charles D, *Secy,* Sierra Arts Found, Reno, NV

Glavin, Ellen Marie, *Prof,* Emmanuel College, Boston, MA

Glazebrook, Mark, *Dir,* San Jose State Univ Art Gallery, CA

Gleason, Katherine, *Secy,* State Univ New York at Binghamton

Gleason, Ron, *Dir,* Tyler Museum of Art, TX

Glen, T, *Asst Prof,* McGill Univ, Montreal, PQ

Glendening, Marilyn, *Secy,* Chautauqua Gallery of Art, NY

Glenn, Constance W, *Dir,* Art Galleries, Long Beach, CA

Glennon, Sister Mary, *Dir Summer School,* College Misericordia, Dallas, PA

Gletner, Frank, *Prog Consult,* Univ Oregon, Museum of Art, Eugene

Glick, Gretchen, *Registrar/Preparator,* Wichita Falls Museum and Art Center, TX

Glicksman, Gretchen, *Registrar,* Univ California, Berkeley

Glicksman, Hal, *Dir,* Otis Art Inst Gallery, Los Angeles, CA

Glidden, Dan, *Vis Prof,* Sam Houston State Univ, Huntsville, TX

Glidden, Robert, *VPres,* American Council for the Arts in Education, see National and Regional Organizations

Glob, Dr P V, *Dir,* Nat Museum, Copenhagen, Denmark

Globus, Dorothy Twining, *Exhib Coordr,* Cooper-Hewitt Museum, New York, NY

Glover, Delone B, *Chmn Bd,* Brigham City Museum-Gallery, UT

Glover, Jack N, *Cur,* Sunset Trading Post Old West Museum, TX

Glover, R Leigh, *Pres,* Artist-Craftsmen of New York, NY

Glover, Tom, *Instr,* Amarillo College, TX

Gluhman, Dr Joseph W, *Head Dept,* Lafayette College, Easton, PA

Glusberg, Jorge, *Pres,* Centro de Arte y Communicacion, Buenos Aires, Argentina

Glusbeg, Leonardo, *VPres,* Centro de Arte y Communicacion, Buenos Aires, Argentina

Gluzinski, W, *Cur,* Muzeum Narodowe We Wroclawiu, Wroclaw, Poland

Gmeiner, Susan, *Prog Adminr,* Monmouth Museum and Cultural Center, Lincroft, NJ

Gnat, Raymond, *Dir,* Indianapolis Marion County Public Library, IN

Goacher, Alice, *Assoc Prof,* Univ Minnesota, Saint Paul

Goad, Albert W, *Acting Chmn,* Ashland College, OH

Goberis, Theodora C, *Instr,* Norwich Art School, CT

Gobin, Henry, *Arts Dir,* Inst of American Indian Arts, Santa Fe, NM

Godbolt, Fred B, *Pres,* Kelly-Griggs House Museum, Red Bluff, CA

Goddard, Jonathan, *Vis Prof,* Univ Bridgeport, CT

Godfrey, Robert, *Dir,* Westminster College Art Gallery, New Wilmington, PA

Godlewski, Henry, *Instr,* Mohawk Valley Community College, Utica, NY

Goehlich, John, *Instr,* Ray-Vogue Schools, Chicago, IL

Goelet, Robert G, *Pres,* New York Historical Society; *Pres,* American Museum of Natural History, New York, NY

Goepper Dr Roger, *Dir,* Museum fur Ostasiatische Kunst, Museen der Stadt Koln, Germany

Goerg, Charles, *Cur,* Musee D'Art et D'Histoire, Geneva, Switzerland

Goetemann, Gordon, *Mem Faculty,* College of Saint Benedict, Saint Joseph, MN

Goethals, Gregor, *Head Dept History Art,* Rhode Island School of Design, Providence

Goetz, Henri, *Prof,* Paris American Academy, France

Goetz, Richard V, *Dir,* Goetz Art School, New York, NY

Goff, Laurens W, *Treas,* Providence Athenaeum, RI

Goff, Lloyd L, *Secy,* Nat Society of Mural Painters, see National and Regional Organizations

Goff, Lila J, *Asst to Dir for Libraries and Museum Coll,* Minnesota Historical Society, Saint Paul

Goff, Ronald J, *Secy,* Univ Pennsylvania Museum, Philadelphia

Goffen, Rona, *Asst Prof,* Duke Univ, Durham, NC

Gogel, Ken, *Prof,* Univ Northern Iowa, Cedar Falls

Goheen, Ellen R, *Cur 20th Century Art,* William Rockhill Nelson Gallery of Art, Kansas City, MO

Goins, Ralph Michael, *Asst Prof,* Univ North Carolina at Wilmington

Goke, Tadaomi, *Cur Lacquer,* Tokyo Kokuritsu Kindai Bijutsukan, Japan

Gold, Debra, *Instr,* East Tennessee State Univ, Johnson City

Gold, Ivan, *Secy/Treas,* Portland Center for the Visual Arts, OR

Gold, Marvin, *VPres,* Erie Art Center, PA

Gold, Muriel, *Dir Dept Performing Arts,* Saidye Bronfman Centre (YM-YWHA & NHS), Montreal, PQ

Goldberg, Dr Gisela, *Cur Old German Paintings,* Bayerischen Staatsgemaldesammlungen, Munich, Germany

Goldberg, Kenneth P, *Asst-Librn,* Cleveland Inst of Art, OH

Goldcamp, Alice, *Educ Dir,* Butler Inst of American Art Museum, Youngstown, OH

Golden, Morton, *Deputy Dir Adminr,* Los Angeles County Museum of Art, CA

Goldenberg, Gottfried, *Pres,* Association of Medical Illustrators, see National and Regional Organizations

Goldfarb, Roslyn, *Dir,* Pratt-Phoenix School of Design, New York, NY

Goldfield, Alfred S, *Pres,* Once Gallery, New York, NY

Goldin, Leon, *Chmn Div Painting and Sculpture,* Columbia University, New York, NY

Golding, Robert D, *Teacher,* Antonelli School of Photography, Philadelphia, PA

Goldman, Dan, *VPres,* Main Line Center of the Arts, Haverford, PA

Goldman, Dorian, *Instr,* Brockton Art Center, MA

Goldman, Jean, *Exhib Dir,* Univ Chicago Bergman Gallery, IL

Goldman, Max, *VPres,* La Casa del Libro, San Juan, PR

Goldman, Saul, *Video Officer,* Centre for Experimental Art and Communication, Toronto, ON

Goldman, Stewart, *Mem Faculty,* Art Academy of Cincinnati, OH

Goldner, George R, *Chmn,* Occidental College, Los Angeles, CA

Goldsmith, Benedict, *Art Gallery Dir,* State Univ New York at Potsdam

Goldsmith, Elsa, *Secy,* Women in the Arts Found, New York, NY

Goldsmith, Morris, *Pres,* Philadelphia Sketch Club, PA

Goldstein, Alan, *Mem Faculty,* Bucks County Community College, Newtown, PA

Goldstein, Gladys, *Assoc Prof,* College of Notre Dame of Maryland, Baltimore

Goldstein, Howard, *Prof,* Trenton State College, NJ

Goldstein, Nathan, *Chmn Found Dept & Gallery Comt,* Art Inst of Boston, MA

Goldstein, Sidney M, *Cur Ancient Glass,* Corning Museum of Glass, NY

Goldwater, Marge, *Cur,* Fort Worth Art Museum, TX

Goldworm, Judith, *Asst to Dir,* Lehigh Galleries, Bethlehem, PA

Golladay, Bea, *Secy,* Buchanan Arts and Crafts, Buchanan Dam, TX

Gollek, Dr Rosel, *Cur,* Stadtische Galerie Im Lenbachhaus, Munich, Germany

Golson, Palmer, *Asst Dir & Librn,* Ships of the Sea Museum, Savannah, GA

Golter, Robert, *Dir,* College of Wooster Art Center Museum, OH

Golub, Leon, *Prof,* Mason Gross School of the Arts, Rutgers, The State Univ New Jersey, New Brunswick

Gombrich, Ernst, *Vis Prof,* Univ Chicago, IL

Gomez-Moreno, Carmen, *Cur In Charge Medieval Art,* Metropolitan Museum of Art, New York, NY

Gomez-Moreno, Maria Elena, *Dir,* Museo Romantico Madrid, Spain

Gómez-Sicre, José, *Dir,* Museum of Modern Art of Latin America, Washington, DC

Gomon, Mrs W R, *Treas,* Museum of Arts and Sciences, Daytona Beach, FL

Gontesky, Michael, *Asst Prof,* Mount Marty College, Yankton, SD

Gonzales, Alex, *Instr,* Monterey Peninsula College, CA

Gonzales, Donald J, *VPres, & Dir Pub Relations,* Colonial Williamsburg Found, VA

Gonzalez, Xavier, *Instr,* Truro Center for the Arts at Castle Hill, MA

Good, Merrie, *Assoc Dir Art Prog,* Chase Manhattan Bank, New York, NY, see Corporate Art Holdings

Goodale, Carol, *Instr,* Pontiac Art Center, MI

Goodall, Donald B, *Dir,* Art Museum, Austin, TX

Goodenough, Ward H, *Cur Oceanian Ethnology,* Univ Pennsylvania Museum, Philadelphia

Goodfriend, Janet R, *Dir,* Studio School of Art and Design, Philadelphia, PA

Goodlett, Henry, *Pres,* Central Florida Community College Art Collection, Ocala

Goodman, Bernard, *Asst Supt,* Independence National Historical Park, Philadelphia, PA

Goodman, Helen J, *Exec Secy,* Carnegie Inst Museum of Art, Pittsburgh, PA

Goodman, John, *Historic Landscape Architect,* Nat Trust for Historic Preservation, Washington, DC

Goodman, Susan, *Chief Cur,* Jewish Museum, New York, NY

Goodnough, Joan, *Asst Dir,* Moose Jaw Art Museum, SK

Goodridge, Edythe, *Cur,* Mem Univ of Newfoundland, Saint Johns

Goodridge, Laurence W, *Mem Faculty,* Art Academy of Cincinnati, OH

Goodspeed, Barbara, *First VPres,* Kent Art Association Gallery, CT

Goodwin, David, *Instr,* Coe College, Cedar Rapids, IA

Goodwin, Elizabeth F, *Mus Aide,* Sheldon Jackson College Museum, Sitka, AK

Goodwin, John A, *VPres,* Lowell Art Association, MA

Goody, Marvin E, *Chmn,* Boston Art Commission, MA

Goodyear, Frank H, Jr, *Cur,* Pennsylvania Acad of Fine Arts Collection, Philadelphia

Goodyear, John Lake, *Prof,* Mason Gross School of the Arts, Rutgers, The State Univ New Jersey, New Brunswick

Goosey, Jim, *Construction Specialist,* Montana State Univ Museum of the Rockies, Bozeman

Goosman, Mildred, *Cur Western Collections,* Joslyn Art Museum, Omaha, NE

Gorchov, Ron, *Artist-in-Residence,* Oxbow Summer Art Workshops, Saugatuck, MI

Gordley, Metz Tran, *Chmn Drawing and Painting,* East Carolina Univ, Greenville, NC

Gordley, Tran, *Acting Dean,* East Carolina Univ, Greenville, NC

Gordon, Dr Albert C, *Dir,* DuPont Gallery, Washington and Lee Univ, Lexington, VA

Gordon, Amorita, *Asst Dir,* Lauren Rogers Library and Museum of Art, Laurel, MS

Gordon, Anne, *Teacher,* Southwestern School of Art, Albuquerque, NM

Gordon, Anne M, *Librn,* Long Island Historical Society, Brooklyn, NY

Gordon, Anne W, *Librn In Charge,* Carnegie Library of Pittsburgh, PA

Gordon, Ayala, *Cur Youth Wing,* Israel Museum, Jerusalem

Gordon, Carol, *Cur Decorative Arts,* Munson-Williams-Proctor Inst Museum of Art, Utica, New York

Gordon, G. Lynn, *Chmn & Prof,* Radford College, VA

Gordon, Ida, *VPres,* Brown County Art Gallery Association, Nashville, IN

Gordon, Irene, *Asst Prof,* John Jay College of Criminal Justice, New York, NY

Gordon, John, *Instr,* Sioux City Art Center, IA

Gordon, Joy, *Asst Cur,* New York Univ Art Collection, New York, NY

Gordon, Joy L, *Dir,* Danforth Museum, Framingham, MA

Gordon, Lida, *Instr,* Louisville School of Art, Anchorage, KY

Gordon, Martha, *Asst Prof,* Tarrant County Junior College, Northeast Campus, Hurst, TX

Gordon, Pat, *Pres,* Calgary Artists Society, AB

Gordon, Thomas, *Chmn Dept Lib Arts Studies,* Ontario College of Art, Toronto

Gordon, Thomas L, *Chmn,* Ohio Northern Univ, Ada

Gore, Frederick, *Head Painting & VPrin,* Saint Martins School of Art, London, England

Gore, Samuel M, *Head Dept,* Mississippi College, Clinton

Gorecki, Claudia, *Assoc Prof,* Cardinal Stritch College & *Secy,* Wisconsin Painters & Sculptors, Milwaukee

Gorelick, Len, *Pres,* New Rochelle Art Association, New Rochelle Public Library, NY

Gorman, Chester F, *Asst Cur In Charge South & Southeast Asia Section,* Univ Pennsylvania Museum, Philadelphia

Gorman, James G, *Asst Prof Art & Art Coordr & Dir Summer School,* Vincennes Univ, IN

Gorman, Joan H, *Assoc Cur,* Brandywine River Museum, Chadds Ford, PA

Gorman, William, *Vice Pres,* Allied Artists of America, see National and Regional Organizations

Gormley, Brian, *Dir,* Lake Placid School of Art Gallery, NY

Gormley, Donald J, *Exec Secy,* Art Commission of the City of New York, NY

Gorney, Diane E, *Admin Coordr,* Women's Art Registry of Minnesota, Minneapolis

Gorove, Margaret J, *Asst Prof,* Univ Mississippi, University

Gorski, Richard K, *Prof,* Northern Michigan Univ, Marquette

Gosley, G S, *Dir,* Dartmouth Heritage Museum, NS

Gosney, Mrs Leila, *Asst Treas,* Museum of Arts and Sciences, Daytona Beach, FL

Gostin, Arlene, *Dept Chairperson & Assoc Prof,* Philadelphia College of Art, PA

Gothberg, Ed, *Mem Faculty,* Casper College, WY

Gottfried, Herbert, *Chmn & Dir Summer School,* Oklahoma State Univ, Stillwater

Gottlieb, Gerald, *Cur Early Children's Books,* Pierpont Morgan Library, New York, NY

Gottselig, Len, *Librn,* Glenbow-Alberta Inst, Calgary, AB

Goudeer, Tangred, *Asst Cur Archaeology,* Nat Museum, Valletta, Malta

Gouger, Regina D, *Pres,* Berks Art Alliance, Reading, PA

Gould, Arthur, *Mem Faculty,* Hamline Univ, Saint Paul, MN

Gouldin, Virginia, *Secy,* Roberson Center, Binghamton, NY

Gouma-Peterson, Thalia, *Chmn,* College of Wooster, OH

Gregory, Mrs Gale, *Librn,* Cedar Rapids Art Center, IA

Gregory, James, *Librn,* New York Historical Society, New York

Gregory, Joan, *Head,* Univ North Carolina at Greensboro

Gregory, Peg, *VPres,* South County Art Association, Kingston, RI

Gregory, Mrs W P, *Pres Bd Trustees,* Gallery at Stratford, ON

Grenn, Raymond S, *Chmn Bd,* Philadelphia Art Alliance, PA

Gresham, Paul A, *Instr,* Oklahoma State Univ, Okmulgee

Gretch, Richard, *Dir Summer School,* College of Great Falls, MT

Greville, H, *Subject Supvr,* George Brown College of Applied Arts and Technology, Toronto, ON

Grey, Clarence, *Asst Prof,* Loma Linda Univ, La Sierra Campus, Riverside, CA

Gribbon, Deborah, *Cur,* Isabella Stewart Gardner Museum, Boston, MA

Grider, Jon L, *Prof,* Los Angeles Harbor College, Wilmington, CA

Griffin, Chris, *Mem Faculty,* State Univ New York College At Old Westbury

Griffin, Christine, *In-House Chair,* Women in the Arts Found, New York, NY

Griffin, Fred, *Mem Faculty,* Burnley School of Professional Art, Seattle, WA

Griffin, Gale, *Picture Specialist,* San Diego Public Library, CA

Griffin, John R, Jr, *Pres,* Five Civilized Tribes Museum, Muskogee, OK

Griffin, Joyce, *Chmn Bd,* Huntsville Museum of Art, AL

Griffin, Lee, *Pres Bd Trustees,* Louisiana Arts and Science Center, Baton Rouge

Griffin, Tommy L, *Designer/Preparator,* Univ Oregon Museum of Art, Eugene

Griffith, Fuller O, *Asst Prof,* George Washington Univ, Washington, DC

Griffith, Robert, *Asst Prof,* Univ Lowell, MA

Griffith, Roberta, *Prof,* Hartwick College, Oneonta, NY

Grigg, Beth, *Secy,* Klamath Art Association, Klamath Falls, OR

Grimaldi, Joseph, *Historic Site Asst,* Schuyler Mansion, Albany, NY

Grimley, Oliver, *Vis Instr,* Ocean City School of Art, NJ

Grimm, Ben, *Dir,* Jersey City Public Library, NJ

Grimm, Eugene H, *Pres,* Society of North American Artists, see National and Regional Organizations

Grimm, Gloria D, *VPres,* Society of North American Artists, see National and Regional Organizations

Grimm, Raymond, *Prof,* Portland State Univ, OR

Grimme, Dr Ernst-Gunther, *Dir,* Suermondt-Ludwig-Museum Der Stadt Aachen, Germany

Grimsson, Tholl, *Cur,* Thjodminjasafn, Reykjavik, Iceland

Griner, Ned H, *Head Art Dept,* Ball State Univ, Muncie, IN

Gripman, Alice, *Mem Faculty,* Art Inst of Philadelphia, PA

Grippi, Salvatore, *Prof,* Ithaca College, NY

Grissom, Eugene E, *Chmn,* Univ Florida, Gainesville

Griswold, A B, *Pres,* Breezewood Found Museum and Garden, Monkton, MD

Griswold, Scott, *Instr,* Ocean City School of Art, NJ

Grittall, John, *Treas,* Royal College of Art Exhibitions, London, England

Grittner, James, *Assoc Prof,* Univ Wisconsin-Superior

Gritz, Dick, *Dir Summer School,* Northeastern Junior College, Sterling, CO

Groberg, Charles M, *Prof,* Weber State College, Ogden, UT

Grocholski, J, *Instr,* Fontainebleau School of Fine Arts, France

Groff, John, *Registrar,* Philadelphia Maritime Museum, PA

Grogan, Kevin, *Library Dir & Assoc Cur,* Phillips Collection, Washington, DC

Groggins, Marjorie, *Registrar,* Brandeis Univ, Waltham, MA

Grom, Franc, *Pres,* Inter-Society Color Council, see National and Regional Organizations

Gronberg, Erik, *Instr,* Miracosta College, Oceanside, CA

Gronberg, Virginia, *Cataloger,* Maine Historical Society, Portland

Groneau, Mary Alix, *Asst Dir,* Dundurn Castle, Hamilton, ON

Groome, Dr Les, *Secy Gen,* Canadian Society for Education Through Art, see National Organizations of Canada

Grooms, Mrs Robert, *Corresp Secy,* Museum of Arts and Sciences, Daytona Beach, FL

Gros, Fredrick D, *Cur Educ,* Huntington Galleries, WV

Grosch, William E, *Assoc Prof,* Clarion State College, PA

Grose, Y, *Asst Librn,* Rijksmuseum, Amsterdam, Netherlands

Grosland, August J, *Art Dept Head,* Western State College, Gunnison, CO

Gross, Chaim, *Treas,* Sculptors Guild, New York, NY

Gross, Charles M, *Assoc Prof,* Univ Mississippi, University

Gross, Kenneth R, *Exec Dir,* Birmingham-Bloomfield Art Association, Birmingham, MI

Gross, Laurence F, *Cur,* Merrimack Valley Textile Museum, North Andover, MA

Gross, Louis, *Prof,* Glendale College, CA

Gross, Priva, *Assoc Prof,* Queensborough Community College, Bayside, NY

Gross, Thomas, *Asst Dir,* Indiana State Museum, Indianapolis

Grossman, Cissy, *Asst Cur Judiaca,* Jewish Museum, New York, NY

Grossman, Grace Cohen, *Cur,* Spertus Museum of Judaica, Chicago, IL

Grossman, Jeanine, *VPres,* Evanston Art Center, IL

Grossman, Linda, *Mem Faculty,* Art Inst of Philadelphia, PA

Grossman, Maurice, *Coordr Crafts,* Univ Arizona, Tucson

Grossman, Oscar, *Treas,* Los Angeles Art Association and Galleries, CA

Grossman, Sheldon, *Cur Later Italian Painting,* Nat Gallery of Art, Washington, DC

Grossvogel, Jill, *Gallery Adminr,* State Univ New York at Binghamton

Grosvenor, Walter, *Assoc Prof,* Whitworth College, Spokane, WA

Ground, John, *Mem Faculty,* Millersville State College, PA

Groutage, Harrison, *Prof,* Utah State Univ, Logan

Grove, Donna, *Vol Librn,* Museum of the Southwest, Midland, TX

Grove, Jerome, *Pres,* Center for Creative Studies, Detroit, MI

Grove, Richard, *Dir,* Univ Washington Henry Art Gallery, Seattle, WA

Grove, Samuel H, *Dir,* Museum of the Southwest, Midland, TX

Grover, Arnold J, *Pres,* John Paul Jones House, Portsmouth, NH

Grubb, Gary, *Head Dept,* Western Wyoming College, Rock Springs

Grube, Dick Dewayne, *Cur,* National Infantry Museum, Fort Benning, GA

Gruber, Doris, *Periodicals,* Trinity College Library, Washington, DC

Gruber, Francis S, *Prof,* George Washington University, Washington, DC

Grude, Helen A, *Pres,* Toledo Artists' Club, OH

Gruen, Erica, *Dir,* Univ Tennessee, Knoxville

Grunberg, Stephanie, *Admin Asst Educ,* Rutgers Univ Art Gallery, New Brunswick, NJ

Grundy, Owen J, *Pres,* Jersey City Museum Association, NJ

Grunwaldt, Nina, *Treas,* Coos Art Museum, Coos Bay, OR

Gruppe, Charles, *Instr,* Guilford Art and Music School, CT

Gruters, William, *Dir College Art Gallery,* Mount Wachusett Community College, Gardner, MA

Grymes, Miriam, *VPres,* Associated Artists of Winston-Salem, NC

Guadarrama, Jorge, *Cur,* Museo de Arte Moderno, Mexico City, Mexico

Gual, Max Jaravia, *Escultor,* Escuela Nacional de Artes Plasticas, Guatemala City, Guatemala

Gualtiere, Joseph P, *Dir,* Slater Memorial Museum & Converse Art Gallery & *Mem Faculty,* Norwich Art School, Norwich Free Academy, CT

Guastella, Dennis, *Asst Prof,* South Dakota State Univ, Brookings

Guayo, *Prof,* Paris American Acad, France

Gubelmann, Walter S, *Pres,* Society of the Four Arts, Palm Beach, FL

Gudehus, Robyn-Lynn, *Educ Liaison,* Bergen Community Museum, Paramus, NJ

Gudjonsson, Elsa E, *Cur Textiles,* Thjodminjasafn, Reykjavik, Iceland

Guenther, Bruce, *Cur,* Washington State Univ Museum of Art, Pullman

Guenther, John R, *Asst Prof,* Indiana Univ Southeast, New Albany

Guenwald, Larry, *Technician,* Tweed Museum of Art, Duluth, MN

Guerin, Charles, *Dir Exhib & Physical Plant,* Colorado Springs Fine Arts Center, CO

Guerra, Luis, *Head Dept,* Austin Community College, TX

Guerrant, Florence, *Pres,* Essex Art Association, CT

Guertin, Joseph, *Instr,* Portland School of Art, ME

Gueury, Marie-Claire, *Asst Cur,* Musees D'Archeologie et D'Arts Decoratifs, Liege, Belgium

Guglielmi-Tragger, Josiane, *Dir of BA Handcrafts,* Edgecliff College, Cincinnati, OH

Guido, Nelida Maria Luisa, *Secy,* Escuela Superior de Bellas Artes Ernesto de la Carcova, Sculpture Museum, Buenos Aires, Argentina

Guidry, Gail, *Cur Pictures,* Missouri Historical Society, St Louis

Guilford, Ben J, II, *Asst Dir,* Miami-Dade Public Library, Miami, FL

Guill, Kenneth, *Asst Prof,* Georgia Southern College, Statesboro

Guillaume, Mme, *Cur,* Musee des Beaux-Arts de Dijon, France

Guillaume, Harry, *Prof,* Univ Northern Iowa, Cedar Falls

Guillemain, M, *Asst,* Musees Saint-Denis, Reim, France

Guillermety, Jose Buscaglia, *Mem Faculty,* Univ Puerto Rico, Rio Piedras

Guillette, Raymond, *Trustee,* Attleboro Museum, MA

Guilmain, Jacques, *Prof,* State Univ New York at Stony Brook

Guinn, Catherine, *Dir,* Art Center, Mt Clemens, MI

Guise, Ina, *Coordr,* Tennessee Valley Art Center, Tuscumbia, AL

Guitar, Carroll, *Librn,* Shelburne Museum, VT

Gulbranson, Rex, *Asst to Dir,* South Dakota State Univ, Brookings

Guldin, Mark F, *Dir,* School of Printing, Rochester Inst of Technology, NY

Gunawardena, Dr W T T P, *Cur Entomology,* Colombo National Museum, Sri Lanka

Gundersheimer, Herman, *Lectr,* La Salle College, Philadelphia, PA

Gunderson, Barry, *Asst Prof,* Kenyon College, Gambier, OH

Gunnion, Vernon S, *Preparator,* Pennsylvania Farm Museum of Landis Valley, Lancaster

Gunstone, Antony J H, *Dir,* Lincolnshire Museums, Lincoln, England

Gunter, Bradley H, *Asst VPres & Secy,* Federal Reserve Bank of Richmond, VA, see Corporate Art Holdings; *VPres,* Federated Arts Council of Richmond

Gunter, Mrs Joe, Jr, *Pres,* Art Patrons League of Mobile, AL

Gunther, Charles F, *Asst Dir Educ,* Toledo Museum of Art, OH

Gursky, Judy, *Secy,* Los Alamos Arts Council, NM

Gursoy, Ahmet, *Pres,* Federation of Modern Painters and Sculptors, see National and Regional Organizations

Gussow, Alan, *Vis Prof,* Santa Rosa Junior College, CA

Gussow, Roy, *Pres,* Sculptors Guild, New York, NY

Gust, Otto, *Secy,* Craft Center Museum, Danbury, CT

Gustafson, Dwight, *Dean,* Bob Jones Univ, Greenville, SC

Gustafson, R David, *Chmn,* Rock Valley College, Rockford, IL

Gustavson, Robert E, *Exec Dir,* Corporate Council for the Arts, Seattle, WA

Gustin, Mickey, *Dir,* Factory of Visual Art, Seattle, WA

Guston, Philip, *Prof,* Boston Univ, MA; *Vis Prof,* American Univ, Washington, DC

Gustow, Hazel, *Libr Dir,* Philadelphia College of Art, PA

Gutekunst, B, *Head Humanities Div,* Mullen Library, Catholic Univ of America, Washington, DC

Guthe, Alfred K, *Dir,* Univ Tennessee, Knoxville

Guthrie, Gerald, *Asst Preparator,* Univ Illinois, Champaign

Gutierrez, Enruque Sanua, *Mem Faculty,* Univ Puerto Rico, Rio Piedras

Gutierrez, Louis, *Instr,* San Jose City College, CA

Gutkind, Sondra D, *Librn-Archivist,* Independence Nat Historical Park, Philadelphia, PA

Gutman, Amy Frank, *Asst Librn,* Wilbour Library of Egyptology, Brooklyn, NY

Gutman, Robert W, *Dean,* Fashion Inst of Technology, New York, NY

Gutridge, Delbert R, *Registrar,* Cleveland Museum of Art, OH

Guy, Betty, *VPres,* Arts for Living Center, Burlington, IA

Guyath, Richard, *Rector & VProvost,* Royal College of Art Exhibitions, London, England

Guzman, Diane, *Librn,* Wilbour Library of Egyptology, Brooklyn, NY

Guzman, Gabriela, *Head Promotion Dept,* Museo Nacional de Antropologia, Mexico City, Mexico

Guzzetti, Alfred, *Studio Prof,* Harvard Univ, Cambridge, MA

Gyer, Jack, *Cur,* Yosemite Museum Collections, CA

Gyllensvard, Bo, *Dir,* Ostasiatiska Museet, Stockholm, Sweden

Gza, Israel Cavazos, *Cur,* Museo Regional de Nuevo Leon, Monterrey, Mexico

Ha, Yeung, *Mem Faculty,* Austin Peay State Univ, Clarksville, TN

Haag, Dr Robert, *Dean Community Services,* El Camino College, Torrance, CA

Haagensen, Lynn, *Asst Prof,* Univ Idaho, Moscow

Haarer, Sister Ann, *Chmn Dept,* College Saint Elizabeth, Convent Station, NJ

Haas, Pauline, *Dept Coordr & Assoc Prof,* Whitworth College, Spokane, WA

Haas, Dr Susanne, *Cur Prehistory, India,* Museum fur Volkerkunde und Schweizerisches Museum fur Volkskunde Basel, Switzerland

Habel, Dorothy, *Asst Prof,* Univ Nebraska at Omaha

Habicht, L, *Dean,* Eesti Nsv Riiklik Kunstiinstituut, Tallinn, Estonia, USSR

Habraken, N John, *Head Dept Architecture,* Massachusetts Inst Technology, Cambridge

Habs, Gail J, *Communications Officer,* Visual Arts Ontario, Toronto

Hache, Alfreda, *Secy,* Univ Moncton Galerie D'Art, NB

Hachey, Paul A, *Asst Cur,* Beaverbrook Art Gallery, Fredericton, NB

Hack, Janet S, *Graphics Designer,* Hall of Fame of the Trotter, Goshen, NY

Hack, Rosalinda, *Asst to Chief,* Chicago Public Library, IL

Hackenbroch, Yvonne, *Cur Sculpture & Decorative Arts,* Metropolitan Museum of Art, New York, NY

Hacker, Susan, *Asst Prof,* Webster College, Webster Groves, MO

Hackett, Edward W, *Dir Summer School,* Univ Maine, Orono

Hackett, Mrs J Vincent, *VPres,* Buck Hill Art Association, Buck Hill Falls, PA

Haddaway, Chester, *Art Librn,* Dallas Public Library, TX

Haden, Eunice, *Treas,* Miniature Painters, Sculptors and Gravers Society, Washington, DC

Hadley, Dayna, *Coordr of Vol,* Omniplex, Oklahoma City, OK

Hadley, Rollin van N, *Dir,* Isabella Stewart Gardner Museum, Boston, MA

Hadwin, Millie, *Dir,* Ella Sharp Museum, Jackson, MI

Hadzi, Dimitri, *Resident Artist & Acting Dir,* Carpenter Center for the Visual Arts, Harvard Univ, Cambridge, MA

Hadzi, Martha Leeb, *Assoc Prof,* Mount Holyoke College, South Hadley, MA

Hafermann, Candy, *Lectr,* Univ Wisconsin, Madison

Hagan, Jane, *Librn,* Brand Library and Art Center, Glendale, CA

Hagan, Kathleen, *Head Weaving & Fibers,* Bowling Green State Univ, OH

Hagarty, Kevin, *Dir,* Tacoma Public Library, WA

Hagelberg, Richard, *First VPres,* Greater Gary Arts Council, IN

Hagelberger, Richard, *Asst Prof,* Wittenberg Univ, Springfield, OH

Hageman, Lee, *Assoc Prof,* Northwest Missouri State Univ, Maryville

Hagen, Gary, *Assoc Prof,* Univ Wisconsin-Stevens Point

Hagener, Toni, *Pres,* Montana Historical Society, Helena

Hageness, Karen, *Prof & Head Art Dept,* Bethany Lutheran College, Mankato, MN

Hager, Hellmut, *Head Dept Art Hist,* Pennsylvania State Univ, University Park

Hagerstrand, M A, *Exec VPres,* Cherokee Nat Historical Society, Tahlequah, OK

Hagerty, Harriet M, *Recording Secy,* Pen and Brush, New York, NY

Haggemann, Robert, *Headmaster,* Elgin Acad Gallery, IL

Hagler, Michael, *Designer & Cur Installations,* William Rockhill Nelson Gallery of Art, Kansas City, MO

Haglich, Bianca, *Chmn,* Marymount College, Tarrytown, NY

Hagon, John, *Instr,* Dean Junior College, Franklin, MA

Hagy, Richard L, *Asst to Pres,* Filson Club, Louisville, KY

Hagy, Ruth K, *Cur,* Chester County Historical Society, West Chester, PA

Hahn, Linda, *Admin Officer,* Scotts Bluff Nat Monument, Gering, NE

Haight, Donald A, *VPres Summer School,* Acad of Art College, San Francisco, CA

Haines, Mary Egan, *Sr Adv,* Ontario College of Art, Toronto

Hair, Norman J, *Chmn,* Gulf Coast Community College, Panama City, FL

Hajek, Dr Lubor, *Chief Oriental Art Coll,* Narodni Galerie v Praze, Prague, Czechoslovakia

Hakkinen, Elisabeth S, *Dir,* Sheldon Museum and Cultural Center, Haines, AK

Halberstadt, Milton, *Vis Prof,* Univ Oregon, Eugene

Halbgebauer, Peter, *Head Conservator,* Gemaldegalerie der Akademie der Bildenden Kunste in Wien, Austria

Hale, Alison B, *Secy,* Ages of Man Found, Amenia, NY

Hale, Elizabeth F, *Librn,* Macdonald-Stewart Library, Society of the Montreal Military & Maritime Museum, PQ

Hale, George, *Treas,* California Historical Society, San Francisco

Hale, Golden Glen, *Chmn,* Alice Lloyd College, Pippa Passes, KY

Hale, Dr Nathan Cabot, *Pres,* Ages of Man Found, Amenia, NY

Hale, Pearl, *Asst Prof,* Herbert H Lehman College, Bronx, NY

Hale, Roger L, *Pres,* Walker Art Center, Minneapolis, MN

Hales, David A, *Head Reader Serv,* Elmer E Rasmuson Library, Univ Alaska Museum, Fairbanks

Haley, Dr Ken, *Asst Prof,* Georgetown Univ, Washington, DC

Hall, Mrs Ariel, *Trustee,* Attleboro Museum, MA

Hall, Carl, *Head Design,* Bowling Green State Univ, OH

Hall, Charles W, *Exec Dir,* Museum of York County, Rock Hill, SC

Hall, Chenoweth, *Chmn Cultural Affairs,* Univ Maine, Machias

Hall, Doug, *Mem Faculty,* Kirkwood Community College, Cedar Rapids, IA

Hall, Douglas, *Keeper,* Scottish Nat Gallery of Modern Art, Nat Gallery of Scotland, Edinburgh

Hall, Edward J, Jr, *Librn,* Kent State Univ Architecture/Urban Studies Library, OH

Hall, Elizabeth Turner, *Assoc Prof,* Southern Connecticut State College, New Haven

Hall, Elton W, *Cur Coll,* New Bedford Whaling Museum, MA

Hall, John, *Assoc Prof,* School of Architecture, Univ Toronto, ON

Hall, Lee, *Pres,* Rhode Island School of Design, Providence

Hall, Linnea, *Cur,* Easton Acad of the Arts, MD

Hall, Marie, *VPres,* San Bernardino Art Association, CA

Hall, Martha, *Readers Serv Librn,* Philadelphia College of Art, PA

Hall, Mary Joan, *Librn,* Solomon R Guggenheim Museum, New York, NY

Hall, Michael D, *Head Sculpture Dept,* Cranbrook Academy of Art, Bloomfield Hills, MI

Hall, Rick, *Mem Faculty,* College of Marin, Kentfield, CA

Hall, Robert, *Cur,* Fisk Univ Museum, Nashville, TN

Hall, Robert M, *Chmn Visual Arts Dept,* Flagler College, Saint Augustine, FL

Hall, Mrs Theodore W, *Secy-Registrar,* Berkshire Museum, Pittsfield, MA

Hall, Walter, *Instr,* Hartford Art School, Univ Hartford, West Hartford, CT

Hallahan, Elyse, *Asst to Dir,* Contemporary Crafts Association and Gallery, Portland, OR

Hallahan, John J, *Dir,* Manchester City Library, NH

Hallam, Hallie Lu, *Chmn,* Rollins College, Winter Park, FL

Hallenbeck, Kenneth L, *Asst to Exec VPres & Acting Mus Cur,* American Numismatic Association, see National and Regional Organizations

Hallett, Harold, *VPres,* Monterey Peninsula Museum of Art, CA

Hall-Humpherson, David, *Chmn Dept Found Studies,* Ontario College of Art, Toronto

Halliday, Richard S, *Dean,* School of Art and Design, Montreal, PQ

Hallman, Herbert, *Exhib Specialist,* Museum of US Department of Interior, Washington, DC

Hallman, Tom, *Pres,* Salem Art Association, OR

Hallmark, Donald P, *Cur & Librn,* Richard W Bock Sculpture Collection & *Chmn Dept Art,* Greenville College, IL

Hallmark, Rick, *Dir,* Ojai Valley Art Center, CA

Hallowell, Sheila A, *Catalog Librn,* Presbyterian Historical Society, Philadelphia, PA

Halm, Robert J, *Assoc Prof Art,* Iowa Central Community College, Fort Dodge

Halper, Susan L, *Exec Asst,* Solomon R Guggenheim Museum, New York, NY

Halperin, Jerome Y, *In Charge of Coll,* Coopers & Lybrand, Detroit, MI, see Corporate Art Holdings

Halpin, Marjorie, *Cur Ethnology,* Univ British Columbia Museum of Anthropology, Vancouver

Halsema, Brenda Van, *Dir Exhib,* Calvin College Center Art Gallery, Grand Rapids, MI

Halter, Florence, *Head Dept,* Concordia College, Bronxville, NY

Halverson, James, *Asst to Dir,* California State Univ Fine Arts Gallery, Los Angeles

Halverson, Marie, *Secy,* Allied Arts Council of the Yakima Valley, Yakima, WA

Halverson, Wayne, *Asst Prof,* Univ Wisconsin-Stevens Point

Ham, Gerald F, *State Archivist,* State Historical Society of Wisconsin, Madison

Ham, Lily, *Dir,* Arizona Watercolor Association, Phoenix

Hamada, S, *Cur,* Nippon Mingei-Kan, Tokyo, Japan

Hamasaki, Kazuo, *VPres & Treas,* Society of Canadian Artists, see National Organizations of Canada

Hamblen, Judith, *Registrar,* Norwich Free Academy, CT

Hames, Clint, *VPres,* Community Arts Council of Chilliwack, BC

Hamidi, Taswir Husain, *Supt Mus,* Nat Museum of Pakistan, Karachi

Hamill, Tim, *Pres,* Boston Printmakers, MA

Hamilton, Elaine, *VPres,* Federal Design Council, Washington, DC

Hamilton, George Heard, *VPres,* Hill-Stead Museum, Farmington, CT

Hamilton, James, *Keeper,* Mappin Art Gallery, Sheffield City Art Galleries, England

Hamilton, James G, Jr, *Exec Asst,* Archaeological Inst of America, see National and Regional Organizations

Hamilton, John, *Instr,* Sierra College, Rocklin, CA

Hamilton, John, *VPres,* Concord Antiquarian Society Museum, MA

Hamilton; L M, *Assoc Prof,* Campbellsville College, KY

Hamilton, Phillip M, *Chmn,* Univ Wisconsin, Madison

Hamilton, Mrs S B, Jr, *Dir,* Lockwood-Mathews Mansion Museum, Norwalk, CT

Hamilton, Mrs W Ed, *Exec Secy,* General Federation of Women's Clubs, see National and Regional Organizations

Hamlin, Gordon, *Secy,* Litchfield Historical Society, CT

Hamm, Garrent W, *Instr,* Central Academy of Commercial Art, Cincinnati, OH

Hammer, Alfred E, *Prof & Head,* Univ Manitoba, Winnipeg

Hammerlund, Howard, *Secy,* Cooper School of Art Gallery, Cleveland, OH

Hammerman, Pat, *Pub Relations,* The Exhibitionists, Jamaica, NY

Hammock, Virgil, *Prof & Head Fine Arts,* Mount Allison Univ, Sackville, NB

Hammond, Betsey, *Teacher,* Coquille Valley Art Association, OR

Hammond, Harmony, *Artist-in-Residence,* Oxbow Summer Art Workshops, Saugatuck, MI

Hammond, Jack, *Mem Faculty,* Maryland College of Art and Design, Silver Spring

Hammond, Natalie Hays, *Dir,* Museum of the Humanities, North Salem, NY

Hammood, Emily, *Asst Prof,* Immaculata College of Washington, DC

Hamoy, Carol, *Publicity Chair,* Women in the Arts Found, New York, NY

Hamper, Mary M, *Dir,* Chicago Acad of Fine Arts, IL

Hancock, Mrs Frank, *Chmn Comt,* Old Gaol Museum, York, ME

Hancock, Paula, *Cur Educ,* High Museum of Art, Atlanta, GA

Hand, John, *Cur Northern European Painting to 1700,* Nat Gallery of Art, Washington, DC

Handleman, Mrs David, *Pres,* Meadow Brook Gallery Associates, Oakland Univ, MI

Handy, Edward O, Jr,, *Pres,* Providence Athenaeum, RI

Handy, Riley, *Librn,* Western Kentucky Univ Museum, Bowling Green

Handy, Susan, *Museum Shop Mgr,* Rhode Island School of Design Museum of Art, Providence

Hanes, James, *Asst Prof,* La Salle College, Philadelphia, PA

Hanes, John W, *Chmn,* Nat Museum of Racing, Saratoga Springs, NY

Haney, William, *Assoc Prof,* New York Inst Technology, Old Westbury

Hanfstaengl, Dr Erika, *Cur,* Stadtische Galerie Im Lenbachhaus, Munich, Germany

Hanft, Margie, *Film Librn,* California Inst Arts Library, Valencia

Hanhart, Rudolf, *Conservator,* Historisches Museum, St Gallen, Switzerland

Hankel, Wayne, *Pres,* Sheyenne Valley Arts and Crafts Association, Fort Ransom, ND

Hanna, Katherine, *Dir,* Taft Museum, Cincinnati, OH

Hanna, Mary Ann, *Supvr School Library & Media Program,* Michigan Dept Education State Library Services, Lansing

Hanna, Paul, *Prof,* Texas Tech Univ, Lubbock

Hannah, William, *Asst Prof,* Black Hawk College, Moline, IL

Hanners, Roger, *Chmn,* Balch House, Beverly Historical Society, MA

Hannibal, Emmett, *Head Pub Prog,* Winnipeg Art Gallery, MB

Hannon, Kenneth M, *Chmn Bd,* Fine Arts Museum of the South, Mobile, AL

Hannon, Martin, *Chmn Bd,* Salmagundi Club, see National and Regional Organization; *Recording Secy,* Artists' Fellowship, New York, NY

Hannon, William J, *Chmn Design,* Massachusetts College of Art, Boston

Hanns, James, *Dir Summer School,* Texas Tech Univ, Lubbock

Hansen, Adrian, *Dir,* Arizona Watercolor Association, Phoenix

Hansen, Arne, *Dir,* Colorado Springs Fine Arts Center, CO

Hansen, Arthur, *Treas,* Jersey City Museum Association, NJ

Hansen, Borge, *Treas,* Louisiana Museum of Modern Art, Humlebaek, Denmark

Hansen, Chris, *Instr,* Milwaukee Area Technical College, WI

Hansen, Mrs Donald, *Chmn,* Harlow House, Mount Holyoke College Art Museum, South Hadley, MA

Hansen, Gail, *Educ Chmn,* Huntsville Art League and Museum Association, AL

Hansen, Gaylen C, *Prof,* Washington State Univ, Pullman

Hansen, Georgian, *Educ & Special Events Coordr,* Burnaby Art Gallery, BC

Hansen, Harry, *Chmn Art Studio,* Univ South Carolina, Columbia

Hansen, James A, *Acting Dir,* Bradley Univ, Peoria, IL

Hansen, James L, *Prof,* Portland State University, OR

Hansen, Jorn Otto, *Cur,* Nordjyllands Kunstmuseum, Aalborg, Denmark

Hansen, Norbert Mrs, *Chmn,* Van Cortlandt Museum, Bronx, NY

Hanson, Anne Coffin, *Dir Undergrad Studies,* Yale Univ, New Haven, CT

Hanson, Bernard, *Dean,* Hartford Art School, Univ Hartford, West Hartford, CT

Hanson, Elloyd, *Instr,* Truro Center for the Arts at Castle Hill, MA

Hanson, Etta, *Cur,* Southwestern at Memphis, TN

Hanson, Dr James A, *Dir,* Panhandle-Plains Historical Society Museum, Canyon, TX

Hanson, Wesley T, *Chmn,* International Museum of Photography, Rochester, NY

Hanssen, Peter, *Assoc Prof,* Kingsborough Community College, Brooklyn, NY

Hara, Teruo, *Assoc Prof,* Mary Washington College, Fredericksburg, VA

Harasimowicz, Allen, *Museum Researcher,* Southern Illinois Univ Museum and Art Galleries, Carbondale

Harbach, Merle S, *Cur Educ,* Worcester Art Museum, MA

Harbour, John W, Jr, *Exec Dir,* Sleepy Hollow Restorations, Tarrytown, NY

Harbour, June, *Exec Secy,* Washington State Univ Museum of Art, Pullman

Harcourt, Richard L, *Pres,* Western States Arts Found, Denver, CO

Hardie, P, *Cur Oriental Art,* City Art Gallery, Bristol, England

Hardiman, George W, *In Charge Art Educ,* Univ Illinois, Urbana-Champaign

Harding, Roger W, *Treas,* Haystack Mountain School of Crafts Gallery, Deer Isle, ME

Hardison, O B, Jr, *Dir,* Folger Shakespeare Library, Washington, DC

Hardisty, Vernon R, *Dir,* Polynesian Cultural Center, Laie, HI

Hardman, Jack N, *Dir,* Burnaby Art Gallery, BC

Hardman, L Edwin, *Pres,* Tampa Bay Art Center, FL

Hardwick, Jon, *Chmn Art Educ,* Southern Methodist Univ, Dallas, TX

Hare, Miss, *Librn,* Worshipful Co of Goldsmiths, London, England

Hargis, Dr William J, Jr, *Pres,* Mariners Museum, Newport News, VA

Hargrove, June E, *Assoc Prof,* Cleveland State Univ, OH

Harithas, James, *Dir,* Everson Museum of Art, Syracuse, NY

Harithas, James, *Dir,* Contemporary Arts Museum Houston, TX

Harker, Suzanne, *Asst Prof,* Mount Mary College, Milwaukee, WI

Harkins, Dennis, *Dir Photography,* Art Inst of Fort Lauderdale, FL

Harkins, Dr Richard, *Dir Summer School,* Bakersfield College, CA

Harkness, Mary Lou, *Librn,* Univ South Florida Galleries Program, Tampa

Harlan, Calvin, *Assoc Prof,* Univ New Orleans, LA

Harlan, Mrs Roger, *Exec Secy,* Rockford Art Association, IL

Harland, Joan M, *Head Dept Interior Design,* Univ Manitoba, Winnipeg

Harle, J C, *Keeper Dept Eastern Art,* Ashmolean Museum, Oxford, Univ, England

Harley, James, *Mem Faculty,* Bowdoin College, Brunswick, ME

Harlow, Bonnie K, *Registrar,* St Joseph Museum, MO

Harlow, Thompson R, *Dir,* Connecticut Historical Society Library, Hartford

Harmes, Michael, *Chmn Dept Technol Studies,* Ontario College of Art, Toronto

Harmon, James W, *Pres,* St. Louis Artists Guild, MO

Harmon, Jean, *Instr,* Missouri Western State College, Saint Joseph

Harmon, Jim W, *Dir,* Art-Mart Studio, Saint Louis, MO

Harms, Gudrun, *Librn,* Kunstsammlung Nordrhein-Westfalen, Dusseldorf, Germany

Harper, Ann Boyce, *Asst Dir for Admin,* Baltimore Museum of Art, MD

Harper, Donard R, *Supt,* Scotts Bluff Nat Monument, Gering, NE

Harper, Eleanor, *Secy,* Rockport Art Association, MA

Harper, George D, *Instr,* Glenville State College, WV

Harper, Grady, *Head Dept,* Northwestern State Univ Louisiana, Natchitoches

Harper, John, *Arts Cur,* Redding Museum and Art Center, CA

Harper, Prudence Oliver, *Cur Ancient Near Eastern Art,* Metropolitan Museum of Art, New York, NY

Harper, R W, *Conservator Prints & Watercolors,* City Art Gallery, Bristol, England

Harper, Rob, *Registrar,* Everson Museum of Art, Syracuse, NY

Harper, Robert L, *Head Librn & Mem Teaching Faculty,* California College of Arts & Crafts, Oakland

Harper, William, *Prof,* Florida State Univ, Tallahassee

Harper, Winifred K, *Deputy Dir Public Serv,* Buffalo and Erie County Public Library, NY

Harprath, Dr Richard, *Cur,* Staatliche Graphische Sammlung, Munich, Germany

Harrel, Ralph, *Dean,* Southwest Texas State Univ, San Marcos

Harrell, Mrs C D, Jr, *Pres,* Percy H Whiting Art Center, Fairhope, AL

Harrell, C Miner, *Pres Elect,* Pensacola Museum of Art, FL

Harrell, Lisa, *Admin Asst,* Museum of Fine Arts, Houston, TX

Harris, A Peter, *Dir,* Rodman Hall Arts Centre, St Catharines, ON

Harris, Allyn O, *Prof,* Community College of Baltimore, MD

Harris, Charlene, *Dir,* Art League of Houston, TX

Harris, David J, *Instr,* North Seattle Community College, WA

Harris, Edwin M A, *Assoc Prof,* Univ Northern Iowa, Cedar Falls

Harris, Mrs Erdman, *Pres,* Hill-Stead Museum, Farmington, CT

Harris, Gene E, *Registrar,* Brandywine River Museum, Chadds Ford, PA

Harris, Harry A, *Dir & Chmn Exhib,* Woodmere Art Gallery, Philadelphia, PA

Harris, Hazel, *Dir Summer School,* Furman Univ, Greenville, SC

Harris, Jean C, *Prof,* Mount Holyoke College, South Hadley, MA

Harris, Jeanne, *Assoc Cur Oriental Art,* William Rockhill Nelson Gallery of Art, Kansas City, MO

Harris, John M, *Dir,* Tippecanoe County Historical Museum, Lafayette, IN

Harris, Josephine M, *Chmn Dept,* Wilson College, Chambersburg, PA

Harris, Paul Rogers, *Dir,* Waco Art Center, TX

Harris, Wilhelmina S, *Supt,* Adams Nat Historic Site, Qunicy, MA

Harris, Willard R, *Chmn,* State Univ New York at Buffalo

Harrison, A, *Head Dept Graphic Design,* Leicester Polytechnic, England

Harrison, B R, *Cur Anthropology,* Panhandle-Plains Historical Society Museum, Canyon, TX

Harrison, Carole, *Assoc Prof,* State Univ New York College at Fredonia

Harrison, Cheryl, *Instr,* Brevard College, NC

Harrison, Darrell W, *Acting Dir,* Southern Illinois Univ Museum and Art Galleries, Carbondale

Harrison, Donald, *Pres,* Washington Depot Art Association, CT

Harrison, Ed, *Pres Bd Gov,* Natural History Museum of Los Angeles County, CA

Harrison, Edward E, *Pres,* Fairfield Historical Society, CT

Harrison, George, *Asst Dir & Exhib Cur,* Asheville Art Museum, NC

Harrison, Helen, *Cur,* Parrish Art Museum, Southampton, NY

Harrison, J Frank, *Pres Bd,* Brick Store Museum, Kennebunk, ME

Harrison, Joseph R, *Chmn Bd Trustees,* Metropolitan Museum and Arts Center, Coral Gables, FL

Harrison, Marc S, *Head Program Industrial Design,* Rhode Island School of Design, Providence

Harrison, Muriel, *Secy,* The Dalles Art Association, OR

Harrison, Newton, *Prof,* Univ California, San Deigo, La Jolla

Harrison, Richard, *Mem Faculty,* Rehoboth Art League, Rehoboth Beach, DE

Harrison, Tony, *Lectr,* Division of Painting and Sculpture, Columbia University, New York, NY

Harrison, W H, *Dir,* Fruitlands Museums, Harvard, MA

Harry, David, *Chmn,* Glenville State College, WV

Harry, O K, *Head Dept,* Riverside City College, CA

Hart, Allen M, *Dir,* Children's Aid Society, New York, NY

Hart, Blanche, *Pres,* Art Barn, Greenwich, CT

Hart, David M, *Dir Consulting Serv,* Society for the Preservation of New England Antiquities, Boston, MA

Hart, Evelyn L, *Head,* George Peabody Branch, Enoch Pratt Free Library of Baltimore City, MD

Hart, Robert A, *Dir,* Faulkner Mem Art Wing, Santa Barbara Public Library, CA

Hart, Robert G, *Gen Mgr,* Indian Arts and Crafts Board, Washington, DC

Hart, William B, *Dir Field Serv,* Society for the Preservation of New England Antiquities, Boston, MA

Hartel, Dr H, *Dir,* Museum of Indian Art, Staatliche Museen Preussischer Kulturbestiz, Berlin, Germany

Harten, Jurgen, *Dir,* Stadtische Kunsthalle, Dusseldorf, Germany

Harter, Donald, *Asst Prof,* Midwestern State Univ, Wichita Falls, TX

Harter, Donald R, *Chmn,* Niagara County Community College, Sanborn, NY

Harter, Harry H, *Chmn Dept Fine Arts,* Maryville College, TN

Hartgen, Vincent A, *Prof & Cur,* Univ Maine, Orono

Hartian, Serena, *Dir,* Scalamandre Museum of Textiles, New York, NY

Hartig, Tom, *Head History,* Ohio Historical Society, Columbus

Hartigan, Grace, *Artist-in-Residence,* Maryland Inst, Baltimore

Hartley, Corinne West, *Teacher,* Venice Painting, Drawing & Sculpture Studio, Inc, CA

Hartman, Dr, *Dir Summer School,* Juniata College, Huntingdon, PA

Hartman, Eleanor C, *Librn,* Los Angeles County Museum of Art, CA

Hartman, George F, Jr, *Supt,* Toledo Museum of Art, OH

Hartman, Joan M, *Dir Pub Relations,* Jewish Museum, New York, NY

Hartman, Mary, *Serv Librn,* Babcock Art Library, Sweet Briar College, VA

Hartman, Russell P, *Acting Dir,* Navajo Tribal Museum, Window Rock, AZ

Hartman, Terry L, *Instr,* Modesto Junior College, CA

Hartman, Walter, *Asst Prof,* Williamsport Area Community College, PA

Hartmann, Hans, *Dir,* Bundner Kunsthaus Chur, Switzerland

Hartmann, James, *Cur Historic Preservation,* Colorado Historical Society, Denver

Hartnett, Marianne, *First VPres,* North Shore Art League, Winnetka, IL

Hartsell, *Vis Prof,* Bethany Nazarene College, OK

Hartsook, Jane, *Dir,* Greenwich House Pottery, New York, NY

Hartwell, Carroll T, *Cur Photography,* Minneapolis Inst of Arts, MN

Hartz-Chambers, Jill, *Admin Aide,* Cornell Univ, Ithaca, NY

Harvath, John, Jr, *Head Fine Arts & Recreation,* Houston Public Library, TX

Harvey, Clifford, *Prof,* West Virginia Univ, Morgantown

Harvey, Dr, *Acad Dean,* Art Center College of Design, Pasadena, CA

Harvey, Donald, *Prof Drawing & Painting & Chmn Dept Visual Arts,* University of Victoria, BC

Harvey, Donald E, *Gallery Dir,* Univ Akron Galleries, OH

Harvey, Jack, *Chmn Humanities,* Weatherford College, TX

Harvey, Karen H, *Art Librn,* Smith College Museum of Art, Northampton, MA

Harvey, Merris, *Dir Summer School,* York College of Pennsylvania

Harvey, Virginia I, *Cur,* Univ Washington Henry Art Gallery, Seattle

Harwick, Eugene, *Assoc Prof,* Fort Hays State Univ, Hays, KS

Harwood, Kitty, *Hon Archivist,* Vizcaya, Miami, FL

Hasbury, Miss S, *Art Documentalist,* Nat Gallery of Canada, Ottawa, ON

Hasebe, Mitsuhiko, *Cur Ceramics,* Tokyo Kokuritsu Kindai Bijutsukan, Japan

Hasegawa, Sabroh, *Cur,* Kokuritsu Seiyo Bijutsukan, Tokyo, Japan

Haseltine, Fred, *Asst to Dir & Head Pub Information Dept,* Virginia Museum of Fine Arts, Richmond

Hasenmueller, Christine, *Assoc Prof,* Vanderbilt Univ, Nashville, TN

Hasenyager, Shirley, *Treas,* Windward Artists Guild, Lihue, HI

Haskell, Barbara, *Cur,* Whitney Museum of American Art, New York, NY

Haskell, Barry S, *Dir Summer School & Asst Dean,* Pierce College, Woodland Hills, CA

Haskins, Katherine, *Librn,* William Rockhill Nelson Gallery of Art, Kansas City, MO

Haslem, Hermine H, *Pres Bd Mgrs,* Sheldon Swope Art Gallery, Terre Haute, IN

Hassan, Gaylord, *Coordr Cultural Arts,* New Muse Community Museum of Brooklyn, NY

Hasselschwert, Harold, *Head Jewelry & Metals,* Bowling Green State Univ, OH

Hassou, Miss S, *Secy,* Haaretz Museum, Tel-Aviv, Israel

Hassrick, Peter, *Vice Chmn,* Wyoming Council on the Arts, Cheyenne

Hastie, Reid, *Prof,* Texas Tech Univ, Lubbock

Haswell, Hollee, *Librn,* Worcester Art Museum, MA

Hathaway, Carol J, *Coordr,* Roger Williams College, Bristol, RI

Hathaway, Walter M, *Dir,* Columbia Museums of Art and Science, SC

Hatmaker, Mrs Paul, *Treas,* Strasburg Museum, VA

Hauberg, John H, *Pres,* Seattle Art Museum, WA

Hauck, Alice H, *Mem Faculty,* Providence College, RI

Haughey, Beverly Jo, *Admin Asst,* Museum of Cultural History, Univ California, Los Angeles

Haughom, Synnove, *Cur,* Bates College, Lewiston, ME

Haugland, Ann, *Art Admin,* Federal Reserve Bank of Minneapolis, MN, see Corporate Art Holdings

Haupt, Margaret, *Registrar,* Muriel Isabel Bostwick Library, Art Gallery of Hamilton, ON

Haupt, Shirley, *Assoc Prof,* Univ Northern Iowa, Cedar Falls

Hauser, Dr Brigitta, *Cur Educ Dept,* Museum fur Volkerkunde Und Schweizerisches Museum fur Volkskunde Basel, Switzerland

Hauser, Robert A, *Mus Conservator,* Merrimack Valley Textile Museum, North Andover, MA

Hausman, Dr Jerome J, *Pres,* Minneapolis College of Art and Design, MN

Hausmann, Albert Charles, *Asst Prof,* Univ North Alabama, Florence

Havas, Edwin, *Instr,* Montclair Art Museum; *VPres,* New Jersey Watercolor Society, Bloomfield; *Asst Prof,* Seton Hall Univ, South Orange, NJ

Havas, Sandra H, *Dir,* Eccles Community Art Center, Ogden, UT

Havel, Lynn B, *Instr,* Butler County Community College, El Dorado, KS

Havens, Neil, *Prof,* Rice Univ, Houston, TX

Haver, Ronald, *Dir Film Prog,* Los Angeles County Museum of Art, CA

Havill, Jeffrey, *Asst Prof,* Alma College, MI

Havis, C Kenneth, *Gallery Dir,* North Texas State Univ, Denton

Havlena, Jarmila, *Prof,* Los Angeles Harbor College, Wilmington, CA

Hawcroft, Francis W, *Keeper,* Whitworth Art Gallery, Univ Manchester, England

Hawk, Shirley A, *Admin Asst,* Canton Art Inst, OH

Hawken, George, *Mem Faculty,* Toronto School of Art, Ontario

Hawkes, Elizabeth, *Archives,* Delaware Art Museum, Wilmington

Hawkins, Ashton, *VPres, Secy & Counsel,* Metropolitan Museum of Art, New York, NY

Hawkins, Frank, *Instr,* Dunedin Fine Arts & Cultural Center, FL

Hawkins, Gregory W, *Chmn,* Eastern Washington Univ, Cheney

Hawkins, John, *Assoc Prof,* Queensborough Community College, Bayside, NY

Hawkins, Rebecca, *Asst Prof,* James Madison Univ, Harrisonburg, VA

Hawley, Helen, *Pres,* Spectrum, Friends of Fine Art, Toledo, OH

Hawley, Henry, *Cur Decorative Arts (Post-Renaissance),* Cleveland Museum of Art, OH

Haworth, Dale, *Asst Chief Prints & Photographs Div,* Library of Congress, Washington, DC

Haworth, Julia C, *Exec Dir,* Tennessee Botanical Gardens and Fine Arts Center, Nashville

Haworth, Stephen K, *Prof,* Univ West Florida, Pensacola

Hawxhurst, Virginia, *Treas,* Brush and Palette Club, Cooperstown, NY

Haxthausen, Charles W, *Asst Cur,* Busch-Reisinger Museum, Harvard Univ, Cambridge, MA

Hay, H James, *Assoc Prof,* Olivet College, MI

Hay, Ike, *Mem Faculty,* Millersville State College, PA

Hayano, Carl, *Grad Coordr,* Northern Illinois Univ, DeKalb

Hayashida, Richard, *Instr,* Leeward Community College, Pearl City, HI

Haycock, Charles M, *Chmn,* Madison Area Technical College, WI

Haycock, Everett, *Prof,* Ohio Wesleyan Univ, Delaware, OH

Hayden, Dorothy, *Librn in Charge,* Regina Public Library, SK

Hayden, Elaine, *Dir Summer School,* Nazareth College of Rochester, NY

Hayden, Robert, *Asst Dir for Operations,* Brooklyn Museum, NY

Haydo, John R, *Asst Prof,* Central Missouri State Univ, Warrensburg

Haydon, Harold, *Dir,* Bergman Gallery, Univ of Chicago, IL

Hayes, Mrs Charles, *Pres,* Mississippi Museum of Art, Jackson

Hayes, Don, *Mem Faculty,* Arkansas Arts Center, Little Rock

Hayes, Joann, *Mem Faculty,* Madison Area Technical College, WI

Hayes, Laura H, *Cur,* Wyoming State Art Gallery, Cheyenne

Hayes, Lloyd D, *Treas,* Nat Gallery of Art, Washington, DC

Hayes, Patrick O'N, *Secy,* Newport Historical Society, RI

Hayes, Richard E, *Asst Prof,* Northeast Louisiana Univ, Monroe

Hayes, Richard L, *Dir Permanent Coll, Art Gallery & Assoc Prof,* Thiel College, Greenville, PA

Hayle, Pamela, *Print Dept Librn,* Boston Athenaeum, MA

Haylett, R C, Jr, *VChmn Comt,* Oglebay Inst Mansion Museum, Wheeling, WV

Haymaker, James, *Dir Art Prog,* Pfeiffer College, Misenheimer, NC

Hayner, Agnes, *Secy,* Springfield Art Association of Edwards Place, IL

Haynes, D, *Prof Art & Design & Chmn Dept & Dir Summer School,* Univ of Alberta, Edmonton

Haynes, Mrs N Fred, *Pres,* Museum of Arts and History, Port Huron, MI

Haynes, R, *Head Dept Art Hist,* Brighton Polytechnic, England

Hayter, Stanley William, *Asst Dir,* Art Information Center, New York, NY

Hayum, Andree, *Assoc Prof,* Fordham Univ, New York, NY

Hayward, Charles B, *Chmn,* Bay Path Junior College, Longmeadow, MA

Hayward, Jane, *Cur,* The Cloisters, Metropolitan Museum of Art, New York, NY

Hazel, Bud, *Dir Summer School,* Gonzaga Univ, Spokane, WA

Hazlehurst, F Hamilton, *Chmn Art Dept,* Vanderbilt Univ, Nashville, TN

Heacock, Dr Walter J, *Gen Dir,* Hagley Museum & *Pres,* Historical Society of Delaware, Wilmington

Head, Albert B, *Dir,* Jay R Broussard Mem Galleries, Baton Rouge, LA

Head, Robert W, *Chmn,* Murray State Univ, KY

Headley, Sherman K, *Exec Dir,* Minnesota Museum of Art Permanent Collection Gallery, St Paul

Heald, Betty, *Asst Prof,* Ohio Wesleyan Univ, Delaware

Heald, Lois, *Corresp Secy,* Tullahoma Fine Arts Center, TN

Healey, Ruth, *Dir,* Russell Sage College New Gallery, Troy, NY

Healy, Deborah, *Children's Classes Instr,* Montclair Art Museum, NJ

Heaney, Howell J, *Rare Book Librn,* Free Library of Philadelphia, PA

Heard, J, *Mem Faculty,* Golden West College, Huntington Beach, CA

Hearn, Millard F, *Chmn,* Univ of Pittsburgh, PA

Heath, Molly, *Treas,* Alaska Association for the Arts, Fairbanks

Hebert, Annabelle, *Sr Cur Educ,* New Orleans Museum of Art, LA

Heckel, Inge, *Mgr Develop & Promotion,* Metropolitan Museum of Art, New York, NY

Hecken, Dorothea, *Registrar,* Royal Ontario Museum, Toronto

Heckman, Dr Philip, *VPres,* Nebraska Art Association, Univ Nebraska Art Gallery, Lincoln

Heckman, Steve, *Head Art Dept & Dir Summer School,* Seward County Community College, Liberal, KS

Heckscher, Morrison H, *Cur American Decorative Arts,* Metropolitan Museum of Art, New York, NY

Hedberg, Gregory H, *Cur Paintings,* Minneapolis Inst of Arts, MN

Heden, Karl-Gustaf, *Dir,* Goteborgs Konstmuseum, Sweden

Hedergott, Dr Bodo, *Chief Cur,* Herzog Anton Ulrich-Museum, Brunswick, Germany

Hedgpeth, Don, *Dir,* Buffalo Bill Association, Cody, WY

Hedin, Thomas, *Asst Prof,* Univ Minnesota, Duluth

Hedley, R, *Dir,* Trent Polytechnic, Nottingham, England

Hedman, Donn, *Chmn Exhib,* Arkansas State Univ Art Gallery, State University

Hedrick, Basil C, *Asst Dir,* Illinois State Museum of Natural History and Art, Springfield

Hedvall, Dr Anders, *Librn,* Kungl Myntkabinettet Statens Museum for Mynt Medalj Och Penninghistoria, Stockholm, Sweden; *Librn,* Statens Historiska Museum, Stockholm, Sweden

Hee, Hon-Chew, *Dir,* Tennent Art Found Gallery, Honolulu, HI

Heefner, William F, *Pres,* Bucks County Historical Society, Doylestown, PA

Heeschen, Carl F, *Prof,* Allegheny College, Meadville, PA

Heffner, Jane E, *Develop Officer,* Solomon R Guggenheim Museum, New York, NY

Heflin, Patricia, *Staff Asst,* Dept State Diplomatic Reception Rooms, Washington, DC

Hefting, Dr P H, *Cur,* Ryksmuseum Kroller-Muller, Otterlo, Netherlands

Heftman, Lily, *Area Chairperson Apparel Arts,* Pasadena City College, CA

Heidel, Frederick H, *Prof,* Portland State Univ, OR

Heideman, Susan, *Instr,* Smith College, Northampton, MA

Heikenen, Patricia, *Dir Program & Publications,* Minnesota Museum of Art Permanent Collection Gallery, St Paul

Heil, Harry, *Dir,* Western State College, Gunnison, CO

Heilmer, Steven, *Instr,* Greenville College, IL

Heiloms, May, *Hon Life Pres,* Painters and Sculptors Society of New Jersey

Heimberg, Bruno, *Restoration Dept,* Bayerischen Staatsgemaldesammlungen, Munich, Germany

Heimdal, George, *Mem Faculty,* Spokane Falls Community Coll, Spokane, WA

Hein, Don, *Cur Art Educ,* Art Gallery of South Australia, Adelaide

Hein, Max, *Prof,* Santa Rosa Junior College, CA

Heindel, Robert, *Adv Bd Mem,* Famous Artists School, Westport, CT

Heinemann, Ernest, *Librn,* Haaretz Museum, Tel-Aviv, Israel

Heinmiller, Carl, *VPres,* Sheldon Museum and Cultural Center, Haines, AK

Heinrich, Neil, *Secy,* Verde Valley Art Association, Jerome, AZ

Heins, Valerie, *Mem Secy,* Allentown Art Museum, PA

Heinz, Sister Lorraine, *Mem Faculty,* Edgewood College, Madison, WI

Heinz, Susan, *Exec Dir,* Palos Verdes Art Center, Rancho Palos Verdes, CA

Heiser, Richard, *Librn,* Navajo Nation Library, Window Rock, AZ

Heitz, Nancy, *Assoc Prof,* Brenau College, Gainesville, GA

Heldt, Carl, *Coordr Graphic Design,* Univ Arizona, Tucson

Helfrich, Paul, *Assoc Prof,* College of William and Mary, Williamsburg, VA

Helgoe, Orlin, *Assoc Prof,* Univ Southern Colorado, Belmont Campus, Pueblo

Heliker, John, *VPres Art,* American Academy and Inst of Arts and Letters, see National and Regional Organizations

Hellberg, Ray W, *Head Dept & Head Summer School,* Utah State Univ, Logan

Hellebrand, Nancy, *Mem Faculty,* Bucks County Community College, Newtown, PA

Heller, Jules, *Dean,* College of Fine Arts, Arizona State Univ, Tempe

Hellier, Bob, *Prog Coordr,* Tampa Bay Art Center, FL

Helliesen, Sidsel, *Keeper Prints & Drawings,* Nasjonalgalleriet, Oslo, Norway

Helliwell, Eleanor, *Corresp Secy,* Seattle Weaver's Guild, WA

Helm, Edwin, *Instr,* Langston Univ, OK

Helm, Robert, *Assoc Prof,* Washington State Univ, Pullman

Helman, Phoebe, *Adjunct Assoc Prof,* New York Inst Technology, Old Westbury

Helmer, Bonnie, *Teacher,* Venice Painting, Drawing & Sculpture Studio, CA

Helmetag, Carl, Jr, *Chmn Bd,* Woodmere Art Gallery, Philadelphia, PA

Helmken, Deborah, *Registrar,* Telfair Acad of Arts & Sciences, Savannah, GA

Helsell, Charles P, *Cur,* Univ Minnesota Gallery, Minneapolis

Helsted, Dr Dyveke, *Dir,* Thorvaldsen Museum, Copenhagen, Denmark

Helvey, Kenneth W, *Chmn,* Fullerton College, CA

Hemming, Sam E, *Pres,* Easton Acad of the Arts, MD

Hemus, Sharon, *Activities Coordr,* Fine Arts Gallery of San Diego, CA

Hench, Robert, Belmont Campus, *Assoc Prof,* Univ Southern Colorado

Hench, Robert, *Dir Gallery & Assoc Prof,* Univ Southern Colorado, Belmont Campus, Pueblo

Hendershot, Jim, *Asst Prof,* St John's Univ, Collegeville, MN

Henderson, Ann, *Cur Educ,* New Orleans Museum of Art, LA

Henderson, George, *Div Head,* Dallas Public Library, TX

Henderson, Mrs Harry, *Dir,* Black Hills Art Center, Spearfish, SD

Henderson, J Welles, *Pres,* Philadelphia Maritime Museum, PA

Henderson, Lana, *Chmn,* North Carolina Central Univ, Durham

Henderson, Maren, *Assoc Prof,* California State Polytechnic Univ, Pomona

Henderson, Dr Robert, *Head Libr & Museum of the Performing Arts,* Shelby Cullom Davis Museum of the Performing Arts, New York Public Library, NY

Henderson, Thomas, *Assoc Prof,* Mount Allison Univ, Sackville, NB

Henderson, Vivian, *Dir Continuing Educ, (Summer School)*, Seton Hill College, Greensburg, PA

Hendrick, Barbara, *Mgr Publns*, Long Beach Museum of Art, CA

Hendricks, Barkley L, *Asst Prof*, Connecticut College, New London

Hendrickson, Thomas, C, *Head Dept*, Univ Wisconsin-Platteville

Hendrix, Mrs Hubert, *Secy*, Arts Council of Spartanburg County, SC

Hendry, Ken, *Coordr*, Colorado State Univ, Fort Collins

Henger, Sue, *Registrar/Editor*, Newport Harbor Art Museum, CA

Hengst, Timothy, *Instr*, Johns Hopkins Univ, Baltimore, MD

Henkel, Kathryn, *Cur*, Hartwick College Fine Arts Museum, Oneonta, NY

Henkel, Margot A, *Exec Dir*, New York Society of Architects, New York

Henle, Jane, *Asst Prof*, Marymount College, Tarrytown, NY

Hennessey, William J, *Cur Western Art*, Univ Kansas, Lawrence

Hennig, Lorna, *Secy*, Raeine Art Association, WI

Hennigh, Gary L, *Dir*, Stanley Hall Gallery, Columbia, MO

Henning, Darrell, *Cur*, Vesterheim, Decorah, IA

Henning, Edward B, *Cur Modern Art*, Cleveland Museum of Art, OH

Henning, Fritz, *Pres & Dir*, Famous Artists School, Westport, CT

Henning, Jane, *Architecture Specialist*, Howe Architecture Library, Arizona State Univ, Tempe

Henning, K Louise, *Reference Librn*, Univ Wisconsin-Madison Mem Union

Henning, William, *Cur Fine Arts Coll*, Colorado gsprings Fine Arts Center, CO

Henning, William T, Jr, *Cur*, Phillips Univ Art Gallery, Enid, OK

Henricks, Duane Ed, *Dir & Reference Librn*, Kent Library, Cape Girardeau, MO

Henriksen, Jorgen, *Instr*, Brockton Art Center, MA

Henry, Esther, *VPres*, Easton Academy of the Arts, MD

Henry, Fred, *Asst Prof*, Southern Arkansas Univ, Magnolia

Henry, Jean, *Asst Prof*, Univ Maine at Portland-Gorham, Gorham

Henry, John B, *Coordr Exhib*, Mississippi Museum of Art, Jackson

Henry, Joseph, *Cur*, Craft Center Museum, Danbury, CT

Henry, Penelope, *Registr*, Parrish Art Museum, & *Librn*, Aline B Saarinen Library, Southampton, NY

Henry, Stuart C, *Dir*, Berkshire Museum, Pittsfield, MA

Hensche, Henry, *Dir*, Cape School of Art, Provincetown, MA

Hensche, Henry, *Vis Prof*, Goetz Art School, New York, NY

Henschen, Dr Eva, *Cur Educ*, Thorvaldsen Museum, Copenhagen, Denmark

Henselman, Frances, *Dir Libr Serv*, Long Beach Public Library, CA

Hensler, Ruth, *Chairperson Art Dept & Dir Summer School*, Saint Louis College at Meramec, St Louis, MO

Hensley, Fred Owen, *Asst Prof*, Univ North Alabama, Florence

Henze, Judy, *Mus Asst*, Ships of the Sea Museum, Savannah, GA

Hepburn, Irene, *Secy-Treas*, Visual Arts of Ontario, Toronto

Hepburn, Tony, *Artist-in-Residence*, Oxbow Summer Art Workshops, Saugatuck, MI

Hepburn, Tony, *Head Dept*, New York State College of Ceramics at Alfred Univ

Hepner, Edward J, *Site Supt*, Bishop Hill Historic Site, IL

Herberg, Mayde, *Instr*, Santa Ana College, CA

Herbert, Al, *Prof*, Macomb County Community College, Warren, MI

Herbst, Florence, *Librn*, Munson-Williams-Proctor Inst Museum of Art, Utica, NY

Herdeg, John A, *Pres*, Winterthur Museum and Gardens, DE

Heredia, Ruben, *Vis Prof*, Butte Community College, Oroville, CA

Herger, Dorothy, *Instr*, Solano Community College, Suisun City, CA

Herman, Lloyd E, *Dir*, Nat Collection of Fine Arts, Washington, DC

Hermansdorfer, M, *Cur*, Muzeum Narodowe We Wroclawiu, Wroclaw, Poland

Hernandez, Gilberto, *Gallery Coordr*, El Museo del Barrio, New York, NY

Hernandez, Jo Farb, *Librn & Acting Dir*, Triton Museum of Art, Santa Clara, CA

Hernandez, Joseph, *Mem Faculty*, Waubonsee Community College, Sugar Grove, IL

Herold, Donald G, *Dir*, Charleston Museum, SC

Herr, Marcianne, *Cur Educ*, Akron Art Inst Museum, OH

Herrara, Alfredo Ramirez, *Admin*, Museo de Arte Moderno, Mexico City, Mexico

Herrero, Susana, *Mem Faculty*, Univ Puerto Rico, Rio Piedras

Herrick, Esther, *Chmn*, Hale House, Beverly Historical Society, MA

Herrick, Mrs Fred R, *Librn & Secy/Receptionist*, Springfield Art & Historical Society, VT

Herring, Dr Jack W, *Dir*, Baylor Univ Art Museum, Waco, TX

Herring, Janis, *Secy*, Peoria Art Guild, IL

Herrold, Clifford, *Prof*, Univ Northern Iowa, Cedar Falls

Herrold, David W, *Instr*, DePauw Univ, Greencastle, IN

Herscher, Fr Irenaeus, *Art Cur*, Saint Bonaventure Univ Art Collection, NY

Hersey, George L, *Dir Grad Studies*, Yale Univ, New Haven, CT

Hershberger, Abner, *Prof*, Goshen College, IN

Hershey, Michael, *Instr*, Doane College, Crete, NE

Hertel, C H, *Prof*, Pitzer College, Claremont, CA

Hertzi, Joseph, R, *Dir*, Canton Art Inst, OH

Hertzman, Gay M, *Coll Research & Publ*, North Carolina Museum of Art, Raleigh

Hertzman, Hohn A, *Vis Prof*, Univ North Carolina at Chapel Hill

Herzbrun, Helene M, *Prof & Dept Chmn*, American Univ, Washington, DC

Herzman, Diane, *Exec Dir*, Art Directors Club, see National and Regional Organizations

Heslin, James J, *Dir*, New York Historical Society, New York, NY

Hess, Grace, *Librn Fine Arts*, Hawaii State Library, Honolulu

Hess, Joyce, *Librn*, Univ Texas at Austin

Hess, Stanley, *Prof*, Drake Univ, Des Moines, IA

Hesse, Charles T, *VPres*, Old Sturbridge Village, MA

Hessel, Tom, *VPres*, Minnesota Artists Association, Minneapolis

Hessemer, Betty, *Mem Faculty*, Rehoboth Art League, Rehoboth Beach, DE

Hesslein, Dr H G, *Pres*, Art Research Service, Chappaqua, NY

Hester, Charles, *Treas*, Newport Harbor Art Museum, CA

Hester, Dr Warren, *Pres*, Coppini Academy of Fine Arts, San Antonio, TX

Heth, Susan, *Dept Secy*, Univ Alberta Art Gallery and Museum, Edmonton

Heubner, Sister M Rosemarita, *Assoc Prof*, Mount Mary College, Milwaukee, WI

Heuler, Henry J, *Assoc Prof*, Univ West Florida, Pensacola

Heuser, Jay, *Tech Dir*, Art Research Center, Kansas City, MO

Hewitt, Clarissa, *Asst Prof*, California Polytechnic State Univ, San Luis Obispo

Hewitt, Duncan, *Asst Prof*, Univ Maine at Portland-Gorham, Gorham

Hewitt, Linda V, *Asst Dir*, Isabella Stewart Gardner Museum, Boston, MA

Hewitt, Peter M, *Secy*, Providence Athenaeum, RI

Hext, Charles, R, *Asst Prof*, Sul Ross State Univ, Alpine, TX

Heyduck, Bill, *Assoc Prof*, Eastern Illinois Univ, Charleston

Heyman, Lawrence, *Head Prog Printmaking*, Rhode Island School of Design, Providence

Heyman, Therese, *Sr Cur Prints & Photographs*, Oakland Museum, CA

Hiatt, Richard, *Dir Summer School*, Eastern Oregon State College, La Grande

Hibbard, Stephen T, *Pres*, Gibson Society, Boston, MA

Hibbs, Vivian A, *Cur Archaeology*, Hispanic Society of America, New York, NY

Hickenbotham, Sister Kathleen, *Head Dept & Instr*, Mount Marty College, Yankton, SD

Hickie, Philip, *Head Div Design*, Nat Art School, Darlinghurst, Australia

Hicklin, Barbara Roe, *Pres*, Alberta Society of Artists, Calgary

Hickl-Szabo, H, *Cur European Dept*, Royal Ontario Museum, Toronto

Hickman, Patricia, *Chmn Textiles*, De Young Museum Art School, San Francisco, CA

Hickman, Ronald D, *Dir*, Phoenix Art Museum, AZ

Hickman, Theresa, *Mem Secy*, Norton Gallery and School of Art, West Palm Beach, FL

Hicks, Ellen C, *Editor*, American Association of Museums, see National and Regional Organizations

Hicks, Dr Fred W, *Dir*, Rollins College, Winter Park, FL

Hicks, Herb, *Assoc Prof*, Univ Lethbridge, AB

Hicks, James H, *Slide Librn*, Portland Art Association, OR

Hicks, Jotin, *Prof*, Drake University, Des Moines, IA

Hicks, Leon, *Assoc Prof*, Webster College, Webster Groves, MO

Hicks, Margaret, *Dir*, Navarro College, Corsicana, TX

Hicks, Ron, *Instr*, Johnson County Community College, Overland Park, KS

Hickson, Howard, *Dir*, Northeastern Nevada Museum, Elko

Hide, P, *Vis Prof*, Univ Alberta, Edmonton

Hidemark, Dr Elisabet, *Keeper Textiles & Dress*, Nordiska Museet, Stockholm, Sweden

Hielkema, Arthur, *Librn*, Northwestern College, Orange City, IA

Hiers, C, *Head*, Auburn Univ, AL

Hiester, Jan, *Registrar*, Charleston Museum, SC

Hiester, John, *Asst Prof*, Jamestown Community College, NY

Higa, Kazuo M A, *Chmn & Prof*, Los Angeles City College, CA

Higa, Yosh, *Assoc Prof*, Southampton College of Long Island Univ, NY

Higgins, Edward, *Assoc Prof*, Mercyhurst College, Erie, PA

Higgins, Janet, *Asst Prof*, Middle Tennessee State Univ, Murfreesboro

Higgins, Mrs Kenneth R, *Pres*, Association for the Preservation of Virginia Antiquities, Richmond

Higgins, Margaret, *Dir Summer School*, College of Mount Saint Vincent, Riverdale, NY

Higgins, Steve, *Chmn Found*, Univ Manitoba, Winnipeg

Higgins, Dr William H, Jr, *Pres*, Virginia Museum of Fine Arts, Richmond

Higgins, Dr Winifred H, *Chmn Dept Art*, San Diego State Univ, CA

High, Jacqueline, *Registrar*, Univ Kentucky Art Museum, Lexington

Highberg, Stephanie, *Instr*, Chamberlayne Junior College, Boston, MA

Hightower, Caroline, *Exec Dir*, American Inst of Graphic Arts, see National and Regional Organizations

Hightower, John B, *Pres*, South Street Seaport Museum, New York, NY

Higuera, Jean, *Art Cur*, Bank of America Corp and Bank of America Found, San Francisco, CA, see Corporate Art Holdings

Hiigel, Dr Lewis, *Dean Fine Arts,* El Camino College, Torrance, CA

Hildebrand, Sam, *Instr,* Claremore College, OK

Hildreth, Joseph, *Asst Prof,* State Univ New York College at Potsdam

Hiliare, Francois, *Keeper,* Musee Nat des Monuments Francais, Paris, France

Hill, Charles V, *Second VPres,* Beaumont Art Museum, TX

Hill, Dr Conrad, *Pres,* South County Art Association, Kingston, RI

Hill, Dr Ed, *Dir Summer School,* Wenatchee Valley College, WA

Hill, Mrs Ed, *Secy,* North Canton Public Library, OH

Hill, Edward G, *Head Dept & Asst Prof,* Wilberforce Univ, OH

Hill, Esther, *Assoc Prof,* Univ North Carolina, Charlotte

Hill, John, *Assoc Prof,* Yale Univ, New Haven, CT

Hill, Mrs John, *Exhib Chmn,* West Baton Rouge Museum, Port Allen, LA

Hill, John R, *Exhib Technician,* Oklahoma Historical Society, Oklahoma City

Hill, Peter, *Prof,* Univ Nebraska at Omaha

Hill, Richard, *Chmn Dept Photo/Elec Arts,* Ontario College of Art, Toronto

Hill, Roger, *Pres Elect,* Arts for Living Center, Burlington, IA

Hill, Sherri Lynn, *Coordr,* Kilcawley Center Art Gallery, Youngstown State Univ, OH

Hill, William M, *Dir,* Santa Monica College Art Gallery, CA

Hiller, Betty R, *Dir,* Univ Nebraska Art Galleries, Omaha

Hiller, Dr Jack, *Chmn Sloan Comt,* Sloan Galleries, Valparaiso Univ, IN

Hilliard, David C, *Pres Auxiliary Bd,* Art Inst of Chicago, IL

Hilliard, Elbert R, *Dir,* Mississippi Dept of Archives and History, Jackson

Hilligoss, Martha, *Chief Art Dept,* St Louis Public Library, MO

Hillis, Jeanne, *Pres,* The Dalles Art Association, OR

Hillix, Virginia, *Educ Dir,* Art Research Center, Kansas City, MO

Hillman, Raymond, *Cur History,* Pioneer Museum and Haggin Galleries, Stockton, CA

Hills, Patricia, *Cur,* Whitney Museum of American Art, New York, NY

Hilson, M Douglas, *In Charge Grad Painting,* Univ Illinois, Urbana-Champaign, Champaign

Hilt, Lyda, *Cur Genealogy,* Tippecanoe County Historical Museum & *Librn Genealogical Section,* Alameda McCollough Library, Lafayette, IN

Hilty, Thomas, *Head Drawing & Graphics,* Bowling Green State Univ, OH

Hime, Gary D, *Asst Librn,* Wichita Public Library, KS

Himmel, Mrs Arthur, *Pres,* Katonah Gallery, NY

Himmelheber, Dr G, *Cur Furniture,* Bayerisches Nationalmuseum, Munich, Germany

Hinckley, Gene P, *Pres,* Cincinnati Art Club, OH

Hind, Jan G, *Educ Coordr,* Museum of Early Southern Decorative Art, Winston-Salem, NC

Hindle, Brook, *Dir,* Nat Museum of History and Technology, Washington, DC

Hinds, Pat, *Mem Faculty,* Antelope Valley College, Lancaster, CA

Hine, Lela M, *Cur/Registrar,* Hermitage Found Museum, Norfolk, VA

Hines, Adrienne G, *Pres,* Federated Arts Council of Richmond, VA

Hines, Charles, *Instr,* Dunedin Fine Arts & Cultural Center, FL

Hines, Felrath, *Conservator,* Nat Portrait Gallery, Washington, DC

Hines, Norman P, *Asst Prof,* Pomona College, Claremont, CA

Hines, Susan, *Pres,* Municipal Arts Commission, City of Los Angeles Municipal Arts Dept, CA

Hing, Glenn, *Gallery Asst,* California State Univ Fine Arts Gallery, Los Angeles

Hios, Theo, *VPres,* Federation of Modern Painters and Sculptors, see National and Regional Organizations

Hiott, John, *Dir Summer School,* Meredith College, Raleigh, NC

Hipp, Jean E, *Office Mgr,* Virginia Beach Arts Center, VA

Hirsch, Barron, *Prof & Chmn Art & Design Dept,* Saginaw Valley State College, University Center, MI

Hirsch, Betty W, *Dir,* Beaumont Art Museum, TX

Hirsch, Joseph, *Adv Bd Mem,* Famous Artists School, Westport, CT

Hirschl, Milton, *Prof,* Pierce College, Woodland Hills, CA

Hirschl, Norman, *VPres,* Art Dealers Association of America, see National and Regional Organizations

Hirshbein, Omus, *Educ Dir,* 92nd Street YMHA-YWHA, New York, NY

Hirshblond, Harold R, *Cur,* Historic Burlington County Prison Museum, Mount Holly, NJ

Hirshler, Eric E, *Prof,* Denison Univ, Granville, OH

Hirshman, Louis P, *Dir Instruction,* Samuel S Fleisher Art Mem, Philadelphia, PA

Hirst, B C C, *Dean Faculty,* Manchester Polytechnic, England

Hiserodt, Donald D, *Dir Summer School,* Yavapai College, Prescott, AZ

Hitch, Henry C, Jr, *VPres,* No Mans Land Historical Society, Goodwell, OK

Hitchcock, D Michael, *Asst Prof,* George Washington Univ, Washington, DC

Hitchcock, Howard G, *Chmn,* California State Univ, Long Beach

Hitchcock, P, *Chmn,* California State Univ, Sacramento

Hitchings, Gladys, *Librn,* Davenport Municipal Art Gallery, IA

Hitchings, Sinclair H, *Keeper Prints,* Albert H Wiggins Gallery, Boston Public Library, MA

Hittle, Sheila, *Mem Secy,* Fine Arts Gallery of San Diego, CA

Hlad, Richard, *Asst Prof,* Tarrant County Junior College, Northeast Campus, Hurst, TX

Hlusicka, Jiri, *Art Historian & Dir,* Moravska Galerie v Brne, Czechoslovakia

Ho, Abraham P, *Cur,* Chung-Cheng Art Gallery, St John's Univ, Jamaica, NY

Ho, Fran, *Assoc Prof,* Washington State Univ, Pullman

Ho, Wai-Kam, *Cur Chinese Art,* Cleveland Museum of Art, OH

Hoadley, Bruce, *Instr,* Truro Center for the Arts at Castle Hill, MA

Hoagland, Joan, *Head Fine Arts Dept,* Cleveland Public Library, OH

Hoare, Sister Gabriel Mary, *Assoc Prof,* Webster College, Webster Groves, MO

Hobbs, Joe F, *Dir,* Univ Oklahoma, Norman

Hobbs, Robert, *Adj Cur Modern Art,* Cornell Univ, Ithaca, NY

Hobbs, Robert D, *Chmn Dept Art,* Clarion State College, PA

Hobday, John, *Nat Dir,* Canadian Conference of the Arts, see National Organizations of Canada

Hobin, James R, *Librn,* Albany Inst of History and Art, NY

Hoblitzell, Alan P, *Treas,* Municipal Art Society of Baltimore City, MD

Hobrecht, Hilary, *Pastor Rev,* Mission San Miguel, CA

Hochman, Marie, *Teacher,* Nutley Art Center, NJ

Hochstetler, T Max, *Mem Faculty,* Austin Peay State Univ, Clarksville, TN

Hockenhull, Jo, *Asst Prof,* Washington State Univ, Pullman

Hockett, Roland L, *Assoc Prof,* Gulf Coast Community College, Panama City, FL

Hockschild, H K, *Pres,* Adirondack Museum of the Adirondack Historical Association, Blue Mountain Lake, NY

Hodge, Dr G Stuart, *Dir,* Flint Inst of Arts Museum, MI

Hodgell, Lois, *Coordr,* Univ Minnesota, Morris

Hodgkinson, T W I, *Dir,* Wallace Collection, London, England

Hodgson, James, *Acquisitions Librn,* Fogg Art Museum, Cambridge, MA

Höegh, Hans, *Pres,* Kunstindustrimuseet I Oslo, Norway

Hoell, Peter, *Mem Faculty,* Saint Louis Community College at Meramec, St Louis, MO

Hoepfner, Gerald R, *Chief Conservator,* Sterling and Francine Clark Art Inst, Williamstown, MA

Hoerl-Binegger, Angelika, *Chmn,* Muiska-Museum, Munich, Germany

Hoermann, Barbara, *Librn,* Univ California Nelson Gallery, Davis

Hoerner, Sister Annette Cecile, *Asst Prof,* Immaculata College of Washington, DC

Hoesen, Lois Van, *Reference Supvr,* Brookline Public Library, MA

Hoetink, H R, *Dir,* Koninklijk Kabinet Van Schilderijen Mauritshuis, The Hague, Netherlands

Hoffeld, Jeffrey, *Mus Dir,* State Univ New York College at Purchase

Hoffman, Mrs Alfred, *Secy,* Florida Gulf Coast Art Center, Clearwater

Hoffman, Barry, *Mgr Dir Center Music, Drama & Art,* Lake Placid School of Art Gallery, NY

Hoffman, L G, *Dir,* Davenport Municipal Art Gallery, IA

Hoffman, Laurence, *Chief Conservator,* Hirshhorn Museum and Sculpture Garden, Washington, DC

Hoffman, Lee M, *Prof,* Univ South Alabama, Mobile

Hoffman, Marilyn, *Dir,* Brockton Art Center, MA

Hoffman, Michael, *Advisor,* Alfred Stieglitz Center, Philadelphia Museum of Art, PA

Hoffman, Roy E, *Dir,* Museum of the Rockies, Montana State Univ, Bozeman

Hoffman, William, *Business & Technical Dept Head,* Wichita Public Library, KS

Hofheimer, Henry Clay, II, *Chmn Bd Trustees,* Chrysler Museum at Norfolk, VA

Hofmann, Earl F, *Artist-in-Residence,* Saint Mary's College of Maryland, Saint Mary's City

Hofmann, Dr Werner, *Dir,* Hamburger Kunsthalle, Germany

Hofstede, Peter, *Scientific Asst,* Groninger Museum Voor Stad En Land, Netherlands

Hogan, Gary, *Assoc Prof,* Hartford Art School, Univ Hartford, West Hartford, CT

Hogan, James, *Assoc Prof,* Saint Louis Community College at Forest Park, MO

Hoge, Robert W, *Dir,* Sanford Museum and Planetarium, Cherokee, IA

Hogg, Mary E, *VPres,* Canadian Crafts Council, see National Organizations of Canada

Hogsett, Ted C, *Owner-Dir,* Southwestern School of Art, Albuquerque, NM

Hohby, Susan, *Secy & Coordr,* Community Arts Council of Chilliwack, BC

Hohl, Robert, *Reference Librn,* Saint Mary's College, Notre Dame, IN

Hohnstone, William H, *Treas,* American Acad in Rome, New York, NY

Hoke, Montee, *Asst Prof,* Southwestern Oklahoma State Univ, Weatherford

Holahan, Elizabeth G, *Pres,* Rochester Historical Society, NY

Holahan, Mary, *Registrar,* Delaware Art Museum, Wilmington

Holcomb, Grant, *Dir Art Mus & Asst Prof,* Mount Holyoke College, South Hadley, MA

Holcomn, Barry, *Dir Fashion,* Art Inst of Fort Lauderdale, FL

Holcroft, Erma, *Secy,* Valley Art Center, Clarkston, WA

Holder, Charles, *Instr,* Dunedin Fine Arts & Cultural Center, FL

Holder, Philancy N, *Mem Faculty,* Austin Peay State Univ, Clarksville, TN

Holder, Thomas J, *Assoc Prof,* Univ Nevada, Las Vegas

Hunter, I A, *Educ Officer,* Nat Art Gallery of New Zealand, Wellington

Hunter, Miss J, *Deputy Librn Coll,* Nat Gallery of Canada, Ottawa, ON

Hunter, J T, *Prin,* Edinburgh College of Art, Scotland

Hunter, Lissa, *Asst Prof,* Mansfield State College, PA

Hunter, Miriam, *Chmn Dept,* Wheaton College, IL

Hunter, Robert Douglas, *Pres,* Guild of Boston Artists, MA

Hunter, Ruth, *Secy-Receptionist,* Remington Art Museum, Ogdensburg, NY

Hunter, Sam, *Prof,* Princeton Univ, NJ

Hunter, Terry J, *Instr,* South Carolina State College, Orangeburg

Hunter, Wilbur, H, *Dir,* Peale Museum, Baltimore, MD

Huntley, Darrell W, *Pres,* Fort Wayne Fine Arts Found, IN

Huntley, David C, *Chmn Dept & Dir Summer School,* Southern Illinois Univ, Edwardsville

Huntley, Rev Joseph, *Secy,* Rolk Public Museum, Lakeland, FL

Hurdle, John H, *Cur,* Ringling Museum of the Circus, John and Mable Ringling Museum of Art, Sarasota, FL

Hurley, Sir John, *Pres,* Museum of Applied Arts and Sciences, Sydney, Australia

Hurley, Michael, *Pres,* Greater Fall River Art Association, MA

Hurst, Elsie, *Dir Admin,* Boston Architectural Center, MA

Hurst, Ralph, *Prof,* Florida State Univ, Tallahassee

Hurt, Jethro M, III, *Educ Coordr,* Chicago Architecture Found, IL

Hurt, Virginia, *Recording Secy,* New Hampshire Art Association, Manchester

Husband, J, *Dir,* Anderson Park Art Gallery, Invercargill, New Zealand

Husband, Timothy, *Asst to Dir,* The Cloisters, Metropolitan Museum of Art, New York, NY

Huskilson, J, *Keeper Admin,* Fitzwilliam Museum, Univ Cambridge, England

Huss, Ardis Hamilton, *Secy,* Minot Art Gallery, ND

Huston, Perry, *Conservator,* Kimbell Art Museum, Fort Worth, TX

Hustrad, Robert, *Mem Faculty,* Millersville State College, PA

Hutchinson, Don, *Instr,* Vancouver Community College, Langara Campus, BC

Hutchinson, Janet, *Dir,* Martin County Historical Society, Stuart, FL

Hutchison, Harold, *Dir Summer School,* Univ Wisconsin-Platteville

Hutchison, Jane C, *Prof & Chmn Art Hist Dept & Dir Summer School,* Univ Wisconsin, Madison

Hutchison, Robin, *Keeper,* Scottish Nat Portrait Gallery, Nat Gallery of Scotland, Edinburgh

Hutson, Bill, *Mem Faculty,* Creighton Univ, Omaha, NE

Hutson, Jean B, *Chief,* Schomburg Center for Research in Black Culture, New York Public Library, New York

Hutt, James E, *Dir,* Adirondack Lakes Center for the Arts, Blue Mountain Lake, NY

Hutter, Dr Heribert R, *Dir,* Gemaldegalerie der Akademie der Bildenden Kunste in Wien, Vienna, Austria

Hutton, Virginia, *Chmn,* Midway College, KY

Hutton, William, *Chief Cur,* Toledo Museum of Art, OH

Huybregts, Brigitte, *Dir,* Pensacola Museum of Art, FL

Huyer, Mrs George, *Dir Art Center,* Greenwich Art Society and Art Center, CT

Hvazda, Gloria, *Sales Desk Mgr,* Allentown Art Museum, PA

Hyams, Ben, *Special Asst to Dir,* Honolulu Academy of Art Collection, HI

Hyatt, Gordon, *Secy,* Municipal Art Society of New York, NY

Hyatt, John D, *Librn,* Rosenberg Library, Galveston, TX

Hyer, Christine D, *Develop Officer,* Univ Rochester Mem Art Gallery, NY

Hyers, Fredric L, *Dir,* Univ Northern Colorado, Greeley

Hyleck, Walter, *Assoc Prof,* Berea College, KY

Hyman, Linda, *Asst Prof,* Emory Univ, Atlanta, GA

Hynes, William, *Mem Faculty,* Shippensburg State College, PA

Hyrkin, Roy, *Lectr,* Ladycliff College, Highland Falls, NY

Hysell, David M, *Assoc Prof,* Rhode Island College, Providence

Hyslin, Richard, *Chmn Ceramics,* Pan American Univ, Edinburg, TX

Hysong, Joe L, *Chairperson Div Creative Arts & Dir Summer School,* Monterey Peninsula College, CA

Iacono, Domenic J, *Cur Coll,* Syracuse University, Joe and Emily Lowe Art Gallery, NY

Iams, James Drake, *Mem Faculty,* Rehoboth Art League, Rehoboth Beach, DE

Ianco-Starrels, Josine, *Dir,* Municipal Art Gallery, City of Los Angeles Municipal Arts Dept, CA

Ibach, Dick, *Mem Faculty,* Spokane Falls Community College, Spokane, WA

Ibsen, Kent, *Vis Prof,* Northern Arizona Univ, Flagstaff

Ide, Mrs George, *Secy,* Mobile Art Association, AL

Igna, Mary Ann, *Cur Exhib,* Cranbrook Academy of Art Museum, Bloomfield Hills, MI

Igoe, Harold E, Jr, *Pres,* Carolina Art Association, Charleston, SC

Iguchi, Yashiro, *Conservator Asiatic Art,* Museum of Fine Arts, Boston, MA

Ihrig, Robert, *Dir,* Kitchener-Waterloo Art Gallery, ON

Ikegawa, Shiro, *Chmn Printmaking,* Otis Art Institute, Los Angeles, CA

Ikemoto, Karen, *Young Adult Librn,* Kauai Regional Library, Lihue, HI

Ikuta, Madoka, *Cur,* Kokuritsu Seiyo Bijutsukan, Tokyo, Japan

Ileckova, Dr Silvia, *Chief Dept Contemporary Art,* Slovenska Narodna Galeria, Bratislava, Czechoslovakia

Iler, Henry, *Assoc Prof,* Georgia Southern College, Statesboro

Iles, William, *Asst Prof,* McNeese State Univ, Lake Charles, LA

Ilgner, Charla, *Mem Faculty,* Laguna Beach School of Art, CA

Ilies, Madeleine, *Reserve Supvr,* Washington Univ Gallery of Art, St Louis, MO

Imai, Haruo, *Dir,* Tokyo-To Bijutsukan, Japan

Imel, William, *Asst Chmn,* Colorado State Univ, Fort Collins

ImOberstag, Ann, *Asst Cur,* Desert Caballeros Western Museum, Wickenburg, AZ

Inayat-ur-Rahman, *Asst Supt Archaeology (Ethnography),* Nat Museum of Pakistan, Karachi

Inez, Sunny, *Asst Prof,* Loma Linda Univ, La Sierra Campus, Riverside, CA

Ingalls, Sarah P, *Cur Natural Hist,* Peabody Museum of Salem, MA

Ingamells, J S, *Asst to Dir,* Wallace Collection, London, England

Ingersoll, Jonathan, *Assoc Prof,* Saint Mary's College of Maryland, Saint Mary's City

Inglis, R R, *Exec Dir,* Association des Musees Canadiens, see National Organizations of Canada

Ingram, Frances, *Asst Dir,* Northport-East Northport Public Library, NY

Injejikian, Lorig, *Gallery Coordr,* Los Angeles Inst of Contemporary Art, CA

Innes, Ian, *Secy-Treas,* Saskatchewan Association of Architects, Saskatoon

Innes, Jacqueline Sione, *Instr,* Univ North Alabama, Florence

Insalaco, Thomas F, *Acting Chmn,* Community College of the Finger Lakes, Canandaigua, NY

Iocovantuno, Yolanda, *Acquisitions & Young Adult Services,* Nutley Public Library, NJ

Iorio, Dominick A, *Dir Summer School,* Rider College, Lawrenceville, NJ

Ipock, Mrs Robert A, *Registrar,* Tryon Palace Restoration Complex, New Bern, NC

Iqbal, Mohd, *Asst in Charge,* Art Gallery Society of Contemporary Art, Rawalpindi, Pakistan

Ireland, Martha, *Cur,* Princeton Antiques Bookservice, Atlantic City, NJ

Irland, Basia, *Asst Prof,* Univ Waterloo, ON

Irons, Helena, *Secy,* Marin Art & Garden Society, Ross, CA

Irvine, Betty Jo, *Fine Arts Librn,* Indiana Univ Art Museum, Bloomington

Irving, D Scott, *Fine Arts Chmn,* Elgin Academy Gallery, IL

Irving, Donald J, *VPres Acad Affairs,* Art Inst of Chicago, & *Dir,* Schools of the Art Inst, IL

Irving, Joan, *Co-Dir,* Brandt Painting Workshops, Corona del Mar, CA

Irving, Mark, *Coordr Pub Relations,* New Muse Community Museum of Brooklyn, NY

Irving, Norbert, *Assoc Prof,* Atlantic Christian College, Wilson, NC

Irwin, Arthur, *Coordr Professional Art,* City College of San Francisco, CA

Irwin, Barbara S, *Reference Librn,* New Jersey Historical Society Museum, Newark

Irwin, G, *Head Dept Fine Arts,* Brighton Polytechnic, England

Irwin, George M, *Pres,* Quincy Society of Fine Arts, IL

Irwin, J C, *Keeper Oriental Dept,* Victoria and Albert Museum, London, England

Irwin, Margaret, *Librn,* American Museum in Britain, Bath, England

Irwin, Patricia S, *Secy,* George Peabody College for Teachers Museum, Nashville, TN

Isaacs, Claire, *Dir,* Junior Arts Center, City of Los Angeles Municipal Arts Dept, CA

Isaacson, Gene L, *Instr,* Santa Ana College, CA

Isaksson, Olov, *Dir,* Statens Historiska Museum, Stockholm, Sweden

Iselin, Lewis, *Pres,* Louis Comfort Tiffany Found, New York, NY

Ishibashi, Shojiro, *Pres,* Bridgestone Bijutsukan, Tokyo, Japan

Ishikawa, Joseph, *Dir Gallery,* Michigan State Univ Art Collection, East Lansing

Isoline, Charles, *Chmn Commercial Design,* Baylor Univ, Waco, TX

Istas, Ivva, *VPres,* Paducah Art Guild, KY

Italiano, Joan N, *Chmn Dept,* College of the Holy Cross, Worcester, MA

Itman, Dr Leszek, *Dir,* Museum Narodowe We Wroclawiu, Wroclaw, Poland

Ito, Miyoko, *Artist-in-Residence,* Oxbow Summer Art Workshops, Saugatuck, MI

Ittmann, John, *Cur Prints & Drawings,* Minneapolis Inst of Arts, MN

Iverson, Floyd, *Prof,* West Shore Community College, Scottville, MI

Ives, Adrienne, *Pres,* McLean County Art Association, Bloomington, IL

Ives, Colta Feller, *Cur in Charge Prints & Photographs,* Metropolitan Museum of Art, New York, NY

Ivey, Carol, *Mem Faculty,* Austin Community College, TX

Ivins, Mildred, *Chmn Fashion Illustration,* Moore College of Art, Philadelphia, PA

Ivory, Paul H, *Adminr,* Chesterwood, Stockbridge, MA

Ivy, Margaret, *Dir,* St Mary's Univ, San Antonio, TX

Izquierdo, Manuel, *Instr,* Museum Art School, Portland, OR

Jachimowicz, Elizabeth, *Cur Costumes,* Chicago Historical Society, IL

Jack, Ann L, *Dir,* College of Marin Art Gallery, Kentfield, CA

Jack, Marlene, *Asst Prof,* College of William and Mary, Williamsburg, VA

Jack, Meredith M, *Instr,* Lamar Univ, Beaumont, TX

Jacka, Mrs G W, *Pres,* San Bernardino Art Association, CA

Jackson, Alexander, B, *Prof,* Old Dominion Univ, Norfolk, VA

Jackson, Anke Tom Dieck, *Educ Dir,* Parrish Art Museum, Southampton, NY

Jackson, Carl, *Dir,* Sharon Arts Center, Peterborough, NH

Jackson, David, *Coordr Spec Prog,* Studio Museum in Harlem, New York, NY

Jackson, Gene E, *Prof,* Sam Houston State Univ, Huntsville, TX

Jackson, Gregg, *Grants & Mem Liaison,* Indiana State Museum, Bloomington

Jackson, Herb, *Dir Art Gallery & Chmn Dept,* Davidson College, NC

Jackson, Jack, *Art Dept Librn,* Boston Athenaeum, MA

Jackson, Judith, *Art & Music Librn,* Brookline Public Library, MA

Jackson, Lyn, *Communications,* Inst of Contemporary Art, Boston, MA

Jackson, Martin, *Instr,* Ocean City School of Art, NJ

Jackson, Martin, *Mem Faculty,* Samuel S Fleisher Art Mem, Philadelphia, PA

Jackson, Rebecca L, *Res Assoc,* Kendall Whaling Museum, Sharon, MA

Jackson, Richard G, *Gallery Dir & Mem Faculty,* Murray State Univ, KY

Jackson, Ruth, *Cur Decorative Arts,* Montreal Museum of Fine Arts, PQ

Jackson, Thomas, *Asst Prof,* Mount Mercy College, Cedar Rapids, IA

Jackson, Ward, *Archivist,* Solomon R Guggenheim Museum, New York, NY

Jackson, William, *Instr,* Simon's Rock Early College, Great Barrington, MA

Jackson, Yvonne, *Asst to Cur,* Banff Centre, AB

Jacob, Mary, *Secy,* Laguna Beach Museum of Art, CA

Jacob, Ray, *Mem Faculty,* Laguna Beach School of Art, CA

Jacob, Dr Sabine, *Asst,* Herzog Anton Ulrich-Museum, Brunswick, Germany

Jacobe, LeOra, *Pres,* Little Gallery of Arts, Vernal, UT

Jacobs, H, *Chmn Textile Design,* Fashion Inst of Technology, New York, NY

Jacobs, John, *Treas,* Peel Museum and Art Gallery, Brampton, ON

Jacobs, John H, *Gallery Dir,* Pasadena City College Art Gallery, CA

Jacobs, John R, *Chmn Dept,* Rio Hondo College, Whittier, CA

Jacobs, Lowell, *Dir Summer School,* Spokane Falls Community College, Spokane, WA

Jacobs, Peter A, *Chmn,* Colorado State Univ, Fort Collins

Jacobs, Stan, *Chmn,* Midland College, TX

Jacobsen, Lolli, *Chairperson Textile Arts,* Mendocino Art Center, CA

Jacobsen, Robert, *Cur Oriental Arts,* Minneapolis Inst of Arts, MN

Jacobsen, Ruth, *Slide Registry Chair,* Women in the Arts Found, New York, NY

Jacobson, Frank, *Dir Prog,* Western States Arts Found, Denver, CO

Jacobson, R I, *Chmn,* Carleton College, Northfield, MN

Jacobson, Thora E, *Adminr,* Samuel S Fleisher Art Mem, Philadelphia, PA

Jacobus, John, *VChmn,* Dartmouth College, Hanover, NH

Jacoby, R B, *VPres,* Mississippi Art Colony, Meridian

Jacqmin, Alice, *A V Librn,* Houston Public Library, TX

Jacques, Michael, *Asst Prof,* Emmanuel College, Boston, MA

Jadger, Don T, *Dir,* Midland Center for the Arts, MI

Jaffar, S M, *Cur,* Peshawar Museum, Pakistan

Jaffarian, Mrs John P, *Secy,* Rensselaer County Historical Society, Troy, NY

Jaffe, A M, *Dir,* Fitzwilliam Museum, Univ Cambridge, England

Jaffe, Richard, *VPres,* Print Club, Philadelphia, PA

Jaffee, Mrs Louis, *VPres,* Irene Leache Mem, Norfolk, VA

Jaffery, Miss Salma, *Tourist Guide,* Lahore Museum, Pakistan

Jahnigan, Debra, *Mem Faculty,* Rehoboth Art League, Rehoboth Beach, DE

Jainschigg, Mrs Gemmell, *Pres,* Society for the Preservation of New England Antiquities, Boston, MA

Jakobsen, Kristian, *Dir,* Aarhus Kunstmuseum, Denmark

Jakstas, Alfred, *Conservator,* Art Inst of Chicago, IL; *Consult Conservation,* Univ Illinois, Champaign

Jalet, Vanessa, *Secy to Dir,* Solomon R Guggenheim Museum, New York, NY

Jameikis, Brone, *Keeper AV Center,* Honolulu Academy of Arts Collection, HI

James, Arloene (Westy), *Assoc Prof,* Bemidji State Univ, MN

James, Christopher, *Mem Faculty,* Greenfield Community College, MA

James, Earl, *Adminr,* Decatur House; *Adminr,* Woodrow Wilson House, Washington, DC

James, Ernest, *Dir,* Univ Lowell, MA

James, Henry, *Librn,* Babcock Art Library, Sweet Briar College, VA

James, Jeanne, *Vis Prof,* Nebraska Wesleyan University, Lincoln

James, Philip, *Asst Prof,* James Madison Univ, Harrisonburg, VA

James, Robert C, *Dept Head & Dir Summer School,* Univ of Oregon, Eugene

James, Sally, *Chmn,* Bemidji State Univ, MN

James, Theodore W, *Asst Dir,* Montgomery Museum of Fine Arts, AL

Jamieson, Charles F, *Assoc Prof,* Maryville College, Saint Louis, MO

Jamison, Alexa, *Pres Bd Dirs,* Evansville Museum of Arts and Science, IN

Jamnik, Dr Irmgard, *Cur,* Brant County Museum, Brantford, ON

Janczak, Roman, *Preparator,* Craft and Folk Art Museum, Los Angeles, CA

Jandova, Dr Libuse, *Deputy Dir & Chief Graphic Art Coll,* Narodni Galerie V Praze, Prague, Czechoslovakia

Janes, Dr Don, *Dir Summer School,* Univ Southern Colorado, Belmont Campus, Pueblo

Janes, Gale, *Educ Head,* Tacoma Art Museum, WA

Janick, Richard N, *Chairperson Dept Art,* Monterey Peninsula College, CA

Janis, Eugenia P, *Assoc Prof,* Wellesley College, MA

Jankowski, Edward, *Asst Prof,* Monmouth College, West Long Branch, NJ

Jann, Gayle, *Instr,* Hinckley School of Crafts, ME

Janosco, Jerry, *Artist-in-Residence,* Oxbow Summer Art Workshops, Saugatuck, MI

Jansen, Dr Beatrice, *Deputy Dir & Head Ancient Art Dept,* Haags Gemeentemuseum, The Hague, Netherlands

Jansen, Catherine, *Mem Faculty,* Bucks County Community College, Newtown, PA

Jansen, Charles, *Asst Prof,* Middle Tennessee State Univ, Murfreesboro

Jansky, Rollin, *Chmn,* Univ Wisconsin-Parkside, Kenosha

Janson, Richard, *Chmn,* Univ Vermont, Burlington

Janssen, Ardene, *Pres,* Humboldt Arts Council, Eureka, CA

Janssen, P L A, *Dir,* Gemeentemuseum Arnhem, Netherlands

Janssen, Dr Walter, *Dept Dir,* Rheinisches Landesmuseum Bonn, Germany

Jardine, Don, *Assoc Dir,* Art Instruction Schools, Minneapolis, MN

Jardine, Miss J, *Recording Secy,* Community Arts Council of Vancouver, BC

Jareckie, Stephen B, *Registrar & Cur Photography,* Worcester Art Museum, MA

Jared, Dorothy, *Secy,* Allen R Hite Art Inst, Univ Louisville, KY

Jaris, Gregory, *Instr,* Grand Valley State Colleges, Allendale, MI

Jarkowski, Stefania, *Art Gallery Dir,* Tuskegee Inst, AL

Jaros, Dr Miroslav, *Dir,* Statni Zidovske Muzeum Prague, Czechoslovakia

Jartun, Marcia, *Dir,* Univ Puget Sound Art Gallery, Tacoma, WA

Jaskevich, Jane, *Prof,* Polk Community College, Winter Haven, FL

Jasper, Alvin Ben, *Chmn Dept,* Augustana College, Rock Island, IL

Jayroe, Kim, *Cur Educ,* Wichita Falls Museum and Art Center, TX

Jean, Rene, *Dir & Cur,* Galerie Restigouche, Campbellton, NB

Jean-Bart, Gabrielle, *Instr,* Traphagen School of Fashion, New York, NY

Jeanroy, Dr Don, *Dir Summer School,* Central Wyoming College, Riverton

Ject-Key, Elsie, *Treas,* American Watercolor Society, see National and Regional Organizations

Jedrey, Micheline, *Processing Librn,* Rotch Library of Architecture and Planning, Massachusetts Inst of Technology, Cambridge

Jefferson, Curtis, *Dean,* Cuyahoga Community College, Cleveland, OH

Jeffords, Walter M, Jr, *VPres,* Nat Museum of Racing, Saratoga Springs, NY

Jeffress, Charles, *Asst Prof,* Louisiana College, Pineville

Jeffries, J H, *VPres Bd Dir,* Museum of Northern British Columbia, Prince Rupert

Jeffries, Dr William W, *Dir,* US Naval Academy Museum, Annapolis, MD

Jeker, Werner, *Head Graphic Design Dept,* Lausanne College of Art & Design, Switzerland

Jelinek, Randall, *Prof,* Linfield College, McMinnville, OR

Jelking, R, *Asst Dir Admin,* Nat Gallery of Canada, Ottawa, ON

Jendrzejewski, Amy Delap, *Asst Prof,* Vincennes Univ, IN

Jenkins, Basil W R, *Cur,* Fowler Museum, Beverly Hills, CA

Jenkins, Donald, *Dir,* Portland Art Association, OR

Jenkins, Harold R, *Librn,* Kansas City Public Library, MO

Jenkins, Harvey C, *Chmn,* Fayetteville State Univ, NC

Jenkins, J G, *Keeper Material Culture,* Welsh Folk Museum, St Fagans, Wales

Jenkins, Norma P H, *Assoc Librn,* Corning Museum of Glass, Corning, NY

Jenkins, Peter, *Clerk,* Worshipful Co of Goldsmiths, London, England

Jenkins, Suzanne, *Registrar,* Nat Portrait Gallery, Washington, DC

Jenkins, William, *Cur,* International Museum of Photography, Rochester, NY

Jenks, David W, *Pres,* David School of Basic Art, Metairie, LA

Jenks, George M, *Librn,* Bucknell Univ, Lewisburg, PA

Jenks, Martha E, *Dir Archives,* International Museum of Photography, Rochester, NY

Jennette, Helen, *Asst Prof,* Nazareth College of Rochester, NY

Jennings, Capt C B, *Dir,* USS North Carolina Battleship Mem, Wilmington

Jennings, Edward, *Dir,* Talladega College, AL

Jennings, John M, *Dir,* Virginia Historical Society, Richmond

Jennings, W Croft, *Chmn Mus Comn,* Columbia Museums of Art and Science, SC

Jensen, Carl, *Asst Prof,* Univ Southern Colorado, Belmont Campus, Pueblo

Jensen, David, *Treas,* Art Barn, Greenwich, CT

Jensen, Grady E, *Secy,* Guild of Book Workers, see National and Regional Organizations

Jensen, H P, *Cur,* Nordjyllands Kunstmuseum, Aalborg, Denmark

Jensen, Judy, *Secy,* Univ Washington Henry Art Gallery, Seattle

Jensen, Knud W, *Dir,* Louisiana Museum of Modern Art, Humlebaek, Denmark

Jensen, Lawrence N, *Prof,* Castleton State College, VT

Jensen, Richard J, *Pres,* Racine Art Association, WI

Jensen, Robert A, *Assoc Prof,* Calvin College, Grand Rapids, MI

Jensen, William M, *Chmn Art History,* Baylor Univ, Waco, TX

Jenson, Marvin G, *Asst Dir,* Territorial Statehouse, Fillmore, UT

Jeppesen, Kent, *Gallery Dir & Assoc Prof,* College of Southern Idaho, Twin Falls

Jeringan, Candy, *Secy,* Provincetown Art Association and Museum, MA

Jerman, Majda, *Cur Exhib,* Moderna Galerija, Ljubljana, Yugoslavia

Jerry, Sylvester, *Educ,* Racine Art Association, WI

Jessiman, John, *Prof,* State Univ New York College at Cortland

Jessup, Kathryn C, *Acting Dir,* Univ Arizona Museum of Art, Tucson

Jeswald, Joseph, *Dir & Dir Summer School,* Montserrat School of Visual Art, Beverly, MA

Jewesson, Ken, *Dir,* School of Art, Museum of Fine Arts, Houston, TX

Jimenez, Priscilla, *Admin Asst,* Sangre De Cristo Arts & Conference Center, Pueblo, CO

Jiménez, Rosario Pastrana, *Leader,* Museo de Arte "Jose Luis Bello y Gonzalez", Puebla, Mexico

Jipson, James W, *Chmn,* Villa Maria College of Buffalo, NY

Joachim, Harold, *Cur Prints & Drawings,* Art Inst of Chicago, IL

Joanice, Sister Mary, *Librn,* Briar Cliff College, Sioux City, IA

Jobrack, Madeleine-Claude, *Mgr,* Printmaking Workshop, New York, NY

Jocoma, Edward, *Assoc Prof,* Alma College, MI

Joglar, Raul, *Adminr,* Inst of Puerto Rican Culture, San Juan

Johannesen, Ole Ronning, *Chief Exec,* Lillehammer Bys Malerisamling, Norway

Johansen, Franz, *Chmn,* Utah State Division of Fine Arts, Salt Lake City

Johanson, George, *Instr,* Museum Art School, Portland, OR

Johnes, Carolyn, *Exec Secy,* Nat Art Museum of Sports, New York, NY

Johns, Gilbert R, *Dean Summer School,* Colorado College, Colorado Springs

Johns, John A, *Pres,* Art Inst of Pittsburgh, PA

Johnson, Al, *Dept Chairperson & Asst Prof,* Philadelphia College of Art, PA

Johnson, Anne, *Periodicals Librn,* Saint Mary's College, Notre Dame, IN

Johnson, Mrs Arthur, *Treas,* Clearwater Art Association, ID

Johnson, Arthur H, *Cur,* Jonson Gallery, Univ New Mexico, Albuquerque

Johnson, Barbara, *Pres,* Museum of American Folk Art, New York, NY

Johnson, Betsey, *Asst Mgr,* Salvador Dali Museum, Beachwood, OH

Johnson, Betty, *Asst Prof,* Univ Northern Colorado, Greeley

Johnson, Bruce, *Cur,* Kemble Collection, California Historical Society, San Francisco

Johnson, Buddy, *Mem Faculty,* Ohio Visual Art Institution, Cincinnati

Johnson, Byron, *Cur History,* Albuquerque Museum of Art, History and Science, NM

Johnson, Carlyle, *Prof,* North Carolina Central Univ, Durham

Johnson, Cathryne, *Cur Publications,* Colorado Historical Society, Denver

Johnson, Cecily Moot, *Pres,* Patterson Library, Westfield, NY

Johnson, Charles W, Jr, *Head Dept & Assoc Prof,* Univ Richmond, VA

Johnson, Charlotte Buel, *Cur Educ,* Albright-Knox Art Gallery, Buffalo, NY

Johnson, Clyde, *Assoc Prof,* Glendale College, CA

Johnson, Dale R, *Asst Prof,* Bethel College, Saint Paul, MN

Johnson, Dana D, *Chmn Dept Art & Dir Summer School,* Memphis State Univ, TN

Johnson, David, *Asst Prof,* Bethel College, Saint Paul, MN

Johnson, David, *Assoc Prof Art & Head Dept Visual Arts,* Judson Baptist College, Portland, OR

Johnson, David B, *Head Dept,* William Jewell College, Liberty, MO

Johnson, Diana, *Chief Cur & Cur Prints & Drawings,* Rhode Island School of Design Museum of Art, Providence

Johnson, Dr Diane Chalmer, *Pres,* Guild of South Carolina Artists, Columbia; *Chmn Dept,* College of Charleston

Johnson, Douglas, *Asst Prof,* Univ Wisconsin-River Falls

Johnson, Edna, *Dir & Resident Artist,* Southampton Art School, ON

Johnson, Edward B, *Second VPres,* Tennessee Valley Art Center, Tuscumbia, AL

Johnson, Elizabeth C, *Cur,* Fairfield Historical Society, CT

Johnson, Ellen H, *Hon Cur Modern Art,* Allen Mem Art Museum, Oberlin College, OH

Johnson, Elma, *Mem Faculty,* Univ of North Carolina at Asheville

Johnson, Eugene, *Prof,* Bethel College, Saint Paul, MN

Johnson, Eugene J, *Chmn Dept,* Williams College, Williamstown, MA

Johnson, Eugenia, *Instr,* Southwestern Technical Inst, Sylva, NC

Johnson, Evert A, *Cur Art,* Southern Illinois Univ Museum and Art Galleries, Carbondale

Johnson, Glorian, *Pres,* Neville Public Museum, Green Bay, WI

Johnson, Ilse, *Assoc Prof,* Trenton State College, NJ

Johnson, Ivan E, *Prof,* Florida State Univ, Tallahassee

Johnson, Jack, *Dir Summer School,* Hamline Univ, Saint Paul, MN

Johnson, James, *Assoc Prof,* Arkansas State Univ, State University

Johnson, James, *Asst Prof,* Ohio Wesleyan Univ, Delaware

Johnson, James E, *Graphic Designer,* Walker Art Center, Minneapolis, MN

Johnson, James R, *Secy-Treas,* American Society for Aesthetics, see National and Regional Organizations

Johnson, Mrs Jan, *Asst Librn,* Babcock Art Library, Sweet Briar College, VA

Johnson, Jean H, *Mgr Fine Arts Dept,* Southeast Banking Corp, Miami, FL see Corporate Art Holdings

Johnson, Joyce, *Dir,* Truro Center of the Arts at Castle Hills, MA

Johnson, Mrs L A, *Exhibit Chmn,* Cody Country Art League, WY

Johnson, Lester, *Chmn,* Cypress College, CA

Johnson, Lois, *Secy,* Print Club, Philadelphia, PA

Johnson, Lynne, *Mem Faculty,* Rivier College, Nashua, NH

Johnson, Marelyn, *Reference Librn/Cataloguer,* Adam L Gimbel Library Parsons School of Design, New York, NY

Johnson, Marianne, *Sales Shop Mgr,* Salt Lake Art Center, UT

Johnson, Marion F T, *Educ Dir,* Delaware Art Museum, Wilmington

Johnson, Michael, *Instr,* Santa Ana College, CA

Johnson, Michael, *Mem Faculty,* Murray State University, KY

Johnson, Paul, *Dir Summer School,* Houghton College, NY

Johnson, Peter, *Instr,* Butler County Community College, El Dorado, KS

Johnson, Peter, *Asst Prof,* Smith College, Northampton, MA

Johnson, Philip, *Asst Prof,* Black Hawk College, Moline, IL

Johnson, Robert Emory, *Art Consult,* Wine Museum of San Francisco, CA

Johnson, Robert F, *Cur Prints & Drawings,* Fine Arts Museums of San Francisco, CA

Johnson, Robert L, *Exec Secy,* King County Arts Commission, Seattle, WA

Johnson, Roger, *Chmn & Dir,* Maine Art Gallery, Lincoln County Cultural and Historical Association, Wiscasset

Johnson, Rosemary, *Art Specialist,* Supplementary Educational Center Art Gallery, Salisbury, NC

Johnson, Ruth Carter, *Pres,* Amon Carter Museum of Western Art, Fort Worth, TX

Johnson, Sue I, *Mgr Records Mgt Dept & Bank Archivist,* Federal Reserve Bank of Richmond, VA, see Corporate Art Holdings

Johnson, Susan, *Instr,* Houston School of Commercial Art, TX

Johnson, Terence, *Chmn Studio Div,* Nova Scotia College of Art and Design, Halifax

Johnson, Thano, College of Marin, Kentfield, CA

Johnson, Theodore E, *Dir & Librn,* Shaker Museum, Poland Spring, ME

Johnson, Tom, *Mem Faculty,* College of Marin, Kentfield, CA

Johnson, W McAllister, *Dir,* Univ Toronto Art Collection, ON

Johnson, Wallace N, *Asst Prof,* Winona State Univ, MN

Johnson, William L, *Cur Coll,* Southern Illinois Univ Museum and Art Galleries, Carbondale

Johnson, William R, *Chief Art & Music Div,* Brooklyn Public Library, NY

Johnsson, Ulf G, *Cur,* Svenska Statens Portrahsamling, Mariefred, Sweden; *Head,* Royal Castles Collection, Nationalmuseum, Stockholm, Sweden

Johnston, Anne, *Educ Officer,* Western Kentucky Univ Museum, Bowling Green

Johnston, Francis E, *Cur Physical Anthropology,* Univ Pennsylvania Museum, Philadelphia

Johnston, Gordon E, *Display Supvr,* Provincial Museum of Alberta, Edmonton

Johnston, James, *Prof,* Macomb County Community College, Warren, MI

Johnston, Leland, *Asst Prof,* Hartford Art School, Univ Hartford, West Hartford, CT

Johnston, Patricia, *Registrar,* Birmingham Museum of Art, AL

Johnston, Peggy, *VPres,* Mid-Southern Watercolorists, Little Rock, AR

Johnston, Philip M, *Cur Dept Decorative Arts,* Wadsworth Atheneum, Hartford, CT

Johnston, Richard, *Assoc Prof,* Univ Utah, Salt Lake City

Johnston, Dr Robert H, *Dean,* College of Fine & Applied Arts & *Dir,* School for American Craftsmen, Rochester Institute of Technology, NY

Johnston, Sona, *Assoc Cur Painting & Sculpture,* Baltimore Museum of Art, MD

Johnston, Thomas V, *Prof & Head Dept,* California Polytechnic State Univ, San Luis Obispo

Johnston, W Robert, *Registrar,* Nat Collection of Fine Arts, Washington, DC

Johnston, William R, *Asst Dir,* Walters Art Gallery, Baltimore, MD

Johonsen, F, *Dir,* NY Carlsberg Glyptothek, Copenhagen, Denmark

Jolles, Arnold, *Acting Dir,* Philadelphia Museum of Art, PA

Jolley, Milt, *Asst Dir,* Utah Travel Council, Salt Lake City

Jolly, Robert, *Head & Assoc Prof,* Presbyterian College, Clinton, SC

Jolly, Robert, *Chmn,* Tennessee Wesleyan College, Athens

Jonas, Mrs Richard S, *Secy,* Newport Harbor Art Museum, CA

Joncev, V, *Pro-Rector & Prof,* Nikolaj Pavlovic Higher Inst of Fine Arts, Sofia, Bulgaria

Jones, Allan L, *Chmn,* Antioch College, Yellow Springs, OH

Jones, Anne, *Exec Secy,* Wichita Falls Museum and Art Center, TX

Jones, Anthony, *Chmn & Prof,* Texas Christian Univ, Fort Worth

Jones, Betsy, *Librn,* Carolina Art Association, Charleston, SC

Jones, Betsy Burns, *Assoc Dir & Cur.* Smith College Museum of Art, Northampton, MA

Jones, Bob, *Chmn Bd,* Bob Jones Univ, Greenville, SC

Jones, Charles J, *Assoc Prof,* Saint Louis Community College at Florissant Valley, Ferguson, MO

Jones, Dancy, *Admin Asst,* Tennessee State Museum, Nashville

Jones, Darleen, *Secy,* Alberta College of Art Gallery, Calgary

Jones, David L, *Cur Educ,* Tucson Museum of Art, AZ

Jones, Frances F, *Cur Coll,* Princeton Univ, NJ

Jones, Frank, *Assoc Prof,* Palomar College, San Marcos, CA

Jones, Gail, *Secy,* Univ Notre Dame Art Gallery, IN

Jones, Gerard, *Secy,* Louis Comfort Tiffany Found, New York, NY

Jones, Harold, *Coordr Photography,* Univ Arizona, Tucson

Jones, Harvey L, *Deputy Cur Art,* Oakland Museum, CA

Jones, Herbert A, *Pres,* Albany Inst History and Art, NY

Jones, Horace, IV, *Treas,* Mystic Art Association, CT

Jones, Howard, *Assoc Prof,* Univ New Orleans, LA

Jones, J Kenneth, *Cur Decorative Arts,* Charleston Museum, SC

Jones, James E, *Assoc Prof,* Morgan State Univ, Baltimore, MD

Jones, Dr Jameson M, *Pres,* Memphis Acad of Arts, TN

Jones, Johanna, *Secy,* Taos Art Association, NM

Jones, Jonah, *Dir,* Nat College of Art and Design, Dublin, Ireland

Jones, Julie, *Cur Primitive Art,* Metropolitan Museum of Art, New York, NY

Jones, Justin, *Staff Asst,* St Gregorys Abbey and College, Shawnee, OK

Jones, Katherine, *Head Librn,* J Paul Getty Museum, Malibu, CA

Jones, Leonard, *Asst Prof,* Virginia State College, Petersburg

Jones, Lora W, *Mgr Community Relations,* E R Squibb & Sons, Princeton, NJ see Corporate Art Holdings

Jones, Margaret, *Corresp Secy,* Coppini Acad of Fine Arts, San Antonio, TX

Jones, Sister Marjorie, *Head Cataloguer,* Saint Mary's College, Notre Dame, IN

Jones, Marvin H, *Assoc Prof,* Cleveland State Univ, OH

Jones, Mary Mildred, *Secy,* Kauai Museum, Lihue, HI

Jones, Melissa, *Cur Educ,* Gaston County Art and History Museum, Dallas, NC

Jones, R E, *Secy,* Peel Museum and Art Gallery, Brampton, ON

Jones, R W, *Mus Dir,* Oklahoma Historical Society, Oklahoma City

Jones, Robert, *VChmn,* Metropolitan Arts Commission, Portland,Or

Jones, Roder H, *Assoc Prof,* Morehead State Univ, KY

Jones, Stan, *Head Dept,* Howe Architecture Library, Arizona State Univ, Tempe

Jones, W J, *Librn,* Nat Museum of Wales, Cardiff

Jones, Mrs Ward T, *First VPres,* Central Louisiana Art Association, Alexandria

Jones, Warren E, *VChmn Bd Trustees,* McMichael Canadian Collection, Kleinburg, ON

Jones, William E, *Cur Decorative Arts,* Los Angeles County Museum of Art, CA

Jones, William K, *Mus Cur,* Dwight D Eisenhower Presidential Library, Abilene, KS

Jonson, Raymond, *Dir,* Johnson Gallery, Univ New Mexico, Albuquerque

Jonsson, Halldor J, *Cur,* Thjodminjasafn, Reykjavik, Iceland

Joosten, Dr E, *Deputy Dir,* Ryksmuseum Kroller-Muller, Otterlo, Netherlands

Joosten, J M, *Research Cur,* Stedelijk Museum-Amsterdam, Netherlands

Joppien, Dr Rudiger, *Asst Cur,* Kunstgewerbemuseum, Museen der Stadt Koln, Germany

Jorda, Jack, *Head Dept & Prof,* Southern Univ in New Orleans, LA

Jordan, Harry, *Asst Dir for Admin,* Nat Collection of Fine Arts, Washington, DC

Jordan, James W, *Assoc Prof,* Antioch College, Yellow Springs, OH

Jordan, Jim, *Film Dept Chmn,* Art Center College of Design, Pasadena, CA

Jordan, Julia, *Dir,* Rocky Mountain Arts and Crafts Center, NC

Jordan, Rose, *Recording Secy,* Tullahoma Fine Arts Center, TN

Jordan, Steven A, *Secy/Treas,* Guild of South Carolina Artist, Columbia

Jordan, William B, *Chmn Exhib Comt,* University Gallery & *Dir,* Meadows Museum, Southern Methodist Univ, Dallas, TX

Jordre, Emma M, *Prog Coordr,* Univ Wisconsin, Madison

Jorgensen, David, *Mem Faculty,* Salve Regina the Newport College, RI

Jorgensen, Doris, *Printing,* Lyme Art Association, Old Lyme, CT

Jorgensen, Sandra, *Chairperson Art Dept,* Elmhurst College, IL

Jorgenson, Dale, *Dean,* Northeast Missouri State Univ, Kirksville

Jorgenson, Lynn, *Exec Dir,* Western Association of Art Museums, see National and Regional Organizations

Jornaes, Dr Bjarne, *Cur,* Thorvaldsen Museum, Copenhagen, Denmark

Joseph, Bruce E, *Educ,* Oklahoma Historical Society, Oklahoma City

Joseph, Philip M, *Asst Prof,* Miami Univ, Oxford, OH

Josephs, John, *Chmn,* Artists Guild Inc of New York, see National and Regional Organizations

Joslin, Elizabeth, *Adminr,* Bundy Art Gallery, Waitsfield, VT

Jossel, Len, *Chmn Graphic Design,* Ringling School of Art, Sarasota, FL

Jost, Barbara L, *Pres,* Federated Art Associations of New Jersey, Lavallette

Jowdy, Mrs W J, *Chmn Art Dept,* Hill Country Arts Found, Ingram, TX

Joy, Carol, *Chmn,* Laney College, Oakland, CA

Joyal, Serge, *VPres,* Musee D'Art DeJoliette, PQ

Joyce, Kathleen, *Assoc Prof,* Rocky Mountain College, Billings, MT

Joyner, Georgia Quimtard, *Asst Dir,* Univ the South Gallery of Fine Arts, Sewanee, TN

Joyner, J Brooks, *Cur,* Univ Calgary, AB

Joyner, Marjorie Hake, *Architectural Librn,* Ball State Univ Art Gallery, Muncie, IN

Ju, I-Hsiung, *Prof,* Washington and Lee Univ, Lexington, VA

Judge, Louisa, *Pub Relations & Librn,* Univ Vermont, Burlington

Judkins, W O, *Chmn & Prof,* McGill Univ, Montreal, PQ

Judson, Andrew, *Chmn Complementary Studies,* Corcoran School of Art, Washington, DC

Judson, J Richard, *Chmn Art,* Univ North Carolina at Chapel Hill

Juergensen, Virginia M, *Assoc Prof,* Mohawk Valley Community College, Utica, NY

Jufii, Hisae, *Cur Prints,* Tokyo Kokuritsu Kindai Bijutsukan, Japan

Juhasz, Elaine, *Assoc Prof,* Youngstown State Univ, OH

Juister, Charles, *Mem Faculty,* Waubonsee Community College, Sugar Grove, IL

Jules, Marvin, *Chmn Art Dept,* City College of New York, NY

Juneau, Andre, *Dir,* Musee du Quebec, PQ

Jung, Michael, *Asst Prof,* Denison Univ, Granville, OH

Jungmeyer, Paul, *Dir Summer School,* McMurry College, Abilene, TX

Juristo, Michelle, *Asst Cur,* Univ South Florida/Galleries Program, Tampa

Juson, William D, *Cur Film Section,* Carnegie Inst Museum of Art, Pittsburgh, PA

Juster, Howard H, *Dir Educ,* Nat Inst for Architectural Education, see National and Regional Organizations

Juttner, Dr Werner, *Cur Art History,* Museen der Stadt Koln, Germany

Jyk-San, *Mem Faculty,* Rudolph Schaeffer School of Design, San Francisco, CA

Kaasa, W H, *Secy,* Alberta Art Found, Edmonton, AB

Kachel, Dr Harold S, *Mus Dir,* No Mans Land Historical Society, Goodwell, OK

Kachel, Joan Overton, *Cur & Secy,* No Mans Land Historical Society and Museum, Goodwell, OK

Kadel, Roger, *VPres,* Springfeld Art Center, OH

Kadish, Skip, *Instr,* Monterey Peninsula College, CA

Kaericher, John, *Exhib Coordr, Assoc Prof Art & Chmn Dept,* Northwestern College, Orange City, IA

Kaganoff, Dr Nathan M, *Librn-Ed,* American Jewish Historical Society, Waltham, MA

Kahlmann, Dr Theodor, *Dir,* Museum of German Folklore, Staatliche Museen Preussischer Kulturbesitz, Berlin, Germany

Kahmeyer, Ray, *Assoc Prof,* Bethany College, Lindsborg, KS

Kahn, David, *Cur,* National Park Service, New York, NY

Kahn, Herbert J, *Dept Photography,* Chicago Acad of Fine Arts, IL

Kahr, Madlyn, *Acting Prof,* Univ California, San Diego, La Jolla

Kahrs, Mrs Daniel, *Pres,* Spartanburg County Art Association, SC

Kain, Jay D, *Prof Art, Chmn Dept & Dir Summer School,* Mansfield State College, PA

Kaiser, George, *Dean Students,* Ringling School of Arts, Sarasota, FL

Kaish, Luise, *VPres Mem,* Sculptors Guild, New York, NY

Kakis, Juris, *Chmn Dept,* Ohio Dominican College, Columbus

Kakudo, Yoshiko, *Cur Japanese Art,* Asian Art Museum, San Francisco, CA

Kakutani, Mitsuo, *Artist-in-Residence,* Earlham College, Richmond, IN

Kalb, Marty J, *Dir Exhib, Gallery & Assoc Prof,* Ohio Wesleyan Univ, Delaware

Kalbacher, Billie, *Off Mgr-Secy,* Guild Hall of East Hampton, NY

Kale, Louise, *Registrar,* College of William and Mary Art Collection, Williamsburg, VA

Kalenberg, Angel, *Dir,* Museo Nacional de Artes Plasticas, Montevideo, Uruguay

Kaleshefski, Martha Rochester, *Asst Prof,* College Misericordia, Dallas, PA

Kaleshefski, Ralph G, *Asst Prof Art & Chmn Dept,* College Misericordia, Dallas, PA

Kalicki, Susan, *Admin Asst,* Yuma Art Center, AZ

Kalitina, Nina Nickolaevna, *Vis Lectr,* Univ Wisconsin, Madison

Kalk, John, *Lectr,* Felician College, Chicago, IL

Kalla, Ron, *Asst Prof,* Beaver College, Glenside, PA

Kallenberg, Lawrence, *Instr,* Abbey School of Jewelry & Art Metal Design, New York, NY

Kallenberger, Klaus, *Assoc Prof,* Middle Tennessee State Univ, Murfreesboro

Kamansky, David, *Dir Pacificulture,* Asia Museum, Pasadena, CA

Kamber, Andre, *Conservator,* Kunstmuseum Solothurn, Switzerland

Kaminsky, Hank, *Chairperson,* Eureka Springs Guild of Artist and Crafts People, AR

Kammer, William, *Mem Faculty,* Junior College of Albany, NY

Kamon, Yasuo, *Exec Dir,* Bridgestone Bijutsukan, Tokyo, Japan

Kampen, Michael, *Preparator,* Univ Georgia Art Collection, Athens

Kampen, Owen, *Mem Faculty,* Madison Area Technical College, WI

Kampiziones, Andrew, *Bd Pres,* Florence Museum, SC

Kamys, Walter, *Dir Univ Art Coll,* Univ Massachusetts, Amherst

Kan, Diana, *Corresp Secy,* Allied Artists of America, see National and Regional Organizations

Kanack, Ronald, *Dir Special Events,* Greenfield Village and Henry Ford Museum, Dearborn, MI

Kane, Jean DuVal, *Dir Coll,* Valentine Museum, Richmond, VA

Kaneko, James S, *Chmn,* American River College, Sacramento, CA

Kaneko, John H, *Mem Faculty,* American River College, Sacramento, CA

Kang, Ingu, *Cur In Charge Archaeology,* Nat Museum of Korea, Seoul

Kang, Shin T, *Cur Ancient Near Eastern Coll,* World Heritage Museum, Univ Illinois at Urbana-Champaign, Urbana

Kangas, Gene, *Assoc Prof,* Cleveland State Univ, OH

Kaplan, Julius, *Chmn Art Dept,* California State College, San Bernardino

Kaplan, Leon, *Asst to Dir,* Arkansas Arts Center, Little Rock

Kaplan, Miss Pat, *Educ Dept,* South African Nat Gallery, Cape Town

Kaplan, Stanley, *Pres,* Society of American Graphic Artists, see National and Regional Organizations

Kaprow, Allan, *Prof,* Univ California, San Diego, La Jolla

Karasek, Lawrence, *Chmn Dept Art & Chmn Summer School,* Univ Montana, Missoula

Karatazas, Steven, *Prof Art & Chmn Dept,* Linvield College, McMinnville, OR

Kardon, Janet, *Dir Exhib,* Philadelphia College of Art, PA

Karesh, Barbara, *Supvr Art School,* Carolina Art Association, Charleston, SC

Karl, Maggie, *Dir,* Coos Art Museum, Coos Bay, OR

Karlan, Clara, *Teacher,* Nutley Art Center, NJ

Karlin, Renata, *Dir,* Henry Street Settlement, New York, NY

Karlson, Mrs Genie, *Librn,* American Numismatic Association, see National and Regional Organizations

Karn, John, *Cur Educ,* Charlotte Nature Museum, NC

Karoblis, Dalija, *Asst Town Librn,* Brookline Public Library, MA

Karolyi, Janet, *Secy,* California State Univ Art Gallery, Chico

Karow, Betty, *Librn,* Milwaukee Art Center, WI

Karp, Aaron, *Gallery Dir,* East Carolina Univ, Greenville, NC

Karpel, Eli, *Prof,* Pierce College, Woodland Hills, CA

Karraker, Jack, *Prof Art & Chmn Dept,* Kearney State College, NE

Karschnick, Ellen, *Corresp. Secy,* San Bernardino Art Association, CA

Karsina, James, *Assoc Prof,* Aquinas College, Grand Rapids, MI

Karterud, Mrs Arvin, *Cur,* Lyman Allyn Museum, New London, CT

Karunanayake, C I, *Librn,* Colombo Nat Museum, Sri Lanka

Kasal, Robert, *Prof,* Portland State Univ, OR

Kassel, Barbara, *Asst Prof,* Colby College, Waterville, ME

Kassiday, Sharlene, *Mem Faculty,* Joliet Junior College, IL

Kassoy, Bernard, *Corresp Secy,* Artists Equity Association of New York, NY; *Mem Faculty,* Harriet FeBland's Advanced Painters Workshop, New Rochelle, NY

Kassoy, Hortense, *VPres,* Artists Equity Association of New York, NY; *Mem Faculty,* Harriet FeBland's Advanced Painters Workshop, New Rochelle, NY

Katavolos, William, *Chmn Curriculum,* Pratt Inst School of Art & Design, Brooklyn, NY

Kathleen, Sister Mary, *Dir Summer School,* College of Saint Elizabeth, Convent Station, NJ

Katka, Patricia K, *Sr Librn,* San Diego Public Library, CA

Katopis, Beverly, *Librn I,* Yonkers Public Library, NY

Katsaros, Aliki, *Registrar,* Fitchburg Art Museum, MA

Katsiff, Bruce, *Chairperson Fine Arts Dept,* Bucks County Community College, Newtown, PA

Katter, Eldon, *Gallery Coordr,* Kutztown State College, PA

Katz, Alice, *Assoc Prof,* Univ Illinois at the Medical Center, Chicago

Katz, Bertram, *Dir Summer School,* Parsons School of Design, New York, NY

Katz, Heidi, *Instr,* Hartford Art School, Univ Hartford, West Hartford, CT

Katz, Janet, *Mus Educ,* Queens Museum, Flushing, NY

Katz, Karl, *Chmn Special Projects,* Metropolitan Museum of Art, New York, NY

Katz, Mel, *VPres,* Portland Center for the Visual Arts, OR

Katz, Sidney L, *Treas,* Nat Inst for Architectural Education, see National and Regional Organizations

Katz, Solomon H, *Cur Physical Anthropology,* Univ Pennsylvania Museum, Philadelphia

Katz, Theodore, *Chief Div Educ,* Philadelphia Museum of Art, PA

Katzive, David H, *Asst Dir Educ & Prog Develop,* Brooklyn Museum, NY

Kau, Dagmar, *VPres,* Windward Artists Guild, Lihue, HI

Kauffman, C, *Keeper Paintings, Prints, Drawings & Photographs,* Victoria and Albert Museum, London, England

Kauffman, Donald, *VPres,* Phoenix Art Museum, AZ

Kaufman, Barbara, *Asst Prof & Cur Exhib,* Seton Hall Univ, South Orange, NJ

Kaufman, Dr C Bud, *Assoc,* Stanley Hall Gallery, Columbia, MI

Kaufman, James C, *Asst Prof,* Miami Univ, Oxford, OH

Kaufman, Suzanne, *Teacher,* Rock Valley College, Rockford, IL

Kaufmann, Dr Christian, *Cur Oceania,* Museum Fur Volkerkunde Und Schweizerisches Museum Fur Volkskunde Basel, Switzerland

Kaufmann, Mrs Richard B, *Pres,* New Orleans Museum of Art, LA

Kaukonen, Toini-Inkeri, *Dir,* Suomen Kansallisinuseo, Helsinki, Finland

Kaul, Marlin, *Assoc Prof,* Bemidji State Univ, MN

Kaulitz, Garry, *Mem Faculty,* Louisville School of Art, Anchorage, KY

Kawa, Florence, *Prof,* Drake Univ, Des Moines, IA

Kawakita, Michiaki, *Dir,* Kyoto Kokuritsu Kindai Bijutsukan, Japan

Kay, Karen J, *Secy,* Allied Arts Council of Lethbridge, AB

Kaya, Douglas, *Head Div,* Leeward Community College, Pearl City, HI

Kayser, Thos, *Asst Dir,* Flint Inst of Arts Museum, MI

Kazak, Nick, *Exhib Chmn,* American Abstract Artists, see National and Regional Organizations

Keam, Grace S, *Reference Librn,* Cincinnati Art Museum, OH

Keane, Joseph, *Dir Summer School,* St Thomas Aquinas College, Sparkhill, NY

Keane, Patricia, *Head Art Section,* Chicago Public Library, IL

Keane, Terence, *Cur,* Elizabet Ney Museum, Austin, TX

Kearney, John W, *Dir,* Contemporary Art Workshop, Chicago, IL

Kearney, Lynn, *Admin Dir,* Contemporary Art Workshop, Chicago, IL

Kearns, Jerry L, *Head Reference Section,* Library of Congress, Washington, DC

Kearse, Dieter Morris, *Dir Planning & Develop,* New Museum, New York, NY

Keating, Patrick, *Chmn Dept & Dir Summer School,* Northeast Technical Community College, Norfolk, NE

Keating, P Warren, *Pres,* Fitchburg Art Museum, MA

Keats, Norman, *Prof,* Univ Wisconsin-Stevens Point

Keaveney, Sydney Starr, *Art & Architecture Librn,* Pratt Inst Library, Brooklyn, NY

Keech, John, *Asst Prof,* Arkansas State Univ, State University

Keefe, John, *Cur European Decorative Arts,* Art Inst of Chicago, IL

Keefe, Katharine Lee, *Cur of Coll,* Bergman Gallery, Univ Chicago, IL

Keefer, Ken, *Mem Faculty,* Spokane Falls Community College, Spokane, WA

Keeler, David, *Chief Office of Exhib & Design,* Nat Collection of Fine Arts, Washington, DC

Keeling, Henry C, *Head Dept,* Morris Harvey College, Charleston, WV

Keeling, Russell, *Dir Summer School,* Southwest Missouri State Univ, Springfield

Keen, Betty, *Cur Prints & Documents,* Putman Museum, Davenport, IA

Keene, Paul, *Mem Faculty,* Bucks County Community College, Newtown, PA

Keeney, Allen L, *Dir,* Sweetwater Community Fine Arts Center, Rock Springs, WY

Keester, George, *Prof & Dept Head,* Heidelberg College, Tiffin, OH

Keeter, Dr Howell, *Treas,* School of the Ozarks, Point Lookout, MO

Kefleyesus, Abeke, *Head Photographic Coll,* Addis Ababa Univ Museum of the Inst of Ethiopian Studies, Ethiopia

Kehde, Martha, *Librn,* Univ Kansas, Lawrence

Kehm, Gladys, *Reference,* Mason City Public Library, IA

Keiser, Dale, *Pres,* Toledo Federation of Art Societies, OH; *Second VPres,* Toledo Artists' Club, OH

Keith, Douglas S, *VPres,* Great Lakes Historical Society, Vermilion, OH

Keith, Marie C, *Asst Librn & Indexer of Photographs,* Frick Art Reference Library, New York, NY

Kelemen, Dr Boris, *Chief Cur Primitive Art,* Galerije Grada Zagreba, Yugoslavia

Kelleher, Radford D, *Publisher,* Metropolitan Museum of Art, New York, NY

Kellenberger, Mrs John A, *Chmn,* Tryon Palace Restoration Complex, New Bern, NC

Keller, Douglas, *Head Dept & Instr,* Coffeyville Community College, KS

Keller, Steven, *Asst to Dean,* Hartford Art School, Univ Hartford, West Hartford, CT

Kelley, C Regina, *Asst Prof,* Univ Maine, Orono

Kelley, Cecilia, *Mem Faculty,* Schoolcraft College, Livonia, MI

Kelley, Donald C, *Art Dept Librn,* Boston Athenaeum, MA

Kelley, Geraldine, *Prog Coordr,* Southern Illinois Univ Museum and Art Galleries, Carbondale

Kelley, Helen, *Prof,* California Polytechnic State Univ, San Luis Obispo

Kelley, Leo, *Mem Staff,* Swain School of Design, New Bedford, MA

Kelley, Thomas, *Develop Dir,* Inst of Contemporary Art, Boston, MA

Kelly, Ardie L, *Librn,* Mariners Museum, Newport News, VA

Kelly, Charlotte, *Cur Slide & Photograph Library & Art History Teaching Coll,* Univ Delaware Art Collection, Newark

Kelly, Clyde, *Prof,* Los Angeles City College, CA

Kelly, Eileen, *Chmn Art History,* Univ Manitoba, Winnipeg

Kelly, Elinor, *Librn,* Eastern Washington State Historical Society, Spokane, WA

Kelly, Miss J, *Asst Cur Registration,* London Public Library and Art Museum, ON

Kelly, Dr James, *Chief Researcher,* Tennessee State Museum, Nashville

Kelly, James J, *Dir Summer School,* Marymount College of Virginia, Arlington

Kelly, Sister M Teresita, *Chmn,* Edgewood College, Madison, WI

Kelly, Moira, *Dir,* AIR Gallery, London, England

Kelly, Perry, *Assoc Prof,* Western Carolina Univ, Cullowhee, NC

Kelly, Ruth, *Rare Bks Librn,* Rosenberg Library, Galveston, TX

Kelly, Vincent M, *Instr,* Yavapai College, Prescott, AZ

Kelly, William, *Assoc Prof,* Bemidji State Univ, MN

Kelly, William, *Dean School of Art,* Victorian College of the Arts, Melbourne, Australia

Kelsey, Darwin, *Dir Admin,* Old Sturbridge Village, MA

Kelsey, Robert, *Secy,* Lahaina Arts Society, HI

Kemeny, Lydia, *Head Fashion Design,* Saint Martins School of Art, London, England

Kemp, Betty R, *Dir,* Lee County Library, Tupelo, MS

Kemp, John R, *Chief Cur,* Louisiana State Museum, New Orleans

Kemp, Paul, *Chmn Crafts Curriculum,* Baylor Univ, Waco, TX

Kempf, Beth, *Secy,* Wayne Art Center, PA

Kempff, Katinka, *Asst Dir,* Pretoria Art Museum, South Africa

Kenamore, Jane, *Cur Special Coll,* Rosenberg Library, Galveston, TX

Kenan, William R, Jr, *Prof,* Univ North Carolina at Chapel Hill

Kendall, George, *Pres,* Sharon Arts Center, Peterborough, NH

Kendall, Thomas, *Head Ceramics Dept,* Kalamazoo Inst of Arts, MI

Kendrick, Diane, *Instr,* Averett College, Danville, VA

Kenfield, Dr John, *Mem Faculty,* Graduate Program in Art History, Rutgers, The State Univ New Jersey, New Brunswick

Kennard, Mary Ed, *Mus Asst,* Ships of the Sea Museum, Savannah, GA

Kennedy, Doreen, *Pres,* Scottsdale Artists' League, AZ

Kennedy, Garry Neill, *Pres,* Nova Scotia College of Art and Design, Halifax

Kennedy, Gene, *Dir,* Grossmont Community College Gallery, El Cajon, CA

Kennedy, Harrient F, *Asst Dir-Registrar,* Museum of the Nat Center of Afro-American Artists, Roxbury, MA

Kennedy, James, *Dir of BA History of Art,* Edgecliff College, Cincinnati, OH

Kennedy, James E, *Head,* Ethnic American Slide Library & *Chmn & Assoc Prof,* Univ South Alabama, Mobile

Kennedy, Paul, *Chmn Photography,* Corcoran School of Art, Washington, DC

Kennedy, Robert, *Prof,* North Carolina Central Univ, Durham

Kennedy, Ronald, *Asst Prof,* Southeastern Louisiana Univ, Hammond

Kennedy, William *Prof & Dir Summer School,* Univ Tennessee, Knoxville

Kenney, Marilyn, *Secy,* Penobscot Marine Museum, Searsport, ME

Kenney, Ray, *Dir Summer School,* Vermilion Community College, Ely, MN

Kennon, Arthur, *Ed,* Kappa Pi International Honorary Art Fraternity, see National and Regional Organizations

Kenny, Aneta, *Secy,* Brandon Allied Arts Council, MB

Kenny, Sister Edith, *Prof,* Marygrove College, Detroit, MI

Kent, Doris, *Cur,* Univ Southern California Art Galleries, Los Angeles, CA

Kent, Krnee, *Slide Librn,* Sarah Lawrence College Library, Bronxville, NY

Kent, Patricia, *Coordr Cultural Prog,* Univ Delaware Art Collections, Newark

Kent, Sherman, *Dir of Educ/Asst Dir,* Omniplex, Oklahoma City, OK

Kent, Susan, *Secy,* Greater Gary Arts Council, IN

Kenway, Corrinne, *Treas,* Southeast Alaska Regional Arts Council, Sitka

Kenyon, Richard A, *Assoc Prof & Dir Summer School,* Rhode Island College, Providence

Keough, Francis P, *Dir,* Springfield City Library, MA

Kepecs, Susan, *Vis Prof,* Jamestown Community College, NY

Kepes, Gregory, *Vis Prof,* Washington Univ, Saint Louis, MO

Kepes, Katherine, *Librn,* Carnegie Library of Pittsburgh, PA

Kerametli, Can, *Dir,* Turk Ve Islam Eserleri Muzesi, Istanbul, Turkey

Keresey, James F, *Pres,* Nat Art Museum of Sports, New York, NY

Kermer, Dr Wolfgang, *Prof & Rector,* Staatliche Akademie Der Bildenden Kunste, Stuttgart, Germany

Kern, Arthur, *Assoc Prof,* Tulane Univ, New Orelans, LA

Kern, Barbara J, *Head Art & Music Dept,* Muttnomah County Library, Portland, OR

Kern, Evan J, *Dean School & Dean Summer School,* Kutztown State College, PA

Kern, Norval C, *Prof Art & Chmn Dept,* Trenton State College, NJ

Kernell, Gunnel, *Asst Cur,* Rohsska Konstslojkmuseet, Goteborg, Sweden

Kerr, Donald A, *Prof,* Grand Valley State Colleges, Allendale, MI

Kerr, Mrs Myrtle, *Treas,* Kappa Pi International Honorary Art Fraternity, see National and Regional Organizations

Kerr, Warren, *Pres,* Klamath Art Association, Klamath Falls, OR

Kershner, Rita E, *Secy,* Washington County Museum of Fine Arts, Hagerstown, MD

Kerslake, Kenneth A, *Prof,* Univ Florida, Gainesville

Kersting, Irene, *Admin Asst,* Albuquerque Museum of Art, History and Science, NM

Kester, Rachael, *Secy,* West Hills Unitarian Fellowship, Portland, OR

Kesterson, *Asst Prof,* College of Mount Saint Joseph, OH

Ketchum, James R, *Cur,* US Senate Commission on Art and Antiquities, Washington, DC

Kettering, Alison, *Asst Prof,* Swarthmore College, PA

Kettlewell, James, *Cur,* Hyde Collection, Glens Falls, NY

Keune, Russell V, *VPres Preservation Serv,* Nat Trust For Historic Preservation, Washington, DC

Key, Dr Archie F, *Dir Information & Research Centre,* Alberta Society of Artists, Calgary

Key, Margaret A, *Registrar,* Bower's Museum, Santa Ana, CA

Keyes, Langley C, *Head Dept Urban Studies & Planning,* Massachusetts Inst of Technology, Cambridge

Keyes, Richard, *Mem Faculty,* Long Beach City College, CA

Keyew, David, *Prof,* Pacific Lutheran Univ, Tacoma, WA

Khandalavala, Karl J, *Chmn,* Lalit Kala Akademi, New Delhi, India

Khendry, Janak K, *Dir,* Sculpture Center, New York, NY

Kho, Irene, *Asst Cur,* Hong Kong Museum of Art

Khuri-Majoli, Pauline, *Prof,* Loyola Marymount Univ, Los Angeles, CA

Khurshid, Mrs Zarina, *Pub Relations Officer,* Lahore Museum, Pakistan

Kiang, Dawson, *Assoc Prof,* Pennsylvania State Univ, University Park

Kibbey, Richard, *Mus Dir,* Museum Without Walls, Rceda Inc, Friendsville, MD

Kidane, Dr Girma, *Mus Cur & Dir,* Addis Ababa Univ Museum of the Inst of Ethiopian Studies, Ethiopia

Kidd, Mary Jane, *Dir Galleries,* Edinboro State College, PA

Kiel, Dorothy M, *Dir,* Emery Gallery, Edgecliff College, Cincinnati, OH

Kiesinger, Kathryn, *Cur European Decorative Arts after 1700,* Philadelphia Museum of Art, PA

Kietzman, William, *Slide Librn,* Lamson Library, Plymouth State College, NH

Kihl, Mrs Harold, *Secy,* Washington Depot Art Association, CT

Kihlstedt, Folke T, *Chmn Dept,* Franklin and Marshall College, Lancaster, PA

Kiihne, Raymond R, *Asst Prof,* Winona State Univ, MN

Kilbourne, John D, *Dir,* Anderson House Museum, Washington, DC

Kilbridge, Maurice Dorney, *Dean,* Harvard Univ, Cambridge, MA

Kilby, Louise, *Secy,* White Rock Painting and Sketch Club, BC

Kilgore, June Q, *Chmn,* Marshall Univ, Huntington, WV

Killoran, Maureen, *Asst Librn,* Worcester Art Museum, MA

Killy, E James, *Asst Prof,* Miami Univ, Oxford, OH

Kilmurry, Irene, *Prof Art,* Cardinal Stritch College, Milwaukee, WI

Kim, Ernie, *Dir,* Richmond Art Center, CA

Kim, Eun-hee, *Librn,* Nat Museum of Korea, Seoul

Kimball, Edwin E, *VPres,* Society for Preservation of Historic Landmarks, York, ME

Kimball, Mary Ellen, *Instr Art,* Southwestern Community College, Creston, IA

Kimble, Warren, *Assoc Prof,* Castleton State College, VT

Kimbrell, Leonard B, *Prof Art History & Head Dept Art & Architecture,* Portland State Univ, OR

Kimbrough, Joseph, *Dir,* Minneapolis Public Library and Information Center, MN

Kimmel, Kent N, *Chmn Art Department,* Salisbury State College, MD

Kimmitt, J S, *Exec Secy,* US Senate Commission on Art and Antiquities, Washington, DC

Kinard, John D, *Dir,* Anacostia Neighborhood Museum, Washington, DC

Kincaid, Clarence, *Prof,* Texas Tech Univ, Lubbock

Kinch, Bruce, *Chmn Photography Dept,* Art Inst of Boston, MA

Kindermann, Helmmo, *Chmn Photography Dept,* Lake Placid School of Art, NY

Kindred, H, *Exten Courses Summer School,* Univ Regina, SK

King, Dr Bruce, *Asst Dir,* Valentine Museum, Richmond, VA

King, Claudia L, *Instr,* Univ Nevada, Las Vegas

King, E, *Keeper Textiles,* Victoria and Albert Museum, London, England

King, Elizabeth Mary, *Keeper Coll,* Univ Pennsylvania Museum, Philadelphia

King, Gerald, *Assoc Prof,* Prince George's Community College, Largo, MD

King, Jack, *Asst Prof,* Augusta College, GA

King, Lyndel, *Acting Dir,* Univ Minnesota Gallery, Minneapolis

King, Muriel, *Librn,* Winnipeg Sketch Club, MB

King, Naomi, *Art Asst,* Junior Museum, Newark Museum, NJ

King, Pauline G, *Prof,* Mary Washington College, Fredericksburg, VA

King, Shirley, *Secy,* Midland Art Council of the Midland Center for the Arts, MI

King, Susan, *Instr,* Howard College, Big Spring, TX

Kingman, Dong, *Mem Faculty,* Famous Artists School, Westport, CT

Kingsley, Charles C, *Pres,* New Haven Colony Historical Society, CT

Kingsley, Robert D, *Asst Prof,* DePauw Univ, Greencastle, IN

Kington, Brent, *Chmn Metals,* Southern Illinois Univ, Carbondale

Kinnaird, Richard W, *Assoc Chmn Studio Art,* Univ North Carolina at Chapel Hill

Kinney, Mary T, *Asst Dean,* Columbus College of Art and Design, OH

Kruger, Barbara, *Vis Prof,* Wright State Univ, Dayton, OH

Kruger, Bruce, *Admin Asst, Librn & Archivist,* Rockford Art Association, IL

Kruk, Arthur, *Prof,* Univ Wisconsin-Superior

Krumrein, John, *Assoc Prof,* Prince George's Community College, Largo, MD

Kruse, Donald, *Assoc Prof,* Indiana Univ-Purdue Univ, Fort Wayne, IN

Kruse, Gerald, *Asst Prof,* South Dakota State Univ, Brookings

Krush, Beth, *Chmn Illustration,* Moore College of Art, Philadelphia, PA

Krushenick, John, *Dir,* Fort Wayne Museum of Art, IN

Krutza, June, *Prof,* Eastern Illinois Univ, Charleston

Krzisnik, Zoran, *Dir,* Moderna Galerija, Ljubljana, Yugoslavia

Kuan, Sister Baulu, *Mem Faculty,* College of Saint Benedict, Saint Joseph, MN

Kubly, Don, *Pres & Dir,* Art Center College of Design, Pasadena, CA

Kuchel, Konrad G, *Coordr Loans,* The American Federation of Arts, see National and Regional Organizations

Kucher, Kathleen, *Assoc Prof,* Fort Hays State Univ, Hays, KS

Kuczynski, John, *Head Art Department & Assoc Prof,* Pierce College, Woodland Hills, CA

Kudlacek, Milton, *Head Art Dept,* Dakota Wesleyan Univ, Mitchell, SD

Kudlawiec, Dennis P, *Chmn,* Livingston Univ, AL

Kudron, Georgeann, *Dir Educ,* Des Moines Art Center, IA

Kuebler, George F, *Dir,* Oklahoma Art Center, OK

Kuehn, Claire, *Archivist & Librn,* Panhandle-Plains Historical Society Museum, Canyon, TX

Kuehn, Edmund K, *Cur Coll,* Columbus Gallery of Fine Arts, OH

Kuehn, Gary, *Assoc Prof,* Mason Gross School of the Arts, Rutgers, The State Univ New Jersey, New Brunswick

Kuehne, Richard E, *Dir,* West Point Museum, NY

Kugler, Richard C, *Dir,* New Bedford Whaling Museum, MA

Kuh, Katharine, *Consult,* First Nat Bank of Chicago, IL, see Corporate Art Holdings

Kuhl, Condon, *Chairperson Dept,* Drake Univ, Des Moines, IA

Kuhl, Helen, *Secy,* San Bernardino Art Association, CA

Kuhlman, Barbara, *Prof,* State Univ New York College At Cortland

Kuhrmann, Dr Dieter, *Dir,* Staatliche Graphische Sammlung, Munich, Germany

Kuhn, Marylou, *Prof,* Florida State Univ, Tallahassee

Kuiper, Dr, John, *Dir Film,* International Museum of Photography, Rochester, NY

Kujundzic, Zeljko, *Assoc Prof Art & Chmn Dept,* Pennsylvania State Univ, Uniontown

Kula, Judith, *Prof,* Florida State Univ, Tallahassee

Kulkarni, Dr K S, *Dean Faculty Music & Fine Arts,* Banaras Hindu Univ, Varanasi, India

Kulla, Linda Claire, *Cur Educ,* Missouri Historical Society, St Louis

Kultzen, Dr Rolf, *Cur Italian Paintings,* Bayerischen Staatsgemaldesammlungen, Munich, Germany

Kummell, Lenore, *Art Gallery Comt Pres,* Peel Museum and Art Gallery, Brampton, ON

Kumnick, Charles, *Asst Prof,* Trenton State College, NJ

Kumpan, Miriam, *Asst Librn,* Haaretz Museum, Tel-Aviv, Israel

Kunda, Judith Lea, *Dir,* Harbor College Art Gallery, Los Angeles, CA

Kuntz, David L, *Exhib Designer,* Illinois State Univ, Normal

Kuo, James K Y, *Prof,* Daemen College, Amherst, NY

Kuony, John H, *Dir & Cur Art,* Oshkosh Public Museum, WI

Kupferman, Norman, *Adult Serv,* Long Beach Public Library, NY

Kurata, Dr Bunsaku, *Dir,* Nara Kokuritsu Hakubutsukan, Japan

Kurcbart, Maria, *Instr,* Hartford Art School, Univ Hartford, West Hartford, CT

Kureshi, B A, *Chmn,* Lahore Museum, Pakistan

Kurey, Joseph M, *Dir Summer School,* Bethany College, WV

Kurka, Donald F, *Head Dept Art,* Univ Tennessee, Knoxville

Kurriger, Patrica, *Mem Faculty,* College of DuPage, Glen Ellyn, IL

Kurth, Constance, *Admin Asst,* Univ Vermont, Burlington

Kurtz, Earl, *Mem Faculty,* Joliet Junior College, IL

Kurtz, Stephen G, *Prin,* Phillips Exeter Acad, NH

Kurtzworth, Harry Muir, *Dir,* American Art Society, Los Angeles, CA

Kurutz, Gary, *Libr Dir,* California Historical Society, San Francisco

Kusama, Tetsuo, *Asst Prof,* Utah State Univ, Logan

Kusel, Heinz, *Prof,* California State Univ, Fresno

Kusnir, Eduardo, *Music Dept,* Centro de Arte y Communicacion, Buenos Aires, Argentina

Kuspit, Donald B, *Prof,* Univ North Carolina at Chapel Hill

Kutcher, Arthur, *Instr,* Abbey School of Jewelry & Art Metal Design, New York, NY

Kutcher, Emily, *Admin,* Dauphin Allied Arts Centre, MB

Kuthy, Dr Sandor, *Cur,* Kunstmuseum Bern, Switzerland

Kutschera, Dr Volker, *Cur Theatrical Sciences & Pub Relations,* Saltzburger Museum Carolino Augusteum, Austria

Kutsky, Irene, *Mem Faculty,* College of New Rochelle, NY

Kuwayama, George, *Sr Cur Far Eastern Art,* Los Angeles County Museum of Arts, CA

Kvaran, Olafur, *Dir,* Listasafn Einars Jonssonar, Reykjavik, Iceland

Kwiecinski, Chet, *Dir,* Abilene Fine Arts Museum, TX

Kyle, Freda, *Mem Faculty,* Goldsboro Art Center, NC

Kyle, J Richard, *Cur Educ,* Chester County Historical Society, West Chester, PA

Lab, Walter F, *Instr,* Modesto Junior College, CA

Labaree, Benjamin, *Dir,* Munson Inst, Mystic Seaport, CT

La Baume, Peter, Dr, *Cur Prehistory,* Provincial Roman Archaeology, Romisch-Germanisches Museum, Museen der Stadt Koln, Germany

Laber, Philip, *Instr,* Northwest Missouri State Univ, Maryville

Labhardt, Dr Ricco, *Dir,* Historisches Museum, St Gallen, Switzerland

Labib, Dr Bahur, *Dir,* Coptic Museum, Cairo, Egypt

Labiche, Walter A, *Dir,* New Orleans Art Inst, LA

Labot, Tony, *Preparator,* Acad of the Museum of Conceptual Art, San Francisco, CA

Labuhn, Erda, *Cur,* Diablo Valley College Museum, Pleasant Hill, CA

LacEachron, David, *Exec Dir,* Japan Society, New York, NY

Lackey, Elaine C, *Pres Bd Trustees,* Mendocino Art Center Gallery, CA

Laclotte, Michel, *Cur Paintings,* Musee du Louvre, Paris, France

Lacouture, Dr Felipe, *Dir,* Museo Nacional de Historia, Mexico City, Mexico

Ladd, Pauline, *Assoc Prof,* Rhode Island College, Providence

Ladely, Dan, *Dir,* Sheldon Film Theater, Univ Nebraska, Lincoln

Ladnowska, Janina, *Cur,* Muzeum Sztuki, Lodz, Poland

Lafferty, Mrs Frederick W, *Recording Secy,* Maryland Historical Society Museum, Baltimore

LaFollette, Curtis K, *Assoc Prof,* Rhode Island College, Providence

Lafon, Dee J, *Chmn & Assoc Prof,* East Central Univ, Ada, OK

Lafond, Robert, *Registrar,* Princeton Univ, NJ

Laforge, Jacques, *Dir,* La Societe des Arts de Chicoutimi, PQ

Lafortune, F, *Chief Librn,* Musee du Quebec, PQ

Lagerberg, Don, *Chmn Dept,* California State Univ, Fullerton

Lago, Fernando Rodriguez, *Instr,* Univ las Americas Galeria de Arte, Cholula, Mexico

LaGrand-Fisher, Susan, *VPres,* Alaska Artists Guild, Anchorage

Lagregren, Paul, *VPres,* Coos Art Museum, Coos Bay, OR

Lahaye, Francois, *Dir,* Centre Culturel de Trois Rivieres, PQ

Laine, Osmo, *VPres,* Turun Taidemuseo, Turku, Finland

Laing, Aileen, *Assoc Prof,* Sweet Briar College, VA

Laing, Richard H, *Dir Summer School & Chmn Art Dept,* Edinboro State College, PA

Laise, C Steven, *Educ Officer,* Mariners Museum, Newport News, VA

Laise, Frederic S, *Sr VPres,* American Red Cross, see National and Regional Organizations

Lakdusinghe, S, *Cur Ethnology,* Colombo Nat Museum, Sri Lanka

Lake, Jerry L, *Asst Prof,* George Washington Univ, Washington, DC

Lakofsky, Charles, *Head Ceramics,* Bowling Green State Univ, OH

Lalli, Mary, *Secy,* Plastic Club, Philadelphia, PA

Lally, Franca P, *Asst Dir,* Caravan of East and West, New York, NY

Lally, John, *Gallery Dir,* Caravan of East and West, New York, NY

Lalonde, Marcel, *Dir,* St Joseph's Oratory, Montreal, PQ

LaMalfa, *Head Dept & Assoc Prof,* Univ Wisconsin Center, Marinette

Lamb, Mrs Condie, *First VChmn,* Guild Hall of East Hampton, NY

Lambert, Anne, *Cur Educ,* Univ Wisconsin-Madison Mem Union

Lambert, Don, *Exec Dir,* Arts Council of Topeka, KS

Lambert, Rose, *Librn,* Louisiana Historical Center Library, New Orleans

Lambert, W E, *Asst Prof,* Del Mar College, Corpus Christi, TX

Lammers, Dr George, *Secy,* Association des Musees Canadiens, see National Organizations of Canada

Lamon, Evelyn, *Exec Asst to Dir,* Portland Art Association, OR

Lamoureux, Richard E, *Chmn Dept,* Assumption College, Worcester, MA

Lampe, Frederick & June, *Co-Owners,* Lampe Gallery of Fine Art, New Orleans, LA

Lampe, George, *Dir,* Stichting de Vrije Academie Psychopolis Voor Beeldende Kunsten, The Hague, Netherlands

Lamph, John, *Assoc Prof,* Mary Washington College, Fredericksburg, VA

Lancaster, John, *Instr,* Malden Bridge School of Art, NY

Lancaster, Madeline E, *Pres,* Springfield Historical Society, NJ

Lancaster, Michael, *Instr,* Malden Bridge School of Art, NY

Landau, Dr E, *Dir,* Inst for Promotion Art & Science, Haaretz Museum, Tel-Aviv, Israel

Landau, John, *Librn,* Palisades Interstate Park Commission, Kingston, NY

Landau, Laureen, *Instr,* Sacramento City College, CA

Landau, Zuki, *Chief Librn,* School of Visual Arts Library, New York, NY

Landfear, Adele, *Recording Secy,* Miniature Art Society of New Jersey, Nutley

Landis, Ellen, *Cur Art,* Albuquerque Museum of Art, History and Science, NM

Landis, Dr M A, *Vis Prof,* Houghton College, NY

Landreau, Anthony N, *Cur Educ,* Carnegie Inst Museum of Art, Pittsburgh, PA

Landry, Lionel, *Exec VPres,* Asia Soc, New York, NY

Landry, Marguerite, *Secy,* Univ Southwestern Louisiana Art Center, Lafayette

Landsley, Patrick, *Registrar,* Concordia Univ, Montreal, PQ

Landwehr, William C, *Dir,* Springfield Art Museum, MO

Lane, Dr Barbara, *Mem Faculty,* Graduate Program in Art History, Rutgers, The State Univ New Jersey, New Brunswick

Lane, C Gardner Jr, *Dir,* Penobscot Marine Museum, Searsport, ME

Lane, Colleen, *Mem Faculty,* Goldsboro Art Center, NC

Lane, John R, *Exec Asst,* Brooklyn Museum, NY

Lane, Larry Scott, *Dir Gallery Theater,* City of Los Angeles Municipal Arts Dept, CA

Lang, James, *Lectr,* La Salle College, PA

Lang, Mike, *Dir Summer School,* Big Bend Community College, Moses Lake, WA

Lang, R Park, *Instr,* Southwestern Oklahoma State Univ, Weatherford

Lang, Thomas, *Assoc Prof,* Webster College, Webster Groves, MO

Lange, Jim *Secy,* Association of American Editorial Cartoonists, see National and Regional Organizations

Lange, Dr Yvonne, *Dir,* Museum of International Folk Art, Santa Fe, NM

Langager, Craig, *Chmn Fine Arts Dept,* Cornish Inst of Allied Arts, Seattle, WA

Langberg, Harald, *Keeper Danish Historical Coll,* Nat Museum, Copenhagen, Denmark

Langenderfer, Colleen, *Corresp Secy,* Spectrum, Friends of Fine Art, Toledo, OH

Langhart, Nicholas, *Adminr,* Museums at Stony Brook, NY

Langhorne, Elizabeth, *Instr,* Tulane Univ, New Orleans, LA

Langland, Harold, *Assoc Prof,* Indiana Univ, South Bend

Langner, Veronica, *Head Dept,* Mount Saint Clare College, Clinton, IA

Lango, Lyyn, *Programs Dir,* Southern Oregon Historical Society, Jacksonville

Langoussis, Andrew, *Prof,* Rockford College, IL

Langstadt, R, *Lectr,* McGill Univ, Montreal, PQ

Langston, Linda, *Coordinating Cur,* Palo Alto Cultural Center, CA

Langvardt, Dr A L, *Acad Dean Summer School,* Hastings College, NE

Lanier, Dana, *Art Dir & Gen Mgr,* Tullahoma Fine Arts Center, TN

Lankford, E Lewis, *Instr,* Grand Canyon College, Phoenix, AZ

Lanmon, Dwight P, *Deputy Dir Coll,* Corning Museum of Glass, Corning, NY

Lanning, Nan, *Acting Dir Summer School,* Corning Community College, NY

Lansbury, Edgar, *VPres,* Nicholas Roerich Museum, New York, NY

Lansdown, Robert R, *Dir,* Woolaroc Museum, Bartlesville, OK

Lantz, Carl, *Develop Officer,* Portland Art Association, OR

Lantz, Randall E, *Horticulturist,* Tennessee Botanical Gardens and Fine Arts Center, Nashville

Lantzy, Don, *Assoc Dean Summer School,* Tyler School of Art of Temple Univ, Philadelphia, PA

Lanyon, Ellen, *Workshop Dir,* Oxbow Summer Art Workshops, Saugatuck, MI

Lao, Lincoln, *Mem Faculty,* Schoolcraft College, Livonia, MI

LaPaglia, Peter, *Cur Coll,* Tennessee State Museum, Nashville

La Palme, Robert, *Cur,* Pavilion of Humour, Montreal, PQ

Lape, Jane M, *Cur & Librn,* Fort Ticonderoga Museum, Ticonderoga, NY

LaPides, Ann, *Cur Asst,* Vassar College Art Gallery, Poughkeepsie, NY

Lapierre, Raymond, *Secy,* Musee D'Art de Joliette, PQ

Lapointe, Anselme, *Pres,* La Societe des Decorateurs-Ensembliers du Quebec, Montreal

LaPorte, Gerald, *Instr,* Del Mar College, Corpus Christi, TX

Lapp, John, *Acad Dean Summer School,* Goshen College, IN

Lapp, Maurice, *Prof,* Santa Rosa Junior College, CA

Lara, Consuelo Perez, *Leader,* Museo de Arte "Jose Luis Bello y Gonzalez", Puebla, Mexico

Laracuente, Mahir, *Prof,* Catholic Univ Puerto Rico, Ponce

Large, Freda M, *Exec Secy,* Architects Association of New Brunswick, Saint John

Large, Dr R G, *Pres Bd Dir,* Museum of Northern British Columbia, Prince Rupert

Largrue, Catherine, *Asst Conservator,* Musee des Beaux-Arts Angers, France

Larkin, Alan, *Asst Prof,* Indiana Univ, South Bend

Larkin, Eugene, *Prof,* Univ Minnesota, Saint Paul

Larkin, James S, *VPres,* Alabama Museum of Photography, Birmingham

Larkin, Jean T, *Mem Secy,* Worcester Art Museum, MA

Larmer, Oscar V, *Prof,* Kansas State Univ, Manhattan

La Rochelle, Peggy, *Develop Asst,* Reynolda House, Winston-Salem, NC

Larochelle, Pierre, *Dir,* L'Universite Laval Art Collection, Quebec, PQ

LaRose, Bruce, *Dir Summer School,* Briarcliff College, Briarcliff Manor, NY

LaRoux, Leonard, *Mem Faculty,* College of St Rose, Albany, NY

LaRow, Sister Magdalen, *Head Dept & Assoc Prof,* Nazareth College of Rochester, NY

LaRowe, Betsy, *Instr,* Laramie County Community College, Cheyenne, WY

Larsen, D, *Cur,* Univ Alaska Museum, Fairbanks

Larsen, Jack Lenor, *Chmn Bd,* Haystack Mountain School of Crafts Gallery, Deer Isle, ME

Larsen, Linda, *Pres,* Southeast Alaska Regional Arts Council, Sitka

Larsen, Paul, *Vice Pres Academic Affairs Summer School,* Dickinson State College, ND

Larsen, Richard, *Chmn,* Lloydminster Barr Colony Museum Committee, SK

Larsen, Mrs William, *Exec,* Southwest Craft Center, San Antonio, TX

Larson, Arthur D, *Asst Dir Admin,* Museum of Fine Arts, Boston, MA

Larson, Clifford J, *Dir,* Laura Musser Art Gallery and Museum, Muscatine, IA

Larson, J. Russell, *Assoc Prof,* Whitworth College, Spokane, WA

Larson, Lester, *Trustee,* Attleboro Museum, MA

Larson, Martha, *Secy,* Pacific Grove Art Center, CA

Larson, Mike, *Prof,* Shoreline Community College, Seattle, WA

Larson, Orland, *Pres,* Canadian Crafts Council, see National Organizations of Canada

Larson, Paul W, *Dir,* Univ Minnesota, St Paul

Larson, Sidney, *Chmn Art Dept,* Columbia College, MO

LaSalle, Barbara, *Registrar,* Brooklyn Museum, NY

Lasansky, Leonardo, Hamline Univ, Saint Paul, MN

Lasansky, William, *Mem Faculty,* Bucknell Univ, Lewisburg, PA

Lash, Ken, *Prof,* Univ Northern Iowa, Cedar Falls

Laske, Lyle, *Assoc Prof,* Moorhead State Univ, MN

Laskin, Dr Myron, Jr, *Research Cur European Art,* Nat Gallery of Canada, Ottawa, ON

Lasko, Peter, *Dir,* Courtauld Inst of Art Galleries, London, England

Laskouski, Peter, *Dir,* Shaker Museum, Old Chatham, NY

Lassaw, Ibram, *Vis Prof,* Mount Holyoke College, South Hadley, MA

Lassen, Erik, *Dir,* Det Danske Kunstindustrimuseum, Copenhagen, Denmark

Lassiter, Dr Frances T, *Chmn Fine Arts Dept,* New York Inst of Technology, Old Westbury

Lasuchin, Michael, *Dept Chmn & Asst Prof,* Philadelphia College of Art, PA

Latchaw/Hirsh, Sharon, *Asst Prof,* Dickinson College, Carlisle, PA

Latcher, Mary Ellen, *Historic Site Asst,* Schuyler Mansion, Albany, NY

Lathrop, Perry Kay, *Pres Board Dir,* Central Wyoming Museum of Art, Casper

Lathrop, William, *Mem Faculty,* Rudolph Schaeffer School of Design, San Francisco, CA

Latocha, Sue, *Mem Faculty,* Joliet Junior College, IL

La Tour, Therese, *Conservator & Ethnographer,* Musee du Quebec, PQ

Latshaw, Charles H B, *Managing Dir,* Florida Gulf Coast Art Center, Clearwater

Latta, George, *Emer Prof,* William Woods/ Westminster Colleges, Fulton, MO

Latzko, Walter, *Staff Asst,* Hall of Fame of the Trotter, Goshen, NY

Lau, Jo, *Secy,* Univ Michigan Museum of Art, Ann Arbor

Lauder, Mrs Ronald, *VPres,* Museum of American Folk Art, New York, NY

Laudicina, Rosario, *Chmn Advertising Design,* Pan American Univ, Edinburg, TX

Laughlin, Mrs Thomas C, *Registrar,* Museum of Fine Arts of St Petersburg, FL

Lauriane, Mary, *Art Dir & Dir Summer School,* Felician College, Chicago, IL

Laury, Zella Brown, *Dir,* Vermilion County Museum Society, Danville, IL

Lauvao, Fa'ailoilo, *Cur,* Jean P Haydon Museum, Pago Pago, American Samoa

Laux, W J, *Asst Comdr,* US Naval Memorial Museum, Washington, DC

Lavallee, Gerard, *Dir & Conservator,* Musee D'Art Saint-Laurent, PQ

Laver, Mrs Samuel, *Assoc Dir,* Buten Museum of Wedgwood, Merion, PA

Laverty, Pater, *Head Div Fine Arts,* Nat Art School, Darlinghurst, Australia

Lavetelli, Mark, *Instr,* Missouri Western State College, Saint Joseph

Lavoie, Mrs E L, *Pres,* Le Comite des Arts D'Arvida, PQ

LaVoy, Walter J, *Prof & Chmn Art Dept,* Central Connecticut State College, New Britain

Law, Aaron, *Chmn Found Prog,* Herron School of Art, Indiana Univ-Purdue Univ, Indianapolis

Law, Alan, *Technician Film/Video,* Queens Museum, Flushing, NY

Law, R, *Dir Summer School,* Western Illinois Univ, Macomb

Lawall, David B, *Cur,* Univ Virginia Art Museum, Charlottesville

Lawder, Standish D, *Assoc Prof & Chmn Dept,* Univ California, San Diego, La Jolla

Lawhorn, James C, *Adminr,* Huntington Galleries, WV

Lawless, Benjamin W, *Asst Dir Exhib,* Nat Museum of History and Technology, Washington, DC

Lawrence, Camille, *Instr,* Davidson County Community College, Lexington, NC

Lawrence, David, *Head Dept,* San Bernardino Valley College, CA

Lawrence, Helen, *Librn,* Southern Methodist Univ Gallery, Dallas, TX

Lawrence, Jacob, *Asst Dir,* Art Information Center, NY

Lawrence, John, *Asst to Cur,* Historic New Orleans Collection, LA

Lawrence, Robert M, *Secy,* American Inst of Architects, see National and Regional Organizations

Lawrence, William A, *Treas,* Concord Antiquarian Society Museum, MA

Lawson, Edward P, *Chief Educ Dept,* Hirshhorn Museum and Sculpture Garden, Washington, DC

Lawson, Noel G, *Prof,* Radford College, VA

Lawson, Pam F, *Asst Prof,* Radford College, VA

Lawson, Stephen, *Prof,* West Virginia Univ, Morgantown

Lawton, Curtis, *Mem Faculty,* Studio School of Art and Design, Philadelphia, PA

Lawton, Mary S, *Asst Prof Art & Acting Chmn Fine Arts Dept,* Loyola Univ, Chicago, IL

Lawton, Thomas, *Dir,* Freer Gallery of Art, Washington, DC

Layborteaux, Ron, *Art Cur,* Junior Arts Center Los Angeles, CA

Lazar, Julie, *Develop Dir,* Hudson River Museum, Yonkers, NY

Lazarus, Diane C, *Asst Cur Painting & Sculpture,* Indianapolis Museum of Art, IN

Lazor, Gloria, *Dir,* Clinton Historical Museum Village, NJ

Lea, Stanley E, *Prof,* Sam Houston State Univ, Huntsville, TX

Leach, David, *Asst Prof,* Wright State Univ, Dayton, OH

Leach, Mrs Ellis, *Secy,* Victoria Society of Maine Women, Portland

Leach, Frederick D, *Chmn Prof,* Hamline Univ, Saint Paul, MN

Leach, Mary E, *Pres,* Owatonna Arts Center, MN

Leach, Maurice, *Librn,* McCormick Library, Washington and Lee Univ, Lexington, VA

Leach, Richard, *Prof,* Albion College, MI

Leach, Sandford B, *Exec VPres,* Rehoboth Art League, Rehoboth Beach, DE

Leachman, James D, *Dir & Librn,* American Baptist Historical Society, Rochester, NY

Leader, Miss Garnet R, *Pres,* Kappa Pi International Honorary Art Fraternity, see National and Regional Organizations

Leaderman, Pamela, *Mem & Pub Relations,* Bergman Gallery, Univ Chicago, IL

Leaf, Bill S, *Chmn Art Dept,* Univ Nevada, Las Vegas

Leaf, Donald, *Supvr Fiscal Mgt & Technical Serv,* Michigan Dept of Education State Library Services, Lansing

Leaf, Ralph, *First VPres,* Beaumont Art Museum, TX

Leahy, Sister John Louise, *Assoc Prof,* Marygrove College, Detroit, MI

Leake, James C, *Secy,* Cherokee Nat Historical Society, Tahlequah, OK

Leake, William W, *Dir Summer School,* Washington and Jefferson College, Washington, PA

Leal, Lou, *Instr,* Hinckley School of Crafts, ME

Leaman, Ellen, *Dir Documents,* Historic New Orleans Collection, LA

Leapard, Mrs J D, *Pres,* Arts and Humanities Council of Tuscaloosa County, AL

Leary, Edward F, *Dir & Dir Summer School,* Boston Univ, MA

Leary, Melody, *Mem Faculty,* Norwich Art School, CT

Leary, Thomas, *Prof,* Salem State College, MA

Leavitt, Thomas W, *Dir,* Merrimack Valley Textile Museum, North Andover, MA

Leavitt, Thomas W, *Dir,* Cornell Univ, Ithaca, NY

le Breux, Jean-Louis, *Dir,* Le Musee Regional de Rimouski, PQ

LeCates, Byron H, *Secy,* Historical Society of York County, PA

Lecavalier, Father Fernand, *Pastor & Dir,* Musee de L'Eglise Notre-Dame, Montreal, PQ

Lederer, Bertha V B, *Coordr Fine Arts Activities,* State Univ New York, College at Geneseo

LeDieu, Sister Salesia, *Chmn Dept,* Cabrini College, Radnor, PA

LeDoux, David, *Assoc Prof,* Middle Tennessee State Univ, Murfreesboro

LeDuc, Paul, *Artistic Cur,* St Joseph's Oratory, Montreal, PQ

Lee, Christopher G, *Dir,* Columbus Chapel, Boal Mansion and Museum, Boalsburg, PA

Lee, Clayton, *Instr,* College of Wooster, OH

Lee, E Franck, *Psychology Research Dir,* American Art Society, Los Angeles, CA

Lee, Ellen, *Assoc Cur Painting & Sculpture,* Indianapolis Museum of Art, IN

Lee, Evelyn N, *Pub Relations,* Flint Inst of Arts Museum, MI

Lee, Hon Ching, *Prof & Dir Gallery,* Rockford College, IL

Lee, Jean Gordon, *Cur Far Eastern Art,* Philadelphia Museum of Art, PA

Lee, L Tennent, III, *VChmn Bd,* Huntsville Museum of Art, AL

Lee, Marielow, *Admin Secy,* Davenport Municipal Art Gallery, IA

Lee, Mathilde Boal, *Dir,* Columbus Chapel, Boal Mansion and Museum, Boalsburg, PA

Lee, Nanyong, *Cur in Charge of Registration,* Nat Museum of Korea, Seoul

Lee, Pat, *Registrar Summer School,* Nebraska Western College, Scottsbluff, NE

Lee, Robert, *Chmn Fine Arts,* Hartnell College, Salinas, CA

Lee, Robert E, *Pres,* Oklahoma Art Center, Oklahoma City

Lee, Robert J, *Assoc Prof,* Marymount College, Tarrytown, NY

Lee, Roland, *Mem Faculty,* Dixie College, St George, UT

Lee, Sherman E, *Dir & Chief Cur Oriental Art,* Cleveland Museum of Art, OH

Lee, Stanley, *Prof,* Indiana Univ-Purdue Univ, Fort Wayne, IN

Lee, Thomas P, *Cur Painting,* Fine Arts Museum of San Francisco, CA

Lee, William, *Mem Faculty,* Elmira College, NY

Lee, Wynn, *Exec Dir Bd Trustees,* Bellegrove, Middletown, VA

Leeam, Arch, *Chmn & Assoc Prof,* St Olaf College, Northfield, MN

Leece, Curtis, *Instr,* Saginaw Valley State College, University Center, MI

Leece, Gayle, *Instr,* Saginaw Valley State College, University Center, MI

Leech, B, *Assoc Cur-in-Charge Conservation Dept,* Royal Ontario Museum, Toronto

Leedy, Walter C, Jr, *Assoc Prof,* Cleveland State Univ, OH

Leek, Thomas A, *Cur,* Southern Utah State College, Cedar City

Lee-Mills, Rowe, *Instr,* Claremore College, OK

Leeper, Mrs John P, *Librn,* Marion Koogler McNay Art Inst, San Antonio, TX

Leeper, John Palmer, *Dir,* Marion Koogler McNay Art Inst, San Antonio, TX

Lees, Avon, Jr, *Pres & Dir,* Tobe-Coburn School for Fashion Careers, New York, NY

Lees, Gary P, *Asst Prof,* Johns Hopkins Univ, Baltimore, MD

Leet, Richard E, *Dir,* Charles H MacNider Museum, Mason City, IA

Leeuw, Dr R A, *Dir,* Stedelijk Museum Het Prinsenhof, Delft, Netherlands

Lefebure, Amelie, *Mus Asst,* Inst de France, Musee Conde, Paris

Lefebvre d'Argence, Rene-Yvon, *Dir & Chief Cur,* Asian Art Museum, San Francisco, CA

Lefevre, Jerry, *Mem Faculty,* School of the Associated Arts, Saint Paul, MN

Leff, Alix, *Mem Faculty,* Clayworks, New York, NY

Leffingwell, Patricia, *Secy,* Maui Historical Society, Wailuku, HI

Leffler, Nadine, *Dir Special Serv,* Orange County Public Library, Garden Grove, CA

Legakis, Brian, *Asst Prof,* Wake Forest Univ, Winston-Salem, NC

Legare, Jerome, *Deputy Dir,* La Societe des Arts de Chicoutimi, PQ

Legner, Dr Anton, *Dir,* Schnutgen Museum, Museen der Stadt Koln, Germany

Legrand, Francine-Claire, *Cur Modern Art,* Musees Royaux des Beaux-Arts de Belgique, Brussels, Belgium; *Dir,* Musee D'Art Ancien, Brussels, Belgium

Lehder, Diane, *Instr,* Xavier Univ of Louisiana, New Orleans

Lehman, Dr Arnold L, *Dir,* Metropolitan Museum and Art Centers, Coral Gables, FL

Lehman, Mark, *Asst Prof,* Trenton State College, NJ

Lehman, Robert, *Cur,* Metropolitan Museum of Art, New York, NY

Lehmann, Yole, *Personnel,* J Paul Getty Museum, Malibu, CA

Lehmer, Steve, *Dir,* Hockaday Center for the Arts, Kalispell, MT

Lehrer, Leonard, *Chmn,* Arizona State Univ, Tempe

Leiberman, Richard, *Faculty,* Mainline Center of the Arts, Haverford, PA

Leibert, Peter, *Assoc Prof,* Connecticut College, New London

Leichty, Erle, *Cur Akkadian Language & Literature,* Univ Pennsylvania Museum, Philadelphia

Leider, Karen, *Cataloger,* Trinity College Library, Washington, DC

Leidy, Susan, *Registrar,* Nat Trust For Historic Preservation, Washington, DC

Leifsen, Marian, *Pub Info Officer,* Museums at Stony Brook, NY

Leigh, Valerie, *Paintings & Sculpture,* South African Nat Gallery, Cape Town

Leighton, David, *Dir,* Banff Centre School of Fine Arts, Alberta

Leijon, Per-Olow, *Cur,* Ostasiatiska Museet, Stockholm, Sweden

Lein, Malcolm E, *Pres,* Minnesota Museum of Art Permanent Collection Gallery, St Paul

Leipen, Neda, *Cur Greek & Roman Dept,* Royal Ontario Museum, Toronto

Leippe, Harry M, *Prof,* New Mexico Highlands Univ, Las Vegas

Leiro, Reinaldo, *Industrial Design Hector Compaired,* Centro de Arte y Communicacion, Buenos Aires, Argentina

Leite, Dr Alicia Dantas, *Head Librn,* Museu de Arte Moderna Brazil, Rio de Janeiro

Leite, Fernanda Passos, *Cur Jewelry,* Museu Nacional de Arte Antiga Lisbon, Portugal

Leitman, Samuel, *VPres,* American Watercolor Society, see National and Regional Organizations

Leitner, Alan M, *Pres & Dir,* The Foundry, Honolulu, HI

Leitner, Alice S, *Secy Admin,* The Foundry, Honolulu, HI

Leja, Michael, *Cur,* Institute of Contemporary Art, Boston, MA

Lekberg, Barbara, *Vis Prof,* Mount Holyoke College, South Hadley, MA

Lekberg, Barbara, *Secy,* Sculpture Center, New York, NY

Lemoine, Pierre, *Cur,* Musee Nat du Chateau de Versailles, France

Lemon, Mrs James, *Dir,* Art Association of Richmond, IN

Lemon, John C, *Mem Faculty,* College of DuPage, Glen Ellyn, IL

Lemon, Kathryn E, *Cataloger,* St Louis Art Museum, MO

Lenertz, John, *Mem Faculty,* School of the Associated Arts, Saint Paul, MN

Lengyel, Mrs Paul, *Art Chmn,* Bridgeport Art League, CT

Lenon, Timothy, *Assoc Conservator,* Art Inst of Chicago, IL

Lent, Donald, *Chmn,* Bates College, Lewistown, ME

Lentel, Allota, *Registrar,* Heritage Plantation of Sandwich, MA

Lenz, Dr Christian, *Cur,* Stadelsches Kunstinstitut, Frankfurt Am Main, Germany

Leon, Dennis, *Instr,* California College of Arts and Crafts, Oakland

Leon, Helen A, *Dir Art Gallery,* Baldwin-Wallace College, Berea, OH

Leonard, Dorothy, *Dir,* Paul Wegel Library, Kansas State Univ, Manhattan

Leonard, Joanne, *Lectr,* Mills College, Oakland, CA

Leonard, William A, *Mem Faculty,* Ohio Visual Art Institution, Cincinnati

Leondar, Arnold, *Chmn,* Tarrant County Junior College, Northeast Campus, Hurst, TX

Leopold, J H, *Scientific Asst Silver,* Groninger Museum Voor Stad En Land, Netherlands

Lepore, James, *Assoc Prof,* Youngstown State Univ, OH

Leppaluoto, Capt A, *Pres Bd Dir,* Maryhill Museum of Art, Goldendale, WA

Lepper, Rita C, *Chmn Art Dept,* Rhode Island Junior College, Warwick

Leppien, Dr Helmut R, *Dir,* Kunsthalle Koln, Museen der Stadt Koln, Germany

Light, Mrs Frank, *Pres,* Emerald Empire Arts Association, Springfield, OR

Light, Raymond E, *Dean,* Univ Wisconsin-Whitewater

Lightdown, R W, *Librn,* Victoria and Albert Museum, London, England

Lightheart, Mrs F, *VPres,* West Vancouver Visual Arts Society, BC

Ligo, Larry L, *Asst Prof,* Davidson College, NC

Likes, James, *Asst Supt,* Bishop Hill Historic Site, IL

Lile, Thomas C, *Dir of Squires,* Virginia Polytechnic Inst & State Univ Art Gallery, Blacksburg

Lillard, Marion, *Chmn Fashion Design,* Pratt Inst School of Art & Design, Brooklyn, NY

Lillis, Loren D, *Registrar,* Univ Mississippi Museum, Oxford

Lilly, Marnee, *Asst Cur,* Bath Marine Museum, ME

Lilyquist, Christine, *Cur Egyptian Art,* Metropolitan Museum of Art, New York, NY

Lim, Dr K W, *Head Dept Asiatic Art,* Rijksmuseum Amsterdam, Netherlands

Lima, Isabel Navarro, *Leader,* Museo de Arte "Jose Luis Bello y Gonzalez" Puebla, Mexico

Limondjian, Hilde, *Program Mgr Concerts & Lectures,* Metropolitan Museum of Art, New York, NY

Limpert, John, *Dir Mem & Develop,* Museum of Modern Art, New York, NY

Lin, Henry H, *Dir,* Anthony G Trisolini Mem Gallery & *Dean,* College Fine Arts, Ohio University, Athens

Linacre, Betty, *Prog Dir,* Hackley Art Museum, Muskegan, MI

Linda, Mary F, *Registrar,* George Walter Vincent Smith Art Museum, Springfield, MA

Lindberg, Ted, *Assoc Cur,* Vancouver Art Gallery, BC

Lindburg, Mrs William, *Exec Dir,* Salem Art Association, OR

Linde, Ruth, *Secy Bd,* Huntsville Museum of Art, AL

Lindemann, Dr Edna M, *Dir,* Burchfield Center, Buffalo, NY

Lindemann, Hans K, *Owner & Founder,* Museum of American Treasures, National City, CA

Lindenheim, Diane, *Mem Faculty,* Bucks County Community College, Newtown, PA

Linder, Jean, *Asst Prof,* Div of Painting and Sculpture, Columbia Univ, New York, NY

Lindfors, Evert, *Mem Faculty,* Sarah Lawrence College, Lacoste, France

Lindgren, Ratchel, *Financial Coordr,* La Jolla Museum of Contemporary Art, CA

Lindop, M J, *Admin Officer,* Walker Art Gallery, Liverpool, England

Lindover, Sally, *Dir,* Provincetown Art Association and Museum, MA

Lindquist, Evan, *Prof Art & Dir Gallery,* Arkansas State Univ, State University

Lindquist, Kenneth H, *Dir,* Arnot Art Museum, Elmira, NY

Lindsay, Dr Alexander J, *Cur Anthropology,* Museum of Northern Arizona, Flagstaff

Lindvald, Steffen, *Cur,* Kobenhavns Bymuseum, Copenhagen, Denmark

Lingelbach, Helen A, *Fine Arts Librn,* Hunt Library, Carnegie-Mellon Univ, Pittsburgh, PA

Lingen, Joan, *Chmn,* Clarke College, Dubuque, IA

Linger, Bernard, *Dir Summer School,* Ohio Northern Univ, Ada

Linhares, Philip, *Dir,* San Francisco Art Inst, CA

Link, Howard A, *Cur Asian Art & Keeper of Ukiyoe Center,* Honolulu Academy of Arts Collection, HI

Link, Lawrence John, *Chairperson Dept & Chairperson Summer School,* Western Michigan Univ, Kalamazoo

Linksz, Dr James J, *Chmn,* Catonsville Community College, MD

Linn, Suellen, *Libr Asst,* Lake Placid School of Art Gallery, NY

Lintault, Roger, *Mem Faculty,* California State College, San Bernardino

Lintelmann, Adela S, *Recording Secy,* Art Students League of New York Gallery, NY

Linton, Kathy, *Secy,* Singing River Art Association, Pascagoula, MS

Linton, Margot, *Dir Mem,* The American Federation of Arts, see National and Regional Organizations; *Pres,* Friends of Neuberger Museum, State Univ New York College at Purchase

Lin-ts'an, Li, *Deputy Dir,* Nat Palace Museum Taiwan, Republic of China

Lintz, Marilee, *Secy,* Northeastern Illinois Gallery, Chicago

Lipchitz, Gretchen D, *Prof,* Boston State College, MA

Lipfert, Nathan, *Asst Cur Exhib,* Bath Marine Museum, ME

Lipke, William C, *Dir,* Univ Vermont, Burlington

Lipofsky, Marvin, *Instr,* California College of Arts and Crafts, Oakland

Lipowicz, Edward, *Cur,* Canajoharie Library and Art Gallery, NY

Lipp, Richard, *Dir Summer School,* Univ New Haven, West Haven, CT

Lippert, Catherine Beth, *Assoc Cur Decorative Arts,* Indianapolis Museum of Art, IN

Lippincott, Barbara, *Museum Shop Mgr,* Flint Inst of Arts Museum, MI

Lipscomb, H Bernard, III, *Coordr Interior Design,* Kean College of New Jersey, Union

Lipsey, Robert, *Mus Supt,* Philadelphia Museum of Art, PA

Lipsey, Dr Roger W, *Art Dept Chmn,* State Univ New York at Potsdam

Lipton, Leah, *Asst Prof,* Framingham State College, MA

Lipzin, Janis Crystal, *Asst Prof,* Antioch College, Yellow Springs, OH

Lis, Edward, *Instr,* Wayne Art Center, PA

Liscombe, Rhodri Windsor, *Asst Prof,* Univ British Columbia, Vancouver

Lisembly, Alan, *Prog Supvr,* Southeast Arkansas Arts and Science Center, Pine Bluff

Liska, Jane, *Asst to Dir,* Madison Art Center, WI

Liskin, Elliot, *Treas,* Artists' Fellowship, New York, NY

Liss, Allen, *Cur Anthropology,* Charleston Museum, SC

Liss, Jan, *Head,* Membership Dept, Portland Art Association, OR

Lister, Cynthia, *VPres,* Print Club, Philadelphia, PA

Listoe, Philip, *Librn,* Nutana Collegiate Inst, Saskatoon, SK

Litt, William A, Jr, *Cur Exhib,* Univ Wyoming Art Museum, Cheyenne

Little, Elsie, *Treas,* Monroe City-County Fine Arts Council, MI

Little, Mrs Robert, *Pres,* Cleveland Art Association, OH

Little, Ruth, *Cur Educ,* Neville Public Museum, Green Bay, WI

Little, T W, *Chmn,* California State Univ, Los Angeles

Littlefield, Doris, *Cur Asst,* Vizcaya, Miami, FL

Littman, Robert R, *Dir,* Grey Art Gallery & Study Center, New York Univ, New York

Litwack, Herman C, *Secy,* Nat Inst for Architectural Education, see National and Regional Organizations

Livesay, Thomas A, *Dir,* Amarillo Art Center, TX

Livet, Anne, *Cur,* Fort Worth Art Museum, TX

Livingston, Jane, *Chief Cur,* Corcoran Gallery of Art, Washington, DC

Livingston, Katherine, *Develop Officer,* Fine Arts Museums of San Francisco, CA

Livingstone, Elaine Biganess, *First VPres,* New Hampshire Art Association, Manchester

Livingstone, Ernest, *Chmn,* Rensselaer Polytechnic Inst, Troy, NY

Lizon, Dr Peter, *Assoc Prof,* Catholic Univ America, Washington, DC

Lizotte, Jack, *Dir Summer School,* Findlay College, OH

Lizzadro, John S, *Dir,* Lizzadro Museum of Lapidary Art, Elmhurst, IL

Ljungberg, Sven, *Dir,* Kungl. Konsthogskolan, Stockholm, Sweden

Llanes, Manuel, *Librn,* Museo Romantico Madrid, Spain

Llewellyn, Frederick, *Dir,* Forest Lawn Museum, Glendale, CA

Llewellyn, Jane E, *Mgr,* Forest Lawn Museum, Glendale, CA

Llisiona, Daniel de Neuda, *Dir,* Escuela Superior de Bellas Artes de San Carlos, Valencia, Spain

Llombart, Felipe-Vicente Garin, *Dir & Conservator,* Museu de Bellas Artes de Valencia, Spain

Lloyd, Alan, *Conservation,* Art Gallery of New South Wales, Sydney, Australia

Lloyd, Mrs J W, *Pres,* Fannie Mebane Ralph Library and Gallery, Bel Haven, NC

Lloyd, Leslie Charles, *Dir,* Dunedin Public Art Gallery, New Zealand

Lloyd, R McAllister, *VPres,* New York Historical Society, New York

Lloyd, Tom, *Dir & Cur,* Store Front Museum, Jamaica, NY

Lobchuk, Bill, *Nat Representative,* Le Front des Artistes Canadiens, Winnipeg, MB

Loche, Dr J L, *Head Modern Art Dept,* Haags Gemeentemuseum, The Hague, Netherlands

Locher, Dr Kurt, *Cur Modern Art,* Wallraf Richartz-Museum, Museen der Stadt Koln, Germany

Lochhead, J, *Chief Nat Prog Div,* Nat Museum of Man, Ottawa, ON

Lochridge, Katherine, *Dir,* Heckscher Museum, Huntington, NY

Lochte, Kate B, *Admin Asst,* Hunter Museum of Art, Chattanooga, TN

Lochtefeld, John, *Prof,* Marymount College, Tarrytown, NY

Locke, John, *Prof,* Dean Junior College, Franklin, MA

Locke, John A, III, *Asst Coordr Visual Arts Gallery & Asst Prof,* Ulster County Community College, Stone Ridge, NY

Lockett, Elizabeth Gaudit, *Librn,* Tulane Univ Exhibition Gallery, New Orleans, LA

Lockhart, Bill, *Prof & Dir Summer School,* Texas Tech Univ, Lubbock

Loeb, Alex M, *Pres,* Mississippi Art Colony, Meridian

Loeb, Jean R, *Secy-Treas,* Mississippi Art Colony, Meridian

Loebel, William, *Exec Dir,* Lakeview Center for the Arts and Sciences, Peoria, IL

Loeffler, Carl E, *Pres,* La Mamelle Inc, San Francisco, CA

Loeffler, Elaine P, *Chairwoman,* Brandeis Univ, Waltham, MA

Loehr, Thomas, *Instr,* Spring Hill College, Mobile, AL

Loerke, William C, *Dir Center for Byzantine Studies,* Dumbarton Oaks Research Library and Collections, Washington, DC

Loft, Deborah, *Mem Faculty,* College of Marin, Kentfield, CA

Lofthus, Else, *Asst Dept Painting & Sculpture,* Statens Museum for Kunst, Copenhagen, Denmark

Loftis, Lynn, *Cur Historical Educ,* Ella Sharp Museum, Jackson, MI

Logan, Anne-Marie, *Art Ref Librn & Photo,* Yale Univ Art Gallery, New Haven, CT

Logan, Dr L H, *VPres Acad Affairs Summer School,* Southern Arkansas Univ, Magnolia

Logan, Oscar, *Instr,* Alabama A&M Univ, Huntsville

Logan, Vernie, *Cur & Librn,* Art Museum & *Lectr,* Baylor University, Waco, TX

Logisz, Sabina, *Asst Librn,* Polish Museum of America, Chicago, IL

Logton, Mrs Richard, *Secy,* Keokuk Art Center, IA

Lohan, Dirk, *Pres,* Soc Contemporary Art, Art Inst of Chicago, IL

Lohden, Bernardine T, *Dir,* Kirkland Art Center, Clinton, NY

Lohe, Richard, *Restorer,* Bayerischen Staatsgemaldesammlungen, Munich, Germany

Lohner, Paul E, *Dir,* Westchester Art Workshop, White Plains, NY

Loiacano, James, *Asst Dir,* Dade County Art Museum, Miami, FL

Loiselle, Bernard R, *Dir,* City of Rockville Maryland Municipal Art Gallery

Loiselle, Jane, *Civic Center Supvr,* City of Rockville Maryland Municipal Art Gallery

Lokensgard, Lynne, *Instr,* Lamar Univ, Beaumont, TX

Lombardo, Daniel J, *Art & Music Librn,* Forbes Library, Northampton, MA

Lombardo, William, *Chmn Ceramics,* Corcoran School of Art, Washington, DC

Londa, Dean, *Exec Dir,* Association of Junior Leagues, see National and Regional Organizations

London, Laurence, *Managing Dir,* Charles B Goddard Center for the Visual and Performing Arts, Ardmore, OK

London, Peter, *Chairperson Art Educ,* Southeastern Massachusetts Univ, North Dartmouth

London, Phyllis, *Lectr,* Regis College, Weston, MA

Londono, Jorge, *Head Urban Studies,* Javeriana Univ Faculty of Architecture and Design, Bogota, Colombia

Lone, Mary, *Assoc Prof,* Texarkana College, TX

Lonergan, Mary Ann, *Instr,* Briar Cliff College, Sioux City, IA

Loney, James, *Cur Educ,* Southeast Arkansas Arts and Science Center, Pine Bluff

Long, Charles, *Pub Information Officer,* Fine Arts Museums of San Francisco, CA

Long, Charles, *Mus Consult,* San Antonio Art League, TX

Long, Chuck, *Treas,* Huntsville Art League and Museum Association, AL

Long, Clarence W, *Pres Bd Trustees,* Indianapolis Museum of Art, IN

Long, Elizabeth, *Admin Dir,* Lighthouse Gallery, Tequesta, FL

Long, Esther, *Educ Dir,* Nat Cowboy Hall of Fame, Oklahoma City, OK

Long, James E, *Pres,* St Augustine Art Association Gallery, FL

Long, Dr John M, *Dean,* Troy State Univ, AL

Long, Meredith, *Gallery Trustee,* Visual Artists and Galleries Association, see National and Regional Organizations

Long, Phillip C, *VPres,* Contemporary Arts Center, Cincinnati, OH

Long, Walter K, *Dir,* Cayuga Museum of History and Art, Auburn, NY

Long, William F, *Dean Summer School,* George Washington Univ, Washington, DC

Long, William, *Cur,* Old Capitol, Kentucky Historical Society Museum, Frankfort

Longen, Sister Leonarda, *Instr & Res Artist,* Mount Marty College, Yankton, SD

Longfellow, Ann, *Reference Librn,* Rotch Library of Architecture and Planning, Massachusetts Inst of Technology, Cambridge

Longin, Tom, *Dean,* Ithaca College, NY

Longley, Cynthia, *Dir Educ,* Oklahoma Museum of Art, Oklahoma City

Longley, Pat, *VPres Publicity,* Miniature Art Society of New Jersey, Nutley, NJ

Longland, Jean R, *Cur Librn,* Hispanic Society of America, New York, NY

Longstreet, Stephen, *Pres,* Los Angeles Art Association and Galleries, CA

Lonier, Teresa, *Instr,* East Tennessee State Univ, Johnson City

Lonsbury, Pierre, *Trustee,* Attleboro Museum, MA

Loomis, Robert A, *Pres Bd Trustees,* Blanden Art Gallery, Fort Dodge, IA

Loomis, Tom, *Asst Prof,* Mansfield State College, PA

Looney, Robert F, *Head Print & Picture Dept,* Free Library of Philadelphia, Pennsylvania

Looy, Glenn Van, *Asst,* International Cultureel Centrum, Antwerpen, Belgium

Lopez, Jesse, *Production Mgr,* Rice Univ, Inst for the Arts, Houston, TX

Lopez, Jorge Martinez, *Dir,* Univ Guadalajara, Mexico

Lopez, Raul A, *Cur New World Coll & Publ Dir,* Museum of Cultural History, Univ California, Los Angeles

Lopez, Silvino, *Instr,* Philippine College of Arts and Trades, Manila

LoPresit, Maryellen, *Librn,* North Carolina State Univ Design Library, Raleigh

Lord, Clifford L, *Dir,* New Jersey Historical Society Museum, Newark

Lord, Eileen, *Prof,* Univ Bridgeport, CT

Lord, J V, *Head Dept Visual Communication,* Brighton Polytechnic, England

Lorenson, Joan, *Curatorial Registrar,* Montclair Art Museum, NJ

Lorentz, Dr Stankslaw, *Dir,* Muzeum Narodowe, Warsaw, Poland

Lorenz, Sister Ellen, *Dir Summer School,* Mount Mary College, Milwaukee, WI

Lorenz, Hella, *Cur,* Suermondt-Ludwig-Museum Der Stadt Aachen, Germany

Lorenzana, Katherine Harper, *Asst Prof,* Loyola Marymount Univ, Los Angeles, CA

Lorenzetti, Constanza, *Prof & Dir,* Accademie de Belle Arti e Liceo Artistico, Naples, Italy

Loso, Mary Jane, *Chairperson Div Humanities,* Eastern Oregon State College, La Grande

Loss, John, *Dir Architecture,* North Carolina State Univ at Raleigh

Lossky, B, *Vis Prof,* Fontainebleau School of Fine Arts, France

Lotreck, Annelaine, *Librn,* Willoughby Wallace Mem Library, Stony Creek, CT

Lottes, John W, *Pres,* Kansas City Art Inst, MO

Louchheim, Mrs Stuart F, *Chmn,* Samuel S Fleisher Art Mem, Philadelphia, PA

Louer, Albert O, *Dir Pub Relations,* Indianapolis Museum of Art, IN

Louis, William, *Chmn Fine Arts,* Avila College Art Gallery, Kansas City, MO

Loupe, Valerie, *Cur Prints,* New Orleans Museum of Art, LA

Lousada, Sir Anthony, *Pro-Provost,* Royal College of Art Exhibitions, London, England

Lovass-Nagy, Klara, *Asst Cur,* Potsdam Public Museum, NY

Lovato, Manuelita, *Cur Functions,* Inst of American Indian Arts Museum, Santa Fe, NM

Love, Frances, *Dir,* Univ Southwestern Louisiana Art Center, Lafayette

Loveall, David, *Asst Dir,* San Francisco Art Inst, CA

Loveday, Amos, *Acting Head Educ Div,* Ohio Historical Society, Columbus

Lovejoy, Carolyn, *Admin Asst & Librn,* Rockwell-Corning Museum, Corning, NY

Loveless, Jim, *Chmn & Prof,* Colgate Univ, Hamilton, NY

Loveall, Mrs Hin-Cheung, *Assoc Cur Chinese Art,* Freer Gallery of Art, Washington, DC

Lovell, Robert O, *Secy Bd Dirs,* New Muse Community Museum of Brooklyn, NY

Lovera, James, *Ceramics Coordr,* San Jose State Univ, CA

Lovett, Peggy, *Lectr,* Marian College, Indianapolis, IN

Lovett, Robert, *Pres,* Beverly Historical Society, MA

Low, Louise, *Treas,* Ojai Valley Art Center, CA

Low, Markus J, *Mgr Corporate Art Serv,* Ciba-Geigy Corp, Ardsley, NY, see Corporate Art Holdings

Low, Rebecca, *Instr,* Northeast Technical Community College, Norfolk, NE

Low, Theodore L, *Dir Educ,* Walters Art Gallery, Baltimore, MD

Lowe, Elsie T, *Secy,* Palette and Chisel Academy of Fine Arts, Chicago, IL

Lowe, Harry, *Asst Dir,* Nat Collection of Fine Arts, Washington, DC

Lowe, J Michael, *Chmn,* St Lawrence Univ, Canton, NY

Lowe, Patricia A, *Secy,* Will Rogers Mem and Museum, Claremore, OK

Lowery, Mrs Cedric, *Pres,* Central Louisiana Art Association, Alexandria

Lowery, Christopher, *VPres,* South Street Seaport Museum, New York, NY

Lowing, Robert, *Mem Faculty,* Millersville State College, PA

Lown, Suzanne E, *Historic Site Asst,* Palisades Interstate Park Commission, Kingston, NY

Lowrance, Miriam A, *Head Dept & Assoc Prof,* Sul Ross State Univ, Alpine, TX

Lowrie, Pamela B, *Mem Faculty,* College of DuPage, Glen Ellyn, IL

Lowry, Keith, *Assoc Prof,* Kearney State College, NE

Loyd, Bess, *Librn,* New Orleans Public Library, LA

Lozinski, Dr Jean S, *Pres Gallery & Chmn Dept of Fine Arts,* Swain School of Design, New Bedford, MA

Lubar, Sheldon B, *Pres Bd Trustees,* Milwaukee Art Center, WI

Lubbers, Lee, *Mem Faculty,* Creighton Univ, Omaha, NE

Lubetkin, Robert, *VPres & Treas,* Des Moines Art Center, IA

Lucas, Arthur, *Chief Restorer,* Nat Gallery of London, England

Lucas, James, *Assoc Prof,* Youngstown State Univ, OH

Lucas, Ken, *Dir Summer School,* Butte Community College, Oroville, CA

Lucas, Margaret O, *Grad Coordr,* North Texas State Univ, Denton

Luck, Meredith, *Asst Prof,* Union Univ; Jackson, TN

Luckert, Walter, *Technician,* State Univ New York at Binghamton

Luckman, Stewart, *Chmn,* Bethel College, Saint Paul, MN

Luckner, Kurt T, *Cur Ancient Art,* Toledo Museum of Art, OH

Luddy, Tony, *Cur Film,* Pacific Film Archive, Univ of Calif, Berkeley

Ludeke, Chuck, *Technical Asst,* Rockford Art Association, IL

Ludgin, Donald, *Secy,* Museum of Contemporary Art, Chicago, IL

Ludmann, Jean-Daniel, *Dir,* Musee des Beaux-Arts Strasbourg, France

Ludmer, Joyce, *Art Librn,* Elmer Belt Library of Vinciana, Univ California, Los Angeles

Ludovice, Leopoldo, *Instr,* Philippine College of Arts and Trades, Manila

Ludwig, Coy, *Dir,* Tyler Art Gallery, State Univ New York at Oswego

Luecking, Stephen, *Asst Prof,* DePaul Univ, Chicago, IL

Luedtke, John, *Cur Oriental, Classical & Decorative Art,* Milwaukee Public Museum, WI

Luehrman, Richard, *Prof,* Central Missouri State Univ, Warrensburg

Lugo, Anthony J, *Assoc Prof,* Palomar College, San Marcos, CA

Luigina, J, *Treas,* New Jersey Watercolor Society Bloomfield, NJ

Lukasiewicz, Ronald, *Preparator,* Univ Georgia Museum of Art, Athens

Lukaszewica, P, *Cur,* Muzeum Narodowe We Wroclawiu, Wroclaw, Poland

Lukonis, W, *Cur,* Naval Amphibious Museum, Norfolk, VA

Lukosius, Richard, *Prof,* Connecticut College, New London

Lukusavitz, Frank, *Chmn Design Dept,* Milwaukee School of the Arts, WI

Lumsden, Ian G, *Cur,* Beaverbrook Art Gallery, Fredericton, NB

Lund, David, *Asst Prof,* Div of Painting and Sculpture, Columbia Univ, New York, NY

Lund, Ed, *Prof,* California State Univ, Fresno

Lund, Nils-Ole, *Rector & Prof,* School of Architecture in Aarhus, Denmark

Lund, Dr R J, *Secy,* Museum Greenwood, SC

Lundberg, Erveen C, *Librn,* John Woodman Higgins Armory, Worcester, Mass

Lunde, Rev Joel, *Head Dept,* Lutheran Brethran Schools, Fergus Falls, MN

Lungy, Kenneth H, *Dir Summer School,* Eastern Connecticut State College, Willimantic

Lunn, Anita, *Head Librn,* Ohio Historical Society, Columbus

McCoy, Katherine, *Head Design Dept,* Cranbrook Academy of Art, Bloomfield Hills, MI

McCoy, L Frank, *Chmn,* Univ Montevallo, AL

McCoy, Michael, *Head Design Dept,* Cranbrook Academy of Art, Bloomfield Hills, MI

McCoy, Mrs Philip, *Pres,* Asian Art Museum, San Francisco, CA

McCoy, T Frank, *Chairperson Fine Art,* Southeastern Massachusetts Univ, North Dartmouth

McCracken, Mrs E A, *Pres,* Grand Prairie Art Council, Stuttgart, AR

McCracken, Edward P, *Admin Officer,* Walters Art Gallery, Baltimore, MD

McCracken, Patrick, *Cur Educ,* Albuquerque Museum of Art, History and Science, NM

McCrady, Mary B, *Dir Summer School,* John McCrady Art School of New Orleans, LA

McCray, Dorothy, *Prof,* Western New Mexico Univ, Silver City

McCready, Eric S, *Dir,* Univ Wisconsin-Madison Mem Union

McCready, Reyburn R, *Librn,* Univ Oregon School of Architecture and Allied Arts Library, Eugene

McCredy, Iris, *Librn,* White Rock Painting and Sketch Club, BC

McCreight, Tim, *Inst,* Craft Center, Worcester, MA

McCue, Harry, *Chmn,* Ithaca College, NY

McCuistion, Mrs Fred, *Pres,* Council of Ozark Artists and Craftsmen, Springdale, AR

McCulloh, Patricia, *Asst Prof,* Kenyon College, Gambier, OH

McCullough, Ed, *Mem Faculty,* Illinois Wesleyan Univ, Bloomington

McCullough, Joseph, *Pres,* Cleveland Inst of Art, OH; *Secy,* Cleveland Art Association, OH

McCurry, Gary, *Instr,* William Woods/Westminster Colleges, Fulton, MO

McDaniel, Susan, *Dir Summer School,* East Carolina Univ, Greenville, NC

McDermand, Robert V, *Coordr Public Serv,* Lamson Library, Plymouth State College, NH

McDermott, Sister Jane, *Dir Summer School,* Albertus Magnus College, New Haven, CT

McDermott, John, *Dir Summer School,* Catholic Univ America, Washington, DC

MacDonald, Alex, *Mgr Pub Affairs,* Art Gallery of Ontario, Toronto

McDonald, Barbara, *Prog Coordr,* King County Arts Commission, Seattle, WA

MacDonald, Bruce K, *Mem Staff,* School of the Museum of Fine Arts, Boston, MA

McDonald, Eloise E, *Librn,* Univ Arkansas, Fayetteville

MacDonald, Jane, *Asst to Dir,* Robert McLaughlin Gallery, Oshawa, ON

McDonald, Jeri, *Dir Public Relations,* Seattle Art Museum, WA

MacDonald, John, *Sr VPres,* Federal Reserve Bank of Minneapolis, MN, see Corporate Art Holdings

MacDonald, Judy, *Registrar,* Confederation Centre Art Gallery and Museum, Charlottetown, PE

Macdonald, Robert R, *Dir,* Louisiana State Museum, New Orleans

MacDonald, William A, *Mem Faculty,* George Washington Univ, Washington, DC

McDonough, Paul, *Head Fashion Dept,* Paris American Acad, France

McDonough, Reginald, *Superior Rev,* Mission San Miguel, CA

McDougal, O J, Jr, *Pres Bd Trustees,* Hastings Museum, NE

McDougal, Rex, *Dean & Assoc Dean Community Educ,* Yuba College, Marysville, CA

MacDougall, E Bruce, *Prof & Head,* Univ Massachusetts, Amherst

McDowell, H Woodward, *Treas,* Presbyterian Historical Society, Philadelphia, PA

McDowell, James, *Chmn Dept,* College of Our Lady of the Elms, Chicopee, MA

McDowell, Paul, *Asst Prof,* Univ Evansville, IN

McDowell, Peggy P, *Chmn Fine Arts,* Univ New Orleans, LA

McDuffee, James, *Asst Dir,* Stephen Foster Center, White Springs, FL

McEndarfer, Ed, *Asst Prof,* Northeast Missouri State Univ, Kirksville

McEvilley, Thomas, *Lectr,* Rice Univ, Houston, TX

McEwen, Amy V, *Asst Dir,* China Inst in America, New York, NY

McFadden, David, *Cur Decorative Arts,* Minneapolis Inst of Arts, MN

McFadden, James L, *Asst Prof,* South Carolina State College, Orangeburg

McFall, Henry S, *Pres,* Historical Society of York County, PA

McFarland, Maighread, *Restorer paper,* Nat Gallery of Ireland, Dublin

McFarland, Mrs. William, *Secy,* Gilpin County Arts Association, Central City, CO

McFarlane, Len, *Technician,* Univ British Columbia Museum of Anthropology, Vancouver

McFee, Doris, *Head Librn,* Chappell Mem Library and Art Gallery, NE

McGaha, Mary Gamble, *VPres,* Huntsville Art League and Museum Association, AL

McGarrell, James, *Artist-in-Residence,* Oxbow Summer Art Workshops, Saugatuck, MI

McGarvey, Elsie Siratz, *Cur Emer Costumes & Textiles,* Philadelphia Museum of Art, PA

McGarvey, Jaune, *Treas,* Kent Art Association Gallery, CT

McGeary, Clyde M, *Chief,* Pennsylvania Dept of Education, Harrisburg

McGeary, George L, *Chmn Fine Arts Dept,* Manhattan College, Bronx, NY

McGee, Carol, *Chmn,* Yuba College, Marysville, CA

McGee, David, *Registrar,* Huntington Galleries, WV

McGee, Melvin C, *Secy,* Buffalo Bill Mem Association, Cody, WY

McGee, Nancy, *Chmn Fashion Design,* Moore College of Art, Philadelphia, PA

McGee, Reginald, *Cur Photography,* Studio Museum in Harlem, New York, NY

McGee, William, *Chmn & Assoc Prof,* Herbert H Lehman College, Bronx, NY

McGee, Winston, *Prof & Chmn Art Dept & Chmn Summer School,* California State College, Stanislaus, Turlock

McGehee, Terry, *Instr,* Agnes Scott College, Decatur, GA

McGeorge, Pauline, *Assoc Prof,* Univ Lethbridge, AB

McGhan, Rena, *Cur,* Sioux Indian Museum, Rapid City, SD

McGill, Esby, *Dir Summer School,* Southern Oregon State College, Ashland

McGill, Forrest, *Coordr Pub Progs,* Univ Michigan Museum of Art, Ann Arbor, MI; *Vis Instr,* Oakland Univ, Rochester, MI

McGill, W A, *Chmn Dept,* Purdue Univ, West Lafayette, IN

McGill, William, *Chmn Art & Design,* Purdue Univ Galleries, West Lafayette, Indiana

McGinnis, Darrell, *Prof,* Fort Hays State Univ, Hays, KS

McGinnis, R Guy, *Chmn Interior/Environmental Design,* Pratt Inst School of Art & Design, Brooklyn, NY

McGough, Carolyn, *Secy,* Twin City Art Found, Monroe, LA

McGough, Charles E, *Dir, Little Gallery & Head Art Dept,* East Texas State Univ Commerce

McGough, Gerry, *Prof,* Southern Baptist College, College City, AR

McGough, Stephen C, *Cur Modern Art,* Allen Mem Art Museum, Oberlin College, OH

McGovern, Robert, *Dept Chairperson & Prof,* Philadelphia College of Art, PA

McGowan, Bette, *Mgr,* Drummer Boy Museum, Brewster, MA

McGowan, Lewis A, *Mgr,* Drummer Boy Museum, Brewster, MA

McGrath, Mrs Don, *Secy,* William Rockhill Nelson Gallery of Art, Kansas City, MO

McGreevy, Susan, *Cur,* Wheelwright Museum, Santa Fe, NM

MacGregor, C, *Acting Head Dept Indust Design,* Manchester Polytechnic, England

MacGregor, D O, *Dir & Librn,* Kootenay School of Art Gallery, Nelson, BC

McGregor, Jack R, *Exec Dir,* San Antonio Museum Association, TX

MacGregor, Janet, *Personal Asst & Secy,* Confederation Centre Art Gallery and Museum, Charlottetown, PE

MacGregor, Leslie, *Instr,* Dunedin Fine Arts & Cultural Center, FL

MacGregor, Nancy, *Assoc Prof,* Ohio State Univ, Columbus

McGregor, Dr Rob Roy, *VPres,* Concord Antiquarian Society Museum, MA

McGuinness, Msgr Brendan, *Rector,* San Carlos Cathedral, Monterey, CA

McGuire, Mrs James, *Educ Coordr,* Lyman Allyn Museum, New London, CT

McGuire, Michael C, *Instr,* Central Acad of Commercial Art, Cincinnati, OH

Machek, Frank, *Assoc Prof Art & Chmn Dept Visual Arts,* Albion College, MI

McHenry, Nadine, *Vis Prof,* Nebraska Wesleyan Univ, Lincoln

Machorro, Silvia Martinez, *Secy,* Museo de Art Jose Luis Bello y Gonzalez, Puebla, Mexico

Macht, Dr Carol, *Sr Cur & Cur Decorative Arts,* Cincinnati Art Museum, OH

Machtel, David, *Chairperson Dept,* Lansing Community College, MI

McHugh, Patricia Tool, *Instr,* Sacramento City College, CA

McHugh, Patricia W, *First Asst Fine Arts Dept,* Detroit Public Library, MI

McHugh, Paul A, *Exec Mgr,* St Louis Artists Guild, MO

Macik, John, *Librn,* Saint Bonaventure Univ Art Collection, NY

McIlhenny, Henry P, *Chmn & Adv Decorative Arts,* Philadelphia Museum of Art, PA

McIlvain, Barbara, *VPres,* Plastic Club, Philadelphia, PA

McIlvain, Douglas L, *Assoc Prof,* Georgian Court College, Lakewood, NJ

McIlvain, Isabel, *Mem Faculty,* Washington and Lee Univ, Lexington, VA

McInerney, M, *Head Dept Fashion & Textiles,* Brighton Polytechnic, England

McIntyre, Ida, *Admin Asst,* Chester County Historical Society, West Chester, PA

McIntyre, Nancy J, *Dir,* Lemoyne Art Found, Tallahassee, FL

McIntyre, Ralph, *Treas,* Roswell Museum and Art Center, NM

Mack, Andrew R, *Chmn,* Stockbridge Mission House Association, MA

Mack, Randy, *Instr,* Univ South Carolina, Columbia

Mack, Mrs William, *Representative of Past Pres,* Cody Country Art League, WY

McKay, Claudine, *Prof,* Xavier Univ Louisiana, New Orleans

MacKay, Don, *Assoc Prof,* Univ Waterloo, ON

Mackay, Linda L, *Library Asst,* College of Architecture Library, Georgia Inst of Technology, Atlanta

Mackay, Phyllis, *Pres,* South Peace Art Society, Dawson Creek, BC

McKechnie, Fred, *Dir,* Univ Club Library, New York, NY

McKee, C V, Jr, *Secy-Treas,* Stark Museum of Art, Orange, TX

McKee, Fred, *Instr,* Miles Community College, Miles City, MT

McKee, Joel, *Adminr,* Clark County Library District Art Activities, Las Vegas, NV

McKee, John, *Mem Faculty,* Bowdoin College, Brunswick, ME

McKee, Ross, *Secy,* Key West Art and Historical Society, FL

McKeeby, Byron, *Prof,* Univ Tennessee, Knoxville

McKeegan, Hugh, *Dir Summer Session,* Bucknell Univ, Lewisburg, PA

MacKeeman, Robert, *Dir,* Nova Scotia College of Art and Design Gallery, Halifax

McKelvy, Susan, *Dir Exhib,* Hunterdon Art Center, Clinton, NJ

McKemie, William, *Asst Secy Treas & Cur,* Agecroft Association Hall, Richmond, VA

Macken, M, *Dir,* Nat Higher Inst of Fine Arts, Antwerp, Belgium

McKenna, George L, *Registrar & Cur Prints,* William Rockhill Nelson Gallery of Art, Kansas City, MO

McKenna, John V, *Exec Dir,* Fort Wayne Fine Arts Found, IN

MacKenzie, Donald, *Prof,* College of Wooster, OH

McKenzie, Wilfred, *Asst Prof,* Winona State Univ, MN

McKeon, Laura, *Instr,* Lake Forest College, IL

McKeon, William E, *VPres,* Marblehead Arts Association, MA

McKern, H H G, *Deputy Dir,* Museum of Applied Arts and Sciences, Sydney, Australia

McKibben, Gael May, *Asst to Dir,* Westbrook College, Portland, ME

McKibbin, David, *Art Librn,* Boston Athenaeum, MA

McKibbin, Robert H, *Asst Prof,* Grinnell College, IA

McKibben, W Alex, *Assoc,* Prof, Miami Univ, Oxford, OH

McKie, Donald, *Librn,* Univ California Central Univ Library, San Diego

Mackie, G, *Instr,* Selkirk College, Nelson, BC

Mackie, Louise W, *Cur Old World,* Textile Museum, Washington, DC

Mackie, Murray, *Pres,* Community Arts Council of Chilliwack, BC

MacKillop, Rod, *Asst Prof,* Univ North Carolina, Charlotte

McKillop, Dr Susan, *Asst Prof,* California State College, Sonoma, Rohnert Park

McKinley, June, *Instr,* Del Mar College, Corpus Christi, TX

McKinney, Claude E, *Dean,* North Carolina State Univ at Raleigh

McKinney, Helen, *Librn,* Society of the Four Arts, Palm Beach, FL

McKinney, John W, *Pres,* Birmingham Gallery, MI

McKinney, Marsha, *Special Projects Coordr,* Bank of Oklahoma, Tulsa, see Corporate Art Holdings

MacKintosh, Kenneth R, *Dir,* Walla Walla Community College, WA

Macklin, Dr A D, *Head Dept,* Virginia State College, Petersburg

McLachlan, Dr Elizabeth, *Mem Faculty,* Graduate Program in Art History, Rutgers, The State Univ New Jersey, New Brunswick

McLanahan, Alexander K, *Pres Bd,* Museum of Fine Arts, Houston, TX

McLaren, Ross, *Film Officer,* Centre for Experimental Art and Communication, Toronto, ON

McLarty, Jack, *Instr,* Museum Art School, Portland, OR

McLary, David, *Cur Exhib,* Indiana State Museum, Indianapolis

McLaughlin, Charles M, *Acting Dir,* Texas Tech Univ Museum, Lubbock

McLaughlin, Eleanor, *Supvr Branches,* Miami-Dade Public Library, FL

McLaughlin, James, *Cur,* Phillips Collection, Washington, DC

McLay, Peter, *Installations Officer & Designer,* Univ Waterloo, ON

McLean, Harriet, *Exec Dir,* Boston Center for Adult Education, MA

McLean, Jessica P, *Instr,* Georgia Inst of Technology, Atlanta

McLean, Linda, *Interpretive Programs Asst,* New York State Dept of Parks and Recreation, Hudson

McLean, Pauline, *Secy,* Council of Delaware Artists, Wilmington

McLean, Peter, *Assoc Prof,* Hartford Art School, Univ Hartford, West Hartford, CT

McLean, Robert, *Instr,* Contra Costa College, San Pablo, CA

MacLeish, Bruce, *Cur Coll,* Western Kentucky Univ Museum, Bowling Green

MacLeish, Patricia, *Registrar,* Western Kentucky Univ Museum, Bowling Green

McLemore, Cosy, *Educ Coordr,* Dallas Historical Society, TX

McLennan, Bill, *Designer,* Univ British Columbia Museum of Anthropology, Vancouver

MacLennan, H K, *Chmn Bd,* Desert Caballeros Western Museum, Wickenburg, AZ

McLeod, David, *Vis Instr,* Univ Nebraska at Omaha

McLeod, Mrs J, *Librn,* Hawkes Bay Art Gallery and Museum, Napier, New Zealand

MacLeod, Robert, *Dir School Architecture,* Univ British Columbia, Vancouver

MacLeod, Robert, *Chmn,* Confederation Centre Art Gallery and Museum, Charlottetown, PE

McLoughlin, Gary, *Technical Asst,* Joe and Emily Lowe Art Gallery, Syracuse Univ, NY

MacMahan, Raymond John, *Chmn,* Birmingham-Southern College, AL

McMahon, Franklin, *Instr,* Famous Artists School, Westport, CT

McMahon, James, *Prof,* Manatee Junior College, Brandenton, FL

McManus, G Louis, *Supt,* Sterling and Francine Clark Art Inst, Williamstown, MA

McMenomy, Robert, *Mem Faculty,* Long Beach City College, CA

McMichael, Dr Robert, *Dir,* McMichael Canadian Collection, Kleinburg, ON

McMillan, Adell, *Dir,* Univ Oregon Museum of Art, Eugene

McMillan, Bruce R, *Dir,* Illinois State Museum of Natural History and Art, Springfield

McMillan, Sister Elizabeth, *Acad Dean Summer School,* Carlow College, Pittsburgh, PA

MacMillan, Ladd, *Cur Arts & Crafts,* Heritage Plantation of Sandwich, MA

McMillan, Leslie, Jr, *VPres,* Arts Council of Spartanburg County, Spartanburg, SC

McMillan, Robert W, *Coordr Painting/Drawing,* Univ Arizona, Tucson

McMullen, Stewart, *Treas,* Evanston Art Center, IL

McMurrough, Eliot S, *Dir,* Eliot McMurrough School of Art, Indialantic, FL

McNalley, Jeff, *VPres,* Association of American Editorial Cartoonists, see National and Regional Organizations

McNally, Rev Dennis, *Lectr,* Saint Joseph's College, Philadelphia, PA

McNally, Dorothy, *Asst to Dir,* Newark Museum, NJ

McNally, Sheila J, *Prof,* Univ Minnesota, Minneapolis

McNamara, Mary Jo, *Cur,* Vassar College Art Gallery, Poughkeepsie, NY

McNaughton, Mrs John N, *Corresp Secy,* Detroit Artists Market, MI

McNeal, Mary Ly, *Dir Summer School,* College of Notre Dame of Maryland, Baltimore

McNealy, Terry A, *Librn,* Bucks County Historical Society Mercer Museum, Doylestown, PA

McNeer, John B, *Dir Summer School,* Richard Bland College, Petersburg, VA

McNeil, Barton, *Mem Faculty,* Illinois Wesleyan Univ, Bloomington

McNeil, David K, *Dir,* Thames Arts Centre, Chatham, ON

McNeil, Donald, *Art Cur,* General Mills, Minneapolis, MN, see Corporate Art Holdings

McNeil, Henry S, *Pres & Chmn Bd,* Pennsylvania Acad of Fine Arts, Philadelphia

McNeil, Robin, *Dir,* Fine Arts Center of Clinton, IL

McNiff, Philip J, *Dir & Librn,* Boston Public Library, MA

McNulty, Kneeland, *Cur Prints, Drawings & Photographs,* Philadelphia Museum of Art, PA

McNutt, Audaleen H, *Mus Secy,* East Tennessee State Univ Museum and Gallery, Johnson City

MacNutt, Glenn, *VPres,* Boston Watercolor Society, Scituate, MA

MacOmber William B, Jr, *Pres,* Metropolitan Museum of Art, New York, NY

McPeak, Thomas E, *Head Dept,* Clemson Univ, SC

McPhail, Donald W, *Pres,* Print Club, Philadelphia, PA

McPhee, J A, *Gallery Officer,* Queen Victoria Museum, Launceston, Australia

McPheeters, E K, *Dean,* Auburn Univ, AL

McPherson, C R, *VPres,* Wilmington Trust Company, DE, see Corporate Art Holdings

McPike, Daniel M, *Cur Anthropology,* Thomas Gilcrease Inst American History and Art, Tulsa, OK

McQuay, Paul L, *Dir Dept,* Williamsport Area Community College, PA

McQueen, Jennifer R, *Acting Secy-Gen,* Nat Museums of Canada, Ottawa, ON

McQueen, Patricia, *Registrar,* Rice Univ, Inst for the Arts, Houston, TX

McQuillan, Frances, *Instr,* Montclair Art Museum, NJ; *VPres,* Art Centre of New Jersey, East Orange

McQuire, Patrick F, *Assoc Prof,* Morgan State Univ, Baltimore, MD

McQuire, Wayne, *Chmn,* Shoreline Community College, Seattle, WA

McRae, Donald C, *Acting Dean,* College of Fine Arts, Univ New Mexico, Albuquerque

McRae, Tru, *Instr & Gallery Dir,* Northeast Missouri State Univ, Kirksville

McRaven, Donald B Jr, *Assoc Prof,* Moorhead State Univ, MN

McShane, Celia, *VPres,* Brush and Palette Club, Cooperstown, NY

McSwain, S O, *Pres,* Arts and Crafts Association, Winston-Salem, NC

MacTavish, Alison M, *Librn,* American Inst of Architects Found & *Cur,* Octagon, Washington, DC

McVean, James E, *Pres,* Jefferson Community College, Watertown, NY

McVeety, Mrs John, *Pres Bd Dir,* Nobles County Art Center Gallery, Worthington, MN

McVicker, Charles, *Pres,* Society of Illustrators, see National and Regional Organizations

McWhirter, David, *Vis Lectr,* Dept of Landscape Architecture, Univ Toronto, ON

McWilliams, David Jackson, *Dir,* La Casa del Libro, San Juan, PR

McWilliams, Harvey, *Instr,* Univ Richmond, VA

Macy, Thaddeus, *Cur Asst,* Westbrook College, Portland, ME

Madden, Charles, *Undergrad Dean Summer School,* Webster College, Webster Groves, Mo

Madden, J Robert, *Prof,* Lamar Univ, Beaumont, TX

Madden, John, *Coordr of Educ,* Tallahassee Junior Museum, FL

Madden, Dr S A, *Dir Summer School,* Virginia State College, Petersburg

Maddick, Russell, *Assoc Prof,* Youngstown State Univ, OH

Maddox, Dawn, *Dir Historic Preservation,* Mississippi Dept of Archives and History, Jackson

Maddox, Gene, *Instr,* College of the Sequoias, Visalia, CA

Maddox, Jerald, *Collections Planner & Coordr,* Library of Congress, Washington, DC

Maddox, Jerrold, *Prof Art, Head Dept & Dir Summer School,* Kansas State Univ, Manhattan

Maddux, Elizabeth, *VPres,* San Antonio Museum Association, TX

Maddy, Kathryn, *Asst Dir & Cur Educ,* Loveland Museum, CO

Madeo, Lynne Robert, *Dir,* Jackson County Historical Society, Independence, MO

Madigan, Richard A, *Dir,* Norton Gallery and School of Art, West Palm Beach, FL

Madigan, Susan, *Mem Faculty,* Hamline Univ, Saint Paul, MN

Madrigal, August, *Assoc Prof,* Univ Bridgeport, CT

Madsen, Mrs, *Asst Dir Summer School,* Kean College of New Jersey, Union

Maeda, Robert, *Mem Faculty,* Tufts Univ, Medford, MA

Maestas, Dr Sigfredo, *Dean Summer School,* New Mexico Highlands Univ, Las Vegas

Maffeo, Edward, *Asst Prof,* Univ New Haven, West Haven, CT

Magavern, Samuel D, *Pres,* Albright-Knox Art Gallery, Buffalo, NY

Magavern, William J, II, *Treas,* Albright-Knox Art Gallery, Buffalo, NY

Magee, Eileen, *Program Coordr,* Athenaeum of Philadelphia, PA

Magill, Betty, *Secy,* Ball State Univ Art Gallery, Muncie, IN

Magnan, Oscar G, *Dir Art Gallery & Chmn Art Dept,* Sain Peter's College, Jersey City, NJ

Magnanimi, Dr Giuseppina, *Dir,* Galleria Nazionale d'Arte Antica-Palazzo Barberini & Palazzo Corsini, Rome, Italy

Magnusson, Fil kan Thor, *Dir,* Thjodminjasafn, Reykjavik, Iceland

Magowan, Mrs Robert A, *VPres,* Society of the Four Arts, Palm Beach, FL

Magruder, Ralph, *Asst,* Texas A&I Univ, Kingsville

Mahdesian, Dr, *Dir Summer School,* St John's Univ, Jamaica, NY

Mahe, John, *Assoc Cur,* Historic New Orleans Collection, LA

Mahey, John A, *Dir,* Univ Rochester Mem Art Gallery, NY

Mahfouz, Nabil, *Libr Archaeologist,* Egyptian Museum, Cairo

Mahlmann, John J, *Exec Dir,* Nat Art Education Association, see National and Regional Organizations

Mahone, Michael, *Chmn,* Trinity College, Hartford, CT

Mahoney, Charles A, *Pres,* Boston Watercolor Society, Scituate, MA

Mahoney, Joella, *Assoc Prof,* La Verne College, CA

Mahoney, Michael, *Chmn Dept Fine Arts & In Charge,* Austin Arts Center, Trinity College, Hartford, CT

Mahoney, Raymond, *Supvr Public Library Prog,* Michigan Dept of Education State Library Services, Lansing

Mahoney, William J, *Chmn,* Department of Art and Education, Columbia Univ, New York, NY

Mahy, Gordon, *Assoc Prof,* Mars Hill College, NC

Maia e Castro, Catarina, *Cur,* Museu Nacional de Soares Dos Reis, Porto, Portugal

Maidment, Ian, *Cur Presentations,* Art Gallery of South Australia, Adelaide

Maidoff, Jules, *Dir & Dean Painting & Drawing,* Studio Art Centers International, Florence, Italy

Mail, Barbara, *Resident Artist,* Peters Valley Craftsmen, Layton, NJ

Mainstone, Mrs M, *Keeper Educ,* Victoria and Albert Museum, London, England

Maitland, Eileen, *Conservator,* Auckland City Art Gallery, New Zealand

Majeski, Thomas H, *Prof,* Univ Nebraska at Omaha

Majewski, Sister Margaret Mary, *Mem Faculty,* Edgewood College, Madison, WI

Major, Lillian, *Cur,* Columbus Chapel, Boal Mansion and Museum, Boalsburg, PA

Majut, Kevin, *Dir,* Univ Tennessee, Knoxville

Makow, Yoram, *Prof,* California State Polytechnic Univ, Pomona

Malcolm, Frances H, *Mgr,* Arts and Crafts Association, Winston-Salem, NC

Malgeri, Dina G, *Librn,* Malden Public Library, MA

Malin, Edward, *Instr,* Museum Art School, Portland, OR

Malinowski, Jerome, *Chmn,* Syracuse Univ, NY

Malke, Dr Lutz S, *Cur,* Stadelsches Kunstinstitut, Frankfurt Am Main, Germany

Malkin, Peter, *Cur,* Vancouver Art Gallery, BC

Mallekote, Mrs W N, *Admin,* Westfries Museum, Hoorn, Netherlands

Mallet, J V G, *Keeper Ceramics,* Victoria and Albert Museum, London, England

Mallia, Francis, S, *Dir,* Nat Museum, Valletta, Malta

Mallory, Clifford D, *Pres,* Mystic Seaport, CT

Mallory, Nina, *Prof,* State Univ New York at Stony Brook

Malm, Eric S, *Secy,* Brookgreen Gardens, Murrells Inlet, SC

Malmanger, Magne, *Keeper Paintings,* Nasjonalgalleriet, Oslo, Norway

Malmer, Brita, *Keeper,* Kungl Myntkabinettet Statens Museum of Mynt Medalj Och Penninghistoria, Stockholm, Sweden

Malmquist, A Keith, *Prof,* Bemidji State Univ, MN

Malone, Alzada, *Cur,* Presidential Museum, Odessa, TX

Malone, Delores, *Exec Secy Bd Trustees,* Fine Arts Museums of San Francisco, CA

Malone, Electra, *Vis Prof,* Northeast Technical Community College, Norfolk, NE

Malone, Lee, *Dir,* Museum of Fine Arts of St Petersburg, FL

Malone, Mrs Robert J, *Secy,* New York Historical Society, New York

Malone, Robert R, *Head Printmaking,* Southern Illinois Univ, Edwardsville

Maloney, Patricia, *Instr,* Washington and Jefferson College, Washington, PA

Maloney, Phyllis Church, *Cur,* Guild of Boston Artists, MA

Maloubier, Jacques, *Instr,* Propersi Galleries and School of Art, Greenwich, CT

Maloy, Laurence, *VPres,* American Crafts Council, see National and Regional Organizations

Mamlow, Lewis, *Pres,* Museum of Contemporary Art, Chicago, IL

Mancinelli, Fabrizio, *Cur for Medieval & Modern Art,* Monumenti Musei e Gallerie Pontificie, Vatican City, Italy

Mancusi-Ungaro, Carol, *Painting Conservator,* Intermuseum Conservation Association, see National and Regional Organizations

Mandel, Howard, *VPres,* Audubon Artists, see National and Regional Organizations

Mandle, Roger, *Assoc Dir,* Toledo Museum of Art, OH

Manetta, Edward J, *Chmn,* St John's Univ, Jamaica, NY

Mangulis, Ingrida, *Prof,* Salem State College, MA

Mangum, William, *Assoc Prof,* Salem Acad and College, Winston-Salem, NC

Manhart, Marcia, *Asst Dir,* Philbrook Art Center, Tulsa, OK

Manin, Dr V S, *Dir,* State Museum of Oriental Art, Moscow, USSR

Manly, Mrs Isaac V, *Pres,* North Carolina Art Society, Raleigh

Mann, Elaine E, *Dir,* Nat Museum of Racing, Saratoga Springs, NY

Mann, Jack, *Instr,* Wittenberg Univ, Springfield, OH

Mann, Linda K, *Dir,* J K Ralston Museum and Art Center, Sidney, MT

Mann, Rev Richard, *Mus Dir,* Cathedral Museum, New York, NY

Manna, Sister Mauro, *Dir Summer School,* College of Notre Dame of Maryland, Baltimore

Manners, L R, *Assoc Prof,* Jacksonville State Univ, AL

Manning, James, *Keeper of Conservation,* Plymouth City Museum and Art Gallery, England

Manning, Jo, *Mem Faculty,* Toronto School of Art, ON

Manning, John R, *Dir,* Munson-Williams-Proctor Inst, Utica, NY

Manning, Peter, *Dean,* Nova Scotia Technical College, Halifax

Manning, Robert Nickerson, *Chmn Film,* Pratt Inst School of Art & Design, Brooklyn, NY

Mannino, James, *Instr,* Mohawk Valley Community College, Utica, NY

Manns, Suzanne, *Instr,* School of Art, Museum of Fine Arts, Houston, TX

Manrique, Dr Julius C, *Dir Summer School,* Modesto Junior College, CA

Mansfield, Joehugh, *Pres,* Creek Council House and Museum, Okmulgee, OK

Mansfield, Patricia K, *Assoc Prof,* Univ Wisconsin, Madison

Manso, Leo, *Dir,* Provincetown Workshop, MA

Mantegna, Douglas, *Pres,* Ontario Crafts Council, Toronto

Mantel, Barbara F, *Asst to Dir,* Ohio Univ, Athens

Manusos, Mary, *Gallery Dir,* Seigfred Gallery, Ohio Univ, Athens

Manville, Reed, *Adminr,* Hudson River Museum, Yonkers, NY

Maortua, Jose A, *Prof,* Morehead State Univ, KY

Maradiaga, Ralph, *Co-Dir,* Galeria de la Raza, San Francisco, CA

Marandel, J Patrice, *Cur Earlier Painting & Sculpture & Classical Art,* Art Inst of Chicago, IL

Marangou, Lila, *Cur Greek-Roman Antiquities Dept & Prof,* Benaki Museum, Athens, Greece

Marantz, Kenneth A, *Chmn Dept Art Educ,* Ohio State Univ, Columbus

Marble, Fran, *Librn,* Warehouse Library, Allied Arts Council of the Yakima Valley, Yakima, WA

Marcellus, Robert, *Instr,* College of the Sequoias, Visalia, CA

March, Paula, *Registrar Legion of Honor,* Fine Arts Museums of San Francisco, CA

Marchant, Sylvia L, *Assoc Dir Educ,* Greenville County Museum of Art, SC

Marchese, Lamar, *Programming Coordr,* Clark County Library District Art Activities, Las Vegas, NV

Marconi, Nello, *Chief Exhib Design,* Nat Portrait Gallery, Washington, DC

Marcoux, Alice, *Head Dept Textile Design,* Rhode Island School of Design, Providence

Marcus, George, *Publ Ed,* Philadelphia Museum of Art, PA

Marcus, Peter, *Chairperson Two Dimensional Dept,* Washington Univ, Saint Louis, MO

Marcus, Richard, *Librn/Dir,* Spertus Museum of Judaica, Chicago, IL

Marcus, Stanley, *Chmn & Assoc Prof,* Univ Texas of Permian Basin, Odessa

Marcusen, Richard B, *Instr,* Yavapai College, Prescott, AZ

Marder, Mrs David, *Registrar,* Asheville Art Museum, NC

Marder, Dr Tad, *Mem Faculty,* Graduate Program in Art History, Rutgers, The State Univ New Jersey, New Brunswick

Marein, Shirley, *Assoc Prof,* New York Inst of Technology, Old Westbury,

Marek, Bernie, *Instr,* Colorado Women's College, Denver

Marforell, Antonio, *Prof,* Inst Puerto Rican Culture, San Juan

Margh, Bob, *Resident Artist,* Peters Valley Craftsmen, Layton, NJ

Margolis, Ann, *Pres,* League of New Hampshire Craftsmen, Concord

Marinho, Dr Gilberto, *VPres,* Museu de Arte Moderna Brazil, Rio de Janerio

Marion, Marjorie, *Chmn Div,* College of Saint Francis, Joliet, IL

Marion, Mrs Oliver, *Pres,* Gilbert Stuart Birthplace, Saunderstown, RI

Marioni, Tom, *Dir,* Acad of the Museum of Conceptual Art, San Francisco, CA

Maris, Arno, *Prof Art & Chmn Dept,* Westfield State College, MA

Maristany, Hiram S, *Dir,* El Museo del Barrio, New York, NY

Mark, Joseph, *Instr,* Williamsport Area Community College, PA

Markham, Nancy, *Cur Formal Educ,* Colorado Historical Society, Denver

Markle, Sam, *VPres,* Professional Art Dealers Association of Canada, see National Organizations in Canada

Markman, Sidney D, *Chmn & Prof Art Dept,* Duke Univ, Durham, NC

Markos, Kessela, *Head Mus Technician,* Addis Ababa Univ Museum of the Inst of Ethiopian Studies, Ethiopia

Markrich, Lilo, *Museum Shop Mgr,* Textile Museum, Washington, DC

Marks, Arthur S, *Dir Summer School,* Univ North Carolina at Chapel Hill

Marks, Paul G, *Pres Bd Trustees,* Danforth Museum, Framingham, MA

Marks, Robert C, *Dean,* Harrington Inst of Interior Design, Chicago, IL

Markson, Eileen, *Head,* Bryn Mawr College, PA

Matranga, Frank P, *Assoc Prof,* Los Angeles Harbor College, Wilmington, CA

Matschke, Donna, *Pres,* Alaska Association for the Arts, Fairbanks

Matson, Judy, *Registrar,* Hudson River Museum, Yonkers, NY

Matsumoto, Moritaka, *Asst Prof,* Univ British Columbia, Vancouver

Mattar, John, *Instr,* Southampton Art School, ON

Matter, Mercedes, *Dean,* New York Studio School of Drawing, Painting and Sculpture, New York

Matthews, Ann M, *Dir,* Tallahassee Junior Museum, FL

Matthews, Mrs Flagler, *Pres & Trustee,* Henry Morrison Flagler Museum, Palm Beach, FL

Matthews, Harriett, *Assoc Prof,* Colby College, Waterville, ME

Matthews, J Eugene, *Chmn Bd Dir,* Sumter Gallery of Art, SC

Matthews, Molly, *Secy,* Univ New Orleans Fine Arts Gallery, LA

Matthews, Mrs Nick S, *VPres Div & Exhibit Chmn,* Council of Ozark Artists and Craftsmen, Springdale, AR

Matthias, Susan M, *Asst Prof,* Indiana Univ Southeast, New Albany

Mattson, Robert, *Head Dept,* Willmar Community College, MN

Mattusch, Carol C, *Asst Prof,* George Mason Univ, Fairfax, VA

Matus, Theodore P, *Asst Prof,* Western Carolina Univ, Cullowhee, NC

Matusiewicz, Dan, *Assoc Dir,* Mississippi Art Association, Jackson

Mauck, Marchita, *Asst Prof,* Louisiana State Univ, Baton Rouge

Maull, Paul, *Exhib Specialist,* Bower's Museum, Santa Ana, CA

Mauner, George, *Prof,* Pennsylvania State Univ, University Park

Mauran, Duncan Hunter, *Pres,* Rhode Island Historical Society, Providence

Mauren, Paul, *Mem Faculty,* College of St Rose, Albany, NY

Maurer, Evan, *Cur Primitive Art,* Art Inst of Chicago, IL

Maurer, Helen B, *Pres,* Arts Council of the Mid-Columbia Region, Richland, WA

Maurice, Alfred, *Acting Dean,* Univ Illinois, Chicago Circle

Maurice, Dr K, *Cur Clocks,* Bayerisches Nationalmuseum, Munich, Germany

Mauriello, Barbara, *Art Asst,* Junior Museum, Newark Museum, NJ

Mauros, Donald O, *Second VPres,* Artist-Craftsmen of New York, NY

Mauthe, Ernest, *Dir,* Mercyhurst College, Erie, PA

Maveety, Dr Patrick, *Dir Oriental Art,* Stanford Univ Museum of Art, CA

Maver, Mrs Quentin, *Chmn,* Spooner House, Mount Holyoke College Art Museum, South Hadley, MA

Mavigliano, George, *Chmn Art History,* Southern Illinois Univ, Carbondale

Mavroudis, Demetrios, *Assoc Prof,* Univ Richmond, VA

Mawn, Peter R, *Cur,* Museum of Art of Ogunquit, ME

Mawson, Robert, *Asst Adminr,* Decatur House; *Asst Adminr,* Woodrow Wilson House, Washington, DC

Maxwell, Allan, *Asst Prof,* Wilkes College, Wilkes-Barre, PA

Maxwell, Debra, *Secy,* Portage and District Arts Council, Portage La Prairie, MB

Maxwell, Derrill M, *Chmn,* West Georgia College, Carrollton

Maxwell, George, *Exhib Chmn,* San Angelo Art Club, TX

Maxwell, Lil, *VPres,* Mystic Art Association, CT

Maxwell, Dr William, *Mem Faculty,* College of New Rochelle, NY

May, A Hyatt, *Pres,* Hispanic Society of America, New York, NY

May, Florence L, *Cur Textiles,* Hispanic Society of America, New York, NY

May, James M, *Asst Prof,* Kearney State College, NE

May, Juanita, *Dir School,* Metropolitan Museum and Art Centers, Coral Gables, FL

Mayall, Myrtle, *Secy,* West Vancouver Visual Arts Society, BC

Mayer, Bena F, *VPres & Secy,* Artists Technical Inst, New York, NY

Mayer, Grace M, *Treas,* Print Council of America, see National and Regional Organizations

Mayer, Herbert, *Dir,* Mayer School of Fashion Design, New York, NY

Mayer, Jessie Hull, *Secy,* Lyme Art Association, Old Lyme, CT

Mayer, Joseph, *Assoc Prof,* Prince George's Community College, Largo, MD

Mayer, Joyce, *Exec Secy,* Buffalo Bill Mem Association, Cody, WY

Mayer, Martin, *Cur,* Suermondt-Ludwig-Museum der Stadt Aachen, Germany

Mayer, Melinda M, *Librn,* Art Museum of South Texas, Corpus Christi

Mayer, Ralph, *Dir,* Artists Technical Inst, New York, NY

Mayes, Steven L, *Head Dept,* West Texas State Univ, Canyon

Mayher, John, *Pres,* Litchfield Historical Society, CT

Mayhew, Dr Edgar deN, *Dir,* Lyman Allyn Museum, New London, CT; *Prof,* Connecticut College, New London

Maylone, R Russell, *Cur Special Coll,* Northwestern Univ Library Art Collection, Evanston, IL

Maynard, Gladys, *Instr,* Chamberlayne Junior College, Boston, MA

Maynard, John, *Exhib Officer,* Auckland City Art Gallery, New Zealand

Maynard, William, *Chmn Fine Arts,* New England School of Art and Design, Boston, MA

Mayne, John, *Asst Prof,* Nicholls State Univ, Thibodaux, LA

Maynor, Dr W, *Dir Summer School,* North Carolina Central Univ, Durham

Mayo, Edward, *Registrar,* Museum of Fine Arts, Houston, TX

Mayo, James E, *Supvry Exhib Specialist,* Anacostia Neighborhood Museum, Washington, DC

Mayo, Noel, *Dept Chmn & Special Adj Prof,* Philadelphia College of Art, PA

Mayor, A Hyatt, *First VPres,* Brookgreen Gardens, Murrells Inlet, SC

Mayor, Robin C, *Prin,* Vancouver School of Art, BC

Mays, John, *Dir,* Nightingale Arts Association, Toronto, ON

Mays, Louise, *Treas,* Tennessee Valley Art Center, Tuscumbia, AL

Maytham, Thomas N, *Dir,* Denver Art Museum, CO

Maza, Herbert, *Pres,* Inst for American Universities, Aix-en-Provence, France

Maze, Clarence Jr, *Pres,* Richard Bland College, Petersburg, VA

Mazeika, George, *Registrar,* William Benton Museum of Art, Storrs, CT

Mazmanian, Arthur B, *Asst Prof,* Framingham State College, MA

Mazonowicz, Douglas, *Dir,* Gallery of Prehistoric Paintings, New York, NY

Mazur, Mrs Alexander, *Pres,* Bridgeport Art League, CT

Mazur, Robert, *Dir Grad Studies,* Bowling Green State Univ, OH

Mazzola, John W, *Managing Dir,* Lincoln Center for the Performing Arts, New York, NY

Mead, John J, *Exec Dir,* American Society of Interior Designers, see National and Regional Organizations

Mead, Katherine H, *Cur Coll,* Santa Barbara Museum of Art, CA

Meadows, Elinor, *Instr,* San Diego Mesa College, CA

Meadows, Mrs Sammie D, *Dir,* Lewis Cooper Junior Mem Library and Arts Center, Opelika, AL

Meagher, Richard, *Dean Summer School,* Fashion Inst of Technology, New York, NY

Meakin, Alexander C, *Pres,* Great Lakes Historical Society, Vermilion, OH

Mears, Mary Ann E, *Asst Prof,* Community College of Baltimore, MD

Meas, Giles W, *Dir,* Natural History Museum of Los Angeles County, CA

Meatyard, Christopher, *Preparator,* Univ Kentucky Art Museum, Lexington

Medaglia, Carlyn, *Dir,* Rustic Canyon Arts & Crafts Center, Santa Monica, CA

Medley, Stephen, *Librn,* Yosemite Museum Collections, CA

Medlock, Ruby, *Prof Head Art Dept,* Asbury College, Wilmore, KY

Meehan, William, *Chmn Art Dept,* DePauw Univ, Greencastle, IN

Meek, William E, *Instr,* Texas Woman's Univ, Denton

Meeker, Barbara, *Mem Faculty,* Purdue Univ, Calumet Campus, Hammond, IN

Meeker, David Olan, Jr, *Exec VPres,* American Inst of Architects, see National and Regional Organizations

Mees, Mary Ann, *Librn,* Portland Art Association, OR

Megee, Lucile K, *Pres,* Rehoboth Art League, Rehoboth Beach, DE

Meglin, Joellen, *Mem Faculty,* Creighton Univ, Omaha

McGonagle, William A, *Dir,* Rockford Art Association, IL

Meier, Nikolaus, *Librn,* Offentliche Kunstsammlung Kunstmuseum Basel, Switzerland

Meier-Arendt, Dr Walter, *Cur Prehistory,* Romisch-Germanisches Museum, Museen der Stadt Koln, Germany

Meigham, Melissa, *Registrar,* The American Federation of Arts, see National and Regional Organizations

Meilhac, Pierre, *Secy,* Union Centrale des Arts Decoratifs Paris, France

Meinhardt, Nevin, *Asst Chmn Advertising Design,* Art Inst of Fort Lauderdale, FL

Meinig, Laurel, *Dir,* Yuma Art Center, AZ

Meir, Norman, *Mem Faculty,* Ray-Vogue Schools, Chicago, IL

Meister, Mark J, *Dir,* Museum of Arts and History, Port Huron, MI

Meister, Peter Wilhelm, *Dir,* Museum fur Kunstandwerk, Frankfurt, Germany

Mejer, Robert Lee, *Gallery Dir,* Quincy College Art Gallery, IL

Melander, Dr Torben, *Cur Archaeology,* Thorvaldsen Museum, Copenhagen, Denmark

Melberg, Jerald, *Cur Exhib,* Mint Museum of Art, Charlotte, NC

Melhorn, Lise, *Educ & Exten Officer,* Laurentian Univ Museum and Arts Centre, Sudbury, ON

Melim, Susan, *Asst Cur Exhib,* Fine Arts Museums of San Francisco, CA

Meline, Elva, *Pres,* San Fernando Valley Historical Society, Mission Hills, CA

Mellen, Frances P, *Secy & Cur,* Concord Art Association, MA

Mellinger, Sydney S, *Acting Librn,* Lake Forest Library, IL

Mellish, Raoul, *Dir,* Queensland Art Gallery, Brisbane, Australia

Mellon, Paul, *Pres,* Nat Gallery of Art, Washington, DC

Meloy, Margaret, *Mem Faculty,* Louisville School of Art, Anchorage, KY

Melrose, Alice G, *Dir,* Nat Acad of Design & School of Fine Arts, New York, NY

Melton, Terry, *VPres,* Western Association of Art Museums, see National and Regional Organizations

Melton, Willard, *Instr,* Sacramento City College, CA

Menaro, Glenn, *Dir Student Union,* Univ Southwestern Louisiana Union Art Gallery, Lafayette

Menase, Ljerka, *Cur Documentation,* Moderna Galerija, Ljubljana, Yugoslavia

Mendenhall, Bethany, *Assoc Librn,* J Paul Getty Museum, Malibu, CA

Mendes, Marcia, *Registrar,* Fort Worth Art Museum, TX

Méndez, Enrique Morales, *Warder,* Museo de Arte Jose Luis Bello y Gonzalez, Puebla, Mexico

Mendla, Joseph, *Chmn Found Dept,* Milwaukee School of the Arts, WI

Mendlow, Philip, *Mem Faculty,* Ivy School of Professional Art, Pittsburgh, PA

Mendro, Donna, *Recordings Librn,* Dallas Public Library, TX

Menear, William H, *Dir,* Hewlett-Woodmere Public Library, Hewlett, NY

Menger, Linda, *Lectr,* Delta College, University Center, MI

Menges, Edward, *Prof,* Saint Louis Community College at Florissant Valley, Ferguson, MO

Menke, Henry, *VChairperson,* Eureka Springs Guild of Artists and Crafts People, AR

Mennen, Muriel, *Treas,* Wisconsin Painters and Sculptors, Milwaukee

Menocal, Narciso, *Asst Prof,* Univ Wisconsin, Madison

Mentz, Sylvia, *Registrar,* Univ Alberta Art Gallery and Museum, Edmonton

Mercader, Yolanda, *Librn,* Museo Nacional de Antropologia, Mexico City, Mexico

Mercer, Bonnie, *Instr,* Northeast Technical Community College, Norfolk, NE

Mercer, Steven, *Exhib & Graphic Designer,* Illinois State Museum of Natural History and Art, Springfield

Meredith, Georgette, *Dir,* World Heritage Museum, Univ Illinois at Urbana-Champaign, Urbana

Meredith, Kenneth, *Asst Prof,* Central Missouri State Univ, Warrensburg

Merino-Antolinez, Fr Jesus M, *Dir,* Univ Santo Tomas Museum of Arts and Sciences, Manila, Philippines

Merkel, Dr Robert, *Pres,* Monroe City-County Fine Arts Council, MI

Merley, Bruce, *Asst to Dir,* Fine Arts Museums of San Francisco, CA

Merrell, C Phelps, *Supt,* Norton Gallery and School of Art, West Palm Beach, FL

Merrick, Gail, *Mem Faculty,* Burnby School of Professional Art, Seattle, WA

Merrick, Robert S, *Trustee,* Merrick Art Gallery, New Brighton, PA

Merrill, Nancy O, *Cur Glass,* Chrysler Museum at Norfolk, VA

Merrill, Pam, *Exhibit Coordr,* Palos Verdes Art Center, Rancho Palos Verdes, CA

Merriman, Mira P, *Chmn Art History,* Wichita State Univ, KS

Merritt, Francis S, *Dir,* Haystack Mountain School of Crafts Gallery, Deer Isle, ME

Merritt, Helen, *Asst Chairperson Dept,* Northern Illinois Univ, DeKalb

Merwin, Mary M, *Dir,* Massillon Museum, OH

Merwin, Nancy, *Secy,* McLean County Art Association, Bloomington, IL

Meseguer, Ines B, *Secy,* Nat Superior School of Fine Arts Etnesto Carcova, Buenos Aires, Argentina

Meshorer, Dr Yaakov, *Chief Cur,* Israel Museum, Jerusalem

Messer, Thomas M, *Dir,* Solomon R Guggenheim Museum, New York, NY

Messersmith, Fred, *Dir Art Gallery & Head Dept,* Stetson Univ, Deland, FL

Mester, Clark, Jr, *Asst Prof,* Bowie State College, MD

Mesterton, Ingrid, *Asst Cur Graphics & Drawings,* Goteborgs Konstmuseum, Sweden

Meszaros, Imre, *Librn,* Washington Univ Gallery of Art, St Louis, MO

Metcalf, C D, *Historic Sites Dir,* Oklahoma Historical Society, Oklahoma City

Metcalf, Mrs Charles W, *Chmn,* Orlando Brown House, Liberty Hall Museum, Frankfort, KY

Metcalf, Kent, *Librn,* Louisville School of Art, Anchorage, KY

Metsopoulos, Marian J, *Exec Dir,* Foothills Art Center, Golden, CO

Metyko, Michael J, *Asst to Dir,* Univ Houston Gallery, TX

Metz, Ted, *Dir,* Univ Montevallo Gallery, AL

Metzker, Dale, *Asst Prof,* Williamsport Area Community College, PA

Mew, T J, *Chmn & Dir Summer School,* Berry College, Mount Berry, GA

Meyer, Barbara, *Cur Educ,* Tyler Museum of Art, TX

Meyer, Barbara, *Chmn & Assoc Prof,* Mary Washington College, Fredericksburg, VA

Meyer, Bernice L, *Adminr,* Univ Rochester Mem Art Gallery, NY

Meyer, Charles E, *Prof,* Western Michigan Univ, Kalamazoo

Meyer, David, *Instr,* Eastern Arizona College, Thatcher

Meyer, Dick, *Chmn Educ,* East Texas State Univ, Commerce

Meyer, Dr Franz, *Dir,* Offentlche Kunstsammlung Kunstmuseum Basel, Switzerland

Meyer, Judy, *Supvr,* Kent State Univ, Architecture/Urban Studies Library, OH

Meyer, Meir, *Dir Public Affairs,* Israel Museum, Jerusalem

Meyer, Roberta, *Mem Faculty,* Madison Area Technical College, WI

Meyer, Ruth K, *Cur,* Contemporary Arts Center, Cincinnati, OH

Meyers, Dale, *Pres,* Allied Artists of America, see National and Regional Organizations

Meyers, Donald E, *Chmn,* Mesa College, Grand Junction, CO

Meyers, Emily *Educ Asst,* Mohawk Valley Museum, Utica, NY

Meyers, John, *Dir Summer School,* Wilkes College, Wilkes-Barre, PA

Michael, John, *Prof,* Miami Univ, Oxford, OH

Michael, Simon, *Head Dept,* Simon Michael School of Fine Arts, Rockport, TX

Michael, Mrs W R, *VPres,* Art Association of Newport, RI

Michala, Mollie, *Mem Faculty,* Emory Univ, Atlanta, GA

Michalove, Carla M, *Cur Educ,* Hunter Museum of Art, Chattanooga, TN

Michalowski, Dr Kazimierz, *VDir,* Muzeum Narodowe, Warsaw, Poland

Michaud, Beverly, *Office Mgr,* Palo Alto Cultural Center, CA

Michaux, Henry, *Prof,* North Carolina Central Univ, Durham

Michel, Delbert, *Assoc Prof,* Hope College, Holland, MI

Micheli, Julio, *Head Dept & Coordr,* Catholic Univ Puerto Rico, Ponce

Michelsen, P, *Keeper Open Air Museum at Sorgenfri,* Nat Museum, Copenhagen, Denmark

Michno, Dorothy, *Editor,* Polish Museum of America, Chicago, IL

Mickens, Charles, *Exhib Mgr,* Anacostia Neighborhood Museum, Washington, DC

Midani, Akram, *Dean,* Carnegie-Mellon Univ, Pittsburgh, PA

Middaugh, Robert, *Cur,* First National Bank of Chicago, see Corporate Art Holdings

Middlebrook, Mrs Robert, *VPres,* Washington Depot Art Association, CT

Middlestadt, Larry, *Mem Faculty,* Toronto School of Art, ON

Middleton, Mrs Edwin, *VPres,* Louisville School of Art Gallery, Anchorage KY

Middleton, Janet, *Librn,* Tasmanian Museum and Art Gallery, Hobart, Australia

Miele, John, *Curriculum Chmn Fashion Illustration,* Art Inst of Fort Lauderdale, FL

Miersen, Emil, *Admin Coordr,* Whatcom Museum of History and Art, Bellingham, WA

Miezajs, Dainis, *Vis Prof,* Toronto School of Art, ON

Mihailovic, Olivera, *Cur,* Bergman Gallery, Univ Chicago, IL

Mihal, Milan, *Assoc Prof,* Vanderbilt Univ, Nashville, TN

Mike, Tyne T, *Head Dept,* Itasca Community College, Grand Rapids, MN

Miki, Tamon, *Chief Cur Fine Art,* Tokyo Kokuritsu Kindai Bijutsukan, Japan

Milam, Evelyn, *Pres,* Cottey College, Nevada, MO

Milan, George, *Dir,* Bureau of Music, City of Los Angeles, Municipal Arts Dept, CA

Milbank, W H, *Dir,* Sarjeant Gallery, Wanganui, New Zealand

Milbrath, Harold A, *Head Dept of Graphic & Applied Arts,* Milwaukee Area Technical College, WI

Milburn, Richard, *Head Libr Public Serv,* Ontario College of Art Gallery Seventy Six, Toronto

Miles, W C, *Prof,* New Mexico State Univ, Las Cruces

Miley, Leslie, *Prof & Chmn Art Dept,* Univ Evansville, IN

Miley, Mimi, *Cur Educ,* Allentown Art Museum, PA

Milford, Howard, *Treas,* Stan Hywet Hall Found, Akron, OH

Milhau, Denis, *Cur,* Musee des Augustins, Toulouse, France

Milhoan, Randy, *Dir,* Colorado Mountain College, Vail

Milkovich, Michael, *Dir,* Dixon Gallery and Gardens, Memphis, TN

Millar, C Blakeway, *VPres,* Royal Canadian Acad of Arts, see National Organizations in Canada

Millar, Dr Dan, *Dir Summer School,* Central Michigan Univ, Mount Pleasant

Millar, David P, *Asst Dir,* Art Gallery of New South Wales, Sydney, Australia

Millard, Charles, *Chief Cur,* Hirshhorn Museum and Sculpture Garden, Washington, DC

Millard, Mark J, *Treas,* Parrish Art Museum, Southampton, NY

Millen, Amy, *VPres,* Federal Design Council, Washington, DC

Miller, Mrs A, *Vol Librn,* Dade County Art Museum, Miami, FL

Miller, Alan C, *Librn,* Univ Oregon School of Architecture and Allied Arts Library, Eugene

Miller, Archibald M, *Chmn,* Univ Rochester, NY

Miller, Arthur, *Instr,* Lower Columbia College, Longview, WA

Miller, Benjamin T, *Mem Faculty,* Indiana Univ Pennsylvania, Indiana, PA

Miller, Constance, *Secy,* Pioneer Museum and Haggin Galleries, Stockton, CA

Miller, Dan, *Instr,* Wayne Art Center, PA

Miller, Daniel M, *Asst Cur,* Univ Western Ontario, London

Miller David, *Dir,* Hathorn Gallery, Skidmore College, Saratoga Springs, NY

Miller, Don, *Asst Prof,* Univ Wisconsin-River Falls

Miller, Donald, *Mem Jury,* Society of Animal Artists, see National and Regional Organizations

Miller, Donna, *Instr,* Weatherford College, TX

Miller, Douglas, *Gallery Asst,* Chautauqua Gallery of Art, NY

Miller, Elizabeth, *Coordr Drawing & Painting,* Iowa State Univ, Ames

Miller, Emil, *Prof,* Glendale College, CA

Miller, Ewing H, *Secy Bd Mgrs,* Sheldon Swope Art Gallery, Terre Haute, IN

Miller, G Lynette, *Registrar,* Heye Found, New York, NY

Miller, Mrs Gavin, *Chmn Bd Trustees,* Junior Arts Center, Los Angeles, CA

Miller, Glen *Mem Faculty,* College of Marin, Kentfield, CA

Miller, Helen, *Coordr,* Essex Art Association, CT

Miller, Hester, *Head Fine Arts Dept,* Albuquerque Public Library, NM

Miller, J Brough, *Prof,* Texas Woman's Univ, Denton

Miller, Jean J, *Art Librn,* Anne Bunce Library, Hartford Art School, West Hartford, CT

Miller, Joan Vita, *Dir,* C W Post Center of Long Island Univ, Greenvale, NY

Miller, Mrs John C, *Corresp Secy,* Historical Society of Early American Decoration, Cooperstown, NY

Miller, Kate, *Registrar,* Univ Maryland, College Park

Miller, Kenneth L, *Dir,* Nevada Art Gallery, Reno

Miller, Kenneth R, *Exec VPres & Librn,* Mitchell Museum, Mount Vernon, IL

Miller, Laurence, *Dir,* Laguna Gloria Art Museum, Austin, TX

Miller, Lawrence K, *Pres,* Shaker Community, Pittsfield, MA

Miller, Lee Anne, *Chmn,* Univ Missouri-Kansas City

Miller, LeNore D, *Cur,* George Washington Univ, Washington, DC

Miller, Margaret, *Research & Development Coordr,* Univ South Florida/Galleries Program, Tampa

Miller, Margaret, *Asst Prof,* Colby College, Waterville, ME

Miller, Marion G, *Asst Prof,* Mount Holyoke College, South Hadley, MA

Miller, Marjorie, *Art Reference Librn,* Fashion Inst of Technology, New York, NY

Miller, Mark, *Dir/Adv,* Arizona State Univ Mem Union Gallery, Tempe

Miller, Marlan, *Mem Faculty,* Mesa Community College, AZ

Miller, Marlene, *Mem Faculty,* Bucks County Community College, Newtown, PA

Miller, Mary Richardson, *Instr,* Wayne Art Center, PA

Miller, Norwood, *Cur Educ,* Historical Society of York County, PA

Miller, Philip E, *Dir,* Hammond Museum, Gloucester, MA

Miller, Mrs R C, *Chmn Comt,* Oglebay Inst Mansion Museum, Wheeling, WV

Miller, Robert, *Mem Faculty,* Ray-Vogue Schools, Chicago, IL

Miller, Robert J, *Dean,* St Mary's College, Raleigh, NC

Miller, J Robert, *Lectr,* McMurry College, Abilene, TX

Miller, Ruane Helen, *Asst Prof,* Lycoming College, Williamsport, PA

Miller, Ruby, *Secy,* Mitchell Museum, Mount Vernon, IL

Miller, Samuel C, *Dir,* Newark Museum, NJ

Miller, William B, *Prof,* Colby College, Waterville, ME

Miller, William B, *Mgr & Librn,* Presbyterian Historical Society, Philadelphia, PA

Millet, N B, *Cur Egyptian Dept,* Royal Ontario Museum, Toronto

Millett, John I, *Pres,* Rensselaer Newman Found Chapel and Cultural Center, Troy, NY

Milley, John C, *Chief Cur,* Independence Nat Historical Park, Philadelphia, PA

Millham, Mrs H C, *VPres Admin,* Community Arts Council of Vancouver, BC

Millis, Judith A, *Head Fiber & Fabrics,* Southern Illinois Univ, Edwardsville

Millon, Henry A, *Dir,* American Acad in Rome, New York, NY

Mills, Charles, *Asst Dir Educ,* Fine Arts Museums of San Francisco, CA

Mills, Cyril, *Pres,* Palette and Chisel Academy of Fine Arts, Chicago, IL

Mills, David, *Asst Dir,* Newfoundland Museum, Saint Johns

Mills, Ernest Andrew, *Assoc Art Educ,* State Education Dept, Albany, NY

Mills, Fred V, *Chmn Art Dept & Dir Summer School,* Illinois State Univ, Normal

Mills, James, *Assoc Prof,* East Tennessee State Univ, Johnson City

Mills, Lawrence, *Prof Art & Head Dept,* Central College, Pella, IA

Mills, Margaret M, *Exec Dir,* American Acad and Institute of Arts and Letters, see National and Regional Organizations

Mills, Paul C, *Dir,* Santa Barbara Museum of Art, CA

Mills, Peter, *Dir Evening & Summer School,* Philadelphia College of Textiles and Science, PA

Millspaugh, Mrs Martin L, *VPres,* Peale Museum, Baltimore, MD

Millstein, Barbara, *Assoc Cur Sculpture Garden,* Brooklyn Museum, NY

Milne, Audrey, *Cur,* York Institute Museum, Saco, ME

Milner, Sue, *Head Dept,* Eastern Wyoming College, Torrington

Milovich, Catherine, *VPres,* St Louis Artists Guild, MO

Milrad, Aaron M, *Admin VPres,* Professional Art Dealers Association of Canada, see National Organizations in Canada

Milrany, Donna J, *Dir Special Events,* Portland Center for the Visual Arts, OR

Milrod, Linda, *Cur Asst,* Queen's Univ Art Centre, Kingston, ON

Mims, Dr Crawford, *Dir Summer School,* Philander Smith College, Little Rock, AR

Mims, Hayden P, *Exec Dir,* Nat Council of Architectural Registration Boards, see National and Regional Organizations

Mims, Maurice, *Secy,* South Arkansas Arts Center, El Dorado

Mims, Thomas E, *Asst Prof,* Univ North Alabama, Florence

Mineko, U, *Rector & Prof,* Nikolaj Pavlovic Higher Inst Fine Arts, Sofia, Bulgaria

Minicki, Josephine, *Librn,* South African Nat Gallery, Cape Town

Mino, Dr Yutaka, *Cur Oriental Art,* Indianapolis Museum of Art, IN

Minot, Michael, *Instr,* Vancouver Community College, Langara Campus, BC

Minton, Robert, *Secy,* Concord Antiquarian Society Museum, MA

Mintz, Dr Donald, *Dean,* Montclair State College, NJ

Minutillo, Richard, *Cur,* Brockton Art Center, MA

Miodonska, Dr Barbara, *In Charge Polish Illuminated Manuscripts,* Muzeum Narodowe W Krakowie, Cracow, Poland

Miotke, Anne, *Mem Faculty & Supr Summer School,* Art Acad of Cincinnati, OH

Miranda, Gregorio Cordero, *Dir,* Museo Nacional de Arqueologia, La Paz, Bolivia

Mirelli, Jerry, *Mgr Data Processing,* Metropolitan Museum of Art, New York, NY

Misfeldt, Willare, *Head Art History,* Bowling Green State Univ, OH

Miss, Mary, *Slide Registry Comt Mem,* Women's Slide Registry, New York, NY

Mitcham, Fred, *Librn,* Dallas Museum of Fine Arts, TX

Mitchell, Alex F, *Chmn Dept & Summer School,* Lake Forest College, IL

Mitchell, Beresford, *Chmn Dept Commun & Design,* Ontario College of Art, Toronto

Mitchell, Charles, *Admin,* Favell Museum of Western Art & Indian Artifacts, Klamath Falls, OR

Mitchell, Mrs Charles, *Asst Admin,* Favell Museum of Western Art & Indian Artifacts, Klamath Falls, OR

Mitchell, Edith, *Treas,* Adirondack Lakes Center for the Arts, Blue Mountain Lake, NY

Mitchell, Ehrman B, Jr, *VPres,* American Inst of Architects, see National and Regional Organizations

Mitchell, Eugene W, *Asst Dir Admin,* Dallas Museum of Fine Arts, TX

Mitchell, J Stuart, *Treas,* Louisville School of Art Gallery, Anchorage

Mitchell, Kenneth Eugene, *Dept Head,* Colby Community College, KS

Mitchell, Lee, *Lectr,* Villa Maria College of Buffalo, NY

Mitchell, Morris, *Chmn Painting,* Ringling School of Art, Sarasota, FL

Mitchell, R E, *Assoc Prof,* Arkansas State Univ, State University

Mitchell, Richard, *Assoc Prof,* Youngstown State Univ, OH

Mitchell, Ramona, *Lectr,* Lake Forest College, IL

Mitchell, Vicki L, *Mem Faculty,* Colby Community College, KS

Mitchell, Mrs William, *Exec Secy,* Federated Arts Council of Richmond, VA

Mitsuda, Mary, *Asst Dir,* Contemporary Arts Center of Hawaii, Honolulu

Mittelberger, Ernest G, *Dir,* Wine Museum of San Francisco, CA

Mittelgluck, Eugene L, *Dir,* New Rochelle Public Library, NY

Mittman, Sima, *Asst Educ Dir,* 92nd Street YMHA-YWHA, New York, NY

Mixter, James M E, *Secy,* Cincinnati Inst of Fine Arts, OH

Miyazaki, Hiroshi, *Instr,* San Diego Mesa College, CA

Mizui, Yasuo, *Mem Faculty,* Sarah Lawrence College, Lacoste, France

Mladenka, Sister Dorcas, *Asst Prof,* Our Lady of the Lake Univ, San Antonio, TX

Mo, Charles, *Registrar,* New Orleans Museum of Art, LA

Moad, Dr John L, *Secy,* School of the Ozarks, Point Lookout, MO

Mobberley, David, *Dean Summer School,* Florida Southern College, Lakeland

Mocasanyi, Paul, *Dir Art Center,* New School for Social Research Art Center, New York, NY

Mochizuki, Tomie, *Librn,* Japan Society, New York, NY

Mocsanyi, Paul, *Dir,* Collectors Inst of the New School, New York, NY

Mode, Robert L, *Assoc Prof,* Vanderbilt Univ, Nashville, TN

Modeen, Mary K, *Mem Faculty,* Ottumwa Heights College, Ottumwa, IA

Model, Elisabeth, *Secy,* Federation of Modern Painters and Sculptors, see National and Regional Organizations

Moe, Richard, *Dir Summer School,* Pacific Lutheran Univ, Tacoma, WA

Moehring, Eugene P, *Cur Educ and Exhib,* Southern Illinois Univ Museum and Art Galleries, Carbondale

Moeller, Robert C, *Cur European Decorative Arts & Sculpture,* Museum of Fine Arts, Boston, MA

Moen, Mrs George J, *Dir,* Youth Cultural Center, Waco, TX

Moerman, I W L, *Cur History,* Stedelijk Museum de Lakenhal, Leyden, Netherlands

Moes, Robert, *Cur Oriental Art,* Brooklyn Museum, NY

Moeser, J, *Dean School of Fine Arts,* Univ Kansas, Lawrence

Moffatt, Fred, *Assoc Prof,* Univ Tennessee, Knoxville

Moffett, Kenworth, *Cur Contemporary Art,* Museum of Fine Arts, Boston, MA

Moffett, Kenworth W, *Prof,* Wellesley College, MA

Moffitt, Elizabeth, *Chmn & Prof,* Univ New Haven, West Haven, CT

Moffitt, John, *Vis Prof,* Florida State Univ, Tallahassee,

Moffitt, John, *Prof,* New Mexico State Univ, Las Cruces

Mohamed, John, *Mem Faculty,* Purdue Univ, Calumet Campus, Hammond, IN

Mohnke, Mary Sue, *Pub Information,* Chicago Architecture Found, IL

Mohsen, Mohammed Ahmed, *Sub-Dir,* Egyptian Museum, Cairo

Moindreau, Mme, *Asst,* Musee des Beaux-Arts, Orleans, France

Moisan, Dr Micheline, *Assoc Cur Dept Prints & Drawings,* Montreal Museum of Fine Arts, PQ

Mol, Janet M, *Mem Faculty,* Norwich Art School, CT

Molaug, Sven, *Dir,* Norsk Sjofartsmuseum, Oslo, Norway

Moldovan, George, *Dir Exhib,* Elizabeth Slocum Gallery & *Assoc Prof,* East Tennessee State Univ, Johnson City

Molen, Larry Ter, *VPres Develop & Public Relations,* Art Inst Chicago, IL

Molfino, Dr Alessandra Mottola, *Dir,* Museo Poldi Pezzoli, Milan, Italy

Molitor, Margaret, *Pres,* Edgecliff College Emery Gallery, Cincinnati, OH

Moll, Loren, *Dir Summer School,* Golden West College, Huntington Beach, CA

Mollema, Peter C, Jr, *Head of Technical Serv,* California State College Art Gallery Stanislaus, Turlock

Moller, Patricia Newton, *Dir,* Henry B Plant Museum, Tampa, FL

Molner, Frank, *Instr,* Santa Ana College, CA

Monaco, Theresa, *Chairperson Dept,* Emmanuel College, Boston, MA

Monaghan, Keith, *Prof,* Washington State Univ, Pullman

Monballieu, Dr A, *Asst Cur,* Koninklijk Museum Voor Schone Kunsten, Antwerp, Belgium

Mondrus, Martin, *Prof,* Glendale College, CA

Moneta, Leslie, *In Charge,* Park Houses, Philadelphia Museum of Art, PA

Monge, Federico Barreda Y, *Mem Faculty,* Univ Puerto Rico, Rio Piedras

Mongi, Ennaifer, *Dir,* Musee Nat du Bardo, Le Bardo, Tunisia

Monies, Leif, *Dir,* Graphic College of Denmark, Copenhagen

Monigle, Joseph P, *Deputy Dir,* Hagley Museum, Wilmington, DE

Moniz, Ray W, *Cur Design,* West Point Museum, NY

Monk, Lorraine, *Dir,* Nat Film Board Photo Gallery, Ottawa, ON

Monkhouse, Christopher, *Cur Decorative Arts,* Rhode Island School of Design Museum of Art, Providence

Monkhouse, Valerie, *Chief Libr Div,* Nat Museums of Canada, Ottawa, ON

Monkman, Betty C, *Registrar,* White House, Washington, DC

Monnier-Raball, Jacques, *Prin,* Lausanne College of Art and Design, Switzerland

Monoian, Anita, *Second VPres,* Allied Arts Council of the Yakima Valley, Yakima, WA

Monroe, Betty Iverson, *Assoc Prof,* Northwestern Univ, Evanston, IL

Monroe, Dan, *Dep Chief Cur,* Alaska State Museum, Juneau

Monroe, P Jensen, *Asst Dir Admin,* Rockwell-Corning Museum, NY

Monsma, Marvin, *Librn,* Calvin College Center Art Gallery, Grand Rapids, MI

Monson, Mrs Ed, *Recording Secy,* Sheyenne Valley Arts and Crafts Association, Fort Ransom, ND

Monson, James P, *Asst Prof,* College of the Holy Cross, Worcester, MA

Monson, Richard, *Assoc Prof,* Central Missouri State Univ, Warrensburg

Montague, Mrs Robert L, *VPres,* Northern Virginia Fine Arts Association, Alexandria

Montanino, Nelsine, *Coordr Young Designers-Competition,* W Braun Co Wolf & Mary Braun Fund, New York, NY

Montenero, Dr Giulio, *Dir,* Civico Museo Revoltella-Galleria D'Arte Moderna, Trieste, Italy

Montes, Amelia, *Secy,* Centro de Arte y Communicacion, Buenos Aires, Argentina

Montgomery, Cara, *Cur,* Norton Gallery and School of Art, West Palm Beach, FL

Montgomery, Colleen, *Registrar,* Univ Vermont, Burlington

Montgomery, Edward K, *Asst Prof,* Miami Univ, Oxford, OH

Montgomery, Jullike, *Asst Cur Graphics & Drawings,* Goteborgs Konstmuseum, Sweden

Montgomery, Katherine, *Instr,* Davidson County Community College, Lexington, NC

Montgomery, Robert P, *Head Dept & Prof,* John Jay College of Criminal Justice, New York, NY

Montmeat, Richard, *First VPres,* Everson Museum of Art, Syracuse, NY

Monton, Pat, *Instr,* West Shore Community College, Scottville, MI

Montplaisir, Isabelle, *Librn,* Musee D' Art Contemporain, Montreal, PQ

Montvel-Cohen, Thomas, *Museum Asst,* Beloit College Theodore Lyman Wright Art Center, WI

Montverde, Dr Mildred, *Assoc Prof,* Univ Southern Colorado, Belmont Campus, Pueblo

Moody, Barbara, *Mem Faculty,* Montserrat School of Visual Art, Beverly, MA

Moody, James W, Jr, *Dir,* Historic Pensacola Preservation Board, FL

Moody, Joe E, *VPres for Real Estate & Legal Services,* Nat Trust for Historic Preservation, Washington, DC

Moody, Margaret, *Registrar,* Shelburne Museum, VT

Moogk, Brig Gen Willis, *Dir,* Dundurn Castle, Hamilton, ON

Moon, Marc, *Instr,* Friends of the Arts and Sciences, Hilton Leech Studio, Sarasaota, FL

Moon, Warren, *Assoc Prof,* Univ Wisconsin, Madison

Moonelio, Judith, *Prof,* Rockford College, IL

Mooney, Sister Ann Austin, *Chmn & Assoc Prof,* College of Mount Saint Joseph, OH

Mooney, James E, *Dir,* Historical Society of Pennsylvania, Philadelphia

Moore, Alfred A, *Chmn,* Contemporary Arts Center, Cincinnati, OH

Moore, Mrs B H Rutledge, *VPres,* Carolina Art Association, Charleston, SC

Moore, Dr Barry E, *Cur International Coll Child Art,* Illinois State Univ, Normal

Moore, Bidez Embry, *Dir,* Creighton Univ Fine Arts Gallery, NE

Moore, Blanche, *Asst to Dir,* Print Club, Philadelphia, PA

Moore, Bobie, *Second VPres Shows,* Arizona Artist Guild, Phoenix

Moore, Charles, *Dir,* Merrick Art Gallery, New Brighton, PA

Moore,, Craig, *Prof,* Taylor Univ, Upland, IN

Moore, Dr Curtis, *Dir Summer School,* Rockford, IL

Moore, David, *Exhibit Designer,* Tennessee Botanical Gardens and Fine Arts Center, Nashville

Moore, Donald Everett, *Acting Chmn & Dir Summer School,* Mitchell Community College, Statesville, NC

Moore, Ethel, *Cur,* Univ Georgia Art Collection, Athens

Moore, Isobel, *Treas,* Prince Rupert Art Club, BC

Moore, Kathleen, *Asst to Art Librn,* Allen R Hite Art Inst, Univ Louisville, KY

Moore, Keiko, *Treas,* Society of Washington Printmakers, Washington, DC

Moore, L A, *Dir,* Plainfield Public Library, NJ

Moore, Lennis, *Asst Dir,* Sanford Museum and Planetarium, Cherokee, IA

Moore, M L, *Dir Found,* Univ Southwestern Louisiana Art Center, Lafayette

Moore, Michael G, *Assoc Prof,* Univ Maine at Portland-Gorham, Gorham

Moore, Russell, *Assoc Dir Library Serv,* Long Beach Public Library, CA

Moore, Russell J, *Dir,* Long Beach Museum of Art, CA

Moore, Stephen, *Dir & Cur,* San Jose State Univ, CA

Moore, Mrs Turner, *Secy,* Star-Spangled Flag House Association, Baltimore, MD

Moorhead, Richard, *VPres Bd Dir,* Plains Art Museum, Moorhead, MN

Moosleitner, Fritz, *Cur Prehistory,* Saltzburger Museum Carolino Augusteum, Austria

Mooz, Dr R Peter, *Dir,* Virginia Museum of Fine Arts, Richmond

Moppett, G, *Asst Cur,* Saskatoon Gallery and Conservatory Corp, SK

Moppett, Ronald, *Sr Cur,* Alberta College of Art Gallery, Calgary

Morales, Luis M Rodriquez, *Exec Dir,* Inst of Puerto Rican Culture, San Juan

Morales, Raymond, *Asst Prof,* Univ Utah, Salt Lake City

Moran, Diane, *Instr,* Sweet Briar College, VA

Moran, Jose, *Mem Faculty,* California State College, San Bernardino

Moran, Lois, *Dir Nat Prog,* American Crafts Council, see National and Regional Organizations

Moran, Mary, *In Charge Newspaper Archives,* Oklahoma Historical Society, Oklahoma City

Moran, Ruth, *Corporate Secy/Treas Operation,* Minnesota Museum of Art Permanent Collection Gallery, St Paul

Moran, Walter J, *Assoc Prof,* Univ Tennessee, Knoxville

Morandi, Thomas, *Assoc Prof,* Eastern Oregon State College, La Grande

Morehart, Mary, *Assoc Prof,* Univ British Columbia, Vancouver

Morehead, Kathleen, *Chmn,* George Walter Vincent Smith Art Museum, Springfield, MA

Morehouse, Willam, *Prof,* California State College, Sonoma, Rohnert Park

Moreland, David, *Assoc Prof,* Univ Idaho, Moscow

Morello, Samuel E, *Chmn Dept & Summer School,* Charles Stewart Mott Community College, Flint, MI

Moreno, Laura, *Asst Dir,* El Museo del Barrio, New York, NY

Morey, Marjorie, *Cur Photographic Coll,* Amon Carter Museum of Western Art, Fort Worth, TX

Morford, Freida, *Adminr,* Louisiana State Museum, New Orleans

Morgan, Edward A, *Pres Bd Trustees,* Huntington Free Library and Reading Room, Bronx, New York

Morgan, Frank A, *Mgr,* Detroit Inst Arts Collections, MI

Morgan, H S, *Pres,* Pierpont Morgan Library, New York, NY

Morgan, Helen, *Assoc Prof,* South Dakota State Univ, Brookings

Morgan, Hugh, *Controller,* Milwaukee Art Center, WI

Morgan, Jane Hale, *Dir,* Detroit Public Library, MI

Morgan, Judith, *Head Librn,* Royal Ontario Museum, Toronto

Morgan, W P, *Dir & Cur,* Regina Public Library, SK

Morgan, Wayne J, *Gen Mgr,* Fort Ticonderoga Museum, Ticonderoga, NY

Morgan, William, *Assoc Prof,* Univ Wisconsin-Superior

Morgan, Wilma D, *Promotions,* Green Country Art Center, Tulsa, OK

Morgan-Curry, Ann, *Newsletter Editor,* Alaska Artists Guild, Anchorage

Morkholm, Otto, *Keeper Royal Coll Coins & Medals,* Nat Museum, Copenhagen, Denmark

Morley, John, *Dir,* Royal Pavilion Art Gallery and Museums, Brighton, England

Mornat, Mlle, *Cur,* Musee des Beaux-Arts de Dijon, France

Morningstar, William, *Instr,* Berea College, KY

Morrin, Peter, *Art Dir,* Vassar College Art Gallery, Poughkeepsie, NY

Morris, Mrs Ben, *Pres,* Ladies Library and Art Association, Independence, KS

Morris, Edward S, *Keeper Foreign Art,* Walker Art Gallery, Liverpool, England

Morris, Gerald, E, *Librn,* G W Blunt White Library, Mystic Seaport, CT

Morris, Gerald E, *Dir,* Maine Historical Society, Portland

Morris, Maj Henry, *Chmn Memorial Hall Comt,* Louisiana Historical Association, New Orleans

Morris, Jack A, Jr, *Exec Dir,* Greenville County Museum of Art, SC

Morris, Jerry W, *Asst Prof,* Miami Univ, Oxford, OH

Morris, Kay, *Registrar,* Colorado Springs Fine Arts Center, CO

Morris, Pat, *Publ,* Art Gallery of Windsor, ON

Morris, Phillip S, *Dean,* Memphis Academy of Arts, TN

Morris, Robert, *Assoc Prof,* Univ Bridgeport, CT

Morris, Robert C, *Asst Dir,* New Jersey Historical Society Museum, Newark

Morris, Terry, *Pres,* Allied Arts Council of Lethbridge, AB

Morrisey, Bob, *Prof,* Polk Community College, Winter Haven, FL

Morrisey, William D, *Cur Educ,* Loch Haven Art Center, Orlando, FL

Morrison, Art, *Asst Prof,* Coe College, Cedar Rapids, IA

Morrison, Barry, *Cur,* Banff Centre, AB

Morrison, Chris, *Librn,* Nat Endowment for the Arts, see National and Regional Organizations

Morrison, Phil, *Installations Dir,* California State Univ Fine Arts Gallery, Northridge

Morrison, Philip R, *Dir,* Hermitage Found Museum, Norfolk, VA

Morrison, Robert, *Assoc Prof Art & Chmn Dept,* Rocky Mountain College, Billings, MT

Morrison, W Stewart, *Pres,* Pensacola Museum of Art, FL

Morrissey, William T, *Dir Summer School,* Boston State College, MA

Morrisson, Stan, *Head Sign Painting,* Butera School of Art, Boston, MA

Morrow, John A, *Pres,* Arts and Letters Club of Toronto, ON

Morrow, Joseph, *Cur Material Culture,* Colorado Historical Society, Denver

Morrow, Lori, *Photography Librn,* Montana Historical Society, Helena

Morsberger, Philip, *Ruskin Master of Drawing,* Ruskin School of Drawings and Fine Arts, Univ of Oxford, England

Morsches, Richard, *VPres Operations,* Metropolitan Museum of Art, New York, NY

Morse, A Reynolds, *Pres,* Salvador Dali Museum, Beachwood, OH

Morse, Carl, *Dir Dept Publication,* Museum of Modern Art, New York, NY

Morse, Irma, *VPres,* Arts and Crafts Association of Meriden, CT

Mortensen, William, *Dir Continuing Educ Dept & Summer School,* Univ of Maine at Portland-Gorham, Gorham

Mortenson, K, *Mem Faculty,* Golden West College, Huntington Beach, CA

Mortimer, Ann, *Secy,* Canadian Crafts Council, see National Organizations of Canada

Morton, James, *Dean,* Cathedral Museum, New York, NY

Morton, Kathryn McCauley, *Mem Faculty,* Providence College, RI

Morton, Terry B, *VPres & Editor Preservation Press,* Nat Trust for Historic Preservation, Washington, DC

Morzinski, Jan, *Mem Faculty,* California State College, San Bernardino

Mosby, Mrs Davenport, Jr, *Pres,* Mississippi Art Association, Jackson

Mosby, Dewey F, *Cur European,* Detroit Inst of Arts Collections, MI

Mosel, Dr Christel, *Cur,* Kestner-Museum, Hanover, Germany

Moseley, Michael, *Instr,* Youngstown State Univ, OH

Moser, Joann, *Cur Coll,* Univ Iowa Museum of Art, Iowa City

Moser, Margaret, *Librn,* Lawrence Lee Pelleiter Library, Allegheny College Galleries, Meadville, PA

Moser, Rex, *Coordr of Educ Serv,* Los Angeles County Museum of Art, CA

Moses, Eva W, *Asst Librn,* R W Norton Art Gallery, Shreveport, LA

Moses, R B, *Chief Librn,* Oakville Public Library and Centennial Gallery, ON

Moskowitz, Marilyn, *Membership,* The Exhibitionists, Jamaica, NY

Mosley, Kim, *Asst Prof,* Saint Louis Community College at Florissant Valley, Ferguson, MO

Moss, Betty, *Secy,* Sculptor's Society of Canada, see National Organizations in Canada

Moss, Dorothy, *Cur,* Art Research Center, Kansas City, MO

Moss, Jacqueline, *Cur Educ & Pub Relations Coordr,* Aldrich Museum of Contemporary Art, Ridgefield, CT

Moss, Joe, *Coordr,* Univ Delaware, Newark

Moss, Michael E, *Cur Art,* West Point Museum, NY

Moss, Dr Roger W, Jr, *Secy & Librn,* Athenaeum of Philadelphia, PA

Motherwell, Robert, *Artist Trustee,* Visual Artists and Galleries Association, see National and Regional Organizations

Motta, Edson, *Dir & Prof,* Museu Nacional de Belas Artes, Rio de Janeiro, Brazil

Motto, Jerry, *Pres,* Las Vegas Art League, NV

Motz, Leslie, *Assoc Prof,* Indiana Univ-Purdue Univ, Fort Wayne, IN

Moubayed, Sylvia, *Exec Dir,* Providence Athenaeum, RI

Moulds, Mrs M, *Exec Secy,* Peace Region Arts Society, Spirit River, AB

Moulton, Alice, *Pres,* Concord Art Association, MA

Moulton, Rosalind, *Mem Faculty,* Stephens College, Columbia, MO

Moulton, Susan, *Dept Chmn,* Sonoma State College Art Gallery, Rohnert Park, CA

Mountjoy, Edie, *Secy,* Art Gallery of Brant, Brantford, ON

Mountsier, Silas R, III, *Second VPres,* Lotos Club, New York, NY

Mousel, Carol, *VPres,* Sierra Arts Found, Reno, NV

Mousseau, P J, *Assoc Prof,* Moorhead State Univ, MN

Moxey, Keith P F, *Head Dept Chmn & Assoc Prof,* Univ Virginia, Charlottesville

Moxham, Sidney, *Recording Secy,* Arizona Artist Guild, Phoenix

Moya, Samuel H, *Asst Prof,* Weber State College, Ogden, UT

Moyer, John R, *Admin,* Riverside Church Arts and Crafts, NY

Mozley, Anita, *Registrar & Cur of Photography,* Museum and Art Gallery, Stanford Univ, CA

Mruskovic, Dr Stefan, *Dir,* Slovenska Narodna Galereia, Bratislava, Czechoslovakia

Mucher, Jean, *Coordr,* Westchester Art Workshop, White Plains, NY

Mudge, Mrs Nina R, *Cur,* Sheldon Art Museum, Middlebury, VT

Muehlenbachs, Ms L, *Head of Extension,* Edmonton Art Gallery, AB

Mueller, Dorothy, *Librn,* Philadelphia Maritime Museum, PA

Mueller, Jean, *Mem & Vol Coordr,* Univ Utah Museum of Fine Arts, Salt Lake City

Mueller, Martha A, *Head Readers Serv,* New York State College of Ceramics at Alfred Univ

Muggeridge, Val, *Dir,* Arizona Watercolor Association, Phoenix

Mugnaini, Joseph, *Mem Faculty,* Univ Southern California, Idyllwild Campus

Muhlberger, Richard, *Dir,* George Walter Vincent Smith Art Museum, Springfield, MA

Muhlberger, Richard, *Chmn Educ,* Detroit Inst of Art Collections, MI

Muhlert, Jan K, *Dir,* Univ Iowa Museum of Art, Iowa City

Muhne, Eric J, *VPres,* Montana Historical Society, Helena

Muick, Paul C, *Prof,* Mary Washington College, Fredericksburg, VA

Mularz, Harriet, *Recording Secy,* Arizona Watercolor Association, Phoenix

Muldavin, Phyllis, *Asst Prof,* Los Angeles City College, CA

Mulford, Theodore, *VPres,* Roberson Center, Binghamton, NY

Mulgrew, John, *Prof,* Pace Univ, White Plains, NY

Mulheard, Sister Flora, *Asst Prof,* College Misericordia, Dallas, PA

Mullen, James, *Pres,* Cooperstown Art Association, NY

Mullen, James M, *Chmn Art Dept,* State Univ New York College At Oneonta

Mullen, Joseph, *Asst to Dir,* Shelburne Museum, VT

Mullen, Philip, *Instr,* Univ South Carolina, Columbia

Mullen, Ray, *Mem Faculty,* Kirkwood Community College, Cedar Rapids, IA

Mullen, Dr Robert J, *Assoc Prof,* Univ Texas at San Antonio

Mullen, Mrs William, *VPres,* Greater Fall River Art Association, MA

Muller, Mrs Frederick, Jr, *Second VPres,* New Orleans Museum of Art, LA

Muller, Jeffrey, *Mem Faculty,* Bowdoin College, Brunswick, ME

Muller, Joan L, *Dir,* School of the Arts Library, Virginia Commonwealth Univ, Richmond

Muller, Mary M, *Adminr,* Carolina Art Association, Charleston, SC

Muller, Norman E, *Conservator,* Worcester Art Museum, MA

Muller, Priscilla E, *Cur Mus Paintings & Metalwork,* Hispanic Society of America, New York, NY

Muller, Robert, *Chief Librn,* Queens College of City Univ of New York Art Collection, Flushing

Mullins, P Joseph, *Dir,* Parkersburg Art Center, WV

Mulloy, Betty, *Librn,* Lauren Rogers Library and Museum of Art, Laurel, MS

Mulloy, Virginia, *Asst Program Coordr,* Clark County Library District Art Activities, Las Vegas, NV

Mulvany, John, *Dir School Art,* Illinois Wesleyan Univ, Bloomington

Mumm, Dianne, *Educ Coordr,* Sioux City Art Center, IA

Munder, Charles, *Pres,* Key West Art and Historical Society, FL

Mundt, Alice, *Cur Japanese Prints,* Worcester Art Museum, MA

Mundy, Jane McKee, *Adminr,* Lynchburg Fine Arts Center, VA

Mundy, Naomi, *Exec Secy,* Stained Glass Association of America, see National and Regional Organizations

Munford, M B, *Asst Cur Decorative Arts,* Baltimore Museum of Art, MD

Munford, Robert, *Assoc Prof,* Southampton College of Long Island Univ, NY

Munhall, Edgar, *Cur,* Frick Collection, New York, NY

Munier, Joyce, *Registrar & Asst Cur,* Wenham Association and Museum, MA

Munns, Lynn, *Mem Faculty,* Casper College, WY

Muno, Rich, *Managing Dir,* Nat Cowboy Hall of Fame, Oklahoma City, OK

Munoz, Ramon, *Head of Means of Expression,* Javeriana Univ Faculty of Architecture and Design, Bogota, Colombia

Munoz, Theresa, *Prof,* Loyola Marymount Univ, Los Angeles, CA

Munro, Alan, *Chief Cur,* Alaska State Museum, Juneau

Munro, J S B, *Dir,* Hawkes Bay Art Gallery and Museum, Napier, New Zealand

Munro, Dr Peter, *Dir,* Kestner-Museum, Hanover, Germany

Munsch, Gene, *Conservator Furniture,* Fine Arts Museums of San Francisco, CA

Munson, Kathy, *Librn,* Canajoharie Library and Art Gallery, NY

Munson, Larom B, *Pres,* Munson Gallery, New Haven, CT

Murata, Hiroshi, *Asst Prof,* Trenton State College, NJ

Murchie, John, *Dir,* Nova Scotia College of Art and Design Gallery Library, Halifax

Murdock, Robert A, *Exec Dir,* Association for the Preservation of Virginia Antiquities, Richmond

Murdock, Robert M, *Cur Contemporary Art,* Dallas Museum of Fine Arts, TX

Murnaghan, Francis D, *Pres, Bd of Trustees,* Walters Art Gallery, Baltimore, MD

Muro, George, *Head,* Allan Hancock College, Santa Maria, CA

Murphy, Sister Catherine, *Assoc Prof,* Elizabeth Seton College, Yonkers, NY

Nelson, Christina H, *Registrar,* Society for the Preservation of New England Antiquities, Boston, MA

Nelson, David, *Asst Dir,* San Francisco Maritime Museum Association, CA

Nelson, Donald K, *Dir Libraries,* Brigham Young Univ, Provo, UT

Nelson, Gary, *Instr,* Burnley School of Professional Art, Seattle, WA

Nelson, Gunvor, *Chmn Filmmaking Dept,* San Francisco Art Inst, CA

Nelson, Harold, *Assoc Cur American & Contemporary Art & Registrar,* Univ Missouri Museum of Art and Archaeology, Columbia

Nelson, Harry B, *Cur,* Topeka Art Guild, KS

Nelson, Helen J, *Secy,* Hartland Art Council, MI

Nelson, James, *Librn & Cur Dept Ancient Art,* Fine Arts Museums of San Francisco, CA

Nelson, Jane, *Asst Prof Art & Chmn Dept & Dir Summer School,* Missouri Western State College, Saint Joseph

Nelson, Jean, *Lectr,* Notre Dame College, Manchester, NH

Nelson, Jeffrey, *Prof,* Butte Community College, Oroville, CA

Nelson, Jon, *Asst to Dir,* Univ Nebraska Art Gallery, Lincoln

Nelson, Kathy, *Educ Specialist,* Walnut Creek Civic Arts Gallery, CA

Nelson, Lee, *Librn,* Timothy Pickering Library, Wenham Historical Association and Museum, MA

Nelson, Lila, *Textiles Cur,* Vesterheim, Decorah, IA

Nelson, Linda, *Librn,* Museum of Fine Arts, Houston, TX

Nelson, Marion J, *Prof & Chmn Art Dept,* Univ Minnesota, Minneapolis

Nelson, Marion John, *Dir,* Vesterheim, Decorah, IA

Nelson, Mary Jean, *Coordr,* Colorado State Univ, Fort Collins

Nelson, Robert Clar, *Chmn,* College of Saint Catherine, Saint Paul, MN

Nelson, Ronald E, *Historian,* Bishop Hill Historic Site, IL

Nelson, William P, *Pres,* Hartland Art Council, MI

Nepean, Donald, *Chmn Creative Arts Div,* Spokane Falls Community College, Spokane, WA

Neprud, Mrs K, *Lectr,* California Lutheran College, Thousand Oaks

Nesbit, G H H, *Head,* Port Elizabeth School of Art, College for Advanced Technical Education, South Africa

Nesim, Lila Halim, *Librn,* Greco-Roman Museum, Alexandria, Egypt

Ness, Mrs Bjarne, *Exec Secy,* Sheyenne Valley Arts and Crafts Association, Fort Ransom, ND

Ness, Dr John H, Jr, *Secy,* United Methodist Church, Lake Junaluska, NC

Nestel, Jeanette, *Secy,* Society of Canadian Artists, see National Organizations in Canada

Nestler, Frank, *Treas,* Nat Watercolor Society, Los Angeles, CA

Netsky, Ronald, *Instr,* Nazareth College of Rochester, NY

Neufeld, Harold, *Treas Bd Dir,* Heritage Museum & Gallery, Leadville, CO

Neugebauer, Margot, *Chairperson Design,* Southeastern Massachusetts Univ, North Dartmouth

Neugebauer, Tom, *Resident Artist,* Peters Valley Craftsmen, Layton, NJ

Neumann, Lynn, *Adminr,* Library Association of La Jolla, CA

Neustadt, Karen, *Cur Educ,* Maitland Art Center & Research Studio, FL

Nevelson, Louise, *VPres,* Federation of Modern Painters and Sculptors, see National and Regional Organizations

Neville, Howard, *Pres,* Univ Maine at Orono

Neville, Mrs S, *VPres Performing Arts,* Community Arts Council of Vancouver, BC

Nevins, Kathy, *Dir Summer School,* Bethel College, Saint Paul, MN

New, George, *Chmn Theatre Arts,* Pratt Inst School of Art & Design, Brooklyn, NY

New, Lloyd, *Chmn,* Indian Arts and Crafts Board, Washington, DC

Newberry, James, *Vis Prof Photography,* Univ Texas at San Antonio

Newberry, John, *Deputy Head Painting,* Univ Oxford, England

Newbert, George W, *Cur Art,* Oakland Museum, CA

Newbold, Theodore T, *VPres,* Fairmount Park Art Association, Philadelphia, PA

Newby, Fletcher, *Deputy Dir,* Chief Plenty Coups Monument, Pryor, MT

Newell, Maurine F, *Registrar,* Brooks Mem Art Gallery, Memphis, TN

Newhouse, Mary, *Instr,* School for Creative Movement in the Arts, New York, NY

Newkirk, Chester H, *Dir,* Morris Museum of Arts and Sciences, Morristown, NJ

Newland, Randa A, *Asst Prof,* Univ Texas at San Antonio

Newman, Anthony, *VPres,* South Street Seaport Museum, New York, NY

Newman, Daniel, *Prof,* Mason Gross School of the Arts, Rutgers, The State Univ New Jersey, New Brunswick

Newman, Jerry, *Prof,* Lamar Univ, Beaumont, TX

Newman, Kirk, *Assoc Dir Educ & Assoc Dir Summer School,* Kalamazoo Inst of Arts, MI

Newman, R K, *Prof,* College of William and Mary, Williamsburg, VA

Newman, Robert C, *Librn,* Berkshire Athenaeum, Pittsfield, MA

Newman, Walter S, *Pres,* Fine Arts Museums of San Francisco, CA

Newmark, Marilyn, *Secy,* Nat Sculpture Society, see National and Regional Organizations

Newsome, Margaret, *Pres,* Santa Cruz Art League, CA

Newton, Douglas, *Chmn Primitive Art,* Metropolitan Museum of Art, New York, NY

Newton, Earle W, *Pres,* College of the Americas, Brookfield, VT

Newton, Harold, *Instr,* Williamsport Area Community College, PA

Newton, Michael, *Pres,* American Council for the Arts, see National and Regional Organizations

Ng, W Tin, *Coordr,* Alberta Art Found, Edmonton

Nibelink, Mrs E A, *Secy,* Historical Society of Early American Decoration, Cooperstown, NY

Nicdao, Diosdado, Jr, *Head Graphics Dept & Dir Summer School,* Philippine College of Arts and Trades, Manila

Nichelson, Jack C, *Assoc Prof,* Univ Florida, Gainesville

Nicholas, Donna, *Chmn Crafts,* Edinboro State College, PA

Nicholls, R, *Keeper Antiquities,* Fitzwilliam Museum, Univ Cambridge, England

Nichols, Adele, *Exhibit Chmn,* Kennebec Valley Art Association, Hallowell, ME

Nichols, Arthur Ray, *Corresp Secy,* Pen and Brush, New York, NY

Nichols, Bernice C, *Cur Peace Collection,* Swarthmore College, PA

Nichols, David, *Asst Prof,* Western Carolina Univ, Cullowhee, NC

Nichols, E E, *Chmn Painting,* Pan American Univ, Edinburg, TX

Nichols, Gerald, *Dept Chmn & Assoc Prof,* Philadelphia College of Art, PA

Nichols, Janie, *Registrar,* Mississippi Museum of Art, Jackson

Nichols, Lynda, *Admin Asst,* Asheville Art Museum, NC

Nichols, Malcolm, *Instr,* San Diego Mesa College, CA

Nichols, Dr Robert, *Dir of Summer School,* State Univ New York, College at Oneonta

Nicholson, Kathleen, *Asst Prof,* Oberlin College, OH

Nicholson, Dr Thomas D, *Dir,* American Museum of Natural History, New York, NY

Nick, George B, *Chmn Fine Arts/2-D,* Massachusetts College of Art, Boston

Nickel, Helmut, *Cur Arms & Armor,* Metropolitan Museum of Art, New York, NY

Nickolson, Richard, *Chmn Painting Prog,* Herron School of Art, Indiana Univ-Purdue Univ, Indianapolis

Nicolaou, Kyriakos, *Cur,* Cyprus Museum, Nicosia

Nicolet, Eric, *Assoc Dean Summer School,* Ventura College, CA

Nicoletti, Joseph, *Mem Faculty,* Bowdoin College, Brunswick, ME

Nicoll, Edward D, *Pres,* Rensselaer County Historical Society, Troy, NY

Nicosia, F, *Dir,* Museo Nazionale G A Sanna, Sassari, Italy

Niederer, Carl, *Head Dept,* Univ Wyoming, Laramie

Niederer, Frances, *Prof,* Hollins College, VA

Niehoff, K R B, *Secy,* Contemporary Arts Center, Cincinnati, OH

Nielsen, H E Norregaard, *Cur French & Danish,* NY Carlsberg Glyptothek, Copenhagen, Denmark

Nielsen, Inger Hjorth, *Asst Dept Prints & Drawings,* Statens Museum for Kunst, Copenhagen, Denmark

Nielsen, Ruby Warp, *Cur,* Pioneer Village, Minden, NE

Niemeijer, Dr J W, *Dir Printroom,* Rijksmuseum Amsterdam, Netherlands

Niesl, Jos, *Instr,* Milwaukee Area Technical College, WI

Niessen, Wolfram F, *Prof,* Northern Michigan Univ, Marquette

Nieuwdorp, Hans M J, *Cur,* Museum Mayer Van Den Bergh, Antwerp, Belgium

Nieves, Miguel A, *Librn,* Inst de Cultura Puertorriquena, San Juan, PR

Niewald, Wilbur, *Chmn Painting/Printmaking,* Kansas City Art Inst, MO

Nightlinger, Elizabeth, *Vis Lectr,* Marymount College of Virginia, Arlington

Nigrosh, Leon, *Instr,* Craft Center, Worcester, MA

Nikirk, Robert, *Librn,* Grolier Club, New York, NY

Niles, Katherine F, *Dir Community Programs,* Pepsico, Inc, Purchase, NY, see Corporate Art Holdings

Nilsen, Edith, *Registrar,* Staten Island Ferry Maritime Museum, NY

Nilsson, Jo H, *Photography & Slide Librn,* Seattle Art Museum, WA

Nilsson, Skans Torsten, *Head Educ & Pub Relations,* Nordiska Museet, Stockholm, Sweden

Nishimura, H, *Chief Cur,* Nara Kokuritsu Hakubutsukan, Japan

Niswonger, Gary, *Asst Prof,* Smith College, Northampton, MA

Nitterauer, Jane, *Registrar,* Albright-Knox Art Gallery, Buffalo, NY

Nixon, Phyllis, *Librn,* Delaware Art Museum, Wilmington

Nobel, Robert, *Chief Cur,* Museum of the Philadelphia Civic Center, PA

Noble, Douglas R, *Dir,* Museum of Arts and Sciences, Macon, GA

Noble, Joseph Veach, *Dir,* Museum of the City of New York, NY

Noble, Joseph Veach, *Pres,* Brookgreen Gardens, Murrells Inlet, SC

Noblecourt, Christian Desroches, *Cur Egyptian Antiquities,* Musee du Louvre, Paris, France

Nock, Walter J, *Museum Specialist,* West Point Museum, NY

Nodelman, Sheldon, *Assoc Prof,* Univ California, San Diego, La Jolla

Nolan, Edith P, *Pres,* Abingdon Square Painters, New York, NY

Nolan, John F, *Pres,* Massachusetts College of Art, Boston

Nolan, Margaret P, *Cmief Photograph & Slide Librn,* Thomas J Watson Library, Metropolitan Museum of Art, New York, NY

Nolan, Patricia J, *Exec Dir,* Vermont State Craft Center at Frog Hollow, Middlebury

Nolan, R P, *Secy,* Nat Gallery of Victoria, Australia

Nolan, William, *Instr,* Atlanta College of Art, GA

Nolf, Richard A, *Dir,* St Joseph Museum, MO

O'Looney, James, *Instr,* Mohawk Valley Community College, Utica, NY

Olpin, Robert S, *Prof,* Univ Utah, Salt Lake City

Olsen, Arthur, *Dir Summer School,* Augustana College, Sioux Falls, SD

Olsen, Dr Harald P, *Cur, Dept Painting & Sculptures,* Statens Museum for Kunst, Copenhagen, Denmark

Olsen, Jan, *Registrar,* Whatcom Museum of History and Art, Bellingham, WA

Olsen, Mel, *Chmn,* Univ Wisconsin-Superior

Olson, Al, *Pres,* Minnesota Artists Association, Minneapolis

Olson, Christi, *Asst Dir Gallery,* Univ California, Davis

Olson, George, *Assoc Prof,* College of Wooster, OH

Olson, Gerald, *Head Art Dept & Coordr,* Dixie College, Saint George, UT

Olson, Jay, *Chmn,* Sioux Falls College, SD

Olson, Joseph, Jr, *Assoc Prof,* Georgia Southern College, Statesboro

Olson, Patricia S, *Dept Communicating Arts,* Chicago Acad of Fine Arts, IL

Olson, Sandra Gordon, *Cur,* William A Farnsworth Library and Art Museum, Rockland, ME

Olsson, Helen, *Libr Asst,* Newark Museum, NJ

Olszewski, Edward J, *VPres & Secy,* Midwest Art History Society, see National and Regional Organizations; *Assoc Prof,* Case Western Reserve Univ, Cleveland, OH

O'Malley, Anne, *Dir,* Hudson County Court House, Jersey City, NJ

O'Malley, E V, Jr, *Secy,* Phoenix Art Museum, AZ

O'Malley, William, *Mem Faculty,* Charles Stewart Mott Community College, Flint, MI

O'Meara, Virginia, *Assoc Prof,* Maryville College, Saint Louis, MO

O'Neal, Eugene, *Instr,* Elizabeth City State Univ, NC

O'Neil, John, *Chmn & Prof,* Univ South Carolina, Columbia

O'Neil, John, *Prof,* Rice Univ, Houston, TX

O'Neill, Mary Jo, *Dir,* Riverside County Art and Cultural Center, Cherry Valley, CA

O'Neill, Robert, *Prof,* Lamar Univ, Beaumont, TX

Onorato, Ronald J, *Dir Exhib,* Univ Rhode Island Gallery, Kingston

Opar, Barbara A, *Architecture Librn,* Ernest Stevenson Bird Library, Syracuse, NY

Opperman, Kathleen, *Admin Asst,* Chesterwood, Stockbridge, MA

Opstad, Lauritz, *Dir,* Kunstindustrimuseet, Oslo, Norway

Orchard, Sharon, *Librn,* Coquille Valley Art Association, OR

O'Riordain, A B, *Keeper Folklife,* Nat Museum of Ireland, Dublin

Orling, Anne, *Pres,* Professional Artists Guild, see National and Regional Organizations

Orlyk, Harry, *Vis Prof,* Nebraska Wesleyan Univ, Lincoln

Orman, Delores, *VPres,* Nome Arts Council, AK

Orman, Jack, *Coordr,* Colorado State Univ, Fort Collins

Ornelia, John, *Asst Prof,* Manhattan College, Bronx, NY

Ornstein-van Slooten, *Cur,* Museum Het Rembrandthuis, Amsterdam, Holland

O'Rourke, Sister Alice, *Pres,* Edgewood College, Madison, WI

O'Rourke, James, *Dir & Secy Bd Dir,* Plains Art Museum & Rourke Art Gallery, Moorhead, MN

Orr, C W, *Dir Summer School,* North Carolina Central Univ, Durham

Orr, Jerome, *Pres,* South Arkansas Arts Center, El Dorado

Orr, Linda L, *Instr,* Guilford Technical Inst, Jamestown, NC

Orr, Loren, *Chmn Div,* Sierra College, Rocklin, CA

Orr, Robert, *Lectr,* Lake Forest College, IL

Orsnes, Mogens, *Keeper Danish Prehistoric Coll,* Nat Museum, Copenhagen

Orszulok, T, *Cur,* Muzeum Narodowe We Wroclawiu, Wroclaw, Poland

Orth, Fredrick, *Chmn,* San Diego Sate Univ, CA

Ortlip, Paul, *Instr,* Montclair Art Museum, NJ

Ortman, George, *Head Painting Dept,* Cranbrook Academy of Art, Bloomfield Hills, MI

Ortolano, Darby, *Mem Faculty,* Clayworks, New York, NY

Ortquist, Richard, *Assoc Dean of Coll & Dir Summer School,* Wittenberg Univ, Springfield, OH

Ory, Norma R, *Dean Junior School,* Museum of Fine Arts, Houston, TX

Orzack, Lucille, *Secy,* Professional Artists ild, see National and Regional Organizations

Osawa, Mamoru, *Pres,* Kanazawa Bijutsu Kogei Daigaku, Japan

Osborn, Daisy, *Founder,* World Museum/Art Centre, Tulsa, OK

Osborn, Don, *Asst Prof,* Bethany College, Lindsborg, KS

Osborn, Jane Ellen, *Educ Coordr,* Parkersburg Art Center, WV

Osborn, T L, & Daisy, *Founders,* World Museum/Art Centre, Tulsa, OK

Osborne, Carol, *Asst Dir,* Stanford Univ Museum of Art, CA

Osborne, Hettie Jane, *Assoc Prof,* Mount Aloysius Junior College, Cresson, PA

Osborne, John, *Mem Faculty,* Swain School of Design, New Bedford, MA

Osborne, Robert, *Dean Faculty,* Ringling School of Art, Sarasota, FL

Osbun, Jack, *Asst Prof,* Wittenberg Univ, Springfield, OH

Osher, Marian S, *Secy,* Federal Design Council, Washington, DC

Oshinsky, Sybil, *Instr,* Pontiac Art Center, MI

Osler, William, *Secy,* Arts and Letters Club of Toronto, ON

Osman, Siham A, *Asst Prof,* York College of Pennsylvania

Ossa, Nena, *Cur,* Museo Nacional de Bellas Artes Chile, Santiago

Ossa, Wilhelm, *Mem Faculty,* Casper College, WY

Osted, Hans, *Pres,* Manisphere Group of Artists, Winnipeg, MB

Osten, Owen K, *Photographer & Publ,* Plains Art Museum & Rourke Art Gallery, Moorhead, MN

Ostermeyer, Denis, *Prof,* Shoreline Community College, Seattle, WA

Ostiguy, J R, *Research Cur & Lectr Canadian Art,* Nat Gallery of Canada, Ottawa, ON

Ostowska, D, *Cur,* Muzeum Narodowe We Wroclawiu, Wroclaw, Poland

Ostrow, Dr Stephen E, *Dir,* Rhode Island School of Design Museum of Art, Providence

Ostrowski, Dr Janusz, *In Charge Greek & Roman Art,* Muzeum Narodowe W Krakowie, Cracow, Poland

O'Sullivan, N, *Educ Officer,* Nat Gallery of Ireland, Dublin

Oszuscik, Philippe, *Instr,* Univ South Alabama, Mobile

Otero, Jose Luis Fuentes, *Dir Gen,* Escuela de Artes Decorativas, Madrid, Spain

O'Toole, Dennis, *Cur Educ,* Nat Portrait Gallery, Washington, DC

O'Toole, Dorothea Barrick, *Prof,* Mount Saint Mary's College, Emmitsburg, MD

Ott, John Harlow, *Dir,* Shaker Community, Pittsfield, MA

Ott, Judith L, *Vis Instr,* Miami Univ, Oxford, OH

Ott, Michael, *Chmn Dept of Painting & Sculpture,* Univ Kansas, Lawrence

Ott, Wendell, *Dir,* Roswell Museum and Art Center, NM

Otter, Janet, *Instr,* Judson Baptist College, Portland, OR

Otto, Martha, *Head Archaeology,* Ohio Historical Society, Columbus

Oubre, Hayward L, *Chmn,* Winston-Salem State Univ, NC

Ouellet, R, *Cur,* Edmonton Art Gallery, AB

Oughton, Larry, *Asst Prof,* Delta College, University Center, MI

Oursel, Herve, *Conservator,* Musee des Beaux-Arts de Lille, France

Outerbridge, John, *Dir,* Watts Towers Arts Center, City of Los Angeles Munipal Arts Dept, CA

Overby, Osmund, *Dir,* Univ Missouri Museum of Art and Archaeology, Columbia

Overdorff, Randall, *Technical Dir,* Museum Without Walls, Rceda Inc, Friendsville, MD

Overland, Carlton, E, *Cur Coll,* Univ of Wisconsin-Madison Mem Union

Overly, Dan, *Exec Dir,* Craftsmen's Guild of Mississippi, Jackson

Overvoorde, Chris Stoffel, *Assoc Prof,* Calvin College, Grand Rapids, MI

Owen, Karl, *Mem Faculty,* College of DuPage, Glen Ellyn, IL

Owen, Katherine M, *Chmn Bd,* Tennessee Valley Art Center, Tuscumbia, AL

Owen, Raymond M, Jr, *Dir,* Bruce Museum, Greenwich, CT

Owen, Jeanne, *Regional Serv Librn,* Clark County Library District Art Activities, Las Vegas, NV

Owen, T M, *Cur,* Welsh Folk Museum, St Fagans, Wales

Owens, Dr George A, *Pres,* Tougaloo College Art Collection, MS

Owens, Mrs Nell, *Pres,* Portage and District Arts Council, Portage La Prairie, MB

Owens, Pam, *Exhib,* Minnesota Museum of Art Permanent Collection Gallery, St Paul

Owens, Wallace, *Chmn Dept,* Langston Univ, OK

Ownbey, Ronald, B, *Chmn Art Dept,* Mount San Antonio College, Walnut, CA

Ownby, Joanna, *Registrar,* E B Crocker Art Gallery, Sacramento, CA

Owsley, David T, *Cur Antiquities Oriental & Decorative Arts,* Carnegie Inst Museum of Art, Pittsburgh, PA

Oxenaar, Dr R W D, *Dir,* Ryksmuseum Kroller-Muller, Otterlo, Netherlands

Oxhammar, Greger, *Head Adminr,* Nordiska Museet, Stockholm, Sweden

Ozatay, Nejat, *Cur Lab Restoration,* Istanbul Arkeoloji Muzeleri, Turkey

Ozegovic, Jack, *Instr,* Northwestern Michigan College, Traverse City

Paarlberg, Mildred, *Cur Coll,* Tippecanoe County Historical Museum, Lafayette, IN

Paasche, Norman, *Assoc Prof,* Lewis and Clark College, Portland, OR

Pabst, Miss S J, *Librn,* Rijksmuseum Vincent Van Gogh, Amsterdam, Netherlands

Pace, Stephen, *Assoc Prof,* American Univ, Washington, DC

Pachter, Marc, *Historian,* Nat Portrait Gallery, Washington, DC

Pachucki, Romek, *Art Conservator,* Tasmanian Museum & Art Gallery, Hobart, Australia

Packard, Helen, *Secy,* Toledo Artists' Club, OH

Packard, Sandra P, *Asst Prof,* Miami Univ, Oxford, OH

Packwood, George, *Cur,* Nat Art Gallery of New Zealand, Wellington

Paddock, Bridget, *Asst Dir,* Phillips Exeter Acad, NH

Padgett, James, *Instr,* Wilberforce Univ, OH

Padgett, R Paul, *Asst Prof,* West Liberty State College, WV

Padghan, Ronald E, *Chmn Found Studies,* Rochester Inst Technology, NY

Page, Addison Franklin, *Dir & Cur,* J B Speed Art Museum, Louisville, KY

Page, Bill, *Asst Prof,* Jacksonville State Univ, AL

Page, Donna, *Mem Faculty,* Illinois Wesleyan Univ, Bloomington

Page, John, *Prof,* Univ Northern Iowa, Cedar Falls

Page, John F, *Dir & Secy,* New Hampshire Historical Society, Concord

Page, Richard C, *Asst Garden Dir,* Tennessee Botanical Gardens and Fine Arts Center, Nashville

Page, Richard K, *Dir,* Philadelphia Maritime Museum, PA

Page, Thomas A, *Treas,* Beaumont Art Museum, TX

Paier, Edward T, *Pres & Dir Summer School,* Paier School of Art, Hamden, CT

Patten, Carol, *Cur,* Stockbridge Mission House Association, MA

Patten, Lloyd L, *Asst Prof,* Univ South Alabama, Mobile

Pattenden, Mrs T, *Secy,* Hawkes Bay Art Gallery and Museum, Napier, New Zealand

Pattershall, Donald F, *Pres,* Lowell Art Association, MA

Patterson, David, *Dir,* El Camino College Art Gallery, Torrance, CA

Patterson, M J, *Cur,* Museum of Northern British Columbia, Prince Rupert

Patterson, Michele, *Libr Asst,* William Hayes Ackland Memorial Art Center, Univ North Carolina, Chapel Hill

Patterson, Nancy-Lou, *Assoc Prof,* Univ Waterloo, ON

Patterson, Phil, *Pres,* Rogue Valley Art Association, Medford, OR

Patterson, Mrs W D M, *Treas,* West Vancouver Visual Arts Society, BC

Patterson, Willis R, *Head Dept,* Central Wyoming College, Riverton

Pattison, Christie R, *Lectr,* Univ North Carolina at Wilmington

Patton, Jack D, *Prof,* Taylor Univ, Upland, IN

Patton, M Ellen, *Asst Prof,* Miami Univ, Oxford, OH

Pattrick, Michael, *Prin,* Central School of Art and Design, London, England

Paukert, Karel, *Cur Musical Arts,* Cleveland Museum of Art, OH

Paul, Arthur, *VPres Corp Art & Graphics, Dir PEI & Art Dir,* Playboy Magazine, Playboy Enterprises, Chicago, IL, see Corporate Art Holdings

Paul, Richard, *Chmn Faculty Gallery Comt,* Purdue Univ Galleries, West Lafayette, IN

Paul, William D, Jr, *Dir,* Univ Georgia Art Collection, Athens

Paulin, Richard C, *Dir,* Univ Oregon Museum of Art, Eugene

Paull, Joy, *Admin Officer,* Univ Regina, SK

Pauls, James, *Asst Prof,* Northeast Missouri State Univ, Kirksville

Paulsen, Richard, *Instr,* Elmhurst College, IL

Paulson, Alan, *Asst Prof,* Colgate Univ, Hamilton, NY

Paulson, Congdon, E, *VPres,* Nebraska Art Association, Univ Nebraska Art Gallery, Lincoln

Paulson, Peter J, *Dir,* New York State Library, Albany

Paulson, Robert, *Chmn 2-D,* Southern Illinois Univ, Carbondale

Pause, Michael, *Dir Basic Design,* North Carolina State Univ at Raleigh

Pauwels, Henri, *Cur Ancient Art,* Musees Royaux des Beaux-Arts de Belgique, Brussels

Pav, John, *Prof,* East Tennessee State Univ, Johnson City

Pavars, Mara E, *Technical Serv,* Nutley Public Library, NJ

Pawel, Nancy, *Lectr,* Incarnate Word College, San Antonio, TX

Paxson, Dr R C, *Head Dept,* Troy State Univ, Alabama

Payne, Woodward, *Mem Faculty,* Mesa Community College, AZ

Payton, Martin, *Instr,* Xavier Univ Louisiana, New Orleans

Paz, Samuel, *Conservator,* Museo Nacional de Bellas Artes Buenos Aires, Argentina

Pazi, M, *Asst Dir,* Topkapi Saray Museum, Istanbul, Turkey

Peace, Bernie K, *Chmn,* West Liberty State College, WV

Peace, Earl G, *Dir Summer School,* Lafayette College, Easton, PA

Peace, Nancy, *Librn,* Rhode Island Historical Society, Providence

Peace, Sandra, *Asst Cur,* Brooks Mem Art Gallery, Memphis, TN

Peak, Robert, *Adv Bd Mem,* Famous Artists School, Westport, CT

Pearce, Mrs B C, *Mgr,* Westover, Charles City, VA

Pearce, Charles G, *Asst Prof,* Clarion State College, PA

Pearce, Dan M, *Instr,* Elizabeth City State Univ, NC

Pearce, Mary L, *Asst Secy, Head Dept & Dir Summer School,* Rehoboth Art League, Rehoboth Beach, DE

Pearl, George C, *Cur,* Tome Parish Museum, NM

Pearlman, Kay, *Sr Libr, Adult Serv,* Ontario City Library, CA

Pearse, Harold, *Chmn Art Educ Div,* Nova Scotia College of Art and Design, Halifax

Pearson, C Jeremy, *Asst Keeper Art,* Plymouth City Museum and Art Gallery, England

Pearson, Clifton, *Head Dept,* Alabama A&M Univ, Huntsville

Pearson, Duane, *Supt,* Nat Park Service, New York, NY

Pearson, John, *Assoc Prof,* Oberlin College, OH

Pearson, Norma, *VPres,* Racine Art Association, WI

Pebworth, Charles A, *Prof,* Sam Houston State Univ, Huntsville, TX

Pechere, R, *Prof,* Fontainebleau School of Fine Arts, France

Pechersky, Jorge, *Industrial Design Hector Compaired,* Centro de Arte y Communicacion, Buenos Aires, Argentina

Peck, Dexter B, *Dir,* Mark Twain Mem, Hartford, CT

Peck, Louis A, *Chmn Dept & Dir Summer School,* Boise State Univ, ID

Peck, Dr Roderick, *Dean Summer School,* California State Univ at Long Beach

Peck, William H, *Cur Ancient, Oriental, African Art,* Detroit Inst of Art Collections, MI

Peckenpaugh, C W, *Chmn Fine Arts Dept,* Milwaukee School of the Arts, WI

Peckham, Anita, *Recording Secy,* Seattle Weaver's Guild, WA

Peckham, Nicholas, *Mem Faculty,* Stephens College, Columbia, MO

Peckham, Suzanne, *VPres,* Essex Art Association, CT

Pecson, Oscar, *Instr,* Philippine College of Arts and Trades, Manila

Pedersen, Margaret, *Pres,* Southern Artists Association, Hot Springs, AR

Pedersen, Marit Lande, *Mus Lectr,* City of Oslo Art Collection, Norway

Pederson, Ronald, *Vis Prof,* Calvin College, Grand Rapids, MI

Pedley, John G, *Dir,* Kelsey Museum of Ancient & Mediaeval Archaeology, Ann Arbor, MI

Peebles, Phoebe, *Archivist,* William Hayes Fogg Art Museum, Harvard Univ, Cambridge, MA

Peek, Lt Comdr Charles, *Asst Dir,* USS North Carolina Battleship Mem, Wilmington

Peerless, Mitchell, *Asst Prof,* Art School, Univ Hartford, West Hartford, CT

Peeters-Demaeyer, Mrs L, *Librn,* Museum Plantin-Moretus, Antwerp, Belgium

Peetz, John E, *Dir,* Oakland Museum, CA

Peirce, Donald, *Asst Cur Decorative Arts,* Brooklyn Museum, NY

Peirce, Robert, *Ed,* Portland Art Association, OR

Peithman, Russell I, *Dir,* Charlotte Nature Museum, NC

Pekarsky, Melvin H, *Chmn,* State Univ New York at Stony Brook

Peladeau, Marius B, *Dir,* William A Farnsworth Library and Art Museum, Rockland, ME

Pelehach, Patricia, *Asst to Dir,* Buten Museum of Wedgwood, Merion, PA

Pelfrey, Robert, *Mem Faculty,* Cuesta College, San Luis Obispo, CA

Pelham, Alfred M, *Treas,* Detroit Inst of Art Collections, MI

Pell, John H G, *VPres,* New York State Historical Association, Cooperstown, NY; *Pres,* Fort Ticonderoga Museum, Ticonderoga, NY

Pell, Robert L, *Asst to Dir Special Events,* Nat Gallery of Art, Washington, DC

Pellegrino, John, *VPres,* Warwick Arts Found, RI

Pelletier, Brenda, *Secy to Dir,* Bowdoin College Museum of Art, Brunswick, ME

Pelletier, Bruce, *Art Dir,* Westerly Public Library, RI

Pelli, Cesar, *Dean,* Yale Univ, New Haven, CT

Pellicciaro, Marid, *Mem Faculty,* Washington and Lee University, Lexington, VA

Pelnar, Patricia Rogers, *Gallery Mgr,* Tufts Univ Gallery Eleven, Medford, MA

Pels, Albert, *Dir,* Pels School of Art, New York, NY

Pelt, Billie Van, *Exec Secy,* Utah Travel Council, Salt Lake City

Pelton, Margaret M, *Chmn Art Dept,* Miami Dade Community College, South Campus, FL

Pelzel, Thomas O, *Assoc Prof,* Univ California, Riverside

Pemberton, Henry R, *VPres,* Historical Society of Pennsylvania, Philadelphia

Pena, Eva Ramirez, *Secy,* Museo de Arte Moderno, Mexico City, Mexico

Penay, Lucianao J, *Assoc Prof,* American Univ, Washington, DC

Pence, Nina, *Chmn Exhib,* Klamath Art Association, Klamath Falls, OR

Pendergast, Dr J F, *Asst Dir Operations,* Nat Museum of Man, Ottawa, ON

Pendergraft, Norman, *Prof Art & Dir Museum,* North Carolina Central Univ, Durham

Pendleton, Eldridge H, *Dir & Cur Coll,* Old Gaol Museum, York, ME

Pendley, Barry, *Instr,* Laramie County Community College, Cheyenne, WY

Penegar, Lucy, *Pres,* Gaston County Art and History Museum, Dallas, NC

Peneguy, Richard A, *Secy,* New Orleans Museum of Art, LA

Penick, S Barksdale, Jr, *Pres,* Montclair Art Museum, NJ

Peniston, Robert C, *Dir,* Lee Chapel and Museum, Washington and Lee Univ, Lexington, VA

Penkowski, Giuseppe, *Cur Ethnographical Coll,* Monumenti Musei e Gallerie Pontificie, Vatican City, Italy

Pennebaker, Dr William, *Dir Summer School,* Univ Alaska, Fairbanks

Penny, Virginia, *Exhib Designer,* Univ Alberta Art Gallery and Museum, Edmonton

Pentecost, David, *Technical Dir,* Electronic Arts Intermix, New York, NY

Pentland, Pam, *Supvr Guest Relations,* Franklin Mint Corp Museum, Franklin Center, PA

Penzes, Eva, *Scientific Secy,* Magyar Nemzeti Galeria, Budapest, Hungary

Pepe, Marie Huper, *Chmn,* Agnes Scott College, Decatur, GA

Peper, Niel, *Div Coordr,* Dowling College, Oakdale, NY

Pepich, Bruce, *Project Dir,* Racine Art Association, WI

Percival, H V T, *Officer In Charge,* Wellington Museum, London, England

Percival, Robert, *Cur Art,* New Brunswick Museum, Saint John

Percival, Sande, *Vis Prof,* Pacific Lutheran Univ, Tacoma, WA

Percy, Ethel, *Secy,* Manisphere Group of Artists, Winnipeg, MB

Pere, Dorothy, *Instr,* Ocean City School of Art, NJ

Pereboom, Bernice, *Treas,* Eureka Springs Guild of Artists and Crafts People, AR

Pereira, Vera Monteiro, *Chief Librn,* Museu Nacional de Belas Artes, Rio de Janeiro, Brazil

Perel, Leonardo, *Industrial Design Hector Compaired,* Centro de Arte y Communicacion, Buenos Aires, Argentina

Perez, Ignacio Cabral, *Instr,* Univ las Americas Galeria de Arte, Cholula, Mexico

Perez, J Esteban, *Installation Designer,* Center for Inter-American Relations Art Gallery, New York, NY

Perez, Vincent, *Instr,* California College of Arts and Crafts, Oakland

Perkins, Constance M, *Dir,* Occidental College Thorne Hall, Los Angeles, CA

Pierce, Delilah W, *Cur Painting,* Smith-Mason Gallery and Museum, Washington, DC

Pierce, Donald, *Dir,* Donald Pierce School of Painting, New York, NY

Pierce, Lloyd, *Mem Faculty,* Spokane Falls Community College, Spokane, WA

Pierotti, Ray, *Dir,* Arrowmont School of Arts and Crafts, Gatlinburg, TN

Pierotti, Ray, *Assoc Prof,* Univ Tennessee, Knoxville

Pierro, Leonard, *Coordr Specialized Studio,* Kean College of New Jersey, Union

Pierron, John, *Exec Dir,* Museum of the Philadelphia Civic Center, PA

Piersol, Lawrence, *VPres,* Civic Fine Arts Association, Sioux Falls, SD

Pierucci, Donal, *Pres,* Arts and Crafts Center of Pittsburgh, PA

Pietrangeli, C, *Dir,* Musei Capitolini, Rome, Italy

Pietraszko, J, *Cur,* Muzeum Narodowe We Wroclawiu, Wroclaw, Poland

Pietroforte, Alfred, *Instr,* College of the Sequoias, Visalia, CA

Pietropaoli, Frank, *Librn,* Nat Museum of History and Technology, Washington, DC

Pietrzak, Ted, *Asst to Dir,* Art Gallery of Hamilton, ON

Pike, Kermit, *Librn,* Western Reserve Historical Society, Cleveland, OH

Pike, Stanley R, Jr, *Admin,* Bennington Museum, VT

Pilat, Peter, *Instr,* Monterey Peninsula College, CA

Pilgrim, Dianne H, *Cur Decorative Arts,* Brooklyn Museum, NY

Pillet, Michel, *Dir,* Univ Southwestern Louisiana, Lafayette

Pillsbury, Edmund P, *Dir,* Yale Univ Art Gallery, New Haven, CT

Pinardi, Brenda, *Assoc Prof Art & Chairperson Dept,* Univ Lowell, MA

Pinardi, Enrico, *Assoc Prof,* Rhode Island College, Providence

Pincus, Debra, *Asst Prof,* Univ British Columbia, Vancouver

Pineau, Capt Roger, *Dir,* US Naval Mem Museum, Washington, DC

Pines, Phillip A, *Dir,* Hall of Fame of the Trotter, Goshen, NY

Pinkney, Helen, *Librn,* Dayton Art Inst, OH

Pinkston, Howell, *Assoc Prof,* Pierce College, Woodland Hills, CA

Pinnow, Phyllis, *Prof,* Rochester Community College, MN

Pinsky, Alfred, *Dean Faculty Fine Arts,* Concordia Univ, Sir George Williams Campus, Montreal, PQ

Pinson, Patricia, *Assoc Prof,* Union Univ, Jackson, TN

Pinto, James, *Dean Faculty,* Instituto Allende, San Maguel de Allende, Mexico

Pinto, Maria Helena Mendes, *Asst Cur Furniture,* Museu Nacional de Arte Antiga Lisbon, Portugal

Pinto, Sandra, *Dir,* Galleria D'Arte Moderna, Galleria Palatina, Florence, Italy

Piombino, EMMY, *Secy,* Queens Museum, Flushing, NY

Piomelli, Rosaria, *Chmn Faculty Affairs,* Pratt Inst School of Art & Design, Brooklyn, NY

Piotrowski, Dr R, *Head Dept & Dir Summer School,* Northern Arizona Univ, Flagstaff

Piper, D T, *Dir,* Ashmolean Museum, Oxford Univ, England

Piper, Douglas, *Instr,* Laramie County Community College, Cheyenne, WY

Piper, Dr Robert E, *Dean Summer School,* Southeastern Massachusetts Univ, North Dartmouth

Pique, Jean Pierre, *Chmn Interior Design & Decoration,* Traphagen School of Fashion, New York, NY

Piro, Jean V, *Adult Serv,* Nutley Public Library, NJ

Pirtle, Judy, *Admin Asst,* Tyler Museum of Art, TX

Pirzada, Abdul Hafeez, *Pres,* Art Gallery Society of Contemporary Art, Rawalpindi, Pakistan

Pisano, Ronald G, *Cur Chase Coll & Archives,* Parrish Art Museum, Southampton, NY

Piskoti, James, *Assoc Prof,* California State College, Stanislaus, Turlock

Pisney, Ramond F, *Dir,* Woodrow Wilson Birthplace Found, Staunton, VA

Pitangui, Dr Ivo, *Pres,* Museu de Arte Moderna Brazil, Rio de Janeiro

Pitt, Paul, *Asst Prof,* Harding College, Searcy, AR

Pittenger, Charles, *Registrar,* Kentucky Historical Society Museum, Frankfort

Pittman, David, *Artmobile Coordr,* Virginia Museum of Fine Arts, Richmond

Pitts, Terence R, *Cur & Librn Photography Archives,* Center for Creative Photography, Tucson, AZ

Pitts, Tom, *Instr,* Berry College, Mount Berry, GA

Pivovar, Ronald A, *Dir,* Sampson Art Gallery; *Assoc Prof & Chmn Dept,* Thiel College, Greenville, PA

Pizzat, Joseph, *Prof,* Mercyhurst College, Erie, PA

Pizzuro, Eugene, *Assoc Dir,* Univ Washington, Seattle

P-Jobb, Andor S, *Asst Prof,* Clarion State College, PA

Place, Bradley E, *Head Dept & Dir Summer School,* Univ Tulsa, OK

Place, Ruth, *VPres,* Riverside Art Center and Museum, CA

Placzek, Adolf K, *Pres,* Society of Architectural Historians, see National and Regional Organizations; *Avery Librn,* Columbia Univ, New York, NY

Plahter, Leif, *Chief Restorer,* Nasjonalgalleriet, Oslo, Norway

Plair, Ann S, *Secy,* South Arkansas Art League, El Dorado

Plaisted, Lola, *Dir Develop,* Minnesota Museum of Art Permanent Collection Gallery, St Paul

Platt, John H, *Head Librn,* Historical Society of Pennsylvania, Philadelphia

Platou, Mrs Ralph V, *Chief Cur,* Historic New Orleans Collection, LA

Platteter, Leo A, *Cur,* Buffalo Bill Mem Association, Cody, WY

Plavwers, Mrs, *Educ Dept,* Stedelyke Musea, Bruges, Belgium

Pledger, Kay, *Asst to Dir,* Dallas Historical Society, TX

Pleer, Ilmar, *Dir,* Johnston Nat Scouting Museum, North Brunswick, NJ

Pletcher, Robert E, *Assoc Prof,* George Peabody College for Teachers, Nashville, TN

Pletscher, Josephine, *Head Fine Arts Div,* Pasadena Public Library, CA

Ploeger, Fred, *Cur Art,* Eastern Washington State Historical Society, Spokane

Plofchan, Thomas, *Dean Continuing Educ,* Marygrove College, Detroit, MI

Plominska, M, *Keeper Educ Dept,* Muzeum Narodowe, Warsaw, Poland

Plotkin, L, *Pres,* Manitoba Association of Architects, Winnipeg

Plous, Phyllis, *Cur,* Univ California Art Museum, Santa Barbara

Plummer, Carlton, *Assoc Prof,* Univ Lowell, MA

Plummer, Jean, *Librn,* Craftsmen's Association of British Columbia, Vancouver

Plummer, John, *Prof,* Princeton Univ, NJ

Plummer, Dr John H, *Cur Mediaeval & Renaissance,* Pierpont Morgan Library, New York, NY

Plummer, Robin J, *Dean,* Brighton Polytechnic, England

Podany, Jerry, *Mem Faculty,* Laguna Beach School of Art, CA

Poe, Robert Harold, *Coordr Visual Studies,* Lander College, Greenwood, SC

Poesch, Jessie J, *Prof,* Tulane Univ, New Orleans, LA

Pogany, Dr G E, *Dir Gen,* Magyar Nemzeti Galeria, Budapest, Hungary

Pogue, Larry, *Head Dept,* East Central Junior College, Union, MO

Pogue, Stephanie, *Asst Prof,* Fisk Univ, Nashville, TN

Poirier, Lynne F, *Chief Cur,* Bucks County Historical Society Mercer Museum, Doylestown, PA

Pokross, David R, *Pres,* American Jewish Historical Society, Waltham, MA

Poland, Maralyn, *Secy,* Providence Art Club, RI

Poleshock, Walter, *Develop Officer,* Whitney Museum of American Art, New York, NY

Poleskie, Steve, *Assoc Prof,* Cornell Univ, Ithaca, NY

Poling, Clark, *Asst Prof,* Emory Univ, Atlanta, GA

Polito, Ronald, *Chairperson Dept,* Boston State College, MA

Polk, Andrew, III, *Instr,* Wake Forest Univ, Winston-Salem, NC

Pollard, G, *Keeper Coins & Medals,* Fitzwilliam Museum, Univ Cambridge, England

Pollock, Luella, *Librn,* Reed College Art Gallery, Portland, OR

Polo, Romulo, *Head Industrial Design,* Javeriana Univ Faculty of Architecture and Design, Bogota, Colombia

Polshek, James Stewart, *Dean,* Columbia Univ, New York, NY

Polster, Joanne, *Librn,* American Crafts Council, see National and Regional Organizations

Polster, Nancy, *Coordr Design,* Iowa State Univ, Ames

Polston, John, *Chmn,* Sinclair Community College, Dayton, OH

Polt, James, *Dir Summer School,* Colorado Women's College, Denver

Polzer, Joseph, *Head Dept,* Queen's Univ, Kingston, ON

Pomarede, F, *Conservator,* Musees Saint-Denis, Reim, France

Pomerantz, Sarah B, *Asst Treas,* Historical Society of Pennsylvania, Philadelphia

Pomeroy, Jim, *Chmn Sculpture Dept,* San Francisco Art Inst, CA

Pomfret, Robert, *Treas,* Providence Watercolor Club, RI

Pond, Freda, *Mem Chair,* Women in the Arts Found, New York, NY

Poole, Dr Jerry D, *Head Dept,* Univ Central Arkansas, Conway

Poole, Frederick, *Pres,* Pontiac Creative Arts Center, MI

Poole, William, *First VPres,* Historical Society of Delaware, Wilmington

Poor, Dr Robert J, *Assoc Prof,* Univ Minnesota, Minneapolis; *Adjunct Cur Asian Art,* Minnesota Museum of Art Permanent Collection Gallery, St Paul

Pope, Marian, *Asst Dir,* Univ New Mexico Art Museum, Albuquerque

Pope, Phyllis B, *Instr,* John Brown Univ, Siloam Springs, AR

Pope, Richard C, *Assoc Prof,* Univ Alabama in Huntsville

Pope, Roy T, *Exhib Technician,* Oklahoma Historical Society, Oklahoma City

Popham, Lewis C, III, *Dir Summer School,* State Univ New York College At Oswego

Poplaski, Alex, *VPres,* Lyme Art Association, Old Lyme, CT

Popolizio, Vincent J, *Chief Bur Art Educ,* State Education Dept, Albany, NY

Popovich, Ljubica D, *Assoc Prof,* Vanderbilt Univ, Nashville, TN

Popp, Janet E, *Secy,* Capitol Univ Schumacher Gallery, Columbus, OH

Poppe, Mary, *Museum Receptionist & Shop Mgr,* Bowdoin College Museum of Art, Brunswick, ME

Porada, Edith, *Hon Cur Seals & Tablets,* Pierpont Morgan Library, New York, NY

Porcelli, Carolyn, *Develop Assoc,* Solomon R Guggenheim Museum, New York, NY

Porebski, Dr Mieczyslaw, *Polish Modern Art Prof,* Muzeum Narodowe W Krakowie, Cracow, Poland

Porfirio, Jose Luis, *Cur Pub Relations,* Museu Nacional de Arte Antiga Lisbon, Portugal

Porinchak, David D, *Chmn,* Hofstra Univ, Hempstead, NY

Port, George, *Vis Prof,* Brandt Painting Workshops, Corona del Mar, CA

Porter, Anastasia, *Corresp Secy,* Lowell Art Association, MA

Porter, Mrs Arthur, *Lect Chmn,* Irene Leache Mem, Norfolk, VA

Porter, Dr Dean A, *Dir,* Univ Notre Dame Art Gallery, IN

Porter, Elmer, *Chmn Art Dept,* Indiana State Univ, Terre Haute

Porter, Elmer J, *Secy,* Kappa Pi International Honorary Art Fraternity, see National and Regional Organizations

Porter, Elwin, *Dir & Dir Summer School,* South Florida Art Inst of Hollywood

Porter, Jeanne C, *Assoc Prof,* Pennsylvania State Univ, University Park

Porter, Raiford, *Assoc Prof,* High Point College, NC

Porter, William L, *Dean,* Massachusetts Inst of Technology, Cambridge

Poser, Mimi, *Pub Affairs Officer,* Solomon R Guggenheim Museum, New York, NY

Posey, Pamela, *Librn,* William A Farnsworth Library and Art Museum, Rockland, ME

Posner, David, *Instr,* Georgia Southern College, Statesboro

Posniak, Richard, *Chmn Sculpture/Metalsmithing,* Moore College of Art, Philadelphia, PA

Post, Jerry L, *Head Dept,* Allegany Community College, Cumberland, MD

Poster, Amy, *Cur Oriental Art,* Brooklyn Museum, NY

Postian, Nancy, *Secy,* London Art Gallery Association, ON

Potemska, Dr Maria, *Cur,* Muzeum Sztuki, Lodz, Poland

Potemski, Mieczyslaw, *Cur,* Muzeum Sztuki, Lodz, Poland

Potoff, Leni, *Painting Conservator,* Intermuseum Conservation Association, see National and Regional Organizations

Potter, R W, *Head Dept Three-Dimensional Design,* City of Birmingham Polytechnic, England

Potter, Ruth, *Secy,* Boothbay Region Art Gallery, Boothbay Harbor, ME

Potter, Ted, *Dir,* Southeastern Center For Contemporary Art, Winston-Salem, NC

Potts, Charles, *Photography Dept Chmn,* Art Center College of Design, Pasadena, CA

Potts, Don, *Asst Prof,* California State College, Sonoma, Rohnert Park

Potts, Marvin, *Pres,* Lighthouse Gallery, Tequesta, FL

Pouliot, J Herman, *Chmn Exec Comt,* Arts and Science Center, Nashua, NH

Poulos, Basilios, *Asst Prof,* Rice Univ, Houston, TX

Poulos, Theodore T, *Head Training Resources Div,* Association des Musees Canadiens, see National Organizations in Canada

Pounds, Bro Joseph, *Cur,* Franciscan Monastery, Washington, DC

Powell, Dean, *Pres,* Artists Guild Inc of New York, see National and Regional Organizations

Powell, George E, *Chmn Bd Govs,* Kansas City Art Inst, MO

Powell, Robert, *Mem Faculty,* Ricks College, Rexburg, ID

Powers, Carolyn, *Asst Prof,* New Mexico Highlands Univ, Las Vegas

Powers, Geneva, *Dir Arts Center,* Council of Ozark Artists and Craftsmen, Springdale, AR

Powers, H Burton, *Pres,* Stowe-Day Found, Hartford, CT

Poynor, Robin, *Cur,* Tweed Museum of Art, Duluth, MN

Prangnell, Peter, *Chmn,* Dept of Architecture, Univ Toronto, ON

Pransky, Shirley, *Mem Staff,* Boston Center for Adult Education, MA

Pratapaditya, Pal, *Cur Indian & Islamic Art,* Los Angeles County Museum of Art, CA

Pratt, Charles C, *Assoc Dir,* Ohio Historical Society, Columbus

Pratt, George O, *Dir,* Staten Island Inst of Arts and Sciences, NY

Pratt, Jean A, *Mem Faculty,* American River College, Sacramento, CA

Pratt, Ralph, *Pres,* West Hills Unitarian Fellowship, Portland, OR

Pratt, Vernon, *Asst Prof,* Duke Univ, Durham, NC

Prebandier, Leon, *Dean,* Lausanne College of Art & Design, Switzerland

Preble, Michael Andrew, *Dir,* Mount San Antonio College Art Gallery, Walnut, CA

Pregno, Adrienne, *Chmn & Assoc Prof,* Ladycliff College, Highland Falls, NY

Preisner, Olga, *Cur,* Pennsylvania State Univ Museum of Art, University Park

Preketes, Beryl, *Recording Secy,* Toledo Federation of Art Societies, OH

Premo, Edward J, *In Charge Coll,* Coopers & Lybrand, Detroit, MI, see Corporate Art Holdings

Prentice, Hattie, *Secy,* Eye Level Gallery, Halifax, NS

Prentiss, Margo, *Secy-Registrar,* Albrecht Art Museum, St. Joseph, MO

Presetnik, Daniela, *Exten Officer,* London Public Library and Art Museum, ON

Press, Nancy S, *Coordr Educ & Cur Crafts,* Cornell Univ, Ithaca, NY

Pressing, Kirk L, *Supvr Central Serv,* Milwaukee Public Library, WI

Pressman, Lenore, *Prof,* North Park College, Chicago, IL

Presteich, Larry, *Instr,* Northeastern Junior College, Sterling, CO

Prestiano, Dr Robert, *Coordr & Assoc Prof,* Angelo State Univ, San Angelo, TX

Preston, Ruth, *Restoration Coordr,* Southern Oregon Historical Society, Jacksonville

Prestwich, Linda, *Asst Cur & Librn,* Highland Area Arts Council, Freeport, IL

Preszler, Robert E, *Cur,* Washington County Museum of Fine Arts, Hagerstown, MD

Pretzer, Dale, *Supvr College & Univ Library Prog,* Michigan Dept of Education State Library Services, Lansing

Preusser, Dr Frank, *Restoration Dept,* Bayerischen Staatsgemaldesammlungen, Munich, Germany

Prewitt, Diana, *Cur Educ,* Brooks Mem Art Gallery, Memphis, TN

Price, Charles, *Chmn,* Connecticut College, New London

Price, Geraldine, *Adv Dir,* Santa Fe Workshops of Contemporary Art, NM

Price, James E, *Dir,* Ohio Visual Art Institution, Cincinnati

Price, Larry, *Asst Librn,* Berkshire Athenaeum, Pittsfield, MA

Price, Lois, *Dir Mus Planning,* Filson Club, Louisville, KY

Price, Michael, *Mem Faculty,* Hamline Univ, Saint Paul, MN

Price, Monroe E, *Dir,* Advocates for the Arts, Los Angeles, CA

Price, Pam, *Asst Prof,* Univ Texas of Permian Basin, Odessa

Price, Priscilla B, *Registrar,* Corning Museum of Glass, NY

Price, Shirley, *Secy,* New Haven Paint & Clay Club, CT

Price, Capt Walter W, *Dir,* Gunston Hall Plantation, Lorton, VA

Prier, Carol Molly, *Lectr,* Mills College, Oakland, CA

Prince, Mrs D L, *Asst Dir,* Contemporary Arts Museum, Houston, TX

Prince, Junius, III, *Pres,* Louisville School of Art Gallery, Anchorage, KY

Prince, Nancy Moyer, *Head Dept,* Pan American Univ, Edinburg, TX

Prince, Paul, *Designer Exhib,* Univ California Art Museum, Santa Barbara

Prince, Richard, *Vis Prof,* Univ British Columbia, Vancouver

Prince, Roger O, *Dir,* Wooster Community Art Center, Danbury, CT

Pritchard, James B, *Cur Biblical Archaeology,* Univ Pennsylvania Museum, Philadelphia

Pritzlaff, Mary Dell, *Pres,* Phoenix Art Museum, AZ

Procario, Saverio, *Deputy Dir Admin,* Sleepy Hollow Restorations, Tarrytown, NY

Prochaska, Thomas A, *Chmn* Wesleyan College, Macon, GA

Prochazka, Dr Vaclav, *Chief Modern Art Coll,* Narodni Galerie v Praze, Prague, Czechoslovakia

Proctor, Letitia B, *Librn,* Brooks Mem Art Gallery, Memphis, TN

Proctor, Valerie, *Cur,* Laurier House, Public Archives of Canada Library, Ottawa, ON

Prodinger, Dr Freidrike, *Dir Ethnology, History of Civilization, Arts & Crafts,* Saltzburger Museum Carolino Augusteum, Austria

Prokop, Peter, *Pres & Cur,* Taras H Shevchenko Museum and Mem Park Found, Oakville, ON

Prokopoff, Stephen S, *Dir,* Inst of Contemporary Art, Boston, MA

Prol, Elbertus, *Cur,* Ringwood Manor House Museum, NJ

Prom, J A, *Head Dept,* Rochester Community College, MN

Pronzas, Betty, *Vis Prof,* Mount Saint Mary's College, Emmitsburg, MD

Propersi, August, *Dir & Instr,* Propersi Galleries and School of Art, Greenwich, CT

Prosdocimi, Dr Alessandro, *Dir,* Museo Civico di Padua, Italy

Prose, Maryruth, *Cur Educ,* Inst and Museum of the Great Plains, Lawton, OK

Proske, Beatrice G, *Cur Emer Sculpture,* Hispanic Society of America, New York, NY

Pross, Lester F, *Chmn Art Dept,* Berea College, KY

Prost, George, *Pres Bd Dirs,* Manisphere Group of Artists, Winnipeg, MB

Protic, Miodrag B, *Dir,* Museum of Modern Art, Belgrade, Yugoslavia

Provencher, Alfred, *Assoc Prof,* Monmouth College, West Long Branch, NJ

Provinzano, Linda, *Librn,* Pacific Film Archive, Univ California, Berkeley

Proweller, William, *Prof,* State Univ New York College at Fredonia

Prud'homme, Robert, *Asst Cur,* Chateau de Ramezay, Montreal, PQ

Pruitt, Nero, *Dir Summer School,* Porterville Community College, CA

Prul, Mirle, *Asst Prof,* Herkimer County Community College, NY

Pruner, Gary L, *Mem Faculty,* American River College, Sacramento, CA

Prytulak, Alexandra, *Chmn Libr Bd,* Woodstock Public Library and Art Gallery, ON

Ptasinski, Margaret, *Children's Librn,* Long Beach Public Library, NY

Puccinelli, Lydia, *Cur Coll,* Museum of African Art, Washington, DC

Puchek, Mrs Michael, *Secy,* Woodmere Art Gallery, Philadelphia, PA

Puerta, Fabio, *Head Advertising Art,* Javeriana Univ Faculty of Architecture and Design, Bogota, Colombia

Puffer, John, *Mem Faculty,* Kirkwood Community College, Cedar Rapids, IA

Pugh, Mary, *Secy,* Hampshire County Public Library, Romney, WV

Pugh, Simon, *Head Complementary Studies,* Saint Martins School of Art, London, England

Pujol, Elliott, *Assoc Prof,* Kansas State Univ, Manhattan

Pulas, Arthur, *Chmn,* Syracuse Univ, NY

Pulford, E B, *Prof,* Mount Allison Univ, Sackville, NB

Pulvino, Mrs, *Exec Secy,* State Univ New York at Buffalo

Pum, Robert, *Head Dept,* Univ Wisconsin-Green Bay

Pumphrey, Richard, *Instr,* Shorter College, Rome, GA

Pumplim, Paula L, *Reference Librn,* Frick Art Reference Library, New York, NY

Punnet, Nan, *VPres,* Midland Art Council of the Midland Center for the Arts, MI

Punt, Rodney L, *Asst Gen Mgr,* City of Los Angeles Municipal Arts Dept, CA

Pura, William, *Chmn Printmaking,* Univ Manitoba, Winnipeg

Purdo, E Dane, *Chmn,* Lawrence Univ, Appleton, WI

Purdy, David, *Chmn Dept,* Columbia College, CA

Purdy, Gerald, *Pres,* Kaysville Community Art League, UT

Purdy, Henry, *Chmn Dept,* Holland College, Charlottetown, PEI

Purrington, Philip F, *Sr Cur,* New Bedford Whaling Museum, MA

Purser, Robert, *Chmn,* Bellevue Community College, WA

Puryear, Thomas, *Chairperson Art History,* Southeastern Massachusetts Univ, North Dartmouth

Pusic, Marija, *Head Documentation,* Museum of Modern Art, Belgrade, Yugoslavia

Putar, Radoslav, *Dir,* Galerije Grada Zabreba, Yugoslavia

Puvogel, Renate, *Librn,* Suermondt-Ludwig-Museum der Stadt Aachen, Germany

Pyle, Gene J, *Asst Prof,* Morehead State Univ, KY

Qamaruddin, Mr, *Tech Officer,* Nat Museum of Pakistan, Karachi

Quall, Alvin, *Dir Summer School,* Whitworth College, Spokane, WA

Qually, Ingolf J, *Prof & Head,* Gettysburg College, PA

Qualters, Robert, *Pres,* Associated Artists of Pittsburgh Arts and Crafts Center, PA

Quanbeck, Lydia, *Dir Summer School,* St Olaf College, Northfield, MN

Quandt, Elizabeth, *Prof,* Santa Rosa Junior College, CA

Quaresma, Maria Clementina, *Cur,* Museu Nacional de Soares dos Reis, Porto, Portugal

Quarre, M, *Cur,* Musee des Beaux-Arts de Dijon, France

Quarterman, George, *VPres,* Amarillo Art Center Association, TX

Quave, Evelyn, *Mem Faculty,* Utica Junior College, MS

Queen, Louis, *Admin Asst,* United Methodist Church, Lake Junaluska, NC

Quick, Birney M, *Head Dept & Prof,* Grand Marais Art Colony, MN

Quick, Michael, *Cur American Art,* Los Angeles County Museum of Art, CA

Quick, Richard, *Museum Asst,* Rahr-West Museum and Civic Center, Manitowoc, WI

Quigley, Donn P, *Chief Cur,* Neville Public Museum, Green Bay, WI

Quigley, Michael A, *Asst Dir,* Univ Pennsylvania Inst of Contemporary Art, Philadelphia

Quimby, George I, *Dir,* Thomas Burke Mem Washington State Museum, Seattle

Quimby, Ian M G, *Ed Publ Office,* Winterthur Museum and Gardens, DE

Quinlan, Sandra, *Secy,* New Mexico Art League, Albuquerque

Quinn, James L, *Dir,* Neville Public Museum, Green Bay, WI

Quinn, James T, *Prof & Chmn Dept Art,* Univ Mississippi, University

Quinn, Patrick J, *Dean,* Rensselaer Polytechnic Inst, Troy, NY

Quinn, Robert M, *Coordr Art History,* Univ Arizona, Tucson

Quinn, Thomas, *Pres Govs Bd,* New York State Dept of Parks and Recreation, Hudson

Quinsac, Annie, *Instr,* Univ South Carolina, Columbia

Quintal, Dr Claire, *Dir Summer School,* Assumption College, Worcester, MA

Quirk, Carol, *Asst Cur,* Nat Art Gallery of New Zealand, Wellington

Quirk, James M, *Asst Prof,* Northern Michigan Univ, Marquette

Quirk, Marie H S, *Mus Dir,* City of Holyoke Museum-Wistariahurst, MA

Quoniam, Pierre, *Dir,* Musee du Louvre, Paris, France

Raab, Tom, *Instr,* Georgia Southern College, Statesboro

Raasch, Cheryl, *Secy,* De Saisset Art Gallery & Museum, Santa Clara, CA

Raasch, L, *Dir,* Junior Museum, Art Inst of Chicago, IL

Rabb, Miriam G, *Adminr & Property Council & Staff,* Nat Trust Interpretors, Oatlands, Leesburg, VA

Rabinovich, Lidia, *Librn,* Centro de Arte y Communicacion, Buenos Aires, Argentina

Rabis, James, *Librn,* Fairfield Public Library and Museum, IA

Rabkin, Leo, *Pres,* American Abstract Artists, see National and Regional Organizations

Racz, Andre, *Prof,* Div Painting and Sculpture, Columbia Univ, New York, NY

Raday, Maria, *Treas,* Main Line Center of the Arts, Haverford, PA

Radde, Bruce, *Art Hist Coordr,* San Jose State Univ, CA

Radecki, Martin, *Conservator,* Indianapolis Museum of Art, IN

Radell, Sheila, *Children's Dept Head,* Topeka Public Library, KS

Rademaker, Pierre, *Assoc Prof,* California Polytechnic State Univ, San Luis Obispo

Radford, Dorothy, *Cur Educ,* Telfair Academy of Arts & Sciences, Savannah, GA

Radich, Anthony J, *Admin-Dir,* Virginia Beach Arts Center, VA

Radley, Russell, *Dir Educ,* American Society of Interior Designers, see National and Regional Organizations

Radosh, Sondra M, *Asst Dir,* Jones Library, Amherst, MA

Radysh, Jeanne, *Mem Faculty,* Ray-Vogue Schools, Chicago, IL

Raedler, Dorothy F, *Dir,* Saint Croix School of the Arts, Christiansted, Virgin Islands

Raferty, Dr J, *Dir & Keeper Antiquities,* Nat Museum of Ireland, Dublin

Raff, Douglass A, *Secy,* Corporate Council for the Arts, Seattle, WA

Raffin, Paul, *Pres,* Maude I Kerns Art Center, Eugene, OR

Ragan, Robert, *Treas,* Gaston County Art and History Museum, Dallas, NC

Raggio, Olga, *Chmn Sculpture & Decorative Arts,* Metropolitan Museum of Art, New York, NY

Rago, Juliet, *Assoc Prof,* Loyola Univ, Chicago, IL

Ragouzis, Perry, *Coordr,* Colorado State Univ, Fort Collins

Rahill, Margaret Fish, *Cur,* Milwaukee Public Library, WI

Rahja, Virginia, *Dir,* School of the Associated Arts, Saint Paul, MN

Raia, Frank, *VPres & Dir Educ,* Art Inst of Fort Lauderdale, FL

Raible, Alton, *Mem Faculty,* College of Marin, Kentfield, CA

Rainbird, Stephen, *Art Educ Officer,* Tasmanian Museum and Art Gallery, Hobart, Australia

Rainer, Otto, *Admin,* Saltzburger Museum Carolino Augusteum, Austria

Rainey, Mrs William, *Pres,* Spiva Art Center, Joplin, MO

Rains, Mickey, *Instr,* Dunedin Fine Arts & Cultural Center, FL

Raiser, Anna, *Instr,* Greenville College, IL

Raiser, C Lane, *Instr,* Greenville College, IL

Rajam, Margarte, *Prof,* West Virginia Univ, Morgantown

Rakocy, William, *Sr Cur,* El Paso Museum of Art, TX

Rakovan, Lawrence, *Assoc Prof,* Univ Maine at Portland-Gorham, Gorham

Ramage, Mrs Edward D, *Asst Librn,* Skaneateles Library Association, NY

Ramage, William, *Instr,* Castleton State College, VT

Rambert, Leonard F, *Pres,* American Swedish Inst, Minneapolis, MN

Ramirez, Adrian N, *Prof,* Catholic Univ Puerto Rico, Ponce

Ramirez, Mari Carmen, *Asst Dir,* Museu de Arte de Ponce, PR

Ramke, Grace, *Assoc Prof,* McNeese State Univ, Lake Charles, LA

Ramkissoon, K K, *Chmn Visual Communications,* Corcoran School of Art, Washington, DC

Ramos, Carlos, *Dir,* Escola Superior de Belas Artes, Oporto, Portugal

Ramos, Cruz Anibal, *Cur,* Museo del Barrio, New York, NY

Ramos, Hope, *First VPres,* Douglas Art Association, AZ

Ramsaran, Helen, *Asst Prof,* John Jay College of Criminal Justice, New York, NY

Ramsauer, Joseph F, *Chmn Dept & Chmn Summer School,* Black Hawk College, Moline, IL

Ramsey, George, *Assoc Prof,* Wittenberg Univ, Springfield, OH

Ramsay, Jane, *Records Researcher,* Presbyterian Historical Society, Philadelphia, PA

Ramsdell, Mrs F A, *Secy,* Potsdam Public Museum, NY

Ramsey, James R, *Asst Prof,* Vanderbilt Univ, Nashville, TN

Ramsey, Robert David, *Chmn,* College of Notre Dame, Belmont, CA

Ramseyer, Dr Urs, *Cur Indonesia,* Museum fur Volkerkunde und Schweizerisches Museum fur Volkskunde Basel, Switzerland

Ramstedt, Nils W, Jr, *Asst Prof,* Univ Nevada, Las Vegas

Rand, Dr Olan A, Jr, *Asst Prof,* Northwestern Univ, Evanston, IL

Randall, Edwin H, *Dir Summer School,* Western State College of Colorado, Gunnison

Randall, Lilian M C, *Cur Manuscripts & Rare Books,* Walters Art Gallery, Baltimore, MD

Randall, Richard H, Jr, *Dir,* Walters Art Gallery, Baltimore, MD

Randall, Willard S, *Instr,* Cultural Arts Center of Ocean City, NJ

Randazzo, Angelo, *Dir Gallery & Summer School,* Craft Center, Worcester, MA

Randolfi, Miss A, *Librn,* New York Chamber of Commerce and Industry, NY

Randolph, Mrs James, *Secy,* Oklahoma Museum of Art, Oklahoma City

Randolph, John, *Head Dept & Prof,* Phillips Univ, Enid, OK

Raneo, Frank, *Chmn Fashion Illustration,* New England School of Art and Design, Boston, MA

Raney, Marcia, *Mem Faculty,* Ohio Visual Art Institution, Cincinnati

Rankin, Alan C, *Treas Bd Mgrs,* Sheldon Swope Art Gallery, Terre Haute, IN

Rankin, Gratia, *Exhib Coordr,* San Jose State Univ, CA

Rankin, Joseph T, *Cur Spencer Coll,* New York Public Library, NY

Rankin, Marjorie E, *Dean & Dir Summer School,* Drexel Univ, Philadelphia, PA

Ranshaw, Ted, *Treas,* Calgary Artists Society, AB

Ransom, Gordon, *Head Graphic Design,* Saint Martins School of Art, London, England

Ransom, William, *Mem Faculty,* Murray State Univ, KY

Ransome-Wallis, Miss, *Cur,* Worshipful Co of Goldsmiths, London, England

Ranspach, E J, *Head Dept,* College of Boca Raton, FL

Rantz, Sylvia M, *Secy-Treas,* Boston Printmakers, MA

Rapalee, Liz, *Libr Asst,* Lake Placid School of Art, NY

Rapaport, Richard, *Dir,* Studio Workshop, New York, NY

Rapp, Brigid, *Librn,* Nat Trust for Historic Preservation, Washington, DC

Rappo, M Michel, *Dir,* Ecoles D'Art de Geneve, Switzerland

Rapson, Ralph E, *Head,* Univ Minnesota, Minneapolis

Raquin, Virginia C, *Asst Prof,* College of Holy Cross, Worcester, MA

Rasch, Arthur Roberts, *Chmn Communication Arts,* East Carolina Univ, Greenville, NC

Rash, Bob, *First VPres,* Allied Arts Council of the Yakima Valley, Yakima, WA

Rash, Gen Dillman A, *Pres Bd Govs,* J B Speed Art Museum, Louisville, KY

Rasmussen, Gail, *Exec Dir,* Artists Equity Association, see National and Regional Organizations

Rasmussen, Gerald E, *Dir,* Stamford Museum and Nature Center, CT

Rasmussen, Glen R, *Dir Summer School,* Morningside College, Sioux City, IA

Rasmussen, H, *Keeper Danish Folk Museum,* Nat Museum, Copenhagen, Denmark

Rasmussen, Marie, *Instr,* Umpqua Community College, Roseburg, OR

Rasmussen, Richard J, *Chmn,* Whitman College, Walla Walla, WA

Rasmussen, Theodore, *Head Dept,* Iowa Wesleyan College, Mount Pleasant

Rasmussen, Waldo, *Dir International Prog,* Museum of Modern Art, New York, NY

Ratcliff, Gary L, *Asst Prof,* Northeast Louisiana Univ, Monroe

Ratcliffe, Mrs Jefferson, *Cur,* Sturdivant Hall, Selma, AL

Ratelle, Marie Jose, *Secy,* La Societe des Decorateurs-Ensembliers du Quebec, Montreal

Rathbum, Joan Nachbaur, *Dir,* Longview Museum and Arts Center, TX

Rathert, Fred, *Pres,* Williams County Historical Society, Williston, ND

Ratner, Hindy, *Exten Cur,* Univ British Columbia Museum of Anthropology, Vancouver

Rattner, Carl, *Chmn,* St Thomas Aquinas College, Sparkhill, NY

Rattray, Alexander, *Head Dept Landscape Archit,* Univ Manitoba, Winnipeg

Rauch, John V, *Assoc Prof,* Northern Michigan Univ, Marquette

Raufer, Mrs William, *Secy,* Quincy Society of Fine Arts, IL

Raup, George B, *Pres,* Clark County Historical Society, Springfield, OH

Raupt, Florita, *Cur Mus Coll,* Traphagen School of Fashion, New York, NY

Rauschenberg, Bradford L, *Research Fellow & Librn,* Museum of Early Southern Decorative Arts, Winston-Salem, NC

Rautboard, Dorothy, *Pres,* Norton Gallery and School of Art, West Palm Beach, FL

Ravel, Nahum, *Exec Dir,* Saidye Bronfman Centre (YM-YWHA & NHS), Montreal, PQ

Ravelli, Shirley, *Secy,* South Peace Art Society, Dawson Creek, BC

Ravenel, Gaillard F, *Cur,* Nat Gallery of Art, Washington, DC

Ravicz, Dr Marilyn Ekdahl, *Research Dir,* Inst for Advanced Studies in Contemporary Art, San Diego, CA

Ravin, Yoram, *Dir Gen,* Israel Museum, Jerusalem

Rawls, William A, *Dir Theatre,* Rocky Mount Arts and Crafts Center, NC

Rawson, Hufty E, *Prof,* Catholic Univ Puerto Rico, Ponce

Ray, Gordan B, *Pres,* John Simon Guggenheim Memorial Found, New York, NY

Ray, Jim, *Dir,* Albrecht Art Museum, St Joseph, MO

Ray, Malde, *Treas,* Tullahoma Fine Arts Center, TN

Ray, P K, *Photographer,* Nat Gallery of Modern Art, New Delhi, India

Ray, Randy, *Preparator,* Museum of the Southwest, Midland, TX

Ray, Timothy, *Assoc Prof,* Moorhead State Univ, MN

Ray, Wade, *Dir & Dir Summer School,* Ray-Vogue Schools, Chicago, IL

Raybon, Phares, *Chmn,* Ouachita Baptist Univ, Arkadelphia, AR

Rayen, James Wilson, *Prof,* Wellesley College, MA

Raymond, Mrs Dana M, *Secy,* Archives of American Art, Washington, DC; *Secy,* Guild Hall of East Hampton, NY

Raymond, Glenn T, *Chmn,* Grand Rapids Junior College, MI

Rayner, Gordon, *Dir,* Three Schools (New School of Art), Toronto, ON

Reach, Milton B, *Pres,* Westfield Athenaeum, MA

Read, Betty, *Corresp Secy,* Arts for Living Center, Burlington, IA

Reak-Johnson, Bridget, *Special Projects Coordr,* Los Angeles Inst of Contemporary Art, CA

Reale, Nicholas, *Instr,* Friends of the Arts and Sciences, Hilton Leech Studio, Sarasota, FL

Reals, Robert L, *Assoc Art Educ,* State Education Dept, Albany, NY

Ream, Fred, *Asst Prof,* Univ Alabama in Birmingham

Reams, Susan, *Secy,* Creative Arts Guild, Dalton, GA

Reardon, John P, *Assoc Prof,* College of Holy Cross, Worcester, MA

Reardon, Michael J, *VPres Art Gallery & Instr,* Blackhawk Mountain School of Art, CO

Reboli, John P, *Asst Prof,* College of Holy Cross, Worcester, MA

Rechtman, Elisheva, *Librn,* Israel Museum, Jerusalem

Recort, Robert, *Asst Prof,* Northwestern State Univ Louisiana, Natchitoches

Redd, Richard J, *Prof,* Lehigh Univ, Bethlehem, PA

Redden, Nigel, *Coordr Performing Arts,* Walker Art Center, Minneapolis, MN

Redding, Mrs Foster, *Chmn Bd,* Detroit Artists Market, MI

Reddix, Roscoe, *Asst Prof,* Southern Univ in New Orleans, LA

Redfern, Mrs Alan, *Pres,* High Plains Museum, McCook, NE

Redjinski, Barbara J, *Registrar,* Montgomery Museum of Fine Arts, AL

Redmond, Arlene, *Recording Secy,* Lowell Art Association, MA

Reeck, Edna, *Gallery Dir,* Waterloo Art Association, IA

Reed, Alan, *Instr,* St John's Univ, Collegeville, MN

Reed, Carl, *Asst Prof,* Colorado College, Colorado Springs

Reed, Doroth, *Secy,* Mount Holyoke College Art Museum, South Hadley, MA

Reed, Elizabeth G S, *Secy,* Westfield Athenaeum, MA

Reed, Fred, *Treas,* Erie Art Center, PA

Reed, Lawrence, *Head Dept,* Campbellsville College, KY

Reed, Mary A, *Instr,* Kearney State College, NE

Reed, Ralph, *Lectr,* Mills College, Oakland, CA

Reed, Raymond, *Dean,* Texas A&M Univ, College Station

Reed, Robert, *Secy,* Art Directors Club, see National and Regional Organizations

Rees, D M, *Keeper,* Nat Museum of Wales, Cardiff

Rees, Philip, *Art Librn,* William Hayes Ackland Memorial Art Center, Univ North Carolina, Chapel Hill

Reese, Alice, *Chmn Bd,* Buchanan Arts and Crafts, Buchanan Dam, TX

Reese, Anne O, *Librn,* Toledo Museum of Art, OH

Reese, Brenda, *Neighborhood Arts Coordr,* Arkansas Arts Center, Little Rock

Reese, Gary, *Chief Librn,* Tacoma Public Library, WA

Reese, Gerard F, *Registrar & Cur Photographic Coll,* New York State Historical Association, Cooperstown

Reeve, James K, *Dir,* Oklahoma Museum of Art, Oklahoma City

Reeves, Mrs Charles M, *VPres,* North Carolina Art Society, Raleigh

Reeves, Robert L, *VPres,* Stan Hywet Hall Found, Akron, OH

Reeves, Thelma, *Asst,* Ponca City Cultural Center and Indian Museum, OK

Reger, Lawrence L, *Dir,* American Association of Museums, see National and Regional Organizations

Regier, Kathleen J, *Chairperson Art Dept,* Webster College, Webster Groves, MO

Regina, A La, *Dir,* Museo Nazionale Romano, Italy

Regina, Sister M, *Dir Summer School,* Caldwell College, NJ

Rehm, Celeste, *Vis Lectr,* California State College, Stanislaus, Turlock

Rehmani, F M Anjum, *Keeper Muslim Period Coll,* Lahroe Museum, Pakistan

Rehnberg, Mats, *Chmn,* Inst Folk Life, Nordiska Museet, Stockholm, Sweden

Reibel, Bertram, *Chmn,* W Braun Co Wolf and Mary Braun Fund, New York, NY

Reich, David L, *Chief Librn,* Chicago Public Library, IL

Reich, Elsa, *Reference & Special Research Librn,* Colorado Springs Fine Arts Center, CO

Reich, Shirley, *Secy,* Triton Museum of Art, Santa Clara, CA

Reichert, Don, *Chmn Painting,* Univ Manitoba, Winnipeg

Reichert, Raphael, *Asst Prof,* California State Univ, Fresno

Reid, Bryan S, Jr, *Secy,* Chicago Historical Society, IL

Reid, D, *Cur, Post Confederation Canadian Art,* Nat Gallery of Canada, Ottawa, ON

Reid, Edward S, *Chmn,* Brooklyn Inst of Arts and Sciences, NY

Reid, Frank P, *Exec Dir,* American Ceramic Society, see National and Regional Organizations

Reid, Jo, *Educ Dir & Dir Summer School,* Coos Art Museum, Coos Bay, OR

Reid, Josie, *Pres,* Coos Art Museum, Coos Bay, OR

Reid, Lawry, *Chairperson Dept,* Dean Junior College, Franklin, MA

Reid, Sir Norman, *Dir,* Tate Gallery, London, England

Reid, Richard, *Asst Prof,* Univ British Columbia, Vancouver

Reid, Robert, *Dir,* Summit Art Center, NJ

Reif, F David, *Assoc Prof,* Univ Wyoming, Laramie

Reiff, Daniel, *Assoc Prof,* State Univ New York College at Fredonia

Reigg, Robert F, *Chmn,* Middlebury College, VT

Reiling, Susan W, *Cur Coll,* Dade County Art Museum; *Cur Decorative Arts,* Vizcaya, Miami, FL

Reilly, Carol, *Lectr,* Georgian Court College, Lakewood, NJ

Reilly, Jerry M, *Instr,* Modesto Junior College, CA

Reilly, John R, Jr, *Pres,* Manchester Historic Association, NH

Reilly, Maureen, *Adminr,* New Museum, New York, NY

Reilly, Rose, *Secy,* Federated Art Associations of New Jersey, Lavallette

Reily, Bill, *Assoc Prof,* Incarnate Word College, San Antonio, TX

Reina, Ruben E, *Cur Latin American Ethnology,* Univ Pennsylvania Museum, Philadelphia

Reinhart, Sister Margaret, *Prof,* Avila College, Kansas City, MO

Reinholtz, Richard, *Assoc Prof,* Univ Missoula, MT

Reininghaus, Ruth R, *Corresp Secy,* Salmagundi Club, see National and Regional Organizations

Reinke, Bernnett, *Librn,* Dickinson State College, ND

Reinold, Dr Marlinde, *Librn,* Stadelsches Kunstinstitut, Frankfurt am Main, Germany

Reinvald, Ilmar, *Dir,* School of Architecture, Montana State Univ, Bozeman

Reipka, *Pres & Prof,* Akademie der Bildenden
Kunste, Munich, Germany

Reischer, Phyllis, *Educ Coordr,* Metropolitan
Museum and Art Centers, Coral Gables, FL

Reitz, Ann, *Cur Coll & Librn,* Flint Inst of Arts
Museum, MI

Reitzel, Dr William, *VPres,* Newport Historical
Society, RI

Reizen, Sandra, *Secy,* Rensselaer County Historical
Society, Troy, NY

Rembert, Virginia, *Pres,* Southeastern College Art
Conference, see National and Regional
Organizations

Remington, R Roger, *Chmn Communications Design,*
Rochester Inst Technology, NY

Remsing, Joseph G, *Instr,* Modesto Junior College,
CA

Renaud, MO, *Gen Mgr,* Manisphere Group of
Artists, Winnipeg, MB

Renfroe, Margie, *Secy,* Galesburg Civic Art Center,
IL

Renfrow, William, *Assoc Prof,* Texas A&I Univ,
Kingsville

Renger, Dr Konrad, *Cur,* Staatliche Graphische
Sammlung, Munich, Germany

Rennie, Dorothy B, *Prog Research & Coordination,*
North Carolina Museum of Art, Raleigh

Rentenbach, Thomas J, *VPres,* Dulin Gallery of Art,
Knoxville, TN

Rentz, Mrs. John, *Pres,* Gilpin County Arts
Association, Central City, CO

Reott, Steve, *Instr,* California College of Arts and
Crafts, Oakland

Replogle, Rex, *Assoc Prof,* Kansas State Univ,
Manhattan

Repper, George, *First VPres,* Lotos Club, New York,
NY

Repplier, Cynthia, *Coordr Vis Serv,* Brandywine
River Museum, Chadds Ford, PA

Reshower, Joe de Cassares, *Lectr,* Georgia Inst of
Technology, Atlanta

Resnick, Nathan, *Chmn,* Long Island Univ
Brooklyn, NY

Resnikoff, Florence, *Instr,* California College of Arts
and Crafts, Oakland

Retana, Graciela Reyes, *Dir,* Museo de San Carlos,
Mexico City, Mexico

Retfalvi, Andrea, *Research Librn,* Univ Toronto Art
Collection, ON

Reuben, Mrs Don S, *Acting Pres,* Textile Society, Art
Inst of Chicago, IL

Reuling, Walter, *Dir Summer School,* Castleton State
College, VT

Reuter, Dr Anneliese, *Dir Educ,* Staatliche
Kunsthalle, Karlsruhe, Germany

Reuter, Laurel J, *Dir & Head Cur,* Univ North
Dakota Art Galleries, Grand Forks

Reuther, Belinda, *Cur,* Louisiana Historical
Association, New Orleans

Reuther, Edward, *Dir Special Prog,* Saint Peter's
College Art Gallery, Jersey City, NJ

Reutlinger, Dagmar E, *Cur Coll,* Worcester Art
Museum, MA

Revicki, Robert, *Prog Adv,* Pennsylvania Dept of
Education, Harrisburg

Revor, Sister M Remy, *Prof,* Mount Mary College
Milwaukee, WI

Rexroth, Nancy, *Instr,* Antioch College, Yellow
Springs, OH

Reyes, Felipe, *Asst Prof,* Univ Texas at San Antonio

Reyman, Dr Janusz, *Polish Coins,* Muzeum
Narodowe W Krakowie, Cracow, Poland

Reynard, Capt Kenneth D, *Fleet Capt,* Maritime
Museum Association of San Diego, CA

Reynolds, Allie, *Pres,* Nat Hall of Fame for Famous
American Indians, Anadarko, OK

Reynolds, Don L, *Asst Dir & Cur Pony Express,* St
Joseph Museum, MO

Reynolds, Donald, *Assoc In Charge Mus Educ,*
Metropolitan Museum of Art, New York, NY

Reynolds, Donald M, *Chmn,* College of Mount Saint
Vincent, Riverdale, NY

Reynolds, Fred J, *Dir,* Public Library of Fort Wayne
and Allen County, IN

Reynolds, Gary, *Registrar-Cur,* New York Univ Art
Collection, NY

Reynolds, Harold M, *Asst Prof,* Central Missouri
State Univ, Warrensburg

Reynolds, Neil, *Pres Bd Dir,* Heritage Museum &
Gallery, Leadville, CO

Reynolds, Robert, *Prof,* California Polytechnic State
Univ, San Luis Obispo

Reynolds, Ron, *Asst Prof,* Arkansas Tech Univ,
Russellville

Reynolds, Stephen, *Vis Prof Ceramics,* Univ Texas at
San Antonio

Reynolds, Valrae, *Cur Oriental Coll,* Newark
Museum, NJ

Reynolds, Wiley R, *VPres,* Society of the Four Arts,
Palm Beach, FL

Rezac, Roselyn, *Coordr,* Univ Minnesota Gallery,
Minneapolis

Rezansoff, Paul, *Chmn,* Saskatchewan Arts Board,
Regina

Rhodes, Curtis, *Assoc Prof,* Western Michigan Univ,
Kalamazoo

Rhodes, Glenda, *Head Fine Arts Dept,* Salt Lake City
Public Library, UT

Rhodes, Jim, *Dept Head Adult Serv,* Topeka Public
Library, KS

Rhodes, Milton, *Exec Dir,* Arts Council, Winston-
Salem, NC

Rhodes, Reilly P, *Dir,* Bower's Museum, Santa Ana,
CA

Rhodes, Rod, *Dir Mus Educ,* Colorado Springs Fine
Arts Center, CO

Rhodes, Silas H, *Dir,* School of Visual Arts, New
York, NY

Rhodes, Thomas A, *Cur Educ,* Montgomery
Museum of Fine Arts, AL

Rhyne, Charles S, *Dir Gallery Prog & Chmn Art Dept*
Reed College, Portland, OR

Ribble, Eva, *VPres,* Wind River Valley Artists
Guild, Dubois, WY

Ricci, Vincent, *Instr,* Montserrat School of Visual
Art, Beverly, MA

Rice, Catherine Teresa, *Dean Summer School,*
Emmanuel College, Boston, MA

Rice, Jacquelyn Ione, *Head Dept Ceramics,* Rhode
Island School of Design, Providence

Rice, Jerry, *Dir Summer School,* Western Carolina
Univ, Cullowhee, NC

Rice, Kristina, *Instr,* Miracosta College, Oceanside,
CA

Rice, Leland, *Lectr,* Pomona College, Clarement,
CA

Rice, Nancy, *Instr,* Maryville College, Saint Louis,
MO

Rice, Norman, *Mem Faculty,* Ivy School of
Professional Art, Pittsburgh, PA

Rice, Norman S, *Dir,* Albany Inst of History and Art,
NY

Ricehill, Ernest, Jr, *Cur,* Sioux City Art Center, IA

Rich, Hester A, *Librn,* Maryland Historical Society
Museum, Baltimore

Rich, Joseph, *Div Chairperson,* Butte Community
College, Oroville, CA

Rich, R D Jr, *Pres,* Stamford Museum and Nature
Center, CT

Rich, Robert E, *VPres,* Albright-Knox Art Gallery,
Buffalo, NY

Richard, Frances, *Exec Dir,* Nat Council for Arts and
Education, see National and Regional
Organizations

Richard, George M, *Dir,* Charles A Wustum
Museum of Fine Arts, Racine, WI

Richard, Jack, *Dir,* Studios of Jack Richard Creative
School of Design & Richard Gallery, Cuyahoga
Falls, OH

Richard, Jim, *Assoc Prof,* Univ New Orleans, LA

Richard, Mervin, *Painting Conservator,*
Intermuseum Conservation Association, see
National and Regional Organizations

Richard, Oscar G, *Dir,* Louisiana State Univ Art
Museum, Baton Rouge

Richards, Bruce, *VPres,* Southern Artists
Association, Hot Springs, AR

Richards, Bruce, *Regional Coordr,* Visual Arts
Ontario, Toronto

Richards, Dick, *Cur Decorative Arts,* Art Gallery of
South Australia, Adelaide

Richards, Karl, *Prof Art & Chmn Dept,* Arkansas
State Univ, State Univ

Richards, Kenneth, *Chmn Fine Arts,* Northeastern
Oklahoma A&M College, Miami

Richards, L W, *Asst Prof,* Nova Scotia Technical
College, Halifax

Richards, Lee, *Prof,* New Mexico State Univ, Las
Cruces, NM

Richards, Louise S, *Cur Prints & Drawings,* Cleveland
Museum of Art, OH

Richards, Milton, *Dept Head & Prof,* Mohawk Valley
Community College, Utica, NY

Richards, Nancy, *Assoc Cur,* Nat Trust For Historic
Preservation, Washington, DC

Richards, J Philip, *Dir,* Sordoni Art Gallery, Wilkes
College, Wilkes-Barre, PA

Richards, Richard, *Prof,* Assumption College,
Worcester, MA

Richards, Violet, *Gallery Dir,* Southern Artists
Association, Hot Springs, AR

Richards, Mrs Willard, *Chmn Antiquarian House,*
Mount Holyoke College Art Museum, South
Hadley, MA

Richardson, Brenda, *Asst Dir Art,* Baltimore
Museum of Art, MD

Richardson, Mrs Donald, *Trustee,* Attleboro
Museum, MA

Richardson, E P, *VPres,* Historical Society of
Pennsylvania, Philadelphia

Richardson, Gail, *Librn,* Helen Palmer Geisel
Library, La Jolla Museum of Contemporary Art,
CA

Richardson, James, *Conservator,* Ella Sharp
Museum, Jackson, MI

Richardson, James L, *Head Dept,* Southwest
Missouri State Univ, Springfield

Richardson, Katherine W, *Asst to Dir,* Essex
Institute, Salem, MA

Richardson, Mrs Pat, *Exec Secy,* Southwest Missouri
Museum Associates, Springfield

Richardson, Roger, *Asst Prof,* Houghton College,
NY

Richenburg, Robert, *Prof,* Ithaca College, NY

Richeson, Joan, *Mem Faculty,* Mount Saint Clare
College, Clinton, IA

Richilieu, Judith, *Librn,* Phillips Collection,
Washington, DC

Richman, Irwin, *Prof,* Pennsylvania State Univ,
Capitol Campus, Middletown

Richman, Stanley M, *Pres,* Arts and Education
Council of Greater St Louis, MO

Richmond, Bill, *Gallery Coordr,* Univ Evansville, IN

Richmond, Larry, *Pres,* Provincetown Art
Association and Museum, MA

Richmond, Neal W, *Art Librn & Cur,* Queens College
of the City Univ New York Art Collection,
Flushing

Richmond, William, *Asst Prof,* Univ Evansville, IN

Richnell, D T, *Dir Gen Reference Div,* British
Library, London, England

Richter, Mrs E, *Asst Art,* Dartmouth Heritage
Museum, NS

Richter, Sister Jean, *Dean,* Rosary College,
Florence, Italy

Ricker, Mrs Walter, *Pres,* Music and Art Found,
Seattle, WA

Ricketts, Mrs Rodney, *Secy,* Peninsula Arts
Association, Newport News, VA

Riddle, Evelyn, *Teacher,* Nutley Art Center, NJ

Riddle, Verna B, *Dir Libr,* Kansas City Art Inst, MO

Ridge, AD, *Provincial Archivist,* Provincial Archives
of Alberta, Edmonton

Ridgway, William C, *Chmn Bd Trustees,* Mystic
Seaport, CT

Ridington, Thomas, *Cur Art Gallery & Asst Prof,* La
Salle College, Philadelphia, PA

Ridley, Bob, *Instr,* Sierra College, Rocklin, CA

Ridley, Donna, *Asst Humanities Reference Librn,*
California State Univ Library, Sacramento

Riedel, Ione, *Treas,* Santa Cruz Art League, CA

Riegger, Hal, *Instr,* Truro Center for the Arts at Castle Hill, MA

Riel, Pamela, *Registrar,* Manchester Inst of Arts and Sciences, NH

Rifai, Maggie, *Secy & Admin Asst,* Kentucky Guild of Artists and Craftsmen, Berea

Riffle, Brenda, *Librn,* Hampshire County Public Library, Romney, WV

Rigacci, Iola, *Chmn Undergrad Div,* Schools of the Art Inst of Chicago, IL

Rigby, Bruce, *Asst Prof,* Trenton State College, NJ

Rigdon, Jerry, *Pres,* Arts for Living Center, Burlington, IA

Rigel, Steven, *Educ Dir,* Craftsmen's Guild of Mississippi, Jackson

Rigg, Mary R, *Res Specialist,* Reading Public Museum and Art Gallery, PA

Riggs, George W, *Asst Adminr,* Nat Gallery of Art, Washington, DC

Riggs, Timothy A, *Cur Prints & Drawings,* Worcester Art Museum, MA

Riggins, Lois, *Cur Educ,* Tennessee State Museum, Nashville

Riglito, Edith A, *Librn,* Montclair Art Museum, NJ

Riisoen, Mrs Thale, *Cur,* Vestlandske Kunstindustrimuseum, Bergen, Norway

Riley, Judith C, *Registrar,* Chrysler Museum at Norfolk, VA

Riley, Orrin, *Conservator,* Solomon R Guggenheim Museum, New York, NY

Riley, Stephen T, *Dir,* Massachusetts Historical Society, Boston

Rindlisbacher, David, *Asst Prof,* West Texas State Univ, Canyon

Rinehart, Michael, *Librn,* Sterling and Francine Clark Art Inst, Williamstown, MA

Ring, Eduardo, *Cur,* Centro de Arte y Communicacion, Buenos Aires, Argentina

Ringle, Steven, *Gallery Mgr,* Massachusetts Inst of Technology, Cambridge

Ringring, Dennis, *Head Drawing & Grad Adv,* Southern Illinois Univ, Edwardsville

Ringsmuth, Charles R, *Assoc Prof,* Corning Community College, NY

Rini, Theresa, *Asst Librn,* Old Sturbridge Village, MA

Rink, Bernard C, *Libr Dir,* Northwestern Michigan College, Traverse City

Rinker, Harry L, *Exec Dir,* Historical Society of York County, PA

Riordon, Bernard, *Cur,* Art Gallery of Nova Scotia, Halifax

Riordan, Claudia, *Researcher,* Northeastern Nevada Museum, Elko

Riordan, James Q, *Treas,* Brooklyn Inst of Arts and Sciences, NY

Riordan, John, *Prof,* State Univ New York College at Potsdam

Riordan, Mary, *Cur Coll,* Cranbrook Academy of Art Museum, Bloomfield Hills, MI

Rios, John F, *Prof,* Texas Woman's Univ, Denton

Ripley, S Dillon, *Secy,* Smithsonian Institution, Washington, DC

Rippel, Evalynne, *Admin Asst,* Wheelwright Museum, Santa Fe, NM

Ripper, Stephen, *Mem Faculty,* Bucks County Community College, Newtown, PA

Rippeteau, Bruce, *State Archaeologist,* Colorado Historical Society, Denver

Ripton, Michael J, *Dir Bur Mus,* Pennsylvania Historical and Museum Commission, Harrisburg

Risatti, Howard, *Asst Prof,* Univ Alabama in Birmingham

Rishel, Joseph, *Cur Paintings Before 1900,* Philadelphia Museum of Art, PA

Rising, Joan, *Art Historian,* Greenfield Community College, MA

Risley, John, *Prof,* Wesleyan Univ, Middletown, CT

Riss, Murray, *Asst Prof,* Southwestern at Memphis, TN

Risser, James, *Prof,* West Virginia Univ, Morgantown

Ristow, Dr Gunther, *Cur Early Christian Archaeology,* Romisch-Germanisches Museum, Museen der Stadt Koln, Germany

Ritch, Andrew J, *Chmn Theater Dept,* Hill Country Arts Found, Ingram, TX

Ritchie, Andrew C, *Asst Dir,* Art Information Center, NY

Ritchie, Ross, *Designer,* Auckland City Art Gallery, New Zealand

Ritger, Carolyn, *Photo Cataloger,* Mariners Museum, Newport News, VA

Ritscher, Carol, *Secy,* Palos Verdes Art Center, Rancho Palos Verdes, CA

Ritter, Harwood, *Coordr,* Univ Delaware, Newark

Ritterskamp, John P, *Assoc Prof,* Antioch College, Yellow Springs, OH

Ritts, Edwin Jr, *Chief Cur/Deputy Dir,* Greenville County Museum of Arts, SC; *Pres Elect,* Guild of South Carolina Artists, Columbia

Rivard, S Noella, *Dir,* Marie de L'Incarnation Center and Museum, PQ

Rivet, Louise, *Coordr,* Dorval Cultural Centre, PQ

Rivoire, Helena G, *Chief Technical Serv,* Bucknell Univ, Lewisburg, PA

Roadruck, Chuck, *Mem Faculty,* Spokane Falls Community College, WA

Robb, David M, Jr, *Chief Cur,* Kimbell Art Museum, Fort Worth, TX

Robbert, Paul, *Prof,* Western Michigan Univ, Kalamazoo

Robbins, Anne, *Asst Prof,* Southwestern at Memphis, TN

Robbins, Caroline, *Pres,* Historical Society of Pennsylvania, Philadelphia

Robbins, Phyllis Y, *Mem Faculty,* American River College, Sacramento, CA

Robbins, Sarah Fraser, *Dir Educ,* Peabody Museum of Salem, MA

Robbins, Warren M, *Dir,* Museum of African Art, Washington, DC

Robels, Dr Hella, *Cur Engravings,* Wallraf-Richartz Museum, Museen der Stadt Koln, Germany

Roberson, Samuel, *Chmn Art Hist Prog,* Herron School of Art, Indiana Univ-Purdue Univ, Indianapolis

Robert, Henry Flood, Jr, *Dir,* Montgomery Museum of Fine Arts, AL

Roberts, Cynthia, *Slide Cur,* School of Visual Arts Library, New York, NY

Roberts, Gail, *Asst,* Brandon Allied Arts Council, MB

Roberts, George, *Prof,* Univ Idaho, Moscow

Roberts, Helene, *Cur Visual Coll,* Fogg Art Museum, Cambridge, MA

Roberts, Jean E, *Children's Serv,* Nutley Public Library, NJ

Roberts, Ken *VPres,* New Mexico Art League, Albuquerque

Roberts, Mary C, *Assoc Prof,* Northwestern State Univ Louisiana, Natchitoches

Roberts, Dr Percival R, III, *Chmn Dept Art,* Bloomsburg State College, PA

Roberts, Ruth, *Cur,* Shaker Museum, Old Chatham, NY

Roberts, William E, Jr, *Assoc Prof,* Wells College, Aurora, NY

Robertshaw, Sister Mary Jane, *Head Dept,* College of New Rochelle, NY

Roberts-Jones, Philippe, *Dir,* Musees Royaux des Beaux-Arts de Belgique, Brussels

Robertson, C M, *Cur Cast Gallery,* Ashmolean Museum, Oxford Univ, England

Robertson, Charles M, *Pres,* School Art League of New York City, Brooklyn, NY

Robertson, Donald, *Prof,* Tulane Univ, New Orleans, LA

Robertson, Donald, *Assoc Prof,* Northwest Missouri State Univ, Maryville

Robertson, Edna, *Cur Coll,* Museum of Fine Arts, Santa Fe, NM

Robertson, George H, *Pres,* Mohawk Valley Community College, Utica, NY

Robertson, Joan E, *Art Cur,* Kemper Insurance Companies, Long Grove, IL, see Corporate Art Holdings

Robertson, Joe Chris, *Chmn,* Mars Hill College, NC

Robertson, John A, *Dir,* Stephen Foster Center, White Springs, FL

Robertson, John K, *Pres,* Professional Art Dealers Association of Canada, see National Organizations in Canada

Robertson, Monica, *Librn & Archivist,* New Brunswick Museum, Saint John

Robeson, Mrs Garland F, *Dir,* Peninsula Arts Association, Newport News, VA

Robillard, Charles, *Treas,* Musee D'Art de Joliette, PQ

Robinson, Andrew, Jr, *Cur Graphic Arts,* Nat Gallery of Art, Washington, DC

Robinson, Chester, *Dean Summer School,* Herbert H Lehman College, Bronx, NY

Robinson, D, *Keeper Paintings & Drawings,* Fitzwilliam Museum, Univ Cambridge, England

Robinson, Mrs D, *Gallery Dir,* Silvermine Guild of Artists, New Canaan, CT

Robinson, Don, *Assoc Prof,* Harding College, Searcy, AR

Robinson, Douglas, *Registrar,* Hirshhorn Museum and Sculpture Garden, Washington, DC

Robinson, Eric, *Downtown Gallery Mgr,* Delaware Art Museum, Wilmington

Robinson, Francis W, *Cur Emer Medieval Art,* Detroit Inst of Art Collections, MI

Robinson, Franklin W, *Dir,* Williams College Museum of Art, Williamstown, MA

Robinson, George, *Assoc Prof,* Bethel College, Saint Paul, MN

Robinson, Grove, *Chmn Dept Art & Dir Summer School,* Union Univ, Jackson, TN

Robinson, Henry S, *Prof,* Case Western Reserve Univ, Cleveland, OH

Robinson, Joyce, *Dir,* Bemis Art School for Children, Colorado Springs Fine Arts Center, CO

Robinson, Julie, *Sr Librn Children's Serv,* Ontario City Library, CA

Robinson, Lilien F, *Chmn,* George Washington Univ, Washington, DC

Robinson, Mary Ann, *Chmn Art Dept,* McPherson College, KS

Robinson, Judge Otto P, *Chmn Trustees,* Everhart Museum, Scranton, PA

Robinson, Susan Barnes, *Asst Prof,* Loyola Marymount Univ, Los Angeles, CA

Robinson, William A, *Dir,* Southern Methodist Univ, Dallas, TX

Robinson, William A, *Dir,* Univ Houston Gallery, TX

Robinson, William F, *Exec Dir Rceda,* Museum Without Walls, Rceda Inc, Friendsville, MD

Robischon, Helen, *Libr Asst,* Univ California Architecture and Fine Arts Library, Los Angeles

Robison, Andrew, *Pres,* Print Council of America, see National and Regional Organizations

Robison, Dr Charles, *Chmn Art & Music,* Angelo State University, San Angelo, TX

Robison, Joan, *Librn,* Baltimore Museum of Art, MD

Robison, Orvetta, *Librn,* Illinois State Museum of Natural History and Art, Springfield

Robson, Ladonna, *Pub Information Officer,* Albuquerque Museum of Art, History and Science, NM

Robson, Mary Louise, *Head,* Malone College, Canton, OH

Roche, James, *Prof,* Florida State Univ, Tallahassee

Roche, Valerie, *Mem Faculty,* Creighton Univ, Omaha, NE

Rocher-Jauneau, Madeleine, *Cur,* Musee des Beaux Arts, Palais St Pierre, Lyon, France

Rochette, Edward C, *Exec VPres,* American Numismatic Association, see National and Regional Organizations

Rochford, Paul A, *Chmn & Dir Summer School,* Hiram College, OH

Rock, John H, *Asst Dir,* Fairbanks Gallery & *Chmn Dept Art,* Oregon State Univ, Corvallis

Rock, William Jr, *Chmn & Assoc Prof Landscape Archit,* Univ Toronto, ON

Rockefeller, David, *VChmn,* Museum of Modern Art, New York, NY

Rockefeller, Mrs John D, III, *Pres,* Museum of Modern Art, New York, NY

Rockmuller, Rebecca, *Chief Pub Serv,* Hewlett-Woodmere Public Library, Hewlett, NY

Rockwell, Ford A, *Head Librn,* Wichita Public Library, KS

Rodger, Bob, *Cur,* Provincetown Art Association and Museum, MA

Rodgers, David, *Cur,* Central Art Gallery, Wolverhampton, England

Rodgers, Ernest B, *Pres Bd Trustees,* Dulin Gallery of Art, Knoxville, TN

Rodgers, Jack A, *Exec Dir,* San Antonio Art Inst, TX

Rodgers, Linda, *Pres & Dir Summer School,* Wayne Art Center, PA

Rodgers, Mary M, *Asst to Dir,* Wine Museum of San Francisco; *Librn,* Alfred Fromm Rare Wine Books Library, San Francisco, CA

Rodriguez, Ada Nivea, *Librn,* Ateneo Puertorriqueno, San Juan, PR

Rodriguez, Carlos, *Dir,* Nat Museum of Colonial Art of la Casa de la Cultura Ecuatoriana, Quito

Rodwell, Marianne, *Lectr,* Cardinal Stritch College, Milwaukee, WI

Roe, Mrs Medford, *VPres,* Art Patrons League of Mobile, AL

Roe, Ruth, *Librn,* Newport Harbor Art Museum, CA

Roehner, Bernice Gottschalk, *Prog Adv,* Pennsylvania Dept of Education, Harrisburg

Roemer, Anna, *Pres,* Brush and Palette Club, Cooperstown, NY

Roerich, Svetoslav, *VPres,* Nicholas Roerich Museum, New York, NY

Rogan, Robert C, *Head Dept & Prof,* Lamar Univ, Beaumont, TX

Roger, David, *Technical Adminr,* Solomon R Guggenheim Museum, New York, NY

Roger, James, III, *Pres Bd,* Lake Placid School of Art Gallery, NY

Rogers, Ann, *Arts Coordr,* Patterson Library, Westfield, NY

Rogers, Charles B, *Dir,* Rogers House Museum Gallery, Ellsworth, KS

Rogers, Don, *Prof Art & Head Dept,* Univ Saskatchewan, Saskatoon Campus

Rogers, Francis D, *VPres,* Associates of the Art Commission, New York, NY

Rogers, Gail, *Exec,* Craftsmen's Association of British Columbia, Vancouver

Rogers, Jac, *Dept Chmn,* Spokane Falls Community College, Spokane, WA

Rogers, James W, *Asst Prof,* Glenville State College, WV

Rogers, John, *Secy,* Stockbridge Mission House Association, MA

Rogers, Millard F, *Dir,* Cincinnati Art Museum, OH

Rogers, Mrs Paul C, *Exec Secy,* Art Association of Newport, RI

Rogers, Mrs Riley, *Dir,* Fine Arts Club 2nd Crossing Gallery, Valley City, ND

Rogers, Robert, *Lectr,* Queensborough Community College, Bayside, NY

Rogers, Samuel S, *Pres,* Merrimack Valley Textile Museum, North Andover, MA

Rogild, Anne-Dorte, *Restorer,* Dept Painting & Sculpture, Statens Museum for Kunst, Copenhagen, Denmark

Rogoff, Anita, *Assoc Prof,* Case Western Reserve Univ, Cleveland, OH

Rohlfing, Christian, *Cur Coll,* Cooper-Hewitt Museum, New York, NY

Rohrmoser, Dr albin, *Cur Art History,* Saltzburger Museum Carolino Augusteum, Austria

Rokujo, Takatsugu, *Chief Cur,* Bridgestone Bijutsukan, Tokyo, Japan

Rolfe, Joanne, *Secy to Dir,* Rodman Hall Arts Centre, St Catharine, ON

Roller, Marion *Chmn Design Dept,* Traphagen School of Fashion, New York, NY

Roller, Russell, *Chmn Dept,* Northeastern Illinois University Gallery, Chicago

Rollins, Caroline, *Info & Mem,* Yale Univ Art Gallery, New Haven, CT

Roloff, Daphne, *Dir Libraries,* Art Inst of Chicago, IL

Rolston, Margaret P, *Librn,* Woodrow Wilson Birthplace Found, Staunton, VA

Roman, Rose D, *Asst Treas,* Providence Watercolor Club, RI

Romanek, V, *Asst Prof,* Pennsylvania State Univ, Uniontown

Romano, Umberto, *Secy,* Nat Acad of Design, New York, NY, *Dir & Instr,* Umberto Romano School of Creative Art, New York, NY

Rombout, Luke, *Dir,* Vancouver Art Gallery, BC

Romney, Hugh N, *Chmn Bd Trustees,* Nat Inst for Architectural Education, see National and Regional Organizations

Ronald, Hugh N, *Pres,* Art Association of Richmond, IN

Roncalli, Francesco, *Cur Etruscan Antiquities,* Monumenti Musei e Gallerie Pontificie, Vatcian City, Italy

Roney, Anne Garwood, *Asst Cur Installations,* London Public Library and Art Museum, ON

Ronte, Dr, Dieter, *Cur Engravings,* Wallraf-Richartz Museum, Museen der Stadt Koln, Germany

Rooney, Alice, *Exec Dir,* Allied Arts of Seattle, WA

Rooney, Mrs Andrew A, *Pres,* Lockwood-Mathews Mansion Museum, Norwalk, CT

Rooney, Paul M, *Dir,* Buffalo and Erie County Public Library, NY

Rooney, Thomas P, *Chmn Summer School,* Catholic Univ America, Washington, DC

Rooney, Walter, *Treas,* Architectural League of New York, NY

Roosevelt, Anna C, *Cur South & Middle America,* Heye Found, New York, NY

Rooston, Maxine, *Cur Prints & Drawings,* Achenbach Foundation for Graphic Arts, Fine Arts Museums of San Francisco, CA

Root, Margaret C, *Asst Cur,* Kelsey Museum of Ancient & Mediaeval Archaeology, Ann Arbor, MI; *Vis Prof,* Univ of Chicago, IL

Root, Mrs Stanley, *Pres,* Philadelphia Museum of Art, PA

Roper, Floyd W. *Treas,* Roberson Center, Binghamton, NY

Roper, Thelma, *Head,* Maryville College, TN

Rorem, Jan, *Assoc Prof,* Black Hawk College, Moline, IL

Rorimer, Anne, *Assoc Cur 20th Century Painting & Sculpture,* Art Inst of Chicago, IL

Rorup, Marianne, *Librn,* Statens Museum for Kunst, Copenhagen, Denmark

Rosa, Joyce, *Assoc Prof,* School of the Arts, C W Post Center of Long Island Univ, Brookville, NY

Rosander, Dr Goran, *Keeper Cultural Field Research,* Nordiska Museet, Stockholm, Sweden

Rosati, Angelo V, *Prof,* Rhode Island College, Providence

Roschwalb, Susanne, *Chief Pub Information,* Nat Portrait Gallery, Washington, DC

Rose, Jack, Curriculum, *Chmn Fashion Merchandising,* Art Inst of Fort Lauderdale, FL

Rose, Jeanne, *Corresp Secy,* Arts Club of Washington, DC

Rose, Larry, *Instr,* Oklahoma State Univ, Okmulgee

Rose, Patricia, *Assoc Prof,* Florida State Univ, Tallahassee

Rose, P D, *Head Dept Combined Arts,* Brighton Polytechnic, England

Rose, Timothy G, *Dir,* Springville Museum of Art, UT

Roseberg, Carl, *Prof,* College of William and Mary, Williamsburg, VA

Roseberry, Helen, *Registrar,* East Tennessee State Univ Museum and Gallery, Johnson City

Rosefelt, Wendy, *Cur Asst,* Marquette Univ Art Gallery, Milwaukee, WI

Rosemfeld, Dr Myra Nan, *Research Cur,* Montreal Museum of Fine Arts, PQ

Rosen, Dr Barry H, *Dir & Archivist,* Univ South Carolina, Columbia

Rosen, Irwin, *Dean,* Ivy School of Professional Art, Pittsburgh, PA

Rosen, James M, *Prof Art, Chmn Dept & Dir Summer School,* Santa Rosa Junior College, CA

Rosen, Steven W, *Cur,* Columbus Gallery of Fine Arts, OH

Rosenbaum, Allen, *Asst Dir,* Princeton Univ, NJ

Rosenberg, Alex, *Gallery Trustee,* Visual Artists and Galleries Association, see National and Regional Organizations

Rosenberg, Amy, *Asst Cur,* Kelsey Museum of Ancient & Mediaeval Archaeology, Ann Arbor, MI

Rosenberg, Barry A, *Asst Prof,* Miami Univ, Oxford, OH

Rosenberg, George, *Asst Prof,* Univ British Columbia, Vancouver

Rosenberg, Marti, *Coordr,* Tenn State Museum Association, Tennessee State Museum, Nashville

Rosenberg, Paul, *Treas,* Danforth Museum, Framingham, MA

Rosenberger, Pat, *Exec Dir,* Valley Art Center, Clarkston, WA

Rosenblatt, Arthur, *VPres Archit & Planning,* Metropolitan Museum of Art, New York, NY

Rosenburg, Jean, *Dir,* New Mexico Art League, Albuquerque

Rosenfeld, L, *Cur Coll,* Edinboro State College, PA

Rosenfeld, Susan, *Information Specialist,* Los Angeles Inst of Contemporary Art, CA

Rosenfield, Rachel, *Asst Cur,* Portland Art Association, OR

Rosengarten, Linda, *Admin Asst,* Univ California Art Gallery, Irvine, CA

Rosenquist, James, *Artist Trustee,* Visual Artists and Galleries Association, see National and Regional Organizations

Rosenstein, Harris, *Exec Adminr,* Rice Inst for the Arts, Houston, TX

Rosenstock, Ron, *Instr,* Craft Center, Worcester, MA

Rosenthal, Earl, *Prof,* Univ Chicago, IL

Rosenthal, Gertrude, *Consult Western Art,* Honolulu Acad of Arts Collection, HI

Rosenthal, Mark, *Cur Coll,* Univ California, Berkeley

Rosenthal, Mark, *Assoc Cur Paintings,* Wadsworth Atheneum, Hartford, CT

Rosenthal, Mark A, *Public Affairs Coordr,* Solomon R Guggenheim Museum, New York, NY

Rosenthal, Robert, *Assoc Prof,* Hanover College, IN

Rosenthal de Sosa, Elsa, *Librn,* Escuela Superior de Bellas Artes Ernesto de La Carcova, Buenos Aires, Argentina

Rosenwald, Lessing, J, *In Charge Coll Prints & Rare Books,* Alverthorpe Gallery, Jenkintown, PA

Rosenzweig, Daphne, *Asst Prof,* Oberlin College, OH

Roskopp, Joanne, *Pres Bd Trustees,* Art Center, Mt Clemens, MI

Roskos, George, *Prof,* Pacific Lutheran Univ, Tacoma, WA

Rosnow, Nancy, *Asst Prof,* New Mexico Highlands Univ, Las Vegas

Ross, Alex, *Librn,* Stanford Univ Museum of Art, CA

Ross, Barbara T, *Custodian Prints & Drawings,* Princeton Univ, NJ

Ross, David, *Chief Cur,* Univ California, Berkeley

Ross, David, *Dir,* New Brunswick Museum, Saint Johns

Ross, Don, *Treas,* Klamath Art Association, Klamath Falls, OR

Ross, Fernande, *Registrar,* Yale Univ Art Gallery, New Haven, CT

Ross, Jack, *Dean & Dir Summer School,* Humber College of Applied Arts and Technology, Rexdale, ON

Ross, John, *Head Dept & Prof,* Manhattanville College, Purchase, NY

Ross, Joseph B, *Asst Prof,* Saint Mary's College of Maryland, Saint Mary's City

Ross, Judy, *Photographer-in-Residence,* Moravian College, Bethlehem, PA

Ross, Kenneth, *Gen Mgr,* City of Los Angeles Municipal Arts Dept, CA

Ross, Lydia A, *Dir,* Peel Museum and Art Gallery, Brampton, ON

Ross, Mary Anne, *Instr,* Delta State Univ, Cleveland, MS

Ross, Mrs Richard M, *Pres,* Columbus Gallery of Fine Arts, OH

Ross, Robert F, *Asst Prof,* Univ Arkansas, Fayetteville

Ross, Robert M, *Art & Music Dept Head,* Kansas City Public Library, MO

Rossell, Mrs William, *Secy,* Gilpin County Arts Association, Central City, CO

Rossman, Michael, *Dept Chairperson & Assoc Prof,* Philadelphia College of Art, PA

Rossman, Ruth, *Pres,* Nat Watercolor Society, Los Angeles, CA

Roster, Laila, *Dir,* Contemporary Arts Center of Hawaii, Honolulu

Roston, Arnold, *Secy,* School Art League of New York City, Brooklyn, NY

Rostworowski, Dr Marek, *European Painting of 15th-17th Centuries,* Muzeum Narodowe W Krakowie, Cracow, Poland

Roters, Ramona, *Slide Librn,* Ernest Stevenson Bird Library, Syracuse, NY

Roth, Carolyn, *Asst Prof,* Univ Evansville, IN

Roth, Dr Leland M, *Asst Prof,* Northwestern Univ, Evanston, IL

Roth, Moira, *Dir,* San Diego State Univ Art Gallery, CA

Roth, Walter, *Lectr,* Catholic Univ America, Washington, DC

Roth, William James, *Ass Cur Paintings & Sculpture,* Brooklyn Museum, NY

Rothe, Janet, *Cur Coll,* Paine Art Center and Arboretum, Oshkosh, WI

Rothenberg, Barbara, *Mem Faculty,* Housatonic Community College, Bridgeport, CT

Rothenberg, Jerome, *Mem Faculty,* Univ California, San Diego, La Jolla

Rothman, Joseph, *VPres,* Artists Equity Association of New York, NY

Rothrock, Dr Dayton, *Dir Summer School,* McPherson College, KS

Rothrock, Ilse S, *Librn,* Kimbell Art Museum, Fort Worth, TX

Rothschild, JoAnn, *Instr,* Brockton Art Center, MA

Rotterdam, Paul, *Sr Lectr,* Harvard Univ, Cambridge, MA

Roudabush, Margaret C, *Exec Secy,* Gunston Hall Plantation, Lorton, VA

Roudzens, Mark, *Prof,* Salem State College, MA

Rouillard, Paul R, *Secy-Treas,* Nat Museum of Racing, Saratoga Springs, NY

Roulston, Pat, *Librn,* Univ Regina, SK

Round, Kathryn, *Dir,* Central Wyoming Museum of Art, Casper

Rourke, Orland J, *Asst Prof,* Concordia College, Moorhead, MN

Rous, Janice, *Educ Dir,* Jewish Museum, New York, NY

Rouse, John R, *Dir School & Cur Gallery,* Wichita Art Association, KS

Rousek, Sister Marie, *Librn,* College of Saint Elizabeth Mahoney, Convent Station, NJ

Rounsavall, Cathryn, *Mem Faculty,* Arkansas Arts Center, Little Rock

Rousseau, Romain, *Pres Exec Comt,* Le Musee Regional de Rimouski, PQ

Rousseve, Numa, *Prof Emer,* Xavier Univ Louisiana, New Orleans

Roux, Emmanuel, *Mgr,* Lotos Club, New York, NY

Roux-Dorlut, C, *Instr,* Fontainebleau School of Fine Arts, France

Rovetti, Paul F, *Dir,* William Benton Museum of Art, Storrs, CT

Row, Brian G, *Chmn,* Southwest Texas State Univ, San Marcos

Rowan, George, *Assoc Prof,* Univ New Orleans, LA

Rowan, Herman, *Prof Studio Art & Chmn Dept,* Univ Minnesota, Minneapolis

Rowan, Madeline Bronsdon, *Cur Ethnology/Pub Prog,* Univ British Columbia, Vancouver

Rowan, Odessa W, *Recording Secy,* Spectrum, Friends of Fine Art, Toledo, OH

Rowe, Ann P, *Asst Cur New World,* Textile Museum, Washington, DC

Rowe, Bobby Louise, *Assoc Prof,* Cleveland State Univ, OH

Rowe, Charles, *Coordr,* Univ Delaware, Newark

Rowe, Donald, *Chmn & Assoc Prof,* Olivet College, MI

Rowe, Donald F, *Dir,* Loyola Univ Chicago Art Collection, IL

Rowe, Harry M, Jr, *County Librn,* Orange County Public Library, Garden Grove, CA

Rowe, M Jessica, *Dir,* Blanden Art Gallery, Fort Dodge, IA

Rowe, Reginald M, *Instr,* San Antonio Art Inst, TX

Rowe, Ria, *Admin Officer,* Univ British Columbia Museum of Anthropology, Vancouver

Rowe, William Thomas, *Assoc Prof,* Saint Mary's College of Maryland, Saint Mary's City

Rowell, Edwin Mrs, *Pres,* Historical Society of Early American Decoration, Cooperstown, NY

Rowell, Henry T, *Pres,* American Acad in Rome, New York, NY

Rowell, Margit, *Cur Special Exhib,* Solomon R Guggenheim Museum, New York, NY

Rowinski, L J, *Dir,* Univ Alaska Museum, Fairbanks

Rowland, Eldon, *Instr,* Friends of the Arts and Sciences, Hilton Leech Studio, Sarasota, FL

Rowland, Katherine L, *Consult Special Projects,* Friends of the Arts and Sciences, Hilton Leech Studio, Sarasota, FL

Rowlett, Elsebet, *Assoc Cur,* Univ Missouri Museum of Anthropology, Columbia

Rowley, Susan, *Instr,* Nazareth College of Rochester, NY

Rowlison, Eric, *Dir,* Nat Gallery of Victoria, Australia

Rowlson, Bob, *VPres,* Ojai Valley Art Center, CA

Roy, Christopher D, *Assoc Prof,* Univ Missouri-Saint Louis

Roy, James, *Chmn,* Saint Cloud State Univ, MN

Roy, Jeanne, Sr, *Supvr,* Musee des Augustines de L'Hotel dieu Quebec, PQ

Roy, Margery, *Admin Asst,* Mount Holyoke College Art Museum, South Hadley, MA

Roy, Richard, *Dir & Dir Summer School,* Paris American Acad, France

Roy, Dr S, *Dir,* Indian Museum, Calcutta, India

Roy, Suzanne Marie, *Chmn,* Annhurst College, Woodstock CT

Royce, Diane, *Head Librn,* Stowe-Day Found, Hartford, CT

Royster, Kathryn, *Secy,* Gaston County Art and History Museum, Dallas, NC

Royster, Kenneth L, *Asst Prof,* Morgan State Univ, Baltimore, MD

Rozen, Melvyn J, *Assoc Prof,* Ohio Dominican Univ, Columbus

Rozman, Joseph, *Asst Prof,* Mount Mary College, Milwaukee, WI

Rozman, Dr Ksenija, *Asst,* Narodna Galerija Yugoslavia, Ljubljana

Rozniatowski, David William, *Chief Librn,* Winnipeg Art Gallery, MB

Rozsa, Eva, *Libr Head,* Magyar Nemzeti Galeria, Budapest, Hungary

Rubenfien, Leo, *Vis Prof,* Swarthmore College, PA

Rubenstein, Benay, *Secy,* American International Sculptors Symposiums, see National and Regional Organizations

Rubenstein, Gerna, *Cur Educ,* Flint Inst of Arts Museum, MI

Rubenstein, Meridel, *Mem Faculty,* College of Santa Fe, NM

Rubin, David, *Instr,* Pomona College, Claremont, CA; *Asst Dir,* Galleries of the Claremont Colleges, CA

Rubin, Helen, *Gen Reference Librn,* Fashion Inst of Technology, New York, NY

Rubin, William, *Dir Painting & Sculpture Coll,* Museum of Modern Art, New York, NY

Rubins, Geoffrey, *Lectr,* Inst for American Univ, Aix-en-Provence, France

Rubow, Jorn, *Dir Dept Painting & Sculpture,* Statens Museum for Kunst, Copenhagen, Denmark

Ruckert, Dr R, *Cur Ceramics,* Bayerisches Nationalmuseum, Munich, Germany

Rudasill, Leroy U, Jr, *Chmn,* Southern Seminary Junior College, Buena Vista, VA

Rudberg, Peggy, *Slide Librn,* Minneapolis College of Art and Design Library and Media Center, MN

Rudd, Barbara, *Secy,* Amarillo Art Center Association, TX

Rudenstine, Angelica, *Research Cur,* Solomon R Guggenheim Museum, New York, NY

Rudman, Joan, *Secy,* Hudson Valley Art Association, White Plains, NY

Rudner, Dr Jack, *Dir Summer School,* Western Connecticut State College, Danbury

Rudolph, Dr Wolf, *Cur,* Indiana Univ Art Museum, Bloomington

Rudy, Andrea, *Adminr,* Nook Farm Visitors Center, Stowe-Day Found, Hartford, CT

Rueppel, Merrill C, *Dir,* Museum of Fine Arts, Boston, MA

Ruffing, Charles, *Supvr Instructional Technology Prog,* Michigan Dept of Education State Library Services, Lansing

Ruffo, Joseph M, *Head Dept Art & Summer School,* Univ Northern Iowa, Cedar Falls

Ruffolo, Robert E, Jr, *Pres,* Princeton Antiques Bookservice, Atlantic City, NJ

Ruger, Dr Christoph B, *Dir,* Rheinisches Landesmuseum Bonn, Germany

Ruggles, Mrs John R, *Acting Dir,* Dulin Gallery of Art, Knoxville, TN

Ruggles, Mervyn, *Head Restoration & Conservation Lab,* Nat Gallery of Canada, Ottawa, ON

Ruhmer, Dr Eberhard, *Cur 19th Century Art,* Bayerischen Staatsgemaldesammlungen, Munich, Germany

Ruhrberg, Karl, *Dir,* Wallraf-Richartz-Museum, Museen der Stadt Koln, Germany

Ruiz, Noemi, *Assoc Chmn,* Inter American Univ Puerto Rico, San German

Ruiz-Avila, Hugo, *Registrar,* Univ Iowa Museum of Art, Iowa City

Rumford, Beatrix T, *Dir,* Abby Aldrich Rockefeller Folk Art Center, Williamsburg, VA

Runestad, Dr Cornell, *Chmn Fine Arts Div,* Wayne State College, NE

Runke, Henry M, *Head Dept of Art & Prof,* Univ Wisconsin-Stevens Point

Runnion, Marjorie, *Secy,* Brattleboro Museum and Art Center, VT

Runyon, Betty S, *Dir Vis Serv & Asst Pub Relations,* Minnesota Museum of Art Permanent Collection Gallery, St Paul

Runyon, John M, *Chmn & Prof,* Corning Community College, NY

Rupe, Bonnie, *Acq Dept Head,* Wichita Public Library, KS

Ruppe, Carol, *Librn,* Heard Museum, Phoenix, AZ

Rus, Alexandra, *Dir,* Muzeul de Arta Cluj-Napoca, Romania

Rush, Kent T, *Instr,* San Antonio Art Inst, TX

Rush, Kent, *Coordr,* San Antonio Art Inst, TX

Rush, Lucile, *Librn,* St Joseph Museum, MO

Rushbrook, Dr John, *Dir Summer School,* Saint Mary's College of Maryland, Saint Mary's City

Rushing, Darla H, *Librn,* Felix J Dreyfous Library, New Orleans Museum of Art, LA

Rushton, Brian, *Publ & Mktg Serv,* Brooklyn Museum, NY

Rusnell, Wesley A, *Registrar & Cur,* Roswell Museum and Art Center, NM

Russell, Ann, *Asst Dir,* DeCordova and Dana Museum and Park, Lincoln, MA

Russell, Dr Crawford L, *Chmn,* Grand Canyon College, Phoenix, AZ

Russell, H Diane, *Cur,* Nat Gallery of Art, Washington, DC

Russell, Jennifer, *Cur,* Whitney Museum of American Art, New York, NY

Russell, John, *Lectr,* John Jay College of Criminal Justice, New York, NY

Russell, John I, *Asst Dir & Exhib Coordr,* Craft Center, Worcester, MA

Russell, Reba, *Cur Educ,* Dixon Gallery and Gardens, Memphis, TN

Russell, Robert, *Assoc Prof,* Pittsburg State Univ, KS

Russell-Jones, P R, *Keeper of Military Coll,* Manchester City Art Galleries, England

Russo, A, *Chmn,* Hood College, Frederick, MD

Russo, Mike, *Pres,* Portland Center for the Visual Arts, OR

Russom, J Michael, *Asst Prof,* Assumption College, Worcester, MA

Rust, David E, *Cur French Painting Since 1700,* Nat Gallery of Art, Washington, DC

Rust, Edwin C, *Dir Emer,* Memphis Acad of Arts, TN

Ruston, Shelley, *Asst Dir Activities,* Santa Barbara Museum of Art, CA

Ruth, Elizabeth E, *Keeper Prints,* New York Public Library, NY

Rutkowski, Dr Walter, *Dir,* George Peabody College for Teachers Museum, Nashville, TN

Rutkowski, Walter E, *Head Dept Fine Arts,* Louisiana State Univ, Baton Rouge

Rutledge, Patricia P, *Librn,* Cincinnati Art Museum, OH

Ruttenberg, Harold J, *Chmn & Pres,* AVM Corp, Pittsburgh, PA, see Corporate Art Holdings

Ruttman, Elena, *Cur,* Plains Indians & Pioneer Historical Found, Woodward, OK

Ruus, Inge, *Cur Asst,* Univ British Columbia Museum of Anthropology, Vancouver

Ruwadi, Raymond, *Clerk-Treas,* Massillon Museum, OH

Ruyle, Kermit, *Instr,* Saint Louis Community College at Florissant Valley, Ferguson, MO

Ruzika, Prof, *Head Dept,* Univ Georgia, Athens

Ryan, James A, *Historic Site Mgr,* Palisades Interstate Park Commission, Kingston, NY

Ryan, Mrs Jean, *Chmn,* Villa Montalvo, Saratoga, CA

Ryan, Mrs Joseph, *Chmn Summer School,* Villa Montalvo, Saratoga, CA

Ryan, Martin, *Assoc Prof,* Monmouth College, West Long Branch, NJ

Ryan, William, *Gift Shop Mgr,* Phillips Collection, Washington, DC

Ryan, William, *Head Design Dept,* Virginia Museum of Fine Arts, Richmond

Ryan, Wilma, *Pres,* Coquille Valley Art Association, OR

Ryberg, H Theodore, *Dir,* Elmer E Rasmuson Library, Univ Alaska Museum, Fairbanks

Rychlewski, Karen, *Assoc Prof,* West Liberty State College, WV

Ryden, Kenneth G, *Head Sculpture,* Southern Illinois Univ, Edwardsville

Rylska, I, *Cur,* Muzeum Narodowe We Wroclawiu, Wroclaw, Poland

Ryndel, Nils, *Cur Modern,* Goteborgs Konstmuseum, Sweden

Rypsam, Russell, *Historian,* Artists' Fellowship, New York, NY

Ryska, Jaroslav, *Asst Prof,* Youngstown State Univ, OH

Ryskamp, Charles, *Dir,* Pierpont Morgan Library, New York, NY

Ryuto, Setsuko, *Admin Asst,* Pioneer Museum and Haggin Galleries, Stockton, CA

Saaltink, H W, *Sr Research Asst,* Westfries Museum, Hoorn, Netherlands

Saari, Sandra, *Chmn,* Eisenhower College, Seneca Falls, NY

Saavedra, E Michale Schanches, *Cur Libr Materials,* Valentine Museum, Richmond, VA

Sabalis, Aldona, *Mus Liaison,* Women in the Arts Found, New York, NY

Sabaroff, Bernard J, *Pres,* Blacksburg Regional Art Association, VA

Sabatini, Raphael, *VPres In Charge Art,* Philadelphia Art Alliance, PA

Sabel, J L, *First VPres,* Montgomery Museum of Fine Arts, AL

Sabin, Robert, *Head Painting & Drawing Dept,* Kalamazoo Inst of Arts, MI

Sabin, Selma, *Admin Asst,* Sterling and Francine Clark Art Inst, Williamstown, MA

Sabol, David, *Gallery Preparator,* Los Angeles Inst of Contemporary Art, CA

Sacher, Joan, *Mem Faculty,* Greenfield Community College, MA

Sachs, Samuel, III, *Dir,* Minneapolis Institute of Arts, MN

Sachs, William R, *VPres,* New York Society of Architects, NY

Sack, Suzanne P, *Conservator,* Brooklyn Museum, NY

Sadek, George, *Dean,* Cooper Union School of Art, New York, NY

Sadek, Dr V, *Deputy Dir,* Statni Zidovske Muzeum Prague, Czechoslovakia

Sadik, Marvin, *Dir,* Nat Portrait Gallery, Washington, DC

Sadir, Helene, *Grad Asst,* American Univ of Beirut Archaeological Museum, Lebanon

Sadler, Randall, *Painting & Drawing Coordr,* San Jose State Univ, CA

Saeed, S M, *Treas,* Art Gallery Society of Contemporary Art, Rawalpindi, Pakistan

Saether, Jan, *Chmn Painting Dept,* Venice Painting, Drawing & Sculpture Studio, CA

Safarik, Dr Eduard A, *Dir,* Galleria Doria Pamphilj, Rome, Italy

Safford, Merritt, *Conservator Prints & Drawings,* Metropolitan Museum of Art, New York, NY

Sagar, Sara, *Educ Cur,* Asheville Art Museum, NC

Sage, Diane, *Special Projects Officer,* Ontario Association of Art Galleries, Toronto

Sage, Konrad, *Dir & Prof,* State College of Fine Arts, Berlin, Germany

Sahlstrand, James, *Dir Art Gallery,* Central Washington Univ, Ellensburg

Sahni, S K, *Guide Lectr,* Nat Gallery of Modern Art, New Delhi, India

Saia, Jorge, *Pres,* Art Metropole, Toronto, ON

Saimond, Paul, *Asst Dean Grad Studies,* State Univ New York at Albany

Sain, Robert, *Coordr Develop,* Walker Art Center, Minneapolis, MN

St Clair, Rita, *VPres,* American Society of Interior Designers, see National and Regional Organizations

St Florian, Friedrich, *Chmn Div of Archit Studies,* Rhode Island School of Design, Providence

St German, Lee, *Secy & Asst to Dir,* Bruce Museum, Greenwich, CT

St John, Betty, *Librn,* Rocky Mountain School of Art, Denver, CO

St John, Terry, *Assoc Cur,* Oakland, Museum, CA

St John, Wayne L, *Chmn Dept Design,* Southern Illinois Univ, Carbondale

St-Louis, Henri-Georges, *Dir Summer School,* Univ Quebec, Trois Rivieres

St Pierre, Carolyn, *Prof,* Boston State College, MA

Saito, Mike, *Mem Staff,* Factory of Visual Art, Seattle, WA

Saito, Sei, *Dir,* Tokyo Kokuritsu Hakubutsukan, Japan

Sajbel, Edward R, *Prof & Art Dept Chmn,* Univ Southern Colorado, Belmont Campus, Pueblo

Sakaguchi, Ben, *Area Chmn Studio Art,* Pasadena City College, CA

Sakai, Kazuya, *Vis Prof Painting,* Univ Texas at San Antonio

Sakai, Robert, *Dean Summer School,* Univ Hawaii, Manoa, Honolulu

Sakakeeny, Donna Tryon, *Assoc Prof,* Palomar College, San Marcos, CA

Salahuddin, Mr, *Modeler,* Lahore Museum, Pakistan

Salam, Dr Heliede, *Asst Prof,* Radford College, VA

Salan, Jean, *Deputy Dir,* Museum of African Art, Washington, DC

Salberg, Lester, *Teacher,* Rock Valley College, Rockford, IL

Salcedo, Dr Alberto Santibanez, *Dir,* Museo de Arte, Lima, Peru

Salcedo, Jaime, *Head Hist & Inst Aesthetic Investigations,* Javeriana Univ Faculty of Architecture and Design, Bogota, Colombia

Saldaña-Guerrero, Caridad, *Warder,* Museo de Arte "Jose Luis Bello y Gonzalez", Puebla, Mexico

Salet, Francis, *Dir,* Musee de Cluny, Paris, France

Salgado, Robert J, *Teacher,* Antonelli School of Photography, Philadelphia, PA

Salgado, Ronald, *Dir,* Muckenthaler Cultural Center, Fullerton, CA

Salisbury, Ralph F, *Dir,* Ralyn Art Center, Lakewood, NJ

Salisian, Steve, *Instr,* San Jose City College, CA

Sallaberry, Carlos A, *Dir Archit Dept,* Centro de Arte y Communicacion, Buenos Aires, Argentina

Salle, David, *Instr,* Hartford Art School, Univ Hartford, West Hartford, CT

Sallick, Robert J, *Pres,* Danbury Scott-Fanton Museum and Historical Society, CT

Sallis, Jane Rose, *Pres,* Dallas Print and Drawing Society, Dallas Public Library, TX

Salmon, Eugene N, *Assoc Humanities Reference Librn,* California State Univ Library, Sacramento

Salmon, Colonel H Morrey, *Treas,* Nat Museum of Wales, Cardiff

Salmon, Larry, *Cur Textiles,* Museum of Fine Arts, Boston, MA

Salter, Peter, *Mem Faculty,* Stephens College, Columbia, MO

Salthouse, Barbara S, *Ref Librn,* Univ Pittsburgh Art Gallery, PA

Saltmarche, Dr Kenneth, *Dir,* Art Gallery of Windsor, ON

Saltzman, Marvin, *Prof,* Univ North Carolina at Chapel Hill

Salveson, Douglas, *Dir, Egner Fine Arts Center & Asst Prof,* Findlay College, OH

Salyer, Ruth Osgood, *Admin Dir,* Laguna Beach School of Art, CA

Sam, Norman, *Dir Summer School,* Lehigh Univ, Bethlehem, PA

Samford, Michael, *Assoc Prof,* George Peabody College for Teachers, Nashville, TN

Sammarjano, Vito, *Prof,* Salem State College, MA

Samoyault, C, *Cur,* Fontainebleau School of Fine Arts, France

Samoyault, Jean-Pierre, *Cur,* Musee Nat du Chateau de Fontainebleau, France

Samoyault-Verlet, Mme, *Cur,* Musee du Chateau de Fontainebleau, France

Samples, Robert, *Bd Chmn,* Metropolitan Cultural Arts Center, Minneapolis, MN

Sampson, June, *Dir & Librn,* W H Over Museum, Univ South Dakota, Vermillion

Sampson, Rose, *Treas,* Galesburg Civic Art Center, IL

Samuel, Evelyn K, *Dir Libr,* New York Univ Art Collection, NY

Samuelson, Fred, *Head Grad Studies,* Instituto Allende, San Maguel de Allende, Mexico

Samuelson, Jerry, *Dean,* California State Univ, Fullerton

Sand, Mary, *Dir & Dir Summer School,* North Dakota State School of Science, Wahpeton

Sande, Theodore A, *Acting VPres Historic Properties,* Nat Trust for Historic Preservation, Washington, DC

Sanders, Albert E, *Cur Natural History,* Charleston Museum, SC

Sanders, Carol, *Office Mgr,* Northeastern Nevada Museum, Elko

Sanders, Ms Scott, *Dir Arts Educ Div,* South Carolina Arts Commission, Columbia

Sanders, Sue, *Secy,* Museum of York County, Rock Hill, SC

Sanders, Val G, *Assoc Prof,* Palomar College, San Marcos, CA

Sanderson, Merle, *Gallery Dir,* Swain School of Design, New Bedford, MA

Sanderson, R O, *Hon Treas,* Community Arts Council of Vancouver, BC

Sandler, Lucy Freeman, *Secy,* College Art Association of America, see National and Regional Organizations

Sandler, Mark H, *Chmn,* State Univ New York College at Potsdam

Sandmann, Herbert, *Prof,* Univ Wisconsin-Stevens Point

Sandok, Flo, *Prof,* Rochester Community College, MN

Sandoz, M Andre, *Pres,* Musee des Beaux-Arts et Societe des Amis des Arts, La Chaux de Fonds, Switzerland

Sandquist, Stormy A, *Mem Chmn,* Florida Artist Group, St. Augustine

Sands, John O, *Asst Dir Coll,* Mariners Museum, Newport News, VA

Sandvik, Karin, *Librn,* M I King Library, Lexington, KY

Sanford, Cynthia, *Trustee & Cur,* Jersey City Museum Association, NJ

Sanford, John, *VPres,* Cooperstown Art Association, NY

Sanger, Helen, *Librn,* Frick Art Reference Library, New York, NY

Sanguinetti, E F, *Dir,* Univ Utah Museum of Fine Arts, Salt Lake City

Sankowsky, Itzhaic, *Mem Faculty,* Mainline Center of the Arts, Haverford, PA

San Martin, Maria L, *Dir,* Nat School of Arts 'Manuel Belgrano', Buenos Aires, Argentina

Santi, Dr Francesco, *Dir,* Galleria Nazionale dell Unbria, Perugia, Italy

Santos, Bob, *Bibliographer,* California State College Art Gallery, Stanislaus, Turlock

Santucci, Jane, *Pres,* Marin Art & Garden Society, Ross, CA

Santucci, Renato, *Video Coordr,* Centro de Arte y Communicacion, Buenos Aires, Argentina

Sanz-Pastor y Fernandez de Pierola, Dr Consuelo, *Dir Found Mus,* Museo Cerralbo, Madrid, Spain

Sarab'ianov, Smitrii, *Vis Prof,* Univ Minnesota, Minneapolis

Sardá, Rafael, *Pub Relations Coordr,* Museum of Modern Art of Latin America, Washington, DC

Sargent, C H, *Dir,* Watkins Inst, Nashville, TN

Sargent, Richard, *Exhib Specialist,* Berkeley Art Center, CA

Sarkany, Iamas, *Asst Keeper,* Kungl Myntkabinettet Statens Museum of Mynt Medalj Och Penninghistoria, Stockholm, Sweden

Sarn, John A, *Asst Prof,* Univ Alabama in Huntsville

Saromines, Barbara, *Instr,* Leeward Community College, Pearl City, HI

Sartor, Joe D, *Asst Prof,* Morehead State Univ, KY

Sartre, Josiane, *Libr Conservator,* Union Centrale des Arts Decoratifs, Paris, France

Sasowaky, Norman, *Coordr,* Univ Delaware, Newark

Sass, Louis D, *Dir,* Pratt Inst Library, Brooklyn, NY

Sasse, Jane M, *Librn,* Lamson Library, Plymouth State College, NH

Satel, Mrs Joseph, *Secy,* San Antonio Art League, TX

Satz, Arthur, *Pres,* New York School of Interior Design, NY

Sauberli, Ronald, *Library Asst,* Illinois State Museum of Natural History and Art, Springfield

Saul, Julie M, *Asst Dir,* Tampa Bay Art Center, FL

Saulnier, Bonny B, *Cur,* Brandeis Univ, Waltham, MA

Saulo, Diana P, *Asst Cur,* Jean P Haydon Museum, Pago Pago, American Samoa

Saunders, Mrs Donald, *Chmn Bd,* Southwest Craft Center, San Antonio, TX

Saunders, J D, *Prof,* Univ Auckland, New Zealand

Sauvageau, Phillippe, *Pres,* Federation des Centres Culturels de la Province de Quebec, Montreal

Sauvageau, Susan, *Asst Prof,* Eisenhower College, Seneca Falls, NY

Savage, *Prof,* Asbury College, Wilmore, KY

Savage, James J, *Dir School of Fine Arts & Exec Dir,* Fine Arts Association, Willoughby, OH

Savage, Roger, *Pres,* Eye Level Gallery, Halifax, NS

Savage, Dr William, *Mus Educ,* Univ South Carolina, Columbia

Savery, Paige, *Librn Photographs & Prints,* Stowe-Day Found, Hartford, CT

Savinar, Barbara, *Registrar,* Oakland Museum, CA

Saw, James T, *Assoc Prof,* Palomar College, San Marcos, CA

Sawa, Ryuken, *Head Dept,* Kyoto City Univ Fine Arts, Japan

Sawdey, Russell, *Prof,* Bemidji State Univ, MN

Sawka, Michaleen, *Cur Secy,* Fine Arts Gallery of San Diego, CA

Sawycky, Roman, *Asst Dir,* Free Public Library of Elizabeth, NJ

Sawyer, Alan, *Prof,* Univ British Columbia, Vancouver

Sawyer, Henry W, III, *VPres,* Fairmount Park Art Association, Philadelphia, PA

Saxton, C, *Head Dept Art,* Leicester Polytechnic, England

Sayad, Homer E, *VPres,* Arts and Education Council of Greater St Louis, MO

Saylor, Harold D, *Pres,* Historical Society of Pennsylvania, Philadelphia

Sayre, C Franklin, *Vis Prof,* Swarthmore College, PA

Sayre, Eleanor A, *Cur Prints & Drawings,* Museum of Fine Arts, Boston, MA

Sayre, Suzanne, *Instr,* William Woods/Westminster Colleges, Fulton, MO

Scafetta, Stefano, *Conservator,* Nat Collection of Fine Arts, Washington, DC

Scaife, Richard M, *Chmn Mus of Art Comt,* Carnegie Inst Museum of Art, Pittsburgh, PA

Scala, Joseph A, *Dir,* Joe and Emily Lowe Art Gallery, Syracuse Univ, NY

Scalamandre, Froanco, *Founder & Pres,* Scalamandre Museum of Textiles, New York, NY

Scanlon, Carole T, *Coordr Interpretive Programs,* Chesterwood, Stockbridge, MA; Cliveden, Philadelphia, PA; Lyndhurst, Tarrytown, NY; Oatlands, Leesburg, VA; Pope-Leighey House, Mount Vernon, VA; Shadows-on-the-Teche, New Iberia, LA; Woodlawn, Mount Vernon, VA

Scannell, Francis X, *State Librn,* Michigan Dept of Education State Library Services, Lansing

Scannell, Joseph, *Asst Prof,* College of the Holy Cross, Worcester, MA

Scannell, Joseph E, *Assoc Dir,* Chapel Arts Center & *Chmn Art Dept,* St Anselm's College, Manchester, NH

Scarborough, Cleve K, *Dir,* Hunter Museum of Art, Chattanooga, TN

Scarlett, Robert, *Librn,* G Pillow Lewis Mem Library, Memphis, TN

Scavotto, Christine, *Mem Faculty,* Saint Louis Community College at Meramec, St Louis, MO

Schaad, Dee, *Asst Prof,* Indiana Central Univ, Indianapolis

Schaber, Ken, *Asst Prof,* Lake Michigan College, Benton Harbor, MI

Schactman, Barry, *Prof & Assoc Dean School Art & Summer School,* Washington Univ, Saint Louis, MO

Schad, Jasper G, *Libr Dir,* Wichita State Univ Museum, Kansas

Schade, William, *Mem Faculty,* Junior College of Albany, NY

Schadler, Dr A, *Cur Sculpture,* Bayerisches Nationalmuseum, Munich, Germany

Schaefer, Aloha Pettit, *Dir,* Pacific Grove Art Center, CA

Schaefer, Fred, *Instr,* Williamsport Area Community College, PA

Schaefer, Jean, *Librn,* Paine Art Center and Arboretum, Oshkosh, WI

Schaefer, Jean O, *Asst Prof,* Univ Wyoming, Laramie

Schaefer, Ronald, *Chmn & Summer School Chmn,* Univ North Dakota, Grand Forks

Schaeffer, August, *Trustee,* Attleboro Museum, MA

Schaeffer, Debra, *Mem Faculty,* Maryland College of Art and Design, Silver Spring

Schaeffer, Harold, *Dir Summer School,* Salisbury State College, MD

Schaeffer, Rudolph, *Dir,* Rudolph Schaeffer School of Design, San Francisco, CA

Schaeffer, William D, *VPres,* Inter-Society Color Council, see National and Regional Organizations

Schaffer, Charles A, *Mgr,* Western Woodcarvings, Custer, SD

Schaffer, Jo, *Cur,* Art Slide Library, State Univ New York College at Cortland

Schaffer, Lillian E, *Mgr,* Western Woodcarvings, Custer, SD

Schaller, Ralph, *Instr,* Missouri Western State College, Saint Joseph

Schanlansky, Della, *Slide Cur I,* California State Univ Library, Sacramento

Schantz, Michael W, *Asst to Cur,* Grunwald Center for the Graphic Arts, Univ California, Los Angeles

Schar, Stuart, *Dir,* College Fine and Professional Art, Kent State Univ, OH

Scharer, Martin R, *Librn,* Schweizerisches Landesmuseum, Zurich, Switzerland

Schatz, Carlotte, *Mem Faculty,* Bucks County Community College, Newtown, PA

Schaub, Gary F, *Dir Civic Arts,* Walnut Creek Civic Arts Gallery, CA

Schauble, Edward R, *Staff Designer,* Northern Trust Company, Chicago, Il, see Corporate Art Holdings

Schaul, Ellie, *Acting Exec Dir,* Charleston Art Gallery of Sunrise, WV

Schaumann, G William, *First VPres,* Historical Society of York County, PA

Scheffler, Deane, *Secy,* Paducah Art Guild, KY

Scheffler, Dr Gisela, *Cur,* Staatliche Graphische Sammlung, Munich, Germany

Scheidt, Patricia M, *Admin Asst,* Arts Club of Chicago, IL

Schele, Linda, *Assoc Prof,* Univ South Alabama, Mobile

Schell, Deborah, *Librn,* Saginaw Art Museum, MI

Schell, Edwin, *Exec Secy & Librn,* United Methodist Historical Society, Baltimore, MD

Schell, Paul E S, *Pres,* Allied Arts of Seattle, WA

Schellstede, Eloise J, *Pres,* Green Country Art Center, Tulsa, OK

Schellstede, Richard Lee, *Exec Dir,* Green Country Art Center, Tulsa, OK

Schenk, C Harlan, *First Asst,* Houston Public Library, TX

Schenker, Leon F, *Chmn,* Ashland College Arts and Humanities Gallery, OH

Scheps, Dr Marc, *Dir & Chief Cur,* Tel Aviv Museum, Israel

Scherba, Sandra, *Treas,* Hartland Art Council, MI

Scherer, Cynthia, *VPres,* Pottstown Area Artists Guild, PA

Scherer, Herbert, *Librn,* Univ Minnesota Gallery, Minneapolis

Sherman, Roger, *Cur,* Plains Art Museum, Moorhead, MN

Scherpereel, Richard, *Chmn Art Dept,* Texas A&I Univ, Kingsville

Scherr, Samuel, *Pres,* American Crafts Council, see National and Regional Organizations

Schetzsle, Letha, *Registrar,* Denison Univ Art Gallery, Granville, OH

Schick, Marjorie, *Assoc Prof,* Pittsburg State Univ, KS

Schidler, Elizabeth, *Staff Mem,* Imperial Calcasieu Museum, Lake Charles, LA

Schier, Peter E, *Acting Chmn Art Dept & Acting Chmn Summer School,* Univ of Bridgeport, CT

Schiferl, Ellen, *Mem Faculty,* Fort Hays State Univ, Hays, KS

Schiffner, R, *Mem Faculty,* Golden West College, Huntington Beach, CA

Schild, Curt, *Cur,* Rosicrucian Egyptian Museum and Art Gallery, San Jose, CA

Schimansky, Dobrila-Donya, *Mus Librn,* Thomas J Watson Library, Metropolitan Museum of Art, New York, NY

Schimmel, Paul, *Cur,* Contemporary Arts Museum Houston, TX

Schimmelman, Janice G, *Vis Instr,* Oakland Univ, Rochester, MI

Schimmelpenninck, L H Graaf, *Trustee,* Teylers Museum, Haarlem, Netherlands

Schlager, Dr Julian, *Dir Summer School,* Plymouth State College, NH

Schlageter, Robert W, *Dir,* Cummer Gallery of Art, Jacksonville, FL

Schlawin, Judy, *Instr,* Winona State University, MN

Schlesinger, Stephen L, *Secy,* John Simon Guggenheim Found, New York, NY

Schling, Dorothy T, *Dir,* Danbury Scott-Fanton Museum and Historical Society, CT

Schloss, Stuart A, Jr, *Treas,* Contemporary Arts Center, Cincinnati, OH

Schlossberg, Dr H, *Dir Summer School,* Shepherd College, Shepherdstown, WV

Schlossberg, Leon, *Asst Prof,* Johns Hopkins Univ, Baltimore, MD

Schlosser, Mary C, *Pres,* Guild of Book Workers, see National and Regional Organizations

Schlosser, Tom, *Chmn Dept,* College of Saint Mary, Omaha, NE

Schlotterback, Thomas, *Chmn,* Western Washington Univ, Bellingham

Schlump, John O, *Prof,* Wittenberg Univ, Springfield, OH

Schluntz, R, *Exec Dir,* Association of Collegiate Schools of Architecture, see National and Regional Organizations

Schluter, Dr Margildis, *Asst Cur,* Kestner-Museum, Hanover, Germany

Schmalenbach, Dr Werner, *Dir,* Kunstsammlung Nordrhein-Westfalen, Dusseldorf, Germany

Schmaljohn, Russell, *Asst Prof,* Northwest Missouri State Univ, Maryville

Schmeller, Dr Alfred, *Dir,* Museum des 20 Jahrhunderts, Vienna, Austria

Schmidt, Carole, *Coordr,* Provincetown Art Association and Museum, MA

Schmidt, Gordon, *Cur Art Dept,* Bruce Museum, Greenwich, CT

Schmidt, Julianne, *Dir Summer School,* Ladycliff College, Highland Falls, NY

Schmidt, Dr Katharina, *Delegate Dir,* Stadtische Kunsthalle, Dusseldorf, Germany

Schmidt, Kathleen, *Mem Faculty,* Northeastern Oklahoma State Univ, Tahlequah

Schmidt, Dr Maria, *Cur Folk Art,* Museen der Stadt Koln, Germany

Schmidt, Mark, *Mem Faculty,* Elmira College, NY

Schmidt, Martin F, *Librn,* Filson Club, Louisville, KY

Schmidt, Maurice, *Assoc,* Texas A&I Univ, Kingsville

Schmidt, Mrs Mott, *Secy,* Katonah Gallery, NY

Schmidt, Myron, *Asst Prof,* Dean Junior College, Franklin, MA

Schmidt, Norman, *Chmn Graphic Design,* Univ of Manitoba, Winnipeg

Schmidt, Philip, *Chmn Hist Art,* Pratt Inst School of Art & Design, Brooklyn, NY

Schmidt, Shirley, *Pres,* Hutchinson Art Association, KS

Schmidt, U, *Dir,* Twin City Art Found, Monroe, LA

Schmidt, Valentine L, *Librn,* John and Mable Ringling Museum of Art, Sarasota, FL

Schmidtke, William A, *Dir, Summer School,* Univ Wisconsin Center, Marinette

Schmiedicki, Dr Joseph, *Dir Summer School,* Edgewood College, Madison, WI

Schmikle, Reed, *Chmn,* Pittsburg State Univ, KS

Schmits, John, *Chmn Dept,* Saint Ambrose College, Davenport, IA

Schmitt, Dr Annegrit, *Nat Cur,* Staatliche Graphische Sammlung, Munich, Germany

Schmitt, Tom, *Asst Dir,* Metropolitan Museum and Art Centers, Coral Gables, FL

Schmitz, Edith, *Secy,* Pensacola Museum of Art, FL

Schmitz, Marie, *Instr,* Univ Missouri-Saint Louis

Schmutzhart, Berthold, *Chmn Sculpture,* Corcoran School of Art, Washington, DC

Schnabel, Clem, *Secy,* Santa Cruz Art League, CA

Schnackenburg, Dr Bernhard, *Asst Cur,* Kunsthalle Bremen, Germany

Schndrr, Emil, *Adj Prof,* Springfield College, MA

Schneck, Marvin, *Exhib Specialist,* Walnut Creek Civic Arts Gallery, CA

Schneider, David, *Mem Staff,* Louisville School of Art, Anchorage, KY

Schneider, Gail K, *Ed & Librn,* Staten Island Inst of Arts and Sciences, NY

Schneider, Dr Hugo, *Dir,* Schweizerisches Landesmuseum, Zurich, Switzerland

Schneider, Janet, *Dir,* Queens Museum, Flushing, NY

Schneider, Dr Jenny, *VDir,* Schweizerisches Landesmseum, Zurich, Switzerland

Schneider, Laurie, *Assoc Prof,* John Jay College of Criminal Justice, New York, NY

Schneider, Richard, *Dir Summer School,* Franklin and Marshall College, Lancaster, PA

Schneider, Richard, *Prof,* Univ Wisconsin-Stevens Point

Schneider, Richard D, *Assoc Prof,* Cleveland State Univ, OH

Schneiderman, Richard, *Cur Graphic Arts,* Univ Georgia Museum of Art, Athens

Schnek, Joseph, B, *Exec Dir,* Anderson Fine Arts Center, IN

Schnell, Lloyd, *Chmn Photography,* Kansas City Art Inst, MO

Schnell, Ronald, *Prof & Chmn Art Dept & Cur Art Collection,* Tougaloo College, MS

Schnepper, Mark, *Cur Exhib,* Evansville Museum of Arts and Science, IN

Schnitter, Mrs, *Guide,* Polish Museum of America, Chicago, IL

Schnorr, Emil G, *Conservator,* George Walter Vincent Smith Art Museum, Springfield, MA

Schnorrenberg, John M, *Chmn & Prof,* Univ of Alabama in Birmingham

Schoeberlein, Elizabeth, *Assoc Prof,* Colorado Women's College, Denver

Schoellkopf, Robert B, *Secy,* Cincinnati Art Club, OH

Schoen, Myron E, *Dir,* Union of American Hebrew Congregations, New York, NY

Schoene, Kathleen S, *Librn,* Missouri Historical Society, St Louis

Schoenwetter, Hilda, *Dean Summer School,* Moore College of Art, Philadelphia, PA

Schofield, Ellice, *Cur,* Stowe-Day Found, Hartford, CT

Schofield, Peg, *Lectr,* Saint Joseph's College, Philadelphia, PA

Scholder, Fritz, *Mem Faculty,* Univ Southern California, Idyllwild Campus

Scholz, Teddi, *Second VPres,* Association of Honolulu Artists, HI

Schomann, Rainer, *Restorer,* Bayerischen Staatsgemaldesammlungen, Munich, Germany

Schon, Gerardo, *Archit Coordr,* Centro de Arte y Communicacion, Buenos Aires, Argentina

Schonberger, Dr Arno, *Chief Dir,* Germanisches Nationalmuseum, Nuremberg

Schoonover, Daniel, *Libr Asst,* The Cloisters, Metropolitan Museum of Art, New York, NY

Schorgl, Thomas B, *Cur,* Art Center, South Bend, IN

Schory, Karen, *Instr,* Johnson County Community College, Overland Park, KS

Schott, Gene A, *Dir,* Heritage Plantation of Sandwich, MA

Schou-Christensen, Jorg Jorgen, *Keeper,* Det Danske Kunstindustrimuseum, Copenhagen, Denmark

Schouse, Maetha, Sister, *Prof,* Marian College, Fond du Lac, WI

Schrader, Jack L, *Cur in Charge,* The Cloisters, Metropolitan Museum of Art, New York, NY

Schrank, H Paul, Jr, *Librn,* Bierce Library, Univ of Akron, OH

Schreckengost, Viktor, *Instr,* Cleveland Inst of Art, OH

Schreiber, Frank *Head Dept & Instr,* North Hennepin Community College, Minneapolis, MN

Schreiberova, Dr Katarina, *Chief Dept Nonprofessional Art,* Slovenska Narodna Galeria, Bratislava, Czechoslovakia

Schremmer, Harold, *Vis Prof,* Portland School of Art, ME

Schroeder, Allen, *Educ Prog Specialist,* W H Over Museum, Univ South Dakota, Vermillion

Schroeder, Ann, *Co-Chairwoman,* Lake Region Art Association, Devils Lake, ND

Schroeder, Ellen, *Lectr,* Leeward Community College, Pearl City, HI

Schroeder, Hans, *Assoc Prof,* New York Inst of Technology, Old Westbury

Schroeder, Howard S, *Mem Faculty,* Rehoboth Art League, Rehoboth Beach, DE

Schroeder, Lee, *Assoc Prof,* Hanover College, IN

Schroeder, Lynn, *Coordr Printmaking,* Univ Arizona, Tucson

Schubert, Mrs J Cardinal *Gallery Technician,* Univ Calgary, AB

Schubert, Patricia, *Ed,* Art Research Center, Kansas City, MO

Schubert, Terrance, *Asst Prof,* Univ Wisconsin-River Falls

Schug, Dr Albert, *Librn,* Museen der Stadt Koln, Germany

Schuldes, Jeanne, *Assoc Cur,* Neville Public Museum, Green Bay, WI

Schuler, Hans C, *Dir School & Dir of Summer School,* Schuler School of Fine Arts, Baltimore, MD

Schulman, Robert, *Pres,* Federal Design Council, Washington, DC

Schulman, William, *Assoc Prof,* Univ Wisconsin-Stout, Menomonie

Schult-Hoffmann, Dr Carla, *Cur 20th Century Art,* Bayerischen Staatsgemaldesammlungen, Munich, Germany

Schultz, Bernie, *Prof,* West Virginia Univ, Morgantown

Schultz, Douglas G, *Cur,* Albright-Knox Art Gallery, Buffalo, NY

Schultz, Jody, *Instr,* Highland Community College, Freeport, IL

Schultz, Leroy, *Asst Prof,* Southwestern Oklahoma State Univ, Weatherford

Schultz, Sharon L, *Asst Dir,* Center for Inter-American Relations Art Gallery, New York, NY

Schultze, Dr Jurgen, *Cur,* Kunsthalle Bremen, Germany

Schultze, Raymond W, *Prof,* Kearney State College, NE

Schulze, Franz, *Prof,* Lake Forest College, IL

Schumacher, Herb *Assoc Prof,* Univ Northern Colorado, Greeley

Schuman, Gary D, *Exec Dir,* Bucks County Historical Society Mercer Museum, Doylestown, PA

Schuman, William, *Treas,* American Acad and Inst of Arts and Letters, see National and Regional Organizations

Schumann, Dr Carl-Wolfgang *Cur,* Kunstgewerbemuseum, Museen der Stadt Koln, Germany

Schupp, Jim, *Chmn Div Fine Arts & Humanities,* Florida Junior College, South Campus, Jacksonville

Schuster, Mrs Edward, *Pres,* Dubuque Art Association, IA

Schutte, Richard, *Treas,* Valley Art Center, Clarkston, WA

Schutte, Thomas F, *Pres,* Philadelphia College of Art, PA

Schutz, Edward E, *Head Dept & Prof,* Northeast Louisiana Univ, Monroe

Schwacha, George, *Treas,* Art Centre of New Jersey, East Orange

Schwalbe, Ole, *Dir,* School Painting, Sculpture & Graphic Arts, Royal Danish Academy of Fine Arts, Copenhagen, Denmark

Schwartz, Carole, *Asst Librn/Mus Archivist,* Cincinnati Art Museum, OH

Schwartz, Donald A, *Treas,* Society of Medalists, see National and Regional Organizations

Schwartz, Douglas W, *Dir,* School of American Research Collections, Santa Fe, NM

Schwartz, Irving D, *Pres,* American Society of Interior Designers, see National and Regional Organizations

Schwartz, Judith, *Prog Adv,* Univ Toronto Art Collection, ON

Schwartz, Lloyd A, *In Charge Coll,* Coopers & Lybrand, Detroit, MI, see Corporate Art Holdings

Schwartz, Stephen H, *Dir,* Kenosha Public Museum, WI

Schwarz, Joseph, *Head Dept & Prof,* Auburn Univ at Montgomery, AL

Schwarz, Marjorie D, *Secy,* Asian Art Museum, San Francisco, CA

Schwarz, Marta, *Librn III & Head Dept,* Yonkers Public Library, NY

Schwarz, William, *Assoc Prof,* Univ Illinois at the Medical Center, Chicago

Schwarzbeck, Ellen L, *Asst to Dir,* Augusta Richmond County Museum, GA

Schwatz, Mrs Alan E, *Secy,* Detroit Inst of Arts Collections, MI

Schwebel, Renata M, *Exec VPres,* Sculptors Guild, New York, NY

Schweiss, Ruth Keller, *Exec Dir,* Acad of Professional Artists, St Louis, MO

Schweitzer, Mary de Paul, *Instr Art & Coordr,* Marian College, Indianapolis, IN

Schweizer, Paul D, *Vis Prof & Cur Art Collection,* St Lawrence Univ, Canton, NY

Schwering, Dr Max-Leo, *Cur Cologne Folklore,* Museen der Stadt Koln, Germany

Schwermer, Sabine, *Librn,* Staatliche Kunsthalle Karlsruhe, Germany

Schwetman, Nan, *Pres,* Lafayette Art Center, IN

Schwidder, Ernst, *Prof,* Pacific Lutheran Univ, Tacoma, WA

Schwieger, C R, *Chmn,* Minot State College, ND

Schwieso, Dr R, *Dir Summer School,* Marycrest College, Davenport, IA

Seyle, Bob, *Asst Prof,* Loma Linda Univ, La Sierra Campus, Riverside, CA

Seymour, Lyle, *Pres Summer School,* Wayne State College, NE

Seymour, Whitney North, Jr, *VPres,* Art Commission of the City of New York, NY

Sgouros, Thomas, *Chmn Div Design,* Rhode Island School of Design, Providence

Shafer, Anders C, *Dir Art Gallery,* Univ Wisconsin-Eau Claire

Shafer, Stan, *Mem Faculty,* College of Saint Benedict, Saint Joseph, MN

Shaffer, Barbara, *Secy,* Nome Arts Council, AK

Shaffer, Diana, *Asst Prof,* Aquinas College, Grand Rapids, MI

Shaffer, Ellen, *Cur,* Silverado Museum, Saint Helena, CA

Shaffer, John J, *Pres,* Nome Arts Council, AK

Shaffstall, James W, *Chmn Dept,* Hanover College, IN

Shainswit, Lisa, *Pub Appearance Chair,* Women in the Arts Found, New York, NY

Shalansky, Ruby, *Exec Dir,* Warwick Arts Found, RI

Shalkop, R L, *Dir,* Anchorage Historical and Fine Arts Museum, AK

Shaman, Floyd D, *Asst Prof,* Delta State Univ, Cleveland, MS

Shaman, Sanford Sivitz, *Dir,* Univ Northern Iowa Gallery of Art, Cedar Falls

Shamonsey, Peter D, *Dir Summer School,* Columbia Univ, New York, NY

Shanahan, Katheleen, *Vis Prof,* Lane Community College, Eugene, OR

Shane, Audrey, *Archivist,* Univ British Columbia Museum of Anthropology, Vancouver

Shaner, Carol, *Exhib Librn,* Sarah Lawrence College Library, Bronxville, NY

Shaner, David, *Pres,* Archie Bray Found, Helena, MT

Shangraw, Clarence F, *Sr Cur,* Asian Art Museum, San Francisco, CA

Shangraw, Sylvia Chen, *Cur Chinese Art,* Asian Art Museum, San Francisco, CA

Shanks, Clarence, *Pres,* Arizona Watercolor Association, Phoenix

Shankwiler, Beverly, *Gallery Dir,* Sill Gallery, Ypsilanti, MI

Shannon, Charles, *Prof,* Auburn Univ at Montgomery, AL

Shannon, Joseph, *Chief Exhib,* Hirshhorn Museum and Sculpture Garden, Washington, DC

Shannon, Joseph, *Prof,* Trenton State College, NJ

Shannon, Mary R, *Cur,* Rochester Historical Society, NY

Shannon, Zella, *Assoc Dir,* Minneapolis Public Library and Information Center, MN

Shantz, Mrs Arthur W, *Secy,* Womens City Club of Cleveland, OH

Shapiro, Barbara, *Dir Pub Relations,* International Center of Photography, New York, NY

Shapiro, F, *Chmn Fine Arts,* Fashion Inst of Technology, New York, NY

Shapiro, Irving, *Dir Acad & Dir Summer School,* American Acad of Art, Chicago, IL

Shapiro, Seymour, *Artist-in-Residence,* Maryland Inst, Baltimore

Sharif, Dr Muhammad, *Asst Supt Archaeology,* Nat Museum of Pakistan, Karachi

Sharp, Dick, *Dir Summer School,* Indian Hills Community College, Centerville, IA

Sharp, Ellen, *Cur Graphic Arts,* Detroit Inst of Art Collections, MI

Sharp, Renata, *Exec Secy,* Stadtische Kunsthalle, Dusseldorf, Germany

Sharpe, Bruce, *Dean,* Pratt Inst School of Art & Design, Brooklyn, NY

Sharpe, David C, *Acting Chmn,* Illinois Inst of Technology, Chicago

Sharpe, John R, *Dir,* Abbey School of Jewelry & Art Metal Design, New York, NY

Sharpe, K, *Keeper,* South London Art Gallery, England

Sharpe, Sara, *Treas,* Plastic Club, Philadelphia, PA

Sharretts, Edward P, Jr, *Secy,* Parrish Art Museum, Southampton, NY

Sharrow, Sheba, *Mem Faculty,* Millersville State College, PA

Shaughnessy, Robert, *Prof,* Southampton College of Long Island Univ, NY

Shaunnessy, Marie, *Funding,* Alaska Artists Guild, Anchorage

Shaver, Shirlee, *Asst Prof,* Texas Woman's Univ, Denton

Shaver, Wes, *Treas,* Abilene Fine Arts Museum, TX

Shaviro, Sol, *Chmn Bd,* Bronx Museum of the Arts, NY

Shaw, Mrs Alfred P, *Pres,* Arts Club of Chicago, IL

Shaw, David, *VPres,* Cornish Inst of Allied Arts Gallery, Seattle, WA

Shaw, Elizabeth, *Dir Pub Information,* Museum of Modern Art, New York, NY

Shaw, H Allen, Jr, *Instr,* Oklahoma State Univ, Okmulgee

Shaw, Luke A, *Head Dept Coordr,* Coppin State College, Baltimore, MD

Shaw, Miss M, *Educ Officer,* Durban Art Gallery, South Africa

Shaw, Marvin, *Asst Prof,* Jacksonville State Univ, AL

Shaw, Mary, *Secy,* Las Vegas Art League, NV

Shaw, Mary M, *Dir,* Johnson-Humrickhouse Museum, Coshocton, OH

Shaw, Wayne L, *Chmn Art Dept & Dir Summer School,* Belleville Area College, IL

Shea, Sister Liliosa, *Assoc Prof,* Notre Dame College, Manchester, NH

Sheaks, Barclay, *Head Dept,* Virginia Wesleyan College, Norfolk

Shear, T Leslie, *Prof & Chmn Prog Classical Archaeology,* Princeton Univ, NJ

Sheardy, Robert, *Mem Faculty,* Muskegon Community College, MI

Shearer, Elizabeth, *VPres,* Cleveland Museum of Art, OH

Shearer, Linda, *Asst Cur,* Solomon R Guggenheim Museum, New York, NY

Shearman, J, *Technician,* Sarjeant Gallery, Wanganui, New Zealand

Shearouse, Henry G, Jr, *Librn,* Denver Public Library, CO

Sheel, Frieda, *Pub Serv Dir,* Rosenberg Library, Galveston, TX

Sheffield, Clinton A, *Assoc Prof,* Dickinson State College, ND

Sheffield, John T, *Treas,* Wichita Art Association, KS

Shehata, Youssef Hanna, *Dir,* Greco-Roman Museum, Alexandria, Egypt

Sheild, Conway, III, *Pres,* Peninsula Arts Association, Newport News, VA

Sheldon, Alan, *Pres,* Medicine Hat Public Library, AB

Sheldon, James L, *Cur Photography,* Addison Gallery of American Art, Andover, MA

Sheldon, Ms Joan, *Fine Arts Coordr,* Lutheran Brotherhood, Minneapolis, MN, see Corporate Art Holdings

Sheldon, Thomas D, *Deputy Comr Elementary, Secondary & Continuing Educ,* State Education Dept, Albany, NY

Shelito, Jean, *Secy,* Kansas Watercolor Society, Wichita

Shelley, Dr Donald A, *Pres,* Greenfield Village and Henry Ford Museum, Dearborn, MI

Shellman, Feay, *Cur Coll,* Telfair Acad of Arts & Sciences, Savannah, GA

Shelly, Barbara, *Instr,* Vancouver Community College, Langara Campus, BC

Shelov, Sidney, *Chmn Resources,* Pratt Inst School of Art & Design, Brooklyn, NY

Shen-Dar, Judith, *Cur,* Museum of Modern Art, Haifa, Israel

Shepard, Fred, *Mem Faculty,* Murray State Univ, KY

Shepard, Mrs Willard, *Secy,* Lyman Allyn Museum, New London, CT

Shepeard, Peter, *Dean,* Univ Pennsylvania, Philadelphia

Shephard, Dorothy G, *Cur Textile,* Cleveland Museum of Art, OH

Shepher, Raymond V, *Adminr & Property Council & Staff,* Nat Trust Interpreters, Cliveden, Philadelphia, PA

Shepherd, Gyde V, *Asst Dir,* Nat Gallery of Canada, Ottawa, ON

Shepherd, Jean, *Cur Asst,* Illinois State Univ, Normal

Shepler, Joseph, *Co-Dir,* Chatham College Art Gallery, Pittsburgh, PA

Sheppard, Carl D, *Treas,* International Center of Medieval Art, New York, NY; *Prof,* Univ Minnesota, Minneapolis

Sheppard, John, *Dir Pub Relations,* Brandywine River Museum, Chadds Ford, PA

Shepperd, John Ben, *Chmn,* Presidential Museum, Odessa, TX

Sher, Alvin I, *Prof,* Hobart & William Smith Colleges, Geneva, NY

Sherbell, Rhoda, *VPres,* Professional Artists Guild, see National and Regional Organizations

Sheridan, Helen, *Head Librn,* Kalamazoo Inst of Art, MI

Sheridan, Lee, *Dir Pub Relations,* Museum of Fine Arts, Springfield, MA

Sheridan, Susan, *Librn,* Danforth Museum, Framingham, MA

Sherker, Michael, *Assoc Prof,* Kinsborough Community College, Brooklyn, NY

Sherman, Elizabeth, *VPres,* Monterey Peninsula Museum of Art, CA

Scioli, Don, *Lectr,* Saint Joseph's College, Philadelphia, PA

Sciotti, Angela M, *Libr Dir,* Swain School of Design, New Bedford, MA

Scoones, Nancy, *Adminr,* Cornell Univ, Ithaca, NY

Scorsone, Dora J, *Secy,* State Univ New York College at Geneseo

Scott, Charles, C, *Prof & Dir Summer School,* Glenville State College, WV

Scott, David W, *Consult Bldg Prog,* Nat Gallery of Art, Washington, DC

Scott, Forrest, *Architect,* City of Los Angeles, Municipal Arts Dept, CA

Scott, G Richard, *Academic Dean,* Avila College Art Gallery, Kansas City, MO

Scott, Jack, *Keeper Archaeology,* Glasgow Museum and Art Galleries, Scotland

Scott, James, *Instr,* Burnley School of Professional Art, Seattle, WA

Scott, John F, *Asst Prof,* Rice Univ, Houston, TX

Scott, John T, *Chmn,* Xavier Univ Louisiana, New Orleans

Scott, Oliver Patrick, *Chmn,* Morgan State Univ, Baltimore, MD

Scott, Paul, *Mem Faculty,* Montserrat School of Visual Art, Beverly, MA

Scott, Suzanne B, *Lectr,* Univ Wisconsin, Madison

Scott, T, *Head Dept Art,* City of Birmingham Polytechnic, England

Scott, Tom, *Dean Summer School,* Maryland Inst, Baltimore

Scott, Violet A, *Cur Art Center,* Honolulu Acad of Arts Collection, HI

Scott, Walter, *VPres,* Nat Society of Painters in Casein and Acrylic, see National and Regional Organizations

Scottez, Annie, *Asst,* Musee des Beaux-Arts de Lille, France

Scott-Gibson, Herbert, *In Charge Community Prog,* Metropolitan Museum of Art, New York, NY

Scranton, William, *Vis Prof,* Emory Univ, Atlanta, GA

Scull, Mrs Ward, III, *VPres,* Peninsula Arts Association, Newport News, VA

Sdunek, Bruce, *VPres,* Hartland Art Council, MI

Seace, Barry, *Asst Prof,* Mount Holyoke College, South Hadley, MA

Seager, Pamela, *Exec Asst,* California Historical Society, San Francisco

Seagrave, Edmund O, *Assoc Mgr,* Jorgensen Auditorium Gallery, Univ Connecticut, Storrs

Seagraves, Mrs Edwin D, *VPres,* Green Hill Art Gallery, Greensboro, NC

Seagren, Alan, *Dir Summer School,* Univ Nebraska, Lincoln

Seal, Leila, *Coordr Mus Serv,* Museum of the Southwest, Midland, TX

Seal, Robert H, *VPres,* San Antonio Museum Association, TX

Seaman, Anne T, *Librn,* Honolulu Acad of Arts, HI

Seamans, David M, *Asst Dir,* Muhlenberg College Center for the Arts, PA

Searing, Helen, *Chairperson Art Dept,* Smith College, Northampton, MA

Sears, Michael E, *VPres,* Hill Country Arts Found, Ingram TX

Sebolt, Alberta, *Dir Educ,* Old Sturbridge Village, MA

Secor, W. Fielding, *VPres,* Mattatuck Historical Society, Waterbury, CT

Sedam, Marvin, *Treas,* Historical Society of York County, PA

Sedlacek, Evelyn A, *Librn,* Joslyn Art Museum, NE

Seeburger, Charles L. *Cur Coll,* American Swedish Historical Found Museum, Philadelphia, PA

Seeden, Helga, *Acting Cur,* American Univ Beirut Archaeological Museum, Lebanon

Seeger, Mrs Nelson V, *Secy,* Stan Hywet Hall Found, Akron, OH

Seegmiller, Betty, *Admin Asst,* Vesterheim, Decorah, IA

Seelig, Christine J, *Admin Asst,* William A Farnsworth Library and Art Museum, Rockland, ME

Seelye, Eugene, A, *Assoc Prof,* Clarion State College, PA

Seeman, Rebecca, *Instr,* College of Wooster, OH

Sefekar, Joseph, *Adminr,* Hirshhorn Museum and Sculpture Garden, Washington, DC

Segerson, Marge, *Librn,* Jose Marti Library, Daytona Beach, FL

Segger, Martin, *Dir & Cur,* Univ Victoria, BC

Segoviano, Jose Luis Mercado, *Head Dept,* Escuela de Artes Decorativas, Madrid, Spain

Segura, Tom, *Rentals Coordr,* Sangre De Cristo Arts & Conference Center, Pueblo, CO

Seibert, Donald C, *Dept Head,* Ernest Stevenson Bird Library, Syracuse, NY

Seidel, Linda, *Assoc Prof,* Univ Chicago, IL

Seifert, *Prof,* Asbury College, Wilmore, KY

Seifert, Johannes, *Librn,* Rheinisches Landesmuseum Bonn, Germany

Seiler, Dr Annemarie, *Cur America,* Museum fur Volkerkunde und Schweizerisches Museum fur Volkskunde Basel, Switzerland

Seiz, John, *Mem Faculty,* Springfield College, IL

Sekino, Tad, *Chmn Ceramics,* De Young Museum Art School, San Francisco, CA

Sekler, Eduard F, *Prof,* Harvard Univ, Cambridge, MA

Selby, Roger, L, *Dir,* Winnipeg Art Gallery, MB

Seley, Jason, *Prof,* Cornell Univ, Ithaca, NY

Seligman, Thomas K, *VDir Educ,* Fine Arts Museums of San Francisco, CA

Seligsohn, Valern, *Asso Prof,* Philadelphia Community College, PA

Sellars, Judith, *Librn,* Museum of International Folk Art, Santa Fe, NM

Sellers, Beth, *Asst Dir,* Boise Gallery of Art, ID

Sellers, William, *Asst Prof,* Herbert H Lehman College, Bronx, NY

Sellon, William, *Dir Summer School,* Bemidji State Univ, MN

Selter, Dan, *Instr,* Transylvania Univ, Lexington, KY

Selz, Dr Paul, *Chmn Art Gallery,* Fairfield Public Library and Museum, IA

Semerad, Marjorie, *Chmn,* Russell Sage College, Troy, NY

Semler, Evelyn, *Reference Librn,* Pierpont Morgan Library, New York, NY

Semmel, Marsha K, *Art Historian/Promotion,* Taft Museum, Cincinnati, OH

Sena, Paul, *Instr,* Springfield College, MA

Senior, Mrs P A, *Dir,* Johannesburg Art Gallery, South Africa

Sennett, Arthur, *Prof,* State Univ New York College at Potsdam

Senti, Marvel, *Exhib Chmn,* Hutchinson Art Association, KS

Sentz, Georgiana D, *Asst Prof,* Houghton College, NY

Senzoku, Nobuyuki, *Cur,* Kokuritsu Seiyo Bijutsukan, Tokyo, Japan

Sepulveda, Teresa, *Head Ethnographical Dept,* Museo Nacional de Antropologia, Mexico City, Mexico

Serafimov, S, *Dean Applied Arts & Assoc Prof,* Nikolaj Pavlovic Higher Inst of Fine Arts, Sofia, Bulgaria

Serafy, Jean, *Chmn,* Texas Southmost College, Brownsville

Serenco, Henry, *Assoc Prof,* Univ Nebraska at Omaha

Serette, David W, *Cur Graphic Arts & Photography,* Shaker Museum, Poland Spring, ME

Serisawa, Sueo, *Mem Faculty,* Southern California, Idyllwild Campus; *Mem Faculty,* Laguna Beach School of Art, CA

Serra, Dr Rosanna Maggio, *Dir,* Museo Civico, Torino, Italy

Serullaz, Maurice, *Cur Drawings,* Musee du Louvre, Paris, France

Settgast, Dr J, *Dir Egyptian Antiquities,* Staatliche Museen Preussischer Kulturbesitz, Berlin, Germany

Sever, Ziya, *Chmn,* Alvin Community College, TX

Severa, Joan, *Cur Decorative Arts,* State Historical Society of Wisconsin, Madison

Severens, Martha R, *Cur Coll,* Carolina Art Association, Charleston, SC

Sevigny, Daniel E, *Asst Cur,* Old Gaol Museum, York, ME

Sevin, Whitney, *Asst Prof,* Grand Valley State Colleges, Allendale, MI

Sevy, Barbara, *Librn,* Philadelphia Museum of Art, PA

Sewell, Darrel, *Cur American Art,* Philadelphia Museum of Art, PA

Sewell, Jack, *Cur Oriental Art & Secy-Treas,* The Orientals, Art Inst of Chicago, IL

Sewell, Stuart, *Mem Faculty,* Waubonsee Community College, Sugar Grove, IL

Sexauer, Donald R, *Chmn Printmaking,* East Carolina Univ, Greenville, NC

Sexstone, Dick, *Resident Artist,* Peters Valley Craftsmen, Layton, NJ

Seyfert, Anna Mary, *Second VPres,* Arizona Watercolor Association, Phoenix

Seylaz, Paul, *Dir & Cur,* Musee des Beaux-Arts et Societe des Amis des Arts, La Chaux De Fonds, Switzerland

Sherman, Helen, *Assoc Prof Art & Art Hist & Chmn Dept,* Marygrove College, Detroit, MI

Sherman, Roger, *Cur,* Plains Art Museum & Rourke Art Gallery, Moorhead, MN

Sherman, Terry J, *Educ Cur,* Montclair Art Museum, NJ

Sherman, Thomas L, *Art Reach Dir,* Delaware Art Museum, Wilmington

Sherman, William A, *Pres,* Newport Historical Society, RI

Shermoe, Raymond, *Exec Dir,* Civic Fine Arts Association, Sioux Falls, SD

Sherrill, Margorie, *Mem,* Tucson Museum of Art, AZ

Sherwin, Brian, *Pres,* Fine Arts Association, Willoughby, OH

Sherwood, Richard E, *Pres,* Los Angeles County Museum of Art, CA

Shestack, Alan, *Dir,* Yale Univ Art Gallery, New Haven, CT

Shetler, Charles, *Librn,* State Historical Society of Wisconsin, Madison

Shevis, Stell, *Asst Dir,* Gallery of Stell & Shevis, Camden, ME

Shevis, William A, *Dir,* Gallery of Stell & Shevis, Camden, ME

Shewhake, Mitzi, *Asst Prof,* Winston-Salem State Univ, NC

Shieber, Phyllis Carol, *Assoc Prof,* Lane College, Jackson, TN

Shields, Jennifer Clark, *Sales Gallery Mgr,* Amarillo Art Center, TX

Shiels, L F, *Secy,* Le Front des Artistes Canadiens, Winnipeg, MB

Shields, Mildred, *Secy,* Racine Art Association, WI

Shifflett, Celia, *Mem Secy,* Industrial Designers Society of America, see National and Regional Organizations

Shigaki, Betty Jean, *Dir,* Rochester Art Center, MN

Shih, Dr Hsio-Yen, *Dir,* Nat Gallery of Canada, Ottawa, ON

Shih, Patricia, *Admin Asst,* Lone Mountain College Art Dept Gallery, San Francisco, CA

Shih, Phoebe, *Instr,* Cultural Arts Center of Ocean City, NJ

Shin, Hyun, *Asst Prof,* Univ Northern Colorado, Greeley

Shindelbower, Daniel N, *Chmn,* Eastern Kentucky Univ, Richmond

Shine, Carolyn R, *Cur Costumes, Textiles & Tribal Arts,* Cincinnati Art Museum, OH

Shipengrover, Judith, *Dir Summer School,* Niagara County Community College, Sanborn, NY

Shipley, Roger Douglas, *Dir,* Art Center Gallery, *Assoc Prof & Chmn Art Dept & Dir Summer School,* Lycoming College, Williamsport, PA

Shirk, George H, *Pres Bd Trustees,* Oklahoma Historical Society, Oklahoma City

Shirley, Karen, *Assoc Prof,* Antiocn College, Yellow Springs, OH

Shirley, Mrs Lawrence W, *Clerk,* Currier Gallery of Art, Manchester, NH

Shissler, Barbara J, *Dir,* Univ Minnesota Gallery, Minneapolis

Shive, Dr Joseph, *Dir Summer School,* Housatonic Community College, Bridgeport, CT

Shoemaker, Innis H, *Asst Dir,* William Hayes Ackland Memorial Art Center, Univ North Carolina, Chapel Hill

Skowronek, Dr Stefan, *Ancient Coins,* Museum Narodowe W Krakowie, Cracow, Poland

Skrade, Dennis, *Junior Libr Asst,* Univ Minnesota Gallery, Minneapolis

Skramstad, Harold K, Jr, *Dir,* Chicago Historical Society, IL

Skreiner, Dr Wilfried, *Dir,* Neue Galerie am Landesmuseum Joanneum, Graz, Austria

Skuja, Lucija, *Head Music & Art Dept,* Grand Rapids Public Library, MI

Slack, Virginia, *Secy,* Hickory Museum of Art, NC

Slader, Duncan, *Artist-in-Residence,* Hinckley School of Crafts, ME

Slade, Rona, *Chmn Found & Second Year,* Corcoran School of Art, Washington, DC

Slade, Roy, *Pres & Dir Museum,* Cranbrook Acad of Art, Bloomfield Hills, MI

Slaney, Steven, *Designer Exhib,* Univ California Art Museum, Santa Barbara

Slate, Joseph, *Prof,* Kenyon College, Gambier, OH

Slattum, Jerry, *Asst Prof,* California Lutheran College, Thousand Oaks

Slavin, Richard E, III, *Cur,* New York State Historical Association, Cooperstown

Slaymaker, Sandy, *VPres,* Wayne Art Center, PA

Slayton, Ronald, *Cur,* Wood Art Gallery, Montpelier, VT

Slee, David W, *Technician,* Kelsey Museum of Ancient & Mediaeval Archaeology, Ann Arbor, MI

Slee, Jacquelynn, *Registrar,* Univ Michigan Museum of Art, Ann Arbor

Sleight, Frederick W, *Exec Dir,* Palm Springs Desert Museum, CA

Slemmons, Rod, *Cur,* Whatcom Museum of History and Art, Bellingham, WA

Slenker, Sister Elizabeth, *Mem Faculty,* St Thomas Aquinas College, Sparkhill, NY

Slepchuk, Mrs P, *Librn,* Ukrainian Arts and Crafts Museum, Edmonton, AB

Slive, Seymour, *Dir,* William Hayes Fogg Art Museum, Harvard Univ, Cambridge, MA

Slivka, Rose, *Ed-in-Chief Crafts Horizons,* American Crafts Council, see National and Regional Organizations

Sloan, John, *Asst Cur & Cur,* Delaware Art Museum, Wilmington

Sloan, Joy Carol, *Prog Consult,* Angelo State Univ Center, San Angelo, TX

Sloan, Dr Thomas L, *Asst Prof,* Northwestern Univ, Evanston, IL

Sloan, William, *Pres,* Association of Canadian Industrial Designers (Ontario), Toronto

Sloane, Eric, *Art Adv Bd,* Society of Medalists, see National and Regional Organizations

Sloane, Joseph C, *Dir,* William Hayes Ackland Memorial Art Center, Univ North Carolina, Chapel Hill

Slobodkina, Esphyr, *Treas,* American Abstract Artists, see National and Regional Organizations

Slocum, Richard, *Dir,* Our Lady of the Lake Univ, San Antonio; TX

Slocum, Mrs Richard C, *Secy,* Columbia Museums of Art and Science, SC

Slomann, Wencke, *Head Early Iron Age Dept,* Universitetets Samling Av Nordiske Oldsaker, Oslo, Norway

Sloshberg, Leah P, *Dir,* New Jersey State Museum, Trenton

Slottman, Helen, *Fist VPres,* Pen and Brush, New York, NY

Slovacek, Joe, *Instr,* San Jacinto College, Pasadena, TX

Slusarski, Peter, *Asst Prof,* Eisenhower College, Seneca Falls, NY

Smaka, J, *Cur,* Muzeum Narodowe We Wroclawiu, Wroclaw, Poland

Small, Carol D, *Instr,* Gettysburg College, PA

Small, David, *Asst Prof,* State Univ New York College at Fredonia

Small, Mrs. Robert N., *Pres,* Everson Museum of Art, Syracuse, NY

Smallenberg, Harry, *Chmn Gen Studies,* Center for Creative Studies, Detroit, MI

Smalley, David, *Chmn & Dir Summer School,* Connecticut College, New London

Smallman, Carol, *Exec Asst,* Archaeological Inst of America, see National and Regional Organizations

Smet, Dany, *Librn,* International Cultureel Centrum, Antwerp, Belgium

Smigocki, Dr. Stephen, *Mem Faculty,* Fairmont State College, WV

Smiter, Janine, *Chief Information & Pub Relations,* Nat Gallery of Canada, Ottawa, ON

Smith, Albert H, *Asst Prof,* Georgia Inst of Technology, Atlanta

Smith, Sir Alex, *Dir,* Manchester Polytechnic, England

Smith, Allen C, *Cur Coll,* Arnot Art Museum, Elmira, NY

Smith, Ann, *Dir,* Mattatuck Historical Society, Waterbury, CT

Smith, Ann Cote, *Dir,* Copper King Mansion, Butte, MT

Smith, Arthur, *Prof,* Salem State College, MA

Smith, Bob, *Dir,* Los Angeles Inst of Contemporary Art, CA

Smith, Bonnie Mae, *Staff Mem,* Imperial Calcasieu Museum, Lake Charles, LA

Smith, Brydon E, *Cur Contemporary Art,* Nat Gallery of Canada, Ottawa, ON

Smith, Carol R, *Secy,* Southern Highland Handicraft Guild, Asheville, NC

Smith, Cathy, *Instr,* Cleveland State Community College, TN

Smith, Charles Lee, *Secy-Treas,* North Carolina Art Society, Raleigh

Smith, D, *Art Technician,* Durban Art Gallery, South Africa

Smith, Miss D C P, *Librn,* Royal Scottish Museum, Edinburgh

Smith, Daniel H, *Exec Secy,* Riverside Art Center and Museum, CA

Smith, Darold, *Assoc Prof,* West Texas State Univ, Canyon

Smith, David, *Vis Prof,* Ithaca College, NY

Smith, David L, *Assoc Prof,* Univ Wisconsin-Stevens Point

Smith, David L, *Mem Faculty,* Swain School of Design, New Bedford, MA

Smith, Donald C, *Prof,* Rhode Island College, Providence

Smith, Dr. Donald E., *Prof & Chmn Dept Art,* Texas Woman's Univ, Denton

Smith, Dorothy O, *Corresp Secy,* St Augustine Art Association Gallery, FL

Smith, Dorothy V, *Librn,* Brush and Palette Club, Cooperstown, NY

Smith, Douglas A, *Asst Prof Art,* Central Oregon Community College, Bend

Smith, Edith, *Pres,* Rutland Area Art Association, VT

Smith, Erin McCawley, *Staff Asst,* Lemoyne Art Found, Tallahassee, FL

Smith, Ernest W, *Dir,* Auckland City Art Gallery, New Zealand

Smith, Ernest W, *Dir,* Dalhousie Univ Art Gallery, Halifax, NS

Smith, Frances K, *Acting Dir & Cur,* Queen's University Art Centre, Kingston, ON

Smith, Frank Anthony, *Assoc Prof,* Univ Utah, Salt Lake City

Smith, Frederick T, *Instr,* Univ Minnesota, Minneapolis

Smith, G Alden, *Pres,* Mid-America College Art Association, see National and Regional Organizations; *Chmn Art Dept & Dir Summer School,* Wayne State Univ, Detroit, MI

Smith, Gary T, *Dir,* Hartnell College Gallery, Salinas, CA

Smith, George, *Adminr,* Woodlawn & Pope-Leighey House, Mount Vernon, VA

Smith, Gladys, *Asst Librn,* Chappell Mem Library and Art Gallery, NE

Smith, Gregory Allgire, *Asst Dir Develop,* Akron Art Inst Museum, OH

Smith, Harriet Ross, *Secy,* Virginia Beach Arts Center

Smith, J B, *Dir Art Museum & Chmn Dept,* Baylor University, Waco, TX

Smith, James, *Asst Prof,* Univ Missouri, Saint Louis

Smith, James E., *Assoc Prof,* Western Carolina Univ, Cullowhee, NC

Smith, James F, *Dean & Found Chmn & Dean Summer Div,* New England School of Art and Design, Boston, MA

Smith, James L, *Pres,* Waterloo Art Association, IA

Smith, James Morton, *Dir,* Winterthur Museum and Gardens, DE

Smith, James Morton, *Dir,* State Historical Society of Wisconsin, Madison

Smith, Jean, *Secy,* Sheldon Museum and Cultural Center, Haines, AK

Smith, Jean, *Arts & Archit Librn,* Pennsylvania State Univ, University Park

Smith, Jo, *Office Mgr,* Marin Art & Garden Society, Ross, CA

Smith, Joan, *Secy,* Main Line Center of the Arts, Haverford, PA

Smith, John P, *Asst Prof,* Univ New Orleans, LA

Smith, John W, *Asst Prof,* Univ Arkansas, Fayetteville

Smith, Joseph Johnson, *Dir,* New Haven Colony Historical Society, CT

Smith, Kathy A, *Instr,* Jefferson Davis State Junior College, Brewton, AL

Smith, Louise, *Educ Chmn,* Huntsville Art League and Museum Association, AL

Smith, Maggie, *Recording Secy,* Kent Art Association, CT

Smith, Marcia, *Librn,* Adirondack Museum of the Adirondack Historical Association, Blue Mountain Lake, NY

Smith, Marie, *Secy,* Rockport Art Association, MA

Smith, Marion Kay, *Staff Asst,* Southeastern College Art Conference, see National and Regional Organizations

Smith, Mark S, *Dir of Galleries & Art Instr,* Texas Woman's Univ, Denton

Smith, Marlene, *Secy,* Canadian Guild of Potters, see National Organizations in Canada

Smith, Melvin T, *Dir,* Utah Division of State History, Salt Lake City

Smith, Meta, *Asst to Cur,* Spertus Museum of Judaica, Chicago, IL

Smith, Micahel J, *Head Painting,* Southern Illinois Univ, Edwardsville

Smith, Moishe, *Prof,* Utah State Univ, Logan

Smith, Morgan K, *Pres,* Concord Antiquarian Society Museum, MA

Smith, Mort E, *Head Dept & Prof,* Univ North Alabama, Florence

Smith, Nancy, *Assoc Prof,* Boston Univ, MA

Smith, Nancy Brown, *Instr,* West Virginia Wesleyan College, Buckhannon

Smith, P, *Head Publns,* Nat Gallery of Canada, Ottawa, ON

Smith, Paul, *Dir,* Museum of Contemporary Crafts of the American Crafts Council, New York, NY

Smith, Paul, *VPres,* Louis Comfort Tiffany Found, New York, NY

Smith, Philip C F, *Cur Maritime History,* Peabody Museum of Salem, MA

Smith, R, *Gen Asst,* Univ Club Library, New York

Smith, Raymond M, *Pres,* Monterey History and Art Association, CA

Smith, Robert, *Dir Summer School,* Anderson College, IN

Smith, Robert, *VPres,* Industrial Designers Society of America, see National and Regional Organizations

Smith, Robert Ross, *Deputy Dir,* Copper King Mansion, Butte, MT

Smith, Ronald, *Dir Summer School,* Fayetteville State Univ, NC

Smith, Stanley M, *Dir Develop,* Society for the Preservation of New England Antiquities, Boston, MA

Smith, Susan, *Property Council & Staff,* Nat Trust Interpretors, Pope-Leighey House & Woodlawn, Mount Vernon, VA

Stein, Claire A, *Exec Dir,* Nat Sculpture Society, see National and Regional Organizations

Stein, Margaret, *Mem Faculty,* Greenfield Community College, MA

Stein, Michael, *Mem Faculty,* Housatonic Community College, Bridgeport, CT; *Assoc Cur,* Housatonic Museum of Art, Bridgeport

Stein, Robert, *Assoc Prof & Dir Summer School,* Philadelphia College of Art, PA

Stein, Virginia, *Librn,* Sill Gallery, Ypsilanti, MI

Steinberg, Ronald M, *Assoc Prof,* Rhode Island College, Providence

Steinborn, B, *Cur,* Muzeum Narodowe We Wroclawiu, Wroclaw, Poland

Steinfeldt, Cecilia, *Sr Cur History & Decorative Arts,* San Antonio Museum Association, TX

Steingraber, Dr E, *Gen Dir,* Bayerischen Staatsgemaldesammlungen, Munich, Germany

Steinhauser, Janice, *Dir Visual Arts Serv,* Western States Arts Found, Denver, CO

Steiro, Carol, *Cur Coll,* Museum of International Folk Art, Santa Fe, NM

Stele-Mozina, Melita, *Cur Mus Coll,* Moderna Galerija, Ljubljana, Yugoslavia

Stemmler, Dr Dierk, *Dir,* Stadtisches Kunstmuseum Bonn, Germany

Stemple, Colette, *Instr,* Lake Placid School of Art, NY

Stene, Larry, *Instr,* Bemidji State Univ, MN

Stephen, Barbara, *Assoc Dir Curatorial,* Royal Ontario Museum, Toronto

Stephens, Arial A, *Dir,* Public Library of Charlotte and Mecklenburg County, Charlotte, NC

Stephens, Fred, *Chmn,* Brescia College, Owensboro, KY

Stephens, John C, *Dean,* Univ Georgia, Athens

Stephens, Michael, *Coordr,* Art Research Center, Kansas City, MO

Stephens, Richard A, *Pres,* Acad of Art College, San Francisco, CA

Stephens, William B, *Chmn & Assoc Prof,* Texas Eastern Univ, Tyler

Stephenson, Dr, *Dir Summer School,* East Central Univ, Ada, OK

Stephenson, Carolynn, *Registrar,* Louisville School of Art Gallery, Anchorage, KY

Stephenson, Garrick C, *First VPres,* Parrish Art Museum, Southampton, NY

Stephenson, Robert E, *Archit Librn,* Virginia Polytechnic Inst & State Univ Art Gallery, Blacksburg

Sterling, William H, *Chmn,* Wilkes College, Wilkes-Barre, PA

Stern, Peter H, *Pres,* Storm King Center, Mountainville, NY

Stern, Robert A M, *Pres,* Architectural League of New York, NY

Sterne, John, *Chmn,* Art Gallery of Brant, Brantford, ON

Sterritt, James, *Chairperson 3D Dept,* Washington Univ, Saint Louis, MO

Stevanov, Zoran, *Dir Exhib,* Fort Hays State Univ, KS

Steven, Dorothy, *City Librn,* Monterey Public Library, CA

Steven, Leland, *Assoc Prof,* Agnes Scott College, Decatur, GA

Steven, Timoth J, *Dir,* Walker Art Gallery, Liverpool, England

Stevens, Arthur D, *Assoc Prof & Chmn Art Dept,* Scripps College, Claremont; CA; *Mem Faculty,* Pomona College, Claremont, CA

Stevens, Elizabeth, *Asst To Pres,* Louis Comfort Tiffany Found, New York, NY

Stevens, George F, *Secy & Dir,* Oregon State Univ Mem Union Art Gallery, Corvallis

Stevens, Hugh, *Head Dept,* Jackson State College, MS

Stevens, Marge, *Registrar,* Brooklyn Museum Art School, NY

Stevens, Martha, *Cur Educ,* Alaska State Museum, Juneau

Stevens, Roger L, *Chmn Bd Trustees,* John F Kennedy Center for the Performing Arts, Washington, DC

Stevens, Susan Stairs, *Secy,* Florida Artist Group, St Augustine

Stevens, Walter, *Prof,* Univ Tennessee, Knoxville

Stevenson, A Brockie, *Chmn Drawing & Design,* Corcoran School of Art, Washington, DC

Stevenson, Branson, *Secy,* Archie Bray Found, Helena, MT

Stevenson, Charles, *Chairperson Fine Arts,* Mendocino Art Center, CA

Stevenson, Harold Ransom, *Head Dept & Instr,* Stevenson Acad of Traditional Painting, New York, NY

Stewart, Albert, *Vis Lectr,* California State College, Stanislaus, Turlock

Stewart, Ann, *Librn,* Nat Gallery of Ireland, Dublin

Stewart, Anne, *Dean Summer School,* American River College, Sacramento, CA

Stewart, Charles A, *Dean,* Howard Payne Univ, Brownwood, TX

Stewart, David M, *Pres,* Montreal Museum of Fine Arts, PQ

Stewart, Donald F, *Exec Dir,* Baltimore Maritime Museum, MD

Stewart, Dorothy, *Pres,* Kent Art Association Gallery, CT

Stewart, Duncan E, *Dir Art Gallery & Asst Prof,* Univ West Florida, Pensacola

Stewart, George R, *Dir,* Birmingham Public Library, AL

Stewart, J Alexander, *Pres,* Filson Club, Louisville, KY

Stewart, Jarvis, *Prof,* Ohio Wesleyan Univ, Delaware

Stewart, Jean C, *Asst Cur Coll,* Carolina Art Association, Charleston, SC

Stewart, John, *Dean,* Univ Montevallo, AL

Stewart, John R, *Chmn Dept,* Dept of Architecture & Landscape Architecture, Oregon State Univ, Corvallis

Stewart, Lawna, *Accessionist/Secy,* Mount Saint Vincent Univ Art Gallery, Halifax, NS

Stewart, Milo V, *Assoc Dir & Chief,* New York State Historical Association, Cooperstown

Stewart, Priscilla, *Prof,* Manatee Junior College, Brandenton, FL

Stewart, Robert G, *Cur,* Nat Portrait Gallery, Washington, DC

Stewart, Rosamond Joy, *Assoc Prof,* Hillsdale College, MI

Stewart, Ruth Chambers, *Exec Secy,* Rehoboth Art League, Rehoboth Beach, DE

Steyaert, John, *Asst Prof,* Univ Minnesota, Minneapolis

Stibbe, Katherine Campbell, *Pres,* Nicholas Roerich Museum, New York, NY

Stickler, Jim, *Mem Faculty,* Murray State Univ, KY

Stieglitz, Mary G, *Assoc Prof,* Univ Wisconsin, Madison

Stiff, Libby, *Asst Cur Educ,* Tucson Museum of Art, AZ

Stiles, Lois Kent, *Chief Art Div,* Public Library of District of Columbia, Washington, DC

Stiles, William F, *Sr Cur,* Heye Found, New York, NY

Stillman, Damie, *Second VPres,* Society of Architectural Historians, see National and Regional Organizations

Stillman, George, *Chmn Art Dept,* Central Washington Univ, Ellensburg

Stirnaman, Loretta, *Newsletter Ed,* San Bernardino Art Association, CA

Stites, Mary Henry, *Secy,* Moravian Historical Society, Nazareth, PA

Stitt, Susan, *Dir,* Museums at Stony Brook, NY

Stittenfeld, Elizabeth B, *Co-Dir & Cur,* Univ Cincinnati Art Gallery, OH

Stiuson, Robert, *Head Painting,* Bowling Green State Univ, OH

Stlot, Dr Franciszek, *Deputy Dir Polish Art of the 16th-18th Centuries,* Muzeum Narodowe W Krakowie, Cracow, Poland

Stockdale, Louise L, *Mgr,* Gunston Hall Plantation, Lorton, VA

Stockwell, Ross, *Instr,* San Diego Mesa College, CA

Stoddard, Dr Donna M, *Coordr Art Dept & Gallery Dir,* Florida Southern College, Lakeland

Stoddart, Stanford C, *Chmn Bd,* Detroit Inst of Art Collections, MI

Stodola, Bruce, *Secy,* American Society of Interior Designers, see National and Regional Organizations

Stodulski, Leon, *Science Assoc,* William Hayes Fogg Art Museum, Harvard Univ, Cambridge, MA

Stoelzel, Martin C, *Chmn Dept,* College of Marin, Kentfield, CA

Stoessell, Pamela, *Instr,* Marymount College of Virginia, Arlington

Stohr, Waldemar, Dr, *Cur Art of Indonesia & South Seas,* Rautenstrauch-Joest Museum fur Volkenkunde, Museen der Stadt Koln, Germany

Stoker, Eloise, *Asst Prof,* Incarnate Word College, San Antonio, TX

Stokes, Charlotte, *Prof,* Oakland Univ, Rochester, MI

Stokstad, Marilyn, *Pres,* College Art Association of America, see National and Regional Organizations; *Cur Art,* Univ Kansas, Lawrence

Stolnitz, Jerome, *Pres,* American Society for Aesthetics, see National and Regional Organizations

Stomps, Walter, *Head Dept,* Western Kentucky Univ, Bowling Green

Stone, Ben, *Cur Indian Coll,* Philbrook Art Center, Tulsa, OK

Stone, Carolyn Rea, *Assoc Prof & Chmn Art Educ,* Delta State Univ, Cleveland, MS

Stone, Dorris, *Exec Secy,* Watkins Inst, Nashville, TN

Stone, R Adm Earl E, *Dir,* Allen Knight Maritime Museum, Monterey History and Art Association, CA

Stone, Karen, *Mem Faculty,* Mesa Community College, AZ

Stone, K Gordon, *Assoc Mus Librn,* Robert Lehman Collection Library, Metropolitan Museum of Art, New York, NY

Stone, Marion, *Second VPres,* San Bernardino Art Association, CA

Stone, Peter G, *Comt Chmn,* Oregon College of Education Gallery 109, Monmouth

Stone, William F, Jr, *Recording Secy,* Monterey Peninsula Museum of Art, CA

Stones, M Alison, *Assoc Prof,* Univ Minnesota, Minneapolis

Stonum, Paul T, *Exec VPres/Dir,* Nat Hall of Fame for Famous American Indians, Anadarko, OK

Stonum, Sally, *Secy,* Nat Hall of Fame for Famous American Indians, Anadarko, OK

Stooker, Patricia D, *Pub Relations Dir,* Denver Art Museum, CO

Storer, Mrs C A, *Chmn Bd Trustees,* Zigler Museum, Jennings, LA

Storer, Inez, *Acting Gallery Dir,* Sonoma State College Art Gallery, Rohnert Park, CA

Storey, Frank J, *Secy,* Confederation Centre Art Gallery and Museum, Charlottetown, PE

Storey, Jackson Grey, *Pres,* Central Acad of Commercial Art, Cincinnati, OH

Story, Lewis, *Secy,* Western Association of Art Museums, see National and Regional Organizations; *Assoc Dir,* Denver Art Museum, CO

Story, William E, *Dir,* Ball State Univ Art Gallery, Muncie, IN

Stotski, Joe, *Dir Summer School,* Ohio Dominican Univ, Columbus

Stotz, Virginia, *Coordr Art Hist,* Kean College of New Jersey, Union

Stoughton, Gen, *Librn,* Oak Ridge Community Art Center, TN

Stoughton, Michael, *Asst Prof,* Univ Minnesota, Minneapolis

Stout, Alan, *VPres,* Gaston County Art and History Museum, Dallas, NC

Stout, Kenneth, *Assoc Prof,* Fontbonne College, Clayton, MO

Stover, Edwin L, *Dir Instr,* San Jose City College, CA

Stowell, Lynn, *Admin Asst,* Univ Kentucky Art Museum, Lexington

Stradling, Anne C, *Dir & Cur,* Stradling Museum of the Horse, Patagonia, AZ

Stradling, Floyd M, *Deputy Dir,* Stradling Museum of the Horse, Patagonia, AZ

Straight, Robert, *Asst Prof,* Connecticut College, New London

Strand, Elizabeth, *Prof,* Concordia College, Moorhead, MN

Stras, Marian, *Secy,* Kingsport Fine Arts Center, TN

Strater, Henry, *Dir,* Museum of Art of Ogunquit, ME

Stratton, Marcel C, *Assoc Prof,* Moorhead State Univ, MN

Straub, Dale, *Asst Prof,* Williamsport Area Community College, PA

Strauss, Helen, *Asst,* Pemaquid Group of Artists, Pemaquid Point, ME

Strauss, Melvin, *Pres,* Cornish Inst of Allied Arts, Seattle, WA

Strawn, Jarrett W, *Head Dept,* Beloit College, WI

Strawn, Mel, *Dir Art School & Dir Summer School,* Univ Denver, CO

Strawn, Phyllis, *Instr,* William Woods/Westminster Colleges, Fulton, MO

Streeter, F S, *Secy,* Grolier Club, New York, NY

Streetman, John W, III, *Dir,* Evansville Museum of Arts and Science, IN

Streety, John, *Dir Summer School,* Southwestern at Memphis, TN

Streibig, Kenneth C, *Dean Summer School,* Monmouth College, West Long Branch, NJ

Strel, Donald O, *Dir Fine Arts Div & Dir Museum of Fine Arts,* Museum of New Mexico, Santa Fe

Streppone, Robert, *Assoc Dir,* Studio Workshop, New York, NY

Stribley, Roger, *Pres,* Craftsmen's Association of British Columbia, Vancouver

Strickland, Alice, *Mus Guide,* Tomoka State Park Museum, Ormond Beach, FL

Strickland, Dianne, *Dir,* Southwest Missouri State Univ Gallery, Springfield

Strickland, Eyck, *Affiliate,* Emory Univ, Atlanta, GA

Strickland, Norma, *Asst Prof,* Saint Mary's College of Maryland, Saint Mary's City

Strider, Maurice, *Assoc Prof,* Morehead State Univ, KY

Strike, Mrs William F A, *Acting Dir,* Concord Antiquarian Society Museum, MA

Striker, Carlene, *Pres,* Seattle Weaver's Guild, WA

Stringer, Mary Evelyn, *Prof,* Mississippi Univ for Women, Columbus

Stroh, Charles, *Chmn Art Dept & Dir Summer School,* Coe College, Cedar Rapids, IA

Strohman, Barbara J, *Assoc Prof,* Bloomsburg State College, PA

Strom, Caryl, *Newsletter Ed,* Alaska Artists Guild, Anchorage ·

Stromei, Susan, *Asst Archives,* International Museum of Photography, Rochester, NY

Strommen, Kim, *Asst Dean Art School,* Washington Univ, Saint Louis, MO

Strong, Barbara, *Instr,* College of the Sequoias, Visalia, CA

Strong, Richard, *Prof,* Dept of Landscape Architecture, Univ Toronto, Ontario

Strong, Dr Roy, *Dir,* Victoria and Albert Museum, London, England

Strong, Susan R, *Head Art Reference & AV Serv,* New York State College of Ceramics at Alfred Univ, NY

Strosahl, William, *Second VPres,* American Watercolor Society, see National and Regional Organizations

Strother, Joseph W, *Dir,* Louisiana Tech Univ, Ruston

Stroud, Peter, *Assoc Prof,* Mason Gross School of the Arts, Rutgers, The State Univ New Jersey, New Brunswick

Strouse, Norman H, *Dir,* Silverado Museum, Saint Helena, CA

Strueber, Michael M, *Dir,* Southern Alleghenies Museum of Art, Loretto, PA

Strull, Virginia, *Dir Develop,* Schenectady Museum, NY

Strump, M, *Chmn Jewelry Design,* Fashion Inst of Technology, New York, NY

Strunck, Juergen, *Artist-in-Residence,* Oxbow Summer Art Workshops, Saugatuck, MI

Struppeck, Jules, *Prof,* Tulane Univ, New Orleans, LA

Struve, Gail, *Pres,* Evanston Art Center, IL

Stuart, Joseph, *Dir,* South Dakota State Univ, Brookings

Stuart, Michelle, *Slide Registry Comt Mem,* Women's Slide Registry, New York, NY

Stuart, Spencer, *Pres Bd Trustees,* Silvermine Guild of Artists Gallery, New Canaan, CT

Stubblebine, Dr James, *Mem Faculty,* Grad Prog in Art History, Rutgers, The State Univ New Jersey, New Brunswick

Stubbs, Maurice, *Univ Art Cur,* Univ Western Ontario, London

Stubbs, Robert, *Admin,* Pennsylvania Acad of Fine Arts Collection, Philadelphia

Stubsjoen, H, *Assoc Prof,* Nova Scotia Technical College, Halifax

Stuckenbruck-Smith, Linda, *Instr,* Texas Woman's Univ, Denton

Stuckey, W Dubose, *Treas,* Greenwood Museum, SC

Stuckhardt, Michael H, *Asst Prof,* Miami Univ, Oxford, OH

Studler, Rene, *Second VPres,* La Societe des Decorateurs-Ensembliers du Quebec, Montreal

Stuffman, Dr Margaret, *Cur,* Stadelsches Kunstinstitut, Frankfurt am Main, Germany

Stuiver, Chitra, *Art Specialist,* Hawaii State Library, Honolulu

Stull, Robert, *Chmn Dept Art,* Ohio State Univ, Columbus

Stumpo, Mary-Anne, *Docent,* Norwich Free Academy & *Mem Faculty,* Norwich Art School, CT

Stuppack, Hermann, *Pres & Prof,* International Summer Acad of Fine Arts, Salzburg, Austria

Sturdy, Kenneth G, *Head,* Alberta College of Art, Calgary

Sturgell, Jack S, *Dir,* Univ Delaware Student Center Art Gallery, Newark

Sturgeon, Eileen, *Dir,* Roberts Art Gallery, Santa Monica High School, CA

Sturges, Michael, *Develop Dir,* Mystic Seaport, CT

Sturr, Henry D, *Asst Dir,* California Museum of Science and Industry, Los Angeles

Sturrock, Alice, *Asst to Dir,* Norton Gallery and School of Art, West Palm Beach, FL

Stutman, Ellen, *Mem Staff,* Boston Center for Adult Education, MA

Styron, Thomas W, *Cur American Art,* Chrysler Museum at Norfolk, VA

Suarez, Linda, *Exec Secy,* Tampa Bay Art Center, FL

Suazo, David C, *Dir,* Ghost Ranch Visitor Center, Abiquiu, NM

Suddith, John T, *Chmn,* Louisiana College, Pineville

Suddon, Alan, *Head Fine Art Dept,* Metropolitan Toronto Library Board, ON

Sudouth, William M, *Acting Dir/Dir Operations,* Omniplex, Oklahoma City, OK

Suelflow, Dr August R, *Dir,* Concordia Historical Inst, St Louis, MO

Suftin, Edward, *Chmn,* Vermont College of Norwich Univ, Montpelier

Sugihara, Nobuhiko, *Chief Crafts Gallery,* Tokyo Kokuritsu Kindai Bijutsukan, Japan

Suitak, Florian, *Educ Dir,* York Acad of Arts, PA

Sulentic, J D, *Pres,* Deadwood Gulch Art Gallery, SD

Sulentic, Margaret, *Secy,* Deadwood Gulch Art Gallery, SD

Sullivan, Arthur L, *Dir Landscape Archit,* North Carolina State Univ at Raleigh

Sullivan, Edward F, *Dir,* Chicago Architecture Found, IL

Sullivan, Eugene E, *Asst Prof,* Framingham State College, MA

Sullivan, Gayle, *Mem Faculty,* Factory of Visual Art, Seattle, WA

Sullivan, Jeannette T, *Art Librn,* Ernest Stevenson Bird Library, Syracuse, NY

Sullivan, Max W, *Dir,* Univ Texas Art Gallery, Arlington

Sullivan, Milton F, *Dir,* Southern Illinois Univ, Carbondale

Sullivan, Paul, *Cur,* Chapel Arts Center, Saint Anselm's College, Manchester, NH

Sullivan, Ronald Dee, *Assoc Prof,* Del Mar College, Corpus Christi, TX

Sultz, Jan, *Lectr,* Webster College, Webster Groves, MO

Sultz, Phil, *Assoc Prof,* Webster College, Webster Groves, MO

Summa, Kathryn, *Circ Head,* Lake Forest Library, IL

Summer, Eugenia, *Assoc Prof,* Mississippi Univ for Women, Columbus

Summerford, Ben L, *Prof & Chmn Art Dept & Dir Summer School,* American Univ, Washington, DC

Summers, Ruth T, *Exec Dir,* Hand Work Shop, Richmond, VA

Summerville, Gabrielle, *Asst to Dir,* Society of the Four Arts, Palm Beach, FL

Sumner, Steven, *Assoc Prof,* State Univ of New York College at Potsdam

Sumpter, Henry, *Asst Prof,* Alcorn State Univ, Lorman, MS

Sundbye, Delores A, *Supvr Arts & AV Serv,* St Paul Public Library, MN

Sunderland, Dr Elizabeth, *Hon Cur Medieval Coll, Museum of Art & Prof,* Duke Univ, Durham, NC

Sunkel, Robert, *Cur,* DeLuce Gallery, *Chmn Dept Art, & Dir Summer School,* Northwest Missouri State Univ, Maryville

Supovitz, Marjory, *Projects Coordr,* Massachusetts Inst of Technology, Cambridge

Suren, Ms M, *Cur,* Municipal Van Abbemuseum Eindhoven, Netherlands

Surovek, John H, *Dir,* Art Center, South Bend, IN

Surpthe, Lanier, *Assoc Prof,* Univ Tennessee, Knoxville

Surtees, Ursula, *Cur/Dir,* Kelowna Centennial Museum & Nat Exhibit Centre, BC

Susovski, Marijan, *Cur Contemporary Art & Librn,* Galerije Grada Zagreba, Yugoslavia

Sussman, Elisabeth, *Cur,* Inst of Contemporary Art, Boston, MA

Sussman, Margaret, *Pres,* Pen and Brush, New York, NY

Suter, Sherwood E, *Art Dept Chmn & Gallery Dir,* Ryan Fine Arts Center, McMurry College, Abilene, TX

Sutherland, A J, *Pres Bd,* Timken Art Gallery, San Diego, CA

Sutherland, Mrs Adair, *Assoc Dir Develop,* San Antonio Museum Association, TX

Sutherland, Martha, *Gallery Coordr,* Univ Arkansas, Fayetteville

Sutter, James, *Assoc Prof,* State Univ New York College at Potsdam

Sutton, B Lee, *Lectr,* Centenary College of Louisiana, Shreveport

Sutton, Judith, *Assoc Dir,* Public Library of Charlotte and Mecklenburg County, Charlotte, NC

Suydam, David, *Pres,* Mystic Art Association, CT

Svendsen, Louise Averill, *Cur,* Solomon R Guggenheim Museum, New York, NY

Swahn, Dr Jan-Ojvind, *Librn-in-Chief,* Nordiska Museet, Stockholm, Sweden

Swain, Charles W, *Staff Photographer,* Rockwell-Corning Museum, Corning, NY

Swain, Dr Jerrol, *Dir Summer School,* Southern Baptist College, College City, AR

Swain, Marjorie, *Coordr Mus Practive Prog,* Univ Michigan Museum of Art, Ann Arbor, MI

Swain, Robert, *Prof,* Hunter College, New York, NY

Swain, Robert, *VPres,* Ontario Association of Art Galleries, Toronto

Swain, Robert F, *Dir,* Gallery/Stratford, ON

Swan, Bradford, *Secy,* Rhode Island Historical
Society, Providence
Swank, Scott T, *Head Educ Div,* Winterthur Museum
and Gardens, DE
Swann, Maureen, *Mem Faculty,* Toronto School of
Art, Ontario
Swanson, Roy, *Prof,* Hutchinson Community Junior
College, KS
Swanson, Sister Thoma, *Chmn,* Albertus Magnus
College, New Haven, CT
Swarz, Sahl, *Asst Prof,* Division of Painting and
Sculpture, Columbia Univ, New York, NY
Swearingen, Eugene, *Chmn Bd & Chief Exec Officer,*
Bank of Oklahoma, Tulsa, see Corporate Art
Holdings
Sweeney, Mr & Mrs David, *Custodians,* Gibson
Society, Boston, MA
Sweeney, Dennis, *Mem Faculty,* Montserrat School
of Visual Art, Beverly, MA
Sweeney, Gray, *Asst Prof,* Grand Valley State
Colleges, Allendale, MI
Sweeney, John A H, *Coordr Research,* Winterthur
Museum and Gardens, DE
Sweeney, Mary Sue, *Pub Relations,* Newark
Museum, NJ
Sweeney, Patrick, *Youth Coordr,* Davenport
Municipal Art Gallery, IA
Sweeney, Robert P, *Assoc Prof,* Univ Arkansas,
Fayetteville
Sweeney, Steven, *Dir Summer School,* College of
New Rochelle, NY
Sweet, Douglass, *Instr,* San Jacinto College,
Pasadena, TX
Sweet, Ernest A, Jr, *Treas,* Currier Gallery of Art,
Manchester, NH
Swenson, Sandra, *Chmn Art History,* Pan American
Univ, Edinburg, TX
Swenson, Ric, *Pres,* Alaska Artists Guild,
Anchorage
Swenson, Ronald, *Dean,* School of the Associated
Arts, Saint Paul, MN
Swiderska, W, *Cur,* Muzeum Narodowe We
Wroclawiu, Wroclaw, Poland
Swierczynski, Henry, *Pres,* Springfield Art &
Historical Society, VT
Swift, Gustavus F, *Dir,* Bergman Gallery, Univ
Chicago, IL
Swift, J W, *Display Officer,* Queen Victoria Museum,
Launceston, Australia
Swift, June M, *Exec Secy,* St Joseph Museum, MO
Swimmer, Ross O, *Pres,* Cherokee Nat Historical
Society, Tahlequah, OK
Swindell, Mrs Murray, *Asst Treas,* Concord
Antiquarian Society Museum, MA
Swords, Cramer, *Assoc Prof,* Central Florida
Community College, Ocala
Swoyer, David, *Asst Cur Educ,* New Orleans
Museum of Art, LA
Swuift, Leslie, *VPres,* Providence Watercolor Club,
RI
Sykes, Lawrence F, *Assoc Prof,* Rhode Island
College, Providence
Sykes, Ronald, *Mem Faculty & Dir Summer School,*
Millersville State College, PA
Sykora, T A, *Secy,* Great Lakes Historical Society,
Vermilion, OH
Symington, Martha F, *Secy,* Frick Collection, New
York, NY
Symington, Sheila, *Pres,* White Rock Painting and
Sketch Club, BC
Synder, R Brant, *Treas,* Norton Gallery and School
of Art, West Palm Beach, FL
Sywak, Zofia, *Archivist,* New Haven Colony
Historical Society, CT
Szablowski, Dr Jerzy, *Pres,* Panstwowe Zbiory Sztuki
na Wawelu, Cracow, Poland
Szabo, Albert, *Prof,* Harvard Univ, Cambridge, MA
Szabo, George, *Cur,* Roker & Lehman Coll,
Metropolitan Museum of Art, New York, NY
Szabo, Pamela, *Librn,* Univ Notre Dame Catalog
Library, IN
Szainer, Armand, *Asst Prof,* Notre Dame College,
Manchester, NH

Szarkowski, John, *Dir Dept Photography,* Museum of
Modern Art, New York, NY
Szege, Dr Balint, *Deputy Dir Gen,* Magyar Nemzeti
Galeria, Budapest
Szeitz, P R, *Chmn,* Moorhead State Univ, MN
Szentleleky, Dr T, *Deputy Dir,* Szepmuveszet:
Muzeum, Budapest, Hungary
Szereszewski, Yaffa, *Chief Librn,* Israel Museum,
Jerusalem
Szilagyi, Eve, *Instr,* Pontiac Art Center, MI
Szilagyi, Dr J Gy, *Head Greek & Roman Antiquities,*
Szepmuveszet: Muzeum, Budapest, Hungary
Tabakoff, Sheila K, *Cur European Decorative Arts,*
Detroit Inst of Art Collections, MI
Tabb, Mrs Cabell Mayo, *First Regent,* Gunston Hall
Plantation, Lorton, VA
Tacha, Athena, *Assoc Prof,* Oberlin College, OH
Tack, A Catherine, *Librn,* Carnegie Library of
Pittsburgh, PA
Tacy, Katie, *Secy,* Brush and Palette Club,
Cooperstown, NY
Tade, George T, *Dean,* Texas Christian Univ, Fort
Worth
Tadlock, Marvin, *Mem Faculty,* Virginia Intermont
College, Bristol
Tadmor, Gabriel, *Dir/Cur,* Museum of Modern Art,
Haifa, Israel
Taflinger, Richard H, *Chmn,* Southernwestern
Oklahoma Univ, Weatherford
Taggart, Ross E, *Senior Cur,* William Rockhill
Nelson Gallery of Art, Kansas City, MO
Taggert, William C, *Admin & Property Council & Staff,*
Nat Trust Interpretors, Lyndhurst, Tarrytown,
NY
Tai, Jane S, *Asst Dir & Dir Exhib,* The American
Federation of Arts, see National and Regional
Organizations
Takacs, Dr M H, *Head Old Pictures,* Szepmuveszet:
Muzeum, Budapest, Hungary
Takahara, Takeshi, *Asst Prof,* Grand Valley State
Colleges, Allendale, MI
Takeuchi, Mavis, *Admin Secy,* Bergman Gallery,
Univ Chicago, IL
Takizawa, Yasushi, *Cur Exhib & International
Exchange,* Tokyo Kokuritsu Kindai Bijutsukan,
Japan
Talbot, Jarold D, *Cur,* Hill-Stead Museum,
Farmington, CT
Talbot, Phillips, *Pres,* Asia Society, New York, NY
Talbot, Mrs William, *Exec Secy,* Washington Depot
Art Association, CT
Talbot, William S, *Assoc Cur Paintings,* Cleveland
Museum of Art, OH
Talbott, Edward L, *Assoc Prof,* Miami Univ, Oxford,
OH
Talley, Dan, *Gallery Cur,* Atlanta Art Workers
Coalition, GA
Talley, William E, *First VPres,* Allied Arts of Seattle,
WA
Tallon, Roy U, *Registrar,* Museum of the City of
Mobile, AL
Tam, L C S, *Cur,* Hong Kong Museum of Art
Tamayo, Daisy, *Sr Art Librn,* Free Public Library of
Elizabeth, NJ
Tamura, Ruth, *Cur Exten Serv,* Honolulu Academy
of Arts Collection, HI
Tanabe, Takao, *Head Art Div,* Banff Centre School of
Fine Arts, AB
Tandy, Jean C, *Coordr Dept Art,* Mount Wachusett
Community College Art Galleries, Gardner, MA
Tanik, John March, *Assoc Prof,* Catholic Univ
America, Washington, DC
Tank, Frida, *Librn,* City of Oslo Art Collection,
Norway
Tanner, Daniel, *Technical Dir,* Pacific Film Archive,
Univ California, Berkeley
Tanous, Joe, *Instr,* Monterey Peninsula College, CA
Tansey, Luraine, *Instr,* San Jose City College, CA
Tanta, Juan Jose Barragan, *Mem Faculty,* Univ
Puerto Rico, Rio Piedras
Taplin, Franklin P, *Dir,* Westfield Athenaeum, MA
Tapscott, Melrose, *Cur Educ,* Reynolda House,
Winston-Salem, NC

Tarantal, Steve, *Dept Chmn & Assoc Prof,*
Philadelphia College of Art, PA
Tarbox, Gurdon L, *Dir & Librn,* Brookgreen
Gardens, Murrells Inlet, SC
Tardo, Barbara, *Asst Prof,* Southeastern Louisiana
Univ, Hammond
Tarvas, P, *Asst Rector,* Eesti Nsv Riiklik
Kunstiinstituut, Tallinn, Estonia, USSR
Tashjean, Catherine, *Librn,* Manhattanville College,
Purchase, NY
Tasse, M. Jeanne, *Chmn Art Dept,* Marietta College,
OH
Taszycka, Dr Maria, *Textiles, Polish Costumes,*
Muzeum Narodowe W Krakowie, Cracow, Poland
Tate, Barbara, *Exec Secy,* Studio Museum in Harlem,
New York, NY
Tate, Henry A, *Prof,* Chamberlayne Junior College,
Boston, MA
Tate, LaDeane V, *Mem Faculty,* Olympic College,
Bremerton, WA
Tatman, Sandra, *Archit Librn,* Athenaeum of
Philadelphia, PA
Tator, Marie A, *Asst Prof,* Salisbury State College,
MD
Taubin, William, *VPres,* Art Directors Club, see
National and Regional Organizations
Tavernetti, Roland, *Treas,* Monterey Peninsula
Museum of Art, CA
Tavins, Paula, *Slide Registry Comt Mem,* Women's
Slide Registry, New York, NY
Taxman, Sarah E, *Asst to Librn,* William Rockhill
Nelson Gallery of Art, Kansas City, MO
Taylor, Alan R, *Assoc Librn,* Johns Hopkins Univ
Archaeological Collection, Baltimore, MD
Taylor, Alton L, *Dir Summer School,* Univ Virginia,
Charlottesville
Taylor, Ben, *Chmn Mus Comt,* Fairfield Public
Library and Museum, IA
Taylor, Charles, *Preparator Exhib,* Philbrook Art
Center, Tulsa, OK
Taylor, Della Brown, *Acting Chmn,* West Virginia
State College, Institute
Taylor, Donald R, *Dir,* Tryon Palace Restoration
Complex, New Bern, NC
Taylor, Elizabeth, *Exhib Dir,* Maritime Art
Association, see National Organizations in Canada
Taylor, Elizabeth H, *Assoc Dir,* Museum of the
Humanities, North Salem, NY
Taylor, Frances J, *Exec Dir,* Cultural Arts Center of
Ocean City; *Exec Dir & Dir Summer School,* Ocean
City School of Art, NJ
Taylor, Mrs George, *Painting Workshop & Painting
Class,* Plastic Club, Philadelphia, PA
Taylor, Harrison C, *Cur Exhib,* Joslyn Art Museum,
Omaha, NE
Taylor, Herman W, Jr, *Mem Faculty,* Washington
and Lee University, Lexington, VA
Taylor, Howard J, *Asst Dir,* Philadelphia Maritime
Museum, PA
Taylor, Hugh A, *Provincial Archivist,* Public Archives
of Nova Scotia, Halifax
Taylor, Hugh H, *Prof,* Washington and Jefferson
College, Washington, PA
Taylor, Ira M, *Head Dept,* Hardin-Simmons Univ,
Abilene, TX
Taylor, Mrs J, *Secy,* Anderson Park Art Gallery,
Invercargill, New Zealand
Taylor, J Allyn, *Chmn Bd Trustees,* McMichael
Canadian Collection, Kleinburg, ON
Taylor, Jean F, *Asst Prof,* Northeast Louisiana Univ,
Monroe; *Secy,* Twin City Art Found, Monroe
Taylor, John Lloyd, *Dir,* Art History Galleries, Univ
Wisconsin-Milwaukee
Taylor, Mrs Joseph, *Cur,* Orlando Brown House,
Liberty Hall Museum, Fankfort, KY
Taylor, Joshua C, *VPres,* College Art Association of
America, see National and Regional
Organizations; *Dir,* Nat Collection of Fine Arts,
Washington, DC
Taylor, Lisa, *Dir,* Cooper-Hewitt Museum, New
York, NY
Taylor, Lonn W, *Cur History,* Dallas Historical
Society, TX

Taylor, Mrs M C, *Cur Drawings,* Nat Gallery of Canada, Ottawa, ON

Taylor, Mack, *Mem Faculty,* La Roche College, Pittsburgh, PA

Taylor, Marilyn S, *Conservator & Cur Coll,* St Joseph Museum, MO

Taylor, Mary C, *Head Dept,* Plymouth State College, NH

Taylor, Michael D, *Assoc Prof,* Univ Missouri-Saint Louis

Taylor, Michael L, *Assoc Prof & Chairperson Art Dept & Dir Summer School,* George Peabody College for Teachers, Nashville, TN

Taylor, Michiko, *Librn,* Museums at Stony Brook, NY

Taylor, P W, *Deputy Cur,* South London Art Gallery, England

Taylor, Prentiss, *Pres,* Society of Washington Printmakers, Washington, DC

Taylor, Dr Rene, *Dir,* Museo de Arte de Ponce, PR

Taylor, Mrs Richard, *VPres,* Museum of American Folk Art, New York, NY

Taylor, Robert S, *Acting Head,* Carnegie-Mellon Univ, Pittsburgh, PA

Taylor, Rod A, *Head Dept,* Norfolk State College, VA

Taylor, Sally, *Admin Asst,* Jacksonville Museum of Arts and Sciences, FL

Taylor, Veda, *Co-Chmn,* Valley Art Center, Clarkston, WA

Taylor, Dr W E, Jr, *Dir,* Nat Museum of Man, Ottawa, ON

Tchakalian, Sam, *Chmn Painting Dept,* San Francisco Art Inst, CA

Teagarden, Jerry, *Vis Instr,* Texas A&I Univ, Kingsville

Teague, Mary, *Dir Pub Information,* South Carolina Arts Commission, Columbia

Teahan, John, *Keeper Art,* Nat Museum of Ireland, Dublin

Tebble, Dr Norman, *Dir Dept Art & Archaeology,* Royal Scottish Museum, Edinburgh, Scotland

Teed, Truman, *Chmn Art Educ,* Univ South Carolina, Columbia

Teholiz, Leo, *Prof & Head Art Dept & Dir Summer School,* West Shore Community College, Scottville, MI

Teichman, Carmela, *Librn,* Israel Museum, Jerusalem

Teilman, Herdis Bull, *Cur Painting & Sculpture,* Carnegie Inst Museum of Art, Pittsburgh, PA

Teis, Daniel K, *Chmn,* Univ Delaware, Newark

Teitz, Richard Stuart, *Dir,* Worcester Art Museum, MA

Teixeira, Maria Emilia Amaral, *Dir,* Museu Nacional de Soares dos Reis, Porto, Portugal

Telfer, Lillie, *Cur Art Gallery,* Woodstock Public Library and Art Gallery, ON

Telford, Elizabeth S, *Registrar,* John and Mable Ringling Museum of Art, Sarasota, FL

Temple, Grace, *Fine Arts Librn,* Adelphi Univ, Garden City, NY

Temple, Tom, *Asst Prof Art,* Central Oregon Community College, Bend

Templeton, Orion A, *Pres,* Lynchburg Fine Arts Center, VA

Templin, Vivian, *Readers Serv,* Trinity College Library, Washington, DC

Tenney, Gerard, *Mem Faculty,* Austin Peay State Univ, Clarksville, TN

Tenney, Nancy, *Admin Asst,* Dartmouth College Museum and Galleries, Hanover, NH

Teoli, Alfred, *Assoc Prof,* Univ Illinois at the Medical Center, Chicago

Teppola, Melody, *Pres Bd Dir,* Contemporary Crafts Association and Gallery, Portland, OR

Terenzio, Anthony, *Prof,* Univ Connecticut, Storrs

Terenzio, Stephanie, *Asst Dir,* William Benton Museum of Art, Storrs, CT

Tereshko, Daniel, *Assoc Prof,* Moravian College, Bethlehem, PA

Terhune, Anne, *Mem Faculty,* College of New Rochelle, NY

Terhune, Dolores, *Asst to Dir,* Ball State Univ, Muncie, IN

Terken, John, *VPres,* Nat Sculpture Society, see National and Regional Organizations

Terrell, James A, *Instr,* Southwestern Oklahoma State Univ, Weatherford

Terrell, Richard, *Assoc Prof Art & Head Dept,* Doane College, Crete, NE

Terrell, Sharrel, *First VPres & Ed,* Association of Honolulu Artists, HI

Terrible, Wilda, *Mem Secy,* Columbus Gallery of Fine Arts, OH

Terrill, Evelyn B, *Pres & Dir Art Exhib,* West Baton Rouge Museum, Port Allen, LA

Terry, George, *Cur Historical Coll,* Univ South Carolina, Columbia

Tervo, Malcolm, *Instr,* Northwest Community College, Powell, WY

Terwilliger, Anne, *Librn,* Traphagen School of Fashion, New York, NY

Teter, Keith, *Industrial Design Chmn,* Art Center College of Design, Pasadena, CA

Tetrau, Richard, *Librn,* Saint Peter's College Art Gallery, Jersey City, NJ

Tetreault, Eva, *Admin Secy,* Federation des Centres Culturels de la Province de Quebec, Montreal

Tetreault, Paul-Andre, *Pres,* Order of Architects of Quebec, Montreal

Tettleton, Robert L, *Prof,* Univ Mississippi, University

Thalacker, Donald W, *Dir Fine Arts Prog,* General Services Administration, see National and Regional Organizations

Thalken, Thomas T, *Dir,* Herbert Hoover Presidential Library, West Branch, IA

Thames, Sandra, *Instr,* Pearl River Junior College, Poplarville, MS

Thayed, Dr Fred, *Asst Prof,* Radford College, VA

Thayer, Russell, *Assoc Prof,* Delta College, University Center, MI

Thebaut, Payne, *Educ Dir,* American Art Society, Los Angeles, CA

Théberge, P, *Cur Adminr,* Nat Gallery of Canada, Ottawa, ON

Theeke, Tina, *Asst Librn,* Minneapolis College of Art and Design Library and Media Center, MN

Thein, John, *Mem Faculty,* Creighton Univ, Omaha, NE

Theis, Andrew, *Mem Faculty,* Studio School of Art and Design, Philadelphia, PA

Thelin, Valfred, *Instr,* Friends of Arts and Sciences, Hilton Leech Studio, Sarasota, FL

Theobald, Sharon A, *Dir,* Lafayette Art Center, IN

Theodore, Crystal, *Prof,* James Madison Univ, Harrisonburg, VA

Theordore, Josephine, *Exec Secy,* Univ Utah Museum of Fine Arts, Salt Lake City

Theriault, Lucien, *Pres,* Musee Historique de Vaudreuil, PQ

Theriault, Normand, *Cur Contemporary Canadian Art,* Montreal Museum of Fine Arts, PQ

Theuer, Mary, *Dir Operations & Registrar Temporary Exhib,* Minnesota Museum of Art Permanent Collection Gallery, St Paul

Theuer, Otto S, *Dir Gallery,* Minnesota Museum of Art Permanent Collection Gallery, St Paul

Thibault, Claude, *Conservator Ancient Art,* Musee du Quebec, PQ

Thieband, Wayne, *Vis Prof,* Santa Rosa Junior College, CA

Thiedeman, Michael, *Asst Prof,* West Virginia Wesleyan College, Buckhannon

Thielen, Greg G, *Registrar,* Springfield Art Museum, MO

Thieme, Otto Charles, *Asst Prof,* Univ Wisconsin, Madison

Thigpen, Dean, *Dir Summer School,* Emory Univ, Atlanta, GA

Thisdale, Hector, *Admin Asst,* Musee D'Art Contemporain, Montreal, PQ

Thivierge, Jean-Marie, *Conservateur,* Musee du Seminaire de Quebec, PQ

Thogerson, Gary, *Librn,* J K Ralston Museum and Art Center, Sidney, MT

Thomas, Anne W, *Secy,* Southeastern College Art Conference, see National and Regional Organizations

Thomas, C David, *Instr,* Emmanuel College, Boston, MA

Thomas, David, *Dir,* Art Gallery of South Australia, Adelaide

Thomas, Elaine F, *Dir & Cur,* Tuskegee Inst, AL

Thomas, Elaine G, *Dir,* International Correspondence Schools Scranton, PA

Thomas, Mrs Elroy, *Treas,* Spiva Art Center, Joplin, MO

Thomas, George, *Dir,* Whatcom Museum of History and Art, Bellingham, WA

Thomas, Hess, *Cur 20th Century Art,* Metropolitan Museum of Art, New York, NY

Thomas, James A, *Maintenance,* Tryon Palace Restoration Complex, New Bern, NC

Thomas, Jean, *Instr,* Emmanuel College, Boston, MA

Thomas, John L, *Pres,* Thomas College, Waterville, ME

Thomas, John Z, *Asst Prof,* Hanover College, IN

Thomas, Katherine, *Dir,* Kingsport Fine Arts Center, TN

Thomas, Linda, *Registrar,* Museum of Fine Arts, Boston, MA

Thomas, Lionel A J, *Assoc Prof,* Univ British Columbia, Vancouver

Thomas, Minor Wine, Jr, *Dir & Chief Cur,* New York State Historical Association, Cooperstown

Thomas, Peter G, *Dean School & Dean Summer School,* Corcoran School of Art, Washington, DC

Thomas, W Radford, *Chmn Art Dept,* East Tennessee State Univ, Johnson City

Thomas, Ralph R, *Asst Dean & Dir Admis,* Indiana Univ, Indianapolis

Thomas, Richard C, *Head Metalsmithing Dept,* Cranbrook Academy of Art, Bloomfield Hills, MI

Thomas, Robin M, *Sr Keeper & Keeper Art,* Plymouth City Museum and Art Gallery, England

Thomas, Ronald, *Mem Faculty,* Saint Louis Community College at Meramec, St Louis, MO

Thomas, Sam, *Asst Prof,* Mansfield State College, PA

Thomas, Troy, *Instr,* Pennsylvania State Univ, Capitol Campus, Middletown

Thomas, William, *Prof,* West Virginia Univ, Morgantown

Thomas, William B, *Treas Bd,* Huntsville Museum of Art, AL

Thomas, William Radford, *Prof Art, Chmn Dept Fine Arts & Dir Summer School,* East Tennessee State Univ, Johnson City

Thomas, Mr & Mrs Windsor P, Jr, *Secy-Treas,* Central Louisiana Art Association, Alexandria

Thomasita, Sister Mary, *Head Dept,* Cardinal Stritch College Art Collection, Milwaukee, WI

Thomason, Herbert L, *Museum Construction Supvr,* School of the Ozarks, Point Lookout, MO

Thompson, Ann, *Exten Serv Coordr,* Clark County Library District Art Activities, Las Vegas, NV

Thompson, Charles, *Dir,* Patterson Library, Westfield, NY

Thompson, Charles, *Asst Prof,* East Tennessee State Univ, Johnson City

Thompson, Colin, *Dir,* Nat Gallery of Scotland, Edinburgh

Thompson, Eleanor E, *Dir,* Wenham Historical Association and Museum, MA

Thompson, Ernest, *VPres,* Pemaquid Group of Artists, Pemaquid Point, ME; *Instr,* Portland School of Art, ME

Thompson, Florence, *Secy,* Pemaquid Group of Artists, Pemaquid Point, ME

Thompson, Frank, *Dir Summer School,* Greenville College, IL

Thompson, Mrs Frederick, *Exec Dir,* Frederick Thompson Found, New York, NY

Thompson, Mrs George A, *Pres Bd Trustees,* Museum of Arts and Sciences, Daytona Beach, FL

Thompson, Holly, *Secy,* Longview Museum and Arts Center, TX

Thompson, Jack, *Chmn Ceramic Design,* Moore College of Art, Philadelphia, PA

Thompson, James E, *Dir,* Charles B Goddard Center for the Visual and Performing Arts, Ardmore, OK

Thompson, John R, *Chmn Ceramics Dept,* Lake Placid School of Art, NY

Thompson, Joseph B, *VPres,* Antonelli School of Photography, Philadelphia, PA

Thompson, Julianne, *Registrar,* Washington State Univ Museum of Art, Pullman

Thompson, Lewis, *Prof,* Hollins College, VA

Thompson, Margaret, *Chief Cur,* American Numismatic Society, see National and Regional Organizations

Thompson, Marjorie S, *Docent Coordr,* Museum of Fine Arts, Houston, TX

Thompson, Marsi, *Pub Relations Dir,* Nat Cowboy Hall of Fame, Oklahoma City, OK

Thompson, Mary, *Dir Summer School,* Manhattanville College, Purchase, NY

Thompson, Meera, *Asst,* Junior Museum, Metropolitan Museum of Art, New York, NY

Thompson, Mercedes, *Prof,* North Carolina Central Univ, Durham

Thompson, Morley P, *Pres,* Taft Museum, Cincinnati, OH; *Pres,* Cincinnati Inst of Fine Arts, OH

Thompson, Paul E, *Exec Dir,* Key West Art and Historical Society, FL

Thompson, Philip, *Chmn,* Augsburg College, Minneapolis, MN

Thompson, Richard P, *Asst to Exec Dir,* Society for the Preservation of New England Antiquities, Boston, MA

Thompson, Ro, *Mem Faculty,* Austin Community College, TX

Thompson, Stuart R, *Chmn Dept,* Seton Hill College, Greensburg, PA

Thompson, Trudy, *VPres,* Kentucky Guild of Artists and Craftsmen, Berea

Thompson, Willard, *Dir Summer School,* Univ of Minnesota, Minneapolis

Thompson, William F, *Dir Research,* State Historical Society of Wisconsin, Madison

Thomsen, Robert E, *Prof,* Glendale College, CA

Thomson, Carol, *Second VPres,* Alaska Association for the Arts, Fairbanks

Thomson, Garry, *Scientific Adv,* Nat Gallery London, England

Thorburn, Dan, *Preparator,* Art Gallery of Hamilton, ON

Thorburn, Dr Neil, *Acad Dean Summer School,* Albion College, MI

Thorkildsen, Jean, *Cur,* Schenectady County Historical Society, NY

Thorn, James C, *Assoc Prof,* Northwestern State Univ Louisiana, Natchitoches

Thorne, Mrs J W, *Secy,* Skaneateles Library Association, NY

Thorns, John C, Jr, *Chmn Dept Art,* Fort Hays State Univ, Hays, KS

Thornton, Anna, *Pres,* Prince Rupert Art Club, BC

Thornton, Clinton, *Asst Prof,* Friends Univ, Wichita, KS

Thornton, Mary, *Instr,* Friends Univ, Wichita, KS

Thornton, P K, *Keeper Furniture,* Victoria and Albert Museum, London, England

Thornton, Richard, *Head Dept,* Univ Connecticut, Storrs

Thornton, Dr William, *Pres,* Meridian Museum of Art, MS

Thorp, Michele, *Secy,* Emerald Empire Arts Association, Springfield, OR

Thorpe, Dr F, *Chief History Div,* Nat Museum of Man, Ottawa, ON

Thorpe, James, *Dir,* Huntington Library, Art Gallery and Botanical Gardens, San Marino, CA

Thorpe, James, *Assoc Prof,* State Univ New York College at Cortland

Thorsten, Liz, *Staff Secy,* Metropolitan Arts Commission, Portland, OR

Thorstvedt, Else Marie, *Librn,* Norsk Sjofartsmuseum, Oslo, Norway

Threatt, Thomas K, *Asst,* Fort Worth Public Library, TX

Thue, Oscar, *Keeper Sculpture,* Nasjonalgalleriet, Oslo, Norway

Thurheimer, David C, *Dir,* Brick Store Museum, Kennebunk, ME

Thurlow, Alan, *Asst Prof,* Mississippi Univ for Women, Columbus

Thurlow, Fearn, *Cur Painting & Sculpture,* Newark Museum, NJ

Thurman, Christa C Mayer, Art Inst of Chicago, IL

Thursz, Frederic, *Prof,* Kingsborough Community College, Brooklyn, NY

Thyssen, Esther, *Cur,* Rensselaer County Historical Society, Troy, NY

Tibbetts, Laurence, *Dir Mem,* Minnesota Museum of Art Permanent Collection Gallery, St Paul

Tidd, Patrick, *Mem Faculty,* Contra Costa College, San Pablo, CA

Tidemann, Viola, *Reference Dept Head,* Wichita Public Library, KS

Tieken, Theodore, *Pres,* Chicago Historical Society, IL

Tierney, Lennox, *Prof,* Univ Utah, Salt Lake City

Tiessen, George W, *Assoc Prof,* Univ Victoria, British Columbia

Tietze, Mary Keim, *Secy,* American Artists Professional League, see National and Regional Organizations; *Judge & Jury Chmn,* Federated Art Associations of New Jersey, Lavallette

Tiff, Georgiana, *Head Arts & Recreation Dept,* Denver Public Library, CO

Tiffany, Joan Thacher, *Projects Specialist,* William Underwood Co, Westwood, MA, see Corporate Art Holdings

Tiffin, Jay H, *Pres Bd Gov,* Florida Gulf Coast Art Center, Clearwater

Tighe, Nancy, *Corresp Secy,* Essex Art Association, CT

Tilford, Kean, *Pres,* Kansas Watercolor Society, Wichita

Tilghman, Douglas, *Asst Dir Admin,* Univ Kansas, Lawrence

Till, C M, *Keeper,* Nat Gallery of Rhodesia, Salisbury

Tilley, Harriette, *Secy & Receptionist, Bookkeeper,* Mohawk Valley Museum, Utica, NY

Tilley, Lewis, *Prof,* Univ Southern Colorado, Belmont Campus, Pueblo

Tillotson, Robert G, *Asst Dir Admin,* Nat Museum of History and Technology, Washington, DC

Tilney, P, *Acting Chief,* Canadian Centre for Folk Culture Studies, Nat Museum of Man, Ottawa, ON

Timm, Kathleen, *Secy,* Humboldt Arts Council, Eureka, CA

Timmerman, Mary Jane, *Mem Faculty,* Murray State Univ, KY

Timmone, Randall, *Mem Faculty,* Arkansas Arts Center, Little Rock

Timms, Peter, *Dir,* Fitchburg Art Museum, MA

Tims, Michael W, *Secy,* Art Metropole, Toronto, ON

Tinelli, Stephen D, *Assoc Prof,* West Virginia Wesleyan College, Buckhannon

Tinley, Glenn, *Head Design Dept,* Winnipeg Art Gallery, MB

Tippetts, Harold J, *Dir,* Territorial Statehouse, Fillmore, UT

Tippit, Jack, *Dir & Cur,* Museum of Cartoon Art, Greenwich, CT

Titman, J L, *Registrar,* Queen's Gallery, Buckingham Palace, London, England

Titus, William, *Registrar,* Heckscher Museum, Huntington, NY

Tivey, Hap, *Vis Prof,* Univ Southern Colorado, Belmont Campus, Pueblo

Toadvnie, Jane E, *Sr Instr,* Miami Univ, Oxford, OH

Tobey, Alton S, *Pres,* Artists Equity Association of New York, NY

Tobias, John L M, *Pres,* Columbia Museums of Art and Science, SC

Tobin, Mrs Edgar, *Pres,* Marion Koogler McNay Art Inst, San Antonio, TX

Tobin, Mrs M, *Exec Secy,* Manitoba Association of Architects, Winnipeg

Tocco, Sylvia, *Secy,* Warwick Arts Found, RI

Todak, Joseph, *Coordr,* Walter Elwood Museum and Art Gallery, Amsterdam, NY

Todd, Mrs Hugh, *Librn,* Ingraham Mem Research Library, Litchfield, CT

Todd, Joe L, *Cur Coll,* Oklahoma Historical Society, Oklahoma City

Todd, Marilyn, *Mem Faculty,* Midland College, TX

Toffel, Alvin E, *Pres,* Norton Simon Museum, Pasadena, CA

Tolles, Bryant F, Jr, *Dir,* Essex Inst, Salem, MA

Tolmatch, Elaine, *Registrar,* Montreal Museum of Fine Arts, PQ

Tolpo, Vincent, *Cur & Dir,* Highland Area Arts Council, Freeport, IL

Tomasini, Wallace J, *Dir School & Dir Summer School,* Univ Iowa, Iowa City

Tomasch, Otto H, *Instr,* York College of Pennsylvania

Tombaugh, Richard F, *Exec Dir,* Arts and Education Council of Greater St Louis, MO

Tomidy, Paul, *Acting Dir,* Mills College Art Gallery, Oakland, CA

Tomiyama, Hideo, *Chief Cur,* Kokuritsu Seiyo Bijutsukan, Tokyo, Japan

Tomlinson, Ann, *VPres,* Ontario Crafts Council, Toronto

Tomlinson, D, *Head Dept Fashion & Textiles,* City of Birmingham Polytechnic, England

Tomlinson, Juliette, *Dir,* Connecticut Valley Historical Museum, Springfield, MA

Tomlinson, Tom, *Exec Dir,* Allied Arts Council of the Yakima Valley, Yakima, WA

Tommi, Thomas, *Dir,* Le Centre D'Art de Perce, PQ

Tomsic, Walt, *Chmn,* Pacific Lutheran Univ, Tacoma, WA

Tonelli, Edith, *Cur,* DeCordova and Dana Museum and Park, Lincoln, MA

Tong, Carin, *Dir Reference Center,* Orange County Public Library, Garden Grove, CA

Tong, Marvin E, Jr, *Dir,* School of the Ozarks, Point Lookout, MO

Toombs, Dr, *Dean Educ Summer School,* Univ Regina, SK

Toon, Jocelyn, *Librn,* Provincial Museum of Alberta, Edmonton

Toperzer, Tom R, *Dir,* Illinois State Univ, Normal

Topolski, Andy, *Lectr,* Villa Maria College of Buffalo, NY

Torcoletti, Enzo, *Asst Prof,* Flagler College, Saint Augustine, FL

Tormey, John L, *VPres,* Stan Hywet Hall Found, Akron, OH

Tormo, Manuel Perez, *Restorer,* Museo Romantico, Madrid, Spain

Tornheim, N, *Mem Faculty,* Golden West College, Huntington Beach, CA

Torreano, John, *Vis Prof,* New Mexico State Univ, Las Cruces

Torrence, Dave, *Chmn,* J K Ralston Museum and Art Center, Sidney, MT

Torrens, Thomas, *Artist-in-Residence,* Pacific Lutheran Univ, Tacoma, WA

Torres, Dorothy, *Asst Dir,* San Jose State Univ, CA

Torrini, Rudolph E, *Prof Art & Chmn Dept,* Fontbonne College, Clayton, MO

Torroella, Isabelle, *Head Art Dept,* School of Fashion Design, Boston, MA

Tostenrud, Don B, *VPres,* Phoenix Art Museum, AZ

Toth, Carl, *Head Photography Dept,* Cranbrook Academy of Art, Bloomfield Hills, MI

Toth, Edwin J, *Horticultural Dir,* Dixon Gallery and Gardens, Memphis, TN

Toth, Judith, *Vis Instr,* Oakland Univ, Rochester, MI

Toth, Richard, *Head,* Utah State Univ, Logan

Toto, Sister Julia, *Dir Summer School,* Cabrini College, Radnor, PA

Touhey, John F, *Inst Dir & Libr Dir,* Fashion Inst of Technology, New York, NY

Touhey, Paula, *Cur Educ,* Kenosha Public Museum, WI

Toulis, Vasilios, *Printmaking,* Pratt Inst School of Art & Design, Brooklyn, NY

Toupin, Juanita, *Librn,* Montreal Museum of Fine Arts, PQ

Tourliere, M, *Dir,* Nat College of Decorative Arts, Paris, France

Tournon-Branly, Marion, *Dir School & Prof Archit,* Fontainebleau School of Fine Arts, France

Toutant, Eileen, *Asst to Cur,* Allen R Hite Art Institute, Univ Louisville, KY

Tovar, Francisco Gil, *Dir,* Colombian Inst of Culture, Bogota, Colombia

Tovish, Harold, *Prof,* Boston Univ, MA

Tow, Terry, *Coordr Crafts,* Iowa State Univ, Ames

Tower, A Wesley, *Head Div,* Culver-Stockton College, Canton, MO

Tower, Whitney, *VPres,* Nat Museum of Racing, Saratoga Springs, NY

Town, Vernon, *Mem Faculty,* Murray State Univ, KY

Towne, Violet, *Dir Summer School,* Herkimer County Community College, NY

Townley, Frances, *Corresp Secy,* Kent Art Association Gallery, CT

Townsend, Arthur, *State Historic Preservation Officer,* Colorado Historical Society, Denver

Townsend, Carol, *Asst Prof,* Daemen College, Amherst, NY

Townsend, Eleanor, *Librn,* Newark Museum, NJ

Townsend, Sally O'C, *Dir Educ,* Newark Museum, NJ

Townsend, Mrs Samuel, *Librn,* Skaneateles Library Association, NY

Toy, Ernest, Jr, *Librn,* California State Univ Art Gallery, Fullerton

Trachtman, Philip, *Pres & Dir Summer School,* Art Inst of Philadelphia, PA

Tracy, Berry B, *Cur in Charge American Decorative Arts,* Metropolitan Museum of Art, New York, NY

Trafford, Hal, *Head Commercial Art,* Butera School of Art, Boston, MA

Trafton, Roland M, *Pres,* Corporate Council for the Arts, Seattle, WA

Traiger, Lynn, *Asst to Dir,* Wadsworth Atheneum, Hartford, CT

Trakis, Louis, *Assoc Prof,* Manhattanville College, Purchase, NY

Trank, Lynn, *Prof,* Eastern Illinois Univ, Charleston

Trapp, Frank, *Dir Art Collection & Chmn Dept,* Amherst College, MA

Trapp, Kenneth R, *Cur,* Cincinnati Art Museum, OH

Trapp, Roy, *Asst Exhib Coordr,* Univ South Florida/ Galleries Program, Tampa

Trappeniers, Dr M, *Cur,* Noordbrabants Museum, Hertogenbosch, Netherlands

Trasatti, Joseph A, *Bldg Supt,* Berkshire Museum, Pittsfield, MA

Trattner, Alfred, *Librn Fine Arts Dept,* Jersey City Public Library, NJ

Trau, Robert A, *Instr,* Central Acad of Commercial Art, Cincinnati, OH

Travis, David, *Assoc Cur Photography,* Art Inst of Chicago, IL

Traylor, Charles, *Dept Head & Dir Summer School,* Kirkwood Community College, Cedar Rapids, IA

Treadway, Beth A, *Prof Art & Gallery Keeper,* Pace Univ, White Plains, NY

Tredennick, Dorothy, *Prof,* Berea College, KY

Tree, Walter Fox, *Prof,* Boston State College, MA

Treese, William, *Art Librn,* Univ California Art Museum, Santa Barbara

Trefry, Philippe, *Librn Asst,* Musee du Quebec, PQ

Tregenza, John, *Cur Historical Coll,* Art Gallery of South Australia, Adelaide

Tremaine, Laurine, *Librn,* Parry Sound Public Library, ON

Tremblay, Anthony, *Dir Summer School,* Franklin Pierce College, Rindge, NH

Tremper, Steven H, *Dir,* Wheelwright Museum, Santa Fe, NM

Trencher, Michael, *Chmn Student Affairs,* Pratt Inst School of Art & Design, Brooklyn, NY

Trenerry, Walter N, *Chmn Bd Trustees,* Minnesota Museum of Art Permanent Collection Gallery, St Paul

Trepp, George, *Asst Dir,* Long Beach Public Library, NY

Tresler, Mrs George W, *Pres,* Cody County Art League, WY

Treuherz, J B, *Keeper Fine Arts,* Manchester City Art Galleries, England

Treuter, Miss Lirl, *Dept Head,* Fort Worth Public Library, TX

Trevithick, Claudia, *Special Projects,* Univ Southwestern Louisiana Art Center, Lafayette

Triano, Anthony Train, *Asst Prof,* Seton Hall Univ, South Orange, NJ

Tribble, Genevieve, *Librn,* Art Complex Museum at Duxbury, MA

Trifiletti, Edith, *Pres,* Miniature Painters, Sculptors and Gravers Society of Washington, DC

Trimble, Mike, *Pres,* New Mexico Art League, Albuquerque

Tringale, Vincent J, *Prof,* Boston State College, MA

Tripp, Powell, *Chmn Advertising Design,* Center for Creative Studies, Detroit, MI

Tripp, Wendell, *Ed Assoc & Chief Libr Serv,* New York State Historical Association, Cooperstown

Trissel, James, *Prof,* Colorado College, Colorado Springs

Tritschler, Thomas, *Chmn Fine Art Dept,* Univ Guelph, ON

Trivigno, Pat, *Chmn Newcomb Art Dept,* Tulane Univ, New Orleans, LA

Trnek, Dr Renate, *Asst,* Gemaldegalerie der Akademie der Bildenden Kunste in Wien, Vienna, Austria

Troemel, Jean Wagner, *Immediate Past Pres,* Florida Artist Group, St Augustine

Trojanova, Dr Eva, *Chief Dept Graphic Art,* Slovenska Narodna Galeria, Bratislava, Czechoslovakia

Trolle, Jorgen, *Pres,* Det Danske Kunstindustrimuseum, Copenhagen, Denmark

TropBlumberg, Sandra, *Asst Dir,* Everson Museum of Art, Syracuse, NY

Troutman, Philip, *Cur Coll,* Courtauld Inst of Art Galleries, London, England

Trovato, Joseph S, *Asst to Dir,* Munson-Williams-Proctor Inst Museum of Art, Utica, New York

Trowell, Ian, *Pres,* Ontario Society of Artists, Toronto

Truax, Harold R, *Prof,* Miami Univ, Oxford, OH

Trubner, Henry, *Cur Dept Asian Art,* Seattle Art Museum, WA

Trudel, J, *Cur Early Canadian Art,* Nat Gallery of Canada, Ottawa, ON

Trudel, Jean, *Dir,* Montreal Museum of Fine Arts, PQ

Trudell, Don, *Mem Faculty,* Madison Area Technical College, WI

Trueb, Verena, *Secy,* Offentliche Kunstsammlung Kunstmuseum Basel, Switzerland

Trueblood, Franklin D, *Secy,* Arts Club of Chicago, IL

Truettner, William H, *Cur 18th & 19th Century Painting & Sculpture,* Nat Collection of Fine Arts, Washington, DC

Trujillo, Dr Rupert A, *Dir,* Div Continuing Education, Univ New Mexico Harwood Found, Taos

Truran, Jane, *Art Librn,* Houston Public Library, TX

Trusty, Janice, *Admin Asst,* Valley Art Center, Clarkston, WA

Tryba, John, *Assoc Prof,* Cardinal Stritch College, Milwaukee, WI

Tryba, Mildred, *Instr,* Cardinal Stritch College, Milwaukee, WI

Trythall, Gilvert, *Dean,* West Virginia Univ, Morgantown

Tsakona, Mrs Pitsa, *Librn,* Benaki Museum, Athens, Greece

Tschinkel, Paul, *Assoc Prof,* Queensborough Community College, Bayside, NY

Tschudy, Karen, *Libr Dir,* Cleveland Inst of Art, OH

Tse, Stephen, *Chmn,* Big Bend Community College, Moses Lake, WA

Tsun-I, Chu, *Pres,* Nat Taiwan Acad of Arts, Taipei, Republic of China

Tuasosopo, Palauni, *Chmn Bd Trustees,* Jean P Haydon Museum, Pago Pago, American Samoa

Tuchman, Maurice, *Sr Cur Modern Art,* Los Angeles County Museum of Art, CA

Tucker, Anne, *Adjunct Cur,* Museum of Fine Arts, Houston, TX

Tucker, James E, *Cur,* Univ North Carolina at Greensboro

Tucker, Janet, *Pres,* Polk Public Museum, Lakeland, FL

Tucker, L Y, *Assoc Prof,* Florida A&M Univ, Tallahassee

Tucker, Laureen, *Educ Coordr,* Brockton Art Center, MA

Tucker, Marcia, *Dir,* New Museum, New York, NY

Tufts, Eleanor, *Chmn,* Southern Methodist Univ, Dallas, TX

Tufts, Roger, *Instr,* Tarrant County Junior College, Northeast Campus, Hurst, TX

Tuhey, Ned, *Mem Faculty,* Mesa Community College, AZ

Tulanowski, Sister Elaine, *Asst Prof,* College Misericordia, Dallas, PA

Tumolo, Camille, *Cur Educ,* Heard Museum, Phoenix, AZ

Tung, Rosemary, *Cur,* Jacques Marchais Center of Tibetan Arts, Staten Island, NY

Tunis, Roselyn, *Cur,* Roberson Center, Binghamton, NY

Tupper, R, *Dean Exten Col,* Central Connecticut State College, New Britain

Turk, Rudy H, *Dir,* Arizona State Univ Art Collection, Tempe

Turk, Sandra Doane, *Pres,* Frontier Times Museum, Bandera, TX

Turley, Geraldine, *Dir,* Southwestern Community College Art Gallery, Chula Vista, CA

Turlington, Lucy B, *Asst VPres & Staff Interior Designer,* United Virginia Bankshares, Richmond, see Corporate Art Holdings

Turnbull, Betty, *Cur Exhib & Coll,* Newport Harbor Art Museum, CA

Turnbull, Christine, *Treas,* Toledo Federation of Art Societies, OH

Turnbull, Krista, *Preparator,* Univ Washington Henry Art Gallery, Seattle

Turnbull, Lucy, *Hon Cur Classics,* Univ Mississippi, Oxford

Turnbull, Paula, *Chmn,* Fort Wright College of Holy Names, Spokane, WA

Turner, A R, *Provincial Archivist,* Provincial Archives of British Columbia, Victoria

Turner, A Richard, *Prof,* Grinnell College, IA

Turner, Anne M, *Dir,* Jones Library, Amherst, MA

Turner, Arthur, *Instr,* School of Art, Museum of Fine Arts, Houston, TX

Turner, B, *VPres,* Association of Collegiate Schools of Architecture, see National and Regional Organizations

Turner, Bruce F, *Chmn,* Wharton County Junior College, Wharton, TX

Turner, David, *Cur Educ,* Amarillo Art Center, TX

Turner, Diana, *Cur Educ,* Asian Art Museum, San Francisco, CA

Turner, Donna H, *Cur Educ,* Columbus Gallery of Fine Arts, OH

Turner, Harvey, *Instr,* Grand Marais Art Colony, MN

Turner, Helen Mary, *Instr, Head Dept & Dir Summer School,* Maple Woods Community Coll, Kansas City, MO

Turner, James, *Mem Faculty,* Bucknell Univ, Lewisburg, PA

Turner, Judith, *Librn,* Milwaukee Public Museum, WI

Turner, Dr Robert B, *Chmn Dept & Chmn Summer School,* Univ Northern Colorado, Greeley

Turner, William K, *Dean,* Tulane Univ, New Orleans, LA

Turpin, Thomas D, *Assoc Prof,* Univ Arkansas, Fayetteville

Tushingham, A D, *Chief Archaeologist,* Royal Ontario Museum, Toronto

Tussey, Karen, *Secy & Registrar,* Rocky Mountain School of Art, Denver, CO

Tuthill, Barbara A, *Supvry Librn,* San Diego Public Library, CA

Tutt, George E, *Chmn Div Fine Arts & Head Art Dept,* William Woods/Westminster Colleges, Fulton, MO

Tuttle, Betsy, *Lectr,* Univ Wisconsin, Madison

Tuttle, Ilene, *Coordr,* Museum on Wheels, Monterey Peninsula Museum of Art, CA

Tuttle, Richard, *Asst Prof,* Tulane Univ, New Orleans, LA

Tutzker, Ralph, *Secy,* Friends of Photography, Carmel, CA

Tvedten-Doran, Jan, *Asst Cur,* Art Research Center, Kansas City, MO

Twamley, William E, *First VPres,* St Augustine Art Association Gallery, FL

Twardowski, Ellen, *Lectr,* Ladycliff College, Highland Falls, NY

Twery, Elliott R, *Chmn Art Dept,* Randolph-Macon Woman's College, Lynchburg, VA

Twery, Thelma L, *Asst Prof,* Lynchburg College, VA

Twigg-Smith, Thurston, *Chmn Bd,* Contemporary Arts Center of Hawaii, Honolulu

Twiggs, Leo F, *Dir Art Program,* South Carolina State College, Orangeburg

Tworkov, Jack, *Vis Prof,* American Univ, Washington, DC

Tyler, B A, *Asst Dir Publns,* Nat Museum of Man, Ottawa, ON

Tyler, Dr Ron, *Dir Publns & Cur History,* Amon Carter Museum of Western Art, Fort Worth, TX

Tyler, William R, *Dir,* Dumbarton Oaks Research Library and Collections, Washington, DC

Tyne, Janet, *Chmn Metal Arts,* De Young Museum Art School, San Francisco, CA

Tyrie, Harold Joffre, *Secy,* Dunedin Public Art Gallery, New Zealand

Tysseling, William, *Pres,* Octagon Center for the Arts, Ames, IA

Ubans, Juris K, *Chmn,* Univ Maine at Portland-Gorham, Gorham

Uchima, A, *Head Dept,* Sarah Lawrence College, Bronxville, NY

Uchiyama, Takeo, *Cur,* Kyoto Kokuritsu Kindai Bijutsukan, Japan

Udall, Ralph O, *Treas,* Art Association of Newport, RI

Ude, Lucy, *Admin Secy,* Washington Univ Gallery of Art, St Louis, MO

Udell, Seymour, *Secy,* Lotos Club, New York, NY

Ueda, Osamu, *Assoc Cur Oriental Art,* Art Inst of Chicago, IL

Uelsmann, Jerry N, *Mem Faculty,* Univ Florida, Gainesville

Uhde, Jan, *Asst Prof,* Univ Waterloo, Ontario

Ullenberg, Frances, *Lectr,* Cardinal Stritch College, Milwaukee, WI

Ulloa, Jorge, *Head Archit Drafting,* Javeriana Univ Faculty of Architecture and Design, Bogota, Colombia

Ulrich, Edwin A, *Dir,* Edwin A Ulrich Museum, Hyde Park, NY

Ulrich, James, *Asst Head,* Alberta College of Art, Calgary

Ulrich, Lisa, *Secy,* Violet Oakley Mem Found, Philadelphia, PA

Ulrich, R, *Asst Prof,* Youngstown State Univ, OH

Ulrich, Theodore, *Asst Treas,* Violet Oakley Mem Found, Philadelphia, PA

Ultan, Roslye, *Cur Permanent Coll & Mem Faculty,* Hamline Univ, St Paul, MN

Umehara, Takeshi, *Dir,* Kyoto City Univ of Fine Arts, Japan

Umlauf, Karl, *Chmn Painting,* East Texas State Univ, Commerce

Umlauf, Madelon, *Mem Faculty,* Austin Community College, TX

Underhill, E H, *Chief Instr,* Selkirk College, Nelson, BC; *Cur,* Kootenay School of Art Gallery, Nelson

Underwood, Genevieve, *Assoc Prof Art & Chmn Dept,* Loyola Marymount Univ, Los Angeles, CA

Underwood, Sandra L, *Instr,* Saint Mary's College of Maryland, Saint Mary's City

Unger, Miss P, *Pub Relations Officer In Charge Activities & Members Organization,* Haaretz Museum, Tel-Aviv, Israel

Unger, William, *Prof,* Northeast Missouri State Univ, Kirksville

Ungerleider, Joy G, *Dir,* Jewish Museum, New York, NY

Unruh, Melvin, *Assoc Prof,* Bethany Nazarene College, OK

Unrult, Jack, *Chmn Advertising,* East Texas State Univ, Commerce

Unser, Sister Carlene, *Dir Art Gallery & Chmn Art Dept,* Viterbo College, La Crosse, WI

Unsworth, Jean, *Prof,* Loyola Univ Chicago, IL

Upchurch, John D, *Chmn,* Brevard College, NC

Upchurch, Mrs W Kendrick, Jr, *Secy,* Montgomery Museum of Fine Arts, AL

Upshaw, Leon R, *Registrar,* Bergman Gallery, Univ Chicago, IL

Upton, Richard, *Dir Summer School,* Skidmore College, Saratoga Springs, NY

Upton, Richard F, *Pres,* New Hampshire Historical Society, Concord

Upton, Ruth, *Young Adult,* Mason City Public Library, IA

Urban, Janos, *Head Gen Artistic Studies,* Lausanne College of Art & Design, Switzerland

Urban, Richard, *Asst Prof,* Univ Alabama in Birmingham

Urban, Thomas, *Craft Center Coordr,* Univ Oregon Museum of Art, Eugene

Urbinato, Lisa, *Asst to Dir & Registrar,* Bergman Gallery, Univ Chicago, IL

Urquhart, A M, *Chmn Dept,* Univ Waterloo, Ontario

Urquhart, Kenneth T, *Librn,* Historic New Orleans Collection, LA

Urschel, Kenneth, *Secy,* Stained Glass Association of America, see National and Regional Organizations

Usher, Elizabeth R, *Chief Librn,* Thomas J Watson Library, Metropolitan Museum of Art, New York, NY

Usui, Kiichi, *Cur,* Oakland Univ, Rochester, MI

Uttech, Tom, *Pres,* Wisconsin Painters and Sculptors, Milwaukee, WI

Utterbach, Rosalie F, *Chmn,* Woodbury College, Los Angeles, CA

Uyemura, Ken, *Mem Faculty,* Univ Miami, Coral Gables, FL

Uzunoglu, Edibe, *Cur,* Museum of Ancient Orient, Istanbul Arkeoloji Muzeleri, Turkey

Vacca, Johanna D, *Mem Faculty,* Norwich Art School, CT

Vaculik, Dr Karol, *Chief Dept Slovak & European Art to 19th Century,* Slovenska Narodna Galeria, Bratislava, Czechoslovakia

Vadeboncoeur, Guy, *Cur,* Society of the Montreal Military & Maritime Museum, PQ

Vait, Richard H, *Mem Faculty,* Chipola Junior College, Marianna, FL

Valcarcel, Dr Luis E, *Pres,* Museo Nacional de la Cultura Peruana, Lima, Peru

Valdes, Karen, *Dir & Cur,* Miami-Dade Community College, South Campus Art Gallery, FL

Valdey, Mrs Frank, *Asst Secy,* San Antonio Museum Association, TX

Valentine, Lanci, *Dir Pub Affairs,* Art Complex Museum at Duxbury, MA

Valentine, Milfred, *Chmn,* Jones County Junior College, Ellisville, MS

Valeri, Linda Ann, *Gallery Dir,* Rio Hondo College Art Gallery, Whittier, CA

Valien, Bonita, *VPres,* Miniature Painters, Sculptors, and Gravers Society of Washington, DC

Valley, Jerry, *Chmn 3-Dimensional Area,* Edinboro State College, PA

Van Alstine, John, *Asst Prof,* Univ Wyoming, Laramie

Van Auker, Alfred, *Prof,* Pierce College, Woodland Hills, CA

Van Baron, Dr Judith, *Dir,* Monmouth Museum and Cultural Center, Lincroft, NJ

Van Bianchi, Peggy, *Mem Faculty,* Factory of Visual Art, Seattle, WA

Van Bodegom, John, *Pub Relations Sr VPres,* First National Bank of Oregon, Portland, see Corporate Art Holdings

van Boven, Dr M M A, *Dir,* Noordbrabants Museum, Hertogenbosch, Netherlands

Vance, Alex, *Dir Educ,* Davenport Municipal Art Gallery, IA

Vance, Carl, *Asst Dir Admin,* Santa Barbara Museum of Art, CA

Vance, Philip, *Chief Conservator,* Intermuseum Conservation Association, see National and Regional Organizations

Vanco, John, *Exec Dir,* Erie Art Center, PA

Van Crimpen, Dr H, *Cur,* Rijksmuseum Vincent Van Gogh, Amsterdam, Netherlands

Vandegrift, David, *Assoc Prof,* Marygrove College, Detroit, MI

Vandemeulebroecke, Erik, *Chmn,* Schiller College, Europe Univ, Strasbourg, France

Vandenbeck, James H, *Secy,* Montana Historical Society, Helena

Vandenberg, Art, *Librn,* Atlanta Art Workers Coalition, GA

van den Berk, Aloys, *Librn,* Municipal Van Abbemuseum, Eindhoven, Netherlands

Vanderhill, Marlene, *Secy,* Calvin College Center Art Gallery, Grand Rapids, MI

Van Derhill, Rein, *Instr,* Northwestern College, Orange City, IA

Vanderhoof, Anne, *Lending Dept,* Newark Museum, NJ

van der Kemp, Gerald, *Cur,* Musee Nat du Chateau de Versailles, France

van der Marck, Jan, *Dir,* Dartmouth College Museum and Galleries, Hanover, NH

van der Mast, Dr W M, *Head History Dept,* Haags Gemeentemuseum, The Hague, Netherlands

Vandermeer, Jos, *Mem Faculty,* University of North Carolina at Asheville

van der Meulen, Jan, *Prof & Chmn,* Cleveland State Univ, OH

Vanderstrappen, Harrie, *Prof,* Univ Chicago, IL

Van Der Tuin, Andrew, *Cur,* Missouri Historical Society, St Louis

van der Vossen-Delbruck, Mrs E, *Librn,* Rijksmuseum Amsterdam, Netherlands

Vanderway, Richard, *Educ Coordr,* Whatcom Museum of History and Art, Bellingham, WA

Vander Weg, Phillip, *Asst Prof,* Middle Tennessee State Univ, Murfreesboro

Van Dien, Dr J, *Dir Summer School,* Trinity College, Washington, DC

van Droffelaar, Mrs J F W, *Cur Communication,* Stedelijk Museum-Amsterdam, Netherlands

van Eijle, R, *Intendant,* Rijksmuseum Amsterdam, Netherlands

van Frankenberg, Gisela, *Pres & Librn,* Muiska-Museum, Munich, Germany

van Gelder, Dr H E, *Cur Coins & Medals,* Teylers Museum, Haarlem, Netherlands

Vango, Eugene, *Asst Prof,* Virginia State College, Petersburg

van Ginkel, Blanche Lemco, *Prof Archit & Dir School,* School of Architecture, Univ Toronto, ON

van Grootheest, T, *Cur Communication Dept,* Stedelijk Museum-Amsterdam, Netherlands

Van Halsema, Brenda, *Instr,* Calvin College, Grand Rapids, MI

VanHook, David H, *Cur/Preparator,* Columbia Museums of Art and Science, SC

Van Horn, Chalmer, *Asst Prof,* Williamsport Area Community College, PA

Van Horn, Rev David, *Mem Faculty,* Siena Heights College, Adrian, MI

Van Horn, Donald, *Asst Prof,* Texas Eastern Univ, Tyler

Van Horn, Mrs Henry, *Exec Secy,* Mansfield Art Center, OH

VanHorn, Walter, *Cur Coll,* Anchorage Historical and Fine Arts Museum, AK

Vanier, Josee, *Secy,* Pavilion of Humour, Montreal, PQ

Van Kooten, C, *Cur,* Gemeentemuseum Arnhem, Netherlands

Van Laar, Timothy, *Instr,* Calvin College, Grand Rapids, MI

van Laarhoven, J C T M, *Cur,* Noordbrabants Museum, Hertogenbosch, Netherlands

van Leeuwen, J M, *Adminr,* Stedelijk Museum de Lakenhal, Netherlands

Van Lierde, Mrs I, *Serials Librn,* Nat Gallery of Canada, Ottawa, ON

van Loenen Martinet, J, *Deputy Dir,* Stedelijk Museum-Amsterdam, Netherlands

Vann, Dr Lowell C, *Chmn,* Samford Univ, Birmingham, AL

Van Ness, James, *Dir Summer School,* St Lawrence Univ, Canton, NY

van Niekerk, Dr Raymund H, *Dir,* South African Nat Gallery, Cape Town

van Oosterwijk, Cecile, *Asst Cur,* Museum Het Rembrandthuis, Amsterdam, Holland

van Nouhuys, L, *Trustee,* Teylers Museum, Haarlem, Netherlands

Van Pelt, Billie, *Exec Secy,* Utah Travel Council, Salt Lake City

van Riemsdijk, Dr J, *Dir,* Rijksakademie Van Beeldende Kunsten, Amsterdam, Netherlands

Van Riper, Tracy, *Historic Site Asst,* Philipse Manor Hall State Historic Site, Yonkers, NY

van Straaten, William, *Pres,* Chicago Art Dealers Association, IL

VanSuchtelen, Adrian, *Assoc Prof,* Utah State Univ, Logan

van Thiel, Dr P J J, *Dir Dept Paintings,* Rijksmuseum Amsterdam, Netherlands

van Velzen, Dr T, *Dir,* Haags Gemeentemuseum, The Hague, Netherlands; *Dir,* Museum Bredius, The Hague

Van Voorst, Philip, *Asst Prof,* Northwest Missouri State Univ, Maryville

Van Wagoner, Richard J, *Chmn & Prof Art & Dir Summer School,* Weber State College, Ogden, UT

Van Why, Joseph S, *Dir & Libr Pres,* Stowe-Day Found, Hartford, CT

Van Zanten, David T, *Secy,* Society of Architectural Historians, see National and Regional Organizations

Vardaman, Dr E J, *Cur,* Southern Baptist Seminary, Louisville, KY

Varde, Ralph, *Prof,* North Park College, Chicago, IL

Vares, J, *Rector,* Eesti Nsv Riiklik Kunstiinstituut, Tallinn, Estonia, USSR

Vargo, Thomas E, *Coordr Summer School,* Williamsport Area Community College, PA

Varian, Elayne H, *Cur Contemporary Art,* John and Mable Ringling Museum of Art, Sarasota, FL

Varriano, John L, *Assoc Prof Art & Chmn Dept,* Mount Holyoke College, South Hadley, MA

Varvaro, Vincent, *Mem Faculty,* Montserrat School of Visual Arts, Beverly, MA

Vascovitch, Joanne M, *Area Head,* Chamberlayne Junior College, Boston, MA

Vaslef, Irene, *Librn,* Dumbarton Oaks Research Library and Collections, Washington, DC

Vasquez, Mario, *Head Museographical Dept,* Museo Nacional de Antropologia, Mexico City, Mexico

Vatasiano, Dr Virgil, *Pres Scientific Council,* Muzeul de Arta Cluj-Napoca, Romania

Vaugel, Martine Olga, *Chmn Sculpture Dept & Dir Summer School,* Venice Painting, Drawing & Sculpture Studio, CA

Vaughan, Alan, *Asst Prof Art & Cur,* Cohen Museum, George Peabody College for Teachers, Nashville, TN

Vaughan, Harrison, *Instr,* East Tennessee State Univ, Johnson City

Vaughan, J Terrell, *Pres,* Missouri Historical Society, St Louis

Vaughan, Thomas, *Dir,* Oregon Historical Society, Portland

Vaught, Marion N, *Head Fine Arts-A V Section,* Hawaii State Library, Honolulu

Vazquez, Paul, *Assoc Prof,* Univ Bridgeport, CT

Veber, Dr Joseph, *Second VPres,* St Augustine Art Association Gallery, FL

Vedder, Alan, *Conservator,* Museum of International Folk Art, Santa Fe, NM

Veeder, Mrs Kirke C, *Secy Bd Dirs,* Ladies Library and Art Association, Independence, KS

Vega, Willam, *Assoc Dean Continuing Educ,* Contra Costa College, San Pablo, CA

Vegeler, Robert H, *Asst Dir,* Public Library of Fort Wayne and Allen County, IN

Veldhuis, Joyce, *Instr,* Ulster County Community College, Stone Ridge, NY

Velick, Mrs Harry, *Secy,* Birmingham-Bloomfield Art Association, Birmingham, MI

Vena, Carolyn, *Chairperson,* Otis Art Gallery Comt & Otis Art Association, Otis Art Inst, Los Angeles, CA

Veneziano, Patricia, *Head Art, Music & Theatre Dept,* Silas Bronson Library, Waterbury, CT

Ventimiglia, John T, *Instr,* Portland School of Art, ME

Vera, Victor, *Secy,* Museo Nacional de Arqueologia, La Paz, Bolivia

Verano, Pedro P Polo, *Acad Dean,* Javeriana Univ Faculty of Architecture and Design, Bogota, Colombia

Verchomin, Mrs J, *Chmn,* Ukrainian Arts and Crafts Museum, Edmonton, AB

Verdery, John D, *Headmaster,* Wooster School, Wooster Community Art Center, Danbury, CT

Verdugo, Rene, *Registrar,* Tucson Museum of Art, AZ

Verkuil, Elsie, *Asst to Dir,* Staten Island Inst of Arts and Sciences, NY

Vermeersch, Dr V, *Cur,* Stedelyke Musea, Bruges, Belgium

Vermeule, Cornelius C, *Cur Classical,* Museum of Fine Arts, Boston, MA

Verner, Abbie, *Secy,* Adirondack Lakes Center for the Arts, Blue Mountain Lake, NY

Verney, Katherine, *Assoc Prof,* Villa Maria College of Buffalo, NY

Vernon, Marlene, *Adv,* Univ Minnesota Gallery, Minneapolis

Verostko, Roman J, *Dean Summer School,* Minneapolis College of Art and Design, MN

Versaci, Nancy R, *Cur,* Brown Univ, Providence, RI

Versailles, Joseph, *Cur,* Chateau de Ramezay, Montreal, PQ

Vervoort, Frank, *Sr Instr,* Alberta College of Art, Calgary

Vetter, Barbara, *Staff Asst,* Brandeis Univ, Waltham, MA

Vey, Dr Horst, *Dir,* Staatliche Kunsthalle Karlsruhe, Germany

Vezzani, Daniel, *Pres,* Lahaina Arts Society, HI

Viana, Maria Teresa, *Cur,* Museu Nacional de Soares Dos Reis, Porto, Portugal

Vice, Lola, *Dir,* Brownville Fine Arts Association, NE

Vicente, Esteban, *Vis Prof,* American Univ, Washington, DC

Vickers, Robert, *Prof,* Hope College, Holland, MI

Victor, Mary O'Neill, *Dir,* Fine Arts Museum of the South, Mobile, AL

Victor, Shirley A, *Asst Cur Libr,* Hispanic Society of America, New York, NY

Viener, Saul, *Chmn Exec Council,* American Jewish Historical Society, Waltham, MA

Viera, Ricardo, *Dir Exhib & Coll, Galleries, Asst Prof Art & Chairperson Pro Tempore Dept Fine Arts,* Lehigh Univ, Bethlehem, PA

Vierneisel, Dr K, *Dir Greek & Roman Antiquities,* Staatliche Museen Preussischer Kulturbesitz, Berlin, Germany

Vieser, Milford A, *Chmn Bd,* New Jersey Historical Society Museum, Newark

Vigiletti, Bob, *Chmn Photography,* Center for Creative Studies, Detroit, MI

Vigtel, Gudmund, *Dir,* High Museum of Art, Atlanta, GA

Vila-Lobos, F R, *Dir,* Naval Amphibious Museum, Norfolk, VA

Vilcek, Marica, *Assoc Cur Central Catalog,* Metropolitan Museum of Art, New York, NY

Vilcins, Miss N, *Reference Librn,* Nat Gallery of Canada, Ottawa, ON

Villa-Arce, Jose, *Exten Supvr,* Provincial Museum of Alberta, Edmonton

Villard, Francois, *Cur Greek & Roman Antiquities,* Musee du Louvre, Paris, France

Villareal, Raymond, *Librn I,* San Antonio Public Library, TX

Vincent, Ellen, *Mem Faculty,* Maryland College of Art and Design, Silver Spring

Vincent, Tom, *Instr,* Montclair Art Museum, NJ

Vinson, Alda, *Mem Faculty,* Lane Community College, Eugene, OR

Vint, Virginia H, *Prof,* Winona State Univ, MN

Vinzani, Bernard, *Asst Prof,* Vincennes Univ, IN

Viola, Carol J, *Chairperson & Asst Dean Instr, Summer School,* Waubonsee Community College, Sugar Grove, IL

Violette, Cherry Lou, *Head Dept,* Wiley College, Marshall, TX

Vitagliano, Maria, *Instr,* Chamberlayne Junior College, Boston, MA

Vitale, Lydia Modi, *Dir,* De Saisset Art Gallery and Museum, Santa Clara, CA

Vitale, Marc, *Fiscal Consult,* De Saisset Art Gallery and Museum, Santa Clara, CA

Vitkavage, Janet, *Instr,* Abbey School of Jewelry and Art Metal Design, New York, NY

Vizzini, Michael, *Chmn Crafts,* Center for Creative Studies, Detroit, MI

Vlack, Don, *Dir,* Shelby Cullom Davis Museum of the Performing Arts, New York Public Library, NY

Vodicka, Julia R, *Dir,* Hampton Inst Museum, VA

Vodnizky, N, *Pub Relations,* Museum of Modern Art, Haifa, Israel

Voelker, Dr A, *Cur Textiles,* Bayerisches Nationalmuseum, Munich, Germany

Voelker, Cecilia, *Asst Prof,* Augusta College, GA

Voelkle, William M, *Assoc Cur Mediaeval & Renaissance Manuscripts,* Pierpont Morgan Library, New York, NY

Voet, Dr L, *Dir,* Museum Plantin-Moretus, Antwerp, Belgium; *Dir,* Stedelijk Prentenkabinet, Antwerp

Voglsamer, Gunther, *Prof,* Akademie der Bildenden Kunste in Nuremberg, Germany

Vogt, Don, *Treas,* King County Arts Commission, Seattle, WA

Vogt, Joel, *Instr,* Avila College, Kansas City, MO

Vogt, John, *Assoc Prof,* Kansas State Univ, Manhattan

Vogt, Judith, *Asst Gallery Coordr,* Los Angeles Inst of Contemporary Art, CA

Vogt, Peter, *Chmn Center Council,* Burchfield Center, Buffalo, NY

Volk, Beverly T, *Exec Dir,* Philadelphia Art Commission, PA

Volk, Dr P, *Cur Sculpture,* Bayerisches Nationalmuseum, Munich, Germany

Volk, Sylvia P, *Educ Prog Coordr,* Burchfield Center, Buffalo, NY

Volkes, Ann, *Distribution Mgr,* Electronic Arts Intermix, New York, NY

Voll, Walter, *Exhib Designer,* W H Over Museum, Univ South Dakota, Vermillion

Volprecht, Dr Klaus, *Cur African Art,* Rautenstrauch-Joest Museum fur Volkerkunde, Museen der Stadt Koln, Germany

von Berckefeldt, Susan, *Mus Serv,* E B Crocker Art Gallery, Sacramento, CA

von Bock, Dr Gisela Reineking, *Chief Cur,* Kunstgewerbemuseum, Museen der Stadt Koln, Germany

von Borries, Dr Johann, *Dir Engraving,* Staatliche Kunsthalle Karlsruhe, Germany von Bothmer, Dietrich, *Chmn Greek & Roman Art,* Metropolitan Museum of Art, New York, NY

von Euw, Dr Anton, *Cur Art of Middle Ages,* Schnutgen Museum, Museen der Stadt Koln, Germany

von Gagcrn, Dr Axel, *Dir,* Rautenstrauch-Joest Museum fur Volkerkunde, Museen der Stadt Koln, Germany

von Gleich, Dr C C J, *Head Music Dept,* Haags Gemeentemuseum, The Hague, Netherlands

von Heusinger, Dr Christian, *Cur,* Herzog Anton Ulrich-Museum, Brunswick, Germany

von Hohenzollern, Dr J G Prinz, *Cur French Paintings,* Bayerischen Staatsgemaldesammlungen, Munich, Germany

Von Huene, Stephan, *Acting Dean,* California Inst of the Arts, Valencia

von Mueller, Dr A, *Dir,* Museum of Pre- and Protohistory, Staatliche Museen Preussischer Kulturbesitz, Berlin, Germany

von Rague, Dr B, *Dir,* Museum of Far Eastern Art, Staatliche Museen Preussischer Kulturbesitz, Berlin, Germany

Von Schaack, Eric, *Prof,* Colgate Univ, Hamilton, NY

vonSchlegell, David, *Assoc Prof,* Yale Univ, New Haven, CT

von Sonnenburg, Dr Hubert Falkner, *Dir Restoration Dept,* Bayerischen Staatsgemaldesammlungen, Munich, Germany

von Stockhausen, Hans Gottfried, *Pro-Rector,* Staatliche Akademie Der Bildenden Kunste, Stuttgart, Germany

Voorhees, Alan Lee, *Educ Cur,* Arnot Art Museum, Elmira, NY

Voorhees, Alan M, *Dean,* Univ Illinois, Chicago Circle

Voorhees, Don, *Pres,* New Jersey Watercolor Society, Bloomfield

Voos, William J, *Pres,* Atlanta College of Art, GA

Voris, Peter, *Prof,* New Mexico State Univ, Las Cruces

Voss, Bill, *Mem Faculty,* Mesa Community College, AZ

Votocek, Otakar, *Dir,* Severoceska Galerie VytvarnehoUmeni, Litomerice, Czechoslovakia

Voyer, Sylvain, *Nat Representative,* Canadian Artists' Representation (CAR), see National Organizations in Canada

Vrhunc, Polonca, *Asst,* Narodna Galerija Yugoslavia, Ljubljana

Vries, P I M, *Adjunct/Dir & Cur Paintings & Drawings,* Groninger Museum Voor Stad En Land, Netherlands

Vrijland, C W D, *Trustee,* Teylers Museum, Haarlem, Netherlands

Vroom, Dr W H, *Head Dept Dutch History,* Rijksmuseum Amsterdam, Netherlands

Vruwink, John, *Assoc Prof,* Central College, Pella, IA

Vyas, Chintamani, *Sr Technical Asst,* Nat Gallery of Modern Art, New Delhi, India

Wachtman, John B, *VPres,* American Ceramic Society, see National and Regional Organizations

Wackernagel, Dr R, *Cur Conservation,* Bayerisches Nationalmuseum, Munich, Germany

Waddell, Carol N, *Asst Dir,* Tippecanoe County Historical Museum, *& Librn Historical Section,* Alameda McCollough Library, Lafayette, IN

Waddington, Murray, *Librn Technical Serv,* Nat Gallery of Canada, Ottawa, ON

Waddington, Súsan R, *Head,* Providence Public Library, RI

Wade, J P, *Cur Art,* Museum of Applied Arts and Science, Sydney, Australia

Wade, Mrs Marion H, *Dir,* Bronxville Public Library, NY

Wade, Robert, *Chief Exhib,* Natural History Museum of Los Angeles County, CA

Wadsworth, Dorothy, *Coordr Commercial Art Prog,* Johnson County Community College, Overland Park, KS

Waehrer, Anita, *Instr,* San Diego Mesa College, CA

Waetzoldt, Dr Stephen, *Dir,* Staatliche Museen Preussischer Kulturbesitz, Berlin, Germany

Wageman, Virginia, *Dir Publns,* Princeton Univ, NJ

Waggoner, Lynda, *Assoc Cur,* Museum Without Walls, Rceda Inc, Friendsville, PA

Waggoner, Warren D, *Asst Prof,* Southwestern Oklahoma State Univ, Weatherford

Wagman, N E, Jr, *Chmn Dept,* Salem State College, MA

Wagner, Elaine, *Educ Chmn,* Art Association School, Spartanburg, SC

Wagner, G Noble, *Dir,* Cheltenham Art Center, PA

Wagner, Gary W, *Dir Develop,* Bacone College Museum, Muskogee, OK

Wagner, Dr Hugo, *Dir,* Kunstmuseum Bern, Switzerland

Wagner, Norman, *Instr,* Atlanta College of Art, GA

Wagner, Wesley, *Asst Prof,* Bethany College, WV

Wagstaff, Marge, *Secy,* Reynolda House, Winston-Salem, NC

Wahl, Jane, *Reference Librn,* Univ Portland, OR

Wahler, William, *Lectr,* Villa Maria College of Buffalo, NY

Wahlgren, David, *Mem Faculty,* Austin Community College, TX

Wailes, Bernard, *Assoc Cur European Archaeology,* Univ Pennsylvania Museum, Philadelphia

Wain-Hobson, D, *Head Dept Fine Arts,* Manchester Polytechnic, England

Wait, Newman E, Jr, *Pres,* Yaddo, Saratoga Springs, NY

Wakefield, Carol, *Children's Librn,* Hillsboro Public Library, OR

Wakeman, Phil, *Instr,* Louisville School of Art, Anchorage, KY

Walberg, Dr G F, *Educ Dept,* Frans Halsmuseum, Haarlem, Netherlands

Walch, John, *Assoc Conservator,* St Gregorys Abbey and College, Shawnee, OK

Walchli, Nancy A, *Admin Asst,* Yale Univ, New Haven, CT

Wald, Palmer, *Adminr,* Whitney Museum of American Art, New York, NY

Walden, Robert Jerry, *Asst Prof,* Delta State Univ, Cleveland, MS

Walden, T A, *Dir,* Glasgow Museums and Art Galleries, Scotland

Waldfogel, Melvin, *Prof,* Univ Minnesota, Minneapolis

Waldman, Diane, *Cur Exhib,* Solomon R Guggenheim Museum, New York, NY

Waldron, Ethna, *Cur,* Hugh Lane Municipal Gallery of Modern Art, Dublin, Ireland

Waldron, Shirley, *Instr,* Cultural Arts Center of Ocean City, NJ

Walker, Barbara, *Assoc Prof,* Southeastern Louisiana Univ, Hammond

Walker, Beverly, *Secy Receptionist,* Remington Art Museum, Ogdensburg, NY

Walker, Brian, *Asst Cur,* Museum of Cartoon Art, Greenwich, CT

Walker, Brooks & Noel, *Dirs,* Walker Museum, Fairlee, VT

Walker, Chris, *Mus Asst,* Ships of the Sea Museum, Savannah, GA

Walker, Daniel S, *Assoc Cur Ancient, Near & Far Eastern Arts,* Cincinnati Art Museum, OH

Walker, David, *Pres,* Sunbury Shores Arts and Nature Centre, Saint Andrews, NB

Walker, Edith G Bradley, *Dir,* Greenville Art Center, NC

Walker, Isabella, *VPres,* Society of Washington Printmakers, Washington, DC

Walker, Jane, *Gallery Dir,* Sumter Gallery of Art, SC

Walker, Larry, *Chmn,* Univ the Pacific, Stockton, CA

Walker, Merle D, *Dir,* League of New Hampshire Craftsmen, Concord

Walker, Nancy H, *Asst Cur,* Kiah Museum, Savannah, GA

Walker, Rima, *Mem Faculty,* Clayworks, New York, NY

Walker-Oni, Roslyn A, *Dir,* Illinois State Univ, Normal

Walkey, Frederick P, *Exec Dir,* DeCordova and Dana Museum and Park, Lincoln, MA

Walkinshaw, Allan, *Cur Asst,* Robert McLaughlin Gallery, Oshawa, ON

Wall, Alexander J, *Pres,* Old Sturbridge Village, MA

Wall, Charles C, *Resident Dir,* Mount Vernon, VA

Wall, Carol, *Secy,* Octagon Center for the Arts, Ames, IA

Wallace, Ann, *Asst Dir,* Lee County Library, Tupelo, MS

Wallace, Anthony F C, *Cur North American Ethnology,* Univ Pennsylvania Museum, Philadelphia

Wallace, Betty, *Dir, Elder Gallery & Prof & Head Art Dept,* Nebraska Wesleyan Univ, Lincoln

Wallace, Charlee, *Corresp Secy,* Arizona Artist Guild, Phoenix

Wallace, Donald, *Dir Summer School,* Drake Univ, Des Moines, IA

Wallace, John, *Instr,* Truro Center for the Arts at Castle Hill, MA

Wallace, Richard W, *Prof Art & Chmn Dept,* Wellesley College, MA

Wallace, Sara E, *Mgr Libr Serv,* Hallmark Cards, Kansas City, MO

Wallace, Victoria, *Dir,* Northport-East Northport Public Library, NY

Wallack, Mark, *Prof,* Albertus Magnus College, New Haven, CT

Walle, T Y v/d, *Archaeology Dept,* Westfries Museum, Hoorn, Netherlands

Wallens, Nancy G, *Reference Librn,* Lake Forest Library, IL

Waller, Bret, *Pres,* Intermuseum Conservation Association, see National and Regional Organizations; *Dir,* Univ Michigan Museum of Art, Ann Arbor

Waller, Catherine, *Vis Asst Prof,* Miami Univ, Oxford OH

Waller, M, *Keeper,* Grange Art Gallery and Museum, Royal Pavilion Art Gallery and Museums, Brighton, England

Waller, Richard, *Community Gallery Coordr,* Brooklyn Museum, NY

Wallin, Franklin, *Pres,* Earlham College, Richmond, IN

Wallin, Hans Erik, *Ed,* Louisiana Museum of Modern Art, Humlebaek, Denmark

Wallin, Jack W, *Supt,* MacArthur Mem, Norfolk, VA

Wallis, Mel R, *Mem Faculty,* Olympic College, Bremerton, WA

Walls, Roger James, *Pres,* Saskatchewan Association of Architects, Saskatoon

Wallschlaeger, *Chmn Dept Industrial Design,* Ohio State Univ, Columbus

Walmsley, William, *Prof,* Florida State Univ, Tallahassee

Walpole, Donald, *Head Dept,* Saint Meinrad College, IN

Walpuck, Kenneth, *Asst Prof,* Queensborough Community College, Bayside, NY

Walsch, Albert J, Jr, *Coordr,* Butte Community College, Oroville, CA

Walsh, Alice, *Assoc Prof,* Regis College, Weston, MA

Walsh, Breffny A, *Dir,* Rensselaer County Historical Society, Troy, NY

Walsh, Richard K, *Pres,* Oregon College of Art, Ashland

Walsh, Thomas, *Chmn Sculpture,* Southern Illinois Univ, Carbondale

Walson, John, *Mem Faculty,* Muskegon Community College, MI

Walter, C Wallace, *Chmn,* School of the Ozarks, Point Lookout, MO

Walter, Elizabeth, *Instr,* Univ North Alabama, Florence

Walters, Betty F, *Exec Secy,* Asian Art Museum, San Francisco, CA

Walters, Mrs Charles D, *Secy*, Green Hill Art Gallery, Greensboro, NC

Walters, Charles Thomas, *Asst Prof*, Bloomsburg State College, PA

Walters, Don, *Chmn Dept & Dir Summer School*, Western Montana College, Dillon

Walters, Sister Louisella, *Dir*, L J Walters, Jr, Gallery & *Prof & Chmn Art Dept*, Regis College, Weston, MA

Walters, Sylvia Solochek, *Assoc Prof & Chairperson Art Dept*, Univ Missouri-Saint Louis

Walters, Walter H, *Dean Col*, Pennsylvania State Univ, University Park

Walther, Karen, *Registrar*, Northeastern Nevada Museum, Elko

Walton, James M, *Pres*, Carnegie Inst Museum of Art, Pittsburgh, PA

Walton, John, *Prin*, Heatherley School of Fine Art, London, England

Walton, K, *Asst Cur Applied Art*, City Art Gallery, Bristol, England

Walton, P H, *Chmn Dept*, McMaster Univ, Hamilton, ON

Walton, Thomas, *Lectr*, Catholic Univ America, Washington, DC

Walton, William, *Chmn Printmaking*, Moore College of Art, Philadelphia, PA

Walusis, Michael, *Asst Prof*, Youngstown State Univ, OH

Walz, Arzella, *Secy*, Ponca City Art Association, OH

Walz, Dr Orville, *Dir Summer School*, Concordia College, Seward, NE

Wands, Robert, *Asst Prof*, Univ Southern Colorado, Belmont Campus, Pueblo

Wantz, John A, *Mem Faculty*, College of DuPage, Glen Ellyn, IL

Wantz, Justine, *Asst Prof*, Loyola Univ Chicago, IL

Wantz, Richard G, *Pres Bd Trustees*, Washington County Museum of Fine Arts, Hagerstown, MD

Warburton, Austen, *Pres*, Triton Museum of Art, Santa Clara, CA

Warburton, Mrs R T, *Pres*, North Canton Public Library, OH

Ward, Christine W, *Manuscripts Librn*, Albany Inst of History and Art, NY

Ward, Elaine, *Chairperson*, Univ Minnesota Gallery, Minneapolis

Ward, Helen, *VPres*, Salem Art Association, OR

Ward, Jan R, *Asst Prof*, Del Mar College, Corpus Christi, TX

Ward, John L, *Assoc Prof*, Univ Florida, Gainesville

Ward, Joseph, *Chmn*, Baptist College at Charleston, SC

Ward, Karl, *Pres*, Chilkat Valley Historical Society, Haines, AK

Ward, Lyle, *Assoc Prof & Head Dept of Art*, College of the Ozarks, Clarksville, AR

Ward, Marietta M, *Librn*, Univ Washington Henry Art Gallery, Seattle

Ward, Melinda, *Coordr Film*, Walker Art Center, Minneapolis, MN

Ward, N Jeanne, *Instr*, Guilford Technical Inst, Jamestown, NC

Ward, N W, *Asst Prof*, George Mason Univ, Fairfax, VA

Ward, Phillip A, *Prof*, Univ Florida, Gainesville

Ward, Robert, *Asst Prof*, Bowie State College, MD

Ward, Robert G, *Assoc Prof*, Northeast Lousiana Univ, Monroe

Ward, William, *Teacher*, Philadelphia Maritime Museum, PA

Ward, William E, *Asst in East Indian Art & Museum Designer*, Cleveland Museum of Art, OH

Wardlaw, George, *Prof & Chmn Art Dept*, Univ Massachusetts, Amherst

Wardwell, Allen, *Dir*, Asia House Gallery, Asia Society, New York, NY

Ware, Hon John H, III, *Pres*, Chester County Historical Society, West Chester, PA

Warehall, Bill, *Mem Faculty*, California State College, San Bernardino

Warfield, Darlene, *Head Circulation*, Clark County Library District Art Activities, Las Vegas, NV

Warford, Fred R, *Dir*, Claremore College, OK

Wargula, Patricia, *Children's Room*, Mason City Public Library, IA

Waricher, George, *Mem Faculty*, Shippensburg State College, PA

Waring, Mrs Sumner, *VPres*, Greater Fall River Art Association, MA

Wark, Robert R, *Cur Art Coll*, Huntington Library, Art Gallery and Botanical Gardens, San Marino, CA

Warner, Deborah, *Chmn Textile Design*, Moore College of Art, Philadelphia, PA

Warner, Douglas, *Mem Faculty*, Charles Stewart Mott Community College, Flint, MI

Warner, H, *Mem Faculty*, Golden West College, Huntington Beach, CA

Warner, John, III, *Secy-Treas*, Fine Arts Center of Clinton, IL

Warner, Mrs John, III, *Pres*, Fine Arts Center of Clinton, IL

Warner, Lewis H, *Pres*, Tracey-Warner School, Philadelphia, PA

Warner, Mary, *Vis Prof*, Univ Montana, Missoula

Warner, Michael, *Asst Dir*, American Association of Museums, see National and Regional Organizations

Warnock, Phyllis, *Dir*, Creek Council House and Museum, Okmulgee, OK

Warp, Harold, *Pres*, Pioneer Village, Minden, NE

Warren, Bea, *Librn*, DeCordova and Dana Museum and Park, Lincoln, MA

Warren, Betty, *Dir & Instr*, Malden Bridge School of Art, NY

Warren, Mrs Claude, III, *Secy*, Art Patrons League of Mobile, AL

Warren, David B, *Assoc Dir*, Museum of Fine Arts, Houston, TX

Warren, Jerri, *Instr*, West Texas State Univ, Canyon

Warren, Joy, *Instr*, Hinckley School of Crafts, ME

Warren, L, *Chief Photographer*, Royal Ontario Museum, Toronto

Warren, Mark, *Librn*, Robert McLaughlin Gallery, Oshawa, ON

Warren, Marlea R, *Head Art, Music & Films Dept*, Minneapolis Public Library and Information Center, MN

Warren, Mary Jane, *Secy*, Museum of the Southwest, Midland, TX

Warren, Ralph, *Dir Gallery*, Bowling Green State Univ Fine Arts Gallery, OH

Warren, Russell, *Instr*, Davidson College, NC

Warrington, Ann, *Photographer*, Southern Oregon Historical Society, Jacksonville

Warrington, John W, *Chmn*, Taft Museum, Cincinnati, OH

Warshasky, Stanford, *Dir*, Silas Bronson Library, Waterbury, CT

Warwick, Katherine, *Asst to Dir Pub Information*, Nat Gallery of Art, Washington, DC

Wasgett, Mary, *Registrar*, William A Farnsworth Library and Art Museum, Rockland, ME

Washburn, Gordon B, *Chmn Art Comt*, China Inst in America, New York, NY

Washburn, Mrs Harold, *Trustee*, Attleboro Museum, MA

Washington, Selden, *Asst Dir*, Honolulu Acad of Arts Collection, HI

Wasilewski, March, *Asst Cur Educ*, George Walter Vincent Smith Art Museum, Springfield, MA

Wasserman, Jack, *Dean*, Tyler School of Art of Temple Univ, Philadelphia, PA

Waterhouse, Dr Alan, *Chmn*, Dept of Urban & Regional Planning, Univ Toronto, ON

Waterman, Donald, *Chmn*, Syracuse Univ, NY

Waterton, Eric C, *Head Cur Human History*, Provincial Museum of Alberta, Edmonton

Watkins, Ben P, *Acting Chmn Dept*, Eastern Illinois Univ, Charleston

Watkins, Debbie, *Secy*, Kingsport Fine Arts Center, TN

Watkins, Ragland, *Assoc Dir Gallery*, Artists Space, New York, NY

Watkins, Raymond, *Cur Exhib*, Inst and Museum of the Great Plains, Lawton, OK

Watkins, Rebecca, *Exhib Asst*, Ivy School of Professional Art Galleries, Pittsburgh, PA

Watkins, Ruth Nagle, *Chmn & Prof*, College of Notre Dame of Maryland, Baltimore

Watkins, William Myers, III, *Exec Dir*, Meridian Museum of Art, MS

Watkinson, Patricia, *Cur*, Washington State Univ Museum of Art, Pullman

Watral, James, *Chmn Ceramics*, East Texas State Univ, Commerce

Watrous, John, *Dir Art Gallery & Prof Art*, Santa Rosa Junior College, CA

Watson, Helen, *Chmn Ceramics*, Otis Art Inst, Los Angeles, CA

Watson, Herb, *Vis Designer*, Univ British Columbia Museum of Anthropology, Vancouver

Watson, Jennifer, *Asst Cur/Registrar*, Robert McLaughlin Gallery, Oshawa, ON

Watson, John, *VPres*, Art Centre of New Jersey, East Orange

Watson, Katharine J, *Dir*, Bowdoin College Museum of Art, Brunswick, ME

Watson, Dr Lorne, *First VPres*, Brandon Allied Art Council, MB

Watson, Lorraine, *Head Teaching Staff*, Cultural Arts Center of Ocean City, NJ & Ocean City School of Art

Watson, Paulette Skirbunt, *Dir*, James Monroe Law Office Museum and Mem Library, Fredericksburg, VA

Watson, Ronald, *Chmn Dept*, Aquinas College, Grand Rapids, MI

Watson, Ross, *Cur British Painting*, Nat Gallery of Art, Washington, DC

Watson, Wendy, *Chief Cur*, Mount Holyoke College Art Museum, South Hadley, MA

Watsztein, Elena, *Educ Serv*, Museo de San Carlos, Mexico City, Mexico

Watt, Dr Norman, *Dir Summer School*, Univ British Columbia, Vancouver

Watt, Virginia J, *Managing Dir*, Guilde Canadianne des Metiers D'Art, Quebec, PQ

Wattenmaker, Richard J, *Chief Cur*, Art Gallery of Ontario, Toronto

Watters, Ann, *Secy*, Breezewood Found Museum and Garden, Monkton, MD

Watts, Melvin E, *Cur*, Currier Gallery of Art, Manchester, NH

Watts, Roland S, *Assoc Prof*, Winston-Salem State Univ, NC

Waufle, Alan D, *Dir*, Gaston County Art and History Museum, Dallas, NC

Waugh, Carlisle J, *Head Dept*, Oklahoma State Univ, Okmulgee

Wavell, Joan B, *Adminr*, Rollins College, Winter Park, FL

Wax, Bernard, *Dir*, American Jewish Historical Society, Waltham, MA

Way, Ed, *Cur Exhib*, Alaska State Museum, Juneau

Way, Mrs Gordon, *Dir*, Cody Country Art League, WY

Wayne, James M, *Instr*, San Jose City College, CA

Wayne, Sam, *Mem Faculty*, Saint Louis Community College at Meramec, St Louis, MO

Wdowka, Wanda, *Dir*, Traphagen School of Fashion, New York, NY

Weare, Shane, *Assoc Prof*, California State College, Sonoma, Rohnert Park

Weaver, Barlow, *Librn*, College of San Meteo Library, CA

Weaver, Chris, *Instr Studio Arts*, Emma Willard School, Troy, NY

Weaver, George, *First VPres*, Chautauqua Gallery of Art, NY

Weaver, Helen, *Teacher*, Southwestern School of Art, Albuquerque, NM

Weaver, Howard S, *Dir*, Yale Univ, New Haven, CT

Weaver, Judy, *Secy*, Museum of the Rockies, Montana State Univ, Bozeman

Weaver, Larry E, *Assoc Prof Art & Chmn Dept*, Univ Lethbridge, AB

Weaver, Marguerite, *Secy-Treas*, Hill-Stead Museum, Farmington, CT

Weaver, Mary Catharine, *Dir,* Martin Mem Library, York, PA

Webb, Beth R, *Mus & Art Librn,* B R Larsen Gallery, Brigham Young Univ, Provo, UT

Webb, Brian, *Instr,* Vermont College of Norwich Univ, Montpelier

Webb, Mrs Edward, *Cur Historic Houses,* Charleston Museum, SC

Webb, Robert L, *Pres,* Adirondack Lakes Center for the Arts, Blue Mountain Lake, NY

Webb, Samuel B, *Pres,* Shelburne Museum, VT

Webber, E Leland, *Dir,* Field Museum of Natural History, Chicago, IL

Webber, Nancy E, *Asst Prof,* Los Angeles Harbor College, Wilmington, CA

Webber, William B, *Pres Bd Mgrs,* Univ Rochester Mem Art Gallery, NY

Weber, Alice, *Pres,* Association of Junior Leagues, see National and Regional Organizations

Weber, Arthur H, *Dean,* Herron School of Art, Indiana Univ-Purdue Univ, Indianapolis

Weber, B M A, *Chmn Art Dept,* California Lutheran College, Thousand Oaks

Weber, Barbara, *Secy/Bookkeeper,* Contemporary Crafts Association and Gallery, Portland, OR

Weber, Sister Donna, *Instr,* Viterbo College, La Crosse, WI

Weber, Dorothy M, *Exec Dir,* Visual Artists and Galleries Association, see National and Regional Organizations

Weber, Jean M, *Dir,* Parrish Art Museum, Southampton, NY

Weber, John, *Assoc Prof,* Elmhurst College, IL

Weber, Joseph A, *Asst Chmn Dept,* Southern Illinois Univ, Edwardsville

Weber, Kathleen, *Chmn,* Howard College, Big Spring, TX

Weber, Michael, *Assoc Dir,* Museum of New Mexico, Santa Fe

Webster, *Prof,* Asbury College, Wilmore, KY

Webster, Mrs Christopher R, *Exec Secy,* North Carolina Art Society, Raleigh

Webster, D B, *Cur Canadian Dept,* Royal Ontario Museum, Toronto

Webster, Douglas, *VPres,* Birmingham Gallery, MI

Webster, M, *Mem Faculty,* Northern Arizona Univ, Flagstaff

Wechsler, Elaine Telsey, *Instr,* School for Creative Movement in the Arts, New York, NY

Wechsler, Jeffrey, *Cur Paintings & Sculpture,* Rutgers Univ Art Gallery, New Brunswick, NJ

Weekly, Nancy, *Art Gallery Asst,* State Univ New York College at Fredonia

Weeks, Dennis, *Lectr,* Saint Joseph's College, Philadelphia, PA

Weeks, Edward F, *Cur,* Birmingham Museum of Art, AL

Weeks, James, *Assoc Prof,* Boston Univ, MA

Weeks, John, *VPres,* Abilene Fine Arts Museum, TX

Weeks, Phil, *Pres,* Jackson County Historical Society, Independence, MO

Weelock, Mrs Andrew, *Clerk,* Greater Fall River Art Association, MA

Weems, Betsy, *Secy,* Meridian Museum of Art, MS

Weers, Rosalind, *Young Adult,* Mason City Public Library, IA

Wees, Beth Carver, *Asst Cur,* Sterling and Francine Clark Art Inst, Williamstown, MA

Wees, J Dustin, *Photograph & Slide Librn,* Sterling and Francine Clark Art Inst, Williamstown, MA

Weet, Barry D, *Asst Dir,* Illinois State Univ, Normal

Weglewski, Linda, *Lectr,* Villa Maria College of Buffalo, NY

Wegner, Nadene, *Mem Faculty,* Louisville School of Art, Anchorage, KY

Wegner, Samuel J, *Cur,* Oglebay Inst Mansion Museum, Wheeling, WV

Weidensee, Victor, *Chmn,* Black Hills State College, Spearfish, SD

Weidl, Beverly, *Cur,* Hopewell Museum, NJ

Weidman, James F, *Develop Officer,* Huntington Galleries, WV

Weidmann, Daniel, *Graphic Designer,* Brooklyn Museum, NY

Weigel, Jan, *Designer,* Taft Museum, Cincinnati, OH

Weihrer, Arthur, *Vis Prof,* Mount Saint Mary's College, Emmitsburg, MD

Weil, Norman, *Asst Prof,* Northwest Missouri State Univ, Maryville

Weil, Mrs Robert S, *Past Pres,* Montgomery Museum of Fine Arts, AL

Weil, Rose R, *Exec Secy,* College Art Association of America, see National and Regional Organizations

Weil, Stephen, *Deputy Dir,* Hirshhorn Museum and Sculpture Garden, Washington, DC

Weiler, Melody, *Mem Faculty,* Murray State Univ, KY

Weill, Eva W, *Secy,* Pittsburgh Plan for Art, PA

Weimerskirch, Robert, *Instr,* School of Art, Museum of Fine Arts, Houston, TX

Wein, Albert, *Art Adv Bd,* Society of Medalists, see National and Regional Organizations

Weinberg, Ephraim, *Dean,* Pennsylvania Acad of Fine Arts, Philadelphia

Weinberger, James, *Librn,* Judah L Magnes Memorial Museum, Berkeley, CA

Weinberger, Oscar, *Treas,* Guild Hall of East Hampton, NY

Weinbrecht, Rudy, *Chmn Libr Comt,* James Monroe Law Office Museum and Mem Library, Fredericksburg, VA

Weinbrecht, Mrs Standau E, *Librn,* James Monroe Museum and Mem Library, Fredericksburg, VA

Weiner, Abe, *Mem Faculty,* Ivy School of Professional Art, Pittsburgh, PA

Weingartner, Fannia, *Ed,* Chicago Historical Society, IL

Weingrod, Carmi, *Slide Cur,* Univ Oregon School of Architecture and Allied Arts Library, Eugene

Weinhardt, Carl J, Jr, *Dir,* Dade County Art Museum, Miami, FL

Weinland, Richard, *Treas,* Katonah Gallery, NY

Weinrich, Peter H, *Exec Dir,* Canadian Crafts Council, see National Organizations in Canada

Weinstein, Edward, *VPres,* West Hills Unitarian Fellowship, Portland, OR

Weinstein, Jeffrey, *Vis Prof,* Grand Valley State Colleges, Allendale, MI

Weinstein, Joyce, *Action Chair,* Women in the Arts Found, New York, NY

Weinstein, M, *Treas,* Lovis Corinth Mem Found, New York, NY

Weis, Helene H, *Librn,* Willet Stained Glass Studios, Philadelphia, PA

Weisberg, Charlene, *Mem Faculty,* Univ Southern California, Idyllwild Campus

Weisberg, Gabriel P, *Cur Educ,* Cleveland Museum of Art, OH

Weisenburger, Patricia, *Asst Dir,* Kansas State Univ, Manhattan

Weiser, Kurt, *Res Dir,* Archie Bray Found, Helena, MT

Weisflog, Donald, *Prof,* Anderson College, IN

Weisl, Edwin L, Jr, *Pres,* International Found for Art Research, see National and Regional Organizations

Weisman, Gustav, *Chmn Dept Exp Art,* Ontario College of Art, Toronto

Weiss, Anton, *Art Dir,* Watkins Inst, Nashville, TN

Weiss, Art, *Dept Chmn & Dir Summer School,* California State Univ, Northridge

Weiss, Dr Evelyn, *Cur Modern Art,* Wallraf-Richartz Museum, Museen der Stadt Koln, Germany

Weiss, Gilbert H, *Teacher,* Antonelli School of Photography, Philadelphia, PA

Weiss, Jack, *Dir Summer School,* Illinois Inst of Technology, Chicago

Weiss, John, *Coordr,* Univ Delaware, Newark

Weiss, Dr Nathan, *Pres,* Kean College of New Jersey Gallery, Union

Weiss, Peg, *Cur Coll,* Everson Museum of Art, Syracuse, NY

Weisser, Renee, *Secy,* Sioux City Art Center, IA

Weisser, Terry Drayman, *Dir Conservation Dept,* Walters Art Gallery, Baltimore, MD

Weisz, Helen, *Mem Faculty,* Bucks County Community College, Newtown, PA

Weitzel, Robert, *Dean Faculty Summer School,* Cleveland Inst of Art, OH

Welber, Beverly Zisla, *Assoc Dir,* Chapel Arts Center, Saint Anselm's College, Manchester, NH

Welch, Ileana, *Dir Cultural Heritage,* City of Los Angeles Municipal Arts Dept, CA

Welch, Kathryn, *Preservation Planner,* Society for the Preservation of New England Antiquities, Boston, MA

Welch, Olga, *Secy,* Cooperstown Art Association, NY

Welch, Paul, *Instr Art, Chmn Dept & Dir Summer School,* Northwestern Michigan College, Traverse City

Welden, Larry, *Instr,* Sacramento City College, CA

Welliver, Jackie, *Instr,* Williamsport Area Community College, PA

Welliver, Dr Kenneth, *Dir Summer School,* West Virginia Wesleyan College, Buckhannon

Wellman, Dave, *Chief Cur & Librn,* Nome Museum, AK

Wellock, Mr, *Chmn,* Fairmont State College, WV

Wells, Augusta, *Secy,* Lighthouse Gallery, Tequesta, FL

Wells, Charles, *Archivist,* Klamath County Museum, Klamath Falls, OR

Wells, Dr Charles, *VPres,* Tennessee Botanical Gardens and Fine Arts Center, Nashville

Wells, James L, *Cur Graphics,* Smith-Mason Gallery and Museum, Washington, DC

Wells, Kimball, *Assoc Prof,* Saint Louis Community College at Forest Park, MO

Wells, Mrs Peter, *Secy,* Beaumont Art Museum, TX

Wells, Sarajane, *Chief Educ Prog,* Chicago Historical Society, IL

Wells, Vern, *Area Chmn Art History,* Pasadena City College, CA

Wells, William, *Chmn Dept Art,* Briar Cliff College, Sioux City, IA

Wells, William, *Keeper Burrell Collection,* Glasgow Museum and Art Galleries, Scotland

Welsh, Alexandra, *Cur of Prints & Cur of Ship Models,* US Naval Academy Museum, Annapolis, MD

Weltzin, Wallace, *Asst Dir,* Horner Museum, Oregon State Univ, Corvallis

Welu, James A, *Assoc Cur,* Worcester Art Museum, MA

Welu, William J, *Chairperson,* Briar Cliff College, Sioux City, IA

Wendel, Charlotte, *Develop Officer,* San Jose Museum of Art, CA

Wenegrat, Saul S, *Adminr Archit Serv,* Port Authority of New York and New Jersey, New York, NY, see Corporate Art Holdings

Weng, Siegfried R, *Dir Emer,* Evansville Museum of Arts and Science, IN

Wenger, Mildred, *Historian,* Alaska Association for the Arts, Fairbanks

Wenig-Horswell, Judy, *Asst Prof,* Goshen College, IN

Wentworth, Mr, *Dir Summer School,* Sarah Lawrence College, Bronxville, NY

Wentworth, John, *VPres,* Rockport Art Association, MA

Wentworth, T T, Jr, *Dir & Cur,* T T Wentworth, Jr, Museum, Pensacola, FL

Wentworth, T W, *Deputy Dir & Secy,* T T Wentworth, Jr, Museum, Pensacola, FL

Werk, Horst, *Instr,* Corning Community College, NY

Werkele, Marilyn, *Instr,* Laramie County Community College, Cheyenne, WY

Werner, Howard, *Resident Artist,* Peters Valley Craftsmen, Layton, NJ

Werner, Susan, *Cur Asst,* Watson Gallery, Wheaton College, Norton, MA

Werness, Hope B, *Vis Lectr,* California State College, Stanislaus, Turlock

Wernig, Raymond, *VChmn,* Stan Hywet Hall Found, Akron, OH

Wert, Ned O, *Chmn Exhib,* Indiana Univ Pennsylvania, PA

Werth, Dr A J, *Dir,* Pretoria Art Museum, South Africa

Werthan, Albert, *Pres,* Tennessee Botanical Gardens and Fine Arts Center, Nashville, TN

Wertheim, Bud, *Asst Prof,* Sullivan County Community College, Loch Sheldrake, NY

Wesaw, Sallie, *Mem Faculty,* Central Wyoming College, Riverton

Wesp, Erwin O, *Exhib Chmn,* Coppini Acad of Fine Arts, San Antonio, TX

Wessel, Frederick, *Instr,* Art School, Univ Hartford, West Hartford, CT

Wessetzky, Dr V, *Head Egyptian Antiquities,* Szepmuveszet: Muzeum, Budapest, Hungary

Wesson, Robert, *Pres,* Main Line Center of the Arts, Haverford, PA

West, Harvey, *Dir,* Washington State Univ Museum of Art, Pullman

West, Jan, *VPres,* Galesburg Civic Art Center, IL

West, Jean, *Arts Workshop.* Newark Museum, NJ

West, Mrs John D, *Bd Chmn,* Rahr-West Museum and Civic Center, Manitowoc, WI

West, Richard Vincent, *Dir,* E B Crocker Art Gallery, Sacramento, CA

West, Sharon, *Head Catalog Dept,* Elmer E Rasmuson Library, Univ Alaska Museum, Fairbanks

Westberg, Alma, *Art & Music Librn,* Santa Cruz Public Library, CA

Westcoast, Wanda, *Chmn Gen Studies,* Otis Art Inst, Los Angeles, CA

Westerberg, Dr Wesley M, *Dir,* American Swedish Inst, Minneapolis, MN

Westergaard, Christine, *Instr,* Umpqua Community College, Roseburg, OR

Westergaard, Hanne, *Cur, Dept Painting & Sculpture* Statens Museum for Kunst, Copenhagen, Denmark

Westermark, Ulla, *Deputy Keeper,* Kungl Myntkabinettet Statens Museum of Mynt Medalj Och Penninghistoria, Stockholm, Sweden

Westers, Dr A, *Dir,* Groninger Museum Voor Stad En Land, Netherlands

Westervelt, Alice, *Museum Shop Mgr,* Rhode Island School of Design Museum of Art, Providence

Westervelt, Robert F, *Assoc Prof,* Agnes Scott College, Decatur, GA

Westhafer, Dorothy H, *Gallery Dir,* Niagara County Community College Art Gallery, Sanborn, NY

Westheimer, Jerome, *Treas,* Charles B Goddard Center for the Visual and Performing Arts, Ardmore, OK

Westheimer, Jerome M, *VPres,* Oklahoma Art Center, Oklahoma City

Westley, David, *Secy,* Pottstown Area Artists Guild, PA

Westmorland, Bob, *Pres,* Ponca City Art Association, OH

Weston, Norman B, *Pres,* Detroit Inst of Art Collections, MI

Westra, Monique, *Acting Cur In Charge Art Dept,* Glenbow-Alberta Inst, Calgary, AB

Westrom, Fred, *Chmn,* Twin City Art Found, Monroe, LA

Wetherbee, Ralph H, Jr, *Chmn Bd,* Springfield Art Center, OH

Wettengel, Jack, *Secy,* Oklahoma Historical Society, Oklahoma City

Wettre, Hakan, *Cur Exhib Dept,* Goteborgs Konstmuseum, Sweden

Wever, Robert C, *Chmn,* Davis and Elkins College, Elkins, WV

Wewer, William J, *Exec Dir,* Pennsylvania Historical and Museum Commission, Harrisburg

Weyerhaeuser, Charles A, *Mus Dir,* Art Complex Museum at Duxbury, MA

Weyl, Dr Martin, *Chief Cur Arts,* Israel Musuem, Jerusalem

Weyman, William M, *Dir School, Prof & Dir Summer School,* Leo Marchutz School of Painting and Drawing, Aix-en-Provence, France

Whang, Dr Ji-hyun, *Cur & Librn,* Museum fur Ostasiatische Kunst, Museen der Stadt Koln, Germany

Wharton, John, *Dir,* Phillips Exeter Academy, NH

Wheat, Gilbert, *Mem Faculty,* College of Marin, Kentfield, CA

Wheatley, Richard, *Instr,* Wilberforce Univ, OH

Wheeler, Anita, *Asst Dir,* Cayuga Museum of History and Art, Auburn, NY

Wheeler, Mayor Charles B, Jr, *Head,* Municipal Art Commission, Kansas City, MO

Wheeler, Claire, *Admin Asst,* Shaker Museum, Old Chatham, NY

Wheeler, Douglas P, *Exec VPres,* Nat Trust for Historic Preservation, Washington, DC

Wheeler, Elbert, *Instr,* Phillips Univ, Enid, OK

Wheeler, Gary, *Asst Prof,* Miami Univ, Oxford, OH

Wheeler, Glyde J, *Dir Educ & Spec Prog,* Charles H MacNider Museum, Mason City, IA

Wheeler, Mark, *Pres,* Art Inst of Fort Lauderdale, FL

Wheeler, Mary Elizabeth, *Cur,* Principia College, Elsah, IL

Wheeler, Meme, *Instr,* Phillips Univ, Enid, OK

Wheeler, Robert C, *Dir,* Minnesota Historical Society, St Paul

Wheeler, Robert G, *VPres/Research & Interpretation,* Greenfield Village and Henry Ford Museum, Dearborn, MI

Wheeling, Kenneth E, *Dir,* Shelburne Museum, VT

Wheelock, Dr Charles, *Dir Summer School,* Glendale College, CA

Whelan, L, *Secy,* Saskatoon Gallery and Conservatory Corp, SK

Wherry, Doroth J, *Secy,* Auckland City Art Gallery, New Zealand

Whetzel, Mrs Jonathan, *Second VPres,* Allied Arts of Seattle, WA

Whipkey, Harry E, *Dir Bur Archives & History,* Pennsylvania Historical and Museum Commission, Harrisburg

Whipple, Enez, *Dir,* Guild Hall of East Hampton, NY

Whistler, Barry, *Dir Installations,* Fort Worth Art Museum, TX

Whitacre, Steven, *Chmn Found,* Kansas City Art Inst, MO

Whitaker, Richard, *Dir School Archit,* Univ Illinois, Chicago Circle

Whitbeck, Gary, *Dir,* Rahr-West Museum and Civic Center, Manitowoc, WI

Whitcomb, Mrs Morton C, *Secy,* Colonel Black Mansion, Ellsworth, ME

Whitcomb, Therese T, *Dir Founders Gallery & Chmn Art Dept,* Univ San Diego, CA

White, Amos, IV, *Assoc Prof,* Bowie State College, MD

White, Barbara, *Asst Prof,* Tufts Univ, Medford, MA

White, Barbara, *Mem Faculty,* Charles Stewart Mott Community College, Flint, MI

White, Mrs C Ridgely, *Pres,* Bellegrove, Middletown, VA

White, Charles, *Chmn Drawing,* Otis Art Inst, Los Angeles, CA

White, Dan, *Mem Faculty,* Lane Community College, Eugene, OR

White, David O, *Mus Dir,* Connecticut State Library, Hartford

White, Donald, *Assoc Cur,* Univ Pennsylvania Museum, Philadelphia

White, E Alan, *Asst Prof,* Univ Tennessee at Chattanooga

White, Evelyn, *Art & Slide Librn,* California Inst of the Arts Library, Valencia

White, Ferrell E, *Second VPres,* Washington Nat Insurance Co, Evanston, IL, see Corporate Art Holdings

White, Ian McKibbin, *Dir,* Fine Arts Museums of San Francisco, CA

White, Jack H, *Dir,* Milwaukee School of the Arts, WI

White, James, *Dir,* Nat Gallery of Ireland, Dublin

White, Jim, *Mem Faculty,* Murray State Univ, KY

White, Joan, *Dir Campus Events,* Reed College Art Gallery, Portland, OR

White, John, *Mem Staff,* Rudolph Schaeffer School of Design, San Francisco, CA

White, Mrs John, *Pres,* Southwest Missouri Museum Associates, Springfield

White, Juanita, *Secy,* St Paul's School, Concord, NH

White, Lelia, *Dir Libr Serv,* Oakland Public Library, CA

White, Leonard, *Chmn,* Meredith College, Raleigh, NC

White, Lionel, *Media Specialist,* Fashion Inst of Technology, New York, NY

White, Patrick J, *Pres,* Stained Glass Association of America, see National and Regional Organizations

White, Paul, *Adv,* Mystic Art Association, CT

White, Rita A, *Chmn,* Palomar College, San Marcos, CA

White, William G, *Chmn & Assoc Prof,* Hollins College, VA

White, William V, *Cur Graphic Reproductions Coll,* Illinois State Univ, Normal

Whitebird, Joanie, *Cur,* Contemporary Arts Museum, Houston, TX

Whitehead, Elizabeth A, *Gen Secy,* Archaeological Inst of America, see National and Regional Organizations

Whitehead, L D, *Pres,* Brandon Allied Arts Council, MB

Whitehill, Florence, *Recording Secy,* Council of American Artist Societies, see National and Regional Organizations

Whitehill, Walter M, *Pres,* Monticello, Charlottesville, VA

Whitenack, Michael, *Supvr Visual Art Resources,* Univ Oregon Museum of Art, Eugene

Whiteside, Forbes J, *Prof,* Oberlin College, OH

Whitesides, Patricia, *Registrar,* Toledo Museum of Art, OH

Whitfield, Frances, *Librn,* J B Speed Art Museum, Louisville, KY

Whitley, Sharon, *Asst Dir,* Mus School of Art, Greenville County Museum of Art, SC

Whitlock, Dr John R, *Dir,* Brooks Mem Art Gallery, Memphis, TN

Whitlock, Mrs Myles, Jr, *Pres,* Arts Council of Spartanburg County, SC

Whitlock, Reverdy, *Secy,* New Haven Colony Historical Society, CT

Whitman, Sue, *Pub Relations Dir,* Norton Gallery and School of Art, West Palm Beach, FL

Whitmore, Doris L, *Dir,* Jacksonville Museum of Arts and Sciences, FL

Whitmore, Quentin R, *Teacher,* Antonelli School of Photography, Philadelphia, PA

Whitney, John, *Chairperson,* City College of San Francisco, CA

Whitney, John Hay, *VPres,* Nat Gallery of Art, Washington, DC

Whitney Maynard, *Dir,* Lyle True Gallery & *Chmn Art Dept,* Colorado Women's College, Denver

Whitney, William, *Dir,* Armstrong Museum of Art and Archaeology & *Prof,* Olivet College, MI

Whitsitt, Marjorie, *Asst Prof,* Univ Wisconsin-Superior

Whitt, Brenda, *Secy,* Morehead State Univ Art Gallery, KY

Whitten, Lee, *Asst Prof,* Los Angeles City College, CA

Whittington, Harrell, *Mem Faculty,* Bob Jones Univ, Greenville, SC

Whittle, Bertram, *Deputy Dir,* Western Australian Art Gallery, Perth

Whitwell, W L, *Assoc Prof,* Hollins College, VA

Whitworth, Phyllis, *Pres,* Brown County Art Gallery Association, Nashville, IN

Wichman, Juliet Rice, *Pres,* Kauai Museum, HI

Wick, Wendy C, *Cur Prints,* Nat Portrait Gallery, Washington, DC

Wickard, Margaret, *Mus Registrar,* Arkansas Arts Center, Little Rock

Wickman, Dr John E, *Dir,* Dwight D Eisenhower Presidential Library, Abilene, KS

Wicks, Eugene C, *Prof & Acting Head Dept & Dir Summer School,* Univ Illinois, Urbana-Champaign, Champaign

Wickstrom, Richard, *Prof,* New Mexico State Univ, Las Cruces

Widenhofer, Allan, *Mem Faculty,* College of Marin, Kentfield, CA

Widiez, George, *Prof,* College Saint-Louis-Maillet, Edmundston, NB

Widman, D, *Head Applied Arts,* Nationalmuseum, Stockholm, Sweden

Widman, Harry, *Acting Dean,* Portland Art Association Museum Art School, OR

Widrig, Walter M, *Asst Prof,* Rice Univ, Houston, TX

Wied, Dr Alexander, *Cur,* Neue Galerie Am Landesmuseum Joanneum, Graz, Austria

Wiedemann, Gladys, *Pres,* Wichita Art Association, KS

Wieder, Charles, *Asst Prof,* Ohio State Univ, Columbus

Wiederspan, Stan, *Dir,* Cedar Rapids Art Center, IA

Wiegmann, Richard, *Dir,* Koenig Art Gallery & *Prof,* Concordia College, Seward, NE

Wiener, Hattie & Jack, *Dir,* School for Creative Movement in the Arts, New York, NY

Wiesendanger, Margaret, *Assoc Conservator,* St Gregorys Abbey and College, Shawnee, OK

Wiesendanger, Martin, *Chief Conservator,* St Gregorys Abbey and College, Shawnee, OK

Wiesner, Jerome B, *Pres,* Massachusetts Inst of Technology, Cambridge

Wiesner, Dr Ulrich, *Cur,* Museum fur Ostasiatische Kunst, Museen der Stadt Koln, Germany

Wike, Antoinette, *Chmn,* Davidson County Community College, Lexington, NC

Wilcox, Arthur, *Pres,* Charleston Museum, SC

Wilcox, Jeffrey, *Assoc Cur Exhib,* Univ Missouri Museum of Art and Archaeology, Columbia

Wilcox, U Vincent, *Cur North America,* Heye Found, New York, NY

Wild, Archie M, *Sr Exhib Specialist,* US Naval Academy Museum, Annapolis, MD

Wild, Bruce, *Mem Faculty,* Lane Community College, Eugene, OR

Wild, Kurt, *Prof,* Univ Wisconsin-River Falls

Wild, Terry, *PT Instr,* Lycoming College, Williamsport, PA

Wilde, Edwin, *Dean Summer School,* Roger Williams College, Bristol, RI

Wilde, Robert, *Lectr,* Saint Joseph's College, Philadelphia, PA

Wilder, Mitchell A, *Dir,* Amon Carter Museum of Western Art, Forth Worth, TX

Wildfeuer, Marvin, *VPres,* Lafayette Art Center, IN

Wilding-White, Mrs M L, *Pres,* John Woodman Higgins Armory, Worcester, MA

Wildung, Dr Dietrich, *Dir,* Staatliche Sammlung Agyptischer Kunst, Munich, Germany

Wilen, Eve, *Exec Secy,* Artists Equity Association of New York, NY

Wilentz, Elias, *Secy,* Art Commission of the City of New York, NY

Wilerson, Dr Thomas A, *Chmn Div Humanities,* Dalton Junior College, GA

Wiley, Hugh, *Instr,* California College of Arts and Crafts, Oakland

Wiley, Sandy, *Instr,* Hinckley School of Crafts, ME

Wilfer, Joseph E, *Dir,* Madison Art Center, WI

Wilfong, Jean A, *Pres,* Clearwater Art Association, ID

Wilhelmi, Tom, *Chmn,* Holyoke Historical Commission, City of Holyoke Museum-Wistariahurst, MA

Wilkerson, Mrs Frederick W, *Pres,* Montgomery Museum of Fine Arts Association, AL

Wilkerson, Sally, *Assoc Prof,* Berea College, KY

Wilkins, David G, *Dir,* Univ Pittsburgh Art Gallery, PA

Wilkins, Marilyn, *Head Librn,* New Orleans Public Library, LA

Wilkinson, Irene, *Head Technical Serv,* Brookline Public Library, MA

Wilkinson, Mrs P Chauvin, *Chmn Empire Bedroom Coll,* West Baton Rouge Museum, Port Allen, LA

Wilkinson, Pam, *Art Registrar,* Glenbow-Alberta Inst, Calgary, AB

Wilkinson, William D, *Dir,* Mariners Museum, Newport News, VA

Willcoxon, Suzanne, *Exec Secy,* Western Colorado Center for the Arts, Grand Junction

Wille, Kay, *Staff Asst,* Univ New Mexico Art Museum, Albuquerque

Willert, Galen R, *Dir,* Minot Art Gallery, ND

Willet, Augusta W, *VPres,* Willet Stained Glass Studios, Philadelphia, PA

Willet, E Crosby, *Pres,* Willet Stained Glass Studios, Philadelphia, PA

Willet, Henry Lee, *Chmn,* Willet Stained Glass Studios, Philadelphia, PA

William, Maudine B, *Head Librn,* Indiana Univ, Indianapolis

Williams, Ann, *Asst Prof,* Beaver College, Glenside, PA

Williams, Benjamin F, *Coll Care & Preparation,* North Carolina Museum of Art, Raleigh

Williams, Dr Beryl W, *Dir Summer School,* Morgan State Univ, Baltimore, MD

Williams, Mrs C E, *Art Dir,* Plains Indians & Pioneer Historical Found, Woodward, OK

Williams, C L, *Assoc Prof,* Florida A&M Univ, Tallahassee

Williams, Catherine, *Dir Fine Art,* Holden School of Art and Design, Charlottesville, VA

Williams, Dr Donald, *Dir Summer School,* Hope College, Holland, MI

Williams, Elizabeth G, *Instr,* Dalton Junior College, GA

Williams, Dr Ellen Reeder, *Cur,* Johns Hopkins Univ Archaeological Collection, Baltimore, MD

Williams, Eunice, *Asst Cur Drawings,* William Hayes Fogg Art Museum, Harvard Univ, Cambridge, MA

Williams, Gretchen, *Secy,* Univ North Carolina at Greensboro

Williams, Rev H, *Pres,* Moravian Historical Society, Nazareth, PA

Williams, H L, *Chmn,* Florida A&M Univ, Tallahassee

Williams, Dr Haydn, *Pres,* Asia Found Gallery, San Francisco, CA

Williams, Hiram D, *Prof,* Univ Florida, Gainesville

Williams, James M, *Dir,* Johnson County Community Colelge, Overland Park, KS

Williams, Jo Ella, *Asst Prof,* Northeast Louisiana Univ, Monroe

Williams, John C, *Pres & Dir,* Agecroft Association Hall, Richmond, VA

Williams, Mrs Juanita N, *Secy,* Art Center, South Bend, IN

Williams, Julia, *Supvr Loan-Own Art Serv,* Virginia Museum of Fine Arts, Richmond

Williams, Lenis, *Slide Librn,* Rotch Library of Architecture and Planning, Massachusetts Inst of Technology, Cambridge

Williams, Lewis C, *Pres,* Cleveland Museum of Art, OH

Williams, Lorraine, *Archaeology/Ethnology,* New Jersey State Museum, Trenton

Williams, Margaret Click, *Chmn Dept & Assoc Prof,* St Mary's College, Raleigh, NC

Williams, Mary Jane, *Registrar,* Arizona State Univ Art Collection, Tempe

Williams, Marylou S, *Dir & Cur,* Theodore Lyman Wright Art Center, Beloit College, WI

Williams, Ranae, *Librn,* Lois Brownell Research Library, Point Lookout, MO

Williams, Dr Richmond, *Dir,* Eleutherian Mills Historical Library, Wilmington, DE

Williams, Roberta L, *Exec Dir,* Louisville Junior Art Gallery, KY

Williams, Roger, *Adjunct Assoc Prof,* New York Inst of Technology, Old Westbury

Williams, Roger, *Dir,* Art Acad of Cincinnati, OH

Williams, Sally, *Secy,* Kirkland Art Center, Clinton, NY

Williams, Sylvia, *Assoc Cur African, Oceanic & New World Cultures,* Brooklyn Museum, NY

Williams, W, *Mem Faculty,* Northern Arizona Univ, Flagstaff

Williams, Wayne, *Prof,* Community College of the Finger Lakes, Canandaigua, NY

Williams, Wesley C, *Pres,* Cleveland Museum of Art, OH

Williams, William H, *Dir,* Wyoming State Archives & Historical Dept, Wyoming State Art Gallery, Cheyenne

Williams, William R, *Dean,* Cuyahoga Community College, Cleveland, OH

Williams, Winifred S, *Assoc Prof,* Texas Woman's Univ, Denton

Williamson, David, *Dir Educ,* Octagon Center for the Arts, Ames, IA

Williamson, James, *Head Educ Serv,* Art Gallery of Ontario, Toronto

Williamson, Dr Moncrieff, *Dir,* Confederation Centre Art Gallery and Museum, Charlottetown, PEI

Williamson, Preston, *Mem Faculty,* Studio School of Art and Design, Philadelphia, PA

Willing, Wanda, *Asst Librn,* Polish Museum of America, Chicago, IL

Willis, J L, *Dir,* Museum of Applied Arts and Science, Sydney, Australia

Willis, William H, Jr, *Pres,* Art Inst of Boston, MA

Willoughby, Roy, *VPres,* Art League of Houston, TX

Wills, J Robert, Jr, *Dean,* Univ Kentucky, Lexington

Wilson, A D P, *Dir,* City Art Gallery, Bristol, England

Wilson, Betty, *Mem Faculty,* College of Marin, Kentfield, CA

Wilson, Dr Charles Z, Jr, *Treas,* Los Angeles County Museum of Art, CA

Wilson, Chris, *Asst Prof,* Atlantic Christian College, Wilson, NC

Wilson, D M, *Dir,* British Museum, London, England

Wilson, Eileen H, *Exec Secy,* Fairmount Park Art Association, Philadelphia, PA

Wilson, Dr Forrest, *Chmn,* Catholic Univ America, Washington, DC

Wilson, Francis C, *Chmn Art Comt & Bd Trustees,* Malden Public Library, MA

Wilson, Fred, *Mem Faculty,* Arkansas Arts Center, Little Rock

Wilson, George, *Dir Summer School,* Interlochen Arts Acad, MI

Wilson, Gillian, *Cur Decorative Arts,* J Paul Getty Museum, Malibu, CA

Wilson, Hugh Allen, *Chmn & Prof,* Union College, Schenectady, NY

Wilson, Jack, *Asst to Exhib Coordr,* Dartmouth College Museum and Galleries, Hanover, NH

Wilson, John L, *Pres Bd Trustees,* Hoyt Inst of Fine Arts, New Castle, PA

Wilson, John M, *Mem Faculty,* Hope College, Holland, MI

Wilson, John R, *Prof,* Butte Community College, Oroville, CA

Wilson, Kenneth, *Dir Coll & Preservation,* Greenfield Village & Henry Ford Museum, Dearborn, MI

Wilson, Kenneth T, *Assoc Prof,* Bloomsburg State College, PA

Wilson, Leon, *Ed-in-Chief,* Metropolitan Museum of Art, New York, NY

Wilson, Malin, *Cur Exhib,* Museum of Fine Arts, Santa Fe, NM

Wilson, Marc F, *Cur Oriental Art,* William Rockhill Nelson Gallery of Art, Kansas City, MO

Wilson, Martha, *Exec Dir,* Franklin Furnace Archive, New York, NY

Wilson, Martha Peitzke, *Exec Secy,* American Acad in Rome, New York, NY

Wilson, Mary, *Asst Prof,* Univ Missouri-Saint Louis

Wilson, Robert, *Vis Prof,* Nebraska Wesleyan Univ, Lincoln

Wilson, Russel H, *Pres,* Jesse Besser Museum, Alpena, MI

Wilson, Stanley, *Assoc Prof,* California State Polytechnic Univ, Pomona

Wilson, Steve, *Dir,* Inst and Museum of the Great Plains, Lawton, OK

Wilson, William, *Prof,* State Univ New York at Albany

Wilson, William H, *Cur European Art,* John and Mable Ringling Museum of Art, Sarasota, FL

Wilton, Andrew, *Cur Prints & Drawings,* Yale Univ Art Gallery, New Haven, CT

Wilwers, Ed, *Head Dept,* Arkansas Tech Univ, Russellville

Wimmer, Charles, *Assoc Prof,* Univ Wisconsin-Stout, Menomonie

Winchell, Karl, *Prof,* California State Polytechnic Univ, Pomona

Winding-White, Mrs M L, *Pres,* John Woodman Higgins Armory, Worcester, MA

Wineberg, Charles, *Adminr,* Mount Clare Mansion, Baltimore, MD

Wineland, Gene, *Chmn,* Pratt Community College, KS

Winer, Helene, *Exec Dir,* Artists Space, New York, NY

Winer, Jane, *Head Dept,* Univ South Carolina at Aiken

Winetrout, Mark, *Acting Dir & Cur Art Coll & Exhibits,* Schenectady Museum, NY

Winfield, Rodney M, *Prof,* Maryville College, Saint Louis, MO

Wing, Stephen, *Prof,* Mars Hill College, NC

Wingate, Adina, *Pub Relations & Media Coordr,* Tucson Museum of Art, AZ

Wingfield, Dr Ruth, *Mem Faculty,* Northern Arizona Univ, Flagstaff

Winiger, Max, *Technical Asst,* Historisches Museum, St Gallen, Switzerland

Wink, Jon D, *Chmn Dept,* Slippery Rock State College, PA

Wink, Jon D, *Chmn,* Stephen F Austin State Univ, Nacogdoches, TX

Winker, Dietmar R, *Mem Faculty,* Illinois Inst of Technology, Chicago

Winkler, Dietmar R, *Dean Col,* Southeastern Massachusetts Univ, North Dartmouth

Winkler, Eldon, *Pres,* American Council for the Arts in Education, see National and Regional Organizations

Winkler, Gail C, *Lectr,* Univ Wisconsin, Madison

Winkler, Paul, *Asst to Dir,* Museum of International Folk Art, Santa Fe, NM

Winland, Carol, *Pres,* Hampshire County Public Library, Romney, WV

Winn, Thomas J, *Dir,* Dakota Art Gallery, Rapid City, SD

Winn, William, *Chmn Pub Relations,* Association of Medical Illustrators, see National and Regional Organizations

Winner, Dr Matthias, *Dir Dept of Prints & Drawings,* Staatliche Museen Preussischer Kulturbesitz, Berlin, Germany

Winningham, Geoffrey, *Assoc Prof,* Rice Univ, Houston, TX

Winokur, James, *VPres,* Pittsburgh Plan for Art, PA

Winrow, Everett, *Asst Prof,* Virginia State College, Petersburg

Winsand, Orvill, *Head Dept Art,* Carnegie-Mellon Univ, Pittsburgh, PA

Winter, F E, *Chmn Dept Fine Arts,* Univ Toronto, ON

Winter, Gerald G, *Chmn,* Univ Miami, Coral Gables, FL

Winter, R B, *Secy,* Ashmolean Museum, Oxford Univ, England

Winter, W J, *Secy,* St Augustine Historical Society, FL

Winter, William F, *Pres Bd Trustees,* Mississippi Dept of Archives and History, Jackson

Winters, John L, *Assoc Prof,* Univ Mississippi, University

Winters, Nathan, *Asst Prof,* Univ Utah, Salt Lake City

Winther, Dr Annemarie, *Asst Cur,* Kunsthalle Bremen, Germany

Wipfler, Heinz, *Asst Prof,* Queensborough Community College, Bayside, NY

Wirgin, Jan, *Cur,* Ostasiatiska Museet, Stockholm, Sweden

Wirtz, Virginia, *Mus Dir,* Maui Historical Society, Wailuku, HI

Wirz, Dadi, *Asst Prof,* Rice Univ, Houston, TX

Wisdon, John M, *Cur,* William Hayes Ackland Memorial Art Center, Univ North Carolina, Chapel Hill

Wise, Howard, *Pres,* Electronic Arts Intermix, New York, NY

Wise, R Gordon, *Dir,* Millersville State College, PA

Wiseman, Howard W, *Cur,* New Jersey Historical Society Museum, Newark; *VPres,* Springfield Historical Society, NJ

Wisniewski, John, *Preparator,* State Univ New York at Albany

Wisnosky, John, *Chmn Dept Art,* Univ Hawaii at Manoa, Honolulu

Wisnovsky, Mary, *Dir Community Serv,* Princeton Univ, NJ

Wistar, Caroline, *Asst Cur,* La Salle College Art Gallery, Philadelphia, PA

Witherow, Dale, *Asst Prof,* Mansfield State College, PA

Withey, Raymond A, *Pres,* Green Mountain College, Poultney, VT

Withington, Charlotte, *Preparator,* Bergen Community Museum, Paramus, NJ

Withrow, William J, *Dir,* Art Gallery of Ontario, Toronto

Witsell, Rebecca Rogers, *Dir Educ,* Arkansas Arts Center, Little Rock

Witt, E C, *Cur Applied Art,* City Art Gallery, Bristol, England

Witt, Ruth E, *Asst Dir,* Univ Missouri Museum of Art and Archaeology, Columbia

Wittenberg, Mrs James K, *VPres,* Walker Art Center, Minneapolis, MN

Witterman, Oliver, *Secy,* Wichita Art Association, KS

Witthoft, Brucia, *Asst Prof,* Framingham State College, MA

Wittman, Harold M, *Asst Dir,* Fine Arts Museum of the South, Mobile, AL

Wittmann, Otto, *Dir,* Toledo Museum of Art, OH

Witz, Herbert E, *Pres,* Star-Spangled Banner Flag House Association, Baltimore, MD

Witzmann, Hugh, *Head Dept & Asst Prof,* St John's Univ, Collegeville, MN

Wixom, William D, *Cur Decorative Arts,* Cleveland Museum of Art, OH

Wlodarczyk, Joyce Anne, *Instr,* Inter American Univ Puerto Rico, San German

Woelffer, Emerson, *Chmn Painting,* Otis Art Inst, Los Angeles, CA

Woitena, Ben, *Instr,* School of Art, Museum of Fine Arts, Houston, TX

Wojcik, Gary, *Asst Prof,* Ithaca College, NY

Woldbye, Vibeke, *Keeper,* Det Danske Kunstindustrimuseum, Copenhagen, Denmark

Wolf, Arthur H, *Cur Coll,* School of American Research Collections, Santa Fe, NM

Wolf, Edwin, II, *Librn,* Library Co of Philadelphia, PA

Wolf, Jean, *Secy,* Midland Art Council of the Midland Center for the Arts, MI

Wolf, Dr John H, *Pres,* Woodmere Art Gallery, Philadelphia, PA

Wolf, Karen, *Lectr,* Marian College, Indianapolis, IN

Wolf, Patricia, *Cur Educ,* Anchorage Historical and Fine Arts Museum, AK

Wolf, Sara, *Librn,* Mint Museum of Art, Charlotte, NC

Wolf, Warren A, *Art Dept Chmn,* Univ Akron, OH

Wolf, William W, III, *Prof Art & Chmn Dept,* Grinnell College, IA

Wolfe, Dr Charles J, *First VPres Bd Trustees,* Museum of Arts and Sciences, Daytona Beach, FL

Wolfe, Helen B, *Gen Dir,* American Association of Univ Women, see National and Regional Organizations

Wolfe, James, *Dir Visual Arts Prog,* Center for Inter-American Relations Art Gallery, New York, NY

Wolfe, Richard O, *Dean Summer School,* Bloomsburg State College, PA

Wolfe, Robert, Jr, *Prof,* Miami Univ, Oxford, OH

Wolfe, Ronnie, *Instr,* Craft Center, Worcester, MA

Wolfe, Townsend D, III, *Exec Dir,* Arkansas Arts Center, Little Rock

Wolfenden, William E, *Dir,* Archives of American Art, Washington, DC

Wolfram, William R, *Prof Art & Head Dept,* Concordia College, Seward, NE

Woll, Gerd, *Cur,* City of Oslo Art Collection, Norway

Wolpert, Lynn David, *Community Outreach Coordr,* Southern Alleghenies Museum of Art, Loretto, PA

Womack, William, *Instr,* Southwestern at Memphis, TN

Wong, Eddie, *Cur,* Univ Wisconsin-Stout, Menomonie

Wong, Jason D, *Cur,* Joe and Emily Lowe Art Gallery, Syracuse Univ, NY

Wood, Barbara, *Dir,* Artists' Workshop & *Dir,* Other Place, Three Schools, Toronto, ON

Wood, Carol, *Dir,* Maude I Kerns Art Center, Eugene, OR

Wood, Carolyn, *Cur,* Huntsville Museum of Art, AL

Wood, Clifford P, *Sr Asst Humanities Reference Librn,* California State Univ Library, Sacramento

Wood, Dan, *Head Dept & Instr,* Vermilion Community College, Ely, MN

Wood, David H, *Dir,* Stockbridge Historical Society, MA

Wood, Gurdon, *Asst Dir,* Natural History Museum of Los Angeles County, CA

Wood, Mrs J Frank, *Pres,* Morris-Jumel Mansion, New York, NY

Wood, James N, *Dir,* St Louis Art Museum, MO

Wood, James W, *Pres,* Mid-Southern Watercolorists, Little Rock, AR

Wood, John J, *Deputy Dir,* Minnesota Historical Society, Minneapolis

Wood, Katharine M, *Chief Reference,* Morris Library, Univ Delaware, Newark

Wood, Leonard E, *Instr,* Independence Community Junior College, KS

Wood, Marcia J, *Mem Faculty,* Kalamazoo College, MI

Wood, Michael, *Pres,* Art League of Houston, TX

Wood, Phyllis, *Corresp Secy,* Association of Medical Illustrators, see National and Regional Organizations

Wood, Richard H, *Keeper Art,* Lincolnshire Museums, Lincoln, England

Wood, Robert S, *Asst Dir,* Herbert Hoover Presidential Library, West Branch, IA

Wood, Rodger H, *Asst Prof,* Univ Mississippi, University

Wood, Stephen, *Artist-in-Residence,* Trinity College, Hartford, CT

Wood, William P, *Pres,* Philadelphia Museum of Art, PA

Woodall, Roy T, *Exec Dir,* Roanoke Fine Arts Center, VA

Wooden, Howard E, *Dir,* Wichita Art Museum, KS

Woodfall, Amy, *Dir,* Whistler House, Lowell Art Association, MA

Woodford, Don, *Mem Faculty,* California State College, San Bernardino

Woodger, Carol, *Reference Librn,* Port Chester Public Library, NY

Woodgerd, Wes, *Dir,* Chief Plenty Coups Monument, Pryor, MT

Woodhead, Daniel, Jr, *Pres,* Lyme Historical Society, Old Lyme, CT

Woodington, Walter, *Cur,* Royal Acad Schools, Royal Acad of Arts, London, England

Woodland, Ms Johan C, *Corresp Secy,* Prince Rupert Art Club, BC

Woodman, George E, *Chmn,* Univ Colorado, Boulder

Woodruff, Marian D, *Dir Educ,* Currier Gallery of Art, Manchester, NH

Woods, Sister Arlene, *Head Dept,* Salve Regina the Newport College, Newport, RI

Woods, Bruce, *Instr,* Bethany College, Lindsborg, KS

Woods, Frank, *Dean Summer School,* Univ Rhode Island, Kingston

Woods, Michael, *Dir Fine Arts,* Acad of Art College, San Francisco, CA

Main Index